THE CLASSIC WRITINGS OF
Billy Graham

The Inspirational Christian Library

THE CLASSIC WRITINGS OF
Billy Graham

ANGELS

HOW TO BE BORN AGAIN

THE HOLY SPIRIT

INSPIRATIONAL PRESS/NEW YORK

Previously published in three separate volumes as:

Angels, copyright © 1975, 1986 by Billy Graham.
How to be Born Again, copyright © 1977, 1989, by Billy Graham.
The Holy Spirit, copyright © 1978, 1988, by Billy Graham.

This collection originally published as The Collected Works of Billy Graham.

Published by Inspirational Press, A Division of BBS Publishing Corporation
        252 W. 38th Street
        New York, NY 10018

By arrangement with the W Publishing Group.

Library of Congress Catalog Card Number: 98-73958

ISBN10: 0-88486-421-9
ISBN 13: 978-0-88486-421-9

Printed in the United States of America.

Contents

SCRIPTURE QUOTATION SOURCES

ANGELS

Unless otherwise indicated, all biblical quotations are taken from the King James Version. Those marked RSV are from the Revised Standard Version of the Bible, copyrighted 1946, 1953, © 1971, 1973 by the Division of Christian Education of the National Council of Churches of Christ in the U.S.A. and are used by permission. Those marked NIV are from the New International Version, copyright © 1978 by the New York Bible Society, and are used by permission.

Those marked TLB are from *The Living Bible*, copyright © 1971 by Tyndale House Publishers and used by permission. Excerpt from *A Prisoner and Yet . . .* by Corrie ten Boom, copyright 1954 by Christian Literature Crusade, London. Christian Literature Crusade, London and Fort Washington. Used by permission.

Those marked NASB are from the New American Standard Bible, copyright © 1975 by The Lockman Foundation and are used by permission. Those marked AB are from the Amplified Bible, copyright © 1965 by the Zondervan Publishing House.

HOW TO BE BORN AGAIN

Unless otherwise noted, Scripture quotations are from *The New American Standard Bible* (copyright 1960, 1962, 1963, 1968, 1971 by the Lockman Foundation and used by permission). Scripture quotations marked *The Living Bible* are from *The Living Bible, Paraphrased* (Wheaton: Tyndale House Publishers, 1971) and are used by permission. Quotations marked NIV are from the New International Version of the Bible (copyright © 1973 by New York Bible Society International). The quotation marked Goodspeed is from The New Testament: An American Translation by Edgar J. Goodspeed (copyright © 1923, 1948 by the University of Chicago). The quotation marked TEV is from the Today's English Version of the Bible (copyright © American Bible Society 1976). The quotations marked Phillips are from *The New Testament in Modern English* (rev. ed.), copyright © 1958, 1960, 1972 by J. B. Phillips.

THE HOLY SPIRIT

Unless otherwise indicated, Scripture quotations are from *The New American Standard Bible* (copyright 1960, 1962, 1968, 1971 by the Lockman Foundation and used by permission). Scripture quotations marked LB are from *The Living Bible Paraphrased* (Wheaton: Tyndale House Publishers, 1971). Quotations marked NIV are from the New International Version of the Bible—New Testament (copyright © 1973 by the New York Bible Society International). Those marked RSV are from The Revised Standard Version of the Bible, copyright 1946, 1952, © 1971, 1973 by the Division of Christian Education of the National Council of the Churches of Christ in the United States of America, and are used by permission. Those marked *Phillips* are from *The New Testament in Modern English* (rev. ed.), copyright © 1958, 1960, 1972 by J. B. Phillips. Quotations marked NEB are from *The New English Bible*, © 1961, 1970 The Delegates of the Oxford University Press and The Syndics of the Cambridge University Press. Those marked KJV are from the King James Version of the Bible.

THE CLASSIC WRITINGS OF
Billy Graham

Angels:
God's Secret Agents

The angels are the dispensers and administrators of the divine beneficence toward us; they regard our safety, undertake our defense, direct our ways, and exercise a constant solicitude that no evil befall us.

JOHN CALVIN

Institutes of the Christian Religion, I

CONTENTS

PREFACE

WHEN I DECIDED to preach a sermon on angels, I found
practically nothing in my library. Upon investigation I soon discovered that little had been written on the subject in this century.
This seemed a strange and ominous omission. Bookstores and
libraries have shelves of books on demons, the occult and the devil.
Why was the devil getting so much more attention from writers
than angels? Some people seem to put the devil on a par with God.
Actually, Satan is a fallen angel.

Even when people in our modern age have had their attention
drawn to the subject of angels from time to time, those ideas have
often been fanciful or unbiblical. As I write this preface to the
second edition, a popular television program tells the story of an
"angel" who has been sent to earth in the form of a man to help
people who are facing problems. The popularity of the program
suggests many people find it great entertainment—but I cannot
help but feel it also reinforces the idea in many minds that angels
are just a product of our imagination, like Santa Clause or magical elves. But the Bible stresses their reality, and underlines their
constant—if unseen—ministry on behalf of God's people. In a
materialistic world which nevertheless is riddled with evil and
suffering, we need to discover afresh the Bible's teaching about
angels.

The English painter, Sir Edward Coley Burne-Jones, wrote to
Oscar Wilde that "the more materialistic science becomes, the
more angels shall I paint: their wings are my protest in favor of
the immortality of the soul."

Angels have a much more important place in the Bible than the
devil and his demons. Therefore, I undertook a biblical study of
the subject of angels. Not only has it been one of the most fascinating studies of my life, but I believe the subject is more relevant
today than perhaps at any time in history.

The Bible teaches that angels intervene in the affairs of nations.
God often uses them to execute judgment on nations. They guide,
comfort and provide for the people of God in the midst of suffering and persecution. Martin Luther once said in *Table Talk*, "An

angel is a spiritual creature without a body created by God for the service of christendom and the church."

As an evangelist, I have often felt too far spent to minister from the pulpit to men and women who have filled stadiums to hear a message from the Lord. Yet again and again my weakness has vanished, and my strength has been renewed. I have been filled with God's power not only in my soul but physically. On many occasions, God has become especially real, and has sent His unseen angelic visitors to touch my body to let me be His messenger for heaven, speaking as a dying man to dying men.

In the midst of a world which seems destined to live in a perpetual state of crisis, the subject of angels will be of great comfort and inspiration to believers in God—and a challenge to unbelievers to believe.

Blaise Pascal, the French philosopher and mathematician, once said, "Certain authors, when they speak of their work say, 'my book,' 'my commentary,' 'my history.' They would be better to say 'our book,' 'our commentary,' 'our history,' since their writings generally contain more of other peoples' good things than their own."

This is *our* book, and I wish to thank all who have helped me with this intriguing and sometimes complicated subject.

In its writing, editing and counseling, I am indebted to—Ralph Williams, who helped with research for my original writing of the manuscript; Dr. Harold Lindsell, former editor of *Christianity Today*, who went through the original manuscript with many helpful suggestions; Mr. Paul Fromer, professor at Wheaton College, who helped with content, style and organization.

To my faithful staff at Montreat who typed, retyped, read and called to my attention many areas of possible improvement— Karlene Aceto, Elsie Brookshire, Lucille Lytle, Stephanie Wills and Sally Wilson.

To Calvin Thielman, Pastor of Montreat Presbyterian Church; and Dr. John Akers for their suggestions.

To my wife, Ruth, who was an encouragement and a help from start to finish.

Especially, to our heavenly Father who helped me see this neglected and important subject.

Through the months I have gathered ideas and even quotations from sources long-since forgotten. To everyone whose books and articles I have read, to every man or woman with whom I have talked or prayed about the subject of angels, I express my gratitude. Each has contributed to this book. I regret it is not possible to list each one by name.

This new edition of the book is largely as it was written in 1975. I have added some new material and expanded certain points.

It is still my prayer that God will use this book to bring comfort to the sick and the dying; to bring encouragement to those who are under the pressures of everyday living; to bring guidance to those who are frustrated by the events of our generation.

BILLY GRAHAM

Montreat, North Carolina

1

Are Angels
God's Secret Agents?

MY WIFE, WHO was born and raised in China, recalls that in her childhood days tigers lived in the mountains. One day a poor woman went up to the foothills to cut grass. To her back was tied a baby, and a little child walked beside her. In her hand she carried a sharp sickle to cut grass. Just as she reached the top of a hill she heard a roar. Frightened almost speechless, she looked around to see a mother tigress springing at her, followed by two cubs.

This illiterate Chinese mother had never attended school or entered a church. She had never seen a Bible. But a year or two earlier a missionary had told her about Jesus, "who is able to help you when you are in trouble." As the claws of the tigress tore her arm and shoulder, the woman cried out in a frenzy, "O Jesus, help me!" The ferocious beast, instead of attacking again to get an easy meal, suddenly turned and ran away.

The Bible says, "He will give his angels charge of you, to guard you in all your ways" (Psalm 91:11, RSV). Had God sent an angel to help this poor ignorant Chinese woman? Are there supernatural beings today who are able to influence the affairs of men and nations?

In *A Slow and Certain Light*, Elizabeth Elliot told about her father's experiences with angelic helpers:

"My father, when he was a small boy, was climbing on an upper story of a house that was being built. He walked to the end of a

board that was not nailed at the other end, and it slowly began
to tip. He knew that he was doomed, but inexplicably the board
began to tip the other way, as though a hand had pushed it down
again. He always wondered if it was an angel's hand."

Help from Angels

A celebrated Philadelphia neurologist had gone to bed after an
exceptionally tiring day. Suddenly he was awakened by someone
knocking on his door. Opening it he found a little girl, poorly
dressed and deeply upset. She told him her mother was very sick
and asked him if he would please come with her. It was a bitterly
cold, snowy night, but though he was bone tired, the doctor dressed
and followed the girl.

As the *Reader's Digest* reports the story, he found the mother
desperately ill with pneumonia. After arranging for medical care,
he complimented the sick woman on the intelligence and persis-
tence of her little daughter. The woman looked at him strangely
and then said, "My daughter died a month ago." She added, "Her
shoes and coat are in the clothes closet there." Amazed and per-
plexed, the doctor went to the closet and opened the door. There
hung the very coat worn by the little girl who had brought him to
tend to her mother. It was warm and dry and could not possibly
have been out in the wintry night.

Could the doctor have been called in the hour of desperate need
by an angel who appeared as this woman's young daughter? Was
this the work of God's angels on behalf of the sick woman?

The Reverend John G. Paton, pioneer missionary in the New
Hebrides Islands, told a thrilling story involving the protective care
of angels. Hostile natives surrounded his mission headquarters one
night, intent on burning the Patons out and killing them. John
Paton and his wife prayed all during that terror-filled night that
God would deliver them. When daylight came they were amazed
to see that, unaccountably, the attackers had left. They thanked
God for delivering them.

A year later, the chief of the tribe was converted to Jesus Christ,
and Mr. Paton, remembering what had happened, asked the chief
what had kept him and his men from burning down the house and

killing them. The chief replied in surprise, "Who were all those men you had with you there?" The missionary answered, "There were no men there; just my wife and I." The chief argued that they had seen many men standing guard—hundreds of big men in shining garments with drawn swords in their hands. They seemed to circle the mission station so that the natives were afraid to attack. Only then did Mr. Paton realize that God had sent His angels to protect them. The chief agreed that there was no other explanation. Could it be that God had sent a legion of angels to protect His servants, whose lives were being endangered?

A Persian colporteur was accosted by a man who asked him if he had a right to sell Bibles. "Why, yes," he answered, "we are allowed to sell these books anywhere in the country!" The man looked puzzled, and asked, "How is it, then, that you are always surrounded by soldiers? I planned three times to attack you, and each time, seeing the soldiers, I left you alone. Now I no longer want to harm you." Were these soldiers heavenly beings?

During World War II, Captain Eddie Rickenbacker and the rest of the crew of the B-17 in which he was flying ran out of fuel and "ditched" in the Pacific Ocean. For weeks nothing was heard of him. The newspapers reported his disappearance and across the country thousands of people prayed. Mayor LaGuardia asked the whole city of New York to pray for him. Then he returned. The Sunday papers headlined the news, and in an article, Captain Rickenbacker himself told what had happened. "And this part I would hesitate to tell," he wrote, "except that there were six witnesses who saw it with me. A gull came out of nowhere, and lighted on my head—I reached up my hand very gently—I killed him and then we divided him equally among us. We ate every bit, even the little bones. Nothing ever tasted so good." This gull saved the lives of Rickenbacker and his companions. Years later I asked him to tell me the story personally, because it was through this experience that he came to know Christ. He said, "I have no explanation except that God sent one of His angels to rescue us."

During my ministry I have heard or read literally thousands of similar stories. Could it be that these were all hallucinations or accidents or fate or luck? Or were real angels sent from God to perform certain tasks?

The Current Cult of the Demonic

Just a few years ago such ideas would have been scorned by most educated people. Science was king, and science was tuned in to believe only what could be seen or measured. The idea of supernatural beings was thought to be nonsense, the ravings of the lunatic fringe.

All this has changed. Think, for example, of the morbid fascination modern society has for the occult.

Walk into a bookstore; visit any newsstand at a modern airport; go to a university library. You will be confronted by shelves and tables packed with books about the devil, Satan worship and demon possession. A number of Hollywood films, television programs and as many as one in four hard-rock pop songs are devoted to, or thematically make reference to, the devil. Years ago the Rolling Stones sang their "Sympathy for the Devil" to the top of the popularity chart; another group answered back with a symphony to the devil.

The Exorcist proved to be one of the biggest moneymakers of any film in history. Arthur Lyons gave his book a title that is frighteningly accurate: *The Second Coming: Satanism in America*. This theme, which intellectuals would have derided a generation ago, is now being dealt with seriously by such people as noted author John Updike and Harvard professor Harvey Cox. Some polls indicate that seventy percent of Americans believe in a personal devil. Some years ago Walter Cronkite announced a poll over his CBS network news showing that the number of Americans who believed in a personal devil has increased twelve percent. This was in the mid–1970s. What would the figure be today? It is ironic that a generation ago, scientists, psychologists, sociologists and even some theologians were predicting that by the late 1970s there would be a sharp decline in the belief in the supernatural. The reverse is true!

Some years ago, in a medium-sized metropolitan area, I turned out of curiosity to the entertainment pages of the local newspaper and studied them carefully. I was unprepared for the shock I received as I read the descriptions of the themes and content of the feature motion pictures being shown in the theaters in that area. They focused on sadism, murder, demon possession and demonism, devil worship and horror, not to mention those that depicted erotic sex. It seemed that each advertisement tried to outdo the others in the degree of shock, horror and mind-bending emotional devastation. The picture hasn't changed. If anything, the movies are even worse today!

Even in the Christian world the presses have turned out a rash of books on the devil by both Catholic and Protestant writers. I myself have thought about writing a book on the devil and his demons.

The Reality and Power of Satan

The Bible does teach that Satan is a real being who is at work in the world together with his emissaries, the demons. In the New Testament they intensified their activities and bent every effort to defeat the work of Jesus Christ, God's Son. The apparent increase in satanic activity against people on this planet today may indicate that the Second Coming of Jesus Christ is close at hand. Certainly, the activity of Satan is evident on every side. We can see it in the wars and other crises that affect all people daily. We can also see it in the attacks of Satan against individual members of the body of Christ.

Some years ago I had dinner with several senators and congressmen in a dining room in the Capitol building. We began discussing the rising interest in the occult with special reference to *The Exorcist*. One of the senators, who had recently passed through a deep religious experience, said that due to his past experience with the occult, whenever he knew of a theater that was showing *The Exorcist* he would drive a block around it. He was afraid even to go near it. He said, "I know that both angels and demons are for real."

Several years ago the late Pope Paul said he was sure that the evil forces attacking every level of society had behind them the work of a personal devil with a whole kingdom of demons at his command. The Roman Catholic Church has been rethinking its position on the reality of the spirit world; and interest in this subject has revived among both theological liberals and evangelicals in Protestant churches everywhere.

Unidentified Flying Objects

The renewed interest in the occult and satanism is not the only evidence of the new openness to the supernatural. It also was revealed in the widespread revival of speculation about the so-called "unidentified flying objects"—UFOs—some years ago. Even some of today's popular movies, like *Cocoon*, center on visitors from outer space.

Some reputable scientists deny and others assert that UFOs do appear to people from time to time. Some scientists have reached the place where they think they can prove that these are possibly visitors from outer space. Some Christian writers have speculated that UFOs could very well be a part of God's angelic host who preside over the physical affairs of universal creation. While we cannot assert such a view with certainty, many people are now seeking some type of supernatural explanation for these phenomena. Nothing can hide the fact, however, that these unexplained events are occurring with greater frequency around the entire world and in unexpected places.

Some years ago, Japan witnessed a typical example of unexplained objects that appeared in the night skies. On 15 January 1975, a squadron of UFO-like objects, resembling a celestial string of pearls, soared silently through the evening skies over half the length of Japan. As government officials, police and thousands of curious citizens stared at the sky in wonder, from fifteen to twenty glowing objects, cruising in straight formation, flew over Japan inside a strange misty cloud. Further, they were sighted and reported in cities seven hundred miles apart in less than an hour.

Hundreds of frantic telephone calls jammed switchboards of police stations and government installations as the spectacular formation sped south. "All the callers reported seeing a huge cloud passing over the city. They said they saw strange objects inside the cloud moving in a straight line," recalled Duty Officer Takeo Ohira. Were they planes? "No," said Hiroshi Mayazawa, "because no planes or natural phenomena appeared on my radar. It was an exceptionally clear night. To me the whole thing is a mystery."

Professor Masatoshi Kitamura watched the dazzling display in the night sky from the Control Room of Tokyo's Meteorological Bureau station near the airport. He said, "I was mystified. Nothing showed up on my radar. I reported my sighting to the airport control tower and they told me nothing showed on their radar either."

Other Explanations

Erich von Daniken's *Chariots of the Gods?*, published many years ago, was re-issued in paperback by Berkeley in 1984. It theorizes that in pre-history astronauts from distant stars visited earth in spaceships. From these visits grew man's idea of gods and many of his conceptions of them. Immanuel Velikovsky in his equally popular *Worlds in Collision* and *Ages in Chaos* put forward the notion that the turbulent history of the Middle East in the second millennium B.C. can be traced to a violent scattering of the solar system that caused ruin on earth. The knowledge of the intense suffering of those times was soon repressed, but lies buried in man's racial memory, explaining his modern self-destructive behavior.

Men would dismiss these grandiose cosmologies lightly if it were not that they, along with a number of other theories, have been put forward with such frequency and serious import that no one can shrug them off. They are being studied seriously at many of our universities. As a theme for talk shows, hardly anything or anyone can top concerns like this.

Some sincere Christians, whose views are anchored in a strong commitment to Scripture, contend that these UFOs are angels. But are they? These people point to certain passages in Isaiah, Ezekiel, Zechariah and the book of Revelation, and draw parallels to the reports of observers of alleged UFO appearances. They take the detailed descriptions, for example, of a highly credible airline crew and lay them alongside Ezekiel 10, and put forward a strong case. In Ezekiel 10 we read, "Each of the four cherubim had a wheel beside him—'The Whirl-Wheels,' as I heard them called, for each one had a second wheel crosswise within, sparkled like chrysolite, giving off a greenish-yellow glow. Because of the construction of these wheels, the cherubim could go straight forward in each of four directions; they did not turn when they changed direction but could go in any of the four ways their faces looked . . . and when they rose into the air the wheels rose with them, and stayed beside them as they flew. When the cherubim stood still, so did the wheels, for the spirit of the cherubim was in the wheels" (Ezekiel 10:9–13,16–17, TLB).

Any attempt to connect such passages with the visits of angels may, at best, be speculation. Nor should we become too preoccupied or overly fascinated with trying to identify contemporary theories and speculations about UFOs or similar phenomena with biblical passages. Secular speculations often, in fact, run counter to the Bible's teaching concerning the origin of life on this planet. What is interesting, however, is that such theories are now being given serious attention even by people who make no claim to believe in the God of the Bible.

A further evidence of the renewed interest in the supernatural is the widespread fascination with extrasensory perception—ESP. The subjective science of parapsychology is now one of the fastest growing fields of academic research in our universities today.

At Duke University, Dr. Joseph B. Rhine took up the study of extrasensory perception in the 1930s and championed it to the point where a department of parapsychology was established at the university. He became its pioneering professor. Today scientists are probing every conceivable frontier for ESP possibilities. Its line-up of protagonists reads like a *Who's Who.* Not only is serious intellectual and scientific study being carried on, but the subject is immensely popular because many of its aggressive proponents profess to be nonreligious. It has gained even more widespread respectability in communist societies (such as in the Soviet Union) than here in the United States. It plays a role of a "substitute religion" in some cases, although it has been used primarily as a technique to influence people.

Notice also the reaction on network talk shows. When a celebrity steps through the grand entrance and strolls to the guest chair, he is asked, "Do you believe in ESP?" To say, "No," in the middle 1980s would be as unfashionable as to have said, "Yes," a generation ago.

Why I Wrote This Book

But why write a book on angels? Isn't talking about angels merely adding to the speculation about supernatural phenomena? What possible value is there in such a discussion? Didn't the fascination with angels vanish with the Middle Ages?

Because all the powers of the evil world system seem to be preying on the minds of people already disturbed and frustrated in our generation, I believe the time has come to focus on the positives of the Christian faith. John the Apostle said, "greater is he that is in you, than he that is in the world" (1 John 4:4). Satan is indeed capable of doing supernatural things—but he acts only by the permissive will of God; he is on a leash. It is God who is all powerful. It is God who is omnipotent. God has provided Christians with both offensive and defensive weapons. We are not to be fearful; we are not to be distressed; we are not to be deceived; nor are we to be intimidated. Rather, we are to be on our guard, calm and alert "Lest Satan should get an advantage of us, for we are not ignorant of his devices" (2 Corinthians 2:11).

One of Satan's sly devices is to divert our minds from the help God offers us in our struggles against the forces of evil. However, the Bible testifies that God has provided assistance for us in our spiritual conflicts. We are not alone in this world! The Bible teaches us that God's Holy Spirit has been given to empower us and guide us. In addition, the Bible—in nearly three hundred different places—also teaches that God has countless angels at His command. Furthermore, God has commissioned these angels to aid His children in their struggles against Satan. The Bible does not give as much information about them as we might like, but what it does say should be a source of comfort and strength for us in every circumstance.

I am convinced that these heavenly beings exist and that they provide unseen aid on our behalf. I do not believe in angels because someone has told me about a dramatic visitation from an angel, impressive as such rare testimonies may be. I do not believe in angels because UFOs are astonishingly angel-like in some of their reported appearances. I do not believe in angels because ESP experts are making the realm of the spirit world seem more and more plausible. I do not believe in angels because of the sudden worldwide emphasis on the reality of Satan and demons. I do not believe in angels because I have ever seen one—because I haven't.

I believe in angels because the Bible says there are angels; and I believe the Bible to be the true Word of God.

I also believe in angels because I have sensed their presence in my life on special occasions.

So what I have to say in the chapters that follow will not be an accumulation of *my* ideas about the spirit world, nor even a reflection of my own spiritual experiences in the spirit realm. I propose to put forward, at least in part, *what I understand the Bible to say about angels.* Naturally, this will not be an exhaustive study of the subject. I hope, however, that it will arouse your curiosity sufficiently for you to dig out from the Bible all that you can find on this subject after you have read this book. More than that, it is my prayer that you will discover the reality of God's love and care for you as evidenced in the ministry of His angels on your behalf, and that you would go forth in faith each day trusting God's constant watch-care over you.

Spiritual forces and resources are available to all Christians. Because our resources are unlimited, Christians will be winners. Millions of angels are at God's command and at our service. The hosts of heaven stand at attention as we make our way from earth to glory, and Satan's BB guns are no match for God's heavy artillery. So don't be afraid. God is for you. He has committed His angels to wage war in the conflict of the ages—and they will win the victory. The apostle Paul has said in Colossians 2:15, "And having spoiled principalities and powers, he made a show of them openly, triumphing over them." Victory over the flesh, the world and the devil is ours now! The angels are here to help and they are prepared for any emergency.

As you read this book, therefore, I pray that God will open your eyes to the resources He has provided for all who turn to Him for strength. I pray also that God will use it to show you your constant need of Him, and how He has sent His Son, Jesus Christ, into the world to deliver you from both the guilt and power of sin.

The British express train raced through the night, its powerful headlight piercing the darkness. Queen Victoria was a passenger on the train.

Suddenly the engineer saw a startling sight. Revealed in the beam of the engine's light was a strange figure in a black cloak standing in the middle of the tracks and waving its arms. The engineer grabbed for the brake and brought the train to a grinding halt.

He and his fellow trainmen clambered down to see what had stopped them. But they could find no trace of the strange figure. On a hunch the engineer walked a few yards further up the tracks. Suddenly he stopped and stared into the fog in horror. The bridge had been washed out in the middle and ahead of them it had toppled into a swollen stream. If the engineer had not heeded the ghostly figure, his train would have plummeted down into the stream.

While the bridge and the tracks were being repaired, the crew made a more intensive search for the strange flagman. But not until they got to London did they solve the mystery.

At the base of the engine's headlamp the engineer discovered a huge dead moth. He looked at it a moment, then on impulse wet its wings and pasted it to the glass of the lamp.

Climbing back into his cab, he switched on the light and saw the "flagman" in the beam. He knew the answer now: the moth had flown into the beam, seconds before the train was due to reach the washed-out bridge. In the fog, it appeared to be a phantom figure, waving its arms.

When Queen Victoria was told of the strange happening she said, "I'm sure it was no accident. It was God's way of protecting us."

No, the figure the engineer saw in the headlight's beam was not an angel . . . and yet God, quite possibly through the ministry of His unseen angels, had placed the moth on the headlight lens exactly when and where it was needed. Truly "He will command his angels concerning you to guard you in all your ways" (Psalm 91:11, NIV).

2

Angels Are for Real

SPECULATION ABOUT THE nature of angels has been around since long before Queen Victoria's time, and it continues down to the present time. Yet through revelation in the Bible God has told us a great deal about them. For this reason, theologians through the ages have universally agreed about the importance of "angelology" (the orderly statement of biblical truth about angels). They judged it worthy of treatment in any book of systematic theology. They wrote at length, distinguishing between good angels and satanology (the study of fallen and thus evil angels). But today we have neglected the theme of good angels, although many are giving the devil and all of his demons rapt attention, even worshiping them.

Angels belong to a uniquely different dimension of creation that we, limited to the natural order, can scarcely comprehend. In this angelic domain the limitations are different from those God has imposed on our natural order. He has given angels higher knowledge, power and mobility than we. Have you ever seen or met one of these superior beings called angels? Probably not, for both the Bible and human experience tell us visible appearances by angels are very rare—but that in no way makes angels any less real or powerful. They are God's messengers whose chief business is to carry out His orders in the world. He has given them an ambassadorial charge. He has designated and empowered them as holy deputies to perform works of righteousness. In this way they assist Him as their creator while He sovereignly controls the universe. So He has given them the capacity to bring His holy enterprises to a successful conclusion.

Angels Are Created Beings

Don't believe everything you hear (and read!) about angels! Some would have us believe that they are only spiritual will-o'-the-wisps. Some view them as only celestial beings with beautiful wings and bowed heads. Others would have us think of them as effeminate wierdos.

The Bible states that angels, like men, were created by God. At one time no angels existed; indeed there was nothing but the Triune God: Father, Son and Holy Spirit. Paul, in Colossians 1:16, says, "For by him were all things created, that are in heaven, and that are in earth, visible and invisible." Angels indeed are among the invisible things made by God, for "all things were created by him, and for him." This Creator, Jesus, "is before all things, and by him all things consist" (Colossians 1:17), so that even angels would cease to exist if Jesus, who is Almighty God, did not sustain them by His power.

It seems that angels have the ability to change their appearance and shuttle in a flash from the capital glory of heaven to earth and back again. Although some interpreters have said that the phrase "sons of God" in Genesis 6:2 refers to angels, the Bible frequently makes it clear that angels are nonmaterial; Hebrews 1:14 calls them ministering "spirits." Intrinsically, they do not possess physical bodies, although they may take on physical bodies when God appoints them to special tasks. Furthermore, God has given them no ability to reproduce, and they neither marry nor are given in marriage (Mark 12:25).

The empire of angels is as vast as God's creation. If you believe the Bible, you will believe in their ministry. They crisscross the Old and New Testaments, being mentioned directly or indirectly nearly 300 times. Some biblical scholars believe that angels can be numbered potentially in the millions since Hebrews 12:22

speaks of "an innumerable [myriads—a great but indefinite number] company of angels." As to their number, David recorded 20,000 coursing through the skyways of the stars. Even with his limited vision he impressively notes, "The chariots of God are twenty thousand, even thousands of angels" (Psalm 68:17). Matthew Henry says of this passage, "Angels are 'the chariots of God,' his chariots of war, which he makes use of against his enemies, his chariots of conveyance, which he sends for his friends, as he did for Elijah . . . , his chariots of state, in the midst of which he shows his glory and power. They are vastly numerous: 'Twenty thousands,' even thousands multiplied."

Ten thousand angels came down on Mount Sinai to confirm the holy presence of God as He gave the Law to Moses (Deuteronomy 33:2). An earthquake shook the mountain. Moses was held in speech-bound wonder at this mighty cataclysm attended by the visitation of heavenly beings. Furthermore, in the New Testament John tells us of having seen ten thousand times ten thousand angels ministering to the Lamb of God in the throne room of the universe (Revelation 5:11). The book of Revelation also says that armies of angels will appear with Jesus at the Battle of Armageddon when God's foes gather for their final defeat. Paul in 2 Thessalonians says, "the Lord Jesus shall be revealed from heaven with his mighty angels" (1:7).

Think of it! Multitudes of angels, indescribably mighty, performing the commands of heaven! More amazingly, even one angel is indescribably mighty, as though an extension of the arm of God. Singly or corporately, angels are for real. They are better organized than were the armies of Alexander the Great, Napoleon, or Eisenhower. From earliest antiquity, when the angel guardians of the gates to the glory of Eden sealed the entrance to the home of Adam and Eve, angels have manifested their presence in the world. God placed angelic sentinels called cherubim at the east of the Garden of Eden. They were commissioned not only to bar man's return into Eden, but with "a flaming sword flashing back and forth to guard the way to the tree of life" (Genesis 3:24, NIV) lest Adam by eating of its fruit should live forever. If Adam had lived in his sin forever—this earth would long ago have been hell. Thus, in one sense death is a blessing to the human race.

Angels Serve God and Regenerate Men

Witness the unprecedented and unrepeated pageantry at Mt. Sinai. When God moves toward man, it is an event of the first magnitude and can include the visitation of angelic hosts. In the billowing clouds that covered Sinai an angelic trumpeter announced the presence of God. The whole mountain seemed to pulsate with life. Consternation gripped the people below. The earth seemed convulsed with a nameless fear. As God came to the mountaintop, He was accompanied by thousands of angels. Moses, the silent, lone witness, must have been overcome with even a limited vision of the forces of God. It staggers the imagination to wonder what kind of a headline would be prompted in the daily press for even a man-sided view of such a heavenly visitation. "And so terrible was the sight, that Moses said, I exceedingly fear and quake" (Hebrews 12:21).

The appearance of God was glorious. He shone like the sun when it goes to its strength. In his commentary Matthew Henry says, "Even Seir and Paran, two mountains at some distance, were illuminated by the divine glory which appeared on Mount Sinai, and reflected some of the rays of it, so bright was the appearance, and so much taken notice to set forth the wonders of the divine providence (Habakkuk 3:3,4; Psalm 18:7–9). The Jerusalem Targum has a strange gloss [note of explanation] upon this, that, 'when God came down to give the law, he offered it on Mount Seir to the Edomites, but they refused it, because they found in it, *Thou shalt not kill.* Then he offered it on Mount Paran to the Ishmaelites, but they also refused it, because they found in it, *Thou shalt not steal;* and then he came to Mount Sinai and offered it to Israel, and they said, *All that the Lord shall say we will do.*'" This account by the Jerusalem Targum is, of course, fictional, but it throws an interesting light on how some Jews later regarded this extraordinary and spectacular event.

Belief in Angels: A General Phenomenon

The history of virtually all nations and cultures reveals at least some belief in angelic beings. Ancient Egyptians made the tombs of their dead more impregnable and lavish than their homes because they felt angels would visit there in succeeding ages. Islamic scholars have proposed that at least two angels are assigned to each person: one angel records the good deeds and the other the bad. In fact, long before Islam arose, and even apart from contact with Scripture, some religions taught the existence of angels. But no matter what the traditions, our frame of reference must be the Scripture as our supreme authority on this subject.

Today some hard-nosed scientists lend credence to the scientific probability of angels when they admit the likelihood of unseen and invisible intelligences. Increasingly, our world is being made acutely aware of the existence of occult and demonic powers. People pay attention as never before to sensational headlines promoting films and books concerning the occult. News accounts of strange happenings around the world fascinate readers and TV viewers everywhere. Ought not Christians, grasping the eternal dimension of life, become conscious of the sinless angelic powers who are for real, and who associate with God Himself and administer His works in our behalf? After all, references to the holy angels in the Bible far outnumber references to Satan and his subordinate demons.

Cosmic Powers

If the activities of the devil and his demons seem to be intensifying in these days, as I believe they are, should not the incredibly greater supernatural powers of God's holy angels be even more indelibly impressed on the minds of people of faith? Certainly the eye of faith sees many evidences of the supernatural display of God's power and glory. God is still in business too.

Christians must never fail to sense the operation of angelic glory. It forever eclipses the world of demonic powers, as the sun does the candle's light.

If you are a believer, expect powerful angels to accompany you in your life experiences. And let those events dramatically illustrate the friendly presence of "the holy ones," as Daniel calls them.

Angels speak. They appear and reappear. They are emotional creatures. While angels may become visible by choice, our eyes are not constructed to see them ordinarily any more than we can see the dimensions of a nuclear field, the structure of atoms, or the electricity that flows through copper wiring. Our ability to sense reality is limited: The deer of the forest far surpass our human capacity in their keenness of smell. Bats possess a phenomenally sensitive built-in radar system. Some animals can see things in the dark that escape our attention. Swallows and geese possess sophisticated guidance systems that appear to border on the supernatural. So why should we think it strange if men fail to perceive the evidences of angelic presence? Could it be that God granted Balaam and his ass a new optical capacity to view the angel? *(See* Numbers 22:23, 31.) Without this special sense they might have thought him to be only a fragment of their imagination.

Reports continually flow to my attention from many places around the world telling of visitors of the angelic order appearing, ministering, fellowshiping and disappearing. They warn of God's impending judgment; they spell out the tenderness of His love; they meet a desperate need; then they are gone. Of one thing we can be sure: angels never draw attention to themselves but ascribe glory to God and press His message upon the hearers as a delivering and sustaining word of the highest order.

Demonic activity and Satan worship are on the increase in all parts of the world. The devil is alive and more at work than at any other time. The Bible says that since he realizes his time is short, his activity will increase. Through his demonic influences he does succeed in turning many away from true faith; but we can still say that his evil activities are countered for the people of God by His ministering spirits, the holy ones of the angelic order. They are vigorous in delivering the heirs of salvation from the stratagems of evil men. They cannot fail.

Believers, look up—take courage. The angels are nearer than you think. For after all (as we have already noted), God has given "his angels charge of you, to guard you in all your ways. On their hands they will bear you up, lest you dash your foot against a stone" (Psalm 91:11, 12, RSV).

3

Angels Visible or Invisible?

THE SPIRIT WORLD and its activities are big news today. And the idea of the supernatural is not only seriously regarded, but is accepted as a fact. Many of the most recent books on the subject border on the sensational, or are purely speculative, or have been dreamed up in somebody's imagination. But those who take the Bible at full value cannot discount the subject of angels as speculation or hollow conjecture. After all, the Scriptures mention their existence almost three hundred times.

Have You Ever Seen an Angel?

I have already said that angels are created spirit beings who can become visible when necessary. They can appear and disappear. They think, feel, will and display emotions. But some people have questions about them that ought not concern us. The old debate about how many angels can dance on the head of a pin is foolish. And to ask how many angels can be crowded into a telephone booth or into a Volkswagen hardly merits our attention. On the other hand, we should know what the Bible teaches about them as oracles of God, who give divine or authoritative decisions and bring messages from God to men. To fulfill this function angels have not infrequently assumed visible, human form. The writer to the Hebrews asks, "Are they [angels] not all ministering spirits?" (1:14). Now, have you ever seen a pure spirit? I can't say that I have. Yet I do know that down through the ages God has chosen to manifest His own spiritual presence in different ways. At the baptism of Jesus, God the Holy Spirit was present in the form of a dove. So God has chosen also to manifest His presence through His angels, who are lesser beings to whom He has given the power to assume forms that occasionally make them visible to men.

Are Angels to Be Worshiped?

It is no mere accident that angels are usually invisible. Though God in His infinite wisdom does not, as a rule, permit angels to take on physical dimensions, people tend to venerate them in a fashion that borders on worship. We are warned against worshiping the creature rather than the Creator (Romans 1:24–25). It's no less than heretical, and indeed is a breach of the first commandment, to worship any manifestation of angelic presence, patron or blesser.

Paul has pointed out that while unusual manifestations may be deeply significant, Jesus Christ the incarnate God, the second person of the Trinity, who is creator of all things and by whom all things exist, is worthy of our worship (Colossians 2:18). We are not to pray to angels. Nor are we to engage in "a voluntary humility and worshiping" of them. Only the Triune God is to be the object of our worship and of our prayers.

Moreover, we should not confuse angels, whether visible or invisible, with the Holy Spirit, the third person of the Trinity and Himself God. Angels do not indwell men; the Holy Spirit seals them and indwells them when He has regenerated them. The Holy Spirit is all knowing, all present, and all powerful. Angels are mightier than men, but they are not gods and they do not possess the attributes of the Godhead.

Not angels, but the Holy Spirit convicts men of sin, righteousness and judgment (John 16:7). He reveals and interprets Jesus Christ to men, while angels remain messengers of God who serve men as ministering spirits (Hebrews 1:14). So far as I know, no Scripture says that the Holy Spirit ever manifested Himself in human form to men. Jesus did this in the incarnation. The glorious Holy Spirit can be everywhere at the same time, but no angel can be in more than one place at any given moment. We know the Holy Spirit as spirit, not flesh, but we can know angels not as spirits alone but sometimes also in visible form.

At the same time, both angels and the Holy Spirit are at work in our world to accomplish God's perfect will. Frankly, we may not always know the agent or means God is using—the Holy Spirit or the angels—when we discern God's hand at work. We can be sure, however, that there is no contradiction or competition between God the Holy Spirit and God's command of the angelic hosts. God Himself is in control to accomplish His will—and in that we can rejoice!

God uses angels to work out the destinies of men and nations. He has altered the courses of the busy political and social arenas of our society and directed the destinies of men by angelic visitation many times over. We must be aware that angels keep in close and vital contact with all that is happening on the earth. Their knowledge of earthly matters exceeds that of men. We must attest to their invisible presence and unceasing labors. Let us believe that they are here among us. They may not laugh or cry with us, but we do know they delight with us over every victory in our evangelistic endeavors. Jesus taught that "there is joy in the presence of the angels of God when our sinner repents" (Luke 15:10, TLB).

Angels Visible? Invisible?

In Daniel 6:22 we read, "My God hath sent his angel, and hath shut the lions' mouths." In the den, Daniel's sight evidently perceived the angelic presence, and the lions' strength more than met its match in the power of the angel. In most instances, angels, when appearing visibly, are so glorious and impressively beautiful as to stun and amaze men who witness their presence.

Can you imagine a being, white and dazzling as lightning? General William Booth, founder of the Salvation Army, describes a vision of angelic beings, stating that every angel was surrounded with an aura of rainbow light so brilliant that were it not withheld, no human being could stand the sight of it.

Who can measure the brilliance of the lightning flash that illuminates the countryside for miles around? The angel who rolled away the stone from the tomb of Jesus was not only dressed in white, but shone as a flash of lightning with dazzling brilliance (Matthew 28:3). The keepers of the tomb shook and became as dead men. Incidentally, that stone weighed several times more than a single man could move, yet the physical power of the angel was not taxed in rolling it aside.

Abraham, Lot, Jacob and others had no difficulty recognizing angels when God allowed them to manifest themselves in physical form. Note, for example, Jacob's instant recognition of angels in Genesis 32:1, 2. "And Jacob went on his way, and the angels of God met him. And when Jacob saw them, he said, This is God's host: and he called the name of that place Mahanaim."

Further, both Daniel and John described the glories of the angels (Daniel 10:6 and Revelation 10:1) visibly descending from heaven with immeasurable beauty and brilliance, shining like the sun. Who has not thrilled to read the account of the three Hebrew children, Shadrach, Meshach and Abednego? They refused to fall in line with the music of obeisance and worship to the king of Babylon. They learned that the angel presence can be observed on occasion by people in the unbelieving world on the outside. After they had refused to bow, the angel preserved them from being burned alive or even having the smell of smoke on their garments from the seven-times-hotter fire. The angel came to them in the midst of the flame without harm and was seen by the king who said, "I see four men . . . in the midst of the fire" (Daniel 3:25).

On the other hand, the Bible indicates angels are more often invisible to human eyes. Whether visible or invisible, however, God causes His angels to go before us, to be with us, and to follow after us. All of this can be fully understood only by believers who know that angelic presences are in control of the battlefield about us, so that we may stand with complete confidence in the midst of the fight. "If God be for us who can be against us?" (Romans 8:31).

What Do You See When You See an Angel?

God is forever imaginative, colorful and glorious in what He designs. Some of the descriptions of angels, including the one of

Lucifer in Ezekiel 28, indicate that they are exotic to the human eye and mind. Apparently angels have a beauty and variety that surpass anything known to men. Scripture does not tell us what elements make up angels. Nor can modern science, which is only beginning to explore the realm of the unseen, tell us about the constitution or even the work of angels.

The Bible seems to indicate that angels do not age, and never says that one was sick. Except for those who fell with Lucifer, the ravages of sin that have brought destruction, sickness and chaos to our earth have not affected them. The holy angels will never die.

The Bible also teaches that angels are sexless. Jesus said that in heaven men "neither marry, nor are given in marriage, but are as the angels of God in heaven" (Matthew 22:30). This may indicate that angels enjoy relationships that are far more thrilling and exciting than sex. The joy of sex in this life may be only a foretaste of something that believers will enjoy in heaven which is far beyond anything man has ever known.

How are we to understand "theophanies"? (This is a theological term for the visible appearances of Jesus Christ in other forms prior to His incarnation.) Some passages in the Old Testament tell us that the second person of the Trinity appeared and was called either "the Lord" or "the angel of the Lord." Nowhere is it clearer than in Genesis 18 where three men appear before Abraham. Their leader is clearly identified with the Lord, whereas the other two are merely angels. There are no grounds for questioning the very early and traditional Christian interpretation that in these cases there is a preincarnation manifestation of the second person of the Trinity, whether He is called 'the Lord' or 'the Angel of the Lord' (*Zondervan Pictorial Encyclopedia of the Bible*).

We must remember, then, that in some cases in the Old Testament God Himself appeared in human form as an angel. This reinforces the idea of the relationship between God and His angels. Nevertheless, in almost all of the cases where angelic personages appear they are God's created angelic beings and not God Himself.

Yes, angels are real. They are not the product of our imagination, but were made by God Himself. Think of it! Whether we see them or not, God has created a vast host of angels to help accomplish His work in this world. When we know God personally through faith in His Son, Jesus Christ, we can have confidence that the angels of God will watch over us and assist us because we belong to Him.

4

Angels—How They Differ from Man

THE BIBLE TELLS us that God has made man "a little lower than the angels." Yet it also says angels are "ministering spirits, sent forth to minister for them who shall be heirs of salvation" (Hebrews 2:5–7;1:13, 14). This sounds like a contradiction: man lower—but eventually higher through redemption. How can we explain this?

First we must remember that this Scripture is speaking both of Jesus Christ and men. Jesus did "stoop" when He became man. And as a man He was a little lower than the angels in His humanity—although without losing in any sense His divine nature. But it also speaks about men other than Jesus. God has made men head over all the creatures of our earth world; but they are lower than angels with respect to their bodies and to their place while here on earth. In his *Institutes*, John Calvin said, "The angels are the dispensers and administrators of the Divine beneficence toward us; they regard our safety, undertake our defense, direct our ways, and exercise a constant solicitude that no evil befall us."

God commands angels to help men since they will be made higher than the angels at the resurrection. So says Jesus in Luke 20:36. God will alter the temporary lower position of man when the kingdom of God has come in its fullness. Now let us examine in detail how God says angels differ from men.

Although angels are glorious beings, the Scriptures make it clear that they differ from regenerated men in significant ways. How can the angels who have never sinned fully understand what it means to be delivered from sin? How can they understand how precious Jesus is to those for whom His death on Calvary brings light, life and immortality? Is it not stranger still that angels themselves will be judged by believers who were once sinners? Such judgment, however, apparently applies only to those fallen angels who followed Lucifer. Thus Paul writes in 1 Corinthians 6:3, "Know ye not that we shall judge angels?" But even the holy angels have limitations, though the Bible speaks of them as being superior to men in many ways.

Is God "Father" to Angels?

God is not called "Father" by the holy angels because, not having sinned, they need not be redeemed. All the fallen angels cannot call God "Father" because they cannot be redeemed. The latter case is one of the mysteries of Scripture: God made provision for the salvation of fallen men, but He made no provision for the salvation of fallen angels. Why? Perhaps because, unlike Adam and Eve, who were enticed toward sin by sinners, the angels fell when there were no sinners, so no one could entice them to sin. Thus, their sinful state cannot be altered; their sin cannot be forgiven; their salvation cannot be achieved.

The wicked angels would never want to call God "Father," though they may call Lucifer "father," as many Satan worshipers do. They are in revolt against God and will never voluntarily accept His sovereign lordship, except in that Day of Judgment when every knee will bow and every tongue confess that Jesus Christ is Lord (Philippians 2:9, 10). Yet even holy angels who might like to call God "Father" could do so only in the looser sense of that word. As Creator, God is the father of all created beings; since angels are created beings, they might think of Him this way. But the term is normally reserved in Scripture for lost men who have been redeemed. So in a real sense, even ordinary men cannot call God "Father" except as their Creator God—until they are born again.

Angels Are Not Heirs of God

Christians are joint heirs with Jesus Christ through redemption (Romans 8:17), which is made theirs by faith in Him based on His death at Calvary. Angels who are not joint heirs must stand aside when the believers are introduced to their boundless, eternal riches. The holy angels, however, who are ministering spirits, have never lost their original glory and spiritual relationship with God. This assures them of their exalted place in the royal order of God's creation. By contrast, Jesus identified Himself with fallen men in the incarnation when He was "made a little lower than the angels for the suffering of death" (Hebrews 2:9). That He chose to taste the death we deserve also shows that the holy angels do not share our sinfulness—nor our need of redemption.

Angels Cannot Testify of Salvation by Grace through Faith

Who can comprehend the overwhelming thrill of fellowship with God and the joy of salvation that even angels do not know? When the local church assembles as a group of Christian believers, it represents in the human sphere the highest order of the love of God. No love could go deeper, rise higher, or extend farther than the amazing love that moved Him to give His only begotten Son. The angels are aware of that joy (Luke 15:10), and when a person accepts God's gift of eternal life through Jesus Christ, angels set all the bells of heaven to ringing with their rejoicing before the Lamb of God.

Yet although the angels rejoice when people are saved and glorify God who has saved them, they cannot do one thing: testify personally to something they have not experienced. They can only point to the experiences of the redeemed and rejoice that God has saved them. This means that throughout eternity we humans alone will give our personal witness to the salvation that God achieved by grace and that we received through faith in Jesus Christ. The man who has never married cannot fully appreciate the wonders of that relationship. The person who has never lost a father or mother cannot understand what that loss means. So angels, great as they are, cannot testify to salvation the same way as those who have experienced it.

Angels Have No Experiential Knowledge of the Indwelling God

Nothing in the Bible indicates that the Holy Spirit indwells angels as He does redeemed people. Since He seals believers when they accept Christ, such sealing would be unnecessary for the angels who never fell and who therefore need no salvation.

But there is a second reason for this difference. Redeemed men on earth have not yet been glorified. Once God has declared them just and given them life, He embarks on a process of making them inwardly holy while they live here below. At death He makes them perfect. So the Holy Spirit takes His abode in the hearts of all believers while they are still on earth, to perform His unique ministry, one that angels cannot perform. God the Father sent Jesus the Son to die; Jesus performed His unique ministry as His part of God's saving process. Likewise, the Holy Spirit has a role, one different from the Son's. Sent by the Father and the Son, He not only guides and directs believers, but also performs a work of grace in their hearts, conforming them to the image of God to make them holy like Christ. Angels cannot provide this sanctifying power.

Furthermore, angels themselves do not need the ministry of the Holy Spirit the way believers do. The angels have already been endowed with authority by virtue of their relationship to God through creation and continuing obedience. They are unspoiled by sin. People, however, are not yet perfect and therefore need what the Holy Spirit alone can give. Someday we will be as perfect as angels are now.

Angels Do Not Marry or Procreate

I have already said that angels do not marry. In Matthew 22:30, Jesus points out that "in the resurrection they [men] neither marry,

nor are given in marriage, but are as the angels of God in heaven."
Because of this we can make a deduction: The number of angels
remains constant. For the obedient angels do not die. The fallen
angels will suffer the final judgment at the time God finishes dealing with them. While we cannot be certain, some scholars estimate that as many as one third of the angels cast their lot with
Satan when he mysteriously rebelled against his Creator. In any
event the book of Hebrews says the angels constitute an "innumerable company," vast hosts that stagger our imagination. A third
of them would likely be counted in the hundreds of thousands—
ones who are now desperate demons.

Just as angels differ from people with respect to marriage, so they
differ in other important ways. Nothing in Scripture says that
angels must eat to stay alive. But the Bible says that on certain
occasions angels in human form did indeed eat. David refers to the
manna eaten by the children of Israel in the wilderness as the bread
of angels. In Psalm 78:25, Asaph says, "Man did eat angels' food."
We can hardly disregard what happened to Elijah after he won a
great victory over the priests of Baal on Mount Carmel. Because
Jezebel threatened his life he needed help from God. So God's angel
came to the tired, discouraged prophet and set before him food and
drink. When he had eaten twice he was sent on his journey; the
food he had eaten was enough to keep him for forty days and forty
nights (1 Kings 19:5). Not without reason some have concluded
that Elijah indeed ate angels' food.

When Abraham was encamped in the plains of Mamre, three
angels visited him, of whom one may have been the Lord Jesus
(Genesis 18:1, 2). These heavenly beings ate and drank what he
provided for them by way of customary entertainment. Shortly
thereafter, when God decided to destroy Sodom and Gomorrah,
two angelic beings came to save backslidden Lot and his family.
Lot made them a feast and there again they ate food, including
unleavened bread (Genesis 19).

It is interesting that after His resurrection, Jesus ate with His
disciples. Luke's account says that the disciples "gave him a piece
of a broiled fish, and of an honeycomb. And he took it, and did
eat before them" (Luke 24:42, 43).

The Knowledge of Angels

Angels excel humankind in their knowledge. When King David was being urged to bring Absalom back to Jerusalem, Joab asked a woman of Tekoah to talk to the king. She said: "My lord is wise, according to the wisdom of an angel of God, to know all things that are in the earth" (2 Samuel 14:20). And angels possess knowledge that men do not have. But however vast is their knowledge, we can be sure they are not omniscient. They do not know everything. They are not like God. Jesus bore testimony to the limited knowledge of the angels when He was speaking of His second coming. In Mark 13:32 He said, "But of that day and that hour knoweth no man, no, not the angels which are in heaven."

Angels probably know things about us that we do not know about ourselves. And because they are ministering spirits, they will always use this knowledge for our good and not for evil purposes. In a day when few men can be trusted with secret information, it is comforting to know that angels will not divulge their great knowledge to hurt us. Rather, they will use it for our good.

The Power of Angels

Angels enjoy far greater power than men, but they are not omnipotent or "all powerful." In 2 Thessalonians 1:7, Paul refers to the "mighty angels of God." From the word translated "mighty" here we get the English word "dynamite." In material power, angels are God's dynamite! In Peter we read, "angels who are greater in might and power [than men] do not bring a reviling judgment against them before the Lord" (2 Peter 2:11, NASB). Peter's testimony here reinforces Paul's. We should also note that it took only one angel to slay the first born of Egypt in Moses' day, and one to shut the lions' mouths for Daniel.

In Psalm 103:20 David speaks about [God's] "angels that excel in strength." Nowhere in Scripture is that strength manifested more dramatically than in the climax of this age. Following the Battle of Armageddon, Scripture pictures what will happen to Satan: He is to be bound and cast into a bottomless pit. But what power, apart from God Himself, can do this to Satan, whose power we all know about and whose evil designs we have experienced? The Bible says that one angel will come from heaven. He will have a great chain in his hand. He will lay hold of Satan and bind him with that chain. And then he will cast him into the pit. How great is the power of one of God's mighty angels.

Do Angels Sing?

There has been much conjecture about angel choirs. We at least assume that angels can and do sing, even if the Scriptures do not pointedly say so. In *Hamlet*, William Shakespeare seemed to underscore the possibility that angels sing when he stated, "Now cracks a noble heart, Good night, sweet prince:/ and flights of angels sing thee to thy rest."

Some Bible students insist that angels do not sing. This seems inconceivable. Angels possess the ultimate capacity to offer praise, and their music from time immemorial has been the primary vehicle of praise to our all-glorious God. Music is the universal language. It is likely that John saw a massive heavenly choir (Revelation 5:11, 12) of many millions who expressed their praise of the heavenly Lamb through magnificent music. I believe angel choirs will sing in eternity to the glory of God and the supreme delight of the redeemed.

While it is partly speculative, I believe that angels have the capacity to employ heavenly celestial music. Many dying believers have testified that they have heard the music of heaven. Most of my close friends tease me because I cannot carry a tune. When I am singing beside people in a congregation I usually throw them off key. But from years of listening I recognize good music when I hear it—even if I can't produce it myself. And there have been times when I have seriously tried to understand and appreciate music I did not like, whether it was a difficult opera or rock. I think before we can understand the music of heaven we will have to go beyond our earthly concept of music. I think most earthly music will seem to us to have been in the "minor key" in comparison to what we are going to hear in heaven.

The Bible tells us of many who sang: Moses (Exodus 15:1), Miriam (Exodus 15:20, 21), David (Psalms), and many others. Thou-

sands of worshipers at the temple continually sang, praising the
Lord (2 Chronicles 5:12). Thousands of singers preceded the ark
of the covenant (1 Chronicles 15:27, 28). We all think of Psalms
as the hymn book of the Bible.

New Testament believers also sang with rapturous joy. Though
the Bible does not say it, it implies that angels, who are of a higher
creative order, are tuned to sing with no discordant note to God
and the Lamb. Paul reminds us that there is a language of man and
a language of angels (1 Corinthians 13:1). Angels have a celestial
language and make music that is worthy of the God who made
them. I believe in heaven we will be taught the language and music
of the celestial world. The wonderful hymn, "Holy, Holy Is What
the Angels Sing," by Johnson Oatman, Jr., and J. Sweney expresses
this thought in verse 4:

> So, altho' I'm not an angel,
> yet I know that over there
> I will join the blessed chorus
> that the angels cannot share;
> I will sing about my Saviour,
> who upon dark Calvary
> Freely pardoned my transgressions,
> died to set a sinner free.

Angels Worship before the Throne

Unquestionably angels ascribe honor and glory to the Lamb of
God. But angels do not spend all their time in heaven. They are
not omnipresent (everywhere present at the same time), so they
can be in only one place at a given time. Yet as God's messengers
they are busy around the world carrying out God's orders. Is it not,
therefore, obvious that when they are engaged in their ministry
here they cannot stand before God's throne? But when angels do
stand before the throne of God, indeed they worship and adore
their creator.

We can look for that future day when angels will have finished
their earthly ministry. Then they will gather with all the redeemed
before the throne of God in heaven. There they will offer their

praise and sing their songs. In that day the angels who veiled their faces and stood mute when Jesus hung on the cross will then ascribe glory to the Lamb whose work is finished and whose kingdom has come. The angels may also stop to listen as the redeemed children of God express their own thanksgiving for salvation. It may well be true as the hymn writer has said in verse 3 of the song, "Holy, Holy Is What the Angels Sing,"

> Then the angels stand and listen,
> For they cannot join that song,
> Like the sound of many waters,
> By that happy, blood-washed throng.

But the children of God will also stop to listen to the angels. They have their own reasons for singing, ones that differ from ours. They have given themselves to the service of God Almighty. They have had a part in bringing in the kingdom of God. They have helped the children of God in difficult circumstances. So theirs shall be a shout and a song of victory. The cause they represent has been victorious; the fight they fought is finished; the enemy they met has been conquered; their wicked companion angels who fell shall vex them no more. The angels sing a different song. But they sing; my, how they sing! And I believe that angels and those of us who have been redeemed will compete with each other for the endless ages of eternity to see who can best ascribe glory and praise to our wonderful God!

Do you have that hope of eternity in your heart right now? Do you know—beyond doubt—that some day you will join the angels in heaven in singing praises to God? If not, make your commitment to Christ today.

Without Christ you are separated from God and without hope of eternal life. You need to have your sins forgiven, and you need to be renewed and cleansed by the power of God. And this can happen, if you will give your life to Christ and trust Him as your personal Lord and Savior. Christ came to take away your sins by His death on the cross. You deserved to die—but He died in your place! "For Christ died for sins once for all, the righteous for the unrighteous, to bring you to God" (1 Peter 3:18, NIV). Right now by a simple prayer of faith you can invite Christ to come into your heart. When you do, He will make you part of His family forever and you can know that some day you will join with the angels and with millions of believers from across the ages in singing praises to God in heaven. Take that step of faith today.

5

Angelic Organization

WE CANNOT STUDY the subject of angels in the Bible without becoming aware of ranks among angelic beings. The evidence shows that they are organized in terms of authority and glory.

Though some see the ranking of celestial powers as conjectural, it seems to follow this pattern: archangels, angels, seraphim, cherubim, principalities, authorities, powers, thrones, might and dominion (Colossians 1:16; Romans 8:38).

Medieval theologians divided angelic beings into ten grades. Some people, however, have asked whether some of these grades—the principalities, authorities, powers, thrones, might and dominion—could not refer to human institutions and human beings. To answer, we must understand Colossians 1:16. Paul is speaking about creation of things both seen and unseen. On this verse Matthew Henry says that Christ "made all things out of nothing, the highest angel in heaven as well as men upon earth. He made the world, the upper and lower world, with all the inhabitants of both. . . . He [Paul] speaks here as if there were several orders of angels: 'Whether thrones, or dominions, or principalities, or powers,' which must signify either different degrees of excellence or different offices and employments." Perhaps any list that ranks angelic beings will err, but we can be sure they differ in power, some having authority others do not possess. While I do not wish to be dogmatic, I think there are different ranks of angels and that the list given in Colossians does refer to these celestial personalities. Let's look at four of them:

1. ARCHANGEL

While Scripture designates only Michael as an archangel (Jude 9), we have biblical grounds for believing that before his fall Lucifer was also an archangel, equal or perhaps superior to Michael. The prefix "arch" suggests a chief, principal or great angel. Thus, Michael is now the angel above all angels, recognized in rank to be the first prince of heaven. He is, as it were, the Prime Minister in God's administration of the universe, and is the "angel administrator" of God for judgment. He must stand alone, because the Bible never speaks of archangels, only *the* archangel. His name means "who is like unto the Lord."

In the Old Testament, Michael seems to be identified primarily with Israel as a nation. Thus, God speaks of Michael as prince of His chosen people, "the great prince which standeth for the children of thy people" (Daniel 12:1). He specially protects and defends God's people whoever they are.

Further, in Daniel he is referred to as "Michael, your prince" (Daniel 10:21). He is God's messenger of law and judgment. In this capacity he appears in Revelation 12:7–12 leading the armies that battle Satan, the great dragon, and all of his demons. Michael with his angels will be locked in the titanic struggle of the universe at the last conflict of the age, which will mark the defeat of Satan and all forces of darkness. Scripture tells us in advance that Michael will finally be victorious in the battle. Hell will tremble; heaven will rejoice and celebrate!

Bible students have speculated that Michael cast Lucifer and his fallen angels out of heaven, and that Michael enters into conflict with Satan and the evil angels today to destroy their power and to give to God's people the prospect of their ultimate victory.

Michael, the archangel, will shout as he accompanies Jesus at His Second Coming. Not only does he proclaim the matchless and exciting news that Jesus Christ returns, but he speaks the word of life to all who are dead in Christ and who await their resurrection. "For the Lord himself shall descend from heaven with a shout, with the voice of the archangel . . . and the dead in Christ shall rise first" (1 Thessalonians 4:16).

2. THE ANGEL GABRIEL

Gabriel is one of the most prominent angels mentioned in Scripture.

"Gabriel," in Hebrew, means "God's hero," or "the mighty one," or "God is great." Scripture frequently refers to him as "the messenger of Jehovah" or "the Lord's messenger." However, contrary to popular opinion and to the poet John Milton, it never calls him an archangel. Yet it refers to his work more often than to Michael's.

Ministry of Gabriel

Gabriel is primarily God's messenger of mercy and promise. He appears four times in the Bible, always bearing good news (Daniel 8:16, 9:21; Luke 1:19, 26). We may question whether he blows a silver trumpet, since this idea arises from folk music and finds only indirect support in Scripture. But the announcements of Gabriel in unfolding the plans, purposes and verdicts of God are of monumental importance.

In Scripture we gain our first glimpse of Gabriel in Daniel 8:15,16. There he announces the vision of God for the "end time." God has charged him to convey the message from the "situation room" of heaven that reveals God's plan in history. In verse 17 Gabriel says, "Understand, . . . the vision belongs to (events that shall occur in) the time of the end" (AB).

Daniel, while in prayer, records Gabriel's second appearance to him: "While I was speaking in prayer, the man Gabriel, whom I had seen in the former vision, being caused to fly swiftly, came near to me and touched me about the time of the evening sacrifice" (Daniel 9:21, AB). To Daniel he said, "Understand the vision" (9:23), and then revealed to him the magnificent sequence of events at the end time. Gabriel, sketching panoramically the procession of earthly kingdoms, assured Daniel that history would culminate in the return of Christ, "the prince of princes," (Daniel 8:25, AB) and conqueror of the "king of fierce countenance" (Daniel 8:23, AB). The prophetic announcement by Daniel in his prayer to God is twofold. He expressly refers to the more immediate judgment upon Israel (Daniel 9:16) and then to the awesome portent of "end time judgment" and "tribulation" which shall be for "seven years" (Daniel 9:27). In a later chapter, "Angels in Prophecy," we will trace how the angels supervise the fearsome events of the end time.

Gabriel in the New Testament

Gabriel first appears in the New Testament in Luke 1. He identifies himself to Zacharias (verse 19), announces the birth of John the Baptist and describes his life and ministry as the forerunner of Jesus.

But in his most important appearance, Gabriel informs the Virgin Mary about Jesus, the incarnate God! What a message to deliver to the world through a teenage girl! What a wonderfully holy girl she must have been, to be visited by the mighty Gabriel. He declares:

> Fear not, Mary: for thou hast found favour with God. And, behold, thou shalt conceive in thy womb, and bring forth a son, and shalt call his name Jesus. . . . And he shall reign over the house of Jacob for ever; and of his kingdom there shall be no end (Luke 1:30–33).

Throughout all time, this divine declaration of Gabriel shall be the Magna Charta of the incarnation and the foundation stone of the world to come: God became flesh to redeem us.

3. SERAPHIM

It would appear from the Bible that celestial and extraterrestrial beings differ in rank and authority. The seraphim and cherubim follow in order after the archangel and angels. These may possibly define the angelic authority to which Peter refers when he speaks of Jesus, "Who is gone into heaven, and is on the right hand of God; angels and authorities and powers being made subject unto him" (1 Peter 3:22).

The word "seraphim" may come from the Hebrew root meaning "love" (though some think the word means "burning ones" or "nobles"). We find the seraphim only in Isaiah 6:1–6. It is an awe-inspiring sight as the worshiping prophet beholds the six-winged seraphim above the throne of the Lord. We can assume that there were several seraphim since Isaiah speaks about "each one" and "one cried unto another."

The ministry of the seraphim is to praise the name and character of God in heaven. Their ministry relates directly to God and His heavenly throne, because they are positioned above the throne—unlike the cherubim, who are beside it. Students of the Bible have not always agreed on the duties of the seraphim, but we know one thing: they are constantly glorifying God. We also learn from Isaiah 6:7 that God can use them to cleanse and purify His servants.

They were indescribably beautiful. "With two [wings] he covered his face, and with two he covered his feet, and with two he did fly" (implying that some angelic beings fly). The Scriptures do not, however, support the common belief that all angels have wings. The traditional concept of angels with wings is drawn from their ability to move instantaneously and with unlimited speed from place to place, and wings were thought to permit such limitless movement. But here in Isaiah 6 only two of the seraphim's wings were employed for flying.

The glory of the seraphim reminds us of Ezekiel's description of the four living creatures. He did not call them seraphim, but they too performed their service for God. Like seraphim they acted as both agents and spokesmen of God. In both cases the glory displayed was a witness to God, though only the seraphim, of course, hovered over the heavenly throne as functionaries and attendants, with a chief duty of praising God. In all these manifestations we see God willing that men should know of His glory. He determines to maintain an adequate witness to that glory in both terrestrial and celestial realms.

4. CHERUBIM

Cherubim are real and they are powerful. But the cherubim in the Bible were often symbolic of heavenly things. "At God's direction they were incorporated into the design of the Ark of the Covenant and the Tabernacle. Solomon's temple utilized them in its decoration" (*Zondervan Pictorial Encyclopedia*). They had wings, feet and hands. Ezekiel 10 pictures the cherubim in detail as having not only wings and hands, but being "full of eyes," encompassed by "wheels within wheels."

But Ezekiel sounds a somber note in chapter 10 also, and the cherubim provide the clue. The prophet presents his vision that prophesies the destruction of Jerusalem. In Ezekiel 9:3, the Lord has descended from His throne above the cherubim to the threshold of the temple, while in 10:1 He returns again to take His seat above them. In the calm before the storm, we see the cherubim stationed on the south side of the sanctuary. Being stationed in position toward the city, they witness the beginning of the gradual withdrawal of God's glory from Jerusalem. The fluttering of their wings indicates immensely important events to follow (10:5). Then the cherubim rise up in preparation for the departure.

While Ezekiel 10 is difficult to understand, one point comes across clearly. The cherubim have to do with the glory of God. This chapter is one of the most mysterious and yet descriptive passages of the glory of God to be found in the Bible, and it involves angelic beings. It should be read carefully and prayerfully. The reader gets a sense of God's greatness and glory as in few other passages in the Bible.

While the seraphim and the cherubim belong to different orders and are surrounded by much mystery in Scripture, they share one thing. They constantly glorify God. We see the cherubim beside the throne of God. "Thou that dwellest between the cherubim, shine forth" (Psalm 80:1). "He sitteth between the cherubim" (Psalm 99:1). God's glory will not be denied, and every heavenly being gives silent or vocal testimony to the splendor of God. In Genesis 3:24, we see cherubim guarding the tree of life in Eden. In the tabernacle in the wilderness designs representing the guardian cherubim formed a part of the mercy seat and were made of gold (Exodus 25:18).

The cherubim did more than guard the most holy place from those who had no right of access to God. They also assured the right of the high priest to enter the holy place with blood as the mediator with God on behalf of the people. He, and he alone, was permitted to enter into the inner sanctuary of the Lord. By right of redemption and in accordance with the position of believers, each true child of God now has direct access as a believer-priest to the presence of God through Jesus. Cherubim will not refuse the humblest Christian access to the throne. They assure us that we can come boldly—because of Christ's work on the cross! The veil in the temple has been rent. As Paul says, "Ye are no more strangers and foreigners, but fellow citizens with the saints, and of the household of God" (Ephesians 2:19). Further, Peter assures that "Ye are a chosen generation, a royal priesthood, an holy nation, a peculiar people; that ye should show forth the praises of him who hath called you out of darkness into his marvelous light" (1 Peter 2:9).

The inner sanctuary of God's throne is always open to those who have repented of sin and trusted Christ as Savior.

Many believe that the "living creatures" often mentioned in the book of Revelation are cherubim. But as glorious as the angelic and heavenly beings are, they become dim beside the inexpressible glory resident in our heavenly Lamb, the Lord of glory, to whom all powers in heaven and on earth bow in holy worship and breathless adoration.

6

Lucifer and the Angelic Rebellion

FEW PEOPLE REALIZE the profound part angelic forces play in human events. It is Daniel who most dramatically reveals the constant and bitter conflict between the holy angels faithful to God and the angels of darkness allied with Satan (Daniel 10:11–14). This Satan, or the devil, was once called "Lucifer, the son of the morning." Along with Michael he may have been one of the two archangels, but he was cast from heaven with his rebel forces, and continues to fight. Satan may appear to be winning the war because sometimes he wins important battles, but the final outcome is certain. One day he will be defeated and stripped of his powers eternally. God will shatter the powers of darkness.

Many people ask, "How could this conflict come about in God's perfect universe?" The apostle Paul calls it "the mystery of iniquity" (2 Thessalonians 2:7). While we have not been given as much information as we might like, we do know one thing for certain: The angels who fell, fell because they had sinned against God. In 2 Peter 2:4 the Scripture says, "God spared not the angels that sinned but cast them down to hell, and delivered them into chains of darkness, to be reserved unto judgment." Perhaps the parallel passage in Jude 6 puts the onus of responsibility more directly on the shoulders of the angels themselves. "The angels," wrote Jude, quite deliberately, "kept not their first estate, but left their own habitation."

Thus, the greatest catastrophe in the history of the universal creation was Lucifer's defiance of God and the consequent fall of perhaps one third of the angels who joined him in his wickedness.

When did it happen? Sometime between the dawn of creation and the intrusion of Satan into the Garden of Eden. The poet Dante reckoned that the fall of the rebel angels took place within twenty seconds of their creation and originated in the pride that made Lucifer unwilling to await the time when he would have perfect knowledge. Others, like Milton, put the angelic creation and fall immediately prior to the temptation of Adam and Eve in the Garden of Eden.

But the important question is not, "When were angels created?" but, "When did they fall?" It is difficult to suppose that their fall occurred before God placed Adam and Eve in the Garden. We know for a fact that God rested on the seventh day, or at the end of all creation, and pronounced everything to be good. By implication, up to this time even the angelic creation was good. We might then ask, "How long were Adam and Eve in the Garden before the angels fell and before Satan tempted the first man and woman?" This question must remain unanswered. All we can say positively is that Satan, who had fallen before he tempted Adam and Eve, was the agent and bears a greater guilt because there was no one to tempt him when he sinned; on the other hand Adam and Eve were faced with a tempter.

Thus, we pick up the story where it began. It all started mysteriously with Lucifer. He was the most brilliant and most beautiful of all created beings in heaven. He was probably the ruling prince of the universe under God, against whom he rebelled. The result was insurrection and war in heaven! He began a war that has been raging in heaven from the moment he sinned and was brought to earth shortly after the dawn of human history. It sounds like a modern world crisis!

Isaiah 14:12–14 records the conflict's origin. Prior to his rebellion, Lucifer, an angel of light, is described in scintillating terms in Ezekiel 28:12–17 (NASB): "You had the seal of perfection, full of wisdom and perfect in beauty. . . . You were the anointed cherub who covers, and I placed you there. You were on the holy mountain of God. You walked in the midst of the stones of fire. You were blameless in your ways from the day you were created, until unrighteousness was found in you. . . . Your heart was lifted up because of your beauty; you corrupted your wisdom by reason of your splendor." When the angel Lucifer rebelled against God and His works, some have estimated that as many as one third of the angelic hosts of the universe may have joined him in his rebellion. Thus, the war that started in heaven continues on earth and will see its climax at Armageddon with Christ and His angelic army victorious.

Leslie Miller in his excellent little book, *All About Angels*, points out that Scripture sometimes refers to angels as stars. This explains why prior to his fall Satan was called, "the star of the morning." And to this description John adds a qualifying detail, "His tail swept a third of the stars out of the sky and flung them to the earth" (Revelation 12:4, NIV).

Rebellion in Heaven

The apostle Paul understood and spoke of the war of rebellion in the heavens when he referred to the former Lucifer, now Satan, as "the prince of the power of the air, the spirit that now worketh in the children of disobedience" (Ephesians 2:2). He also says that in fighting the organized kingdom of satanic darkness, we struggle against "the worldforces of this darkness . . . the spiritual forces of wickedness in the heavenly places" (Ephesians 6:12, NASB).

We can describe all unrighteousness and transgression against God as "self-will" against the will of God. This definition applies to human beings today as well as to angels.

Lucifer's Five "I Wills"

Lucifer, the son of the morning, was created, as were all angels, for the purpose of glorifying God. However, instead of serving God and praising Him forever, Satan desired to rule over heaven and creation in the place of God. He wanted supreme authority! Lucifer said (Isaiah 14), "I will ascend into heaven." "I will exalt my throne above the stars of God." "I will sit also upon the mount of the congregation." "I will ascend above the heights of the clouds." "I will be like the most high." I . . . I . . . I . . . I . . . I.

Lucifer was not satisfied with being subordinated to his creator. He wanted to usurp God's throne. He exulted at the thought of being the center of power throughout the universe—he wanted to be the Caesar, the Napoleon, the Hitler of the entire universe. The "I will" spirit is the spirit of rebellion. His was a bold act to dethrone the Lord Most High. Here was a wicked schemer who saw himself occupying the superlative position of power and glory. He wanted to be worshiped, not to worship.

Satan's desire to replace God as ruler of the universe may have been rooted in a basic sin that leads to the sin of pride I have already mentioned. Underneath Satan's pride lurked the deadliest of all sins, the sin of covetousness. He wanted what did not belong to him. Virtually every war ever fought began because of covetousness. The warfare in heaven and on earth between God and the devil certainly sprang from the same desire—the lust for what belonged to God alone.

Today as always in the past, virtually no one can sin alone. The influences of sin are contagious. The Bible speaks of "the dragon . . . and his angels" (Revelation 12:7), indicating that along with Lucifer, myriads of angels also chose to deny the authority of God and subsequently lost their high position. They chose to participate in the "war program" of Lucifer. As a result of their fall, those angels have been "reserved unto judgment" (2 Peter 2:4) and have their part with Lucifer in the "everlasting fire, prepared for the devil and his angels" (Matthew 25:41). But until this happens they constitute a mighty force—capable of wreaking havoc among individuals, families and nations! Watch out, they are dangerous, vicious and deadly. They want you under their control and they will pay any price to get you!

Satan, the fallen prince of heaven, has made his decision to battle against God to the death. He is the master craftsman who has plotted destruction during all the ages since he first rebelled. His "I will" spirit has worked through his consuming hatred of God to write his tragic story in the annals of human history. In his warfare against God, Satan uses the human race, which God created and loved. So God's forces of good and Satan's forces of evil have been engaged in a deadly conflict from the dawn of our history. Unless world leaders and statesmen understand the true nature of this warfare, they will continue to be blind leaders of the blind. They can only patch a little here and patch a little there. We will find no final solution to the world's great problems until this spiritual warfare has been settled. And it will be settled in the last war of history—Armageddon. Then Christ and His angelic armies will be the victor!

Past, Present and Future in Perspective

Lucifer became Satan, the devil, the author of sin; and it is sin that has always deceived, disturbed, betrayed, depraved and destroyed all that it has touched.

Will there never be an end to this Battle of the Ages, this war against God lustfully conceived in Lucifer and perpetrated on earth?

Not only does the battle rage on earth, but it rages in heaven. "And there was war in heaven: Michael and his angels fought against the dragon; and the dragon fought and his angels . . . and the great dragon was cast out" (Revelation 12:7, 9).

Satan and his demons are known by the discord they promote, the wars they start, the hatred they engender, the murders they initiate, the opposition to God and His commandments. They are dedicated to the spirit of destruction. On the other hand the holy angels obey their Creator. No discordant note sounds among the angels of heaven. They are committed to fulfill the purpose for which all true children of God pray, "Thy kingdom come. Thy will be done . . . as it is in heaven" (Matthew 6:10).

The Bible refers to Lucifer and the fallen angels as those who sinned and did not keep their first position (Jude 6). They committed the sins of consummate pride and covetousness. The sin of pride particularly has caused the downfall of Lucifer in heaven; most certainly it can bring mortal man down too. We must be on guard against pride, or we are headed for a fall patterned after the fall of Lucifer and his angels, who turned into demons.

Could it be that God wanted to be sure that men would not question the existence of Satan and his demon-hosts? Perhaps He had this in mind when He inspired the writing of Ezekiel 28, which sets forth the typology of Satan in the earthly sense. This account by the prophet Ezekiel speaks of an earthly prince of the city of Tyre. He seems to be an earthly symbol of Satan. It is clear from the passage that the king of Tyre became a devil incarnate, and an earthly illustration of the heavenly Lucifer who became the devil.

We live in a perpetual battlefield—the great War of the Ages continues to rage. The lines of battle press in ever more tightly about God's own people. The wars among nations on earth are merely popgun affairs compared to the fierceness of battle in the spiritual, unseen world. This invisible spiritual conflict is waged around us incessantly and unremittingly. Where the Lord works, Satan's forces hinder; where angel beings carry out their divine directives, the devils rage. All this comes about because the powers of darkness press their counterattack to recapture the ground held for the glory of God.

Were it not for the angel hosts empowered by God to resist the demons of Satan, who could ever hope to press through the battlements of the fiendish demons of darkness to the Lord of eternal liberty and salvation? Paul speaks the truth when he says that the forts of darkness are impregnable. Yet they yield to the warfare of faith and light as angel hosts press the warfare to gain the victory for us (2 Corinthians 10:4, 5).

Satan on the Attack

Revelation 12:10 speaks of Satan as "the accuser of the brethren" and Ephesians 6:12 (NIV) describes the "rulers . . . authorities . . . the powers of this dark world . . . the spiritual forces of evil in the heavenly realms." Although Satan and his evil followers press their warfare in the heavens, it seems that their primary endeavor is to destroy faith in the world.

Isaiah 13:12–14 clearly points up Satan's objectives: he works to bring about the downfall of nations, to corrupt moral standards and to waste human resources. Corrupting society's order, he wants to prevent the attainment of order, and to shake the kingdoms of our God. He uses his destructive power to create havoc, fire, flood, earthquake, storm, pestilence, disease and the devastation of peoples and nations. The description of Satan's great power ends with the words, "who opened not the house of his prisoners" (Isaiah 14:17). This undoubtedly refers to the prison house of Satan, Hades or the abode of the dead so clearly pictured in Luke 16:19–31.

Satan has great power. He is cunning and clever, having set himself against God and His people. He will do everything in his power to hold people captive in sin and to drag them down to the prison of eternal separation from God.

Since the fall of Lucifer, that angel of light and son of the morning, there has been no respite in the bitter Battle of the Ages. Night and day Lucifer, the master craftsman of the devices of darkness, labors to thwart God's plan of the ages. We can find inscribed on every page of human history the consequences of the evil brought to fruition by the powers of darkness with the devil in charge. Satan never yields an inch, nor does he ever pause in his opposition to the plan of God to redeem the "cosmos" from his control. He forever tries to discredit the truthfulness of the Word of God; he coaxes men to deny the authority of God; and he persuades the world to wallow in the deluding comforts of sin. "He was a murderer from the beginning, not holding to the truth, for there is no truth in him. When he lies, he speaks his native language, for he is a liar and the father of lies" (John 8:44, NIV). Sin is the frightful fact in our world. It writes its ruin in vice and lust, in the convulsions of war, in selfishness and sorrow, and in broken hearts and lost souls. It remains as the tragedy of the universe and the tool of Satan to blunt or destroy the works of God.

Satanic Intrigue

God cannot tolerate sin forever if He is just. He will not permit the perversions of Lucifer to mock Him, for the inescapable answer to the evil of the world is found in the unalterable law of the Word of God that "the wages of sin is death; but the gift of God is eternal life through Jesus Christ our Lord" (Romans 6:23). Satan's attacks, which began at the dawn of history, will continue until God begins to bring down the curtain on this frightening drama at Armageddon.

Satan's ideology is based on the little word "if." Through all time he has sought to discredit God by making Him out a liar in the eyes of man. He never ceases trying to discredit the claims of the Word of God and to rob mankind of the strength and comfort of faith. The all-time tool of Lucifer is an "if," but God declares that there are no "ifs," "buts" or "ands" about His program for salvation. God's plan is unalterable; His antidote for the satanic "if" works and is unchangeable. God assures us that through the work of Christ and the labors of His angelic deputies we can look for the triumphant and victorious warfare over the armies of Lucifer.

It is not surprising that the fallen Lucifer hatched his plot to usurp the preeminence of God in His creation. In the first conversation in the Garden, the serpent embodying Lucifer asked, "Hath God said, Ye shall not eat of every tree of the garden?" (Genesis 3:1). To this question Eve replied, "But God did say, 'You must not eat fruit from the tree that is in the middle of the garden, and you must not touch it, or you will die" (Genesis 3:3, NIV).

Hear Lucifer reply, if you eat of the fruit of this tree "ye shall not surely die" (Genesis 3:4). He says in effect that God does not know what He is talking about. Satan often works by interjecting a question to raise doubts. It is deadly to doubt God's Word! Satan's strategy is to persuade us to rationalize. Eve probably began to reason with the enemy: Is it possible that God would be so unjust and unkind as to forbid this seemingly innocent thing?—"it was pleasant to the eyes" (Genesis 3:6).

Eve foolishly parleyed with the tempter. In her own mind she began to doubt the truth and the wisdom of God. How easily Satan covers with a light color ideas that are dark. His intrigue comes to us colored in the light of our own desires. Time after time he injects his subtle "ifs." "This tree is to be desired to make one wise." Eve listened; she reasoned with herself, she took, she tasted. Satan never fails to appeal to the appetites of the flesh and to the seeming sensual satisfactions that come from the inventions of sin.

Our senses are inlets through which Satan can work, prod and inject his deadly "ifs."

The Genesis account states that Eve ate first, and then gave some to Adam to eat. If they had fixed their minds on God and trusted His wisdom, recognizing the danger that lurked in the fruit He had forbidden, all history would have been radically different and had another ending. Had they only realized the consequences of disobedience, had they only seen the danger of the satanic "if," had they only envisioned the flaming sword barring them forever from the Garden! Had they only realized the terrible consequences of a single "innocent" moment, they would not have had to stand over the silent, lifeless form of their son Abel. His tragic death was the fruit of the seductive power of sin in their own lives. Apart from it our world would have been paradise today!

Had Adam and Eve resisted the devil, he would have fled, forever defeated. But they fell, and thus death passed upon all men (Genesis 3:13). This is where death began! Sin works the same with all of us, whatever our condition, nature or environment. We are depraved by nature because we inherited it from our parents (Romans 3:19). The stream has been polluted. We must bear the sentence of guilt and the stain of sin. Each must give account of himself to God.

Listen to Satan's "ifs" of death being injected into the minds of people today: "if" you live a good life, "if" you do what is right, "if" you go to church, "if" you work for the benefit of others—if, if, if. But the Bible teaches that these "ifs" are not enough to meet God's requirements for salvation. Our good works and intentions are not enough. Jesus said, "Ye must be born again" (John 3:7). Only when we turn to Christ in faith and trust, confessing our sins to Him and seeking His forgiveness, can we be assured of our salvation. Satan will do all in his power to make us trust ourselves instead of Christ. But only Christ can save us—and He will, if we will commit our lives to Him and trust His work on the cross for our salvation. "For God so loved the world that he gave his one and only Son, that whosoever believes in him shall not perish but have eternal life" (John 3:16, NIV).

These are Satan's approaches today. The hiss of the serpent is the "if" of death. The stench of death is everywhere today! As

C. S. Lewis points out, "War does not increase death—death is total in every generation." But we can find eternal life when we believe in Jesus Christ.

Have you made your personal commitment to Christ, and are you trusting Him alone for your salvation? If you have never taken that step of faith, or if you are unsure about your relationship to Christ, turn to Him today and receive Him as your personal Lord and Savior. "To all who received him, to those who believed in his name, he gave the right to become children of God" (John 1:12, NIV). This can be your experience today if you will ask Christ to come into your heart by faith.

7

Angels as Messengers of God

Angels minister to us personally. Many accounts in Scripture confirm that we are the subjects of their individual concern. In his book, *Table Talk*, Martin Luther said, "An angel is a spiritual creature created by God without a body, for the service of Christendom and the church."

We may not always be aware of the presence of angels. We can't always predict how they will appear. But angels have been said to be our neighbors. Often they may be our companions without our being aware of their presence. We know little of their constant ministry. The Bible assures us, however, that one day our eyes will be unscaled to see and know the full extent of the attention angels have given us (1 Corinthians 13:11, 12).

Many experiences of God's people suggest that angels have been ministering to them. Others may not have known they were being helped, yet the visitation was real. The Bible tells us that God has ordered angels to minister to His people—those who have been redeemed by the power of Christ's blood.

Daniel and the Angel

In the Old Testament, Daniel vividly describes the bitter conflict between the angelic forces of God and the opposing demons of darkness. Before the angel came to him he had spent three weeks mourning (Daniel 10:3). He ate no bread, meat or wine, nor did he anoint himself. As he stood by the Tigris River, a man appeared clothed in linen. His face looked like lightning and his eyes like flaming torches. His voice sounded like the roar of a crowd.

Daniel alone saw the vision. The men who were with him did not. Yet a great dread came upon them, and they ran away to hide. Left alone with the heavenly visitor, Daniel's strength departed from him, so great was the effect of this personage on him.

Daniel was held in the bonds of a great sleep, yet he heard the voice of the angel. A hand touched him and the angel described an experience he himself had just had. The angel had started to come to Daniel from the moment he began to pray, but en route was waylaid by a demon prince who engaged him in conflict and delayed him. Then Michael came to help this subordinate angel, freeing him to fulfill his mission to Daniel.

The angel had a message. He was to show Daniel what God foresaw would befall the world—especially Israel in the latter days. Daniel then found himself weak and unable to speak, so the angel touched his lips and also restored his strength. Having finished his mission, the angel told Daniel he was returning to fight with the demon prince in the unending struggle of the forces of good versus the forces of evil. In all this Daniel was having no hallucination or dream. It was a genuine experience with a real person, and no one could ever have persuaded Daniel otherwise.

He had pleaded with God for the sons of Israel. His prayer session, accompanied by fasting, had lasted for three weeks. At that moment he received the news from the "angel visitor" sent from heaven that his prayer had been heard. This incident makes it clear that delays are not denials, and that God's permissive will is involved in all of life.

Unseen Forces at Work

During several world crises I have had the privilege of talking with some heads of state or secretaries of state. During the 1967 Middle East war, for example, Secretary of State Dean Rusk, who was visiting my home town of Montreat, North Carolina, invited me to his room. While we were discussing the war that had just broken out, I told him I believed "supernatural forces are at work."

On the eve of one of his missions abroad during the Ford Administration, Secretary of State Kissinger briefed me on some of the staggering problems facing the world. I told him I believed the world was experiencing an unseen spiritual war in which the powers of darkness were attacking the forces of God. As we have moved through the turbulent events of the past decade, I have become more convinced than ever that the activities of the unseen demonic forces are increasing. A well-known television newscaster said to me in his office, "The world is out of control." It seems incredible that such a warfare is taking place—but the Bible says it is!

Dr. A. C. Gaebelein has called it "the conflict of the ages." It will be resolved only when Jesus Christ returns to earth. This is why the world is crying for "a leader." The Anti-Christ, who will be Satan's "front," will arrive on the scene for a brief time and seemingly be The Answer. But after only a few months the world will be thrown back into chaos and conflict. He will prove to be "The Lie" (2 Thessalonians 2:3–10). Then the One whom God chose and anointed before time began will return to earth with His mighty, holy angels. At the end of the age He will throw the devil and his demons into the lake of fire. Thus, for the true believer the conflict now raging will end as God intends. Righteousness will prevail.

Jacob's Experience

The experience of Jacob with angels is a splendid illustration of their ministry for God to men. In some ways Jacob was a cheat. He had stolen the birthright from his brother. He lied to his father and deceived him when his sight was almost gone. He fled from his brother, who would have killed him. He married his Uncle Laban's two daughters, and when their father and brothers no longer looked on him with favor he took his family and flocks back to Canaan.

Though Jacob was a cunning schemer and skilled in deception, God was concerned for him as the one who was in "the line of promise." From him the twelve tribes of Israel were to come. While he was en route home the Scripture tells us that "the angels of God met him." So overcome was he by what happened that he said, "This is God's army!" (verse 2, Genesis 32, AB), and called the place Mahanaim, meaning "two camps." He called the angels, "God's hosts." But the story does not end there. Having formerly cheated his brother Esau, he now feared him, not knowing whether he would be welcomed or killed. So Jacob prayed, admitting he was not worthy of the least of God's mercies. He asked to be delivered from the hand of his brother Esau.

The night before Jacob met Esau he was alone, his family and servants having gone ahead. Suddenly a man appeared and wrestled with him until daybreak, when he finally touched Jacob's thigh, "and the hollow of the thigh was out of joint." At this, Jacob realized the man was a heavenly visitor, and would not let him go until the man had blessed him. When he had told the stranger his name, the man said, "Thy name shall be called no more Jacob, but Israel: for as a prince hast thou power with God and with men and hast prevailed." When Jacob asked the man to identify himself, he received no reply. But the man blessed him there. Jacob called the place Peniel, meaning "face of God" saying, "I have seen God face to face, and my life is preserved" (Genesis 32:24–30).

It may well be that the wrestler was Jesus, appearing fleetingly in human form. In the former part of the story many angels were surrounding Jacob. Through the two experiences, God revealed His will for Jacob's life more fully, and promised that he would be a prince. The next day he therefore went forward cheerfully to meet Esau; everything turned out well for him and his family. Centuries later Hosea testified to this incident, saying that the God of heaven had appeared to Jacob, ministering to him in the person of an angel (Hosea 12:3–6).

Moses and Abraham are perhaps the two greatest Old Testament characters; angels were involved in their lives on important occasions. We have already seen how angels ministered to Abraham. We must look at the experience of Moses at the burning bush (Exodus 3).

Moses Meets an Angel

The background is important. For forty years Moses had lived amid the splendors of Egypt, coming to know its language, customs and laws. He lived a life of luxury and occupied an important position in the social structure. Then because of the misadventure of slaying an Egyptian he fled to the desert. For forty years more he was tutored as a sheepherder in the "university of solitude." Scripture says little about that period, but it represented a great change in circumstances to go from the court of Pharaoh to a field of grazing sheep. It was not exactly an occupation that ranked high in the social order. He was an outcast, a lonely figure compared to his former life. And it took God forty years to bring him to the place where he was serviceable for the job God had in mind for him. So it was that at eighty years of age when the life work of most people has already been completed, Moses was ready for God's call.

One day as he was going about his duties, Moses saw a bush burning. It struck him as peculiar because the bush was not consumed. More than that, "the angel of the Lord appeared to him in a flame of fire out of the midst of the bush." Since we have no reason to suppose that Moses had ever seen an angel before, this must have been an extraordinary visitation to him. Further, his curiosity was aroused. Then it was that God Himself spoke to Moses out of the bush.

Moses was profoundly moved. Having told him to remove his shoes because he was standing on holy ground, God identified Himself as the God of Abraham, Isaac and Jacob. At this Moses was awestruck, and hid his face, fearing to look at God. God then disclosed to Moses His plan to release the Israelites from their captivity in Egypt, using Moses as their leader. When asked by Moses whom he should say had told him this when he approached the Israelites, God responded, "Say I AM hath sent me unto you."

Moses was not at all enthusiastic about what God told him to do. He began to offer what he thought were compelling reasons to be excused from that service. First he said that the people of Israel would never believe him, and therefore would not accept his leadership. In answer, God asked him what he had in his hand. Moses said, "a rod." "Cast it on the ground," God said, and suddenly it became a serpent. But when Moses picked it up, it again became a rod. Then at God's command he put his hand in his robe, and withdrawing it found it leprous. But putting it back a second time and withdrawing it, he found it free of all disease. By such signs, God said, would He show the people Moses' divine commission.

Then Moses made another excuse: He said he couldn't talk, professing to be slow of speech. Perhaps this was the result of forty years in virtual silence on the backside of the desert, but God even refused this excuse, saying He would send Aaron to be his voice. And so Moses went from the desert to Egypt to begin the work of deliverance. But the incident is important in our study because it is tied closely to the angel of the Lord in the burning bush. This again shows that God used angels (or appeared as an angel) to make His will known and communicate His decisions to men.

The presence of angels became part of "the Exodus experience." Thus, in Numbers 20:16 the Bible says, "When we cried unto the Lord, he heard our voice, and sent an angel, and hath brought us forth out of Egypt." Isaiah says that "In all their affliction he was afflicted, and the angel of his presence saved them: in his love and in his pity he redeemed them; and he bare them, and carried them all the days of old" (63:9). It may well be that some of these instances involved angelic forms taken by Jesus Christ, the second person of the Trinity. We can only speculate. In that event, it makes alive the thrilling testimony of Paul who declared that "Jesus Christ [is] the same yesterday, and today, and forever" (Hebrews 13:8).

The Mystery of Angels

Therefore, just as Jesus is with us now through the Holy Spirit, revealing Himself and His will, so was He with His people in ages past, and so shall He be for all time to come, the angel of God's presence who leads us. To His "faithful" of past ages, God the Father revealed His presence through angels; through the angel of the Lord, God the Son, Jesus Christ, He revealed Himself and redeemed us by the Son's crucifixion, death and resurrection. Here is mystery too deep for any of us to fathom fully.

Jewish scholars called the angel of the Lord by the name, "Metatron," "the angel of countenance," because He witnesses the countenance of God continuously and, therefore, works to extend the program of God for each of us.

God has given us the fullest revelation—Jesus Christ in the flesh—so He no longer needs to manifest Himself in the form of "the angel of the Lord" in this age of grace. Consequently, the angels who appear in the New Testament or even today are always "created spirits" and not God in that special angel form He used now and then in the Old Testament. The appearance of God the Son in physical form (a theophany) in the Old Testament is no longer necessary. Consider the presence of angels in the New Testament subsequent to the thrilling account of the birth of God the Son in the flesh through His incarnation at Bethlehem. The angels then were to minister the message of God and to establish the message of the gospel of Christ, but never to supplant it or to detract from it.

Angels Are Ministering Spirits

God uses both men and angels to declare His message to those who have been saved by grace. "Are they [angels] not all ministering spirits, sent forth to minister for them who shall be heirs of salvation?" (Hebrews 1:14.) What a glorious honor it will be for angels to know us by name because of our faithful witness to others. Angels will share our rejoicing over those who repent (Luke 15:10), even though they cannot preach the gospel themselves.

In this regard, consider Philip the deacon, whom God was using as a minister of revival in Samaria. An angel appeared with instructions for him to go to the desert (Acts 8:26), and by God's appointment he met the Ethiopian to whom he became the voice for God in preaching the word of truth.

Angels visited John, too. As he looked out upon the lonely seas from the Isle of Patmos and wondered why he was isolated from all but heaven, the angel of the apocalypse came to announce the message that formed the book of Revelation with its prophecies of the end time (Revelation 1:1–3).

An angel ministered in a somewhat similar way in an incident in Daniel's life. Chapter 5 describes a great feast ordered by Belshazzar in Babylon. It had been prepared ostensibly to show the glory of the kingdom, but in reality Belshazzar meant it to parade his own personal greatness. It was a feast for the thousands of his kingdom's greatest nobles. But on this occasion they desecrated the sacred vessels taken from the Temple at Jerusalem by using them for an ignoble purpose: They ate, drank and offered homage to idols of wood and stone, silver and gold. The god of material- ism was in power. Suddenly the fingers of a man's hand appeared and traced on the wall a record of God's judgment on Babylon. "Mene, Mene, Tekel, Upharsin," the hand wrote—"You have been weighed in the balances and been found wanting. Your kingdom is finished" (verses 25–27). It was one of God's angels sent to announce the impending judgment. Not only were the days of King Belshazzar numbered, but God was finished with him.

Later Daniel prayed for the people, "And he [Gabriel] informed me, and talked with me, and said, O Daniel, I am now come forth to give thee skill and understanding. . . . therefore, understand the matter, and consider the vision" (Daniel 9:22–23). In answer to Daniel's prayer, God gave him a panoramic view of the future "history" of the human race. It is my belief that the world is now possibly reaching the climax of those great visions that God gave Daniel.

The scene in the time of Belshazzar seems almost contemporary, those times and conditions resembling so closely what we see and hear today. It may even be that God is writing another story of impending judgment through the crises of the hour. He is telling men everywhere that unless they repent for their sins, their days like Belshazzar's are numbered and they are finished.

Let us conclude this study of the personal ministry of angels by noting some further incidents when God used angels to declare His plan to men.

The Angel Gabriel

At the beginning of the New Testament, Zacharias the priest saw the angel of the Lord, receiving from him the message that pro- claimed the birth of John, who was to prepare the way for the promised Messiah. The angel (Gabriel in this instance, a special angelic minister of promise) encouraged Zacharias to believe the miracle surrounding the birth of John.

Later Gabriel appeared to the Virgin Mary, announcing to her the divinely conceived plan of the incarnation by which God's Son, Jesus Christ, should be conceived miraculously in her womb by the power of the Holy Spirit. Whatever Mary's questions may have been, they were answered by the angel's witness, "The Holy Ghost shall come upon thee, and the power of the Highest shall overshadow thee: therefore also that holy thing which shall be born of thee shall be called the Son of God" (Luke 1:35). Not only did Gabriel, the special angel of ministry and revelation, bring this message to Mary, but either he or another angel also confirmed to Joseph that he should take Mary as his wife, "For that which is conceived in her is of the Holy Ghost" (Matthew 1:20). He also told Joseph the plan of God that Jesus should "save his people from their sins" (Matthew 1:21).

The special angels of proclamation having faithfully bridged the centuries, carrying the message of God's will in times of oppression, discouragement and waning endurance. God's restoring servants, His heavenly messengers, have encouraged, sustained and lifted the spirits of many flagging saints; and they have changed many hopeless circumstances into bright prospect. Angels have ministered the message, "All is well," to satisfy fully the physical, material, emotional and spiritual needs of His people. They could testify, "The angel of the Lord came unto me."

8

Angels Protect and Deliver Us

THE ENEMIES OF Christ who attack us incessantly would often be thwarted if we could grasp God's assurance that His mighty angels are always nearby, ready to help. Tragically, most Christians have failed to accept this fact so frequently expressed in the Bible. I have noticed, though, that in my travels the closer I get to the frontiers of the Christian faith the more faith in angels I find among believers. Hundreds of stories document extraordinary divine intervention every year: God is using His angels as ministering spirits.

Angels Are Divine Protectors

God's angels often protect His servants from potential enemies. Consider 2 Kings 6:14–17. The king of Syria had dispatched his army to Dothan, learning that Elisha the prophet was there. Upon dressing in the morning, the prophet's helper exclaimed excitedly to Elisha that the surrounding countryside bristled with armies and implements of war. Elisha assured him, "Don't be afraid! . . . our army is bigger than theirs" (verse 16, TLB). Elisha then prayed that God would open the eyes of the young man to see the hosts of protective angels: as He did so, the young man "could see horses and chariots of fire everywhere on the hills surrounding the city."

This passage has been one of the great assurances and comforts to me in my ministry.

The angels minister to God's servants in time of hardship and danger. We find another outstanding illustration of this in Acts 27:23–25. Paul on his way to Rome faced shipwreck with more than two hundred others on board. Speaking to the fear-ridden crew he said, "Last night an angel of the God whose I am and whom I serve, stood beside me and said, 'Do not be afraid, Paul. You must stand trial before Caesar; and God has graciously given you the lives of all who sail with you'" (verses 23, 24, NIV).

Some believe strongly that each Christian may have his own guardian angel assigned to watch over him or her. This guardianship possibly begins in infancy, for Jesus said, "See that you do not look down on one of these little ones. For I tell you that their angels in heaven always see the face of my Father in heaven" (Matthew 18:10).

Angels at Work for Us

The most important characteristic of angels is not that they have power to exercise control over our lives, or that they are beautiful, but that they work on our behalf. They are motivated by an inexhaustible love for God and are jealous to see that the will of God in Jesus Christ is fulfilled in us.

David says of angels, "He who dwelleth in the secret place of the Most High shall abide under the shadow of the Almighty. . . . For he shall give his angels charge over thee, to keep thee in all thy ways. They shall bear thee up . . . lest thou dash thy foot against a stone" (Psalm 91:1,11,12).

My wife, Ruth, tells of a strange incident in a Christian bookroom in Shanghai, China. She learned of it through her father, the late Dr. L. Nelson Bell, who served in the hospital in Tsing-kiangpu, Kiangsu province. It was at this store that Dr. Bell bought his gospel portions and tracts to distribute among his patients.

The incident occurred in 1942, after the Japanese had won control of certain areas of China. One morning around nine o'clock, a Japanese truck stopped outside the bookroom. It was carrying five marines and was half-filled with books. The Christian Chinese shop assistant, who was alone at the time, realized with dismay that they had come to seize the stock. By nature timid, he felt this was more than he could endure.

Jumping from the truck, the marines made for the shop door; but before they could enter, a neatly dressed Chinese gentleman entered the shop ahead of them. Though the shop assistant knew practically all the Chinese customers who traded there, this man was a complete stranger. For some unknown reason the soldiers seemed unable to follow him, and loitered about, looking in at the four large windows, but not entering. For two hours they stood around, until after eleven, but never set foot inside the door. The stranger asked what the men wanted, and the Chinese shop assistant explained that the Japanese were seizing stocks from many of the bookshops in the city, and now this store's turn had come. The two prayed together, the stranger encouraging him, and so the two hours passed. At last the soldiers climbed into their truck and drove away. The stranger also left, without making a single purchase or even inquiring about any items in the shop.

Later that day the shop owner, Mr. Christopher Willis (whose Chinese name was Lee), returned. The shop assistant said to him, "Mr. Lee, do you believe in angels?"

"I do," said Mr. Willis.

"So do I, Mr. Lee." Could the stranger have been one of God's protecting angels? Dr. Bell always thought so.

Corrie ten Boom writes of a remarkable experience at the terrible Nazi Ravensbruck prison camp:

"Together we entered the terrifying building. At a table were women who took away all our possessions. Everyone had to undress completely and then go to a room where her hair was checked.

"I asked a woman who was busy checking the possessions of the new arrivals if I might use the toilet. She pointed to a door, and I discovered that the convenience was nothing more than a hole in the shower-room floor. Betsie stayed close beside me all the time. Suddenly I had an inspiration, 'Quick, take off your woolen underwear,' I whispered to her. I rolled it up with mine and laid the bundle in a corner with my little Bible. The spot was alive with cockroaches, but I didn't worry about that. I felt wonderfully relieved and happy. 'The Lord is busy answering our prayers, Betsie,' I whispered. 'We shall not have to make the sacrifice of all our clothes.'

"We hurried back to the row of women waiting to be undressed. A little later, after we had had our showers and put on our shirts and shabby dresses, I hid the roll of underwear and my Bible under my dress. It did bulge out obviously through my dress; but I prayed, 'Lord, cause now Thine angels to surround me; and let them not be transparent today, for the guards must not see me.' I felt perfectly at ease. Calmly I passed the guards. Everyone was checked, from the front, the sides, the back. Not a bulge escaped the eyes of the guard. The woman just in front of me had hidden a woolen vest under her dress; it was taken from her. They let me pass, for they did not see me. Betsie, right behind me, was searched.

"But outside awaited another danger. On each side of the door were women who looked everyone over for a second time. They felt over the body of each one who passed. I knew they would not see me, for the angels were still surrounding me. I was not even surprised when they passed me by; but within me rose the jubilant cry, 'O Lord, if Thou dost so answer prayer, I can face even Ravensbruck unafraid.'"

Divine Surveillance

Every true believer in Christ should be encouraged and strengthened! Angels are watching; they mark our path. They superintend the events of our lives and protect the interest of the Lord God, always working to promote His plans and to bring about His highest will for us. Angels are interested spectators and mark all we do, "for we are made a spectacle unto the world, and to angels, and to men" (1 Corinthians 4:9). God assigns angelic powers to watch over us.

Hagar, Sarah's maid, had fled from the tents of Abraham. It is ironic that Abraham, after having scaled such glorious heights of faith, should have capitulated to his wife's conniving and scolding, and to the custom of that day, to father a child by Hagar. And it is ironic that Sarah his wife should have been so jealous that when their own son, Isaac, was born years later, she wanted to get rid of both Hagar and the earlier child, Ishmael. So Abraham's self-indulgence led to sorrow and he thrust Hagar out of his home.

Nonetheless, God sent His angel to minister to Hagar. "And the angel of the Lord found her by a fountain of water in the wilderness, by the fountain in the way to Shur" (Genesis 16:7). The angel spoke as an oracle of God, turning her mind away from the injury of the past with a promise of what she might expect if she placed her faith in God. This God is the God not only of Israel but the God of the Arab as well (for the Arabs come from the stock of Ishmael). The very name of her son, Ishmael, meaning "God hears," was a sustaining one. God promised that the seed of Ishmael would multiply, and that his destiny would be great on the earth as he now undertook the restless pilgrimage that was to characterize his descendants. The angel of the Lord revealed himself as the protector of Hagar and Ishmael. Hagar in awe exclaimed, "Thou God seest me" (Genesis 16:13), or as it may be better translated, "I have seen Thou who seest all and who sees me."

Psalm 34:7 underscores the teaching that angels protect and deliver us, "The angel of the Lord encampeth round about those who fear him, and delivereth them." We also find this idea reflected in one of Charles Wesley's songs:

> Angels, where ere we go,
> Attend our steps whate'er betide.
> With watchful care their charge attend,
> And evil turn aside.

Miraculous Deliveries

The great majority of Christians can recall some incident in which their lives, in times of critical danger, have been miraculously preserved—an almost plane crash, a near car wreck, a fierce temptation. Though they may have seen no angels, their presence could explain why tragedy was averted. We should always be grateful for the goodness of God, who uses these wonderful friends called angels to protect us. Evidence from Scripture as well as personal experience confirms to us that individual guardian, guiding angels attend at least some of our ways and hover protectively over our lives.

The Scriptures are full of dramatic evidences of the protective care of angels in their earthly service to the people of God. Paul admonished Christians to put on all the armor of God that they may stand firmly in the face of evil (Ephesians 6:10–12). Our struggle is not against flesh and blood (physical powers alone), but against the spiritual (superhuman) forces of wickedness in heavenly spheres. Satan, the prince of the power of the air, promotes a "religion" but not true faith; he promotes false prophets. So the powers of light and darkness are locked in intense conflict. Thank God for the angelic forces that fight off the works of darkness. Angels never minister selfishly; they serve so that all glory may be given to God as believers are strengthened. A classic example of the protective agency of angels is found in Acts 12:5–11.

As the scene opened, Peter lay bound in prison awaiting execution. James, the brother of John, had already been killed, and there was little reason to suppose that Peter would escape the executioner's axe either. The magistrates intended to put him to death as a favor to those who opposed the gospel and the works of God. Surely the believers had prayed for James, but God had chosen to deliver him through death. Now the church was praying for Peter.

As Peter lay sleeping an angel appeared, not deterred by such things as doors or iron bars. The angel came into the prison cell, shook Peter awake and told him to prepare to escape. As a light shone in the prison Peter's chains fell off, and having dressed, he followed the angel out. Doors supernaturally opened because Peter could not pass through locked doors as the angel had. What a mighty deliverance God achieved through His angel!

Angelic Intervention

Many experiences in both Old and New Testaments grew out of the imprisonment of God's saints, calling either for God to deliver directly, or to intervene through angels acting in His name. Many today who are captive in the chains of depression can take courage to believe in the prospect of deliverance. God has no favorites and declares that angels will minister to all the heirs of faith. If we, the sons of God, would only realize how close His ministering angels are, what calm assurance we could have in facing the cataclysms of life. While we do not place our faith directly in angels, we should place it in the God who rules the angels; then we can have peace.

Hebrews 11 contains a long list of men and women of faith. For most of them God performed miracles, delivering them from disease, calamity, accidents and even death. Someone has called this chapter, "God's Hall of Fame." Angels helped these great men and women to subdue kingdoms, obtain promises, stop the mouths of lions, quench the violence of fire, escape the edge of the sword, and when they were weak, stand with the help of angels to defeat entire armies.

But the tempo changes in verse 35, with the opening words, "and others were tortured, not accepting deliverance." Those now mentioned were of equal faith and courage: they had to endure the trial of cruel mockings and scourgings. They suffered bonds and imprisonment. They were stoned, they were sawn asunder, they were slain with the sword. They wandered about in goatskins, being destitute, afflicted and tormented. Time after time they must have called on God to send His mighty angels to help. No delivering angel came. They suffered and endured almost as though there were no God.

God's Winners

Why? We find a clue when our Lord faced Calvary as He prayed, "If it be possible let this cup pass from me" (Matthew 26:39); but then He added, "nevertheless not my will, but thine, be done" (Luke 22:42). In the sufferings and death of these great saints not physically delivered, God had a mysterious plan, and was performing His will. Knowing this, they suffered and died *by faith*. This latter part of Hebrews 11 indicates that those who received no visible help in answer to prayer will have a far greater heavenly reward because they endured by "faith" alone. But having died, they did enjoy the ministry of angels who then escorted their im-

Billy Graham

mortal souls to the throne of God. If the first part of Hebrews 11 is called "God's Hall of Fame," the second should be called, "God's Winners of the Medal of Honor."

Once when I was going through a dark period I prayed and prayed, but the heavens seemed to be brass. I felt as though God had disappeared and that I was all alone with my trial and burden. It was a dark night for my soul. I wrote my mother about the experience, and will never forget her reply: "Son, there are many times when God withdraws to test your faith. He wants you to trust Him in the darkness. Now, Son, reach up by faith in the fog and you will find that His hand will be there." In tears I knelt by my bed and experienced an overwhelming sense of God's presence. Whether or not we sense and feel the presence of the Holy Spirit or one of the holy angels, by faith we are certain God will never leave us nor forsake us.

9

Angels—God's Agents in Judgment

THE BIBLE SAYS that throughout history angels have worked to carry out God's judgments, directing the destinies of nations disobedient to God. For example, God used angels in scattering the people of Israel because of their sins. He also used angels in bringing judgment on Sodom and Gomorrah, and eventually on Babylon and Nineveh. Further, at "the end of the age" angels will execute judgment on those who have rejected God's love.

The writer of Hebrews speaks of angelic forces as executors of God's judgments: "Who maketh his angels spirits, and his ministers a flame of fire" (Hebrews 1:7). The flaming fire suggests how awful are the judgments of God and how burning is the power of the angels who carry out God's decisions. Angels administer judgment in accord with God's principles of righteousness.

Unknown to men they have undoubtedly in the past helped destroy evil systems like Nazism, because those governments came to the place where God could no longer withhold His hand. These same angels will carry out fearful judgments in the future, some of which the book of Revelation vividly describes.

We often get false notions about angels from plays given by Sunday school children at Christmas. It is true that angels are ministering spirits sent to help the heirs of salvation. But just as they fulfill God's will in salvation for believers in Jesus Christ, so they are also "avengers" who use their great power to fulfill God's will in judgment. God has empowered them to separate the sheep from the goats, the wheat from the chaff, and one of them will blow the trumpet that announces impending judgment when God summons the nations to stand before Him in the last great judgment.

Angels Warn of Judgment

In the case of Sodom and Gomorrah, there was no way judgment could be averted. Their wickedness had become too great. God had judged them; they had to be destroyed. But before God sends judgment, He warns. In this case, He used angels to point out to Abraham the approaching doom of Sodom and Gomorrah for their wickedness (Genesis 18). Abraham, whose nephew, Lot, and his family lived among these wicked people, began to plead with God to spare the two cities. Abraham asked God if He would avert judgment if fifty righteous people lived in Sodom. God told Abraham He would not destroy the city if there were fifty such people. Then Abraham asked for a stay of execution if there were only forty-five righteous people. God agreed. Then Abraham asked for deliverance if there were thirty righteous people. God agreed. Abraham then asked for twenty; then for ten. God agreed to withhold judgment if as many as ten righteous people could be found in Sodom. But not even ten such people lived there. Notice that God answered Abraham every time he asked. And He did not leave off answering until Abraham left off asking.

After this, God ordered the angelic ministers of judgment to rain destruction on these two wicked cities and all their inhabitants. Prior to the destruction of the cities, however, two unidentified heavenly messengers visited Sodom to warn Lot and his family to flee from the wrath about to come. So evil were the inhabitants of Sodom that they wanted to molest the angels physically. The angels blinded them and prevented them from carrying out their iniquitous conduct. In his book, *All About Angels*, C. Leslie Miller states, "It is significant that although Lot, Abraham's nephew, had drifted far from the holy standards of his uncle and had sought the companionship and material benefits of an unholy alliance, yet the angels of the Lord were there to spare his life and assist him in avoiding the consequences of his own poor judgment."

Thus, we see something of the mercy, grace and love of God

toward even those who profess His name and try sincerely to live a God-honoring life in the midst of the most difficult circumstances.

The Angel Who Destroyed the Assyrian Army

In 2 Kings 19, Scripture dramatically underscores God's use of angels to execute His judgments. King Hezekiah had received a letter from the commander of the Assyrian forces and immediately sought God's counsel. God gave Isaiah the answer, saying that not one Assyrian arrow would be fired into the city. He promised to defend Jerusalem on that occasion for David's sake. Dramatically, that night, just one angel struck the Assyrian encampment and 185,000 soldiers were found dead on the field of battle the next morning (verse 35).

The Angel Who Almost Destroyed Jerusalem

Nowhere in the Old Testament is there a more significant use of angelic power in judgment against God's own people than when David defied God's command by numbering Israel. God sent a pestilence among the Israelites and 70,000 died. He also sent a single angel to destroy the city of Jerusalem. David "saw the angel of the Lord stand between the earth and the heaven, having a drawn sword in his hand stretched out over Jerusalem" (1 Chronicles 21:16).

When David pleaded for mercy, the angel told him to set up an altar on the threshing floor of Araunah the Jebusite. God then accepted David's sacrifice there and said to the destroying angel, "It is enough: stay now thine hand" (2 Samuel 24:16). The Scripture significantly says that the same angel had already slain the 70,000 men (verse 17). Indeed angels are God's agents in judgment.

New Testament history also records incidents where avenging angels judged the unrighteous acts of men and nations.

The Angel Who Smote Herod Agrippa

We have already referred to the case of Herod. Dressed in his royal apparel, he appeared before the people to make a speech.

When he finished the people shouted, "It is the voice of a god, and not of a man" (Acts 12:22). Instead of disclaiming any such thing Herod delighted in the impact he had made. God's response to this idolatrous act was prompt, and for Herod, disastrous. "Because he gave not God the glory," he "was eaten of worms, and gave up the ghost" (verse 23). "The angel of the Lord smote him."

The Angel Who Destroyed the Egyptian First Born

One fateful night in Egypt just before the Exodus, the destroying angel was about to sweep over the land with a visitation of death (Exodus 12:18–30). How deeply must anxiety have etched itself upon the hearts of the Israelites. Believing Jews had offered sacrifices and generously sprinkled the blood over doorposts and lintels of their homes. Then in accord with God's time schedule, judgment fell on Egypt as the dark and awesome moment of midnight arrived. The destroying angel (1 Corinthians 10:10; Hebrews 11:28) was God's minister of judgment, leaving death in his wake. The first born of every unbelieving Egyptian or Israeli household died under the judgment of a holy God who, however, had respect for the blood.

Down through the centuries this heart-rending account has been the theme of Jews and Christians alike: "When I see the blood, I will pass over you." It has been the text of thousands of sermons by rabbis and Christian clergymen. It was not the quality of life of the people in the blood-sprinkled houses that counted. It was their faith, apart from works, that they showed by sprinkling the blood. God had respect for only one thing: the blood sprinkled by faith.

How fearful it is to have these mighty angels carry out the judgments of an all-powerful God.

The Angel Who Stopped Abraham

In Genesis 22, God, wanting to test the reality of Abraham's faith, told him to sacrifice his beloved "son of promise," Isaac. God said, "Abraham . . . take now thy son, thine only son Isaac, whom thou lovest, and get thee into the land of Moriah; and offer him there for a burnt offering upon one of the mountains which I will tell thee of" (Genesis 22:1–2). What great suffering must have haunted and hurt the heart of Abraham through the long night as he considered what this supreme sacrifice entailed. Nevertheless, with nothing to go on but God's Word, Abraham by sheer, naked faith took fire, wood and his son, and set off to do God's bidding. The Bible records no greater act of faith.

Having prepared the altar, Abraham placed Isaac, bound hand and foot, on the altar; then, unsheathing his knife, he raised his face toward the heaven in submission to the Father's will. As Abraham lifted the knife in the air to plunge it into the heart of Isaac, "the angel of the Lord called unto him out of heaven, and said, Abraham, Abraham . . . Lay not thine hand upon the lad, neither do thou any thing unto him; for now I know that thou fearest God, seeing thou hast not withheld thy son, thine only son from me" (Genesis 22:11–12).

The double use of the name always implies the importance of the message about to be given. When he heard his name called, faithful Abraham responded immediately, and God rewarded him for his unqualified obedience. "Abraham lifted up his eyes, and looked, and, behold, behind him a ram caught in a thicket by his horns: and Abraham went and took the ram, and offered him up for a burnt offering in the stead of his son" (Genesis 22:13).

Many scholars believe, as I do, that the angel here is a "theophany," an appearance of the Lord Jesus Christ Himself. He assumed the role of an angel and God showed the principle of substitutionary atonement: God had demanded of Abraham the death of his son. The demand for the burnt offering had to be met, and it was met. But in the place of Isaac, God through an angel accepted the animal substitute. That same principle applies to us. True judgment demands that we die. And the judgment must be executed. But Jesus Christ Himself was the substitute offering. He died so that we do not have to die. He took our place so that the words used here, "in the stead of," can be wonderfully applied to every person who trusts in Christ. He died "in the stead of" all who believe on Him.

How could God have asked for a human sacrifice? How could He have asked Abraham to slay Isaac when He had forbidden the killing of people (Genesis 9:6)? Is not this inconsistent with the nature of God? He gives us the answer to these questions about judgment by death in the Epistle to the Romans. "He that spared not his own Son, but delivered him up for us all, how shall he not with him also freely give us all things?" (Romans 8:32). God could ask Abraham to slay Isaac because He Himself was willing to let His own Son die. He was not asking Abraham to do anything more than He was willing to do with His only begotten Son.

Neither Abraham nor Isaac had to drink the cup God presented. Isaac did not die and Abraham did not slay him. But when we come to another cup in the Garden of Gethsemane, the picture is startlingly different. Jesus has now come; as the guiltless one for the guilty, as the sinless one for sinners, He was willing to accept the condemnation of God for the world's guilt, identifying Himself with it through His own death on Calvary.

Neither man nor angel could ever understand what was implied in the "cup" Jesus took in the Garden of Gethsemane that was to lead to His awful suffering, condemnation and death (Mark 14:36; Luke 22:42). In the Garden as He wrestled over the cup He was to drink, no ministering angel could spare Him from it or alleviate His suffering. It was His and His alone. It settled down on the Savior as a cup of judgment He accepted and took upon Himself as the righteous one bearing the guilt of the wicked. The angels would have helped Him in that hour, but Christ did not call for their help. This one who said No to angel help said, in effect, "I will die for the sins of men because I love them so much." And in dying He was forsaken by men, by angels, and by the Father who is of purer eyes than to look upon sin and who in His Son's atoning agony turned His face from Him. That is why Jesus cried from the cross, "My God, my God, why hast thou forsaken me?" (Matthew 27:46). He died alone. Angels were ready to rescue Him, but He refused.

Angels and Those Who Reject Jesus

It is clear in Scripture that angels will be God's emissaries to carry out His judgment against those who deliberately reject Jesus Christ and the salvation God offers through Him. While all men are sinners by nature, choice and practice, yet it is their deliberate rejection of Jesus Christ as Savior and Lord that causes the judgment of eternal separation from God.

God has assigned angels at the end of the age to separate the sheep from the goats, the wheat from the tares, the saved from the lost. We are not called upon to obey the voice of angels. But we are to heed and obey the Word of God and the voice of God that calls upon us to be reconciled to Him by faith in Jesus Christ. If not, we will have to pay the penalty of unforgiven sin. The angels will administer that penalty. They "shall cast them into the furnace of fire" (Matthew 13:50). I am constantly astounded that God's decrees and warnings are considered so lightly in our modern world—even among Christians.

Angels and Eternal Life

Every son of Adam's race is confronted with two ways of life: one, to eternal life; the other, to eternal death. We have seen how angels execute God's judgment on those who reject Jesus; the angels cast them into the furnace of fire. But there is a totally different judgment: It is the good and wonderful judgment unto everlasting life. God gives the angels a place in this too. He commissions them to escort each believer to heaven and to give him a royal welcome as he enters the eternal presence of God. Each of us who trusts Christ will witness the rejoicing of angelic hosts around the throne of God.

In the story of the rich man and Lazarus (Luke 16), Jesus told of a beggar who died in the faith. He had never owned many of this world's goods, but he was rich in faith that counts for eternity. When he died he was "carried by the angels into Abraham's bosom." Here were angelic pallbearers who took his immortal spirit to the place of glory where he was to be eternally with God—the place the Bible calls "heaven."

Another beautiful account of this kind comes from the life of the martyr Stephen (Acts 6:8–7:60). The "council, looking stedfastly on him, saw his face as it had been the face of an angel." Then Stephen in a powerful sermon declared that even unbelievers "received the law by the disposition of angels, and have not kept it" (Acts 7:53). When he had finished his discourse Stephen saw the glory of God and Jesus at the Father's right hand. Immediately his enemies stoned him to death and he was received into heaven. Even as the angels escorted Lazarus when he died, so we can assume that they escorted Stephen; and so they will escort us when by death we are summoned into the presence of Christ. We can well imagine what Stephen's abundant entrance to heaven was like as the anthems of the heavenly host were sung in rejoicing that the first Christian martyr had come home to receive a glorious welcome and to gain the crown of a martyr.

Do you fear the judgment of God? Or do you know that Christ has taken your judgment upon Himself by His death on the cross? When you know Christ you need not fear God's judgment, for He has fully and completely purchased your salvation. Don't delay your decision for Christ, but open your heart to Him and you too will know the joy of sharing in His fellowship throughout all eternity in heaven.

10

Angels and the Gospel

WHILE GOD HAS delegated angels to make special pronouncements for Him, He has not given them the privilege of proclaiming the gospel message. Why this is so, Scripture does not say. Perhaps spirit-beings who have never experienced the effects of separation from fellowship with God because of sin would be unable to preach with understanding.

But notice what the writer says in "Holy, Holy Is What the Angels Sing:"

> Holy, Holy is what the angels sing,
> And I expect to help them make the
>   courts of heaven ring.
> And when I sing redemption's story,
> They will fold their wings,
> For angels never felt the joy
>   that our salvation brings.

Down through the ages man's heart has remained unchanged. Whatever the color of his skin, whatever his cultural or ethnic background, he needs the gospel of Christ. But who has God ordained to bring that gospel to fallen men? Fallen angels cannot do it; they cannot even be saved from their own sins. Yet unfallen angels cannot preach the gospel either. Presumably they do not hear the gospel the way we do; in their purity they have escaped the effects of sin and are unable to comprehend what it means to be lost.

Rather, God has commanded the church to preach. This great task is reserved to believers. God has no other means. Only man can speak salvation's experience to man.

God has, however, assigned angels to assist those who preach. Their assistance includes the use of miraculous and corroborating signs. Missionaries of the eighteenth and nineteenth centuries have reported many wonderful incidents where angels seemed to help them proclaim the gospel. My wife, whose parents were missionaries to China, can remember many instances in her life where angels must have intervened in the ministry of her father and his fellow missionaries.

At any rate, you and I have the privilege of conveying a message to men from God in heaven, a message that angels cannot speak. Think of that! The story is told of a question asked of God: "In the event that men fail to preach the gospel as you have commanded, what other plan have you in mind?" "I have no other plan," He said.

No angel can be an evangelist. No angel can pastor a church, although angels watch over particular churches. No angel can do counseling. No angel can enjoy sonship in Jesus or be partaker of the divine nature or become a joint heir with Jesus in His kingdom. You and I are a unique and royal priesthood in the universe, and we have privileges that even angels cannot experience.

The Angel and Zacharias

The birth of John the Baptist was dynamically connected with the "evangel" (a term meaning the gospel, the good news of God's salvation in Jesus Christ). His parents, Zacharias and Elizabeth, were both old, Elizabeth being beyond the age to bear children. She and her husband were descendants of Aaron and thus connected with the priesthood. Both walked blameless before the Lord and kept His commandments. They illustrate how God works through godly parents; not infrequently we find that some of His greatest servants have enjoyed the benefits of a godly home. John and Charles Wesley, founders of the Methodist Church, came from a godly home and were profoundly influenced by their mother. Adoniram Judson, the great missionary to Burma, came from a minister's home. Jonathan Edwards, pastor, evangelist and educator in early America, was from a line of godly forebears.

When the angel appeared to Zacharias to announce the good news that Elizabeth would, despite her age, give birth to a son, his words were immersed in the evangel. He predicted John's ministry: "Many of the children of Israel shall he turn to the Lord their God" (Luke 1:16). Thus, we learn that no one should presume that any person is saved, not even one born to a believing home, who has believing forebears, and grows up in a believing church. Moreover John was "to make ready a people prepared for the Lord" (verse 17).

How great the message of the angel was and how seriously Zacharias regarded it can be seen from events some months later. Zacharias lost his ability to speak following the angel's visit; he did not regain it until the birth of John. But at that time his tongue was loosed and he was filled with the Holy Spirit. His thinking—curing the long months while Elizabeth awaited the birth of the baby—now burst out in his first words, which reflect the angel's visit and concern for the evangel. Zacharias says, "Blessed be the Lord God of Israel; for he hath visited and redeemed his people, and hath raised up an horn of salvation for us in the house of his servant David." A moment later he added, "And thou, child, [that is, John] shalt . . . give knowledge of salvation unto his people by the remission of their sins, through the tender mercy of our God; whereby the dayspring from on high hath visited us, to give light to them that sit in darkness and in the shadow of death, to guide our feet into the way of peace" (Luke 1:76–79).

Now that was really a message! And all of it rises from the visit of the angel, who told Zacharias about God's intention for John. But notice especially that the angel came, not simply to announce the birth of John, but to make it clear that John was to live his life as the forerunner of the Messiah, and as one who would bring the knowledge of salvation and the remission of sins to his fellow Israelites.

The Angel and the Evangel
in the Birth of Jesus

The announcement to Mary that she was to be the mother of Jesus was made by no ordinary angel. It was Gabriel, one of three angels whose names have been given us in Scripture, who made the announcement. And it was connected with the evangel. This was true both of the words Gabriel spoke and the words Mary spoke while she was pregnant and looking toward the birth of her son. The angel told Mary that Jesus would be the Son of the Highest, that He would inherit the throne of His father David, would reign over the house of Jacob forever, and would be an everlasting kingdom. This was something far different from anything promised anyone else in Scripture. It was not promised to Abraham, or David, or Solomon. Only Jesus' name is connected with these promises, and all of them are inextricably connected with both personal and national salvation.

After Mary became pregnant she visited Elizabeth and sang one of the sweetest songs known to literature. In it she makes evident that she has grasped what the angel told her. And what he told her she describes as salvation and the remission of sins: "My spirit hath rejoiced in God my Saviour" (Luke 1:47). Here was the news that Mary herself needed a Savior, and had found Him. The very baby who was encased in her womb would one day offer Himself as a propitiation for her and for all men. And that baby in her womb was God Almighty who had humbled Himself in order to dwell among us in the flesh.

Indeed she cries out that God's "mercy is on them that fear him from generation to generation." What is this but the glorious evangel, gospel, that God was in Christ reconciling the world to Himself? And this was the message Gabriel brought to Mary. He could not preach it himself, but he could bear witness to the gospel that was to be preached by Jesus Christ and His followers through all ages.

The Angel, the Evangel and Joseph

Joseph, the husband of Mary, was caught up in a seemingly abysmal situation. He was legally engaged to a girl who was pregnant.

He knew he was not the father because they had not yet consummated their forthcoming marriage. Yet Mary was apparently guilty of adultery under Jewish law, unless Joseph was willing to believe her story that the Holy Spirit had come upon her, and that she had never engaged in sexual relations with a man. As the innocent party, Joseph was thinking seriously of putting Mary away according to the custom of that day. The Scripture says that "while he thought on these things" (Matthew 1:20), an angel appeared to him in a dream and told him the true story of the incarnation and the role of Mary. Responding, Joseph believed the angel. But the announcement contained more than the simple fact that Mary was innocent of any transgression and that Joseph was the chosen vessel of God in affording her protection in this extraordinary event.

The angel also told Joseph something that was to witness to the gospel. Though the angel could not preach to Joseph, he struck at the root of the matter when he proclaimed, "He shall save his people from their sins" (Matthew 1:21). Here was the gospel in all of its beauty, simplicity and purity. According to the witness of the angel, sins can be forgiven. There is someone who can forgive sins. This is Jesus the Christ. The Savior has a people about whom He is concerned and guarantees that their sins will be forgiven. In the midst of the wonder of the incarnation we should not overlook the fact that the angel was here bearing witness to the "evangel," the gospel. Jesus was not coming simply as God. He was coming as Redeemer and Savior to make men right with His Father and to assure them of the gift of everlasting life.

Gabriel, the Evangel and Daniel

Long before the days of Zacharias, Elizabeth, Mary, Joseph and John the Baptist, the angel Gabriel had borne witness of the evangel to the prophet Daniel. He had done this in connection with the prophecy of the seventy weeks. Daniel was deep in prayer, confessing both his sin and that of his people. While he was praying, Gabriel appeared to him. Notice again that Gabriel did not preach the word of salvation, but he bore eloquent testimony to it. He said that the seventy weeks were designed "to finish the transgression, to make an end of sins, and to make reconciliation for iniquity" (Daniel 9:24). Then he foretold the cutting off of the

Messiah, an event that Isaiah 53 had prophesied and depicted so dramatically.

The Jews had had difficulty understanding the notion of a suffering Messiah, rather picturing Him as one who would come in power and glory to overthrow their enemies and to reign triumphantly over them. But Gabriel told Daniel that sin is a reality, and must be paid for. The Messiah will do this by being cut off; that is, He will die for the sins of men. Then the power of sin to separate us from God will end, and men will be reconciled to Him. We see that though Gabriel could not preach, he could prophesy! And how beautifully the prophecies of the Old Testament are linked together with the fulfillment in the New Testament. How gracious God was to use His angels as agents to make it plain to all they visited in all ages that their business was to witness to the evangel.

The Angel, the Evangel and the Shepherds

Does it not seem mysterious that God brought the first message of the birth of Jesus to ordinary people rather than to princes and kings? In this instance, God spoke through His holy angel to the shepherds who were keeping sheep in the fields. This was a lowly occupation, so shepherds were not well educated. But Mary in her song, the Magnificat, tells us the true story: "He hath put down the mighty from their seats, and exalted them of low degree. He hath filled the hungry with good things, and the rich he hath sent empty away" (Luke 1:52, 53). What a word for our generation!

What was the message of the angel to the shepherds? First, he told them not to be afraid. Over and over again the presence of angels was frightening to those to whom they came. But unless they came in judgment, the angels spoke a word of reassurance. They calmed the people to whom they came. This tells us that the appearance of angels is awe-inspiring, something about them awakening fear in the human heart. They represent a presence that has greatness and sends a chill down the spine. But when the angel had quieted the fears of the shepherds, he brought this message, one forever to be connected with the evangel:

"For behold I bring you good tidings of great joy, which shall be to all people. For unto you is born this day in the city of David a

Saviour, which is Christ the Lord" (Luke 2:10, 11). I could preach a dozen sermons on those two verses for they contain so many important theological themes. But note once more that the angel does not preach the gospel. Rather, he witnesses to it and demonstrates again the overwhelming concern angels have for it.

What did the angel say? First, he brought good tidings, not bad ones. The shepherds already knew the bad news—the human race had sinned and was lost. But the angel had come to tell them that God was doing something about their lostness. And he pointed out that the good news was not simply for the people of one nation, but for the whole world. Isaiah said, "The God of the whole earth shall he be called" (Isaiah 54:5). Jonah learned the same truth when he was sent to preach repentance to the people of Nineveh. The angel told the shepherds that the good tidings were for all people.

The good tidings were that the Savior had come. They needed somebody who could bring them back into fellowship with God, because the blood of bulls and goats could not do this in any permanent way. But the blood of the Savior could. The angel message was that God had come, redemption was possible, the Lord had visited His people with salvation. What a testimony to the evangel this was. And it was further validated when the angel who was accompanied by "a multitude of the heavenly host" began to chant or sing, "Glory to God in the highest, and on earth peace, good will toward men." Where could there be sweeter music? What hymn writer could match those words?

Angels and the Evangel in the Book of Acts

We might call two wonderful instances "case studies" of how angels see to it that unbelievers hear the gospel, respond to it and become saved. It shows again the concern of angels for the evangel and the steps they take to implement it.

The first case is that of the Ethiopian nobleman, a man of great authority. While reading the Old Testament Scriptures, he came to Isaiah and, unable to understand what the prophet meant, needed someone to interpret the Scripture to him. An angel knew of this situation. But the angel did not and could not do what the Ethiopian needed. He could not preach the gospel. But he could assist the Ethiopian eunuch by sending someone to him who could.

So the Scripture tells us that the angel spoke to Philip and specifically instructed him to go "toward the south unto the way that goeth down from Jerusalem unto Gaza, which is desert" (Acts 8:26). Philip obeyed the angel and approached the chariot. Then he interpreted the Scripture for him. Later the angel led him up and took him away. And the Ethiopian went on his way rejoicing. If the angel had been unconcerned about the evangel he would not have sent Philip to preach the gospel to this interested inquirer.

The second instance has to do with Peter and the conversion of Cornelius. In this case the situation is reversed. The angel had told Philip what to do so the Ethiopian could be saved. In this case he did not tell Peter what to do, but rather ordered Cornelius to send for Peter, who would then tell him the story of the gospel so he could be saved. Would it not have been much easier for the angel to have preached the gospel to Cornelius than to have had him send for Peter? After all, Peter was not a willing witness. He had the notion that it was wrong to preach the gospel for the salvation of Gentiles. Cornelius, however, followed the word of the angel and sent for Peter. Then God had to appear in a dream and convince Peter that it was all right for him to witness to a Gentile. Peter finally went and Cornelius was wonderfully saved. But it was done through the auspices of the angel who was deeply concerned with the evangel, and for the salvation of this Roman soldier.

One other story in the Acts of the Apostles is somewhat different, though no less worthy of consideration. It has to do with Paul on his way to Rome. He was shipwrecked en route. But while it appeared that the ship would sink with all hands lost, an angel of the Lord appeared to Paul at night. He told those aboard the ship that they would all be saved. Then he said something that illuminates the concern of angels for the salvation of men and the witness of Christians to the unsaved. "Fear not, Paul; thou must be brought before Caesar" (Acts 27:24). Here we see that same principle. The angel could not witness to Caesar, but Paul could. And God in His providence was sending him to Rome for precisely this purpose. If Paul had not fully known the will of God before, it was clear at this moment. God intended that Caesar should hear the gospel. And the angel, by bringing the message, revealed his own interest in the evangel.

The Sound of Angel Voices

The keynote of evangelism is couched in the heavenly proclamation I have mentioned, "Unto you is born this day. . . a Saviour which is Christ the Lord." And the task of world evangelization will be completed by men and women whom the Holy Spirit uses. But wherever and whenever we see the gospel working in its power to transform, there is a possibility that in some ways angels may be involved. This is a mystery that we will never quite understand until we get to heaven.

It is not unreasonable to ask, "What did the angel voices sound like?" And "What did they say when they spoke?" Angels seemed to communicate terse commands. Often the angel messengers urged haste, and this is understandable since they were communicating a directive from God. Dr. Miller points out that the contemporary expression, "Hurry up," would fit most angel commands. The words, "Get up," were sometimes literally used. The angel said to Peter, "Rise quickly." The angel said to Gideon, "Arise and go in this thy might." The angel said to Joseph, "Go quickly," and to Philip, "Arise and go."

In the same way any evangelistic ministry sounds the note of urgency concerning the gospel. We have no time to waste because we can never reclaim this moment. We may never have a second chance to witness if we neglect the first.

We can illustrate this from the sinking of the *Titanic*. The greatest ship of its day, weighing 46,000 tons, it was considered unsinkable. But on the night of 14 April 1912, while moving through the ocean at 22 knots, it struck an iceberg. Because it carried only half as many life jackets as passengers, when it sank 1,513 people drowned. Even though this event occurred more than 70 years ago, there is still a great fascination about it. The recent discovery of the hulk of the *Titanic* has revived our interest in the whole tragic story.

Out of tragedy, however, God can still bring triumph.

One passenger, John Harper, was on his way to preach at Moody Church in Chicago. Trying to stay afloat in the ocean he drifted toward a young man holding onto a plank. Harper asked, "Young man, are you saved?" The man said, "No." A wave separated them. After a few minutes they drifted within speaking distance of each other, and again Harper called to him, "Have you made your peace with God?" The young man said, "Not yet." A wave overwhelmed John Harper and he was seen no more, but the words, "Are you saved?" kept ringing in the young man's ears.

Two weeks later a youth stood up in a Christian Endeavor meeting in New York, told his story and said, "I am John Harper's last convert."

11

Angel Ministries in the Life of Jesus

IT WOULD TAKE an entire book to spell out in detail how the life of Jesus was intertwined with the attending ministry of angels. Before He was here they followed His orders. And since He ascended into heaven they have worshiped Him before the throne of God as the Lamb slain for our salvation.

To prepare for the coming of Jesus an angel appeared to Zacharias to inform him that his wife would be the mother of John the Baptist (Luke 1:13). Gabriel, one of the mighty angels of God, announced to Mary that she would give birth to the Messiah. An angel and a multitude of the heavenly host spread the good news of Jesus' coming to the shepherds in the field (Luke 2:9). These angelic incidents preceded and accompanied His birth, but when Jesus began His public ministry angels were intimately involved in His life as well.

Perhaps the most difficult period in the life of Jesus before His crucifixion was His temptation by the devil in the wilderness. After He had fasted forty days and nights, Satan tried to break Him down. In Christ's weakened human condition, Satan began his attack, seeing this as his greatest opportunity to defeat the program of God in the world since his victory in the Garden of Eden. He was out to shipwreck the hope of the human race. Wishing to prevent the salvation of sinners, he struck at the moment when Christ's physical weakness made Him most susceptible to temptation. Satan always directs his sharpest attack at his victim's weakest point. He knows where the Achilles' heel may be and he does not fail to strike at the opportune time.

Three times Satan attempted to defeat Jesus. Three times Jesus quoted Scripture, and three times Satan went down to defeat. Then the Bible declares that "he [Satan] departed from him [Jesus] for a season" (Luke 4:13). It was at this point that angels came to His assistance—not to help Him resist Satan as they help us, for He did that by Himself, but to help Him after the battle was won. The angels "ministered" to Jesus. The Greek word *diakoneo* says it well, for they served Him as a deacon would serve. "Behold, angels came and ministered unto him" (Matthew 4:11). Angelic ambassadors supported, strengthened and sustained Him in that trying hour. From that moment on our Lord Jesus Christ, "who has been tempted in every way, just as we are—yet was without sin" (Hebrews 4:15, NIV), could sympathize and help Christian believers for the ages to come, and lead them to victory in their hour of temptation.

The Angel with Jesus in the Garden of Gethsemane

The night before His crucifixion Jesus was in the Garden of Gethsemane. Only a short time later He was to be seized by the soldiers, betrayed by Judas Iscariot, set before the rulers, beaten and at last crucified. Before He was hung on the cross He went through the terrible agony in the Garden which made Him sweat, as it were, drops of blood. It was in this situation that the Son of man needed inner strength to face what no other being in heaven, hell or earth had ever known. In fact, He was to face what no created being could have faced and gone through in victory. He was about to take upon Himself the sins of men. He was to become sin for us.

Jesus had taken Peter, James and John with Him to the Garden. They could have provided Him with reinforcement and encouragement, but instead they fell asleep. The Son of man was all alone. He prayed, "Father, if thou be willing, remove this cup from me: nevertheless not my will, but thine, be done" (Luke 22:42). Then it was at that crucial moment that the angel came to assist Him, "strengthening Him." The Greek word for strengthening is *eniskuo,* which means to make strong inwardly. Where the disciples of the Lord Jesus had failed to share His agony, as they slept the angel came to help.

Angels Waiting at the Cross

The tragedy of sin reached its crescendo when God in Christ became sin. At this point He was offering Himself as the sacrifice required by the justice of God if man was to be redeemed. At this moment Satan was ready to try his master stroke. If he could get Christ to come down from the cross, and if Christ allowed the mockery of the crowd to shame or anger Him, then the plan of salvation would be jeopardized. Again and again they shouted, "If thou be the Son of God, come down from the cross" (Matthew 27:40). He knew He could come down if He chose; He knew He could get help from more than twelve legions of angels who hovered about with drawn swords.

Yet for our salvation He stayed there. The angels would have come to the cross to rescue the King of kings, but because of His love for the human race and because He knew it was only through His death that they could be saved, He refused to call for their help. The angels were under orders not to intervene at this terrible, holy moment. Even the angels could not minister to the Son of God at Calvary. He died alone to take the full death penalty you and I deserved.

We can never plumb the depths of sin, or sense how terrible human sin is, until we go to the cross and see that it was "sin" that caused the Son of God to be crucified. The ravages of war, the tragedy of suicide, the agony of the poverty-stricken, the suffering and irony of the rejected of our society, the blood of the accident victim, the terror of rape and mugging victims of our generation—these all speak as with a single voice of the degradation that besets the human race at this hour. But no sin has been committed in the world today that can compare with the full cup of the universe's sin that brought Jesus to the cross. The question hurled toward heaven throughout the ages has been, "Who is He and why does He die?" The answer comes back, "This is my only begotten Son, dying not only for your sins but for the sins of the whole world." To you sin may be a small thing; to God it is a great and awful thing. It is the second largest thing in the world; only the love of God is greater.

When we comprehend the great price God was willing to pay for the redemption of man, we only then begin to see that something is horribly wrong with the human race. It must have a Savior, or it is doomed! Sin cost God His very best. Is it any wonder that the angels veiled their faces, that they were silent in their consternation as they witnessed the outworking of God's plan? How inconceivable it must have seemed to them, when they considered the fearful depravity of sin, that Jesus should shoulder it all. But they were soon to unveil their faces and offer their praises again. A light was kindled that day at Calvary. The cross blazed with the glory of God as the most terrible darkness was shattered by the light of salvation. Satan's depraved legions were defeated and they could no longer keep all men in darkness and defeat.

The Angels at the Resurrection

On the third day after His death the Bible says, "And behold there was a great earthquake; for the angel of the Lord descended from heaven, and came and rolled back the stone from the door, and sat upon it. His countenance was like lightning, and his raiment white as snow: And for fear of him the keepers did shake, and became as dead men" (Matthew 28:2–4).

Though some Bible students have tried to estimate how much this stone weighed, we need not speculate because Jesus could have come out of that tomb whether the stone was there or not. The Bible mentions it so that generations to come can know something of the tremendous miracle of resurrection that took place. I have often wondered what those guards must have thought when, against the brightness of the rising sun, they saw the angel rolling away the gigantic boulder with possibly the lightest touch of his finger! The guards, though heavily armed, were paralyzed with fear.

As Mary looked into the tomb she saw "two angels in white sitting, the one at the head, and the other at the feet, where the body of Jesus had lain" (John 20:11, 12). Then one of the angels who was sitting outside the tomb proclaimed the greatest message the world has ever heard: "He is not here, but is risen" (Luke 24:6). Those few words changed the history of the universe. Darkness and despair died; hope and anticipation were born in the hearts of men.

Angels and the Ascension of Jesus

We find the story of the ascension of Jesus in Acts 1. Verse 9 says, "And when he had spoken these things, while they beheld, he was taken up; and a cloud received him out of their sight." Jesus had been accompanied to earth by an angelic host. I believe that the word "cloud" suggests that angels had come to escort Him back to the right hand of God the Father.

The watching disciples were sad and despondent. Tears filled their eyes. But again two angels, looking like men and dressed in white raiment, appeared and said, "Ye men of Galilee, why stand ye gazing up into heaven? This same Jesus, which is taken up from you into heaven, shall so come in like manner as ye have seen him go into heaven" (Acts 1:11).

Thus, the angels escorted the resurrected Lord of glory back to be seated at the Father's right hand; then even the morning stars ascribed honor, glory and praise to Him as the Son of the Living God. On the other hand, some angels remained behind to assure those early disciples that they would always be near, ready to help God's people throughout the ages to come—until Christ returns in person with the angelic host.

12

Angels in Prophecy

ANGELS HAVE AN important role in future events! Human history began at Eden where God planted a garden and made man for His eternal fellowship. Angels were there. They have never failed to attend the human scene. And they will continue on the scene throughout the succeeding ages till time runs into eternity.

Just as millions of angels participated in the dazzling show when the morning stars sang together at creation, so will the innumerable hosts of heaven help bring to pass God's prophetic declarations throughout time and into eternity.

When God decrees it, Satan (Lucifer) will be removed from the world of disorder so God can establish righteousness everywhere, and a true theocracy. Not until that event takes place will the human race know perfect peace on earth. Paul tells us in Romans 8 that the whole creation groans and travails as it awaits the day of Christ's victory.

The prophets spoke of a wonderful day when God would lift the curse, when lion and lamb would lie down together, and when nations would learn war no more (Isaiah 2:4; 11:6). Angel hosts will fulfill His royal decrees and oversee God's purpose in the universe. Christ is coming in great power, and all His holy angels will be with Him. In Acts 1:10, 11 angels gave counsel to the disciples after Jesus had ascended to heaven. As we have already seen, when He had left the Mount of Olives, angels appeared, saying, "Ye men of Galilee, why stand ye gazing up into heaven? This same Jesus

... shall so come in like manner as ye have seen him go into heaven" (Acts 1:11). Angels encouraged those downcast believers who had seen Jesus Christ disappear from their view into a cloud. After this, angels figure prominently in the prophetic plan of God that continued on into the future events of Bible prophecy.

In every age, the true believers have asked, "Will this conflict of the ages ever end?" Each period of history seemingly has its own trials and convulsions. Each generation seems to have to "fight it out." Behind it all is the unseen struggle of the ages. We thought that modern technology would solve many of the great problems of the human race. In some ways it has, by eliminating the fear of diseases like polio and smallpox. But it has also given us Frankenstein weapons of destruction. Poverty, hunger, greed, injustice, prejudice, terrorism, lust, war and death are still with us. This is the same war that began mysteriously in the heart of Lucifer. It seems that our world is on a suicidal course; but God has other plans. Light shines at the end of the tunnel. Someday Satan and his demons will go down in defeat. The Bible declares that righteousness will eventually triumph, Utopia will come to earth, the kingdom of God will ultimately prevail. In bringing all this about angels will have a prominent part.

A little girl heard a clock strike thirteen times. Breathlessly she ran to her mother and said, "Mother, it's later than it's ever been before." Almost everyone throughout the world will agree. It's later than it's ever been before. The human race is rushing madly toward some sort of climax, and the Bible accurately predicts what the climax is! A new world is coming. Through modern technology and scientific achievement we are catching glimpses of what that new world is. If it were not for depraved human nature, man could achieve it himself. But man's rebellion against God has always been his stumbling block. The penalty for man's rebellion is death. The best leaders and the best brains have many times been stopped by death. The Bible teaches that "it is appointed unto men once to die" (Hebrews 9:27). Today the world longs for a leader such as Abraham Lincoln—but death took him from us.

God will use the angels to merge time into eternity, creating a new kind of life for every creature. Even today's intellectual world speaks of a point when time will be no more. Most scientists agree that the clock of time is running out. Ecologically, medically, scientifically, morally, time seems to be running out. In almost every direction we look, man's time on earth seems to be running out. Self-destruction is overtaking us as a human race.

Will man destroy himself? No! God has another plan!

Since the beginning of time, man has been interested in what lies beyond the short span of life. Modern man is turning to the occult, Eastern mysticism, palm readers and every other kind of help available to tell him about the future. Strangely, only a minority turn to the Bible, the only book that accurately foretells the future. The Bible teaches that Jesus Christ is coming back again with His holy angels. It refers to His coming as like "a thief in the night" (2 Peter 3:10), a day of wrath (Romans 2:5), and the judgment of the great day (Jude 6), with many other references both direct and indirect. The Age of Utopia will be preceded by unparalleled events of suffering for the human race—totalitarianism, poverty, disease, earthquakes, moral collapse, war—until men's hearts will fail them for fear (Luke 21:26).

Luke 21 says there will be "wars and commotions . . . Nation shall rise against nation, and kingdom against kingdom: And great earthquakes shall be in divers places, and famines, and pestilences; and fearful sights and great signs shall there be from heaven" (verses 9–11).

Believing Christians and believing Jews alike will be persecuted. Men will deliver "you up to the synagogues, and into prisons, being brought before kings and rulers for my name's sake. . . . And ye shall be betrayed both by parents, and brethren, and kinsfolk, and friends; and some of you shall they cause to be put to death. And ye shall be hated of all men for my name's sake. . . . And when ye shall see Jerusalem compassed with armies, then know that the desolation thereof is nigh. . . . And there shall be signs in the sun, and in the moon, and in the stars; and upon the earth distress of nations, with perplexity; the sea and the waves roaring; Men's hearts failing them for fear, and for looking after those things which are coming on the earth: for the powers of heaven shall be shaken" (verses 12–26).

Jesus continued in verse 27, "And then shall they see the Son of man coming in a cloud with power and great glory."

Even as in the beginning of time angelic forces waged war in heaven (Revelation 12:7–9), so in the very last days angels will wage still another war; Satan will make his last stand. As the time draws near he intensifies his activities.

But it will be a victorious day for the universe, and especially planet earth, when the devil and his angels are thrown into the lake of fire, never again to tempt and destroy man. To the angels God has assigned this task, and Scripture assures us that they will be victorious (Matthew 13:41, 42).

Angels Will Gather God's Elect

Linked to this idea Jesus says that "When the Son of man shall come in his glory, and all the holy angels with him, then shall he sit upon the throne of his glory" (Matthew 25:31). In other words, when Jesus returns, He will be accompanied by the hosts of heaven. The holy angels will be with Him! As He says in Matthew 13:41–42, "The Son of man shall send forth his angels, and they shall gather out of his kingdom all things that offend, and them which do iniquity; And shall cast them into a furnace of fire: there shall be wailing and gnashing of teeth."

Earlier in this same chapter, Jesus has related a significant little story commonly called the Parable of the Tares and Wheat (Matthew 13:24–30, 36–43). Both had been allowed to grow together until the harvest, but then the reapers were to gather them up in bundles. The tares were to be burned; the wheat gathered. We often wonder why God permits so much sin in the world, why He withholds His right arm of judgment. Why doesn't God put an end to sin now? We can give an answer from this text where Jesus said, "Let both grow together," the evil with the good (verse 30). If we were to try to wipe all evil from the face of the earth, who could count on justice? Pure justice does not exist here, because everyone is guilty, including the judges who sit in judgment. We are all guilty of sin.

Man must do his best in meting out justice, but his best is not complete justice. To angels will be delegated the ministry of separating the good from the bad, discerning even attitudes. God's judgment will be so pure that even those who are condemned will bow their knee and confess, "Thou art just." As someone has said, "When I die I do not want justice—I want mercy!" That mercy has been provided by the Lord Jesus Christ.

So angels will not only accompany Christ when He returns, but will be assigned the responsibility of gathering out of His kingdom all things that offend and work iniquity, that they might be judged (Matthew 13:47–50).

It boggles the mind to try to imagine the kind of earth this is going to be when God eliminates the devil and sin. Our minds are staggered at the thought of "Christ on the throne." The great southward-moving Sahara Desert of Africa will bloom and blossom. Mankind will be able to grow new foods; land that today is useless will grow twelve crops a year. The urge in man's heart toward immorality will have vanished. In that day the great drive in man will be a thirst for righteousness. It takes a great deal of faith in these days of despondency to believe this, but it is the clear teaching of the Bible. Without this hope of the future I do not know what modern man does, except turn to drugs and alcohol.

Today we have the choice of whether or not to receive the ministry of angels. In choosing to follow Jesus Christ we also choose the protective watch and care of the angels of heaven. In the time of the Second Coming, we will no longer be afforded the privilege of choice. If we delay now, it will be too late, and we forfeit forever the gracious ministry of angels and the promise of salvation to eternal life.

Angels in Our Future

Dr. Miller asks the question, "What does the future hold for this weary old world? . . . for the physical earth? The answers to such questions are not to be found in astrology or necromancy but in the divinely inspired Word of God. And we may be certain that, as the passing of time fulfills the prophetic Scriptures, the holy angels will be deeply involved in the fulfillment." God will renovate the earth, order the New Jerusalem to descend from heaven, and give redeemed man a position above the angels—what a future!

Elijah was one of the greatest prophets, suddenly appearing on the scene in one of Israel's darkest hours (1 Kings 17). He was a strong, suntanned son of the desert. At times he could be bold as a lion, and at times crushed with frustration. On one occasion he challenged the prophets of the heathen god Baal to a duel to see who was the true God (1 Kings 18:19). When the prophets of Baal could get no answer from their false god, and Elijah's God answered by fire, Queen Jezebel, unable to accept the prophet's verdict, determined to take his life and pursued him with her chariot for many miles. Elijah, weary from his flight and desperately hungry, lay down under a juniper tree to rest. Feeling extremely sorry for himself, he went to sleep, to be wakened by an angel's touch. Then food was set before him to eat, and the angel said, "Arise, eat."

"And he looked, and, behold, there was a cake baken on the coals, and a [jar] of water at his head. And he did eat and drink, and laid him down again. And the angel of the Lord came again the second time, and touched him, and said, Arise and eat; because the journey is too great for thee. And he arose, and did eat and drink, and went in the strength of that meat forty days and forty nights unto Horeb the mount of God" (1 Kings 19:6–8).

God did not let his faithful prophet down. He provided just what he needed physically, psychologically and spiritually. Many of us despair of coping with the pressures of our lives, but if we are living Spirit-filled and Spirit-directed lives, we can claim God's promises. The prophetic Scriptures give us "hope." Without Scripture's plan of God for the future and the hope it brings, I do not know what the average thinking person does. Certainly a person will not find the answer by wringing his hands, or by committing suicide, or by turning to the occult. We find the answer to the future in Holy Scripture. It is summed up in the person of Jesus Christ. God has centered all our hopes and dreams on Him. He is the Commander-in-Chief of these angelic armies that will accompany Him on His return.

Angel Authority

New Testament writers have reaffirmed the badge of authority given to angels to fulfill the prophetic dictates of God. The apostle Peter emphasized this truth when speaking of Christ, who was at the right hand of God, having gone into heaven after "angels and authorities and powers [had been] made subject unto him" (1 Peter 3:22). The time is coming when the twenty-four elders of His angelic creation will fall down before the Lamb and sing their new song (Revelation 5:9–10). Thereafter, the holy angels will gather round the throne and join in a great testimony to the Lamb, expressing praise with such words as, "Worthy is the Lamb that was slain to receive power and riches and wisdom and might and honor and glory and blessing" (Revelation 5:12, NASB). While angels have tremendous authority, it is limited to doing only the will of God. They never deviate from God's message, never dilute His message, never change God's plan. Throughout the ages they have glorified only Him, never themselves.

The Bible teaches that the demons are dedicated to controlling this planet for their master, Satan. Even Jesus called him "the prince of this world" (John 12:31). He is the master-organizer and strategist.

Many times throughout biblical history, and possibly even today, angels and demons engage in warfare. Many of the events of our times may very well be involved in this unseen struggle.

We are not left in doubt about who will ultimately triumph. Time after time Jesus has assured us that He and the angels would be victorious. "When the Son of man shall come in his glory, and all the holy angels with him, then shall he sit upon the throne of his glory" (Matthew 25:31). The apostle Paul wrote, "The Lord Jesus shall be revealed from heaven with his mighty angels in flaming fire . . ." (2 Thessalonians 1:7, 8).

Jesus also taught that "Whosoever shall confess me before men, him shall the Son of man also confess before the angels of God" (Luke 12:8). It is impossible to comprehend one's suffering of eternal loss when he learns that angels do not acknowledge him because he has been false in his claims to know Christ. But what a moment it is going to be for believers throughout all the ages, from every tribe, nation and tongue, when they are presented in the Court of Heaven. Scripture calls it, "the marriage supper of the Lamb" (Revelation 19:9). This is the great event when Jesus Christ is crowned King of kings and Lord of lords. Both believers of all ages, and all the angelic hosts will join in bowing their knees and confessing that He is Lord.

The book of Revelation, from chapter four to nineteen, gives us a picture of judgments to befall the earth such as the world has never known. Angels will be involved in all of these judgments. But after these terrifying events, Christ will come with His holy angels to set up His kingdom.

Whether the battle between the forces of Satan and the forces of God involve other planets and galaxies we do not know. But we do know that the earth is the scene of the conflict; however, it is a gigantic struggle that affects the entire universe. It is mind-boggling that you and I, with such a short period of time on this planet, play a part in this battle of the ages. It is almost incredible to us that supernatural beings from outer space are engaged in a struggle for this planet.

It all started in the Garden of Eden, a place located somewhere between the Tigris and the Euphrates rivers in the Middle East. It is significant that the nations prominent in early history are once again becoming prominent: Israel, Egypt, Syria, Iran, and so on. In that Garden God gave a great promise, "And I will put enmity between thee and the woman, and between thy seed and her seed; it shall bruise thy head, and thou shalt bruise his heel" (Genesis 3:15). As we approach the end of the age, the head of Satan is being battered and bruised as the forces of God gain momentum. Under the command of God, Michael the archangel is now organizing his forces for the last battle—Armageddon. The last picture in the Bible is one of heaven.

Many years ago I was visiting the dining room of the United States Senate. As I was speaking to various people, one of the senators called me to his table. He said, "Billy, we're having a discussion about pessimism and optimism. Are you a pessimist or an optimist?" I smiled and said, "I'm an optimist." He asked, "Why?" I said, "I've read the last page of the Bible."

The Bible speaks about a city whose builder and maker is God, where those who have been redeemed will be superior to angels. It speaks of "a pure river of water of life, clear as crystal proceeding out of the throne of God and of the Lamb" (Revelation 22:1). It says, "And they shall see his face; and his name shall be in their foreheads. And there shall be no night there; and they need no candle, neither light of the sun; for the Lord God giveth them light: and they shall reign for ever and ever" (verses 4, 5).

The next verse has a thrilling last word to say about angels: "These sayings are faithful and true: and the Lord God of the holy prophets sent his angel to shew unto his servants the things which must shortly be done."

Christian and non-Christian alike should meditate on the seventh verse where God says, "Behold I come quickly: blessed is he that keepeth the sayings of the prophecy of this book."

13

The Angels and Death

THE ANGEL WHO came to the garden where Jesus' body lay, rolled away the stone and permitted fresh air and morning light to fill His tomb. The sepulcher was no longer an empty vault or dreary dormitory; rather it was a life-affirming place that radiated the glory of the living God. No longer was it a dark prison but a transformed reminder of the celestial light that sweeps aside the shadows of death. Jesus' resurrection changed it.

An unknown poet has said of the tomb, "'Tis now a cell where angels used to come and go with heavenly news." No words of men or angels can adequately describe the height and depth, the length and breadth of the glory to which the world awakened when Jesus came forth to life from the pall of death. As Charles Wesley says in his hymn:

> 'Tis mystery all! Th' Immortal dies!
> Who can explore His strange design?
> In vain the first-born seraph tries
> To sound the depths of love Divine!
> 'Tis mercy all! Let earth adore!
> Let angel minds inquire no more.

In contrast to Jesus, we all still have to die. Yet just as an angel was involved in Christ's resurrection, so will angels help us in death. Only one thin veil separates our natural world from the spiritual world. That thin veil we call death. However, Christ both vanquished death and overcame the dark threats of the evil fallen angels. So now God surrounds death with the assurance of angelic help to bring pulsing life out of the darkness of that experience for believers. We inherit the kingdom of God.

Christians at Death

Death for the Christian cuts the cord that holds us captive in this present evil world so that angels may transport believers to their heavenly inheritance. Death is the fiery chariot, the gentle voice of the King, the invitation to non-stop passage into the banquet house of the world of glory.

In another connection I have already mentioned Lazarus, whom angels escorted to Abraham in heaven. This story has always been a tremendous comfort to me as I think about death. I will actually be taken by angels into the presence of God. These ministering spirits who have helped me here so often will be with me in my last great battle on earth. Death is a battle, a profound crisis event. Paul calls it "the last enemy" (1 Corinthians 15:26). While the sting of death has been removed by the work of Christ on the cross, and by His resurrection, yet the crossing of this valley still stimulates fear and mystery. However, angels will be there to help us. Could not the "rod and staff," which help us in the valley of the shadow of death (Psalm 23:4), be these holy angels?

We who have made our peace with God should be like the evangelist D. L. Moody. When he was aware that death was at hand, he said, "Earth recedes, heaven opens before me." It appeared as though he was dreaming. Then he said, "No, this is no dream . . . it is beautiful, it is like a trance. If this is death, it is sweet. There is no valley here. God is calling me, and I must go."

After having been given up for dead, Moody revived to indicate that God had permitted him to see beyond that thin veil separating the seen from the unseen world. He had been "within the gates, and beyond the portals," and had caught a glimpse of familiar faces whom he had "loved long since and lost awhile." Then he could remember when he had proclaimed so vociferously earlier in his ministry, "Some day you will read in the papers that D. L. Moody of East Northfield is dead. Don't you believe a word of it. At that moment I shall be more alive than I am now. I shall have gone up higher, that is all—out of this old clay tenement into a house that is immortal; a body that death cannot touch, that sin cannot taint, a body fashioned like unto His glorious body. . . . That which is born of the flesh may die. That which is born of the Spirit will live forever" (*The Life of Dwight L. Moody,* by W. R. Moody). If Moody were to witness to us now, he would surely tell us of the glowing experience that became his as the angelic hosts ushered him into the presence of the Lord.

Phillips Brooks, the writer of "O Little Town of Bethlehem," was one of the greatest pulpit orators and best loved preachers of the nineteenth century. No greater tribute could be paid him than the words of a five-year-old Boston girl, who exclaimed after her mother had told her that the beloved Mr. Brooks had died, "Mother, how happy the angels will be!"

Death is not natural, for man was created to live and not to die. It is the result of God's judgment because of man's sin and rebellion. Without God's grace through Christ, it is a gruesome spectacle. I have stood at the bedside of people dying without Christ; it was a terrible experience. I have stood at the bedside of those who were dying in Christ; it was a glorious experience. Charles Spurgeon said of the glory that attends the death of the redeemed, "If I may die as I have seen some die, I court the grand occasion. I would not wish to escape death by some by-road if I may sing as they sang. If I may have such hosannas and alleluias beaming in my eyes as I have seen as well as heard from them, it were a blessed thing to die."

Death is robbed of much of its terror for the true believer, but we still need God's protection as we take that last journey. At the moment of death the spirit departs from the body and moves through the atmosphere. But the Scripture teaches us that the devil lurks then. He is "the prince of the power of the air" (Ephesians 2:2). If the eyes of our understanding were opened, we would probably see the air filled with demons, the enemies of Christ. If Satan could hinder the angel of Daniel 10 for three weeks on his mission to earth, we can imagine the opposition a Christian may encounter at death.

But Christ on Calvary cleared a road through Satan's kingdom. When Christ came to earth, He had to pass through the devil's territory and open up a beachhead here. That is one reason He was accompanied by a host of angels when He came (Luke 2:8–14). And this is why holy angels will accompany Him when He comes again (Matthew 16:27). Till then, the moment of death is Satan's final opportunity to attack the true believer; but God has sent His angels to guard us at that time.

In telling the story in Luke 16 Jesus says that the beggar was "carried by the angels." He was not only escorted; he was *carried.* What an experience that must have been for Lazarus! He had lain begging at the gate of the rich man until his death, but then suddenly he found himself carried by the mighty angels of God!

Once I stood in London to watch Queen Elizabeth return from an overseas trip. I saw the parade of dignitaries, the marching bands, the crack troops, the waving flags. I saw all the splendor that accompanies the homecoming of a queen. However, that was nothing compared to the homecoming of a true believer who has said good-by here to all of the suffering of this life and been immediately surrounded by angels who carry him upward to the glorious welcome awaiting the redeemed in heaven.

The Christian should never consider death a tragedy. Rather he should see it as angels do: They realize that joy should mark the journey from time to eternity. The way to life is by the valley of death, but the road is marked with victory all the way. Angels revel in the power of the resurrection of Jesus, which assures us of our resurrection and guarantees us a safe passage to heaven.

Hundreds of accounts record the heavenly escort of angels at death. When my maternal grandmother died, for instance, the room seemed to fill with a heavenly light. She sat up in bed and almost laughingly said, "I see Jesus. He has His arms outstretched toward me. I see Ben [her husband who had died some years earlier] and I see the angels." She slumped over, absent from the body but present with the Lord.

When I was a student in a Bible school a godly young missionary volunteer was suddenly taken ill. The physician said she had only a few hours to live. Her young husband and one or two faculty members were in the room when she suddenly exclaimed, "I see Jesus. I can hear the singing of the angels."

The Reverend A. A. Talbot, missionary to China, was at the bedside of a dying Chinese Christian. Suddenly the room was filled with heavenly music. The Chinese Christian looked up with a radiant smile exclaiming, "I see Jesus standing at the right hand of God, and Margaret Gay is with Him." (Margaret Gay was the Talbot's little daughter who had died months before.)

Susanna Wesley said, "When I am gone, sing a song of praise to God."

Dying patients are given so many drugs today that we do not hear as many of these stories now. But to those who face death in Christ it is a glorious experience. The Bible guarantees every believer an escorted journey into the presence of Christ by the holy angels.

The angelic emissaries of the Lord are often sent not only to catch away the redeemed of the Lord at death, but also to give hope and joy to those who remain, and to sustain them in their loss. He has promised to give "the oil of joy for mourning, the garment expressive of praise instead of a heavy, burdened and failing spirit . . . (Isaiah 61:3, AB).

Today man has been overtaken by an increasing sense of gloom about life. In his *Responding to Suicidal Crisis*, Doman Lum quotes Minna Field on the inadequacy of the counsel and treatment given by those who merely "attempt to escape what is to them an unbearable prospect by a pat on the back and by telling the patient that he is talking nonsense." Death seminars are now being held in major medical centers, and teams of psychiatrists, psychologists and therapists are constantly encouraged to become involved. Robert J. Lifton, in studying the cessation of life, points out in the same book some interesting views held by survivors of the atomic destruction of Hiroshima. He says that "There was a lasting sense of an overwhelming and permanent encounter with death. As a result, there was a breakdown of faith or trust in any human structure, a psychological closure in which people literally numbed themselves to any emotional feelings regarding death, and an overwhelming sense of guilt and self-condemnation as if they were responsible for the tragedy. . . . We are obsessed with the fear of sudden death . . . and recognize the unpredictable nature of life."

In popular thinking you and I have heard people speaking of death as "crossing the Jordan." It is found in spirituals and in some hymns of the Christian faith. It comes, of course, from the victorious march of the Israelites who crossed the Jordan to enter the Promised Land. They passed over Jordan on dry ground. By analogy we can consider that the ministering angels will see us safely across the Jordan River of death as we enter the promised land of heaven. So the Christian does not sorrow as those who have no hope (1 Thessalonians 4:13).

When the apostle Paul spoke of his own approaching death, he said, "We are confident, I say, and willing rather to be absent from the body, and to be present with the Lord" (2 Corinthians 5:8). When that glorious physical and spiritual separation takes place, the angels will be there to escort us into the presence of our Savior with abounding joy, and it will mean "life everlasting."

The Wonderful Welcome to Come

I believe that death can be beautiful. I have come to look forward to it, to anticipate it with joy and expectation. I have stood at the side of many people who died with expressions of triumph on their faces. No wonder the Bible says, "Precious in the sight of the Lord is the death of his saints" (Psalm 116:15). No wonder David said, "Even though I walk through the valley of the shadow of death, I will fear no evil, for you are with me . . ." (Psalm 23:4, NIV).

You may be filled with dread at the thought of death. Just remember that at one moment you may be suffering, but in another moment, you will be instantly transformed into the glorious likeness of our Savior. The wonders, beauties, splendor and grandeur of heaven will be yours. You will be surrounded by these heavenly messengers sent by God to bring you home where you may rest from your labors, though the honor of your works will follow you (Revelation 14:13).

No wonder the apostle Paul said, "Therefore, my dear brothers, stand firm. Let nothing move you.

Always give yourselves fully to the work of the Lord, because you know that your labor in the Lord is not in vain" (1 Corinthians 15:58, NIV).

Are you ready to face life? Are you ready to face death? No one is truly ready to die who has not learned to live for the glory of God. You can put your confidence in Jesus because He died for you, and in that last moment—the greatest crisis of all—He will have His angels gather you in their arms to carry you gloriously, wonderfully into heaven.

14

Angel Spectators

HOW WOULD YOU live if you knew that you were being watched all the time, not only by your parents, wife, husband or children, but by the heavenly host? The Bible teaches in 1 Corinthians 4:9 that angels are watching us. Paul says we are a "spectacle" to them. A. S. Joppie points out that the word referred to the arenas where first-century crowds went to see animals killed for sport, men battle to the death and, later, Christians torn apart by lions. In using the word spectacle, Paul is picturing this world as one vast arena. All true Christians participate in this great drama as they seek to obey Christ since this throws them into severe conflict with the forces of evil, who are bent on humiliating them. Yet Scripture says, "They did not love their lives so much as to shrink from death" (Revelation 12:11, NIV).

During this conflict, which was not limited to the arena, the angels were watching them, longing to hasten to their rescue to set free those men and women who often went joyfully to their death. Yet God forbade the angels to rush in as armies of deliverance. Nor had He allowed them to rescue Jesus at the cross when He tasted the death of separation from God the Father. The angel spectators were poised and ready to intervene; the attack order never came. Why? Because God's moment of final victory over the vicious forces of evil had not yet come.

As I mentioned earlier we face many perplexing questions today, such as: Why does God permit evil? Why doesn't God intervene and punish sin? Why does God allow disease? Why does God permit catastrophe? Yet God's timing is precise! Angel hosts who witness everything that transpires in our world are not free to bear up the righteous and deliver the oppressed until God gives the signal. One day He will. Christ has reminded us that the wheat and the tares, the righteous and the unrighteous, are to grow in the field together until the harvest time when the holy angels gather God's elect and bring them into His kingdom.

Angels at Attention

As God's angels have watched the drama of this age unfolding they have seen the Christian church established and expand around the world. They miss nothing as they watch the movements of time, "To the intent that now unto the principalities and powers in heavenly places might be known by the church the manifold wisdom of God" (Ephesians 3:10). Dr. Joppie reminds us that the word "now" actually covers the vast expanse of this Church age. Angel hosts have witnessed the formation of the Church of Christ Jesus, and have watched the walk of each believer as the Lord worked His grace, love and power into each life. The angels were observing firsthand the building of the body of the true Church in all places of His dominion this very hour.

But what are they thinking as we live in the world's arena? Do they observe us as we stand fast in the faith and walk in righteousness? Or may they be wondering at our lack of commitment? These two possibilities seem evident from Ephesians 3:10: "(The purpose is) that through the church the complicated, many-sided wisdom of God in all its infinite variety and innumerable aspects might now be made known to the angelic rulers and authorities (principalities and powers) in the heavenly sphere" (AB).

Our certainty that angels right now witness how we are walking through life should mightily influence the decisions we make. God is watching, and His angels are interested spectators too. The Amplified Bible expresses 1 Corinthians 4:9 this way: "God has made an exhibit of us . . . a show in the world's amphitheater—

with both men and angels (as spectators)." We know they are watching, but in the heat of the battle, I have thought how wonderful it would be if we could hear them cheering.

Incentives for Righteousness

The charge to live righteously in this present world sobers us when we realize that the walk and warfare of Christians is the primary concern of heaven and its angelic hosts. Paul said, "I solemnly charge you in the presence of God and of Christ Jesus and of the chosen angels, that you guard and keep (these rules) . . ." (1 Timothy 5:21, AB). Paul was stirring up Timothy to remember that the elect angels were constantly watching how he served the Savior and lived the Christian life. What fact could provide a greater motivation to righteous living than that? I must say to myself, "Careful, angels are watching!"

It must give the angels great satisfaction to watch the Church of Jesus Christ minister the unsearchable riches of Christ to lost men everywhere. If the angels rejoice over one sinner who repents (Luke 15:10), then the angel hosts are numbered among the spectators in the heavenly grandstands. They are included among those who are referred to as "so great a cloud of witness" (Hebrews 12:1); and they never miss any of the details of our earthly pilgrimage. Yet they do not jeer as did the Greek crowds of Paul's day. Rather as we declare the gospel and see our friends saved, they rejoice with us.

In his book, *Though I Walk Through the Valley*, Dr. Vance Havner tells of an old preacher who worked into the night on a sermon for his small congregation. His wife inquired why he spent so much time on a message that he would give to so few. To this the minister replied, "You forget, my dear, how large my audience will be!" Dr. Havner adds that "Nothing is trivial here if heaven looks on. We shall play a better game if, 'seeing we are encompassed,' we remember who is in the grandstand!"

Our valleys may be filled with foes and tears; but we can lift our eyes to the hills to see God and the angels, heaven's spectators, who support us according to God's infinite wisdom as they prepare our welcome home.

15

Angels in Our Lives Today

IN THE EARLY days of World War II, Britain's air force saved it from invasion and defeat. In her book, *Tell No Man*, Adela Rogers St. John describes a strange aspect of that weeks-long air war. Her information comes from a celebration held some months after the war, honoring Air Chief Marshal Lord Hugh Dowding. The King, the Prime Minister and scores of dignitaries were there. In his remarks, the Air Chief Marshal recounted the story of his legendary conflict where his pitifully small complement of men rarely slept, and their planes never stopped flying. He told about airmen on a mission who, having been hit, were either incapacitated or dead. Yet their planes kept flying and fighting; in fact, on occasion pilots in other planes would see a figure still operating the controls. What was the explanation? The Air Chief Marshal said he believed angels had actually flown some of the planes whose pilots sat dead in their cockpits.

That angels piloted planes for dead men in the battle for Britain we cannot finally prove. But we have already seen from Scripture some of the things angels have certainly done, can do, and are yet going to do as history approaches its climax. The important question for each of us is how angels can assist us in our lives here and now: How do they help us attain victory over the forces of evil? What is our continuing relationship to them?

We know that God has given His angels charge over us so that without their help we could never get the victory over Satan. The apostle Paul said, "For we wrestle not against flesh and blood, but against principalities, against powers, against the rulers of the darkness of this world, against spiritual wickedness in high places" (Ephesians 6:12). Let's consider how we can gain help from God through angels.

The God of This Age

Lucifer, our archenemy, controls one of the most powerful and well-oiled war machines in the universe. He controls principalities, powers and dominions. Every nation, city, village and individual has felt the hot breath of his evil power. He is already gathering the nations of the world for the last great battle in the war against Christ—Armageddon. Yet Jesus assures us that Satan is already a defeated foe (John 12:31; 16:11). In 2 Timothy 1:10 Paul says that Jesus Christ has abolished death and brought life and immortality to light through the gospel. Peter declares that Jesus "has gone into heaven and is at God's right hand—with angels, authorities and powers in submission to him" (1 Peter 3:22, NIV).

The Defeat of Satan

While Satan is a defeated foe in principle, obviously God has not yet eliminated him from the world scene. The Bible teaches, however, that God will use angels to judge and totally eliminate him from the universe. In Revelation 12 we read of Satan's earlier defeat: "Michael and his angels fought against the dragon; and the dragon fought and his angels, And prevailed not; neither was their place found any more in heaven. And the great dragon was cast out, that old serpent, called the Devil, and Satan, which deceiveth the whole world: he was cast out into the earth, . . ." (verses 7–9). In chapter 20 John describes how Satan's present earthly rule will be temporarily restricted: "And I saw an angel come down from heaven, having the key of the bottomless pit and a great chain in his hand. And he laid hold on the dragon, that old serpent, which is the Devil, and Satan, and bound him a thousand years, And cast him into the bottomless pit, and shut him up, and set a seal upon him, that he should deceive the nations no more, . . ." John then tells us that after a temporary release followed by the last great battle, God will cast Satan into the lake of fire and brimstone, there to be tormented forever (Revelation 20:10).

Some will say, "It is well and good to talk about the final defeat of the devil but until that happens it doesn't help me because I have to contend with him every day." But this is not the whole story. We have been given specific instructions in Scripture about how to get victory over the devil.

We are told, for example, "Do not give the devil a foothold" (Ephesians 4:27, NIV). In other words, don't leave any vacant places in your heart for him. The apostle Peter taught, "Be sober, be vigilant; because your adversary the devil, as a roaring lion, walketh about, seeking whom he may devour" (1 Peter 5:8). Thus, we cannot be too careful. This includes the injunction to join God's resistance movement: "Whom resist stedfast in the faith" (1 Peter 5:9). And James says, "Resist the devil, and he will flee from you" (James 4:7).

But these admonitions to be vigilant and to resist tell only part of the story. We are not in the battle alone, nor must we rely on our strength alone. Instead, we are to rely on the Holy Spirit, who dwells within us and is willing and able to help us in every situation if we will turn to Him. In addition we can count on the powerful presence of angels many times more numerous and powerful than Satan and his demons. As Increase Mather wrote centuries ago in *Angelographia*, "Angels both good and bad have a greater influence on this world than men are generally aware of. We ought to admire the grace of God toward us sinful creatures in that He hath appointed His holy angels to guard us against the mischiefs of wicked spirits who are always intending our hurt both to our bodies and to our souls."

We have already considered Elisha at Dothan, ringed by apparently overwhelming enemy forces. Yet if we, like his servant, had open spiritual eyes, we would see not only a world filled with evil spirits and powers—but also powerful angels with drawn swords, set for our defense.

At Dothan thousands of soldiers surrounded the city and intended to do Elisha harm. Yet he had peace. His servant, however, did not, and needed his eyes opened. We, who are troubled, confused, fearful, frustrated Christians need God to open our eyes this very moment. As Vance Havner says, "Our primary problem is not light, but sight. Light is of no value to a blind man. Reading books galore on the subject will not reveal the angels unless our eyes are touched by faith."

We must not get so busy counting demons that we forget the holy angels. Certainly we are up against a gigantic war machine. But we are encompassed by a heavenly host so powerful that we need not fear the warfare—the battle is the Lord's. We can boldly face Satan and his legions with all the confidence of the old captain who, when told that his outfit was completely surrounded, shouted, "Good, don't let any of them escape." If your valley is full of foes, raise your sights to the hills and see the holy angels of God arrayed for battle on your behalf.

When Abraham sent his eldest servant back to his blood relations to look for a bride for Isaac he urged him to go confidently because of God's angel: "he shall send his angel before thee, . . . and prosper thy way" (Genesis 24:7, 40). Isaiah the prophet said, "In all their affliction he [the Lord] was afflicted, and the angel of his presence saved them" (63:9). God promised Moses in the midst of all his exasperations, "Mine angel shall go before thee" (Exodus 23:23). The Bible also says we may see the angels God has sent, but fail to recognize them: "Be not forgetful to entertain strangers: for thereby some have entertained angels unawares" (Hebrews 13:2). Angels, whether noticed by men or not, are active in our twentieth-century world too. Are we aware of them?

It was a tragic night in a Chinese city. Bandits had surrounded the mission compound sheltering hundreds of women and children. On the previous night the missionary, Miss Monsen, had been put to bed with a bad attack of malaria, and now the tempter harassed her with questions: "What will you do when the looters come here? When firing begins on this compound, what about those promises you have been trusting?" In his book, *1,000 New Illustrations*, Al Bryant records the result. Miss Monsen prayed, "Lord, I have been teaching these young people all these years that Thy promises are true, and if they fail now, my mouth shall be forever closed; I must go home."

Throughout the next night she was up, ministering to frightened refugees, encouraging them to pray and to trust God to deliver them. Though fearful things happened all around, the bandits left the mission compound untouched.

In the morning, people from three different neighborhood families asked Miss Monsen, "Who were those four people, three sitting and one standing, quietly watching from the top of your house all night long?" When she told them that no one had been on the housetop, they refused to believe her, saying, "We saw them with our own eyes!" She then told them that God still sent angels to guard His children in their hour of danger.

We have also noted the provision of angels. On occasion they have even given food, as we know from the life of Elijah, following his triumph over the priests of Baal. Fearful, tired and discouraged, "As he lay and slept under a juniper tree, behold, then an angel touched him, and said . . . Arise and eat" (1 Kings 19:5–7). God has promised, "Are they not all ministering spirits, sent forth to minister for them who shall be heirs of salvation?" (Hebrews 1:14). Need we think this provisioning by angels ceased thousands of years ago?

When I was visiting the American troops during the Korean War, I was told of a small group of American marines in the First Division who had been trapped up north. With the thermometer at twenty degrees below zero, they were close to freezing to death. And they had had nothing to eat for six days. Surrender to the enemy seemed their only hope of survival. But one of the men, a Christian, pointed out certain verses of Scripture, and taught his comrades to sing a song of praise to God. Following this they heard a crashing noise, and turned to see a wild boar rushing toward them. As they tried to jump out of his way, he suddenly stopped in his tracks. One of the soldiers raised his rifle to shoot, but before he could fire, the boar inexplicably toppled over. They rushed up to kill him only to find that he was already dead. That night they feasted on meat, and began to regain their strength.

The next morning just as the sun was rising they heard another noise. Their fear that an enemy patrol had discovered them suddenly vanished as they found themselves face to face with a South Korean who could speak English. He said, "I will show you out." He led them through the forest and mountains to safety behind their own lines. When they looked up to thank him, they found he had disappeared.

Angels in Judgment

As we continue to study how to gain the help of angels in our lives today, we need to look soberly once again at the relation of angels to judgment.

Just before fire and brimstone fell on Sodom because of its sins, the angel said, "For we will destroy this place . . . the Lord hath sent us to destroy it" (Genesis 19:13).

In Daniel 7:10 the Word of God says, "A fiery stream issued and came forth from before him . . . the judgment was set, and the books were opened." In scores of places in the Bible God tells us that He will use angels to execute His judgments on all those who have refused to obey His will by failing to receive Christ as Savior and Lord. As Jesus said, "The Son of man shall send forth his angels, and they shall gather out of his kingdom all things that offend, and them which do iniquity; and shall cast them into a furnace of fire: there shall be wailing and gnashing of teeth" (Matthew 13:41, 42). Jesus also said, "It shall be more tolerable for Tyre and Sidon at the day of judgment, than for you" (Matthew 11:22). And again, "every idle word that men shall speak, they shall give account thereof in the day of judgment" (Matthew 12:36). "For there is nothing covered, that shall not be revealed; neither hid, that shall not be known" (Luke 12:2).

God is recording not only the words and actions but all the thoughts and intents of our hearts. Someday you and I will have to give an account, and at that time our final destiny will be determined by whether we have received or rejected Jesus. Paul said that God would give "to you who are troubled rest with us, when the Lord Jesus shall be revealed from heaven with his mighty angels, in flaming fire taking vengeance on them that know not God and that obey not the gospel of our Lord Jesus Christ" (2 Thessalonians 1:7–8).

Justice demands that the books of life be balanced, but without a final judgment this would be impossible. Laws too are meaningless unless accompanied by a penalty for those who break them.

Reason alone should tell us that there must come a time when God will call upon the Hitlers and the Idi Amins of the world for an accounting. Otherwise there is no justice in the universe.

Thousands of wicked men have lived evil lives and perpetrated their evil designs upon others without seeming to pay any penalty for their misdeeds in this life. However, the Bible says that a time will come when the crooked places will be made straight (Isaiah 45:2). In the great day of God's judgment men will call on Him for mercy, but it will be too late. In that day if men were to seek God, they would not be able to find Him. It would be too late. They could cry out for angels to deliver them, but it would be of no avail.

Angels Rejoice in the Salvation of Sinners

While angels will play an important role in executing the judgment of God on those who refuse Jesus Christ as Savior and Lord, yet at the same time the Bible informs us that they also rejoice in the salvation of sinners. Jesus tells several striking stories in Luke 15. In the first, a man had a hundred sheep. When one was lost, he left the ninety-nine in the wilderness to seek him. When he found the sheep he slung it over his own shoulders and brought it back to the fold. At home he summoned all his friends, saying, "Rejoice with me: for I have found my sheep which was lost" (verse 6). Jesus said, "I say unto you, that likewise joy shall be in heaven over one sinner that repenteth, more than over ninety and nine just persons, which need no repentance" (verse 7).

His second story is that of a woman who lost a valuable silver coin. She looked everywhere. She swept her house carefully. At last when she recovered the coin she called all her friends and neighbors saying, "Rejoice with me; for I have found the piece which I had lost" (verse 9). "Likewise, I say unto you, there is joy in the presence of the angels of God over one sinner that repenteth" (Luke 15:10).

In these two parables is not Jesus telling us that the angels of heaven have their eyes on every person? They know the spiritual condition of everybody on the face of the earth. Not only does God love you, but the angels love you too. They are anxious for you

to repent and turn to Christ for salvation before it is too late. They
know the terrible dangers of hell that lie ahead. They want you
to turn toward heaven, but they know that this is a decision that
you and you alone will have to make.

A rich young ruler came running to kneel before Christ one day,
and asked, "Good Master, what shall I do that I may inherit eternal life?" (Mark 10:17). When Peter had preached his great sermon
at Pentecost, Luke says the people were "pricked in their heart,
and said unto Peter, . . . what shall we do?" (Acts 2:37).

The African nobleman riding in the chariot across the desert
talked with Philip the evangelist. Suddenly the nobleman stopped
his chariot and said, "What doth hinder me to be baptized?" (Acts
8:36). At midnight the Philippian jailer asked Paul and Silas, "Sirs,
what must I do to be saved?" (Acts 16:30). Modern man forever
asks this same question. It is old, but always new. It is just as relevant today as it was in the past.

Just what must you do to cause the angels to rejoice? How do
you become reconciled to God? How do you repent of your sin?
A simple question demands a simple answer. Jesus made everything so simple, and we have made it so complicated. He spoke
to people in short sentences, using everyday words, illustrating His
message with never-to-be-forgotten stories. He presented the message of God in such simplicity that many were amazed at what
they heard. They could hardly believe their ears, because the message was so simple.

In the Acts of the Apostles, the Philippian jailer asked the apostle
Paul, "What must I do to be saved?" Paul gave him a very simple
answer, "Believe on the Lord Jesus Christ, and thou shalt be saved"
(Acts 16:30, 31). This is so simple that millions stumble over it.
The one and only way you can be converted is to believe on the
Lord Jesus Christ as your own personal Lord and Savior. You don't
have to straighten out your life first. You don't have to try to give
up some habit that is keeping you from God. You have tried all
that and failed many times. You can come "just as you are." The
blind man came just as he was. The leper came just as he was. The
thief on the cross came just as he was. You can come to Christ
right now wherever you are and just as you are—and the angels of
heaven will rejoice!

Some of the greatest and most precious words recorded in all of Scripture were spoken by Satan himself (not that he intended it to be so). In his discussion with God about Job, he said, "Hast not thou made an hedge about him, and about his house, and about all that he hath on every side? thou hast blessed the work of his hands, and his substance is increased in the land" (Job 1:10).

As I look back over my life I remember the moment I came to Jesus Christ as Savior and Lord. The angels rejoiced! Since then I have been in thousands of battles with Satan and his demons. As I yielded my will and committed myself totally to Christ—as I prayed and believed—I am convinced that God "put a hedge about me," a hedge of angels to protect me.

The Scripture says there is a time to be born and a time to die. And when my time to die comes an angel will be there to comfort me. He will give me peace and joy even at that most critical hour, and usher me into the presence of God, and I will dwell with the Lord forever. Thank God for the ministry of His blessed angels!

How to
Be Born Again

CONTENTS

PREFACE

TODAY BEING "BORN again" is big news. *Time* magazine carries a feature story on "Born Again Faith." Political candidates give the subject as much attention as the latest economic statistics or the energy crisis. A former Black Panther leader and radical of the 1960s returns from exile and announces, "My life has turned 180 degrees. I have been born again." A man who was deeply involved in one of the most publicized political scandals of our time writes a best seller explaining the change in his life as a result of being born again. A Gallup poll comes up with the astonishing conclusion that "more than one-third of those who are old enough to vote have experienced 'born again' religious conversions."

Born again!

Is it possible? Can life be transformed?

What's it all about? What does it mean?

Is it real? Will it last?

How is a person "born again"?

The expression "born again" is not a new term, invented by modern journalists to describe recent religious trends. The term "born again" is almost two thousand years old. One dark night, in the ancient city of Jerusalem, Jesus turned to one of the best-known intellectuals of his time and said, "I say to you, unless one is born again, he cannot see the kingdom of God" (John 3:3). In those words Jesus told us of both the necessity and the possibility of new birth—of spiritual transformation. Since that time untold millions throughout the ages have attested to the reality and the power of God in their lives through being born again.

A young Marine Corps officer, a veteran of the Vietnam War, described publicly the night battle in Vietnam when he and his troops came under enemy attack. Only a few were lifted out alive by helicopter. The sixteen surgical operations he endured had helped to restore his physical powers, but now he was speaking of the spiritual rebirth he had received since returning home. He said, "We bear an allegiance to the flag of our country, but unless we have been born again through faith in Christ, all our religion is worth nothing."

This lieutenant had been born again.

I think of the great Dutch Christian, Corrie ten Boom, who is now in her 80s. Her story of courage in the midşt of Nazi persecution has inspired millions. She tells of an experience when she was only five years old when she said, "I want Jesus in my heart." She described how her mother took her little hand in hers and prayed with her. "It was so simple, and yet Jesus Christ says that we all must come as children, no matter what our age, social standing, or intellectual background."

Corrie ten Boom, at the age of five, had been born again.

I have had countless people tell me, in person and by letter, how they were born again and their lives were changed. A man from Milwaukee wrote, "Tonight my wife and I had come to the brink of ending our marriage. We felt we could no longer stay together under the conditions in which we were living. Both of us admitted that we thought we no longer loved each other. I no longer enjoyed her company nor appreciated my home life. We made bitter statements about each other. We could make no compromise, nor could we agree on how to improve our marriage even if we were to try.

"I believe it was God's will that I turned on the television and listened to your message about spiritual rebirth. As my wife watched with me, we began to search our hearts and felt a new life within us. I prayed that God would come into my heart and truly make me a new man and help me begin a new life. Our troubles seem rather slight now."

Both this man and his wife were born again.

What does it mean to be born again? It is not just a remodelling job, performed somehow by us on ourselves. Today we hear a lot about recycling, reconstruction, and reshaping. We renovate houses and add on more rooms. We tear down old buildings and build new ones in our cities, calling it urban renewal. Millions and millions of dollars are spent every year on health spas, beauty resorts, and exotic cosmetics—all by people hoping to reshape their faces or renew their bodies.

In like manner, people frantically pursue all sorts of promised cures for the renewal of their inner lives. Some people hunt for renewal at the psychiatrist's office. Others search for spiritual renewal in exotic oriental religions or processes of inward meditation. Still others seek for inner peace and renewal in drugs or alcohol. Whatever the path, however, they eventually come to a dead end. Why? Simply because man cannot renew himself. God created us. Only God can recreate us. Only God can give us the new birth we so desperately want and need.

I believe this is one of the most important subjects in the entire world. Governments may be elected or may topple. Military machines may advance and retreat. Men may explore outer space or probe the ocean depths. All of these events are part of the grand plan for humans on this planet.

But the central theme of the universe is the purpose and destiny of every individual. Every person is important in God's eyes. That is why God is not content to stand with His arms folded (as it were) and simply watch the human race wallow in misery and destruction. The greatest news in the universe is that we can be born again! "For God so loved the world, that He gave His only begotten Son, that whoever believes in Him should not perish, but have eternal life" (John 3:16).

This new birth happens in all kinds of ways. It may seem to happen over a period of time or in a moment. The paths which people take to reach that point of decision may be very direct or very circuitous. Whatever the path, we always find Christ at the end to welcome us. And that encounter with Christ, that new birth, is the beginning of a whole new path in life under His control. Lives can be remarkably changed, marriages excitingly improved, societies influenced for good—all by the simple, sweeping surge of individuals knowing what it is to be born again.

It may be that down inside you sense an unnamed need you cannot describe. Perhaps you have been consciously searching all your life to fill a void in your heart and to find a purpose for living. Perhaps outwardly you have been very successful in life, but you know it has not brought you peace and true happiness. Perhaps your life is an unbroken chain of heartaches and shattered dreams. Maybe you are just curious.

Whatever your background may be, I pray that God will use this little book to give you hope—to show you that you, too can be born again.

How to be Born Again is not for the theologians or the philosophers. There are many learned works of theology which probe the meaning of the new birth (or "regeneration," as theologians often call it). I know there have been different emphases among theologians concerning the new birth. Some have stressed the importance of what God does to bring us to faith. Some have stressed the importance of man's search for faith. Some have thought of the new birth as a single event in time, while others use the term to speak of all God wills to do in our lives. Ultimately there is a mystery about the new birth; we cannot understand everything about it, for our minds are finite.

However much the theologians may disagree about fine points of doctrine, the central truth of the new birth is clear: Man apart from God is spiritually dead. He needs to be born again. Only by God's grace through faith in Christ can this new birth take place.

My concern has been to make this book practical. Although we may not be able to say everything possible about the new birth, I have wanted to say everything that was necessary to help people who really want to know God. I want to help them come to have this life-changing experience. I want them—I want you—to be born again. I believe God wants you to be born again.

I was already working on this book when the term "born again" became big news. I have sensed the blessing of God as I have continued writing, and have sensed also that God may have led me to write this book at just the right time as millions wonder about being born again.

I gave my original manuscript to my friends Paul Fromer and Carole Carlson—and asked for help. Then with the added help of my wife and of Cliff and Billie Barrows, we finished it in a little apartment provided by dear Mexican friends while I recuperated from an illness.

Thus, my deepest appreciation to Bill and Vivian Mead of Dallas, Texas, and our wonderful friends the Servitje family in Mexico for making our working, recuperating period possible; to Paul Fromer, professor at Wheaton College, and to my secretary Stephanie Wills, who typed and retyped the manuscript, for the wonderful encouragement and help from my wife, Ruth, for the comments of Dr. John Akers and Mrs. Millie Dienert; but especially to Carole Carlson for the magnificent work she did in helping to simplify what may have been too deep and theological for people all over the world who I pray will read this book and experience "the new birth."

BILLY GRAHAM

Montreat, North Carolina

Author's Note. I am using the words *born again* and *regeneration* in their widest possible terms in this book. I recognize that in one sense they can be narrowly defined theologically, and in another sense cover the whole range of what we mean by "salvation." (The term *new birth* has been used in a wide and in a restricted sense; it may signify the whole process of salvation including the preparatory work of conviction and the concluding work of discipleship and, ultimately, glorification; or it can be used only for that act of imparting spiritual life, excluding the preparation phase and the lifetime phase.

I recognize that different denominations have slightly different interpretations. For example, the Roman Catholic Church regards regeneration as meaning everything in the transition from a position of condemnation on earth to a state of salvation in Heaven. The Augsburg Confession and the Formula Concordie use the new birth or regeneration in the wide meaning but distinguish between justification and sanctification. In the Reformed Churches, such as the Presbyterians, the term is used in the wide significance, but also distinguishes between justification and sanctification. Thus reformed theologians include not only the new birth but all that comes from it. Calvin taught that the new birth was the restoration of the Divine image within us. He believed that the new birth came not only by an instantaneous act of Divine life being infused to the spiritually dead, but also the various processes of spiritual growth that followed. The Westminster Confession of Faith never used the term regeneration, but used the term *effectual calling.* This meant the entire work of the Holy Spirit in the application of total redemption.

Sometimes these uses of the terms *new birth* and *regeneration* have led to semantic differences. In this book I am not making these distinctions but simply stating what most denominations basically believe historically—that man needs regeneration and to be born again—and how he may go about it if he lacks the assurance or if he has never made this commitment, whether he is a church member or not.

I
MAN'S PROBLEM

1

Why Am I So Empty?

WHEN THE VIKING landed on Mars, the world exclaimed, "Unbelievable! Magnificent!" The mysterious Red Planet
had been penetrated. An ingeniously designed robot which was the
result of one billion dollars and the probing minds of hundreds of
scientists had accomplished a task that man had dreamed about
for generations.

Exploring the great mysteries of the universe, trying to predict
the quirks of nature, attempting to predict a trend in society or
politics are all modern concerns.

In the business world, for instance, men search for ways to
improve their efficiency. On office walls and on bulletin boards
of sales organizations we see slogans like "Plan Ahead" or "Plan
Your Work and Work Your Plan." Corporations hire firms at large
fees to determine how they can improve their planning. Business,
world politics, and economics change so fast that in a few days
the direction of an entire country can change. Companies called
"Think Factories" project thinking a decade or more in advance
to keep abreast of the changing times.

In our daily lives we keep a calendar, trying to mark down
appointments and schedule our days. If there were no planning,
children would never get to the dentist, mothers would never make
the community meeting, businesses and labor unions would col-

lapse. We are always searching for ways to streamline our lives, to simplify daily living.

But what about the greater issues of life and death? Do we plan? Do we need to search for answers to the deep moral and spiritual questions so that our lives are more orderly? Man has always thought so, which is why we have philosophers, psychologists, and theologians. Today, however, much of the world in search of knowledge and fulfillment ignores God!

I knew a brilliant young lawyer who did not seem to find a need for God during his intense years of concentration as a student. Later, he began to write a book about a famous person. While he was working on this book we had a conversation during the course of which I detected that he was on a personal spiritual quest. He hoped to find somewhere in the life of the man who was the subject of his book a spiritual fulfillment which he himself wanted. He knew this person believed in God and had accepted Christ into his heart. He also seemed reassured that the one about whom he was writing had doubts from time to time.

This young man who has been searching for so long has now become interested in spiritual things. In my earlier contacts with him I thought he was an agnostic, interested only in gaining knowledge at the university and later at law school. Now I suspect that all through adolescence and his twenties he was searching for God without knowing it.

The Self-made Man

We are taught to be independent, to make it on our own. As we look at an individual we may say, "Now there's someone who's made it!" We admire him and respect his ability to "pull himself up by his bootstraps."

We have even had a well-known TV commercial that says, "Please, mother, I'd rather do it myself."

And yet within each of us is a deep-seated frustration: "I ought to be better. I believe I was made for something more; there must be more to life than this. Why am I so empty?"

Such feelings, often subconscious, cause us to struggle toward some unknown, unnamed goal. We may try to evade this quest, we may detour into a fantasy world, we may even regress to lower levels of life and seek to escape. We may throw up our hands in disgust and say, "What's the use? I'm O.K. just working and keeping out of trouble." But somehow, deep inside is a compulsion which invariably leads us to take up the search again.

This is one of the reasons the nation became fascinated by *Roots*, the product of Alex Haley's ten-year search for identity. My friend Rod McKuen felt rootless and a strange "vacuum" in his heart as he began his search for his true father. The oldest book in the possession of the human race is *Job*, and Job once exclaimed "Oh that I knew where I might find Him" (Job 23:3).

This search transcends race, age, economic status, sex, and educational background. Either man began nowhere and is looking for some place to go, or he began somewhere and lost his way. In either case, he's searching. None of us will ever find "total satisfaction" until we find that our roots are in eternity.

A famous scientist at an eastern university asked to see me. Somewhat surprised, I met him in a quiet room at the Student Union. Suddenly this brilliant man, admired by many and respected as a leader in his field, broke down. When he regained his composure he told me: "I'm at the point of ending my life. . . . My home is a wreck, I'm a secret alcoholic, my children don't respect me. I've never really had a guiding principle in my life except to be recognized in my field of physics. I've come to realize that I don't really know the true values of living. I've watched you on TV and although I don't understand all you're trying to communicate, I have a conviction that you know what the real meaning of life is."

He hesitated, and I'm sure the next thing this famous, self-made man said was very difficult for him: "I've come to you for help." It was a desperate cry.

From every culture, every country—from those who cannot read to Nobel Prize winners—there is the age-old phenomenon, the mystery of *anthropos*, the "upward-looking one," the one who is searching, inquiring for life's deeper and often hidden meaning.

In airports, on planes, in hotel lobbies across the world, people have come to me with serious questions about broken family relationships, ill health, or financial catastrophes. But more often they reveal empty souls. On an airplane flight a man poured out his life story to me. It was a saga of shattered dreams, broken hopes, and emptiness. Before we parted he had said "yes" to Christ. Tremendous relief came over his face as he whispered, "Thank you."

When we landed, I watched him embrace his wife and talk excitedly to her at the same time. I don't know what their conversation was, but from his expression he was evidently telling her of his new relationship with the Lord. I can only imagine how amazed she must have been at the change, because he had told me how his temper and unfaithfulness had just about broken their marriage.

I don't know if his marriage was put back together, because I never saw him again, but his direction was certainly changed on that plane trip.

Fame and Fortune

One of our best known show biz personalities asked me to come to his dressing room after a show on which I had appeared. He motioned me in and said, "I make people laugh . . . but inside I feel like hell. I've been married twice; both marriages have broken up. It's been mostly my fault, I guess, but I don't think I could make a go of a third marriage unless I could find some sort of fulfillment which I don't know how to get."

He stopped and looked at me. "Do you think what I'm really looking for is summed up in the word *God?*"

All of his fame and money had not satisfied his searching heart.

A man who was destined to be very influential in the life of Charles Colson, of Watergate fame, was Tom Phillips. Colson writes in his book, *Born Again*, that Phillips said: "'It may be hard to understand . . . but I didn't seem to have anything that mattered. It was all on the surface. All the material things in life are meaningless if a man hasn't discovered what's underneath them. . . .

"'One night I was in New York on business and noticed that Billy Graham was having a Crusade in Madison Square Garden,' Tom continued. 'I went—curious, I guess—hoping maybe I'd find some answers. What Graham said that night put it all into place for me. I saw what was missing—the personal relationship with Jesus Christ, the fact that I hadn't ever asked Him into my life, hadn't turned my life over to Him. So I did it—that very night at the Crusade.'"[1]

Once again a man was forced to examine his soul.

I was in another country at one time and was invited to have lunch with a man who, materially speaking, had everything this world could offer. In fact, he expressed to me how he could buy anything he wanted. He had traveled extensively in business; everything he touched seemed to turn to gold. He was leader of his social set, and yet in his own words he said, "I'm a miserable old man, doomed to die. If there is a hell, that's where I'm headed."

I looked through the beautiful old windows at the snow falling gently on the manicured lawn and thought about others, like him, who had expressed to me similar thoughts about the emptiness of life without God—the meaninglessness of life for a man who has everything to live with, but nothing to live for. My attention came back with a start as I heard him say, "I've asked you here today to read the Bible to me and to talk to me about God. Do you think it's too late? My father and mother were strong believers in God and often prayed for me."

The verse from Matthew 4:4 flashed across my mind: "Man shall not live on bread alone." And Luke 12:15 tells us, "Not even when one has an abundance does his life consist of his possessions."

We read every day about the rich, the famous, the talented, who are disillusioned. Many of them are turning to the occult, or Transcendental Meditation, or Eastern religions. Some are turning to crime. The questions they thought were answered are left dangling: What is man? Where did he come from? What is his purpose on this planet? Where is he going? Is there a God who cares? If there is a God, has He revealed Himself to man?

Is the Intellectual Searching?

The men and women who are considered part of the intellectual community are searching for the same meaning, the same sense of fulfillment, but many are hampered by their own sense of pride. They would like to save themselves, because pride nourishes self-esteem, making us believe we can manage ourselves without God.

The famous English writer and philosopher, Bertrand Russell, wrote prolifically concerning ethics, morals, and human society, trying to prove what he believed were fallacies in the Bible. When it came to the pride of the intellectual, Russell wrote, "Every man would like to be God, if it were possible; some few find it difficult to admit the impossibility."[2]

From the very beginning of time, man has said, like Lucifer, "I will be like the Most High" (Isa. 14:14, KJV).

The search continues. The heart needs filling, and most intellectuals come to a point in their lives when the academe, the scientific community, the business or political activities are no longer enough.

A brilliant analyst of the cultural scene wrote: "Man, being human, however, tries again and again to evade the logic of his own position, and searches for his true self, his humanity, his freedom, even if he can only do so by means of sheer irrationality or completely unfounded mysticism."[3]

We see the results of man searching for his true self in mystic experiences, new cults, and what is called the New Consciousness. "Man today wants to experience God. It is not faith or knowledge which is the key word, but experience."[4]

As the desire for this experience increases, the false philosophies and false gods become acceptable. A European intellectual says: "For centuries there has been the search for the attainment of that ideal which the Greeks called ataraxia, the idea of quiet calm, of deep inner contentment, beyond the restlessness, frustrations, and tensions of normal living. Many searched for this via philosophy and religion, but always there has been the parallel search for short cuts."[5]

An American scholar writes, "As man's search for new experiences, new leaders, new hopes, increases in intensity, there will be that continued desire to find an alternative route into what appears to be a dark future."[6]

Men desperately want peace, but the peace of God is not absence from tension or turmoil, but peace in the midst of tension and turmoil.

In Calcutta, India, I wanted to see a great woman of God who is known to the world as Mother Theresa. I arrived early in the evening and the sisters hated to disturb Mother Theresa, because three men had died in her arms that day and she had just gone to her room to get a bit of rest. However, the official who brought me there sent a note to Mother Theresa, and in a few minutes she was there. I immediately had the impression of this saintly woman as a person who has peace in the midst of turmoil. It's the peace that passes all understanding, and all misunderstanding, too.

How desperately we need that kind of peace during a generation which is being torn apart by internal unrest and despair. The daily newspapers are classics in negative outlook. Terrorism, bombings, suicide, divorce, general pessimism are the diseases of the day because in his pride man refuses to turn to God!

The honest intellectual, however, the one who keeps an open mind along with his searching heart, is the one who makes a thrilling discovery. Dr. Rookmaaker says: "We cannot understand God fully, nor know His work completely. But we are not asked to accept in blind faith. On the contrary: we are asked to look around us, and know that the things He tells us through His Son and His prophets and apostles are true, real, and of this world, the cosmos He has made.

"Therefore our faith can never be just 'out of the box,' irrational. Faith is not a sacrifice of the intellect if we believe in the biblical account of history."[7]

Who Needs Help?

In the rash of disaster movies in the middle 70s there was one called *Earthquake*. When the devastating quake hit, two of the main characters in the movie found shelter under a sturdy car from the flying debris and the terror of unleashed nature. At that moment they didn't reason about what had happened; they didn't analyze what they were going to do; they knew they needed help and dove for shelter.

The person who is on the bottom of life's circumstances wants help immediately. He doesn't need to analyze and examine how help comes; he only knows he needs to be saved.

When it comes to the disasters of our inner earthquakes some intellectuals want to know the source of help and all the details concerning that source. The intellectual has a certain set of beliefs which are self-sufficient and he believes his system is complete. Other intellectuals accept blindly the counterfeits which may be veiled in such complex language and thought patterns that the denial of their premises would sound ignorant. It's very difficult for some to say, "That doesn't really make good sense and I don't understand what is being said."

Nevertheless, many intellectual searchers have opened their minds and hearts to the truth of the Good News and found new life.

A young Hindu who was doing graduate study in nuclear medicine at UCLA was just beginning her second year of study when she came to a Crusade. At the end of the service she accepted Christ as her Savior and was born again.

A brilliant surgeon who came to a Crusade heard me say that if gaining Heaven depended upon good deeds I wouldn't expect to get there. He had devoted his life to helping humanity, but at that moment he realized his training, his years of hard work and devotion, his sleepless nights with patients, and his love for his profession wouldn't earn him a place with God. This man, who had seen many births himself, knew what it was to be born twice.

Many people think Christ talked only to down-and-outers or children. One of His greatest encounters during His teaching ministry was with an intellectual. This man, whose name was Nicodemus, had a very rigid philosophical and theological system, and it was a good plan, with God at the center. However this "intellectual" structured his philosophical religious system without the new birth—found only in Jesus Christ!

What did Jesus, the carpenter from Nazareth, tell this well-educated man? He said, in words like these, "Nicodemus, I'm sorry I can't explain it to you. You have seen something that troubles you, that doesn't fit your system. You admit I am more than an ordinary man, that I act with the power of God. This may not make sense to you, but I can't explain it to you because your assumptions do not allow for a starting point. Nicodemus, to you it's not 'logical.' Nothing in your thought patterns permits it. You cannot see with spiritual insight until you are born spiritually. You will just have to be born again."

Nicodemus was baffled. "'And how can a man who's getting old possibly be born?' replied Nicodemus. 'How can he go back into his mother's womb and be born a second time?'" (John 3:4, Phillips).

The intellectual asks, "How can a man be born twice?"

If anyone is to find the answer to his search he must reject much of his old system and plunge into a new one. He will see the possibility of what he thought was impossible.

"That is also why only this uniquely 'impossible' faith—with a God who is, with an Incarnation that is earthly and historical, with a salvation that is at cross-purposes with human nature, with a Resurrection that blasts apart the finality of death—is able to provide an alternative to the sifting, settling dust of death and through a new birth open the way to new life."[8]

In the mountains near our home there was a small plane lost with four people on board. At the same time a fifteen-year-old girl was lost in approximately the same area in the Great Smoky Mountains. It was a sad time for our little community because the four were killed and the girl was never found.

As my wife talked to a man who helps us about the tragic events of these people, he told her a story from his own experience. He was born and raised in these mountains, he said, and thought he could never get lost. The mountains were his playground as a child and his hunting area as an adult. One day, however, he found himself groping through the brush and clambering over the rocks, hopelessly confused. He wandered and retraced his steps and suddenly, to his relief, came upon an old man in a mountain cabin. He told Ruth that he would never forget the advice the old man gave him: "When you find yourself lost in the mountains, never go down—always go up. At the top of the ridge you can get your bearings and find your way again."

We can become lost in the mountain of life. We have two choices: we can either go down and get caught in drugs, depression, emptiness, and confusion, or we can keep heading up. The direction we go will determine whether we find ourselves or not.

In this Age of Quest the most important is our personal search for answers concerning life and about God. That search will propel us in the only true direction, in only one way, and we will be embarked on that journey when we are born again.

2

Can Anyone Tell Me Where to Find God?

A DRUNK WAS LOOKING for something on the sidewalk one night under a street light. He groped along the ground, feeling the cement, occasionally grabbing the pole for support. A passerby asked what he was looking for. "Lost my wallet," the drunk replied. The passerby offered to help him look, but with no success.

"Are you sure you lost it here?" he asked the drunk.

"'Course I didn't!" the drunk replied. "It was half a block back there."

"Then why aren't you looking back there?"

"Because," answered the drunk with baffling logic, "there ain't no street lights back there."

Searching is important, but it doesn't do any good unless we search in the right places.

The governor of one of our states entertained us in his home and after dinner asked to talk to me privately. We went into his study and I could see that he was struggling with his emotions, but finally he said, "I'm at the end of my rope. I need God. Can you tell me how to find Him?"

A young man, toughened in the Green Berets, so strong that his hands had been insured as lethal weapons, fell upon the floor of his room one night, weeping like a helpless child. "God, God, where are you?"

From the ghetto to the mansion, from community leader to

prisoner on death row, man wonders if there is a God. And if there is, what is He like?

A remarkable fact for all seekers of God is that belief in some kind of God is practically universal. Whatever period of history we study, whatever culture we examine, if we look back in time we see all peoples, primitive or modern, acknowledging some kind of deity. During the past two centuries archaeology has unearthed the ruins of many ancient civilizations, but none has ever been found that did not yield some evidence of a god who was worshiped. Man has worshiped the sun and carved idols. Man has worshiped a set of rules, animals, and other men. Some seem to worship themselves. Man has made gods out of his imagination, although basically through a fog of confusion he believes that God does exist.

Some people give up the pursuit of God in frustration, calling themselves "atheists" or "agnostics," professing to be irreligious. Instead they find it necessary to fill the vacuum left within them with some other kind of deity. Therefore man makes his own "god"—money, work, success, fame, sex, or alcohol, even food.

Today many use their nation as an object of worship, espousing the gospel of nationalism. They mistakenly attempt to displace the true and living God with the religion of nationalism. Others make a god of their cause. Although many radical groups deny faith in God, thousands willingly lay down their lives and suffer privation and poverty because of their belief in "the cause" or "the revolution."

Failing to find the true God, millions declare their allegiance to lesser gods and causes. They find no ultimate answers or satisfaction, however. Just as Adam was made for fellowship with God, so are all men. Jesus commented on the First Commandment by saying, "And you shall love the Lord your God with all your heart, and with all your soul, and with all your mind, and with all your strength" (Mark 12:30).

He meant that man, unlike a stone or an animal, has the capacity to love God.

Two-Way Search

Although the wise person seeks God, we have seen that he doesn't have the intellectual capacity to reason his way through to God. He must raise a serious personal question: "Is there any hope of being successful in this search? Can I really know God?"

Once when being interviewed by Ludovic Kennedy on BBC in London, I was asked, "Who made God?" The answer was simple. "No one made God." God is self-existent.

"In the beginning God" are the words which build the cornerstone of all existence. Without God there would have been no beginning and no continuing. God was the creating power and the cohesive force that brought cosmos out of chaos. By divine fiat He brought form out of shapelessness, order out of disorder, and light out of darkness.

Scientists cannot see God in a test tube or a telescope. God is God and the mind of man is too small!

Blaise Pascal, the celebrated seventeenth century French physicist, said, "A unit joined to infinity adds nothing to it any more than one foot added to infinite length. The finite is swallowed up by the infinite and becomes pure zero. So are our minds before God."

As we seek this great God, what route are we to take? How can a created, finite human being, limited by time and space, understand an infinite God?

Our failure to comprehend God fully should not strike us as strange. After all, we live surrounded by mysteries we cannot explain—mysteries far simpler. Who can explain why objects are always attracted to the center of the earth? Newton formulated the law of gravity, but he couldn't explain it. Who can explain reproduction? For years scientists have tried to reproduce a living cell and solve the mystery of procreation. They believe they are coming close, but as yet they are without success.

We have become accustomed to accepting as fact many mysteries we cannot explain. I am amazed when my wife mixes corn meal, shortening, eggs, baking powder, and buttermilk, and I see the soupy mixture slowly rise in the oven and come out light and fluffy with a crispy brown crust. I don't understand it, but I accept the results.

God is far more complex than some of the earthly phenomena we cannot understand. However, we could present many arguments before a very skeptical jury which would suggest the existence of God. In the scientific realm we know that whatever is in motion must be moved by something else, since motion is the response of matter to power. Yet in the world of matter there can be no power without life, and life presupposes a being who produces the power to move such things as tides and planets.

Another argument says that nothing can be the cause of itself. It would be prior to itself if it caused itself to be, and that is an absurdity!

Consider the law of life. We see objects that have no intellect, such as stars and planets, moving in a consistent pattern, cooperating ingeniously with one another. It is evident that they achieve their movements not by accident but by design.

Whatever lacks intelligence cannot move intelligently. What gives direction and design to these inanimate objects? It is God. He is the underlying, motivating force of life.

Many evidences and arguments suggest God's existence, yet the plain truth is that God cannot be proved by intellectual arguments alone. If the human mind could fully prove God, He would be no greater than the mind that proves Him!

Ultimately you must come to God by faith. Faith is the link between God and man. The Scriptures say you must believe that *He is.* "Faith" is used many times in the Bible, and God has taken it upon Himself to encourage that faith. God continues to pursue man—just as man is searching for Him.

In spite of man's repeated rebellion, God loves man with an everlasting love. Some earthly fathers give up on their children when they fall into habits and company that are despicable. A father might order his son or daughter out of the house and tell them never to return. On the other hand, some fathers and even mothers deny their children before they are born. We know young people—even grown ones—whose lives are scarred by parental rejection. The only way such a person can be healed is to accept the fact and ask the Lord to supply the lack. The Bible says, "When my father and my mother forsake me, then the Lord will take me up" (Ps. 27:10, KJV).

God has never forsaken man. The most dramatic quest of the centuries is God's loving and patient pursuit of man.

When man chose in the Garden of Eden to defy God's law, to break the line of communication between himself and God, they could no longer have fellowship. Light and darkness could not live side by side. Why did this barrier come between God and His creation? The cause is a characteristic of God that the average person does not comprehend. God is absolute "holiness."

Long ago God said to Israel, "I the Lord your God am holy" (Lev. 19:2).

In the book of Revelation the cry in heaven night and day is, "HOLY, HOLY, HOLY, is THE LORD GOD, THE ALMIGHTY, who was and who is and who is to come" (Rev. 4:8).

A holy God recoils from our evil; He cannot look upon sin because it is ugly and revolting to Him. Because man was stained with sin, God could no longer have fellowship with him. However, *God loves us—in spite of ourselves!*

God had a plan to restore fellowship with man, in spite of his sin. If God didn't have a plan, certainly no one else can! He had said to Adam and Eve at the very beginning when they broke His law, "You shall surely die" (Gen. 2:17). In a later chapter we will discuss the three dimensions of death. Man had to die or God would have had to go back on His word, and God cannot be a liar or He would no longer be God.

We can see that because man still sins, still defies authority and still acts independently of God, a great gulf exists between him and God. Twentieth-century man and woman are no different from Adam and Eve. We may have added some sophisticated technology, built a few skyscrapers, and written several million books, but there is still a chasm between sinful man and holy God. Yet across this dark, barren abyss, God calls, even pleads, with man to be reconciled to Him.

God loves us.

The Apostle John said that "God is love" (1 John 4:8).

The prophet Jeremiah quotes God as saying, "'I have loved you with an everlasting love; therefore I have drawn you with loving-kindness'"(Jer. 31:3).

Another prophet, Malachi, said, "'I have loved you,' says the Lord" (Mal. 1:2).

In every good novel or play there must be conflict. But even Shakespeare could not have created a more powerful plot than the divine dilemma. We know that man is sinful and separated from God. Because God is holy, He couldn't automatically forgive or ignore man's rebellion. Because God is love, He couldn't completely cast man aside. Conflict. How could God be just and the justifier? This is the question Job posed: "But how can a man be in the right before God?" (Job 9:2).

God Speaks

Radio was just coming of age when I was a boy. We would gather around a crude homemade set and twist the three tuning dials in an effort to establish contact with the transmitter. Often all the sound that came out of the amplifier was the squeak and squawk of static. It wasn't very exciting to listen to all those senseless sounds, but we kept at the controls with anticipation. We knew that somewhere out there was the unseen transmitter, so if contact was established and the dials were in adjustment we could hear a voice loud and clear. After a long time of laborious tuning the far distant sound of music or a voice would suddenly break through and a smile of triumph would brighten the faces of everyone in the room. At last we were tuned in!

Perhaps you have been puzzled that the prophets said God spoke to them. Does He speak to us? Does He tell us where He is—how we can find Him—how we can be right with Him? How God has answered these questions in His Word is the subject of part 2 of this book, which deals with the kind of person Jesus Christ was and the work He did. God has solved the problem, He does tell us about Himself and his loving concern. The key is a line of communication which is "revelation."

Revelation means "to make known" or "to unveil." Revelation requires a "revealer," who in this case is God. It also requires "hearers"—the chosen prophets and apostles who recorded in the Bible what He told them. Revelation is communication in which God is at one end and man is at the other.

In the revelation that God established between Himself and us we can find a new dimension of living, but we must "tune in." Levels of living we have never attained await us. Peace, satisfaction, and joy we have never experienced are available to us. God is trying to break through. The heavens are calling and God is speaking!

Have you heard God's voice? At the same time you are searching for God, He is speaking to you.

3

Does God Really Speak to Us?

GOD HAS SPOKEN to us from the beginning. Adam heard the voice of the Lord in the Garden of Eden. God also spoke to Eve, and she knew who was speaking and must have trembled because she knew she had disobeyed Him.

Two people, a man and a woman, chose to disobey God and plunged into a world that was spiritually dark and dead—and physically unproductive except by hard work and suffering. The world was under the judgment of God. The Bible teaches that man is in a period of spiritual blackout. "The god of this world has blinded the minds of the unbelieving" (2 Cor. 4:4).

Isaiah, the great Hebrew prophet, said, "We grope along the wall like blind men, we grope like those who have no eyes; we stumble at midday as in the twilight, among those who are vigorous we are like dead men" (Isa. 59:10).

Isaiah was giving a vivid description of what sounds like physical blindness, but which is the darkness of the spirit.

To be trapped in physical darkness can be an uncanny experience. When Cliff Barrows and I were in England just after World War II we drove down the streets in fog so thick that one of us had to walk in front of the car to prevent it from running into the curb. This was a new experience, a type of "blackout" which was frightening.

How much worse it is to be forever spiritually blacked out and trapped! There are those who have physical blindness and yet are able to "see" better than a sighted person.

There is a beautiful Korean girl with a voice that has been described as "electric." She also plays the piano beautifully, and yet she is physically blind. Kim sees more than many with 20-20 vision and does not consider her blindness a handicap, but a gift from God. I have found her to have mental, psychological, and spiritual insights which are absolutely amazing.

Man is also spiritually deaf. Another great prophet said, people have "ears to hear but do not hear" (Ezek. 12:2). Jesus said it with more force: "If they do not listen to Moses and the Prophets, neither will they be persuaded if someone rises from the dead" (Luke 16:31).

The difference between physical deafness and spiritual deafness is illustrated to me vividly at the Crusades. We have a section for the deaf and I have often stopped to shake hands with these men and women. At one Crusade about a dozen deaf persons were brought to see me in my office and I sat and talked to them through an interpreter. The light of Christ was quite obvious on the faces of many of them.

The world of the physically deaf is one which those of us with normal hearing find difficult to comprehend. But we walk in the world of the spiritually deaf every day.

Spiritually, many men and women are more than deaf and blind, they are dead. "You were dead in your trespasses and sins" (Eph. 2:1).

For the spiritually dead there is no communication with God. Millions of persons long for a world of joy, light, harmony, and peace, instead they are engulfed in a world of pessimism, darkness, discord, and turmoil. They search for happiness, but it eludes them, just as a sunbeam or a shaft of light eludes a child who tries to catch it.

Many give up and give in to pessimism. Often their despondent attitude leads to a circle of cocktail parties or bars where they obliterate the reality of their world with the unreality of alcohol. Sometimes they are led to drugs or an all-consuming pursuit of a hobby or a sport. All these are symptoms of the great escapist disease caused by an insidious infection called sin.

Many persons want to dissect God under their own microscopes. After establishing their own methods of analysis they come to no conclusions. God remains the great cosmic silence, unknown and unseeing. However, God does communicate with those who are willing to obey Him. He penetrates the dark silence with free, life-giving discoveries in nature, the human conscience, Scripture, and the Person of Jesus Christ.

God Speaks in Nature

I was present when our youngest son was born, and our three sons-in-law and our oldest son were present at the births of their children. We all felt that we had experienced a miracle. As one of the doctors said, "How can anyone deny the existence of God after witnessing birth?"

In its own language, nature speaks of God's existence, whether it is the cry of a baby or the song of a meadowlark. It is the language of order, beauty, perfection, and intelligence. The intricacies of a flower are God's work; the instincts of the birds are within His plans. God speaks in the regularity of the seasons; in the movements of the sun, moon, and stars; in the balance of the elements which allow us to breathe. "The heavens are telling of the glory of God; and the firmament is declaring the work of His hands. Day to day pours forth speech, and night to night reveals knowledge" (Ps. 19:1,2).

The very size of the universe has always been incomprehensible to man, but as twentieth century exploration has taken man into space our minds have become boggled. Every scientist who lacks belief in God must be completely baffled when he surveys how small man is on this earth—part of an estimated 100 billion galaxies, with 100 billion stars and planets in each galaxy.

With the exploration of the universe this generation has also looked at the other end of the scale. The electron microscope and biochemical research have enabled investigators to examine cells which have been magnified up to 200,000 times. There are so many molecules in one drop of water that if they could be transformed into grains of sand there would be enough sand to pave a road from Los Angeles to New York!

The Apostle Paul said, "For since the creation of the world His invisible attributes, His eternal power and divine nature, have been clearly seen, being understood through what has been made" (Rom. 1:20).

God says that we can learn a great deal about Him just by observing nature. Since He has spoken through His universe men and women are without excuse for not believing Him. This is the reason the Psalmist writes, "The fool has said in his heart, 'There is no God'" (Ps. 14:1).

God speaks in nature but we cannot know Him simply by sitting under a tree and gazing at the sky. He has another avenue of revelation for us which is often called that "still small voice."

God Speaks in Our Conscience

What is a conscience? A dictionary definition is "the sense of right and wrong; ideas and feelings within a person that tell him when he is doing right and warn him of what is wrong."

"Let your conscience be your guide" is sometimes wise advice, but not always. God shows Himself in our conscience. Sometimes it is a gentle teacher, prodding us in the right direction like the usher in a darkened theater leading us to our seats. Other times our conscience is our worst enemy, torturing us day and night with agonizing unrest.

Paul describes the working of conscience in this way: "For when Gentiles who do not have the Law do instinctively the things of the Law, these, not having the Law, are a law to themselves, in that they show the work of the Law written in their hearts, their conscience bearing witness, and their thoughts alternately accusing or else defending them" (Rom. 2:14,15).

"A man's conscience is the Lord's searchlight exposing his hidden motives" (Prov. 20:27, *The Living Bible*).

When we realize that God takes a powerful light and shines it into the darkest recesses of our minds, examining not just our actions, but the motives behind those actions, it becomes clear that God does indeed speak through our conscience.

Even people who are not Christians realize the existence of something within themselves which is a guiding force. Thomas

Jefferson wrote almost two hundred years ago that "the moral sense, or conscience, is as much a part of man as his leg or arm. It is given to all human beings in a stronger or weaker degree, as force of members is given them in a greater or less degree."

Some persons, even without God, have a stronger sense of conscience than others. But the one with a seared or dead conscience is like an airplane without a pilot or a boat without a rudder—confused and directionless, on a collision course with circumstances. Through sin the conscience can become hardened, and even dead.

God Speaks in Scripture

The Bible is the textbook of revelation. In God's great classroom there are three textbooks—one called nature, one called conscience, and one named Scripture. The laws God revealed in nature have never changed. In the written textbook of revelation—the Bible—God speaks through words. The Bible is the one book which reveals the Creator to the creature He created! No other book that man has conceived can make that statement and support it with fact.

The Bible is unique in its claims, its teachings, and its survival. Today there are many persons who are looking at books which are supposed to give the answers to the great questions of life and death; many of these books are products of Eastern religions or humanistic philosophy. In his book *Evidence That Demands a Verdict,* Josh McDowell quotes a former professor of Sanskrit who spent forty-two years studying Eastern books and said this in comparing them with the Bible: "Pile them, if you will, on the left side of your study table; but place your own Holy Bible on the right side—all by itself, all alone—and with a wide gap between them. For, . . . there is a gulf between it and the so-called sacred books of the East which severs the one from the other utterly, hopelessly, and forever . . . a veritable gulf which cannot be bridged over by any science of religious thought.'"[1]

Skeptics have attacked the Bible and retreated in confusion. Agnostics have scoffed at its teaching, but are unable to produce an intellectually honest refutation. Atheists have denied its

validity, but must surrender to its historical accuracy and archaeological verification.

I picked up a reputable news magazine and read that a certain
head of state made a remark about the economic trends. Nothing
very startling about that. You and I read statements made by men
and women every day. If we hear them from several different
sources, we are inclined to believe that they're true and to tell
someone else.

If we were confronted with a book which said in hundreds of
different situations that, for instance, the Queen of England spoke,
we would believe that she actually had been making statements.
No doubt about it!

The writers of the Bible spoke in many ways to indicate that
God gave them their information. In the Old Testament alone they
said 3000 times that God spoke! Just in the first five books of the
Bible we find such phrases as these:

"The Lord God called to the man"
"The Lord God said to the woman"
"The Lord said to Noah"
"God spoke unto Israel"
"God said"
"The Lord spoke saying"
"The Lord commanded"
"Hear the words of the Lord"
"Says the Lord"

Did God speak to these men as they were inspired to write? If
He didn't, then they were the most blatant and consistent liars the
world has ever known, or they were mentally deranged. Would a
variety of men from different areas, many of them not knowing
each other, tell more than 3000 lies on one subject? If they were
mistaken in this area why should we believe anything they said?
If we cannot believe that God spoke to men in the Bible, then we
cannot believe that the prophecies of these great men came true—
and yet they did!

If someone lies to you two or three times, you begin to distrust
him. You find it difficult, if not impossible, to believe anything

he says. However, we would have to negate everything in the Bible if we thought that the Bible writers lied when they said God spoke.

Jesus quoted frequently from the Old Testament. He knew it well and never doubted the Scriptures. He said, "Scripture cannot be broken" (John 10:35).

The Apostles often quoted the Old Testament Scriptures. Paul said, "All Scripture is inspired by God" (2 Tim. 3:16). Peter said, "For no prophecy was ever made by an act of human will, but men moved by the Holy Spirit spoke from God" (2 Pet. 1:21).

Many people get their belief about the Bible from secondhand sources. A smattering of biblical movie epics, some television reruns, hearsay, and courses on comparative religion give them man's view of Scripture. In high school or college classes students take courses in "the Bible as Literature." Many times these classes are used to undermine the faith of young people unless there is a teacher who understands the Bible and has a strong faith in God. I know students who have studied such topics as the "Myths and Discrepancies of the Bible."

Secondhand sources will not do.

A verse or a story in the Bible may speak to someone in a way someone else could not imagine. It was a firsthand source in a secondhand bookstore that changed the lives of an entire family.

My wife has a weakness for books—especially old, choice religious books which are now out of print. At one time Foyles in London had a large secondhand religious book department. One day during the 1954 London Crusade she was browsing through the books in Foyles when a very agitated clerk popped out from behind the stacks and asked if she was Mrs. Graham. When she told him that she was, he began to tell her a story of confusion, despair, and frustrations. His marriage was on the rocks, his home was breaking up, and business problems were mounting. He explained that he had explored every avenue for help and as a last resort planned to attend the services at Harringay arena that night. Ruth assured him that she would pray for him, and she did. That was in 1954.

In 1955 we returned to London. Again my wife went into Foyles' secondhand book department. This time the same clerk appeared from behind the stacks, his face wreathed in smiles. After expressing how happy he was to see her again, he explained that he had gone to Harringay that night in 1954 as he had said he would, that he had found the Savior, and that the problems in his life had sorted themselves out.

Then he asked Ruth if she would be interested in knowing what verse it was that "spoke to him." She was. Again he disappeared behind all the books and reappeared with a worn Bible in his hand. He turned to Psalm 102, which I had read the night that he had attended the Crusade. He pointed out verse 6, "I am like a pelican of the wilderness; I am like an owl of the desert" (KJV). This had so perfectly described to him his condition that he realized for the first time how completely God understood and cared. As a result he was soundly converted to the Lord Jesus Christ. And subsequently so was his entire family.

My wife was in London during 1972 at the time of a Harringay reunion. As the ceremonies closed, a gentleman came up to speak to her, but he didn't have to introduce himself. She recognized the clerk from Foyles. He was radiantly happy, introduced his Christian family, and explained how they were all now in the Lord's work—all because God spoke to him when he was "an owl of the desert!"

Make use of this tool of communication by which God speaks to us—namely, the Bible! Read it, study it, memorize it. It will change your entire life. It is not like any other book. It is a "living" book that works its way into your heart, mind and soul.

Speaking In Dark Places

In places where there is easy accessibility to the Bible, it may gather dust on the shelf. In countries where the Bible is subversive literature, God speaks in unusual ways.

A famous violinist was invited years ago by Chow En Lai to teach at one of the famous universities in the People's Republic of China. He was told that if he wanted to leave he would be able to do so. After seven years this violinist was completely disillusioned.

When he went to the exit permit office to apply for the right to leave, he was refused. However, he returned every day, and one day a piece of paper was slipped into his pocket. On returning home he found it there and pulled it out, only to discover that it was a page from the Bible. He read it with interest and found that it strangely spoke to his heart. On one of his subsequent visits a man came up to him and asked if he would like another page from the Bible. He said he would.

Each day when he returned to the exit permit office he was supplied with another page from the Bible. There in the People's Republic of China he was soundly converted to Jesus Christ. Ultimately he received his exit permit and went to Hong Kong. He is now a professor in another country.

When Corrie ten Boom was in Ravensbruck prison camp it was the studying and teaching of the Word of God which kept her mind clear so that when she was released she was mentally alert. Many inmates upon their release were little more than vegetables and had to be cared for until they regained some form of normalcy.

A similar story is told of a missionary who was imprisoned by the Japanese in China. At this concentration camp the penalty for owning even a portion of the Scriptures was death. However, a small Gospel of John was smuggled to her in a winter coat. At night when she went to bed she pulled the covers over her head and with her flashlight read a verse and then put herself to sleep memorizing that verse. In this way, over a period of time, she memorized the entire Gospel of John.

When she went to wash her hands she would take one page at a time, dissolve it in the soap and water, and flush it down the drain. "And that is the way," she said, "that John and I parted company."

This little missionary was interviewed by a *Time* reporter just before the prisoners were released. The reporter happened to be standing at the gates when the prisoners came out. Most of them shuffled along, eyes on the ground, little more than automatons. Then out came the little missionary, bright as a button. One of the reporters was heard to ask, "I wonder if they managed to brainwash her?"

The *Time* reporter overheard the remark and said, "God washed her brain!"

The Word of God hidden in the heart is a stubborn voice to suppress. Ruth had another experience in London which emphasizes this fact. During the meetings in Earls Court in 1966 she made friends with a little Cockney beatnik. Each night as we arrived, this thoroughly likable, irrepressible little rebel would be waiting for Ruth. During the Earls Court Crusade she would frequently sit with Ruth, or sometimes just walk with her to her seat. They began an unusual, but lasting friendship.

Ruth learned that the girl had, previous to her conversion, been on drugs. Ruth told her to memorize several verses which she felt would be important to her, like John 3:16, 1 John 1:8, and the last two verses of Jude. One night she even warned her that, because of her past background, when she hit a snag in life she would have two choices: one was to go back on drugs, the other was to go forward with the Lord Jesus Christ.

One night during the service the usher gave my wife a note saying, "I am on drugs and I need you. Please come help me." It was signed by this young friend.

Ruth slipped out of the meeting and found her waiting—white-faced, hollow-eyed, and obviously drugged. Ruth, having had little previous experience with drug-users, thought that they were handled as drunks and took her to a coffee stand to get her a cup of coffee. She didn't realize that was the last thing she should have done. On the way she asked the girl why she had done this, only to receive the reply, "Me best friend died on an overdose today."

Ruth wanted her to hear the sermon, and they sat down on a step within earshot of the service. The girl was in no condition to hear. Realizing that her little friend was fast passing out, Ruth wrote on the little card found at the bottom of a pocket package of Kleenex, something to this effect: "God loves me. Jesus died for me. No matter what I have done, He will forgive me if I repent and ask Him to forgive me."

The following year, 1967, we were back in London at Earls Court for another series of meetings. One evening Ruth was having tea with her young beatnik friend. The girl fished into her sack and brought out the crumpled Kleenex card on which Ruth had written the words the previous year. She asked Ruth when she had written these words. Ruth told her, but the girl had no recollection of what had happened that night. Then she repeated the verses of Scripture that Ruth told her to learn and asked when it was that she had learned them. Ruth explained to her, but she didn't remember the occasion. It is interesting that the drugs could cause amnesia up to a certain point, but they had not been able to take away the Word of God which she had hidden away in her heart.

A similar situation happened when Ruth fell out of a tree while trying to build a pipeslide for our grandchildren. She suffered a severe concussion and was unconscious for the better part of a week. As she regained consciousness, the thing that concerned her the most was that she could remember so little. Her greatest loss was that of the Bible verses which she had memorized down through the years.

In her notebook she has written how one night as she was fuzzily praying about this fact, out of nowhere came the words, "I have loved thee with an everlasting love, therefore with loving kindness have I drawn thee." There was no recollection of when or where she had memorized the verse, for her mind was still foggy. And yet—there it was!

God Speaks in Jesus Christ

God speaks most clearly in the person of His Son Jesus Christ. "God, . . . in these last days has spoken to us in His Son" (Heb. 1:1,2).

Throughout the ages many people have believed that God is a spirit within everyone. Tolstoi, the great Russian writer, said, "Every man recognizes within himself a free and rational spirit, independent of his body. This spirit is what we call God."

Philosophers have found God in everything. In the first century the Roman philosopher Seneca set the stage for belief throughout the ages when he wrote, "Call it nature, fate, fortune: all are but names of the one and same God."

Seneca was, of course, wrong. But so have millions of men throughout the ages been equally mistaken.

In most religions of the world we find some references to a belief that God would visit the earth. There have been many men who have come claiming they are God. One man from Korea during our time has drawn many followers by claiming to be the "Lord of the Second Advent."

However, it was not until the "fulness of time" when all the conditions were right, when all the prophecies were fulfilled, that God "sent forth His Son, born of a woman" (Gal. 4:4).

In a little town in the Middle East almost 2000 years ago, the prophecy in Micah 5:2 was fulfilled when God "was revealed in the flesh" (1 Tim. 3:16). This revelation came in the person of Jesus Christ.

The Scripture says about Christ, "In Him all the fulness of Deity dwells in bodily form" (Col. 2:9).

This revelation is the most complete God ever gave to the world. Do you want to know what God is like? All you have to do is look at Jesus Christ.

Nature has perfection and beauty; we see order, power, and majesty in the physical world around us. All of these descriptions apply to Jesus Christ. In the working of our conscience and the magnificence of the written Scriptures we find justice, mercy, grace and love. These are attributes of Jesus Christ. "The Word [logos] became flesh, and dwelt among us" (John 1:14).

To His disciples and to all of us living in this twentieth-century world, Jesus said, "Believe in God, believe also in me" (John 14:1). This sequence of faith is inevitable. If we believe in what God made and what God said, we must believe in the One whom God sent.

How can we believe? The means of understanding these facts of salvation is "faith." We are not always challenged to understand everything, but we are told to believe. "But these have been written that you may believe that Jesus is the Christ, the Son of God; and that believing you may have life in His name" (John 20:31).

Every need to know God, every expectation of eternal life, every desire for a new social order—all must be tied to the only One who can accomplish these goals—Jesus Christ. When we come to Jesus Christ, the unknown becomes known; we experience God Himself.

When our groping darkened lives experience the light of the eternal presence of God, we are able to see that another world stretches beyond the confusion and frustration of the world we live in.

A small child, not even old enough for school, went into one of those mirrored mazes at an amusement park. When her father discovered that she had slipped away he saw her trying to find her way out and beginning to cry in fear. She became increasingly confused by all the paths, until she heard her daddy call out, "Don't cry, darling. Put your hands out and reach all around. You'll find the door. Just follow my voice."

As he spoke the little girl became calm and soon found her way out and ran to the security of her father's outstretched arms.

God has revealed Himself to the human race on this little planet through nature, conscience, the Bible—and fully in the person of Jesus Christ.

4

But I'm Not Religious!

THE QUESTION IS often heard, "What about all the other religions of the world? Isn't one religion just as good as another?"

Few terms in the language of man have been so distorted and misunderstood as that of "religion." The 18th century German philosopher Immanuel Kant described religion as "morality or moral action." Hegel, the philosopher who influenced Hitler's thinking, said religion was "a kind of knowing."

"Religion" has many meanings for many people. It can mean the sadistic symbolism of the Manson girls, who cut an "x" on their foreheads; it can be the rituals of Transcendental Meditation or the chants of various cults; or it can suggest quiet meditation within the comforting walls of a church.

Many people say rather proudly, "I'm not very religious," but in spite of some of his own objections man is a religious being. The Bible, anthropology, sociology, and other sciences teach us that people long for some sort of religious experience.

My major in college was anthropology, which the dictionary explains as a science dealing with the races, customs, and beliefs of mankind. I have also had the privilege of traveling extensively on every continent. I have found from personal experience that what I learned from anthropology is true: man has naturally and universally a capacity for religion—and not only a capacity, for the vast majority of the human race practices or professes some form of religion.

Religion can be defined as having two magnetic poles, the biblical and the naturalistic. The biblical pole is described in the teachings of the Bible. The naturalistic pole is explained in all the man-made religions. In humanistic systems there are always certain elements of truth. Many of these faiths have borrowed from Judeo-Christianity; many use portions and incorporate their own fables. Other religions or faiths have in fragments what Christianity has as a whole.

The Apostle Paul described the naturalistic pole when he said that men "exchanged the glory of the incorruptible God for an image in the form of corruptible man and of birds and four-footed animals and crawling creatures" (Rom. 1:23).

All false religions cut away parts of God's revelation, add ideas of their own, and come out with various viewpoints that differ from God's revelation in the Bible. Natural religion does not come from God, but from the natural world He created and that turned away from Him in its pride.

A false religion is like the imitation of high fashion. I've read that after an exclusive showing of original designs in one of the fashion centers of the world like Paris, copies will soon appear in the mass merchandising stores under different labels. The very presence of counterfeits prove the existence of the real. There would be no imitations without a genuine product.

God's original design has always had imitators and counterfeits!

The Birth of Religion

How did all the religions of the world get started? A famous military conqueror from the past was able to state a truth, without realizing that he had charged right past the real Truth. Napoleon Bonaparte stated, "I would believe in a religion if it existed ever since the beginning of time, but when I consider Socrates, Plato, Muhammad, I no longer believe. All religions have been made by man."

Paul Bunyan once said, "Religion is the best armor that a man can have, but it's the worst cloak."

When did man invent this maze of religion? It began with a couple of fellows who are rather well known. When Adam and Eve had their sons, we might have thought they would have been able to instill in both of them the importance of a right relationship with God. However, Cain wanted to do it his own way. He approached the first altar with his offering of "the fruit of the ground," trying to regain "paradise" without accepting God's plan of redemption. Cain brought what he had grown, the distinctive elements of his own culture. Today we would call Cain's gift his attempt at salvation by works. But God never said we could work our way to heaven.

His brother, Abel, obeyed God and humbly offered the first of his flock in a sacrifice of blood. Abel agreed with God that sin deserved death and could be covered before God only through the substitutionary death of a guiltless sacrifice. Cain deliberately rejected this plan. God demanded a blood sacrifice.

The Bible writers knew that blood was absolutely essential for life. A person or an animal might get along without a leg or an eye, but no animal or man could live without blood. That is why the Old Testament said, "For the life of the flesh is in the blood" (Lev. 17:11).

Thus, the Bible teaches that atonement for sin comes only through the shedding of blood. "In fact, the law requires that nearly everything be cleansed with blood, and without the shedding of blood there is no forgiveness" (Heb. 9:22, NIV).

When we speak of the blood of Christ, therefore, we are saying that He died for us. Blood sacrifice underlined the seriousness of sin. Sin was a life-and-death matter. Only the shedding of blood could atone for sin. The death of Christ also underlined the principle of substitution. In the Old Testament a sacrificed animal was seen as a substitute; the innocent animal took the place of the guilty person. In the same way, Christ died in our place. He was innocent, but He freely shed His blood for us and took our place. We deserved to die for our sins, but He died in our place.

Because of Christ's death for us, we can know His life—now and eternally. "Knowing that you were not redeemed with perishable things . . . but with precious blood . . . of Christ" (1 Pet. 1:18,19).

When Cain chose to go his way, not God's way of blood, something bitter happened to his heart. He began to hate his brother, Abel. Just as the true Christian believer will often not be accepted by those who have their man-made religion, Abel was not accepted by Cain, and this hatred festered until Cain killed his brother.

Pride, jealousy, and hatred have been in the human heart in all cultures and all ages. Many years ago when I was a student in Florida a young man killed his older brother in a fit of jealousy. His father and mother had both been killed in an automobile crash, and when the will was read it indicated that the older brother had received two-thirds of an orange grove, leaving only a third to the younger brother. He became moody and depressed, angry at his deceased parents, and intensely jealous of his brother. Then the older brother disappeared, and about six weeks later his body was found tied with wire to the trunk of a cypress tree in a river.

Times haven't changed. Millions want salvation, but on their own terms; they want to chart their own courses and devise all kinds of routes to lead to God.

If Christianity is true, it is not a religion. Religion is man's effort to reach God. The dictionary describes religion as a "belief in God or gods . . . or worship of God or gods." Religion can be anything! But true Christianity is God coming to man in a personal relationship.

The modern interest in the occult and in Eastern religions is indicative of man's eternal search for God. We cannot escape the fact that man is instinctively religious, but God has chosen to reveal Himself to us through nature, conscience, the Scriptures, and through Jesus Christ. The Scripture says there is no excuse for a person not to know God!

In the Name of "Religion"

It's no wonder that people say with satisfaction, "I'm not religious." Extreme cruelties and great injustices have been perpetrated in the name of religion.

In China when my wife was growing up, frequently babies who died before cutting their teeth were thrown out to be eaten by pariah dogs. The people feared that if evil spirits thought they cared too much for the children they would come and take another one. They tried to prove their indifference in this crude way. "Religion" impressed Ruth as being grim and joyless, and often cruel.

I once saw a man in India lying on a bed of spikes. He had been there for many days, eating no food and drinking little water. He was attempting to atone for his sins. Another time in Africa I saw a man walk on coals of fire. Supposedly, if he came through unscathed, he was accepted by God; if he was burned, he was considered to be a sinner in need of more repentance.

In India a missionary who passed the banks of the Ganges noticed a mother sitting by the river bank with two of her children. On her lap was a beautiful new baby and whimpering beside her was a painfully retarded child of about three. On her return home that night, the missionary saw the young mother still sitting at the river bank, but the baby was gone and the mother was trying to comfort her little retarded child. Horrified at what she thought might be true, the missionary hesitated a moment and then walked over to the mother and asked her what had happened. With tears streaming down her cheeks, the mother looked up and said, "I don't know about the god in your country, but the god in mine demands the best." She had given her perfect baby to the god of the Ganges.

People have made human sacrifices in the name of religion. They have worshiped all types of idols, from brass monkeys to trees. In some of the Pacific islands, for instance, some of the islanders believe that the souls of their ancestors are in certain trees. Offerings are made to the tree, and they believe that if any injury occurs to the tree, some misfortune will come upon the village. They fear that if the tree were cut down, the village and all its inhabitants would inevitably perish.

In the name of religion, kings, emperors, and leaders of nations and tribes have been worshiped as gods. One English scholar wrote, "At a certain stage of early society the king or priest is often thought to be endowed with supernatural powers or to be an incarnation of a deity; . . . he is held responsible for bad weather, failure of the crops, and similar calamities."[1]

An example of the class of monarchs worshiped as deity was the Mikado, the spiritual emperor of Japan. In an official decree he received the title of "manifest or incarnate deity." An early account says of the Mikado: "It was considered as a shameful degradation for him even to touch the ground with his foot. . . . None of the superfluities of the body were ever taken from him, neither his hair, his beard, nor his nails were cut."[2]

Many people will shrug at "religion" and agree with the philosophy professor from a prestigious American university who wrote: "The term 'religion' has come into use as a label for referring all at once to Judaism, Christianity, Islam, Buddhism, Hinduism, Taoism, and Confucianism, as well as a great many other siblings, some of whom have proper names and some of whom do not, but all of whom are taken to be sufficiently similar to the seven mentioned here to make it useful to lump them together."[3]

Can we really lump Christianity with every "religion" of the world?

Without Excuse

From the very beginning of time, "natural" religion was introduced onto the human stage as a substitute for God's plan. The Apostle Paul describes this phenomenon in his letter to the Romans, using references to images resembling birds, animals, and serpents to illustrate man-made religion. But this doesn't describe all its forms. Today there are many new and more sophisticated religious expressions—especially at some universities—but they are really from the same root: man seeking God consciously or unconsciously.

Paul describes man's corruption of God's revelation: "For since the creation of the world His invisible attributes, His eternal power and divine nature, have been clearly seen, being understood through what has been made, so that they are without excuse. For even though they knew God, they did not honor Him as God, or give thanks; but they became futile in their speculations, and their foolish heart was darkened. Professing to be wise, they became fools. . . . For they exchanged the truth of God for a lie, and worshiped and served the creature rather than the Creator, who is blessed forever" (Rom. 1:20–25).

Paul is simply saying that all men everywhere possess at least a primitive knowledge of God. Some people greet this idea with cynicism, which initiates the inevitable question: What about the pagans who have never heard of Jesus?

What about the pagans on Main Street, U.S.A., or the pagans at Oxford or the Sorbonne? God created all of us in His image; everyone is answerable to the light that He revealed to them. How can a just God condemn people who have never had the opportunity of hearing the Gospel? The answer is in Genesis 18:25: "Shall not the Judge of all the earth do right?" (KJV).

God's nature will bear witness of a divine power and person to whom everyone will answer. On the other side, God's justice will be exhibited against those who fail to live up to the light that He has given them.

In my lifetime, I have heard of many instances in which people have been given insight into the "eternal power and divine nature" of God, without benefit of a Bible or an evangelistic crusade.

In the middle 1950s, we held a major Crusade in Madras, India. One man walked over 120 miles to attend these meetings. I was told that this man came from a village that had never had a missionary and, so far as anyone knew, the gospel of Christ was completely unknown. Yet he longed with all his heart to know the true and living God. He heard that a "guru" from America was going to be speaking, and his desire for God was so intense that he came and found Christ. Eight months later when Bishop Newbigin of the Church of South India (who told me the story) visited the village, he found the entire community had been turned into a church. Everyone had been led to Christ by this one man.

When we were preaching in northeast India in 1972, people walked for as much as ten days, carrying all their belongings on their shoulders, bringing their entire families from such places as Nepal, Sikkim, and Burma. We were told that a number of those people had never heard the name of Jesus Christ. They just heard that a religious meeting was going to be held and they wanted to come and see what it was about. Many stayed to find Christ.

I am convinced that when a man sincerely searches for God with all his heart, God will reveal Himself in some way. A person, a Bible, or some experience with believers will be used by God to reach the one who seeks.

A famous Bible teacher, Dr. Donald Barnhouse, told about a boat trip he had to take through the middle of Africa on a river. When he got into the boat, he noticed a chicken and thought it was probably for their next meal. After two or three hours he heard a roar in the distance and realized that they were approaching very turbulent water. The nationals who were rowing the boat steered it over to the bank, got out, and took the chicken into the woods. There they made a very crude altar. Preparatory to sacrificing the chicken, they chopped off its head and sprinkled the blood over the front of the boat. Dr. Barnhouse said he realized once more that even without a missionary and without God's Word having been taught to those people, they knew a sacrifice was necessary.

So Paul says that God has seen to it that all people everywhere possess basic knowledge of Him, His attributes, power, and divine nature. Through what they can observe, and through their consciences, they can respond to Him if they wish.

But humankind has turned away from Him. Their minds did not love the truth enough, their wills didn't desire to obey Him, their emotions were not excited by the prospect of pleasing Him.

What happened? What is still happening? Man suppresses the truth, mixes it with error, and develops the religions of the world.

Humanistic religions are often offended by biblical faith, which is the belief that accepts the Bible as the authoritative source of what sin is, and how through the life and atoning death of Christ, God can declare sinners "just." Natural religion contains just enough truth to make it deceptive. It may contain elements of the truth, or high ethical standards. Some of its followers at times use terms which sound like the language of the Bible. The English scholar C. S. Lewis said that all religions are really a preview or a perversion of Christianity.

Religion of man may have a very pleasant sound. Thomas Paine wrote, "The world is my country, all mankind are my brethren, and to do good is my religion." While morality or "do-goodness" may win the approval of men, it is not acceptable to God, nor does it reflect His full moral demands. In fact, some of the crudest immorality in human history has had the approval of natural religion.

There is a great counterfeiter who adapts himself to every culture, even deceiving true believers at times. He doesn't charge on the scene clothed in red and wearing a hideous mask but charms his way as an "angel of light." This is how Satan operates. Thousands of people have entered churches without discovering a vital experience with Jesus Christ. The substitutes have been handed them in the guise of religious rituals, good works, community effort, or social reform, all of which are commendable actions in themselves, but none of which can gain a person a right relationship with God.

There are many people who say, "I guess I'm a Christian," or "I try to be a Christian." There's no guess or "try to" in the Christian life. Even some of the great intellects of our time have not come to grips with this truth: The simplicity of the gospel can reach the mentally retarded as well as the geniuses.

The Compromisers

Where there is truth and error there is always compromise. Within some churches there is a movement to reshape the Christian message to make it more acceptable to modern man. A view held by many is that "the Christian churches have been, and still are, fountainheads of anti-intellectualism and opposition to critical thinking."[4]

Books are written and sermons preached scoffing at the Bible and the basic beliefs of the Christian faith. One thick volume is called *Bible Myths* and the chapter titled "The Miracles of Christ" starts this way: "The legendary history of Jesus of Nazareth, contained in the books of the New Testament, is full of prodigies and wonders. These alleged prodigies, and the faith which the people seem to have put in such a tissue of falsehoods, indicate the prevalent disposition of the people to believe in everything, and it was among such a class that Christianity was propagated."[5]

Time magazine, in a lengthy article on the Bible, said, "Questions about the Bible's truth are nothing new; they have arisen from its earliest days."[6]

There was an archaeology professor I knew at Wheaton College who was also studying at the University of Chicago. Frequently the Chicago professor would bring up some point to undermine the trustworthiness of the Scriptures. On each occasion the archaeology teacher would bring out some archaeological find which proved the authenticity of the Scriptures. At one point that professor at the University of Chicago exclaimed in exasperation, "That's the trouble with you evangelical archaeologists! You're always digging up something to prove us wrong and the Bible right!"

Archaeology has never uncovered anything that disproved the Scriptures.

Among some of those who are theologians but who fail to agree among themselves on which part of the New Testament to retain and which part to reject. Some of them seem to agree that the miracles were myths. They regard the resurrection as a subjective experience of the disciples rather than an objective historical event. They question that Jesus Christ was supernatural and reject any explanation that says part of His excellence came from the fact that He was God as well as man.

C. S. Lewis was baffled by biblical critics who would pick and choose among the supernatural events they accepted. "He wondered at the selective theology of the Christian exegete who, 'after swallowing the camel of Resurrection, strains at such gnats as the feeding of the multitudes.'"[7]

The Deceivers

From compromise to deceit is a small step. All through the Bible we are warned about false prophets and false teachers. Jesus said, "Beware of the false prophets, who come to you in sheep's clothing, but inwardly are ravenous wolves. . . . So then, you will know them by their fruits" (Matt. 7:15,20).

Sometimes the "sheep's clothing" is a clergyman's robe. He may be a liberal or a fundamentalist. The liberal is like the Sadducees of old, denying biblical truth. The extreme fundamentalists, like the Pharisees of old, may accept sound theology but add so much nonbiblical material to it. Other times the clothing may be worn by someone with a string of degrees, who speaks with logical-sounding phrases. It's difficult sometimes for a Christian to discern a false teacher, since in some ways he resembles the true teacher. Jesus spoke of false prophets who "show great signs and wonders, so as to mislead, if possible, even the elect" (Matt. 24:24).

The person behind the Great Deception is Satan himself. He is crafty and clever, working in such subtle and secretive ways that no Christian should brag that he is beyond the assaults of Satan.

The Apostle Paul warned Timothy, "But evil men and imposters will proceed from bad to worse, deceiving and being deceived" (2 Tim. 3:13). He also warned the church at Ephesus, "Let no one deceive you with empty words" (Eph. 5:6); and again, "As a result, we are no longer to be children, tossed here and there by waves, and carried about by every wind of doctrine, by the trickery of men, by craftiness in deceitful scheming" (Eph. 4:14).

A woman who now leads hundreds of women each week in a Bible class in California said that for years her pseudo-intellectualism had her grabbing onto every "religious thought" that was presented. After accepting Jesus Christ as her Savior and being born again spiritually, she said, "I'm no longer a child . . . carried about by every wind of doctrine."

This is a time when more false teachers will appear. We may be living in a time in history when this age may be drawing to an end. The Apostle Peter said: "But false prophets also arose among the people, just as there will also be false teachers among you, who will secretly introduce destructive heresies, even denying the Master who bought them, bringing swift destruction upon themselves. And many will follow their sensuality, and because of them the way of the truth will be maligned; and in their greed they will exploit you with false words; their judgment from long ago is not idle, and their destruction is not asleep" (2 Pet. 2:1–3).

When we realize that the heresies and the deceptions are secretly introduced, it should make us even more alert. The Sunday school, the Bible class, the pulpit, the classroom, and the mass media are being invaded en masse. Some of the terms of Christianity are even being used, for example, *peace, love, born again*. Watch for the words which pepper secular literature and have entirely different meanings; *messiah, a christ, redemption, regenerate, genesis, conversion, mercy, salvation, apostle, prophet, deliverer, savior, a spiritual leader*. Even great theological terms like *evangelical, infallible Bible*, etc. are rapidly losing their former meaning.

Thousands of untaught Christians are being deceived today, as are millions of people who are rejecting or ignoring the true Christ. Deceivers with intellectual arguments which sound like the epitome of scholarship are beguiling many.

Paul is not gentle with the false teachers. He says, "But the Spirit explicity says that in later times some will fall away from the faith, paying attention to deceitful spirits and doctrines of demons, by means of the hypocrisy of liars" (1 Tim. 4:1,2).

The Bible is very clear that many have turned away because they listened to Satan's lies and deliberately chose to accept the doctrines of devils rather than the truth of God.

Back to Basics

Church members and spiritually thirsty non-church members have been hungry for a personal, vital experience with Jesus Christ. Many have been turning to other forms of worship in addition to the church service.

In 1965 I wrote in my book *World Aflame* that "unless the church quickly recovers the authoritative biblical message, we may witness the spectacle of millions of Christians going outside the institutional church to find spiritual food." This is exactly what has happened.

We now estimate that there are over two million prayer groups and Bible study groups meeting in homes and churches in the United States that were not meeting ten years ago. One of the great hopes we see is that denominational leadership is beginning to recognize this and promote Bible studies conducted on a lay level with adequate leadership.

Our own Crusade preparation has revealed in recent years a far greater increase in actual home prayer meeting groups. In our most recent Crusades we established a prayer group on every block in the city. The result is that thousands of additional prayer meeting groups are being held in connection with the Crusades—in some cities as many as 5,000.

With nearly 50 million adult Americans having experienced "born again" religious conversions, I believe it is important to have a clear understanding of what this is all about.

An Old Cliché

Nothing could be more grossly wrong than the old cliché that "any religion will do, as long as you're sincere." What if the same line of reasoning were used with a baby? The mother would say,

"I don't have any milk, but I truly want my baby to be fed, so I'll just put some coke or a little wine in the bottle. After all, they're all liquids." Ridiculous as that may sound, it is no more so than the old "sincerity" answer.

Who invented religion? Let's go back to the brothers again. The two altar fires outside Eden illustrate the difference between true and false religion. One belonged to Abel, who made an offering to the Lord God from the first-born of his flock. Abel acted in love, adoration, humility, reverence, and obedience. And the Bible says that the Lord held Abel and his offering in high regard.

His older brother, Cain, brought a bloodless, cheap offering to the altar, and the Bible says of God that "for Cain and for his offering He had no regard" (Gen. 4:5).

Was God being unfair? After all, didn't Cain attempt to please God? Wasn't he sincere?

This story was put in the Bible to teach us there is a right way and a wrong way to make contact with God. Abel brought a sacrifice of blood as God had instructed; Cain made his vegetable sacrifice selfishly and superficially, disobeying God by coming without faith. When God didn't bless his sacrifice, Cain killed his brother. Cain's worship was empty religiosity, hollow as his whole life became. He left his family and walked the earth as a bitter man, crying out to the Lord, "My punishment is too great to bear" (Gen. 4:13).

Cain was sincere—but wrong.

Humanistic religion emerges under the very noses of great men of God. While Moses was on Mount Sinai receiving the tablets of stone "written with the finger of God," false religion was erupting in the camp of Israel. The people said to Aaron, "Come, make us a god who will go before us." Aaron was carried along with the idea of a new religion and said, "Tear off the gold rings which are in the ears of your wives, your sons, and your daughters, and bring them to me." Out of this gold he made a molten calf and the people said, "This is your god, O Israel, who brought you up from the land of Egypt" (Exod. 32:1–4).

Throughout time other idolatrous beliefs have eroded the foundations of truth. Whether ancient or modern, all have posed alternatives to the biblical way of approaching God.

Men and women may devise plans to satisfy their inner long-ings, but in the midst of all the "religions" of the world God's way is available in the Bible for all who will come to Him on His terms. For the person who searches, the answers are available.

5

What Is This Thing Called Sin?

THERE'S A STORY about a jet which was traveling from Chicago to Los Angeles. As the gigantic plane leveled out at 40,000 feet, the passengers heard a voice over the loud speaker.

"This is a recording. You have the privilege of being the first to fly in a wholly electronic jet. This plane took off electronically. It is now flying at 40,000 feet electronically. It will land in Los Angeles electronically.

"This plane has no pilot, no co-pilot, no flight engineer. But don't worry. Nothing can go wrong . . . go wrong . . . go wrong . . . go wrong . . . go wrong . . ."

Something has gone wrong with our jet age. It's supposed to be scientifically sophisticated and morally liberated. But it isn't. What's gone wrong?

In every major city in America and Europe crime is up. The crime wave has hit the world with hurricane force. A news magazine reported that in the U.S. "in the past 14 years, the rate of robberies has increased 255%, forcible rape 143%, aggravated assault 153% and murder 106%."[1]

Statistics are cold until they happen to you. I was told that at a fine private university in a small town in the West the girls don't go out of their rooms at night for fear of mugging or rape. The father who told me this said he had sent his daughter there to get her away from the dangerous areas of the large cities. This was worse.

There is no longer a safety zone in any city. A woman may be pistol-whipped while parking her car in an underground structure, or a man beaten on his way out of his office. Criminals have no respect for age, with older citizens living in many areas in a nightmare of fear. In New York City, police charged a gang of six teenagers—one of whom was thirteen—with murdering three elderly and penniless men by asphyxiation. One man died with his prayer shawl stuffed into his mouth.

Man is a contradiction. On one side is hatred, depravity, and sin; on the other side is kindness, compassion, and love. Man is a helpless sinner on one hand and has capacities which would relate him to God on the other. No wonder Paul spoke of man's disease as "the mystery of iniquity."

Some people don't like the word *sin*. They believe this is for the other person, not them. But everyone recognizes that the human race is sick and that whatever the disease is, it has affected all of life.

What is this thing called sin? The Westminster Confession defines it as "any want of conformity to or transgression of the law of God." Sin is anything contrary to the will of God.

The Beginning of Sinning

Where did sin begin and why did God allow it? The Bible hints at the answer to this riddle when it teaches that sin did not originate with man, but with the angel whom we know as Satan. This was no ordinary angel, but the most magnificent of creatures!

The prophet Ezekiel describes this noble being this way: "'You were the anointed cherub who covers; and I placed you there. You were on the holy mountain of God. . . . You were blameless in your ways from the day you were created, *until unrighteousness was found in you*'" (Ezek. 28:14,15, emphasis mine). Here is a glimpse of where it started. In some unknown past, sin was found in the heart of this magnificent creature of heaven.

The prophet Isaiah gives us another hint of the origin of evil: "'How you have fallen from heaven, O star of the morning [Lucifer], son of the dawn! You have been cut down to the earth, you who have weakened the nations! But you said in your heart, "*I will* ascend to heaven; *I will* raise my throne above the stars of God, and *I will* sit on the mount of assembly in the recesses of the north. *I will* ascend above the heights of the clouds; *I will* make myself like the Most High." Nevertheless you will be thrust down to Sheol, to the recesses of the pit'" (Isa. 14:12–15, emphasis mine).

There's the picture. Lucifer's sin was that of the five "I wills." He fell and became Satan because of his undue ambition. He wanted to be like God! He wanted to be equal to God. This was conceit in its strongest form. The New Testament gives us a glimpse of the sin of pride or conceit when it speaks of a person who might "become conceited and fall into the condemnation incurred by the devil" (1 Tim. 3:63).

From Satan to Sinners

Sin began with the revolt of Lucifer and continued with man's revolt against God. In place of "living for God," sin substitutes "living for self."

The Bible makes it quite clear how sin entered the human race. In that luscious garden of Eden there were many trees. One tree symbolized the knowledge of good and evil, and God in His wisdom said, "You shall not eat." Adam and Eve with one or two bites violated what they knew to be God's will (see Rom. 5:12–19; Gen. 3:1–8; 1 Tim. 2:13,14).

God could have created us as human robots who would respond mechanically to His direction. Obviously this would be a response over which man had no control. But instead, God created us in His image, and He desires that the creature worship the Creator as a response of love. This can be accomplished when "free will" is exercised. Love and obedience which are compelled do not satisfy. God wanted sons, not machines.

A pastor friend who was having dinner with us one evening told us about his son who was attending a state university and becoming "very wise." "Dad," he said to his father one day, "I'm not sure that when I get out of school I will be able to follow you in your simple Christian faith." Our friend looked his son in the eyes and replied, "Son, that is your freedom—your terrible freedom."

And that is what God gave Adam and Eve—and what he gives us—our freedom to choose. Our "terrible freedom." God gave humankind the gift of freedom. Our first parents had the choice: whether to love God or rebel and build their world without Him. The tree of the knowledge of good and evil was their test—and they flunked.

Sin Is Rebellion

Why did Adam and Eve, with all Paradise to enjoy, choose to rebel? The cause of rebellion was "the lust of the flesh and the lust of the eyes and the boastful pride of life" (1 John 2:16). And this is the type of lust to which Eve submitted. "When the woman saw that the tree was good for food, and that it was a delight to the eyes, and that the tree was desirable to make one wise, she took from its fruit and ate; and she gave also to her husband with her, and he ate" (Gen. 3:6).

Centuries later, Christ faced the same three temptations in the wilderness. He overcame all of them and thereby showed us that it is possible to resist the temptations of Satan (Matt. 4: 1–11).

The Ten Commandments tell us not to covet or lust. However, all moral law is more than a test; it's for our own good. Every law which God has given has been for our benefit. If a person breaks it, he is not only rebelling against God, he is hurting himself. God gave "the law" because he loves man. It is for man's benefit. God's commandments were given to protect and promote man's happiness, not to restrict it. God wants the best for man. To ask God to revise His commandments would be to ask Him to stop loving man.

Children usually accuse their parents of "not understanding" and being too strict. When a father says to his teen-ager, "Be in at 11 o'clock, and let me know exactly where you are going to be," he is protecting his child, not punishing him. God is a loving father.

When Adam and Eve broke God's commandment, they died spiritually and faced eternal death. The consequences of that act were immediate and fearful. Sin became and is the stubborn fact of life.

In our universe we live under God's law. In the physical realm, the planets move in split-second precision. There is no guesswork in the galaxies. We see in nature that everything is part of a plan which is harmonious, orderly, and obedient. Could a God who made the physical universe be any less exacting in the higher spiritual and moral order? God loves us with an infinite love, but He cannot and will not approve of disorder. Consequently, He has laid down spiritual laws which, if obeyed, bring harmony and fulfillment, but, if disobeyed, bring discord and disorder.

What were the results of Adam and Eve's sin? When both Satan and Adam challenged God's law, they did not break it; they broke themselves upon it. The life of beauty, freedom, and fellowship that Adam had known was gone; his sin resulted in a living death. Nature became cursed and the poison of sin infected the entire human family. The whole of creation was thrown into disharmony and the earth was now a planet in rebellion!

Missing the Target

One of the translations of the term *sin* in the New Testament means "a missing of the target." Sin is failure to live up to God's standards. All of us miss the target; there is not one person who is capable of fulfilling all of God's laws at all times.

For some people, even the standards of the world seem unattainable. One of the most intense and exciting spectacles we ever view is the World Olympics. Athletes who have trained for years, disciplining their minds and bodies to attain greater and greater goals, often fall short of their target. One of the finest figure skaters said she was particularly afraid that a fall would ruin her performance. She said, "Think how much time I've put into this, and how much other people have to help me. With one mistake, it could all go down the drain."[2]

In our spiritual lives we are constantly falling. There is no way we can turn in a perfect performance. King David said, "They have all turned aside; together they have become corrupt; there is no one who does good, not even one" (Ps. 14:3).

The prophet Isaiah confessed, "All of us like sheep have gone astray, each of us has turned to his own way" (Isa. 53:6).

We have all been touched by the sin of Adam. David said, "Behold, I was brought forth in iniquity, and in sin my mother conceived me" (Ps. 51:5). This doesn't mean that he was born out of wedlock, but that he inherited the tendency to sin from his parents.

"Why do we have to be punished for what Adam did?" Think about it. Would you have done any better than Adam? I know I wouldn't have.

We are all sinners by choice. When we reach the age of accountability and face the choice between good and evil, we will slip. We may choose to get angry, to lie, or to act selfishly. We will gossip or slander someone's character. None of us can really trust his heart, any more than we can trust a lion. In an animal preserve in East Africa the lions are allowed to roam around as if they were in their native habitat. People drive their cars or jeeps through the area, watching the lions, but are warned not to get near them. One woman rolled down the window in her car to get a better look, and without warning a lion charged, critically mauling her. That lion looked so tame, acted so docile, and yet became ferocious in one frightening instant.

The Bible applies this principle like this: "Sin is crouching at the door" (Gen. 4:7). Most of us are capable of almost anything, given the right circumstances. David was a classic example. Under circumstances of fleshly desire he took a woman who belonged to another man, then saw to it that her husband was murdered by putting him in the front line of battle.

You may be saying, "You make everyone out to be so rotten, and that isn't really true." Of course it isn't. A person may be a very moral individual and yet lack the love for God which is the fundamental requirement of the law.

Because we fail to meet God's requirements, we are guilty and under condemnation. Being guilty means that we deserve punishment. The very holiness of God reacts against sin: "For the wrath of God is revealed from heaven against all ungodliness and unrighteousness of men . . ." (Rom. 1:18).

Guilty of What?

The Bible says that sin is falling short of the glory of God. Many people are unaware of the nature of the target, so they can't understand why they are told that they are missing it.

Let's imagine that someone puts a blindfold around your eyes and ties it so tight you are completely in the dark. Then you are told there is a dart board across the room and you are to hit it with a dart. You throw in exactly the direction you are told, but when the blindfold is removed you find that your dart is stuck in a lampshade, three feet from the target. You aimed in the right direction, but you missed.

This is where the world is today, missing the target. It's what Solomon meant when he said, "There is a way which seems right to a man, but its end is the way of death" (Prov. 14:12).

When God begins to open our blindfolds so that a small amount of light begins to seep through, we may begin to see an outline, at least, of the target. We can see, for instance, how God was beginning to reveal a general sense of direction to a girl who wrote me: "I'm not in any serious trouble or anything, but I do need the help of Jesus Christ. This is my first attempt to reach out to Him. I'm seventeen, and seriously want to consider myself a Christian. I'm reaching out . . . please don't disappoint me."

Her letter shows that she senses "something" is wrong with her present life. Just what is wrong in her life and right in Christ's life she isn't yet able to say, but her life without Christ carries a kind of odor of death to it, and she wants to replace it by the fragrance of Christ. When she says she isn't in any "serious trouble," she means that she hasn't been arrested, or shamed before the community. But she has an uneasiness in her heart.

To help us see that something is terribly wrong in our lives and that death—spiritual death—will result, God gives us "the law," that is, a set of standards to sharpen our moral judgment so that we can recognize sin. The Ten Commandments form the backbone of the law. They are a giant x-ray machine to reveal the bone structure of our sinfulness. The first four x-ray plates concern our direct relation to God. The last six concern our relationships with others.

Reading the X-rays

"You shall have no other gods before Me" (Exod. 20:3). Another god is not necessarily a brass Buddha or a carved totem pole. Whatever captures our highest interest is our god. Sports can be a

god—or work, or money. Sex may be a god to some, while travel may be a god to another. But our highest interest should be God. He alone is worthy of our worship. Jesus said that the great commandment was to love God with all our heart, soul, mind, and strength. If we were able to do this, we would be demonstrating that we have no other god except the Lord.

"You shall not make for yourself an idol" (Exod. 20:4). The first commandment dealt with whom we worship. This one concerns how. We are told to worship sincerely, with a heart for God. "Man looks at the outward appearance, but the Lord looks at the heart" (1 Sam. 16:7). When we sit in a church, full of piety, but ignoring God, we make an idol of the church building.

"You shall not take the name of the Lord your God in vain" (Exod. 20:7). This does not just apply to swearing, but even using the name for deity, such as God or Lord, without thinking of God Himself. If we vaguely mouth the words of a hymn, or call ourselves Christians without knowing Christ personally, we take the name of God in vain.

There is a story of Alexander the Great who met a disreputable character whose name was also Alexander. Alexander the Great said, "Either change your way of life or change your name."

"Remember the sabbath day, to keep it holy" (Exod. 20:8). A day in seven set apart for special worship and rest is called for in Scripture. Jesus said, "The Sabbath was made for man, and not man for the Sabbath" (Mark 2:27). This means that we need that special day. God in His wisdom tells us that our bodies need it for rest, just as our spirits need it for worship.

The practice of turning weekends into long periods of leisure and entertainment to the exclusion of worship means that we lose the advantage of both leisure and worship.

We know that a nation or an individual that works seven days a week, suffers physically, psychologically, and spiritually. All machinery needs occasional rest.

"Honor your father and your mother" (Exod. 20:12). This passage sets no age limit on such honor. In addition, it does not say they must be honorable to be honored. This doesn't necessarily mean that we must "obey" parents who may be dishonorable. Not

only while we are children, but as long as our parents live, we must honor them if we are to obey God. Honor has many shapes: affection, humor, financial aid, respect. And yet, harsh words are often heard in the home more than anywhere else. We say things to our parents that we would never say to our friends at work or in church.

"You shall not murder" (Exod. 20:13). In the older translation of this command the word *kill* was used, but the original Hebrew properly refers to murder. The outward act of murder is the final act of many emotions. Behind it are the attitudes of irritation, envy, and hatred. Jesus said, "You have heard that men were told in the past, 'Do not murder; anyone who commits murder will be brought before the judge.' But now I tell you: whoever is angry with his brother will be brought before the judge; whoever calls his brother 'You good-for-nothing!' will be brought before the Council; and whoever calls his brother a worthless fool will be in danger of going to the fire of hell" (Matt. 5:21–22).

Is anyone able to say that he has never been angry with someone else? We all stand condemned before such a law, even if we have never forcefully taken someone's life.

"You shall not commit adultery" (Exod. 20:14). One scholar said: "One of the extraordinary things is that in the non-Christian religions time and time again immorality and obscenity flourish under the very protection of religion. It has often been said and said truly that chastity was the one completely new virtue which Christianity brought into this world."[3] Although that may be true, this commandment goes beyond chastity. It involves more than dishonoring a wife or husband by having sexual relations with others; it deals with the mentality which is occupied with sex. It means even looking at a man or woman with an attitude of desire or lust. To God, purity is first a matter of the heart, then of action.

Put in those terms you might say, "That's ridiculous. No one can live up to that commandment." And you would be right.

"You shall not bear false witness against your neighbor" (Exod. 20:16). We think of a witness as one being in court. If we were to lie on a stand and say, "But, your honor, my dog was provoked into biting my neighbor. He started to hit my animal with a large

stick and so he attacked in self-defense," when, in fact, your dog had taken a chunk out of your neighbor's leg without provocation, then you would be bearing false witness.

But what if you gossip in a "harmless" way? The commandment is just as shattered!

"You shall not covet" (Exod. 20:17). When we take something that belongs to another, that's stealing. It is an act. Coveting is an attitude. When we desire something which belongs to someone else, that's coveting. How many marriages have ended in divorce because a man replaced thoughts about his own wife with thoughts about the desirability of his neighbor's wife? We are told not to covet anything, and that means our neighbor's new house, his car, his TV set, or the camper in his driveway.

Results of the X-Rays

Can anyone read the Ten Commandments with insight and not feel condemned by them? They reveal our hearts. The Apostle James made the comment that even one commandment broken would be enough to destroy us. If we are suspended over a pit by a chain of ten links, how many links have to break for us to fall into the pit? "For whoever keeps the whole law and yet stumbles in one point, he has become guilty of all" (James 2:10).

The Bible and our consciences tell us that we have seriously missed the target and are sinners. What does a holy God do? How does God deal with our sin?

We see a glimpse of this in the words of a young man who became painfully aware of the commandment, "You shall not steal." He said, "My life was not a rosy one. Before I was thirteen years old I was a thief in heart, word, and action. I had been arrested many times. I spent time in a boy's reformatory and less than a week after I left I was stealing again." He said that his family gave up on him and thought that his future was destroyed. One night he heard the gospel on television, found a Bible, and started to read it. As a result he asked Christ to forgive him for his past. He is now looking to Christ to build a new foundation and give him a new future.

How can God forgive us? What happens if sin becomes a pattern in our lives? What if we are really caught up in the sin syndrome? Is there any hope?

If there weren't any hope I wouldn't be writing this book! If there weren't answers, you probably wouldn't be reading!

6

Does God Have a Cure for Spiritual Disease?

A DOCTOR IN Australia told me of a conversation between a man and his barber. As the scissors worked, the barber said, "Hmm—see you have a sore on your lip."

"Yep," said the man. "My cigarettes have done that."

"Well," said the barber, "it doesn't seem to be healing."

"Oh, it will—it will," replied the man confidently.

A month later he came into the shop again. His lip was split and ugly.

"Don't worry about it," he told the barber, "I've switched to a cigarette holder. It'll heal soon."

The barber had been concerned about his customer so he obtained some medical photographs that showed what lip cancer looked like. He urged his friend to compare them in the mirror with his own lip.

"Well, they look a lot alike," admitted the man, "but I'm not worried."

On the third month the man failed to come for his regular haircut. When the barber called his friend's home to inquire about him he was told, "Oh, didn't you know? He died of cancer two days ago."

Sin is like cancer. It destroys step by step. Slowly, without realizing its insidious onslaught, it progresses until finally the diagnosis is pronounced: sick to death.

A man was describing to us how he had been brought up in a godly European home, had come to this country as a young man to seek his fortune, had been converted to Christ, and then had gotten sidetracked. Temptation yielded to another temptation until finally he found himself in what he thought was a hopeless condition. I'll never forget how he described the process. "It was like being in the ocean when there is a strong undertow," he said. "You don't realize how far you're drifting from shore until all of a sudden you find yourself beyond your depth, trying desperately to swim, but unable to hold your own against the outgoing tide."

But, unless we know some of the signs of danger, how can we seek help? We can find the help the Bible provides when we know the parts of a person that sin strikes and corrupts.

Mind Attack

A person may be brilliant in some areas, but inadequate about spiritual realities. The Bible teaches us that a veil lies over our minds and that before we can know Christ this veil must be lifted. Without this spiritual sight we cannot come to God.

You may have heard someone ask, "How can any intelligent person believe in the Bible and all those myths and contradictions?" (implying that the gospel of Jesus Christ is anti-intellectual). The implication is contrary to truth. Understanding demands the use of the mind, but when the mind is diseased by sin it is clouded and confused.

Joel Quinones was a living example of a person whose mind was under attack. I met him in San Diego and heard his amazing story.

Joel was first thrown into prison at the age of eight for trying to kill a sadistic man who had beaten him and burned him with cigarettes. When Joel was released, he came out a bundle of hatred and from then on did everything he could to show his scorn to society. As a result Joel found himself in San Quentin at the age of nineteen and spent the next eleven years there. He was turned over to the prison psychiatrists who examined him, gave him shock treatments, and finally diagnosed him as "criminally insane."

Joel was placed in with the incorrigibles. When they were fed, the food was placed on what appeared to be a large shovel with the handle long enough to push it under two separate security doors. "You don't even feed a tiger that way," Joel told us, "but that's the way they fed us."

After all those years in San Quentin, it was decided to get rid of the undesirable aliens, and Joel, along with a number of other Mexicans, was taken across the border and turned loose. He had a godly mother, a cook at a Bible school, who had been in the courtroom when Joel had been convicted for the first time. She had said to him then, "Joel, this isn't the end. Jesus has work for you to do."

When he was released in Mexico, his mother was there to greet him. Putting her arms around him, she said, "Joel, you need the Lord Jesus; you need to ask Him to forgive your sins, to give you a new heart and a new life."

Joel struggled with this, but before the Lord was finished with him he was a transformed person. He went to Bible school, married one of the graduates, and is today a prison chaplain in Mexico. He has won so many prisoners to Christ that he is busy trying to build a halfway house, a "City of Refuge" to which these prisoners can come for rehabilitation before returning to normal life.

Sin had affected Joel's mind, but the transforming power of Christ had given him new gifts.

As I write this, I'm looking at a bone-handled knife with a five-inch blade that once belonged to Joe Medina. Joe's story is one of the most unbelievable, comic, awe-inspiring demonstrations of the power of God in what the ordinary person would have termed a hopeless life that I have ever heard. Mind attack? Joe simply couldn't think straight.

Joe was brought up in a Bronx ghetto. His mother and both of his grandmothers were spirit mediums. The streets of New York had been his home since babyhood, and gang warfare, knife fighting, stealing, and lying were simply a way of life. He was one of those disenchanted, rebellious youths of the sixties—a drug-user and accomplished thief.

Joe, however, went to a meeting at which Akbar Haqq, one of our associate evangelists, was speaking. Before the evening was over, Joe had given his heart to Jesus Christ. The day after his conversion, one of his best buddies was trying to induce Joe to go with him to get drugs and Joe didn't want to be bothered. The friend pulled a knife and threatened to cut Joe up. That was a big mistake. Joe was small, but like lightning, with a knife, and before he knew what had happened, he had plunged the knife (yes, the one on my desk) into his buddy. The boy he attacked was in the hospital for two weeks.

Joe had no Christian background to fall back on and he had many ups and downs in his spiritual life. He enrolled in a small college near us but quit school before the year was up. I'm still not sure what his reason was, but I think he had some vague notion that he had to get back to share his faith with his buddies in the Bronx.

My wife talked to Joe before he left and urged him to come to Madison Square Garden, where we were having a meeting. I found out later that Joe had rounded up some of his tough buddies and gotten to the Garden at 7:30, only to find it closed because it was full, and the policeman wouldn't let him in. There had been a threat on my life that night and the policemen were taking a dim view of any suspicious-looking characters. Joe and his friends qualified for that description.

They went into a huddle and decided to rush the police. They succeeded in getting to the top floor of the Garden but suddenly found themselves face to face with a wall of plainclothes men advancing on them. Turning to run the other way, they confronted another formidable wall of police. They were thrown out of the Garden without further ceremony. When I heard about this later I thought, "Oh no! Just the ones we were trying to reach!"

However, Joe was undaunted and brought his sister and brother the next night. They both came forward to receive Christ.

Joe had a lot of trouble for a while getting values straightened out. He called Ruth one time and said he had to see her. When he arrived, she could tell something was wrong. "What have you done now, Joe?" she asked.

"Ruth, I robbed a filling station."

"Oh, Joe, why did you do that?"

"Well, it's this way—I have this buddy, you know. Well, he needed some money and he'd never robbed a filling station before. Golly, Ruth, I just felt it was my Christian duty to help him."

Ruth asked him how much he had taken and then asked him if his buddy were a Christian. He was not, Joe said. Ruth explained to Joe that he would have to be responsible for returning the entire amount. Joe looked as if she had hit him in the stomach with her fist. She then asked him point-blank if he had anything else in his possession that he had stolen. He looked at her in amazement and exclaimed, as if that were the dumbest question ever asked, "Everything I own!"

Joe returned all the stolen goods. After more advances and retreats in his Christian growth than I care to relate, he was finally admitted to Columbia Bible College. In his senior year he became vice president of the student body and is today a graduate student there with an amazing knowledge and love of the Bible.

On a recent weekend he came to visit us, and the Presbyterian pastor of our community, Calvin Thielman, asked him to give his testimony and talk about his ministry. Joe told how he related to the drug-users, the dropouts, the rebels. His story was full of such wit, humor, and compassion that the audience was left with the reassurance that "nobody's hopeless."

Only those who knew Joe from the beginning can fully appreciate the marvels of the new birth in this young man's life. His mind had been so attacked by sin that it took a long time for the healing process. We are born again as babies, not mature Christians, and babies need a lot of love and patience!

The Bible teaches that sin affects the mind, whether that mind is of superior intelligence or average. A person may be intellectually brilliant, but spiritually ignorant. "A natural man does not accept the things of the Spirit of God; . . . and he cannot understand them, because they are spiritually appraised" (1 Cor. 2:14).

An intellectual mind can be turned into a first-class mind when Christ penetrates the heart. Gerhard Dirks, one of the most brilliant men in the world, is reported to have an IQ of 208. He has over 140 patents with IBM and has even attempted theoretically to reconstruct the human brain. He became completely bewildered and shaken, however, when confronted with the complexity and utter impossibility of such a reconstruction. He didn't know what to do or where to run. His choice was two-fold: either the human brain came about by a fantastic chance or by intelligent planning. When faced with the alternative he knew he had only one choice, and he became a believer in God as it was revealed to him through Jesus Christ, whose intellect he could not surpass.

Dr. Boris Botsenko, a brilliant Russian physicist-mathematician, was attending a conference of scientists in Edmonton, and in his hotel picked up a Gideon Bible. He read it and through it accepted Jesus Christ and was born again. He is now in the research department of the University of Toronto.

Attack on the Will

Sin attacks another facet of our being—will. Jesus said, "Every one who commits sin is the slave of sin" (John 8:34). Even in countries where there is political freedom, there are millions who live under the tyranny of pride, jealousy, or prejudice. Countless others are slaves to alcohol, barbiturates or narcotics. They possess traits or are consumed by desires they hate but are powerless in their grip. They want to be free, and some search for freedom through avenues offered by other men. But Christ said, "You shall know the truth, and the truth shall make you free" (John 8:32). Christ is the truth.

I have known many persons who found freedom from the bondage of will and desire. On May 9, 1972, in a little church outside of Nashville, Tennessee, a pastor gave a Gospel invitation and a man named Johnny Cash got up and went down the aisle and knelt at the altar of the church. Johnny Cash says that he gave his life to Jesus Christ that day. Here is a man whose life had been hurt by drugs and imprisonment, and who has become a hero to the world of country music. He is now a force for good in the world and is being used in the cause of Christ.

I have in my possession a hashish pipe as a reminder of a young man who was a slave to drugs. He had made a terrible mess of his life and also the life of the girl he loved. As a result, he drove to a lonely, deserted parkway where he slit his wrists. Evidently he didn't do a very good job, because the blood wasn't coming out fast enough and he thought at that rate it was going to take him too long to die. So he crawled under the tailpipe of his car with the motor still going, covered himself with a blanket, and proceeded to inhale the fumes.

He said that while he became drowsy from the fumes he uttered a prayer asking God to forgive him for what he was doing. Suddenly a horrible black feeling came over him and he knew that what he was about to do did not please God. In his weakness, with bleeding wrists and drugged mind, he drove to a pastor's home. The pastor took him to the hospital. After the young man was treated, the pastor explained to him that Christ alone can make atonement for our sins and give us release from guilt and the joy of being forgiven.

This young man is now happily married and is a positive influence on the lives of others.

Unresolved hatred is a tyranny which can make anyone a slave to sin as it attacks the will. Just a few years ago Dr. William P. Wilson, then Professor of Psychiatry at Duke University Medical Center, systematically took Bibles away from his patients at the center. But his life and medical practice have been transformed by the power of Jesus Christ, and he now uses the insights he has gained from the gospel in treating his patients. He keeps copies of the Bible in his office and gives them out. Dr. Wilson says, "One of the greatest causes of mental illness is unresolved guilt. Feelings of shame, inadequacy, missing the mark, not measuring up, are some sources of guilt feelings. The answer to guilt is grace and the new birth. The new birth leads to the forgiveness of sin."

Forgiveness is hard for many to believe. Dr. Warren Wiersbe of Chicago calls forgiveness "the greatest miracle in the Bible."

I have a letter from a young man who said, "In 1971 I was a drug-dealing dropout from Northwestern University. During your Chicago Crusade I came forward at the invitation and prayed for the Lord to save me, even though I personally didn't feel bad about my ungodly practices. I also asked that He forgive me my sins (I could intellectually conceive of them, but not personally feel them) and that He would make Himself known in a personal way.

"I was expecting a lightning bolt from heaven to knock me down, or for God to put me through a mental breakdown so He could straighten out my mind and use it for His glory. Needless to say, He didn't do that. I began to feel quite disappointed and also somewhat scared and thought this God thing might easily turn out to be a hoax after all. At that instant a middle-aged, short-haired, suit-wearing, Bible-carrying counselor came up to me and put a Jesus sticker on my shirt and shook my hand. 'God bless you, young man,' he said. Think of it! This establishment dude shaking my hand—me, a freaked-out hippie. The love of God coming through him showed me that Jesus loved me regardless of how I dressed or abused society. That simple act hit me and I suddenly realized the simplicity of God's salvation. He didn't want to put me through pain of a mental breakdown—all He wanted me to do was to receive His Son as I had just done!"

When Conscience Fails

Sin not only affects the mind and the will, but also the conscience. A person becomes very slow to detect the approach of sin. It's like telling an untruth: the first time you tell a story it really bothers you; but with repetition your conscience is no longer your guide, and soon the lie is woven so strong that you are convinced it's the truth. You no longer have sensitivity to things you know are wrong.

One day Joe Medina, to whom I referred earlier in the chapter, called Ruth from a telephone booth and said, "Ruth, I'm not drunk, but I just wanted to tell you something."

Ruth asked him what he was doing in a phone booth. He explained that he was riding around with a buddy who had a fifth of whiskey with him. Joe explained that his friend didn't have a North Carolina driver's license and shouldn't drive the car, especially while drinking. So Joe said, with his typical logic, "Ruth, I felt it was my Christian duty to drink that fifth of whiskey for him."

The patience of my wife never ceases to amaze me. She said, "Joe, you drank that fifth of whiskey because you wanted to drink that fifth of whiskey."

There was a long pause. Then, "Ruth, you're exactly right."

Joe had been trained in calling badness "good." He knew how to lie, cheat, and rationalize out of any situation. But for the grace of God, he would still be that way today.

The results of the infection of no longer knowing the difference between good and evil are reflected in every part of the Scriptures. When David first looked at Bathsheba, a train of events began which led from adultery to deceit to murder. David was forgiven for his sins, but he had to pay the natural consequences. He reaped a bitter harvest and his reign was clouded with constant trouble.

In view of the way we allow our consciences to become dulled, it is amazing that God is so patient. The Bible says, "The Lord is not slack concerning his promise, as some men count slackness, but is longsuffering toward us, not willing that any should perish, but that all should come to repentance" (2 Pet. 3:9, KJV).

No matter how patient God is, He is also just. When man hardens his heart, God continues to speak. But man cannot hear. Genesis 6:3 says, "My Spirit shall not always strive with man." Eventually, if God sees that man won't repent, "There is a sin unto death" (1 John 5:16, KJV). This refers to blasphemy against the Holy Spirit, which is final rejection of God's plan of salvation, and it is also described in Hebrews 6:4–6:

"For in the case of those who have once been enlightened and have tasted of the heavenly gift and have been made partakers of the Holy Spirit, and have tasted the good word of God and the powers of the age to come, and then have fallen away, it is impossible to renew them again to repentance, since they again crucify to themselves the Son of God, and put Him to open shame."

When a man's conscience is gone he uses all kinds of excuses to justify his action. He blames his family, his business associates, his bad breaks, anything. He can cheat on his income tax because the laws are unjust. He can cheat on his wife (or a wife can be unfaithful to her husband) because the other one is cold—or thoughtless. The good and bad are gone and life is lived in grey tones.

In Athens the columns and statues of the Parthenon have been eroding in recent years at an accelerated rate. It hasn't been storms or time which have caused the imminent destruction of these priceless ancient works of art, but the pollution of the wastes of modern society. In the same way, it's not the heavy storms of life that erode us, but the insidious, gradual pollution of sin which leads to our destruction.

Sick to Death

Crime requires punishment and sin has a penalty. Although this may be a subject we would like to ignore, it is an unavoidable fact.

Not only does everyone suffer as a result of sin in this life, but everyone must face the judgment to come. "For the wages of sin is death" (Rom. 6:23).

First, there is *physical death*. The Bible says, "It is appointed for men to die once" (Heb. 9:27). Incidentally, this completely rules out the possibility of reincarnation.

Death is inevitable and unpredictable in many cases. For each of us there is a day, an hour, a minute, when physically we are no longer earth beings. If God had not given the judgment of physical death, the earth would soon become uninhabitable, because men would live forever in their sins.

Because life is brief, the Bible teaches that we must "Prepare to meet [our] God" (Amos 4:12). In the course of my life I have known many people who are thoroughly prepared to meet God. There is a startling difference between them and people who have lived a life without God.

I will never forget the summer of 1973. That was the year that one of the greatest Christians I ever knew entered heaven. He was my father-in-law, Dr. L. Nelson Bell. Dr. Bell served Christ for years in China as a missionary surgeon. In 1972 he had been Moderator of the Presbyterian Church in the United States, the highest honor his denomination could bestow. The night before he died he spoke for the World Missions Conference in a large auditorium in Montreat.

At the end of his talk he said, "Before I pray I have a few words today. After hearing that singing, no one can deny that our Presbyterian Church is waking up. Now in this place there are two groups of people. There are those who know they are saved and love the Lord Jesus Christ, and there are those here who as yet may not know Christ. My hope is that before you leave this place you will come to know Him as your personal Lord and Savior. The Lord said, 'Behold, I stand at the door and knock; if any man hears my voice, and open the door, I will come in to him, and will sup with him and he with me."

Those were the last words that Dr. Bell said in public. That night he went to sleep and when he awoke he was in the presence of his Lord. His life had come full circle. His favorite hymn was "All the Way My Saviour Leads Me," and when I saw him that morning, it was a great comfort to see the face of one so peaceful.

He was prepared to meet God.

I remember hearing of the last words said by Pearl Goode, a wonderful woman who through the years was one of our most faithful prayer supporters, often going into seclusion and praying night and day for the Crusade team wherever they were. She walked in such close fellowship with God that when it was her time to go, she sat up in bed and said, "Well, there He is. There's Jesus!" She was prepared to meet God.

In the summer of 1976 there was a flash flood in Colorado that took the lives of a great many people. Among the victims were some young Christian girls who had been at a retreat in the mountains. The men who had the job of searching out the bodies of those who were killed reported later that most of the people had expressions of horror on their faces, but they were astounded to see that every one of the girls appeared to be at peace. They were prepared to meet their God.

Life is so short. The Bible says that we must be prepared to meet God at all times. We never know when we step into our car, walk out the door of our home, or just open our eyes to a new day, what lies ahead. "'Since his days are determined, the number of his months is with Thee, and his limits Thou hast set so that he cannot pass'" (Job 14:5).

The second dimension of death is *spiritual death*. Millions of people on earth are walking around physically alive, but spiritually dead. When your eyes and ears become attuned to the cries of others, you hear those who say they are empty and lost. They are separated from the source of life and like a lamp which is unattached, they are dark and lifeless. The lamp may be very expensive, may have a beautiful shade which draws attention, but has no light without being plugged into the source of energy. Jesus said, "I am the life."

Newspapers and magazines throughout the world carried the story of the suicide of Freddie Prinze. At the age of twenty-two he had attained one of the highest status roles in show business. He was the darling of television and had just performed for an incoming president at the Inaugural gala in Washington. Yet something was terribly wrong in the life of this talented comedian. A close friend, comedian David Brenner, explained to *Time* magazine,

"There was no transition in Freddie's life. It was an explosion. It's tough to walk off a subway at age 19 and then step out of a Rolls Royce the next day." Producer Komack, also a close confidant, said, "Freddie saw nothing around that would satisfy him. He would ask me 'Is this what it is? Is this what it's all about?'" Mr. Komack said, "His real despondency, whether he could articulate it or not, concerned the questions: 'Where do I fit in? Where is my happiness?' I would tell him, 'God, Freddie, your happiness is right here. You're a star.' He'd say, 'No. That's not happiness for me any more.'" As *Time* magazine commented at the end of the story, "For one of the most singular escape stories in ghetto history, escape was not enough."

We may be physically alive, but spiritually dead, like the woman who is described as "dead even while she lives" (1 Tim. 5:6).

The third dimension of death is *eternal death*. This may be a subject which most try to avoid. We hear a lot about "hell on earth," but there is another hell which is more real and certain, and that's the hell of eternal death. Jesus Himself spoke frequently about hell. He warned of a hell to come. The Scripture teaches us that we'll be in hell alone and bearing pain alone. There is no fellowship in hell except fellowship with darkness. I have heard some people say, "If I thought my father [or some other loved one] were in hell, that's where I want to be, too!" What an illusion! Hell is the loneliest place imaginable.

Jesus warned men, "And these will go away into eternal punishment" (Matt. 25:46). He also said, "The Son of Man will send forth His angels, and they will gather out of His kingdom all stumbling blocks, and those who commit lawlessness, and will cast them into the furnace of fire; in that place there shall be weeping and gnashing of teeth" (Matt. 13:41,42).

There is never such an urgency to talk about eternity as there is when physical death confronts us. A friend of mine told me that the day after her son was killed in an airplane accident, while their house was full of people offering love and consolation, something went wrong with the furnace. A repair man was called. After looking at the heater, he said, "Lady, if you had waited a little while longer to call me that furnace might have blown up." In the midst of her own grief she paused, looked the repair man squarely in the eyes. "There's only one thing that's important right now," she said. "If that furnace had exploded while you were working on it, do you know for sure where you would spend eternity?"

Before he left the house he learned how to have assurance of his eternal destiny.

Two Faces of Man

Man has two faces. One shows his ingenuity, his capacity to create, to be kind, to honor truth. The other face reveals him using his ingenuity maliciously. We see him doing kind acts in a shrewd manner in order to forward a private desire. We see one side of him enjoying a sunset, but at the same time working in a job that fills the atmosphere with waste products that nearly obscure the sunset. His search for truth often degenerates into a rat race to discover a scientific fact so the credit will be his.

Man is both dignified and degraded.

The need for spiritual rebirth is evident to the most casual observer of human nature. Man is fallen and lost, alienated from God. From the very beginning, all attempts to recover man from his lostness have revealed one or the other of two ways.

Plan A and Plan B

Remember Cain and Abel? The sons of Adam and Eve represent Plan A and Plan B of salvation. One of them, Cain, came his own way: he initiated Plan A; the other, Abel, was obedient and came God's way, Plan B.

Cain was the self-sufficient materialist and religious humanist. He brought to the altar an expression of his own labors; he became the prototype of all who dare approach God without the shedding of blood.

Cain's way didn't work for him. It has never worked for anyone, and it will not work today. Only God can properly diagnose our disease and provide the cure. God chose blood as the means of our redemption. The Apostle John wrote that Jesus Christ "washed us from our sins in his own blood" (Rev. 1:5, KJV).

When Jesus Christ, the perfect God-man, shed His blood on the cross, He was surrendering His pure and spotless life to death as an eternal sacrifice for man's sin. Once and for all, God made complete provision for the cure of man's sins. Without the blood of Christ, it is a fatal disease.

Each of us makes his choice between the two ways—man's way or God's way. Which?

II
GOD'S ANSWER

7

The Man Who Is God

IT'S JUST AFTER Christmas as I write this chapter. The cards are still coming in each day, bulging the mailbox and dazzling the eye. Many of them have pictures of Jesus, some as a baby in a rough-hewn cradle, others as a shepherd, surrounded by children. The world is fascinated with how He might look. From the magnificent cathedrals of Europe to Sunday school classrooms in the U.S.A., we see pictures of artists' conceptions of Jesus. I was in Africa a few days before Christmas and saw Jesus depicted as a black baby. Last year we were in the Orient just before Christmas and saw Him depicted as an Oriental.

What is the image the world has of Jesus Christ? Some visualize him as a pale, blue-eyed man, smiling rather weakly beneath an ethereal halo. In America, the new popular Jesus is a handsome, virile type with robust charm and appeal. Probably Jesus looked Middle Eastern, with a swarthy colored skin—we really don't know. And it's just as well that we don't know what He really looked like physically—because today He belongs to the world!

No matter how we imagine Him to be, Jesus Christ has no stronger portrait than the one in the Bible. It is a picture of the man who is God. The claim that Jesus Christ is deity is the focal point for all belief. It is the foundation of Christianity. Since the quickest way to destroy any edifice is to tear out or weaken its base, men have always tried to disprove, ignore, or scoff at the claims of Christ. However, our hope of redemption from sin is dependent upon the deity of Christ.

Who is He?

Jesus: Unique in All Ways

We know that Jesus lived. He was a man in history, as well as a man for all times. Tacitus, perhaps the greatest Roman historian born in the first century, speaks of Jesus. Josephus, a Jewish historian born A.D. 37, tells of the crucifixion of Jesus. A contemporary Bible scholar said that "the latest edition of the *Encyclopaedia Britannica* uses 20,000 words in describing this person, Jesus. His description took more space than was given to Aristotle, Cicero, Alexander, Julius Caesar, Buddha, Confucius, Mohammed or Napoleon Bonaparte."[1]

Rousseau said, "It would have been a greater miracle to invent such a life as Christ's than to be it."

Jesus lived, taught, and died on earth in a small area of the Middle East, mostly in what is in Israel today. That is a confirmed fact of history.

His Intellect

Many men in history have been admired and many have been given honors for their intellectual achievements, but no man has had the incisive intellect of Jesus. In all circumstances, whether tired from a long journey, or plagued by his enemies, Jesus was able to confound some of the greatest minds of His day.

He had three years of intellectual encounters with the religious leaders of His day. These men often tried to put Him on the spot by asking questions which were difficult to answer. On one occasion, when He was teaching in the temple, the chief priests and elders questioned Him belligerently. They asked, "By what authority are You doing these things, and who gave You this authority?" (Matt. 21:23).

Here were the men who had control of all the religious teaching, and this Jesus, a carpenter from Nazareth, who was not their pupil, was teaching in their territory. Can you imagine what would happen at one of our prestigious seminaries if the janitor suddenly stepped onto the platform and began to instruct the students?

Jesus answered the question of the religious authorities with another question. "I will ask you one thing too, which if you tell Me, I will also tell you by what authority I do these things. The baptism of John was from what source, from heaven or from men?"

Now John the Baptist had not been ordained by them either, and he had urged his followers to obey Jesus. The religious leaders were thrown into confusion. They knew if they said "From heaven," that Jesus would say, "Then why didn't you believe him?" On the other hand, if they answered "From men," they feared that the people would become irate, because they believed John was a prophet. So they simply said, "We don't know."

Jesus replied, "Neither will I tell you by what authority I do these things" (Matt. 21:27).

Jesus possessed a mental agility that has astounded scholars for 2,000 years.

His Frankness

No matter what the consequences, Jesus was very open and frank. The members of the religious establishment of His day were meticulously following certain rites for cleansing the dishes they ate from each day. Using this practice as an illustration, Jesus said, "Woe to you, scribes and Pharisees, hypocrites! For you clean the outside of the cup and of the dish, but inside they are full of robbery and self-indulgence. You blind Pharisee, first clean the inside of the cup and of the dish, so that the outside of it may become clean also" (Matt. 23:25,26).

The charge Jesus made is just as applicable today. True belief in God is inward and has to do with a personal commitment and attitude, rather than strict observance of rituals and rules. Most of us would be reticent to speak so frankly to church leaders of our time. Jesus, however, was a man who was frank, bold and honest in every situation.

His Openness

Jesus had the ability to understand all people, no matter what their position in society. On one occasion He was dining with a prominent religious leader named Simon. While they were eating, a repentant prostitute came into the hall where the meal was being served and began to wash the feet of Jesus with her tears and to dry them with her hair. The religious leader was shocked and began to look at Jesus with doubt. He thought, "If this man were a prophet He would know who and what sort of person this woman is who is touching Him . . ."

Jesus, sensing his thoughts, told him this story: "A certain money-lender had two debtors; one owed five hundred denarii [a denarius was then a day's wage], and the other fifty. When they were unable to repay, he graciously forgave them both. Which of them therefore will love him more?"

Simon must have wondered, what's the purpose of this story? He probably shrugged as he answered, "I suppose the one to whom he forgave more."

Jesus told him that was the right answer. Then He reminded Simon that when He had come into his house as a guest, Simon had ignored all the normal courtesies of the day. "You gave Me no water for My feet, but she has wet My feet with tears, and wiped them with her hair. You gave Me no kiss; but she, since the time I came in, has not ceased to kiss My feet."

Then Jesus turned to the woman and reassured her that her sins had been forgiven.

The other guests at the dinner party were astounded. They asked, "Who is this man who even forgives sins?" (Luke 7).

We know that Jesus often dined with the social elite but defended the social outcasts.

His Forgiving Spirit

His opponents were powerful and persistent. They mocked Him, plotted against Him, and finally maneuvered the crowds to support His death by crucifixion.

As He was hanging on the cross, bleeding and suffering from the pain and the hot sun, many jeered at Him, saying, "Save Yourself, and come down from the cross!" (Mark 15:30).

Under such extreme circumstances, Jesus exhibited a trait that was beyond our comprehension. He spoke to God the Father and said, "Father forgive them; for they do not know what they are doing" (Luke 23:34).

How many mere men could forgive their persecutors under such brutal circumstances?

His Moral Authority

The pictures of Jesus as a vague, colorless man do not fit the true account of His strength and moral authority. At the end of His life the establishment, both religious and political, had united together to end His work by sending officers to arrest Him. The burly henchmen approached Jesus, but stopped to listen to what He was saying. They returned to their superiors without Him.

"Why didn't you bring Him?" they were asked.

The officers replied in astonishment, "Never did a man speak the way this man speaks" (John 7:45,46). They were experiencing what the crowds of ordinary people already knew. "The multitudes were amazed at His teaching," Matthew reported, "for He was teaching them as one having authority, and not as their scribes" (Matt. 7:28,29).

Jesus Christ lived the type of life He taught. There are many men we know who are noble, intelligent, frank, open, and who speak with authority. But only in Jesus do we find the human characteristics which we would expect God to display if He were to become a man.

Jesus' claim to deity is fully supported by His character. He was unique in history.

More Than Just a Man

If this were all we had to say about Jesus Christ, He would have very little more to offer than many great men of history. However, the uniqueness of Christ is that in His life on earth He displayed every known attribute or characteristic of deity.

What is an attribute? One Bible scholar offered this simple definition: "The attributes of God are those distinguishing characteristics of the nature of God which are inseparable from the idea of deity, and which constitute the basis and grounds for His various manifestations to His creatures."[2]

Jesus Christ was the supreme manifestation of God. "God was in Christ reconciling the world to Himself" (2 Cor. 5:19).

He was no ordinary man. Several hundred years before He was born, Isaiah, the prophet, said, "Behold, a virgin will be with child and bear a son" (Isa. 7:14). No other man in all history could say that his mother was a virgin. The Scriptures teach that He did not have a human father; if He had, He would have inherited the sins and infirmities that all men have, since "that which is born of the flesh is flesh" (John 3:6). Since He was conceived not by natural means, but by the Holy Spirit, He stands as the one man who came forth pure from the hand of God. He could stand before His fellowmen and ask, "Which of you can truthfully accuse Me of one single sin?" (John 8:46, *The Living Bible*). He was the only man since Adam who could say, "I am pure."

If we honestly probe our minds, we have to admit that there are mysteries about the incarnation that none of us can ever understand. In fact, Paul speaks of God, manifest in the flesh, as a "mystery" (1 Tim. 3:16).

Paul explained the Man who is God in another epistle: "Have this attitude in yourselves which was also in Christ Jesus, who, although He existed in the form of God, did not regard equality with God a thing to be grasped, but emptied Himself, taking the form of a bond-servant, and being made in the likeness of men" (Phil. 2:5–7).

First, *God is holy*. This is a characteristic possessed by Jesus Christ which is central to the entire Christian faith. What does "holiness" mean? It is a term used in reference to people, places, and sometimes circumstances. However, this very common word, often misused and misunderstood, means "self-affirming purity." No mere human being now or ever could possess pure holiness and moral perfection.

In the Old Testament, God is described as "holy in all His ways" (Ps. 145:17) and the prophet Isaiah, in his vision of the Lord God, declares "Holy, holy, holy, is the Lord of hosts" (Isa. 6:3). In the New Testament this unique attribute is possessed by Jesus Christ, the holy child, the sinless man. Thus Jesus Christ had a characteristic that only God could possess.

Second, *God is also just.* In order to guard His holiness, God must exercise justice. Since all sin is an offense to God, the principle of God's justice is vital to an orderly universe, just as a nation must have certain laws and codes. But unlike human government, which uses justice in ways that are suitable to the rulers or heads of government, God's justice is pure; no mistake is ever made.

Jesus Christ was just. During His earthly career He exhibited this characteristic when He drove the racketeers out of the temple with a whip. He is also described as faithful and just in forgiving us our sins. When He died for our sins it was "the Just" dying for the unjust.

Third, *God is mercy.* This characteristic of deity was seen in the entire life of Jesus Christ. When the woman who was an adulteress was brought before the authorities and condemned to be stoned, Jesus defended her with the charge, "Let him who is without sin cast the first stone." Her accusers retreated in embarrassment. Jesus Christ, exhibiting God's mercy, told her to go and sin no more. The love, mercy, and compassion of Jesus comes out time after time throughout His public ministry. In the opening address that Jesus gave at His hometown of Nazareth, He had quoted Isaiah the prophet, "The Spirit of the Lord is upon Me, because He anointed Me to preach the gospel to the poor. He has sent Me to proclaim release to the captives, and recovery of sight to the blind, to set free those who are downtrodden, to proclaim the favorable year of the Lord" (Luke 4:18).

Fourth, *God is love.* The first songs children learn in Sunday school, when they are barely able to carry a tune, are about God's love. A child can understand God's love, but the depths are so infinite that an adult finds it difficult to fathom. God's love is the continuing result of His holiness, justice, and mercy.

As a holy God, He hates sin and can have no fellowship with sin. Because the Bible tells us that the soul that sins must surely die, we can see that separation from God is a result of sin. However, because God is also mercy, He longs to save the guilty sinner and must then provide a substitute which will satisfy His divine justice. He provided that substitute in Jesus Christ. There is God's love: "For God so loved the world, that He gave His only begotten Son, that whoever believes in Him should not perish, but have eternal life" (John 3:16).

God and Jesus Christ the Same

Fifth, Jesus Christ possesses the three great "omni's" of God. This prefix means "completely or all" and when used within the word *omnipotent* it means that the possessor has all power. The dictionary has one word to describe the Omni-potent, and that is God.

While a man on earth, Jesus Christ performed many miracles. He raised people from the dead; He took a few loaves and fishes and multiplied them to feed thousands; He cured the chronically sick and healed the crippled. But why should this be surprising? Jesus said, "All power is given unto me in heaven and in earth" (Matt. 28:18, KJV). That is a startling statement if it were made by any ordinary man. Only God could make such a claim.

Jesus Christ was *omniscient*. This means that He knew all things, and He still knows all things. The Scriptures say, "Jesus knowing their thoughts" (Matt. 9:4); "He knew all men . . . He Himself knew what was in man" (John 2:24,25); "In whom are hidden all the treasures of wisdom and knowledge" (Col. 2:3).

Do you know anyone of your acquaintance, or any person in history who knew everything? Have you ever heard of a person who could know, without a mistake, the minds of men? Only an all-powerful God knows everything, and Jesus Christ was omniscient.

Probably no idea is more difficult for man to comprehend than the thought of *omnipresence*. How can God be everywhere at once? From our viewpoint we are bound by time and space. We are physical creatures who can only be one place at a time. We frequently complain, "I can't be everyplace at once!" God transcends time and space, and so does Jesus Christ. He existed before time began. "Before Abraham was born, I AM" (John 8:58). "He is before all things" (Col. 1:17).

Jesus is not earthbound. He said, "Wherever two or more of you are gathered together in My Name there am I in the midst of you." He can be with a gathering of believers in a primitive hut in New Guinea or a businessman's luncheon in Dallas. He can be at the supper table of a family or in the banquet hall of royalty. Jesus Christ is omnipresent.

Jesus Christ claimed to be God. He said, "I and the Father are one" (John 10:30) and, "He who beholds Me beholds the One who sent Me" (John 12:45). He made it very clear when He spoke to the religious leaders of his time who He was. "I am He who bears witness of Myself, and the Father who sent Me bears witness of Me." Members of the local church hierarchy said to Him, "Where is Your Father?" Jesus answered, "You know neither Me, nor My Father; if you knew Me, you would know My Father also."

Christ represents Himself as having been "sent from God" and being "not of this world." He declares that He is "the light of the world," "the way, the truth, and the life," and "the resurrection and the life." He promises eternal life to everyone who believes in Him as Lord and Savior.

Knowing the claims of Jesus Christ, you are faced with this vital decision—

What Will You Do With Jesus?

Question: Who do you think Jesus Christ is? If He is not who He claimed to be, He is a deceiver or an egomaniac. We cannot settle for a middle-of-the-road answer that He was "a good man," or the modern form of adulation as a "superstar." He Himself eliminates a neutral answer. Either we decide He is a liar or a lunatic, or we must declare Him to be Lord.

In light of the evidence of Scripture and the physical fact of the Resurrection, the only wise conclusion is that He is God, worthy of our worship and trust. When I decide to be a Christian, I am deciding who Jesus Christ is. Trust in Him makes me a believer in Him and leads to being truly alive!

Out of His Private Wilderness

We heard about a young couple who were separated during
World War II. While the father was gone the mother gave birth to
a baby girl. The months passed and the mother kept a large picture of her husband on the desk so that the little girl would grow
up knowing what her daddy looked like. She learned to say
"Daddy" and associated the name with the picture on the desk.
Finally the day came when her father returned home from the war.
The whole family gathered to watch the little girl when she saw
her father for the first time. Imagine their disappointment when
she would have nothing whatever to do with him. Instead, she ran
to the photograph on the desk, saying, "That's my daddy." Day
after day the family had to blink back the tears as they saw the
young father on his knees trying his best to get acquainted with
his little daughter, explaining as simply as he could that he was
her daddy. But each time she would shake her head, then run to
the picture on the desk and exclaim, "That's my daddy." This went
on for some time, but one day something happened. The little girl,
having gone repeatedly to the picture on the desk, returned to her
father and looked carefully into his face. Then she went back to
the picture on the desk and studied it. The family held their breath.
After several trips the little face lit up as the child exclaimed excitedly, "They're both the same daddy!"

C. S. Lewis describes his experience: "You must picture me alone
in that room in Magdalen, night after night, feeling, whenever my
mind lifted even for a second from my work, the steady unrelented
approach of Him whom I so earnestly desired not to meet. That
which I greatly feared had at last come upon me. In the Trinity
Term of 1929 I gave in, and admitted that God was God, and knelt
and prayed: perhaps, that night, the most dejected and reluctant
convert in all England. I did not then see what is now the most
shining and obvious thing; the Divine humility which will accept
a convert even on such terms. The Prodigal Son at least walked
home on his own feet. But who can duly adore that Love which
will open the high gates to a prodigal who is brought in kicking,
struggling, resentful, and darting his eyes in every direction for a
chance of escape? The words *compelle intrare*, compel them to

come in, have been so abused by wicked men that we shudder at them; but, properly understood, they plumb the depth of the Divine mercy. The hardness of God is kinder than the softness of men, and His compulsion is our liberation."[3]

A certain professor said that in over forty years on campus he had never been asked, "Are you a Christian?" When he was a student he had read books that explained away Christ's miracles; he considered himself well informed and sophisticated on the subject. As a result, on the one hand he disbelieved the deity of Jesus Christ while on the other hand he kept some vague belief in God.

In practice, however, he said, "I usually chose to ignore Him in my early post-college days. This started the path into my own personal wilderness. I tried to satisfy my inner needs by reading and studying literature and science. These studies often confirmed my opinion that I could leave Christ out of my life because He was just another prophet."

Then one day a student entered this professor's "private wilderness" to invite him to hear a campus talk on the deity of Christ. The professor later recalled, "I was confronted with the positive side of Christ's deity for the first time since I was a child. I didn't expect to have my disbelief in the deity of Christ changed.

"As I listened that evening, partly in skepticism, partly in hope, I admit I also yearned to be convinced. The speaker had scarcely completed half of his remarks before I was convinced of the deity of Christ. A lifetime's assumption that Jesus was just another gifted teacher was destroyed. The turnabout in my convictions was simple."

I must agree with the professor. It is simple. Jesus is God. Our earthly lives and eternal destinies depend on our belief in that fact.

8

What Happened
at the Cross

IN JEWELRY STORES from Fifth Avenue to the airport in
Rome one piece of jewelry is universally displayed—the cross.
Clerical robes have this emblem sewn on the front or back.
Churches display the cross in wood, bronze, concrete, or brass. The
last month of the year some office buildings light certain windows
at night to form a cross which can be seen for miles.

What does the cross of Jesus mean? If we stopped people on the
street and asked that question we might hear, "It's a symbol for
Christianity, I guess." Or, "Jesus was a martyr and was nailed to
a cross." Others might say it was a myth, or a history major might
say it was an example of Roman justice.

Another answer to the question "What does the cross mean?"
was given by the poet, Thomas Victoria. He tried to express how
Jesus Himself might speak of the cross if we asked Him. The poet
pictured Jesus on the cross, surrounded by men who were intent
upon killing him.

Jesus looks at them and says:

> Oh, how sweet the wood of the cross,
> How sweet the nails,
> That I could die for you.

This deeply personal, intimate view of the cross is what the
Apostle Paul taught when he said, "In human experience it is a

rare thing for one man to give his life for another, . . . though there have been a few who have had the courage to do it. Yet the proof of God's amazing love is this: that it was *while we were sinners* that Christ died for us" (Rom. 5:7,8, Phillips).

The focus of Paul's whole ministry to the great commercial city of Corinth was summed up when he said, "For I determined to know nothing among you except Jesus Christ, and Him crucified" (1 Cor. 2:2).

The average person in Corinth would have answered a question about the cross in the same way as the man on the street in the USA or any European, African, or Asian country. Corinthians lived in a city which was known for its depraved moral character. It was the kind of town in which we wouldn't want to raise our families. The Corinthians were a sophisticated, sexually dissolute bunch, who thought that the cross was ridiculous, foolish, and even idiotic. Commenting on this view, Paul said, "The foolishness of God is wiser than men, and the weakness of God is stronger than men" (1 Cor. 1:25).

In Corinth the preaching of the Cross of Christ was a stumbling block to the Jews, and idiocy to the philosophic Greeks. The philosophers believed they could unravel divine mysteries because they were overconfident of their own mental capacities. However, Paul said that the natural man (meaning the man who does not have the Spirit of God indwelling him) cannot understand the things of God. He meant that sin has twisted our understanding of truth so that we cannot recognize the truth about God.

Before the teaching in the Bible about the cross can mean anything to us, the Spirit of God must open our minds. The Scriptures teach that a veil covers our minds as a result of our separation from God.

To an "outsider" the cross must appear to be ridiculous. But to those who have experienced its transforming power, it has become the only remedy for the ills of each person, and of the world.

In spite of this available power, the gospel about Christ who was crucified is still unimportant to millions. They reflect the failure Paul analyzed when he questioned, "What have the philosopher, the writer and the critic of this world to show for all their wisdom? Has not God made the wisdom of this world look foolish?

For it was after the world in its wisdom had failed to know God, that he in his wisdom chose to save all who believe by the 'simple-mindedness' of the gospel message" (1 Cor. 1:20,21, Phillips).

How can we brand the message of the cross as foolishness? Have we done so well with our private lives, with our families, and with our society that we can claim wisdom? It's time we abandoned the pretense of being intellectual and recognize that our best minds are baffled by life.

God successfully changes men and women by the message that centers in the cross. His approach recognizes our disease and presents the right medicine. He offers His wisdom as an alternative to our failures.

In our everyday life we profit from many helps that we can't understand. We go to the sink and turn on the water tap, never stopping to figure out the source of the water, or how it was carried through the pipes to us. What about a prescription from a doctor? We can't read it or analyze it. We pay a sum we may think is too much because we rely on the doctor's knowledge and authority to make us well.

In the same way we may not be able to fully comprehend the deep significance of the cross, but we can benefit from it because the Bible gives us the authoritative answer to the problem of sin.

What Happened at the Cross?

The cross is the focal point in the life and ministry of Jesus Christ. Some think that God didn't want Christ to die, but was forced to adjust His plans to adapt to it. Scripture makes it very clear, however, that the cross was no afterthought with God. Christ was "delivered up by the predetermined plan and foreknowledge of God" (Acts 2:23).

God designed the cross to defeat Satan, who by deception had obtained squatters' rights to the title deed of the world. When Satan with all of his clever promises separated man from God in the Garden of Eden, he was more than the deceiver of Adam and Eve. In some mysterious manner he began to exert a kind of pseudosovereignty over man. In his arrogant violence, Satan unleashed his fiercest attack to stop Christ's ministry by seeing that He was murdered. But Satan was stopped by God and caught in his own trap. He hadn't realized that God loved the world so intensely that He could let His own Son be subjected to the worst Satan could do. Satan miscalculated. He didn't comprehend the greatness of God's love and the wisdom of His plan.

Satan's power was broken at the cross. "The Son of God appeared for this purpose, that He might destroy the works of the devil" (1 John 3:8).

What a blow was dealt to Satan! Although he is still a wily pretender, his destruction was made certain by the victory of Christ at the cross. "That through death he might render powerless him who had the power of death, that is, the devil" (Heb. 2:14). What seemed to be the biggest defeat of history turned into the greatest triumph.

Through the cross, God not only overpowered Satan but brought Himself and man together. Christ rescued the slaves that Satan held captive and reconciled them to Himself. The Bible describes this amazing divine plan in these words: "We speak God's wisdom in a mystery, the hidden wisdom, which God predestined before the ages to our glory; the wisdom which none of the rulers of this age has understood; for if they had understood it, they would not have crucified the Lord of Glory" (1 Cor. 2:7,8).

The cross revealed an eternal secret. This was "the mystery which has been kept secret for long ages past, but now is manifested" (Rom. 16:25,26).

If it were possible for one man, Adam, to lead mankind to ruin, why shouldn't it be possible for one man to redeem it? The Bible says, "For as in Adam all die, so also in Christ all shall be made alive" (1 Cor. 15:22).

What Did the Cross Cost God?

As human beings filled with our own hurts and desires and emotions, we find it almost impossible to stretch our minds enough to conceive the cost to God in allowing His only Son to go to the cross. If He could have forgiven our sins by any other method, if the problems of the world could have been solved in any other way, God would not have allowed Jesus to die.

In the garden of Gethsemane on the night before He was killed, Jesus prayed, "My Father, if it is possible, let this cup pass from Me" (Matt. 26:39), in other words, if there is any other way to redeem the human race, Oh God, find it! There was no other way. And then He prayed, "Not as I will, but as Thou wilt" (Matt. 26:39).

It's important to understand that when Jesus prayed that prayer, He was not just considering the simple act of dying. Just as His life was unique, so was His death. What happened to Him when He died had never happened to any person in the past and would never happen to anyone in the future. To be able to understand this we need to look into God's revelation before Christ's earthly ministry, back to the Old Testament.

The orthodox Jewish religion was founded on God's grace. God entered into a covenant relationship with Israel, declaring Himself to be their God and stating in a special way that they were to be His people (Deut. 7:6). With this type of relationship, how were they to express their love for Him? The answer was by doing His will as it was described in the Old Testament law. But the people could not keep the law perfectly, and when they broke it, they sinned. As the Bible says, "Sin is the transgression of the law" (1 John 3:4 KJV).

The sacrifices in the temple were meant by God to show graphically that a person's guilt and penalty for sin could be transferred from him to another. In the case of the Old Testament, a perfect animal symbolically bore the penalty and was killed.

Why did God give the law if He knew people couldn't possibly keep it? The Bible teaches that the law was given as a mirror. When we look into it, we see what true righteousness is. The Ten Commandments describe the life that pleases God. If we are separated from God by sin, the law exposes our sin and faces us with our true spiritual condition. The mirror does not reveal a very attractive image!

Sin had to be paid for, so in the beginning God instituted the sacrificial system by which we finally could be brought into a right relationship with God. In Old Testament times, those who had sinned brought sacrifices of animals and offered them to God. These sacrifices were shadows of The Great Sacrifice who was yet to come.

In Leviticus 4, Moses describes a situation in which a leader needs to offer a sacrifice. We can think of it in seven steps:

1. "When a leader sins . . .
2. he shall bring for his offering a goat,
3. a male without defect.
4. And he shall lay his hand on the head of the male goat,
5. and slay it . . . ; it is a sin offering.
6. Then the priest is to take some of the blood of the sin offering . . . and put it on the horns of the altar. . . .
7. Thus the priest shall make atonement for him in regard to his sin, and he shall be forgiven" (vv. 22–26).

Notice the sequence. Man sinned and wants forgiveness of God. He brings an animal, a perfect specimen, to the priest and lays his hand on its head. Symbolically, at that point the guilt and punishment he bears because of his sin passes to the animal. He then kills it as a sin offering, and the priest places some of the blood on the altar.

What is the significance? It is an atonement for the man in regard to his sin. In place of a broken relationship between God and the sinner, "atonement" results and "he shall be forgiven" by God.

The sacrifices were visual aids to show sinners that there was hope because the punishment for sin could be transferred to another. However, they were only symbols, because, "It is impossible for the blood of bulls and goats to take away sins" (Heb. 10:4). But God could forgive them in the light of what He would one day do at the cross. Jesus, "having offered one sacrifice for sins for all time, sat down at the right hand of God" (Heb. 10:12).

God did not initiate the sacrifices because He was bloodthirsty or unjust. He wanted us to zero in on two things: first, the loathsomeness of sin, and second, the cross on which God Himself would satisfy forever the demands of His justice. "Not through the blood of goats and calves, but through His own blood He [Jesus] entered the holy place once for all, having obtained eternal redemption" (Heb. 9:12).

When Christ atoned for sin, He stood in the place of guilty men and women. If God had forgiven sin by a divine decree, issuing some sort of a heavenly document written across the sky, without the atonement which involved the personal shame, agony, suffering, and death of Christ, then we might assume that God was indifferent to sin. Consequently we would all go on sinning, and the earth would become a living hell.

In the suffering of Jesus we have the participation of God in the act of atonement. Sin pierced God's heart. God felt every searing nail and spear. God felt the burning sun. God felt the scorn of His tormenters and the body blows. In the cross is the suffering love of God bearing the guilt of man's sin. This love alone is able to melt the sinner's heart and bring him to repentance for salvation. "He [God the Father] made Him who knew no sin [Jesus] to be sin on our behalf" (2 Cor. 5:21).

The Reason for Communion

Many people do not understand communion. For them, the communion service has no mystical meaning. And yet the cross is what communion is all about. In the Lord's Supper, Jesus likens Himself to the Lamb that was offered in the sacrifice or atonement and says to His disciples and to all who will believe in Him, "This is my body broken for you." This is symbolic of what He did on the cross. When the cup is offered the emphasis is upon the fact that His blood is shed for the remission of sins. The elements of bread and wine convey to us the reality of atonement and forgiveness. We can touch them, taste them and see them. We have bread in our hands, but we have Christ in our hearts. We have the cup in our hand, but we have the benefits of forgiveness through His blood in our hearts.

One of the most famous Scottish theologians was John Duncan of New College in Edinburgh. As communion was being held in a Church of Scotland on one occasion, when the elements came to a little sixteen-year-old girl, she suddenly turned her head aside. She motioned for the elder to take the cup away—that she couldn't drink it. John Duncan reached his long arm over, touched her shoulder, and said tenderly, "Take it, lassie, it's for sinners!"

How Can I Understand All This?

There is a mystery to the death of Christ that is beyond our human understanding. The depths of God's love in sending His Son to pay such an awful price is beyond the measure of the mind of man. But we must accept it on faith or we will continually bear the burdens of guilt. We must accept the atonement which Christ has made to try to make our own atonement, and this we can never do. Salvation is by Christ alone through faith alone, and for the glory of God alone.

Christ took the punishment which was due us.

My friend and associate, Cliff Barrows, told me this story about bearing punishment. He recalled the time when he took the punishment for his children when they had disobeyed. "They had done something I had forbidden them to do. I told them if they did the same thing again I would have to discipline them. When I returned from work and found that they hadn't minded me, the heart went out of me. I just couldn't discipline them."

Any loving father can understand Cliff's dilemma. Most of us have been in the same position. He continued with the story: "Bobby and Bettie Ruth were very small. I called them into my room, took off my belt and my shirt, and with a bare back, knelt down at the bed. I made them both strap me with the belt ten times each. You should have heard the crying! From them, I mean! They didn't want to do it. But I told them the penalty had to be paid and so through their sobs and tears they did what I told them."

Cliff smiled when he remembered the incident. "I must admit I wasn't much of a hero. It hurt. I haven't offered to do that again, but I never had to spank them again, either, because they got the point. We kissed each other when it was over and prayed together."

In that infinite way that staggers our hearts and minds, we know that Christ paid the penalty for our sins, past, present, and future.

That is why He died on the cross.

9

The King's Courtroom

THE UNITED STATES has a Presidential election every four years. Changes are usually made in the White House, the Congress, and in many governor's mansions. When one elected leader is about to step down for his successor, he may grant some pardons to prisoners under his jurisdiction. It's always interesting to see who might benefit from these last-minute gestures.

If you or I were in prison and were told, "You're free. The President just granted you a pardon," we would certainly pack up and get out fast! That pardon would change our lives.

In the courtroom of the King of kings, a pardon means much more. At the cross, God not only delivered the believer in Christ from punishment, He also welcomed Him with open arms into His family. He opens His home to us.

At the cross we have not only acquittal, but also justification (just-as-if-I'd-never-sinned); not only pardon, but also acceptance. We saw in the last chapter that God Himself bore the burden of our sin and suffered for us. Now we must see that the cross offers us more than a pardon.

The issue involved is not just in Jesus' blood, which cleanses us from sin, but also in His righteousness. The key is in the word "justified." We are "justified as a gift by His grace through the redemption which is in Christ Jesus" (Rom. 3:24).

Several years ago I was to be interviewed at my home for a well-known television show and, knowing that it would appear on nationwide television, my wife took great pains to see that everything looked nice. She had vacuumed and dusted and tidied up the whole house but had gone over the living room with a fine-tooth comb since that was where the interview would be filmed. When the film crew arrived with all the lights and cameras, she felt that everything in that living room was spic and span. We were in place along with the interviewer when suddenly the television lights were turned on and we saw cobwebs and dust where we had never seen them before. In the words of my wife: "I mean, that room was festooned with dust and cobwebs which simply did not show up under ordinary light."

The point is, of course, that no matter how well we clean up our lives and think we have them all in order, when we see ourselves in the light of God's Word, in the light of God's holiness, all the cobwebs and all the dust do show up.

Picture a courtroom. God the Judge is seated in the judge's seat, robed in splendor. You are arraigned before Him. He looks at you in terms of His own righteous nature as it is expressed in the moral law. He speaks to you:

GOD: John (or) Mary, have you loved Me with all your heart?
JOHN/MARY: No, Your Honor.
GOD: Have you loved others as you have loved yourself?
JOHN/MARY: No, Your Honor.
GOD: Do you believe you are a sinner and that Jesus Christ died for your sins?
JOHN/MARY: Yes, Your Honor.
GOD: Then your penalty has been paid by Jesus Christ on the cross and you are pardoned.

I have my pardon, but there is much more. When the Bible says that the person who believes in Jesus is justified as a gift by His grace (see Romans 3:24), this sounds like more than a mere pardon. And it is. If I'm a criminal whom the president or the governor pardons, everyone knows I'm still guilty. I simply don't have to serve my sentence. But if I'm justified, it's *just-as-if-I'd* never sinned at all.

Both pardon and justification come to us when we believe in

Jesus. On the one hand God pardons our sin because of the death of Christ. He paid our penalty. On the other hand God actually declares us "righteous" (a word which means the same as "just").

GOD: Because Christ is righteous, and you believe in Christ, I now declare you legally righteous.

How can God do that and remain "just" Himself—when He attached the penalty of death to sin? The answer is in the righteousness of Jesus Christ. He lived an unblemished, perfect life. His character perfectly supported His claim to deity, as we saw in chapter 7, "The Man Who Is God." It's easy to see God the Father declaring Jesus just, because He was. But how does that help me, a sinner? Paul gives the answer in 2 Corinthians 5:21. To make it clear we'll substitute the words *God* and *Christ* where the words *He* and *Him* appear. "God made Christ who knew no sin to be sin on our behalf, that we might become the righteousness of God in Christ."

God put my sin on Christ, who had no sin; He punished Him in my place, as we have seen. But He did one other thing, according to this verse. By God's action the righteousness of Christ was put on us who believe, "that we might become the righteousness of God in Him."

The Judge, God, has transferred Christ's righteousness to your legal account if you have believed in Christ. Now He examines you according to law. What does He see? All of your past evil deeds and thoughts? Your sinful actions of the present?

No. He doesn't see your sin because that has been transferred to Christ when God made Christ to be sin. Rather He looks at you carefully and sees the righteousness of Christ.

But you may say, "Look, am I not still a sinful person?"

The answer is "Yes and No." If you mean that you have the legal status of a sinner before God, the answer is "No." To Him, legally, you are just. You are in right standing before Him, and "standing" is the issue in the courtroom.

Do you still have the capacity to sin? The answer is "Yes." Of course you are not perfect. You may still at times think and act in ways contrary to God's desires. But your character and mine aren't the issue here. Our legal standing is. And legally we are declared just.

Am I Free to Sin?

"Love God and live as you please!" Now are we free to sin without restraint? Can we run out of the courtroom, pardoned and justified, and do anything we want? Yes. But you are now "born again." You don't want to do the same old wrong things; your desires are changed.

If you have trusted Jesus and seen what depth of concern He had for you at the cross, you can say with the Apostle Paul, "It is Christ's love that controls me" (2 Cor. 5:14, Goodspeed). The inner changes God begins to achieve in our character will be the subject of a later chapter. But they are all based on a change in status. We who were properly condemned are now properly declared just if we have trusted Christ.

Can you imagine what a newspaper man would do with this event?

SINNER PARDONED—GOES
TO LIVE WITH JUDGE

It was a tense scene when John and Mary stood before the Judge and had the list of charges against them read. However, the Judge transferred all of the guilt to Jesus Christ, who died on a cross for John and Mary.

After John and Mary were pardoned the Judge invited them to come to live with Him forever.

The reporter on a story like that would never be able to understand the irony of such a scene, unless he had been introduced to the Judge beforehand and knew His character.

Pardon and Christ's righteousness come to us only when we totally trust ourselves to Jesus as our Lord and Savior. When we do this, God welcomes us into His intimate favor. Clothed in Christ's righteousness we can now enjoy God's fellowship and "come boldly unto the throne of grace, that we may obtain mercy, and find grace to help in time of need" (Heb. 4:16, KJV).

Conclusions from the Testimony

If I were a lawyer, I'm sure I would study the procedures of great trials of the past, the evidences presented, and the conclusions reached by the findings.

There are some vital conclusions we can draw from the death of Christ. First, at the cross we see the strongest evidence of the guilt of the world. Here sin reached its climax when its terrible display occurred. Sin was never blacker or more hideous than on the day Christ died.

Some people have said that man has improved since then and that if Christ returned today He wouldn't be crucified but might even be given a glorious reception. I am convinced that if Christ came today He might be tortured and put to death even more quickly than He was two thousand years ago, though perhaps in different, more sophisticated ways. But sinful people would still shout, "Away with Him."

Human sinful nature has not changed. As we look at the cross we see clear proof that all men have "sinned and fallen short of the glory of God." This is God's inescapable verdict.

The second conclusion we see at the cross is that God hates sin and loves righteousness. He has told us repeatedly that the soul that sins shall die, and that He cannot forgive our sin unless our debt has been paid. The Scripture says, "Without the shedding of blood there is no forgiveness of sins" (Heb. 9:22, RSV).

God will not tolerate sin. As the moral judge of the entire universe, He cannot compromise if He is to remain just. His holiness and His justice demand the penalty for broken law. There are some schools of thought which feel that such a view of God is too severe. Sin, they say, has its psychological basis. Some time ago a young man was executed for killing two other young men. The newspapers were full of the legal arguments, the debates over the death penalty, and the frequent postponements of the execution date. Why did he do it? What events or people in his past influenced his twisted mind?

Many say they are not responsible for what they do. Poor parents, bad environment, the government are all blamed. But God says that we are responsible. When we look at the cross, we see how drastically God deals with sin. The Bible says, "He who did not spare His own Son, but delivered him up for us all, how will He not also with Him freely give us all things?" (Rom. 8:32). "For our sake he [God] made him [Christ] to be sin who knew no sin" (2 Cor. 5:21, RSV).

If God had to send His only Son to the cross to pay the penalty for sin, then sin must be terrible indeed in His sight.

However, we see that God loves righteousness and clothes the believer in His righteousness because of the cross. It is amazing to think about! We are clothed, we are covered, protected, shielded. A wonderful old hymn says, "Jesus, thy blood and righteousness, My beauty are, my glorious dress."[1] This is not self-righteousness, but "the righteousness which comes from God on the basis of faith" (Phil. 3:9).

God is now at work through the Holy Spirit to make the believer righteous in his inner character. Peter shows how intimately this is based on the cross also when he says of Christ that "He Himself bore our sins in His body on the cross, that we might die to sin and live to righteousness" (1 Pet. 2:24).

What other conclusion must we reach from the testimony of the cross? We see the greatest demonstration of God's love. "For God so loved the world, that He gave His only begotten Son, that whoever believes in Him should not perish, but have eternal life" (John 3:16).

In our own weakness as humans, we tend to grade sins. Here's a little sin on our scale, but over here there's a very, very heavy sin. We may see God as able to forgive the small sin, but incapable of forgiving and accepting the gross sinner. I recall a story out of World War II that illustrates this graphically. Hitler and his Third Reich had gone down to defeat at the hands of the Allies. Many of the men who had been Nazi leaders in some of the most infamous crimes known to man were brought to trial in Nuremberg. The world watched as sentences of imprisonment and death were brought against these war criminals.

However, out of the Nuremberg trials came an amazing account by Chaplain Henry Gerecke. He was called upon to be prison chaplain to the former Nazi high command. He described himself as a humble preacher, a one-time Missouri farm boy, and then he was given this extremely difficult assignment.

Chaplain Gerecke recalls the sincere conversion to faith in Jesus Christ by some of these men who had committed despicable crimes. One of them was a former favorite general of Hitler. At first the chaplain was very leery of confessions of faith. He said the first time he saw this criminal reading his Bible he thought, "a phony." However, as he spent time with him he wrote, "But the longer I listened, the more I felt he might be sincere. He said he had not been a good Christian. He insisted he was very glad that a nation which would probably put him to death thought enough of his eternal welfare to provide him with spiritual guidance." With this Bible in his hand he said, "I know from this book that God can love a sinner like me."[2]

What an amazing love God exhibited for us at the cross!

The fourth conclusion we can reach from the testimony at the cross is that it is the basis for true world brotherhood. There are many groups which espouse the brotherhood of man and make appeals in behalf of peace. Only when we are brought into the family of God through the Fatherhood of God can there be any true brotherhood of man. God is not our Father automatically (except by creation) when we are born; He must become our Father spiritually.

The Bible teaches that we can experience glorious brotherhood and Fatherhood through the cross. "For He Himself is our peace, who made both groups into one, and broke down the barrier of the dividing wall, by abolishing in His flesh the enmity, which is the Law of commandments contained in ordinances, that in Himself He might make the two into one new man, thus establishing peace" (Eph. 2:14,15).

Outside the work of the cross we see bitterness, intolerance, hatred, prejudice, lust, and greed. Within the powerful working of the cross grow love, new life, and new brotherhood. The only human hope for peace lies at the cross of Christ, where all men, no matter what their background of nationality or race, can become a new brotherhood.

You are probably familiar with the story of Hansei. Her book *Hansei* describes vividly her absolute dedication to Adolph Hitler and the Nazi movement as a member of the Hitler Youth; her subsequent disenchantment and disillusionment; then her conversion to Jesus Christ. My wife has a letter from Hansei telling of her first meeting with Corrie ten Boom, whose book *The Hiding Place* tells of the ten Boom family's experiences during World War II. The family was arrested and put in prison for hiding Jews, and Corrie's father and sister died there.

One day Hansei and Corrie were at a convention and were seated in the same building, autographing their books. Hansei waited as long as she could, then made her way to Corrie because she simply had to ask forgiveness for what she had done. Hansei pushed through those standing in line with their books for Corrie to sign, knelt in front of Corrie with tears streaming down her cheeks and said, "Corrie, I'm Hansei." Corrie's reaction was not only absolute forgiveness, but love and acceptance. This could only happen between Christians and illustrates what the cross does.

Captain Mitsuo Fuchida was the Japanese Naval air commander who led the bombing attack on Pearl Harbor. He relates that when the Japanese war prisoners were returning from America he was curious as to what kind of treatment they had received. An ex-prisoner he questioned told him what made it possible for those in the camp to forget their hate and hostility toward their captors. One young girl had been extremely kind and helpful and had shown such love and tenderness for them that their hearts were touched. They wondered why she was so good to them and were amazed when she told them it was because her parents had been killed by the Japanese army! She explained that her parents had been Christian missionaries in the Philippines at the beginning of the war but when the Japanese landed they were forced to flee to the mountains. They were later found by the Japanese, accused of being spies and put to death. But before they were killed they had asked for thirty minutes of time to pray, which was granted. The girl was convinced that her parents had spent that thirty minutes praying for forgiveness for their executioners, and because of this she was able to allow the Holy Spirit to remove the hate from her heart and replace it with love.

Captain Fuchida could not understand such love. Several months passed and one day in Tokyo he was given a leaflet as he left a railroad station. This told the story of Sergeant Jacob DeShazer who was captured by the Japanese, tortured, and held prisoner of war for forty months. While in prison camp he received Christ through reading the Bible. God's Word removed the bitter hatred for the Japanese from his heart and replaced it with such love that he was compelled to return to tell the Japanese people of this marvelous love of Christ.

Captain Fuchida bought a Bible and began to read. He faced the scene of the crucifixion of Christ and was struck by Jesus' words "Father forgive them; for they do not know what they are doing" (Luke 23:34). Jesus prayed for the very soldiers who were about to thrust the spear into His side. In his book *From Pearl Harbor to Golgotha* Captain Fuchida tells how he found the source of this miracle love that can forgive enemies, and how he could now understand the story of the American girl whose parents had been slain and the transformation in Jake DeShazer's life.

Personal Questions the Cross Answers

"Why can't I seem to solve my problems?" This question reminds me of a Peanuts cartoon. It pictures Lucy in her psychiatrist's booth giving counsel to Charlie Brown. Charlie has lost another ball game and feels depressed and defeated. Lucy, the psychiatrist, is explaining to him that life is made of ups and downs. Charlie goes away screaming, "But I hate downs, all I want is ups."

I'm afraid that often those of us who teach the Christian message give the impression that once we have accepted Jesus Christ we will never again have any problems. This isn't true, but we do have Someone to help us face our problems. I have a paraplegic friend who has been that way for over thirty years. In spite of overwhelming problems for which there is no solution, she has learned not only to live with her condition, but to be radiant and triumphant, blessing and winning others to Christ.

Paul Tournier, one of the great Swiss psychiatrists, has stated that the Christian life we have to realize that each day will present new circumstances and there will always be adjustments that have to be made. If I drive my car into a city, I can't rigidly place my hands on the steering wheel and drive at a set rate of speed. I have to stop and start and turn to make adjustments. The same thing is true in daily living. There is always a price to being a person; part of that price is pain and problems, but we have the promise Christ made that He will always be with us.

In Psalm 34 there are three great statements about our problems:

"This poor man cried and the Lord heard him; and saved him out of all his troubles" (v. 6).

"The righteous cry and the Lord hears, and delivers them out of all their troubles" (v. 17).

"Many are the afflictions of the righteous; but the Lord delivers him out of them all" (v. 19).

The Christian life is not a way "out" but a way "through" life. The "out of" in these verses refers to deliverance not from but through difficulty. The English scholar Dr. Arthur Way phrased it, "Deliverance out of, not from the crisis of trial. So that the sense appears to be, 'bring me safely out of the conflict'" and, "not simply keep me from entering into it."

Another question: "I feel so guilty—how can I find relief?"

Guilt is a very debilitating feeling. It can destroy our attitude, our personal relationships, and our outreach. Sometimes we feel guilty because we've done things that are wrong for which we must accept the responsibility and also accept God's forgiveness.

I have been told by doctors that a large percentage of the patients in psychiatric hospitals could be released if only they could be assured of the fact that they had been forgiven.

It's so easy to blame someone or something else. Anna Russell, the British comedienne, has an interesting little poem about guilt:

I went to my psychiatrist to be psychoanalized.
To find out why I kicked the cat, and blacked my wifey's eyes.
He laid me on his downy couch to see what he could find,
And this is what he dredged up from my subconscious mind.
When I was one my mama hid my dolly in a trunk,
And so it falls naturally that I am always drunk.
When I was two I suffered from ambivalence toward my
   brothers,

And so it falls naturally I poisoned all my lovers.
Now I am so glad that I have learned the lessons this has taught,
That everything I do that's wrong is someone else's fault.

For some people guilt is an excuse. They won't accept the forgiveness that is offered to them; it is so hard to believe. It seems too good to be true that God should let us go eternally scot-free from our sins—and yet that is the message that the Gospel brings to us. When we cling to our guilt we do not honor God and we handicap our own lives terribly.

Forgiveness is an opportunity that Christ extended to us on the cross. When we accept His forgiveness and are willing to forgive ourselves, then we find relief.

After the sewage plants of London have reclaimed all that is usable of sewage, sludge barges on the river Thames collect the residue and carry it out to sea a certain number of miles and dump it. Apparently it is only a matter of minutes before the sea water is as pure as it was before! This is a beautiful illustration of how He has buried our sins in the depths of the sea.

Corrie ten Boom tells a story of a little girl who broke one of her mother's treasured demitasse cups. The little girl came to her mother sobbing, "Oh, mama, I'm so sorry I broke your beautiful cup."

The mother replied, "I know you're sorry and I forgive you. Now don't cry any more." The mother then swept up the pieces of the broken cup and placed them in the trash can. But the little girl enjoyed the guilty feeling. She went to the trash can, picked out pieces of the cup, brought them to her mother and sobbed, "Mother, I'm so sorry that I broke your pretty cup."

This time her mother spoke firmly to her, "Take those pieces and put them back in the trash can and don't be silly enough to take them out again. I told you I forgave you so don't cry any more, and don't pick up the broken pieces any more."

Guilt is removed with confession and cleansing. "If we confess our sins, he is faithful and just to forgive us our sins, and to cleanse us from all unrighteousness" (1 John 1:9, KJV).

However, the story of David's sin (Ps. 51) shows that forgiveness does not preclude the natural consequences of our sin. Murder can be forgiven, but that does not bring the dead to life again.

There is a well-known story of some fishermen in Scotland who had spent the day fishing. That evening they were having tea in a little inn. One of the fishermen, in a characteristic gesture to describe the size of the fish that got away, flung out his hands just as the little waitress was getting ready to set the cup of tea at his place. The hand and the teacup collided, dashing the tea against the whitewashed walls. Immediately an ugly brown stain began to spread over the wall. The man who did it was very embarrassed and apologized profusely, but one of the other guests jumped up and said, "Never mind." Pulling a pen from his pocket, he began to sketch around the ugly brown stain. Soon there emerged a picture of a magnificent royal stag with his antlers spread. That artist was Landseer, England's foremost painter of animals.

This story has always beautifully illustrated to me the fact that if we confess not only our sins but our mistakes to God, He can make out of them something for our good and for His glory. Somehow it's harder to commit our mistakes and stupidities to God than it is our sins. Mistakes and stupidities seem so dumb, whereas sin seems more or less to be an outcropping of our human nature. But Romans 8:28 tells us that if they are committed to God He can make them work together for our good and His glory.

When you bake a cake, you put in raw flour, baking powder, soda, bitter chocolate, shortening, etc., none of which taste very good in themselves, but which work together to make a delicious cake. And so with our sins and our mistakes—although they are not good in themselves, if we commit them in honest, simple faith to the Lord, He will work them out His own way and in His own time make something of them for our good and His glory.

Question: "Do I have to understand all this about Christ's death?"

The depths of God's love in sending His Son to pay such an awful price is beyond the measure of the mind of man. We must accept it on faith or we will continually bear the burden of guilt. Salvation is by Christ alone, through faith alone, for the glory of God alone.

Jesus never said, "Only understand." He said, "Only believe."

10

Jesus Christ Is Alive

IN A MAUSOLEUM in Moscow's Red Square lie the embalmed remains of Lenin. A crystal casket in that tomb has been viewed by millions of people. On the casket it says: "For he was the greatest leader of all people of all time. He was the lord of the new humanity; he was the savior of the world."

The tribute to Lenin is stated in past tense. What a startling contrast to the triumphant words of Christ. "I am the resurrection, and the life; he who believes in Me shall live even if he dies" (John 11:25).

The basis for our belief in Jesus Christ is in His resurrection. Karl Barth, the great Swiss theologian, said that without belief in the physical resurrection of Jesus Christ there is no salvation.

If Christ were entombed someplace in a grave near Jerusalem where the millions who visit Israel each year could walk by a grave and worship Him, then Christianity would be a fable. The Apostle Paul said, "If Christ has not been raised, then our preaching is in vain and your faith is in vain. . . . If Christ has not been raised, your faith is futile and you are still in your sins" (1 Cor. 15:14,17, RSV).

We usually hear a sermon about the resurrection every Easter, and that's about all. But when the early apostles preached, the cross and resurrection were their constant themes. Without the resurrection, the cross is meaningless.

Shall Man Live Again?

Some say we are nothing but bone, flesh, and blood. After we have died, nothing happens—we don't go anywhere. Or if we do go somewhere it is to a nebulous location, devised by the imagination to represent almost anything.

Does science help? I have questioned scientists concerning life after death and most of them say, "We just don't know." Science deals in formulas and test tubes; the spiritual world is beyond its reach.

Many who do not believe in life after death fill their writings with tragedy and pessimism. Gore Vidal, Truman Capote, Dalton Trumbo, and many others write with almost unrelieved pessimism. How different are the words of Jesus Christ, who said, "Because I live, you shall live also" (John 14:19). We must base our hope of immortality on Christ alone—not on any longings, arguments, or instinctive feelings of immortality.

The Bible speaks of the resurrection of Jesus as something which could be examined by the physical senses. The disciples saw Him under many different conditions after He had been raised. A single disciple saw Him on one occasion, five hundred on another. Some saw Jesus separately, some together; some for a moment, some for a long time.

The disciples heard Him in conversation. They were told to touch Him to verify His physical reality. They touched Him, walked with Him, conversed with Him, ate with Him, and examined Him. This took the resurrection appearances of Jesus out of the realm of hallucination and put them into the realm of demonstrable physical fact.

Historical fact provides the basis for our belief in the bodily resurrection of Christ. We have more evidence for it than for any other event of that time, secular or religious.

What about the Other Religions?

Most of the world religions are based upon philosophical thought, except for Judaism, Buddhism, Islam, and Christianity. These four are based upon personalities. Only Christianity claims resurrection for its founder.

Abraham, the father of Judaism, died about nineteen centuries before Christ. There are no evidences for his resurrection.

Buddha lived about five centuries before Christ, and taught principles of brotherly love. It is believed that he died at the age of eighty. There are no evidences for his resurrection.

Muhammad died A.D. 632, and his tomb at Medina is visited by thousands of devout Mohammedans. His birthplace at Mecca sees many pilgrims each year. However, there are no evidences for his resurrection.

Evidences of Christ's Resurrection

There is something called "the swoon theory" which says that Jesus didn't actually die, but only fainted. Since there could be no resurrection without a death, this thought denies His resurrection. Yet the evidence for His death is strong.

The soldiers were positive Jesus was dead, so they didn't need to induce death by shock through breaking His legs, which they did to the two thieves beside Him. It was not the friends of Jesus, but His enemies who vouched for His death. Also, they made certain when they thrust a spear into His heart.

One of the wealthiest men in the world, Howard Hughes, died recently. The events and circumstances surrounding his death are still shrouded in mystery, and yet he had an entourage of men who followed and guarded him for years.

In a city in the Middle East, however, there is more historical evidence for the death of one man, alone on a cross between two thieves, than any other in history. The great Bible student Wilbur Smith said, "Let it simply be said that we know more about the details of the hours immediately before, and the actual death of Jesus, in and near Jerusalem, than we know about the death of any other one man in all the ancient world."[1]

Jesus was buried. We know more about the burial of Jesus than we know of the burial of any character in ancient history. His body was taken from the cross and wrapped in fine linen with spices. Joseph of Arimathea, a rich man and a secret disciple of Jesus, mustered up his courage and asked Pilate for the body of Jesus. When his request was granted, we are told, he took Him down from the cross and wrapped Him in a linen sheet (Matt. 27:59).

We are told that Nicodemus (the same religious leader who had asked Jesus how to be born again) came and brought a very expensive mixture of myrrh and aloes to wrap in with the linens, as was the custom of Jewish burial.

The body of Jesus was placed in Joseph's own tomb, which was located in the garden. This burial procedure shows that it was the body of Jesus which was buried, not His spirit. Spirits are immaterial and cannot be buried.

After Jesus was buried, a huge stone was placed against the face of the tomb and a seal placed upon that. Anyone trying to move the stone from the entrance to the tomb would have had to break the Roman seal and face the consequences of the harsh Roman law.

To make sure that His disciples didn't steal His body, a Roman guard was then placed in front of the sealed stone. The enemies of Jesus didn't want to take any chances that the prophecy about his resurrection would take place.

What about the Roman guards? These men weren't cowards. Their discipline was so severe that the punishment for quitting their post, or even falling asleep on the job, was death.

Historians say there were probably four guards on watch at the tomb, all of them outfitted with strong weapons and shields. No chances were taken that this Jesus would be removed from the tomb.

The empty tomb. It was the third day, the day Jesus said he would arise. Around the tomb the earth began to shake, and along with it the armor of the Roman soldiers must have clattered wildly. And then an angel of the Lord came from heaven and easily rolled away the stone and sat on it. He didn't even have to say, "Hi, fellas!" The guards just looked at him and became like dead men. The angel spoke to Mary Magdalene and Mary, too, but the Bible says that they took action and ran to tell the disciples that He had risen.

When Peter and John came running to the tomb, John peeped in and saw the linen clothes Christ had been wrapped in lying there empty. Peter, who, true to his character, blundered right in, saw that Jesus' body was missing. He was gone.

The bodily resurrection was a fact attested to by hundreds of eyewitnesses. We have records of thirteen different appearances of

Jesus under widely different circumstances. His body was both similar and dissimilar to the one nailed to the cross. It was so similar to an ordinary human body that Mary mistook Him for the caretaker of the garden by the tomb when He appeared to her. He could eat, speak to people, and occupy space.

However, his body was not like a normal body. He could pass through closed doors or vanish in a moment. Christ's body was physical, and also spiritual. Why should this be surprising? Paul said to King Agrippa, "Why should it be thought a thing incredible with you, that God should raise the dead?" (Acts 26:8, KJV).

Over and over again the Bible affirms the fact of the bodily resurrection of Christ. Luke says it very directly in the book of Acts. He reports that Jesus "presented Himself alive, after His suffering, by many convincing proofs, appearing to them over a period of forty days" (Acts 1:3).

In speaking about those "convincing proofs," C. S. Lewis says, "The first fact in the history of Christendom is a number of people who say they have seen the Resurrection. If they had died without making anyone else believe this 'gospel' no gospels would ever have been written."[2]

The Resurrection Essential

There is a series of events that form links in a chain from eternity to eternity. These include the incarnation of Jesus, His crucifixion, resurrection, ascension, and return. Any missing link and the chain is destroyed.

All of Christianity as a system of truth collapses if the resurrection is rejected. As Paul said, "If Christ has not been raised, then our preaching is vain, your faith also is vain" (1 Cor. 15:14).

In addition to breaking the chain of redemptive events, if the resurrection were not essential, then the good news of salvation would be flat, lifeless, and negative. Resurrection is central to the gospel. Paul said: "Now I make known to you, brethren, the gospel which I preached to you, which also you received, in which also you stand, by which also you are saved, if you hold fast the word which I preached to you, unless you believed in vain. For I delivered to you as of first importance what I also received, that

Christ died for our sins according to the Scriptures, and that He was buried, and that He was raised on the third day according to the Scriptures" (1 Cor. 15:1–4).

In my book *World Aflame,* I told the story about Auguste Comte, the French philosopher, and Thomas Carlyle, the Scottish essayist. Comte said he was going to start a new religion that would supplant the religion of Christ. It was to have no mysteries and was to be as plain as the multiplication table; its name was to be positivism. "Very good, Mr. Comte," Carlyle replied, "very good. All you will need to do will be to speak as never a man spake, and live as never a man lived, and be crucified, and rise again the third day, and get the world to believe that you are still alive. Then your religion will have a chance to get on."

Today many "new religions" are springing up, like toadstools after a summer rain. I wonder how many could meet the criteria that Carlyle told his friend?

We have been emphasizing throughout this book the experience of being born again. A personal salvation experience is directly related to belief in the resurrection. Paul gave the formula for saving faith and showed that it centered in this belief: "If you confess with your mouth Jesus as Lord, and believe in your heart that God raised him from the dead, you shall be saved; for with the heart man believes, resulting in righteousness, and with the mouth he confesses, resulting in salvation" (Rom. 10:9,10).

It couldn't be clearer in the Scriptures. Yet there are churches where ministers say they believe in the resurrection, but that this means Jesus immediately rose from death into spiritual life with God. They say they believe in a "spiritual" but not a "physical" resurrection. This is what some modern preachers proclaim on Easter morning—though I am thankful they are diminishing in number.

No wonder there are many who sit in some churches week after week, year after year, without hearing the whole gospel and knowing what it is to be born again. They hear a gospel which is incomplete, and consequently not good news at all. The resurrection was not disembodied, it was physical. Eyewitnesses said, "We saw his glory"; "You will see him"; "He appeared"; "I have seen Jesus the Lord."

Within the short span of three days both events, the death and resurrection, took place bodily and not symbolically—tangibly, not spiritually—watched by men of flesh and blood, not fabricated by hallucination.

The resurrection was also the pledge and the promise of our own resurrection.

To understand this we need to see that, in the Bible, death affects both personality and body. (Remember the three dimensions of death?) The body, too, has to be retrieved from condemnation. Only by resurrecting the body could God make a complete conquest of death. He started with the body of Jesus, but He will also work in a similar manner with the bodies of all who believe. As the judgment of death was total, so salvation from its penalty is total, involving the physical, spiritual, and eternal.

Obviously our resurrection bodies will be recognizable, but they can't possibly be the exact bodies we have here. However, they must be like Christ's resurrected body. He had the nail prints and the wound in His side, and yet he could pass through closed doors. When it was time for Him to go to heaven He was able to ascend.

What a promise this is! "For if we believe that Jesus died and rose again, even so God will bring with Him those who have fallen asleep in Jesus (1 Thess. 4:14).

Jesus staked everything upon His rising from the dead. By His resurrection He would be judged true or false.

What Does the Resurrection Mean to Us Today?

Christ lives with every person who puts his trust in Him. The resurrection means the presence of the living Christ. He said, "Lo, I am with you always, even unto the end of the world" (Matt. 28:20, KJV). This is Christ's own guarantee: life has a new meaning. After the crucifixion, the disciples were in despair. They said, "We had hoped that he was the one to redeem Israel" (Luke 24:21, RSV). They were full of anguish because they thought of Christ's death as such a tragedy. Life had lost its meaning for them. But when he rose from the grave, they saw the living Christ, and life took on purpose once more.

We can also claim the prayers of the living Christ. The Bible says, "Christ Jesus is He who died, yes, rather who was raised, who is at the right hand of God, who also intercedes for us" (Rom. 8:34). We don't have to think that our prayers are bouncing off the ceiling. The living Christ is sitting at the right hand of God the Father. God the Son retains the same humanity He took to save us, and is now living in a body that still has nail prints in its hands. He is our great High Priest, interceding for us with God the Father.

The resurrection presence of Christ gives us power to live our lives day by day and to serve Him. "Truly, truly, I say to you, he who believes in Me, the works that I do shall he do also; and greater works than these shall he do; because I go to the Father" (John 14:12).

The resurrected body of Jesus is the design for our bodies when we are raised from the dead also. No matter what afflictions, pain, or distortions we have in our earthly bodies, we will be given new bodies. What a glorious promise of things to come! "For our citizenship is in heaven, from which also we eagerly wait for a Savior, the Lord Jesus Christ; who will transform the body of our humble state into conformity with the body of His glory, by the exertion of the power that He has even to subject all things to Himself" (Phil. 3:20,21).

Thousands of people today are excited about Bible prophecy. The revelation of what the Bible says about events past, present, and future, has become more prominent in the themes of books, sermons, and conferences. The Second Coming of Christ is becoming a closer and closer reality for those of us who study the Bible and the world scene.

The entire plan for the future has its key in the resurrection. Unless Christ was raised from the dead, there can be no kingdom and no returning King. When the disciples stood at the place Jesus left this earth, which is called the place of ascension, they were given assurance by angels that the Christ of resurrection would be the Christ of returning glory. "Men of Galilee, why do you stand looking into the sky? This Jesus, who has been taken up from you into heaven, will come in just the same way as you have watched Him go into heaven" (Acts 1:11).

The resurrection is an event which prepares us and confirms for us that future event when He will return again.

Yes, Jesus Christ is alive.

Obviously Christ's physical resurrection is an essential part of God's plan to save us. Have you given yourself to this living Christ?

A woman wrote us this: "Last evening I was alone and watching television. I had no *TV Guide*. Something urged me to turn the dial to the station where the gospel was being preached. I had been really wrestling with a great problem. I was and am facing death, and may or may not be helped through surgery. I had been putting off the operation because I was afraid I had been cut off from God.

"I began to really seek the Lord. The message I heard was God's way of speaking to me and answering my prayers. Now I feel entirely at peace in my soul."

If you trust the resurrected Christ as your Lord and Savior, He will be with you when you die, and will give you life with Him forever. Because of the resurrection, you can be "Born Again."

III

MAN'S RESPONSE

11

The New Birth Is for Now

THE COFFEE SEEMS bitter and the toast cold when the morning newspaper is finished. Another riot in Egypt. Africa torn apart by rival factions. The Middle East seemed quiet until another border incident set off new hostilities. Three coeds murdered on the campus of a prominent state university.

What can the average person do? He feels inadequate, powerless. All of the committees, the resolutions, the changes in governments don't seem to change society.

We see that if mankind is to be saved, something radical needs to be done quickly. The forces building up in our world are so overwhelming that men and women everywhere are beginning to cry out in desperation. They feel like the man John Bunyan describes in the beginning of *Pilgrim's Progress*. ". . . he was greatly distressed in his mind, he burst out, as he had done before, crying, 'What shall I do to be saved?'"

So much in our world seems to improve, but man doesn't. We can send a spaceship to the moon and take close-up pictures of Mars, but we can't walk safely on the streets at night. The subtle sins of selfishness and indifference are everywhere. Seemingly upright men and women admit to desires of the grossest sort. (And who is shocked any more?) Human viciousness breaks out as people steal, cheat, lie, murder, and rape.

Someone in the movie industry said that all we would have to do is contrast the titles of some of the old movie classics with current movie offerings to see the change in morality during the past generation. It's a long way from *Indian Love Call* to *Deep Throat.*

Man has made many attempts to change himself. We have tried without success to achieve moral goals by improvement in our environment and many are disillusioned with the results.

How can we change human nature?

From the Outside In

Studies in anthropology, psychology, and sociology to discover the laws of human behavior are an important part of educational research. Too often however, the researchers themselves ignore the fact of human sin and see a human being as proceeding from a combination of genes and chromosomes, and then shaped by his environment. At a meeting of the American Anthropological Association a new discipline was introduced to the academic community by a Harvard zoologist. He calls it "sociobiology," and it is described as "the study of the biological basis for social behavior in every species; its practitioners believe that some—and perhaps much—of human behavior is genetically determined."[1]

The sociobiologists imply that "a good deal more of mankind's morality may be genetically based."[2] They fail to give a proper place to the inborn twist toward selfishness, viciousness, and indifference to God, so many of their conclusions are only pseudo-scientific.

If we are shaped by our genes, and molded by our environment, then all we need to do is develop a way to alter genetic bases in humans or cure man's environment in terms of bad housing, slums, poverty, unemployment, and racial discrimination.

A best-selling author said this: "Many ministers today 'keep their cool' about questions of the sin and repentance of individuals and have turned their attack on the sin of society, in an attempt to make society squirm. This 'attack' varies from a mild sociology lecture to an angry assault against social injustice. However, slums and ghettos and put-downs are not going to disappear in society unless slums and games disappear from the hearts of people."[3]

But as Christians we need to do something about social injustice, slums and ghettos. We cannot sit back with the attitude that the problems are too overwhelming or insoluble. We need to get involved in helping to make this world a better place to live for the unfortunate whose standard of living is so low as to defy imagination, and for those who live under terrible political oppression. Ultimately, however, society is not going to be changed with coercion and force because when it is changed that way, man usually loses his freedom. It can be changed by a complete transformation of the human heart.

Man also attempts to change himself by *chemistry*. Scientists have developed methods to control behavior by drugs, which in some cases have been helpful. A great deal of research is being done that may benefit the mentally ill. The danger is that these same drugs in the hands of a world dictator could control an entire population of normal people. Stories from prisoners in oppressed countries verify how present-day mind manipulators misuse drugs to influence human actions.

One of them wrote: "I personally witnessed the treatment undergone by political prisoners in psychiatric hospitals when they tried to protest by refusing the food and the 'treatments' inflicted upon them. They were tied up, injected with paralyzing sulphur and force fed. . . . [They] have invented a powerful means to get rid of those who do not think as they do. Not only do they not hesitate to confine them in hospital-prisons, but they also compound their crime by injecting prisoners with chemical substances in order to destroy their personality and intellect."[4]

Changes in our body chemistry may benefit us or damage us permanently. The determining question is, "Who administers the drugs and for what purpose?"

Experiments are being made to try to give one person the intellectual capacities of another by what the mind-manipulators call "artificial reincarnation." In a study that came out of Russia, it was reported that one of the country's top physicists had experimented with "tuning one mind to another telepathically." The scientist explained, "'When this happens, the teacher can teach a student beyond the normal capacity of his mind by broadcasting over the defense mechanism into the normally empty 90 percent of the brain.'" He continues to explain that he "reincarnated a European mathematical genius in a college math student."[5]

Another human attempt to solve man's problems concerns *microbiology.* The increasing success with organ transplants may in time lead to a vast movement to change people by replacing certain organs connected with thinking, conscience, and emotions. However, the gospel of microbiology, administered by scientists who themselves are sinners, and who have access only to the substance of a fallen world, must likewise fail.

Many writers of science fiction consider their *interplanetary speculations* as the only source for solving man's problems. But the fundamental difficulty is that sin is too deeply ingrained in human nature to be rooted out by such influences. When God is ignored, the problem-solvers themselves participate in the problems. The superpowers are now frantically preparing for a "space" war. As a newspaper editorial says, "Whoever wins this race could control the world."

Many people today are trying to find a solution to man's problems by turning to *the occult world.* They seek knowledge and power from sources the Bible says we should wholeheartedly resist. The Apostle Paul says, "For our struggle is not against flesh and blood, but against the rulers, against the powers, against the world-forces of this darkness, against the spiritual forces of wickedness in the heavenly places" (Eph. 6:12). The occult world is a source only of terror and destruction.

The methods men use to change themselves from the outside in are truly varied, and sometimes amazing.

From the Inside Out

Jesus said that God can change men and women from the inside out. It was a challenge—a command. He didn't say, "It might be nice if you were born again," or, "If it looks good to you you might be born again." Jesus said, "You *must be* born again" (John 3:7).

It has always astounded me that He made this statement to a devout religious leader, Nicodemus, who must have been shocked by it. After all, Nicodemus was a good, moral, religious man. His neighbors probably said of him, "He's a wonderful man. You could trust him with your life. He's a great theologian." Nicodemus fasted two days a week; he spent two hours a day in prayer at the temple and tithed all his income. He was a professor of theology at the local seminary. If a pastor-seeking committee were looking for the best man they could get for their local church, they would seek a man like Nicodemus. But Jesus said all his piety and goodness weren't enough. He said, "You must be born again."

In spite of all of his education and professional standing, Nicodemus saw something very special in Jesus Christ—something he couldn't understand. He saw in Jesus a new quality of living. He was honestly seeking to find out what this dimension of life was.

When Jesus told him that unless one is born again he cannot see the kingdom of God, he was explaining to Nicodemus that he didn't have to improve his moral standards or increase his educational credits, he needed to receive a new quality of life—eternal life—that begins in this world and carries into the next world.

On returning home from a trip one day I found my desk, as usual, piled high with letters to be answered. In this particular pile there happened to be two from two separate mental hospitals in different states. A glance at the handwriting and a reading of the letters made it clear that the writers needed to be in a mental institution. Yet each spoke of the Lord Jesus and the comfort He was.

I could not help thinking how kind and understanding and compassionate God has been in choosing to reveal Himself to man through simple childlike faith rather than the intellect. There would otherwise be no chance for little children or the mentally retarded or brain damaged. And yet the brilliant scientist, the true intellectual, the genius, must all come the same way. As Jesus said in Matthew 18:3, "Unless you are converted and become like children, you shall not enter the kingdom of heaven."

John Hunter, the English Bible scholar, tells the story about a young man who came up to him after he had been preaching on John 3. "He, like Nicodemus, was obviously very well educated, and he said: 'What you have been saying has really challenged me; in fact, if I could fully understand what you have told us, I would become a real Christian.' He was quite sincere in what he said, so

I questioned him and talked further with him. He was a graduate of a university, trained to think and evaluate facts.

"I asked, 'If you could really understand the full meaning of the gospel, you would become a Christian?'

"'Yes,' he replied, 'I would.'

"'Well, consider this,' I went on. 'I have a friend who is a missionary in the Congo. He works among the Pygmies, people with little capacity for understanding. If, in order to become a Christian, we had to understand the gospel message, how could these simple people ever be blessed?'

"His reply was quite honest: 'You know, I never thought of that!'

"'No,' I replied, 'but God did. The gospel message doesn't have to be understood by the seeking soul, only to be received in simple faith. It isn't fully understanding the gospel that gives me the blessing, but simply believing and receiving it.'

"Nicodemus began by 'knowing,' but he continued by believing and receiving."[6]

There are many people sitting in churches today who have never heard this message of the new birth. Some churches preach good works, social change, government legislation, and neglect the one thing that will help solve the problems of our world—changed men and women. Man's basic problem is first spiritual, then social. He needs a complete change from inside out.

Some time ago I attended a historic conference in Africa. Every country except one from the whole continent of Africa was represented by delegates. Never before had there been such a Christian gathering. Time after time I heard African leaders express appreciation for what Christian missions had done, especially in the fields of evangelism, medical aid, and education. One of the speakers said, "85 percent of all education south of the Sahara has been done by Christian missions."

An Anglican bishop from England told us, "Every social agency in England from the Society for the Prevention of Cruelty to Animals, on up, was founded as a result of a conversion to Christ and a spiritual awakening." We must be careful not to put the cart before the horse.

The Bible refers many times to this change Jesus talked about. Through the prophet Ezekiel, God said, "I will give you a new heart and put a new spirit within you" (Ezek. 36:26). In the book of Acts, Peter called it repenting and being converted. Paul speaks of it in Romans as being "alive from the dead" (Rom. 6:13). In Colossians Paul calls it "(a putting off of) the old self with its evil practices, and (a putting on of) the new self who is being renewed to a true knowledge according to the image of the One who created him" (Col. 3: 9, 10). In Titus he calls it "the washing of regeneration and renewing by the Holy Spirit" (Tit. 3:5). Peter said it was being "partakers of the divine nature" (2 Pet. 1:4). In the Church of England catechism it is called "a death unto sin and a new birth unto righteousness."

The context of John 3 teaches that the new birth is something that God does for man when man is willing to yield to God. We have seen that the Bible teaches that man is dead in trespasses and sins, and his great need is life. We do not have within ourselves the seed of the new life, this must come from God Himself.

One of the great Christian writers of this century, Oswald Chambers, said, "Our part as workers for God is to open men's eyes that they may turn themselves from darkness to light; but that is not salvation, that is conversion—the effort of a roused human being. I do not think it is too sweeping to say that the majority of nominal Christians are of this order; their eyes are opened, but they have received nothing. . . . When a man is born again, he knows that it is because he has received something as a gift from Almighty God and not because of his own decision."[7]

Conversion means "turning." The Bible is full of this concept and God pleads with man to turn to Him. He spoke through the prophet Ezekiel, "Repent . . . and *turn* your faces away from all your abominations" (Ezek. 14:6, emphasis mine). Another prophet, Isaiah, spoke, "*Turn* to Me, and be saved, all the ends of the earth; For I am God, and there is no other" (Isa. 45:22, emphasis mine).

The new birth is not just being reformed, it's being transformed. People are always making resolutions to do better, to change, and breaking those resolutions soon afterwards. But the Bible teaches us that through the new birth we can enter a new world.

The contrasts used in the Bible to express the change which comes over us when we are born again are very graphic; from lust to holiness; from darkness to light; from death to resurrection; from stranger to the kingdom of God to now being its citizen. The Bible teaches that the person who is born again has a changed will, changed affections, changed objectives for living, changed disposition, new purpose. He receives a new nature and a new heart. He becomes a new creation.

Before and After

The Bible is full of people from all walks of life who have been changed by an encounter with Jesus Christ. Christ met a woman in Samaria who was a prostitute and an outcast in her own town. To avoid meeting other women she went to a well during the heat of the day when she knew she wouldn't encounter other villagers. But there she met Christ. She was changed immediately into a new person. In fact, she became an instant missionary and rushed to her own city, where she was despised and scorned, to tell others about Jesus Christ. And we are told, "Many of the Samaritans believed in Him because of the word of the woman who testified, 'He told me all the things that I have done!'" (John 4:39).

Andrew was an ordinary fellow. He didn't seem to be the big personality man, but he was very quick to respond to Christ; in fact, he was on fire from the moment he met Jesus. The first thing he did was to go and find his brother to tell him the wonderful news about the Messiah. He may not have been a flaming evangelist, but wherever he appears in the biblical account, he is fruitful.

In these days of high taxes, the yearly or quarterly tax reports are not exactly greeted with enthusiasm. It wasn't any different in Jesus' time. Zacchaeus, a tax collector, and not a very honest one at that, was skillful in defrauding people, but when he met Jesus all that changed. He repented and wanted to make amends for his deceitful acts. "Behold, Lord, half of my possessions I will give to the poor, and if I have defrauded anyone of anything, I will give back four times as much" (Luke 19:8).

A young intellectual named Saul was on a journey along the road to Damascus, persecuting Christians, when he met Jesus Christ. To this day we speak about "Damascus Road experiences," because

Saul was never the same again. He became the great Apostle Paul. Many times he referred to that encounter, even recalling the very day and moment when he met Christ.

On the day of Pentecost a dramatic change occurred in three thousand people who were born again. In the morning they were lost, uncertain about the purpose of life, many of them guilty over the death of Christ. Others were afraid of either the secular or religious authorities. But at the end of the day they had been born into the kingdom of God. Each one had passed out of death into life. "'Truly, truly, I say to you, he who hears My word, and believes Him who sent Me, has eternal life, and does not come into judgment, but has passed out of death into life'" (John 5:24).

Any person who is willing to trust Jesus Christ as his personal Savior and Lord can receive the new birth now. It's not something to be received at death or after death; it is for now. "Now is the accepted time; behold, now is the day of salvation" (2 Cor 6:2, KJV).

The New Birth Is for Now

The "before and after" advertisements for diet remedies or face-lifts cannot match the impact of the testimonies of those who have been born again. From corporate president to prison inmate, stories unfold of lives turned right side up.

A young woman wrote us: "Until last January I was a stranger to Jesus. I was a rebel, thief, a drunkard, a hard drug taker, an adulteress, a hippie, and a self-centered, confused young woman. Thinking I was going to stump everyone with my cynical questions, I went to a Bible study about a year ago out of curiosity. That night I became sincerely interested in the Bible. Finally after searching and studying the Scriptures for months, John 3:16 spoke to my heart and I gave my life to Christ. I never knew that this kind of happiness could exist. God shows you how to love and what it feels like to be loved. He was what I had been looking for since my early teens. He was 'the bag' I hadn't found. It seemed to me that drugs, liquor, free love, and bumming around the country would make me free, but they were all traps. Sin was the trap that led me to confusion, unhappiness, guilt, and near-suicide.

Christ has made me free. Being a Christian is exciting because there is always a new challenge, so much to learn. Now I wake up glad to see the day.

"He has made me new."

Johnny Cash says, "A few years ago I was hooked on drugs. I dreaded to wake up in the morning. There was no joy, peace, or happiness in my life. Then one day in my helplessness I turned my life completely over to God. Now I can't wait to get up in the morning to study my Bible. Sometimes the words out of the Scriptures leap into my heart. This does not mean that all my problems have been solved, or that I have reached any state of perfection. However, my life has been turned around. I have been born again!"

12

The New Birth Is Not Just a "Feeling"

A MAN WHO was persuaded to go to a large evangelistic meeting recalled the following events:

"It was here, I believe for the first time in my life, that I heard the claims of Jesus Christ presented, simply and authoritatively.

"At the end of his talk the speaker invited those who wished to know more to come to the front of the auditorium. I went and was introduced to the speaker and we talked for a while. There were other people who wanted to ask questions, so I made my way to the exit, very interested in what he had said, but still in a deep fog.

"Just as I was about to go out the door I was confronted by a man who looked me in the eye and said:

"'Are you a Christian?'

"'Strange question,' I thought, putting on my best Sunday school smile and saying, 'Oh yes, I think so.'

"'Are you a Christian?' he insisted, a light in his eye.

"'Crank,' I thought, 'Humor him and then escape!'

"So I replied, 'Well, I'm trying to be.'

"'Ever try to be an elephant?'

"Grinning at my dumb astonishment, he took me by the arm, sat me down in a chair and explained that no amount of trying could ever transform me into a Christian (any more than it could turn me into an elephant). Then he began to explain what New Testament Christianity was all about. That Jesus Christ had died in *my* place. That HE had paid the full penalty which *my* sins demanded. As I was, I stood condemned before a holy God; I needed a Savior. Jesus alone could save me. Forgiveness for the past was possible in Him. Moreover, in His resurrection, He was offering me power to live the sort of life I had hitherto considered hopelessly out of reach.

"What a stupendous offer! If the living God were really asking to come into my wretched, tarnished life, to take over what I was only wasting and spoiling—how dare I refuse Him! He was promising, 'Behold I stand at the door and knock.'

"I flung open the door. He was as good as His word."

This man was born again. He had a turnabout. He thought he was a Christian, but he had never personally made a commitment to Jesus Christ.

Jesus made everything so simple and we have made it so complicated. He spoke to the people in short sentences and everyday words, illustrating his messages with parables and stories.

Paul told the Philippian jailer who asked what he must do to be saved, "Believe in the Lord Jesus, and you shall be saved" (Acts 16:31).

It's so simple that it's often overlooked. Although the gospel message is heard—especially in America—on radio stations, presented on television, sung on streetcorners, presented from pulpits, and explained in books, and tracts, millions overlook it. All you have to do to be born again is to repent of your sins and believe in the Lord Jesus as your personal Lord and Savior. You don't clean up, give up, or turn around yourself, you just come as you are. This is why we sing the hymn, "Just As I Am" at our Crusades.

Key Word: Repentance

In the New Testament Peter says, "Repent, therefore, and be *converted*, that your sins may be blotted out, [so that] the times of refreshing shall come from the presence of the Lord" (Acts 3:19, KJV, emphasis mine).

A person cannot turn to God to repent, or even to believe, without God's help. God must do the turning. Many times the Bible tells how men and women did that very thing, "Turn thou me, and I shall be turned; for thou art the Lord my God" (Jer. 31:18, KJV).

To many the word "repentance" is old-fashioned. It doesn't seem to have a proper place in a twentieth-century vocabulary. But repentance is one of the two vital elements in conversion and simply means recognition of what we are, and a willingness to change our minds toward sin, self, and God.

Repentance involves first of all an acknowledgment of our sin. When we repent we are saying that we recognize that we are sinners and that our sin involves us in personal guilt before God. This type of guilt does not mean incriminating self-contempt; it means seeing ourselves as God sees us, and saying, "God be merciful to me a sinner" (Luke 18:13, KJV). It is not just the corporate guilt of society we are acknowledging—it's so easy to blame the government, the school system, the church, the home, for our own personal guilt. The Bible teaches that when we reach the age of accountability—usually somewhere around ten or eleven years of age—God looks upon us as fullgrown adults, making moral and spiritual choices for which we will be held accountable at the judgment. Each of us has an individual guilt before God. From the moment we are conceived we have the tendency toward sin; then we become sinners by choice and, ultimately, sinners by practice. That is why the Bible says we have all sinned and come short of the glory of God.

Every person throughout the world, of whatever race, color, language, or culture, needs to be born again. We are guilty of "sin" (singular) which is expressed in "sins" (plural). We break God's laws and rebel against Him because we are sinners by nature. It is this disease of sin (singular) that Christ dealt with on the cross.

We have heard so much about "roots." The roots of man's individual and corporate problems lie deep in his own heart. We are a diseased human race. This disease can only be dealt with by the blood of Christ, just as in the Old Testament blood was shed on hundreds of altars, looking forward to the day when Jesus Christ would come and be "the Lamb of God who takes away the sin of the world" (John 1:29). He became the cosmic scapegoat for the entire world. All of our sins were laid on Him. This is why God can now forgive us. This is why He can infuse new life into us—which is called regeneration, or the new birth.

When we look at the attributes of God and realize how far short we fall of His perfection, there is no alternative to the recognition of our sinful nature. The Apostle Peter had been involved in sinful acts and harbored sinful thoughts, but far deeper than the physical or mental admission of wrongdoing, Peter realized that he had a twisted nature. He said, "Depart from me, for I am a sinful man, O Lord!" (Luke 5:8). Notice that he didn't say, "I sin," but "I am a sinful man."

Job saw how corrupt he was in relation to God's perfection, and said, "I have heard of thee by the hearing of the ear; but now mine eye seeth thee: Wherefore I abhor myself, and repent in dust and ashes" (Job 42:5,6, KJV). Job compared himself with God and repented; he recognized what he was before God.

Repentance also involves a genuine *sorrow* for sin. Sorrow is an emotion, and we are creatures who vary greatly in the degree of sorrow we may experience. Repentance without sorrow is hollow, however. The Apostle Paul said, "I now rejoice, not that you were made sorrowful, but that you were made sorrowful to the point of repentance; for you were made sorrowful according to the will of God, in order that you might not suffer loss in anything through us" (2 Cor. 7:9).

With repentance comes a change of purpose, a willing turnaround from sin. If we had to repent without God's help, then we would be almost helpless. The Scripture teaches that we are dead in trespasses and in sins. A dead man can do nothing; therefore we need God's help even in our repenting. Sometimes this involves "restitution." If we have stolen, lied, or cheated to the hurt of other people, we must go and make this right if at all possible.

I've had hundreds of letters from people who have told me that they have had money returned to them that had been stolen by people who claimed to be "born again." Many people, before their conversion, have been shoplifters. Many have felt that they must go back to the store, discuss their wrongdoing with the manager, and make restitution.

When my wife was counseling with Joe Medina after he was tempted and helped a friend rob a filling station, she told him that his repentance would never be real unless he confessed his crime. He did. He earned the money that summer and returned it in full. The filling station owner forgave him. Today that young man has finished four years at a Bible college and is now a minister.

When Jim Vaus, the underworld figure, came to Christ in 1949, he spent many weeks looking up people whom he had offended, injured, and stolen from. He returned everything he possibly could and apologized to all those whom he had offended.

This type of restitution is rare today, but it is most certainly taught in the Scriptures. It helps complete our repentance. It shows to those whom we have offended, and to the world, that we mean business with God.

When emotions are contrary to our willingness to turn from sin, hypocrisy enters the life of a believer, and doubts begin to grow. There are so many things in the Bible that seem so difficult to believe. When we become a new creature in Christ, we are propelled into an exhilarating, joyful, exciting experience which carries us emotionally for a time. Then doubts may enter our lives, quietly at first, but then more boldly as the questions begin to crowd out the trust. "How can I be willing to turn over my life to God when He might make me do something I don't want to do?"

When a wealthy, beautiful woman who was a leader in her community was converted, one of the first persons she told, a friend of many years, said, "Well, Dorothy, what are you going to do now—go to Africa as a missionary?"

Dorothy struggled with her emotions, but answered with her surrendered will, "If that's where God wants me, I'll go."

But it's not that easy for most to be willing to turn over the action and direction to God.

A wonderful old woman who wrote one of the classics in Christian books told a story about a young man of great intelligence who was having tremendous difficulties in his new Christian experience with this matter of will. He was a great doubter, and emotionally nothing seemed real to him. He was given this piece of advice: "'A man's will is really the man's self; . . . what his will does, he does. Your part then is simply to put your will . . . over on God's side, making up your mind that you will believe what He says [in the Bible], because He says it, and that you will not pay any regard to the feelings that make it seem so unreal. God will not fail to respond, sooner or later, with His revelation to such a faith.'

"The young man paused a moment, and then said solemnly, 'I understand, and will do what you say. I cannot control my emotions, but I can control my will; and the new life begins to look possible to me, if it is only my will that needs to be set straight in the matter. I can give my will to God, and I do.'"[1]

Biblical repentance is the fuel which is used to propel our life with God at the controls. Until we utilize that fuel, we are earth-bound, tied down by our ego, our pride, our troubles and guilt. Young people are often chained in a prison of purposelessness, uncertainty, and even guilt. Many an older person faces old age and death with dread and fear. True repentance can release those chains.

Thus, repentance is *first*, and absolutely necessary, if we are to be born again. It involves simple recognition of what we are before God—sinners who fall short of His glory; *second*, it involves genuine sorrow for sin; *third*, it means our willingness to turn from sin.

Key Word: Faith

In considering conversion we have seen that it has a "turning-from" side called repentance. It also has a "turning-to" side, called faith.

Faith is first of all belief—belief that Christ was who He said He was. Second, faith is belief that He can do what He claimed He could do—He can forgive me, and come into my life. Third, faith is trust, an act of commitment, in which I open the door of my heart to Him. In the New Testament the words "faith," "belief," and "believe," are translations of similar Greek words so they are interchangeable.

Placing your faith in Christ means that first you must make a choice. The Scripture says, "Whoever believes in him [Jesus] is not condemned, but whoever does not believe stands condemned already because he has not believed in the name of God's one and only Son" (John 3:18, NIV). The person who believes is not condemned; the person who has not believed is condemned. In order not to be condemned you must make a choice—you must choose to believe.

So we can see how important belief is. The Bible says that without faith it is impossible to please God. But what does it mean to believe? It means to "commit" yourself to Christ, to "surrender" to Him. Believing is your response to God's offer of mercy, love, and forgiveness. God took the initiative and did everything that was needed to make the offer of salvation possible. When Christ bowed His head on the cross and said, "It is finished," He meant just that (John 19:30). God's plan for our reconciliation and redemption was complete in His Son. But only by believing in Jesus— committing yourself to Him, surrendering to Him—are you saved.

Belief is not just a feeling; it is the assurance of salvation. You may look at yourself in the mirror and say, "But I don't feel saved— I don't feel forgiven." But don't depend on feelings for your assurance. Christ has promised, and He cannot lie. Belief is a deliberate act of committing one's self to the person of Jesus Christ. It's not a "hanging on" to some vague idea. It is an act of trust in the God-Man, Jesus Christ.

The New Testament never used the words "belief" and "faith" in the plural. Christian faith does not mean accepting a long list of dos and don'ts. It means a single, individual relinquishment of mind and heart toward the one person, Jesus Christ. It does not mean believing everything or just anything. It is belief in a person, and that person is the Christ described in Scripture.

Faith is not anti-intellectual. Faith involves a very logical premise— that is, trusting that God's superior ability is able to save us.

Francis Schaeffer, a brilliant Christian living in Switzerland, explains that faith is not only logical, but that lack of faith is illogical. He writes: "Man is made in the image of God; therefore, on the side of the fact that God is a personal God the chasm stands not between God and man, but between man and all else. But on the side of God's infinity, man is as separated from God as the atom or any other finite [object] of the universe. So we have the answer to man's being finite and yet personal.

"It is not that this is the best answer to existence; it is the *only* answer. That is why we may hold our Christianity with intellectual integrity. The only answer for what exists is that he, the infinite-personal God, really is there."[2]

Faith in Christ is also voluntary. A person cannot be coerced, bribed, or tricked into trusting Jesus. God will not force His way into your life. The Holy Spirit will do everything possible to disturb you, draw you, love you—but finally it is your personal decision. God not only gave His Son on the cross where the plan of redemption was finished: He gave the law as expressed in the Ten Commandments and the Sermon on the Mount to show you your need of forgiveness; He gave the Holy Spirit to convict you of your need. He gives the Holy Spirit to draw you to the cross, but even after all of this, it is your decision whether to accept God's free pardon or to continue in your lost condition.

Faith also involves the whole person. In his book *Knowing God*, J. I. Packer says, "Knowing God is a matter of *personal involvement, in mind, will, and feeling*. It would not, indeed, be a fully personal relationship otherwise."[3]

So faith is not just an emotional reaction, an intellectual realization, or a willful decision; faith is all-inclusive. It involves the intellect, the emotion, and the will.

Steps Leading to Conversion

We have seen that conversion occurs when we repent and place our faith in Christ. But what is the process like as we approach the point of conversion? How long will it take? Will it be emotional or dramatic? My answer is, I don't know. If everyone had the same reaction we could apply a neat little chemical formula with predetermined results. The key word is *variety*.

We can see this clearly if we stop for a moment to reflect on God. First, the point we are heading for is a point where God Himself is going to do something; He is the one who converts us when we repent and believe in Christ. "Salvation is of the Lord." Second, His help starts coming long before that point. As we have already seen, during the time before conversion He is preparing us for repentance by the conviction of the Holy Spirit and by making us want to turn from our sins. Also He is preparing us for faith by showing us how forgiving and majestic Christ is.

Questions about length of time and amount of emotion in the conversion process, consequently, are very personal. God looks at each of us differently, because each of us is different. He will relate to you just as you are. He will relate to me just as I am. Of course, in His concern His goal for each of us will be the same—our new birth. But to help us to that point He will be just as personal as a shepherd who knows each of his sheep by name.

We could go to the experiences of people we know, or to your own experience. If you have not been born again, the very fact that you are reading this book right now may be the process God is using in your life to lead you toward a decision.

God knows the needs of your heart. When we look at the process He used with different people in the Bible prior to their conversion, we see that He understands their individuality. In John 1, for instance, He talked to several men who had not yet been converted. On being approached by Andrew and a friend, Jesus asked a question, "What do you seek?" (John 1:38) and then invited them to spend the day with Him where He was staying. Quiet conversation was Andrew's need if he was to gain a sense of his sin and a trust in Jesus.

Andrew brought along his erratic brother, Simon. Christ acted very differently toward him. Regarding him seriously, Jesus said, "You are Simon the son of John; you shall be called 'Cephas' (which translated means Peter)," the word for rock. Jesus revealed a flash of His majesty by telling this volatile young man that in trusting Him his character would be changed to a rocklike steadiness (John 1:42). To be converted Peter needed to see his sin of relying on himself, which made him such a changeable personality, and he needed to trust Christ as the one who had the power and concern to change him.

The next day Jesus found Philip and treated him in still another way. He simply said, "Follow Me" (John 1:43). Unlike Andrew or Peter, Philip needed a straightforward command. Philip then brought Nathanael, a very religious man of prayer who was seeking an experience with God. Jesus adapted to his special needs in John 1:51, saying, "Truly, truly, I say to you, you shall see the heavens open, and the angels of God ascending and descending upon the Son of Man.

Andrew, Peter, Philip, and Nathanael were all different. So Jesus treated them all differently. They all needed a personal relationship with Christ. This is essentially what the new birth is. To some of them the realization of what was happening came slowly. It took months of training by Jesus Himself. This is why I urge new converts to take plenty of time in Bible study and prayer before getting on a public platform to testify. The Scripture warns against "a novice." We have often unwittingly been guilty of this in our Crusades—putting up to give a testimony young converts who had really not grown in the grace and knowledge of Christ enough. Through long years of experience we have become far more careful.

After the conversion of the Apostle Paul he took three years of study in Arabia. It took God forty years to train Moses on the back side of a desert before he made his public appearance. In these days we often hear of a person who is in jail one day, and a few weeks later is on a public platform testifying concerning his conversion before a large crowd. Sometimes this is followed by a great tragedy—the so-called new convert had really not been born again; he had only professed Christ but had not been willing to pay the price of following Christ.

I know a young man who seemed to be gloriously converted in one of our Crusades, and I believe he was. He did have a rather long period of getting over his drug habit and growing in the knowledge of the Scriptures. We urged him to attend a Bible school, which he did for a year. His testimony was so thrilling that the invitations began to pour in from across America for him to give his witness. It wasn't long before this attention had caused him to backslide terribly, to the point of even leaving his wife and family. I am glad to report that he has been restored to fellowship with God, realizes his sins and mistakes, and is now going back to finish his studies.

What can we expect the process to be like as we approach the new birth? It will be tailored to our own environment, temperament, secret needs, and hopes. That is the way God works.

How Long Are the Steps?

The length of time and degree of emotion involved in the process which leads to our conversion is also varied. Some, but not all, will face an emotional crisis with symptoms similar to those accompanying mental conflict. They may experience deep feelings and even tears of repentance. The Holy Spirit is convicting them of sin. This is their way of responding to Him. Each of us may have a different emotional experience. The night I came to Christ there were several people around me weeping. I had no tears at all and wondered if my act of commitment was genuine.

I have learned since that many have had a much quieter conversion, with a shorter time in the process. Perhaps one person, reading the Scripture or singing a hymn, comes upon a simple statement and applies it to himself then and there. Another person hears a sermon and with no stress or conflict receives its message and believes in Christ. Conversion is no less real to these quiet people than to the more expressive or dramatic ones.

Acts 16 records two conversions which were striking contrasts. Lydia was a businesswoman in the city of Philippi. She had shown enough interest in God to be spending time and prayer by the side of a river, where she heard Paul preach. The Lord opened her heart to respond to the gospel message, and she was converted without fanfare or a strong emotional display.

Then there was the jailer in the city of Philippi where Paul was imprisoned. An earthquake came and the jailer panicked as he realized his prisoners could escape. He thought the only way out of his crisis was to kill himself. Just as he was drawing his sword he heard the Apostle Paul say, "Do yourself no harm, for we are all here!" (Acts 16:28).

The jailer couldn't believe what he heard! Why hadn't the prisoners escaped? He was shaking from head to foot, and called for a light. He took one look at Paul and Silas, his prisoners, and fell down at their feet, crying, "What must I do to be saved?" Paul told him to believe in the Lord Jesus Christ and he would be saved, and he was converted right there, in the rubble of the prison.

Jesus described the conversion experience like the movement of the wind. "The wind blows where it wishes and you hear the sound of it, but do not know where it comes from and where it is going; so is every one who is born of the Spirit" (John 3:8).

Wind can be quiet, gentle, or it can reach cyclone proportions. So it is with conversion, sometimes easy and tender, and other times a tornado which alters the entire landscape.

Is there one definite point in time, one hour of one day of one year when a person can say, "That was when I was born again"? I know many people who can point to that time and say with assurance, "That was my spiritual birthday." However, I know there are people who today are walking in fellowship with Jesus Christ, but have no memory of an exact time when they deliberately committed themselves to Him, and cannot remember when they did not love and trust Him. My wife is one of those great Christians in this category. However, it is my opinion that they may be the exception rather than the rule. Scripture teaches that belief is an act of the will, so whether they can remember the time or not, there was a moment when they crossed over the line from death to life.

Nevertheless, the issue for a person now is not so much "when" as "whether." When we were saved is not so important as whether we are now saved. We often cannot tell the exact moment when night becomes day, but we know when it is daylight. So the great question for a person to answer who has never by a conscious act of will committed himself to Christ as his Lord and Savior is this: "Are you now living in the day, in touch with Christ?"

How to Receive Christ

Just after I received Christ someone gave me a little tract entitled "Four Things God Wants You To Know," by an English writer. I often used those four points in my earlier preaching, and they were excellent. Years later, Bill Bright of Campus Crusade developed "The Four Spiritual Laws" which have been widely used throughout the world in helping people to understand how to be born again. Our own organization developed what we called "Four Steps to Peace with God," taken largely from one of my earlier books, *Peace With God.* I do not believe however, that there is a tidy little formula, or a recipe which has the Good Housekeeping seal of approval. However, I do believe these have provided little handles which help people to understand how to receive Christ.

Here are some guidelines from the Bible which will help you accept Christ as your Lord and Savior. You have seen the need, the direction, and the steps in previous chapters, and you may already have reached your own conclusions. Just the same, let me summarize what you must do.

First, you must recognize what God did: that He loved you so much He gave His Son to die on the cross. Substitute your own name for "the world" and "whoever" in this familiar verse: "For God so loved the world, that He gave His only begotten Son, that whoever believes in Him should not perish, but have eternal life" (John 3:16). "The Son of God . . . loved me, and delivered Himself up for me" (Galatians 2:20).

Second, you must repent for your sins. Jesus said, "Unless you repent, you will . . . perish" (Luke 13:3). He said, "Repent and believe" (Mark 1:15). It's not enough to be sorry; repentance is that turnabout from sin that is emphasized.

Third, you must receive Jesus Christ as Savior and Lord. "But as many as received Him, to them He gave the right to become children of God, even to those that believe in His name" (John 1:12). This means that you cease trying to save yourself and accept Christ as your only Lord and your only Savior. Trust Him completely, without reservation.

Fourth, you must confess Christ publicly. This confession is a sign that you have been converted. Jesus said, "Every one therefore who shall confess Me before men, I will also confess him before My Father who is in heaven" (Matt. 10:32). It is extremely important that when you receive Christ you tell someone else about it just as soon as possible. This gives you strength and courage to witness.

Make it happen *now*. "Now is the accepted time . . . now is the day of salvation" (2 Cor. 6:2, KJV). If you are willing to repent for your sins and to receive Jesus Christ as your Lord and Savior, you can do it now. At this moment you can either bow your head or get on your knees and say this little prayer which I have used with thousands of persons on every continent:

O God, I acknowledge that I have sinned against You. I am sorry for my sins. I am willing to turn from my sins. I openly receive and acknowledge Jesus Christ as my Savior. I confess Him as Lord. From this moment on I want to live for Him and serve Him. In Jesus' name. Amen.

These are the steps and the prayer which many years ago, in a book I wrote, were read by people just like yourselves who responded and wrote of their changed lives.

If you are willing to make this decision and have received Jesus Christ as your own Lord and Savior, then you have become a child of God in whom Jesus Christ dwells. You do not need to measure the certainty of your salvation by your feelings. Believe God. He keeps His word. You are born again. You are alive!

(If you would like more help and literature, please feel free to write me:

Billy Graham
Minneapolis, Minnesota

—that's all the address you need.)

13

Alive and Growing

"AFTER THINKING ABOUT it for three days, I realized I needed Jesus Christ, and I accepted Him. Now that my life has been turned over to Jesus Christ, I can function with an extra power bestowed by God."

Who made a statement like that? Someone down on the bottom of life's heap, struggling for worth and identity? No. A handsome, young University of Southern California athlete, John Naber, who gained international attention by earning four gold medals with his swimming achievements in the 1976 Olympics. John Naber said he was searching for something meaningful in his life and after attending one of our meetings he began to wake up to the realization of Jesus Christ. He was born again.

More and more celebrities, especially in the sports, entertainment, and political worlds, are telling of their new experiences of being made alive in Christ. While it is thrilling to hear about it, there are also dangers (as I have already expressed) in a "novice" who has very little grounding in the Word of God. Yet I cannot help rejoicing in every one of them and believe that God has been moving mightily in reaching out for people of extraordinary gifts and talents all over the world. Many of them He is greatly using to win others to Christ. A newspaper feature said that "evidence of a current religious revival is everywhere," and then related how famous personalities were "pinpointing the exact moment of spiritual turn-around" with their "often unbelievable accounts of being born again. Some say they have met Jesus Christ. Others experience a sensation similar to an electric shock. In all cases the new believers experience overwhelming feelings of love and joy."

Dean Jones, a Walt Disney film veteran, relates, "I was performing in summer stock at a New Jersey lodge and had gone to my room to be alone. Nothing was satisfying me. I looked out that window and felt fear and confusion. Impulsively, I knelt by the bed and spelled out my doubts to God; I don't know why I was moved to do this. I said to God, 'If you bring meaning to my life, I'll serve you.'"

There is nothing more exciting than a personal testimony from a person who has experienced a spiritual rebirth. This is more than an interesting story or fascinating experience. A new born man or woman has been given so many riches by God. We will outline them and then discuss how to draw from that wealthy potential.

Forgiven!

"Your sins are forgiven you for His name's sake" (1 John 2:12). What a stupendous promise! Throughout the New Testament we learn that the one who receives Christ as Lord and Savior also receives, immediately, the gift of forgiveness. The Bible says, "As far as the east is from the west, so far has He removed our transgressions from us" (Ps. 103:12).

"Forgive me." "I'm sorry." "I didn't mean it." How often we use those words and they echo back with a hollow sound. But God's forgiveness is not just a casual statement; it is the complete blotting out of all the dirt and degradation of our past, present, and future. The only reason our sins can be forgiven is because Jesus Christ paid their full penalty on the cross.

Guilt feelings provide the basis for many dramatic plots. Shakespeare's line from *Macbeth* is famous: "Out, damned spot! Out!" Guilt feelings are the focal point of much psychiatric counseling. Many feel like Judas, who, after he betrayed Christ, said, "I have betrayed innocent blood." So tremendous is the weight of our guilt that the great and glorious concept of forgiveness should be shouted by every believer in Jesus Christ.

God's goodness in forgiving us goes even farther when we realize that when we are converted we are also declared just—which means that in God's sight we are without guilt, clothed forever with Christ's righteousness.

As we saw in "The King's Courtroom," forgiveness and justification are God's free gifts.

Adopted by the King

When you were converted, God adopted you as His son or daughter. As an adopted child each of us can claim to be joint heir with Jesus Christ. "God sent forth His Son . . . that He might redeem those who were under the Law, that we might receive the adoption as sons" (Gal. 4:4,5).

I know a lawyer and his wife who have two adopted children, a boy and a girl. The little girl looks very much like her mother, and the young man could easily be the natural son of his father. The fact that they were chosen by their parents has given them a great sense of security and love.

To be the son or daughter of the Lord of the universe is a powerful realization.

The Indwelling Holy Spirit

When you were converted, the Spirit of God immediately came to live in you. Before He ascended into heaven, Jesus Christ said, "I will ask the Father, and He will give you another Helper, that He may be with you forever; that is the Spirit of truth . . . you know Him, because He abides with you, and will be in you" (John 14:16,17).

When Christ lived on this earth, He could be with only a small group of people at any one time. Now Christ dwells through the Holy Spirit in the hearts of all those who have received Him as Lord and Savior. Lloyd Ogilvie, pastor of the First Presbyterian Church in Hollywood, refers to the Holy Spirit as "the contemporary Christ." Paul wrote to the Romans, "He [God] will also give life to your mortal bodies through His Spirit who indwells you" (Rom. 8:11).

At the historic Congress on World Evangelization in Switzerland in 1974, the Holy Spirit was the subject of many addresses and discussions. The Reverend Gottfried Osei-Mensah of Nairobi, Kenya, said, "The Spirit is our Master. It is the work of the Holy Spirit, living in us, to free us from the rule of sin in our daily lives, and to help us live the new life we share with Christ."

How long does the Holy Spirit live in the heart of a believer? Forever. God does not give a gift as powerful as the Holy Spirit and then take it back. By faith you accept God's statements that you are indwelt by the Spirit of God, but you can watch Him at work, too. The Holy Spirit can rejuvenate a tired Christian, captivate an indifferent believer, and empower a dry church.

A clergyman from Buenos Aires, Argentina, said, "The Holy Spirit today is renewing the fruit of the Spirit—love, joy, peace. All those things are going to be the elements that show the world that we are his people."

The Holy Spirit is there to give you special power to work for Christ. He is there to give you strength in the moment of temptation.

Jesus promised that we would receive power from the Holy Spirit (Acts 1:8). Perhaps you have heard the story of the woodpecker who was pecking with his beak against the trunk of a tree. At that very moment, the lightning struck the tree, splitting it from top to bottom. When he'd recovered from the shock, the woodpecker flew away exclaiming, "I didn't know there was so much power in my beak!" I don't ask you, have you the Holy Spirit, but does the Holy Spirit have you?

Victory over Temptation

The Bible teaches that the new believer in Jesus Christ—the converted person—is to "abhor what is evil" (Rom. 12:9). Here is another strong admonishment, "in reference to your former manner of life, you lay aside the old self, which is being corrupted in accordance with the lusts of deceit" (Eph. 4:22).

Now wait a minute. How are we supposed to be able to stop doing some of the sinful things we have done for years, or get rid of some of the negative, suspicious, hateful, greedy attitudes which are ingrained in our personality? "I just can't do it myself," you might say.

You're right. However, the capacity to resist sin and obey God comes from the Holy Spirit, who lives in every true believer. It's not up to us to struggle against temptation alone. God lives in our hearts to help us resist sin. It is His job to work, and our job to yield.

What about the old bugaboo of temptation? The Bible doesn't say we won't be tempted; that would be foolish. We know that we live in a world full of temptations, most of them tied up in very attractive packages and offered as something we must try or buy—just once! But the converted man or woman has the offer of victory over temptation. "No temptation has overtaken you but such as is common to man; and God is faithful, who will not allow you to be tempted beyond what you are able; but with the temptation will provide the way of escape also, that you may be able to endure it" (1 Cor. 10:13).

To be tempted is not a sin; as a believer in Jesus Christ you do not need to blame yourself for an increase in the temptations that surround you. The indwelling Holy Spirit gives us strength to resist temptation.

Temptation is very powerful and will become even more so after you have been born again. The Scriptures tell us that we are in a spiritual warfare and that our enemies have more power and skill to tempt us than we have ever encountered before. Here is where many new believers make a big mistake. They think that when they are converted they will become perfect right away, that they will live on a continual high. Then they find themselves being tempted, in conflict, and even at times yielding to temptation. The new believer takes a look at himself and doesn't like what he sees. He is filled with discouragement and frustration. This is normal. The devil tempts you and God tests you. Often they are two sides to the same coin—God allows the devil to tempt you, and He uses it as a test, or as an experience to help deepen your faith and let you see how fragile you really are if you depend on yourself. He wants you to depend totally and completely on Him.

An old allegory illustrates this well: "Satan called together a council of his servants to consult how they might make a good

man sin. One evil spirit started up and said, 'I will make him sin.'—
'How will you do it?' asked Satan. 'I will set before him the pleasures of sin,' was the reply; 'I will tell him of its delights, and the
rich rewards it brings.'—'Ah,' said Satan, 'that will not do; he has
tried it, and knows better than that.' Then another imp started up
and said, 'I will make him sin.'—'What will you do?' asked Satan.
'I will tell him of the pains and sorrows of virtue. I will show him
that virtue has no delights, and brings no rewards.'—'Ah, no!'
exclaimed Satan, 'that will not do at all; for he has tried it, and
knows that "Wisdom's ways *are* ways of pleasantness, and all her
paths are peace."'—'Well,' said another imp, starting up, 'I will
undertake to make him sin.'—'And what will you do?' asked Satan,
again. 'I will discourage his soul,' was the short reply. 'Ah, that
will do!" cried Satan; 'that will do! We shall conquer him now.'"[1]

Spiritual conflict is at work in the heart of every believer. It is
true that the Christian possesses a new nature, but the old sin
nature is still there. It is now up to us, day by day, to yield to the
new nature which Christ dominates.

There is the story of a housewife who found a mouse in her
kitchen and took a broom to it. The mouse didn't waste its time
contemplating either the housewife or the broom, but got busy
looking for the hole. And so it is with us when we are caught by
temptation. We don't spend time contemplating the temptation
but get busy looking for a way out. The Scripture says, "God . . .
will not allow you to be tempted beyond what you are able; but
with the temptation will provide the way of escape also" (1 Cor.
10:13).

When the Christian sins he is miserable. Sometimes he avoids
other Christians, stops going to church, believes that he is misunderstood. However, every Christian has access to God through
prayer and when he confesses his sin God restores fellowship with
him. This is the difference between the believer and the unbeliever.
The unbeliever makes sin a practice; the believer does not.

A word about how believers should treat a "fallen" brother:
Some years ago we knew a young college student recently converted from a life of drugs. Shortly after his conversion he agreed
to turn informer for a narcotics agent in order to try and catch the
pushers in that area. Fellow Christians warned him against doing

this, but he had already committed himself and the inevitable happened. He blew his Christian witness when he had to pretend to be a drug-user himself in order to convince the pusher that he was for real, at one point having to take two shots of heroin. (Incidentally, the shots had an effect on him opposite to that before his conversion—instead of getting high he had violent withdrawals.) The Sunday before he left the school to return to his home, he stood up before the Sunday school class to tell them what had happened. The pusher had been caught, and although this young man had blown his Christian witness, he wanted the students to know that he was still a believer and a follower of the Lord. He stood up before the class, holding two fingers together to explain, "Me and Jesus are just like this." This gave the teacher an opportunity to talk to the students on how a brother should be treated when he has apparently fallen. During the time when he was trying to assist the narcotics agent, all the Christians on campus thought he had backslidden and gave him the cold shoulder. Actually, when we see a brother fall (or one whom we think has fallen) we should, like the Good Samaritan, get down and help him up again and do what we can to encourage him, pray for him, and let him know that we love him and believe in him.

The believer hates sin and wants to abide by God's commands. Paul says believers "do not walk according to the flesh, but according to the Spirit" (Rom. 8:4). The Holy Spirit who indwells us convicts us in various ways. A believer will begin to realize that the dirty jokes which were once a part of his office repertoire are sticking in his throat. The cocktail parties which were once so interesting and funny have become dull and boring. Ruth and I have sometimes gone to cocktail parties in various parts of the world. Always we have taken a soft drink and tried to be a witness. The first convert of the New York Crusade was a direct result of my going to a cocktail party like this on board a ship coming from Japan in the early 1950s. Such occasions may afford a great opportunity for Christian witness. We have often had a whole group of people gather around us and ask spiritual questions. In this same way Jesus talked with publicans and sinners, and for a clear purpose. On the other hand, going to cocktail parties just to be one of the gang not only often becomes boring, but carries the painful risk of hearing someone swear and take the name of the Lord in vain.

The choices of a new believer are made from a new perspective. He may hand himself over to sin (and feel miserable in it) or give himself over to God. Paul's advice is excellent: "I urge you therefore, brethren, by the mercies of God, to present your bodies a living and holy sacrifice, acceptable to God, which is your spiritual service of worship. And do not be conformed to this world, but be transformed by the renewing of your mind, that you may prove what the will of God is, that which is good and acceptable and perfect" (Rom. 12:1,2).

The transformation by "renewing of your mind" may happen quickly and dramatically, as the addict who experiences instant withdrawal, or it may permeate into your lifestyle more gradually.

Growing Slowly, Almost Imperceptibly —but Growing!

Many people grow into Christian maturity very rapidly; others much more slowly, almost imperceptibly. I once saw a picture on television of flowers growing, budding, and opening. This was done by slow-motion photography over a long period of time. If you had watched the same process with your naked eye in your garden it would have taken days. In the same way, we watch our lives from day to day and often get discouraged at the slow growth. But if you wait for a year or two and then look back over your life you will see how much you have grown. You've become kinder, more gracious, more loving. You love the Scriptures more. You love to pray more. You are a more faithful witness. You never will reach that point of full maturity in Christ until you see Him face to face in heaven.

Abrupt or gradual, the changes in a converted person are a part of his growth. He is not reborn full-grown; rather he is reborn with the energies of new life that will mature him as time passes. This growth is spiritual and moral. It's just like a baby learning to crawl, then toddle, then walk, then run. It takes time, study, patience, and discipline.

A person can attempt to imitate Christian growth by religious effort, but the result is like a plaster of Paris model of Michelangelo's David. It's phoney and easily broken.

A Christian grows as the life of God exerts its new power from deep in the center of his personality. The unconverted person cannot duplicate that life, no matter how religious he tries to act. He lacks the sources for growth because he has not been reborn.

A group of students at Harvard once tried to fool the famous professor of zoology Agassiz. They took parts from a number of different bugs and with great skill attached them together to make a creation they were sure would baffle their teacher. On the chosen day they brought it to him and asked that he identify it. As he inspected it with great care, the students grew more and more sure they had tricked this genius.

Finally, Professor Agassiz straightened up and said, "I have identified it." Scarcely able to control their amusement, they asked its name. Agassiz replied, "It is a humbug."

A person with genuine life from God will detect the counterfeit and think, "Humbug."

The new convert is a babe in Christ. A babe must be nourished in order to grow. He must be protected because he has been born into a world of many enemies. His primary battle will be with "the world," "the flesh," and "the devil." This is why he needs the encouragement of his family, Christian friends, and especially the Church. At the time of birth the child of God is born into great riches, and has a marvelous inheritance, but it takes some time to find out about all his wealth.

The most important thing in the beginning of new life is to be nourished and strengthened. Here are the important nutrients to use.

Get a Bible

If you have a Bible, fine. If the Scriptures are a whole new world to you, however, I would advise that you get one of the newer translations which may be easier for you to understand. It is important for you to begin reading the New Testament, and the Gospel of John is a good place to start.

Saturate yourself in the Word of God. Don't worry about under-standing everything you read, because you won't. Pray before you read and ask the Holy Spirit to clarify what you are reading. The Scriptures are the greatest source of hope you will find in this hopeless world. "For whatever was written in earlier times was written for our instruction, that through perseverance and the encouragement of the Scriptures we might have hope" (Rom. 15:4).

Memorize portions of the Word of God. "Thy word have I hid in mine heart, that I might not sin against thee" (Ps. 119:11, KJV). Try taking a Bible verse that speaks to your needs and typing it on a file card. Put it in your pocket or purse and refer to it fre-quently. Review it daily, and by the end of the week you will have a verse memorized.

Satan is the great discourager. He doesn't want you to read the Bible or memorize Scripture. In the past you may not have been attacked by Satan, but now you've done something which makes him very angry. You've left his camp and joined the army of God. You're a Christian soldier and Satan will unleash all of his secret weapons. From now on it's upstream all the way against the cur-rent of the evils of this world.

But you can overcome everything he hurls at you with the weapon God has provided—"the sword of the Spirit, which is the word of God" (Eph. 6:17). Not only is the Word of God a sword to be used in offense, but you also have a shield to be used in defense. You have "the shield of faith with which ye shall be able to quench all the fiery darts of the wicked" (Eph. 6:16, KJV).

When Christ was in the wilderness He was tempted by Satan, and every time he met temptation with Scripture, saying, "It is written" (Matt. 4).

Christ needed this mighty weapon, and so do we.

Learn to Pray

There are complete books written about prayer, seminars held which deal in prayer, and hundreds of sermons on the power of prayer. The new believer is sometimes baffled by what and how to pray.

Jesus said, "Men ought always to pray" (Luke 18:1, KJV). The Apostle Paul said, "Pray without ceasing" (1 Thess. 5:17).

A prayer does not have to be eloquent or contain the language and terms of a theologian. When you made your decision for Christ, you were given the privilege of addressing God as Father. You pray to Him as a child talking to his loving and gracious father. In the beginning you may not be fluent, but it's important to begin. My wife has a notebook she has kept of our children as they were beginning to talk with us. She treasures these first attempts, mistakes and all. She said, "I wouldn't take anything for that book."

When Paul said we should pray without "ceasing," he chose a term used in his day to describe a persistent cough. Off and on, throughout our day we should be turning quickly to God to praise and thank Him, and to ask for His help. Prayers should be specific. God is interested in everything you do and nothing is too great or too insignificant to share with Him.

Find Christian Fellowship

God doesn't intend for you to live the Christian life alone. This is why he has brought other believers together to form fellowships. A church where the Bible is taught and believed is the first place a reborn man or woman must seek. I do not advise that just any church will do. Is the pastor teaching the Word of God or expounding his own or some other philosophy of living? You'll know. Does the church have Bible classes for all ages?

Without the fellowship of believers, a newly born Christian has a tendency to wither. The writer of the book of Hebrews says, "Let us consider how to stimulate one another to love and good deeds, not forsaking our own assembling together, as is the habit of some but encouraging one another" (Heb. 10: 24,25).

Perhaps there's a Bible class or prayer group in your community. It's exciting to find a whole new set of friends, people who are in various stages of their own Christian growth, growth, to share with and strengthen your faith.

One of my daughters lives in a high middle-class neighborhood. Some of the social leaders of the city are her neighbors. After a

great deal of prayer she decided that she would go to her neighbors' houses and ask them if they would like to have a Bible study.
She knocked on the door of house after house, and in almost every
instance the women not only said "yes," but some of them burst
into tears and said, "I've been waiting for someone to ask me to a
Bible class so I could learn the Bible." Today, my daughter teaches
a weekly Bible class of three hundred women, with many on the
waiting list to get in. If there's not a Bible class in your community, perhaps you could start one. You will find your neighbors
"hungrier" and "thirstier" than you had ever dreamed. They are
just waiting for someone to take the initiative. At first it may be
that only two or three of you will meet, read a passage in the Bible,
discuss it, have prayer over a cup of coffee. There are tens of thousands of such Bible classes springing up throughout the world in
homes, in offices, in professional football teams. Even the touring
golf professionals have a weekly Bible class that attracts anywhere
from ten to fifty of the golfers and their wives.

You are no longer alone. The fatherhood of God forms the true
brotherhood of man, an ideal which the philosophers and moral-
ists have sought from the beginning of time. This brotherhood
erases barriers of language, cultural background, and race. One of
the greatest joys a Christian experiences is that of meeting a fellow believer in an unexpected place. The waitress in the restau-
rant finds a common bond with her customer. The passenger on
an airplane discovers that the stewardess is a believer. You are in
a foreign country and immediately feel at home when you encounter another Christian. No lengthy introductions are necessary. You
share the greatest bond on earth. There is no fellowship on earth
to compare with it.

At the beginning of this book I said that I believed the most
important subject in the entire world is that of the new birth. It
is the most important event which can happen to any man,
woman, or child.

It is only when you are born again that you can experience all
the riches God has in store for you. You are not just a living person, you are truly ALIVE!

NOTES

Preface

1. Corrie ten Boom, *In My Father's House* (Old Tappan, N.J.: Fleming Revell Publishing Co., 1976), p. 24.
2. *Los Angeles Times*, September 23, 1976, pp. 3, 30.
3. *Time*, September 27, 1976, p. 86.

Chapter One

1. Charles Colson, *Born Again* (Old Tappan, N.J.: Chosen Books, 1976), p. 110.
2. Bertrand Russell, *Power: A New Social Analysis* (New York: Norton, 1938), p. 11.
3. H. R. Rookmaaker, *Modern Art and the Death of a Culture* (London: Inter-Varsity Press, 1970), p. 196.
4. Ibid., p. 202.
5. Os Guinness, *Dust of Death* (Downers Grove, Ill.: Inter-Varsity Press, 1973), p. 233.
6. Hal Lindsey, *The Terminal Generation* (Old Tappan, N.J.: Fleming H. Revell Co., 1976), p. 83.
7. Rookmaaker, *Modern Art*, p. 233.
8. Guinness, *Dust of Death*, p. 392.

Chapter Three

1. Josh McDowell, *Evidence That Demands a Verdict* (Campus Crusade for Christ, 1972), p. 17 ff.

Chapter Four

1. Sir James Frazer, *The Golden Bough* (New York: Macmillan Co., 1960), p. 194.
2. Ibid., p. 196.
3. Walter Kaufmann, *Critique of Religion and Philosophy* (New York: Harper and Row, 1958), p. 74.
4. Ibid., p. 88.
5. Tw. W. Doane, *Bible Myths* (New York: University Books, 1971), p. 252.

6. *Time*, December 30, 1974, p. 38.
7. Ibid., p. 40.

Chapter Five

1. *Time*, June 30, 1975, p. 10.
2. *Time*, February 2, 1976, p. 62.
3. William Barclay, *Letters to Timothy* (Philadelphia: Westminster Press, 1960), p. 44.

Chapter Six

1. *Time*, February 7, 1977, p. 37.

Chapter Seven

1. Josh McDowell, *Evidence That Demands A Verdict* (Campus Crusade, 1972), p. 89.
2. Harry Rimmer, *The Magnificence of Jesus* (Grand Rapids, Mich.: Wm. B. Eerdmans Publishing Co., 1943), p. 112.
3. C. S. Lewis, *Surprised By Joy* (New York: Harcourt, Brace & World, 1955), pp. 228 ff.

Chapter Nine

1. Nicolaus von Zinzendorf, 1739, tr. John Wesley, 1940.
2. *Saturday Evening Post*, September 1, 1951, p. 19.

Chapter Ten

1. Josh McDowell, *Evidence That Demands a Verdict* (Campus Crusade, 1972), p. 193.
2. Ibid., p. 233.

Chapter Eleven

1. *Time*, December 13, 1976, p. 93.
2. Ibid., E-3, p. 94.

3. Thomas Harris, *I'm OK—You're OK* (New York: Harper & Row, 1967), p. 229.
4. Sergiu Grossu, *The Church in Today's Catacombs* (New Rochelle, N.Y.: Arlington House Publishers, 1975), p. 43.
5. Ostrander and Schroeder, *Psychic Discoveries Behind the Iron Curtain* (Englewood Cliffs, N.J.: Prentice-Hall, 1970), pp. 151 ff.
6. John Hunter, *Impact* (Glendale, Calif.: Regal Books, 1966), pp. 45, 46.
7. Oswald Chambers, *My Utmost for His Highest* (New York: Dodd Mead & Company, 1946), p. 10.

Chapter Twelve

1. Hannah Pearsall Smith, *The Christian's Secret of a Happy Life* (London: Nisbet and Co. Ltd., 1945), p. 88.
2. Francis A. Schaeffer, *He is There and He is Not Silent*, (Wheaton, Ill.: Tyndale House, 1972), p. 15.
3. J. I. Packer, *Knowing God* (Downers Grove, Ill.: Inter-varsity Press, 1973), p. 35.

Chapter Thirteen

1. Hannah Pearsall Smith, *The Christian's Secret of a Happy Life*, p. 133.

The Holy Spirit

CONTENTS

PREFACE

AN OLD AMERICAN Indian legend tells of an Indian who came down from the mountains and saw the ocean for the first time. Awed by the scene, he requested a quart jar. As he waded into the ocean and filled the jar he was asked what he intended to do with it. "Back in the mountains," he replied, "my people have never seen the Great Water. I will carry this jar to them so they can see what it is like."

Before he died, Pope John was asked what church doctrine most needed reemphasis today. He replied, "The doctrine of the Holy Spirit."

A number of years ago, my wife and I had the privilege of spending a brief vacation in Switzerland as the guests of Dr. Karl Barth, the noted Swiss theologian. During the course of our conversations I asked him what he thought the next emphasis on theology would be. He replied without hesitation, "The Holy Spirit."

Attempting to write a book on so vast a subject as the Holy Spirit is like trying to capture the ocean in a quart jar. The subject is so infinite—and our minds are so finite.

This book really began as part of my personal spiritual pilgrimage. Throughout my ministry as an evangelist I have had a growing understanding of the ministry of the Holy Spirit. In recent years my attention has been drawn in a fresh way to the ministry of the Holy Spirit because of the renewed interest in His work in many parts of the world. Sensing my own need for further understanding, I began a systematic study of what the Bible teaches about the person and work of the Holy Spirit. It was not my original intention to write a book, but as I began to examine the subject in more depth I became concerned over the misunderstanding and even ignorance in some Christian circles concerning the Third Person of the Trinity.

In some ways I have been hesitant to write this book. But writing it has given me new insight into the ministry of the Holy Spirit; it has also helped me understand some of the movements of the Holy Spirit in our world today. My hope and prayer is that this book will be informative and clarifying for many Christians. I also pray it will be a unifying book. The Holy Spirit did not come to divide Christians but, among other reasons, He came to unite us.

My sole concern has been to see what the Bible has to say about the Holy Spirit. The Bible—which I believe the Holy Spirit inspired—is our only trustworthy source, and any reliable analysis of the person and work of the Holy Spirit must be biblically-based. As never before I have realized that there are some things we cannot know completely, and some issues are open to differences of interpretation by sincere Christians. About areas where there are honest differences among Christians I have tried not to be dogmatic.

I am thankful the Holy Spirit is at work in our generation, both in awakening the Church and in evangelism. May God use this book to bring renewal and challenge to many.

I owe a great debt to many people who have helped me during the writing of this book. I am grateful for my colleague Roy Gustafson who first suggested writing on this subject. Several people have been especially helpful in reading early drafts of the manuscript, either in part or the whole, and making constructive suggestions—including Dr. Harold Lindsell (former editor of *Christianity Today*), Mr. Paul Fromer (Wheaton College), Canon Houghton (former chairman of British Keswick), Dr. Thomas Zimmerman (General Superintendent of the Assemblies of God), Dr. Merrill C. Tenney (Dean Emeritus, Wheaton Graduate School), and Dr. Donald Hoke (Secretary, Lausanne Committee for World Evangelization). I am also thankful for the graciousness of Mr. and Mrs. Bill Mead, whose generosity enabled my wife, Ruth, and me to join them for several periods of work on the book. I will never forget those days of sitting around in a circle with the Meads and my longtime colleagues, the Cliff Barrows, the Fred Dienerts, and the Grady Wilsons, discussing various chapters of the book. I am also thankful for the suggestions of my colleague, Dr. John Akers, the help of the Reverend Ralph Williams of our Minneapolis office, and of Sally Wilson in Montreat who suggested illustrations and Scriptures to add to my original notes. My secretary, Stephanie Wills, has patiently typed and retyped the manuscript through its various drafts.

Introduction:
Man's Cry—God's Gift

MAN HAS TWO great spiritual needs. One is for forgiveness. The other is for goodness. Consciously or unconsciously, his inner being longs for both. There are times when man actually cries for them, even though in his restlessness, confusion, loneliness, fear, and pressures he may not know what he is crying for.

God heard that first cry for help, that cry for forgiveness, and answered it at Calvary. God sent His only Son into the world to die for our sins, so that we might be forgiven. This is a gift for us— God's gift of salvation. This gift is a permanent legacy for everyone who truly admits he has "fallen short" and sinned. It is for everyone who reaches out and accepts God's gift by receiving Jesus Christ as his Lord and Savior. Paul calls it God's "indescribable" gift (2 Cor. 9:15).

But God also heard our second cry, that cry for goodness, and answered it at Pentecost. God does not want us to come to Christ by faith, and then lead a life of defeat, discouragement, and dissension. Rather, He wants to "fulfill every desire for *goodness* and the work of faith with power; in order that the name of our Lord Jesus Christ may be glorified in you" (2 Thess. 1:11, 12). *To the great gift of forgiveness God adds also the great gift of the Holy Spirit.* He is the source of power who meets our need to escape from the miserable weakness that grips us. He gives us the power to be truly good.

If we are to live a life of sanity in our modern world, if we wish to be men and women who can live victoriously, we need this two-sided gift God has offered us: first, the work of the Son of God *for* us; second, the work of the Spirit of God *in* us. In this way God has answered mankind's two great cries: the cry for forgiveness and the cry for goodness.

As a friend of mine has said, "I need Jesus Christ for my eternal life, and the Holy Spirit of God for my internal life."

If you believe in Jesus Christ, a power is available to you that can change your life, even in such intimate areas as your marriage, your family relationships, and every other relationship. Also, God offers power that can change a tired church into a vital, growing body, power that can revitalize Christendom.

Unfortunately, this power has been ignored, misunderstood, and misused. By our ignorance we have short-circuited the power of the Holy Spirit.

Many books are written about this power, many prayers are said pleading for this power. Scores of Christians would like to have it, but they aren't sure what it is.

When the world looks at a Christian, certain mental clichés come to mind: it sees the believer as a stiff-necked, sober-faced person without a sense of humor; a person who can't make it himself so he uses "God as a crutch"; one who has left his brains in kindergarten.

Now, if this cold stereotype applies in any way to us or the Church, then we need to know about the exciting, revolutionary power available exclusively to Christian believers. No one can buy it, claim it, or use it without first knowing its source.

The Holy Spirit Was Promised

When Jesus was teaching His disciples, preparing them for what He knew was the end, His heart ached for them because He knew they were confused and sad. I can imagine that He moved from one to another, putting His arms around them. To each He explained in simple fashion, as we do to our children, the important truths He wanted them to understand. At one point He said,

"But now I am going to Him who sent Me; and none of you asks Me, 'Where are You going?' But because I have said these things to you, sorrow has filled your heart. But I tell you the truth, it is to your advantage that I go away; for if I do not go away, the Helper shall not come to you; but if I go, I will send Him to you" (John 16:5–7).

There was a promise! The coming of the Spirit was based upon the word of the Lord Jesus Christ. No conditions were attached. Jesus didn't say that He would send the Helper (or "Comforter") to some believers and not to others. Nor did He say that we had to belong to some special organization or be higher on the scale of spiritual performance than someone else. He simply said, "If I go, I will send Him to you."

When Jesus Christ makes a promise, He does not break or forget it. We may doubt the promises of friends or family; we may even doubt our own promises to others. But we have never been given a promise by Jesus that has not been a certainty.

Some people dismiss Jesus Christ as a "great teacher" or one of the outstanding religious leaders of the world. However, when it comes to promises, it's interesting to contrast His words with other great religious and philosophical leaders. For example, as the founder of Buddhism was bidding his followers farewell he said, "You must be your own light." Or when Socrates was about to take that fatal cup, one of his disciples mourned that he was leaving them orphans. The leaders of the world's religions and philosophies were unable to promise that they would never leave their followers.

The disciples of Jesus Christ, however, were not left alone. He said, "I will not leave you as orphans; I will come to you" (John 14:18). It is interesting that the Greek word for "orphans" is the same as the word used by the disciple of Socrates when he realized that his master was going to leave him alone.

The Promise Fulfilled

Jesus said He would leave His disciples for a while, and He did. During the dreadful hours of the crucifixion, death, and burial, agonizing doubt gripped the minds of those who loved Him. He had not yet been "glorified," so the promise of His Spirit was not yet a fact.

But we know what happened. God raised Him from the dead and gave Him glory. Addressing Christians, the Scriptures say that Christ came "for the sake of you who through Him are believers in God, who raised Him from the dead and gave Him glory, so that your faith and hope are in God" (1 Peter 1:20, 21).

God had said to "wait" for the Spirit to come. Jesus rose from the dead and was seen by His disciples. Unable to grasp what was happening, they failed to recognize Him at first, and were frightened because they thought they were seeing a ghost. To confirm His physical reality, Jesus told them to touch Him, and even asked for something to eat. A spirit didn't have flesh, did it? A ghost couldn't eat, could it?

So this was truly Jesus, not the Spirit He had promised. However, He told them still to wait! The time was not yet.

Fifty days later the promise was fulfilled at Pentecost. What a day it was! It is difficult for us to imagine, with our practical, earthbound, scientific mentality, the amazing happening of that day.

"And when the day of Pentecost had come, they were all together in one place. And suddenly there came from heaven a noise like a violent, rushing wind, and it filled the whole house where they were sitting. And there appeared to them tongues as of fire distributing themselves, and they rested on each one of them. And they were all filled with the Holy Spirit and began to speak with other tongues, as the Spirit was giving them utterance" (Acts 2:1–4).

The one for whom they were asked to "wait" had come!

What a difference the emphasis of one word makes in the description of a happening of such world-shaking importance! Before the day of Pentecost the emphasis was on the word "ask." "If you then, being evil, know how to give good gifts to your children, how much more shall your Heavenly Father give the Holy Spirit to those who *ask* Him?" (Luke 11:13, italics mine).

After Pentecost the emphasis was on the word "receive." In his powerful sermon that day, Peter said, "Repent, and let each of you be baptized in the name of Jesus Christ for the forgiveness of your sins; and you shall *receive* the gift of the Holy Spirit" (Acts 2:38, italics mine).

This is the good news: we are no longer waiting for the Holy Spirit—He is waiting for us. We are no longer living in a time of promise, but in the days of fulfillment.

The members of the early Church, those men, women, and children who knew the reality of the Holy Spirit as a force, were totally transformed. The rush of power they experienced on the day of Pentecost is characteristic of the age that gave us the New Testament. The Holy Spirit was promised, the promise was fulfilled, the disciples were changed, and the glory of it for us is that He is present in every true believer today. And so His power is available today.

Who is this Person whom Christ promised to send to earth in His place? Who is this Person whom He uses to transform human nature? Who is this Person who can give you supernatural power to face any crisis? And how can you and I know His power in our lives day by day?

We will find out.

1

Who Is
the Holy Spirit?

SOME YEARS AGO a teacher in a fifth-grade class asked his students if anyone could explain electricity. One boy raised his hand. The teacher asked, "How would you explain it, Jimmy?" Jimmy scratched his head a moment and then replied, "Last night I knew it, but this morning I've forgotten." The teacher shook his head sadly and said to the class, "What a tragedy. The only person in the world ever to understand electricity, and he's forgotten!"

That teacher's position may describe you and me when we study the doctrine of the Trinity. We accept the fact that the Holy Spirit is God, just as much God as God the Father and God the Son. But when it comes to explaining it, we are at a loss.

In recent years people have talked more about the Holy Spirit and written more books about Him than possibly any religious theme other than the occult. This has come about largely because of the influence of the charismatic movement, which has been called Christendom's "third force" alongside Catholicism and Protestantism. The more recent charismatic movement, which has some of its roots in historic Pentecostalism and stresses the Holy Spirit, is now deeply entrenched in most of the mainline denominations and in Catholicism. We may feel that it is such a vast subject and we know so little about it. Nevertheless, God in His Word has revealed all we should know.

Many questions will arise in this book for which answers are being sought by puzzled and at times untaught believers. In fact, millions of Christians on every continent are now asking these questions. They are seeking and deserve biblical answers.

For example: What is the baptism of the Holy Spirit? When does it take place? Is speaking in tongues *possible* or necessary today? Is there an experience called a "second blessing"?

To start our study, we need to ask a critical question at the very beginning: Who is the Holy Spirit?

The Holy Spirit Is a Person

The Bible teaches that the Holy Spirit is a *person*. Jesus never referred to "it" when He was talking about the Holy Spirit. In John 14, 15 and 16, for example, He spoke of the Holy Spirit as "He" because He is not a force or thing but a person. Whoever speaks of the Holy Spirit as "it" is uninstructed, or perhaps even undiscerning. In Romans 8:16 the King James Version refers to the Holy Spirit as "itself." This is a mistranslation. Nearly all of the newer translations have changed "itself" to "himself."

We see from the Bible that the Holy Spirit has intellect, emotions, and will. In addition to this, the Bible also ascribes to Him the acts we would expect of someone who was not just a force, but a real person.

He speaks: "He who has an ear, let him hear what the Spirit says to the churches. To him who overcomes, I will grant to eat of the tree of life, which is in the Paradise of God" (Rev. 2:7).

"And while they were ministering to the Lord and fasting, the Holy Spirit said, 'Set apart for Me Barnabas and Saul for the work to which I have called them'" (Acts 13:2).

He intercedes: "And in the same way the Spirit also helps our weakness; for we do not know how to pray as we should, but the Spirit Himself intercedes for us with groanings too deep for words" (Rom. 8:26).

He testifies: "When the Helper comes, whom I will send to you from the Father, that is the Spirit of truth, who proceeds from the Father, He will bear witness of Me" (John 15:26).

He leads: "And the Spirit said to Philip, 'Go up and join this chariot'" (Acts 8:29).

"For all who are being led by the Spirit of God, these are sons of God" (Rom. 8:14).

He commands: "And they passed through the Phrygian and Galatian region, having been forbidden by the Holy Spirit to speak the word in Asia; and when they had come to Mysia, they were trying to go into Bithynia, and the Spirit of Jesus did not permit them" (Acts 16:6, 7).

He guides: "When the Spirit of truth comes, he will guide you into all the truth; for he will not speak on his own authority, but whatever he hears he will speak, and he will declare to you the things that are to come" (John 16:13 RSV).

He appoints: "Be on guard for yourselves and for all the flock, among which the Holy Spirit has made you overseers, to shepherd the church of God which He purchased with His own blood" (Acts 20:28).

He can be lied to: "But Peter said, 'Ananias, why has Satan filled your heart to lie to the Holy Spirit, and to keep back some of the price of the land? While it remained unsold, did it not remain your own? And after it was sold, was it not under your control? Why is it that you have conceived this deed in your heart? You have not lied to men, but to God'" (Acts 5:3, 4).

He can be insulted: "How much severer punishment do you think he will deserve who has trampled under foot the Son of God, and has regarded as unclean the blood of the covenant by which he was sanctified, and has insulted the Spirit of grace?" (Heb 10:29).

He can be blasphemed: "Therefore I say to you, any sin and blasphemy shall be forgiven men, but blasphemy against the Spirit shall not be forgiven. And whoever shall speak a word against the Son of Man, it shall be forgiven him; but whoever shall speak against the Holy Spirit, it shall not be forgiven him, either in this age, or in the age to come" (Matt. 12:31, 32).

He can be grieved: "And do not grieve the Holy Spirit of God, by whom you were sealed for the day of redemption" (Eph. 4:30)

Each of the emotions and acts we have listed are characteristics of a person. The Holy Spirit is not an impersonal force, like gravity or magnetism. He is a Person, with all the attributes of personality. But not only is He a Person; He is divine as well.

The Holy Spirit Is a Divine Person: He Is God

Throughout the Bible it is clear that the Holy Spirit is God Himself. This is seen in the attributes which are given to the Holy Spirit in Scripture, for example. Without exception these attributes are those of God Himself.

He is eternal: This means that there never was a time when He was not. "How much more will the blood of Christ, who through the eternal Spirit offered Himself without blemish to God, cleanse your conscience from dead works to serve the living God?" (Heb. 9:14).

He is all-powerful: "And the angel answered and said to her, 'The Holy Spirit will come upon you, and the power of the Most High will overshadow you; and for that reason the holy offspring shall be called the Son of God'" (Luke 1:35).

He is everywhere present (that is, omnipresent) at the same time: "Where can I go from Thy Spirit? Or where can I flee from Thy presence?" (Ps. 139:7).

He is all-knowing (that is, omniscient): "For to us God revealed them through the Spirit; for the Spirit searches all things, even the depths of God. For who among men knows the thoughts of a man except the spirit of the man, which is in him? Even so the thoughts of God no one knows except the Spirit of God" (1 Cor. 2:10, 11).

The Holy Spirit is called God: "But Peter said, 'Ananias, why has Satan filled your heart to lie to the Holy Spirit, and to keep back some of the price of the land? While it remained unsold, did it not remain your own? And after it was sold, was it not under your control? Why is it that you have conceived this deed in your heart? *You have not lied to men, but to God'"* (Acts 5:3, 4, italics mine).

"And we all, with unveiled face, beholding the glory of the Lord, are being changed into his likeness from one degree of glory to another; for this comes from the Lord who is the Spirit" (2 Cor. 3:18 RSV).

He is the Creator: The first biblical reference to the Holy Spirit is Genesis 1:2 (Moffatt) where we are told "the spirit of God was hovering over the waters." Yet Genesis 1:1 says, "In the beginning God created the heavens and the earth." And in Colossians 1 where

Paul is writing to the Church at Colossae about the Lord Jesus Christ, among other tremendous truths he tells us, "For in Him all things were created, both in the heavens and on earth, visible and invisible, whether thrones or dominions or rulers or authorities—all things have been created through Him and for Him. And He is before all things, and in Him all things hold together" [cohere] (Col. 1:16, 17).

Thus, God the Father, God the Son, and God the Holy Spirit were together creating the world. To understand and accept these facts is of the greatest importance to every Christian, both theologically and practically.

One day I made a few of these assertions about the Holy Spirit to some seminary students. One asked, "But He is usually mentioned last. Doesn't that imply inferiority?" Yet in Romans 15:30 He is not mentioned last: "Now I urge you, brethren, by our Lord Jesus Christ and by the love of the Spirit, to strive together with me in your prayers to God for me." And in Ephesians 4:4 Paul says, "There is one body and one Spirit, just as also you were called in one hope of your calling."

But more than this, the usual placement of the three persons of the Trinity in the New Testament has to do with their order and function. Thus we say that we pray to the Father through the Son and in the power of the Holy Spirit. Moreover, I have already shown that *functionally* the Father came first, then the Son became incarnate, died and rose again. Now the Spirit does His work in this age of the Spirit. The order has nothing to do with equality, but only with function and chronology.

The Trinity

When I first began to study the Bible years ago, the doctrine of the Trinity was one of the most complex problems I had to encounter. I have never fully resolved it, for it contains an aspect of mystery. Though I do not totally understand it to this day, I accept it as a revelation of God.

The Bible teaches us that the Holy Spirit is a living being. He is one of the three persons of the Holy Trinity. To explain and illustrate the Trinity is one of the most difficult assignments to a

Christian. Dr. David McKenna once told me that he was asked by his small son, Doug, "Is God the Father God?" He answered, "Yes." "Is Jesus Christ God?" "Yes." "Is the Holy Spirit God?" "Yes." "Then how can Jesus be His own Father?" David thought quickly. They were sitting in their old 1958 Chevrolet at the time. "Listen, son," he replied, "under the hood is one battery. Yet I can use it to turn on the lights, blow the horn, and start the car." He said, "How this happens is a mystery—but it happens!"

The Bible *does* teach us the reality of the Trinity, both in the Old and New Testaments. Let us look at some of the major passages.

God unfolds His revelation of Himself in the Bible progressively. But there are indications from the very beginning of the Book of Genesis that God subsists in three persons—the Father, the Son, and the Holy Spirit—and that these three persons constitute the one God. Christianity is trinitarian, not unitarian. There is only one God, not three, so it is clear that the Christian faith is not polytheistic.

The Bible begins with the majestic statement: "In the beginning God created the heavens and the earth" (Gen. 1:1).

Hebrew scholars have told me there are three numbers in the Hebrew language: Singular, one; dual, two; plural, more than two. The word translated "God" in Genesis 1:1 is plural, indicating more than two. The Hebrew word used here is *Elohim*. Matthew Henry says it signifies "the plurality of persons in the Godhead, Father, Son, and Holy Ghost. This plural name of God . . . [confirms] our faith in the doctrine of the Trinity, which, though but darkly intimated in the Old Testament, is clearly revealed in the New."[1]

As we have seen concerning creation, even from the beginning God gives us glimpses of the truth that the Godhead consists of more than one person. I have italicized some of the key words. In Genesis 1:26, God said, "Let *us* make man in *our* image, according to *our* likeness; and let them rule over the fish of the sea and over the birds of the sky and over the cattle and over all the earth, and over every creeping thing that creeps on the earth." Further, in Genesis 3:22 the Lord God said, "Behold, the man has become like one of *Us*, knowing good and evil." And in Genesis 11: 6, 7, the

Lord said, "Behold, they are one people, and they all have the same language. And this is what they began to do, and now nothing which they purpose to do will be impossible for them. Come, let *Us* go down and there confuse their language, that they may not understand one another's speech." When Isaiah heard the voice of the Lord saying, "Whom shall I send, and who will go for *us*?" he answered, "Here am I. Send me!" (Isa. 6:8).

The New Testament's doctrine of the Trinity is much more fully developed than that of the Old Testament. Since revelation is progressive, more light is thrown on this subject as God more fully disclosed Himself at the time of Christ and the apostles.

The last command of Jesus before His ascension is recorded in Matthew 28:18–20. In it He ordered His followers to "make disciples of all the nations," baptizing converts "in the name of the Father and the Son and the Holy Spirit, teaching them to observe all that I commanded you; and lo, I am with you always, even to the end of the age." Here Jesus taught that after He left this earth, His followers were to carry His gospel message to all nations. The Holy Spirit was to use them to call out a people for His name. This trinitarian commission to baptize associates the Holy Spirit with God the Father and God the Son as their equal. He is God the Holy Spirit.

It is thrilling to note that Jesus says believers will not be left alone. Through the Holy Spirit whom He and the Father sent, He will never leave us nor forsake us (Heb. 13:5). He will remain with every believer right to the end. This thought has encouraged me a thousand times in these dark days when satanic forces are at work in so many parts of the world.

Along this line the apostle Paul also said, "The grace of the Lord Jesus Christ, and the love of God, and the fellowship of the Holy Spirit, be with you all" (2 Cor. 13:14). This benediction clearly indicates that the Holy Spirit is one with the Father and one with the Son in the Godhead. *It is not one plus one plus one equals three. It is one times one times one equals one.* The Holy Spirit is one with the Father and the Son. If the Father is God, and Jesus is God, then the Holy Spirit is also God.

The chief problem connected with the doctrine of the Trinity concerns Christianity's claim to be also monotheistic. It rejects polytheism, the belief in more than one God. The answer is that trinitarianism preserves the unity of the Godhead, and at the same time it acknowledges that there are three persons in that Godhead which is still of one essence. God is one, but that oneness is not simple—it is complex.

This is a terribly difficult subject—far beyond the ability of our limited minds to grasp fully. Nevertheless, it is extremely important to declare what the Bible holds, and be silent where the Bible is silent. God the Father is fully God. God the Son is fully God. God the Holy Spirit is fully God. The Bible presents this as fact. It does not explain it. Nevertheless, many explanations have been suggested, some of which sound logical, but they do not preserve the truth of Scriptural teaching.

One Christian heresy in the early church was called "modalism." It taught that God appeared at different times in three different modes or forms—as Father, then as Son, and finally as Holy Spirit. Those who held this view thought it preserved the unity of monotheism. But it also meant that when Jesus prayed, He had to be talking to Himself. Further, to say, as Acts 2 does, that the Father and the Son sent the Holy Spirit, makes little sense if we accept modalism. Moreover, it violated the clearest presentation of the Trinity-in-unity as expressed in Matthew's statement by Jesus in the Great Commission. It was Jesus who said that His disciples were to baptize their converts "in the name of the Father and the Son and the Holy Spirit." The Greek construction makes it clear that Jesus is referring to three separate persons. He clearly taught the doctrine of the Trinity.

We have seen that the Holy Spirit is a person, and is God, and is a member of the Trinity. Anyone who fails to recognize this is robbed of his joy and power. Of course a defective view of any member of the Trinity will bring about this result because God is all important. But this is especially true for the Holy Spirit, for although the Father is the source of all blessing, and the Son is the channel of all blessing, it is through the Holy Spirit at work in us that all truth becomes living and operative in our lives.

The most important point I can make in summary is this: there is nothing that God is that the Holy Spirit is not. All of the essential aspects of deity belong to the Holy Spirit. We can say of Him exactly what was said of Jesus Christ in the ancient Nicene Creed: He is very God of very God! So we bow before Him, we worship Him, we accord Him every response Scripture requires of our relationship to Almighty God.

Who is the Holy Spirit? He is God!

2

When the Holy Spirit Has Come

AS I WAS writing this chapter, my wife and I sat on the porch in the hot spring sun, and we talked about the refreshment of the wind as evening came. We especially discussed the power and the mystery of the wind.

It is interesting that in Scripture, in both the original Hebrew and Greek languages, the word used in speaking of the Spirit is the word that can also mean "wind." In like-manner, the Holy Spirit works in different ways in our lives, and in different times in history.

I have seen tornadoes in Texas and Oklahoma, and even in my home state of North Carolina when I was a boy. Yes, I have seen the power of the wind. I have seen the air-brakes that use the wind, or the air, to stop the giant truck going down the highway. That same force can lift a giant airplane.

"The manager of a granite quarry in North Carolina said: 'We supplied the granite for the municipal building in New York City. We can lift an acre of solid granite ten feet thick to almost any height we desire for the purpose of moving it. We do it with air. We can do it as easily as I can lift a piece of paper.'

"Air! Air—this invisible envelopment in which we live and move, this substance so immaterial that we can move our hands through it as though it had no reality at all. But the power it possesses! How great, how terrible!"[1]

We have seen something of the nature and personality of the Holy Spirit. Now we must catch a vision of His distinctive work in each of the great ages of time. But first, to place it in perspective, we must see how the Triune God is at work in every age.

The elements of mystery in this make it difficult for the human mind to comprehend fully. Simultaneously the Father, the Son, and the Holy Spirit have different functions to perform that are distinctive to each. For instance, it was not the Father or the Holy Spirit who died on the cross of Calvary. It was God the Son. We need to understand such facts, especially when we think of this present age and the work of God in it.

As we study the Bible, the work of God the Father is especially emphasized in the Old Testament. The work of God the Son is emphasized in the Gospels. From the day of Pentecost until the present, however, the emphasis is on the work of God the Holy Spirit. And yet the Bible also tells us God the Holy Spirit has been at work throughout history, from the beginning of the world. Therefore, we begin our study of the work of the Holy Spirit by examining briefly His activities in the eras before Pentecost, before concentrating on His unique ministry since then.

The Spirit's Work from Creation to Bethlehem

As we have seen in the previous chapter, the Holy Spirit was at work in creation. According to Genesis 1:2, "The earth was formless and void, and darkness was over the surface of the deep." Immediately, we are told that "the Spirit of God was moving over the surface of the waters." The Hebrew word for "moving" means "brooding" or "hovering." Just as a hen broods over her eggs for the purpose of hatching them and bringing forth new life, so the Holy Spirit brooded over the original creation of God for the purpose of filling its void with life in various forms. The creation recorded in the rest of Genesis 1, together with Genesis 2, resulted. Thus, from the beginning the Holy Spirit was active in creation along with the Father and the Son.

When God "formed man of dust from the ground" (Gen. 2:7), the Holy Spirit was involved. We learn this indirectly in Job 33:4, "The Spirit of God has made me, And the breath of the Almighty gives me life." A play on words here shows how intimately God's Spirit and our breath are related: both "Spirit" and "breath" are from the same Hebrew word.

Genesis 2:7 also says that the Lord God "breathed into his nostrils the breath of life; and man became a living being." While the Hebrew word translated "breath" here is not the one also meaning spirit, clearly man owes his very life to God according to this passage. And the breath of God that started man on his earthly journey was, in fact, the Holy Spirit, as Job 33:4 tells us.

Psalm 104:30 carries our understanding of the Spirit in creation a step further. Not only was the Spirit at work in the formation of the earth and the first man, but the Spirit is always the creator of life. "Thou [God] dost send forth Thy Spirit, they are created; And Thou dost renew the face of the ground." Who are the "they" whom the Spirit creates? The entire psalm clarifies this, but just in verses 18–26 we learn that included are wild goats and rock badgers (18), beasts of the forest such as young lions (20, 21), man (23), and whatever lives on the earth or in the sea (24, 25).

Understanding that the Spirit gives life, a married woman in the Old Testament who was unable to bear a child would go to the tabernacle or temple. There either she prayed or the priest petitioned God to open her womb. Now, such a woman knew the basic facts of life just as we do, although she did not possess as much scientific knowledge about the birth process as we do today. Yet even to us it is still one of the mysteries of nature and one of nature's miracles that sperm can penetrate an ovum and initiate a new life. This is simply a medical or biological way of describing the touch of God's hand in the creation of life.

Hannah is a classic illustration of this. She went to the tabernacle to pray for a son. Eli, the high priest, thought at first that she was drunk, but she informed him she was a woman in sorrow who had poured out her soul to the Lord. Eli responded, "Go in peace; and may the God of Israel grant your petition that you have asked of Him" (1 Sam. 1:17). She later conceived and Samuel the prophet was born. While in the story itself God's spirit is not mentioned, our understanding of His place according to Psalm 104:30 (and Job 33:4) shows us that the life-giving function distinctively belonged to God's Spirit.

Yet Psalm 104:30 says more than just that we owe our creation to the Spirit. The face of the ground is also renewed by Him. God feeds what He creates.

So believers in the Old Testament were rightly convinced that God had something to do with the growing of crops. They attributed a good harvest to Him: "He causes the grass to grow for the cattle, And vegetation for the labor of man, So that he may bring forth food from the earth" (Ps. 104:14). In Deuteronomy 28 the conditions for blessing or cursing in the promised land were enunciated. If Israel obeyed God there was the promise: "Blessed shall be the offspring of your body and the produce of your ground," and "The Lord will make you abound . . . in the produce of your ground" (Deut. 28:4, 11). Israel's Feast of Firstfruits formally recognized that God was responsible for abundance. Today as we bow our heads before meals to thank God for the food we continue to acknowledge God as the One who sustains us.

However, God both blesses and curses, delivers and punishes. The Old Testament often attributes the salvation of Israel to the Spirit of God. He strove with people before the flood (Gen. 6:3). I believe that He is striving with people today exactly as He did before the flood. Jesus said, "And just as it happened in the days of Noah, so it shall be also in the days of the Son of Man" (Luke 17:26). The same sick perversions, moral decay, and erosions are prevalent today. The Holy Spirit is mightily striving but the vast majority of the human race will not listen.

Then from time to time the Holy Spirit took possession of certain men in order to deliver God's people. For instance, in the Book of Judges alone, He came upon Othniel (3:10), Gideon (6:34), Jephthah (11:29), and Samson (13:25).

The three main expressions used in the Old Testament for the work of the Holy Spirit on human beings are:

(1) He *came* upon men: "Then the Spirit of God came on Zechariah" (2 Chron. 24:20). (2) He *rested* on men: "the Spirit rested upon them" (Num. 11:25). (3) He *filled* men: "I have filled him with the Spirit of God" (Exod. 31:3).

The Spirit used not only judges and prophets to deliver Israel, but also kings. They were anointed with oil, a symbol that they were empowered with the Holy Spirit. So when Samuel anointed David in 1 Samuel 16:13, "the Spirit of the Lord came mightily upon David from that day forward."

Yet the next verse sounds a note of solemnity. While in Judges the Spirit often departed when the select person's task was done, He also might withdraw when the chosen one disobeyed. This occurred to Saul according to 1 Samuel 16:14, and also to Samson, as we see by comparing Judges 14:19 with 16:20. David's concern that the Spirit might withdraw from him occasioned his prayer, "Do not take Thy Holy Spirit from me" (Ps. 51:11).

God's great deliverance, of course, came not with a human anointed king, but with the Messiah, a title that means "Anointed." Isaiah had recorded prophetically that the Messiah would say, "The Spirit of the Lord God is upon me, Because the Lord has anointed me" (Isa. 61:1). And Jesus, reading this in the synagogue 800 years later, said, "Today this Scripture has been fulfilled in your hearing" (Luke 4:21).

It is not always easy to separate the roles of the Father, the Son, and the Holy Spirit in the Old Testament. But we do know that Jesus appeared from time to time in "theophanies" which are simply appearances of our Lord before the Incarnation. We also know that the use of the name of God in the Old Testament can refer to different members of the Trinity.

In summary, we have seen that the Holy Spirit was at work before the world began. Then He renewed and fed His creation. He was active throughout the Old Testament, both in the world of nature and among His people, guiding and delivering them through the judges, prophets, kings, and others. And He told of a coming day when the Anointed One would come.

The Spirit's Work from Bethlehem to Pentecost

During the period of time covered by the four Gospels, the work of the Holy Spirit centered around the person of Jesus Christ. The God-man was begotten of the Spirit (Luke 1:35), baptized by the Spirit (John 1:32, 33), led by the Spirit (Luke 4:1), anointed by the Spirit (Luke 4:18; Acts 10:38), and empowered by the Spirit (Matt.

12:27, 28). He offered Himself as an atonement for sin by the Spirit (Heb. 9:14), was raised by the Spirit (Rom. 8:11), and gave commandments by the Spirit (Acts 1:2).

Without a doubt one of the most awe-inspiring passages in Scripture relates what the angel said to Mary: "The Holy Spirit will come upon you, and the power of the Most High will overshadow you; and for that reason the holy offspring shall be called the Son of God" (Luke 1:35). Overly skeptical people, and others with too limited a view of science, may scoff in utter disbelief, but the angel dispelled all doubt when he said, "For nothing will be impossible with God" (Luke 1:37).

For Christians, any suggestion that God the Holy Spirit was not capable of bringing the virgin birth to pass is nonsense. If we believe that God is God—and that He rules His universe—nothing is too great for His limitless power. At all times God does whatever He chooses. When He planned the Messiah's birth, He performed a miracle. He bypassed one link in the normal physiological chain of birth: no human male participated. The life that was formed in the womb of the virgin was none other than the incarnate life of God the Son in human flesh. The virgin birth was a sign so extraordinary that it was obviously God and not man at work in the Incarnation. There are some so-called theologians today who deny the Incarnation—they reject the deity of Jesus Christ. In so doing they come very close to blaspheming the Holy Spirit!

The Holy Spirit was also at work among the disciples of Jesus before Pentecost. We know this because Jesus said of them, "He [the Holy Spirit] abides with you" (John 14:17). Jesus also said to Nicodemus, "Unless one is born of water and the Spirit, he cannot enter into the kingdom of God" (John 3:5). Again, He said, "You must be born again" (John 3:7).

Yet the operation of the Spirit among men in Jesus' day differed from His work today. For in John 7:39 we are told by the apostle John concerning the word of Jesus: "But this He [Jesus] spoke of the Spirit, whom those who believed in Him were to receive; for the Spirit was not yet given, because Jesus was not yet glorified."

Exactly what the difference was the Bible does not reveal completely. However, we know that the coming of the Spirit at Pentecost was in a far greater measure than anything they had ever experienced before. At any rate, we have seen that the Holy Spirit was at work in various ways in the birth and life of our Lord Jesus Christ and in the lives and ministries of His disciples.

The Spirit's Work from Pentecost till Now

In Acts, Luke records the ascension of Jesus into heaven (Acts 1:9–11). In chapter 2 he depicts the descent of the Holy Spirit to earth (Acts 2:1–4). Jesus had said, "If I do not go away, the Helper [Holy Spirit] shall not come to you; but if I go, I will send Him to you" (John 16:7). It was in fulfillment of this promise that Peter, speaking of the glorified Christ, said, "Therefore having been exalted to the right hand of God, and having received from the Father the promise of the Holy Spirit, He has poured forth this which you both see and hear" (Acts 2:33).

Many years ago a great Arctic explorer started on an expedition to the North Pole. After two long years in the lonely northland he wrote a short message, tied it under the wing of a carrier pigeon, and prepared to turn it loose to make the two thousand mile journey to Norway. The explorer gazed around him at the desolation. Not a creature to be seen. There was nothing but ice, snow, and never-ending bitter cold. He held the trembling little bird in his hand for a moment and then released her into the icy atmosphere. The bird circled three times, and then started her southward flight for multiplied hundreds of miles over ice and frozen ocean wastes until at last she dropped into the lap of the explorer's wife. By the arrival of the bird, his wife knew that all was well with her husband in the dark night of the arctic North.

Likewise the coming of the Holy Spirit, the Heavenly Dove, proved to the disciples that Christ had entered the heavenly sanctuary. He was seated at the right hand of God the Father, for His atoning work was finished. The advent of the Holy Spirit fulfilled Christ's promise; and it also testified that God's righteousness had been vindicated. The age of the Holy Spirit, which could not commence until Jesus was glorified, had now begun.

Unquestionably the coming of the Holy Spirit on the day of Pentecost marked a crucial turning point in the history of God's dealings with the human race. It is one of five past events, all of which are essential components of the Christian gospel: the Incarnation, the Atonement, the Resurrection, the Ascension, and Pentecost. A sixth component is still future: the Second Coming of Jesus.

The Incarnation as the first event marked the redemptive entrance of God into human life as true man. The second event in the series was the means by which God could remain just and yet justify guilty men—the Atonement. The third, the Resurrection, demonstrated that man's three great enemies—death, Satan, and hell—had been dealt their death blow. The fourth—the Ascension—showed that the Father had accepted the atoning work of the Son and that His righteous demands had been met. Pentecost, the fifth, assures us that the Spirit of God has come to achieve His certain purposes in the world, in the church, and in the individual believer!

The Jewish religious calendar centered in a number of annual feasts. However, the three most important were those in which all males were required to appear before the Lord (Deut. 16:16). These were the feasts of Passover, Tabernacles, and Pentecost.

"The Feast of Passover" commemorated the time when the Israelites were miraculously freed from a long period of slavery in Egypt. After killing an "unblemished" lamb (Exod. 12:5), the Israelites placed the blood over the door of each Israelite house and the lamb was roasted and eaten. The blood of the lamb brought about deliverance from God's judgment. The Old Testament passover found its final fulfillment in the death of Christ on Calvary, "For Christ our Passover also has been sacrificed" (1 Cor. 5:7). The Book of Hebrews teaches us that there is therefore no more need for the offering of the blood of bulls and goats. Jesus Christ, once and forever, offered Himself for the salvation of men by shedding His blood.

"The Feast of Tabernacles" (the present-day word for tabernacle is "booths" or "tents") reminded Israel of the days during the exodus from Egypt when the people lived not in houses, but in booths made of cut branches. The celebration came when the harvests were in, so it is called the "Feast of Ingathering" in Exodus 23:16. Perhaps celebration of deliverance from Egypt was fulfilled in the greater deliverance and blessing that came with redemption in Christ. John 7:38 may suggest that the coming of the Holy Spirit quenches thirst as neither the water of the desert nor the rain needed for harvest could do.

Pentecost was known as the "Feast of Weeks" because it was celebrated on the day following the passage of seven sabbaths—a Week of Weeks—from Passover. Because it fell on the fiftieth day, it gained the name "Pentecost," from the Greek word for "fiftieth." The Feast of Pentecost celebrated the beginning of the harvest; in Numbers 28:26 it was called "the day of the first fruits." In a real sense, the Day of Pentecost in the New Testament on which the Holy Spirit came was "a day of first fruits"—the beginning of God's harvest in this world, to be completed when Christ comes again. Pentecost in the New Testament marked the commencement of the present age of the Holy Spirit. Believers are under His guidance even as the disciples of Jesus were under Him. From heaven Jesus still exercises lordship over us, but, not being physically with us now, He transmits His directions by means of the Holy Spirit who makes Christ real to us. Since Pentecost the Holy Spirit is the link between the first and second advents of Jesus. He applies the work of Jesus Christ to men in this age, as we will see in the pages that follow.

When I began studying about the Holy Spirit shortly after I became a Christian, one of the first questions I asked myself was: Why did the Holy Spirit have to come? I soon found the answer in my Bible study. He came because He had a work to do in the *world*, in the *Church*, and in the individual *Christian*, as we will now discover.

The Holy Spirit's Present Work in the World

In regard to the world, the Spirit's work is twofold. First, He has come to reprove it of sin, righteousness, and judgment (John 16:7–11). The Bible teaches us, and we know from experience, that all have sinned and are coming short of the glory of God (Rom. 3:23). Sinful man cannot inherit eternal life. Everyone who has ever been born recapitulates Adam's fall. Everyone is born with the seed of sin within him which, with the coming of the age of accountabil-

ity, culminates in a multitude of sins. There is a difference between
sin and sins. Sin is the root, sins are the fruit.

However, a person may not be consciously aware that his deepest problem is sin, or that his sin has separated him from fellowship with God. Therefore, it is the work of the Holy Spirit to disturb and convict him in his sin. Until this takes place he cannot
experience salvation. In our crusade meetings I have seen people
walk out shaking their fists at me as I was preaching. They are not
actually hostile toward me, I know, but they have been brought
under conviction by the Holy Spirit. Often people like this later
return to find Christ.

But the Holy Spirit not only convicts of sin, He convinces men
that Jesus is the righteousness of God. He shows sinners that Jesus
is the way, the truth, and the life, and that no one comes to the
Father but by Him.

The Holy Spirit also convicts the world of judgment, because
the prince of this world is judged, and all will be judged if they
refuse God's offer of everlasting life. When the apostle Paul testified before Agrippa, he said that on the Damascus road at the time
of his conversion God had told him the nature of his ministry. It
would concern Gentiles and be "to open their eyes so that they
may turn from darkness to light and from the dominion of Satan
to God, in order that they may receive forgiveness of sins . . ." (Acts
26:18).

At the moment Jesus Christ died on the cross, Satan suffered an
overwhelming defeat. That defeat may not be apparent as we read
our newspapers and watch the television screens, but Satan is a
defeated enemy in principle. He still wages his wicked warfare, and
his total destruction and removal from the earth are near at hand.
But until then, he will intensify his activities. It is quite apparent
to Christians all over the world that new demons are abroad. Perversions, permissiveness, violence, and a hundred other sinister
trends are now rampant on a world-wide scale perhaps unknown
since the days of Noah. The Holy Spirit has come to show us these
things, for He is deeply involved in biblical prophecy, as we will
see later.

The Holy Spirit's work in the world is not confined to the ministry of conviction concerning sin, righteousness, and judgment,

however. His *second work* in the world is to hinder the growth of lawlessness, that is, to engage in the ministry of preservation. The apostle Paul said, "For the mystery of lawlessness is already at work; only he who now restrains will do so until he is taken out of the way" (2 Thess. 2:7).

The Scripture makes it clear that this planet would already be a literal hell on earth were it not for the presence of the Holy Spirit in the world. The unbelieving world little knows what it owes to the restraining power of the Holy Spirit.

Several theologians to whom I have talked recently, both in Europe and America, hold the view that the Holy Spirit is gradually being withdrawn from the world as we enter what may be the climactic moments of the end of the present age. When He is totally withdrawn "all hell will break loose." The world will experience wars, violence, eruptions, perversions, hatred, fear—of which we are only seeing glimpses today. The human race will be in a hell of its own making. Free from the restraints of the Holy Spirit the Antichrist will reign supreme for a short period until he is crushed by the coming of the Lord Jesus Christ and the armies of heaven!

The Holy Spirit also *acts through* the people of God, who are called the salt of the earth and the light of the world by Jesus in His Sermon on the Mount (Matt. 5:13, 14). These are apt metaphors because salt and light are forces that operate silently and unobtrusively, yet with great effect. Salt and light speak of the influence Christians can exercise for good in society. We who are believers sometimes find it difficult to understand what influence we can have when we are such a minority, are so often divided, and are disobedient from time to time. By the power of the Spirit, however, we can restrain evil and do good!

To spell out the metaphors further, salt and light are essential in our homes: light dissipates the darkness, and salt prevents decay. The Bible tells us that the state of the world will grow darker as we near the end of the age. The world has no light of its own— and it is marked by a process of accelerating decay. However, Jesus taught us that we who are His followers, though weak and small in number, act as salt so that we can hinder the process of decline. Christians at work in the world are the only real spiritual light in the midst of great spiritual darkness. In studying the Old Testament prophets we discover that a part of the judgment on the wicked is the destruction of the righteous.

This places a tremendous responsibility on all of us. Only as the world sees our good works do they know that a light is shining. Only as the world senses our moral presence are they conscious of the salt. This is why Christ warned against the salt losing its saltness, and the light dimming. He said, "Let your light shine" (Matt. 5:16). If you and I filled this role faithfully, there would be a dramatic but peaceful revolution in the world almost overnight. We Christians are *not* powerless. We have the mighty power of God available through God the Holy Spirit, even in this world.

The Holy Spirit's Work in the Church

The Spirit is active not only in the world, but also in the Church. When speaking of the Church, I am not talking about the Presbyterian, Baptist, Methodist, Anglican, Lutheran, Pentecostal, or Catholic churches, but the whole body of believers. The word "Church" comes from the Greek word that means "called together ones."

Although the Church was veiled in mystery in the Old Testament, yet Isaiah proclaimed, "Therefore thus says the Lord God, 'Behold, I am laying in Zion for a foundation a stone, a tested stone, a precious cornerstone, of a sure foundation'" (Isa. 28:16 RSV). The New Testament speaks of Christ as that "sure foundation" of His Church, and all believers are little building stones built into a holy temple in the Lord (1 Peter 2:5). Christ is also the head of His body, the universal Church. And He is the head of every local congregation of believers. Every person who has repented of his sin and received Jesus Christ as Savior and Lord is a member of this body called the Church. So the Church is more than a religious organization. It is an organism with Christ as its living head. It is alive, with the life of Christ made living in each member.

What part does the Holy Spirit play in this? *First*, the Bible beautifully tells us that the Church was brought into being by Him: "For by one Spirit we were all baptized into one body, whether Jews or Greeks, whether slaves or free, and we were all made to drink of one Spirit. For the body is not one member, but many" (1 Cor. 12:13, 14).

Second, by the Spirit God lives in the Church: "And in him [Christ] you too are being built together to become a dwelling in which God lives by his Spirit" (Eph. 2:22 NIV). God does not dwell today in temples made with hands. But if we recognize that in our church gatherings God is really in our midst personally, it will deepen our worship.

One point about the relation of the Holy Spirit and Jesus Christ needs clarification. The Scriptures speak of "Christ in you," and some Christians do not fully understand what this means. As the God-man, Jesus is in a glorified body. And wherever Jesus is, His body must be also. In that sense, in His work as the second person of the Trinity, Jesus is now at the right hand of the Father in heaven.

For example, consider Romans 8:10 (KJV), which says, "If Christ is in you, the body is dead because of sin." Or consider Galatians 2:20, "Christ lives in me." It is clear in these verses that if the Spirit is in us, then Christ is in us. Christ dwells in our hearts by faith. But the Holy Spirit is the person of the Trinity who actually dwells in us, having been sent by the Son who has gone away but who will come again in person when we shall literally see Him.

Believers are indeed the dwelling place of the Spirit. But, unfortunately, they are often lacking in the fruit of the Spirit. They need to be quickened and given new life. This was brought home to me forcefully by Bishop Festo Kivengere. In an article on the remarkable revivals that have swept East Africa, he said: "I want to share with you . . . the glorious work of the Holy Spirit in bringing new life to a dead church. . . . You can call it renewal, coming to life or whatever you choose. . . . The Lord Jesus in his risen power through the power of the Holy Spirit began to visit a church which was scattered like bones. . . . It may surprise some of you . . . that you can be evangelical and dry, but you can. And then Jesus Christ came. . . . The attraction, the growing power came through a simple presentation of the New Testament and the Holy Spirit took men and women, including myself, from our isolation and drew us to the center, the Cross. The theme of East African revival was the Cross and we needed it. . . . The Holy Spirit drew men and women from their isolation, and changed us—sins were sins in the glare of God's love and hearts were melted."[2]

For example, I have a pastor friend in Florida. His various degrees came from one of America's most prestigious eastern universities. He pastored a church in New England. Through his much learning, he had become almost an "agnostic," though deep in his heart he still believed. He said he watched his church in New England dwindle around him. There was no authority or power in his ministry. Then through a series of events he came to accept the Bible as the infallible Word of God. He began to live and speak with power. The fruit of the Spirit was evident in his life and spiritual power was evident in his ministry. He saw his church blossom like a rose. People began to come from all around to hear him preach.

Third, the Holy Spirit gives gifts to specific people in the Church "for the equipping of the saints for the work of service, to the building up of the body of Christ" (Eph. 4:12). Since we will examine these gifts more closely in later chapters, it is enough to say here that the Holy Spirit gives every Christian some gift the moment he receives Christ. No Christian can say, "I have no gift." Every believer has at least one gift from the Holy Spirit. A weakness in today's churches is the failure to recognize, cultivate, and use fully the gifts God has given people in the pews.

I have a pastor friend on the west coast of the United States. One Sunday he passed out blank slips of paper to his congregation. He said, "I want you to spend a week studying, thinking, and praying about what gift you have from the Holy Spirit. Write it on this slip of paper. Then we will collect the slips next Sunday morning." More than 400 slips of paper were turned in the following Sunday. Some listed only one gift—some listed two or three—and some said they were not certain about their gift. However, as a result the entire congregation was mobilized. All the gifts began to be used. It transformed the church into a "growth" church and a spiritually revitalized membership. Until then the people were expecting the pastor to have all the gifts and to do all the work. They were simply spectators. Now they realized that they had as great a responsibility to use their gifts as the pastor has to use his gifts.

The Holy Spirit's Work in the Believer's Life

Having considered the Holy Spirit's work in the world and the Church, we must now consider each believer. *First,* the Holy Spirit illumines (enlightens) the Christian's mind: "For to us God revealed them through the Spirit; for the Spirit searches all things, even the depths of God" (1 Cor. 2:10); "And do not be conformed to this world, but be transformed by the renewing of your mind" (Rom. 12:2); "And that you be renewed in the spirit of your mind" (Eph. 4:23).

In a small book stressing the importance of allowing God to develop and use our converted minds, John R. W. Stott says: "Nobody wants a cold, joyless, intellectual Christianity. But does this mean we should avoid 'intellectualism' at all costs?. . . Heaven forbid that knowledge without zeal should replace zeal without knowledge! God's purpose is both, zeal directed by knowledge, knowledge fired with zeal. As I once heard Dr. John Mackay say, when he was President of Princeton Seminary, 'Commitment without reflection is fanaticism in action. But reflection without commitment is the paralysis of all action.'"[3]

Dr. Stott stresses how mistaken are those who say that what matters in the end is "not doctrine but experience." In rebuttal he says, "This is tantamount to putting our subjective experience above the revealed truth of God."[4] It is the business of the Holy Spirit to lift the veil Satan has put over our minds, and to illuminate them so that we can understand the things of God. He does this especially as we read and study the Word of God, which the Holy Spirit has inspired.

Second, the Holy Spirit not only illumines the Christian's mind, but also indwells his body. "Do you not know that your body is a temple of the Holy Spirit who is in you, whom you have from God, and that you are not your own?" (1 Cor. 6:19).

If we Christians realized that God Himself in the person of the Holy Spirit really dwells within our bodies, we would be far more careful about what we eat, drink, look at, or read. No wonder Paul said, "But I buffet my body and make it my slave, lest possibly, after I have preached to others, I myself should be disqualified"

(1 Cor. 9:27). Paul disciplined his body for fear of God's disapproval. This should drive us to our knees in confession.

In other ways I need not enlarge upon now the Holy Spirit works in the lives of believers. For example, He comforts them (Acts 9:31); He guides them (John 16:13); He sanctifies them (Rom. 15:16); He tells His servants what to preach (1 Cor. 2:13); He directs missionaries where to go (Acts 13:2); He helps us in our infirmities (Rom. 8:26); and He even tells believers where they are not to go (Acts 16:6,7).

In summation, broadly speaking, the operations of the Holy Spirit among men in the three periods of human history may be defined by three words: "upon," "with," "in." In the Old Testament He came *upon* selected persons and remained for a season (Judg. 14:19). In the Gospels He is represented as dwelling *with* the disciples in the person of Christ (John 14:17). From the second chapter of Acts onward He is spoken of as being *in* the people of God (I Cor. 6:19).

3

The Holy Spirit and the Bible

"SOME TIME AGO a man took his worn New Testament to a bookbinder to bind it with a fine Morocco leather cover and to print *The New Testament* on the edge in gold leaf letters.

"At the appointed time he returned to find his New Testament beautifully bound. The bookbinder had one apology, however: 'I did not have small enough type in my shop to print out fully the words on the edge so I abbreviated them.' Looking on the edge of his Book, the man saw—T.N.T.

"This is true! It is God's dynamite."[1]

In the New Testament Paul declares that all Scripture comes from God. In fact, he says: "All Scripture is inspired by God and profitable for teaching, for reproof, for correction, for training in righteousness" (2 Tim. 3:16). He used a Greek word for "inspired" that literally means "God-breathed." Somewhat as God breathed life into man and made him a living soul, so also He breathed life and wisdom into the written Word of God. This makes the Bible the world's most important book, especially to everyone who believes in Christ. The Bible is the constant fountain for faith, conduct, and inspiration from which we drink daily.

The Holy Spirit Was the Inspirer of Scripture

Hundreds of passages indicate—either directly or indirectly—that God the Holy Spirit inspired the men who wrote the Bible.

We do not know exactly how He imprinted His message on the minds of those He chose to write His Word, but we know He did lead them to write what He wanted. "For no prophecy was ever made by an act of human will, but men moved by the Holy Spirit spoke from God" (2 Peter 1:21).

It seems that each book of the Bible came into being because of a special need at that time. Yet even as God was meeting a particular need, He was looking into the distant future too. He designed the Bible to meet the needs of all people in all ages. For this reason, biblical writers sometimes wrote about future events they did not understand fully but saw only dimly. Isaiah may not have fully understood the fifty-third chapter of his book as he detailed the suffering of Jesus Christ more than 700 years before it took place. "As to this salvation, the prophets who prophesied of the grace that would come to you made careful search and inquiry, seeking to know what person or time the Spirit of Christ within them was indicating as He predicted the sufferings of Christ and the glories to follow" (1 Peter 1:10, 11).

Throughout both the Old and New Testaments we find constant references to the Spirit of God inspiring the men of God who would write the Scriptures. For example, the Bible teaches that the Spirit spoke through David, who wrote many of the Psalms: "The Spirit of the Lord spoke by me, and His word was on my tongue" (2 Sam. 23:2).

He also spoke through the great prophet Jeremiah: "I will put My law within them, and on their heart I will write it; and I will be their God, and they shall be My people. And they shall not teach again, each man his neighbor and each man his brother, saying, 'Know the Lord,' for they shall all know Me, from the least of them to the greatest of them," declares the Lord, "for I will forgive their iniquity, and their sin I will remember no more" (Jer. 31:33, 34).

Ezekiel said: "The Spirit then entered me and made me stand on my feet, and He spoke with me and said to me, 'Go, shut yourself up in your house'" (Ezek. 3:24).

The apostle Peter spoke of "all things, about which God spoke by the mouth of His holy prophets from ancient time" (Acts 3:21).

The Book of Hebrews quotes from the Law (Heb. 9:6–8), the prophets (Heb. 10:15–17), and the Psalms (Heb. 3:7–10), in each case attributing authorship to the Holy Spirit.

Jesus assured the disciples in advance that the Holy Spirit would inspire the writers of the New Testament: "The Holy Spirit . . . will teach you all things, and bring to your remembrance all that I said to you" (John 14:26). This embraces the four Gospels, Matthew to John. Jesus' statement, "He will guide you into all the truth" (John 16:13), takes in the books from Acts to Jude. "He will disclose to you what is to come" (John 16:13), covers the Book of Revelation as well as many other passages throughout the New Testament. Thus, as someone has said, Scripture is literature indwelt by the Spirit of God.

Just as God the Holy Spirit inspired the writing of the Scriptures, so He was instrumental in the selection of the sixty-six books that comprise the canon of the Bible. Contrary to the opinion of many, the question of what books were included in the Bible was not settled simply by the human choice of any church council. The Holy Spirit was at work in Spirit-filled believers who selected the sixty-six books we have in our Bibles. And at last, after years and even centuries of discussion, prayer, and heartsearching, the canon of Scripture was closed. The Holy Spirit in His work did not bypass the human processes, but instead, He worked through them.

"Inspiration by the Spirit" Defined

When discussing the inspiration of the Bible, we immediately touch one of the most controversial questions of the ages. Ever since Satan questioned Eve in the Garden of Eden, "Indeed, has God said . . . ?" men have attacked the Word of God. But every time in history they have doubted it, dire consequences have resulted—whether in the life of an individual, a nation (ancient Israel), or the Church. Without exception the individual, the nation, or the Church went into a period of spiritual decline. Often idolatry and immorality followed.

Competent scholars agree that the Holy Spirit did not merely use the biblical writers as secretaries to whom He dictated the

Scriptures, although some sincere Christians think He did this. The Bible itself does not state in detail just *how* the Holy Spirit accomplished His purpose in getting the Scripture written. However, we do know that He used living human minds and guided their thoughts according to His divine purposes. Moreover, it has always been clear to me that we cannot have inspired ideas without inspired words.

It would be helpful if we define the important words associated with God-breathed Scripture. The first is *inspiration*.

When we speak of the *total* (or *plenary*) *inspiration* of the Bible, we mean that all of the Bible, not just some parts of it, are inspired. Dr. B. H. Carroll, founder of the largest theological seminary in the world (Southwestern Baptist Theological Seminary of Fort Worth, Texas), spoke and wrote at length on this subject:

> . . . the Bible is called holy because it is that infallible, *theopneustos* [God-breathed-out], product of the Holy Spirit. . . .
>
> A great many people say, "I think the Word of God is in the Bible, but I don't believe that all of the Bible is the Word of God; it contains the Word of God, but it is not the Word of God."
>
> My objection to this is that it would require inspiration to tell the spots in it that were inspired. It would call for an inspiration more difficult than the kind that I talk about, in order to turn the pages of the Bible and find out which part is the Word of God. . . .
>
> In other words, with reference to the Scriptures, inspiration is plenary, which means full and complete, hence my question is, "Do you believe in the plenary inspiration of the Bible?" If the inspiration is complete, it must be plenary.
>
> My next question is this: "Do you believe in plenary verbal inspiration?"
>
> I do, for the simple reason that the words are mere signs of ideas, and I don't know how to get at the idea except through the words. If the words don't tell me, how shall I know? Sometimes the word is a very small one, maybe only one letter or a mere element. The word with one letter—the smallest letter—shows the inspiration of the Old Testament. The man that put that there was inspired.
>
> Take the words of Jesus. He says, "Not one jot or tittle of that law shall ever fail."
>
> The "jot" is the smallest letter in the Hebrew alphabet and the "tittle" is a small turn or projection of a Hebrew letter. He says the heavens may fall, but not one jot or tittle of that law shall fail. Then He says that the Scriptures cannot be broken.

What is it that cannot be broken? Whatever is written cannot be broken if it is *theopneustos*. But the word is not inspired if it is not *theopneustos*, which means God-breathed, or God-inspired."2

We could say much more about the complete trustworthiness of the Bible. By way of illustration, hundreds of times the Bible uses phrases like "God said," or "The word of the Lord came unto me saying." It is also interesting that Jesus never once told us to doubt the difficult passages of the Old Testament Scriptures. For example, He accepted as fact, not fiction, the stories of Jonah and the fish, Noah and the ark, and the creation of Adam and Eve. If these stories had not been literally true, He surely would have told us so. But time after time Jesus (and the New Testament writers) quoted the Scriptures as authoritative and as the very Word of God.

Of course, inspiration by the Holy Spirit does not refer to the many English translations, but to the original languages. No modern language, whether English, French, or Spanish, has in it the exact equivalent for every Greek or Hebrew word. However, numerous scholars agree that most of the translations, even with their variations, do not alter or misrepresent the basic theological teachings of the Scriptures—especially those dealing with salvation and Christian living.

My wife has more than twenty different translations available at all times. By the time she has compared the various wordings of all these, she can be reasonably sure that she has a good idea of the meaning the Holy Spirit intended to convey in any passage of Scripture.

It is also interesting that some words could not be translated into other languages so it was necessary to lift them from the original tongue. The Greek word for "baptism" had no English equivalent, so it came to *be* the English word. The Holy Spirit has seen to it that the Bible is not a dead book but a living vehicle for Him to use as He wishes.

There is a second word we should discuss when we talk about the Bible. Not only is the Bible inspired, but it is also *authoritative*. When we say the Bible is authoritative, we mean that it is God's binding revelation to us. We submit to it because it has come from God. Suppose we ask: What is the source of our religious knowledge? The answer is, the Bible, and it is authoritative for us. As Dr. John R. W. Stott has written,

"To reject the authority of either the Old Testament or the New Testament is to reject the authority of Christ. It is supremely because we are determined to submit to the authority of Jesus Christ as Lord that we submit to the authority of Scripture. . . . submission to Scripture is fundamental to everyday Christian living, for without it Christian discipleship, Christian integrity, Christian freedom and Christian witness are all seriously damaged if not actually destroyed."[3]

Yes, every area of our lives is to be under the Lordship of Jesus Christ. And that means the searchlight of God's Word must penetrate every corner of our lives. We are not free to pick and choose the parts of the Bible we want to believe or obey. God has given us all of it, and we should be obedient to all of it.

Having declared what I believe about the authority, inspiration, and infallibility of the Bible, I must still answer one further question. On what basis have I come to believe all of this about the Bible? There are various reasons for having confidence in the Bible as God's Word, but it is at this point that the work of the Holy Spirit is most plainly manifested. The truth of the matter is that the same Holy Spirit who was the author of the Scriptures through the use of human personalities also works in each of us to convince us the Bible is the Word of God to be trusted in all its parts.

In his *Institutes of the Christian Religion*, John Calvin has a word about the testimony of the Holy Spirit that I like:

"The same Spirit, therefore, who has spoken through the mouths of the prophets must penetrate into our hearts to persuade us that they faithfully proclaimed what had been divinely commanded. . . . Until he illumines their minds, they ever waver among many doubts! . . . Let this point therefore stand: that those whom the Holy Spirit has inwardly taught truly rest upon Scripture, and that Scripture indeed is self-authenticated; hence, it is not right to subject it to proof and reasoning. And the certainty it deserves with us, it attains by the testimony of the Spirit. For even if it wins reverence for itself by its own majesty, it seriously affects us only when it is sealed upon our hearts through the Spirit."

Calvin continues, "Therefore, illumined by his power, we believe neither by our own nor by anyone else's judgment that Scripture is from God; but above human judgment we affirm with utter certainty (just as if we were gazing upon the majesty of God himself) that it has flowed to us from the very mouth of God by the ministry of men. We seek no proofs, no marks of genuineness upon which our judgment may lean; but we subject our judgment and wit to it as to a thing far beyond any guesswork! This we do, not as persons accustomed to seize upon some unknown thing, which, under closer scrutiny, displeases them, but fully conscious that we hold the unassailable truth!"[4]

The Illumination of the Spirit

That the writers of the Old and New Testaments were inspired by the Holy Spirit is one part of the story. In addition, He illumines the minds and opens the hearts of its readers. We find spiritual response to the Word of God described in scores of ways. Jeremiah said, "Thy words were found and I ate them, And Thy words became for me a joy and the delight of my heart; For I have been called by Thy name, O Lord God of hosts" (Jer. 15:16). Furthermore, Isaiah said, "The grass withers, the flower fades, But the word of our God stands forever" (Isa. 40:8).

Jesus warned the Sadducees of His day that they entertained many errors in their teachings because they did not know the Scriptures or the power of God (Matt. 22:29). This links the Scriptures to the power of the Holy Spirit, who effects change through the Bible. Moreover, John records Jesus' words, "the Scripture cannot be broken" (John 10:35). Jesus also said, "You are already clean because of the word which I have spoken to you" (John 15:3).

So through the Bible the Holy Spirit not only gives us doctrinal and historical truth; He also uses it as the vehicle for speaking to our hearts. This is why I constantly urge people to study the Scriptures—whether they fully understand what they are reading or not. The reading of Scripture itself enables the Holy Spirit to enlighten us and to do His work in us. While we read the Word, its message saturates our hearts, whether we are conscious of what is happening or not. The Word with all its mysterious power touches our lives and gives us its power.

This is seen, for example, in a statement Paul made: "Eye hath not seen, nor ear heard, neither have entered into the heart of man, the things which God hath prepared for them that love him. But God hath revealed them unto us by his Spirit . . ." (1 Cor. 2:9, 10 KJV).

Note that Paul does not say God reveals these wonderful things to us by His *Word* (although it is there that we find them), but rather He does it by His *Spirit* through His Word. "We have received, not the spirit of the world, but the Spirit who is from God, that we might know the things freely given to us by God" (1 Cor. 2:12).

As the Reverend Gottfried Osei-Mensah of Kenya said at the Lausanne Congress on Evangelization in 1974: "It is the work of the Holy Spirit to reveal truths previously hidden from human search and understanding, and to enlighten men's minds to know and understand them (1 Cor. 2:9, 10). . . . If the role of the Holy Spirit is to teach, ours is to be diligent students of the Word."[5]

This has been my experience as I have studied the Scriptures. Things I may have known intellectually for years have come alive to me in their fuller spiritual significance almost miraculously. As I have studied the Scriptures, I have also learned that the Spirit always lets more light shine from the Word. Almost every time I read an old, familiar passage I see something new. This happens because the written Word of God is a living Word. I always come to the Scriptures with the Psalmist's prayer, "Open my eyes, that I may behold wonderful things from Thy law" (Ps. 119:18).

The Unity of the Spirit and the Word

A glorious unity exists between the Holy Spirit and the Word of God. On the day of Pentecost Peter illustrated this in quoting from the Old Testament, "This is that which was spoken by the prophet Joel" (Acts 2:16 KJV). "This" refers to the promised Spirit. "That" refers to the written Word. "This is that" shows the wonderful unity that exists between the Spirit and the Word.

"Where the word of a king is, there is power" (Eccl. 8:4 KJV), and "where the Spirit of the Lord is, there is liberty" (2 Cor. 3:17). These two things—power and liberty—will characterize the utterances of that man who, filled with the Spirit, proclaims the Word of God. James Hervey describes the change that took place in Wesley when he was controlled by the Spirit. "Wesley's preaching," he says, "once was like the firing of an arrow—all the speed and force depended on the strength of his arm in bending the bow; now it was like the fire of a rifle ball—the force depending upon the power, needing only a finger touch to let it off."

I believe effective preaching must be biblical preaching, whether it is the exposition of a single word in the Bible, a text, or a chapter. The Word is what the Spirit uses. So the important element is that the Word of God be proclaimed. Thousands of pastors, Sunday school teachers and Christian workers are powerless because they do not make the Word the source of their preaching or teaching. When we preach or teach the Scriptures, we open the door for the Holy Spirit to do His work. God has not promised to bless oratory or clever preaching. He has promised to bless His Word. He has said that it will not return to Him "empty" (Isa. 55:11).

It is the Word of God which changes our lives also. Remember, God has given us His Word "for teaching, for reproof, for correction, for training in righteousness; that the man of God may be adequate, equipped for every good work" (2 Tim. 3:16, 17). Are these things happening in our lives? Are we learning God's truth? Jesus said, "Thy word is truth" (John 17:17). Are we being convicted of sin in our lives, and our need of God's correction and God's righteousness, as we read the Word of God? The Bible says, "For the word of God is living and active and sharper than any two-edged sword, and piercing as far as the division of soul and spirit, of both joints and marrow, and able to judge the thoughts and intentions of the heart. And there is no creature hidden from His sight, but all things are open and laid bare to the eyes of Him with whom we have to do." (Heb. 4:12, 13). Let the study of the Bible become central in your life—not just so you will know it, but that you will obey it. Let Job's statement be yours: "I have not departed from the command of His lips; I have treasured the words of His mouth more than my necessary food" (Job 23:12).

George Muller (the great founder of the Bristol Orphanage in the last century) once said, "The vigor of our Spiritual Life will be in exact proportion to the place held by the Bible in our life and thoughts. . . . I have read the Bible through one hundred times, and always with increasing delight. Each time it seems like a new book to me. Great has been the blessing from consecutive, diligent, daily study. I look upon it as a lost day when I have not had a good time over the Word of God."[6]

The Spirit Is Using the Word Today

The Spirit has the power to transform and inspire lives today through the Bible. Here are some situations where He has recently touched people:

A former surgeon-general of Portugal was out walking one rainy day. When he returned to his home, he found a piece of paper sticking to his shoe. When he pulled it off, he discovered it to be a tract that presented the Gospel by using Scripture. On reading it, he was soundly converted to Jesus Christ.

Dr. J. B. Phillips writes in the preface to his *Letters to Young Churches* that he was "continually struck by the living quality of the material" on which he worked; often he "felt rather like 'an electrician rewiring an ancient house without being able to turn the mains off'."[7]

Many prisoners in the "Hanoi Hilton" during the Vietnam war were gloriously sustained by the Spirit through the Word of God. These men testified to the strength they received from the Word of God. Howard Rutledge, in his book *In the Presence of Mine Enemies*, tells how the prisoners developed a code system that the enemy was never able to break. By it they communicated with one another, sharing names and serial numbers of every prisoner. They also passed along other messages as well, including Scripture verses that they knew.

Geoffrey Bull, a missionary on the borders of Tibet, said in his book, *When Iron Gates Yield*, that during his three years of imprisonment he was relentlessly brainwashed and would have succumbed had it not been for Scriptures he had committed to memory. He repeated them over and over to himself when he was in solitary confinement. Through them God strengthened him to face the torture designed to break him down.

I have written here mainly of those who were imprisoned or in desperate circumstances. Yet much could be said about the daily nourishment and reinforcement of faith we all receive from studying the Word of God, and the wisdom it provides us for day-to-day living. It reminds me of Hebrews 11:32, "And what more shall I say? For time would fail me to tell of Gideon, Barak, Samson, Jephthah . . ." (RSV). Tens of thousands of God's saints and sufferers through the ages have found their dark nights lightened and tortured souls strengthened because they found help from the Spirit in the Word of God.

As we approach the end of the age, persecution is going to be intensified. We are already seeing evidences in many parts of the world. The Scriptures you memorize now and the teachings of the Word of God you learn now will sustain you in that hour!—if you are called on to suffer physically and mentally for the name of Christ!

4

The Holy Spirit and Salvation

DURING ONE OF our London Crusades, a Russian nobleman came one evening. He spoke no English. Yet when the invitation was given to receive Christ he responded. The trained Russian-speaking counselor asked him how, knowing no English, he had understood enough of the message to respond so intelligently. "When I entered this place," the nobleman replied, "I was over-whelmed with a longing for God. Tell me, how can I find Him?"

This is but one of hundreds of similar stories that have come to my attention during my years of ministry. In our Crusades we have counselors who speak various languages. For example, in our recent Crusade in Toronto, trained counselors were available to help in twenty-eight languages. It is amazing that in almost every service people respond to the "invitation" who understand little or no English. To me, this is clearly the work of the Holy Spirit drawing people to the Savior in spite of the language barrier.

When a person comes to Christ, the Bible tells us the Holy Spirit has been at work in a number of ways. Some of these we may not fully understand, and yet this does not alter the fact that the Holy Spirit is deeply involved in our salvation. In this chapter we will look at some of the ways the Spirit works to bring us to Christ.

The Need for Spiritual Rebirth

We live in a revolutionary, changing world. Man's moral capacities lag far behind his technological skills and discoveries.

This could mean disaster for the human race. In light of this, the greatest need in the world is to bring about the transformation of human nature. Many of our technologists are saying there is a great need for a new breed of man. Even the political radicals and the humanists talk about the "new man." From this it is clear that they acknowledge that man, as he is, is not good enough. So they also look for the arrival of the new man who, they say, will come into being when society has been changed so that a new environment can produce him.

There are also the technocrats who believe that technology is now advancing so rapidly that we will soon be able to create an entirely new human race. We have genetic engineers who believe that by the end of this century they will be able to create any type of person they want.

But there is only one ultimate answer to the need of man to be changed. Science and technology cannot change man's basic nature. Economic restructuring cannot change man's basic nature. No amount of self-improvement or wishful thinking can change man's basic nature. Only God—the One who created us—can recreate us. And that is precisely what He does when we give ourselves to Jesus Christ. The Bible says, "Therefore if any man is in Christ, he is a new creature; the old things passed away; behold, new things have come" (2 Cor. 5:17). What a tremendous statement!

The Bible speaks of this change in various ways. One of the most vivid is the term "born again." Just as we have been born physically, so we can be born again—spiritually. "For you have been born again not of seed which is perishable but imperishable, that is, through the living and abiding word of God" (1 Peter 1:23).

Certainly few passages in the New Testament speak as directly about the Holy Spirit's role in our salvation as the third chapter of John. In it, John recounts for us an interview Jesus had with a very influential religious leader named Nicodemus. Nicodemus was wealthy, and a member of the Sanhedrin, the ruling council of the Jewish nation. He probably fasted several times a week, and spent time each day in the Temple in prayer. He tithed his income, and was apparently a noted religious teacher. He would have been considered a model Christian in some circles today. But Jesus said all his goodness was not enough. Instead, Jesus said, "You must be born again" (John 3:7).

Jesus went on to explain that this new birth—this spiritual regeneration—is accomplished by the Holy Spirit. "The wind blows where it wishes and you hear the sound of it, but do not know where it comes from and where it is going; so is every one who is born of the Spirit" (John 3:8). There is something mysterious about this; we cannot fully understand how the new birth comes to us. It is from above, not from the earth or from within our human nature. It comes because of the love and grace of God. It comes because of the death and resurrection of Jesus Christ. It comes because of the action of the Holy Spirit.

In its notes on John 3 the *Open Bible* describes the encounter between Jesus and Nicodemus this way: "What a shock it must have been [to Nicodemus] to learn that his religion was not enough! It never is. He came to Jesus, addressing Him as 'a teacher come from God.' Jesus knew Nicodemus, as He knows all men [John 2:24, 25], and Jesus knew that he needed more than a teacher—he needed a Saviour. He needed more than religion—he needed regeneration. He needed more than law—he needed life. Jesus began by going right to the point when He said, 'Ye must be born again.' Nicodemus asked, 'How can a man be born when he is old?' [This was a very natural question for Nicodemus to ask.] Then Jesus pointed out the dissimilarity in the two births: 'That which is born of flesh is flesh' (the flesh will never change); and 'that which is born of the Spirit is spirit' (the Spirit will never change). [John 3:6]"[1]

Jesus knew what lies in the hearts of all men—the fatal disease that causes lying, cheating, hate, prejudice, greed, and lust. He said, "For out of the heart come evil thoughts, murders, adulteries, fornications, thefts, false witness, slanders. These are the things which defile the man" (Matt. 15:19, 20). Psychologists realize something is wrong with the human race, but they disagree as to the problem. The Bible says man's problem is the direct result of his decision as an intelligent, moral, responsible being to revolt against the will of his Maker. Man's disease is called S-I-N in the Bible.

Sin is a transgression of the law (1 John 3:4). It is falling short of doing one's duty, a failure to do what one knows he ought to do in God's sight. It is iniquity—a turning aside from a straight path. Isaiah said, "All of us like sheep have gone astray, each of us has turned to his own way" (Isa. 53:6). The Bible teaches that the sinner is "dead" before God when it says that "through one man sin entered into the world, and death through sin, and so death spread to all men, because all sinned" (Rom. 5:12). Thus a radical change is needed in the inner being of every man. This is a change man cannot earn, nor is it something he can do for himself. It is a change science cannot accomplish for him; it is something God alone can and must do.

The Holy Spirit Convicts Us and Calls Us

One of the most devastating effects of sin is that it has blinded us to our own sin. "The god of this world has blinded the minds of the unbelieving, that they might not see the light of the gospel of the glory of Christ, who is the image of God" (2 Cor. 4:4). Only the Holy Spirit can open our eyes. Only He can convict us of the depth of our sin, and only He can convince us of the truth of the gospel. That is one reason the Holy Spirit is called "the Spirit of truth" in John 14:17. In speaking of the Holy Spirit, Jesus said, "And He, when He comes, will convict the world concerning sin, and righteousness, and judgment; concerning sin, because they do not believe in Me; and concerning righteousness, because I go to the Father, and you no longer behold Me; and concerning judgment, because the ruler of this world has been judged" (John 16: 8-11).

J. Gresham Machen wrote: "There must be the mysterious work of the Spirit of God in the new birth. Without that, all our arguments are quite useless. . . . What the Holy Spirit does in the new birth is not to make a man a Christian regardless of the evidence, but on the contrary to clear away the mists from his eyes and enable him to attend to the evidence."[2]

We should also remember that it is the truth of the Word of God which is used by the Holy Spirit to bring conviction to our hearts. The Bible tells us, "So faith comes from hearing, and hearing by the word of Christ" (Rom. 10:17). Or again we read that, "The word of God is living and active and sharper than any two-edged sword, and piercing as far as the division of soul and spirit, of both joints and marrow, and able to judge the thoughts and intentions of the heart" (Heb. 4:12). God the Holy Spirit can take the humblest preaching or the feeblest words of our witness to Christ, and transform them by His power into a convicting word in the lives of others.

Apart from the ministry of the Holy Spirit we would never clearly see the truth of God concerning our sin, or the truth of God about our Savior. I believe this is what Jesus meant in John 6:44: "No one can come to Me, unless the Father who sent Me draws him; and I will raise him up on the last day."

However, the Bible also gives us a solemn warning about resisting the calling of the Holy Spirit. In Genesis 6:3 we read: "My Spirit shall not strive with man forever." Without the "striving" of the Spirit it would be impossible for a person to come to Christ. Yet, there is also the danger that we will pass the point of no return, and that our hearts will be so calloused and hardened by sin that we will no longer hear the voice of the Spirit.

Again, there is much we may not understand fully about this, and it is not our place to say when that point has been reached in another person's life. No man could have been more hardened, seemingly, than King Manasseh in the Old Testament, and yet he eventually repented of his sin and was forgiven by God in His grace (2 Chron. 33). But we dare not neglect the warning of the Bible that tells us, "Now is the time of God's favor, now is the day of salvation" (2 Cor. 6:2 NIV). The writer of Proverbs said, "A man who hardens his neck after much reproof will suddenly be broken beyond remedy" (Prov. 29:1).

The Holy Spirit Regenerates Us

Along with repentance and faith, one of the works of the Spirit of God in the heart of man is regeneration. "Regeneration" is another term for renewal or rebirth. "He saved us, not on the basis of deeds which we have done in righteousness, but according to His mercy, by the washing of regeneration and renewing by the Holy Spirit" (Titus 3:5). Actually the Greek word translated "regeneration" here is a compound of two Greek words; it literally means "birth again" or new birth.

This is a once-for-all change, though it has continuing effects. In John 3:3 the Bible speaks of one being "born again," and the Amplified Version suggests "born anew" or "born from above" to clarify the meaning. The sinner in his natural state is spiritually dead in trespasses and sins. In regeneration that which is dead is made alive. He is justified by God from the guilt of a broken law, and he is forgiven of every sin. Further, by the new birth the justified sinner becomes a new creation—a new creature (2 Cor. 5:17; Gal. 6:15 RSV). Moreover, regeneration, like justification, is immediate and constitutes a one-time act of the Holy Spirit, though the person who is "born again" might, or might not, be conscious of the exact time. Theologians have long debated exactly when regeneration actually takes place in a person's life. In spite of some disagreements, the central issue is clear: it is the Holy Spirit who regenerates us within.

The gift of new or divine life to the regenerated person comes to the soul from Christ through the Holy Spirit. Jesus said that the new birth is "a mystery." He uses the illustration of the wind blowing: we sense its effects but we cannot see where it comes from or where it is going. Thus regeneration is a hidden transaction in the same sense that it is something which takes place within the individual heart and may or may not be known to the one who receives it—and often it is not immediately visible to people around him. The results that flow from the new birth are so incalculably significant that they deserve to be called "a miracle"— the greatest of all miracles! Even as unbelieving men did not know Jesus on earth, and failed to realize that God incarnate was standing before them, so it is possible for "the new man" in Christ to go unrecognized for at least a while. Yet, known or unknown to the world, the new man exists within. Sooner or later the new birth will manifest itself in godly living. But the divine life, which will abide forever, is there, and the "new man" who possesses the kingdom of God is there (2 Cor. 5:17)—a new creature.

This is not to deny the importance of personal faith and decision. We do not passively sit back and wait for the Spirit to do His work before we come to Christ. We are commanded to "Ask, and it shall be given to you; seek, and you shall find; knock, and it shall be opened to you" (Matt. 7:7). We have the promise of God: "And you will seek Me and find Me, when you search for Me with all your heart" (Jer. 29:13). Furthermore, the Scripture tells us that even faith itself is a gift of God's grace. "Because of his kindness you have been saved through trusting Christ. And even trusting is not of yourselves; it too is a gift from God" (Eph. 2:8 LB). We therefore have everything we need to decide for Christ, but we still have a responsibility to respond to the call and conviction of the Holy Spirit.

When a person is born again, the process is uncomplicated from the divine perspective. The Spirit of God takes the Word of God and makes the child of God. We are born again through the operation of the Holy Spirit, who in turn uses the divinely inspired Word of God. God's Spirit brings life to men. At this point the Holy Spirit indwells a person for life. He receives *eternal* life.

As an evangelist for over thirty-five years, I have watched hundreds of thousands of people come down aisles in auditoriums, stadiums, churches, tents, and brush arbors, to make what has often been referred to as a "decision" for Christ. Years ago I tried to change the terminology to "inquirers." Walking down an aisle in an evangelistic meeting does not necessarily mean a person has been or will be regenerated. Going forward to make some kind of public commitment to Christ is only a visible, though an important, act. It may or may not reflect what is going on or has already taken place in the human heart. Regeneration is *not* the work of the evangelist; it is the work of God's Spirit. The indispensable condition of the new birth is repentance and faith, but repentance and faith itself does not save. Genuine faith is God's gift to a person—as I have said, even helping us to repent. When a person displays that kind of repentance and faith, we may be sure that God the Holy Spirit accompanies it with regeneration. In this we see the love and grace of God shed abroad toward judgment-bound sinners through Jesus Christ.

Thus, to be born again means that "as the Father raises the dead and gives them life, even so the Son also gives life to whom He wishes" (John 5:21). In Acts, Peter called it "repenting" or "being converted." In Romans 6:13, Paul spoke of it as being "alive from the dead." To the Colossians, Paul said, ". . . you laid aside the old self with its evil practices, and have put on the new self who is being renewed to a true knowledge according to the image of the One who created him" (Col. 3:9, 10).

You and I cannot inherit regeneration: Rather, "as many as received Him [Jesus], to them He gave the right to become children of God, even to those who believe in His name" (John 1:12). A person may have been baptized, as Hitler and Stalin were, but that is no guarantee that he has been regenerated. Simon the Sorcerer was baptized by Philip after having "believed" in some fuzzy mental sense, but Peter told him, "Your heart is not right before God" (Acts 8:21).

A person may be confirmed in one of the more liturgical churches, but that does not necessarily mean he has been regenerated. In the Book of Acts we read, "The Lord was adding to their number day by day those who were being saved" (Acts 2:47). The one indispensable condition for admission to the fellowship of the early church was that each one first had to have been regenerated.

Nor can one be regenerated by doing good works: "He saved us, not on the basis of deeds which we have done in righteousness, but according to His mercy, by the washing of regeneration and renewing by the Holy Spirit" (Titus 3:5). A man can join every club in town and become involved in every charitable event and be a "good," "moral" person all his life, and still not know what it means to be regenerated.

Others try to be regenerated by reformation. They do their best to reform by making new resolutions. But the Bible says, "All our righteous deeds are like a filthy garment" in the sight of God (Isa. 64:6).

Some well-meaning people even try to find salvation through imitating Christ in their lives. But this is not acceptable to God, because no one can really imitate Christ. Christ was pure. Men are sinners, *dead* in sin. What they need is life, and this can be supplied only by the Holy Spirit through regeneration.

Have you been regenerated by the power of the Spirit of God? Nothing less can bring true spiritual rebirth to your life. But God sent His Son into the world to give us new life. God has given us His Word, and the power of the Holy Spirit can take it and bring regeneration—spiritual rebirth—to us.

The new birth will bring about a change in your relationship with God, a change in your relationship with your family, a change in your relationship with yourself, a change in your relationship with your neighbors. Gradually, if you are an obedient believer, it will bring about a change in disposition, affection, aims, principles, and dimensions.

The Holy Spirit Assures Us

After we receive Christ as Savior we may be confused sometimes because many of the old temptations have not disappeared. We still sin. Sometimes we lose our tempers. Pride and jealousy may still crop up from time to time. This is not only confusing, it is discouraging and sometimes leads to spiritual depression. We may even have some particular "besetting sin" which plagues us, and which we do not seem to be able to conquer.

But the moment you and I received Christ and were regenerated by the Holy Spirit we were given a new nature. Thus, those of us who are born again have two natures. The old nature is from our first birth; the new is from our new birth. By the old birth we are children of the flesh; by the new birth we are children of God. This is why Jesus told Nicodemus that he "must be born again."

Whatever the problem, whenever the old nature within us asserts itself, a new believer may begin to doubt whether or not he has really been born again. Satan would want us to doubt the reality of our salvation—which is really doubting God's Word to us. We will write more fully about the assurance of our salvation in a later chapter, but at this point we need to remind ourselves that the Holy Spirit also gives us assurance that we have been born again and have become members of the family of God. "And the Holy Spirit also bears witness to us" (Heb. 10:15). By the written Word of God, and by the quiet work of the Spirit in our hearts, we know we have been born again—regardless of the accusations of Satan. "The Spirit Himself bears witness with our spirit that we are children of God" (Rom. 8:16).

How to Become Born Again

First, realize that you are a sinner in God's eyes. You may not consider yourself a bad person, because you know you have lived a fairly decent life. On the other hand, you may be carrying a burden of guilt over some sins committed in the past. Whatever your background, the Bible tells us "there is none righteous, no, not one" (Rom. 3:10 KJV). We have all broken the Law of God, and we all deserve nothing but God's judgment and wrath.

Second, realize that God loves you and sent His Son to die for you. You deserve to die for your sins, but Christ died in your place. "For Christ also died for sins once for all, the just for the unjust, in order that He might bring us to God" (1 Peter 3:18). That is the wonder of the gospel—that God loves us! He loves you, in spite of the fact you are a sinner.

Third, repent of your sins. Repentance comes from a Greek word meaning "a change of mind." It means that I admit I am a sinner, and that I feel sorry for the fact I have sinned. But repentance also means I actually turn my back on my sins—I reject them—and determine by God's grace to live as He wants me to live. Jesus said, "unless you repent, you will all likewise perish" (Luke 13:3). Repentance involves a willingness to leave sin behind, and turn my life over to Jesus Christ as Lord of my life. We see ourselves as God sees us and we pray, "God, be merciful to me, the sinner!" (Luke 18:13).

Fourth, come by faith and trust to Christ. Salvation, the Bible tells us, is a free gift. God has done everything possible to make salvation available to us, but we must respond and make that gift our own. "For the wages of sin is death, but the free gift of God is eternal life in Christ Jesus our Lord" (Rom. 6:23).

How do you accept this gift? By a simple act of faith in which you say "yes" to Christ. If you have never accepted Christ into your life, I invite you to do it right now before another minute passes. Simply tell God you know you are a sinner, and you are sorry for your sins. Tell Him you believe Jesus Christ died for you, and that you want to give your life to Him right now, to follow Him as Lord the rest of your life. "For God so loved the world, that He gave His only begotten Son, that whoever believes in Him should not perish, but have eternal life" (John 3:16).

If you have done that, God has forgiven all your sins. What a wonderful thing to know that every sin you ever committed—even the things you did not realize were sins—are all washed away by the blood of Jesus Christ, "in whom we have redemption, the forgiveness of sins" (Col. 1:14). More than that—you can accept by faith now that you are a new creation in Christ.

In their conversation Jesus reminded Nicodemus of an incident in the wilderness journey of the ancient Israelites. God had judged His sinning people by sending among them serpents whose bites were fatal. Many Israelites were suffering and dying. Then God told Moses to fashion a serpent of brass and lift it high on a pole. All who looked upon that serpent by faith after they had been bitten would be saved. That sounded like an insult to their intelligence. There was no healing quality in brass. And they knew that rubbing medicine on their bites would not heal them. Fighting the serpents was of no avail. Making an offering to the serpent on the pole wouldn't help. Prayer to the serpent would not save them from death. Even Moses the prophet of God could not help them.

Rather, *all* they had to do was look at the serpent of brass in childlike faith that God would save them totally by His grace. When they looked at the serpent of brass, they were looking beyond the serpent to God Himself. So it is as if Jesus said, "I am going to be lifted up—look unto me and be saved." Of course, His "lifting up" was to take place at His forthcoming death on the cross. No one can come to Christ unless the Holy Spirit draws him to the cross, where Jesus by His blood cleanses away the sin of each person who places his faith in Him.

As with the Israelites in the wilderness, God does not mean to insult our intelligence. But if you have not believed in Christ, your mind has been blinded spiritually by the devil and affected by sin. That is why the apostle Paul said, "For since in the wisdom of God the world through its wisdom did not come to know God, God was well-pleased through the foolishness of the message preached to save those who believe" (1 Cor. 1:21).

At first it looks foolish to believe that Jesus Christ, who died on a cross and rose again 2,000 years ago, can transform your life radically today by the Holy Spirit. Yet millions of Christians on every continent would rise at this moment to testify that He has transformed their lives. It happened to me many years ago. It could happen to you—today!

5

Baptism
with the Spirit

MANY YEARS AGO when I was attending a small Bible
school in Florida, I visited what was called a "brush arbor revival
meeting." The speaker was an old-fashioned Southern revival
preacher. The little place seated about two hundred people and was
filled. The speaker made up in thunder what he lacked in logic,
and the people loved it.

"Have you been baptized with the Holy Spirit?" he asked the
audience during the sermon.

Apparently he knew a great many in the audience because he
would point to someone and ask, "Brother, have you been baptized
with the Spirit?" And the man would answer, "Yes, bless God."

"Young man," he said, spotting me, "have you been baptized
with the Holy Spirit?" "Yes, sir," I replied.

"When were you baptized with the Holy Spirit?" he asked. He
had not questioned the others on this.

"The moment I received Jesus Christ as my Savior," I replied.
He looked at me with a puzzled expression, but before going to
the next person he said, "That couldn't be."

But it could! It was.

I do not doubt the sincerity of this preacher. However, in my
own study of the Scriptures through the years I have become convinced that there is only one baptism with the Holy Spirit in the
life of every believer, and that takes place at the moment of con-

version. This baptism with the Holy Spirit was initiated at Pentecost, and all who come to know Jesus Christ as Savior share in that experience and are baptized with the Spirit the moment they are regenerated. In addition, they may be filled with the Holy Spirit; if not, they need to be.

The scriptural usage of the word *baptism* shows that it is something initiatory both in the case of water baptism and Spirit baptism, and that it is *not repeated*. I can find no biblical data to show that the baptism with the Spirit would ever be repeated.

"For by one Spirit we were all baptized into one body" (1 Cor. 12:13). The original Greek of this passage makes it clear that this baptism of the Spirit is a completed past action. (The King James Version incorrectly translates it into the present tense rather than the past.)

Two things stand out in that verse: first, the baptism with the Spirit is a collective operation of the Spirit of God; second, it includes every believer. Dr. W. Graham Scroggie once said at Keswick, "Observe carefully to whom the Apostle is writing and of whom he is speaking." He uses the word *"all"*—"It is not to the faithful Thessalonians, nor to the liberal Philippians, nor to the spiritual Ephesians, but to the carnal Corinthians (1 Cor. 3:1)," Scroggie went on. The clear indication is that baptism with the Spirit is connected with our *standing* before God, not our current subjective *state*; with our *position* and not our *experience*.

This becomes still clearer if we examine the experiences of the Israelites described in 1 Corinthians 10:1–5. In these verses there are five *alls*. "All under the cloud," "all passed through the sea," "all were baptized," "all ate," "all drank." It was after all these things happened to all the people that the differences came: "Nevertheless, with most of them God was not well-pleased" (1 Cor. 10:5).

In other words, they were all part of the people of God. This did not mean, however, that all lived up to their calling as God's holy people. In like manner, all believers are baptized with the Holy Spirit. This does not mean, however, that they are filled or controlled by the Spirit. The important thing is the great central truth—when I come to Christ, God gives His Spirit to me.

Differences That Divide Us

I realize that baptism with the Holy Spirit has been differently understood by some of my fellow believers. We should not shrink from stating specific differences of opinion. But we should also try to understand each other, pray for each other, and be willing to learn from each other as we seek to know what the Bible teaches. The differences of opinion on this matter are somewhat similar to differences of opinion about water baptism and church government. Some baptize babies; others do not. Some sprinkle or pour; others only immerse. Some have congregational church polity; others have presbyterian or representative democracy; still others have the episcopal form. In no way should these differences be divisive. I can have wonderful Christian fellowship, especially in the work of evangelism, with those who hold various views.

On the other hand, the question of the baptism with the Holy Spirit, in my judgment, is often more important than these other issues, especially when the doctrine of the baptism with the Spirit is distorted. For example, some Christians hold that the Spirit's baptism only comes at some time subsequent to conversion. Others say that this later Spirit baptism is necessary before a person can be fully used of God. Still others contend that the baptism with the Spirit is always accompanied with the outward sign of a particular gift, and that unless this sign is present the person has not been baptized with the Spirit.

I must admit that at times I have really wanted to believe this distinctive teaching. I, too, have wanted an "experience." But I want every experience to be biblically based. The biblical truth, it seems to me, is that we are baptized into the body of Christ by the Spirit at conversion. This is the only Spirit baptism. At this time we can and should be filled with the Holy Spirit, and afterward, be refilled, and even filled unto all fullness. As has often been said, "One baptism, but many fillings." I do not see from Scripture that this filling by the Holy Spirit constitutes a second baptism, nor do I see that speaking in tongues is a necessary accompaniment of being filled with the Spirit.

Sometimes these different opinions are really only differences in semantics. As we shall see in the next chapter, what some people call the baptism of the Spirit may really be what the Scripture calls the filling of the Spirit, which may take place many times in our lives after our conversion.

There are, incidentally, only seven passages in the New Testament which speak directly of the baptism with the Spirit. Five of these passages refer to the baptism with the Spirit as a future event; four were spoken by John the Baptist (Matt. 3:11; Mark 1:7, 8; Luke 3:16; and John 1:33) and one was spoken by Jesus after His resurrection (Acts 1:4, 5). A sixth passage looks back to the events and experiences of the day of Pentecost (Acts 11:15–17) as fulfilling the promises spoken by John the Baptist and Jesus. Only one passage— 1 Corinthians 12:13—speaks about the wider experience of all believers.

During my ministry I have known many Christians who agonized, labored, struggled, and prayed to "get the Spirit." I used to wonder if I had been wrong in thinking that having been baptized by the Spirit into the body of Christ on the day of my conversion I needed no other baptism. But the longer I have studied the Scriptures the more I have become convinced that I was right. Let's trace out what God did in Christ's passion week, and fifty days later at Pentecost, to see that we need not seek what God has already given every believer.

Calvary and Pentecost

When Jesus died on the cross, He bore our sins: "God sending his own Son in the likeness of sinful flesh, and for sin, condemned sin in the flesh" (Rom. 8:3 KJV).

Isaiah prophesied, "The Lord hath laid on him the iniquity of us all" (Isa. 53:6 KJV). Paul said, "He hath made him to be sin for us, who knew no sin" (2 Cor. 5:21 KJV). This made the holy Jesus represent sin for the whole world.

Quite clearly Jesus did not say that His death on the cross would mark the cessation of His ministry. The night before His death He repeatedly told the disciples that He would send the Holy Spirit.

The night before He was to die, He told His disciples, "It is expedient for you that I go away: for if I go not away, the Comforter will not come unto you; but if I depart, I will send him unto you" (John 16:7 KJV). Before He could send the Holy Spirit, who is the Comforter, Jesus had to go away: first, to the death of the cross; then to the resurrection; then, to the ascension into heaven. Only then could He send the Holy Spirit on the day of Pentecost. And after His death and resurrection He commanded them to remain in Jerusalem to await the gift of the Spirit, "Tarry ye in the city . . . until ye be endued with power from on high" (Luke 24:49 KJV). Before He ascended He told them to stay in Jerusalem until they were "baptized with the Holy Spirit not many days hence" (Acts 1:5 KJV).

That's why John the Baptist proclaimed the twofold mission of Christ: first, he proclaimed the ministry of Christ as "the Lamb of God, which taketh away the sin of the world" (John 1:29 KJV); second, he predicted that Christ's ministry at Calvary would be followed by His ministry through baptism with the Holy Spirit (John 1:33).

When Christ rose from the dead this baptism with the Spirit that was to signify the new age still lay in the future; but it was to occur fifty days after the resurrection.

Ten days after the ascension, Pentecost dawned. The promise was fulfilled. The Holy Spirit came on 120 disciples. A little later when Peter was explaining it to a much larger crowd, he referred to the gift as "the gift of the Holy Spirit." He urged his audience, "Repent, and be baptized . . . and ye shall receive the gift of the Holy Spirit" (Acts 2:38 KJV).

John Stott reminds us, "The 3,000 do not seem to have experienced the same miraculous phenomena (the rushing mighty wind, the tongues of flame, or the speech in foreign languages). At least nothing is said about these things. Yet because of God's assurance through Peter they must have inherited the same promise and received the same gift (verses 33, 39). Nevertheless, there was this difference between them: the 120 were regenerate already, and received the baptism of the Spirit only after waiting upon God for ten days. The 3,000 on the other hand were unbelievers, and received the forgiveness of their sins and the gift of the Spirit simultaneously—and it happened immediately they repented and believed, without any need to wait.

"This distinction between the two companies, the 120 and the 3,000, is of great importance, because the *norm* for today must surely be the second group, the 3,000, and not (as is often supposed) the first. The fact that the experience of the 120 was in two distinct stages was due simply to historical circumstances. They could not have received the Pentecostal gift before Pentecost. But those historical circumstances have long since ceased to exist. We live after the event of Pentecost, like the 3,000. With us, therefore, as with them, the forgiveness of sins and the 'gift' or 'baptism' of the Spirit are received together."[1]

From that day onward, the Holy Spirit has lived in the hearts of all true believers, beginning with the 120 disciples who received Him at Pentecost. When they received the Holy Spirit, He united them by His indwelling presence into one body—the mystical body of Christ, which is the Church. That is why when I hear terms like "ecumenicity," or "ecumenical movement," I say to myself: an ecumenicity already exists if we have been born again. We are all united by the Holy Spirit who dwells within our hearts whether we are Presbyterian, Methodist, Baptist, Pentecostal, Catholic, Lutheran, or Anglican.

There were, it is true, several other occasions recorded in the Book of Acts which were similar to Pentecost, such as the so-called "Samaritan Pentecost" (Acts 8:14–17) and the conversion of Cornelius (Acts 10:44–48). Each of these, however, marked a new stage in the expansion of the Church. Samaritans were a mixed race, scorned by many as unworthy of the love of God. Their baptism by the Spirit was a clear sign that they too could be part of God's people by faith in Jesus Christ. Cornelius was a Gentile, and his conversion marked still another step in the spread of the Gospel. The baptism of the Spirit which came to him and his household showed conclusively that God's love extended to the Gentiles as well.

In view of all this, no Christian need strive, wait, or "pray through to get the Spirit." He has received Him already, not as a result of struggle and work, agonizing and prayer, but as an unmerited and unearned gift of grace.

W. Graham Scroggie once said something like this at Keswick, "On the day of Pentecost all believers were, by the baptism of the

Spirit, constituted the body of Christ, and since then every separate believer, every soul accepting Christ in simple faith, has in that moment and by that act been made partaker of the blessing of the baptism. It is not therefore a blessing which the believer is to seek and receive subsequent to the hour of his conversion."

Three Possible Exceptions Explained

I have just suggested that all believers have the Holy Spirit, who comes to dwell within them at the time of their regeneration or conversion. However, some have urged that the Book of Acts gives us several examples of people who did not receive the Holy Spirit when they first believed. Instead, some contend, these incidents indicate that a baptism with the Spirit occurs subsequent to our incorporation into the body of Christ. Three passages are of particular interest at this point. Personally I found these passages difficult to understand when I was a young Christian (and to some extent I still do) and I know many people have had the same experience. I would not pretend to have all the answers to the questions raised by these passages, but my own study has led me to some observations which might be helpful.

The first passage is found in Acts 8 where Philip's trip to Samaria is recounted. He preached Christ and performed a number of miracles. The Samaritans were emotionally stirred. Many of them professed faith and were baptized. The apostles in Jerusalem were so concerned about what was happening in Samaria that they sent two of their leaders, Peter and John, to investigate. They found a great stir and a readiness to receive the Holy Spirit. "Then they began laying their hands on them, and they were receiving the Holy Spirit" (Acts 8:17).

As we compare Scripture with Scripture, we immediately discover one extraordinary feature in this passage: When Philip preached in Samaria, it was the first time the gospel had been proclaimed outside Jerusalem, evidently because Samaritans and Jews had always been bitter enemies. This gives us the clue to the reason the Spirit was withheld till Peter and John came: It was so they might see for themselves that God received even hated Samaritans who believed in Christ. There could now be no question of it.

Notice too what happened when the Spirit of the Lord suddenly removed Philip, taking him down to Gaza where he witnessed to the Ethiopian eunuch. When the Ethiopian believed and received Christ, he was baptized with water. But at no time did Philip lay hands on him and pray for him to receive the Holy Spirit, nor was anything said about a second baptism. Thus the situation in Samaria as recounted in Acts 8 was unique and does not fit with other passages of Scripture as we compare Scripture with Scripture.

A second passage that gives some people difficulty deals with the conversion of Saul on the road to Damascus as recorded in Acts 9. Some say that when he was later filled with the Spirit in the presence of Ananias (v. 17), he experienced a second baptism of the Spirit.

Here again the situation is unique. God had chosen this persecutor of the Christians "to bear My name before the Gentiles and kings and the sons of Israel" (v. 15). When Saul called Jesus "Lord," he used a term that can mean "my very own lord," signifying his conversion, or simply "Sir," a title of respect rather than a confession of faith. We do know that later Ananias called Paul "brother," as most of our English translations phrase it (v. 17). But here again, most of the Jews of that day called each other "brother." He might have been calling Saul a brother in the sense that American black people often refer to each other as "brother."

In other words, when did Saul's regeneration take place? Was it on the Damascus road, or could it have been over a period of three days of witnessing by Ananias (which would cover the period of Saul's blindness)? I am convinced that the new birth is often like natural birth: the moment of conception, nine months of gestation, and then birth. Sometimes it takes weeks of conviction by the Holy Spirit. I've seen people in our crusades come forward more than once, and not experience the assurance of their salvation until the third or fourth time. When were they regenerated? Only God the Holy Spirit knows; it might have been at baptism or confirmation and they came forward for assurance. It may be that some are coming (as I sometimes have said) to "re-confirm their confirmation."

Furthermore, Acts 9:17 says Paul is to be filled with the Holy Spirit. The verse does not use the word baptism, and when he was filled it does not say he spoke in other tongues. My point is that even if Paul was regenerated on the Damascus road, his later filling is not presented as a second baptism. And possibly his regeneration did not occur until Ananias came to him. So the passage does not teach that Paul was baptized twice with the Spirit.

A third text that has given rise to some controversy is Acts 19: 1–7. Paul visited Ephesus and found twelve professing disciples who had not received the Holy Spirit. On reading this passage the question immediately arises: Were these twelve people true Christians before their meeting with Paul? They seemed to be ignorant about the Holy Spirit and Jesus. Also they talked about John's baptism. Certainly, Paul did not reckon their earlier baptism sufficient grounds for calling them believers. He had them undergo water baptism in the name of Christ.

Probably thousands of people had heard John or Jesus during the previous few years. John's baptism had made a deep impression on them, but during the intervening period of time they probably had lost all contact with the teachings of both John and Jesus. Thus, again we have a unique situation. The very fact that the apostle asked such searching questions would indicate that he doubted the genuineness of their conversion experience.

However, we must still deal with Acts 19:6: "And when Paul had laid his hands upon them, the Holy Spirit came on them; and they began speaking with tongues and prophesying." Dr. Merrill Tenney calls them "belated believers." The interesting thing is that all these events took place simultaneously. Whether the tongues spoken of here were the tongues to which Paul refers in 1 Corinthians 14, or Luke speaks about at Pentecost, we are not told. The word "prophesying" here carries with it the idea of testimony or proclamation. Apparently they went about telling their friends how they had come to believe in Jesus Christ. In my thinking, this does not suggest a second baptism with the Spirit subsequent to a baptism with the Spirit at regeneration. Rather, it appears that they were regenerated and baptized with the Spirit at the same time.

To summarize, it is my belief that Pentecost instituted the Church. Then all that remained was for Samaritans, Gentiles and "belated believers" to be brought into the Church representatively. This occurred in Acts 8 for Samaritans, Acts 10 for Gentiles (according to Acts 11:15), and Acts 19 for belated believers from

John's baptism. Once this representative baptism with the Spirit had occurred, the normal pattern applied—baptism with the Spirit at the time each person (of whatever background) believed on Jesus Christ.

Our Share in Pentecost

Pentecost was an event then which included not only those who participated at that moment but also those who would participate in the centuries ahead. Perhaps we can use the atonement here by way of analogy. Christ died once for all; He died for members of His body who were not yet born or regenerated. Thus, you and I became members of His body by regeneration through the one-time shedding of His blood. So also you and I in similar fashion now participate in the new reality, the Church. What was formed by the baptism with the Spirit at Pentecost is, on our part, entered into when we were made to "drink of one Spirit" (1 Cor. 12:13) so that each believer comes into the benefits of it at the moment of his regeneration even as, at the same time, he comes into the benefits of the shed blood of Jesus for justification. So the Lord adds to the Church those who are being saved (Acts 2:47).

It may sound strange to speak of present-day believers as sharing in an event that took place 2,000 years ago. However, the Bible offers many examples similar to those of the atonement and the baptism with the Spirit. In Amos 2:10 (kjv), God said to His erring people, "I brought *you* up from the land of Egypt, and led you forty years through the wilderness" (italics mine), although the people whom the prophet addressed lived hundreds of years after the Exodus. The fact is that the nation was regarded as one and continuous; and so it is with the Church.

One Baptism and Regeneration

Since the baptism with the Spirit occurs at the time of regeneration, Christians are never told in Scripture to seek it. I am convinced that many of the things some teachers have joined to baptism with the Holy Spirit really belong to the fullness of the Spirit. Thus, the purpose of the baptism with the Holy Spirit is to bring the new Christian into the body of Christ. No interval of time falls between regeneration and baptism with the Spirit. The moment we received Jesus Christ as Lord and Savior we received the Holy Spirit. He came to live in our hearts. "Any one who does not have the Spirit of Christ does not belong to him," said Paul in Romans 8:9 (RSV). It is not a second blessing, or third, or fourth. There are and will be and should be *new fillings*—but not *new baptisms.*

Nowhere in the New Testament is there a command to be baptized with the Holy Spirit. Surely if baptism with the Spirit were a necessary step in our Christian lives, the New Testament would be full of it. Christ Himself would have commanded it. But we are not commanded as Christians to seek something that has already taken place. Thus, when I was asked as a young Bible school student in Florida if I had received the baptism of the Spirit, it was correct for me to respond that I had already received it at the moment of my conversion.

The Unity of the Spirit

In 1 Corinthians 12:13, the apostle Paul writes, "For by one Spirit we were all baptized into one body—Jews or Greeks, slaves or free—and all were made to drink of one Spirit" (RSV). Paul has been talking about the need for *unity* in the disobedient and carnal Corinthian church. David Howard says: "Notice the emphasis in these phrases: 'the same Spirit' (vv. 4, 8, 9); 'one Spirit' (vv. 9, 13. . .); 'one and the same Spirit' (v. 11); 'the same Lord' (v. 5);. . . 'the body is one' (v. 12); 'one body' (v. 12, 13); 'there are many parts, yet one body' (v. 20); 'that there may be no discord in the body' (v. 25)."[2]

Howard later continues, "In this context of unity Paul says, 'For by one Spirit we were all baptized into one body—Jews or Greeks, slaves or free—and all were made to drink of one Spirit.' John R. W. Stott [*The Baptism and Fullness of the Holy Spirit,* p. 22] points out in this connection, 'So the baptism of the Spirit in this verse, far from being a dividing factor . . . is the great uniting factor.'"[3]

The Conclusion of the Matter

This much all Christians are agreed upon: Every true believer must be baptized by the Spirit into the body of Christ. Beyond that opinions differ significantly, however. But even here we should never forget a crucial area of agreement.

To see it, we must first recall that we all believe salvation is past, present, and future: We *have been saved* (justification), we *are being saved* (sanctification), and we *will be saved* (glorification). Between the time we are justified and the time when we shall be glorified falls that period in our pilgrim journey we call sanctification.

This has to do with holiness. And holiness proceeds from the work of the Spirit in our hearts. Whatever may be our differences about a second Spirit baptism, tongues, and Spirit-filling, all Christians are agreed that we should seek after *holiness*—without which no man shall see the Lord. Let us, therefore, seek ardently the kind of life that reflects the beauty of Jesus and marks us as being what saints (in the best sense of that word) ought to be!

How does this kind of life come? It comes as we are filled with the Holy Spirit—as He works in and through us as we are yielded to God and His will. It is to this subject of the filling of the Spirit that we must now turn in the next chapter.

6

The Seal, the Pledge, and the Witness of the Holy Spirit

AN ENGLISH MISSIONARY died in India in the early part of this century. Immediately after his death his former neighbors broke into his house and started carrying away his possessions. The English Consul was notified, and since there was no lock on the door of the missionary's house, he pasted a piece of paper across it and affixed the seal of England on it. The looters did not dare break the seal because the world's most powerful nation stood behind it.

The sealing of the Holy Spirit is one of a series of events that take place simultaneously, of which we may not even be aware, the moment we repent of our sins and receive Christ as Savior. First, of course, God regenerated and justified us. Second, the Holy Spirit baptized us into the body of Christ. Third, the Holy Spirit took up His abode in our hearts immediately. Several other events accompanying our salvation, together with His continuing work in us, are the focus of this and the next chapters.

The Seal

The fourth event is what the Bible calls "the Seal." It translates a Greek word that means to confirm or to impress. This word is used three times in the New Testament in connection with believers. It is also mentioned in the life of Jesus. John says that "on Him [Jesus] the Father, even God, has set His seal" (John 6:27). Here we see that the Father sealed the Son.

At the moment of conversion, however, believers are sealed with the Spirit for the day of redemption: "Having also believed, you were sealed in Him with the Holy Spirit of promise" (Eph. 1:13; cf. 4:30).

It seems to me that Paul had two main thoughts in mind concerning our sealing by the Holy Spirit. One concerns security, and the other, ownership. Sealing in the sense of security is illustrated in the Old Testament when the king sealed Daniel into the lion's den so that he could not get out. Also, in ancient times, as when Esther was queen (Esth. 8:8), the king often used his own ring to affix his mark or seal to letters and documents written in his name. Once he had done this, no one could reverse or countermand what he had written.

Pilate did much the same when he ordered the soldiers to secure the tomb of Jesus. He said, "'You have a guard; go, make it as secure as you know how.' And they went and made the grave secure, and along with the guard they set a seal on the stone" (Matt. 27:65, 66). "Seal" in this passage is the same Greek word used in passages which speak of the sealing of the Holy Spirit. A. T. Robertson says that the sealing of the stone was "probably by a cord stretched across the stone and sealed at each end as in Dan. 6:17. The sealing was done in the presence of the Roman guard who were left in charge to protect this stamp of Roman authority and power."[1] In an even more meaningful way, when the Holy Spirit seals us or puts His mark on us, we are secure in Christ.

One of the most thrilling thoughts that has ever crossed my mind is that the Holy Spirit sealed me. And He has sealed you— if you are a believer.

Nothing can touch you. "For I am convinced that neither death, nor life, nor angels, nor principalities, nor things present, nor things to come, nor powers, nor height, nor depth, nor any other created thing, shall be able to separate us from the love of God, which is in Christ Jesus our Lord" (Rom. 8:38, 39).

Yet this sealing with the Holy Spirit signifies more than security. It also means ownership. In the Old Testament we read that Jeremiah bought a piece of property, paid for it in front of witnesses, and sealed the purchase according to the Law and custom (Jer. 32:10). He was now the owner.

The allusion to the seal as the proof of purchase would have been especially significant to the Ephesians. The city of Ephesus was a seaport, and the shipmasters of the neighboring ports carried on an extensive trade in timber. The method of purchase was this: the merchant, after selecting his timber, stamped it with his own signet—an acknowledged sign of ownership. In due time the merchant would send a trusted agent with the signet; he would locate all the timbers that bore the corresponding impress, and claim them. Matthew Henry sums it up: "By him [the Holy Spirit] believers are sealed; that is, separated and set apart for God, and distinguished and marked as belonging to him."[2] You and I are God's property forever!

The Pledge

As we trust in Christ, God gives us the Spirit not only as a seal, however. He is also our pledge, or, as some translations read, "earnest," according to such passages as 2 Corinthians 1:22 and Ephesians 1:14.

"Now He who establishes us with you in Christ and anointed us is God, who also sealed us and gave us the Spirit in our hearts as a pledge" (2 Cor. 1:21, 22).

In the apostle Paul's day, businessmen considered a pledge to do three things: it was a down payment that sealed a bargain, it represented an obligation to buy, and it was a sample of what was to come.

Suppose you were to decide to buy a car. The pledge would first be a down payment sealing the transaction. It would also represent an obligation to buy the car. And it would be a sample of what was to come—the remaining portion of the selling price.

The Holy Spirit likewise seals God's purchase of us. And His presence shows God's sense of obligation to redeem us completely. Perhaps best of all, the presence of the Holy Spirit, living in fellowship with us, provides us with a foretaste, a sample, of our coming life and inheritance in God's presence.

In Numbers 13 when the spies of Israel set out to scout the land of Canaan, they reached it at the time of the first ripe grapes. They came to "the valley of Eshcol and from there cut down a branch with a single cluster of grapes" (Num. 13:23). This they brought back with them for the people of Israel to see. The cluster of grapes was the pledge of their inheritance. It was a small foretaste of what lay before them in the Promised Land. This was God's pledge that as they moved forward in faith, they would receive in full what they now had only in part.

Recently, one of New York's leading grocery stores exhibited a basket of choice and beautiful grapes in the window. A notice appeared above the basket announcing: "A whole carload like this sample basket is expected in a few days." The grapes were a "pledge" of what was to come. The firstfruits are but a handful compared with the whole harvest; so, reasoning from the known to the unknown, we ask with the hymnwriter:

"What will Thy presence be,
If such a life of joy can crown
Our walk on earth with Thee?"

The New Testament refers to the pledge of the Spirit three times:

1. "[God] also sealed us and gave us the Spirit in our hearts as a pledge" (2 Cor. 1:22). Here the Spirit's presence in our lives is God's pledge that He will fulfill His promise.

2. "Now He who prepared us for this very purpose is God, who gave to us the Spirit as a pledge" (2 Cor. 5:5). The context here suggests that the Spirit in our lives is God's pledge that we shall receive spiritual bodies at Christ's coming.

3. "[The Holy Spirit] is given as a pledge of our inheritance, with a view to the redemption of God's own possession, to the praise of His glory" (Eph. 1:14). Here the Spirit is God's pledge guaranteeing our inheritance until the future brings the total redemption of those who are God's possession.

In summary, we can say that when we are baptized into the body of Christ, the Spirit enters our lives and by His presence seals us. He is God's pledge assuring us of our inheritance to come.

The conclusion of the matter has been graphically expressed by Matthew Henry: "The earnest [this is the King James version's word for 'pledge'] is part of payment, and it secures the full sum: so is the gift of the Holy Ghost; all his influences and operations, both as a sanctifier and a comforter, are heaven begun, glory in the seed and bud. The Spirit's illumination is an earnest [pledge] of everlasting light; sanctification is an earnest of perfect holiness; and his comforts are earnests of everlasting joys. He is said to be the earnest, *until the redemption of the purchased possession*. It may be called here the possession, because this earnest makes it as sure to the heirs as though they were already possessed of it; and it is purchased for them by the blood of Christ. The redemption of it is mentioned because it was mortgaged and forfeited by sin; and Christ restores it to us, and so is said to redeem it, in allusion to the law of redemption."[3]

The Witness of the Spirit

Not only is the Holy Spirit our seal and our pledge, but He is also our witness within, assuring us of the reality of our salvation in Jesus Christ.

Jesus personally spoke to His disciples and provided them with assurance when He was with them. In like manner the Holy Spirit witnesses to and in the hearts of all true believers. Several passages in the New Testament touch on this subject.

First, the Scripture teaches us the Holy Spirit is a witness to the finality and sufficiency of Jesus Christ's atonement for us. We find this in Hebrews 10:15–17, where the writer contrasts the ineffectiveness of the oft-repeated Levitical sacrifices with the sacrifice of Christ, which was offered *one* for all and *once* for all. Our conscience could never be finally relieved of its burden of sin by the continual animal sacrifices. But on the other hand, "by one offering He [Jesus Christ] has perfected for all time those who are sanctified. And the Holy Spirit also bears witness to us" (Heb. 10:14, 15). It is a witness linked to Jeremiah 31, "I will forgive their iniquity, and their sin I will remember no more" (v. 34). Since this witness to us is engraved in the written Word of God that never varies, its comfort relieves us of our fears through all the changing scenes of time.

Second, the Scripture also teaches us the Holy Spirit witnesses that we have become, by faith in Jesus Christ and His work on the cross, the children of God. "The Spirit Himself bears witness with our spirit that we are children of God" (Rom. 8:16). We have not only been saved and baptized into the body of Christ, but we have been adopted into the family of God. "And because you are sons, God has sent forth the Spirit of His Son into our hearts, crying, 'Abba! Father!' Therefore you are no longer a slave, but a son; and if a son, then an heir through God" (Gal. 4:6, 7). Because we are declared sons of God by the Spirit's witness we can cry out from our hearts, "Abba, Father." This is the Magna Charta of the Christian's liberation from the power of sin to the privileges and wealth of Christ. The fact of our sonship is repeatedly declared. Each day you and I should sing, "I am a child of the King."

C. S. Lewis wrote this about the Christian's personal relationship with God: "To put ourselves thus on a personal footing with God could, in itself and without warrant, be nothing but presumption and illusion. But we are taught that it is not; that it is God who gives us that footing. For it is by the Holy Spirit that we cry 'Father.' By unveiling, by confessing our sins and 'making known' our requests, we assume the high rank of persons before Him. And He, descending, becomes a Person to us."'

Thus, by the Holy Spirit the Christian has a witness within himself. "The one who believes in the Son of God has the witness in himself" (1 John 5:10). Our sins and iniquities are remembered against us no more. We have been adopted into the heavenly family. The Spirit bears witness that as believers in the Lord Jesus Christ we have eternal life.

Finally, the Scripture teaches us the Holy Spirit witnesses to the truth of every promise God has given us in His Word. The Spirit, who inspired the written Word of God, also works in our hearts to assure us that its promises are true, and that they are for us. We know Christ is our Savior, because the Bible tells us this and the Spirit assures us it is true. We know we have become children of God because the Bible tells us this and the Spirit again assures us it is true. "But when He, the Spirit of truth, comes, He will guide you into all the truth" (John 16:13). "Thy word is truth" (John 17:17). Sometimes I speak with people who tell me they are lacking the assurance of their salvation. When I inquire further, I often find they have been neglecting the Word of God. "And the witness is this, that God has given us eternal life, and this life is in His Son. He who has the Son has the life; he who does not have the Son of God does not have the life. These things I have *written* to you who believe in the name of the Son of God, in order *that you may know that you have eternal life*" (1 John 5:11–13, italics mine).

The Spirit therefore witnesses in our hearts, convincing us of the truth of God's presence and assurance. This is something often difficult to explain to an unbeliever, but countless believers know of the Spirit's assurance in their hearts.

John Wesley, the founder of the Methodist church, once observed, "It is hard to find words in the language of men, to explain the deep things of God. Indeed, there are none that will adequately express what the Spirit of God works in His children. But ... by the testimony of the Spirit, I mean, an inward impression on the soul, whereby the Spirit of God immediately and directly witnesses to my spirit, that I am a child of God; that Jesus Christ hath loved me, and given Himself for me; that all my sins are blotted out, and I, even I, am reconciled to God."[5]

We can see then that God places a *seal* on us when we receive Christ. And that seal is a person—the Holy Spirit. By the Spirit's presence God gives us security and establishes His ownership over us.

Further, the Spirit is God's *pledge.* He not only seals the arrangement, but He represents God's voluntary obligation to see us through. And fellowship with the Spirit is a sample of what we can expect when we come into our inheritance in heaven.

Finally, the Spirit *witnesses* to us by His Word and within our hearts that Christ died for us, and by faith in Him we have become God's children. What a wonderful thing to know the Holy Spirit has been given to us as a seal—a pledge—and a witness! May each of these give us new assurance of God's love for us, and give us confidence as we seek to live for Christ. And with the apostle Paul may we say, "Thanks be to God for His indescribable gift!" (2 Cor. 9:15).

7

The Christian's Inner Struggle

AN ESKIMO FISHERMAN came to town every Saturday afternoon. He always brought his two dogs with him. One was white and the other was black. He had taught them to fight on command. Every Saturday afternoon in the town square the people would gather and these two dogs would fight and the fisherman would take bets. On one Saturday the black dog would win; another Saturday, the white dog would win—but the fisherman always won! His friends began to ask him how he did it. He said, "I starve one and feed the other. The one I feed always wins because he is stronger."

One or Two Natures?

This story about the two dogs is apt because it tells us something about the inner warfare that comes into the life of a person who is born again.

We have two natures within us, both struggling for mastery. Which one will dominate us? It depends on which one we feed. If we feed our spiritual lives and allow the Holy Spirit to empower us, He will have rule over us. If we starve our spiritual natures and instead feed the old, sinful nature, the flesh will dominate.

Every Christian can identify with the apostle Paul when he said, "For that which I am doing, I do not understand; for I am not practicing what I would like to do, but I am doing the very thing I hate. . . . I find then the principle that evil is present in me . . . but I see a different law in the members of my body, waging war against the law of my mind, and making me a prisoner of the law of sin which is in my members" (Rom. 7:15, 21, 23).

Many young Christians have said things like this to me from time to time: "Since I became a Christian, I have had struggles within that I never had before. I didn't know I was such a sinner! I never wanted to sin like this before. I thought God had saved me from my sins!"

Actually, strange as it may seem, this condition is something to be thankful for. It is an evidence that the Holy Spirit has come into your life, illuminating the darkness of sin, sensitizing your conscience to sin, awakening in you a new desire to be clean and free from sin before God. Those old sins were there before. Those old temptations were there strongly before, but they didn't appear evil to you then. But now the Holy Spirit has come into your life. You are a new person, born again by this same Spirit. And everything looks different now.

The Struggle within

Now you have become keenly aware of the basic problem in a Christian's life, the struggle with sin. In the New Testament the apostle Paul talks of every Christian being in an intense spiritual battle: "For our struggle is not against flesh and blood, but against the rulers, against the powers, against the world forces of this darkness, against the spiritual forces of wickedness in the heavenly places" (Eph. 6:12). So there are external spiritual forces which are at work in this world, seeking to keep us from God and His will. But we must not always blame Satan for everything that goes wrong or every sin we commit. Often it is our own sinful nature which is at work within us. "For the flesh sets its desire against the Spirit, and the Spirit against the flesh; for these are in opposition to one another, so that you may not do the things that you please" (Gal. 5:17).

And this is not just external to us. This battle goes on inside of us. And that's the theme of Romans 7, especially verses 7 through

25. Look at Romans 7:7 and 8, for example. (Read it in a good modern translation of the Bible.) Let me paraphrase what Paul is saying:

Before I heard the law of God and the good news of salvation, I didn't know covetousness was sin, but then I heard the tenth commandment, "Thou shalt not covet." God's law showed me this sin in my heart, and I suddenly became keenly aware how much covetousness was a live, writhing evil within me. And I realized how great a sinner I was, doomed to die—but for Christ! As a Christian I began to fight this evil desire in me. And what a struggle! I tried to stop coveting and envying, but I couldn't.

That's the picture, and I'm sure you have often felt just as Paul did. Maybe your sin is wrong sexual desires, pride, gluttony, laziness, or anger, or some other besetting sin (Heb. 12:1 KJV). But you feel the same inner struggle. Sometimes you conclude just as Paul did in Romans 7:22–24 which I quoted above.

But don't stop there! Note Paul's glorious conclusion in verse 25 and 8:2 (there were no chapter divisions in Paul's original letter!): "Thanks be to God through Jesus Christ our Lord! . . . For the law of the Spirit of life in Christ Jesus has set you free from the law of sin and of death." As a great saint said many years ago, "Sin no longer reigns, but it still fights!"

Horatius Bonar was a brilliant theologian, a great saint, and a compassionate pastor. He died at the age of 33, but not before a great revival had taken place in his church in Scotland. His sermons and books have blessed God's people for the last 150 years. He spoke honestly for all of us when he said: "While conversion calms one kind of storm it raises another, which is to be lifelong."[1] Efforts to explain this struggle by theologians have gone on for centuries. Some have taken Paul's words and spoken of the "two natures" in the Christian—the "old man" and the "new man." This terminology comes from such passages as Ephesians 4:22–24 where Paul says, "That, in reference to your former manner of life, you lay aside the *old self*, which is being corrupted in accordance with the lusts of deceit . . . and put on the *new self*, which in the likeness of God has been created in righteousness and holiness of the truth" (italics mine).

Speaking of this in the footnote on that passage, *The New Scofield Reference Bible* says, "The 'new man' is the regenerate man as distinguished from the old man . . . and is a new man as having become a partaker of the divine nature and life . . . in no sense the old man made over, or improved."[2] In a footnote on Romans 7:15, Scofield continues, "The apostle personifies the struggle of the two natures within the believer—the old or Adamic nature, and the divine nature received through the new birth."[3]

How can we visualize and understand what is going on inside of us? I think Romans 8:1–13 describes it best. Let me try to paraphrase what Paul is saying here, and let me put it in the first person—this is how it applies to me:

I was born in sin. For years I was controlled by sin and didn't know it. I was literally "dead in trespasses and sin" (Eph. 2:1). Then I heard the Word of God, the law and the Gospel. I was convicted. I saw my sins for the first time. I accepted Christ. And now the law of God is speaking to me every day through the Word of God.

Now I have become conscious of sins I didn't know I had. Sometimes I despair (like Paul in Romans 7:24: "Wretched man that I am!"), but, praise the Lord, I know now there is no condemnation anybody can bring against me because I am in Christ (Rom. 8:1). Christ has set me free from the law of sin and death (Rom. 8:2). I am still me—with my old sinful personality and nature, sinful habits that have grown strong in the many years before I was a Christian. But now the Holy Spirit has come into my life. He shows me my sin. He actually condemns the sin in me (Rom. 8:3). And by His power He helps me to meet the requirements of God's law (Rom. 8:4).

If I keep thinking about my old life and my sins, I will go back to that life. The old "me" will continue to sin. But if I put my mind on Christ and try to listen and obey the Holy Spirit (Rom. 8:5), the Holy Spirit will give me life and peace (Rom. 8:6). If a man is a Christian, he has the Holy Spirit (Rom. 8:9). His spirit has been made alive (Rom. 8:10). The Holy Spirit is giving life to his body, bringing it back from the deadness of sin (Rom. 8:11) and bringing abundant new life in Christ.

The Two Natures

God uses many strong figures of speech to describe what the Holy Spirit does for us throughout the Bible. We have already noticed this in John 3. He says we are "born again" by the Holy

Spirit. This is clearly an illustration to describe, in physical terms, a great spiritual truth. And here in regard to our Christian life in Romans 7 and 8 and in Ephesians 4, God uses psychological terms—"new nature . . . old nature" or "new man and old man"—to try to make us understand the radical change that takes place in our Christian life when we are controlled by the Holy Spirit.

We consciously feel that we are just one person. When I have sinned, deep down I know that I did it. I felt the pull of temptation. I responded and at some point willed to sin. At some point I said "Yes" to the devil as he tempted me through my old habits, my old desires, my old motives, or appealed to my old goals in life. This is what Paul means in talking about the "old nature" or the sin principle. But it is really me. I am one person before God. I am responsible for my sins. I can't blame the sin principle that still lives within. I have a choice either to yield to the Spirit—the new impetus in my life—or the old force of sin.

But now the Holy Spirit has come into my heart. He has given me new life—God's quality of eternal life. And He Himself is in me to break the old habits, to purify my motives, to set my eyes on new goals, especially the goal of becoming like the Lord Jesus Christ (Rom. 8:29).

So for the rest of my Christian life until Christ comes and calls me home, I am being sanctified (growing more and more into spiritual maturity) by the Holy Spirit through the Word of God. Best of all, the Holy Spirit is daily, quietly making me to be conformed more and more to the Lord Jesus Christ if I am cooperating with Him: "But we all, with unveiled face beholding as in a mirror the glory of the Lord, are being transformed into the same image from glory to glory, just as from the Lord, the Spirit" (2 Cor. 3:18).

But never forget there will always be a struggle, both without and within. The devil is an implacable enemy. He never gives up. Through "the world" and the flesh, he appeals to the old force within me to reassert itself. He appeals to my lusts, my covetousness, and my pride, just as he did to Eve and Adam (Gen. 3). I will always feel the pull of temptation. My old tendencies will be awakened and will want to sin. *But* I have the Holy Spirit within me, a more powerful principle or force: "Greater is He who is in you than he who is in the world" (1 John 4:4). If I cooperate with

Him and turn to Him for help, He will give me the power to resist temptation. He will make me stronger as a result of every test.

Perhaps the next time the devil will appeal to a different weakness in *"the flesh."* I have a different set of temptations. But the Holy Spirit is always in my heart to give me victory over this new struggle, and as I win victory after victory I get stronger. Dr. Bonar says that God recognizes the saint's inner conflict "as an indispensable process of discipline, as a development of the contrast between light and darkness, as an exhibition of the way in which God is glorified in the infirmities of His saints, and in their contests with the powers of evil."[4]

In Romans 7 Paul is not saying he cannot help but sin because of his old nature which he can't control. Rather, Paul is describing the struggle all of us are going to have and telling us we can have victory in Christ by the power of His Holy Spirit that lives within us (Rom. 8:4).

Sanctification

The word sanctification comes from the Greek word which means "to be separate" or "set apart for a purpose." Paul speaks of the believer as having been "sanctified by the Holy Spirit" (Rom. 15:16). He wrote to the Corinthians saying that they, *having been sanctified*, are called to be saints (1 Cor. 1: 2). We Christians are to be "progressively sanctified" or "made righteous" in holiness as we daily abide in Christ—and obey His Word. Abiding and obedience are the keys to a successful Spirit-dominated life. We are as much sanctified as we are possessed by the Holy Spirit. It is never a question of how much you and I have of the Spirit, but how much He has of us.

The Scriptures teach that "sanctification" has *three parts* to it. *First*, the moment you receive Christ there is an immediate sanctification. *Second*, as we progress in the Christian life there is a "progressive sanctification." *Third*, when we go to heaven there will be total and "complete" sanctification, which is called "glorification."

We have a friend on one of the Caribbean islands who purchased the ruins of an old mansion. In his eyes he sees it as it will someday be, beautiful, restored, perfect. It is "sanctified." In the meantime, he is working on it with his limited resources, his ingenuity, and his love. To the average beholder it may look like something out of a horror movie, with its scraps of lumber, patched tin roof, fabulous tile floor. But to our friend it is special. Loved. He sees it as it will be someday. Perhaps the world sees the body of Christ (the true Church) as others see this mansion. But God sees it as it will eventually be. Perfect, complete. It is being sanctified. In our friend's eyes, the mansion is already beautiful, because he sees in his mind's eye the finished product. When he begins work on it, it will be in the process of being restored. And someday our friend will complete his work, and the mansion will be in reality what he always hoped it would be.

In a far greater way, God looks on us in Jesus Christ. He sees us now as fully sanctified, because He knows what we will be some day. Also He is at work in us restoring us—we are being sanctified. And some day that process will be complete when we go to be with Him throughout all eternity. We will be fully sanctified.

J. B. Phillips says that God predestinates us "to bear the family likeness of his Son" (Rom. 8:29). That is what is happening to us now as believers. We are being progressively sanctified—to spiritual maturity—to bear the family likeness of His Son. Remember that Jesus Christ was perfect—and we are to strive for perfection. While this will be complete only in heaven, it should be our goal right now. This is what the Bible means when it commands us, "Like the Holy One who called you, be holy yourselves also in all your behavior; because it is written, 'You shall be holy, for I am Holy' " (1 Peter 1:15, 16). Whether we realize it or not we are growing spiritually through the conflicts, turbulence, troubles, temptations, testings, and so on that afflict all Christians slowly or rapidly. But there is coming a day when all of this will be past, and we will be completely sanctified, "We know that, when He appears, we shall be like Him, because we shall see Him just as He is" (1 John 3:2).

In the meantime, Christians, day by day, week by week, and month by month, are told to walk in the Spirit. Walking in the Spirit means being led and directed by the Holy Spirit. This comes as we progressively yield various areas of our lives to the Spirit's control. Paul said, "Walk by the Spirit, and you will not carry out the desire of the flesh" (Gal. 5:16). Now desire in itself is not wrong, it's *what* we desire or lust for that is wrong—and *when* we yield.

The Old Self-Life

When Eve had a desire to "know" (but based on self)—Satan turned healthy desire into unhealthy. And Eve disobeyed God. Flesh is the Bible's word for unperfected human nature. Leaving off the "h" and spelling it in reverse we have the word *self*. Flesh is the self-life: it is what we are when we are left to our own devices. At times our *self* behaves itself very well. It can do good things, it can be moral, and it can have extremely high ethical standards. But sooner or later your self and mine will show itself to be *selfish*.

We try to educate self, to train and discipline it. We pass laws to compel it to behave. But Paul said that the flesh has a mind of its own and that "the natural mind" is not subject to the law of God. God clearly says He has no confidence in our flesh. Paul declared, "I know that nothing good dwells in me, that is, in my flesh" (Rom. 7:18). The moment we realize this and yield to the dictates of the Holy Spirit in our lives, greater victory, greater spiritual maturity, greater love, joy, peace and other fruits will manifest themselves.

Recently, a friend of ours was converted to Christ. He had previously led a wild life. One of his old friends said to him, "I feel sorry for you. You now go to church, pray, and read the Bible all the time. You no longer go to the nightclubs, get drunk, or enjoy your beautiful women." Our friend gave a strange reply. He said, "I do get drunk every time I want to. I do go to nightclubs every time I want to. I do go with the girls when I want to." His worldly friend looked puzzled. Our friend laughed and said, "Jim, you see, the Lord took the *want* out when I was converted and He made me a new person in Christ Jesus."

St. Augustine once said, "Love God and live as you please." If we truly love God we will want to do what pleases Him. It is as the Psalmist says in Psalm 37, "Delight yourself in the Lord; And He will give you the desires of your heart" (v. 4). Delighting in the Lord alters the desires.

The Battle with the Flesh

If we as Christians try to make ourselves better or good or even acceptable to God by some human effort, we will fail. Everything we have and are and do comes through the Holy Spirit. The Holy Spirit has come to dwell in us, and God does His works in us by the Holy Spirit. What we have to do is yield ourselves to the Spirit of God so that He may empower us to put off the old and put on the new.

Paul makes all of this clear in Galatians 5:17, "For the flesh sets its desire against the Spirit, and the Spirit against the flesh; for these are in opposition to one another." This indicates what the real conflict is in the heart of every true believer. The flesh wants one thing and the Spirit wants another. The black dog and the white dog are often fighting. As long as there is not the surrender of mind and body every moment of the day, the old nature will assert itself.

Conscious of my own weakness, sometimes on rising in the morning I have said, "Lord, I'm not going to allow this or that thing to assert itself in my life today." Then the devil sends something unexpected to tempt me, or God allows me to be tested at that exact point. Many times in my life the thing I never meant to do in my mind I did in the flesh. I have wept many a bitter tear of confession and asked God the Spirit to give me strength at that point. But this lets me know that I am engaged in a spiritual warfare every day. I must never let down my guard—I must keep armed.

Many of the young people I meet are living defeated, disillusioned, and disappointed lives even after coming to Christ. They are walking after the flesh because they have not had proper teaching at this precise point. The old man, the old self, the old principle, the old force, is not yet dead or wholly renewed: it is still there. It fights every inch of the way against the new man, the new force, that God made us when we received Christ. Only as we yield and obey the new principle in Christ do we win the victory.

"Yielding" is the secret! Paul said, "I appeal to you therefore, brethren, and beg of you in view of [all] the mercies of God, to make a decisive dedication of your bodies—presenting all your members and faculties—as a living sacrifice, holy (devoted, consecrated) and well pleasing to God, which is your reasonable (rational, intelligent) service and spiritual worship" (Rom. 12:1, *Amplified*). When total surrender occurs, there is another "experience." For most Christians it is not just a second experience—but it comes many times throughout our lives.

The Works of the Flesh

Thus, we see that there is a continuing conflict going on in every one of us between the flesh on the one hand and the Spirit on the other. When Paul uses the word "flesh," he really means human nature in all its weakness, its impotence, and its helplessness. The flesh is the lower side of man's nature. The flesh is all that man is without God and without Christ. Paul lists the works of the flesh in Galatians 5:19–21. When we read this terrible list, we should also read Romans 1:17–32. In these passages the depravity of human nature is pictured for us. We see it for what it is.

Every day we read about this depravity in our newspapers. We watch it on the newscasts on our television screens daily. Everywhere, unregenerate human nature calls the signals and produces the works of the flesh. The sins of the flesh are flaunted shamelessly. They are committed blatantly and without repentance by unregenerate men. However, the Christian can sometimes temporarily yield to one or more of these terrible things. He is immediately convicted by the Holy Spirit and quickly repents and finds forgiveness.

In Galatians 5 there is a catalog of fifteen *works of the flesh* which range from sexual sins to drunkenness and include idolatry and sorcery. What strikes terror in every Christian heart is the knowledge that these sins can easily creep into our lives unless we are spiritually vigilant and strong. "Therefore let him who thinks he stands take heed lest he fall" (I Cor. 10:12). With this in mind, let us look at the list of sins Paul lists in Galatians 5, so we will be better prepared to fight against the flesh.

Some have suggested that these can be divided into three categories, or sets. The first set are sexual immorality, impurity, and sensuality (Gal. 5:19).

1. Immorality. The Greek word here is broad enough to cover all kinds of sexual wickedness and is, incidentally, the word (*porneia*) from which the word "pornography" comes. Premarital sex, extramarital sex, abnormal sex, incest, prostitution, and surely sex sins in the heart are part of what the apostle has in mind here.

2. Impurity. Here the Greek word suggests any kind of impurity, whether in thought or deed. It might even include unnatural lust as described by Paul in Romans 1:24. It surely would cover some of the modern films, pornographic literature, and "evil imaginations." William Barclay describes it as the pus of an unclean wound; a tree that has never been pruned; material that has never been sifted.

3. Sensuality. This Greek word can be thought of as wantonness or debauchery. But there may be more to it than that. It has in it the notion of reckless shamelessness, or even an open indulgence in impurity. The same word is used in 2 Peter 2:7 when the apostle speaks of the licentiousness of Sodom and Gomorrah. It can be no less than lewdness and sensuality of any kind.

The second set of the works of the flesh enumerated by Paul are these:

1. Idolatry. The Greek word for idolatry is the worship of false gods of which there are many today. By implication we think of it as including anything that comes between us and God. Money can become an idol if we worship it above our worship of God. Pleasure can become an idol, even a relationship to another person can become an idol if it takes the place of God.

2. Sorcery. The Greek word here can be translated witchcraft; the idea especially is the administering of magical potions and drugs. Thus it is related also to the use of drugs; we get our word "pharmacy" from this Greek word, *pharmakia.* Throughout Scripture, witchcraft and sorcery are condemned. This evil is spreading rapidly in Western societies at an alarming rate.

3. Enmities. The Greek word for enmities has to do with hatred. Hatred contains within it the idea of something latent, like an animal ready to spring on its prey. Hostility, antipathy, antagonism, animosity, rancor, and intense dislike are all comparable terms for what is translated here as hatred.

4. Strife. The Greek word refers to variance, contentions, strife, fighting, discord, wrangling, and quarreling. Many churches are hard hit by internal discord that divides laymen from pastors, and laymen from laymen. When members of a congregation do not speak to each other and when they fight with one another, this sin is at work and the Spirit of God is quenched. Numerous families are infected by this spirit. Many marriages, even Christian ones, are being destroyed by this sin.

5. Jealousy—a very common sin. It involves envy when someone gets an honor we wanted, or it can mar a marriage relationship when a husband or a wife is jealous of his or her partner. We read of murders being committed because of jealousy, of friends who have not spoken for years. On the other hand, there is the beautiful example of Jonathan who was *not* jealous of David (1 Sam. 20).

6. Outbursts of anger. The Greek word for wrath means unrighteous fits of rage, passionate outbursts of anger and hostile feelings. John uses the same root word in the Apocalypse about the righteous wrath of God. Man's wrath can be righteous or unrighteous, but God's wrath is always righteous for He cannot sin. There is a righteous wrath, but it is not a fit of anger. Here anger or wrath is a sin we must cast out of our lives. Someone has well said, "Righteous indignation is usually one part righteous and nine parts indignation."

7. Disputes. This Greek word for disputes or strife means selfish ambition, self-seeking, and selfishness. This violates both parts of the Ten Commandments (Exod. 20). First it is a sin against God when selfish ambition replaces the will of God for our lives. Then it violates the command to love our neighbors, for acts of self-seeking are always committed at someone else's expense.

8. Dissensions. The Greek word means seditions, dissensions, or divisions. Believers are to be of one mind. "He is the God that maketh men to be of one mind in an house" is the Prayer Book version of Psalm 68:6.[5] Unless principles are at stake or the Word of God is threatened, then discord can become sinful. We are to contend for the faith, but even when doing so we are not to be contentious. Truth often divides, but when truth is not at stake, God's people should be able to live together in love by the grace of the Holy Spirit.

9. Factions. The Greek word for factions, or heresies, has to do with sects and sectarianism. It means to choose that which is bad, or to form an opinion contrary to the revelation of God in Scripture. This is the same word found in 2 Peter 2:1 (NIV): "But there were also false prophets among the people, just as there will be false teachers among you. They will secretly introduce destructive heresies, even denying the sovereign Lord who bought them—bringing swift destruction on themselves." Thus this is a serious sin. As Alexander said, "Error is often plausibly dressed in the outer garb of truth."

10. Envyings. This Greek word means resentment at the excellence or good fortune of another, a jealous spirit. We may envy someone his beautiful voice, his great wealth, his superior position, or his athletic attainments. Or we may begrudge a girl her beauty, a person his position in public office. Envy has been the downfall of many a Christian. Normally, there can be no envy that does not involve covetousness.

11. Drunkenness. This Greek word means overindulgence in alcohol. Alcohol may be used for medicine, but it can also become a terrible drug. The way it is used in our world is probably one of the great evils of our day. It is a self-inflicted impediment that springs from "a man taking a drink, a drink taking a drink, and drink taking the man." Distilled liquors as we have them today were unknown in Bible times. This modern use of alcohol is far more dangerous than the use of wine, which was also condemned when taken to excess. Teetotalism or nonteetotalism cannot be proven from Scriptures. Whatever we do, we should do it to the glory of God (1 Cor. 10:31).

I had a wonderful Christian friend in England many years ago. He was a godly man with a great knowledge of the Scriptures and a deep and holy walk with God. Once when we had a meal with him he said, "I serve wine at my table to the glory of God. I know you don't take wine, to the glory of God, so we have provided ginger ale for you." He continued, "We are taught to respect each other's liberty and each other's conscience."

12. Carousings. In the Greek this means orgies. In Romans 13:13 and 1 Peter 4:3 it is associated with illicit sex, drunkenness, and other evils in which no Christian should indulge.

There may be someone reading this who has been guilty of one, or even all of the sins listed here. Does this mean you can never enter the kingdom of Heaven; that the door is forever closed to you? Certainly not. The Bible says that by repentance and faith anyone can be forgiven (1 John 1:9).

However, Galatians 5:21 constitutes the most serious warning to those who may think they can sin that grace may abound. The apostle sternly says, "Those who practice such things [i.e. those things just enumerated] shall not inherit the kingdom of God." Paul's whole terrible list when practiced by men violates God's will for them. God hates these things so much that He will judge those who do them. People whose lives are characterized by such deviations from the will of God will be separated from Him and lost in outer darkness. The reason I have listed all this is because millions of professing Christians are only just that—"professing." They have never possessed Christ. They live lives characterized by the flesh. Tens of thousands have never been born again. They will go into eternity lost—while thinking they are saved because they belong to the church, or were baptized, and so on.

But there is another truth we should not forget. Today people do many of these forbidden things in the name of freedom. What they fail to see is that such activities actually enslave those who become involved in them. And when liberty becomes license, liberty not only is misconstrued—those who misconstrue are themselves shackled so that they lose the liberty of which Scripture speaks. True freedom consists not in the freedom to sin, but the freedom *not* to sin.

Another truth is that those who live in the flesh can be changed only by the Spirit of God. This is why a deep spiritual awakening is so desperately needed today. You cannot legislate successfully against these problems. No matter how many laws are passed, or how many good intentions there may be, in those persons outside of Christ the old nature is in control. It may be subdued at times; it may be controlled by sheer discipline on other occasions, but there will come times when these works of the flesh will manifest themselves by boiling over in strife and eventually war.

However, the Christian has become a new creation. He can come under the control of the Holy Spirit and produce the fruit of the Spirit, which is a whole new set of principles that develop a new man and could eventually produce a new society.

Paul says, "Now those who belong to Christ Jesus have crucified the flesh with its passions and desires" (Gal. 5:24). During the lifetime of our Lord Jesus Christ, He lived as a man, He was tempted as a man, yet He kept the whole law of God and had victory over the flesh. Those of us who are bound to Him by faith are, in principle at least, finished with all that belongs to the flesh. Yet Paul recognizes that these old fleshly tendencies still lurk within us and that we must almost hourly yield to the Holy Spirit to have total and complete victory.

The Scripture does not say, "They that are Christ's *should* crucify the flesh." This took place positionally and legally when Jesus Christ hung on the cross. Galatians 2:20 reads, "I *have been* crucified with Christ" (italics mine). Romans 6:6 says, "Knowing this, that our old self *was crucified* with Him" (italics mine). It is a completed action, a settled matter. Since we believers have already been crucified even as we have already been saved, we are now called upon to work out that crucifixion in the flesh so that we do not make provision for the works of the flesh. We have been buried with Christ and now are raised from the dead unto the new life in Him.

Many people say, "I cannot live a life like this. I cannot hold out." If it were up to you and me, we could not. The apostle Paul says, "Consider yourselves to be dead to sin" (Rom. 6:11). He also said sin shall no longer reign in our mortal bodies. This means that "by faith" we accept what Jesus Christ has done for us at the cross. By faith we turn over our lives totally and completely and without reservation to the Holy Spirit. Christ sits on the throne of our hearts. No one, or anything, is going to push Him off. The Holy Spirit produces the "fruit of the Spirit." While the works of the flesh would like very much to manifest themselves—and sometimes do—they no longer reign, they are no longer in control. It is no longer a practice; it is no longer a habit; we are transformed by His grace and live the new life in Christ. But this is only possible as we are filled with the Holy Spirit. It is to this important topic that we now turn.

8

The Fullness of the Spirit

OUR HOME IS supplied by a reservoir fed by two mountain springs. These two springs on the mountain above the house, according to the mountain people who lived here before we did, never fluctuate. Rainy season or dry, they remain the same. We draw on the water as we need it, and the springs continually flowing into the reservoir keep it filled to overflowing. That is literally what it means to "be being filled with the Spirit."

All Christians are committed to be filled with the Spirit. Anything short of a Spirit-filled life is less than God's plan for each believer.

What does the Bible mean when it speaks of the fullness of the Holy Spirit? Let's define the fullness of the Spirit. To be Spirit-filled is to be controlled or dominated by the Spirit's presence and power. In Ephesians 5:18 Paul says, "And do not get drunk with wine, for that is dissipation, but be filled with the Spirit." Here he draws a contrast between two things. A person who is filled with alcohol is controlled or dominated by alcohol. Its presence and power have overridden his normal abilities and actions.

It is interesting that we often say someone is "under the influence" of alcohol. Now that is somewhat the meaning of being filled with the Spirit. We are "under the influence" of the Spirit. Instead of doing things only with our own strength or ability, He empowers us. Instead of doing only what we want to do, we now are guided by Him. Unfortunately millions of God's people do not enjoy the unlimited spiritual wealth at their disposal because they are not filled with the Holy Spirit.

I remember a great woman Bible teacher by the name of Ruth Paxson whom I heard speak on this theme many times. She was a guest in our home, and I still have some of the notes I made from her lectures.

As she reminded us, the lives of many reflect the practices and standards of this present world. True, they have been baptized with the Holy Spirit into the body of Christ, and they are going to heaven. But they are missing so much of what God wants them to have in this life. Consciously or unconsciously they are more interested in imitating the world system dominated by Satan than in imitating Christ. They do not really want to share the reproach of Christ outside the camp (Heb. 13:13). Their gifts are often unused, and spiritual fruit is absent from their lives. Nor do they have any great concern to evangelize the spiritually needy in their own community. Their zeal to walk in obedience to the commandments of Christ grows weak. Their devotional life is uneven, if not totally neglected, and they anticipate reading the newspaper more than reading the Word of God. If they do pray, it is a cheerless duty and a tedious task rather than a joy. As with Lot in Sodom, sin for them has lost some of its sinfulness; their sensitivity to sin has been numbed and the edge of conscience blunted. Known sins remain unconfessed.

Christians have more equipment and technology for evangelizing the world than ever before. And there are better trained personnel. But one of the great tragedies of the present hour is this: Christians so often lack the fullness of the Spirit with its true dependence on God's power for their ministry. Illustrations of the kind of spiritual power they need but lack abounded in the first century. It was said of the Christians in one city, "These men who have turned the world upside down have come here also" (Acts 17:6 RSV). And from time to time in later centuries this same Holy Spirit power was unleashed upon the world. Isolated instances of it exist right now. But what if the *full* power of the Holy Spirit were to be loosed today through all true believers? The world could again be turned upside down.

The Biblical Basis for Being Filled with the Spirit

I think it proper to say that anyone who is not Spirit-filled is a defective Christian. Paul's command to the Ephesian Christians, "Be filled with the Spirit," is binding on all of us Christians everywhere in every age. There are no exceptions. We must conclude that since we are ordered to be filled with the Spirit, we are sinning if we are not filled. And our failure to be filled with the Spirit constitutes one of the greatest sins against the Holy Spirit.

It is interesting to note that the command to "Be filled with the Spirit" actually has the idea of continuously being filled in the original Greek language which Paul used. We are not filled once for all, like a bucket. Instead, we are to be filled constantly. It might be translated, "Be filled and keep on being filled," or "Be being filled."

Ephesians 5:18 literally says, "Keep on being filled with the Spirit." Dr. Merrill C. Tenney has compared this to the situation of an old-time farmhouse kitchen. In one corner was a sink; above it was a pipe through which came a continuous stream of water from the spring outside. The water, by running constantly, kept the sink brimful of good water. In like manner the Christian is not to let himself be emptied of the Spirit that he may later become full again; rather he is constantly to accept the direction and energy of the Spirit so he is always overflowing.

The overflowing rivers and the abundant life are available blessings for all Christians. Rivers of living water fail to flow in our lives not because God denies them to us, but because we do not want them or we refuse to meet the conditions to get them.

This continuous filling by the Holy Spirit is also what Jesus was teaching in John 4, in speaking to the Samaritan woman at Jacob's well: "Everyone who drinks of this water shall thirst again; but whoever drinks of the water that I shall give him shall never thirst; but the water that I shall give him shall become in him a well of water springing up to eternal life" (John 4:13, 14). Jesus spoke of the Holy Spirit in the same way in John 7:38: "He who believes in Me, as the Scripture said, 'From his innermost being shall flow rivers of living water.'" The overflowing spring and the continual river speak of the constant supply of the Holy Spirit's blessing available to all Christians. This living water of which Jesus speaks—this continual filling by the Holy Spirit—fails to flow in our lives not because God denies it to us, but because we do not want it or we refuse to meet the conditions God sets up to get it.

In reading John 7:38 one day, I was stopped short and struck with awe by the grandeur of Jesus' words. He did not speak of drops of blessings, few and far between, as in a light shower on a spring day. He spoke of rivers of living water. Consider the Mississippi, the Amazon, the Danube, or the Yangtze Rivers: However much may be taken from them, they do not run dry but continue to flow generously. The sources from which they come keep sending water down their course. These rivers illustrate the life of the Spirit-filled Christian. The supply is never exhausted because it has its source in the Holy Spirit who is inexhaustible.

Bishop Moule once said, "Never shall I forget the gain to conscious faith and peace which came to my own soul not long after a first decisive and appropriating view of the crucified Lord as the sinner's sacrifice of peace." What was the cause of this gain? He says it was "a more intelligent and conscious hold upon the living and more gracious personality of the Spirit through whose mercy the soul had got that blessed view. It was a new contact as it were with the inner and eternal movements of redeeming goodness and power. A new discovery in divine resources."

One of the prayers of the great Welsh revival was:

> "Fill me, Holy Spirit, fill me,
> More than fulness I would know:
> I am smallest of Thy vessels,
> Yet, I much can overflow."[1]

We must make ourselves available to the Holy Spirit so that when He fills us we will become vessels of blessing to the world, whether large and beautiful in great service, or small and unnoticed by men. To me the Corinthian church was one of the saddest and most tragic churches in the New Testament. Its members had been baptized with the Spirit; they had been given many of the gifts of the Spirit; and therefore they had much to commend them. Yet Paul said they were fleshly and unspiritual. "And I, brethren, could not speak to you as to spiritual men, but as to men of flesh, as to babes in Christ. . . . for you are still fleshly" (1 Cor. 3:1, 3). This means that you and I may have one or more gifts of the Spirit and still be unspiritual, lacking in "the fullness of the Spirit." To say that having the gift of evangelism, or the gift of a pastor, or of a teacher, or the gift of tongues, or the gift of healing (or any other gift), is proof that we have the fullness of the Spirit is misleading. Furthermore, any gift we may have will never be used to its fullest potential for God unless it is brought under the control of, and empowered by, the Holy Spirit. There is nothing more tragic than a gift of God which is misused for selfish or unspiritual purposes.

So it is critical that we be filled with the Spirit. In considering this, however, we must not be confused by mere terminology. Some Christians have used terms like "the second baptism" or "the second blessing" or "a second work of grace." None of these terms are used in the Bible, but I realize that for many people they are simply semantic equivalents for the fullness of the Spirit. The name we give the experience is less important than that we actually *be* filled with the Spirit.

I prefer not to use these terms, however, since they can lead to confusion in some people's minds. Personally I believe the Bible teaches there is one baptism in the Spirit—when we come to faith in Christ. The Bible teaches there are many fillings—in fact, we are to be continuously filled by the Holy Spirit. One baptism—many fillings! I do not personally find anything in Scripture which indicates there must be some later "baptism of the Spirit" into our lives after conversion. He is already there, and we are called to yield to Him continually, but never do I condemn those who hold a different view. Many of those holding a different view are among my closest friends. Differences at this point do not constitute a basis for division of Christian fellowship.

Maybe we need to reverse the figure we use. When we are filled with the Spirit, it is not a question of there being more of Him, as though His work in us is quantitative. It is not how much of the Spirit *we* have, but how much the Spirit has of *us*. He is in us in all His fullness, whether we see this exhibited in our lives or not. When we receive Christ as Savior and Lord, you and I receive Him in full, not just in part. Then as we come to understand more and more of Christ's lordship, we surrender and yield more and more. So, seeking the fullness of the Spirit, we receive and enjoy His filling and His fullness more and more.

When we receive Christ as Savior, our spiritual capacities are extremely small. At that moment we have surrendered to Him as Savior and Lord as best we know how. It may even be proper to say we are filled with the Spirit at that time, in the sense that we are under His influence and control. However, there are still many areas of our lives which need to be yielded to His control, and we may not even be aware of them at that moment. As we grow in the grace and knowledge of Christ, our spiritual capacities enlarge. We soon discover in our Christian life that we are not yet "perfect." We often stumble and fall into sins—including sins of which we may not be conscious at the time. There are many sins of omission also—things we should be doing or attitudes we should be having, but they have not become part of us yet. Part of the work of the Holy Spirit is to convict us of these sins and bring us to true repentance. At such a time we need a new filling of the Holy Spirit, that He might control and dominate us. There also may be new tasks or challenges that God gives us, and this should always cause us to seek afresh the power and presence—the filling—of the Holy Spirit.

It is also common for a young Christian to believe that he must rely on his own wisdom and strength to fight sin in his life, or to undertake some task God has given him. Such a person may realize that his salvation is based totally on what God has done in Christ, but at the same time be unaware that he is just as dependent on God the Holy Spirit for his Christian growth. Often he will fight bravely and struggle against temptations, or zealously seek to witness for Christ, and yet see little or no real progress. Why? It is because he is doing everything in the energy of the flesh, not in the power of the Spirit. Such a person needs to understand God's provision of the Holy Spirit and be yielded to His control. He needs to be filled with the Spirit.

Sometimes in this situation the Holy Spirit may fill such a person in deeply moving and memorable ways. Other Christians who may be more mature may still have an overwhelming spiritual experience in which the Holy Spirit fills them in fresh and wonderful ways. Some people call this a "baptism of the Spirit," but I think it is more Scriptural to speak of it as "a new filling of the Holy Spirit." This experience may come at a critical point in one's life when he is facing some crucial decision or some particularly difficult problem or challenge. Or this experience may come very quietly. In fact, there can even be times in which the filling of the Holy Spirit is very real, and yet we may be almost completely unaware of it.

Both of these experiences have been true in my own life. There have been times of deep awareness of the Holy Spirit's presence. There have been other times in which I have felt weak and inadequate, and yet in retrospect I know the Holy Spirit was in control of my life.

In my own life there have been times when I have also had the sense of being filled with the Spirit, knowing that some special strength was added for some task I was being called upon to perform.

We sailed for England in 1954 for a crusade that was to last for three months. While on the ship, I experienced a definite sense of oppression. Satan seemed to have assembled a formidable array of his artillery against me. Not only was I oppressed, I was overtaken by a sense of depression, accompanied by a frightening feeling of inadequacy for the task that lay ahead. Almost night and day I prayed. I knew in a new way what Paul was telling us when he spoke about "praying without ceasing." Then one day in a prayer meeting with my wife and colleagues, a break came. As I wept before the Lord, I was filled with deep assurance that power belonged to God and He was faithful. I had been baptized by the Spirit into the body of Christ when I was saved, but I believe God gave me a special anointing on the way to England. From that moment on I was confident that God the Holy Spirit was in control for the task of the 1954 Crusade in London.

That proved true.

Experiences of this kind had happened to me before, and they have happened to me many times since. Sometimes no tears are shed. Sometimes as I have lain awake at night the quiet assurance has come that I was being filled with the Spirit for the task that lay ahead.

However there have been many more occasions when I would have to say as the apostle Paul did in 1 Corinthians 2:3: "I was with you in weakness and in fear and in much trembling." Frequently various members of my team have assured me that when I have had the least liberty in preaching, or the greatest feeling of failure, God's power has been most evident.

In other words it is still true, as Paul continued in his letter to the church at Corinth, "My message and my preaching were not in persuasive words of wisdom, but in demonstration of the Spirit and of power, that your faith should not rest on the wisdom of men, but on the power of God" (1 Cor. 2:4, 5).

But note, those who *heard* the word sensed the power, not necessarily the one who proclaimed it. Filling does not necessarily imply "feeling."

Full and Filled

Two words used in the New Testament sometimes puzzle Christians: the words are *full* and *filled*. Some people make a distinction between them. I agree that there may be some distinction, but it is only minor. For instance, to be *full* of the Spirit seems to me to refer to the "state of being" of the believer. I think that John the Baptist and the apostle Paul were full of the Spirit all the time; that is, it was a continuous state. However, for them to be "filled with the Spirit" might also refer to a particular and occasional empowering or "anointing" for special purposes and special tasks. On occasion some of the New Testament saints God used for special assignments were said to be "filled with the Spirit." They might not have been able to bear it if that surcharge of power filled them all the time. But in moments of great need they could bear it for a season.

I believe God gives us the strength of the Holy Spirit commensurate with the tasks He gives us.

We have a friend who is a retired Presbyterian clergyman. His father operated a pile driver. He once told of watching the great pile drivers driving the posts into the river bed of the Mississippi in the process of building a bridge. Each pole was lifted into place and then with a mighty pounding of the pile driver each pole was driven securely into the riverbed.

That evening the little boy, Grier Davis, was playing in his sandpile and trying to reenact what he had seen earlier. But try as he would, he could not drive the sticks into the sand as he had seen the pile driver drive the poles into the Mississippi River bottom. Then he had a bright idea. Running to his father he asked if he might have permission to borrow one of the pile drivers. With a chuckle the father explained that the pile driver was much too powerful for the small job he was attempting to accomplish, and that a hammer would be more like it.

So it is with the power of the Holy Spirit. When God calls us to any task He also supplies the power for that task.

Thus it should be the normal situation of the Christian to be filled with the Spirit because we keep on being filled. But, then, what are we to make of the repeated, specific times of filling mentioned in the Book of Acts? Dr. Merrill C. Tenney uses a city house to illustrate this:

Most homes are connected to a water main. This supplies the house with adequate water for normal life. But suppose a fire breaks out. Then firemen tap a nearby hydrant to secure a much greater flow of water to meet the emergency. To be "full" of the Spirit is like a house supplied continuously with adequate water. But to be "filled" on occasion, as the apostles were in Acts 4:31, is to be given extra energy and power for special service. "And when they had prayed, . . . they were all filled with the Holy Spirit, and began to speak the word of God with boldness" (Acts 4:31). For the special task of persisting in evangelism, even when the religious leadership violently opposed them, the apostles needed a special filling of God's power. They had been "full of the Spirit" all along. Now they needed "extra filling" to meet the extra demands on them.

Filled for a Purpose

Of course, God has a purpose in wanting us to be filled with the Spirit. We saw this in Acts 4:31, "And they were all filled with the Holy Spirit, and began to speak the word of God with boldness." In other words, the disciples were filled *for a purpose*—to proclaim the Word of God. The great question every believer must face is, "What is my motivation in wanting to be filled with the

Spirit? Do I desire this fullness merely in the interest of self-enjoyment and self-glorification, or in order that Christ might be glorified?"

Often a Christian may sincerely seek the power of the Holy Spirit, and yet—either by ignorance or design—seek it for the wrong reasons. Some look for some type of emotional experience and want the fullness of the Spirit simply to give them a new (and even spectacular) experience. Some seek certain sensations because they see other Christians who may have had a particular form of experience which they believe has come from the Holy Spirit. Perhaps out of a misguided desire to be spiritually like others, or even spiritually superior, a person seeks the Spirit's fullness. Or again, a person may seek the Spirit's fullness only because he is encountering some particular problem, and he is hoping he can get out of the difficulty by having an experience of the Spirit's power. In short, people may yearn for the Spirit's power for all kinds of reasons.

It is true that the Spirit may bring some of these happenings into our lives. On occasion He may give us a deeply emotional sense of His presence, or make us particularly happy, or help us overcome a particularly troublesome difficulty. But we must be very careful that we do not seek His fullness for selfish reasons. He has come that we might glorify Christ.

The purpose of filling is that those who are filled may glorify Christ. The Holy Spirit came for this purpose. Jesus said, "He shall glorify Me; for He shall take of Mine, and shall disclose it to you" (John 16:14). That is, the Holy Spirit does not draw attention to Himself, but to Christ. Jesus said, "When the Helper comes, whom I will send to you from the Father, that is the Spirit of truth, who proceeds from the Father, He will bear witness of Me" (John 15:26). I believe this is one of the tests of a Spirit-filled life. Is Christ becoming more and more evident in my life? Are people seeing more of Him, and less of me?

For this reason I was hesitant about writing a book like this. I am a bit suspicious of people who make a fetish of talking about Him: "The Holy Spirit . . . this," and "the Holy Spirit . . . that." The Holy Spirit did not come to glorify Himself; He came to glorify Christ.

One other point—a person who is filled with the Spirit may not even be conscious of it. Not one biblical character said, "I am filled with the Spirit." Others said it about them, but they did not claim it for themselves. Some of the most godly people I have known were not conscious that they were filled with the Spirit. Someone has said that the nearer to heaven we get, the more conscious of hell we feel.

We've been considering power for use, but what about its abuse? What about those who want the Spirit's power for wrong reasons? One example in the New Testament of a person wanting the power of the Spirit for selfish reasons is found in Acts 8. Simon the sorcerer "believed," was baptized, and then was amazed by the signs and great miracles performed by the apostles. He was particularly interested when he noted how the converts received the Holy Spirit. Offering Peter and his fellow workers money, he said, "Give me also this power, that any one on whom I lay my hands may receive the Holy Spirit" (Acts 8:19 RSV). Peter immediately rebuked him, saying "your heart is not right before God" (v. 21). The Holy Spirit's power is for a purpose—but that purpose is always for the glory of God, not personal advantage or advancement.

Power for a Holy Life

Ultimately we need the filling of the Holy Spirit so that we may glorify Christ. But how do we glorify Christ? We glorify Christ when we live for God—trusting, loving, and obeying Him. Jesus said, "Let your light shine before men in such a way that they may see your good works, and glorify your Father who is in heaven" (Matt. 5:16). Paul said, "Whether, then, you eat or drink or whatever you do, do all to the glory of God" (1 Cor. 10:31). What a concept—everything we do should glorify God!

And yet this brings us to the heart of the problem. Why do we need the fullness of the Holy Spirit? *Because only in the power of the Spirit can we live a life that glorifies God.* We cannot glorify God in the energy of the flesh. This was Paul's cry in Romans 7: "I do not understand my own actions. For I do not do what I want, but I do the very thing I hate. . . . I can will what is right, but I cannot do it. For I do not do the good I want, but the evil I do not want is what I do" (Rom. 7:15, 18, 19 RSV). But in the power of the Holy Spirit we can live a life that increasingly glorifies God. God the Holy Spirit gives us power for a purpose—power to help us glorify God in every dimension of our lives.

In the Christian life, power is dynamically related to a Person. This Person is the Holy Spirit Himself, indwelling the Christian and filling him with the fullness of His power. As we said earlier, He supplies His power for a purpose; it is to be used. Although His limitless resources are available to us, He will permit us to have only as much power as He knows we will use or need. Unfortunately, many Christians are disobedient and, having prayed for power, have no intention of using it, or else neglect to follow through in active obedience. I think it is a waste of time for us Christians to look for power we do not intend to use: for might in prayer, unless we pray; for strength to testify, without witnessing; for power unto holiness, without attempting to live a holy life; for grace to suffer, unless we take up the cross; for power in service, unless we serve. Someone has said, "God gives dying grace only to the dying."

Power for Service

We glorify God by living lives that honor Him, and we can only do this in the power of the Holy Spirit. But we also glorify God as we serve Him, and we can only do that in the power of the Holy Spirit also. We are filled by the Spirit to serve.

Peter was so filled with the Holy Spirit that when he preached, 3,000 people were saved in one day at Pentecost. It is interesting that the Bible is full of statistics; this is one of them. Someone must have counted the number who were converted on that day, and Luke, inspired by the Holy Spirit, wrote down the number. In Acts 4:4 he says the number of men who believed "came to be about five thousand." And the same Spirit who inspired this keeping of statistics, saw to it that they were kept accurately.

In Acts 4:8 Peter and John, who had been arrested for preaching, were brought before the religious leaders. Then Scripture says Peter, "filled with the Holy Spirit," fearlessly proclaimed the death and resurrection of Christ. This same Peter, now full of the Holy

Spirit, was so bold he was ready to face death for Christ. Yet only a few weeks earlier he had denied Him with curses. The fullness of the Holy Spirit made the difference.

Shortly afterward, Peter and his companions went to a prayer meeting. As we have already seen when they prayed "they were all filled with the Holy Spirit, and began to speak the word of God with boldness" (Acts 4:31). The filling was given to them to serve Christ by boldly proclaiming the gospel. It is significant to me that here Peter had two fillings. He was filled before he preached (v. 8), and he was filled again after he and his fellow workers prayed (v. 31).

But the filling of the Spirit for power was not limited to preaching. The apostles became so tied down with the daily ministrations to the multiplied new believers that they were unable to devote themselves fully to the ministry of the Word. So they asked for seven men to be appointed for this practical job—a job of administration.

They laid down three qualifications for the officeholders: they were to be "of good reputation, full of the Spirit and of wisdom" (Acts 6:3).

This admonition tells us something important. If all the believers were "of good reputation, full of the Spirit and of wisdom," then the instructions make no sense. Some must have lacked some vital requirement. A good reputation, being full of the Holy Spirit, and wisdom were all required.

No man should be an officer in the church today who does not possess these qualifications. Of how many church members today can it be said they are "of good reputation, full of the Spirit and of wisdom"? Yet these requirements were for a practical, not a spiritual, ministry.

Does this not show us that to carry out the most practical job to the glory of God (be it as a craftsman, an administrator, a housekeeper, or secretary) we need to be filled with God's Holy Spirit— as well as of good reputation and wisdom?

We could go on and on because the early Church was empowered for every form of service by the filling of the Holy Spirit.

I am convinced that to be filled with the Spirit is not an option, but a necessity. It is indispensable for the abundant life and for fruitful service. The Spirit-filled life is not abnormal; it is the normal Christian life. Anything less is subnormal; it is less than what God wants and provides for His children. Therefore, to be filled with the Spirit should never be thought of as an unusual or unique experience for, or known by, only a select few. It is intended for all, needed by all, and available to all. That is why the Scripture commands all of us, "Be filled with the Spirit."

9

How to Be Filled with the Holy Spirit

IN MY MINISTRY I am frequently asked, "How can I be filled with the Spirit?" We have been commanded to be filled, but how do we obey? How does the presence and power of the Holy Spirit become a reality in each of our lives? This is the heart of the matter. Everything I have said so far about the filling of the Spirit will only be an intellectual curiosity, unrelated to our lives, unless we learn in our own experience what it means to be filled with the Spirit.

It is interesting that the Bible nowhere gives us a neat, concise formula for being filled with the Spirit. I believe that may be because most believers in the first century did not need to be told how to be filled. They knew that the Spirit-filled life was the normal Christian life. It is a sad commentary on the low level of our spiritual lives today that we are so confused about the filling of the Spirit.

And yet the Bible does say a great deal about this subject, and when we look at the New Testament as a whole there can be little doubt in our minds either about the meaning of the Spirit-filled life, or how the Spirit-filled life becomes a reality in our lives. *I believe the New Testament's teaching on how to be filled with the Holy Spirit can be summarized in three terms: Understanding, Submission, and Walking by Faith.*

Understanding

The first step in being filled with the Spirit is *understanding*. That is, there are certain things we must know and *understand*— certain truths God has revealed to us in His Word, the Bible. Some of these we have already mentioned, but let us be sure we have them clearly in our minds. What are these truths?

The first truth we must understand is that God has given us His Holy Spirit, and that He dwells within us. If I have accepted Christ as my Savior, the Spirit of God dwells within me. Remember—I may not necessarily *feel* His presence, but that does not mean He is absent. It is the *fact* of His presence that we must understand. God has promised that the Spirit lives within you if you belong to Christ, and God cannot lie. *We accept this fact by faith.*

We also must understand that God *commands* us to be filled with the Spirit. That means it is His will for you to be filled—and to refuse to be filled with the Spirit is to act contrary to the will of God. It is His command, and therefore it is His will. Just to make it even clearer—God *wants* to fill us with His Spirit. That is a wonderful truth to me. God does not give us a full measure of the Spirit grudgingly or unwillingly. No, He wants us to live our lives controlled and guided by the Holy Spirit. "If you then, being evil, know how to give good gifts to your children, how much more shall your heavenly Father give the Holy Spirit to those who ask Him?" (Luke 11:13). If I fail to be filled with the Spirit, remember that it is not because of God's reluctance. The fault is entirely on my side.

This leads to a further point we must understand, and that is the presence of sin in our lives. What is it that blocks the work of the Holy Spirit in our lives? It is sin. *Before we can be filled with the Holy Spirit we must deal honestly and completely with every known sin in our lives.* This may be very painful for us, as we face up to things that we have hidden or not even realized about our lives. But there will be no filling by the Holy Spirit apart from cleansing from sin, and the first step in cleansing from sin is awareness of its presence.

Most of us have had the experience at one time or another of having pipes clogged in our homes so that the water came through only in a trickle, or perhaps was stopped entirely. Where I live in North Carolina we rarely have extremely cold weather, but once in a while I have seen the temperature go below zero. Even though the pipes are buried quite deep coming from the spring into our house in a natural flow, I have seen them completely frozen. On one occasion we had to dig up the hard frozen ground and use blowtorches to melt the ice at an elbow in the pipe. So it is with sin in our lives. Sin is like the ice in our pipes—our spiritual lives have been "frozen" by a hostile world. There is only one solution, and that is repentance to clear the blockage and restore the flow of the Holy Spirit.

We are all familiar with "hardening of the arteries" as being one of the dangerous diseases to which a large percentage of the population is subject. The arteries become clogged with substances that still baffle medical experts. They still do not know how to unclog these arteries so that the blood can have free flow. Frequently bypass surgery is used, but medical opinion is divided even over this method in some instances. Vast amounts of money are being spent on medical research in many countries of the world trying to discover a chemical that will unclog arteries and save millions from death every year.

In the same way, our lives need that chemical provided by the blood of Christ to unclog the pipes, or arteries, of our lives so that the vital sap of the vine may flow. Sin is the great clogger, and the blood of Christ is the great cleanser when applied by repentance and faith.

Sometimes new believers are startled to find they are still sinners, and they not only continue to be tempted but they can still yield to temptation. Actually this should be no surprise, because the old sin nature is still within us. Before a person comes to Christ there is only one force at work in him—the old carnal nature. But when we accept Christ into our lives the Holy Spirit comes to dwell within us. Now there are two natures at work in our lives— the old sinful nature that wants us to live for self, and the new spiritual nature that wants us to live for God. The question is— which of these two natures will rule over our actions? This is why being filled with the Holy Spirit is so important. Unless the Spirit controls our lives, we will be dominated by our old sinful nature.

The Spirit's work will be blocked, however, as long as we allow sin to remain.

So we must deal completely with sin in our lives if we are to know the infilling of the Holy Spirit. This is not easy for several reasons. For one thing, it may be extremely painful for us to face the reality of sin in our lives. Pride is often at the root of our sins, and our pride is often deeply wounded when we honestly admit before God and before men that we are not as good as we had thought we were.

Dealing with sin in our lives is also hard because (as we shall see) we must not only know our sin, but we must repent of it. And some of us may be harboring sin and tolerating it, unwilling to give it up. Like the rich young ruler in Mark 10, we want what Jesus has for us, but we want to cling to our sin even more.

There is a further reason it is difficult for us to deal with sin in our lives, and it is simply this: sin blinds us spiritually, and one of the things about which we are blinded often is the awesome depth of sin. We do not see how much it has invaded every area of our lives, and just how much it has infected everything we say and think and do. It is all too easy to confess the sins which we see in our lives, and yet fail to see the many other sins possibly hindering even more directly our walk with the Lord.

That is why the Bible is so vital in this matter. We must not be content with a casual examination of our lives, thinking that only the sins which seem to give us the most trouble are worthy of being confessed. Instead, as we prayerfully study the Word of God, the Holy Spirit—who is, remember, the author of Scripture—will convict us of other areas of sin which need confessing to God. We must confess not only what we think is sin, but what the Holy Spirit labels as sin when we really listen to His voice from the Word of God. "All Scripture is inspired by God and profitable for teaching, for reproof, for correction, for training in righteousness" (2 Tim. 3:16).

Confession should be as broad as sin. The Song of Solomon warns us about "the little foxes, that spoil the vines" (2:15 KJV). This is a picture of the way "little" sins can destroy our fruitfulness for the Lord. There may be pride, jealousy, or bitterness in our lives. There may be backbiting, impatience, unkindness, or an uncontrolled temper—any one of which can make life miserable for those around us. Unclean thoughts may need to be brought to God for cleansing. Gluttony or laziness may need to be faced. Or the Holy Spirit may speak to us about our use of time, our use of money, or our lifestyle, or our use (or abuse) of some gift He has given us. Perhaps our treatment of someone near to us has become cold and indifferent. In other words, every sin that we can identify we should bring to God for confession. Sin takes all sorts of forms, and the Holy Spirit must guide us as we prayerfully examine our lives.

A young man came to me recently and said that he had lost the Holy Spirit. I replied that he had not lost the Holy Spirit, but he might well have grieved the Spirit through some particular sin. He replied that he could not think of a single thing in his life that stood between him and God. I asked him, "What about your relationship with your parents?" In response he said, "Well, it's not the best." I dug deeper and asked him, "Do you honor your father?" He agreed that he had sinned in this area. I said, "Why don't you go and have a straight, frank talk with him, and confess your sin, if you have been wrong?" He did that, and a few days later he came to me with a broad smile and said, "Fellowship restored!"

There is one other point we need to make about confession of our sins. We must not only be honest about the various sins in our lives, but we must get down to the deepest sin of all—our failure to let Christ rule our lives. *The most basic question any Christian can ask is this: Who is ruling my life, self or Christ?*

Sin will always be a continuing problem—our lives will always be marked by defeat and discouragement—as long as we try to keep "self" at the center of our lives. It is amazing how many Christians never really face this issue of Christ's Lordship, and yet the New Testament is full of statements about Christ's demand for our full commitment. "If anyone wishes to come after Me, let him deny himself, and take up his cross daily, and follow Me" (Luke 9:23). How easy it is for us to set up our own goals, operate by our own motives, and seek our own desires, without ever asking God for His will above all else. He calls us to renounce our plans and practices, and seek His way. He asks us to step off the throne of our lives, and let Him rule in every area of every thing we are and do. "And He died for all, that they who live should no longer live for themselves, but for Him who died and rose again on their behalf" (2 Cor. 5:15). Have you seen how completely—and tragically—sin has dominated your life, and are you willing to yield to Christ's authority and rule in everything?

We also need to understand that the Holy Spirit is in us, and God wants our lives to be controlled by Him. But we must understand our sin in all its dimensions. Most of all we need to face the crucial question of who is controlling our lives—we or Christ? Only when we understand these matters can we move to the second step.

Submission

The second step in being filled by the Holy Spirit is what we might term *submission*. What do I mean by this? By submission I mean that we renounce our own way and seek above all else to submit to Christ as Lord and be ruled by Him in every area of our lives.

The importance of this will be seen from what we said above about the way sin blocks the control of the Spirit in our lives. The essence of sin is self-will—placing ourselves at the center of our lives instead of Christ. The way to be filled—controlled and dominated—by the Spirit is to place Christ at the center of our lives, instead of self. This only happens as we submit to Him—as we allow Him to become Lord of our lives.

How does submission become a reality in our lives? There are, I believe, two steps.

First, there is the step of confession and repentance. We have just seen that one of the things we must understand is the depth of our sin. But we must move beyond understanding. Sin must be confessed to God and we must repent of it. There are many people who know they are sinners, and they can tell you what particular sins are a problem to them. They may even feel sorry for their sins and wish things were different. But there is never any change. Why? Because they have never confessed their sins to God and repented of them.

There is actually a difference between confession and repentance, although I believe the Bible sees them as being intimately related, like two sides of the same coin. Confession is acknowledgment of sin. It is admitting before God that I know I am a sinner, because I have committed certain sins which are known to me. The wonderful thing is that God has promised to forgive us when we turn to Him in humble confession. One of the great promises of the Bible is 1 John 1:9: "If we confess our sins, He is faithful and righteous to forgive us our sins and to cleanse us from all unrighteousness."

To repent means to *renounce* sin. In the Greek (the language in which the New Testament was originally written) the word "repent" meant a complete and total change of mind. To repent is not only to feel sorry for my sin, or even just to confess it to God. To repent of my sin is to turn from it, and to turn to Christ and His will.

If I have been guilty of evil thoughts, I renounce them when I repent of them and determine by God's grace to fill my mind with things that honor Him. If I have mistreated someone and acted in an unloving way toward him, I determine to do whatever is necessary to replace my mistreatment with loving acts toward that person. If my lifestyle is not pleasing to God, I will change it to bring it more in line with God's will. Repentance is a conscious turning from my sins. "Remember therefore from where you have fallen, and repent" (Rev. 2:5).

If the first step in our submission is confession and repentance of every known sin in our lives, *the second step is yielding ourselves to God and His will.* Confession and repentance might be described as the negative side of submission; this involves getting rid of everything which hinders God's control over our lives. Yielding to God might be described as the positive side; this involves placing ourselves totally and completely (as best we know how) into the hands of God in complete submission to His will for our lives.

This step of yielding ourselves to God is clearly presented in the sixth chapter of Romans. In that passage Paul talks vividly about the way sin has ruled our lives in the past. But now we belong to

Christ—we are no longer living for our old master, sin—we are now living for Christ, our new Master. Therefore we should not yield to sin, but yield ourselves to God. "Neither yield ye your members as instruments of unrighteousness unto sin: but yield yourselves unto God, as those that are alive from the dead" (Rom. 6:13 KJV). Paul then goes on to tell us that we have been set free from our slavery to sin—we no longer belong to sin. We have changed masters. Just as a slave in the first century might be sold and come under the ownership of a new master, so we have been purchased with the blood of Christ, and we belong now to God. "Having been freed from sin, you became slaves of righteousness" (Rom. 6:18).

In the original Greek language the words which are translated "yield yourselves to God" in the King James Version have a beautiful meaning. The thought has been translated in various ways by other versions: "Put yourselves in God's hands" (Phillips); "offer yourselves to God" (NIV); "present yourselves to God" (New American Standard Version). However, the fullest meaning of the word "yield" is "to place yourself at the disposal of someone." In other words, when we yield ourselves to Christ, we do not simply sit back and hope that God will somehow work through us. No, instead we place ourselves at His disposal—we say, in effect, "Lord, I am Yours, to be used in whatever way You want to use me. I am at Your disposal, and You may do with me whatever You will. I seek Your will for my life, not my own will." "Put yourselves at the disposal of God" (Rom. 6:13 NEB).

The same term is used in Romans 12:1: "I urge you therefore, brethren, by the mercies of God, to present your bodies a living and holy sacrifice, acceptable to God." This includes every area of our lives. It includes our abilities, our gifts, our possessions, and our families—our minds, wills, and emotions. Nothing is excluded. We can hold nothing back. In principle He must control and dominate us in the whole and the part. This verse reminds us of the sacrifices in the Old Testament, which the worshiper presented wholly to God. He could keep back no part of it, and it was all consumed on the altar. In the same way our surrender—our submission and yielding—must be total. It is a surrender without any conditions attached.

More and more I am coming to see that this *surrender* is a definite and conscious act on our part in obedience to the Word of God. It should, in fact, occur at the time of our conversion when we repent and receive Christ not only as our Savior but as our Lord. But for many people it may well be a crisis event which comes after conversion.

Perhaps we have not understood fully what it means to follow Christ as Lord, but later we begin to see that Jesus Christ calls us not simply to believe in Him but to follow Him without reserve as His disciples. If we find ourselves fuzzy and confused about Christ's Lordship, we should take action immediately. Our intention should be a complete and final act of submission in principle, even though in months ahead the Holy Spirit may well show us other areas of our lives that need to be surrendered. This is, in fact, one of the signs of our yieldedness—as we place ourselves at God's disposal, He leads us into new areas of commitment.

The Holy Spirit may test us many times to see if we really mean business. He may even call on us to surrender something in principle that He really does not want us to surrender in fact, but which He wants us to be willing to surrender. We must be open to everything He wants to do in and through our lives.

Perhaps several illustrations will help us understand more clearly this matter of yielding ourselves to God's will. In Romans 6, Paul (as we have seen) uses the illustration of a slave who has a new master. Professor William Barclay reminds us about the real meaning of Paul's analogy:

"When we think of a servant, in our sense of the word, we think of a man who gives a certain agreed part of his time to his master, and who receives a certain agreed wage for doing so. Within that agreed time he is at the disposal and in the command of his master. But, when that time ends, he is free to do exactly as he likes. . . . But, in Paul's time, the status of the slave was quite different. Quite literally he had no time which belonged to himself. He had no moment when he was free. Every single moment of his time belonged to his master. He was the absolutely exclusive possession of his master, and there was not one single moment of his life when he could do as he liked. In Paul's time a slave could never do what he liked; it was impossible for him to serve two masters, because he was the exclusive possession of one master. That is the picture that is in Paul's mind."[1]

Now the parallel between the slave of Paul's time and the Christian is not exact (as Paul himself says) because there is a sense in which the Christian is the freest person in the world since he knows the spiritual freedom Christ brings. But on the other hand, you and I are called to belong to God, and to be His people. We are called to be at His disposal, ready and eager to do His will. Paul told Titus that Christ "gave himself for us to redeem us from all wickedness and to purify for himself a people that are his very own, eager to do what is good" (Titus 2:14 NIV).

Perhaps another illustration will help me make my point. The principle of yielding to Christ is like the commitment a bride and groom make when they are linked together in marriage. A new situation is created that becomes an enduring reality. In principle it is a complete and final act once they have repeated the vows and consummated the marriage. They are married, in fact and in principle, but—and this is a crucial thing—in practice husband and wife discover that their lives have to be constantly surrendered to each other in line with the new fact of their mutual commitment to each other in marriage.

Two people are not less married because there are defects in their lives and problems in the everyday details of living. Instead, they each grow, learning more of what it means to love each other and adjust to each other as a result of that love. Likewise in our spiritual pilgrimage we see sins which mar our relationship with God, but beneath it is a commitment which seeks to move beyond to a higher life, based on wholehearted surrender to God.

Have you ever submitted your life to God? Have you ever confessed your sin to Him, and repented of your sin as best you know how? Are there particular sins that are obstacles to your full commitment? Are there other sins, which you have not even begun to admit? Most of all, have you ever really told God—as fully and as simply as you know how—that you want His will in your life, whatever it may be?

There are people who suggest we should pray for God to fill us with His Holy Spirit. While this may be a valid prayer, I personally see little or no example of this in the New Testament. Instead, I believe we should pray that God will take possession of our lives totally and completely. We should pray that we will be emptied of self—self-love, self-will, self-ambition—and be placed completely at His disposal.

If you have never taken the step of submission to God and His will, I urge you to get on your knees before you read another page of this book, and give your life without reserve to your Master and Lord. "Therefore, shake off your complacency and repent. See, I stand knocking at the door. If anyone listens to my voice and opens the door, I will go into his house and dine with him, and he with me" (Rev. 3:19, 20 *Phillips*).

Faith

We now come to the last step in the infilling of the Holy Spirit, which I like to call "Walking in Faith." We must first *understand* certain things—then we must *submit* and yield ourselves to God— and then we must learn the secret of *walking in faith*.

The main point is this: When we are yielded to God and His will, we are filled with the Holy Spirit. The Holy Spirit controls and dominates us. Now we are to *act* on that truth and *walk* or live with full assurance that God has already filled us, and we are under His control.

The Apostle Paul puts it this way: "Likewise reckon ye also yourselves to be dead indeed unto sin, but alive unto God through Jesus Christ our Lord" (Rom. 6:11 KJV). The word in Greek which we translate "reckon ye" was sometimes used in accounting or mathematics. After a business transaction, for example, the amount of money would be computed and entered in the books. The entry in the accounting books demonstrated that the transaction had already taken place and payment had been made. Now when we yield ourselves to Christ and follow Him as Lord of our lives, we know that something has happened. The Holy Spirit has taken over our lives, to guide and empower us. We are now to walk in faith, reckoning ourselves to be dead to sin and alive to God.

We *are* filled with the Holy Spirit; now we *are to live* in light of this truth. This is not pretending; it is acting on God's promise. Dr. John Stott puts it this way:

"Now 'reckoning' is not make-believe. It is not screwing up our faith to believe something we do not believe. We are not to pretend that our old nature has died when we know perfectly well that it has not. . . . We are simply called to 'reckon' this—not to pretend it, but to realize it. It is a fact. And we have to lay hold of it. We have to let our minds play upon these truths. We have to meditate upon them until we grasp them firmly."

Dr. Stott then continues: "Can a married woman live as though she were still a single girl? Well, yes, I suppose she can. It is not impossible. But let her feel that ring on the fourth finger of her left hand, the symbol of her new life, the symbol of her identification with her husband, let her remember who she is, and let her live accordingly. . . . Our minds are so to grasp the fact and the significance of our death and resurrection with Christ, that a return to the old life is unthinkable. A born-again Christian should no more think of going back to the old life than an adult to his childhood, a married man to his bachelorhood, or a discharged prisoner to his prison cell."[2]

If you have fulfilled the Scriptural requirements for being filled with the Holy Spirit—especially the repentance and submission we have considered—then you and I can privately say to ourselves, "By faith I know I am filled with the Holy Spirit." I've never known a person whom I thought was truly filled with the Holy Spirit who went out and bragged about it, or sought to draw attention to himself. If we are filled with the Holy Spirit others will soon notice it, because the filled person produces the fruit of the Spirit. But we may not even be aware of this. In fact, some of God's greatest saints have indicated that the closer they came to Christ the more sinful they felt. My friend and associate, Roy Gustafson, once said, "The Holy Spirit didn't come to make us Holy-Spirit-conscious, but Christ-conscious." Thus, when we say to ourselves that we are filled with the Spirit it means that every known sin and hindrance is out of the way and then we claim by faith that we are filled.

There are, I believe, several things we should remember at this point.

First, we must remember that the filling of the Spirit is not a matter of feeling, but of faith. We may feel strongly the closeness of God when we are filled, or we may not. Instead of trusting in our feelings, we must trust God's promises. We must reckon ourselves to be filled by His Spirit. James McConkey put it this way:

"Nothing is more hurtful than to be constantly inspecting our own inner lives to see if God is fulfilling His promise in our experience. It is like the child constantly digging up the seed to see if it has sprouted. The question of the experience of fullness of the Spirit belongs to the Lord."[3]

Also, we must remember that the filling of the Spirit does not mean we are perfect and without sin. It means we are controlled by the Spirit, but sin is still a reality, lurking around the corner ready to lunge at the first opportunity. We may be blameless in our desire to serve Christ, but that does not make us without fault. A Scottish preacher of another generation explained it this way:

"I have lying on the table beside me a letter, which will illustrate the point at issue. I received it when I was away in New Zealand on a mission tour, in 1891. It was from my eldest daughter, then a child of five years of age. It reads: 'Dear father, I wrote all this myself. I send you a kiss from Elsie.' The fact of the matter is, that it is not writing at all, but an attempt at printing in large capitals, and not one of the letters is properly formed; there is not as much as one straight stroke on the page. . . . Now, this letter which I prize so dearly is certainly not a 'faultless' production; it is as full of faults as it is full of letters, but most assuredly it is 'blameless.' I did not blame my child for her crooked strokes, and answer with a scold, for I judged her work by its motive. I knew it was the best she could do, and that she had put all the love of her little heart into it. She wanted to do something to please me, and she succeeded. By the grace of the indwelling Christ . . . this is what our daily life, our daily life-work may be, viz., 'blameless.'"

This brings me to the last truth about the filling of the Holy Spirit: *the filling of the Holy Spirit should not be a once-for-all event, but a continuous reality every day of our lives.* It is a process. We must surrender ourselves to Him daily, and every day we must choose to remain surrendered. In every situation involving conflict between self and God's will, we must make our decisions on the basis of our constant submission to Christ.

As we have seen, the Greek verb used by Paul in his command in Ephesians 5:18, "Be filled with the Spirit," carries with it the idea that we should keep on being filled with the Spirit. We are already the temple of God, indwelt by the Holy Spirit, but He wants to fill us. However, He can fill only those who wish to be emptied of self and yielded to Him. Therefore, this active surrender must continue day by day, concerning little things as well as big ones. If we sin we need to repent so that He can fill us again. And if on occasion we face exceptional pressure, we need to pray for His additional help.

And so the four steps we have outlined above are not only a beginning, but a process. Each day we should seek to understand more from God's Word. We should pray that God will help us see our sin each day. Each day we should confess and repent. And each day we should submit our wills to His will. We should so walk in faith that He is continually filling us as we submit to Him. Each day we should walk in obedience to His Word.

Personally I find it helpful to begin each day by silently committing that day into God's hands. I thank Him that I belong to Him, and I thank Him that He knows what the day holds for me. I ask Him to take my life that day and use it for His glory. I ask Him to cleanse me from anything which would hinder His work in my life. And then I step out in faith, knowing that His Holy Spirit is filling me continually as I trust in Him and obey His Word. Sometimes during the day I may not be aware of His presence; sometimes I am. But at the end of the day, I can look back and thank Him, because I see His hand at work. He promised to be with me that day—and He has been!

This can be your experience also as you daily yield to the Lordship of Jesus Christ in your life. May you yield each day to Him. And may you be able to look back at the end of each day and know that His Holy Spirit has been your guide and your strength as you have yielded to Him.

10

Sins against the Holy Spirit

ONE OF THE most solemn themes in all Scripture concerns sins against the Third Person of the Trinity, the Holy Spirit. Believers and unbelievers alike can and do sin against Him. What is the nature of these sins, and how can we guard ourselves against committing them?

Blaspheming the Holy Spirit

Of all the sins men commit against the Holy Spirit none is worse than that of blaspheming Him. The reason for this is clear: It is the one sin for which there is no forgiveness. All other sins against the Holy Spirit are committed by *believers*. We can repent of them, be forgiven, and make a new start.

Not so with blaspheming the Spirit. This sin is committed by *unbelievers* and is often called "the unpardonable sin." It was committed by the enemies of Jesus when they accused Him of casting out devils by the power of Satan after Jesus had clearly stated that they were cast out by the power of the "Spirit of God." He then continued: "Therefore I say to you, any sin and blasphemy shall be forgiven men, but blasphemy against the Spirit shall not be forgiven. And whoever shall speak a word against the Son of Man, it shall be forgiven him; but whoever shall speak against the Holy Spirit, it shall not be forgiven him, either in this age, or in the age to come" (Matt. 12:31, 32).

When my father was a young man, he attended a revival meeting in North Carolina and became convinced through a sermon on this subject that he had committed the unpardonable sin.

And he lived with this awful thought for many years. He agonized over it, was frightened by it, and thought of himself as a doomed man who could never repent of his sin. In time he discovered that his sin was not one which excluded him from the mercy and grace of God. He came to know that the Holy Spirit would not be convicting and wrestling with him and drawing him to Christ if he had really committed this unpardonable sin.

Perhaps I can venture a definition of what I understand the unpardonable sin to be. It seems to me, negatively, that no one has committed this sin who continues to be under the disturbing, convicting, and drawing power of the Holy Spirit. So long as the Spirit strives with a person he has not committed the unpardonable sin. But when a person has so resisted the Holy Spirit that He strives with him no more, then there is eternal danger. In other words, the unpardonable sin involves the total and irrevocable rejection of Jesus Christ.

I believe this is what Stephen was talking about in the sermon he preached just prior to his martyrdom. In that message he said, "You . . . who are stiff-necked . . . are always resisting the Holy Spirit" (Acts 7:51).

The context makes it clear that Stephen was saying, first of all, that just as their fathers had refused to take seriously the proclamations of the prophets and messengers of God, or to believe them, so his listeners were guilty of like sins. In the Old Testament we read that some opposed, maligned, persecuted, and ridiculed the prophets. Since the prophets were inspired by the Holy Spirit, these people were in fact resisting the Spirit. So Stephen says that when the people to whom he was speaking refused to hear Christ's apostles and chosen ones, who were speaking through the Holy Spirit, they were in effect resisting the Holy Spirit.

Now the fatal infection of sin in the hearts of unregenerate people will always cause them to resist the Holy Spirit. The flesh and the reprobate mind always fight Him. When people do this, they will not receive the Word of God in its power unless the Holy Spirit gains victory over them.

But Stephen was saying something more, too. He was telling them and us that just as God the Spirit strove in vain with people in the Old Testament and they were doomed, so his listeners would be doomed if they did not heed the work of the Spirit in their hearts. Resisting the Spirit is a sin committed only by unbelievers. But it is a sin that, when carried on long enough, leads to eternal doom. Only certain judgment remains for those who so resist the Spirit.

The only way any sinner can be forgiven for resisting the Holy Spirit is to cease resisting and to embrace Jesus Christ, to whom the Spirit bears witness. That person has hope only if he repents immediately and allows the Spirit to work in his heart.

I think pastors, teachers, evangelists, and all Christian workers should handle this subject very carefully. For the most part Christian workers should be extremely hesitant to draw their own conclusions dogmatically as to when someone has committed the unpardonable sin. Let the Holy Spirit and God the Father make that decision. We should always urge men everywhere to repent and turn to Jesus since we do not know when the Spirit has stopped dealing with them. And let us pray that those about whom we are most uncertain may yet respond to the good news that Jesus saves.

Are you perhaps one of those who worries about having committed the unpardonable sin? If so, you should face squarely what the Bible says on this subject, not what you may have heard from others. The unpardonable sin is rejecting the truth about Christ. It is rejecting, completely and finally, the witness of the Holy Spirit, which declares that Jesus Christ is the Son of God who alone can save us from our sins. Have you rejected Christ in your own life, and said in your heart that what the Bible teaches about Him is a lie? Then I tell you as solemnly and as sincerely as I know how that you are in a very dangerous position. I urge you without delay to accept the truth about Christ, and come to Him in humble confession and repentance and faith. It would be tragic for you to persist in your unbelief, and eventually go into eternity without hope and without God.

On the other hand you may be a believer, but you have committed some sin which you have thought might keep you from being saved. No matter what it is, remember that God loves you, and He wants to forgive you of that sin. Right now you need to confess that sin to Him and seek His forgiveness. You need to be freed from the burden of guilt and doubt that has oppressed you. Christ died to free you from it. If you have come to Christ, you know on the basis of God's Word that this sin—whatever it is—is not the unpardonable sin. It will not send you to hell, because you are saved by faith in the shed blood of Christ. But you need to put it out of your life by casting it on Christ. Remember the words of the Psalmist, "As far as the east is from the west, so far has He removed our transgressions from us" (Ps. 103:12).

Grieving the Spirit

We now come to two sins against the Holy Spirit which can be committed by *Christians*. One is to grieve the Holy Spirit, and the other is to quench the Spirit. These are inclusive terms, for almost any wrong action we take can be included under one of these two headings. Let us look first at grieving the Spirit.

Paul warns his readers that they are not to "grieve the Holy Spirit of God, by whom you were sealed for the day of redemption" (Eph. 4:30). It is important and consoling to hear Paul say that we are "sealed for the day of redemption." This means we are and will remain Christians. So he is not speaking of judgment in the sense that what we do here will separate us from the love of God and cause us to go to hell. He is speaking rather of things we do that are inconsistent with the nature of the Holy Spirit and thus hurt His heart and wound Him in His own selfhood. We can bring pain to the Spirit by what we do.

"Grieve" is a "love" word. The Holy Spirit loves us just as Christ did, "Now I urge you, brethren, by our Lord Jesus Christ and by the love of the Spirit, to strive together with me in your prayers to God for me" (Rom. 15:30). We may hurt or anger one who has no affection for us, but we can grieve only a person who loves us.

I once heard a father tell his son, "Unless you are good, I won't love you any more." This was unfortunate. He had every right to tell the boy to be good, but he had no reason to tell him that he would withdraw his love. A father should always love his son—whether he is good or bad. But when he is bad, his father's love for him is mixed with pain and even sorrow and anguish.

How do Christians grieve the Holy Spirit? In Ephesians 4:20–32 Paul says that whatever is unlike Christ in conduct, speech, or disposition grieves the Spirit of grace. In one of her books, Ruth Paxson suggests that we can know what hurts the Spirit when we consider our conduct in light of the words Scripture uses to depict the Spirit. The Holy Spirit is the Spirit of:

1. *Truth* (John 14:17); so anything false, deceitful, or hypocritical grieves Him.

2. *Faith* (2 Cor. 4:13); so doubt, distrust, anxiety, worry, grieve Him.

3. *Grace* (Heb. 10:29); so whatever in us is hard, bitter, malicious, ungracious, unforgiving, or unloving grieves Him.

4. *Holiness* (Rom. 1:4); so anything unclean, defiling or degrading grieves Him.

What happens when we grieve the Holy Spirit? Ordinarily He delights to take the things of Christ and reveal them to us. He also imparts to us joy, peace, and gladness of heart. But when we grieve Him this ministry is suspended.

I come from that region of the United States where the textile industry is prominent. Some years ago I walked through a very large factory where hundreds of looms were spinning cloth made of very fine linen threads. The manager of the mill said, "This machinery is so delicate that if a single thread out of the whole thirty thousand which are weaving at this moment should break, all of these looms would stop instantly." To demonstrate it he stepped to one of the machines and broke a single thread. Instantly every loom stopped until the thread had been fixed; then they went on automatically.

This mechanical wonder provides a rough analogy of "that which is spiritual." When I commit one sin, one disobedient act, one departure from the clearly seen pathway of the will and the fear of God, then the ministry of the Spirit in my life is impaired. While the ministry of the Spirit in my life is withdrawn it is not stopped. Unlike the machinery, it is impaired. As soon as the broken thread has been repaired the full ministry of the Spirit commences again as He illuminates my mind, satisfies my heart needs, and makes the ministry of Christ effective to me.

There is one glorious and gracious aspect to this, however. To grieve the Holy Spirit is not to lose Him in my life. He does not cease to seal me; He does not remove Himself from me. Indeed a believer cannot grieve Him so that He goes away totally. I have been singularly blessed by the hymns of William Cowper, who was an associate of John Newton. But these lines have always troubled me:

> Return, O holy Dove! return,
> Sweet messenger of rest!
> I hate the sins that made Thee mourn,
> And drove Thee from my breast.[1]

I have the uneasy impression that these words suggest more than just causing the Spirit within me to stop His wonderful work. They imply that I lose Him. If that is what Cowper meant, I think he was mistaken.

It is possible that the sense of the Holy Spirit's presence may be taken away or withdrawn from men. Psalm 51 makes this clear when David cried, "Do not take Thy Holy Spirit from me" (v. 11). But remember that the Holy Spirit has sealed every believer for the day of redemption, that is, the redemption of our bodies (Eph. 1:13; 4:30; Rom. 8:23). You and I may backslide, but this is quite different from falling from grace, or having the Holy Spirit totally withdrawn from us.

If the Spirit were to withdraw Himself from a believer He has sealed, would He not be denying the whole scheme of salvation? But when He is grieved, He does bring about an absence of joy and power in our lives until we can renounce and confess the sin. Though we may appear happy, we are inwardly wretched when we are out of communion with the Holy Spirit. This is not because the Spirit has abandoned us, but because He deliberately makes us wretched until we return to Christ in brokenness, contrition, and confession. Psalm 32—which many think was written by David after his sin with Bathsheba—is an excellent example of this: "When I kept silent about my sin, my body wasted away through my groaning all day long. For day and night Thy hand was heavy upon me; My vitality was drained away as with the fever-heat of summer. I acknowledged my sin to Thee, and my iniquity I did not hide; I said, 'I will confess my transgressions to the Lord'; and Thou didst forgive the guilt of my sin. . . . Be glad in the Lord and rejoice you righteous ones, and shout for joy all you who are upright in heart" (Ps. 32:3–5, 11).

I believe that once we have been baptized into the body of Christ and indwelt by the Holy Spirit we will never be abandoned by the Spirit again. We are sealed forever. And He is the earnest, the pledge, of what is to come. I realize that many of my brethren in the faith hold a different view, but as far as I have light at this moment, I believe we are kept by the Holy Spirit.

On the one hand the Holy Spirit who indwells us secures us for God. He does this on the basis of Christ's blood in which we have trusted and by which we know we have been redeemed. On the other hand, He gives us continuous enjoyment in the knowledge that we belong to God; that enjoyment is interrupted only when some work of the flesh grieves the One who has sealed us. As translated by Weymouth, James 4:5 says He "yearns jealously over us." I seriously doubt if, this side of heaven, we will ever know how great is the power of the force we could have utilized in this life: the power of the Holy Spirit, which we tap through prayer.

When we yield ourselves totally every moment of every day to Jesus Christ as Lord, the wonder-working power of the Holy Spirit in our lives and witness will be overwhelming. It is at this point of surrender that the secret of purity, peace, and power lies. I believe it also carries with it what George Cutting used to call Safety, Certainty, and Enjoyment. It also conveys the thought of outward achievement and inward rest.

Yes, as the Spirit of love the Holy Spirit is grieved when we sin, because He loves us.

Quenching the Spirit

To blaspheme the Spirit is a sin committed by unbelievers. Grieving and quenching the Spirit are sins committed by believers. Now we must consider what is meant by quenching the Spirit.

Paul's terse admonition is this: "Do not quench the Spirit" (1 Thess. 5:19). The word *grieve* suggests the sense of being hurt, of being made sorrowful. This has to do with the way we bruise the heart of the Spirit in our individual lives. The word *quench* means "to put out, to put a damper on." It is pertinent to the Scripture's reference to the Holy Spirit as a fire. When we quench the Spirit, we put the fire out. This does not mean we expel Him, but that we extinguish the love and power of the Spirit as He seeks to carry out His divine purpose through us. We may quench Him in a number of ways, but the figure of fire suggests two aspects by way of warning.

A fire goes out when the fuel supply is withdrawn. When we do not stir up our souls, when we do not use the means of grace, when we fail to pray, witness, or read the Word of God, the fire of the Holy Spirit is banked. These things are channels through which God gives us the fuel that keeps the fire burning. And the Holy Spirit wants us to use those gifts to maintain His burning in our lives.

The second way to put out a fire is to extinguish it, by throwing water on it or smothering it with a blanket or a shovelful of dirt. In a similar way, willful sin quenches the Spirit. When we criticize, act unkindly, belittle the work of others by careless or unappreciative words, we smother the fire and put it out. This happens many times when there is a fresh, new, or different movement of the Spirit of God—perhaps not using the old traditional methods in proclamation or service. For example, when some Christians sometimes seek to block what God may be doing in a new way.

I want to be very clear at one point: No Christian *must* sin. Yet, conversely, he has not been rendered *incapable* of sinning. I believe a Christian *can* sin, but he does not *have to.* It is possible to keep the fire burning; it is possible to avoid grieving the Spirit. God never would have told us to reject evil acts if in point of fact we could not help but do them. Thank God we need not sin, even though we can sin!

I do not know their source, but the following words about the Holy Spirit have been a help to me: "Resist not His incoming; grieve not His indwelling; quench not His outgoing. Open to Him as the Incomer; please Him as the Indweller; obey Him as the Outgoer in His testimony of the things concerning Christ, whether through yourself or others."

Have you in any sense grieved the Spirit, or quenched the Spirit in your life? These are serious matters, and they call for our careful attention. If this has been the case, realize that now is the time to confess these to God, and repent of them. And then walk each day in the fullness of the Spirit, sensitive to His leading and power in your life.

11

Gifts of the Spirit

WHEN OUR CHILDREN were growing up, Christmas morning would find the Christmas tree surrounded by gifts. They had been selected lovingly according to each child's enjoyment and need. Each would be opened with anticipation and excitement—accepted with expressions of love and appreciation—enjoyed and used (depending on age) all day. Alas, however, (again depending on age) by evening jealousy and squabbling had begun.

Is this not somewhat true of spiritual gifts (with the exception that spiritual gifts were given for service, not for personal enjoyment)? Still, the spiritually immature wind up eyeing with a bit of jealousy gifts which they have not received. Sometimes there is a touch of smugness and pride on the part of the receiver. But the spirit in which the gift was given cannot be judged by the attitudes of the receivers.

The New Testament lists "the gifts of the Spirit" in three passages—Romans 12:6–8; 1 Corinthians 12:8–10; and Ephesians 4:11. (There is a fourth listing in 1 Peter 4:10, 11, although it seems to duplicate material included in the previous lists.)

Gifts and the Body

The Bible teaches that every redeemed person is given at least one gift by the Holy Spirit: "Now there are varieties of gifts, . . . But to each one is given the manifestation of the Spirit for the common good" (1 Cor. 12:4, 7). God holds us responsible for the way we use our gifts.

The apostle Paul likens the Church to our physical bodies, where each member has a unique function yet all parts work together. Paul said, "For the body is not one member, but many. If the foot should say, 'Because I am not a hand, I am not a part of the body,' it is not for this reason any the less a part of the body. . . . But now God has placed the members, each one of them, in the body, just as He desired." Paul continued by saying that "there are many members, but one body. And the eye cannot say to the hand, 'I have no need of you'; or again the head to the feet, 'I have no need of you'" (1 Cor. 12:14–21). He added that even those members of the body that seem the most feeble or the least needed are necessary parts of the perfect body. They are all essential for the body's proper functioning.

As with the human body, so the body of Christ is a complete organism made by God. Yet each member of the body is unique. There can never be another "you" or "me." In a sense, your gift or mine is unique. God often gives similar gifts to different people, but there is a uniqueness about this that makes each of us distinct from any other person who has ever lived. And if any one of us is missing, the body is incomplete, lacking some part.

The Meaning of Charisma

The New Testament uses the Greek word *charisma* (plural, *charismata*) to speak of the various gifts God has given by the Holy Spirit to Christians. Actually, the word "charisma" has come into our English language to describe someone who has a certain indefinable quality which attracts people to his personality. We speak of certain well-known people as having charisma. A biblical illustration might be Apollos (Acts 18:24–28). This New Testament evangelist and Bible teacher seemed to have charisma, in its modern English sense. The apostle Paul lacked it. However, both men had definite spiritual gifts—*charismata*—that God had supernaturally given them. In the worldly sense charisma is an intangible influence that no one can put his finger on. But in the biblical use of the word *charisma*, it means "a gift of holy grace." Thus the word *charisma* in the Bible has a different meaning from the one the world thinks of when it says a man has "charisma."

The word *charismata* is the plural of *charisma* and, except for one passage in 1 Peter, is found only in the writings of the apostle Paul. If we define it precisely, it means "manifestations of grace," and is translated, "gifts." This word was used to denote the various spiritual gifts given to individuals for the benefit of the Church, and these gifts are the subject of this chapter. In Ephesians 4 Paul uses two other words translated "gifts," *dorea* and *doma*. They are similar to *charismata* and indeed to a fourth word for "gifts," *pneumatika*, which, precisely defined, means "things belonging to the Spirit." These various Greek terms lie behind our single English translation, "gifts," and mean about the same thing.

The Origin of Spiritual Gifts

Before dealing with the gifts of the Spirit more specifically I must emphasize one point. These gifts come to us from the Holy Spirit. He chooses who gets which gifts, and He dispenses them at His good pleasure. While we are held accountable for the use of any gifts He gives us, we have no responsibility for gifts we have not been given. Nor are we to covet what someone else has or be envious of that person. We may wish to have certain gifts and even ask for them, but if it is not the will of the Holy Spirit, we will not get what we ask for. And if we are dissatisfied because the Holy Spirit does not give us the gifts we want, we sin. In my case I believe God has given me the gift of evangelism, but I did not ask for it.

If I had the gift of evangelism and failed to use it, it would be a sin for me. If, on the other hand, someone else does not have the gift of evangelism, and yet is disgruntled because he does not have it, he also is sinning. There are many things I cannot do very well, but that is because there are some gifts I do not have, nor should I be discontented. The gifts you and I have are the ones God has seen fit to give us, and we should seek to discover and use them for His glory.

One other point should be stressed. We have talked about the fruit of the Spirit (and will have three chapters devoted to the fruit), and we have shown that every one of the fruits of the Spirit should be characteristic of every single Christian. But the gifts of the Spirit are different. Every believer should have the same fruit as every other believer, but not every believer will have the same gifts as every other believer. No, the Holy Spirit distributes the gifts in such a way that every believer has at least one gift which is uniquely his. You may have been given a certain gift by God, but it would be a mistake for you to say everyone else should have that same gift.

Spiritual Gifts and Talents

In studying the three passages where the gifts are listed, we find a total of about twenty. In addition, the Old Testament mentions a number of gifts not listed in the New Testament. Many of these seem quite similar to natural abilities or talents people may have, although others are clearly spiritual in character.

Certainly, most of us know of people who have a special gift of "music" which is not listed among these twenty. Moreover, many people wonder what the difference is between a spiritual gift and a natural talent. One may have the talent of making beautiful handicrafts; another may have a talent for music. Actually, most people have talents of one kind or another, and these too come from the Creator.

It appears that God can take a talent and transform it by the power of the Holy Spirit and use it as a spiritual gift. In fact, the difference between a spiritual gift and a natural talent is frequently a cause for speculation by many people. I am not sure we can always draw a sharp line between spiritual gifts and natural abilities—both of which, remember, come ultimately from God. Nor do I believe it is always necessary to make a sharp distinction. On most occasions, however, in the context we are discussing, the gifts I have in mind are supernatural ones the Spirit gives a person for the good of the Church.

A gift might also be called a "tool" or an instrument that is to be used, rather than a piece of jewelry for decoration, or a box of candy for personal enjoyment. We could think of the different types of tools a carpenter uses, or the different types of tools a surgeon needs. These "tools" have been given to people for use in the functioning of the Body of Christ.

There's an interesting passage in Exodus 31 about Bezalel. The Bible says, "And I have filled him with the Spirit of God in wisdom, in understanding, in knowledge, and in all kinds of craftsmanship, to make artistic designs for work in gold, in silver, and in bronze, and in the cutting of stones for settings, and in the carving of wood, that he may work in all kinds of craftsmanship" (vv. 3–5). This indicates that many of the skills and talents that people have are gifts of God.

This unique ability of Bezalel, given by the Spirit, included not only manual skill but also the intellectual wisdom and understanding essential to all art. Artistic talent of every kind is a divine gift. "Every good thing bestowed and every perfect gift is from above, coming down from the Father of lights, with whom there is no variation, or shifting shadow" (James 1:17). God has given to mankind aesthetic faculties which, like all the human faculties, were corrupted by man's rebellion against God in the Garden of Eden—but they are still there!

Purpose of Gifts

Paul says that the purpose of these spiritual gifts is, "for the equipping of the saints for the work of service, to the building up of the body of Christ" (Eph. 4:12). In other words, God has given each of us a task to do, and supernatural gifts to equip us for it. If we fail to perform this task we face censure at the "judgment seat of Christ."

Scripture teaches that every believer will someday have to stand before the judgment seat of Christ to give an account of how faithfully he used his gifts, as well as his personal life before God and man. This is called the "bema" or the judgment seat of Christ: "For we must all appear before the judgment seat of Christ, that each one may be recompensed for his deeds in the body, according to what he has done, whether good or bad" (2 Cor. 5:10). This will not be a judgment for the unbelieving world. That is called the Great White Throne judgment. This will be a special judgment for Christians. Our sins have been atoned for by Christ on the cross, but after salvation every work must come into judgment. The result is reward or loss (1 Cor. 3:11–15) "but he himself [the believer] shall be saved."

In 1 Corinthians 12:7, the apostle Paul says the gifts are given "for the common good" so we are not to use them selfishly. Instead, we are to use them to help each other. As Paul says in Philippians 2:3, 4, "Do nothing from selfishness or empty conceit, but with humility of mind let each of you regard one another as more important than himself; do not merely look out for your own personal interests, but also for the interests of others."

God has also designed the gifts to help "unite" the body of Christ. Just before listing the gifts in Ephesians 4:3–7, the apostle Paul urges us to be "diligent to preserve the unity of the Spirit in the bond of peace. There is one body and one Spirit, just as also you were called in one hope of your calling; one Lord, one faith, one baptism, one God and Father of all who is over all and through all and in all. But to each one of us grace [a special gift] was given according to the measure of Christ's gift." Notice how Paul emphasizes unity by repeating the word "one."

Thus the gifts of the Spirit should never divide the body of Christ; they should unify it.

How to Recognize Your Gift

I am often asked, "How can I discover what gift I have?" And "How can I utilize my gift to the best advantage?" I would make the following suggestions:

First, realize that God has given you at least one spiritual gift, and He wants you to know what it is and to use it for His glory. Paul wrote to young Timothy and said, ". . . kindle afresh the gift of God which is in you" (2 Tim. 1:6). Just as the first step in being filled with the Spirit is understanding that God has given us the Spirit, so the first step in finding our spiritual gifts is understanding God's provision.

Second, I believe the discovery of our spiritual gifts should be a matter of careful and thoughtful prayer on our part. We should pray that God will guide us to know our spiritual gifts. Also we should be sure we are willing to make use of our spiritual gifts in a way that is honoring to God. For example, if God showed you that you had the gift of teaching others, would you be willing to put that gift to use in a Sunday school class? If we find we are reluctant to know God's gifts because we are afraid of what He might call us to do with them, this needs to be faced and confessed before God.

Along with this is a third step, which involves an intelligent understanding of what the Bible says about spiritual gifts. It is my prayer that this book will be a reliable guide, but there is no substitute for firsthand study of the Bible's teaching on the gifts of the Spirit.

A fourth step in finding out your spiritual gifts involves a knowledge of yourself and your abilities. There may be certain experiences in your personal background which would tend to lead you one way or another. We may find we like to do certain things, and we may discover we are good at them. There are few short-cuts here; we simply have to discover specific ways in which our gifts begin to emerge. Often it is good to try a variety of situations— for example, in various ministries of the church. Other people can help us. For example, we may not be aware of an ability we have to be a good listener and counselor to people. But as time goes along we find more and more people coming to us and sharing their personal problems with us; we also may find other Christians telling us they think we have certain gifts along this line.

The process of discovering our spiritual gifts may be a lengthy one, and we may even find gifts emerging as the years go by and we confront new opportunities and challenges. However, we cannot let that discourage us. God wants to use us, and we will never be used by Him in the fullest way until we know our gifts and have committed them to Him. Actually, I believe a person who is Spirit-filled—constantly submitting to the Lordship of Christ—will come to discover his gifts with some degree of ease. He wants God to guide in his life, and that is the kind of person God stands ready to bless by showing him the gifts the Holy Spirit has bestowed on him.

Humbly and gratefully accept the gift God appears to have given you, and use it as fully as possible. We should accept ourselves as we are and use the gifts we have. Our gift may call us to service in some prominent position, with its own difficulty and danger. But it may also mean we are to serve in some humble sphere. I rather like David Howard's comment: "God has not called a spiritual elite to carry out the work of the ministry, bypassing the ordinary believer in the church. Rather, '*to each* is given the manifestation of the Spirit for the common good' (1 Cor. 12:7 [RSV])."[1]

This does not do away with the office of elder or bishop, or the deacon either, for that matter. It simply means that the laity as well as elders and deacons have a role to play and obligations to discharge in the congregation.

What we have said so far lays the groundwork for discussing each gift Paul lists. When it comes to the gifts of the Spirit mentioned by the apostle Paul, we see that he does not group gifts by category and no grouping I'm familiar with is wholly satisfactory. In the rest of this chapter we will limit ourselves to those five gifts listed in Ephesians 4:11 (apostle, prophet, evangelist, pastor, and teacher); several of these are also mentioned in 1 Corinthians 12:28. In a separate chapter we will deal with other gifts mentioned in 1 Corinthians 12 and Romans 12. A further chapter will deal with the sign gifts.

Apostle

The Greek word for this gift means "one sent with a commission." John R. W. Stott says, "The word 'apostle' is probably used in *three senses* in the New Testament. . . . [*Firstly,*] in the general sense that all of us are sent into the world by Christ and thus share in the apostolic mission of the church (Jn. 17:18; 20:21), all of us are in the broadest term 'apostles'. . . . [*Secondly,*] the word is used at least twice to describe 'apostles of the churches' (2 Cor. 8:23; Phil. 2:25), messengers sent on particular errands from one church to another. In this sense the word might be applied to missionaries and other Christians sent on special missions. . . . [*Thirdly,*] the gift of apostleship which is thus given precedence must refer, therefore, to that small and special group of men who were 'apostles of Christ', consisting of the Twelve (Lk. 6:12, 13), together with Paul (e.g. Gal. 1:1), . . . They were unique in being eyewitnesses of the historic Jesus, especially of the risen Lord. . . . In this primary sense, therefore, in which they appear in the lists, they have no successors, in the very nature of the case, although there are no doubt 'apostles' today in the secondary sense of 'missionaries'."[2] (italics mine)

Dr. Merrill C. Tenney has suggested that a present-day missionary may have this gift in its secondary meaning if he is a church planter. He would then need (1) to be sent with a message, (2) to be responsible to establish a church, and (3) to exercise authority in setting policies and enforcing them. I have a friend in the Caribbean who has spent a lifetime going from one community to another establishing churches. During his life he has established more than fifty. There are hundreds, and perhaps thousands, of men and women of God throughout the world today who are doing just that—even though the church may meet in a storefront building or a home.

Prophet

The English word *prophecy* derives from the Greek word meaning "public expounder." In apostolic times the gift of prophecy had two parts. One concerned the communication of words from God to men through the prophet. This was a supernatural gift. And in order for men to discern between false and true prophets, the Spirit gave the gift of "discerning the spirits" to other believers. The very fact that a prophet spoke by revelation virtually assured the existence of false prophets, too, as we note from both Old and New Testaments. New Testament Christians were not to despise prophesying but they were told to test all things.

According to 1 Corinthians 14:3, the second part of the prophetic office was the edification, instruction, consolation, and exhortation of the believers in local congregations. The prophet, who was usually an itinerant, took precedence over the local minister. But as time went on the gift of prophecy was exercised by local ministers who preached the Word of God for the edification of their parish members.

The gift of prophecy in the first sense, that of foretelling or predictive prophecy, no longer exists to the extent it did in first century Christianity.

I am aware of the evidence for rare instances in which Christians believe they have been given foreknowledge about future events. Hans Egede (1686–1758), the pioneer missionary to Greenland, was said to have prophesied the coming of a vessel with food at a time when starvation was close at hand. And the vessel came as he predicted. But instances of this sort are rare, not ordinary and frequent. I would not wish to rule out such occurrences as impossible to a sovereign God, though they are not binding on believers as scriptural prophecy. Also, I would think of them as distinct from what is the normal or ordinary function of the gift of prophecy today, which is the ability to understand and to engage in the exposition of the Word of God.

God no longer directly reveals "new truth"; there is now a back cover to the Bible. The canon of Scripture is closed. I understand the gift of prophecy to be used "in the extended sense of presenting God's people truths received, not by direct revelation, but from careful study of the completed and infallible Word of God."[3]

It is the work of the Holy Spirit to illumine the minds of those who are called to the prophetic office so they understand the Word of God and apply it with a depth impossible to those who do not have the gift of prophecy. It may sound like new truth freshly revealed—but to be biblical it must be based on the Word of God. There is a difference between doctrine and direction. There is nothing new in doctrine, but God does give new directions, which many times are mistaken as prophecies.

When prophecy is mentioned in connection with speaking in tongues another dimension appears. As I understand it from some of my brethren, individuals in the congregation might prophesy in tongues and then be interpreted by someone who has that latter gift. I am willing to grant that possibility, with the understanding that it does not involve *new* revelation but something the Holy Spirit would do that would be dynamically related to the written Word of God. The gift of prophecy deserves a stronger emphasis, perhaps, than that of either pastor or evangelist. Apparently, the New Testament prophets instructed, exhorted, rebuked, and warned of judgment.

I listened to a tape sometime ago that was reputed to be a new prophecy by an outstanding charismatic leader. However, upon listening to the tape I found that almost everything he said was biblically based. It was nothing new—only his emphasis was new. He gave biblical truth in a dramatic way, applying it to our own world.

In my own preaching I have done all these things. And I have encountered some evangelists whom I thought were prophets/ evangelists/teachers/pastors; they had all these gifts and the gifts overlapped. The Old Testament prophets foretold the future, especially the future as it related to judgment to fall on cities and nations, or to the coming of Messiah. The New Testament prophets had ministries more like that of the evangelists. They proclaimed the Word of God and called upon people to repent of their sins; they disturbed people in their sins. The apostle Paul devotes a large portion of 1 Corinthians 14 to the subject of prophecy. The people of Corinth were so taken with the sign gifts that Paul chose to emphasize the importance of prophecy.

One word of caution, however. The Scriptures plainly teach that we are to exercise the gift of discernment—because many false prophets will appear. As a matter of fact, both in the writings of Jesus and the apostles, there is warning after warning that false prophets would appear, especially as we approach the end of the age. Many of them will be wolves in sheep's clothing. They will often fool God's own people. Thus the Christian must have those who can distinguish between false and true prophets. Paul was concerned about the Corinthians because they seemed to have little discernment, and they welcomed anyone as a true prophet of Christ. "For if someone comes to you and preaches a Jesus other than the Jesus we preached, or if you receive a different spirit from the one you received, or a different gospel from the one you accepted, you put up with it easily enough. . . . such men are false apostles, deceitful workmen, masquerading as apostles of Christ" (2 Cor. 11:4, 13 NIV).

There is a sense in which every Christian should be discerning, ascertaining truth from falsehood. This is so because every Christian should be rooted in the Bible, and he should know what the Bible teaches. However, the Bible also indicates some Christians have the gift of discernment in special measure.

What about people who claim to foretell the future? I have often been asked this question. The requirement (or test) of the true prophet (the forthteller) in the Scriptures was that he be 100 percent accurate. Not 50 percent. Not 75 percent. Not even 99 percent. But 100 percent accurate.

Evangelist

The term "evangelist" comes from a Greek word meaning "one who announces good news."

In his excellent book, *Good News Is for Sharing*, Leighton Ford points out something that comes as a surprise to some Bible students. The word translated "evangelist" occurs only three times in the New Testament: (1) Luke called Philip an evangelist (Acts 21:8); (2) Paul said God gave evangelists to the churches (Eph. 4:11); (3) he also urged Timothy to "do the work of an evangelist" (2 Tim. 4:5). The gift of evangelism, then, is simply a special ability in communicating the gospel.

The evangelist's message almost necessarily centers around the "content" of the gospel. The evangelist primarily is a "messenger"; he is a deliverer of "the good news." Incidentally, the evangelist in his proclamation may teach and do the work of a pastor, but his primary message centers in the death, burial, and resurrection of Christ, His coming again, and the need for all men everywhere to repent and believe.

The evangelist is the special proclaimer of the good news that God was in Christ reconciling the world to Himself. The Church through history has missed great blessings because some denominations have not as clearly recognized the gift of the evangelist as they have that of the teacher or pastor. Indeed, sometimes evangelists have been ignored or opposed by churches, as in the case of John Wesley, whose mission was rejected by his own church. Despite this, in almost every generation God has raised up evangelists, who often have had to pursue their calling outside the structured church.

Caricatures of evangelists abound because false evangelists in the Elmer Gantry image have libeled the hundreds of true ones throughout the world. But then the same can be said of some pastors, or teachers, who turn out to be false. A well-known pastor, teacher, or evangelist is often a special target of Satan. The higher the visibility, the easier the target. That's the reason those well known for their gifts need to be surrounded by prayer constantly on the part of God's people.

True evangelism speaks to the intellect and may or may not produce emotion, but its main job is to speak to the will. At times the gifts of teaching and evangelism are given to the same person. Some of the most effective evangelists I have known were essentially teachers who informed the minds of people even as they pricked their consciences by their use of the Word of God. I have known many teachers and expository preachers who claimed they were not evangelists—but indeed they did have the gift of evangelism! For example, though the late Dr. Donald Grey Barnhouse was a pastor/teacher, I have met many people who received Christ through his ministry.

Unfortunately, some evangelists spend too much time thinking and even planning about how to achieve visible results. This is an easy trap to fall into. Evangelists rightly desire to see results, but the gift itself is not a guarantee that these will be immediate.

The Reverend James R. Graham, Sr., pioneer missionary to China, proclaimed the gospel for three years without seeing results. When asked if he ever became discouraged, he replied, "No. 'The battle is the Lord's, and He will deliver it into our hands.'"

Nowhere do the Scriptures tell us to seek results, nor do the Scriptures rebuke evangelists if the results are meager. Men and women do make decisions wherever the gospel is proclaimed; whether publicly or privately, some say yes, some say no, and some procrastinate. No one ever hears the gospel proclaimed without making some kind of decision!

We should never forget that Noah was a preacher of righteousness. Yet after an evangelistic and prophetic ministry of 120 years only those in his immediate family believed and entered the ark (Heb. 11:7). On the other hand, some who obviously had the gift of evangelism have modestly subdued their gift because they are afraid of being accused of nonintellectualism, emotionalism, commercialism, or being too concerned with statistics. These are subtleties of Satan to keep the man with the gift of evangelism from being used.

For example, I remember there was a time in my own ministry when we quit keeping statistics (due to criticism). We found almost immediately that the public press exaggerated what was happening, and often used the wrong terminology. For example, we were in one city and the newspaper the next day reported, "1,000 saved at Billy Graham Crusade." Two things were wrong with that headline. First, only God knows whether they were saved or not—that is the reason we call them inquirers and not decisions. Second, it was not 1,000, but less than 500 (over half of those who came forward were trained counselors). Thus, we went back to giving accurate statistics.

Evangelism is not limited to professional evangelists, that is, those whose lives are wholly spent in this calling. The gift of evangelism is also given to many lay people. Philip is the only person in the Bible who was called an evangelist, and he was a deacon! In some sense every Christian who is not called to the vocation of evangelism is still called upon to do the *work* of an evangelist.

People often misunderstand the methods of evangelism. One can use hundreds of different methods, but it is the message that counts. Let us take note, however, of what evangelists cannot do. They cannot bring conviction of sin, righteousness, or judgment; that is the Spirit's work. They cannot convert anyone; that is the Spirit's work. The evangelist can invite men to receive Christ, and exhort them. But the effectual work is done by the Spirit as He works on the minds, hearts, and wills of the unsaved. We are to take care of the possible and trust God for the impossible.

Yet there is more. If the evangelist is to carry on a truly effective ministry to the glory of the Lord, the message must be backed by a Spirit-filled, fruit-producing life. Jesus promised, "Follow Me, and I will make you become fishers of men" (Mark 1:17). He provides the strength, through the Spirit. I urge all Christians to do the work of an evangelist—whether they go into full-time evangelism or not! I believe they have no option. It is a command from our Lord Jesus Christ, and the general injunction of Scripture. "Go therefore and make disciples of all the nations, baptizing them in the name of the Father and the Son and the Holy Spirit, teaching them to observe all that I commanded you; and lo, I am with you always, even to the end of the age" (Matt. 28:19, 20).

Pastor

The Bible does not often use the word *pastor*. In the Old Testament it occasionally translates the Hebrew word for shepherd. The New Testament uses the word *pastor* only once with the root idea of "shepherd" (Eph. 4:11). Here it is closely linked with the Old Testament translation of the word for shepherd. It is also closely linked with the word for teacher. Forms of the underlying Greek word also appear in two other places.

Among many Christians the word *pastor* is one of the most commonly preferred designations for ordained clergy. Its use is consistent with the ministry of our Lord who applies the term "shepherd" to Himself. So those called to the pastoral ministry by the Holy Spirit are undershepherds of the sheep.

Jesus Christ is called "the good shepherd" (John 10:11), and "the great Shepherd of the sheep" (Heb. 13:20). Peter talks about the "Chief Shepherd" who will someday appear (1 Peter 5:4). If Jesus is the chief shepherd, then there must be assistant shepherds; these include ministers of the gospel and unordained saints in the congregation who have gifts of counseling, guiding, warning, and guarding the flock. A number of people have acted as spiritual shepherds in my own life although they were never formally ordained to the ministry.

Many youth counselors, Sunday school teachers, and leaders of home Bible studies and Christian nurture groups actually perform functions that are part of the pastoral gift. Three of Paul's letters, 1 and 2 Timothy and Titus, were called pastoral epistles. They tell the shepherds how to watch over the flock. In our crusades, we use a "shepherd plan": Each person who comes forward as an inquirer talks to a trained counselor (or shepherd). This person may be a layman or an ordained pastor. We ask the counselor (or shepherd) to follow up with letters, phone calls, and visits until the inquirer is either in a warm Christian atmosphere, has made other Christian contacts, or is in a nurture group or prayer group. If he is in forced solitude (in prison), the shepherd teaches him to study the Bible on his own.

I believe that thousands of Christians throughout the world who will never become pastors of churches do have the gift of a pastor that can be used to assist the clergy in their work. Those who have the gift should use it as fully as possible, remembering that failure to do so is to grieve the Holy Spirit. Many pastors of churches are overworked and could use a little help. Each of us might well ask his pastor what to do to help him.

Teacher

The Greek word in Ephesians 4:11 for the gift of teacher means "instructor." When the message of the gospel has resulted in conversions, the new Christians must then be taught. In the Great Commission (Matt. 28:18–20), the command to disciple is followed immediately by the injunction, "teaching them to observe all that I commanded you."

One of the great needs in the Church at the present hour is for more teachers of the Bible. Yet this, too, is in the sovereign hands of God. Teaching is simply a Spirit-given ability to build into the lives of Christians a knowledge of God's Word and its application to their thinking and conduct. Teaching has for its goal the conformity of Christians to the likeness of Jesus. It can and should be done both simply, compassionately, and searchingly. Many years ago I had two doctrine professors. Both had earned doctors' degrees and were scholars in their own right. Both had one thing in common. When they taught their classes, they did it with such great brokenness and compassion that often tears would come to their eyes. I have long ago forgotten a great deal of what they taught, but I still remember those "tears."

Along this line, I am told that Paul's Greek phrasing of the list of gifts in Ephesians 4 suggests such a close connection between the gift of pastor and teacher that his words could almost be translated "pastor-teacher" as if it were one gift. This reinforces the idea that the spiritual teacher must have a compassionate sensitivity to the needs of the taught.

Some of the best teachers of the Word to whom I have listened have not had much formal education. By contrast, some of the poorer teachers have had Ph.D. degrees in various biblically related disciplines, but they lacked the teaching gift with which to communicate their knowledge. It is unfortunate that some seminaries fall into the secular world's qualifications for teachers—and some of the best Bible teachers do not have earned degrees. Therefore they are not qualified to teach in a modern seminary. I believe to the extent that this is practiced it could be dangerous to the future of the Church. That does not mean God does not use our intellectual abilities when they are committed to Him, but spiritual teaching, like all spiritual gifts, is a supernatural ability the Holy Spirit gives, not a university degree. In recent years I have changed my emphasis somewhat: in my proclamation of the gospel I have emphasized the cost of discipleship and the need for learning. God has providentially brought into being thousands of Bible classes as a result of our emphasis in the preparation and follow-up of our Crusades. Likewise, God has raised up hundreds of evangelical Bible schools and seminaries throughout the world. But the Church still lacks enough teachers. Yet I believe that the Spirit has given the gift of teaching to hundreds and perhaps thousands of people who either do not know they have the gift, or are not using it!

The gift of teaching may be used in all kinds of contexts—from a theological seminary and Bible school to a Sunday school class or home Bible study. The important thing for a person who has this gift is to use it whenever and wherever God leads.

One of the first verses of Scripture that Dawson Trotman, founder of the Navigators, made me memorize was, "The things that thou hast heard of me among many witnesses, the same commit thou to faithful men, who shall be able to teach others also" (2 Tim. 2:2 KJV). This is a little like a mathematical formula for spreading the gospel and enlarging the Church. Paul taught Timothy; Timothy shared what he knew with faithful men; these faithful men would then teach others also. And so the process goes on and on. If every believer followed this pattern, the Church could reach the entire world with the gospel in one generation! Mass crusades, in which I believe and to which I have committed my life, will never finish the Great Commission; but a one-by-one ministry will.

Apostle—prophet—evangelist—pastor—teacher: five of the gifts of the Holy Spirit. But perhaps you are saying, "I'm not a pastor or an evangelist. These are someone else's gifts, not mine. What do they have to do with me?" They have much to do with you!

First, it may be God *has* given you one of these gifts. God may be calling you to be a pastor, or an evangelist, or a teacher of the Bible. Perhaps you are a young person whom God is calling to the mission field. You may be older, and God wants to use you to teach a Sunday school class or a home Bible study group.

Second, the Bible commands us to support those whom God has called as leaders in the Church. For example, you should pray regularly for your pastor, for missionaries, and for others who are involved in God's work. "Pray on my behalf" the apostle Paul said (Eph. 6:19). Let them know you are supporting their work and are interested in what God is doing through them.

Third, learn from those God has placed in positions of Christian leadership. "Remember those who led you . . . imitate their faith. . . . Obey your leaders" (Heb. 13:7, 17). Give thanks to God for the gifts He has given to these leaders "for the equipping of the saints for the work of service, to the building up of the body of Christ" (Eph. 4:12).

12

Further Gifts of the Spirit

In THE LAST chapter we studied the gifts Paul lists in Ephesians 4. Next we will consider others that he mentions in 1 Corinthians 12 (which are somewhat duplicated in Romans 12) where we find the primary list of gifts, the ones probably best known to most of us. Because the sign gifts (such as tongues) have caused so much controversy, we will deal with them in a separate chapter.

We must note first that Paul says, "Now there are varieties of gifts, but the same Spirit" (v. 4). Whatever I say about the gifts is based on a crucial presupposition: these gifts are supernatural gifts from the Spirit. The Christian himself cannot manufacture or produce them in any way. This does not mean, of course, that we should understand the gifts apart from the written Word of God. We are to study the Word and apply it.

The Spirit grants some people special wisdom, knowledge, faith, and the like, but the granting of these special gifts does not mean other Christians are barren. Rather, such spiritual gifts are often heightened forms of a rudimentary ability God gives all Christians. The gift of wisdom illustrates this. We all have some spiritual wisdom, but a person with this *gift* has wisdom in a very special degree. On the other hand, I believe the gift of healing or miracles is one a believer has or does not have. And God gives such a gift to very few, a policy He appears to have followed throughout the history of the Church. At any rate, we must now consider the first two spiritual gifts Paul mentions in 1 Corinthians 12.

We can possess three kinds of wisdom. The first comes to us naturally. The second comes from learning, so it is something we can be taught. But the highest kind of wisdom comes directly from God and is associated with the particular work of the Holy Spirit. Though He is the fountainhead of all truth from whatever source, yet He gives believers wisdom in a unique way—through the Scriptures. In addition, He gives a special gift or capacity for wisdom to some.

Dr. Merrill C. Tenney of Wheaton College defines this gift as "the ability to make correct decisions on the basis of one's knowledge."

This then leads us to a second gift, the gift of knowledge, which concerns acquaintance with spiritual information. Yet we all know believers with striking information about God and doctrine, but who do not know how to apply this to practical situations. I have a friend whose head is crammed full of biblical knowledge, yet the tragic mistakes he has made in judgment have almost destroyed his ministry. For this reason, the gifts of wisdom and knowledge must work together, that is, they illustrate the need for those with varying gifts to cooperate.

Jesus discusses a case where a believer may need both gifts. He says, "And when they bring you to trial and deliver you up, do not be anxious beforehand what you are to say; but say whatever is given you in that hour, for it is not you who speak, but the Holy Spirit" (Mark 13:11 RSV). Time after time Jesus' disciples had to defend themselves before mobs, governors, princes, and kings; the apostle Paul may have made his defense before Caesar himself. That knowledge which is the gift of the Spirit is based on long hours of disciplined study in which God teaches us. But the capacity to apply what we learn to actual situations goes beyond study and comes directly from the Holy Spirit. Wisdom is the gift from the Spirit which shows us how to use knowledge. Paul defended himself by using both. In doing this he illustrated Peter's advice about "always being ready to make a defense to every one who asks you to give an account for the hope that is in you, yet with gentleness and reverence" (1 Peter 3:15).

It is interesting that Peter also said we are to "grow in the grace and knowledge of our Lord and Savior Jesus Christ" (2 Peter 3:18). Through our communion with God we gain a higher knowledge and a higher wisdom than the world has. And believers given these in a peculiar degree can consider that they have the gift of knowledge or wisdom.

All of us face pressures, dilemmas, and problems for which we have no answer humanly speaking. A board of twenty-six capable men and women, both black and white, handles the personnel and financial affairs of our evangelistic association. From the very beginning of our ministry we have tried to be scrupulous in the way our business affairs are handled. Time after time in our board meetings when we reached an impasse about priorities, or when we were faced with critical financial needs, or had to face an unjust attack from some quarter, we would get on our knees to ask God for wisdom. He gave us answers immediately again and again. Every fellowship of believers needs at least one person with the gift of wisdom to aid in practical decisions. Such a person would often be the one, after we had prayed, who came up with the direction for the right decision we should make.

Faith

Faith comes from a Greek word meaning faithfulness or steadfastness: "To another faith by the same Spirit" (1 Cor. 12:9). In this passage the apostle Paul assumes the existence of saving faith. The Scripture says, "By grace you have been saved through faith" (Eph. 2:8). We are also told that "we walk by faith, not by sight" (2 Cor. 5:7). However, faith in 1 Corinthians 12 is a very special gift the Holy Spirit gives at His good pleasure.

We must distinguish between the grace of faith and the gift of faith. The grace of faith means that we can believe God will do whatever He has promised to do in His Word. All Christians have the grace of faith. Therefore, if we do not have faith in what the Bible promises, we sin. But many things come into our lives concerning which there are no specific promises from the Word. Therefore, when we pray, we add, "if it be Thy will." But sometimes the Holy Spirit gives us the gift of faith to believe for things about which the Bible is silent. If we do not have this special gift of faith, it is not sin.

We see a classic example of the gift of faith in the life of George Muller of Bristol, England, who cared for thousands of orphans over a period of many years. Muller refused to ask anyone for a single penny, but he prayed the money in. This is the gift of faith described by Jesus when He said, "If you have faith as a mustard seed, you shall say to this mountain, 'Move from here to there,' and it shall move; and nothing shall be impossible to you" (Matt. 17:20).

At times in my own ministry it has seemed to me that I was a man of little faith, and yet there have been a number of occasions when the Holy Spirit has given me the special gift of faith and forced me into seemingly impossible situations where there was no specific promise from God in the Word.

For example, in our 1957 New York Crusade, Madison Square Garden had been packed out night after night for six weeks and thousands had made their commitment to Christ. However, though we were scheduled to close at the Yankee Stadium on July 20, a burden grew in the hearts of a few of us that the Crusade should continue. Some felt that returning to the Garden after the Yankee Stadium would be anticlimactic; people would no longer be interested, especially with vacation time at hand.

I became so terribly burdened that I found it impossible to sleep at night. I knew that the ultimate decision would be up to me and my longtime colleague, Cliff Barrows, before God. Finally, one night while on my knees before God I said, "Lord, I do not know what is right, but by faith I am going to tell the committee tomorrow we shall go on." I called Cliff on the phone and he indicated God seemed to be saying the same thing to him.

Based on that decision we continued on for ten more weeks, ending with an open-air rally in Times Square where 75,000 people jammed the streets. The service was carried live on television and radio to the nation on prime evening time. Now, if that decision had not been made on the basis of the gift of faith from the Holy Spirit, hundreds of people who now know Christ might not have known Him.

I firmly believe there are times in all our lives when we make decisions on the basis of the will of God, and we are given faith by the Spirit to do what God wants us to do, regardless of the consequences.

Discernment of Spirits

The word *discernment* in 1 Corinthians 12:10 comes from a Greek word embodying several ideas: to see, consider, examine, understand, hear, judge closely. The New American Standard Bible calls the capacity for this gift, "the distinguishing of spirits."

As I stated in the last chapter, the Bible points out that many false prophets and deceivers will emerge inside and outside the Church through the ages. However, at the end of the age they will intensify their activities. Paul said, "Even Satan disguises himself as an angel of light. Therefore it is not surprising if his servants also disguise themselves as servants of righteousness" (2 Cor. 11:14, 15). I am convinced that hundreds of religious leaders throughout the world today are servants not of God, but of the Antichrist. They are wolves in sheep's clothing; they are tares instead of wheat.

Spiritism, the occult, the worship of Satan, and the activities of demons have increased rapidly throughout the Western world. False teachings (Paul calls them "doctrines of demons" in 1 Timothy 4:1) have gone hand in hand with their rise.

The great question is: How can we know the false from the true? This is why believers need the gift of discernment, or at least respect for the opinions of those who have it. The apostle John said, "Beloved, do not believe every spirit, but test the spirits to see whether they are from God; because many false prophets have gone out into the world" (1 John 4:1). In other words, believers are to test the various spirits and doctrines that abound today. Most of all we are to test them against the standard of the Word of God, the Bible. However, God gives to some individuals extraordinary abilities to discern the truth. In 1 Corinthians 12:10 we read, "to another [is given] the distinguishing of spirits."

A man named Joe Evans had this gift, I believe. I always called

him "Uncle" Joe. He was probably the closest friend of Dr.
V. Raymond Edman, the late president of Wheaton College. Many
times the three of us (and sometimes members of my team) knelt
down for long and glorious periods of prayer when we were faced
with challenges, opportunities, or problems. At certain periods in
my ministry I have been tempted to accept offers to move from
evangelism to some other field. Many times, offers came through
"an angel of light." I needed discernment. Since I did not always
have it myself, one person to whom I went was "Uncle" Joe so I
could profit from his special gift of discernment. I sought his advice
and prayer. It is important to realize that a person with the gift of
discernment can often tell the difference between what is of God
and what is not. Such a person can often point out false teachings
or false teachers—he has an almost uncanny ability to perceive
hypocrisy, shallowness, deceit, or phoniness.

Certainly, this gift enabled Peter to see through the hypocrisy
of Ananias and Sapphira. He also saw through Simon of Samaria
who claimed to be converted and baptized in the Spirit but who
turned out to be a counterfeit (Acts 8:9ff). Paul warned that "in
later times some will fall away from the faith, paying attention to
deceitful spirits and doctrines of demons" (1 Tim. 4:1).

Scripture teaches us everywhere that anything religious should
be evaluated very carefully; that even the churches to which we
go must be examined to see if they are sound in the faith.

Helps

The gift of "helps," mentioned in 1 Corinthians 12:28, gains its
name from the Greek word having the idea of supporting, or
assisting.

We have an example of the use of helps when the apostles
decided to appoint deacons to take over the business affairs of the
church (Acts 6). Their duties consisted primarily in waiting on
tables and in the distribution of funds to the poor. The use of this
gift makes it possible for thousands of lay people to engage in
helping to promote the kingdom of God in such ways as counseling, prayer, handling the business affairs of the church
and parachurch organizations, and witnessing. But, also, "helps"

embodies the idea of social service, such as assisting the oppressed who suffer from social injustice and caring for orphans and widows. It could mean preparing a meal for a sick neighbor, writing a letter of encouragement or sharing what we have with someone in need. Helps is the gift of showing mercy. It also carries with it the idea of helping in some of the ordinary activities of Christian service so that others, endowed with other gifts, can be released to utilize them more freely. "If anyone serves, he should do it with the strength God provides, so that in all things God may be praised through Jesus Christ" (I Peter 4:11 NIV).

During my early crusades I had a compulsion to be involved in virtually all aspects of our evangelism ministry. Obviously, this meant demands so heavy upon me that I was physically exhausted most of the time. I remember how Dawson Trotman, whom I had asked to head our counseling, came to me one night. "Billy," he said, "you are wearing yourself out." He added, "Why can't we go at this as a team? Let Cliff Barrows lead the singing, you do the preaching, and trust me and those I have trained to do the counseling." I agreed to give it a try. This was one of the most momentous and profitable decisions of my life. For the first time I began to realize that God can and does use others to take charge of certain phases of the work of evangelism just as effectively as he could use me or Cliff Barrows or some of the other leaders on our team. This is an illustration of how God can use all the gifts to help one another, but that the gift of "helps" is special.

My later study of Scripture showed me that even our Lord gathered a team of people around Him and then sent them out on one occasion to minister two by two. Mark was the helper for Paul and Barnabas (Acts 12:25). Paul traveled continually with a team of workers, without whom he could never have carried on his ministry effectively. At the end of his letters Paul usually mentioned some of those faithful helpers. In Romans the list contains more than a score of names, many of them women. Writing to the Philippians, Paul mentions Epaphroditus who "ministered to my wants" (Phil. 2:25 KJV).

While I was writing this chapter, my wife Ruth and I, along with Grady and Wilma Wilson, were the guests of Mr. and Mrs. Bill Mead of Dallas, Texas. Every morning we had a Bible study. One morning Grady Wilson suggested that we break into our regular Bible study schedule and go instead to the Book of Philemon. I thought this was rather strange, but we went along with him. As we studied Philemon I prayed, "Thank you, Lord, for giving me a perfect illustration of one who had the gift of helps." The example was Onesimus, the slave. Paul wrote to his master Philemon and said, Onesimus was "useful . . . to me" (Philem. 11).

Do you have the particular gift of "helps"? You could be a businessman faithfully serving on a board of a parachurch organization or missionary society. Or you could be involved in a Bible society or be a trustee or deacon of a church. One could be a busy housewife and mother. Another could be a student.

A relative of mine named Uncle Bo used to take every Saturday afternoon to clean the little church in the heart of Charlotte where he was a member. He mowed the grass and cut the hedges. Few people ever noticed the helps he gave so cheerfully. This was about all he could do. He couldn't preach; he couldn't teach; he had a difficult time praying in public; but he had the gift of helps. And God used him.

The Gift of Governments

This gift gains its name from the Greek word carrying the idea of steering, piloting, or directing. Some versions call it the gift of administrations (1 Cor. 12:28). Certain people have been given the gift of leadership that is recognized by the Church.

The Scriptures teach that churches must have government; they require leadership, whether professional or nonprofessional. Christ spent more than half His time with just twelve men, developing them into leaders who would carry on His work after He ascended to heaven. Wherever the apostles went they appointed leaders over the churches they founded. The Scripture says that Paul and Barnabas "appointed elders for them in every church" (Acts 14:23). In 1 Timothy 3:1–7 Paul gives qualifications for "bishops" (KJV). The word for "bishop" is thought by many to be equivalent to "pastor," carrying the idea of overseer, superintendent, or governor.

While some churches and assemblies attempt to conduct the work of the Lord without an appointed leadership, I believe this is virtually impossible. Some Christian groups do not have an appointed ordained leader. Yet services are conducted decently and in order, and the other ministries of the group are carried out. There are those who exercise leadership, even if the official titles are not given to them. If we do not recognize this gift it leads to confusion, and it appears to me to be unbiblical since it hinders the work of the Holy Spirit who gives men the gift of government. The writer of the Book of Hebrews went so far as to say, "Obey your leaders, and submit to them" (Heb. 13:17). Certainly he was talking about those who had authority in the Church.

The qualifications of a leader are listed several times in the New Testament. He must not be dictatorial, egotistical, or dogmatic; he is to be anything but that. Rather he is to be humble, gracious, courteous, kind, and filled with love; yet at times he must be very firm. For this reason the gift of knowledge combined with wisdom is necessary. Further, the leadership idea outlined in the New Testament is decisively in opposition to the notion of great pomp and pageantry. Rather, it emphasizes the graces of humility and service.

The Lord Jesus Christ is the most perfect example of a governor, or a leader. "For even the Son of Man did not come to be served, but to serve, and to give His life a ransom for many" (Mark 10:45). He humbled Himself to become a servant (Phil. 2:7); He washed the disciples' feet and then said, "A servant is not greater than his master" (John 13:16 RSV). Jesus, by example, tells us that every true leader should be a helper, a servant, or even a bondslave. We are exhorted to, "through love serve one another" (Gal. 5:13). This is a command, not a suggestion, and applies with special force to leaders.

The End of the Matter

God did not ordain that the Church should drift aimlessly in the seas of uncertainty without compass, captain, or crew. By His Spirit He has provided for the operation of the Church in history through the gifts of His Spirit, and we are told to "earnestly desire the greater gifts" (1 Cor. 12:31). Whether the Holy Spirit gives us one or several, it is important for us to do two things: First we should recognize the gift or gifts God has given us. Second, we should nurture those gifts and do everything, humanly speaking, to improve them as we use them. One who has the gift of prophecy should be better able to fill this role with the passage of every year of his life. And the person with the gift of wisdom should be wiser at the end than he was at the beginning.

Some day all of us will give account of the way we have used the gifts God has given. The person to whom much has been given will find much required of him. Let's use our gifts as fully as possible and wait with expectation for our Lord's "Well done, good and faithful servant" (Matt. 25:21 RSV) at the judgment of the saints.

13

The Sign Gifts

I THINK A WORD of explanation and caution will be helpful here in connection with the so-called sign gifts listed in 1 Corinthians 12:9, 10. By "sign gifts" I mean those gifts of the Holy Spirit which are often obvious outward indications or signs of the working of God. The sign gifts include *healings, miracles,* and *tongues.* They seem to rate the most attention in the Church today, exciting the imagination and producing outward manifestations that attract multitudes.

One Christian leader said that if he heard a clergyman down the street was preaching the gospel, he would just turn on his T.V. and go back to watching his favorite program. But if he was told that someone down the street was performing miracles, he would drop everything to see what was happening. Why is this? Simply because we seem to be fascinated by the spectacular and the unusual. This kind of curiosity is not necessarily good or helpful, but it is, nevertheless, very common.

It is interesting to note that in the Bible's four discussions of the gifts of the Spirit (Rom. 12:6–8; 1 Cor. 12:8–10; Eph. 4:11; and 1 Peter 4:10, 11), these sign gifts are listed together only in the first letter to Corinth, a church that was abusing at least one of these gifts. Christians should remember that the Holy Spirit did not intend gifts to be misused so that they become divisive, or disrupt our fellowship. When this occurs the greatest of all manifestations of the Spirit, love, is diminished.

Healing

The Holy Spirit gives the gift of healing (literally, the gift of cures). Many cases of healing appear in the Old Testament, and certainly the New Testament is full of instances when Jesus and His disciples healed the sick. Throughout the history of the Christian Church countless instances of physical healing have been recorded.

The ministry of physical healings through spiritual means is sometimes associated with faith healers. Many of these claim to have the gift of healing or at least some special power. Tens of thousands of people flock to these healers. And thousands more are urged to write certain radio and television preachers who claim to have this gift of healing. Indeed, mass attention has been focused in recent years on the Christian faith and physical healing.

Yet sickness and infirmity are a part of life: no one can escape them at last. All people, including the most famous faith healers, get sick, and all eventually die. Kathryn Kuhlman, the famous faith healer, died early in 1976. For years she had suffered from a heart condition, and late in 1975 underwent open heart surgery from which she never recovered. People were healed under her ministry. She was not. Sickness brought death to her at last.

However, we must distinguish the operation of what the Bible calls the gift of healing from a second method of healing. Some place their emphasis on the faith of the one who needs healing— telling him it will happen if only he believes. By this they mean more than those who believe that forgiveness, cleansing, and acceptance with God spring from the atoning work of Jesus on the cross. They think that any Christian who becomes ill can claim healing by faith. Note that this has nothing to do with the gift of healing as such. Such teachers may believe, for example, that physical healing for disease is in the atonement of Jesus Christ. To them the death of Christ on the cross not only results in the offer of forgiveness for our sins, but also physical healing for the body. Both, they believe, come to us by faith.

This kind of healing has to do with *faith* rather than just the gift of healing itself.

In support of this position it is pointed out that the Old Testament foretold the coming of the Messiah and said of Him, "And by His scourging we are healed" (Isa. 53:5). Personally I do not believe the Scripture makes it clear to us that Christ's work on the cross included physical healing. The passage found in Isaiah 53:5 is quoted once in the New Testament in 1 Peter 2:24: "And He Himself bore our sins in His body on the cross, that we might die to sin and live to righteousness; for by His wounds you were healed." It seems clear from this that the "healing" of the Savior is primarily spiritual in nature, not physical.

Some Christians, regardless of whether they believe God heals through the spiritual gift or through the exercise of faith alone, believe it is unnecessary to consult a physician when they are ill, except possibly as a last resort. Several avenues are open to them: They can believe God for healing, in which case it does not involve the gift of healing but rather the gift of faith. Or they may go to someone whom they believe has the gift of healing. The gift of healing means that a person so gifted can do exactly what Jesus did; by that power which is his as a gift from the Holy Spirit he can make the sick well immediately and permanently: a broken arm is mended instantly, a cancer disappears, the process of pneumonia stops and the lungs become well.

Healing from illnesses must be considered from a broader perspective, I feel. James teaches that all good gifts come from above. I believe that healing can and may come from God through the gift of healing and the gift of faith, but it also comes from Him through the use of medical means. Paul told Timothy to take some medicinal wine for his stomach problems (1 Tim. 5:23). We must keep in mind that Luke was a physician and accompanied Paul on many of his trips, and probably gave him medical help.

I know the Lord has used physicians and medicine to cure illnesses I have suffered. Furthermore, we must be open to the idea that it may not be the will of God for us to be cured of all our infirmities, something true of the apostle Paul (see 2 Cor. 12:7–10). I think Christians should therefore use God-given wisdom to determine whether they should seek the use of natural means or rely solely on prayer or those with the genuine gift of healing.

If medication is not available, or if doctors have pronounced a case incurable, and God lays it on our hearts to look to Him in simple faith for the impossible, then we must follow His leading. But this leading must come from God, not the urging of fellow Christians.

However, if medication and doctors are available, to ignore them in favor of asking God to heal seems to me to border on presumption.

I had a friend who was struck with a deadly disease. The doctors knew there was no hope. He knew there was no hope. So he sent for one he knew to have the gift of healing. After prayer and spiritual counseling, the healer laid her hands on my friend. Immediately he felt what seemed to be an electric shock, and he was healed instantly. When he was checked by the doctors, all evidence of the disease had disappeared.

Overjoyed, he became totally taken up with the sign-gifts: healing, miracles, speaking in tongues and their interpretation. The person and work of Christ were all but ignored. The fruit of the Spirit was not in evidence. Three years later the disease recurred with a vengeance. This time God did not choose to heal him. He died slowly, bitterly disillusioned, as if all glory plus the Lord Himself were not awaiting him.

Prudence differs from presumption, and we ought not tempt God. If a sick Christian resorts to faith for healing, he should be certain God has given him that faith. Lacking it, he ought to seek the help of physicians. And in my judgment it is normal for a Christian to use the medical help God provides. Medicine and physicians (such as Luke) are of God, too.

Sometime ago I conversed with a psychiatrist of impeccable qualifications. In the conversation he underscored a well-known fact: People suffer from both organic and functional diseases. Under the latter category the medical books list many diseases which have no organic basis but are psychosomatic. Yet they do produce outward physical ailments which cannot be cured by ordinary medical treatment; they can be cured, however, when the mind is treated. When the mind is made well, the physical manifestations stemming from this functional situation disappear. The Romans had a famous saying: *mens sana in corpore sano,* a sound mind in a sound body. A diseased mind can produce disease in the body. A healthy mind will keep the body from functional diseases that derive from disease of the mind.

Having said all this, I do know that God heals under certain circumstances in accordance with His will. My own sister-in-law is an outstanding example. She was dying of tuberculosis. The X-rays showed the seriousness of her condition, but she asked her surgeon father for permission to discontinue medical treatment because she believed God was going to heal her. It was granted, and some godly men and women anointed her with oil and prayed the prayer of faith. Then a new series of X-rays was taken, and to the astonishment of the physicians at the sanatorium she no longer showed any signs of active tuberculosis. Immediately she began to gain weight, and thirty-five years later she is an active Bible teacher, a healthy person. Obviously, she was healed. But note that the healing came, not through someone who had the gift of healing, but through faith.

It is interesting to note that Jesus did not always heal people the same way. On some occasions He simply spoke the word and the healing took place. At other times He used what might be considered *means*. Jesus took the hand of Simon Peter's mother-in-law, and she was healed instantly (Matt. 8:15). When Jesus raised Lazarus from the dead, He cried out with a loud voice, "Lazarus, come out" (John 11:43 RSV). But Jesus healed the man born blind in quite a different way: He mixed clay and spittle, spread it on the eyes of the blind man, and commanded him to wash it off in the pool of Siloam (John 9:1ff). In the case of the centurion's servant, the sick man was not even near Jesus when he was healed (Matt. 8:5ff). And the woman with the issue of blood was healed simply by touching the garment of the Lord (Matt. 9:18ff).

The laying on of hands or the anointing with oil has both spiritual and psychological significance. The sick and those who anoint them must not suppose that the healing is due to the laying on of hands, the anointing with oil, their own personal faith, or even their prayers. The healing is from God and is of God. "The *Lord* will raise him up" (James 5:15, italics mine).

But God does not always choose to heal us. As I have said, I can find no evidence in Scripture that it is the will of God to heal all people of all illnesses. If the Holy Spirit gives a sick person or someone who is praying for a sick person the gift of faith that the person will be healed, then we can be sure the person will be healed. But God does not always give the gift of faith. This means that sick people and their loved ones should certainly pray for the one who is ill, but in the absence of the gift of faith they must pray, "If it be Thy will." I believe that true faith involves a complete surrender of our life to the will of God, whatever it is, even when God does not choose to heal us. This means we are willing to be healed, or willing to remain afflicted, or willing to die—willing for whatever God wants!

We have the classic example of Job who was afflicted with boils from head to foot. Satan was responsible for this, but it is interesting to note that Satan had to get God's permission before he could even touch Job's possessions, much less Job.

Yet the Book of Job is the result of the situation. What would believers have done down through the centuries without this tremendous account?

Then there is the example of Amy Carmichael of India who spent over fifty years ministering to children. The last twenty years of her life were spent in bed in almost constant pain due to an injury from a severe accident. Yet it was during these years that she did all her writing—poems, devotional books, and accounts of the ministry of the Dohnavur Fellowship. These books continue to minister to thousands throughout the world though she has long since gone to be with the Lord. Had she not been confined to her bed, she would never have had the time to write.

I have attended a number of healing meetings. Some sickened me because of the emotional hysteria present. I have also attended healing meetings where the services were conducted decently and in order. At those, I have witnessed the quiet moving of the Spirit of God in a way that could offend no one. In meetings like that the Spirit used God's servants with special gifts to do His will.

Every sickness, every infirmity, and every wrong thing in our lives can be traced back to original sin. But this does not mean that those of us who experience these difficulties do so because we have been guilty of overt transgressions. Certainly in some cases we do suffer from illnesses that are the direct or indirect result of some evil we have committed. But not always.

One day Jesus encountered a man who was blind from birth. And it was His disciples, not the Pharisees or the Sadduccees who asked this question, "Who sinned, this man or his parents, that he should be born blind?" (John 9:2). Even Jesus' disciples could not conceive of blindness that was not a direct result of sin. Jesus told them, "It was neither that this man sinned, nor his parents; but it was in order that the works of God might be displayed in him" (v. 3).

When we see someone with an infirmity or illness, we should be careful not to assume he is suffering because of his sin. Many illnesses are not the result of the person's sin. Accidents or inherited defects can cause sickness. Neither the sin of a retarded baby or its parents caused its misfortune, though all illness arises from original sin. God never meant for us to get sick and die, but man's rebellion against God in the Garden of Eden changed all that. We must remember, too, that the devil spitefully tries to use every sickness to hinder our fellowship with God, to cause us to have a neurotic sense of guilt, or even to charge God with injustice, lack of love for us, or harshness.

At the same time we have the promise of God that some day all the effects of sin on this creation will be destroyed, including sickness. "And He shall wipe away every tear from their eyes; and there shall no longer be any death; there shall no longer be any mourning, or crying, or pain; the first things have passed away" (Rev. 21:4).

Many Christians do suffer physical, mental, and even spiritual illnesses from time to time. Chronic physical impediments, minds disposed to periods of depression, or weak spirits subject to doubt all cause acute suffering. God's help is available for those impediments, and His sympathy and understanding abound. We can expect the Holy Spirit to be present and to work in our lives. "The Spirit also helpeth our infirmities" (Rom. 8:26 KJV), and through Hebrews 4:16 God promises us help: "Let us therefore draw near with confidence to the throne of grace, that we may receive mercy and may find grace to help in time of need."

In circumstances like these the Holy Spirit takes over. He is called "the divine Paraclete." The Greek word *parakletos* occurs five times in the New Testament. Four times it is translated "helper" (John 14:16, 26; 15:26; 16:7) and once "advocate" (1 John 2:1). It means "one who walks by our side as our counselor, helper, defender, and guide."

The Holy Spirit *does* help us in the midst of our sicknesses, infirmities, and weaknesses. Sometimes these very sicknesses indicate that we are Spirit-filled. Three times the apostle Paul asked God to remove the "thorn" that gave him great difficulty, but God answered, "No." He also said, "My grace is sufficient for you, for power is perfected in weakness" (2 Cor. 12:9). Paul responded quickly, "Most gladly, therefore, I will rather boast about my weaknesses, that the power of Christ may dwell in me" (2 Cor. 12:9). He went even further: "I am well content with weaknesses, with insults, with distresses, with persecutions, with difficulties, for Christ's sake; for when I am weak, then I am strong" (2 Cor. 12:10). Paul, even while being filled with the Holy Spirit, bore a sickness in his body that God allowed him to suffer for His glory.

So if God allows a sickness and refuses healing, we should accept it with gratitude. And we should ask Him to teach us all He wants us to learn through the experience, including how to glorify Him in it.

Paul's experience teaches us a lesson concerning healing in relation to the atonement of our Lord. Matthew says that "He took our infirmities and bore our diseases" (Matt. 8:17 RSV). This is absolutely true. By His death on Calvary we are assured that we shall be delivered from every infirmity and every disease. But God permits some of us to be afflicted with infirmities and diseases now. So we know that deliverance from them was never meant for all God's people, and for all diseases at all times, including today.

There are a growing number of churches that hold occasional healing services. When I inquired about these healing services, it was explained that few of the healings had to do with physical illness—rather they deal with relationships, memories, attitudes, guilt feelings. As a result, marriages have been healed; parents reconciled with children; employers with employees.

To summarize, there is no doubt in my mind that there is a gift of healing—that people are healed in answer to the prayer of faith—

and that there are other healings, such as healings of relationships. There is also need for a word of caution. There are many frauds and charlatans in the fields of medicine and faith healing. Again, one must have spiritual discernment.

Miracles

The gift of performing miracles takes its key term, "miracles," from a Greek word meaning "powers" (2 Cor. 12:12). A miracle is an event beyond the power of any known physical law to produce; it is a spiritual occurrence produced by the power of God, a marvel, a wonder. In most versions of the Old Testament the word "miracle" is usually translated "a wonder" or "a mighty work." Versions of the New Testament usually refer to miracles as "signs" (John 2:11) or "signs and wonders" (John 4:48; Acts 5:12; 15:12).

Clearly, the wonders performed by Jesus Christ and the apostles authenticated their claim of authority and gave certitude to their message. And we must remember that people did ask Jesus and the apostles this question, "How do we know that you are what you say you are, and that your words are true?" That was not an improper question. And at strategic moments God again and again manifested Himself to men by miracles so they had outward, confirming evidence that the words they heard from God's servants were true.

One notable case that illustrates this principle has to do with Elijah on Mount Carmel. He was engaged in a terrible battle in which the people of Israel had to decide between God and Baal. Elijah challenged the priests of Baal to set up an altar and lay an animal sacrifice on it. He told the people of Israel they should look for a confirming sign to convince them whether the true God was Baal or the Lord. The priests of Baal cried out in desperation to their god, but nothing happened. Then Elijah poured barrels of water over the animal sacrifice on his altar, and God sent fire from heaven that consumed the sacrifice in spite of the water. This was a miracle!

Paul argues that men could know he was an apostle when he said, "The signs of a true apostle were performed among you with all perseverance, by signs and wonders and miracles" (2 Cor. 12:12).

The Holy Spirit gave the gift of performing miracles to the early apostles as an evidence that they were Christ's messengers for a special task: that of ushering in a new era in mankind's history.

However, it has always interested me that many of the great men of both the Old and New Testaments performed no miracles. John the Baptist illustrates this: "And many came to Him; and they were saying, 'While John performed no sign, yet everything John said about this man was true.' And many believed in Him there" (John 10:41, 42). So though John performed no miracles, he exalted the Lord Jesus Christ, whom many then received. Remember that Jesus said of John, "Truly, I say to you, among those born of women there has not arisen anyone greater than John the Baptist" (Matt. 11:11).

Why do we not see the spectacular miracles today that we read about in the Bible? Are few such miracles occurring because our faith is small—or could it be that God does not will the spectacular right now? Could it be that signs and wonders were gifts particularly appropriate to the special circumstances of the early Church? I think so. And today when the gospel is proclaimed on the frontiers of the Christian faith that approximate the first century situation, miracles still sometimes accompany the advance of the gospel. As indicated by both the prophets Hosea and Joel, as we approach the end of the age we may expect miracles to increase.

Yet Jesus, referring to His miracles, told the disciples they would perform "greater works than these" (John 14:12). What could be greater than the works He did: healing the sick, restoring sight to the blind, raising the dead, casting out demons? It has been said, "Jesus did not come to preach the gospel but in order that there might be a gospel to preach."

Because of His death and resurrection we now have a gospel that can provide forgiveness of sins and the transformation of lives. A transformed life is the greatest of all miracles. Every time a person is "born again" by repentance of sin and faith in Jesus Christ, the miracle of regeneration is performed.

This is not to reject the further truth that in some places in the world the Holy Spirit has sovereignly appointed certain people to be workers of miracles. I have just stated that as we approach the end of the age I believe we will see a dramatic recurrence of signs and wonders which will demonstrate the power of God to a skeptical world. Just as the powers of Satan are being unleashed with greater intensity, so I believe God will allow signs and wonders to be performed.

Tongues

A leading minister in the Church of Scotland lay in the Intensive Care Unit of a Glasgow infirmary. He knew that his life hung in the balance—at any minute he might be seeing his Lord face to face. And so, he began talking to Him. As he did, he found himself praying in a language he had never heard before. After confiding this to a friend, he never mentioned it again. He recovered to serve His Lord for several more years.

A frantic young wife and mother, for whom everything had gone wrong one day, sat up in her bed that night literally "fussing at God."

"Have you ever heard of praying in tongues?" she paused to ask my wife when she was recounting the incident. Ruth nodded. "Well, I never had. I'd never heard of it. I'd never asked for it. I didn't even know what was happening. And suddenly it was as if I were orbiting the earth in a spaceship and as I passed over each continent I thought of the Christians there, mentioning the missionaries I knew by name. In this way I circled the entire globe. Then I glanced at the clock, thinking I had been praying at least thirty minutes. To my amazement it was dawn. And I was refreshed. The burden was lifted. The frustration, the anger, the complaining—it was all gone. And I felt as if I'd had a good night's sleep."

A Sunday school class was studying the person and work of the Holy Spirit in a neighborhood where speaking in tongues had become a divisive issue among believers. After one particularly exciting meeting the college Sunday school teacher was asked to speak on the Holy Spirit. One by one the students shared their experience with this phenomenon. The teacher, recalling the class some months later, mentioned three people who stood out in his memory. One, whose testimony had the ring of truth to it, for a few months after his experience became totally preoccupied with tongues, speaking of little else, and doing his best to see that other believers had the same experience. Eventually, however, he leveled off, realizing that the Holy Spirit has been given to enable us to glorify the Lord Jesus in differing ways. Today he is a uniquely gifted minister of the gospel.

A second class member, who also claimed to speak in tongues, was expelled from his college a few weeks later for open, repeated, and unrepentant immorality.

A third who stands out in the teacher's memory was a recently converted street-fighter from one of our large cities. After the class, he had taken the teacher to one side and confided that he had been in the same meeting where he had recognized the language spoken. When the teacher asked him what language it was, he replied, "The language I used to hear when I assisted my grandmother who was a spirit medium." The teacher told me he thought these cases illustrated three sources for what are called tongues: (1) the Holy Spirit; (2) psychological influence; (3) satanic influence.

While I do not pose as an expert on the subject of tongues, my opinions have come from my study of the Bible and from my experience and conversations with many people. Of one thing I'm certain: neither the Holy Spirit nor any of His gifts were given to divide believers. This does not mean that we ought not have our own opinions about what the Bible teaches on tongues. Or that we should not have local congregations in which prominence is given to tongues as well as those in which tongues are not prominent. But I am certain about one thing: when the gift of tongues is abused and becomes divisive, then something has gone wrong. Sin has come into the body of Christ.

Historical Background

For almost a century speaking in tongues has been given an important role among many Christians and certain churches. For them tongues-speaking is related to the life of the Christian subsequent to conversion.

It is true, however, that thousands of so-called "charismatic" believers have never spoken in tongues. Yet they are accepted as true believers in the Lord Jesus. Thus, among many churches which consider themselves charismatic, speaking in tongues is not regarded as an essential sign of having been born again. They agree that regenerated believers have been baptized into the body of Christ by the Spirit, of which water baptism is an outward sign. At the time of regeneration the Spirit took up His abode in their hearts. But for them the baptism in the Spirit is something that occurs after regeneration.

More recently the neo-Pentecostal or charismatic movement has come into being. Many of these people hold their memberships in mainline denominations and some of them are Roman Catholics. They agree with Pentecostal churches in their emphasis on healing and often accept speaking in tongues as a sign of baptism with the Holy Spirit, an experience occurring subsequent to regeneration. But the old-time Pentecostal churches are bothered because they do not always see a change in lifestyle among the neo-Pentecostals, something they cherish as being intrinsic to the Spirit-anointed life.

No one can escape the fact that the neo-Pentecostal emphasis has brought Protestants and Roman Catholics closer together in some parts of the world, not on the basis of having worked out their theological disagreements on matters like justification by faith, the sacrifice of the Mass, or the infallibility of the Pope, but on the basis of speaking in tongues and baptism with the Holy Spirit. However, I have met many Roman Catholics, like Protestants, who call themselves charismatic but have never spoken in tongues. For them it has been a new discovery of a personal relationship with Christ.

The Biblical Data on Tongues

Speaking in tongues (or "glossolalia," a term formed from the equivalent Greek words) is mentioned in *only two* New Testament books: The Acts of the Apostles and Paul's First Letter to the Corinthians (though it is mentioned in Mark 16:17, which most scholars believe is not in the original manuscripts). The word seems to be used in two different ways. One way is found in connection with the events at Pentecost, when the promised coming of the Holy Spirit occurred. A careful study of that passage in Acts 2 indicates that the "tongues" were known languages which were understood by foreign visitors in Jerusalem. Thus the little band of Christians was given a supernatural ability to speak in other languages.

What happened at Pentecost? The second chapter of Acts tells us that four things took place which signaled the advent of the new age. First, a sound from heaven like that of a violent wind filled the house. Second, something that looked like tongues of fire sat on each one of the people in the upper room. Third, all of them were filled with the Holy Spirit. Fourth, all of them spoke in tongues as the Spirit gave them the ability to do so. These tongues were languages known to the people from all over the Roman Empire who had come to Jerusalem for Pentecost. Some believe that the miracle took place in the ears of the hearers. Others believe that the apostles were given a supernatural gift of speaking in a foreign language that they did not know. Whatever position we take, a "miracle" took place!

The same basic word for "filled" appears in Acts 4:8 where Peter, "filled with the Holy Spirit" (speaking in tongues is not mentioned), preached his short sermon to the high priest and the rulers of the Jews. The same root word is used in connection with John the Baptist in Luke 1:15 where the Scripture says that "he will be filled with the Holy Spirit, while yet in his mother's womb." However, we have no record that John ever spoke in tongues. In Paul's conversion experience we are told that Ananias came to him "that you may regain your sight, and be filled with the Holy Spirit" (Acts 9:17). His sight then returned, he was baptized, and "immediately he began to proclaim Jesus in the synagogues, saying, 'He is the Son of God'" (Acts 9:20). Again, speaking in tongues is not mentioned.

Acts 19 recounts the story of Paul at Ephesus. He found some believers there who had heard nothing about the Spirit's coming. We are then told that "when Paul had laid his hands upon them, the Holy Spirit came on them, and they began speaking with tongues and prophesying" (Acts 19:6). Here the Scripture does not say they were filled with the Spirit. At any rate they spoke with tongues and prophesied, though there were no tongues of fire nor rushing mighty wind as at Pentecost. Moreover, the account in Acts 19 does not say whether the tongues spoken were languages the people there understood nor does it say interpreters were present. At least we can assume they spoke in tongues used somewhere in the world.

When I go to a foreign country, I speak in English. This is an unknown tongue to the majority of my listeners. For example, in northeast India I spoke to many thousands at each meeting; seventeen separate interpreters were used to translate my message into seventeen different dialects so that the people could understand my "unknown tongue." In my judgment this is analogous to what happened at Pentecost, except there it was a divine miracle. Either a given speaker spoke in a language certain listeners knew, or the Holy Spirit interpreted what was being said to each listener in his own language, the miracle then being in his capacity to understand.

"Unknown" Tongues in 1 Corinthians

In 1 Corinthians speaking in tongues appears to be something quite different from the occurrences in the Acts of the Apostles, although the same Greek word is used in Acts and 1 Corinthians to speak of "tongues."

At Pentecost the disciples spoke in tongues known to the people visiting Jerusalem. The Spirit-empowered speakers did not know these languages, but their listeners did. However, in 1 Corinthians the listeners did not hear a language they knew, so interpreters were required. The question is whether or not the tongues in 1 Corinthians were known languages. Some Bible students suggest they were, while others say they were simply some form of ecstatic utterance unrelated to any known human language. Personally, I lean toward the latter position. Actually, however, it probably makes little difference in our understanding of the passage, although some point out that if the Corinthian gift of tongues was a known language, then it is unrelated to much of what is labeled as "tongues" today. The fact that "interpretation" is seen as a spiritual gift makes me believe that the gift of tongues mentioned in 1 Corinthians was not a known language which might be understood by someone who naturally spoke that language.

First Corinthians 13 has its own puzzle. Paul mentions tongues of men and of angels. Now it should be apparent that angelic tongues are not known to any of us, yet the implication is there that some might speak in such tongues. However, in Corinthians Paul speaks of tongues as a gift that comes from the Holy Spirit, so He might give someone the ability to speak an angelic tongue. Of course, Paul makes it quite plain that not everyone is given this particular gift. It is for these reasons that I have difficulty linking the filling of the Holy Spirit to a second baptism and to a necessary accompanying sign, speaking in tongues. I cannot see solid Scriptural proof for the position that tongues as a sign is given to all who are baptized with the Spirit while tongues as a gift is given only to some.

Furthermore, I sometimes think the modern usage of the term "charismatic" may be incorrect. In 1 Corinthians, the Greek word for gifts God gives believers is *charismata.* No one can get such a gift by himself. According to Paul, the gifts, as we shall see in a moment, come from the sovereign operation of the Spirit of God "distributing to each one individually just as He wills" (1 Cor. 12:11). Paul says, "For by one Spirit we [for that is what the Greek says] were all baptized into one body" (1 Cor. 12:13). But in addition to this the Spirit distributes gifts to the various members of the body. Thus, every believer gets some gift. And *every* believer is therefore a charismatic!

Moreover, Paul does not indicate that any one gift belongs to every believer. He says only that each receives "some" gift. He does tell the Corinthians to "covet" (which Cruden's Concordance defines as "to earnestly desire") the best gifts, however. And in I Corinthians 13 he insists that any gift unaccompanied by love is worthless.

Observations on the Gift of Tongues

Concerning the gift of tongues as mentioned in 1 Corinthians 12:30 and the lengthy discourse on the subject in 1 Corinthians 14, the following points must be noted:

First, there is a definite gift of tongues apparently different from the one expressed at Pentecost because no interpretation was required there. And other signs accompanied it: the tongues as of fire and the violent rushing wind. These are nowhere mentioned in connection with the gifts of the Spirit in 1 Corinthians.

Although there is honest disagreement among Christians about the validity of tongues today, I personally cannot find any biblical justification for saying the gift of tongues was meant exclusively for New Testament times. At the same time, it easily becomes a misunderstood and even divisive issue; the fact that Paul found it necessary to deal with it at such length in 1 Corinthians 12–14 is testimony to this. (While stressing it was the least of the gifts, Paul also devoted the most space to discussing it of any of the gifts.) Therefore, when it does occur today it must be surrounded very carefully with the biblical safeguards Paul sets forth.

Also, while the gift of tongues may occur today as a valid spiritual gift, this does not mean every manifestation of tongues is according to the will of God and should be approved uncritically by us.

Second, it should be stressed, as is clearly indicated in 1 Corinthians 12–14, that tongues is a gift of the Holy Spirit, not a fruit of the Spirit. As we shall see, the fruit of the Spirit outlined in Galatians 5:22, 23 should mark every Christian who is walking in the Spirit. On the other hand, gifts are distributed among believers by the sovereign will of God. Therefore, it is a gift that some may have but not others. I simply cannot find any biblical reason for saying that tongues is a gift God desires to give to all believers. Some may be given the gift, while many others will not be given it. It would be wrong for someone who has not been given the gift of tongues to feel he is somehow a "second-rate" Christian, or earnestly covet this gift if God has not seen fit to give it to him. It would be equally wrong for someone who has this gift to try to compel others to have it, or to teach that everyone must experience it.

Third, the gift of tongues mentioned in 1 Corinthians 12–14 is clearly one of the less important gifts of the Spirit—in fact, it appears to be the least important. The reason for this is that it often does not give any spiritual benefit to other believers. The other gifts clearly are exercised to build up and strengthen the body of Christ, however. While tongues may do this in a public worship service (if there is an interpreter present), the other gifts are more directly involved in the mutual strengthening of believers.

This is why the gift of tongues should not be thought of as the high point of Christian maturity. In fact, millions of spiritually mature Christians have never spoken in tongues, and many who have spoken in tongues are not spiritually mature.

Fourth, the gift of tongues is not necessarily a sign of the baptism of the believer by the Holy Spirit into the body of Christ. That is especially true in 1 Corinthians, because these people had already been incorporated once-for-all into the body of Christ. Nowhere in the Bible do I find it said that the gift of tongues is a necessary evidence of being baptized with the Holy Spirit into Christ's body, the Church. Even in Acts where speaking in tongues is mentioned there is no indication it was necessary evidence that one had been baptized with the Holy Spirit.

In like manner the gift of tongues is not necessarily to be equated with being filled with the Spirit. We may be Spirit-filled and never speak in tongues. The filling of the Spirit may result in many different experiences in our lives, of which tongues on occasion may be only one evidence. Some of the most Spirit-filled Christians I have ever known had never experienced the gift of tongues, but they were no less filled with the Spirit.

Fifth, both the Bible and experience warn us that the gift of tongues may easily be abused and in fact may be dangerous. For example, the gift of tongues has often led to spiritual pride. Perhaps someone experiences the gift of tongues and immediately believes he is better or more spiritual than other believers who have not been given this gift. Such an attitude is directly contrary to the proper attitude of a Spirit-filled believer.

Other dangers should be mentioned. For example (as has been indicated), tongues may easily lead to divisiveness. Often this happens because of pride or because a person with the gift of tongues tries to force it on others. On the other hand, it is possible for some people to be proud because they don't speak in tongues, and that is equally wrong!

One of the greatest dangers in this matter of tongues is imbalance. That is, sometimes a person who has experienced this gift will become almost completely absorbed or preoccupied with tongues. The other gifts of the Spirit are forgotten (except, perhaps, the other sign gifts which are also spectacular or impressive), and there is often little interest in holy living and the fruit of the Spirit. Some who insist on making it their central focus to call others to seek this gift, fail to show any interest in evangelism, an emphasis the Spirit wants to give. I am thinking, for instance, of a small group of tongues-speaking people who rarely win other souls to Christ. They wait until someone else does the soul-winning, and then approach the new convert in an effort to persuade him that he must speak in tongues to grow in the Lord.

Still another danger is that some would see an experience of speaking in tongues as a short-cut to spiritual power and maturity. A member of my staff was in seminary with a young man who was going to various meetings constantly hoping to get the gift of tongues. When asked why he wanted this gift, he said it was because he felt a deep lack of power and fellowship with God, and he thought this would give him both spiritual power and a sense of God's presence. When asked if he prayed with any frequency, or read his Bible regularly, or spent much time in fellowship with other believers, he admitted he did not do any of these. God had given him the means of spiritual growth—prayer, the Bible, fellowship—but he was unwilling to be disciplined enough to make use of them. For him, tongues would be a short-cut to spiritual maturity. It was probably no accident that he dropped out of seminary shortly after this and gave up his plans to become a minister.

One final danger might be mentioned, and that is the possibility that the gift may sometimes be counterfeited. This may be due to deliberate deception, or possibly because the "gift" sometimes has its sources not in God but in our psychological make-up. It also may be the result of demonic activity.

Perhaps it should be noted that the ancient Greek oracle of Delphi spoke what might be called "tongues," as did the priests and priestesses at the great temple above Corinth. Dr. Akbar Abdul-Haqq tells me it is not an uncommon phenomenon in India among non-Christian religions today.

Also, there are certain well-substantiated instances of demon-possessed people given the ability to speak in certain known languages with which they were totally unfamiliar when in their right minds. The Bible records how Pharaoh's magicians were able to duplicate God's miracles up to a certain point.

No wonder John says, "Do not believe every spirit, but test the spirits to see whether they are from God" (I John 4:1). We have already gone into this in the discussion of the gift of discernment in chapter 12.

Even Christians have counterfeited this gift. One girl who attended a charismatic meeting wanted desperately to receive the gift of tongues as had so many of her friends. So, having been raised in another country, she prayed in that native language, pretending it was the operation of a spiritual gift. The others thought she had received the gift of tongues. As a result, in this little circle where speaking in tongues was so important, she was finally accepted!

No experience—no matter how much it may mean to us, or how impressive it may seem to be—must take the place of God's Word in our lives. Our experiences must always be judged in light of the Bible; we must not judge the Bible by our experiences. God the Holy Spirit has given us the Bible, and no gift which is truly from the Holy Spirit will contradict the Bible.

Sixth, what about the private, devotional use of tongues as a means of praising God and experiencing His fellowship? A number of friends have told me that after they had prayed for a long period of time, they suddenly found themselves speaking in an unknown language. For the most part they have kept it private and have not said everyone else must have the same experience. They have not said that all Christians must speak in tongues as a sign of spiritual maturity. Everyone knew that Corrie ten Boom had spoken in tongues, but she never talked about it and never discussed it. She often rebuked those who did talk about it excessively.

Actually, the Bible has little to say about this. The private use of tongues is implied by Paul when he remarks that "I speak in tongues more than you all; however, in the church I desire to speak five words with my mind, that I may instruct others also, rather than ten thousand words in a tongue" (1 Cor. 14:18, 19). Some have suggested that Paul's command to "pray at all times in the Spirit" (Eph. 6:18) involves praying in tongues, but the emphasis on specific prayer requests (in which the mind is clearly at work concentrating on the subjects of the prayer) in this passage would indicate this is not what is implied by Paul.

In conclusion, I must say I cannot help but be impressed by the wide differences of opinion about tongues on the part of the people who would call themselves charismatic. Many feel it is utterly wrong to say that tongues are essential to being baptized or filled with the Holy Spirit. A large group of evangelicals do not even regard tongues as a relevant gift of the Spirit today, just as the office of the apostolate is no longer a relevant gift.

I know of one Bible conference ministry which has been greatly used of God, but it would not knowingly invite to its platform anyone, however gifted and acceptable he might be in evangelical circles, who professed to speak in tongues. Others may disagree with this policy, but the leaders of this ministry are sincere in their convictions and should be respected for their views.

On the other hand, many evangelicals who do not themselves profess to speak in tongues now adopt an entirely neutral stance. They have seen the charismatic movement penetrate deeply into all the denominations with great blessing and renewal. So they are prepared to recognize that all the supernatural gifts of 1 Corinthians 12 are relevant today and therefore to be accepted as gifts of the Spirit.

In fairness to some of my charismatic friends I must add that even though I disagree with them on the issue of the "baptism with the Spirit" as accompanied by the sign of tongues, yet I do know and teach the need for believers to be filled with the Spirit. Setting aside the issue of tongues as the necessary sign, we may be talking about a phase of the same experience. In my judgment the Bible says that any believer can enjoy the filling of the Holy Spirit and know His power even though he or she has not had any sign such as speaking in tongues. On the occasion of a particular infilling, tongues may be a sign God gives some, but I do not find that it is a sign for all. I do think it is important, though, for each of us to hold our opinion without rancor and without breaking our bonds of fellowship in Jesus Christ. We worship the same Lord, and for this we are grateful.

In 1 Corinthians 14 Paul certainly says that prophesying is greater than speaking in tongues. At the same time he says, "Do not forbid to speak in tongues" (1 Cor. 14:39). Paul apparently spoke in many different tongues, but he did not emphasize this unduly. We must be careful not to put the Holy Spirit into a position where He must work our way. The Holy Spirit is sovereign; He gives His gifts as He wills! Peter Wagner says: "It must be remembered that the body of Christ is universal, with many local manifestations. Spiritual gifts are given to the body universal, and therefore certain ones may or may not be found in any particular local part of the body. This explains why, for example, a local church or even an entire denomination may not have been given the gift of tongues, while other parts of the body might have it."[1]

To summarize. *First*, there is a real, as contrasted with a counterfeit, gift of tongues. Many of those who have been given this gift have been transformed spiritually—some temporarily and some permanently!

Second, God uses tongues at certain times, in certain places, especially on the frontiers of the Christian mission, to further the kingdom of God and to edify believers.

Third, many are convinced that we may be living in what Scripture calls "the latter days." Both Joel and Hosea prophesy that in those days great manifestations of the Spirit and many of the sign gifts will reappear. We may be living in such a period of history. Certainly we cannot blind ourselves to the fact that many of the sign gifts which vindicate the authenticity of the gospel are reappearing at this hour.

Many years ago in a class discussion at the Florida Bible Institute a teacher said something on the subject of tongues that has stayed with me. He advised his students to "seek not; forbid not."

Indeed, tongues is a gift of the Spirit. Today there are Presbyterians, Baptists, Anglicans, Lutherans, and Methodists, as well as Pentecostals, who speak or have spoken in tongues—or who have not, and do not expect to.

But if tongues is the gift of the Holy Spirit, it cannot be divisive in itself. When those who speak in tongues misuse it so that it becomes divisive, it indicates a lack of love. And those who forbid it do the Church a disservice because they appear to contradict the teaching of the apostle Paul. Those believers who do speak in tongues and those who do not should love each other and work for the greater glory of God in the evangelization of the world, remembering one thing: those who do speak in tongues and those who do not *will* live with each other in the New Jerusalem.

Is this a gift God has seen fit to give you? Don't let it be a source of pride or preoccupation. Become grounded in the whole Word of God. And above all, learn what it means to love others, including believers who may not agree with your emphasis.

Is this a gift you do not have? Don't let it preoccupy you either, and don't let it be a source of division between you and other believers if at all possible. There may be other believers who have a different emphasis from you, but they are still your brothers and sisters in Christ.

Above all, we are called to "walk by the Spirit, and you will not carry out the desire of the flesh" (Gal. 5:16).

The sign gifts—healings, miracles, and tongues—probably attracted as much attention in the first century as they do today. They also sometimes caused confusion and abuses just as they do today. Nevertheless, God the Holy Spirit gave them to some within the Church, to be used for His glory. They must never be exploited for selfish reasons, nor must they ever become sources of either division or pride. We are not to become preoccupied or obsessed with them, and most of all whenever gifts of this nature are given, they must be used strictly in accordance with the principles God has set forth in the Bible. This should also contribute to the unity of the Spirit. And if God chooses to give these gifts to some today, we should always pray that they will be used "for the common good" (1 Cor. 12:7) and the furtherance of the kingdom of God.

14

The Fruit of the Spirit

A HANDFUL OF men had been waiting at a dock on the Thames since five o'clock that bitter cold winter morning. Along with scores of others, they had been selected to unload a docked freighter. This was done by balancing a wheelbarrow on planks that stretched from the dock to a barge and from the barge to the freighter. Among the working men, unknown to them, was a clergyman. Deeply concerned for the men of that area, he had decided that the only way he could communicate with them was to live and work among them. Dressed like them, he denied himself even a cup of hot tea before leaving his room, and went without an overcoat. He knew the men who would be standing in line for jobs along the docks that day would not have had the comfort of a cup of tea, and would, for the most part, be inadequately clothed.

In the days before he landed a job, he learned what it was to be treated as a stranger. He learned what it was to stand all day in the cold and the fog, only to be told there were no jobs available. These men would have to go back to inadequate lodgings and face hungry families without so much as a piece of bread for them.

But this day he had been fortunate and was hired. On his twelfth trip, as he was crossing the plank with his loaded wheelbarrow, it began to jiggle so that he lost his footing and fell into the Thames, amid roars of laughter on all sides.

Fighting to control his temper, he managed finally to struggle to his feet, grinning as he did so. One of the workmen (the culprit who had jiggled the plank) had shouted, "Man overboard," and stood there laughing. As he watched the unrecognized clergyman struggling good-naturedly in the mud, some better impulse seemed to move him to drop some empty boxes into the slush and jump down to help the man out. His would-be rescuer's first remark justified the clergyman's attitude which the Holy Spirit had prompted.

"You took that all right," his former tormenter said as he helped the clergyman to clamber onto the boxes. He did not have the accent of a cockney, for he was not the usual docker.

"You haven't been long at this game," the clergyman remarked.

"Neither have you," replied his tormenter-turned-rescuer. The clergyman agreed, then invited the man to accompany him to his rooming house.

As they talked, the clergyman learned to his amazement that the man had once been a highly successful physician, but due to heavy drink he had lost a thriving practice and his lovely wife and family. The outcome of the story was that the clergyman was able to lead this man to Christ and eventually see him reunited with his family.

Perhaps this is what the fruit of the Spirit is all about. If life were always kind to us, if people were always pleasant and courteous, if we never had headaches, never knew what it was to be tired or under terrific pressure, the fruit of the Spirit might go unnoticed.

But life is not always like that. It is in the midst of difficulties and hardships that we especially need the fruit of the Spirit, and it is in such times that God may especially work through us to touch other people for Christ. As we bear the fruit of the Spirit in our lives, others will see in us "the family likeness of his Son" (Rom. 8:29, Phillips) and be attracted to the Savior.

It is no accident that the Scriptures call the Third Person of the Trinity the *Holy* Spirit. One of the main functions of the Holy Spirit is to impart the holiness of God to us. He does this as He develops within us a Christlike character—a character marked by the fruit of the Spirit. God's purpose is that we would "become mature, attaining the full measure of perfection found in Christ" (Eph. 4:13, NIV).

Fruit: God's Expectation

God the Holy Spirit uses the word *fruit* frequently in Scripture to denote what He expects of His people in the way of character. We have noted in the chapters on the gifts of the Holy Spirit that believers are given various gifts. I may have a gift someone else does not have, while another person may have been given gifts I do not have. However, when we come to the Bible's teaching on the fruit of the Spirit, we find there is a basic difference between the *gifts* of the Spirit and the *fruit* of the Spirit.

Unlike the gifts of the Spirit, *the fruit of the Spirit is not divided among believers*. Instead, *all* Christians should be marked by *all* the fruit of the Spirit. The fruit of the Spirit is God's expectation in our lives. This is clearly seen in many passages of Scripture. In Matthew 13 Jesus told the familiar parable of the seed and the sower. He likens the work of anyone who declares the Word of God—a pastor, teacher, evangelist or any other Christian—to a man sowing seed. Some seed falls by the wayside and is eaten by the birds; some falls on rocky ground and withers in the sun; still other seed begins to grow but is choked by thorns. The fourth group of seeds falls into good soil, takes root, and brings forth fruit abundantly. So you and I are to bear fruit, as the Word of God begins to work in our lives in the power of the Spirit.

It is interesting that the Bible talks of the *fruit* of the Spirit rather than *fruits*. A tree may bear many apples, but all come from the same tree. In the same way, the Holy Spirit is the source of all fruit in our lives.

Put in simplest terms, the Bible tells us we need the Spirit to bring fruit into our lives because we cannot produce godliness apart from the Spirit. In our own selves we are filled with all kinds of self-centered and self-seeking desires which are opposed to God's will for our lives. In other words, two things need to happen in our lives. *First*, the sin in our lives needs to be thrust out. *Second*, the Holy Spirit needs to come in and fill our lives, producing the fruit of the Spirit. *"Put to death*, therefore, whatever belongs to your earthly nature: . . . as God's chosen people, holy and dearly loved, *clothe yourselves* with compassion, kindness, humility, gentleness and patience" (Col. 3:5, 12 NIV, italics mine).

Let me use an illustration. Many people have a fence around their home with a gate for entering and leaving. Remember, a gate can be used for two purposes: it can be opened to let people in, or it can be shut to keep people out.

Spiritually our lives are like this gate. Inside our lives are all sorts of things that are wrong and unpleasing to God. We need to let these things out, and allow the Holy Spirit to come in and control the very center of our lives. But we do not have the power even to open the gate. Only the Holy Spirit can do that, and when He does—as we yield to Him and look to Him for His fullness— He not only comes in but He helps us thrust out the evil things in our lives. He controls the gate, and as He purges the heart of its wickedness He can bring in new attitudes, new motivations, new devotion and love. He also strengthens the door with bars that keep out evil. So the works of the flesh depart and the fruit of the Spirit comes in. The Scripture says that the Holy Spirit wants us to have fruit—and then more fruit, and even much fruit.

In his book, *The Fruit of the Spirit,* Manford George Gutzke compares the fruit of the Spirit to light: "All the colors of the rainbow are in every beam of sunlight. They all are there at any one time. They may not always come into vision, but they are all present. It is not necessary to think of them as being so many separate colors. Just as these colors of the rainbow are present in light, so these traits of personal conduct are in the working of the Holy Spirit."[1]

How the Fruit Grows

How does the Holy Spirit work in our lives to produce the fruit of the Spirit? There are two passages of Scripture especially helpful in answering this question.

The first passage is Psalm 1, which compares the godly man to a tree planted by a river: "But his delight is in the law of the Lord, and in His law he meditates day and night. And he will be like a tree firmly planted by streams of water, which yields its fruit in its season, and its leaf does not wither; and in whatever he does, he prospers" (Ps. 1:2,3). Here the bearing of spiritual fruit is clearly related to the place the Word of God has in our lives. (Notice, it does not just say read, but meditate.) As we read and meditate on the Bible, the Holy Spirit—who, we remember, inspired the Bible—convicts us of sin which needs to be purged and directs us to God's standard for our lives. Apart from the Word of God there will be no lasting spiritual growth or fruit-bearing in our lives.

The second passage is found in John 15, where Jesus compares our relationship to Him to the branches of a vine. "Abide in Me, and I in you. As the branch cannot bear fruit of itself, unless it abides in the vine, so neither can you, unless you abide in Me. I am the vine, you are the branches; he who abides in Me, and I in him, he bears much fruit; for apart from Me you can do nothing" (John 15:4,5).

There are many wonderful truths in this passage, but there are several points we should especially notice. First, this is a command to every believer: "Abide in Me." By that is meant we are to have the closest, most intimate relationship with Christ, with nothing coming between us. This is one reason why the disciplines of prayer, Bible study, and fellowship with other believers are so important.

Also, this tells us that we can *only* bear spiritual fruit if we abide in Christ: "Apart from me you can do nothing." It may be possible for us to make use of the *gifts* of the Spirit even when we are out of fellowship with the Lord. But we cannot display the *fruit* of the Spirit all the time when our fellowship with Christ has been interrupted by sin. We can see, then, how crucial it is to be filled with the Spirit, and we are being filled as we abide in Christ, the vine. The secret of abiding is obedience. As we, through obedient living, abide in Christ, the life of Christ (like the life-giving sap in a vine) flows into us, producing fruit to the glory of the Father and the nourishment and blessing of others.

I believe there is something about this relationship which we cannot fully understand. If we were to ask a branch on a grape-vine, "How do you grow such luscious fruit?" the branch would probably reply, "I don't know. I don't grow any of it; I just bear it. Cut me off from this vine and I will wither away and become useless." Without the vine the branch can do nothing. So it is with our lives. As long as I strain and work to produce the fruit of the Spirit from within myself, I will end up fruitless and frustrated.

But as I abide in Christ—as I maintain a close, obedient, dependent relationship with Him—God the Holy Spirit works in my life, creating in me the fruit of the Spirit. That does not mean we instantly become mature, bearing all the fruit of the Spirit fully and immediately. The fruit on a fruit tree takes time to mature, and pruning may be necessary before fruit is produced in quantity. So it may be with us.

My wife and I enjoy the beautiful trees surrounding our house in North Carolina. In the autumn most leaves drop off and are blown away, but thousands of the old dead leaves cling to the branches even in March and April. However, when the sap in the trees begins to flow, the new leaves form—and life and power pulsate and surge through every living branch. Then all of the old dry leaves fall off, unnoticed. What an analogy for the Christian! "Old things have passed away; behold, new things have come" (2 Cor. 5:17).

Furthermore, each summer we cut down some of the trees that obstruct the view or keep out the sunlight. And some have been badly damaged during the winter storms. Similarly, we have trees in our lives to which the axe must be laid—trees which either lie rotting on the ground or produce only ugly sights. Jesus said, "Every plant which My heavenly Father did not plant shall be rooted up" (Matt. 15:13). We have a few fruit trees on our property. We take special care of those with the best fruit—pruning, feeding, and spraying at proper times. A good tree brings forth good fruit and should be kept. But whether a tree is worth keeping or cutting down depends on the distinction Jesus made. He said, "You will know them by their fruits" (Matt. 7:20 RSV).

Then there are a few grapevines. Some years we pick only a small crop of substandard grapes for personal use. But we do not cut the vines down. Rather, we prune them carefully. Then the next year the vines bring forth more and better fruit. Similarly, as the pruning process goes on in our lives under the guidance of the Holy Spirit, the vines, speaking spiritually, are useful for the production of more spiritual fruit.

Remember, the picture in John 15 is of the Lord Jesus as the vine, we as the branches, and God as the husbandman, or gardener.

Verse three says, "You are already clean because of the word which I have spoken to you," or as J. B. Phillips translates it, "Now, you have already been pruned by my words." There is no better way for the child of God to be pruned than through studying and applying the Bible to his own heart and situation. Somehow God can correct us, tell us where we have fallen short and gone astray, without once discouraging us.

In the Acts of the Apostles we read of Apollos whose earnestness, love, and great gift of oratory appealed to the hearts of Priscilla and Aquila. However, he was immature and unprepared to lead others into the deeper Christian life. He had progressed barely beyond the baptism of John. But this godly couple, instead of laughing at his ignorance or decrying his lack of understanding of true biblical orthodoxy, took him into their home and in love expounded the way of the Lord more perfectly to him (Acts 18:26). Then he began to use his great gifts for the glory of God and the winning of souls. He left an indelible impression on the early Church and helped promote the kingdom of God in the first century.

Are you abiding in Christ? This is the primary condition God sets down for us before we can really bear the fruit of the Spirit. Is there any unconfessed sin in your life which is keeping you from a close walk with Christ? Is there any lack of discipline? Is there any broken relationship with another person which needs healing? Whatever the cause may be, bring it to Christ in confession and repentance. And then learn what it means each day to "Abide in Me."

15

The Fruit of the Spirit:
Love, Joy, Peace

OF ALL THE passages in the Bible which sketch the character of Christ and the fruit which the Spirit brings to our lives, none is more compact and challenging than Galatians 5:22, 23. "But the fruit of the Spirit is love, joy, peace, patience, kindness, goodness, faithfulness, gentleness, self-control." In the next three chapters we will examine in detail the meaning of each of these. For purposes of study, we can divide these nine words into three "clusters" of fruit. Love, joy, and peace make up the first cluster. They especially speak of our Godward relationship. The second "cluster"—patience, kindness, and goodness—especially are seen in our manward relationship, i.e. our relationship with other people. The third "cluster" of faithfulness, gentleness, and self-control are especially seen in our inward relationship—the attitudes and actions of the inner self.

At the same time, of course, these three "clusters" are all related to each other, and *all* should characterize our lives. And all *will* characterize our lives when we abide in Christ and allow the Holy Spirit to do His work in us.

The Fruit of the Spirit: Love

There should be no more distinctive mark of the Christian than love. "By this all men will know that you are My disciples, if you have love for one another" (John 13:35). "We know that we have passed out of death into life, because we love the brethren" (1 John 3:14). "Owe nothing to anyone except to love one another; for he who loves his neighbor has fulfilled the law" (Rom. 13:8).

No matter how else we may bear our testimony for the Lord Jesus Christ, the absence of love nullifies it all. Love is greater than anything we can say, or anything we can possess, or anything we can give. "If I speak with the tongues of men and of angels, but do not have love, I have become a noisy gong or a clanging cymbal. And if I have the gift of prophecy, and know all mysteries and all knowledge; and if I have all faith, so as to remove mountains, but do not have love, I am nothing. And if I give all my possessions to feed the poor, and if I deliver my body to be burned, but do not have love, it profits me nothing" (1 Cor. 13:1–3).

The greatest chapter on love in the Bible is 1 Corinthians 13. Its description of love should be written in letters of gold on every Christian heart. If any chapter of the Bible should be memorized besides John 3, it is 1 Corinthians 13. When we reflect on the meaning of love, we see that it is to the heart what the summer is to the farmer's year. It brings to harvest all the loveliest flowers of the soul. Indeed, it is the loveliest flower in the garden of God's grace. If love does not characterize our lives, they are empty. Peter said, "Above all, keep fervent in your love for one another, because love covers a multitude of sins" (1 Peter 4:8).

In his little book, *The Four Loves*, C. S. Lewis discusses the different Greek words translated "love" in English. When Scripture describes God's love for us and the love God wants us to have, it often uses the Greek word *agape* (pronounced ah-*gah*-pay). *Agape* love is found everywhere in the New Testament. When Jesus said, "Love your enemies," Matthew in his Gospel used the word *agape*. When Jesus said we were to love one another, John used the word *agape*. When Jesus said, "Thou shalt love thy neighbor," Mark used the word *agape*. When the Scripture says, "God is love," it uses the word *agape*. The New Bible Dictionary defines *agape* love in Greek as "that highest and noblest form of love which sees something infinitely precious in its object."[1]

God's greatest demonstration of *agape* love was at the cross where He sent His Son Jesus Christ to die for our sins. Since we are to love as God does, believers should have *agape* love. But we do not have it naturally, nor can we develop it, for the works of the flesh cannot produce it; it must be supernaturally given to us by the Holy Spirit. He does this as we yield ourselves to the will of God.

We should be clear about one thing concerning *agape* love. All too often today love is seen only as an emotion or feeling. Certainly there is emotion involved in love, whether it is love for others or love for God. But love is more than an emotion. Love is not a feeling—love is doing. True love is love which *acts*. That is the way God loves us: "For God so loved the world, that He *gave* His only begotten Son" (John 3:16, italics mine). "Little children, let us not love with word or with tongue, but in deed and truth" (1 John 3:18).

Love is, therefore, an act of the will—and that is why our wills must first be yielded to Christ before we will begin to bear the fruit of love. Bishop Stephen Neill has defined love as "a steady direction of the will toward another's lasting good."[2] He points out that much human love is really selfish in nature, while *agape* love involves self-giving. As Neill says:

"The first love [human love] says, 'I wish to make my own something that another has, and which it is in his power to give me.'

"The second love [God's love] says, 'I wish to give to this other, because I love him.'

"The first love wishes to make itself richer by receiving a gift which some other can give.

"The second love wishes to make another richer by giving all that it has.

"The first love is a matter of feeling and desire. This love comes and goes as it will; we cannot call it into being by any effort of our own.

"The second love is much more a matter of the will, since to give or not to give is largely within our power."[3]

We are to love as the Good Samaritan loved (Luke 10:25–38), which is nothing less than love finding its best demonstration in action. This is a love which reaches out to all—wives, husbands, children, neighbors, and even people we have never met on the other side of the world. It will include those who are easy to love, because they are like us, and those who are hard to love because they are so different. It will even extend to people who have harmed us or brought sorrow to us.

A young wife and mother whose husband had become unfaithful and left her to live with another woman was bitter and full of resentment. However, as she began to think about the love of Christ for us she found a new love growing in her for others—including the woman who had taken her husband. At Christmas time she sent the other woman one red rose with a note: "Because of Christ's love for me and through me, I can love you!" This is *agape* love, the fruit of the Spirit.

The command to love is not an option; we are to love whether we feel like it or not. Indeed, we may say that love for others is the first sign that we have been born again and that the Holy Spirit is at work in our lives.

Certainly above all, love should be the outstanding mark among believers in every local congregation. Dr. Sherwood Wirt has written: "I have learned there is no point in talking about strong churches and weak churches, big churches and little churches, warm churches and cold churches. Such categories are unrealistic and beside the point. There is only a loving church or an unloving church."[4]

It can be so easy at times to say we love people, and be completely honest and sincere in our expression. But so often we don't see the lonely person in the crowd, or the sick or destitute man or woman whose only hope of escape may be the love we can give through Christ. The love God would have us show reaches down to each person.

A friend of ours is a well-known singing star. I have noticed that when he enters a room full of people he does not look around to find the people he knows. He looks for the little guy, unknown, uneasy, out of place, and he walks right over, hand out, his rugged face alight with a kindly smile as he introduces himself, "Hello, I'm. . . ."

As a young boy growing up in Boston a dear friend of mine of many years, Allan Emery, had an experience which made a deep impression upon him. His father received a call saying a well-known Christian had been found at a certain place drunk on the sidewalk. Immediately his father sent his chauffered limousine to pick the man up, while his mother prepared the best guest room. My friend watched wide-eyed, as the beautiful coverlets were turned down on the exquisite old four-poster bed, revealing the monogrammed sheets.

"But, mother," he protested, "he's drunk. He might even get sick."

"I know," his mother replied kindly, "but this man has slipped and fallen. When he comes to, he will be so ashamed. He will need all the loving encouragement we can give him."

It was a lesson the son never forgot.

Jesus looked at the multitudes of people and was moved with compassion for each of them. He loved as no human is able to love. His love engulfed the whole world, the whole human race, from time's beginning to end. His love knew no bounds, no limit, and no one was excluded. From the lowliest beggar to the greatest monarch, from the deepest sinner to the purest saint—His love embraced them *all*. Nothing but the Spirit of God working in our lives can produce such fruit, and it will be evident in our public as well as private lives.

The Fruit of the Spirit: Joy

Returning from his young son's grave in China, my father-in-law wrote to his mother in Virginia, "There are tears in our eyes, but joy in our hearts." The joy which the Spirit brings to our lives lifts us above circumstances. Joy can be ours, even in the midst of the most trying situations.

The Greek word for joy is used repeatedly in the New Testament to denote joy from a spiritual source such as "the joy of the Holy Spirit" (1 Thess. 1:6). The Old Testament likewise uses phrases like "the joy of the Lord" (Neh. 8:10) to point to God as the source.

Just before Calvary our Lord met with His disciples in the Upper Room. He told them He had spoken as He did "that My joy may be in you, and that your joy may be made full" (John 15:11). Bishop Stephen Neill has remarked: "It was because they were a joyful people that the early Christians were able to conquer the world."[5]

Today's world is joyless, full of shadows, disillusionment, and fear. Freedom is rapidly disappearing from the face of the earth. Along with the loss of freedom, a great many of the superficial joys and pleasures of life are also disappearing, but this need not alarm us. The Scriptures teach that our spiritual joy is not dependent on circumstances. The world's system fails to tap the *source* of joy. God, by His Spirit, directs His joy to our bleak, problem-riddled lives, making it possible for us to be filled with joy regardless of our circumstances.

America's Declaration of Independence speaks of "the pursuit of happiness," but nowhere in the Bible are we told to pursue this. Happiness is elusive, and we don't find it by seeking it. It comes when outward conditions are favorable, but joy goes much deeper. Joy is also different from pleasures. Pleasures are momentary, but joy is deep and abiding despite the worst circumstances of life.

Not only are we given the source of joy which is the person of Christ, but we are assured that it is constantly available to the Christian, no matter what the circumstances.

I once visited Dohnavur in South India where Amy Carmichael had lived for fifty years, caring for hundreds of girls originally dedicated to temple service. As I said earlier, she was bedridden for the last twenty years of her life, during which time she wrote many books that have blessed millions. Joy filled her sick room so that everyone who visited her came away praising God. In her book *Gold by Moonlight* she said, "Where the things of God are concerned, acceptance always means the happy choice of mind and heart of that which He appoints, because (for the present) it is His good and acceptable and perfect will."[6]

Even after her death, when I visited the room where she had served the Lord for twenty years, writing from her bed, I was asked by her former nurse to lead in prayer. I began, but was so overwhelmed by a sense of God's presence I broke down (a thing I seldom ever do). So I indicated to my companion that he should continue. The same thing happened to him. As I left that room, I sensed the joy of the Lord in my own heart. Many times I have visited sick people to encourage them. Some suffered from terminal illnesses. Strangely enough, I have come away blessed in my own soul by their contagious joy.

Deep joy crowned the apostle Paul's final testimony as he wrote his last letter to young Timothy from death row. Despite the suffering he had endured, the horror of prison, and the frequent threat of death, the joy of the Lord filled his heart.

Charles Allen puts it this way, "Just as all the water in the world cannot quench the fire of the Holy Spirit, neither can all the troubles and tragedies of the world overwhelm the joy which the Spirit brings into the human heart."[7]

It has been said that "Joy is the flag that flies above the palace when the King is in residence."

The Fruit of the Spirit: Peace

Peace carries with it the idea of unity, completeness, rest, ease, and security. In the Old Testament the word was *shalom.* Many times when I meet Jewish friends I greet them with *"Shalom."* And often, when I greet my Arab friends I use a similar term that they use for peace, *salam.*

Recently as I watched the televised report of passengers disembarking from a hijacked plane, I saw terror, horror, and fear on their faces. But one woman had a little child in her arms, calmly sleeping through it all. Peace in the midst of turmoil.

Isaiah said, "Thou wilt keep him in perfect peace, whose mind is stayed on thee: because he trusteth in thee" (Isa. 26:3 KJV). This is the picture of any Christian who stands alone on the battlefield, by faith garrisoned round about with God's holy weapons, and in command of the situation. Such a man is not troubled about the future, for he knows who holds the key to the future. He does not tremble on the rock, for he knows who made the rock. He does not doubt, for he knows the One who erases all doubt.

When you and I yield to worry, we deny our Guide the right to lead us in confidence and peace. Only the Holy Spirit can give us peace in the midst of the storms of restlessness and despair. We should not grieve our Guide by indulging in worry or paying undue attention to self.

There are different kinds of peace, such as the peace of a graveyard, or that of tranquilizers. But for the Christian, peace is not simply the absence of conflict, or any other artificial state the world has to offer. Rather it is the deep, abiding peace only Jesus Christ brings to the heart. He describes it in John 14:27: "Peace I leave with you; My peace I give to you; not as the world gives, do I give to you." This is the peace that can come only from the Holy Spirit.

The peace *of* God that can reign in our hearts is always preceded by peace *with* God, which must be the starting point. When this is so, the peace of God can follow. From this standpoint, Christ's work of salvation has two stages: First He was able to end the war between sinful man and the righteous God. God indeed was angry with man because of his sin. But Jesus by His blood made peace. The war ended; peace came. God was satisfied. The debt was cancelled, and the books were balanced. With his accounts settled, man was set free, if willing to repent and turn in faith to Christ for salvation. God is now able to look on him with favor.

But Jesus Christ not only freed us from bondage and war. He also made possible a further stage—we can have the peace *of* God in our hearts here and now. For us, peace with God is not simply an armistice; it is a war ended forever; and now the redeemed hearts of former enemies of the cross are garrisoned with a peace that transcends all human knowledge and outsoars any wings of flight we can possibly imagine.

Concerning the peace of God, Spurgeon said: "I looked at Christ, and the dove of peace flew into my heart; I looked at the dove of peace, and it flew away." So we should not look at the fruit itself, but at the source of all peace, because Christ through the Holy Spirit wisely cultivates our lives to allow us to bring forth peace. The greatest psychiatric therapy in the world is appropriating what Jesus promised, "I will give you rest"—or peace (Matt. 11:28). King David became living proof of the spiritual therapy for the soul which the Holy Spirit dispenses when he said, "He maketh me to lie down" (Ps. 23:2 KJV). This is peaceful resting. But David continues, "He restoreth my soul." This is peaceful renewing. Though men continue to seek peace, they will not find it until they come to the simple realization that "Christ is peace."

A woman full of despair and frustration wrote me that her case was hopeless because God could not possibly forget all her gross sins. In reply I said that although she felt forsaken by God and others, He had not forsaken her, but had allowed distress and despair to flood her heart so she might realize her need for God's forgiveness and peace. She wrote later that she jumped up and down with delight when she realized she could have God's peace. Jesus said that not our peace but His peace makes the difference: "My peace I give to you; not as the world gives" (John 14:27).

In Romans Paul gives us these wonderful words, "May the God of hope fill you with all joy and peace in believing, so that by the power of the Holy Spirit you may abound in hope" (15:13 RSV). How can joy and peace be any better described? Indeed the fruit of the Spirit is peace—do you have it in your heart?

16

The Fruit of the Spirit: Patience, Kindness, Goodness

THE FIRST CLUSTER of the fruit of the Spirit has a primary Godward relationship with outward results others can see. Thus, we speak of the love of God, the joy of the Lord, and the peace of God. The second cluster—patience, kindness, and goodness—has to do with the kind of Christians we are in our outward relationships. If we are short-tempered, unkind, and rude, we lack the second cluster of the fruit of the Spirit. But when the Spirit controls us, He works to transform us so that the buds of patience, kindness, and goodness begin to blossom and then to be fruitful.

The Fruit of the Spirit: Patience

The English word *patience* (or *long-suffering* in the King James Version) comes from a Greek word that speaks of a person's steadfastness under provocation. Inherent in the word is the thought of patiently enduring ill-treatment without anger or thought of retaliation or revenge. Thus, this part of the fruit of the Spirit is seen in our relationship to our neighbors. It is patience personified—love's patience. If we are irritable, vengeful, resentful, and malicious to our neighbors, we are short-suffering, not long-suffering. And when that condition exists, the Holy Spirit is not in control.

Patience is the transcendent radiance of a loving and tender heart which, in its dealings with those around it, looks kindly and graciously upon them. Patience graciously, compassionately and with understanding judges the faults of others without unjust criticism. Patience also includes perseverance—the ability to bear up under weariness, strain, and persecution when doing the work of the Lord.

Patience is part of true Christlikeness, something we so often admire in others without demanding it of ourselves. Paul teaches us that we can be "strengthened with all might, according to his glorious power, unto all patience and longsuffering with joyfulness" (Col. 1:11 KJV). Patience in our lives springs from God's power based upon our willingness to learn it. Whenever we are selfish, or when anger or ill will begins to build, or when impatience or frustration overtakes us, we must recognize that we are the source of our problems, not God. We must refuse, renounce, and repudiate the situation immediately. It comes from the old sinful nature.

Patience and Testing

Patience is closely related to testings or trials in the Bible, and that is only logical. We may be patient in ordinary life, but how do we react when trials come? It is then that we especially need the fruit of the Spirit—patience. This is one reason why the Bible tells us that trials can be good for us, because they allow us to be strengthened, and especially they allow patience to be developed by the Spirit. "Consider it all joy, my brethren, when you encounter various trials, knowing that the testing of your faith produces endurance" (James 1:2, 3).

If this is true, we should welcome trials and testings when they come, because they force us to draw more and more upon the source of all strength, producing more of the patience which is the fruit of the Spirit. It is the regular exercise of patience and longsuffering in the small day-to-day frustrations and irritations which prepares us to endure when the great battles come.

Inner erosion of the heart leaves us vulnerable to the cunning, and often disguised, attacks of Satan. But the heart that has learned to call *instantly* in prayer on the Holy Spirit at the first sign of temptation has no reason to fear any such erosion. In a short time prayer will become so automatic and spontaneous that we will have uttered the prayer almost before we are aware of the need. The Bible says we are to be "patient in tribulation; continuing instant in prayer" (Rom. 12:12 KJV). For me, the best time to pray is the *very moment* a tense situation or an unspiritual attitude overtakes me. God the Holy Spirit is always there, ready to help me gain victory in the spiritual battles I face—big or small. However, in order for prayer to become an involuntary, or subconscious reaction to my problem, I must voluntarily and consciously practice it day after day until it becomes an integral part of my being.

A dear friend and trusted counselor once told me that sometimes the greatest test comes to us when we ask God the question, "Why?"

As Charles Hembree has pointed out, "In the full face of affliction it is hard to see any sense to things that befall us and we want to question the fairness of a faithful God. However, these moments can be the most meaningful of our lives."[1]

One of God's great servants, Paul Little, was killed in an automobile accident in 1975. I immediately asked God, "Why?" Paul was one of God's outstanding young strategists and Bible teachers. He was a theological professor, a leader of Inter-Varsity Christian Fellowship, and a former member of our team. I am sure his wife, Marie, must have asked in the agony of her heart, "Why?" And yet, a few months later when she came to our team retreat, she manifested a marvelous spirit as she shared her victory with the wives of our team members. Instead of our comforting her, she was comforting us.

We may suffer affliction or discipline, yet the Psalmist said, "Weeping may last for the night, but a shout of joy comes in the morning" (Ps. 30:5). No Spirit-filled Christian will fail to evince long-suffering and patience if he has faithfully endured "the fellowship of His sufferings" (Phil. 3:10).

In order for the fruit to appear in our lives God allows us to face chastening, discipline, affliction, and persecution. Had Joseph not been sold into slavery by his brothers who hated him, and been wrongly accused by Potiphar who put him in prison, he would not have developed the fruit of patience and long-suffering that was to become the hallmark of his life. Even after he had told Pharaoh's cupbearer he would be restored to the king's court and asked him to tell Pharaoh of his unjust imprisonment, he had to wait two more years for release from prison.

As we wait upon the Lord, God may sometimes seem slow in coming to help us, but He never comes too late. Paul wrote, "For momentary, light affliction is producing for us an eternal weight of glory far beyond all comparison" (2 Cor. 4:17). Jesus told His disciples, "By your perseverance you will win your souls" (Luke 21:19). It is this long-suffering and patience that the Holy Spirit uses to bless others.

We must guard against one thing, however, when we speak about long-suffering. Sometimes we use it as an excuse for failing to take specific action when it is called for. Sometimes we enjoy a kind of neurotic self-flagellation because we don't want to face the truth, and we mistakenly call it long-suffering. But Jesus vigorously "drove out all who sold and bought in the temple, and he overturned the tables of the money-changers and the seats of those who sold pigeons" (Matt. 21:12 RSV). Moreover He furiously castigated the scribes and the Pharisees (Matt. 21:13ff). It is the Spirit-filled Christian who knows when to have "righteous indignation" and when to be patient, and who knows when long-suffering becomes an excuse for inaction or a crutch to hide a defect of character.

The Fruit of the Spirit: Kindness

Kindness, or *gentleness*, is the *second segment* of the fruit that grows outward. This term comes from a Greek word referring to the kindness that pervades and penetrates the whole nature. Gentleness washes away all that is harsh and austere. Indeed, gentleness is love enduring.

Jesus was a gentle person. When He came into the world, there were few institutions of mercy. There were few hospitals or mental institutions, few places of refuge for the poor, few homes for orphans, few havens for the forsaken. In comparison to today, it was a cruel world. Christ changed that. Wherever true Christianity has gone His followers have performed acts of gentleness and kindness.

The word gentleness occurs only a few times in our English Bible. It is spoken of in connection with the three persons of the Trinity. In Psalm 18:35, it is the gentleness of God; in 2 Corinthians 10:1, the gentleness of Christ; and in Galatians 5:23, the gentleness of the Holy Spirit.

Charles Allen points out: "In one's disdain of sin, one can be harsh and unkind toward a sinner. . . . Some people seem to have such a passion for righteousness that they have no room left for compassion for those who have failed."[2]

How easy it is to be impatient or harsh toward those who may have failed in life! When the hippie movement began in America, many people reacted to it with a critical and unloving attitude toward the hippies themselves. The Bible teaches us otherwise. Jesus would have responded to them with loving "kindness" or "gentleness." The only people with whom He dealt harshly were the hypocritical religious leaders, but to everyone else He manifested a wonderful gentleness. Many sinners on the verge of repentance have been disillusioned by a pharisaical and coldly rigid Christianity that hangs on to a legalistic religious code minus the quality of compassion. But Jesus dealt tenderly, gently, and kindly with everyone. Even small children sensed His gentleness and approached Him eagerly and without fear.

Paul told his young friend Timothy, "The servant of the Lord must not strive; but be gentle unto all men" (2 Tim. 2:24 KJV). James said, "The wisdom that is from above is first pure, then peaceable, gentle, and easy to be entreated" (James 3:17 KJV).

Some claim that gentleness is a sign of weakness, but they are wrong! Abraham Lincoln was well-known for his gentleness and humility, but it can never be said that he was weak. On the contrary, it was the combination of his great strength of character and his gentle and compassionate spirit that made him the great person he was.

In *Fruits of the Spirit,* Hembree says, "In our age of guided missiles and misguided men there is desperate need for us to learn how to share gentleness. It seems strange that in an age when we can reach the moon, bounce signals off far planets, and receive pictures from whirling satellites we have great difficulty communicating tenderness to those about us."[3]

The logical place to turn for guidance and instruction in such things of the Spirit is the minister in the pulpit, and the compelling need of this generation is to be exposed to great preaching. But however eloquent, however well prepared, and however gifted any preacher may be, if his ministry lacks tenderness and gentleness, he will be unable to lead many people to Jesus Christ. The gentle heart is the broken heart—the heart that weeps over the sins of the bad as well as the sacrifices of the good.

The Fruit of the Spirit: Goodness

The *third element* in this trio is *goodness*. This is derived from a Greek word referring to that quality found in the person who is ruled by and aims at what is good, that which represents the highest moral and ethical values. Paul writes, "For the fruit of the light consists in all goodness and righteousness and truth" (Eph. 5:9). He also says, "To this end also we pray for you always that our God may count you worthy of your calling, and fulfill every desire for goodness and the work of faith with power; in order that the name of our Lord Jesus may be glorified in you" (2 Thess. 1:11, 12). Again Paul says in commending the church in Rome, "And concerning you, my brethren, I myself also am convinced that you yourselves are full of goodness, filled with all knowledge, and able also to admonish one another" (Rom. 15:14).

As I said in an earlier chapter, on the grounds that surround our home we have a number of fresh water springs. One spring sends forth a never ending supply of pure water, and from it we get the water for our house. The comment of the man who tested it was, "It's the purest water I've ever found." A good heart, like a good spring, perpetually pours out goodness.

The word "good" in the language of Scripture literally means "to be like God," because He alone is the One who is perfectly good. It is one thing, however, to have high ethical standards but quite another for the Holy Spirit to produce the goodness that has its depths in the Godhead. The meaning here is more than just "doing good." Goodness goes far deeper. Goodness is love in action. It carries with it not only the idea of righteousness imputed, but righteousness demonstrated in everyday living by the Holy

Spirit. It is doing good out of a good heart, to please God, without expecting medals and rewards. Christ wants this kind of goodness to be the way of life for every Christian. Man can find no substitute for goodness, and no spiritual touch-up artist can imitate it.

Thoreau wrote, "If a man does not keep pace with his companions, perhaps it is because he hears a different drummer. Let him step to the music which he hears, however measured or far away."[4] As Christians we have no alternative but to march to the drumbeat of the Holy Spirit, following the measured steps of goodness, which pleases God.

We can do good deeds, and by practicing principles of goodness can witness to those around us that we have something "different" in our lives—perhaps something they themselves would like to possess. We may even be able to show others how to practice the principles of goodness in their own lives. But the Bible says, "Your goodness is as a morning cloud, and as the early dew it goeth away" (Hosea 6:4 KJV). True goodness is a "fruit of the Spirit," and our efforts to achieve it in our own strength alone can never succeed.

We should be careful that any goodness the world may see in us is the genuine fruit of the Spirit and not a counterfeit substitute, lest we unwittingly lead someone astray.

We must be constantly aware that Satan can take any human effort and twist it to serve his own purposes, but he cannot touch the spirit that is covered by the blood of Christ and rooted deep in the Holy Spirit. Only the Spirit can produce the goodness that can stand up under any test.

Goodness is never alone so far as the outward facets of the fruit of the Spirit are concerned, but it is always accompanied by patience and kindness. These three go together and all were beautifully manifested in the life of the One who is the perfect prototype of what you and I ought to be. By the power of the Holy Spirit these traits of character become part of our lives that we might remind others of Him.

17

The Fruit of the Spirit: Faithfulness, Gentleness, Self-Control

AUTHENTIC CHRISTIAN LIVING has its own order of priority in our lives: God first, others second, self third. It is proper, therefore, when speaking about the third cluster of the fruit of the Spirit to focus our attention upon the *inward man*. The Spirit works *in* us that He might work through us. "Being" is far more important than "doing." But when we are what we should be inside, we will bring forth fruit, more fruit, and much fruit. This is the ultimate purpose the apostle Paul had in mind when he wrote, "It is God who is at work in you, both to will and to work for His good pleasure" (Phil. 2:13). He also says, "He who began a good work in you will perfect it until the day of Christ Jesus" (Phil. 1:6).

The third cluster of the spiritual fruit has to do with the inward man. It includes faithfulness, gentleness, and self-control.

The Fruit of the Spirit: Faithfulness

The reference to faithfulness (or "faith" in the KJV) is not to faith exercised by the Christian, but rather to *faithfulness* or *fidelity*, produced by the Holy Spirit in a yielded Christian life.

The same word occurs in Titus 2:10 where it is translated "fidelity" in the King James Version. This trait of character is highly commended in Scripture. Fidelity in little things is one of the surest tests of character, as our Lord indicated in the parable of the talents: "You were faithful with a few things, I will put you in charge of many things" (Matt. 25:21). Morality is not so much a matter of magnitude, but of quality. Right is right, and wrong is wrong, in small things as well as in big things.

Peter contrasts those who walk faithfully with God over against those who become entangled again with the pollution of the world. He writes, "For it had been better for them not to have known the way of righteousness, than, after they have known it, to turn from the holy commandment delivered unto them. But it is happened unto them according to the true proverb, The dog is turned to his own vomit again; and the sow that was washed to her wallowing in the mire" (2 Peter 2:21, 22 KJV).

The Third Epistle of John contains only fourteen verses. Diotrephes and Demetrius are the two main characters. The faithful follower was Demetrius who is described as receiving a "good testimony from everyone, and from the truth itself" (v. 12). He is commended because in word and in truth, in practice and in precept, he followed the Lord faithfully.

A familiar expression in industry is "turn around time," the time that elapses between the receipt of an order and the day it is delivered. Many Christians will some day regret the self-imposed time lag that came between the point when God first showed them His plan for them, and the point when they took action. The ancient Israelites could have completed their journey from Egypt to Canaan in a few months. Instead, the journey took forty years and a whole generation died because of their unfaithfulness.

Lack of faithfulness is actually a sign of spiritual immaturity. One sign of emotional immaturity is the refusal to accept responsibility. A young person may want all the privileges of adulthood, but refuse to accept the responsibilities. The same thing is true spiritually. God has given us certain responsibilities as mature Christians. When we are disobedient and refuse to accept these responsibilities, we are unfaithful. On the other hand, when we are faithful, it means we have accepted the responsibilities God has given us. This is a sign of spiritual maturity, and it is one of the important fruits the Spirit brings to our lives.

Surely most of us grow at a slower rate than we should because we refuse to allow the Holy Spirit to control all areas of our lives.

Rather, our faithful obedience to allow God the Holy Spirit to remove any vile habit or developing infection should be immediate. We can become impatient when we discover it takes so long to become like Him, but we should be patient and faithful, for becoming like Him is worth waiting for. However, even if we could become totally mature Christians I am not sure that we would be conscious of it. Who of us can claim total perfection in this life? But we know that when we stand with Him in eternity, we will be glorified with Him. And the Holy Spirit will begin to perform the deeper work of God's plan in our lives any time we are willing to faithfully say "yes" to His will!

The Scriptures are replete with stories of men like Abraham (Heb. 11:8–10), who were faithful in their walk before God. The entire eleventh chapter of Hebrews should be studied as it recounts the men and women whom God calls faithful.

It is dangerous to tempt God, as did "unfaithful" men in the day of Amos. To them God declared, "Behold, days are coming . . . when I will send a famine on the land, not a famine for bread, or a thirst for water, but rather for hearing the words of the Lord" (Amos 8:11).

Rather we should heed the advice of James: "Blessed is a man who perseveres under trial; for once he has been approved, he will receive the crown of life, which the Lord has promised to those who love him" (1:12). James later says, "One who looks intently at the perfect law, the law of liberty, and abides by it, not having become a forgetful hearer but an effectual doer, this man shall be blessed in what he does" (1:25).

Over and over we are admonished to be *faithful.* As we saw earlier we read in the Bible about a number of judgments at the end of this age. One of these is called the judgment seat of Christ. Someday all Christians will stand before Jesus Christ to give an account of the works we have done since our conversion. We will be judged, not on the basis of how successful we were in the eyes of the world, but on how faithful we were in the place God put us. The apostle Paul indicates this in 1 Corinthians 3:9–16: faithfulness will be the basis on which God renders judgment.

Sometimes the greatest test of our faithfulness is how much time we spend reading the Scriptures, praying, and living in accord with the principles of righteousness when we have been blessed with prosperity. A devout Christian surprised me recently by saying, "It's hard to be a faithful Christian in modern-day America." It is so easy to forget and to forsake our God in the midst of prosperity and especially when materialism is rampant. This is the reason Jesus told us that it is hard for rich men to enter the kingdom of God. Rich men can be saved—but the Bible talks about "the deceitfulness of riches" (Matt. 13:22). The burdens and cares of this world often interfere with our faithful walk before the Lord. In the midst of material prosperity we should beware lest we fall into the same pitfall as the Laodiceans, who incurred God's wrath and displeasure because they felt they had need of nothing since they were materially rich (Rev. 3:17). "But those who want to get rich fall into temptation and a snare and many foolish and harmful desires which plunge men into ruin and destruction. For the love of money is a root of all sorts of evil, and some by longing for it have wandered away from the faith, and pierced themselves with many a pang" (1 Tim. 6:9, 10).

If we could carve an epitaph on the tombstone of the apostle Paul, it might read: "Faithful unto death." As he awaited execution Paul could say without hesitation, "I have fought a good fight, I have finished my course, I have kept the faith: Henceforth there is laid up for me a crown of righteousness, which the Lord, the righteous judge, shall give me at that day" (2 Tim. 4:7, 8 KJV). Whatever the failures of Paul and however short he fell of perfection, he knew that he had been faithful to the Lord to the end.

This wonderful segment of the cluster of the fruit of the Spirit—faithfulness—constitutes faithfulness to our testimony, faithfulness to our commitments and calling, and faithfulness to the commands of Christ. And the ultimate reward for faithfulness is given in Revelation 2:10: "Be faithful until death, and I will give you the crown of life."

The Fruit of the Spirit: Gentleness

The word gentleness here (or in the KJV, meekness) comes from a Greek word meaning "mild; mildness in dealing with others." Jesus said, "Blessed are the gentle, for they shall inherit the earth" (Matt. 5:5). Nowhere in Scripture does this word carry with it the idea of being spiritless and timid. In biblical times gentleness or meekness meant far more than it does in modern day English. It carried the idea of being tamed, like a wild horse that has been brought under control. Until tamed by the Holy Spirit Peter was a rough and ready character. Then all of his energy was used for the glory of God. Moses was called the meekest of men, but prior to God's special call to him he was an unbroken, high-spirited man who needed forty years in the desert before he was fully brought under God's control. A river under control can be used to generate power. A fire under control can heat a home. Meekness is power, strength, spirit, and wildness under control.

In another sense, gentleness can be likened to modesty in that it is the opposite of a flamboyant and self-indulgent spirit. Rather, it displays a sensitive regard for others and is careful never to be unfeeling for the rights of others.

Gentleness enjoys a quiet strength that confounds those who think of it as weakness. This is seen in the response of Jesus following his arrest—throughout His trial, torture, and crucifixion he endured the emotional and physical pain inflicted mercilessly by his captors and taunting spectators. "He was oppressed and He was afflicted, yet He did not open His mouth; Like a lamb that is led to slaughter, and like a sheep that is silent before its shearers, so He did not open His mouth" (Isa. 53:7). Meekness is referred to as love under discipline. Charles Allen states, "God never expects us to be less than we really are. . . . Self-belittlement is an insult to the God who made us. Meekness comes another way. . . . Pride comes from looking only at ourselves, meekness comes through looking at God."[1]

All Christian growth, including meekness, takes place in the heavy atmosphere of hostility. This kind of spiritual poise and inward quiet strength as a growing work of the Holy Spirit does not come on a playground, but on a spiritual battleground.

In still another definition of meekness, David Hubbard says that meekness is making ourselves consistently available to those who count on us; we are at peace with our power, so we do not use it arrogantly or hurtfully. When speaking of meekness, DeWitt Talmadge said, "As the heavens prophetically are taken by violence, so the earth is taken by meekness, and God as proprietor wants no tenants more or grants larger leases than to the meek of heart and spirit."

In his appraisal of Andrew Murray, the great Keswick speaker, Dr. V. R. Edman states in his book, *They Found the Secret*, "Such indeed is the abiding life that draws its sustenance and strength from the Vine. By the refreshing and reviving flow of the Holy Spirit through that life there is prayer that prevails, preaching that is powerful, love that is contagious, joy that overflows, and peace that passes understanding. It is the adoration that is stillness to know God for one's self. It is the obedience that does the Saviour's bidding in the light of the Word. It is the fruitfulness that arises spontaneously from abiding in the Vine."[2]

Another illustration that has helped me to understand gentleness is the iceberg. I have seen some of them from shipboard when crossing the Atlantic. However high an iceberg may be above the water line, the greater part of it is submerged. Icebergs are particularly formidable and destructive when they drift along the sea lanes.

But the greatest threat to icebergs comes from something beneficent, the sun. The sun's rays bring warmth to life, and death to icebergs. As gentleness is a powerful force, so the sun proves to be more powerful than the mightiest iceberg. God's gentleness, or meekness, in us permits the rays of the sun of God's Holy Spirit to work on our icebound hearts, transforming them into instruments for good and for God. Spiritually, the gentle, Spirit-filled Christian is a prism through whom the rays of the sun's spectrum are gathered to minister to the icebergs of our carnality.

How do you and I apply gentleness to ourselves? Jesus set before us His own example by calling upon us to be "gentle and humble in heart" (Matt. 11:29).

First, we do not rise up defensively when our feelings are ruffled, as did Peter when he slashed the ear of the soldier at the arrest of Jesus in the garden, only earning His Lord's rebuke (Matt. 26:51, 52).

Second, we do not crave to have the preeminence, as Diotrephes did (3 John 9). Rather, we desire that in all things Jesus Christ might have the preeminence (Col. 1:18).

Third, we do not seek to be recognized and highly regarded, or to be considered the voice of authority, as Jannes and Jambres did (2 Tim. 3:8). These magicians of Egypt rejected the Lord's authority through Moses, and opposed him just before the Exodus. "Do not think of yourself more highly than you ought, but rather think of yourself with sober judgment, . . . Be devoted to one another in brotherly love. Honor one another above yourselves" (Rom. 12:3, 10 NIV).

The enthronement of Jesus Christ in our lives makes it possible for meekness to become one of our virtues. Gentleness may be the most tangible sign of greatness displayed in us. You and I may never be respected as voices of authority; we may never gain the plaudits of the world; we may never rule or swing the baton of power. But one day the meek will inherit the earth (Matt. 5:5), for no one can take away our rightful share of God's divine and delightful bequest to us.

The Fruit of the Spirit: Self-control

Self-control (temperance in the KJV) is the third fruit in this cluster. It comes from a Greek word meaning strong, having mastery, able to control one's thoughts and actions.

John Wesley's mother once wrote him while he was a student at Oxford that "anything which increases the authority of the body over the mind is an evil thing." This definition has helped me understand "self-control."

Intemperance has brought about the fall of kings and tycoons. History illustrates this. Someone has said: "There are men who can command armies, but cannot command themselves. There are men who by their burning words can sway vast multitudes who cannot keep silence under provocation or wrong. The highest mark of nobility is self-control. It is more kingly than regal crown and purple robe."

Elsewhere it has been said:

> "Not in the clamor of the crowded street,
> Not in the shouts and plaudits of the throng,
> But in ourselves, are triumph and defeat."[3]

Past history and current public examples illustrate how the excesses of uncontrolled appetite and fleshly indulgence wreak damage in our hearts.

The sin of intemperance, lack of self-control, springs from two causes: first, physical appetite; second, mental habit.

When we think of temperance we usually think of alcohol. This is not unexpected because of the great efforts of temperance leaders who for years sought to eradicate this poison that affects so many people in the world. But somehow we silently countenance gluttony, which the Bible condemns as clearly as drunkenness. We also tend to overlook unkindness, gossip, pride, and jealousy. It is possible to be intemperate in all these areas, too. The Scripture says, "Those who live according to their sinful nature have their minds set on what that nature desires; but those who live in accordance with the Spirit have their minds set on what the Spirit desires" (Rom. 8:5 NIV). Temperance, self-control, as a fruit of the Spirit is the normal Christian life taking its exercise.

Temperance in our use of food is moderation. Temperance with respect to alcohol is soberness. Temperance in sexual matters is abstinence for those who are not married. Even for those of us who are married there may be times for temperance, when we abstain by mutual consent from legitimate sexual activity so we can give ourselves more fully to the study of God's Word, prayer, and good works (see 1 Cor. 7:5).

Temperance in regard to temper is self-control. Recently I was with a man who parked in a prohibited zone at the airport. An attendant kindly asked him if he would move the car as he was in a no-parking zone. Angrily he replied, "If you don't have police credentials, shut your mouth." This Christian was so nervous and tense from shouldering so many responsibilities that he had almost totally lost control of his temper. He was intemperate. It was just as much a sin as if he had become drunk.

Temperance in matters of dress is appropriate modesty. Temperance in defeat is hopefulness. Temperance in relation to sinful pleasure is nothing short of complete abstinence.

Solomon wrote, "He who is slow to anger is better than the mighty, and he who rules his spirit, than he who captures a city" (Prov. 16:32). The Living Bible paraphrases the latter part of that verse to read, "It is better to have self-control than to control an army." The writer of Proverbs said, "A man without self-control is as defenseless as a city with broken-down walls" (25:28 LB).

Paul taught the importance of self-control. Any athlete who would win a race must train himself to become the complete master of his body, he told his readers. He emphasized that the goal was not merely a corruptible, but an incorruptible crown: "Everyone who competes in the games exercises self-control in all things. They then do it to receive a perishable wreath, but we an imperishable. . . . but I buffet my body and make it my slave, lest possibly, after I have preached to others, I myself should be disqualified" (1 Cor. 9:25, 27).

In Peter's list of Christian virtues, he says, "Add . . . to knowledge temperance; and to temperance patience" (2 Peter 1:5, 6 KJV). All these go together. And it is quite clear that when we allow our passions to rule us, the outcome at last is far more undesirable than can be imagined during the moment of pleasurable fulfillment.

Who is to say where temperance stops and intemperance begins? Some Christians have an elastic conscience when it comes to their own foibles—and an ironbound conscience when it comes to the foibles of others. Maybe that's why it is so easy for some Christians to condemn a person who takes an occasional sip of wine but never rebuke themselves for the sin of habitual overeating. Compulsive overeating is one of the most widely accepted and practiced sins of modern Western Christians. It is easy to condemn an adulterer, but how can the one who condemns do so when he is guilty of some other form of intemperance? Should each of us not have clean hands and a pure heart in all of life? Is one form of slavery more wrong in principle than another? Are we not just as tightly bound if the chains are made of ropes as of steel?

The appetite that controls one person may differ from the appetite that controls another. But if one person submits to a craving for possessions, is he so different from others who crave sex, gambling, gold, food, alcohol, or drugs?

The need for temperance in *every* aspect of life has never been greater than it is today. At a time when violence, selfishness, apathy, and undisciplined living threaten to destroy this planet, it is imperative that Christians set an example. The world needs this example—something, steadfast it can hold on to, an anchor in a raging sea.

For centuries Christians have proclaimed Christ as the anchor. If we who have the Holy Spirit living and working within us falter and fail, what hope is there for the rest of the world?

Space for Fruit-growing

We have now considered these nine wonderful facets that comprise the fruit of the Spirit: love, joy, peace, patience, kindness,
goodness, faithfulness, gentleness, and self-control. It is my prayer
that they will characterize your life and mine.

The Holy Spirit is already in every Christian heart, and He
intends to produce the fruit of the Spirit in us. However, there
must be a displacement. A boat does not sink when it is in
the water, but it does sink when the water comes into the boat.
We do not fail to enjoy the fruit of the Spirit because we live in
a sea of corruption; we fail to do so because the sea of corruption
is in us.

The internal combustion engine's worst enemy is the deadly
carbon that builds up in the cylinder chamber. It reduces the power
and causes the motor to lose efficiency. Oil will improve the
engine's performance, but it will not remove the carbon so that
the motor can run more efficiently. Mechanical surgery must be
performed to remove the carbon so that the oil can do its best work
and the motor perform as it was designed to do. Similarly, we must
eliminate the works of the flesh from our inner lives so that deadly
carbon and grit do not impair the effectiveness of our spiritual
performance. One oil company advertised, "More power for
smoother performance." Spiritually this is possible only as we
yield our lives to the control of the Holy Spirit. We must let the
searchlight of God's Word scan us to detect the abiding sins and
fruitless qualities which impair our personal growth and fruitfulness.

The story is told of a man who glanced at the obituary column
in his local newspaper. To his surprise he saw his own name,
indicating that he had just died. At first he laughed about it. But
soon the telephone began to ring. Stunned friends and acquaint-
ances called to inquire and to offer their sympathy. Finally, in
irritation, he called the newspaper editor and angrily reported that
even though he had been reported dead in the obituary column
he was very much alive. The editor was apologetic and embarrassed. Then in a flash of inspiration he said, "Do not worry, sir,

I will make it all right, for tomorrow I will put your name in the births column."

This may sound like merely a humorous incident, but it is actually a spiritual parable. Not until we have allowed our old selves to be crucified with Christ can our new selves emerge to display the marvelous fruit characteristic of the life of Jesus Christ.

And only the Holy Spirit can make possible the out-living of the in-living Christ. The kind of persons God wants us to be can never be produced through human effort. But when the Holy Spirit fills us, He brings forth His fruit in people who manifest a growing likeness to Christ, the prototype of what we will someday be.

18

The Need
of the Hour

THE 1850s IN America brought a marked decline in religion in the United States. The discovery of gold in California, as well as a number of other developments, had turned people's minds and hearts away from religion and toward material things. The political turmoil over slavery and the threatened disintegration of the nation also preoccupied public attention. A severe financial panic in the late 1850s led to even greater concern about material things.

In September of 1857 a quiet businessman named Jeremiah Lanphier decided to invite other businessmen to join him in a noonday prayer meeting once a week, seeking for the renewing work of the Holy Spirit. He distributed hundreds of handbills advertising the meeting, but the first day only half a dozen showed up, meeting in the rear of a church on Fulton Street. Two weeks later there were forty, and within six months some ten thousand were gathered daily for prayer in New York City alone. Awakening swept the country, and within two years an estimated one million people had professed faith in Christ.

The effects of the awakening were profound, both in individual lives and in society. Tragically, the awakening was too late to avoid the Civil War which threatened the very life of the nation. But untold good came from the awakening, including many movements for evangelism and social betterment.

The Need for Spiritual Revival

The world today is again in desperate need of a spiritual awakening. It is the only hope for the survival of the human race. In the midst of the vast problems which face our world Christians are strangely silent and powerless, almost overwhelmed by the tides of secularism. And yet Christians are called to be "the salt of the earth" (Matt. 5:13), keeping a decaying world from further corruption. Christians are to be "the light of the world" (Matt. 5:14), illuminating the darkness caused by sin and giving guidance to a world that has lost its way. We are called to be "children of God above reproach in the midst of a crooked and perverse generation, among whom you appear as lights in the world" (Phil. 2:15).

Why are we not "salt" and "light" as we should be? Why are we not doing much more to bring the kingdom of God to the hearts and lives of humanity?

There certainly are many instances of Christians who have been touched by God, and are in turn touching the lives of others for Christ. But for every instance of that, there are many more Christians who are living defeated, joyless lives. These people have no sense of victory over sin or effectiveness in witnessing. They have little impact on those around them for the sake of the Gospel.

If, then, the greatest need of our world is to feel the effects of a spiritual awakening, the greatest need within the Christian Church throughout the world today is to experience the touch of the Holy Spirit, bringing true "revival" and "renewal" to the lives of countless Christians.

Many centuries ago God gave Ezekiel, the prophet, a remarkable vision in which he saw national Israel scattered among the nations. Israel's bones were described as many and dry. All hope for the future seemed to be gone. According to the word of the prophet, Israel might as well be buried as far as the secular world was concerned. However, Ezekiel was staggered when God asked this question: "Can these bones live?" (Ezek. 37:3). To this the prophet replied, "Thou knowest." Then the man of God was commanded to speak the word of God and the bones stood up, a great host of men who were clothed with flesh. But they still seemed strangely impotent. They lacked spirit or breath. Then the Spirit of God gave them breath and they became a mighty army.

Again we face a dark time in the history of God's people. In spite of some encouraging signs, the forces of evil seem to be gathering for a colossal assault on the work of God in the world. Satan has unleashed his power in a way perhaps unparalleled in the history of the Christian Church. If ever there was a time we needed renewal, it is now. Only God can thwart the plans of Satan and his legions, because only God is all-powerful. Only His Holy Spirit can bring true spiritual awakening which will stem the tide of evil and reverse the trend. In the darkest hour God can still revive His people, and by the Holy Spirit breathe new vigor and power into the body of Christ.

Our world needs to be touched by Christians who are Spirit-filled, Spirit-led, and Spirit-empowered. Are you that kind of Christian? Or is there in your own life the need for a new touch of the Spirit? Do you stand in need of genuine spiritual renewal within your own life? If so, know that God the Holy Spirit wants to bring that renewal to you right now.

The Time Is Now

The time for spiritual revival is *now*. We must not delay. Dr. Samuel Johnson wore a watch on which was engraved the words from John 9:4, "The Night Cometh." We Christians ought to carry written in our hearts the solemn truth of how short is our opportunity to witness for Christ and live for Him. We do not know—any of us—how much time we have left on this earth. Death may cut our lives short. Christ could come again at any moment.

I once read about a sundial on which was inscribed the cryptic message, "It is later than you think." Travelers would often pause to meditate on the meaning of that phrase. We Christians have a sundial—the Word of God. From Genesis to Revelation it bears its warning, "It is later than you think." Writing to the Christians of his day Paul said, "It is already the hour for you to awaken from sleep; for now salvation is nearer to us than when we believed. The night is almost gone, and the day is at hand. Let us therefore lay aside the deeds of darkness and put on the armor of light" (Rom. 13:11, 12).

Billy Bray, a godly clergyman of another generation, sat by the bedside of a dying Christian who had been very shy about his testimony for Christ during his life. The dying man said, "If I had the power I'd shout glory to God." Billy Bray answered, "It's a pity you didn't shout glory when you had the power." I wonder how many of us will look back over a lifetime of wasted opportunities and ineffective witness and weep because we did not allow God to use us as He wanted. "Night is coming, when no man can work" (John 9:4).

If ever we are to study the Scriptures, if ever we are to spend time in prayer, if ever we are to win souls for Christ, if ever we are to invest our finances for His kingdom—it must be *now*. "Since all these things are to be destroyed in this way, what sort of people ought you to be in holy conduct and godliness, looking for and hastening the coming of the day of God, on account of which the heavens will be destroyed by burning, and the elements will melt with intense heat! But according to His promise we are looking for new heavens and a new earth, in which righteousness dwells. Therefore, beloved, since you look for these things, be diligent to be found by Him in peace, spotless and blameless" (2 Peter 3:11–14).

The Effects of an Awakening

What would happen if revival were to break into our lives and our churches today? I believe there are at least *eight characteristics* of such an outpouring of the Holy Spirit.

1. There will be a new vision of the majesty of God. We must understand that the Lord is not only tender and merciful and full of compassion, but He is also the God of justice, holiness, and wrath. Many Christians have a caricature of God. They do not see God in all of His wholeness. We glibly quote John 3:16, but we forget to quote the following verse, "he who does not believe has been judged already" (v. 18). Compassion is not complete in itself, but must be accompanied by inflexible justice and wrath against sin and a desire for holiness. What stirs God most is not physical suffering but sin. All too often we are more afraid of physical pain than of moral wrong. The cross is the standing evidence of the fact that holiness is a principle for which God would die. God cannot clear the guilty until atonement is made. Mercy is what we need and that is what we receive at the foot of the cross.

2. There will be a new vision of the sinfulness of sin. Isaiah saw the Lord upon a throne high and lifted up, His train filling the temple, and he saw the seraphim bowing in reverence as they cried, "Holy, Holy, Holy, is the Lord of hosts, the whole earth is full of His glory" (Isa. 6:3). Then it was that Isaiah realized his own unworthiness and his utter dependence upon God. When Simon Peter, on the Sea of Galilee, realized that it was the very Lord with him in the boat, he said, "Depart from me, for I am a sinful man, O Lord!" (Luke 5:8). The consciousness that Jesus was God Himself brought to Peter's mind his own human sinfulness. In the presence of God, Job said, "I abhor myself" (Job 42:6 ASV).

When a man is tempted, James tells us, his own passions carry him away and serve as a bait (James 1:14, 15). And whatever his lust may be it conceives and becomes the parent of sin, and sin when fully matured gives birth to death. We need to see sin as it really is. The greatest vision of sin that a person can ever receive is to look at the cross. If Jesus Christ had to die for sin, then sin indeed must be dark and terrible in the sight of God.

3. There will be an emphasis on the necessity of repentance, faith, and the new birth. Jesus came preaching repentance and saying that unless a man is born from above he cannot see the kingdom of God. He said that sinners love darkness and will not come to the light for fear their deeds will be exposed and condemned. Those whose hearts have been changed are new creatures. They come to the light out of love for truth and for God. If anyone is in Christ Jesus, he is a new creature, for the old things have passed away and everything has become new.

4. There will be the joy of salvation. The prayer expressed in the Psalm was for a requickening "That Thy people may rejoice in Thee" (Ps. 85:6). David's desire was for a restoration of the joy of salvation. The express purpose of Jesus for the disciples was "that your joy may be made full" (John 15:11). When Philip went down to Samaria and led a great spiritual awakening, Scripture says, "There was much rejoicing in that city" (Acts 8:8). Jesus also tells us that there is joy in heaven, joy in the presence of the angels of God over one sinner who repents (Luke 15:7). So a true revitalization of the Church would bring about the salvation of tens of thousands of sinners, and this in turn would bring joy in heaven as well as joy here on earth.

If there were no heaven and no hell I would still want to be a Christian because of what it does for our homes and our own families in this life.

5. *There will be a new realization of our responsibility for world evangelization.* John the Baptist pointed his hearers to "the Lamb of God" and his two disciples followed Jesus from then on (John 1:36, 37). Andrew first found his own brother Peter and told him that they had found the Christ. When Philip had begun to follow Christ he went after Nathanael (John 1:40–45). The apostles were to be witnesses anywhere and everywhere, even unto the uttermost part of the earth (Acts 1: 8). And when persecution scattered the church which was at Jerusalem, they went everywhere preaching Christ and the glorious gospel (Acts 8:4). One of the first and best evidences of being a true believer is the concern which we feel for others.

6. *There will be a deep social concern.* In Matthew 22:37–39, Jesus said, "You shall love the Lord your God with all your heart, and with all your soul, and with all your mind. . . . You shall love your neighbor as yourself." Our faith is not only vertical, it is horizontal. We will become interested in the hurts of those around us and those far away. But I would have to say that to a world which really wants to be saved from the consequences of its own sin and folly a revived Christianity can have only one message, "Repent." Too many people today want a brotherly world in which they can remain unbrotherly; a decent world in which they can live indecently. Too many individuals want economic security without spiritual security. But the revitalization that we long for must be biblical. If it is Christian, it will be Bible-centered. If this is true, then its leaders must have the courage of Amos to condemn those who "buy the helpless for money and the needy for a pair of sandals" (Amos 8:6).

We must lift high the moral, ethical, and social teachings of Jesus, agreeing that He offers the only standard for personal and national character. The Sermon on the Mount is for today and every day. We cannot build a new civilization on the chaotic foundation of hatred and bitterness.

7. *There will be increased evidence of both the gifts and the fruit of the Spirit.* Renewal is brought by the Holy Spirit, and when He

comes in all His power upon the Church there will be clear evidences of the gifts and the fruit of the Spirit. Believers will learn what it means to minister to one another and build each other up through the gifts the Holy Spirit has given. They will be given a new measure of love for each other and for a lost and dying world. No longer will the world say that the Church is powerless and silent. No longer will our lives seem ordinary and indistinguishable from the rest of the world. Our lives will be marked by the gifts only the Holy Spirit can give. Our lives will be marked by the fruit only He can bring.

8. There will be renewed dependence upon the Holy Spirit. There are already evidences that this is taking place in many parts of the world. No spiritual revitalization can come without Him. The Holy Spirit is the one who reproves, convicts, strives, instructs, invites, quickens, regenerates, renews, strengthens, and uses. He must not be grieved, resisted, tempted, quenched, insulted, or blasphemed. He gives liberty to the Christian, direction to the worker, discernment to the teacher, power to the Word, and fruit to faithful service. He reveals the things of Christ. He teaches us how to use the sword of the Spirit which is the Word of God. He guides us into all truth. He directs in the way of godliness. He teaches us how to answer the enemies of our Lord. He gives access to the Father. He helps us in our prayer life.

There are things which money cannot buy; which no music can bring; which no social position can claim; which no personal influence can assure; and which no eloquence can command. No clergyman however brilliant, no evangelist no matter how eloquent or compelling, can bring about the revival we need. Only the Holy Spirit can do this. Zechariah said, "Not by might nor by power, but by My Spirit, says the Lord of hosts" (Zech. 4:6).

Steps to Awakening

If spiritual revival is the great need for many Christians today, how does it come? What are the steps to revival in our own lives and the lives of others? I believe there are three steps which the Bible sets forth.

The first step is admitting our spiritual poverty. All too often we are like the Laodicean Christians who were blinded to their own spiritual needs, "You say, 'I am rich, and have become wealthy, and have need of nothing,' and you do not know that you are wretched and miserable and poor and blind and naked" (Rev. 3:17).

Is there sin in our lives which is blocking the work of the Holy Spirit in and through us? We must not be too quick to answer "no." We must examine ourselves in the light of God's Word, and pray that the Holy Spirit will reveal to us every sin which hinders us. It may be something we are doing that is wrong—a habit, a relationship, an evil motive or thought. It may be something we are neglecting—a responsibility we are shirking or an act of love we have failed to perform. Whatever it is, it must be faced honestly and humbly before God.

The second step in spiritual renewal is confession and repentance. We can know we have sinned, and still do nothing about it. But we need to bring our sin to God in confession and repentance, not only acknowledging our sins before Him but actually turning from sin and seeking to be obedient to Him. One of the great promises of the Bible is 1 John 1:9, "If we confess our sins, He is faithful and righteous to forgive us our sins and to cleanse us from all unrighteousness." The prophet Isaiah said, "Seek the Lord while He may be found; call upon Him while He is near. Let the wicked forsake his way, and the unrighteous man his thoughts; and let him return to the Lord" (Isa. 55:6, 7).

It is no accident that some of the great awakenings in history have begun in prayer. A prayer meeting under a haystack in a rainstorm in 1806 led to the first large-scale American missionary efforts. In 1830 some 30,000 people were converted in Rochester, New York, under the ministry of Charles Finney; later Finney said the reason was the faithful praying of one man who never attended the meetings but gave himself to prayer. In 1872 the American evangelist Dwight L. Moody began a campaign in London, England, which was used of God to touch countless lives. Later Moody discovered that a humble bedridden girl had been praying. The list could go on and on.

Are you praying for revival, both in your own life and in the lives of others? Are you confessing sin to Him and seeking His blessing on your life?

The third step is a renewed commitment on our part to seek and do the will of God. We can be convicted of sin—we can pray and confess our sin—we can repent—but the real test is our willingness to obey. It is no accident that true revival is always accompanied by a new hunger for righteousness. A life touched by the Holy Spirit will tolerate sin no longer.

What is it that is hindering spiritual revival in your life today? Ultimately, of course, it is sin. Sometimes it hurts deeply to face the truth about our own lack of spiritual zeal and dedication. But God wants to touch us and make us useful servants for Himself. "Let us also lay aside every encumbrance, and the sin which so easily entangles us, and let us run with endurance the race that is set before us, fixing our eyes on Jesus, the author and perfecter of faith" (Heb. 12:1, 2). James A. Stewart has observed, "A church that needs to be revived is a church that is living below the norm of the New Testament pattern. . . . It is a tragic fact that the vast majority of Christians today are living a sub-normal Christian life. . . . the Church will never become normal until she sees revival."[1]

Are you living a "subnormal" Christian life—a life that is ineffective, lukewarm, and lacking in love for Christ and for others? Let God the Holy Spirit bring you in humility to God, confessing sin and seeking His face. Let Him touch you as you yield yourself to Him. The greatest need in the world today is for fully committed Christians.

Over 100 years ago, two young men were talking in Ireland. One said, "The world has yet to see what God will do with a man fully consecrated to Him." The other man meditated on that thought for weeks. It so gripped him that one day he exclaimed, "By the Holy Spirit in me I'll be that man." Historians now say that he touched two continents for Christ. His name was Dwight L. Moody.

This can happen again, as we open our lives to the recreating power of the Holy Spirit. No person can seek sincerely the cleansing and blessing of the Holy Spirit, and remain the same afterward. No nation can experience the touch of awakening in its midst, and remain the same afterward.

As we have seen in this book, Pentecost was the day of power of the Holy Spirit. It was the day the Christian Church was born.

We do not expect that Pentecost will be repeated any more than that Jesus will die on the cross again. But we do expect pentecostal blessings when the conditions for God's moving are met, and especially as we approach "the latter days." We as Christians are to prepare the way. We are to be ready for the Spirit to fill and use us.

NOTES

Chapter 1

1. Matthew Henry, *Commentary on the Whole Bible*, Vol. 1 (Old Tappan, N. J.: Fleming H. Revell Co.), p. 2.

Chapter 2

1. W. A. Criswell, *The Holy Spirit in Today's World* (Grand Rapids: Zondervan Publishing House, 1966), p. 87.
2. J. D. Douglas, ed., *Let the Earth Hear His Voice* (Minneapolis: World Wide Pub., 1975), p. 277.
3. John R. W. Stott, *Your Mind Matters* (Downers Grove, IL: Inter-Varsity Press, 1973), pp. 5, 7.
4. Ibid, p. 10.

Chapter 3

1. Al Bryant, *1,000 New Illustrations* (Grand Rapids: Zondervan Publishing House, 1960), p. 30.
2. B. H. Carroll, *Inspiration of the Bible* (New York, Chicago, London, Edinburgh: Fleming H. Revell Co., 1930), p. 54ff.
3. John R. W. Stott, *The Authority of the Bible* (Downers Grove, IL: Inter-Varsity Press, 1974), pp. 30, 40.
4. John Calvin (Trans. Ford Lewis Battles) ed. John McNeill, *Institutes of the Christian Religion* (Philadelphia: Westminster Press, 1960) Book One, Chapter 7, Sections 4 & 5, pp. 79, 80.
5. J. D. Douglas, ed., *Let the Earth Hear His Voice* (Minneapolis: World Wide Pub., 1975), p. 259.
6. Henry H. Halley, *Halley's Bible Handbook* (Grand Rapids: Zondervan Publishing House, 1962), p. 5.
7. J. B. Phillips, *Letters to Young Churches* (New York: The Macmillan Company, 1955), p. xii.

Chapter 4

1. *The Open Bible* (Nashville: Thomas Nelson, 1975), p. 988.
2. J. Gresham Machen, *The Christian Faith in the Modern World* (Grand Rapids: Wm. B. Eerdmans Co., 1947), p. 63.

Chapter 5

1. John R. W. Stott, *Baptism and Fullness* (London: Inter-Varsity Press, 1975), p. 28f.
2. David Howard, *By the Power of the Holy Spirit* (Downers Grove, IL: Inter-Varsity Press, 1973), p. 34f.
3. Ibid.

Chapter 6

1. A. T. Robertson, *Word Pictures in the New Testament*, Vol. 1 (Nashville: Broadman Press, 1930), p. 239.
2. Matthew Henry, *Commentary on the Whole Bible*, Vol. 6 (Old Tappan, N.J.: Fleming H. Revell Co.), p. 688f.
3. Ibid.
4. C. S. Lewis, *Letters to Malcolm: Chiefly on Prayer* (London and Glasgow: Collins Fontana Books, 1966), p. 22f.
5. John Wesley, *A Compend of Wesley's Theology*, eds. Burtner and Chiles (Nashville: Abingdon Press, 1954), p. 95.

Chapter 7

1. Horatius Bonar, *God's Way of Holiness* (Chicago: Moody Press, 1970), p. 93.
2. C. I. Scofield, ed., *The New Scofield Reference Bible* (New York, Oxford University Press, 1967), p. 1276.
3. Ibid, p. 1219.
4. Bonar, *God's Way of Holiness*, p. 91.

Chapter 8

1. *Keswick Week* (London: Marshall Brothers, 1907), p. 105.

Chapter 9

1. William Barclay, *The Daily Study Bible: The Letter to the Romans* (Philadelphia: Westminster Press, 1957), p. 90.
2. John R. W. Stott, *Men Made New* (London: Inter-Varsity Fellowship, 1966), pp. 49–51.

3. James H. McConkey, *The Threefold Secret of the Holy Spirit* (Chicago: Moody Press, 1897), p. 65.
4. John MacNeil, *The Spirit-filled Life* (Chicago: Moody Press, n.d.), pp. 58–59.

Chapter 10

1. "Oh For a Closer Walk," in *Christian Praise* (London: Tyndale Press, 1963), p. 337.

Chapter 11

1. David Howard, *By the Power of the Holy Spirit* (Downers Grove, IL: Inter-Varsity Press, 1973), p. 101.
2. John R. W. Stott, *Baptism and Fullness*, p. 99ff.
3. Merrill C. Tenney, ed. *The Zondervan Pictorial Encyclopedia of the Bible*, Vol. 4 (Grand Rapids: Zondervan Publishing House, 1977), p. 903.

Chapter 13

1. Peter Wagner, *Frontiers in Missionary Strategy* (Chicago: Moody Press, 1971), p. 71.

Chapter 14

1. Manford George Gutzke, *The Fruit of the Spirit* (Atlanta: The Bible For You, n.d.), pp. 10, 11.

Chapter 15

1. J. D. Douglas, ed., *The New Bible Dictionary* (London: The Inter-Varsity Fellowship, 1965), p. 753.
2. Stephen Neill, *The Christian Character* (New York: Association Press, 1955), p. 22.
3. Ibid., p. 21.
4. Sherwood Wirt, *Afterglow* (Grand Rapids: Zondervan Publishing House, 1975), p. 82.

5. Neill, *The Christian Character*, p. 29.
6. Amy Carmichael, *Gold by Moonlight* (Fort Washington, PA: Christian Literature Crusade, n.d.), p. 31.
7. Charles Allen, *The Miracle of the Holy Spirit* (Old Tappan, N.J.: Fleming H. Revell Co., 1974), p. 56.

Chapter 16

1. Charles Hembree, *Fruits of the Spirit* (Grand Rapids: Baker Book House, 1969), pp. 57, 58.
2. Charles Allen, *The Miracle of the Holy Spirit* (Old Tappan, NJ.: Fleming H. Revell Co., 1974), p. 60.
3. Hembree, *Fruits of the Spirit*, p. 74.
4. Henry David Thoreau, *Walden* (Boston: Houghton, Mifflin & Co., 1906), p. 358ff.

Chapter 17

1. Charles Allen, *The Miracle of the Holy Spirit* (Old Tappan, N.J.: Fleming H. Revell Co., 1974), p. 63.
2. V. Raymond Edman, *They Found the Secret* (Grand Rapids: Zondervan Publishing House, 1960), p. 98.
3. Henry Wadsworth Longfellow, *The Poets*, quoted from Bartlett's *Familiar Quotations* (Boston: Little, Brown, and Co., 1968), p. 624b.

IMPORTANT FAMILIES OF ORGANIC COMPOUNDS

	Family					
	Alkane	**Alkene**	**Alkyne**	**Arene**	**Haloalkane**	**Alcohol**
Specific Example	CH_3CH_3	$CH_2{=}CH_2$	$HC{\equiv}CH$	(benzene ring)	CH_3CH_2Cl	CH_3CH_2OH
IUPAC Name	Ethane	Ethene or Ethylene	Ethyne or Acetylene	Benzene	Chloro-ethane	Ethanol
Common Name	Ethane	Ethylene	Acetylene	Benzene	Ethyl chloride	Ethyl alcohol
General Formula	RH	$RCH{=}CH_2$ $RCH{=}CHR$ $R_2C{=}CHR$ $R_2C{=}CR_2$	$RC{\equiv}CH$ $RC{\equiv}CR$	ArH	RX	ROH
Functional Group	C—H and C—C bonds	$\diagdown C{=}C \diagdown$	—C≡C—	Aromatic Ring	$-\overset{\mid}{\underset{\mid}{C}}-X$	$-\overset{\mid}{\underset{\mid}{C}}-OH$

Family						
Ether	Amine	Aldehyde	Ketone	Carboxylic Acid	Ester	Amide
CH_3OCH_3	CH_3NH_2	$\overset{\displaystyle O}{\overset{\|}{CH_3CH}}$	$\overset{\displaystyle O}{\overset{\|}{CH_3CCH_3}}$	$\overset{\displaystyle O}{\overset{\|}{CH_3COH}}$	$\overset{\displaystyle O}{\overset{\|}{CH_3COCH_3}}$	$\overset{\displaystyle O}{\overset{\|}{CH_3CNH_2}}$
Methoxy-methane	Methan-amine	Ethanal	Propanone	Ethanoic Acid	Methyl ethanoate	Ethanamide
Dimethyl ether	Methyl-amine	Acetal-dehyde	Acetone	Acetic acid	Methyl acetate	Acetamide
ROR	RNH_2 R_2NH R_3N	$\overset{\displaystyle O}{\overset{\|}{RCH}}$	$\overset{\displaystyle O}{\overset{\|}{RCR}}$	$\overset{\displaystyle O}{\overset{\|}{RCOH}}$	$\overset{\displaystyle O}{\overset{\|}{RCOR}}$	$\overset{\displaystyle O}{\overset{\|}{RCNH_2}}$ $\overset{\displaystyle O}{\overset{\|}{RCNHR}}$ $\overset{\displaystyle O}{\overset{\|}{RCNR_2}}$
—C—O—C—	—C—N—	$\overset{\displaystyle O}{\overset{\|}{-C-H}}$	$-C-\overset{\displaystyle O}{\overset{\|}{C}}-C-$	$\overset{\displaystyle O}{\overset{\|}{-C-OH}}$	$\overset{\displaystyle O}{\overset{\|}{-C}}-O-C-$	$\overset{\displaystyle O}{\overset{\|}{-C}}-N-$

ORGANIC CHEMISTRY

FIFTH EDITION

ORGANIC CHEMISTRY

T. W. GRAHAM SOLOMONS
University of South Florida

JOHN WILEY & SONS, INC.
New York Chichester Brisbane Toronto Singapore

The 3D molecular images on the cover and chapter openers throughout this book are exact computer-generated models of actual molecular data. These were created using the computer-aided molecular design package, SYBYL®, developed by TRIPOS Associates, Inc., St. Louis, MO. TRIPOS also performed the electronic capture and reproduction of these images.

Cover image created by Patricia A. Chernovitz, Tripos Associates, Inc.

Fig. 14-38 Diasonics, Inc.

Acquisitions Editor	Nedah Rose
Production Manager	Joe Ford
Designer	Madelyn Lesure
Production Supervisor	Elizabeth Austin
Manufacturing Manager	Lorraine Fumoso
Supervising Copy Editor	Elizabeth Swain
Copy Editor	Jeannette Stiefel
Photo Research Manager	Elaine Bernstein
Photo Researcher	John Schultz, PAR/NYC
Illustration	John Balbalis

Recognizing the importance of preserving what has been written, it is a policy of John Wiley & Sons, Inc. to have books of enduring value published in the United States printed on acid-free paper, and we exert out best efforts to that end.

Library of Congress Cataloging in Publication Data:

Solomons, T. W. Graham.
  Organic chemistry / T. W. Graham Solomons. — 5th ed.
      p.   cm.
  Includes bibliographical references and index.

  1. Chemistry, Organic.   I. Title.
QD251.2.S66   1992   91-23206
547—dc20   CIP

Printed in the United States of America

10 9 8 7 6 5 4 3 2 1

For Judith

ABOUT THE AUTHOR

T. W. GRAHAM SOLOMONS did his undergraduate work at The Citadel and received his doctorate in organic chemistry in 1959 from Duke University where he worked with C. K. Bradsher. Following this he was a Sloan Foundation Postdoctoral Fellow at the University of Rochester where he worked with V. Boekelheide. In 1960 he became a charter member of the faculty of the University of South Florida and became Professor of Chemistry in 1973. He is a member of Sigma Xi, Phi Lambda Upsilon, and Sigma Pi Sigma. He has received research grants from the Research Corporation and the American Chemical Society Petroleum Research Fund. For several years he was director of an NSF-sponsored Undergraduate Research Participation Program at USF. His research interests have been the areas of heterocyclic chemistry and unusual aromatic compounds. He has published papers in the *Journal of the American Chemical Society,* the *Journal of Organic Chemistry,* and the *Journal of Heterocyclic Chemistry.* He has received several awards for distinguished teaching. His organic chemistry textbooks have been widely used for 16 years and have been translated into Japanese, Chinese, Korean, Malaysian, Arabic, Portuguese, Spanish, and Italian.

He has spent several years in England as a visiting member of the faculty at the University of Sussex. He and his wife Judith have a 500-year-old cottage in Sussex, and this is where he has done most of his writing for his textbooks. They have a daughter who is a geophysicist and two younger sons.

TO THE STUDENT

A Study Guide for the textbook is available through your college bookstore under the title **Study Guide to accompany *ORGANIC CHEMISTRY,* Fifth Edition** by **T. W. Graham Solomons and Jack E. Fernandez.** The Study Guide can help you with course material by acting as a tutorial, review, and study aid. If the Study Guide is not in stock, ask the bookstore manager to order a copy for you.

PREFACE

My goal in writing this fifth edition has been the same as with earlier editions: to make it the most effective and up-to-date text possible for teaching the fascinating subject of organic chemistry. I have learned much that has helped with this task from kind colleagues who have supplied me with suggestions, and from my own students. The aim of this edition is, as it has been from the first edition, to bring a realistic approach to the study of mechanisms, to bring real functional group chemistry into the first term of the course, and to provide an emphasis on the biological, environmental, and medical applications of organic chemistry that are so important to students.

This edition, the most extensively revised of any so far, retains many features that have made earlier editions successful. However, it differs from previous editions in ways that will improve its usefulness to students and instructors.

ORGANIZATION

The basic organization is one that combines the best aspects of the *functional group approach* the the *reaction mechanisms approach*. The primary organization is by functional groups. The mechanisms that unify the underlying chemistry are presented, in most instances, in the context of chapters organized around a particular functional group. This is not always the case, however. For example, I do not follow the traditional method of describing radical chemistry in the chapter on alkanes. Because I wish to introduce ionic mechanisms first, and because I want to give radical chemistry a much-deserved broader scope, I have a separate chapter (Chapter 7) on radical chemistry.

NEW TO THIS EDITION

Among the many features of this new edition are:

- New early chapters on acids and bases in organic chemistry (Chapter 3)
- Ionic and radical mechanisms introduced early in back-to-back chapters beginning with ionic reactions
- Stronger emphasis on the biological, environmental, medical and industrial applications of organic chemistry
- Greater emphasis on organic synthesis and on using retrosynthetic analysis to plan syntheses
- Early introduction (Chapter 11) of the structure and reactivity of carbonyl compounds, oxidation – reduction reactions, and syntheses using Grignard and organolithium reagents
- Extensive revision of the chapters that deal with bio-organic chemistry (Chapters 22 – 25)
- Reaction summaries for all functional group chapters.

ACID-BASE REACTIONS

I have added a new early chapter on acids and bases in organic chemistry (Chapter 3). There are several reasons for doing this. Acid-base chemistry is fundamental; it finds its way into almost all of the rest of the book and into much of the laboratory work that the students will do. Acid-base reactions, moreover, are relatively simple, and they are reactions that students have studied previously in their general chemistry course. They also lend themselves especially well to the introduction of several important topics that students need to know about early in the course: (1) the curved arrow notation for illustrating mechanisms; (2) free energy changes and their relationship to equilibrium constants; (3) enthalpy and entropy changes and how they affect reactions under equilibrium control; and (4) solvent effects. Furthermore, acid-base reactions even provide an introduction to synthesis when they are used to prepare deuterium- and tritium-labeled compounds.

MECHANISMS

Ionic and radical mechanisms are now introduced in back-to-back chapters (Chapters 6 and 7). I begin with ionic reactions because they are fundamentally simpler than radical chain reactions, and I introduce the study of mechanisms with the S_N2 reaction of an alkyl halide. This, I believe, is a good starting point because it is important to show students the connection between experimental evidence and our theories about reaction mechanisms. With a simple S_N2 reaction it is easy to show how the formulation of the mechanism comes from kinetic and stereochemical studies. With other possible leadoff reactions — a radical chain reaction or the addition of a hydrogen halide to an alkene, for example — the kinetics are complicated and the opportunity to make an important connection will be missed.

Chapter 6 has been rewritten so as to use transition state theory and free energies of activation rather than collision theory and energies of activation as was done in the previous edition. Mechanisms of radical reactions are discussed in a revised and modernized way in Chapter 7. Here, too, it is explained how in certain instances it is possible to make reasonable predictions about the extent of reaction on the basis of the enthalpy change, and how in these instances energies of activation can be used in place of free energies of activation to predict reactivity.

One benefit of the new back-to-back approach for ionic and radical reactions comes when the addition reactions of alkenes are discussed in Chapter 9. Here, because both mechanistic types have been presented, students can understand both the Markovnikov and anti-Markovnikov addition of HBr. A discussion of the synthesis of addition polymers via radical reactions is also possible.

APPLICATIONS

New material in this edition provides an even stronger emphasis on the biological, environmental, medical, and industrial applications of organic chemistry that have characterized previous editions and that interest all students. A few examples of new applications that I have added are how chirality pervades nature (Section 5.2), radicals in industry, biology, and medicine (Section 7.1), autoxidation and vitamin E (Section 7.10D), partially hydrogenated vegetable oils and saturated and unsaturated fats (Section 8.6), how glycolipids and glycoproteins determine antibody–antigen interactions (Section 22.16), cholesterol and heart disease (Section L.5), and medical applications of purine chemistry (Section 25.4).

ORGANIC SYNTHESIS

There is also a greater emphasis on organic synthesis and on using retrosynthetic analysis to plan syntheses in this edition. Retrosynthetic analysis is introduced in Chapter 4 using syntheses based on the coupling reactions of lithium dialkylcuprates as a vehicle for illustrating the disconnection approach to retrosynthetic analysis. Then in Chapter 6 the idea of a functional group interconversion is explained using conversions made possible by S_N2 reactions. In Chapter 9, a section entitled "Synthetic Strategies Revisited" describes all of the major aspects of synthesis: construction of the carbon skeleton, functional group interconversion, control of regiochemistry, and control of stereochemistry. A brief optional section illustrates the meanings of synthons and synthetic equivalents. Here, too, students are urged to begin assembling a notebook that will become their "Toolkit for Organic Synthesis."

RICHER CHEMISTRY IN THE FIRST TERM

To ensure that students will have ample opportunities to put into practice what they have learned about planning syntheses, Chapter 11 now introduces the structure and reactivity of carbonyl compounds, oxidation-reduction reactions, and syntheses using Grignard and organolithium reagents. This will also bring more interesting chemistry to the first-semester's work and provide greater scope for the accompanying laboratory work.

BIO-ORGANIC CHEMISTRY

The chapters that deal with bio-organic chemistry (Chapters 22–25) have all been revised and brought up to date. Many recent research developments now enhance the basic chemistry of these chapters. In the chapter on carbohydrates, for example, some of the classical chemistry has been deleted to make room for recent developments in the chemistry of amino sugars and of glycolipids and glycoproteins. In the chapter on lipids there is an expanded discussion of the structure of cell membranes. The chapter on proteins has an important new section entitled "Introduction to Enzymes." The principles learned there are applied in another new section describing mechanisms of enzyme activity of the serine proteases. Finally, the chapter on nucleic acids now includes sections describing the determination of the base sequence of DNA, the laboratory synthesis of antisense oligonucleotides, and the important polymerase chain reaction.

REACTION SUMMARIES AND GLOSSARIES

Chapters that describe functional group chemistry now have sections that provide reaction summaries, and some have flow diagrams that interrelate functional groups from several chapters. Other chapters have a glossary of important terms and concepts.

SPECIAL TOPICS

Fifteen Special Topics, interspersed at appropriate places in the text, augment the basic textual material. This is a feature not found in other textbooks. The purpose of these special topics is to give instructors flexibility in designing their courses. Special topics can be omitted or included as the instructor desires, because the special topics stand apart from the material in the 25 basic chapters. An understanding of the special topics is not required for an understanding of the material in the basic chapters or for working problems given in them.

Even if the special topics are not included in the course, and most instructors will not include them all, they give inquisitive students an opportunity to explore more deeply into areas that they find interesting. The special topics also make this text more useful to students as a reference book for later courses.

The special topics include such subjects as divalent carbon compounds, addition polymers, mass spectrometry, condensation polymers, transition metal organic compounds, lithium enolates, lipid biosynthesis, the photochemistry of vision, and reactions controlled by orbital symmetry.

ILLUSTRATIONS

All drawings of molecular models have been replaced with modern computer-generated models, and a standard color scheme for atoms of different types in models is used throughout the text. Many other new full-color diagrams have been added as well. When combined, these features will make this the most effectively illustrated organic textbook available.

STUDY GUIDE

A *Study Guide for Organic Chemistry,* 5th Ed. by T. W. Graham Solomons and J. E. Fernandez contains **worked-out solutions** to all of the problems in this text. It also contains **reaction summaries** and **flow diagrams, self-tests** for each chapter, **supplementary problems,** a section on the **calculation of empirical and molecular formulas,** a **glossary** of important terms, and **molecular model exercises.**

INSTRUCTOR'S SUPPLEMENTS

To aid instructors, a Test Bank is available, containing more than 1,500 questions. The Test Bank is available in both a printed and a computerized (Macintosh and IBM) version. Also available is a set of Overhead Transparencies.

T. W. Graham Solomons

ACKNOWLEDGMENTS

I am especially grateful to the following people who provided reviews that helped me prepare this new edition:

Ronald Baumgarten
University of Illinois at Chicago

Wayne Brouillette
University of Alabama

George Clemans
Bowling Green State University

William Closson
State University of New York at Albany

Brian Coppola
University of Michigan

Phillip DeShong
University of Maryland

Trudy Dickneider
University of Scranton

Paul Dowd
University of Pittsburgh

Gideon Fraenkel
The Ohio State University

Roy Gratz
Mary Washington College

John Helling
University of Florida

John Hogg
Texas A & M University

Robert G. Johnson
Xavier University

Michael Kzell
Orange Coast College

Frank Robinson
University of Victoria, British Columbia

Jonathan Sessler
University of Texas at Austin

John Sevenair
Xavier University of Louisiana

Doug Smith
University of Toledo

James Van Verth
Canisius College

Darrell Watson
GMI Engineering and Management Institute

Desmond Wheeler
University of Nebraska

Darrell Woodman
University of Washington

I am also grateful to the many people who have provided the reviews that have guided me in preparing earlier editions of my textbooks:

Winfield M. Baldwin
University of Georgia

David Ball
California State University, Chico

Paul A. Barks
North Hennepin State Junior College

Harold Bell
Virginia Polytechnic Institute
and State University

Newell S. Bowman
The University of Tennessee

Edward M. Burgess
Georgia Institute of Technology

Robert Carlson
University of Minnesota

William D. Closson
State University of New York at Albany

Phillip Crews
University of California, Santa Cruz

James Damewood
University of Delaware

O. C. Dermer
Oklahoma State University

Robert C. Duty
Illinois State University

ACKNOWLEDGMENTS

Stuart Fenton
University of Minnesota

Jeremiah P. Freeman
Notre Dame University

M. K. Gleicher
Oregon State University

Wayne Guida
Eckerd College

Philip L. Hall
Virginia Polytechnic Institute
and State University

Lee Harris
University of Arizona

William H. Hersh
University of California, Los Angeles

Jerry A. Hirsch
Seton Hall University

John Holum
Augsburg College

Stanley N. Johnson
Orange Coast College

John F. Keana
University of Oregon

David H. Kenny
Michigan Technological University

Robert C. Kerber
State University of New York
at Stony Brook

Karl R. Kopecky
The University of Alberta

Paul J. Kropp
University of North Carolina
at Chapel Hill

John A. Landgrebe
University of Kansas

Allan K. Lazarus
Trenton State College

Philip W. LeQuesne
Northeastern University

Robert Levine
University of Pittsburgh

Samuel G. Levine
North Carolina State University

John Mangravite
West Chester University

Jerry March
Adelphi University

John L. Meisenheimer
Eastern Kentucky University

Gerado Molina
Universidad de Puerto Rico

Everett Nienhouse
Ferris State College

John Otto Olson
Camrose Lutheran College

Allen Pinhas
University of Cincinnati

William A. Pryor
Louisiana State University

Thomas R. Riggs
University of Michigan

Stephen Rodemeyer
California State University, Fresno

Yousry Sayed
University of North Carolina
at Wilmington

Ronald Starkey
University of Wisconsin — Green Bay

James G. Traynham
Louisiana State University

Daniel Trifan
Fairleigh Dickinson University

Desmond M. S. Wheeler
University of Nebraska

James K. Whitesell
The University of Texas at Austin

Joseph Wolinski
Purdue University

Darrell J. Woodman
University of Washington

I thank my colleagues at the University of South Florida for the many helpful
suggestions that they have offered. In this regard, I think especially of: Raymond N.
Castle, Jack E. Fernandez, George R. Jurch, Leon Mandell, George R. Newkome,
Terence C. Owen, Douglas J. Raber, Stewart W. Schneller, George R. Wenzinger,
Robert D. Whitaker and Andy Zetzker.

ACKNOWLEDGMENTS

I am especially grateful to Robert G. Johnson of Xavier University who not only provided a very helpful review of the previous edition, but also gave me page-by-page comments on this edition. I also thank him and James G. Traynham of Louisiana State University for their help in proofreading.

I am much indebted to Jeannette Stiefel for copyediting and proofreading.

I am grateful to many people at Wiley for their help, especially Nedah Rose, Chemistry Editor, Kaye Pace, Publisher, Elizabeth Austin, Production Supervisor, Madelyn Lesure, Designer, John Balbalis, Illustration Designer, Elizabeth Swain, Copyediting Supervisor, Elaine Bernstein, Acting Photo Research Manager, and Joan Kalkut, Supplements Editor.

I also thank Pat Chernovitz and Bruce Meyer of Tripos Associates for providing the fine computer-generated graphics for the chapter openers and the cover.

And, finally, I thank my wife, Judith Taylor Solomons, for her encouragement and for her editing and proofreading.

T. W. Graham Solomons

CONTENTS

1
CARBON COMPOUNDS AND CHEMICAL BONDS

2
REPRESENTATIVE CARBON COMPOUNDS

3

ACIDS AND BASES IN ORGANIC CHEMISTRY

4

ALKANES AND CYCLOALKANES. CONFORMATIONS OF MOLECULES

5

STEREOCHEMISTRY. CHIRAL MOLECULES

6

IONIC REACTIONS—NUCLEOPHILIC SUBSTITUTION AND ELIMINATION REACTIONS OF ALKYL HALIDES

7

RADICAL REACTIONS

8

ALKENES AND ALKYNES I. PROPERTIES AND SYNTHESIS

9

ALKENES AND ALKYNES II. ADDITION REACTIONS

10

ALCOHOLS AND ETHERS

11

ALCOHOLS FROM CARBONYL COMPOUNDS. OXIDATION– REDUCTION AND ORGANOMETALLIC COMPOUNDS

12

CONJUGATED UNSATURATED SYSTEMS

FIRST REVIEW PROBLEM SET   510

13

AROMATIC COMPOUNDS

14

SPECTROSCOPIC METHODS OF STRUCTURE DETERMINATION

15

ELECTROPHILIC AROMATIC SUBSTITUTION

16

ALDEHYDES AND KETONES I. NUCLEOPHILIC ADDITIONS TO THE CARBONYL GROUP

17

ALDEHYDES AND KETONES II. ALDOL REACTIONS

18

CARBOXYLIC ACIDS AND THEIR DERIVATIVES. NUCLEOPHILIC SUBSTITUTION AT THE ACYL CARBON

19

AMINES

20

SYNTHESIS AND REACTIONS OF β-DICARBONYL COMPOUNDS. MORE CHEMISTRY OF ENOLATE IONS

21

PHENOLS AND ARYL HALIDES. NUCLEOPHILIC AROMATIC SUBSTITUTION

22

CARBOHYDRATES

23

LIPIDS

24

AMINO ACIDS AND PROTEINS

25

NUCLEIC ACIDS AND PROTEIN SYNTHESIS

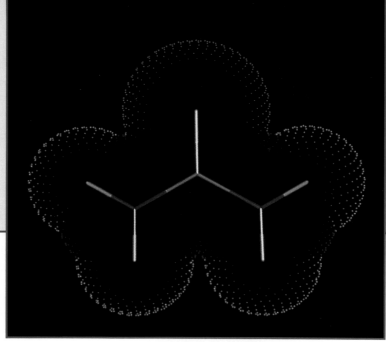

Urea (see Section 1.2A).

CHAPTER

1

CARBON COMPOUNDS AND CHEMICAL BONDS

1.1 INTRODUCTION

Organic chemistry is *the study of the compounds of carbon.* The compounds of carbon constitute the central chemicals of all living things on this planet. Carbon compounds include deoxyribonucleic acids (DNAs), the giant molecules that contain the genetic information for all living species. Carbon compounds make up the proteins of our blood, muscle, and skin. They make up the enzymes that catalyze the reactions that occur in our bodies. Together with oxygen in the air we breathe, carbon compounds in our diets furnish the energy that sustains life.

It was not always so. Considerable evidence indicates that several billion years ago most of the carbon atoms on the earth existed in the form of the gas, CH_4, called methane. This simple organic compound, along with water, ammonia, and hydrogen were the main components of the primordial atmosphere. It has been shown experimentally, that when electrical discharges and other forms of highly energetic radiation pass through this kind of atmosphere, many of these simple compounds become fragmented into highly reactive pieces. These pieces combine into more complex compounds. Compounds called amino acids, formaldehyde, hydrogen cyanide, purines, and pyrimidines can form in this way. It is thought that these, and other compounds produced in the primordial atmosphere in the same way, were carried by rain into the sea until the sea became a vast storehouse containing all of the compounds necessary for the emergence of life. Amino acids apparently reacted with each other to form the first proteins. Molecules of formaldehyde reacted with each other to become sugars, and some of these sugars, together with inorganic phosphates, combined with purines and pyrimidines to become simple molecules of ribonucleic acids (RNAs) and DNA. Molecules of RNA, because they can carry genetic information and can act as enzymes, were apparently instrumental in the emergence of the first primitive self-replicating systems. From these first systems, in a manner far from understood, through the long process of natural selection came humans and all the other living things on this earth today.

Not only are we composed largely of organic compounds, not only are we derived from and nourished by them, *we also live in an Age of Organic Chemistry.* The clothing we wear, whether a natural substance such as wool or cotton or a synthetic such as nylon or a polyester, is made up of carbon compounds. Many of the materials that go into the houses that shelter us are organic. The gasoline that propels our automobiles, the rubber of their tires, and the plastic of their interiors are all organic. Most of the medicines that help us cure diseases and relieve suffering are organic. Organic pesticides help us eliminate many of the agents that spread diseases in both plants and animals.

Organic chemicals are also factors in some of our most serious problems. Many of the organic chemicals introduced into the environment have had consequences far beyond those originally intended. A number of insecticides, widely used for many years, have now been banned because they harm many species other than insects and they pose a danger to humans. Organic compounds called polychlorobiphenyls (PCBs) are responsible for pollution of the Hudson River that may take years to reverse. Organic compounds used as propellants for aerosols have been banned because they threatened to destroy the ozone layer of the outer atmosphere, a layer that protects us from extremely harmful radiation.

Thus for good or bad, organic chemistry is associated with nearly every aspect of our lives. We would be wise to understand it as best we can.

1.2 THE DEVELOPMENT OF ORGANIC CHEMISTRY AS A SCIENCE

Humans have used organic compounds and their reactions for thousands of years. Their first deliberate experience with an organic reaction probably dates from their discovery of fire. The ancient Egyptians used organic compounds (indigo and alizarin) to dye cloth. The famous "royal purple" used by the Phoenicians was also an organic substance, obtained from mollusks. The fermentation of grapes to produce ethyl alcohol and the acidic qualities of "soured wine" are both described in the Bible and were probably known earlier.

As a science, organic chemistry is less than 200 years old. Most historians of science date its origin to the early part of the nineteenth century, a time in which an erroneous belief was dispelled.

1.2A VITALISM

During the 1780s scientists began to distinguish between **organic compounds** and **inorganic compounds.** Organic compounds were defined as compounds that could be obtained from *living organisms.* Inorganic compounds were those that came from *nonliving sources.* Along with this distinction, a belief called "vitalism" grew. According to this idea, the intervention of a "vital force" was necessary for the synthesis of an organic compound. Such synthesis, chemists held then, could take place only in living organisms. It could not take place in the flasks of a chemistry laboratory.

Between 1828 and 1850 a number of compounds that were clearly "organic" were synthesized from sources that were clearly "inorganic." The first of these syntheses was accomplished by Friedrich Wöhler in 1828. Wöhler found that the organic compound urea (a constituent of urine) could be made by evaporating an aqueous solution containing the inorganic compound ammonium cyanate.

$$NH_4^+NCO^- \xrightarrow{heat} H_2N \overset{\overset{\textstyle O}{\|}}{-C} - NH_2$$

Ammonium cyanate   **Urea**

Although "vitalism" disappeared slowly from scientific circles after Wöhler's synthesis, its passing made possible the flowering of the science of organic chemistry that has occurred since 1850.

Despite the demise of vitalism in science, the word "organic" is still used today by some people to mean "coming from living organisms" as in the terms "organic vitamins" and "organic fertilizers." The commonly used term "organic food" means that the food was grown without the use of synthetic fertilizers and pesticides. An "organic vitamin" means to these people that the vitamin was isolated from a natural source and not synthesized by a chemist. While there are sound arguments to be made against using food contaminated with certain pesticides, and while there may be environmental benefits to be obtained from organic farming, it is impossible to argue that "natural" vitamin C, for example, is healthier than the "synthetic" vitamin, since the two substances are identical in all respects. In science today, the study of compounds from living organisms is called biochemistry.

1.2B EMPIRICAL AND MOLECULAR FORMULAS

In the eighteenth and nineteenth centuries extremely important advances were made in the development of qualitative and quantitative methods for analyzing organic substances. In 1784 Antoine Lavoisier first showed that organic compounds were composed primarily of carbon, hydrogen, and oxygen. Between 1811 and 1831, *quantitative* methods for determining the composition of organic compounds were developed by Justus Liebig, J. J. Berzelius, and J. B. A. Dumas. A great confusion was dispelled in 1860 when Stanislao Cannizzaro showed that the earlier hypothesis of Amedeo Avogadro (1811) could be used to distinguish between **empirical** and **molecular formulas.** As a result, many molecules that had appeared earlier to have the same formula were seen to be composed of different numbers of atoms. For example, ethylene, cyclopentane, and cyclohexane all have the same empirical formula: CH_2. However, they have molecular formulas of C_2H_4, C_5H_{10}, and C_6H_{12}, respectively. Appendix A of the Study Guide that accompanies this book contains a review of how empirical and molecular formulas are determined and calculated.

1.3 THE STRUCTURAL THEORY OF ORGANIC CHEMISTRY

Between 1858 and 1861, August Kekulé, Archibald Scott Couper, and Alexander M. Butlerov, working independently, laid the basis for one of the most fundamental theories in chemistry: **the structural theory.** Two central premises are fundamental:

1. The atoms of the elements in organic compounds can form a fixed number of bonds. The measure of this ability is called **valence**. Carbon is *tetravalent;* that is, carbon atoms form four bonds. Oxygen is *divalent;* oxygen atoms form two bonds. Hydrogen and (usually) the halogens are *monovalent;* their atoms form only one bond.

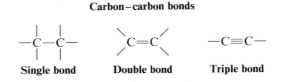

| Carbon atoms are tetravalent | Oxygen atoms are divalent | Hydrogen and halogen atoms are monovalent |

2. A carbon atom can use one or more of its valences to form bonds to other carbon atoms.

Carbon–carbon bonds

| Single bond | Double bond | Triple bond |

In his original publication Couper represented these bonds by lines much in the same way that most of the formulas in this book are drawn. In his textbook (published in 1861), Kekulé gave the science of organic chemistry its modern definition: *a study of the compounds of carbon.*

We can appreciate the importance of the structural theory if we consider now one simple example. These are two compounds that have the *same* molecular formula, C_2H_6O, but these compounds have strikingly different properties (see Table 1.1). One compound, called *dimethyl ether,* is a gas at room temperature; the other compound, called *ethyl alcohol,* is a liquid. Dimethyl ether does not react with sodium; ethyl alcohol does, and the reaction produces hydrogen gas.

TABLE 1.1   Properties of ethyl alcohol and dimethyl ether

	ETHYL ALCOHOL C_2H_6O	DIMETHYL ETHER C_2H_6O
Boiling point (°C)	78.5	−24.9
Melting point (°C)	−117.3	−138
Reaction with sodium	Displaces hydrogen	No reaction

Because the molecular formula for these two compounds is the same, it gives us no basis for understanding the differences between them. The structural theory remedies this situation, however. It does so by giving us **structural formulas** for the two compounds and these structural formulas (Fig. 1.1) are different.

One glance at the structural formulas for these two compounds reveals their difference. The two compounds differ in their **connectivity**: The atoms of ethyl alcohol are connected in a way that is different from those of dimethyl ether. In ethyl alcohol there is a C—C—O linkage; in dimethyl ether the linkage is C—O—C. Ethyl alcohol has a hydrogen atom attached to oxygen; in dimethyl ether all of the hydrogen atoms are attached to carbon. It is the hydrogen atom covalently bonded to oxygen in ethyl alcohol that is displaced when this alcohol reacts with sodium:

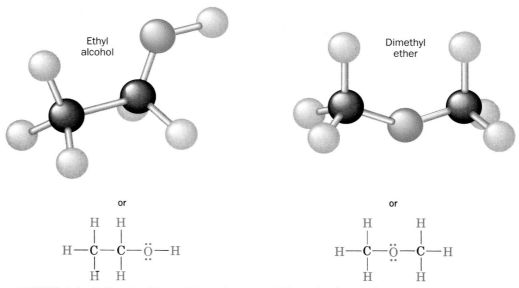

FIGURE 1.1 Ball-and-stick models and structural formulas for ethyl alcohol and dimethyl ether.

$$2\ \text{H—C—C—O—H} + 2\ \text{Na} \longrightarrow 2\ \text{H—C—C—O}^-\text{Na}^+ + \text{H}_2$$

This is just the way water reacts with sodium:

$$2\ \text{H—O—H} + 2\ \text{Na} \longrightarrow 2\ \text{H—O}^-\text{Na}^+ + \text{H}_2$$

Hydrogen atoms that are covalently bonded to carbon are normally unreactive toward sodium. As a result, none of the hydrogen atoms in dimethyl ether is displaced by sodium.

> The hydrogen atom attached to oxygen also accounts for the fact that ethyl alcohol is a liquid at room temperature. As we shall see in Section 2.16, this hydrogen atom allows molecules of ethyl alcohol to form hydrogen bonds to each other and gives ethyl alcohol a boiling point much higher than that of dimethyl ether.

1.3A ISOMERISM. CONSTITUTIONAL ISOMERS

More than 7 million organic compounds have now been isolated in a pure state and have been characterized on the basis of their physical and chemical properties. Additional compounds are added to this list by the tens of thousands each year. A look into *Chemical Abstracts* or Beilstein's *Handbuch der Organischen Chemie,* where known organic compounds are catalogued, shows that there are dozens and sometimes hundreds of *different compounds that have the same molecular formula.* Such compounds are called **isomers.** Different compounds with the same molecular formula are said to be **isomeric,** and this phenomenon is called **isomerism.**

Ethyl alcohol and dimethyl ether are examples of what are now called **constitutional isomers.*** *Constitutional isomers are different compounds that have the same molecular formula, but differ in their connectivity, that is, in the sequence in which their atoms are bonded together.* Constitutional isomers usually have different physical properties (e.g., melting point, boiling point, and density) and different chemical properties. The differences, however, may not always be as large as those between ethyl alcohol and dimethyl ether.

1.3B THE TETRAHEDRAL SHAPE OF METHANE

In 1874, the structural formulas originated by Kekulé, Couper, and Butlerov were expanded into three dimensions by the independent work of J. H. van't Hoff and J. A. Le Bel. van't Hoff and Le Bel proposed that the four bonds of the carbon atom in methane, for example, are arranged in such a way that they would point toward the corners of a regular tetrahedron, the carbon atom being placed at its center (Fig. 1.2). The necessity for knowing the arrangement of the atoms in space, taken together with an understanding of the order in which they are connected, is central to an understanding of organic chemistry, and we shall have much more to say about this later, in Chapters 4 and 5.

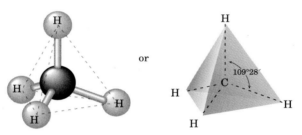

FIGURE 1.2 The tetrahedral structure of methane.

1.4 CHEMICAL BONDS: THE OCTET RULE

The first explanations of the nature of chemical bonds were advanced by G. N. Lewis (of the University of California, Berkeley) and W. Kössel (of the University of Munich) in 1916. Two major types of chemical bonds were proposed.

1. The **ionic** (or **electrovalent**) bond, formed by the transfer of one or more electrons from one atom to another to create ions.
2. The **covalent** bond, a bond that results when atoms share electrons.

The central idea in their work on bonding is that atoms without the electronic configuration of a noble gas generally react to produce such a configuration.

The concepts and explanations that arise from the original propositions of Lewis and Kössel are satisfactory for explanations of many of the problems we deal with in

---

*An older term for isomers of this type was **structural isomers.** The International Union of Pure and Applied Chemistry (IUPAC) now recommends that use of the term "structural" when applied to isomers of this type be abandoned.

organic chemistry today. For this reason we shall review these two types of bonds in more modern terms.

1.4A IONIC BONDS

Atoms may gain or lose electrons and form charged particles called *ions.* An ionic bond is an attractive force between oppositely charged ions. One source of such ions is the interaction of atoms of widely differing electronegativities (Table 1.2). **Electro-negativity measures the ability of an atom to attract electrons.** Notice in Table 1.2 that electronegativity increases as we go across a horizontal row of the periodic table from left to right:

Li Be B C N O F

Increasing electronegativity

and that it decreases as we go down a vertical column:

F
Cl
Br
I

Decreasing
electronegativity

An example of the formation of an ionic bond is the reaction of lithium and fluorine atoms.

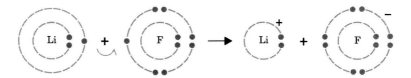

Lithium, a typical metal, has a very low electronegativity; fluorine, a nonmetal, is the most electronegative element of all. The loss of an electron (a negatively charged species) by the lithium atom leaves a lithium cation (Li^+); the gain of an electron by the fluorine atom gives a fluoride anion (F^-). Why do these ions form? In terms of the Lewis–Kössel theory both atoms achieve the electronic configuration of a noble gas by becoming ions. The lithium cation with two electrons in its valence shell is like an

TABLE 1.2   Electronegativities of some of the elements

			H			
			2.1			
Li	Be	B	C	N	O	F
1.0	1.5	2.0	2.5	3.0	3.5	4.0
Na	Mg	Al	Si	P	S	Cl
0.9	1.2	1.5	1.8	2.1	2.5	3.0
K						Br
0.8						2.8

atom of the noble gas helium, and the fluoride anion with eight electrons in its valence shell is like an atom of the noble gas neon. Moreover, crystalline lithium fluoride forms from the individual lithium and fluoride ions. In this process negative fluoride ions become surrounded by positive lithium ions, and positive lithium ions by negative fluoride ions. In this crystalline state, the ions have substantially lower energies than the atoms from which they were formed. Lithium and fluorine are thus "stabilized" when they react to form crystalline lithium fluoride.

We represent the formula for lithium fluoride as LiF, because this is the simplest formula for this ionic compound.

Ionic substances, because of their strong internal electrostatic forces, are usually very high melting solids, often having melting points above 1000 °C. In polar solvents, such as water, the ions are solvated (see Section 2.16E), and such solutions usually conduct an electric current.

Ionic bonds form only when atoms of very different electronegativities transfer electrons to become ions.

1.4B COVALENT BONDS

When two or more atoms of the same or similar electronegativities react, a complete transfer of electrons does not occur. In these instances the atoms achieve noble gas configurations by *sharing electrons. Covalent* bonds form between the atoms, and the products are called *molecules.* Molecules may be represented by electron-dot formulas or, more conveniently, by dash formulas where each dash represents a pair of electrons shared by two atoms. Some examples are shown here. These formulas

$$H_2 \qquad H\cdot + \cdot H \longrightarrow H\!:\!H \quad \text{or} \quad H\!-\!H$$

$$Cl_2 \qquad :\!\ddot{C}l\cdot + \cdot\ddot{C}l\!: \longrightarrow :\!\ddot{C}l\!:\!\ddot{C}l\!: \quad \text{or} \quad :\!\ddot{C}l\!-\!\ddot{C}l\!:$$

$$CH_4 \qquad \cdot\dot{C}\cdot + 4\,H\cdot \longrightarrow \begin{matrix} H \\ H\!:\!\ddot{C}\!:\!H \\ \ddot{H} \end{matrix} \quad \text{or} \quad \begin{matrix} H \\ | \\ H\!-\!C\!-\!H \\ | \\ H \end{matrix}$$

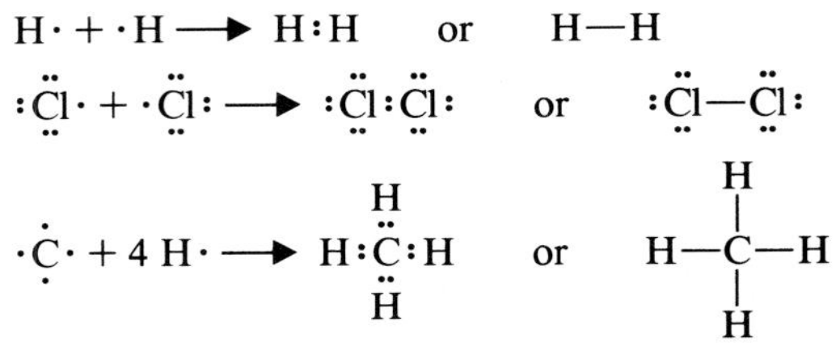

are often called **Lewis structures;** in writing them we show only the electrons of the valence shell.

In certain cases, multiple covalent bonds are formed; for example,

$$N_2 \qquad :\!N\!:\!:\!N\!: \quad \text{or} \quad :\!N\!\equiv\!N\!:$$

and ions themselves may contain covalent bonds.

$$\overset{+}{N}H_4 \qquad \begin{matrix} H \\ \ddot{} + \\ H\!:\!\overset{}{N}\!:\!H \\ \ddot{H} \end{matrix} \quad \text{or} \quad \begin{matrix} H \\ | \\ H\!-\!\overset{+}{N}\!-\!H \\ | \\ H \end{matrix}$$

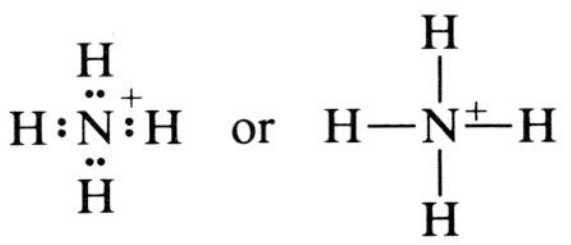

1.5 WRITING LEWIS STRUCTURES

When we write Lewis structures (electron-dot formulas) we assemble the molecule or ion from the constituent atoms showing only the valence electrons (i.e., the electrons of the outermost shell). By having the atoms share or transfer electrons, we try to give each atom the electronic configuration of a noble gas. For example, we give hydrogen atoms two electrons because by doing so we give them the structure of helium. We give carbon, nitrogen, oxygen, and fluorine atoms eight electrons because by doing this we give them the electronic configuration of neon. The number of valence electrons of an atom can be obtained from the periodic table because it is equal to the group number of the atom. Carbon, for example, is in Group **IVA** and it has four valence electrons; fluorine, in Group **VIIA** has seven; hydrogen in Group **IA**, has one.

Sample Problem

Write the Lewis structure of CH_3F.

Answer:

1. We find the total number of valence electrons of all the atoms:

$$4 + 3(1) + 7 = 14$$
$$\uparrow \quad \uparrow \quad \uparrow$$
$$C \quad H_3 \quad F$$

2. We use pairs of electrons to form bonds between all atoms that are bonded to each other. We represent these bonding pairs with lines. In our example this requires four pairs of electrons (8 of our 14 valence electrons).

$$\begin{array}{c} H \\ | \\ H-C-F \\ | \\ H \end{array}$$

3. We then add the remaining electrons in pairs so as to give each hydrogen 2 electrons (a duet) and every other atom 8 electrons (an octet). In our example, we assign the remaining 6 valence electrons to the fluorine atom in three nonbonding pairs.

$$\begin{array}{c} H \\ | \\ H-C-\ddot{\underset{\cdot\cdot}{F}}\colon \\ | \\ H \end{array}$$

If the structure is an ion, we add or subtract electrons to give it the proper charge.

Sample Problem

Write the Lewis structure for the chlorate ion (ClO_3^-).

Answer:

1. We find the total number of valence electrons of all the atoms including the extra electron needed to give the ion a negative charge:

$$7 + 3(6) + 1 = 26$$

Cl O_3 e^-

2. We use three pairs of electrons to form bonds between the chlorine atom
    and the three oxygen atoms:

```
        O
        |
    O — Cl — O
```

3. We then add the remaining 20 electrons in pairs so as to give each atom an
    octet.

$$\left[\begin{array}{c} :\ddot{O}: \\ | \\ :\ddot{O} - \overset{}{Cl} - \ddot{O}: \end{array} \right]^-$$

If necessary, we use multiple bonds to give atoms the noble gas configuration. The
carbonate ion ($CO_3{}^{2-}$) illustrates this.

$$\left[\begin{array}{c} :\ddot{O} \\ \| \\ C \\ \diagup \quad \diagdown \\ :\ddot{O} \quad \ddot{O}: \end{array} \right]^{2-}$$

The organic molecules ethene (C_2H_4) and ethyne (C_2H_2) have a double and triple
bond, respectively.

$$\begin{array}{cc} H & H \\ \diagdown \quad \diagup \\ C = C \\ \diagup \quad \diagdown \\ H & H \end{array} \quad \text{and} \quad H - C \equiv C - H$$

1.6 EXCEPTIONS TO THE OCTET RULE

Atoms share electrons, not just to obtain the configuration of an inert gas, but
because sharing electrons produces increased electron density between the positive
nuclei. The resulting attractive forces of nuclei for electrons is the "glue" that holds
the atoms together (cf. Section 1.11). Elements of the second period of the periodic
table can form only four bonds (i. e., have eight electrons around them) because these
elements have only $2s$ and $2p$ orbitals available for bonding and a total of eight
electrons fills these orbitals (Section 1.11). The octet rule, therefore, only applies to
these elements, and even here, as we shall see in compounds of boron, it does not
apply strictly. Elements of the third period, and beyond, have d orbitals that can be
used for bonding. These elements can accommodate more than eight electrons in
their valence shell and therefore can form more than four covalent bonds. Examples
are compounds such as PCl_5 and SF_6.

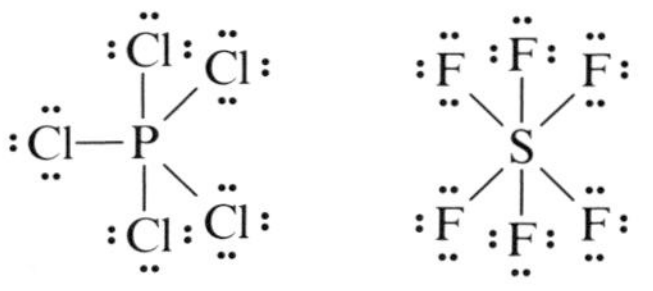

$$
\begin{array}{cc}
\ddot{\underset{..}{Cl}} : \ddot{Cl}: & \ddot{F}\ :\ddot{F}:\ \ddot{F}: \\
:\overset{|}{\underset{..}{Cl}}{-}\overset{\diagup}{P} & \diagdown\overset{|}{S}\diagup \\
:\underset{..}{Cl}:\ \ddot{\underset{..}{Cl}}: & :\ddot{F}\ :\ddot{F}:\ \ddot{F}:
\end{array}
$$

Sample Problem

Write a Lewis structure for the sulfate ion (SO_4^{2-}).

Answer:

1. We find the total number of valence electrons including the extra 2 electrons needed to give the ion a negative charge:

$$
\underset{\underset{S}{\uparrow}}{6} + \underset{\underset{O_4}{\uparrow}}{4(6)} + \underset{\underset{2e^-}{\uparrow}}{2} = 32
$$

2. We use pairs to form bonds between the sulfur atom and the four oxygen atoms:

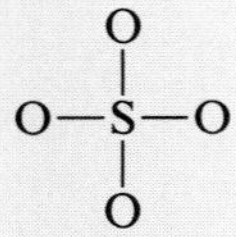

$$
\begin{array}{c}
O \\
| \\
O{-}S{-}O \\
| \\
O
\end{array}
$$

3. We add the remaining 24 electrons as unshared pairs on oxygen atoms and as double bonds between the sulfur atom and two oxygen atoms. This gives each oxygen 8 electrons and the sulfur atom 12.

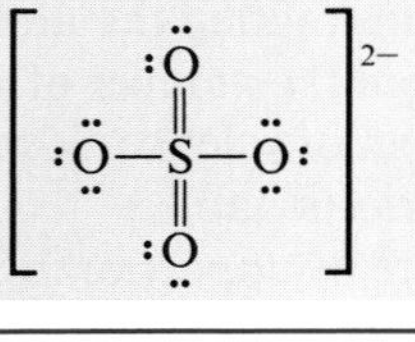

$$
\left[
\begin{array}{c}
:\ddot{O} \\
\| \\
:\ddot{O}{-}S{-}\ddot{O}: \\
\| \\
:\ddot{O}
\end{array}
\right]^{2-}
$$

Some highly reactive molecules or ions have atoms with fewer than eight electrons in their outer shell. An example is boron trifluoride (BF_3). In the BF_3 molecule the central boron atom has only six electrons around it.

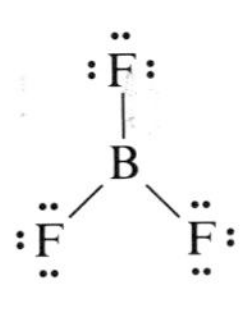

$$
\begin{array}{c}
:\ddot{F}: \\
| \\
B \\
\diagup\ \ \diagdown \\
:\ddot{F}\qquad\ddot{F}:
\end{array}
$$

Finally, one point needs to be stressed: Before we can write some Lewis structures, *we must know how the atoms are connected to each other.* Consider nitric acid, for example. Even though the formula for nitric acid is often written HNO_3, the hydrogen is actually connected to an oxygen, not to the nitrogen. The structure is $HONO_2$ and not HNO_3. Thus the correct Lewis structure is

$$H-\ddot{\underset{\cdot\cdot}{O}}-N\overset{\displaystyle\overset{O}{\diagup}}{\underset{\underset{\cdot\cdot}{\ddot{O}}}{\diagdown}} \quad \text{and not} \quad H-N-\ddot{\underset{\cdot\cdot}{O}}-\ddot{\underset{\cdot\cdot}{O}}:$$

This knowledge comes ultimately from experiments. If you have forgotten the structures of some of the common inorganic molecules and ions (such as those listed in Problem 1.1), this may be a good time for a review of the relevant portions of your general chemistry text.

Problem 1.1

Write Lewis structures for each of the following molecules or ions.

(a) HBr   (e) H_2O_2 (i) NF_3 (m) NH_4Cl ($NH_4^+Cl^-$)

(b) Br_2 (f) SiH_4 (j) CH_3Cl (n) NaOH (Na^+OH^-)

(c) CO_2 (g) NH_3 (k) H_2O (o) H_2SO_4

(d) CH_4 (h) PCl_3 (l) OH^- (p) HSO_4^-

1.7 FORMAL CHARGE

When we write Lewis structures, it is often convenient to assign unit positive or negative charges, called **formal charges,** to certain atoms in the molecule or ion. This is nothing more than a bookkeeping method for electrical charges, because *the arithmetic sum of all of the formal charges equals the total charge on the molecule or ion.*

We calculate formal charges on individual atoms **by subtracting the number of valence electrons assigned to an atom in its bonded state from the number of valence electrons it has as a neutral free atom.** (Recall that the number of valence electrons in a neutral free atom is equal to its **group number** on the periodic table.)

We assign valence electrons to atoms in the bonded state by apportioning them. **We divide shared electrons equally between the atoms that share them and we assign unshared pairs to the atom that possesses them.**

Consider first the ammonium ion, an ion that has no unshared pairs. We divide all of the valence electrons equally between the atoms that share them. Each hydrogen is assigned *one electron* (e^-) and we subtract this from *one* (the number of valence electrons in a neutral hydrogen atom) to give a formal charge of 0 for each hydrogen atom. The nitrogen atom is assigned *four electrons.* We subtract this from *five* (the number of valence electrons in a neutral nitrogen atom) to give a formal charge of $+1$. In effect, we say that because the nitrogen atom in the ammonium ion lacks one electron when compared to a neutral nitrogen atom (in which the number of protons and electrons are equal) it has a formal charge of $+1$.*

---

* An alternative method for calculating formal charge is to use the equation:

$$F = Z - S/2 - U$$

where F is the formal charge, Z is the group number, S equals the number of shared electrons, and U is the number of unshared electrons.

1.7 FORMAL CHARGE

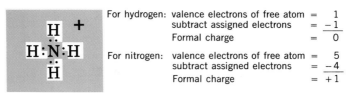

For hydrogen: valence electrons of free atom = 1
subtract assigned electrons = −1
Formal charge = 0

For nitrogen: valence electrons of free atom = 5
subtract assigned electrons = −4
Formal charge = +1

Charge on ion = (4)(0) + 1 = +1

Let us next consider the nitrate ion (NO_3^-), an ion that has oxygen atoms with unshared electron pairs. Here we find that the nitrogen atom has a formal charge of +1, that two oxygen atoms have formal charges of −1, and that one oxygen has a formal charge equal to 0.

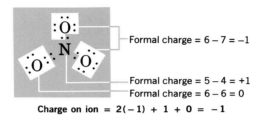

Formal charge = 6 − 7 = −1

Formal charge = 5 − 4 = +1
Formal charge = 6 − 6 = 0

Charge on ion = 2(−1) + 1 + 0 = −1

Molecules, of course, have no net electrical charge. Molecules, by definition, are neutral. Therefore, the sum of the formal charges on each atom making up a molecule must be zero. Consider the following examples:

Ammonia

H—N̈—H   or   H:N̈:H

Formal charge = 5 − 5 = 0
Formal charge = 1 − 1 = 0

Charge on molecule = 0 + 3(0) = 0

Water

H—Ö—H   or   H:Ö:H

Formal charge = 6 − 6 = 0
Formal charge = 1 − 1 = 0

Charge on molecule = 0 + 2(0) = 0

Problem 1.2

Calculate the formal charge on each atom, and verify the total charge on the molecule or ion, for each of the following species:

(a) BH_4^-
(b) OH^-
(c) BF_4^-
(d) H_3O^+

(e) CO_3^{2-}
(f) :CH_3^- (a carbanion)
(g) CH_3^+ (a carbocation)
(h) ·CH_3 (a free radical)

(i) :CH_2 (a carbene)
(j) :NH_2^-

1.7A SUMMARY OF FORMAL CHARGES

With this background it should now be clear that each time an oxygen atom of the type —$\ddot{\text{O}}$: appears in a molecule or ion it will have a formal charge of −1, and that each time an oxygen atom of the type =$\ddot{\text{O}}$: or —$\ddot{\text{O}}$— appears it will have a formal charge of 0. Similarly; —$\overset{|}{\underset{|}{\text{N}}}$— will be +1, and —$\overset{}{\underset{|}{\text{N}}}$— will be zero. It is much easier to memorize these common structures than to calculate their formal charges each time they are encountered. These common structures are summarized in Table 1.3.

TABLE 1.3   A summary of formal charges

GROUP	FORMAL CHARGE OF +1			FORMAL CHARGE OF 0				FORMAL CHARGE OF −1		
3				—B—				—$\overset{|}{\underset{|}{\text{B}}}\underline{}$		
4	—$\overset{+}{\text{C}}$—	=$\overset{+}{\text{C}}$	≡$\overset{+}{\text{C}}$	—$\overset{|}{\underset{|}{\text{C}}}$—	=C—	≡C—		—$\overset{\cdot\cdot}{\text{C}}\underline{}$	=$\ddot{\text{C}}$:⁻	≡C:⁻
5	—$\overset{|}{\text{N}}\overset{+}{\underset{|}{}}$—	=$\overset{+}{\text{N}}$—	≡$\overset{+}{\text{N}}$—	—$\overset{\cdot\cdot}{\underset{|}{\text{N}}}$—	=$\ddot{\text{N}}$—	≡N:		—$\overset{\cdot\cdot}{\underset{\cdot\cdot}{\text{N}}}\underline{}$	=$\ddot{\text{N}}$:⁻	
6	—$\overset{\cdot\cdot}{\text{O}}\overset{+}{\underset{|}{}}$—	=$\overset{}{\underset{+}{\text{O}}}$—	—$\ddot{\text{O}}$—	=$\ddot{\text{O}}$:				—$\ddot{\text{O}}$:⁻		
7	—$\overset{\cdot\cdot}{\underset{\cdot\cdot}{\text{X}}}\overset{+}{\underline{}}$			—$\overset{\cdot\cdot}{\underset{\cdot\cdot}{\text{X}}}$: (X = F, Cl, Br, or I)	:$\ddot{\text{X}}$:⁻					

Problem 1.3

Using the chart given in Table 1.3, determine the formal charge on each colored atom of the following molecules and ions. (*Remember:* With respect to formal charge, —$\ddot{\text{O}}$— is equal to =$\ddot{\text{O}}$:, —$\overset{\cdot\cdot}{\underset{|}{\text{N}}}$— is equal to ≡N:, and so on.)

(a) 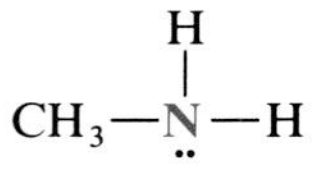 CH_3—$\overset{\text{H}}{\underset{\cdot\cdot}{\text{N}}}$—H

(an amine)

(d) 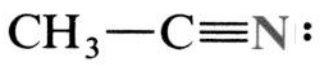 CH_3—C≡N:

(a nitrile)

(g) 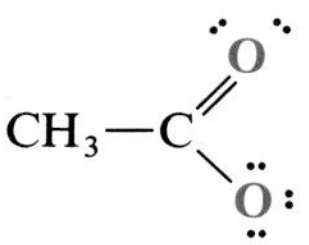 CH_3—C$\overset{\ddot{\text{O}}}{\underset{\ddot{\text{O}}:}{}}$

(a carboxylate ion)

(b)  CH_3—$\ddot{\text{N}}$=$\ddot{\text{O}}$:

(a nitroso compound)

(e) 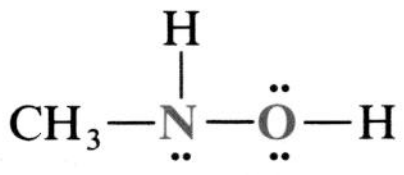 CH_3—$\overset{\text{H}}{\underset{\cdot\cdot}{\text{N}}}$—$\ddot{\text{O}}$—H

(a hydroxylamine)

(h) CH_3CH_2—$\overset{\cdot\cdot}{\underset{\text{H}}{\text{O}}}$—H

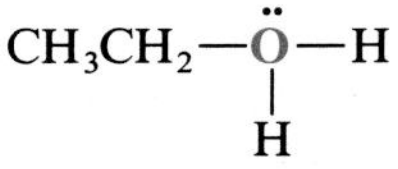

(a protonated alcohol)

(c) 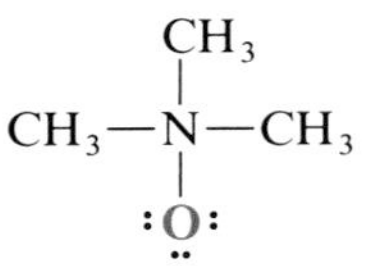 $CH_3-\overset{\overset{\textstyle CH_3}{|}}{\underset{\underset{\textstyle :\ddot{O}:}{|}}{N}}-CH_3$ 　　(f) $CH_3-N\overset{\nearrow\ddot{\ddot{O}}}{\underset{\searrow\underset{\cdot\cdot}{\ddot{O}}\cdot\cdot}{}}$ 　　(i) $CH_3CH\overset{}{\underset{\underset{\cdot}{Br}}{-}}CHCH_3$

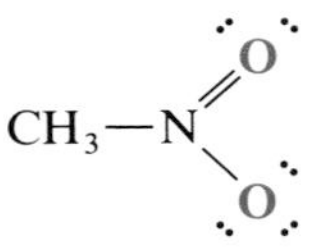

(an amine oxide) 　　　**(a nitro compound)** 　　　**(a bromonium ion)**

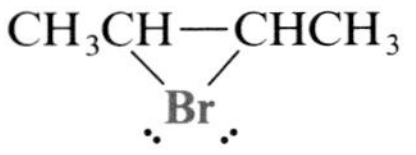

1.8 RESONANCE

One problem with Lewis structures is that they impose an artificial **location** on the electrons. As a result, more than one *equivalent* Lewis structure can be written for many molecules and ions. Consider, for example, the carbonate ion (CO_3^{2-}). We can write three *different* but *equivalent* structures, **1–3.**

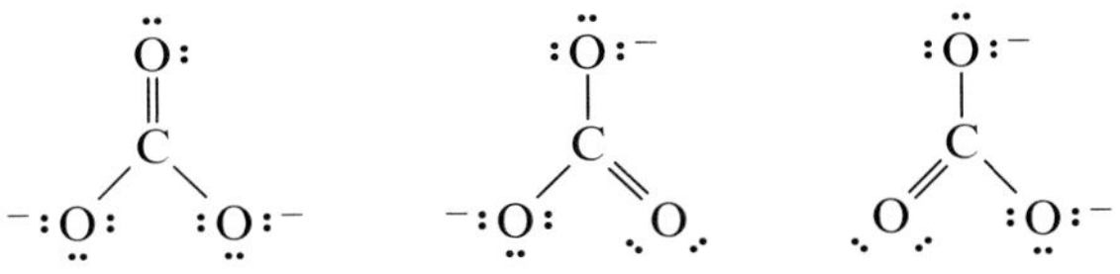

Notice two important features of these structures. First, each atom has the noble gas configuration. Second, *and this is especially important,* we can convert one structure into any other by *changing only the positions of the electrons.* We do not need to change the relative positions of the atomic nuclei. For example, if we move the electron pairs in the manner indicated by the curved arrows* in structure **1,** we change structure **1** into structure **2:**

In a similar way we can change structure **2** into structure **3:**

Structures **1–3,** although not identical, *are equivalent.* None of them, however, fits important data about the carbonate ion.

---

* The use of curved arrows is described in more detail later (Section 3.2). We should point out now that the curved arrows show movement of electrons, not atoms, and that the tail of the arrow begins at the current position of the electron pair, while the head of the arrow shows the new location.

X-ray studies have shown that carbon–oxygen double bonds are shorter than single bonds. The same kind of study of the carbonate ion shows in addition that all of its carbon–oxygen bonds are of equal length. One is not shorter than the others as would be expected from the representations **1, 2,** or **3.** Clearly none of the three structures agrees with this evidence. In each structure, **1–3,** one carbon–oxygen bond is a double bond and the other two are single bonds. None of the structures, therefore, is correct. How, then, should we represent the carbonate ion?

One way is through a theory called **resonance theory.** This theory states that whenever a molecule or ion can be represented by two or more Lewis structures *that differ only in the positions of the electrons,* two things will be true:

1. None of these structures, which we call **resonance structures** or **resonance contributors,** will be a correct representation for the molecule. None will be in complete accord with the physical or chemical properties of the substance.

2. The actual molecule or ion will be better represented by a *hybrid of these structures.*

Resonance structures, then, are not structures for the actual molecule or ion; they exist only in theory. As such they can never be isolated. No single contributor adequately represents the molecule or ion. In resonance theory we view the carbonate ion, which is, of course, a real entity, as having a structure that is a **hybrid** of these three **hypothetical** resonance structures.

What would a hybrid of structures **1–3** be like? Look at the structures and look especially at a particular carbon–oxygen bond, say, the one at the top. This carbon–oxygen bond is a double bond in one structure (**1**) and a single bond in the other two (**2** and **3**). The actual carbon–oxygen bond, since it is a hybrid, must be something in between a double bond and a single bond. Because the carbon–oxygen bond is a single bond in two of the structures and a double bond in only one it must be more like a single bond than a double bond. It must be like a one- and one-third bond. We could call it a partial double bond. And, of course, what we have just said about any one carbon–oxygen bond will be equally true of the other two. Thus all of the carbon–oxygen bonds of the carbonate ion are partial double bonds, and *all are equivalent.* All of them *should be* the same length, and this is exactly what experiments tell us. They are all 1.28 Å long, a distance which is intermediate between that of a carbon–oxygen single bond (1.43 Å) and that of a carbon–oxygen double bond (1.20 Å).

One other important point: By convention, when we draw resonance structures, we connect them by double-headed arrows to indicate clearly that they are hypothetical, not real. For the carbonate ion we write them this way:

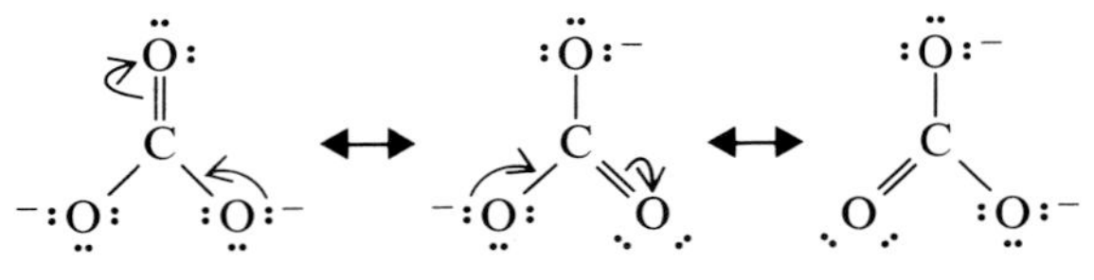

We should not let these arrows, or the word "resonance," mislead us into thinking that the carbonate ion fluctuates between one structure and another. These structures exist only on paper; therefore, the carbonate ion cannot fluctuate among them. It is also important to distinguish between resonance and **an equilibrium.** In an equilibrium between two, or more, species, it is quite correct to think of different structures and moving (or fluctuating) atoms, *but not in the case of resonance* (as in the carbonate ion). Here the atoms do not move, and the "structures" exist only on paper. An equilibrium is indicated by $\rightleftharpoons$ and resonance by $\longleftrightarrow$.

How can we write the structure of the carbonate ion in a way that will indicate its actual structure? We may do two things: we may write all of the resonance structures as we have just done and let the reader mentally fashion the hybrid or we may write a non-Lewis structure that attempts to represent the hybrid. For the carbonate ion we might do the following:

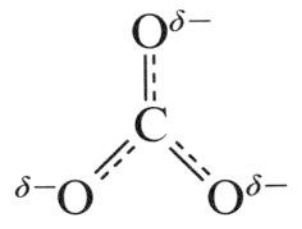

The bonds are indicated by a combination of a solid line and a dashed line. This is to indicate that the bonds are something in between a single bond and a double bond. As a rule, we use a solid line whenever a bond appears in all structures, and a dashed line when a bond exists in one or more but not all. We also place a $\delta-$ (read partial minus) beside each oxygen to indicate that something less than a full negative charge resides on each oxygen atom. (In this instance each oxygen atom has two thirds of a full negative charge.)

Sample Problem

The following is one way of writing the structure of the nitrate ion.

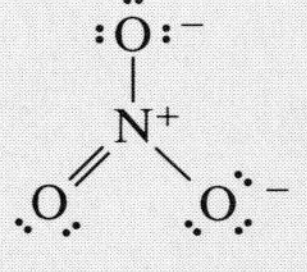

However, considerable physical evidence indicates that all three nitrogen–oxygen bonds are equivalent and that they have a bond distance between that expected for a nitrogen–oxygen single bond and a nitrogen–oxygen double bond. Explain this in terms of resonance theory.

Answer:

We recognize that if we move the electron pairs in the following way, we can write three *different* but *equivalent* structures for the nitrate ion:

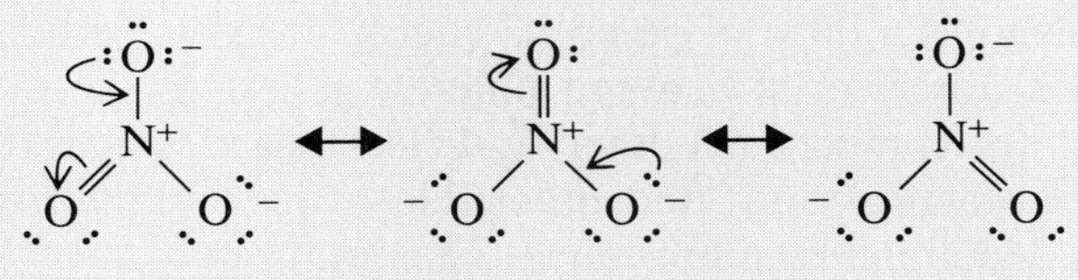

Since these structures differ from one another *only in the positions of their electrons,* they are *resonance structures* or *resonance contributors*. As such, no single structure taken alone will adequately represent the nitrate ion. The actual molecule will be best represented by a *hybrid of these three structures*. We might write this hybrid in the following way to indicate that all of the bonds are equivalent and that they are more than single bonds and less than double bonds. We also indicate that each oxygen atom bears an equal partial negative charge. This charge distribution corresponds to what we find experimentally.

$$
\begin{array}{c}
O^{\delta-} \\
\| \\
N^{+} \\
\delta-O \diagdown\ \diagup O^{\delta-}
\end{array}
$$

Hybrid structure for the nitrate ion

1.9 ENERGY CHANGES

Since we will be talking frequently about the energies of chemical systems, perhaps we should pause here for a brief review. *Energy* is defined as the capacity to do work. The two fundamental types of energy are **kinetic energy** and **potential energy.**

Kinetic energy is the energy an object has because of its motion; it equals one half the object's mass multiplied by the square of its velocity (i.e., $\frac{1}{2} mv^2$).

Potential energy is stored energy. It exists only when an attractive or repulsive force exists between objects. Two balls attached to each other by a spring can have their potential energy increased when the spring is stretched or compressed (Fig. 1.3). If the spring is stretched, an attractive force will exist between the balls. If it is compressed, a repulsive force will exist. In either instance releasing the balls will cause the potential energy (stored energy) of the balls to be converted into kinetic energy (energy of motion).

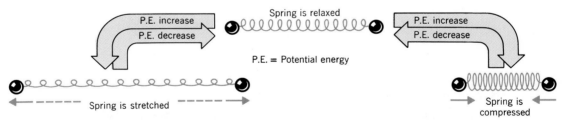

FIGURE 1.3 Potential energy (P.E.) exists between objects that either attract or repel each other. When the spring is either stretched or compressed, the P.E. of the two balls increases. (Adapted with permission from J. E. Brady and G. E. Humiston, *General Chemistry: Principles and Structure,* 1st ed., Wiley, New York, p. 18.)

Chemical energy is a form of potential energy. It exists because attractive and repulsive electrical forces exist between different pieces of the molecules. Nuclei attract electrons, nuclei repel each other, and electrons repel each other.

It is usually impractical (and often impossible) to describe the *absolute* amount of potential energy contained by a substance. Thus we usually think in terms of their *relative potential energies.* We say that one system has *more* or *less* potential energy than another.

Another term that chemists frequently use in this context is the term **stability** or **relative stability.** ***The relative stability of a system is inversely related to its relative potential energy.*** The *more* potential energy an object has, the *less stable* it is. Consider, as an example, the relative potential energy and the relative stability of snow when it lies high on a mountainside and when it lies serenely in the valley below. Because of the attractive force of gravity, the snow high on the mountain *has greater potential energy and is much less stable* than the snow in the valley. This greater potential energy of the snow on the mountainside can become converted to the enormous kinetic energy of an avalanche. By contrast, the snow in the valley with its lower potential energy and with its greater stability is incapable of releasing such energy.

1.9A POTENTIAL ENERGY AND COVALENT BONDS

Atoms and molecules possess potential energy — often called chemical energy — that can be released as heat when they react. Because heat is associated with molecular motion, this release of heat results from a change from potential energy to kinetic energy.

From the standpoint of covalent bonds, the state of greatest potential energy is the state of free atoms, the state in which the atoms are not bonded to each other at all. This is true because the formation of a chemical bond is always accompanied by the lowering of the potential energy of the atoms (cf. Fig. 1.9). Consider as an example the formation of hydrogen molecules from hydrogen atoms:

$$H \cdot + H \cdot \longrightarrow H{-}H + 104 \text{ kcal mol}^{-1} \quad (435 \text{ kJ mol}^{-1})*$$

The potential energy of the atoms decreases by 104 kcal mol^{-1} as the covalent bonds form. This potential energy change is illustrated graphically in Fig. 1.4.

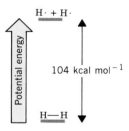

FIGURE 1.4 The relative potential energies of hydrogen atoms and hydrogen molecules.

A convenient way to represent the relative potential energies of molecules is in terms of their relative **enthalpies** or **heat contents,** H. (*Enthalpy* comes from the German word *enthalten* meaning to contain.) The difference in relative enthalpies of reactants and products in a chemical change is called the enthalpy change and is symbolized by $\Delta H°$. [The Δ (delta) in front of a quantity usually means the difference, or change, in the quantity. The superscript ° indicates that the measurement is made under standard conditions.]

By convention, the sign of $\Delta H°$ for **exothermic** reactions (those evolving heat) is negative. **Endothermic** reactions (those that absorb heat) have a positive $\Delta H°$. The heat of reaction, $\Delta H°$, measures the change in enthalpy of the atoms of the reactants as they are converted to products. For an exothermic reaction the atoms have a

---

*A kilocalorie of energy (1000 cal) is the amount of energy in the form of heat required to raise by 1 °C the temperature of 1 kg (1000 g) of water at 15 °C. The unit of energy in SI units is the joule, J, and 1 cal = 4.184 J. (Thus 1 kcal = 4.184 kJ.)

smaller enthalpy as products than they do as reactants. For endothermic reactions, the reverse is true.

We express the exothermic reaction of hydrogen atoms to form hydrogen molecules this way:

$$H \cdot + H \cdot \longrightarrow H—H \qquad \Delta H° = -104 \text{ kcal mol}^{-1} \qquad (-435 \text{ kJ mol}^{-1})$$

The reverse reaction is endothermic. Energy has to be supplied to break the covalent bonds:

$$H—H \longrightarrow H \cdot + H \cdot \qquad \Delta H° = +104 \text{ kcal mol}^{-1} \qquad (+435 \text{ kJ mol}^-)$$

The covalent bond of a fluorine molecule is weaker than that of a hydrogen molecule. Less energy is released when it forms and, consequently, less energy is required to break it:

$$F \cdot + F \cdot \longrightarrow F—F \qquad \Delta H° = -38 \text{ kcal mol}^{-1} \qquad (-159 \text{ kJ mol}^{-1})$$
$$F—F \longrightarrow F \cdot + F \cdot \qquad \Delta H° = +38 \text{ kcal mol}^{-1} \qquad (+159 \text{ kJ mol}^{-1})$$

The bond of hydrogen fluoride is very strong:

$$H \cdot + F \cdot \longrightarrow H—F \qquad \Delta H° = -136 \text{ kcal mol}^{-1} \qquad (-569 \text{ kJ mol}^{-1})$$
$$H—F \longrightarrow H \cdot + F \cdot \qquad \Delta H° = +136 \text{ kcal mol}^{-1} \qquad (+569 \text{ kJ mol}^{-1})$$

When molecules react with each other, the reaction can be either exothermic or endothermic. Generally speaking, if the bonds of the products are collectively stronger than those of the reactants, the reaction will be exothermic. An example is the reaction of hydrogen with fluorine:

$$H—H + F—F \longrightarrow 2 H—F \qquad \Delta H° = -130 \text{ kcal mol}^{-1} \qquad (-544 \text{ kJ mol}^{-1})$$

Because the bonds of the H—F molecules are collectively stronger than those of hydrogen and fluorine, the reaction evolves heat. The heat of reaction or enthalpy change is negative. The product molecules with their stronger bonds have lower potential energy than those of the reactants (Fig. 1.5).

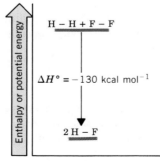

FIGURE 1.5 The energy change that accompanies the reaction $H_2 + F_2 \longrightarrow 2$ HF.

1.10 QUANTUM MECHANICS

In 1926 a new theory of atomic and molecular structure was advanced independently and almost simultaneously by three men: Erwin Schrödinger, Werner Heisenberg, and Paul Dirac. This theory, called **wave mechanics** by Schrödinger or **quantum mechanics** by Heisenberg, has become the basis from which we derive our modern understanding of bonding in molecules.

The formulation of quantum mechanics that Schrödinger advanced is the form that is most often used by chemists. In Schrödinger's publication the motion of the electrons is described in terms that take into account the wave nature of the electron.* Schrödinger developed a way to convert the mathematical expression for the total energy of the system consisting of one proton and one electron — the hydrogen atom — into another expression called a **wave equation.** This equation is then solved to yield not one but a series of solutions called **wave functions.**

Wave functions are most often denoted by the Greek letter psi (ψ), and each wave function (ψ function) corresponds to a different state for the electron. Corresponding to each state, and calculable from the wave equation for the state, is a particular energy.

Each state is a sublevel where one or two electrons can reside. *The solutions to the wave equation for a hydrogen atom can also be used* (with appropriate modifications) *to give sublevels for the electrons of higher elements.*

A wave equation is simply a tool for calculating two important properties: These are the energy associated with the state and the relative probability of an electron residing at particular places in the sublevel (Section 1.11). When the value of a wave equation is calculated for a particular point in space relative to the nucleus, the result may be a positive number or a negative number (or zero). These signs are sometimes called **phase signs.** They are characteristic of all equations that describe waves. We do not need to go into the mathematics of waves here, but a simple analogy will help us understand the nature of these phase signs.

Imagine a wave moving across a lake. As it moves along, the wave has crests and troughs; that is, it has regions where the wave rises above the average level of the lake or falls below it (Fig. 1.6). Now, if an equation were to be written for this wave, the wave function (ψ) would be plus (+) in regions where the wave is above the average level of the lake (i.e., in crests) and it would be minus (−) in regions where the wave is below the average level (i.e., in troughs). The relative magnitude of ψ (called the

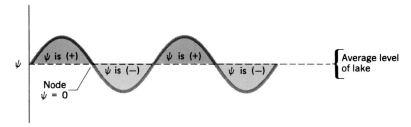

FIGURE 1.6 A wave moving across a lake is viewed along a slice through the lake. For this wave the wave function, ψ, is plus (+) in crests and minus (−) in troughs. At the average level of the lake it is zero; these places are called nodes.

*The idea that the electron has the properties of a wave as well as those of a particle was proposed by Louis de Broglie in 1923.

amplitude) will be related to the distance the wave rises above or falls below the average level of the lake. At the places where the wave is exactly at the average level of the lake, the wave function will be zero. Such a place is called a **node.**

One other characteristic of waves is their ability to reinforce each other or to interfere with one another. Imagine two waves approaching each other as they move across a lake. If the waves meet so that a crest meets a crest, that is, so that *waves of the same phase sign meet each other,* the waves **reinforce** each other, they add together, and the resulting wave is larger than either individual wave. On the other hand, if a crest meets a trough, that is, if waves of opposite sign meet, the waves **interfere** with each other, they subtract from each other, and the resulting wave is smaller than either individual wave. (If the two waves of opposite sign meet in precisely the right way, complete cancellation can occur.)

The wave functions that describe the motion of an electron in an atom or molecule are, of course, different from the equations that describe waves moving across lakes. And when dealing with the electron we should be careful not to take analogies like this too far. Electron wave functions, however, are like the equations that describe water waves in that they have phase signs and nodes, and *they undergo reinforcement and interference.*

1.11 ATOMIC ORBITALS

For a short time after Schrödinger's proposal in 1926, a precise physical interpretation for the electron wave function eluded early practitioners of quantum mechanics. It remained for Max Born, a few months later, to point out that the square of ψ *could* be given a precise physical meaning. According to Born, ψ^2 for a particular location (x,y,z) expresses the **probability** of finding an electron at that particular location in space. If ψ^2 is large in a unit volume of space, the probability of finding an electron in that volume is great — we say that the **electron probability density** is large. Conversely if ψ^2 for some other unit volume of space is small, the probability of finding an electron there is low.* Plots of ψ^2 in three dimensions generate the shapes of the familiar s, p, and d atomic orbitals, which we use as our models for atomic structure.

The f orbitals are practically never used in organic chemistry, and we shall not concern ourselves with them in this book. The d orbitals will be discussed briefly later when we discuss compounds in which d orbital interactions are important. The s and p orbitals are, by far, the most important in the formation of organic molecules and, at this point, we shall limit our discussion to them.

An orbital is a region of space where the probability of finding an electron is large. The shapes of s and p orbitals are shown in Fig. 1.7. There is a finite, but very small, probability of finding an electron at greater distances from the nucleus. The volumes that we typically use to illustrate an orbital are those volumes that would contain the electron 90–95% of the time.

Both the $1s$ and $2s$ orbitals are spheres (as are all higher s orbitals). The sign of the wave function, ψ_{1s}, is positive (+) over the entire $1s$ orbital (Fig. 1.7). The $2s$ orbital contains a nodal surface, that is, an area where $\psi = 0$. In the inner portion of the $2s$ orbital, ψ_{2s} is negative.

---

* Integration of ψ^2 over all space must equal 1; that is, the probability of finding an electron somewhere in all of space is 100%.

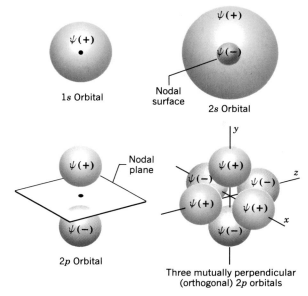

FIGURE 1.7 The shapes of some *s* and *p* orbitals.

The 2*p* orbitals have the shape of two almost-touching spheres. The phase sign of the wave function, ψ_{2p}, is positive in one lobe (or sphere) and negative in the other. A nodal plane separates the two lobes of a *p* orbital, and the three *p* orbitals are arranged in space so that their axes are mutually perpendicular.

You should not associate the sign of the wave function with anything having to do with electrical charge. As we said earlier the (+) and (−) signs associated with ψ are simply the arithmetic signs of the wave function in that region of space. The (+) and (−) signs do not imply a greater or lesser probability of finding an electron either. The probability of finding an electron is ψ^2, and ψ^2 is always positive. (Squaring a negative number always makes it positive.) Thus the probability of finding the electron in the (−) lobe of a *p* orbital is the same as that of the (+) lobe. The significance of the (+) and (−) signs will become clear later when we see how atomic orbitals combine to form molecular orbitals and when we see how covalent bonds are formed.

There is a relationship between the number of nodes of an orbital and its energy: ***The greater the number of nodes, the greater the energy.*** We can see an example here; the 2*s* and 2*p* orbitals have one node each and they have greater energy than a 1*s* orbital, which has no nodes.

The relative energies of the lower energy orbitals are as follows. Electrons in 1*s* orbitals have the lowest energy because they are closest to the positive nucleus. Electrons in 2*s* orbitals are next lowest in energy. Electrons of 2*p* orbitals have equal but still higher energy. (Orbitals of equal energy are said to be **degenerate orbitals.**)

We can use these relative energies to arrive at the electronic configuration of any atom in the first two rows of the periodic table. We need only follow a few simple rules.

1. **The aufbau principle:** Orbitals are filled so that those of lowest energy are filled first. (*Aufbau* is German for "building up.")
2. **The Pauli exclusion principle:** A maximum of two electrons may be placed in each orbital *but only when the spins of the electrons are paired.* An electron spins

about its own axis. For reasons that we cannot develop here, an electron is permitted only one or another of only two possible spin orientations. We usually show these orientations by arrows, either ↑ or ↓. Thus two spin-paired electrons would be designated ↑↓. Unpaired electrons, which are not permitted in the same orbital, are designated ↑ ↑ (or ↓ ↓).

3. **Hund's rule:** When we come to orbitals of equal energy (degenerate orbitals) such as the three *p* orbitals, we add one electron to each *with their spins unpaired* until each of the degenerate orbitals contains one electron. Then we begin adding a second electron to each degenerate orbital so that the spins are paired.

If we apply these rules to some of the second-row elements of the periodic table, we get the results shown in Fig. 1.8.

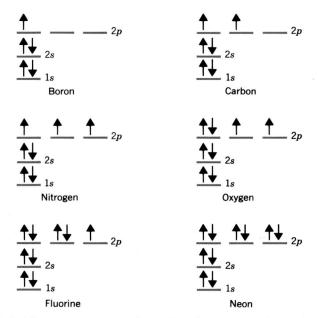

FIGURE 1.8 The electron configuration of some second-row elements.

Problem 1.4

Provide an explanation for Hund's rule.

1.12 MOLECULAR ORBITALS

For the organic chemist the greatest utility of atomic orbitals is in using them as models in understanding how atoms combine to form molecules. We shall have much more to say about this subject in subsequent chapters for, as we have already said, covalent bonds are central to the study of organic chemistry. First, however, we shall concern ourselves with a very simple case: the covalent bond that is formed when two hydrogen atoms combine to form a hydrogen molecule. We shall see that the description of the formation of the H—H bond is the same as, or at least very similar to, the description of bonds in more complex molecules.

Let us begin by examining what happens to the total energy of two hydrogen atoms with electrons of opposite spins when they are brought closer and closer together. This can best be shown with the curve shown in Fig. 1.9.

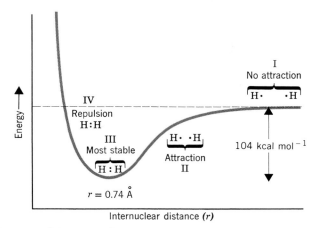

FIGURE 1.9   The potential energy of the hydrogen molecule as a function of internuclear distance.

When the atoms of hydrogen are relatively far apart **(I)** their total energy is simply that of two isolated hydrogen atoms. As the hydrogen atoms move closer together **(II)**, each nucleus increasingly attracts the other's electron. This attraction more than compensates for the repulsive force between the two nuclei (or the two electrons), and the result of this attraction *is to lower the energy of the total system.* When the two nuclei are 0.74 Å apart **(III)**, the most stable (lowest energy) state is obtained. This distance, 0.74 Å, corresponds to the *bond length* for the hydrogen molecule. If the nuclei are moved closer together **(IV)** the repulsion of the two positively charged nuclei predominates, and the energy of the system rises.

There is one serious problem with this model for bond formation. We have assumed that the electrons are essentially motionless and that as the nuclei come together they will be stationary in the region between the two nuclei. Electrons do not behave that way. Electrons move about, and according to the **Heisenberg uncertainty principle,** we cannot know simultaneously the position and momentum of an electron. That is, we cannot pin the electrons down as precisely as our explanation suggests.

We avoid this problem when we use a model based on quantum mechanics and *orbitals,* because now we describe the electron in terms of probabilities (ψ^2) of finding it at particular places. By treating the electron in this way we do not violate the uncertainty principle, because we do not talk about where the electron is precisely. We talk instead about where the *electron probability density* is large or small.

Thus an orbital explanation for what happens when two hydrogen atoms combine to form a hydrogen molecule is the following: As the hydrogen atoms approach each other, their 1s orbitals (ψ_{1s}) begin to overlap. As the atoms move closer together, orbital overlap increases until the **atomic orbitals (AO's)** combine to become **molecular orbitals (MO's).** The molecular orbitals that are formed encompass both nuclei and, in them, the electrons can move about both nuclei. They are not restricted to the vicinity of one nucleus or the other as they were in the separate atomic orbitals.

Molecular orbitals, like atomic orbitals, *may contain a maximum of two spin-paired electrons.*

When atomic orbitals combine to form molecular orbitals, ***the number of molecular orbitals that result always equals the number of atomic orbitals that combine.*** Thus in the formation of a hydrogen molecule the *two* atomic orbitals combine to produce *two* molecular orbitals. Two orbitals result because the mathematical properties of wave functions permit them to be combined by either *addition* or *subtraction.* That is, they can combine either *in* or *out of* phase. What are the natures of these new molecular orbitals?

One molecular orbital, called the **bonding molecular orbital** (ψ_{molec}) contains both electrons in the lowest energy state, or *ground* state, of a hydrogen molecule. It is formed when the atomic orbitals combine in the way shown in Fig. 1.10. Here atomic orbitals combine by *addition,* and this means that atomic *orbitals of the same phase sign overlap.* Such overlap leads to *reinforcement* of the wave function in the region between the two nuclei. Reinforcement of the wave function not only means that the value of ψ is larger between the two nuclei, it means that ψ^2 is larger as well. Moreover, since ψ^2 expresses the probability of finding an electron in this region of space, we can now understand how orbital overlap of this kind leads to bonding. It does so by increasing the electron probability density in exactly the right place—in the region of space between the nuclei. When the electron density is large here, the attractive force of the nuclei for the electrons more than offsets the repulsive force acting between the two nuclei (and between the two electrons). This extra attractive force is, of course, the "glue" that holds the atoms together.

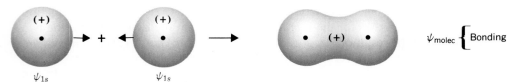

FIGURE 1.10 The overlapping of two hydrogen 1s atomic orbitals to form a bonding molecular orbital.

The second molecular orbital, called the **antibonding molecular orbital** (ψ^*_{molec}) contains no electrons in the ground state of the molecule. It is formed by subtraction in the way shown in Fig. 1.11. [Subtraction means that the phase sign of one orbital has been changed from (+) to (−).] Here, because *orbitals of opposite phase overlap,* the wave functions *interfere* with each other in the region between the two nuclei and

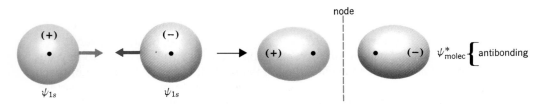

FIGURE 1.11 The overlapping of two hydrogen 1s atomic orbitals to form an antibonding molecular orbital.

a node is produced. At the node $\psi = 0$, and on either side of the node ψ is small. This means that in the region between the nuclei ψ^2 is also small. Thus if electrons were to occupy the antibonding orbital, the electrons would avoid the region between the nuclei. There would be only a small attractive force of the nuclei for the electrons. Repulsive forces (between the two nuclei and between the two electrons) would be greater than the attractive forces. Having electrons in the antibonding orbital would not tend to hold the atoms together; it would tend to make them fly apart.

What we have just described has its counterpart in a mathematical treatment called the LCAO (linear combination of atomic orbitals) method. In the LCAO treatment, wave functions for the atomic orbitals are combined in a linear fashion (by addition or subtraction) in order to obtain new wave functions for the molecular orbitals.

Molecular orbitals, like atomic orbitals, correspond to particular energy states for an electron. Calculations show that the relative energy of an electron in the bonding molecular orbital of the hydrogen molecule is substantially less than its energy in a ψ_{1s} atomic orbital. These calculations also show that the energy of an electron in the antibonding molecular orbital is substantially greater than its energy in a ψ_{1s} atomic orbital.

An energy diagram for the molecular orbitals of the hydrogen molecule is shown in Fig. 1.12. Notice that electrons are placed in molecular orbitals in the same way that they were in atomic orbitals. Two electrons (with their spins opposed) occupy the bonding molecular orbital, where their total energy is less than in the separate atomic orbitals. This is, as we have said, the *lowest electronic energy state* or *ground state* of the hydrogen molecule. (An electron may occupy the antibonding orbital in what is called an *excited state* for the molecule. This state forms when the molecule in the ground state absorbs a photon of light of proper energy.)

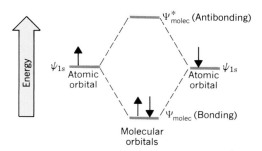

FIGURE 1.12 Energy diagram for the hydrogen molecule. Combination of two atomic orbitals. ψ_{1s} gives two molecular orbitals, ψ_{molec} and ψ_{molec}^*. The energy of ψ_{molec} is lower than that of the separate atomic orbitals, and in the lowest electronic energy state of molecular hydrogen it contains both electrons.

1.13 THE STRUCTURE OF METHANE: sp^3 HYBRIDIZATION

The s and p orbitals used in the quantum mechanical description of the carbon atom, given in Section 1.10, were based on calculations for hydrogen atoms. These simple s and p orbitals do not, when taken alone, provide a satisfactory model for the *tetravalent-tetrahedral* carbon of methane (see Problem 1.5). However, a satisfactory model of methane's structure that is based on quantum mechanics *can* be obtained through an approach called **orbital hybridization.** Orbital hybridization, in its simplest terms, is nothing more than a mathematical approach that involves the combining of individual wave functions for s and p orbitals to obtain wave functions for new orbitals. The new orbitals have, *in varying proportions,* the properties of the original orbitals taken separately. These new orbitals are called **hybrid atomic orbitals.**

According to quantum mechanics the electronic configuration of a carbon atom in its lowest energy state — called the *ground state* — is that given here.

$$C \quad \uparrow\downarrow \quad \uparrow\downarrow \quad \uparrow \quad \uparrow \quad \underline{\hspace{1cm}}$$
$$1s \quad 2s \quad 2p \quad 2p \quad 2p$$

Ground state of a carbon atom

The valence electrons of a carbon atom (those used in bonding) are those of the *outer level,* that is, the $2s$ and $2p$ electrons.

Hybrid atomic orbitals that account for methane's structure can be obtained by combining the wave functions of the $2s$ orbital of carbon with those of the three $2p$ orbitals. The mathematical procedure for hybridization can be approximated by the illustration that is shown in Fig. 1.13.

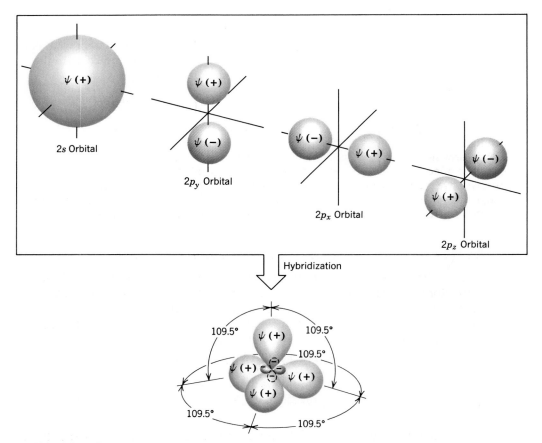

FIGURE 1.13 Hybridization of atomic orbitals of a carbon atom to produce sp^3-hybrid orbitals.

In this model, four orbitals are mixed—or hybridized—and four new hybrid orbitals are obtained. The hybrid orbitals are called *sp³* orbitals to indicate that they have one part the character of an *s* orbital and three parts the character of a *p* orbital. The mathematical treatment of orbital hybridization also shows that *the four sp³ orbitals should be oriented at angles of 109.5° with respect to each other.* This is precisely the spatial orientation of the four hydrogen atoms of methane.

If, in our imagination, we visualize the formation of methane from an *sp³*-hybridized carbon atom and four hydrogen atoms, the process might be like that shown in Fig. 1.14. For simplicity we show only the formation of the *bonding molecular orbital* for each carbon–hydrogen bond. We see that an *sp³*-hybridized carbon gives a *tetrahedral structure for methane, and one with four equivalent C—H bonds.*

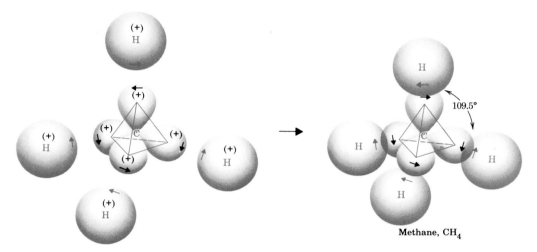

FIGURE 1.14 The formation of methane from an *sp³*-hybridized carbon atom. In orbital hybridization we combine orbitals, *not* electrons. The electrons can then be replaced in the hybrid orbitals as necessary for bond formation, but always in accordance with the Pauli principle of no more than two electrons (with opposite spin) in each orbital. In this illustration we have placed one electron in each of the hybrid carbon orbitals. In this illustration, too, we have shown only the bonding molecular orbital of each C—H bond because these are the orbitals that contain the electrons in the lowest energy state of the molecule.

Problem 1.5

(a) Consider a carbon atom in its ground state. Would such an atom offer a satisfactory model for the carbon of methane? If not, why not? (*Hint:* Consider whether or not a ground state carbon atom could be tetravalent, and consider the bond angles that would result if it were to combine with hydrogen atoms.)
(b) What about a carbon atom in the excited state:

$$C \quad \underset{1s}{\uparrow\downarrow} \quad \underset{2s}{\uparrow} \quad \underset{2p_x}{\uparrow} \quad \underset{2p_y}{\uparrow} \quad \underset{2p_z}{\uparrow}$$

Excited state of a carbon atom

Would such an atom offer a satisfactory model for the carbon of methane? If not, why not?

In addition to accounting properly for the shape of methane, the orbital hybridization model also explains the very strong bonds that are formed between carbon and hydrogen. To see how this is so, consider the shape of the individual sp^3 orbital shown in Fig. 1.15.

FIGURE 1.15   The shape of an sp^3 orbital.

Because the sp^3 orbital has the character of a p orbital, the positive lobe of the sp^3 orbital is large and is extended quite far into space.

It is the positive lobe of the sp^3 orbital that overlaps with the positive $1s$ orbital of hydrogen to form the bonding molecular orbital of a carbon–hydrogen bond. Because the positive lobe of the sp^3 orbital is large and is extended into space, the overlap between it and the $1s$ orbital of hydrogen is also large, and the resulting carbon–hydrogen bond is quite strong.

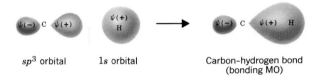

The bond formed from the overlap of an sp^3 orbital and a $1s$ orbital is an example of a **sigma bond** (Fig. 1.16). The term *sigma bond* is a general term applied to those bonds in which orbital overlap gives a bond that is *circularly symmetrical in cross section when viewed along the bond axis.* ***All purely single bonds are sigma bonds.***

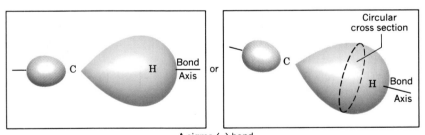

FIGURE 1.16   A sigma (σ) bond.

From this point on we shall often show only the bonding molecular orbitals because they are the ones that contain the electrons when the molecule is in its lowest energy state. Consideration of antibonding orbitals is important when a molecule absorbs light and in explaining certain reactions. We shall point these instances out later.

1.14 THE STRUCTURE OF BORANE: sp^2 HYBRIDIZATION

Borane (BH_3), a molecule that can be detected only at low pressures, has a triangular (trigonal planar) shape with three equivalent boron–hydrogen bonds. In its ground state the boron atom has the following electronic configuration. Only one orbital contains a single electron that might be used to overlap with an s orbital containing the unpaired electron in a hydrogen atom.

B ↑↓ ↑↓ ↑ __ __
    1s 2s 2p 2p 2p

Boron atom ground state

Triangular structure of BH$_3$

Clearly, the s and p orbitals of the ground state will not furnish a satisfactory model for the trivalent and triangularly bonded boron of BH$_3$.

Problem 1.6

(a) What valence would you expect a boron atom in its ground state to have?
(b) Consider an excited state of boron in which one $2s$ electron is promoted to a vacant $2p$ orbital. Show how this state of boron also fails to account for the structure of BH$_3$.

Once again we use a model based on the mathematical process of orbital hybridization. Here, however, we combine the $2s$ orbital with only two of the $2p$ orbitals. Mixing three orbitals as shown in Fig. 1.17 gives three equivalent hybrid orbitals and

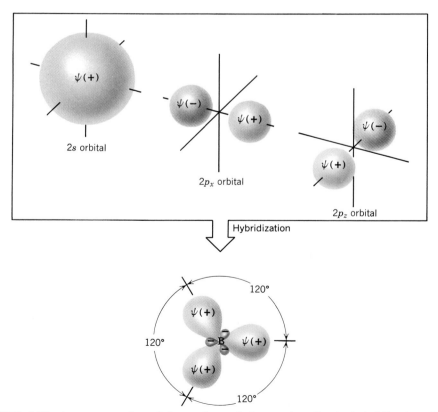

FIGURE 1.17 A representation of the mathematical procedure for the hybridization of one $2s$ orbital and two $2p$ orbitals of boron to produce three sp^2-hybrid orbitals.

these orbitals are sp^2 orbitals. They have one part the character of an s orbital and two parts the character of a p orbital. Calculations show that these orbitals are pointed toward the corners of an equilateral triangle with angles of 120° between their axes. These orbitals, then, are just what we need to account for the trivalent, trigonal planar boron atom of borane.

By placing one of the valence electrons in each of the three sp^2 orbitals and allowing these orbitals to overlap with a s orbital containing one electron from each of three hydrogen atoms, we obtain the structure shown in Fig. 1.18. Notice that the boron atom still has a vacant p orbital, the one that we did not hybridize.

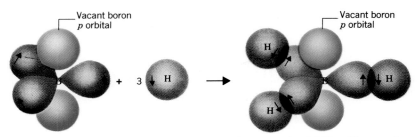

FIGURE 1.18 A representation of the formation of the bonding MO's of borane from an sp^2-hybridized boron atom and three hydrogen atoms.

We shall see in Section 2.4 that sp^2 hybridization offers a satisfactory model for carbon atoms that form double bonds.

1.15 THE STRUCTURE OF BERYLLIUM HYDRIDE: *sp* HYBRIDIZATION

Beryllium hydride (BeH_2) is a linear molecule; the bond angle is 180°.

$$\overset{\frown\;180°\;\frown}{H-Be-H}$$

In its ground state the beryllium atom has the following electronic configuration:

$$Be \quad \uparrow\downarrow \quad \uparrow\downarrow \quad \underline{\quad}\;\underline{\quad}\;\underline{\quad}$$
$$1s \quad 2s \quad 2p \quad 2p \quad 2p$$

In order to account for the structure of BeH_2 we again need a model based on orbital hybridization. Here (Fig. 1.19) we hybridize one s orbital with one p orbital and obtain two sp orbitals. Calculations show that these sp orbitals are oriented at an angle of 180°. The two p orbitals that were not mixed are vacant. Beryllium can use these hybrid orbitals to form bonds to two hydrogen atoms in the way shown in Fig. 1.20.

We shall see in Section 8.3 that sp hybridization offers a satisfactory model for carbon atoms that form triple bonds

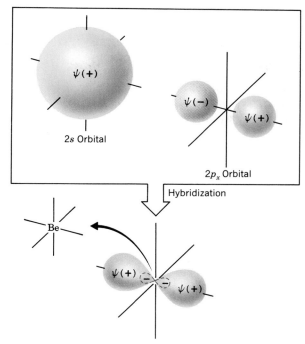

FIGURE 1.19 A representation of the mathematical procedure for the hybridization of one 2s orbital and one 2p orbital of beryllium to produce two *sp*-hybrid orbitals.

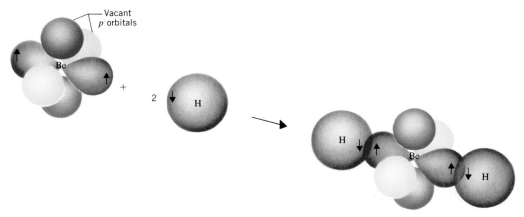

FIGURE 1.20 A representation of the formation of the bonding MO's of BeH_2 from an *sp*-hybridized beryllium atom and two hydrogen atoms.

1.16 A SUMMARY OF IMPORTANT CONCEPTS THAT COME FROM QUANTUM MECHANICS

1. An **atomic orbital (AO)** corresponds to a region of space about the nucleus of a single atom where there is a high probability of finding an electron. Atomic orbitals called *s* orbitals are spherical; those called *p* orbitals are like two almost-tangent spheres. Orbitals can hold a maximum of two electrons when their spins are paired. Orbitals are described by a wave function, ψ, and each orbital has a

characteristic energy. The phase signs associated with an orbital may be (+) or (−).

2. When atomic orbitals overlap, they combine to form **molecular orbitals (MO's).** Molecular orbitals correspond to regions of space encompassing two (or more) nuclei where electrons are to be found. Like atomic orbitals, molecular orbitals can hold up to two electrons if their spins are paired.

3. When atomic orbitals with the same phase sign interact they combine to form a **bonding molecular orbital:**

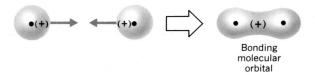

Bonding
molecular
orbital

The electron probability density of a bonding molecular orbital is large in the region of space between the two nuclei where the negative electrons hold the positive nuclei together.

4. An **antibonding molecular orbital** forms when orbitals of opposite phase sign overlap:

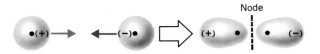

An antibonding orbital has higher energy than a bonding orbital. The electron probability density of the region between the nuclei is small and it contains a **node**—a region where $\psi = 0$. Thus, having electrons in an antibonding orbital does not help hold the nuclei together. The internuclear repulsions tend to make them fly apart.

5. The **energy of electrons** in a bonding molecular orbital is less than the energy of the electrons in their separate atomic orbitals. The energy of electrons in an antibonding orbital is greater than that of electrons in their separate atomic orbitals.

6. The **number of molecular orbitals** always equals the number of atomic orbitals from which they are formed. Combining two atomic orbitals will always yield two molecular orbitals—one bonding and one antibonding.

7. **Hybrid atomic orbitals** are obtained by mixing (hybridizing) the wave functions for orbitals of a different type (i.e., s and p orbitals) but from the same atom.

8. Hybridizing three p orbitals with one s orbital yields four **sp^3 orbitals.** Atoms that are sp^3 hybridized direct the axes of their four sp^3 orbitals toward the corners of a tetrahedron. The carbon of methane is sp^3 hybridized and **tetrahedral.**

9. Hybridizing two p orbitals with one s orbital yields three **sp^2 orbitals.** Atoms that are sp^2 hybridized point the axes of three sp^2 orbitals toward the corners of an equilateral triangle. The boron atom in BF_3 is sp^2 hybridized and **trigonal planar.**

10. Hybridizing one p orbital with one s orbital yields two **sp orbitals.** Atoms that are sp hybridized orient the axes of their two sp orbitals in opposite directions (at an angle of 180°). The beryllium atom of BeH_2 is sp hybridized and BeH_2 is a **linear** molecule.

11. A sigma bond (a type of single bond) is one in which the electron density has circular symmetry when viewed along the bond axis. In general, the skeletons of organic molecules are constructed of atoms linked by sigma bonds.

1.17 MOLECULAR GEOMETRY: THE VALENCE SHELL ELECTRON-PAIR REPULSION (VSEPR) MODEL

We have been discussing the geometry of molecules on the basis of theories that arise from quantum mechanics. It is possible, however, to predict the arrangement of atoms in molecules and ions on the basis of a theory called the **valence shell electron-pair repulsion (VSEPR) theory.** Consider the following examples found in Sections 1.17A–F.

We apply VSEPR theory in the following way:

1. We consider molecules (or ions) in which the central atom is covalently bonded to two or more atoms or groups.
2. We consider all of the valence electron pairs of the central atom — both those that are shared in covalent bonds, called **bonding pairs,** and those that are unshared, called **nonbonding pairs** or **unshared pairs.**
3. Because electron pairs repel each other, the electron pairs of the valence shell tend to stay as far apart as possible. The repulsion between nonbonding pairs is generally greater than that between bonding pairs.
4. We arrive at the geometry of the molecule by considering all of the electron pairs, bonding and nonbonding, but we describe the shape of the molecule or ion by referring to the positions of the nuclei (or atoms) and not by the positions of the electron pairs.

Consider the following examples.

1.17A METHANE

The valence shell of methane contains four pairs of bonding electrons. Only a tetrahedral orientation will allow four pairs of electrons to have the maximum possible separation (Fig. 1.21). Any other orientation, for example, a square planar arrangement, places the electron pairs closer together.

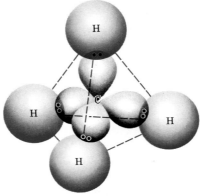

FIGURE 1.21 A tetrahedral shape for methane allows the maximum separation of the four bonding electron pairs.

Thus, in the case of methane, the VSEPR model accommodates what we have known since the proposal of van't Hoff and Le Bel (Section 1.3B): The molecule of methane has a tetrahedral shape.

Problem 1.7

Part of the reasoning that led van't Hoff and Le Bel to propose a tetrahedral shape for molecules of methane was based on the number of compounds that are theoretically possible for substituted methanes, that is, for compounds in which one or more hydrogen atoms of methane have been replaced by some other group. For example, only one compound of the type CH_2X_2 has ever been found. (a) Is this consistent with a tetrahedral shape? (b) With a square planar shape? Explain.

The bond angles for any atom that has a regular tetrahedral structure are 109.5°. A representation of these angles in methane is shown in Fig. 1.22.

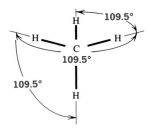

FIGURE 1.22 The bond angles of methane are 109.5°.

1.17B AMMONIA

The geometry of a molecule of ammonia is a **trigonal pyramid.** The bond angles in a molecule of ammonia are 107°, a value very close to the tetrahedral angle (109.5°). We can write a general tetrahedral structure for the electron pairs of ammonia by placing the nonbonding pair at one corner (Fig. 1.23). A *tetrahedral arrangement* of the electron pairs explains the *trigonal pyramidal* arrangement of the four atoms. The bond angles are 107° (not 109.5°) because the nonbonding pair occupies more space than the bonding pairs.

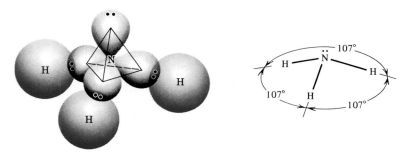

FIGURE 1.23 The tetrahedral arrangement of the electron pairs of an ammonia molecule that results when the nonbonding electron pair is considered to occupy one corner. This arrangement of electron pairs explains the trigonal pyramidal shape of the NH_3 molecule.

1.17C WATER

A molecule of water has an **angular** or **bent geometry.** The H—O—H bond angle in a molecule of water is 105°, an angle that is also quite close to the 109.5° bond angles of methane.

We can write a general tetrahedral structure for the electron pairs of a molecule of water *if we place the two nonbonding electron pairs at corners of the tetrahedron.* Such a structure is shown in Fig. 1.24. A *tetrahedral arrangement* of the electron pairs accounts for the *angular arrangement* of the three atoms. The bond angle is less than 109.5° because the nonbonding pairs are effectively "larger" than the bonding pairs.

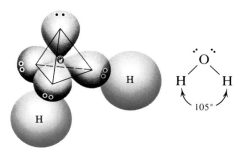

FIGURE 1.24 A tetrahedral arrangement of the electron pairs of a molecule of water that results when the pairs of nonbonding electrons are considered to occupy corners. This arrangement accounts for the angular shape of the H_2O molecule.

1.17D BORON TRIFLUORIDE

Boron, a Group **IIIA** element, has only three outer level electrons. In the compound boron trifluoride (BF_3) these three electrons are shared with three fluorine atoms. As a result, the boron atom in BF_3 has only six electrons (three bonding pairs) around it. Maximum separation of three bonding pairs occurs when they occupy the corners of an equilateral triangle. Consequently, in the boron trifluoride molecule the three fluorine atoms lie in a plane at the corners of an equilateral triangle (Fig. 1.25). Boron trifluoride is said to have a *trigonal planar structure.* The bond angles are 120°.

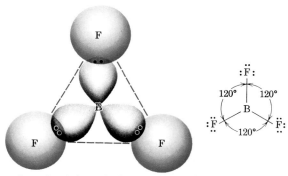

FIGURE 1.25 The triangular (trigonal planar) shape of boron fluoride maximally separates the three bonding pairs.

1.17E BERYLLIUM HYDRIDE

The central beryllium atom of BeH_2 has only two electron pairs around it; both electron pairs are bonding pairs. These two pairs are maximally separated when they are on opposite sides of the central atom as shown in the following structures. This arrangement of the electron pairs accounts for the linear geometry of the BeH_2 molecule and its bond angle of 180°.

$$H:Be:H \quad \text{or} \quad H-Be-H$$

Linear geometry of BeH₂

Problem 1.8

Predict the general shapes of the following molecules and ions:

(a) SiH_4 (c) CH_3^+ (e) CCl_4 (g) BH_4^- (i) BH_3

(b) $:CH_3^-$ (d) BF_4^- (f) $BeCl_2$ (h) BeH_2

1.17F CARBON DIOXIDE

The VSEPR method can also be used to predict the shapes of molecules containing multiple bonds if we assume that *all of the electrons of a multiple bond act as though they were a single unit,* and, therefore, are located in the region of space between the two atoms joined by a multiple bond.

This principle can be illustrated with the structure of a molecule of carbon dioxide (CO_2). The central carbon atom of carbon dioxide is bonded to each oxygen atom by a double bond. Carbon dioxide is known to have a linear shape; the bond angle is 180°.

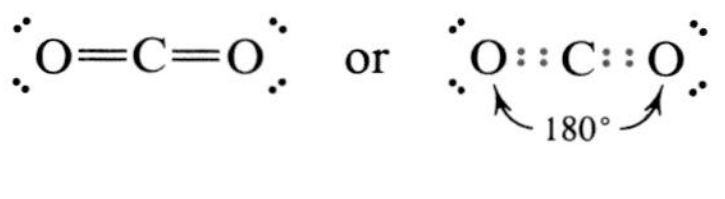

$$\overset{\cdot\cdot}{O} = C = \overset{\cdot\cdot}{O} \quad \text{or} \quad \overset{\cdot\cdot}{O} :: C :: \overset{\cdot\cdot}{O}$$

The four electrons of each double bond act as a single unit and are maximally separated from each other

Such a structure is consistent with a maximum separation of the two groups of four bonding electrons. (The nonbonding pairs associated with the oxygen atoms have no effect on the shape.)

Problem 1.9

Predict the bond angles of (a) $CH_2 = CH_2$, (b) $HC \equiv CH$, (c) $HC \equiv N$.

The shapes of several simple molecules and ions as predicted by VSEPR theory are shown in Table 1.4. In this table we have also included the hybridization state of the central atom.

TABLE 1.4   Shapes of molecules and ions from VSEPR theory

NUMBER OF ELECTRON PAIRS			HYBRIDIZATION STATE OF CENTRAL ATOM	SHAPE OF MOLECULE OR ION[a]	EXAMPLES
Bonding	Nonbonding	Total			
2	0	2	sp	Linear	BeH_2
3	0	3	sp^2	Trigonal planar	BF_3, CH_3^+
4	0	4	sp^3	Tetrahedral	CH_4, NH_4^+
3	1	4	$\sim sp^3$	Trigonal pyramidal	NH_3, CH_3^-
2	2	4	$\sim sp^3$	Angular	H_2O

[a] Excluding nonbonding pairs.

1.18 POLAR COVALENT BONDS

When two atoms of different electronegativities form a covalent bond, the electrons are not shared equally between them. The atom with greater electronegativity draws the electron pair closer to it, and a **polar covalent bond** results. (One definition of *electronegativity* is *the ability of an element to attract electrons that it is sharing in a covalent bond*.) An example of such a polar covalent bond is the one in hydrogen chloride. The chlorine atom, with its greater electronegativity, pulls the bonding electrons closer to it. This makes the hydrogen atom somewhat electron deficient and gives it a *partial* positive charge ($\delta+$). The chlorine atom becomes somewhat electron rich and bears a *partial* negative charge ($\delta-$).

$$\overset{\delta+}{H} \quad \overset{\delta-}{:\ddot{Cl}:}$$

Because the hydrogen chloride molecule has a partially positive end and a partially negative end, it is a dipole, and it has a **dipole moment.**

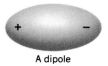

A dipole

The dipole moment is a physical property that can be measured experimentally. It is defined as the product of the magnitude of the charge in electrostatic units (esu) and the distance that separates them in centimeters (cm).

Dipole moment = charge (in esu) × distance (in cm)

$$\mu = e \times d$$

The charges are typically on the order of 10^{-10} esu and the distances are on the order of 10^{-8} cm. Dipole moments, therefore, are typically on the order of 10^{-18} esu cm. For convenience, this unit, 1×10^{-18} esu cm, is defined as one **debye** and is abbreviated D. (The unit is named after Peter J. W. Debye, a chemist born in the

Netherlands, but who taught at Cornell University from 1936–1966. Debye won the Nobel prize in 1936.)

The direction of polarity of a polar bond can be symbolized by a vector quantity $\longmapsto$. The crossed end of the arrow is the positive end and the arrow head is the negative end.

$$(\text{positive end}) \longmapsto (\text{negative end})$$

In HCl, for example, we would indicate the direction of the dipole moment in the following way:

$$\text{H—Cl}$$
$$\longmapsto$$

If necessary, the length of the arrow can be used to indicate the magnitude of the dipole moment. Dipole moments, as we shall see in Section 1.19, are very useful quantities in accounting for physical properties of compounds.

Problem 1.10

Predict the direction of the dipole (if any) in the following molecules:
(a) HBr, (b) ICl, (c) H_2, (d) Cl_2.

1.19 POLAR AND NONPOLAR MOLECULES

In the discussion of dipole moments in Section 1.18, our attention was restricted to simple diatomic molecules. Any *diatomic* molecule in which the two atoms are *different* (and thus have different electronegativities) will, of necessity, have a dipole moment. If we examine Table 1.5, however, we find that a number of molecules (e.g., CCl_4, CO_2) consist of more than two atoms, have *polar* bonds, *but have no dipole moment*. Now that we have an understanding of the shapes of molecules we can understand how this can occur.

TABLE 1.5   Dipole moments of some simple molecules

FORMULA	μ (D)	FORMULA	μ (D)
H_2	0	CH_4	0
Cl_2	0	CH_3Cl	1.87
HF	1.91	CH_2Cl_2	1.55
HCl	1.08	$CHCl_3$	1.02
HBr	0.80	CCl_4	0
HI	0.42	NH_3	1.47
BF_3	0	NF_3	0.24
CO_2	0	H_2O	1.85

1.19 POLAR AND NONPOLAR MOLECULES

Consider a molecule of carbon tetrachloride (CCl_4). Because the electronegativity of chlorine is greater than that of carbon, each of the carbon–chlorine bonds in CCl_4 is polar. Each chlorine atom has a partial negative charge, and the carbon atom is considerably positive. Because a molecule of carbon tetrachloride is tetrahedral (Fig. 1.26), however, *the center of positive charge and the center of negative charge coincide, and the molecule has no net dipole moment.*

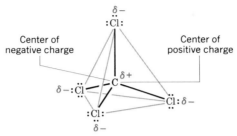

FIGURE 1.26 Charge distribution in carbon tetrachloride.

This result can be illustrated in a slightly different way: If we use arrows ($\longmapsto$) to represent the direction of polarity of each bond, we get the arrangement of bond moments shown in Fig. 1.27. Since the bond moments are vectors of equal magnitude arranged tetrahedrally, their effects cancel. Their vector sum is zero. The molecule has *no net dipole moment.*

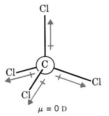

FIGURE 1.27 A tetrahedral orientation of equal bond moments causes their effects to cancel.

The chloromethane molecule (CH_3Cl) has a net dipole moment of 1.87 D. Since carbon and hydrogen have electronegativities (Table 1.2) that are nearly the same, the contribution of three C—H bonds to the net dipole is negligible. The electronegativity difference between carbon and chlorine is large, however, and this highly polar C—Cl bond accounts for most of the dipole moment of CH_3Cl (Fig. 1.28).

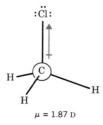

FIGURE 1.28 The dipole moment of chloromethane arises mainly from the highly polar carbon–chlorine bond.

Problem 1.11

A molecule of carbon dioxide (CO_2) is linear (Section 1.17F). Show how this accounts for the fact that CO_2 has no dipole moment.

Problem 1.12

Tetrachloroethene ($CCl_2=CCl_2$) does not have a dipole moment. Explain this fact on the basis of the shape of $CCl_2=CCl_2$.

Problem 1.13

Sulfur dioxide (SO_2) has a dipole moment. (The dipole moment of SO_2 is 1.63 D.) What does this fact indicate about the shape of an SO_2 molecule?

Unshared pairs of electrons make large contributions to the dipole moments of water and ammonia. Because an unshared pair has no atom attached to it to partially neutralize its negative charge, an unshared electron pair contributes a large moment directed away from the central atom (Fig. 1.29). (The O—H and N—H moments are also appreciable.)

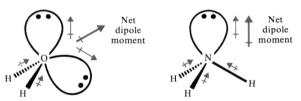

FIGURE 1.29 Bond moments and the resulting dipole moment of water and ammonia.

Problem 1.14

Nitrogen trifluoride ($:NF_3$) has a shape very much like that of ammonia. It has, however, a very low dipole moment ($\mu = 0.24$ D). How can you explain this?

Problem 1.15

Boron trifluoride (BF_3) has no dipole moment. How can this be explained?

1.20 REPRESENTATION OF STRUCTURAL FORMULAS

Organic chemists use a variety of ways to write structural formulas. The most common types of representations are shown in Fig. 1.30. The **dot structure** shows all of the valence electrons, but writing it is tedious and time consuming. The other representations are more convenient and are, therefore, more often used.

1.20 REPRESENTATION OF STRUCTURAL FORMULAS

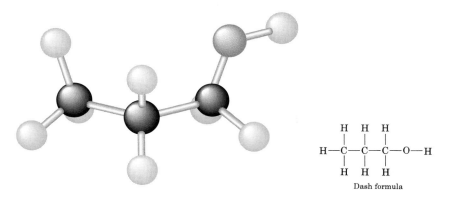

Dash formula

CH₃CH₂CH₂OH
Condensed formula

FIGURE 1.30 Structural formulas for propyl alcohol.

In fact, we often omit unshared pairs when we write formulas unless there is a reason to include them. For example,

$$H:\overset{..}{\underset{\overset{|}{H}}{\overset{|}{C}}}:\overset{..}{O}:\overset{..}{\underset{\overset{|}{H}}{\overset{|}{C}}}:H \quad = \quad H-\overset{\overset{\displaystyle H}{|}}{\underset{\underset{\displaystyle H}{|}}{C}}-O-\overset{\overset{\displaystyle H}{|}}{\underset{\underset{\displaystyle H}{|}}{C}}-H \quad = \quad CH_3OCH_3$$

Dot structure **Dash formula** **Condensed formula**

1.20A DASH STRUCTURAL FORMULAS

If we look at the model for propyl alcohol given in Fig. 1.30 and compare it with the formulas given there, we find that the chain of atoms is straight in all the formulas. In the model, which corresponds more accurately to the actual shape of the molecule, the chain of atoms is not at all straight. Also of importance is this: ***Atoms joined by single bonds can rotate relatively freely with respect to one another.*** (We discuss this point further in Section 2.2B.) This relatively free rotation means that the chain of atoms in propyl alcohol can assume a variety of arrangements like those that follow:

It also means that all of the dash structures that follow are *equivalent* and all represent propyl alcohol. (Notice that in these formulas we represent the bond angles as being 90° not 109.5°. This convention is followed simply for convenience in printing.)

```
                            H                      H
                            |                      |
                        H—C—H                  H—C—H
        H  H  O—H            H                      O—H
        |  |  |              |                      |
    H—C—C—C—H   or   H—C—C—H   or   H—C—C—H
        |  |  |              |                      |  |
        H  H  H              H  O—H                 H  H
```

Equivalent dash formulas for propyl alcohol

Structural formulas such as these indicate the way in which the atoms are attached to each other and *are not* representations of the actual shapes of the molecule. They show what is called the **connectivity** of the atoms. *Constitutional isomers (Section 1.3A) have different connectivity, and, therefore, must have different structural formulas.*

Consider the compound called isopropyl alcohol, whose formula we might write in a variety of ways:

```
            H                                      H  O—H
            |                  H  H  H             |  |
        H  O  H                |  |  |         H—C—C—H
        |  |  |                |  |  |             |
    H—C—C—C—H   or   H—C—C—C—H   or            H
        |  |  |                |  |  |         H—C—H
        H  H  H                H  O  H             |
                                  |               H
                                  H
```

Equivalent dash formulas for isopropyl alcohol

Isopropyl alcohol is a constitutional isomer (Section 1.3A) of propyl alcohol because its atoms are connected in a different order and both compounds have the same molecular formula, C_3H_8O. In isopropyl alcohol the OH group is attached to the central carbon; in propyl alcohol it is attached to an end carbon.

One other point: In problems you will often be asked to write structural formulas for all the isomers with a given molecular formula. Do not make the error of writing several equivalent formulas, like those that we have just shown, mistaking them for different constitutional isomers.

Problem 1.16

There are actually three constitutional isomers with the molecular formula C_3H_8O. We have seen two of them in propyl alcohol and isopropyl alcohol. Write a dash formula for the third isomer.

1.20B CONDENSED STRUCTURAL FORMULAS

Condensed structural formulas are easier to write than dash formulas, and when we become familiar with them, they will impart all the information that is contained in the dash structure. In condensed formulas all of the hydrogen atoms that are attached to a particular carbon are written immediately after that carbon. In fully condensed formulas, all of the atoms that are attached to the carbon are usually written immediately after that carbon. For example,

$$H-\underset{\underset{H}{|}}{\overset{\overset{H}{|}}{C}}-\underset{\underset{Cl}{|}}{\overset{\overset{H}{|}}{C}}-\underset{\underset{H}{|}}{\overset{\overset{H}{|}}{C}}-\underset{\underset{H}{|}}{\overset{\overset{H}{|}}{C}}-H$$

$$CH_3CHCH_2CH_3 \quad \text{or} \quad CH_3CHClCH_2CH_3$$
$$\underset{Cl}{|}$$

Dash formula   **Condensed formulas**

The condensed formula for isopropyl alcohol can be written in four different ways:

$$H-\underset{\underset{H}{|}}{\overset{\overset{H}{|}}{C}}-\underset{\underset{\underset{\underset{H}{|}}{O}}{|}}{\overset{\overset{H}{|}}{C}}-\underset{\underset{H}{|}}{\overset{\overset{H}{|}}{C}}-H$$

$$CH_3CHCH_3 \qquad CH_3CH(OH)CH_3$$
$$\overset{}{O}H$$

$$CH_3CHOHCH_3 \quad \text{or} \quad (CH_3)_2CHOH$$

Dash formula   **Condensed formulas**

Sample Problem

Write a condensed structural formula for the compound that follows:

$$H-\underset{\underset{H}{|}}{\overset{\overset{H}{|}}{C}}-\underset{\underset{\underset{\underset{H}{|}}{C}-H}{|}}{\overset{\overset{H}{|}}{C}}-\underset{\underset{H}{|}}{\overset{\overset{H}{|}}{C}}-\underset{\underset{H}{|}}{\overset{\overset{H}{|}}{C}}-H$$

Answer:

$$CH_3CHCH_2CH_3 \quad \text{or} \quad CH_3CH(CH_3)CH_2CH_3 \quad \text{or} \quad (CH_3)_2CHCH_2CH_3$$
$$\underset{CH_3}{|}$$

$$\text{or} \quad CH_3CH_2CH(CH_3)_2 \quad \text{or} \quad CH_3CH_2CHCH_3$$
$$\underset{CH_3}{|}$$

1.20C CYCLIC MOLECULES

Organic compounds not only have their carbon atoms arranged in chains, they can also have them arranged in rings. The compound called cyclopropane has its carbon atoms arranged in a three-membered ring.

$$\underset{\underset{H}{\diagup}\quad\underset{H}{\diagdown}}{\overset{H\diagdown\quad\diagup H}{\underset{C-C}{C}}} \quad \text{or} \quad \underset{H_2C-CH_2}{\overset{H_2}{C}} \qquad \begin{array}{l}\text{Formulas}\\\text{for}\\\text{cyclopropane}\end{array}$$

1.20D BOND-LINE FORMULAS

More and more organic chemists are using a very simplified formula called a **bond-line formula** to represent structural formulas. The bond-line representation is the quickest of all to write because it shows only the carbon skeleton. The number of hydrogen atoms necessary to fulfill the carbon atoms' valences are assumed to be present, but we do not write them in. Other atoms (e.g., O, Cl, N) *are* written in. Each intersection of two or more lines and the end of a line represents a carbon atom unless some other atom is written in

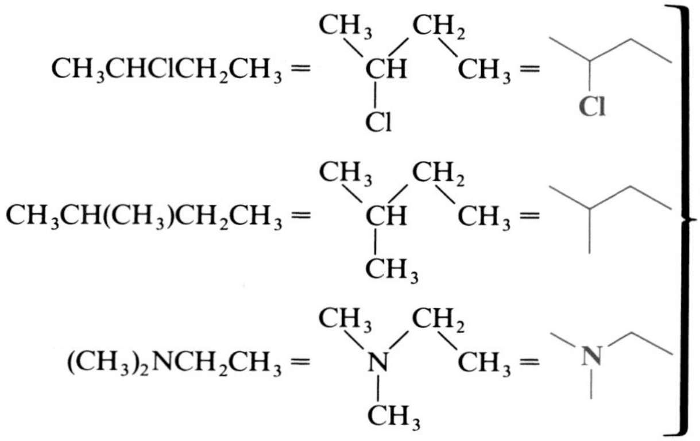

$$CH_3CHClCH_2CH_3 = \quad \text{(structure)} = \quad \text{(bond-line)}$$

$$CH_3CH(CH_3)CH_2CH_3 = \quad \text{(structure)} = \quad \text{(bond-line)}$$

$$(CH_3)_2NCH_2CH_3 = \quad \text{(structure)} = \quad \text{(bond-line)}$$

Bond-line
formulas

Bond-line formulas are often used for cyclic compounds:

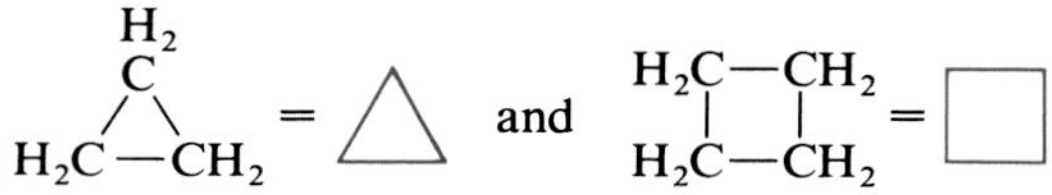

$$\text{cyclopropane} = \triangle \quad \text{and} \quad \text{cyclobutane} = \square$$

Multiple bonds are also indicated in bond-line formulas. For example,

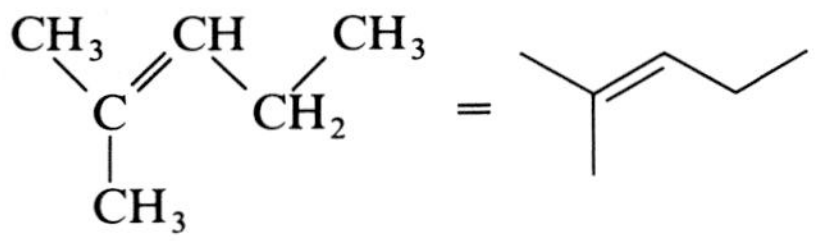

$$\text{(2-methyl-2-butene structure)} = \text{(bond-line)}$$

Sample Problem

Write the bond-line formula for $CH_3CHCH_2CH_2CH_2OH$.
$$\quad\quad\quad\quad\quad\quad\quad\quad\quad\quad | $$
$$\quad\quad\quad\quad\quad\quad\quad\quad\quad CH_3$$

Answer:

First, we outline the carbon skeleton, including the OH group as follows:

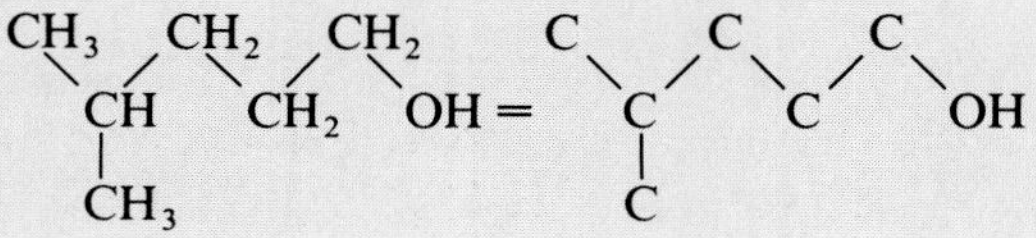

$$\text{(carbon skeleton with } CH_3, CH_2, CH_2, CH, CH_2, OH, CH_3 \text{)} = \text{(C C C C C OH, C)}$$

Thus, the bond-line formula is

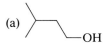

Problem 1.17

Rewrite each of the following condensed structural formulas, as *dash formulas* and as *bond-line formulas:*

(a) $CH_3CCl_2CH_2CH_3$ (f) $CH_3CH_2CH_2CH_2OH$

(b) $CH_3CH(CH_2Cl)CH_2CH_3$

(c) $(CH_3)_3CCH_2CH_3$

(d) $CH_3CHClCHClCH_3$ (g) $CH_3\overset{\overset{\textstyle O}{\|}}{C}CH_2CH(CH_3)_2$

(e) $CH_3CH(OH)CH_2CH_3$ (h) $CH_3CH_2CH(OH)CH(CH_3)_2$

Problem 1.18

Are any of the compounds listed in Problem 1.17 constitutional (structural) isomers of each other? If so, which ones are?

Problem 1.19

Write dash formulas for each of the following bond-line formulas:

(a)   (b)   (c)   (d)

1.20E THREE-DIMENSIONAL FORMULAS

None of the formulas that we have described so far conveys any information about how the atoms of a molecule are arranged in space. There are several types of representations that do this. The type of formula that we shall use is shown in Fig. 1.31. In this representation, bonds that project upward out of the plane of the paper are indicated by a wedge (—), those that lie behind the plane are indicated with a dashed wedge (⸺), and those bonds that lie in the plane of the page are indicated by a line (—).

Problem 1.20

Write three-dimensional (wedge – dashed wedge – line) representations for each of the following: (a) CH_3Cl, (b) CH_2Cl_2, (c) CH_2BrCl, (d) CH_3CH_2Cl.

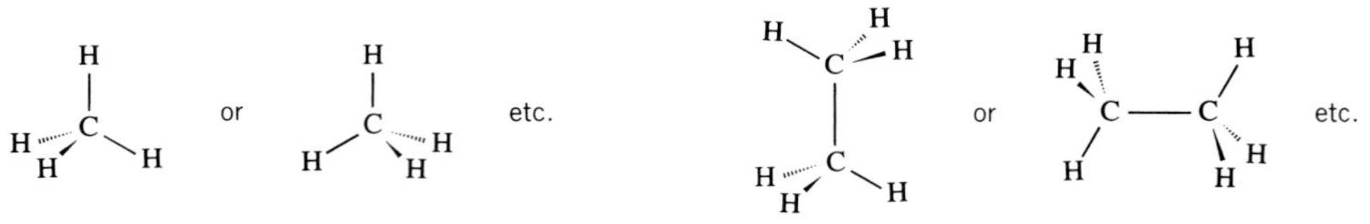

Methane

Ethane

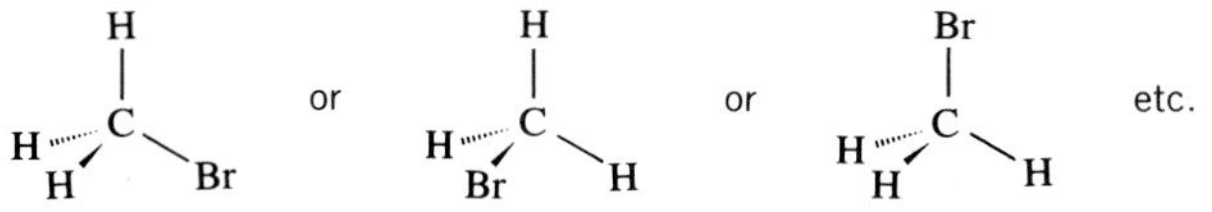

Bromomethane

FIGURE 1.31 Three-dimensional formulas using wedge–dashed wedge–line formulas.

Additional Problems

1.21 Show an electron-dot formula, including any formal charge, for each of the following compounds:

(a) CH_3NCS (c) CH_3ONO_2 (e) CH_2CO (g) KNH_2 (i) CH_2O

(b) CH_3CNO (d) CH_3NCO (f) CH_2N_2 (h) NaN_3 (j) HCO_2H

1.22 (a) Write out the ground state electron configuration for each of the following atoms. (b) Make a sketch of the atom showing the orbital arrangement, shape, and the disposition of the electrons in *s* and *p* orbitals.

(1) Be   (2) B   (3) C   (4) N   (5) O

1.23 Give the formal charge (if one exists) on each atom of the following:

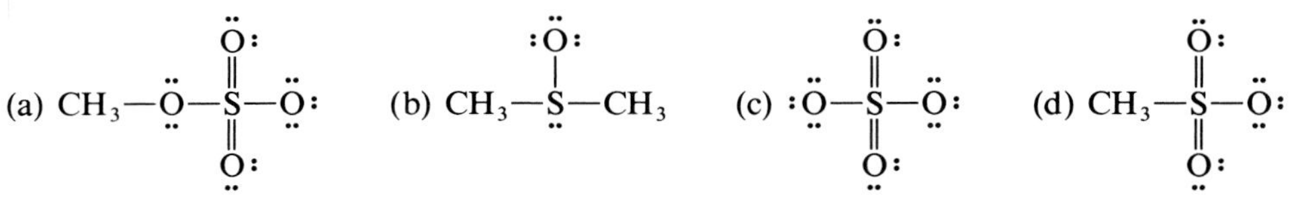

1.24 Write a condensed structural formula for each compound given here.

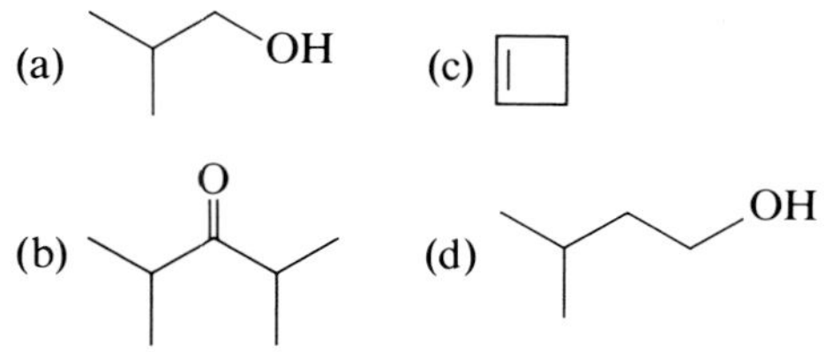

1.25 What is the molecular formula for each of the compounds given in Problem 1.24?

1.26 Consider each pair of structural formulas that follow and state whether the two formulas represent the same compound, whether they represent different compounds that are constitutional isomers of each other, or whether they represent different compounds that are not isomeric.

(a) 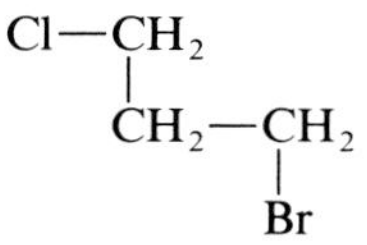 $Cl-CH_2$
   $\quad\quad CH_2-CH_2$
   $\quad\quad\quad\quad\quad\quad |$
   $\quad\quad\quad\quad\quad\quad Br$

and

$$\begin{array}{ccc} H & H & H \\ | & | & | \\ H-C & -C & -C-Br \\ | & | & | \\ H & H & H \end{array}$$

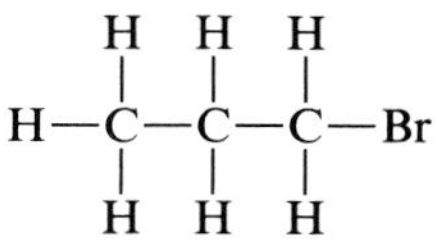

(b) 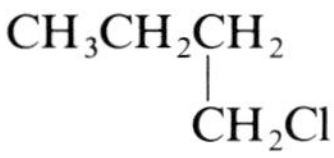 $CH_3CH_2CH_2$
   $\quad\quad\quad |$
   $\quad\quad\quad CH_2Cl$

and $ClCH_2CH(CH_3)_2$

(c) 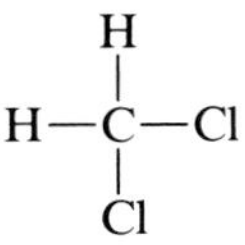 $H-\overset{\displaystyle H}{\underset{\displaystyle Cl}{C}}-Cl$ and $Cl-\overset{\displaystyle H}{\underset{\displaystyle H}{C}}-Cl$

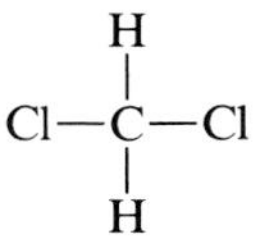

(d) 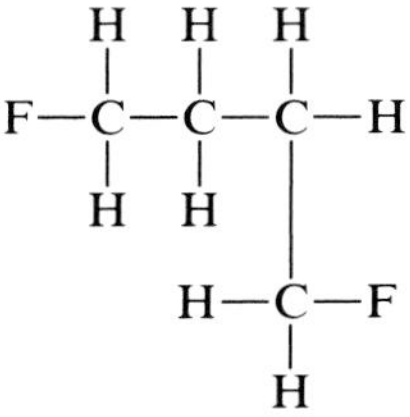 $F-\overset{\displaystyle H}{\underset{\displaystyle H}{C}}-\overset{\displaystyle H}{\underset{\displaystyle H}{C}}-\overset{\displaystyle H}{C}-H$ and $CH_2FCH_2CH_2CH_2F$
$\quad\quad\quad\quad\quad\quad\quad\quad |$
$\quad\quad\quad\quad\quad\quad H-C-F$
$\quad\quad\quad\quad\quad\quad\quad\quad |$
$\quad\quad\quad\quad\quad\quad\quad\quad H$

(e) 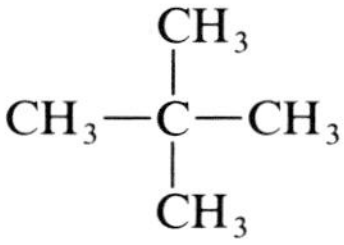 $CH_3-\overset{\displaystyle CH_3}{\underset{\displaystyle CH_3}{C}}-CH_3$ and $(CH_3)_3C-CH_3$

(f) $CH_2{=}CHCH_2CH_3$ and
$$\overset{\displaystyle CH_3}{\underset{\displaystyle H_2C-CH_2}{\overset{|}{CH}}}$$

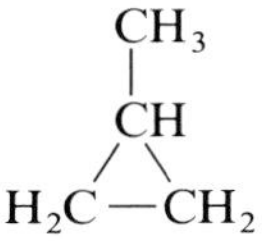

(g) $CH_3OCH_2CH_3$ and $CH_3-\overset{\displaystyle O}{\overset{\|}{C}}-CH_3$

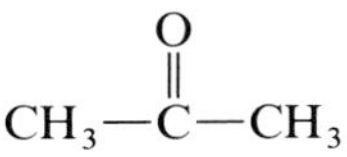

(h) 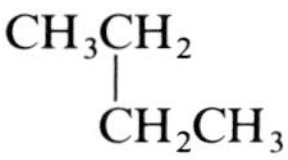 CH_3CH_2
   $\quad\quad |$
   $\quad\quad CH_2CH_3$

and $CH_3CH_2CH_2CH_3$

(i) $CH_3OCH_2CH_3$ and
$$\overset{\displaystyle O}{\underset{\displaystyle H_2C-CH_2}{\overset{\|}{C}}}$$

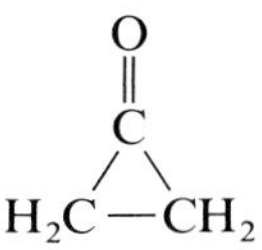

(j) $CH_2ClCHClCH_3$ and $CH_3CHClCH_2Cl$

(k) $CH_3CH_2CHClCH_2Cl$ and CH_3CHCH_2Cl
$\quad\quad\quad\quad\quad\quad\quad\quad\quad\quad\quad\quad |$
$\quad\quad\quad\quad\quad\quad\quad\quad\quad\quad\quad\quad CH_2Cl$

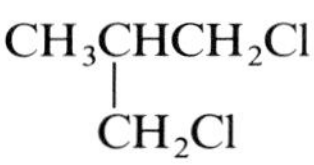

(l) 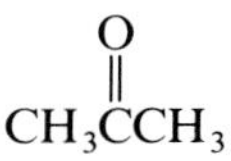 $CH_3\overset{\displaystyle O}{\overset{\|}{C}}CH_3$ and
$$\overset{\displaystyle O}{\underset{\displaystyle H_2C-CH_2}{\overset{\|}{C}}}$$

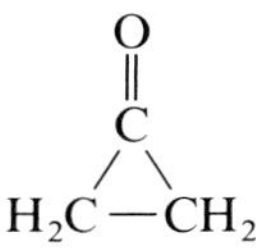

(m) H—C(Cl)(H)—Br   and   Cl—C(H)(H)—Br

(n) CH₃—C(CH₃)(H)—H   and   CH₃—C(H)(H)—CH₃

(o) [H, H, H, C—C, F, H, F] and [H, H, H, C—C, F, F, H]

(p) [H, H, H, C—C, F, F, H] and [F, H, H, C—C, F, H, H]

1.27 Write a three-dimensional formula for each of the following molecules. If the molecule has a net dipole moment, indicate its direction with an arrow, ⟶ . If the molecule has no net dipole moment, you should so state. (You may ignore the small polarity of C—H bonds in working this and similar problems.)

(a) CH_3F (c) CHF_3 (e) CH_2FCl (g) BeF_2 (i) CH_3OH

(b) CH_2F_2 (d) CF_4 (f) BCl_3 (h) CH_3OCH_3 (j) CH_2O

1.28 Rewrite each of the following using bond-line formulas:

(a) $CH_3CH_2CH_2\overset{O}{\overset{\|}{C}}CH_3$

(d) $CH_3CH_2\underset{CH_3}{CH}CH_2\overset{O}{\overset{\|}{C}}OH$

(b) $CH_3\underset{CH_3}{CH}CH_2CH_2\underset{CH_3}{CH}CH_2CH_3$

(e) $CH_2{=}CHCH_2CH_2CH{=}CHCH_3$

(c) $(CH_3)_3CCH_2CH_2CH_2OH$

(f)

1.29 Write a dash formula for each of the following showing any unshared electron pairs:

(a)   (b) 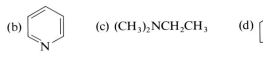   (c) $(CH_3)_2NCH_2CH_3$ (d)

ADDITIONAL PROBLEMS

1.30 Write structural formulas of your choice for all of the constitutional isomers with the molecular formula C_4H_8.

1.31 Write two resonance structures for the nitrite ion (NO_2^-), and show the formal charge on each atom in each structure. Do these structures account for the fact that the nitrogen bonds are of equal length?

1.32 (a) Taking into account the shape of an ammonia molecule (Section 1.17B), in what kind of orbital would you expect the unshared electron pair to be found? (b) In what kind(s) of orbitals would you expect the electron pairs of a water molecule to be found? Explain.

1.33 Chloromethane (CH_3Cl) has a larger dipole moment ($\mu = 1.87$ D) than fluoromethane (CH_3F) ($\mu = 1.81$ D), even though fluorine is more electronegative than chlorine. Explain.

1.34 Cyanic acid ($H—O—C\equiv N$) and isocyanic acid ($H—N=C=O$) differ in the positions of their electrons but their structures do not represent resonance structures. (a) Explain. (b) Loss of a proton from cyanic acid yields the same anion as that obtained by loss of a proton from isocyanic acid. Explain.

1.35 Boron trifluoride reacts readily with ammonia to form a compound, BF_3NH_3. (a) What factors account for this reaction taking place so readily? (b) What formal charge is present on boron in the product? (c) On nitrogen? (d) What hybridization state would you expect for boron in the product? (e) For nitrogen?

1.36 Consider the substances, H_3O^+, H_2O, and OH^-; or NH_3 and NH_4^+; or H_2S and SH^-, and describe the relationship between formal charge and acid strength.

1.37 Ozone (O_3) is found in the upper atmosphere where it absorbs highly energetic ultraviolet (UV) light and thus provides the surface of the earth with a protective screen (cf. Section 7.10). (a) Given that ozone molecules are not cyclic, and that all of the electrons are paired, write resonance structures for ozone. (b) Would you expect the two oxygen–oxygen bonds of ozone to be equivalent? (c) Given that ozone has a dipole moment ($\mu = 0.52$ D) what does this indicate about the shape of an ozone molecule? (d) Is this the shape you would predict on the basis of VSEPR theory? Explain.

1.38 In Problem 1.2 you wrote the Lewis structure for the methyl cation (CH_3^+). In Problem 1.8 you were able to predict its shape on the basis of VSEPR theory. Now describe the methyl cation in terms of orbital hybridization. (Pay special attention to the hybridization state of the carbon atom and be sure to include any vacant orbitals.)

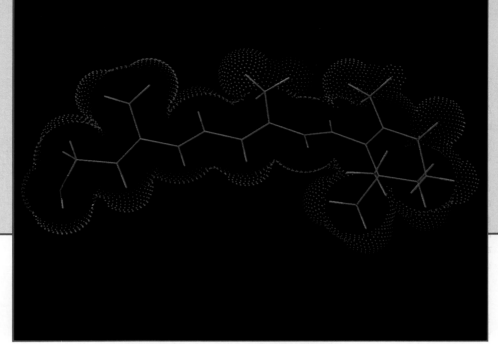

Vitamin A (see Problem 2.15).

REPRESENTATIVE CARBON COMPOUNDS

2.1 CARBON–CARBON COVALENT BONDS

Carbon's ability to form strong covalent bonds to other carbon atoms is the single property of the carbon atom that—more than any other—accounts for the very existence of a field of study called organic chemistry. It is this property too that accounts in part for carbon being the element around which most of the molecules of living organisms are constructed. Carbon's ability to form as many as four strong bonds to other carbon atoms and to form strong bonds to hydrogen, oxygen, sulfur, and nitrogen atoms as well, provides the necessary versatility of structure that makes possible the vast number of different molecules required for complex living organisms.

2.2 METHANE AND ETHANE: REPRESENTATIVE ALKANES

Methane (CH_4) and ethane (C_2H_6) are two members of a broad family of organic compounds called **hydrocarbons.** Hydrocarbons, as the name implies, are compounds whose molecules contain only carbon and hydrogen atoms. Methane and ethane also belong to a subgroup of hydrocarbons known as **alkanes** whose members do not have multiple bonds between carbon atoms. *Hydrocarbons whose molecules have a carbon–carbon double bond* are called *alkenes,* and *those with a carbon–carbon triple bond* are called *alkynes.* Hydrocarbons that contain a special ring that we shall introduce in Section 2.7 and study in Chapter 13 are called aromatic hydrocarbons.

Generally speaking, compounds such as the alkanes, whose molecules contain only single bonds are referred to as **saturated compounds** because these compounds contain the maximum number of hydrogen atoms that the carbon compound can possess. Compounds with multiple bonds, such as alkenes, alkynes, and aromatic hydrocarbons are called **unsaturated compounds,** because they possess fewer than the maximum number of hydrogen atoms, and are capable of reacting with hydrogen under the proper conditions. We shall have more to say about this in Chapter 6.

2.2A SOURCES OF METHANE

Methane was one major component of the early atmosphere of this planet. Methane is still found in the atmosphere of Earth, but no longer in appreciable amounts. It is, however, a major component of the atmosphere of Jupiter, Saturn, Uranus, and Neptune. Recently, methane has also been detected in interstellar space — far from the Earth (10^{16} km) in a celestial body that emits radio waves in the constellation Orion.

On Earth, methane is the major component of natural gas, along with ethane and other low molecular weight alkanes. The United States is currently using its large

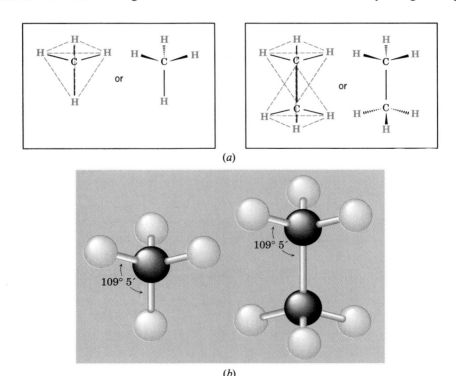

(a)

(b)

FIGURE 2.1 (a) Two ways of representing the structures of methane and ethane that show the tetrahedral arrangements of the atoms around carbon. (b) Ball-and-stick models of methane and ethane.

reserves of natural gas at a very high rate. Because the components of natural gas are important in industry, efforts are being made to develop coal-gasification processes to provide alternative sources.

Some living organisms produce methane from carbon dioxide and hydrogen. These very primitive creatures called *methanogens* may be the Earth's oldest organisms, and they may represent a separate form of evolutionary development. Methanogens can survive only in an anaerobic (i.e., oxygen-free) environment. They have been found in ocean trenches, in mud, in sewage, and in cows' stomachs.

2.2B THE STRUCTURE OF ETHANE

The bond angles at the carbon atoms of ethane, and of all alkanes, are also tetrahedral like those in methane. In the case of ethane (Fig. 2.1), each carbon atom is at one corner of the other carbon atom's tetrahedron; hydrogen atoms are situated at the other three corners.

A satisfactory model for ethane (and for other alkanes as well) can be provided by sp^3-hybridized carbon atoms (Section 1.13). Figure 2.2 shows how we might imagine the bonding molecular orbitals of an ethane molecule being constructed from two sp^3-hybridized carbon atoms and six hydrogen atoms.

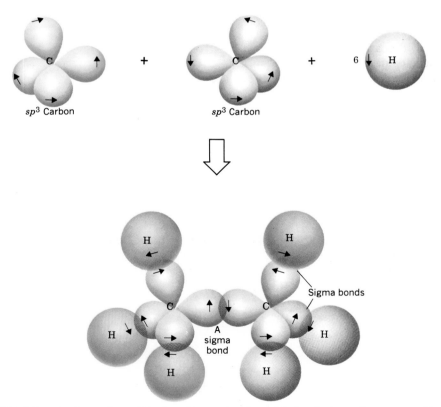

FIGURE 2.2 The formation of the bonding molecular orbitals of ethane from two sp^3-hybridized carbon atoms and six hydrogen atoms. All of the bonds are sigma bonds. (Antibonding sigma molecular orbitals—called σ^* orbitals—are formed in each instance as well, but for simplicity these are not shown.)

The carbon–carbon bond of ethane is a *sigma bond* (Section 1.13), formed by two overlapping sp^3 orbitals. (The carbon–hydrogen bonds are also sigma bonds. They are formed from overlapping carbon sp^3 orbitals and hydrogen s orbitals.)

Because a sigma bond (i.e., any nonmultiple bond) has circular symmetry along the bond axis, *rotation of groups joined by a single bond does not usually require a large amount of energy.* Consequently, groups joined by single bonds rotate relatively freely with respect to one another. (We discuss this point further in Section 4.6.)

2.3 ALKENES: COMPOUNDS CONTAINING THE CARBON–CARBON DOUBLE BOND; ETHENE AND PROPENE

The carbon atoms of virtually all of the molecules that we have considered so far have used their four valence electrons to form four single covalent bonds to four other atoms. We find, however, that many important organic compounds exist in which carbon atoms share more than two electrons with another atom. In molecules of these compounds some bonds that are formed are multiple covalent bonds. When two carbon atoms share two pairs of electrons, for example, the result is a carbon–carbon double bond.

$$\ddot{C}::\ddot{C} \quad \text{or} \quad \overset{\diagdown}{\underset{\diagup}{C}}=\overset{\diagup}{\underset{\diagdown}{C}}$$

Hydrocarbons whose molecules contain a carbon–carbon double bond are called **alkenes.** Ethene (C_2H_4) and propene (C_3H_6) are both alkenes. (Ethene is also called ethylene, and propene is sometimes called propylene.)

H   H   H   H
 \\   /   \\   /
  C=C   C=C
 /   \\   /   \\
H   H   H₃C   H

Ethene   **Propene**

In ethene the only carbon–carbon bond is a double bond. Propene has one carbon–carbon single bond and one carbon–carbon double bond.

The spatial arrangement of the atoms of alkenes is different from that of alkanes. The six atoms of ethene are coplanar, and the arrangement of atoms around each carbon atom is triangular (Fig. 2.3). In Section 2.4 we shall see how the structure of ethene can be explained on the basis of the same kind of orbital hybridization, sp^2, that we learned about for BH_3 (Section 1.14).

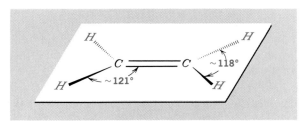

FIGURE 2.3   The structure and bond angles of ethene.

2.4 ORBITAL HYBRIDIZATION AND THE STRUCTURE OF ALKENES

A satisfactory model for the carbon–carbon double bond can be based on sp^2-hybridized carbon atoms.*

The mathematical mixing of orbitals that furnish the sp^2 orbitals for our model can be visualized in the way shown in Fig. 2.4. The $2s$ orbital is mathematically mixed (or hybridized) with two of the $2p$ orbitals. (The hybridization procedure applies only to the orbitals, not to the electrons.) One $2p$ orbital is left unhybridized. One electron is then placed in each of the sp^2-hybrid orbitals and one electron remains in the $2p$ orbital.

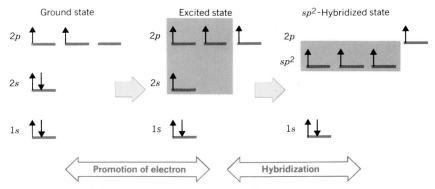

FIGURE 2.4 A process for obtaining sp^2-hybridized carbon atoms.

The three sp^2 orbitals that result from hybridization are directed towards the corners of a regular triangle (with angles of $120°$ between them). The carbon p orbital that is not hybridized is perpendicular to the plane of the triangle formed by the hybrid sp^2 orbitals (Fig. 2.5).

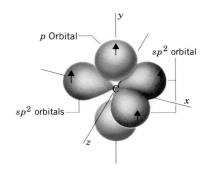

FIGURE 2.5 An sp^2-hybridized carbon atom.

In our model for ethene (Fig. 2.6) we see that two sp^2-hybridized carbon atoms form a sigma (σ) bond between them by the overlap of one sp^2 orbital from each. The remaining sp^2 orbitals of the carbon atoms form σ bonds to four hydrogen atoms

*An alternative model for the carbon–carbon bond is discussed in an article by W. E. Palke, *J. Am. Chem. Soc.*, **1986**, *108*, 6543–6544.

through overlap with the $1s$ orbitals of the hydrogen atoms. These five bonds account for 10 of the 12 bonding electrons of ethene, and they are called the **σ-bond framework.** The bond angles that we would predict on the basis of sp^2-hybridized carbon atoms (120° all around) are quite close to the bond angles that are actually found (Fig. 2.3).

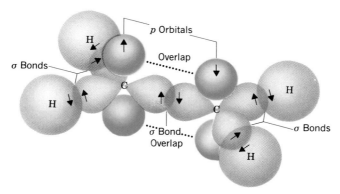

FIGURE 2.6 A model for the bonding molecular orbitals of ethene formed from two sp^2-hybridized carbon atoms and four hydrogen atoms.

The remaining two bonding electrons in our model are located in the p orbitals of each carbon atom. We can better visualize how these p orbitals interact with each other if we replace the $σ$ bonds by lines. This is shown in Fig. 2.7. We see that the parallel p orbitals *overlap above and below the plane of the σ framework.* This sideways overlap of the p orbitals results in a new type of covalent bond, known as a **pi (π) bond.** Note the difference in shape of the bonding molecular orbital of a $π$ bond as contrasted to that of a $σ$ bond. A $σ$ bond has cylindrical symmetry about a line connecting the two bonded nuclei. A $π$ bond has a nodal plane passing through the two bonded nuclei.

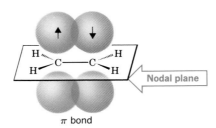

FIGURE 2.7 The overlapping p orbitals of ethene to make a $π$ bond.

According to molecular orbital theory, both bonding and antibonding $π$ molecular orbitals are formed when p orbitals interact in this way to form a $π$ bond. The bonding $π$ orbital (Fig. 2.8) results when p-orbital lobes of like signs overlap; the antibonding $π$ orbital is formed when p-orbital lobes of opposite signs overlap.

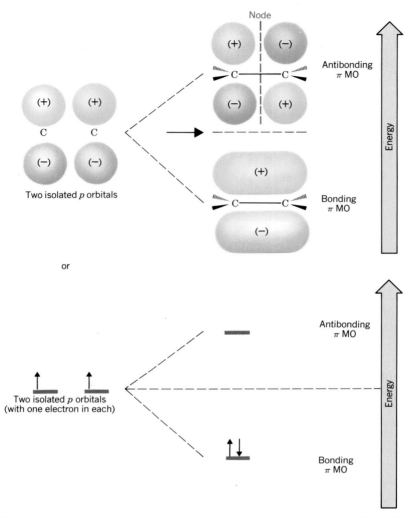

FIGURE 2.8 How two *p* orbitals combine to form two π (pi) molecular orbitals. The bonding MO is of lower energy. The higher energy antibonding MO contains an additional node. (Both orbitals have a node in the plane containing the C and H atoms.)

The bonding π orbital is the lower-energy orbital and contains both π electrons (with opposite spins) in the ground state of the molecule. The region of greatest probability of finding the electrons in the bonding π orbital is a region generally situated above and below the plane of the σ-bond framework between the two carbon atoms. The antibonding π* orbital is of higher energy, and it is not occupied by electrons when the molecule is in the ground state. It can become occupied, however, if the molecule absorbs light of the right frequency, and an electron is promoted from the lower energy level to the higher one. The antibonding π* orbital has a nodal plane between the two carbon atoms.

To summarize: In our model based on orbital hybridization, the carbon–carbon double bond is viewed as consisting of two different kinds of bonds, *a σ bond and a π bond*. The σ bond results from two overlapping *sp²* orbitals end-to-end and is symmetrical about an axis linking the two carbon atoms. The π bond results from a sideways overlap of two p orbitals; it has a nodal plane like a p orbital. In the ground state the electrons of the π bond are located between the two carbon atoms but generally above and below the plane of the σ-bond framework.

Electrons of the π bond have greater energy than electrons of the σ bond. The relative energies of the σ and π molecular orbitals (with the electrons in the ground state) are shown in the following figure. (The σ^* orbital is the antibonding sigma orbital.)

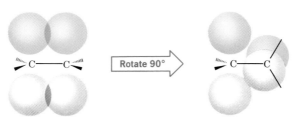

2.4A RESTRICTED ROTATION AND THE DOUBLE BOND

The $\sigma-\pi$ model for the carbon–carbon double bond also accounts for an important property of the double bond: *There is a large barrier to free rotation associated with groups joined by a double bond.* Maximum overlap between the p orbitals of a π bond occurs when the axes of the p orbitals are exactly parallel. Rotating one carbon of the double bond 90° (Fig. 2.9) breaks the π bond, for then the axes of the p orbitals are perpendicular and there is no net overlap between them. Estimates based on thermochemical calculations indicate that the strength of the π bond is 63 kcal mol^{-1}. This, then, is the barrier to rotation of the double bond. It is markedly higher than the rotational barrier of groups joined by carbon–carbon single bonds (3–6 kcal mol^{-1}). While groups joined by single bonds rotate relatively freely at room temperature, those joined by double bonds do not.

FIGURE 2.9   Rotation of a carbon atom of a double bond through an angle of 90° results in the breaking of the π bond.

2.4B CIS–TRANS ISOMERISM

Restricted rotation of groups joined by a double bond causes a new type of isomerism that we illustrate with the two dichloroethenes written in the following structures.

cis-1,2-Dichloroethene   *trans*-1,2-Dichloroethene

CHAPTER 2. REPRESENTATIVE CARBON COMPOUNDS

These two compounds are isomers; they are different compounds that have the same molecular formula. We can tell that they are different compounds by trying to superpose a model of one on a model of the other. We find that it cannot be done. By superpose we mean that we attempt to place one model on the other *so that all parts of each coincide.*

We indicate that they are different isomers by attaching the prefixes cis or trans to their names (cis, Latin: on this side; trans, Latin: across). *cis*-1,2-Dichloroethene and *trans*-1,2-dichloroethene are not constitutional isomers because the connectivity of the atoms is the same in each. The two compounds **differ only in the arrangement of their atoms in space.** Isomers of this kind are classified formally as **stereoisomers,** but often they are called simply cis–trans isomers. (We shall study stereoisomerism in detail in Chapters 4 and 5.)

The structural requirements for cis–trans isomerism will become clear if we consider a few additional examples. 1,1-Dichloroethene and 1,1,2-trichloroethene do not show this type of isomerism.

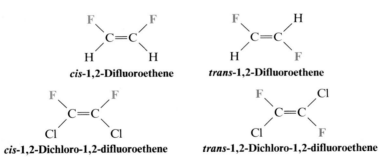

1,2-Difluoroethene and 1,2-dichloro-1,2-difluoroethene do exist as cis–trans isomers. Notice that we designate the isomer with two identical groups on the same side as being cis.

Clearly, then, *cis–trans isomerism of this type is not possible if one carbon atom of the double bond bears two identical groups.*

Problem 2.1

Which of the following alkenes can exist as cis–trans isomers? Write their structures.

(a) CH_2=$CHCH_2CH_3$ (c) CH_2=$C(CH_3)_2$

(b) CH_3CH=$CHCH_3$ (d) CH_3CH_2CH=$CHCl$

Cis–trans isomers have different physical properties. They have different melting points and boiling points, and often cis–trans isomers differ markedly in the

TABLE 2.1   Physical properties of cis–trans isomers

COMPOUND	MELTING POINT (°C)	BOILING POINT (°C)	DIPOLE MOMENT (D)
cis-1,2-Dichloroethene	−80	60	1.90
trans-1,2-Dichloroethene	−50	48	0
cis-1,2-Dibromoethene	−53	112.5	1.35
trans-1,2-Dibromoethene	− 6	108	0

magnitude of their dipole moments. Table 2.1 summarizes some of the physical properties of two pairs of cis–trans isomers.

Problem 2.2

(a) How do you explain the fact that trans-1,2-dichloroethene and trans-1,2-dibromoethene have no dipole moments ($\mu = 0$), whereas the corresponding cis isomers have rather large dipole moments (for cis-1,2-dichloroethene, $\mu = 1.90$ D, and for cis-1,2-dibromoethene, $\mu = 1.35$ D)?   (b) Account for the fact that cis-1,2-dichloroethene has a larger dipole moment than cis-1,2-dibromoethene.

Problem 2.3

Write structural formulas for   (a) all of the compounds that could be obtained by replacing one hydrogen of propene with chlorine;   (b) all of the compounds that could be obtained by replacing two hydrogen atoms of propene with chlorine;   (c) three hydrogens;   (d) four hydrogens;   (e) five hydrogens.   (f) In each instance [(a)–(e)] designate pairs of cis–trans isomers.

2.5 ALKYNES: COMPOUNDS CONTAINING THE CARBON–CARBON TRIPLE BOND; ETHYNE (ACETYLENE) AND PROPYNE

Hydrocarbons in which two carbon atoms share three pairs of electrons between them, and are thus bonded by a triple bond, are called **alkynes.** The two simplest alkynes are ethyne and propyne.

$$H—C\equiv C—H \qquad CH_3—C\equiv C—H$$

Ethyne   **Propyne**
(acetylene)   (C_3H_4)
(C_2H_2)

   Ethyne, a compound that is also called acetylene, consists of linear molecules. The $H—C\equiv C$ bond angles of ethyne molecules are 180°.

$$H\overset{\frown}{—}C\equiv C\overset{\frown}{—}H$$
180°   180°

2.6 ORBITAL HYBRIDIZATION AND THE STRUCTURE OF ALKYNES

We can account for the structure of ethyne on the basis of orbital hybridization as we did for ethane and ethene. In our model for ethane (Section 2.2B) we saw that the carbon orbitals are sp^3 hybridized, and in our model for ethene (Section 2.4) we saw that they are sp^2 hybridized. In our model for ethyne we shall see that the carbon atoms are *sp hybridized* and resemble the hybrid orbitals of BeH_2 (Section 1.15).

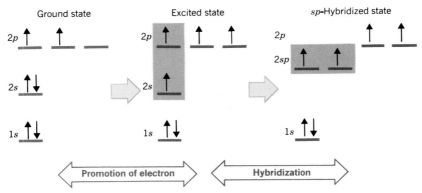

FIGURE 2.10 A process for obtaining *sp*-hybridized carbon atoms.

The mathematical process for obtaining the *sp*-hybrid orbitals of ethyne can be visualized in the following way (Fig. 2.10). The 2s orbital and one 2p orbital of carbon are hybridized to form two *sp* orbitals. The remaining two 2p orbitals are not hybridized. Calculations show that the *sp*-hybrid orbitals have their large positive lobes oriented at an angle of 180° with respect to each other. The 2p orbitals that were not hybridized are perpendicular to the axis that passes through the center of the two *sp* orbitals (Fig. 2.11).

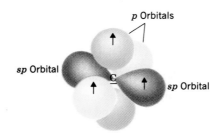

FIGURE 2.11 An *sp*-hybridized carbon atom.

We envision the bonding molecular orbitals of ethyne being formed in the following way (Fig. 2.12). Two carbon atoms overlap *sp* orbitals to form a sigma bond between them (this is one bond of the triple bond). The remaining two *sp* orbitals at each carbon atom overlap with *s* orbitals from hydrogen atoms to produce two sigma C—H bonds. The two *p* orbitals on each carbon atom also overlap side to side to form two π bonds. These are the other two bonds of the triple bond. If we replace the σ bonds of this illustration with lines, it is easier to see how the *p* orbitals overlap. Thus we see that the carbon–carbon triple bond consists of two π bonds and one σ bond.

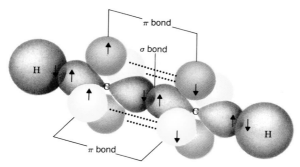

FIGURE 2.12 Formation of the bonding molecular orbitals of ethyne from two *sp*-hybridized carbon atoms and two hydrogen atoms. (Antibonding orbitals are formed as well but these have been omitted for simplicity.)

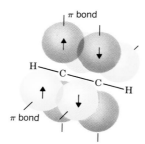

2.6A BOND LENGTHS OF ETHYNE, ETHENE, AND ETHANE

The carbon–carbon triple bond is shorter than the carbon–carbon double bond, and the carbon–carbon double bond is shorter than the carbon–carbon single bond. The carbon–hydrogen bonds of ethyne are also shorter than those of ethene, and the carbon–hydrogen bonds of ethene are shorter than those of ethane. This illustrates a general principle: *The shortest C—H bonds are associated with those carbon orbitals with the greatest s character.* The *sp* orbitals of ethyne — 50% *s* (and 50% *p*) in character — form the shortest C—H bonds. The *sp*³ orbitals of ethane — 25% *s* (and 75% *p*) in character form the longest C—H bonds. The differences in bond lengths and bond angles of ethyne, ethene, and ethane are summarized in Fig. 2.13.

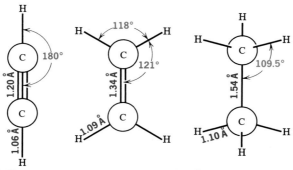

FIGURE 2.13 Bond angles and bond lengths of ethyne, ethene, and ethane.

2.7 BENZENE: A REPRESENTATIVE AROMATIC HYDROCARBON

In Chapter 13 we shall study a group of cyclic hydrocarbons known as **aromatic hydrocarbons.** Benzene is a typical example. The structure of benzene can be represented as a resonance hybrid of the two forms (called Kekulé structures) that follow:

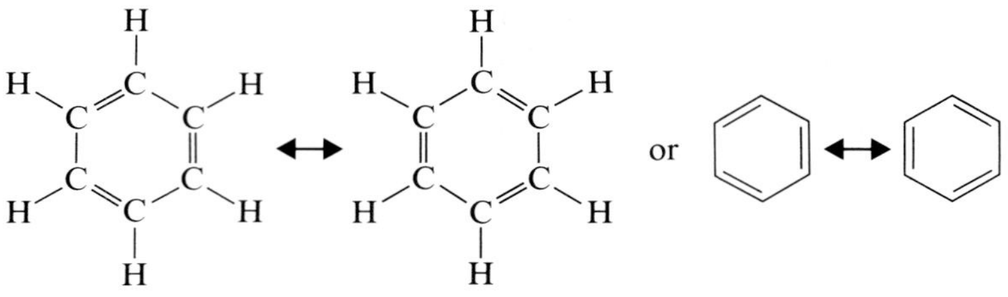

We generally write the structure of benzene by using one of the Kekulé structures or by writing a hexagon with a circle in the middle to indicate that benzene is a resonance hybrid.

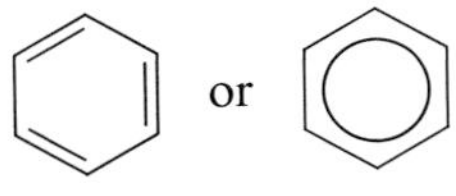

Two ways of representing the structure of benzene

When the benzene ring is attached to some other group of atoms in a molecule, it is called a **phenyl group** and it is represented in several ways:

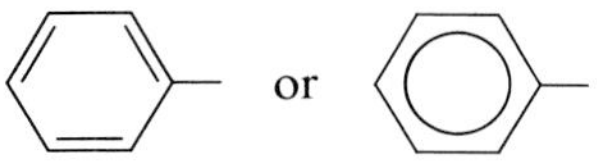

Ways of representing a phenyl group

The combination of a phenyl group and a $-CH_2-$ group is called a **benzyl group.**

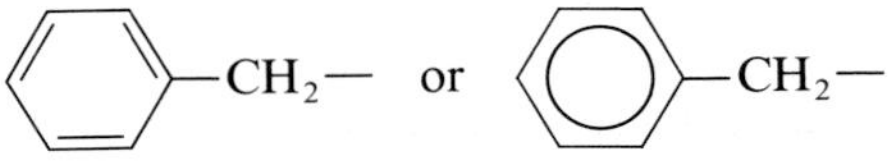

Ways of representing a benzyl group

We shall defer a detailed study of benzene and other aromatic compounds until Chapter 13.

2.8 FUNCTIONAL GROUPS

One great advantage of the structural theory is that it enables us to classify the vast number of organic compounds into a relatively small number of families based on their structures. (The end papers inside the front cover of this text give the most important of these families.) The molecules of compounds in a particular family are characterized by the presence of a certain arrangement of atoms called a **functional group.**

2.8 FUNCTIONAL GROUPS

A functional group is the part of a molecule where most of its chemical reactions occur. It is the part that effectively determines the compound's chemical properties (and many of its physical properties as well). The functional group of an alkene, for example, is its carbon–carbon double bond. When we study the reactions of alkenes in greater detail in Chapter 9, we shall find that most of the chemical reactions of alkenes are the chemical reactions of the carbon–carbon double bond.

The functional group of an alkyne is its carbon–carbon triple bond. Alkanes do not have a functional group. Their molecules have carbon–carbon single bonds and carbon–hydrogen bonds, but these bonds are present in molecules of almost all organic molecules, and C—C and C—H bonds are, in general, much less reactive than common functional groups.

2.8A ALKYL GROUPS AND THE SYMBOL R

Alkyl groups are the groups that we identify for purposes of naming compounds. They are groups that would be obtained by removing a hydrogen atom from an alkane:

Alkane	Alkyl Group	Abbreviation
CH_4 Methane	CH_3- Methyl group	Me—
CH_3CH_3 Ethane	CH_3CH_2- or C_2H_5- Ethyl group	Et—
$CH_3CH_2CH_3$ Propane	$CH_3CH_2CH_2-$ Propyl group	Pr—
$CH_3CH_2CH_3$ Propane	$CH_3-CH-CH_3$ or $CH_3\overset{\underset{\displaystyle CH_3}{\|}}{CH}-$ Isopropyl group	i-Pr—

While only one alkyl group can be derived from methane and ethane (the **methyl** and **ethyl** groups, respectively), two groups can be derived from propane. Removal of a hydrogen from one of the end carbon atoms gives a group that is called the **propyl** group; removal of a hydrogen from the middle carbon atom gives a group that is called the **isopropyl** group. The names and structures of these groups are used so frequently in organic chemistry that you should learn them now.

We can simplify much of our future discussion if, at this point, we introduce a symbol that is widely used in designating general structures of organic molecules: The symbol R. *R is used as a general symbol to represent any alkyl group.* For example, R might be a methyl group, an ethyl group, a propyl group, or an isopropyl group.

$$
\left.
\begin{array}{ll}
CH_3- & \text{Methyl} \\
CH_3CH_2- & \text{Ethyl} \\
CH_3CH_2CH_2- & \text{Propyl} \\
CH_3\underset{|}{CH}CH_3 & \text{Isopropyl}
\end{array}
\right\}
\begin{array}{l}
\text{All of} \\
\text{these} \\
\text{can be} \\
\text{designated}
\end{array}
\text{ by } \mathbf{R}
$$

Thus, the general formula for an alkane is R—H.

Using R, we can write also a general formula for any monosubstituted alkene (i.e., one having only one alkyl group attached to a doubly bonded carbon) such as propene. We write the formula in the following way:

$$R{-}CH{=}CH_2$$

Similarly, we can write a general formula for any monosubstituted alkyne (i.e., one with only one alkyl group attached to the triply bonded carbon atom) such as propyne:

$$R{-}C{\equiv}CH$$

2.9 ALKYL HALIDES OR HALOALKANES

Alkyl halides are compounds in which a halogen atom (fluorine, chlorine, bromine, or iodine) replaces a hydrogen atom of an alkane. For example, CH_3Cl and CH_3CH_2Br are alkyl halides. Alkyl halides are also called **haloalkanes.**

Alkyl halides are classified as being primary (1°), secondary (2°), or tertiary (3°).* ***This classification is based on the carbon atom to which the halogen is directly attached.*** If the carbon ***atom*** that bears the halogen is attached to only one other carbon, the carbon atom is said to be a **primary carbon atom** and the alkyl halide is classified as a **primary alkyl halide.** If the carbon that bears the halogen is itself attached to two other carbon atoms, then the carbon is a **secondary carbon** and the alkyl halide is a **secondary alkyl halide.** If the carbon that bears the halogen is attached to three other carbon atoms, then the carbon is a **tertiary carbon** and the alkyl halide is a **tertiary alkyl halide.** Examples of primary, secondary, and tertiary alkyl halides are the following:

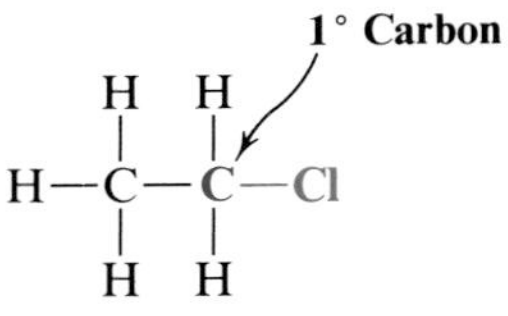

1° Alkyl
chloride

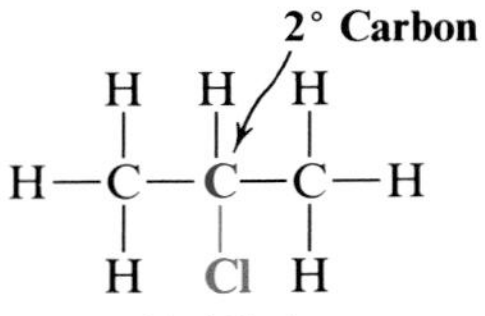

2° Alkyl
chloride

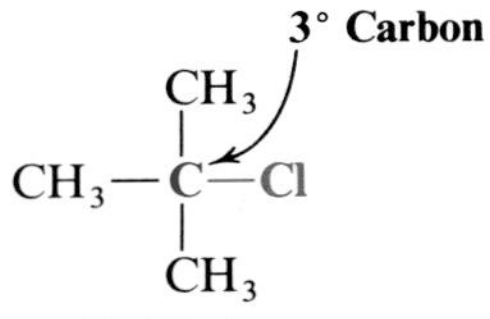

3° Alkyl
chloride

Problem 2.4

Using X to represent any halogen, write the general formula (a) for a primary alkyl halide, (b) for a secondary alkyl halide, (c) for a tertiary alkyl halide, and (d) for *any* alkyl halide regardless of its classification.

Problem 2.5

Although we shall discuss the naming of organic compounds later when we consider the individual families in detail, one method of naming alkyl halides is so straightforward that it is worth describing here. We simply give the name of

*Although we use the symbols 1°, 2°, 3°, we do not *say* first degree, second degree, and third degree; we say *primary, secondary,* and *tertiary.*

the alkyl group attached to the halogen and add the word *bromide, chloride,* and so forth. Write formulas for (a) propyl chloride and (b) isopropyl bromide. What are names for (c) CH_3CH_2F, (d) CH_3CHICH_3, and (e) CH_3I ?

2.10 ALCOHOLS

Methyl alcohol (more systematically called methanol) has the structural formula CH_3OH and is the simplest member of a family of organic compounds known as **alcohols.** The characteristic functional group of this family is the hydroxyl (OH) group attached to a tetrahedral carbon atom. Another example of an alcohol is ethyl alcohol, CH_3CH_2OH (also called ethanol).

This is the functional group of an alcohol

Alcohols may be viewed in two ways structurally: (1) as hydroxy derivatives of alkanes, and (2) as alkyl derivatives of water. Ethyl alcohol, for example, can be seen as an ethane molecule in which one hydrogen has been replaced by a hydroxyl group, or as a water molecule in which one hydrogen has been replaced by an ethyl group. That the latter way of regarding ethyl alcohol is valid is shown by observing that the C—O—H bond angle of ethyl alcohol is similar in size to the H—O—H bond angle of water.

Ethyl group

CH_3CH_2

CH_3CH_3

Hydroxyl group

Ethane

Ethyl alcohol (ethanol)

Water

As with alkyl halides, alcohols are classified into three groups; primary (1°), secondary (2°), or tertiary (3°) alcohols. *This classification is also based on the degree of substitution of the carbon to which the hydroxyl group is directly attached.* If the carbon has only one other carbon attached to it, the carbon is said to be a **primary carbon** and the alcohol is a **primary alcohol.**

1° Carbon

(a 1° alcohol)

CH_2OH

Geraniol (a 1° alcohol with the odor of roses)

CH_2OH

Benzyl alcohol (a 1° alcohol)

If the carbon atom that bears the hydroxyl group also has two other carbon atoms attached to it, this carbon is called a secondary carbon, and the alcohol is a secondary alcohol, and so on

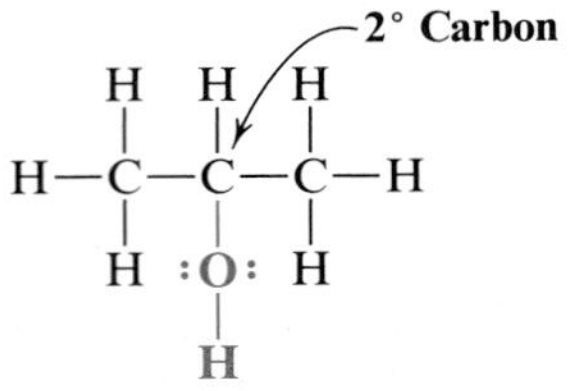

(a 2° alcohol)

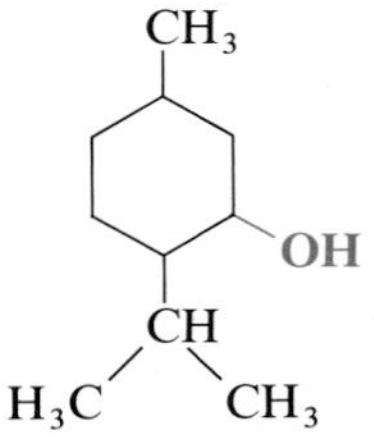

Menthol
(a 2° alcohol found
in peppermint oil)

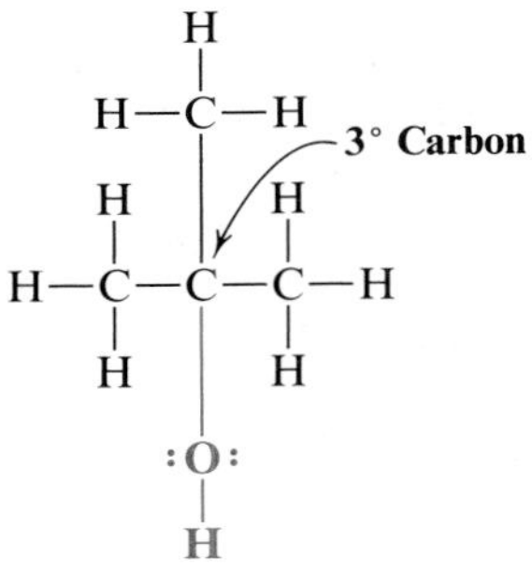

(a 3° alcohol)

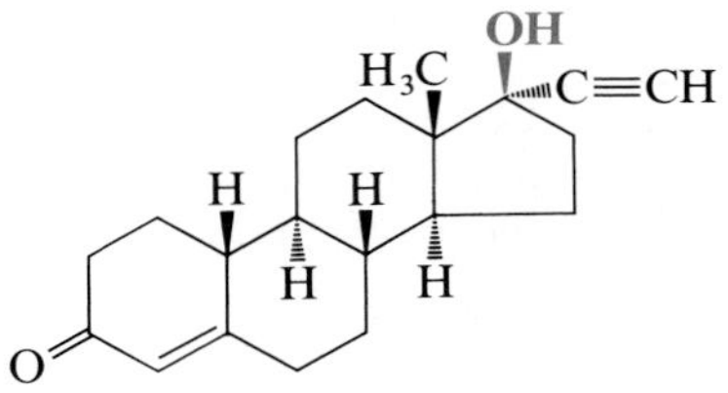

Norethindrone
(an oral contraceptive that contains a 3° alcohol
group, as well as a ketone group and carbon–
carbon double and triple bonds)

Problem 2.6 _____

Using the symbol R, write a general formula for (a) a primary alcohol, (b) a secondary alcohol, and (c) a tertiary alcohol.

Problem 2.7 _____

One way of naming alcohols is to name the alkyl group that is attached to the —OH and add the word *alcohol.* Write the structures of (a) propyl alcohol and (b) isopropyl alcohol.

2.11 ETHERS

Ethers have the general formula R—O—R or R—O—R′ where R′ may be an alkyl group different from R. They can be thought of as derivatives of water in which both hydrogen atoms have been replaced by alkyl groups. The bond angle at the oxygen atom of an ether is only slightly larger than that of water.

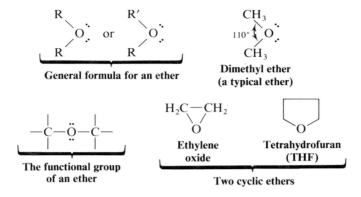

Problem 2.8

One way of naming ethers is to name the two alkyl groups attached to the oxygen atom in alphabetical order and add the word *ether*. If the two alkyl groups are the same, we use the prefix *di-*, for example, as in *dimethyl ether*. Write structural fomulas for (a) ethyl methyl ether, (b) dipropyl ether, (c) isopropyl methyl ether. (d) What name would you give to $CH_3CH_2OCH_2CH_2CH_3$, (e) to $(CH_3)_2CHOCH_2CH_2CH_3$, and (f) to $CH_3OC_6H_5$?

2.12 AMINES

Just as alcohols and ethers may be considered as organic derivatives of water, amines may be considered as organic derivatives of ammonia.

$$H—\overset{..}{N}—H \qquad R—\overset{..}{N}—H \qquad C_6H_5CH_2CHCH_3 \qquad H_2NCH_2CH_2CH_2CH_2NH_2$$
$$\underset{H}{|} \qquad\qquad \underset{H}{|} \qquad\qquad\qquad \underset{NH_2}{|}$$

Ammonia   **(an amine)**   **Amphetamine**   **Putrescine**

                      (a dangerous stimulant)   **(found in decaying meat)**

Amines are classified as primary, secondary, or tertiary amines. **This classification is based on *the number of organic groups that are attached to the nitrogen atom:***

$$R—\overset{..}{N}—H \qquad R—\overset{..}{N}—H \qquad R—\overset{..}{N}—R''$$
$$\underset{H}{|} \qquad\qquad \underset{R'}{|} \qquad\qquad \underset{R'}{|}$$

A primary (1°)   **A secondary (2°)**   **A tertiary (3°)**
    amine   **amine**   **amine**

Notice that this is quite different from the way alcohols and alkyl halides are classified. Isopropylamine, for example, is a primary amine even though its $—NH_2$ group is attached to a secondary carbon atom. It is a primary amine because only one organic group is attached to the nitrogen atom.

H H H
| | |
H—C—C—C—H
| | |
H   H

:NH₂

Isopropylamine
(a 1° amine)

(a cyclic 2° amine)

Problem 2.9

One way of naming amines is to name the alkyl groups attached to the nitrogen atom, using the prefixes *di-* and *tri-* if the groups are the same. Then *-amine* is added as a suffix (not as a separate word). An example is isopropylamine given previously. Write formulas for   (a) dimethylamine,   (b) triethylamine, and (c) ethylmethylpropylamine. What are names for   (d) $(CH_3)_2CHNHCH_3$, (e) $(CH_3CH_2CH_2)_2NCH_3$,   (f) $(CH_3)_2CHNH_2$, and   (g) $(C_6H_5)_3N$?

Problem 2.10

Which amines in Problem 2.9 are (a) primary amines, (b) secondary amines, and (c) tertiary amines?

Amines are like ammonia (Section 1.17B) in having a trigonal pyramidal shape. The C—N—C bond angles of trimethylamine are 108.7°, a value very close to the H—C—H bond angles of methane. Thus, for all practical purposes, the nitrogen atom of an amine can be considered to be sp^3 hybridized. This means that the unshared electron pair occupies an sp^3 orbital, and thus it is considerably extended into space. This is important because, as we shall see, the unshared electron pair is involved in almost all of the reactions of amines.

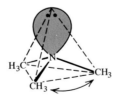

Bond angle = 108.7°

Problem 2.11

(a) What general hybridization state would you expect for the oxygen atom of an alcohol or an ether (cf. Sections 2.10 and 2.11)?   (b) What kind of orbitals would you expect the unshared electron pairs to occupy?

2.13 ALDEHYDES AND KETONES

Aldehydes and ketones both contain the **carbonyl group**—a group in which a carbon atom has a double bond to oxygen.

$$\text{C}=\overset{..}{\underset{..}{\text{O}}}:$$

The carbonyl group

The carbonyl group in aldehydes is bonded to at least one *hydrogen atom,* and in ketones it is bonded to *two carbon atoms.* Using R, we can designate the general formula for an aldehyde as

$$\text{R}-\overset{\overset{..}{\underset{..}{\text{O}}}:}{\underset{}{\overset{\|}{\text{C}}}}-\text{H} \qquad \text{R may also be H}$$

and the general formula for a ketone as

$$\text{R}-\overset{\overset{..}{\underset{..}{\text{O}}}:}{\underset{}{\overset{\|}{\text{C}}}}-\text{R} \quad \text{or} \quad \text{R}-\overset{\overset{..}{\underset{..}{\text{O}}}:}{\underset{}{\overset{\|}{\text{C}}}}-\text{R}'$$

(where R′ may be an alkyl group different from R).
    Some examples of aldehydes and ketones are

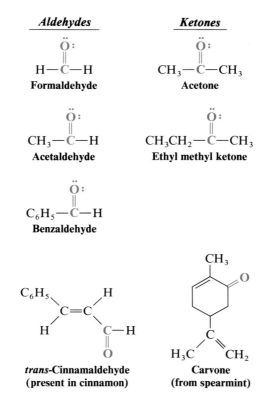

Aldehydes	*Ketones*

$$\text{H}-\overset{\overset{..}{\underset{..}{\text{O}}}:}{\underset{}{\overset{\|}{\text{C}}}}-\text{H}$$
Formaldehyde

$$\text{CH}_3-\overset{\overset{..}{\underset{..}{\text{O}}}:}{\underset{}{\overset{\|}{\text{C}}}}-\text{CH}_3$$
Acetone

$$\text{CH}_3-\overset{\overset{..}{\underset{..}{\text{O}}}:}{\underset{}{\overset{\|}{\text{C}}}}-\text{H}$$
Acetaldehyde

$$\text{CH}_3\text{CH}_2-\overset{\overset{..}{\underset{..}{\text{O}}}:}{\underset{}{\overset{\|}{\text{C}}}}-\text{CH}_3$$
Ethyl methyl ketone

$$\text{C}_6\text{H}_5-\overset{\overset{..}{\underset{..}{\text{O}}}:}{\underset{}{\overset{\|}{\text{C}}}}-\text{H}$$
Benzaldehyde

trans-Cinnamaldehyde
(present in cinnamon)

Carvone
(from spearmint)

Aldehydes and ketones have a trigonal planar arrangement of groups around the carbonyl carbon atom. The carbon atom is sp^2 hybridized. In formaldehyde, for example, the bond angles are as follows:

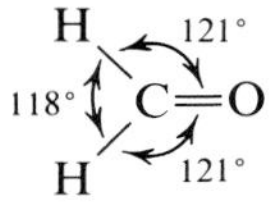

$$\begin{array}{c} H \\ 118° \quad C = O \\ H \end{array} \quad \begin{array}{c} 121° \\ 121° \end{array}$$

2.14 CARBOXYLIC ACIDS, AMIDES, AND ESTERS

2.14A CARBOXYLIC ACIDS

Carboxylic acids have the general formula $R-\overset{\overset{\displaystyle O}{\|}}{C}-O-H$. The functional group, $-\overset{\overset{\displaystyle O}{\|}}{C}-O-H$, is called the **carboxyl group** (**carb**onyl + hydr**oxyl**). (Colloquially, carboxylic acids are often just called "organic acids.")

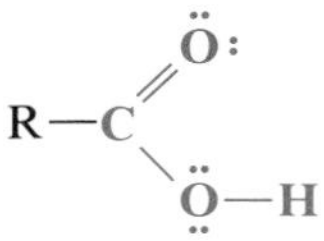

$$R-C\overset{\ddot{O}:}{\underset{\ddot{O}-H}{}} \qquad \text{or} \quad RCO_2H \quad \text{or} \quad RCOOH$$

A carboxylic acid

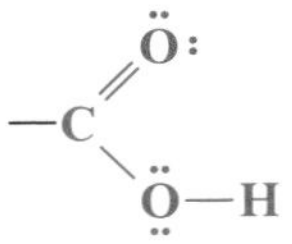

$$-C\overset{\ddot{O}:}{\underset{\ddot{O}-H}{}} \qquad \text{or} \quad -CO_2H \quad \text{or} \quad -COOH$$

The carboxyl group

Examples of carboxylic acids are formic acid, acetic acid, and benzoic acid.

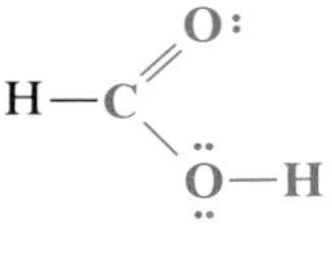

$$H-C\overset{\ddot{O}:}{\underset{\ddot{O}-H}{}} \qquad \text{or} \quad HCO_2H \quad \text{or} \quad HCOOH$$

Formic acid

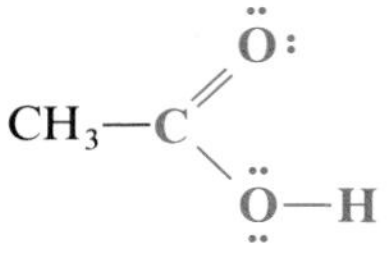

$$CH_3-C\overset{\ddot{O}:}{\underset{\ddot{O}-H}{}} \qquad \text{or} \quad CH_3CO_2H \quad \text{or} \quad CH_3COOH$$

Acetic acid

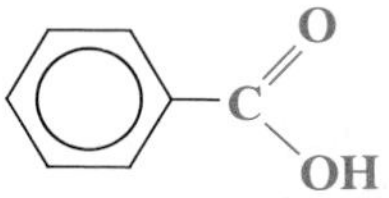

$$\bigcirc-C\overset{O}{\underset{OH}{}} \qquad \text{or} \quad C_6H_5CO_2H \quad \text{or} \quad C_6H_5COOH$$

Benzoic acid

Formic acid is an irritating liquid produced by ants. (The sting of the ant is caused, in part, by formic acid being injected under the skin.) Acetic acid, the substance responsible for the sour taste of vinegar, is produced when certain bacteria act on the ethyl alcohol of wine and cause the ethyl alcohol to be oxidized by air.

2.14B AMIDES

Amides have the formulas $RCONH_2$, RCONHR', or RCONR'R''. Specific examples are the following:

Acetamide   *N*-Methylacetamide   *N*,*N*-Dimethylacetamide

The *N*- and *N*,*N*- indicate that the substituents are attached to the nitrogen atom.

2.14C ESTERS

Esters have the general formula RCO_2R' (or RCOOR').

       or RCO_2R' or   RCOOR'

General formula for an ester

   or $CH_3CO_2CH_2CH_3$ or $CH_3COOCH_2CH_3$

A specific ester called ethyl acetate

Esters can be made from an acid and an alcohol through the loss of a molecule of water. For example:

Acetic acid   Ethyl alcohol   Ethyl acetate

2.15 SUMMARY OF IMPORTANT FAMILIES OF ORGANIC COMPOUNDS

A summary of the important families of organic compounds is given in Table 2.2. You should learn to identify these common functional groups as they appear in other more complicated molecules.

TABLE 2.2 Important families of organic compounds

Family

	ALKANE	ALKENE	ALKYNE	ARENE	HALOALKANE	ALCOHOL	ETHER	AMINE	ALDEHYDE	KETONE	CARBOXYLIC ACID	ESTER	AMIDE
Specific example	CH_3CH_3	$CH_2{=}CH_2$	$HC{\equiv}CH$	 (benzene ring)	CH_3CH_2Cl	CH_3CH_2OH	CH_3OCH_3	CH_3NH_2	$\overset{O}{CH_3CH}$	$\overset{O}{CH_3CCH_3}$	$\overset{O}{CH_3COH}$	$\overset{O}{CH_3COCH_3}$	$\overset{O}{CH_3CNH_2}$
IUPAC name	Ethane	Ethene	Ethyne	Benzene	Chloro-ethane	Ethanol	Methoxy-methane	Methan-amine	Ethanal	Propanone	Ethanoic acid	Methyl ethanoate	Ethanamide
Common name*	Ethane	Ethylene	Acetylene	Benzene	Ethyl chloride	Ethyl alcohol	Dimethyl ether	Methyl-amine	Acetal-dehyde	Acetone	Acetic acid	Methyl acetate	Acetamide
General formula	RH	$RCH{=}CH_2$ $RCH{=}CHR$ $R_2C{=}CHR$ $R_2C{=}CR_2$	$RC{\equiv}CH$ $RC{\equiv}CR$	ArH	RX	ROH	ROR	RNH_2 R_2NH R_3N	$\overset{O}{RCH}$	$\overset{O}{RCR}$	$\overset{O}{RCOH}$	$\overset{O}{RCOR}$	$\overset{O}{RCNH_2}$ $\overset{O}{RCNHR}$ $\overset{O}{RCNR_2}$
Functional group	C—H and C—C bonds	$\mathrm{C{=}C}$	$-C{\equiv}C-$	Aromatic ring	$-\overset{\,}{\underset{\,}{C}}-X$	$-\overset{\,}{\underset{\,}{C}}-OH$	$-\overset{\,}{\underset{\,}{C}}-O-\overset{\,}{\underset{\,}{C}}-$	$-\overset{\,}{\underset{\,}{C}}-N-$	$\overset{O}{-C-H}$	$\overset{O}{-\overset{\,}{\underset{\,}{C}}-C-\overset{\,}{\underset{\,}{C}}-}$	$\overset{O}{-C-OH}$	$\overset{O}{-C-O-\overset{\,}{\underset{\,}{C}}-}$	$\overset{O}{-C-N-}$

*These names are also accepted by the IUPAC.

74

2.16 PHYSICAL PROPERTIES AND MOLECULAR STRUCTURE

So far, we have said little about one of the most obvious characteristics of organic compounds, that is, *their physical state or phase.* Whether a particular substance is a solid, or a liquid, or a gas would certainly be one of the first observations that we would note in any experimental work. The temperatures at which transitions occur between phases, that is, melting points and boiling points, are also among the more easily measured physical properties. Melting points and boiling points are also useful in identifying and isolating organic compounds.

Suppose, for example, we have just carried out the synthesis of an organic compound that is known to be a liquid at room temperature and 1-atm pressure. If we know the boiling point of our desired product, and the boiling points of other byproducts and solvents that may be present in the reaction mixture, we can decide whether or not simple distillation will be a feasible method for isolating our product.

In another instance our product might be a solid. In this case, in order to isolate the substance by crystallization, we need to know its melting point and its solubility in different solvents.

The physical constants of known organic substances are easily found in handbooks and journals.* Table 2.3 lists the melting and boiling points of some of the compounds that we have discussed in this chapter.

Often in the course of research, however, the product of a synthesis is a new compound — one that has never been described before. In these instances, success in isolating the new compound depends on making reasonably accurate estimates of its

TABLE 2.3 Physical properties of representative compounds

COMPOUND	STRUCTURE	mp (°C)	bp (°C) (1 atm)
Methane	CH_4	−182	−162
Ethane	CH_3CH_3	−183	−88.2
Ethene	$CH_2{=}CH_2$	−169	−102
Ethyne	$HC{\equiv}CH$	−82	−84 subl[a]
Chloromethane	CH_3Cl	−97	−23.7
Chloroethane	CH_3CH_2Cl	−138.7	13.1
Ethyl alcohol	CH_3CH_2OH	−115	78.5
Acetaldehyde	CH_3CHO	−121	20
Acetic acid	CH_3CO_2H	16.6	118
Sodium acetate	CH_3CO_2Na	324	dec[a]
Ethylamine	$CH_3CH_2NH_2$	−80	17
Diethyl ether	$(CH_3CH_2)_2O$	−116	34.6
Ethyl acetate	$CH_3CO_2CH_2CH_3$	−84	77

[a]In this table dec = decompose and subl = sublimes.

*Two useful handbooks are *Handbook of Chemistry,* N. A. Lange, Ed., McGraw-Hill, New York and *CRC Handbook of Chemistry and Physics,* CRC, Boca Raton, FL.

melting point, boiling point, and solubilities. Estimations of these macroscopic physical properties are based on the most likely structure of the substance and on the forces that act between molecules and ions. The temperatures at which phase changes occur are an indication of the strength of these intermolecular forces.

2.16A ION–ION FORCES

The **melting point** of a substance is the temperature at which an equilibrium exists between the well-ordered crystalline state and the more random liquid state. If the substance is an ionic compound, such as sodium acetate (Table 2.3), the forces that hold the ions together in the crystalline state are the strong electrostatic lattice forces that act between the positive and negative ions in the orderly crystalline structure. In Fig. 2.14 each sodium ion is surrounded by negatively charged acetate ions, and each acetate ion is surrounded by positive sodium ions. A large amount of thermal energy is required to break up the orderly structure of the crystal into the disorderly open structure of a liquid. As a result, the temperature at which sodium acetate melts is quite high, 324 °C. The *boiling points* of ionic compounds are higher still, so high that most ionic organic compounds decompose before they boil. Sodium acetate shows this behavior.

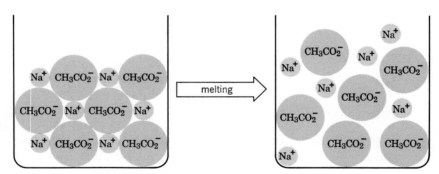

FIGURE 2.14   The melting of sodium acetate.

2.16B DIPOLE–DIPOLE FORCES

Most organic molecules are not fully ionic, but rather have a *permanent dipole moment* resulting from a nonuniform distribution of the bonding electrons (Section 1.19). Acetone and acetaldehyde are examples of molecules with permanent dipoles because the carbonyl group that they contain is highly polarized. In these compounds, the attractive forces between molecules are much easier to visualize. In the liquid or solid state, dipole–dipole attractions cause the molecules to orient themselves so that the positive end of one molecule is directed toward the negative end of another (Fig. 2.15).

FIGURE 2.15   Dipole–dipole interactions between acetone molecules.

2.16C HYDROGEN BONDS

Very strong dipole–dipole attractions occur between hydrogen atoms bonded to small, strongly electronegative atoms (O, N, or F) and nonbonding electron pairs on other such electronegative atoms (Fig. 2.16). This type of intermolecular force is called a **hydrogen bond.** The hydrogen bond (bond dissociation energy about $1-9$ kcal mol^{-1}) is weaker than an ordinary covalent bond, but is much stronger than the dipole–dipole interactions that occur in acetone.

$$\overset{\delta-}{:Z}\!-\!\overset{\delta+}{H}\ \cdots\cdots\ \overset{\delta-}{:Z}\!-\!\overset{\delta+}{H}$$

FIGURE 2.16 The hydrogen bond. Z is a strongly electronegative element, usually oxygen, nitrogen, or fluorine.

Hydrogen bonding accounts for the fact that ethyl alcohol has a much higher boiling point ($+78.5$ °C) than dimethyl ether (-24.9 °C) even though the two compounds have the same molecular weight. Molecules of ethyl alcohol, because they have a hydrogen atom covalently bonded to an oxygen atom, can form strong hydrogen bonds to each other.

$$CH_3CH_2\diagdown O\!-\!H \cdots :O\diagup^{H}_{CH_2CH_3}$$

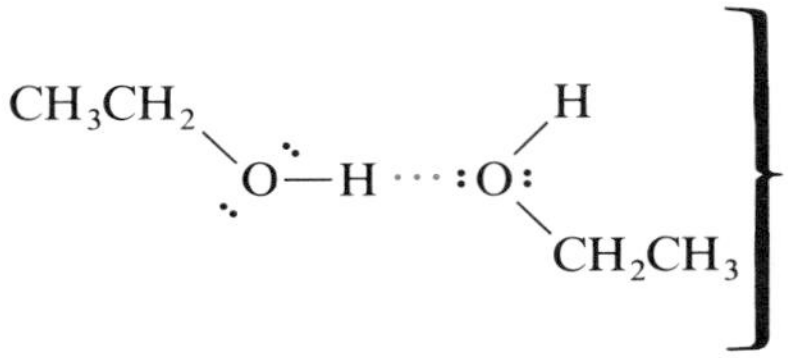

The dotted bond is a hydrogen bond. Strong hydrogen bonding is limited to molecules having a hydrogen atom attached to an O, N, or F atom

Molecules of dimethyl ether, because they lack a hydrogen atom attached to a strongly electronegative atom, cannot form strong hydrogen bonds to each other. In dimethyl ether the intermolecular forces are weaker dipole–dipole interactions.

Problem 2.12

Explain why $(CH_3)_3N$ (trimethylamine) has a considerably lower boiling point (3 °C) than $CH_3CH_2CH_2NH_2$ (propylamine) (49 °C), even though these two compounds have the same molecular weight.

A factor (in addition to polarity and hydrogen bonding) that affects the *melting point* of many organic compounds is the compactness and rigidity of their individual molecules. Molecules that are symmetrical and rigid generally have abnormally high melting points. *tert*-Butyl alcohol, for example, has a much higher melting point than the other isomeric alcohols shown here.

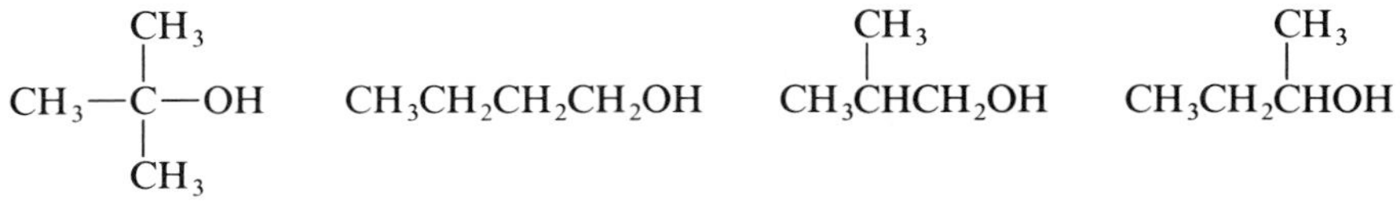

$CH_3\!-\!\overset{\displaystyle CH_3}{\underset{\displaystyle CH_3}{\overset{\mid}{\underset{\mid}{C}}}}\!-\!OH$	$CH_3CH_2CH_2CH_2OH$	$\overset{\displaystyle CH_3}{\overset{\mid}{CH_3CHCH_2OH}}$	$\overset{\displaystyle CH_3}{\overset{\mid}{CH_3CH_2CHOH}}$
tert-Butyl alcohol mp, 25 °C	Butyl alcohol mp, -90 °C	Isobutyl alcohol mp, -108 °C	*sec*-Butyl alcohol mp, -114 °C

Problem 2.13

Which compound would you expect to have the higher melting point, propane or cyclopropane? Explain your answer.

2.16D van der WAALS FORCES

If we consider a substance like methane where the particles are nonpolar molecules, we find that the melting point and boiling point are very low: $-183\ °C$ and $-162\ °C$, respectively. Rather than ask, "Why does methane melt and boil at low temperatures?" a more appropriate question might be "Why does methane, a nonionic, nonpolar substance, become a liquid or a solid at all?" The answer to this question can be given in terms of attractive intermolecular forces called **van der Waals forces** (or **London forces**).

An accurate account of the nature of van der Waals forces requires the use of quantum mechanics. We can, however, visualize the origin of these forces in the following way. The average distribution of charge in a nonpolar molecule (like methane) over a period of time is uniform. At any given instant, however, *because electrons move,* the electrons and thus the charge may not be uniformly distributed. Electrons may, in one instant, be slightly accumulated on one part of the molecule and, as a consequence, *a small temporary dipole will occur* (Fig. 2.17). This temporary dipole in one molecule can induce opposite (attractive) dipoles in surrounding molecules. It does this because the negative (or positive) charge in a portion of one molecule will distort the electron cloud of an adjacent portion of another molecule causing an opposite charge to develop there. These temporary dipoles change constantly, but the net result of their existence is to produce attractive forces between nonpolar molecules, and thus make possible the existence of their liquid and solid states.

FIGURE 2.17 Temporary dipoles and induced dipoles in nonpolar molecules resulting from a nonuniform distribution of electrons at a given instant.

One important factor that determines the magnitude of van der Waals forces is the relative **polarizability** of the electrons of the atoms involved. By polarizability we mean *the ability of the electrons to respond to a changing electric field.* Relative polarizability depends on how loosely or tightly the electrons are held. In the halogen family, for example, polarizability increases in the order $F < Cl < Br < I$. Fluorine atoms show a very low polarizability because their electrons are very tightly held; they are close to the nucleus. Iodine atoms are large and hence are more easily polarized. Their electrons are far from the nucleus. Atoms with unshared pairs are generally more polarizable than those with only bonding pairs. Thus a halogen substituent is more polarizable than an alkyl group of comparable size. Table 2.4 gives the relative magnitude of van der Waals forces and dipole–dipole interactions for several simple

TABLE 2.4   Attractive energies in simple molecular solids

MOLECULE	DIPOLE MOMENT (D)	ATTRACTIVE ENERGIES (kcal mol^{-1})		MELTING POINT (°C)	BOILING POINT (°C)
		DIPOLE-DIPOLE	VAN DER WAALS		
H_2O	1.85	8.7^a	2.1	0	100
NH_3	1.47	3.3^a	3.5	−78	−33
HCl	1.08	0.8^a	4.0	−115	−85
HBr	0.80	0.2	5.2	−88	−67
HI	0.42	0.006	6.7	−51	−35

^{a}These dipole–dipole attractions are called hydrogen bonds.

compounds. Notice that except for the molecules where strong hydrogen bonds are possible, van der Waals are far more important than dipole–dipole interactions.

The *boiling point* of a liquid is the temperature at which the vapor pressure of the liquid equals the pressure of the atmosphere above it. For this reason, the boiling points of liquids are *pressure dependent,* and boiling points are always reported as occurring at a particular pressure, as 1 atm (or at 760 torr), for example. A substance that boils at 150 °C at 1-atm pressure will boil at a substantially lower temperature if the pressure is reduced to, for example, 0.01 torr (a pressure easily obtained with a vacuum pump). The normal boiling point given for a liquid is its boiling point at 1 atm.

In passing from a liquid to a gaseous state the individual molecules (or ions) of the substance must separate considerably. Because of this, we can understand why ionic organic compounds often decompose before they boil. The thermal energy required to completely separate (volatilize) the ions is so great that chemical reactions (decompositions) occur first.

Nonpolar compounds, where the intermolecular forces are very weak, usually boil at low temperatures even at 1-atm pressure. This is not always true, however, because of other factors that we have not yet mentioned: the effects of molecular weight and molecular size. Heavier molecules require greater thermal energy in order to acquire velocities sufficiently great to escape the liquid surface, and because their surface areas are usually much greater, intermolecular van der Waals attractions are also much larger. These factors explain why nonpolar ethane (bp, −88.2 °C) boils higher than methane (bp, −162 °C) at a pressure of 1 atm. It also explains why, at 1 atm, the even heavier and larger nonpolar molecule decane ($C_{10}H_{22}$) boils at +174 °C.

Fluorocarbons (compounds containing only carbon and fluorine) have extraordinarily low boiling points when compared to hydrocarbons of the same molecular weight. The fluorocarbon C_5F_{12}, for example, has a slightly lower boiling point than pentane (C_5H_{12}) even though it has a far higher molecular weight. The important factor in explaining this behavior is the very low polarizability of fluorine atoms that we mentioned earlier, resulting in very small van der Waals forces. The fluorocarbon polymer called *Teflon* [$-(CF_2CF_2)_n$, see Section 9.10] has self-lubricating properties, which are exploited in making "nonstick" frying pans and lightweight bearings.

2.16E SOLUBILITIES

Intermolecular forces are of primary importance in explaining the **solubilities** of substances. Dissolution of a solid in a liquid is, in many respects, like the melting of a solid. The orderly crystal structure of the solid is destroyed, and the result is the formation of the more disorderly arrangement of the molecules (or ions) in solution. In the process of dissolving, too, the molecules or ions must be separated from each other, and energy must be supplied for both changes. The energy required to overcome lattice energies and intermolecular or interionic attractions comes from the formation of new attractive forces between solute and solvent.

Consider the dissolution of an ionic substance as an example. Here both the lattice energy and interionic attractions are large. We find that water and only a few other very polar solvents are capable of dissolving ionic compounds. These solvents dissolve ionic compounds by **hydrating** or **solvating** the ions (Fig. 2.18).

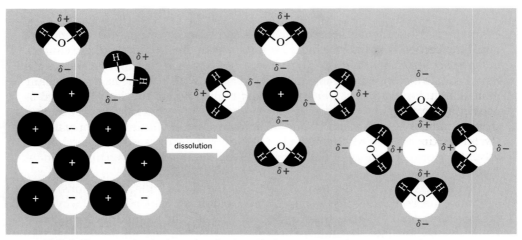

FIGURE 2.18 The dissolution of an ionic solid in water showing the hydration of positive and negative ions by the very polar water molecules. The ions become surrounded by water molecules in all three dimensions, not just the two shown here.

Water molecules, by virtue of their great polarity, as well as their very small compact shape, can very effectively surround the individual ions as they are freed from the crystal surface. Positive ions are surrounded by water molecules with the negative end of the water dipole pointed toward the positive ion; negative ions are solvated in exactly the opposite way. Because water is highly polar, and because water is capable of forming strong hydrogen bonds, the *dipole–ion* attractive forces are also large. The energy supplied by the formation of these forces is great enough to overcome both the lattice energy and interionic attractions of the crystal.

A rule of thumb for predicting solubilities is that "like dissolves like." Polar and ionic compounds tend to dissolve in polar solvents. Polar liquids are generally miscible with each other. Nonpolar solids are usually soluble in nonpolar solvents. On the other hand, nonpolar solids are insoluble in polar solvents. Nonpolar liquids are usually mutually miscible, but nonpolar liquids and polar liquids "like oil and water" do not mix.

We can understand why this is true if we understand that when substances of similar polarities are mixed, the "new" intermolecular forces that form in the solution are very much like those that existed in the separate substances. The miscibility of nonpolar carbon tetrachloride with a nonpolar alkane would be an example. Very polar water molecules are probably capable of inducing polarities in alkane molecules that are sufficiently large to form attractive forces between them. Water and alkanes are not soluble in each other, however, because dissolution of the alkane in water requires the separation of strongly attractive water molecules from each other.

Ethanol and water, by contrast, are miscible in all proportions. In this example, both molecules are highly polar and the new attractive forces are as strong as those they replace and, in this instance, both compounds are capable of forming strong hydrogen bonds.

$$CH_3CH_2 \overset{\delta-}{O} \cdots \overset{\delta+}{H} \longrightarrow \text{Hydrogen bond}$$

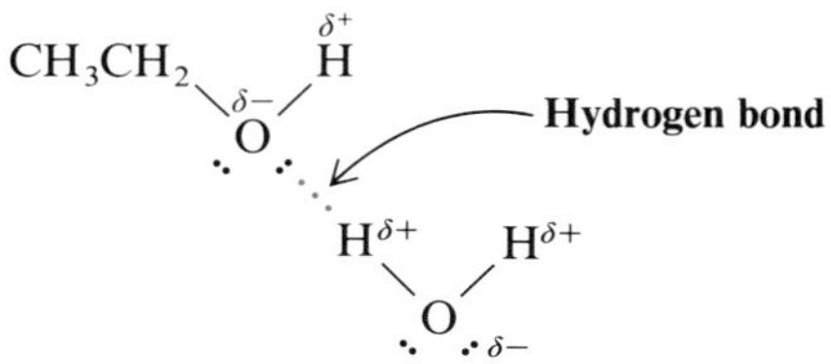

If the carbon chain of an alcohol is long, however, we find that the alcohol is much less soluble in water. Decyl alcohol (see following structure) with a chain of 10 carbon atoms is only very slightly soluble in water. Decyl alcohol resembles an alkane more than it does water. The long carbon chain of decyl alcohol is said to be **hydrophobic** (*hydro,* water; *phobic,* fearing or avoiding — "water avoiding"). Only the OH group, a rather small part of the molecule, is **hydrophilic** (*philic,* loving or seeking — "water seeking"). On the other hand, decyl alcohol is quite soluble in nonpolar solvents.

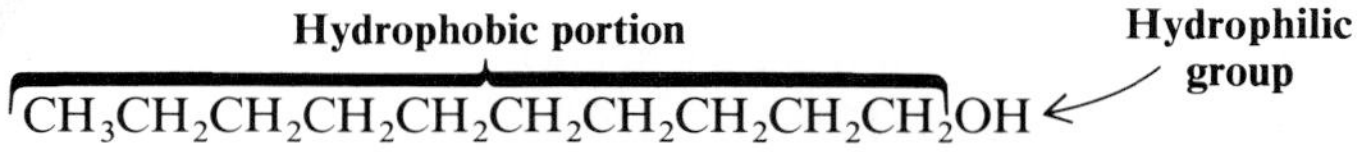

Hydrophobic portion   **Hydrophilic group**

$$CH_3CH_2CH_2CH_2CH_2CH_2CH_2CH_2CH_2CH_2OH$$
Decyl alcohol

2.16F GUIDELINES FOR WATER SOLUBILITY

Organic chemists usually define a compound as water soluble if at least 3 g of the organic compound dissolve in 100 mL of water. We find that for compounds containing nitrogen or oxygen atoms — and thus capable of forming strong hydrogen bonds — the following approximate guidelines hold: Compounds with one to three carbon atoms are water soluble, compounds with four or five carbon atoms are borderline, and compounds with six carbon atoms or more are insoluble.

2.16G INTERMOLECULAR FORCES IN BIOCHEMISTRY

Later, after we have had a chance to examine in detail the properties of the molecules that make up living organisms, we shall see how intermolecular forces are extremely important in the functioning of cells. Hydrogen bond formation, the hydration of polar groups, and the tendency of nonpolar groups to avoid a polar environment all cause complex protein molecules to fold in precise ways — ways that allow them to function as biological catalysts of incredible efficiency. The same factors allow molecules of hemoglobin to assume the shape needed to transport oxygen. They allow proteins and molecules called glycosphingolipids to function as cell membranes.

TABLE 2.5   Attractive electric forces

ELECTRIC FORCE	RELATIVE STRENGTH	TYPE	EXAMPLE
Cation–anion (in a crystal)	Very strong	$\oplus$ $\ominus$	Lithium fluoride crystal lattice
Covalent bonds	Strong (36–125 kcal mol^{-1})	Shared electron pairs	H—H (104 kcal mol^{-1}) CH$_3$—CH$_3$ (88 kcal mol^{-1}) I—I (36 kcal mol^{-1})
Ion–dipole	Moderate	$\delta+ \delta-$ $(+)$ $\delta- \delta+$	Na$^+$ in water (see Fig. 2.18)
Dipole–dipole (including hydrogen bonds)	Moderate–weak (1–9 kcal mol^{-1})	$\overset{\delta-}{—Z}:\cdots\overset{\delta+}{H}—$ and $\delta+\delta-$ $\delta+\delta-$	R, :O:$\cdots$H—O, R and CH$_3$—Cl CH$_3$—Cl
van der Waals	Variable	Transient dipole	Interactions between methane molecules

Hydrogen bonding alone gives molecules of certain carbohydrates a globular shape that makes them highly efficient food reserves in animals. It gives molecules of other carbohydrates a rigid linear shape that makes them perfectly suited to be structural components in plants.

2.17 SUMMARY OF ATTRACTIVE ELECTRIC FORCES

The attractive forces occurring between molecules and ions that we have studied so far are summarized in Table 2.5.

Additional Problems

2.14   Classify each of the following compounds as an alkane, alkene, alkyne, alcohol, or aldehyde, and so forth.

(a) CH$_3$C≡CCH$_3$ (b) CH$_3$CHCH$_2$COH   (c)   (d)

(e) $\underset{\displaystyle CH_3}{CH_3\underset{|}{C}HCH_2CH_2CH_2CH_2CH_2CH_2CH_2CH_2CH_2CH_2CH_2CH_2CH_2CH_3}$

A sex attractant of the female tiger moth

(f) 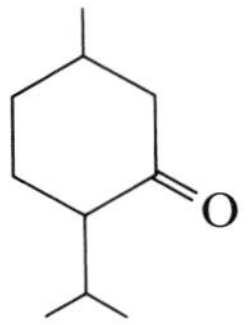 **Obtained from peppermint oil**

2.15 Identify all of the functional groups in each of the following compounds:

(a) 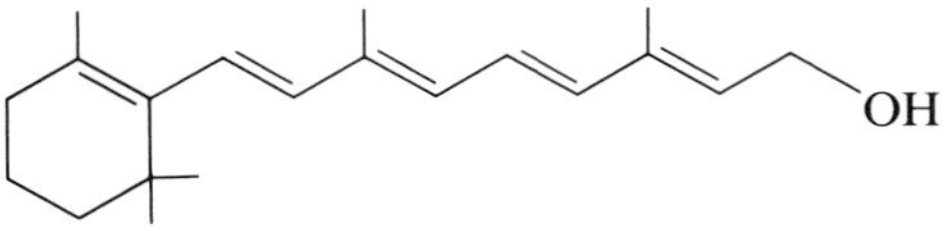

Vitamin A$_1$

(b) 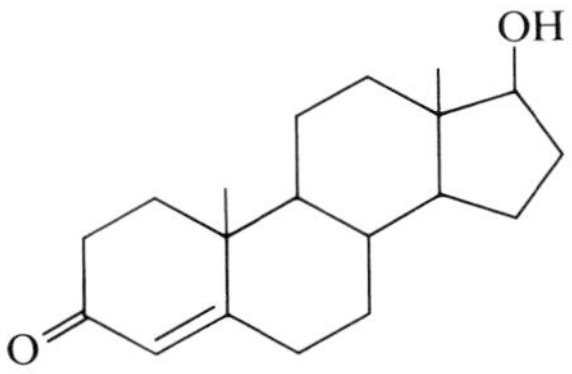 **Testosterone, a male sex hormone**

(c) 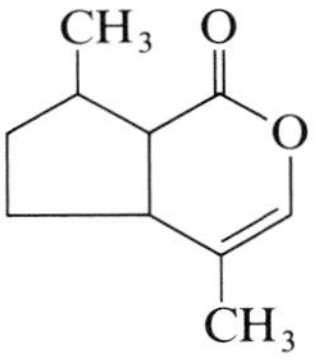 **Nepetalactone (one constituent of catnip)**

(d) $\left[NH{+}CH_2{+}_6 NH\overset{O}{\overset{\|}{C}}{+}CH_2{+}_4\overset{O}{\overset{\|}{C}} \right]_n$

A nylon

(e) 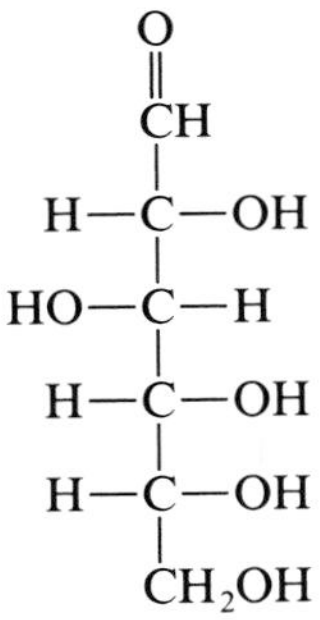

Glucose
(a sugar)

(f) $CH_2{=}CH{-}O{-}CH{=}CH_2$

An anesthetic

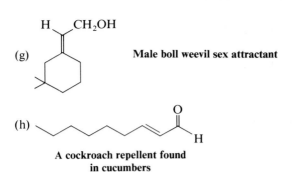

(g)   Male boll weevil sex attractant

(h)

A cockroach repellent found
in cucumbers

(i)

A synthetic cockroach repellent

2.16 There are four alkyl bromides with the formula C_4H_9Br. Write their structural formulas and classify each as to whether it is a primary, secondary, or tertiary alkyl bromide.

2.17 There are seven isomeric compounds with the formula $C_4H_{10}O$. Write their structures and classify each compound according to its functional group.

2.18 Write structural formulas for four compounds with the formula C_3H_6O and classify each according to its functional group.

2.19 Classify the following alcohols as primary, secondary, or tertiary.
(a) $CH_3CH_2CH_2CH_2OH$ (d) $CH_3CH(CH_3)CH(OH)CH_3$

(b) $CH_3CH_2CH_2CH(OH)CH_3$ (e) ⬡—OH

(c) $CH_3CH_2C(OH)(CH_3)_2$ (f) △—CH_3 / OH

2.20 Classify the following amines as primary, secondary, or tertiary.

(a) $CH_3CH_2NHCH_2CH_3$ (c) $CH_3NCH_2CH_2CH_3$ / CH_3 (e) ▷—$NHCH_3$

(b) $CH_3CH(NH_2)CH_2CH_3$ (d) ⬠—NH_2

2.21 Write structural formulas for each of the following:
(a) An ether with the formula C_3H_8O
(b) A primary alcohol with the formula C_3H_8O
(c) A secondary alcohol with the formula C_3H_8O
(d) Two esters with the formula $C_4H_8O_2$

ADDITIONAL PROBLEMS

(e) A primary alkyl halide with the formula C_4H_9X

(f) A secondary alkyl halide with the formula C_4H_9X

(g) A tertiary alkyl halide with the formula C_4H_9X

(h) An aldehyde with the formula C_4H_8O

(i) A ketone with the formula C_4H_8O

(j) A primary amine with the formula $C_4H_{11}N$

(k) A secondary amine with the formula $C_4H_{11}N$

(l) A tertiary amine with the formula $C_4H_{11}N$

(m) An amide of ammonia with the formula C_4H_9NO

(n) An N-substituted amide with the formula C_4H_9NO

(o) A tertiary alcohol with the formula C_4H_8O containing no multiple bonds

2.22 Which compound in each of the following pairs would have the higher boiling point?

(a) Ethyl alcohol (CH_3CH_2OH) or methyl ether (CH_3OCH_3)

(b) Ethylene glycol ($HOCH_2CH_2OH$) or ethyl alcohol (CH_3CH_2OH)

(c) Pentane (C_5H_{12}) or heptane (C_7H_{16})

(d) Acetone $\left(CH_3 \overset{\overset{\displaystyle O}{\|}}{C} CH_3 \right)$ or propyl alcohol ($CH_3CH_2CH_2OH$)

(e) *cis*-1,2-Dichloroethene, 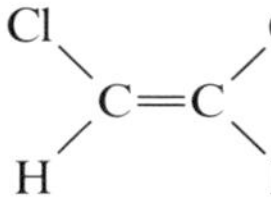 or *trans*-1,2-dichloroethene,

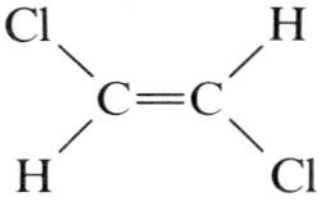

(f) Propionic acid $\left(CH_3CH_2 \overset{\overset{\displaystyle O}{\|}}{C} OH \right)$ or methyl acetate $\left(CH_3 \overset{\overset{\displaystyle O}{\|}}{C} {-} OCH_3 \right)$

2.23 There are four amides with the formula C_3H_7NO. (a) Write their structures. (b) One of these amides has a melting and boiling point that is substantially lower than that of the other three. Which amide is this? Explain your answer.

2.24 Cyclic compounds of the general type shown here are called lactones. What functional group do they contain?

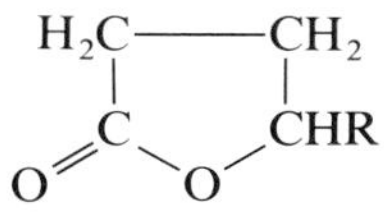

2.25 Hydrogen fluoride has a dipole moment of 1.82 D; its boiling point is 19.34 °C. Ethyl fluoride (CH_3CH_2F) has an almost identical dipole moment and has a larger molecular weight, yet its boiling point is −37.7 °C. Explain.

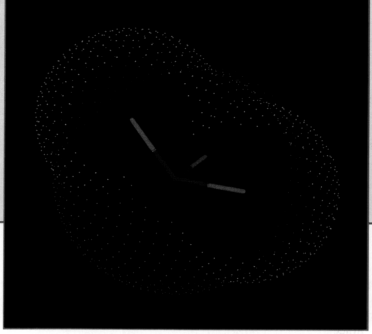

The hydronium ion (see Section 3.1).

CHAPTER

3

ACIDS AND BASES IN ORGANIC CHEMISTRY

3.1 INTRODUCTION

We begin our study of chemical reactivity by examining some of the basic principles of acid–base chemistry. There are several reasons for doing this: Many of the reactions that occur in organic chemistry are either acid–base reactions outright, or they involve an acid–base reaction at some stage. The acid–base reaction is a simple, fundamental reaction that will enable you to see how organic chemists think about what are called *mechanisms of reactions,* and how they use curved arrows to illustrate the process of bond breaking and bond making that inevitably occurs as molecules react. Acid–base reactions also allow us to examine important ideas about the relationship between the structures of molecules and their reactivity, and to see how certain thermodynamic parameters can be used to predict how much of the product will be formed when a reaction reaches equilibrium. Acid and base reactions also provide an illustration for the important role solvents play in chemical reactions. They even give us a brief introduction to organic synthesis. Finally, acid–base chemistry is something that you will find familiar because of your studies in general chemistry. We begin, therefore, with a brief review.

3.1A THE BRØNSTED–LOWRY DEFINITION OF ACIDS AND BASES

According to the Brønsted–Lowry theory, an acid is a substance that can donate a proton, and a base is a substance that can accept a proton. Let us consider, as an example of this concept, the reaction that occurs when gaseous hydrogen chloride dissolves in water:

$$H-\overset{..}{\underset{|}{\overset{..}{O}}}: + H-\overset{..}{\underset{..}{Cl}}: \longrightarrow H-\overset{..}{\underset{|}{\overset{+}{O}}}-H + :\overset{..}{\underset{..}{Cl}}:^-$$

H	H

Base (proton acceptor)	Acid (proton donor)	Conjugate acid of H_2O	Conjugate base of HCl

Hydrogen chloride, a very strong acid, transfers its proton to water. Water acts as a base and accepts the proton. The products that result from this reaction are a hydronium ion (H_3O^+) and a chloride ion (Cl^-).

The molecule or ion that forms when an acid loses its proton is called **the conjugate base** of that acid. The chloride ion, therefore, is the conjugate base of HCl. The molecule or ion that forms when a base accepts a proton is called **the conjugate acid** of that base. The hydronium ion, therefore, is the conjugate acid of water.

Other strong acids that completely transfer a proton when dissolved in water are hydrogen iodide, hydrogen bromide, and sulfuric acid.*

$$HI + H_2O \longrightarrow H_3O^+ + I^-$$

$$HBr + H_2O \longrightarrow H_3O^+ + Br^-$$

$$H_2SO_4 + H_2O \longrightarrow H_3O^+ + HSO_4^-$$

$$HSO_4^- + H_2O \rightleftharpoons H_3O^+ + SO_4^{2-}$$

Because sulfuric acid has two protons that it can transfer to a base, it is called a diprotic (or dibasic) acid. The proton transfer is stepwise; the first proton transfer occurs completely, the second only to the extent of ~ 10%.

Hydronium ions and hydroxide ions are the strongest acids and bases that can exist in aqueous solution in significant amounts. When sodium hydroxide (a crystalline compound consisting of sodium ions and hydroxide ions) dissolves in water, the result is a solution containing solvated sodium ions and solvated hydroxide ions.

$$NaOH_{(solid)} \longrightarrow Na_{(aq)}^+ + OH_{(aq)}^-$$

Sodium ions (and other similar cations) become solvated when water molecules donate unshared electron pairs to their vacant orbitals. Hydroxide ions (and other anions with unshared electron pairs) become solvated when water molecules form hydrogen bonds to them.

---

*The extent to which an acid transfers protons to a base like water is a measure of its strength as an acid. Acid strength is, therefore, a measure of the percentage of ionization and not of concentration.

Solvated sodium ion   Solvated hydroxide ion

When an aqueous solution of sodium hydroxide is mixed with an aqueous solution of hydrogen chloride (hydrochloric acid), the reaction that occurs is between hydronium and hydroxide ions. The sodium and chloride ions are called **spectator ions** because they play no part in the acid–base reaction.

Total Ionic Reaction

$$H-\overset{..}{\underset{H}{O}}{}^{\pm}-H + :\overset{..}{\underset{..}{Cl}}:^- + Na^+ + {}^-:\overset{..}{\underset{..}{O}}-H \longrightarrow 2\,H-\overset{..}{\underset{H}{O}}: + Na^+ + :\overset{..}{\underset{..}{Cl}}:^-$$

Spectator ions

Net Reaction

$$H-\overset{..}{\underset{H}{O}}{}^{\pm}-H + {}^-:\overset{..}{\underset{..}{O}}-H \longrightarrow 2\,H-\overset{..}{\underset{H}{O}}:$$

What we have just said about hydrochloric acid and aqueous sodium hydroxide is true when solutions of all aqueous strong acids and bases are mixed. The net ionic reaction is simply:

$$H_3O^+ + OH^- \longrightarrow 2\,H_2O$$

3.1B THE LEWIS DEFINITION OF ACIDS AND BASES

Acid–base theory was broadened considerably by G. N. Lewis in 1923. Striking at what he called "the cult of the proton," Lewis proposed that acids be defined as **electron-pair acceptors** and bases be defined as **electron-pair donors.** In the Lewis theory, the proton is not the only acid; many other species are acids as well. Aluminum chloride and boron trifluoride, for example, react with ammonia in the same way that a proton does. Using curved arrows to show the donation of the electron pair of ammonia (the Lewis base), we have the following examples:

$$H^+ \quad + \quad :NH_3 \quad \longrightarrow \quad H-\overset{+}{N}H_3$$

Lewis acid   Lewis base
(electron-pair   (electron-pair
acceptor)   donor)

3.1 INTRODUCTION

$$\text{Cl-Al} + :NH_3 \longrightarrow \text{Cl-Al}\overset{+}{=}NH_3$$

Lewis acid **Lewis base**
(electron-pair (electron-pair
acceptor) donor)

$$\text{F-B} + :NH_3 \longrightarrow \text{F-B}\overset{+}{=}NH_3$$

Lewis acid **Lewis base**
(electron-pair (electron-pair
acceptor) donor)

In these examples, aluminum chloride and boron trifluoride accept the electron pair of ammonia just as a proton does, by using it to form a covalent bond to the nitrogen atom. They do this, because the central aluminum and boron atoms have only a sextet of electrons and are, therefore, electron deficient. When they accept the electron pair, aluminum chloride and boron trifluoride are, in the Lewis definition, *acting as acids*.

Bases are much the same in the Lewis theory and the Brønsted–Lowry theory, because in the Brønsted–Lowry theory a base must donate a pair of electrons in order to accept a proton.

The Lewis theory, by virtue of its broader definition of acids, allows acid–base theory to include all of the Brønsted–Lowry reactions and, as we shall see, a great many others.

Any *electron-deficient atom* can act as a Lewis acid. Many compounds containing Group **IIIA** elements such as boron and aluminum are Lewis acids because Group **IIIA** atoms have only a sextet of electrons in their outer shell. Many other compounds that have atoms with vacant orbitals also act as Lewis acids. Zinc and iron(III) halides (ferric halides) are frequently used as Lewis acids in organic reactions. Two examples that we shall study later are the following:

$$R-\ddot{O}-H + ZnCl_2 \longrightarrow R-\overset{\pm}{\ddot{O}}-ZnCl_2^-$$
$$\qquad\qquad\qquad\qquad\qquad\qquad H$$

Lewis base **Lewis acid**
(electron-pair (electron-pair
donor) acceptor)

$$:\ddot{B}r-\ddot{B}r: + FeBr_3 \longrightarrow :\ddot{B}r-\overset{\pm}{\ddot{B}}r-FeBr_3^-$$

Lewis base **Lewis acid**
(electron-pair (electron-pair
donor) acceptor)

Problem 3.1

Write equations showing the Lewis acid–base reaction that takes place when:

(a) BF_3 reacts with an alcohol.

(b) $AlCl_3$ reacts with a tertiary amine.

(c) BF_3 reacts with a ketone.

In each instance you should use a curved arrow to indicate the donation of an electron pair.

Problem 3.2 _____

Identify the Lewis acid and Lewis base in each of the following reactions:

(a) $CH_3Cl + AlCl_3 \longrightarrow CH_3Cl^+ - AlCl_3^-$

(b) $ROH + H^+ \longrightarrow ROH_2^+$

(c) $(CH_3)_3C^+ + Cl^- \longrightarrow (CH_3)_3C - Cl$

(d) $CH_3\overset{\displaystyle O}{\overset{\displaystyle \|}{C}} - OCH_2CH_3 + OH^- \longrightarrow CH_3\overset{\displaystyle O^-}{\underset{\displaystyle OH}{\overset{\displaystyle |}{\underset{\displaystyle |}{C}}}} - OCH_2CH_3$

(e) $CH_2{=}CH_2 + H^+ \longrightarrow CH_3 - CH_2^+$

(f) $CH_3CH_2:^- + CH_3 - \overset{\displaystyle O}{\overset{\displaystyle \|}{C}} - H \longrightarrow CH_3 - \overset{\displaystyle O^-}{\underset{\displaystyle CH_2CH_3}{\overset{\displaystyle |}{\underset{\displaystyle |}{C}}}} - H$

3.2 THE USE OF CURVED ARROWS IN ILLUSTRATING REACTIONS

In Section 3.1B we showed the donation of an electron pair by the Lewis bases with a curved arrow. This type of notation is commonly used by organic chemists to show *the direction of electron flow in a reaction. The curved arrow does not show the movement of atoms,* however. The atoms are assumed to follow the flow of electrons. Organic chemists use curved arrows because they are interested in what are called mechanisms of reactions. That is, they are interested in theories that outline step-by-step descriptions of the way chemical reactions occur. Inevitably in organic reactions, certain covalent bonds are broken and others are formed. The curved arrow notation is a useful method for indicating which bonds form and which bonds break.

Although our study of reaction mechanisms will not begin in detail until we reach Chapter 6, we can now illustrate some of the basic ideas of the curved-arrow notation with simple Lewis acid–base reactions. Consider as an example the reaction of hydrogen chloride with water.

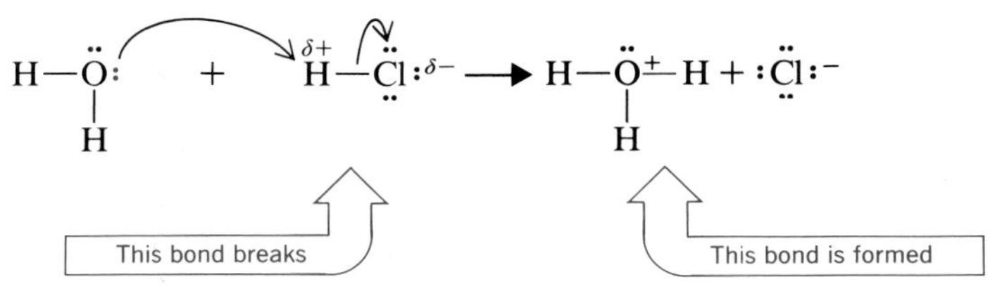

Typically, a curved arrow begins with a covalent bond or unshared electron pair (a site of higher electron density) and points toward a site of electron deficiency. We see here that as the water molecule collides with a hydrogen chloride molecule, it uses one of its unshared electron pairs (shown in blue) to form a bond to the proton of HCl. This bond forms because the negatively charged electrons of the oxygen atom are attracted to the positively charged proton. As the bond between the oxygen and the proton forms, the hydrogen–chlorine bond of HCl breaks, and the chlorine of HCl departs with the electron pair that formerly bonded it to the proton. (If this did not happen, the proton would end up forming two covalent bonds, which, of course, a proton cannot do.) We, therefore, use a curved arrow to show the bond cleavage as well. By pointing to the chlorine, the arrow indicates that the electron pair leaves with the chloride ion.

The following acid–base reactions give other examples of the use of the curved-arrow notation:

$$H-\overset{+}{\underset{\underset{H}{|}}{O}}-H + {}^-:\overset{\cdot\cdot}{\underset{\cdot\cdot}{O}}-H \longrightarrow 2\ H-\overset{\cdot\cdot}{\underset{\underset{H}{|}}{O}}:$$

$$\underset{\textbf{Acid}}{} \qquad \underset{\textbf{Base}}{}$$

$$CH_3-\overset{\overset{\cdot\cdot}{\underset{\|}{O}}}{C}-\overset{\cdot\cdot}{\underset{\cdot\cdot}{O}}-H + :\overset{\cdot\cdot}{\underset{\underset{H}{|}}{O}}-H \rightleftharpoons CH_3-\overset{\overset{\cdot\cdot}{\underset{\|}{O}}}{C}-\overset{\cdot\cdot}{\underset{\cdot\cdot}{O}}:{}^- + H-\overset{+}{\underset{\underset{H}{|}}{O}}-H$$

$$\underset{\textbf{Acid}}{} \qquad \underset{\textbf{Base}}{}$$

$$CH_3-\overset{\overset{\cdot\cdot}{\underset{\|}{O}}}{C}-\overset{\cdot\cdot}{\underset{\cdot\cdot}{O}}-H + {}^-:\overset{\cdot\cdot}{\underset{\cdot\cdot}{O}}-H \longrightarrow CH_3-\overset{\overset{\cdot\cdot}{\underset{\|}{O}}}{C}-\overset{\cdot\cdot}{\underset{\cdot\cdot}{O}}:{}^- + H-\overset{\cdot\cdot}{\underset{\cdot\cdot}{O}}-H$$

$$\underset{\textbf{Acid}}{} \qquad \underset{\textbf{Base}}{}$$

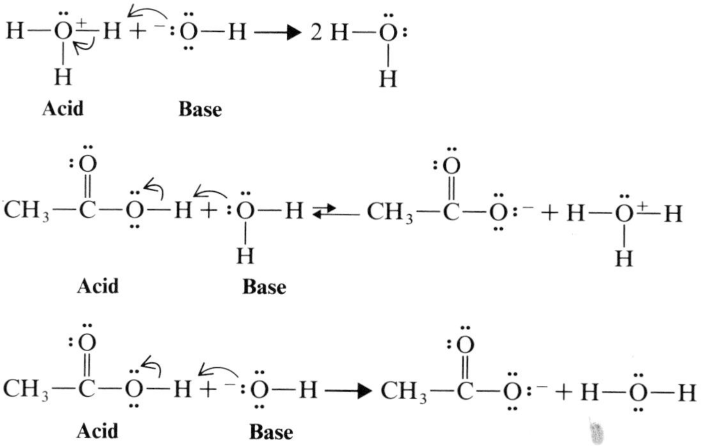

Problem 3.3

Rewrite the acid–base reactions in Problem 3.2 using the curved-arrow notation.

3.3 THE STRENGTH OF ACIDS AND BASES: K_a AND pK_a

In contrast to the strong acids, such as HCl and H_2SO_4, acetic acid is a much weaker acid. When acetic acid dissolves in water, the following reaction does not proceed to completion.

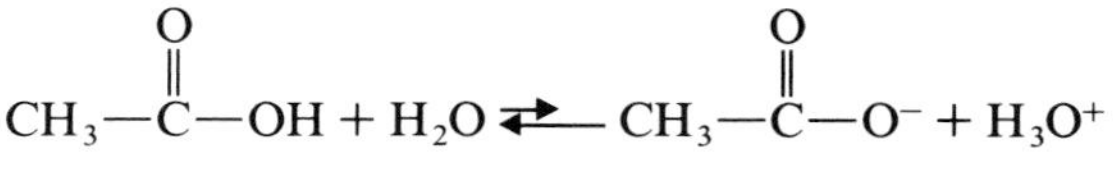

$$CH_3-\overset{\overset{O}{\|}}{C}-OH + H_2O \rightleftharpoons CH_3-\overset{\overset{O}{\|}}{C}-O^- + H_3O^+$$

Experiments show that in a 0.1 M solution of acetic acid at 25 °C only about 1% of the acetic acid molecules ionize by transferring their protons to water.

3.3A THE ACIDITY CONSTANT, K_a

Because the reaction that occurs in an aqueous solution of acetic acid is an equilibrium, we can describe it with an expression for the equilibrium constant.

$$K_{eq} = \frac{[H_3O^+]\,[CH_3CO_2^-]}{[CH_3CO_2H]\,[H_2O]}$$

For dilute aqueous solutions, the concentration of water is essentially constant ($\sim 55.5\ M$), so we can rewrite the expression for the equilibrium constant in terms of a new constant (K_a) called **the acidity constant.**

$$K_a = K_{eq}\,[H_2O] = \frac{[H_3O^+]\,[CH_3CO_2^-]}{[CH_3CO_2H]}$$

At 25 °C, the acidity constant for acetic acid is 1.76×10^{-5}.

We can write similar expressions for any weak acid dissolved in water. Using a generalized hypothetical acid (HA) the reaction in water is

$$HA + H_2O \rightleftharpoons H_3O^+ + A^-$$

and the expression for the acidity constant is

$$K_a = \frac{[H_3O^+]\,[A^-]}{[HA]}$$

Because the concentrations of the products of the reaction are written in the numerator and the concentration of the undissociated acid in the denominator, **a large value of K_a means the acid is a strong acid, and a small value of K_a means the acid is a weak acid.** If the K_a is greater than 10, the acid will be, for all practical purposes, completely dissociated in water.

Problem 3.4 _____

Trifluoroacetic acid (CF_3CO_2H) has a $K_a = 1$ at 25 °C. (a) What are the molar concentrations of hydronium ion and trifluoroacetate ion $(CF_3CO_2^-)$ in a $0.1\ M$ aqueous solution of trifluoroacetic acid? (b) What percentage of the trifluoroacetic acid is ionized?

3.3B ACIDITY AND pK_a

Chemists usually express the acidity constant, K_a, as its negative logarithm, pK_a.

$$pK_a = -\log K_a$$

This is analogous to expressing the hydronium ion concentration as pH.

$$pH = -\log[H_3O^+]$$

3.3 THE STRENGTH OF ACIDS AND BASES: K_a AND pK_a

For acetic acid the pK_a is 4.75:

$$pK_a = -\log(1.76 \times 10^{-5}) = -(-4.75) = 4.75$$

Notice that there is an inverse relationship between the magnitude of the pK_a and the strength of the acid. **The larger the value of the pK_a, the weaker is the acid.** For example, acetic acid with a $pK_a = 4.75$ is a weaker acid than trifluoroacetic acid with a $pK_a = 0$ ($K_a = 1$). Hydrochloric acid with a $pK_a = -7$ ($K_a = 10^7$) is a far stronger acid than trifluoroacetic acid. (It is understood that a positive pK_a is larger than a negative pK_a.)

$$CH_3CO_2H < CF_3CO_2H < \qquad HCl$$

$$pK_a = 4.76 \qquad pK_a = 0 \qquad pK_a = -7$$

Weak acid **Very strong acid**

Increasing acid strength

Table 3.1 lists pK_a values for a selection of acids relative to water as the base. The values in the middle of the table are the most accurate because they can be measured in aqueous solution. Special methods must be used to estimate the pK_a values for the very strong acids at the top of the table and for the very weak acids at the bottom.* The pK_a values for these very strong and weak acids are, therefore, approximate. All of the acids that we shall consider in this book will have strengths in between that of ethane (an extremely weak acid) and that of $HSbF_6$ (an acid that is so strong that it is called a "superacid"). As you examine Table 3.1 take care not to lose sight of the vast range of acidities that it represents.

Problem 3.5

(a) An acid (HA) has a $K_a = 10^{-7}$. What is its pK_a? (b) Another acid (HB) has a $K_a = 5$, what is its pK_a? (c) Which is the stronger acid?

Water, itself, is a very weak acid and undergoes self-ionization even in the absence of acids and bases.

$$H-\ddot{O}: + H-\ddot{O}: \rightleftharpoons H-\overset{+}{\underset{H}{\ddot{O}}}-H + \ ^-:\ddot{O}-H$$

In pure water at 25 °C, the concentrations of hydronium and hydroxide ions are equal to 10^{-7} M. Since the concentration of water in pure water is 55.5 M, we can calculate the K_a for water.

$$K_a = \frac{[H_3O^+][OH^-]}{[H_2O]} \qquad K_a = \frac{(10^{-7})(10^{-7})}{(55.5)} = 1.8 \times 10^{-16} \qquad pK_a = 15.7$$

---

* Acids that are stronger than a hydronium ion and bases that are stronger than a hydroxide ion react completely with water (see Sections 3.1A and 3.8). Therefore, it is not possible to measure acidity constants for these acids in water. Other solvents and special techniques are used, but we do not have the space to describe these methods here.

TABLE 3.1   Relative strength of selected acids and their conjugate bases

	ACID	APPROXIMATE pK_a	CONJUGATE BASE	
Strongest Acid	$HSbF_6$	> -12	SbF_6^-	Weakest Base
	HI	-10	I^-	
	H_2SO_4	-9	HSO_4^-	
	HBr	-9	Br^-	
	HCl	-7	Cl^-	
	$C_6H_5SO_3H$	-6.5	$C_6H_5SO_3^-$	
	H_3O^+	-1.74	H_2O	
	HNO_3	-1.4	NO_3^-	
	CF_3CO_2H	1.0	$CF_3CO_2^-$	
	HF	3.2	F^-	
	CH_3CO_2H	4.76	$CH_3CO_2^-$	
	NH_4^+	9.2	NH_3	
	C_6H_5OH	9.9	$C_6H_5O^-$	
	$CH_3NH_3^+$	10.6	CH_3NH_2	
	H_2O	15.74	OH^-	
	CH_3CH_2OH	16	$CH_3CH_2O^-$	
	$(CH_3)_3COH$	18	$(CH_3)_3CO^-$	
	$HC{\equiv}CH$	25	$HC{\equiv}C^-$	
	H_2	35	H^-	
	NH_3	38	NH_2^-	
	$CH_2{=}CH_2$	44	$CH_2{=}CH^-$	
Weakest Acid	CH_3CH_3	50	$CH_3CH_2^-$	Strongest Base

Increasing acid strength (left arrow, upward) Increasing base strength (right arrow, downward)

Problem 3.6

Show calculations proving that the pK_a of the hydronium ion (H_3O^+) is -1.74 as given in Table 3.1.

3.3C PREDICTING THE STRENGTH OF BASES

In our discussion so far we have dealt only with the strengths of acids. Arising as a natural corollary to this is a principle that allows us to estimate the strengths of bases. Simply stated, the principle is this: **The stronger the acid, the weaker will be its conjugate base.**

We can, therefore, **relate the strength of a base to the pK_a of its conjugate acid. The larger the pK_a of the conjugate acid, the stronger is the base.** Consider the following as examples:

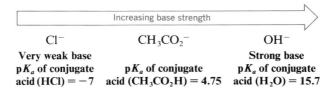

We see that the hydroxide ion is the strongest base of these three bases because its conjugate acid, water, is the weakest acid. (We know that water is the weakest acid because it has the largest pK_a.)

Amines are like ammonia in that they are weak bases. Dissolving ammonia in water brings about the following equilibrium.

$$\overset{..}{N}H_3 + H-\overset{..}{\underset{..}{O}}-H \rightleftharpoons \overset{+}{N}H_4 + {}^-:\overset{..}{\underset{..}{O}}-H$$

| Base | Acid | Conjugate acid | Conjugate base |

$$pK_a = 9.2$$

Dissolving methylamine in water causes the establishment of a similar equilibrium.

$$CH_3\overset{..}{N}H_2 + H-\overset{..}{\underset{..}{O}}-H \rightleftharpoons CH_3\overset{+}{N}H_3 + {}^-:\overset{..}{\underset{..}{O}}-H$$

| Base | Acid | Conjugate acid | Conjugate base |

$$pK_a = 10.6$$

Again we can relate the basicity of these substances to the strength of their conjugate acids. The conjugate acid of ammonia is the ammonium ion, NH_4^+. The pK_a of the ammonium ion is 9.2. The conjugate base of methylamine is the $CH_3NH_3^+$ ion. This ion, called the methylaminium ion, has a $pK_a = 10.6$. Since the conjugate acid of methylamine is a weaker acid than the conjugate acid of ammonia, we can conclude that methylamine is a stronger base than ammonia.

Problem 3.7

The pK_a of the anilinium ion ($C_6H_5\overset{+}{N}H_3$) is equal to 4.6. On the basis of this fact, decide whether aniline ($C_6H_5NH_2$) is a stronger or weaker base than methylamine?

3.4 PREDICTING THE OUTCOME OF ACID-BASE REACTIONS

Table 3.1 gives the approximate pK_a values for a range of representative compounds. While you may not be expected to memorize all of the pK_a values in Table 3.1 now, it is a good idea to begin to learn the general order of acidity and basity for some of the common acids and bases. The examples given in Table 3.1 are representative of their class or functional group. For example, acetic acid has a $pK_a = 4.76$, and carboxylic acids generally have pK_a values near this value (in the range $pK_a = 3-5$). Ethyl alcohol is given as an example of an alcohol, and alcohols generally have pK_a values near that of ethyl alcohol (in the range $pK_a = 15 - 18$), and so on. (There are exceptions, of course, and we shall learn what these exceptions are as we go on.)

By learning the relative scale of acidity of common acids now, you will be able to predict whether or not an acid–base reaction will occur as written. The general principle to apply is this: **Acid–base reactions always favor the formation of the weaker acid and the weaker base.** The reason for this is that the outcome of an acid–base reaction is determined by the position of an equilibrium. Acid–base reactions, are said, therefore, to be **under equilibrium control,** and reactions under equilibrium control always favor the formation of the most stable (lowest potential energy) species. The weaker acid and weaker base are more stable (lower in potential energy) than the stronger acid and stronger base.

Using this principle, we can predict that a carboxylic acid (RCO_2H) will react with aqueous NaOH in the following way because the reaction will lead to the formation of the weaker acid (H_2O) and weaker base (RCO_2^-).

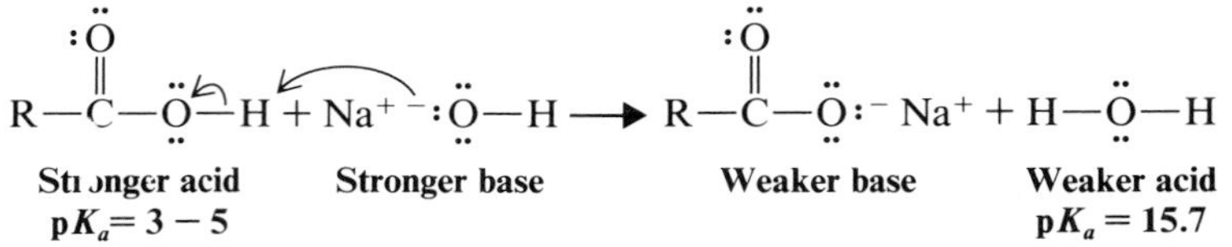

Because there is a large difference in the value of the pK_a of the two acids, the position of equilibrium will greatly favor the formation of the products. In instances like these we commonly show the reaction with a one-way arrow even though the reaction is an equilibrium.

Although acetic acid and other carboxylic acids containing fewer than five carbon atoms are soluble in water, many other carboxylic acids of higher molecular weight are not appreciably soluble in water. Because of their acidity, however, *water-insoluble carboxylic acids dissolve in aqueous sodium hydroxide;* they do so by reacting to form water-soluble sodium salts.

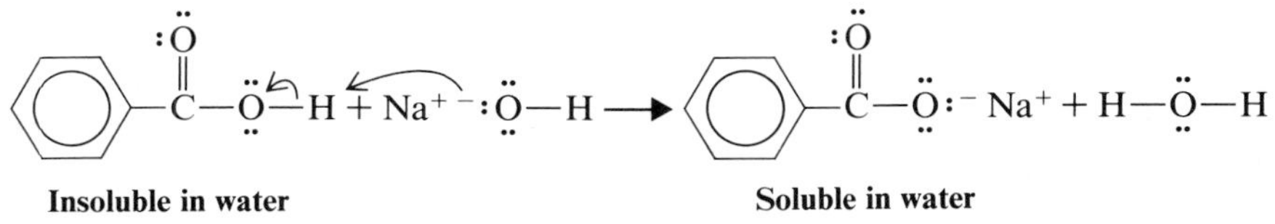

We can also predict that an amine will react with aqueous hydrochloric acid in the following way:

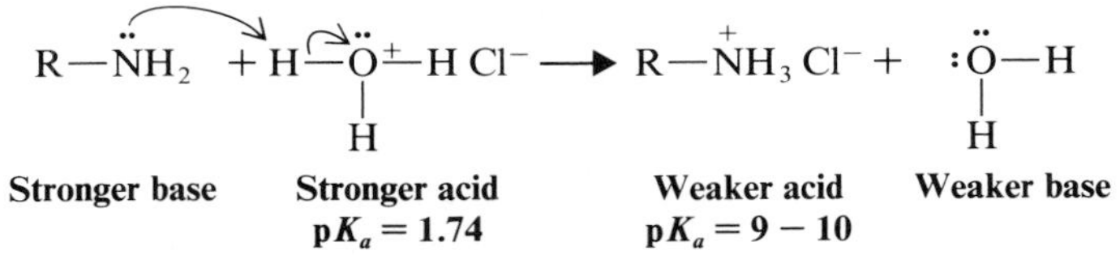

While methylamine and most amines of low molecular weight are very soluble in water, amines with higher molecular weights, such as aniline ($C_6H_5NH_2$), have limited water solubility. However, these water-insoluble amines dissolve readily in hydrochloric acid because the acid–base reactions convert them to soluble salts.

$$C_6H_5-\ddot{N}H_2 + H\overset{\frown}{\longrightarrow}\overset{+}{\underset{\underset{H}{|}}{\ddot{O}}}-H\ Cl^- \longrightarrow C_6H_5-\overset{+}{N}H_3\ Cl^- + :\underset{\underset{H}{|}}{\ddot{O}}-H$$

Water insoluble   **Water-soluble salt**

3.5 THE RELATIONSHIP BETWEEN STRUCTURE AND ACIDITY

The strength of an acid depends on the extent to which a proton can be separated from it and transferred to a base. Removing the proton involves breaking a bond to the proton, and it involves making the conjugate base more electrically negative. *The strength of the bond to the proton is the dominating effect if we compare compounds in a vertical column of the periodic table.* The acidities of the hydrogen halides furnish an example:

Acidity increases ⟶

H—F	H—Cl	H—Br	H—I
$pK_a = 3.2$	$pK_a = -7$	$pK_a = -9$	$pK_a = -10$

Acidity increases as we descend a vertical column: H—F is the weakest acid and H—I is the strongest. The important factor is the strength of the H—X bond, the *stronger* the bond the *weaker* the acid. The H—F bond is by far the strongest and the H—I bond is the weakest.

Because HI, HBr, and HCl are such strong acids, *their conjugate bases (I⁻, Br⁻, Cl⁻) are all very weak bases.* The fluoride ion is considerably more basic. Overall the basicity of the halide ions increases in the following way:

⟵ Basicity increases

F⁻   Cl⁻   Br⁻   I⁻

We see the same trend of acidities and basicities in other vertical columns of the periodic table. Consider, for example, the column headed by oxygen:

Acidity increases ⟶

H_2O H_2S H_2Se

and

⟵ Basicity increases

OH^- SH^- SeH^-

Here the strongest bond is the O—H bond and H_2O is the weakest acid; the weakest bond is the Se—H bond and H_2Se is the strongest acid.

When we compare compounds in the same horizontal row of the periodic table, bond strengths are roughly the same and *the dominant factor becomes the electronegativity of the atom bonded to the hydrogen.* The electronegativity of this atom affects acidity in two related ways. It affects the polarity of the bond to the proton and it affects the relative stability of the anion (conjugate base) that forms when the proton is lost. Let us compare two hypothetical acids, H—A and H—B.

$$\overset{\delta+ \ \ \delta-}{\text{H—A}} \quad \text{and} \quad \overset{\delta+ \ \ \delta-}{\text{H—B}}$$

Let us assume that A is more electronegative than B. The greater electronegativity of A will cause atom A to be more negative than atom B, and the hydrogen (proton) of H—A will be more positive than that of H—B. The proton of H—A, consequently, will be held less strongly, and it will separate and be transferred to a base more readily. The greater electronegativity of A will also mean that atom A will acquire a negative charge more readily than B, and that the A⁻ anion will be more stable than the B⁻ anion. H—A, therefore, will be the stronger acid.

We can see an example of this effect when we compare the acidities of the compounds CH_4, NH_3, H_2O, and HF. These compounds are all hydrides of first-row elements, and electronegativity increases across a row of the periodic table from left to right (see Table 1.2).

Electronegativity increases ⟩
C   N   O   F

Because fluorine is the most electronegative, the bond in H—F is most polarized, and the proton in H—F is the most positive. Therefore, H—F loses a proton most readily and is the most acidic:

Acidity increases ⟩

$$\overset{\delta- \ \ \delta+}{\text{H}_3\text{C—H}} \quad \overset{\delta- \ \ \delta+}{\text{H}_2\text{N—H}} \quad \overset{\delta- \ \ \delta+}{\text{HO—H}} \quad \overset{\delta- \ \ \delta+}{\text{F—H}}$$

$$pK_a = 48 \qquad pK_a = 38 \qquad pK_a = 15.7 \qquad pK_a = 3.2$$

Because H—F is the strongest acid, its conjugate base, the fluoride ion (F⁻) will be the weakest base. Fluorine is the most electronegative atom and it accommodates the negative charge most readily.

⟨ Basicity increases
CH_3^- H_2N^- HO^- F^-

The methanide ion (CH_3^-) is the least stable anion of the four, because carbon being the least electronegative element is least able to accept the negative charge. The methanide ion, therefore, is the strongest base. [The methanide ion and the amide ion (NH_2^-) are exceedingly strong bases because they are the conjugate bases of extremely weak acids. We shall discuss some uses of these powerful bases in Section 3.9.]

3.5A THE EFFECT OF HYBRIDIZATION

The protons of ethyne are more acidic than those of ethene, which in turn, are more acidic than those of ethane.

Ethyne	Ethene	Ethane
$pK_a = 25$	$pK_a = 44$	$pK_a = 50$

We can explain this order of acidities on the basis of the hybridization state of carbon in each compound. Electrons of $2s$ orbitals have lower energy than those of $2p$ orbitals because *electrons in 2s orbitals tend, on the average, to be much closer to the nucleus than electrons in 2p orbitals.* (Consider the shapes of the orbitals: $2s$ Orbitals are spherical and centered on the nucleus; $2p$ orbitals have lobes on either side of the nucleus and are extended into space.) With hybrid orbitals, therefore, **having more *s* character means that the electrons of the anion will, on the average, be lower in energy, and the anion will be more stable.** The sp orbitals of the C—H bonds of ethyne have 50% s character (because they arise from the combination of one s orbital and one p orbital), those of the sp^2 orbitals of ethene have 33.3% s character, while those of the sp^3 orbitals of ethane have only 25% s character. This means, in effect, that the sp carbon atoms of ethyne act as if they were the most electronegative when compared to the sp^2 carbon atoms of ethene, and the sp^3 carbon atoms of ethane. (Remember: Electronegativity measures an atom's ability to hold bonding electrons close to its nucleus, and having electrons closer to the nucleus makes them more stable.)

Now we can see how the order of relative acidities of ethyne, ethene, and ethane parallels the effective electronegativity of the carbon atom in each compound:

Relative Acidity

$$HC\equiv CH > H_2C=CH_2 > H_3C-CH_3$$

Being the most electronegative, the sp-hybridized carbon atom of ethyne polarizes its C—H bonds to the greatest extent, causing its protons to be most positive. Therefore, ethyne donates a proton to a base more readily. And in the same way, the ethynide ion is the weakest base because the more electronegative carbon of ethyne is best able to stabilize the negative charge.

Relative Basicity

$$H_3C-CH_2:^- > H_2C=CH:^- > HC\equiv C:^-$$

Notice that the explanation given here is the same as that given to account for the relative acidities of HF, H_2O, NH_3, and CH_4.

3.5B INDUCTIVE EFFECTS

The carbon–carbon bond of ethane is completely nonpolar because at each end of the bond there are two equivalent methyl groups.

$$CH_3-CH_3$$
Ethane
The C—C bond is nonpolar

This is not the case with ethyl fluoride, however.

$$\overset{\delta+}{CH_3} \!\!>\!\!\!-\!\! \overset{\delta+}{CH_2} \!\!>\!\!\!-\!\! \overset{\delta-}{F}$$
$$\quad\; 2 \qquad\quad 1$$

One end of the bond, the one nearer the fluorine atom is more positive than the other. This polarization of the carbon–carbon bond results from an intrinsic electron-attracting ability of the fluorine (because of its electronegativity) that is transmitted *through space* and *through the bonds of the molecule.* Chemists call this kind of effect an **inductive effect.** The inductive effect here is **electron attracting** (or **electron withdrawing**), but we shall see later, inductive effects can also be **electron releasing.** *Inductive effects weaken steadily as the distance from the substituent increases.* In this instance, the positive charge that the fluorine imparts to C-1 is greater than that imparted to C-2 because the fluorine is closer to C-1.

Transmission of the effect through bonds results from the polarization of one bond causing polarization of an adjacent bond. In ethyl fluoride, the C—F bond is polarized (C-1 is made positive because the highly electronegative fluorine atom draws in its direction the electrons it is sharing with C-1). The C—C bond becomes polarized, too, because the positively charged C-1 pulls in its direction the electrons that it is sharing with C-2. The positive charge on C-2, however, is smaller than that on C-1. (Even the hydrogen atoms of C-2 are made slightly positive because the C—H bonds are slightly polarized by the positive charge on C-2.)

Transmission of the effect through space is known to be the more important mode of transmission; it results from simple electrostatic effects. In this instance, because the positive end of the C—F dipole is closer to C-2, it attracts the electrons around C-2 and makes C-2 positive, and so on.

Inductive effects help us to understand why carboxylic acids are much more acidic than alcohols. Most unsubstituted carboxylic acids have pK_a values in the range of 3–5 ($K_a = 10^{-3} - 10^{-5}$); alcohols have pK_a values in the range of 15–18 ($K_a = 10^{-15} - 10^{-18}$). A new understanding of the greater acidity of carboxylic acids has been provided by recent experimental and theoretical work.* To see how this work applies let us consider, as examples, two compounds of about the same molecular proportions, but with very different acidities: acetic acid and ethyl alcohol.

$$\overset{\displaystyle O}{\overset{\displaystyle \|}{CH_3-C-OH}} \qquad CH_3-CH_2-OH$$

Acetic acid   **Ethyl alcohol**
$pK_a = 4.74$ $pK_a = 15.9$

In both compounds the O—H bond is highly polarized by the greater electronegativity of the oxygen atom. The key to the much greater acidity of acetic acid is the powerful electron-attracting inductive effect of its carbonyl group (C=O group), when compared with the CH_2 group in the corresponding position of ethyl alcohol. The carbonyl group is highly polarized; the carbon of the carbonyl group bears a large positive charge because of the electronegativity of the carbonyl oxygen and because

---

* An older explanation for the greater acidity of acids was based on resonance stabilization of the carboxylate ion. We now know that this resonance stabilization is only a minor factor. Those who may be interested in pursuing this subject further, should consult the following articles: M. R. F. Siggel and T. D. Thomas, *J. Am. Chem. Soc.* **1986**, *108*, 4360–4362, and M. R. F. Siggel, A. R. Streitwieser, Jr., and T. D. Thomas, *J. Am. Chem. Soc.,* **1988** *110*, 8022–8028.

the second resonance structure below is an important contributor to the overall resonance hybrid (Section 1.8). That is to say, if we were to visualize the carbonyl group, it would show a considerable resemblance to the second structure below.

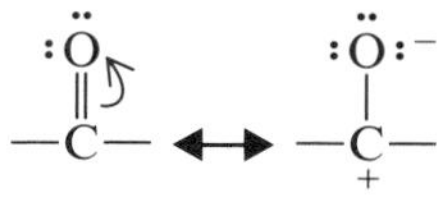

$$\begin{array}{ccc} :\overset{\cdot\cdot}{O} & & :\overset{\cdot\cdot}{O}:^- \\ \| & \longleftrightarrow & | \\ -C- & & -\overset{+}{C}- \end{array}$$

Resonance structures for the carbonyl group

The carbonyl group of acetic acid, because its carbon bears a large positive charge, adds its electron-attracting effect to that of the oxygen of the hydroxyl group attached to it; this makes the hydroxyl proton much more positive than the proton of the alcohol. This greater positive charge on the proton of the acid means that the proton separates more readily. The electron-attracting effect of the carbonyl group also stabilizes the anion that forms from the carboxylic acid (the carboxylate ion), and, therefore, the carboxylate ion is a weaker base than the ethoxide ion.

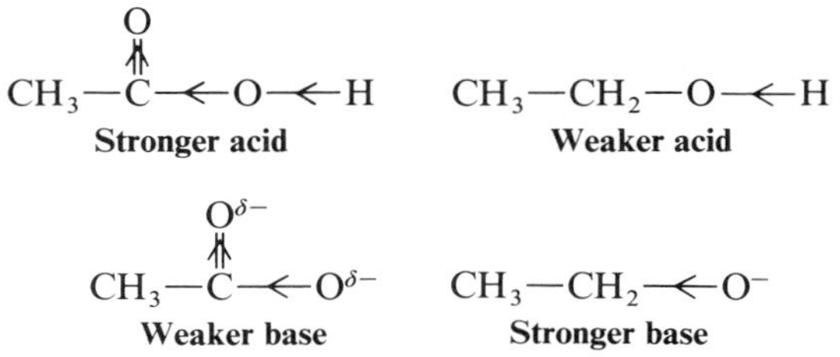

$$\underset{\textbf{Stronger acid}}{CH_3-\overset{\overset{\textstyle O}{\|}}{C}\!\!\leftarrow\!\!O\!\!\leftarrow\!\!H} \qquad \underset{\textbf{Weaker acid}}{CH_3-CH_2-O\!\!\leftarrow\!\!H}$$

$$\underset{\textbf{Weaker base}}{CH_3-\overset{\overset{\textstyle O^{\delta-}}{\|}}{C}\!\!\leftarrow\!\!O^{\delta-}} \qquad \underset{\textbf{Stronger base}}{CH_3-CH_2\!\!\leftarrow\!\!O^-}$$

Problem 3.8 ―――――――――――――――――――――

Use resonance theory to explain two related facts: The carbon–oxygen bond distances in the acetate ion are the same and the oxygen atoms of the acetate ion bear equal negative charges.

――――――――――――――――――――――――――――――

The acid-strengthening effect of electron-attracting groups can also be shown by comparing the acidities of acetic acid and chloroacetic acid:

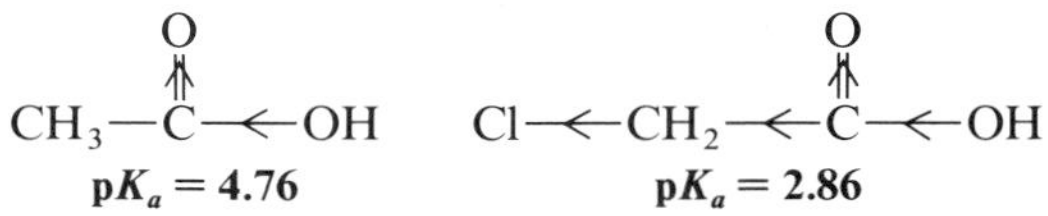

$$\underset{\textbf{p}K_a = 4.76}{CH_3-\overset{\overset{\textstyle O}{\|}}{C}\!\!\leftarrow\!\!OH} \qquad \underset{\textbf{p}K_a = 2.86}{Cl\!\!\leftarrow\!\!CH_2\!\!\leftarrow\!\!\overset{\overset{\textstyle O}{\|}}{C}\!\!\leftarrow\!\!OH}$$

The greater acidity of chloroacetic acid can be attributed, in part, to the extra electron-attracting inductive effect of the electronegative chlorine atom. By adding its effect to that of the carbonyl group and the oxygen, it makes the hydroxyl proton of chloroacetic acid even more positive than that of acetic acid. It also stabilizes the chloroacetate ion that is formed when the proton is lost *by dispersing its negative*

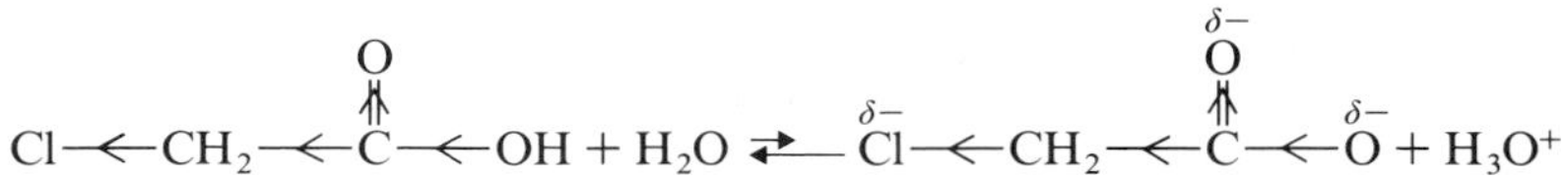

$$Cl\!\!\leftarrow\!\!CH_2\!\!\leftarrow\!\!\overset{\overset{\textstyle O}{\|}}{C}\!\!\leftarrow\!\!OH + H_2O \rightleftarrows \overset{\delta-}{} Cl\!\!\leftarrow\!\!CH_2\!\!\leftarrow\!\!\overset{\overset{\textstyle \overset{\delta-}{O}}{\|}}{C}\!\!\leftarrow\!\!\overset{\delta-}{O} + H_3O^+$$

charge. The negative charge is more spread out in the chloroacetate ion because it resides partially on the chlorine atom. Dispersal of charge always makes a species more stable, and, as we have seen now in several instances, any factor that stabilizes the conjugate base of an acid will increase the strength of the acid. (In Section 3.7, we shall see that entropy changes in the solvent are also important in explaining the increased acidity of chloroacetic acid.)

Problem 3.9

Which would you expect to be the stronger acid? Explain your reasoning in each instance.

(a) CH_2ClCO_2H or $CHCl_2CO_2H$ (c) CH_2FCO_2H or CH_2BrCO_2H

(b) CCl_3CO_2H or $CHCl_2CO_2H$ (d) CH_2FCO_2H or $CH_2FCH_2CO_2H$

3.6 THE RELATIONSHIP BETWEEN THE EQUILIBRIUM CONSTANT AND THE STANDARD FREE-ENERGY CHANGE, $\Delta G°$

An important relationship exists between the equilibrium constant and the standard free-energy change* ($\Delta G°$) that accompanies the reaction.

$$\Delta G° = -2.303 \, RT \log K_{eq}$$

R is the gas constant and equals $1.987 \, cal \, K^{-1} \, mol^{-1}$; T is the absolute temperature in kelvins (K).

It is easy to show with this equation that **a negative value of $\Delta G°$ is associated with reactions that favor the formation of products when equilibrium is reached,** and for which the equilibrium constant is greater than 1. Reactions with a $\Delta G°$ more negative than about $-3 \, kcal \, mol^{-1}$ are said *to go to completion,* meaning that almost all ($>99\%$) of the reactants are converted to products when equilibrium is reached. Conversely, **a positive value of $\Delta G°$ is associated with reactions for which the formation of products at equilibrium is unfavorable** and for which the equilibrium constant is less than 1. Inasmuch as K_a is an equilibrium constant, it is related to $\Delta G°$ in the same way.

The free-energy change ($\Delta G°$) has two components, the enthalpy change ($\Delta H°$) and the entropy change ($\Delta S°$). The relationship between these three thermodynamic quantities is

$$\Delta G° = \Delta H° - T\Delta S°$$

We have seen (Section 1.9) that $\Delta H°$ is associated with changes in bonding that occur in a reaction. If, collectively, stronger bonds are formed in the products than existed in the starting materials, then $\Delta H°$ will be negative (i.e., the reaction is *exothermic*). If the reverse is true, then $\Delta H°$ will be positive (the reaction is *endother-*

---

* By standard free-energy change ($\Delta G°$) we mean that the products and reactants are taken as being in their standard states (1 atm of pressure for a gas, and 1 M for a solution). The free-energy change is often called the **Gibbs free-energy change,** to honor the contributions to thermodynamics of J. Willard Gibbs, a professor of mathematical physics at Yale University from 1871 until the turn of the century. Gibbs ranks as one of the greatest scientists produced by the United States.

mic). A negative value for $\Delta H°$, therefore, will contribute to making $\Delta G°$ negative, and will, consequently favor the formation of products. For the ionization of an acid, the less positive or more negative the value of $\Delta H°$ the stronger the acid will be.

Entropy changes have to do with *changes in the relative order of a system.* **The more random a system is, the greater is its entropy.** Therefore, a positive entropy change $(+\Delta S°)$ is always associated with a change from a more ordered system to a less ordered one. A negative entropy change $(-\Delta S°)$ accompanies the reverse process. In the equation $\Delta G° = \Delta H° - T\Delta S°$, the entropy change (multiplied by T) is preceded by a negative sign; this means that *a positive entropy change (from order to disorder) makes a negative contribution to $\Delta G°$ and is energetically favorable for the formation of products.*

For many reactions in which the number of molecules of products equals the number of molecules of reactants (e. g., when two molecules react to produce two molecules) the entropy change will be small. This means that except at high temperatures (where the term $T\Delta S°$ becomes large even if $\Delta S°$ is small) a large value of $\Delta H°$ will determine whether or not the formation of products will be favored. If $\Delta H°$ is large and negative (if the reaction is exothermic), then the reaction will favor the formation of products at equilibrium. If $\Delta H°$ is positive (if the reaction is endothermic) then the formation of products will be unfavorable.

3.7 THE EFFECT OF THE SOLVENT ON ACIDITY

In the absence of a solvent, (i. e., in the gas phase) most acids are far weaker than they are in solution. In the gas phase, for example, acetic acid is estimated to have a pK_a of about 130 (a K_a of $\sim 10^{-130}$)! The reason for this: When an acetic acid molecule donates a proton to a water molecule in the gas phase, the ions that are formed are oppositely charged particles and these particles must become separated.

$$CH_3-\overset{\overset{\textstyle O}{\|}}{C}-OH + H_2O \rightleftharpoons CH_3-\overset{\overset{\textstyle O}{\|}}{C}-O^- + H_3O^+$$

In the absence of a solvent, separation is difficult. In solution, solvent molecules surround the ions, insulating them from one another, stabilizing them, and making it far easier to separate them than in the gas phase.

In a solvent such as water, called a **protic solvent,** solvation by hydrogen bonding is important (Section 2.16C). **A protic solvent is one that has a hydrogen atom attached to a strongly electronegative element such as oxygen or nitrogen.** Molecules of a protic solvent, therefore, can form hydrogen bonds to the unshared electron pairs of oxygen (or nitrogen) atoms of an acid and its conjugate base, but they may not stabilize both equally.

Consider, for example, the ionization of acetic acid in aqueous solution. Water molecules solvate both the undissociated acid (CH_3CO_2H) and its anion $(CH_3CO_2^-)$ by forming hydrogen bonds to them (Section 3.1A). However, hydrogen bonding to $CH_3CO_2^-$ is much stronger than to CH_3CO_2H because the water molecules are more attracted by the negative charge. This differential solvation, moreover, has important consequences for the entropy change that accompanies the ionization. Solvation of any species decreases the entropy of the solvent because the solvent molecules become much more ordered as they surround molecules of the solute. Because solvation of $CH_3CO_2^-$ is stronger, the solvent molecules become more orderly around it.

TABLE 3.2 Thermodynamic values for the dissociation of acetic and chloroacetic acids in H_2O at 25 °C[a]

ACID	pK_a	$\Delta G°$ (kcal mol^{-1})	$\Delta H°$ (kcal mol^{-1})	$-T\Delta S°$ (kcal mol^{-1})
CH_3CO_2H	4.76	+6.5	−0.1	+6.6
$ClCH_2CO_2H$	2.86	+3.9	−1.1	+5.0

[a] Table adapted from J. March, *Advanced Organic Chemistry,* 3rd ed., Wiley, New York, 1985 p. 236.

The entropy change ($\Delta S°$) for the ionization of acetic acid, therefore, is negative. This means that the $-T\Delta S°$ term in the equation $\Delta G° = \Delta H° - T\Delta S°$, makes an acid-weakening positive contribution to $\Delta G°$. In fact, as Table 3.2 shows, the $-T\Delta S°$ term contributes more to $\Delta G°$ than $\Delta H°$ does, and accounts for the fact that the free-energy change for the ionization of acetic acid is positive (unfavorable).

We saw in Section 3.5B that chloroacetic acid is a stronger acid than acetic acid, and we attributed this increased acidity to the presence of the electron-withdrawing chlorine atom. Table 3.2 shows us that both $\Delta H°$ and $-T\Delta S°$ are more favorable for the ionization of chloroacetic acid ($\Delta H°$ is more negative by 1.0 kcal mol^{-1}, and $-T\Delta S°$ is less positive by 1.6 kcal mol^{-1}). The larger contribution is clearly in the entropy term. Apparently, by stabilizing the chloroacetate anion, the chlorine atom makes the chloroacetate ion less prone to cause an ordering of the solvent because it requires less stabilization through solvation.

3.8 ACID AND BASES IN NONAQUEOUS SOLUTIONS

If you were to add sodium amide ($NaNH_2$) to water in an attempt to carry out a reaction using the very powerful base, the amide ion (NH_2^-) in aqueous solution, the following reaction would take place immediately.

$$H-\ddot{O}-H \: + \: :NH_2^- \longrightarrow H-\ddot{O}:^- \: + \: \ddot{N}H_3$$

Stronger acid	Stronger base	Weaker base	Weaker acid
$pK_a = 15.7$			$pK_a = 38$

The amide ion would react with water to produce a solution containing hydroxide ions (a much weaker base) and ammonia. This example illustrates what is called **the leveling effect** of the solvent. The solvent here, water, converts any base stronger than a hydroxide ion to a hydroxide ion by donating a proton to it. Therefore, *it is not possible to use a base stronger than hydroxide ion in aqueous solution.*

We can use bases stronger than hydroxide ion, however, by using solvents that are weaker acids than water. We can use amide ion (e. g., $NaNH_2$) in a solvent such as hexane, diethyl ether, or in liquid NH_3 (the liquified gas, not the aqueous solution that you may have used in your general chemistry laboratory). All of these solvents are very weak acids, and, therefore they will not convert the amide ion to a weaker base by donating a proton to it.

We can, for example, convert ethyne to its conjugate base by treating it with sodium amide in liquid ammonia.

3.8 ACID AND BASES IN NONAQUEOUS SOLUTIONS

$$H-C\equiv C-H + :NH_2^- \xrightarrow[NH_3]{liquid} H-C\equiv C:^- + :NH_3$$

Stronger acid $pK_a = 25$	Stronger base (from NaNH$_2$)	Weaker base	Weaker acid $pK_a = 38$

Most alkynes with a proton attached to a triply bonded carbon (called **terminal alkynes**) have pK_a values of about 25, therefore, all react with sodium amide in liquid ammonia in the same way that ethyne does. The general reaction is

$$R-C\equiv C-H + :NH_2^- \xrightarrow[NH_3]{liquid} R-C\equiv C:^- + :NH_3$$

Stronger acid $pK_a = 25$	Stronger base	Weaker base	Weaker acid $pK_a = 38$

Alcohols are often used as solvents for organic reactions because being somewhat less polar than water, they dissolve less polar organic compounds. Using alcohols as solvents also offers the advantage of using RO$^-$ ions (called **alkoxide ions**) as bases. Alkoxide ions are somewhat stronger bases than hydroxide ions because alcohols are weaker acids than water. For example, we can create a solution of sodium ethoxide (CH$_3$CH$_2$ONa) in ethyl alcohol by adding sodium hydride (NaH) to ethyl alcohol. We use a large excess of ethyl alcohol because we want it to be the solvent. Being a very strong base, the hydride ion reacts readily with ethyl alcohol:

$$CH_3CH_2\ddot{O}-H + :H^- \xrightarrow{ethyl\ alcohol} CH_3CH_2\ddot{O}:^- + H_2$$

Stronger acid $pK_a = 16$	Stronger base (from NaH)	Weaker base	Weaker acid $pK_a = 35$

The *tert*-butoxide ion, (CH$_3$)$_3$CO$^-$, in *tert*-butyl alcohol, (CH$_3$)$_3$COH, is a stronger base than the ethoxide ion in ethyl alcohol, and it can be prepared in a similar way.

$$(CH_3)_3C\ddot{O}-H + :H^- \xrightarrow{ethyl\ alcohol} (CH_3)_3C\ddot{O}:^- + H_2$$

Stronger acid $pK_a = 17$	Stronger base (from NaH)	Weaker base	Weaker acid $pK_a = 35$

Although the carbon–lithium bond of an alkyllithium (RLi) has covalent character, it is polarized so as to make the carbon negative.

$$\overset{\delta-}{R} \longleftarrow \overset{\delta+}{Li}$$

Alkyllithiums react as though they contained alkanide (R$^-$) ions, and being the conjugate bases of alkanes, alkanide ions are the strongest bases that we shall encounter. Ethyllithium (CH$_3$CH$_2$Li), for example, will react with ethyne in the following way:

$$H-C{\equiv}C-H + \quad {}^-{:}CH_2CH_3 \quad \xrightarrow{\text{hexane}} \quad H-C{\equiv}C{:}^- + CH_3CH_3$$

Stronger acid	**Stronger**	**Weaker**	**Weaker**
$pK_a = 25$	**base**	**base**	**acid**
	(from CH_3CH_2Li)		$pK_a = 50$

Alkyllithiums can be easily prepared by allowing an alkyl bromide to react with lithium metal in an ether solvent (such as diethyl ether).

General Reaction

$$RBr + 2\ Li \xrightarrow[\text{ether}]{\text{diethyl}} \quad RLi \quad + LiBr$$
$$\textbf{Alkyllithium}$$

Specific Example

$$CH_3CH_2Br + 2\ Li \xrightarrow[\text{ether}]{\text{diethyl}} CH_3CH_2Li + LiBr$$
$$\textbf{Ethyllithium}$$

In this reaction lithium acts as a reducing agent; each lithium atom donates an electron to the alkyl bromide producing the alkyllithium and lithium bromide.

Problem 3.10

Write equations for the acid–base reaction that would occur when each of the following compounds or solutions are mixed. In each case label the stronger acid and stronger base, and the weaker acid and weaker base. (If no appreciable acid–base reaction would occur, you should indicate this.)

(a) NaH is added to CH_3OH

(b) $NaNH_2$ is added to CH_3CH_2OH

(c) Gaseous NH_3 is added to ethyllithium in hexane

(d) NH_4Cl is added to sodium amide in liquid ammonia

(e) $(CH_3)_3CONa$ is added to H_2O

(f) NaOH is added to $(CH_3)_3COH$

3.9 ACID–BASE REACTIONS AND THE SYNTHESIS OF DEUTERIUM- AND TRITIUM-LABELED COMPOUNDS

Chemists often use compounds in which deuterium or tritium atoms have replaced one or more hydrogen atoms of the compound as a method of "labeling" or identifying particular hydrogen atoms. Deuterium (^2H) and tritium (^3H) are isotopes of hydrogen with masses of 2 and 3 atomic mass units (amu), respectively.

For most chemical purposes, deuterium and tritium atoms in a molecule behave in much the same way that ordinary hydrogen atoms behave. The extra mass and additional neutrons associated with a deuterium or tritium atom often makes its position in a molecule easy to locate by certain spectroscopic methods that we shall study later. Tritium is also radioactive, which makes it very easy to locate. (The extra mass associated with these labeled atoms may also cause compounds containing deuterium or tritium atoms to react more slowly than compounds with ordinary hydrogen atoms. This effect called an "isotope effect" has been useful in studying the mechanisms of many reactions.)

One way to introduce a deuterium or tritium atom into a specific location in a molecule is through the acid–base reaction that takes place when a very strong base is treated with D_2O or T_2O. For example, treating a solution containing $(CH_3)_2CHLi$ (isopropyllithium) with D_2O results in the formation of propane labeled with deuterium at the central atom:

$$CH_3CH{:}^-Li^+ + D_2O \xrightarrow{hexane} CH_3CH-D + OD^-$$

Isopropyl-lithium (stronger base) + (stronger acid) → 2-Deuterio-propane (weaker acid) + (weaker base)

Sample Problem

Assuming you have available propyne, a solution of sodium amide in liquid ammonia, and T_2O, show how you would prepare the tritium-labeled compound $(CH_3C{\equiv}CT)$.

Answer:
First add the propyne to the sodium amide in liquid ammonia. The following acid–base reaction will take place:

$$CH_3C{\equiv}CH + NH_2^- \xrightarrow{liq.\ ammonia} CH_3C{\equiv}C{:}^- + NH_3$$

Stronger acid + Stronger base → Weaker base + Weaker acid

Then adding T_2O (a much stronger acid than NH_3) to the solution will produce $CH_3C{\equiv}CT$.

$$CH_3C{\equiv}C{:}^- + T_2O \xrightarrow{liq.\ ammonia} CH_3C{\equiv}CT + OT^-$$

Stronger base + Stronger acid → Weaker acid + Weaker base

Problem 3.11

Complete the following acid–base reactions:

(a) $HC{\equiv}CH + NaH \xrightarrow{hexane}$

(b) The solution obtained in (a) + $D_2O \longrightarrow$

(c) $CH_3CH_2Li + D_2O \xrightarrow{hexane}$

(d) $CH_3CH_2OH + NaH \xrightarrow{hexane}$

(e) The solution obtained in (d) + $T_2O \longrightarrow$

(f) $CH_3CH_2CH_2Li + D_2O \xrightarrow{hexane}$

3.10 SOME IMPORTANT TERMS AND CONCEPTS

A *Brønsted–Lowry acid* is a substance that can donate a proton; a *Brønsted–Lowry base* is a substance that can accept a proton.

A *Lewis acid* is an electron-pair acceptor; a *Lewis base* is an electron-pair donor.

A *mechanism for a reaction* is a step-by-step description of how a reaction takes place.

Curved arrows (⤿) are used to show the direction of electron flow when mechanisms are written. The arrow begins with a site of higher electron density and points toward a site of electron deficiency.

The *strength of an acid* can be expressed by its acidity constant, K_a,

$$K_a = \frac{[H_3O^+] \, [A^-]}{[HA]}$$

or by its pK_a,

$$pK_a = -\log K_a$$

The *larger* the value of the K_a, or the *smaller* the value of the pK_a, the *stronger* is the acid.

The *strength of a base* is inversely related to the strength of its conjugate acid; the *weaker* the conjugate acid, the *stronger* is the base. Therefore the larger the pK_a of the conjugate acid, the stronger is the base.

The *outcome of acid–base reactions* can be predicted on the basis of the principle that acid–base reactions proceed toward equilibrium *so as to favor the formation of the weaker acid and the weaker base.*

An inductive effect reflects the ability of a substituent to attract or release electrons because of its electronegativity. The effect, transmitted through space and, less effectively, through bonds, weakens steadily as the distance from the substituent increases.

Dispersal of electrical charge always makes a chemical entity more stable.

The *relationship between K_{eq} and the standard free-energy change* ($\Delta G°$) is as follows:

$$\Delta G° = -2.303 \, RT \log K_{eq}$$

A negative value of $\Delta G°$ is associated with reactions that favor the formation of products when equilibrium is reached.

The relationship between $\Delta G°$, and the *enthalpy change* ($\Delta H°$) and the *entropy change* ($\Delta S°$) is as follows:

$$\Delta G° = \Delta H° - T\Delta S°$$

A *negative enthalpy change* (associated with an exothermic reaction) and a *positive entropy change* (associated with the products being less ordered than the reactants) favors the formation of products when equilibrium is reached.

ADDITIONAL PROBLEMS

A *protic solvent* is one that has a hydrogen atom attached to a strongly electronegative atom (i.e., to an oxygen, nitrogen, or fluorine atom).

Additional Problems

3.12   What is the conjugate base of each of the following acids?

(a) NH_3 (d) $HC{\equiv}CH$
(b) H_2O (e) CH_3OH
(c) H_2 (f) H_3O^+

3.13   List the bases you gave as answers to Problem 3.12 in order of decreasing basicity.

3.14   What is the conjugate acid of each of the following bases?

(a) HSO_4^- (d) NH_2^-
(b) H_2O (e) $CH_3CH_2^-$
(c) CH_3NH_2 (f) $CH_3CO_2^-$

3.15   List the acids you gave as answers to Problem 3.14 in order of decreasing acidity.

3.16   Designate the Lewis acid and Lewis base in each of the following reactions:

(a) 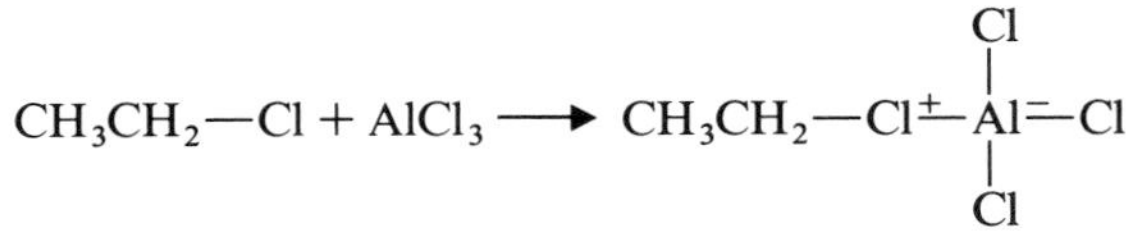 $CH_3CH_2{-}Cl + AlCl_3 \longrightarrow CH_3CH_2{-}Cl{\pm}Al{=}Cl$ with Cl above and Cl below the Al

(b) 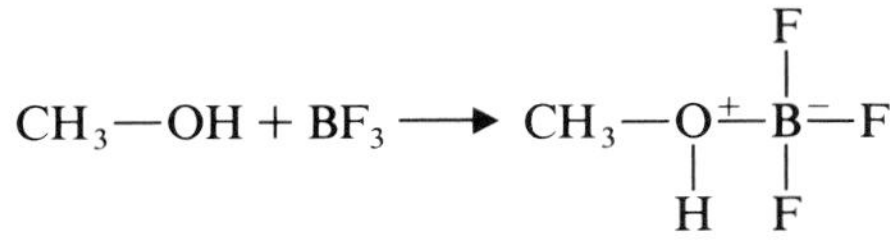 $CH_3{-}OH + BF_3 \longrightarrow CH_3{-}O{\pm}B{=}F$ with F above, H and F below

(c) 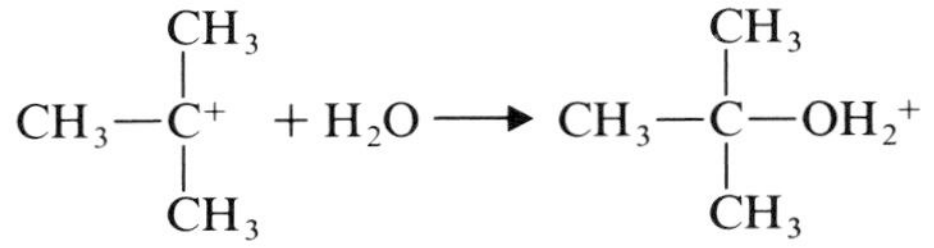 $CH_3{-}C^+$ (with CH_3 above and CH_3 below) $+ H_2O \longrightarrow CH_3{-}C{-}OH_2^+$ (with CH_3 above and CH_3 below)

3.17   Rewrite each of the following reactions using curved arrows and show all nonbonding electron pairs.

(a) $CH_3OH + HI \longrightarrow CH_3OH_2^+ + I^-$
(b) $CH_3NH_2 + HCl \longrightarrow CH_3NH_3^+ + Cl^-$

(c) 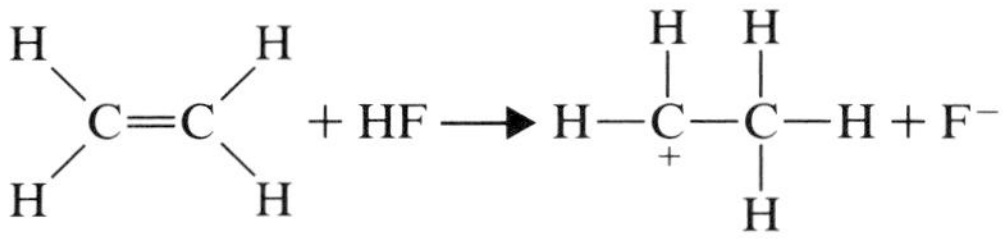 $H_2C{=}CH_2 + HF \longrightarrow H{-}CH_2{-}CH_2{-}H + F^-$

3.18   When methyl alcohol is treated with NaH, the product is $CH_3O^-Na^+$ (and H_2) and not $Na^+ {}^-CH_2OH$ (and H_2). Explain why this is so.

3.19   What reaction will take place if ethyl alcohol is added to a solution of $HC{\equiv}C\colon^-Na^+$ in liquid ammonia?

3.20   (a) The K_a of formic acid (HCO_2H) is 1.77×10^{-4}. What is the pK_a?   (b) What is the K_a of an acid whose p$K_a = 13$?

3.21   Acid HA has a p$K_a = 20$; acid HB has a p$K_a = 10$.   (a) Which is the stronger acid? (b) Will an acid–base reaction with an equilibrium lying to the right take place if Na^+A^- is added to HB? Explain your answer.

3.22   Write an equation, using the curved-arrow notation, for the acid–base reaction that will take place when each of the following are mixed. If no appreciable acid–base reaction takes place, because the equilibrium is unfavorable, you should so indicate.

(a) Aqueous NaOH and $CH_3CH_2CO_2H$

(b) Aqueous NaOH and $C_6H_5SO_3H$

(c) CH_3CH_2ONa in ethyl alcohol and ethyne

(d) CH_3CH_2Li in hexane and ethyne

(e) CH_3CH_2Li in hexane and ethyl alcohol

3.23   Show how you would synthesize each of the following, starting with an alkyl bromide and using any other needed reagents.

(a) $CH_3CH_2CH_2D$

(b) CH_3CHDCH_3

(c)
$$CH_3-\underset{\underset{CH_3}{|}}{\overset{\overset{CH_3}{|}}{C}}-D$$

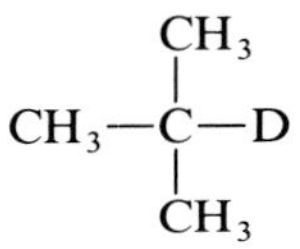

3.24   Starting with appropriate unlabeled organic compounds show syntheses of each of the following:

(a) $CH_3-C{\equiv}C-T$ (b) $CH_3-\underset{\underset{CH_3}{|}}{CH}-O-D$ (c) $CH_3CH_2CH_2OD$

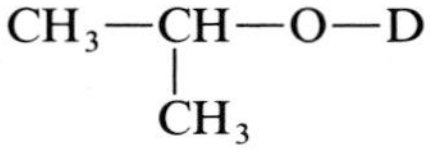

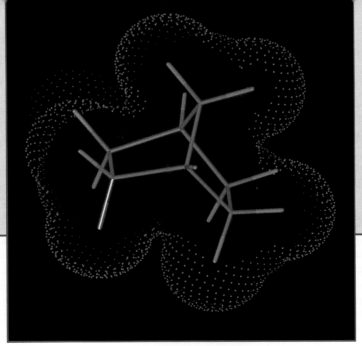

Bicyclo[2.2.1]heptane (see Section 4.4B).

CHAPTER

4

ALKANES AND CYCLOALKANES: CONFORMATIONS OF MOLECULES

4.1 INTRODUCTION TO ALKANES AND CYCLOALKANES

We noted earlier that the family of organic compounds called hydrocarbons can be divided into several groups based on the type of bond that exists between the individual carbon atoms. Those hydrocarbons in which all of the carbon–carbon bonds are single bonds are called *alkanes;* those hydrocarbons that contain a carbon–carbon double bond are called *alkenes;* and those with a carbon–carbon triple bond are called *alkynes.*

Cycloalkanes are alkanes in which all or some of the carbon atoms are arranged in a ring. Alkanes have the general formula C_nH_{2n+2}; cycloalkanes containing a single ring have two fewer hydrogen atoms and thus have the general formula C_nH_{2n}.

Alkanes and cycloalkanes are so similar that many of their properties can be considered side by side. Some differences remain, however, and certain structural features arise from the rings of cycloalkanes that are more conveniently studied separately. We shall point out the chemical and physical similarities of alkanes and cycloalkanes as we go along.

4.1A SOURCES OF ALKANES: PETROLEUM

The primary source of alkanes is petroleum. Petroleum is a complex mixture of organic compounds, most of which are alkanes and aromatic hydrocarbons (cf. Chapter 13). It also contains small amounts of oxygen-, nitrogen-, and sulfur-containing compounds.

4.1B PETROLEUM REFINING

The first step in refining petroleum is distillation; the object here is to separate the petroleum into fractions based on the volatility of its components. Complete separation into fractions containing individual compounds is economically impractical and virtually impossible technically. More than 500 different compounds are contained in the petroleum distillates boiling below 200 °C and many have almost the same boiling points. Thus the fractions taken contain mixtures of alkanes of similar boiling points (cf. Table 4.1). Mixtures of alkanes, fortunately, are perfectly suitable for uses as fuels, solvents, and lubricants, the primary uses of petroleum.

4.1C CRACKING

The demand for gasoline is much greater than that supplied by the gasoline fraction of petroleum. Important processes in the petroleum industry, therefore, are concerned with converting hydrocarbons from other fractions into gasoline. When a mixture of alkanes from the gas oil (C_{12} and higher) fraction is heated at very high temperatures (~ 500 °C) in the presence of a variety of catalysts, the molecules break apart and rearrange to smaller, more highly branched alkanes containing 5 – 10 carbon atoms (see Table 4.1). This process is called **catalytic cracking.** Cracking can also be done in the absence of a catalyst — called **thermal cracking** — but in this process the products tend to have unbranched chains, and alkanes with unbranched chains have a very low "octane rating."

TABLE 4.1   Typical fractions obtained by distillation of petroleum

BOILING RANGE OF FRACTION (°C)	NUMBER OF CARBON ATOMS PER MOLECULE	USE
Below 20	C_1—C_4	Natural gas, bottled gas, petrochemicals
20–60	C_5—C_6	Petroleum ether, solvents
60–100	C_6—C_7	Ligroin, solvents
40–200	C_5—C_{10}	Gasoline (straight-run gasoline)
175–325	C_{12}—C_{18}	Kerosene and jet fuel
250–400	C_{12} and higher	Gas oil, fuel oil, and diesel oil
Nonvolatile liquids	C_{20} and higher	Refined mineral oil, lubricating oil, grease
Nonvolatile solids	C_{20} and higher	Paraffin wax, asphalt, and tar

Adapted with permission from John R. Holum, *Elements of General and Biological Chemistry,* 8th ed., Wiley, New York, 1991.

The highly branched compound 2,2,4-trimethylpentane (called "isooctane" in the petroleum industry) burns very smoothly (without knocking) in internal combustion engines and is used as one of the standards by which the octane rating of

$$CH_3-\underset{\underset{\displaystyle CH_3}{|}}{\overset{\overset{\displaystyle CH_3}{|}}{C}}-CH_2-\underset{\overset{\displaystyle CH_3}{|}}{CH}-CH_3$$

2,2,4-trimethylpentane
("isooctane")

gasolines is established. According to this scale 2,2,4-trimethylpentane has an octane rating of 100. Heptane, $CH_3(CH_2)_5CH_3$, a compound that produces much knocking when it is burned in an internal combustion engine, is given an octane rating of 0. Mixtures of 2,2,4-trimethylpentane and heptane are used as standards for octane ratings between 0 and 100. A gasoline, for example, that has the same characteristics in an engine as a mixture of 87% 2,2,4-trimethylpentane–13% heptane would be rated as 87-octane gasoline.

4.2 SHAPES OF ALKANES

A general tetrahedral orientation of groups — and thus sp^3 hybridization — is the rule for the carbon atoms of all alkanes and cycloalkanes. We can represent the shapes of alkanes as shown in Fig. 4.1.

Butane and pentane are examples of alkanes that are sometimes called "straight-chain" alkanes. One glance at their three-dimensional models shows that because of the tetrahedral carbon atoms their chains are zigzagged and not at all straight. Indeed, the structures that we have depicted in Fig. 4.1 are the straightest possible arrangements of the chains, for rotations about the carbon–carbon single bonds produce arrangements that are even less straight. The better description is **unbranched.** This means that each carbon atom within the chain is bonded to no more than two other carbon atoms and that unbranched alkanes contain only primary and secondary carbon atoms. (Unbranched alkanes used to be called "normal" alkanes or *n*-alkanes, but this designation is archaic and should not be used now.)

Isobutane, isopentane, and neopentane (Fig. 4.2) are examples of branched-chain alkanes. In neopentane the central carbon atom is bonded to four carbon atoms.

Butane and isobutane have the same molecular formula: C_4H_{10}. The two compounds have their atoms connected in a different order and are, therefore, *constitutional isomers*. Pentane, isopentane, and neopentane are also constitutional isomers. They, too, have the same molecular formula (C_5H_{12}) but have different structures.

Problem 4.1

Write condensed structural formulas for all of the constitutional isomers of C_6H_{14}. Compare your answers with the condensed structural formulas given in Table 4.2.

CHAPTER 4. ALKANES AND CYCLOALKANES: CONFORMATIONS OF MOLECULES

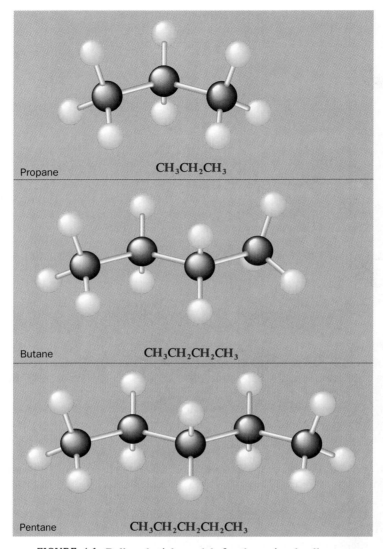

Propane $CH_3CH_2CH_3$

Butane $CH_3CH_2CH_2CH_3$

Pentane $CH_3CH_2CH_2CH_2CH_3$

FIGURE 4.1   Ball-and-stick models for three simple alkanes.

Constitutional isomers, as stated earlier, have different physical properties. The differences may not always be large, but constitutional isomers will always be found to have different melting points, boiling points, densities, indexes of refraction, and so forth. Table 4.2 gives some of the physical properties of the C_4H_{10}, C_5H_{12}, and C_6H_{14} isomers.

As Table 4.3 shows, the number of constitutional isomers that are possible increases dramatically as the number of carbon atoms in the alkane increases.

The large numbers in Table 4.3 are based on calculations that must be done with a computer. Similar calculations that take into account stereoisomers (Chapter 5), as well as constitutional isomers, indicate that an alkane with the formula $C_{167}H_{336}$ would, in theory, have more possible isomers than there are particles in the observed universe!

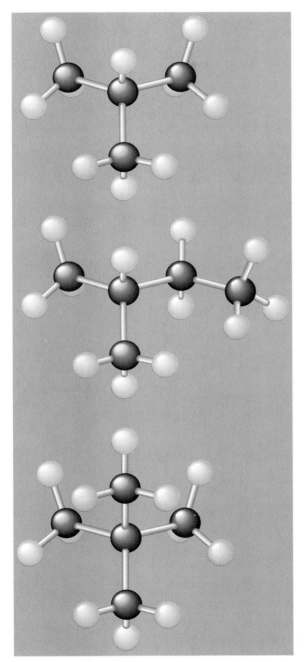

$CH_3\!-\!CH\!-\!CH_3$
$|$
CH_3

Isobutane

$CH_3\!-\!CH\!-\!CH_2\!-\!CH_3$
$|$
CH_3

Isopentane

CH_3
$|$
$CH_3\!-\!C\!-\!CH_3$
$|$
CH_3

Neopentane

FIGURE 4.2 Ball-and-stick models for three branched-chain alkanes. In each of the compounds one carbon atom is attached to more than two other carbon atoms.

TABLE 4.2 Physical constants of the butane, pentane, and hexane isomers

MOLECULAR FORMULA	STRUCTURAL FORMULA	mp (°C)	bp (°C)[a] (1 atm)	DENSITY[b] (g mL^{-1})	INDEX OF REFRACTION[c] (n_D, 20 °C)
C_4H_{10}	$CH_3CH_2CH_2CH_3$	−138.3	−0.5	0.6012^0	1.3543

C_4H_{10}	CH_3CHCH_3
	    |
	   CH_3
		−159	−12	0.603^0	

C_5H_{12}	$CH_3CH_2CH_2CH_2CH_3$	−129.72	36	0.6262^{20}	1.3579

C_5H_{12}	$CH_3CHCH_2CH_3$
	    |
	   CH_3
		−160	27.9	0.6197^{20}	1.3537

C_5H_{12}	$\quad\quad CH_3$ $\quad\quad\ \|$ $CH_3{-}C{-}CH_3$ $\quad\quad\ \|$ $\quad\quad CH_3$	−20	9.5	0.61350^{20}	1.3476
C_6H_{14}	$CH_3CH_2CH_2CH_2CH_2CH_3$	−95	68	0.65937^{20}	1.3748

C_6H_{14}	$CH_3CHCH_2CH_2CH_3$
	    |
	   CH_3
		−153.67	60.3	0.6532^{20}	1.3714

C_6H_{14}	$CH_3CH_2CHCH_2CH_3$
	       |
	     CH_3
		−118	63.3	0.6643^{20}	1.3765

C_6H_{14}	$CH_3CH{-}CHCH_3$
	   | |
	  CH_3 CH_3
		−128.8	58	0.6616^{20}	1.3750

C_6H_{14}	$\quad\quad CH_3$ $\quad\quad\ \|$ $CH_3{-}C{-}CH_2CH_3$ $\quad\quad\ \|$ $\quad\quad CH_3$	−98	49.7	0.6492^{20}	1.3688

[a] Unless otherwise indicated, all boiling points are at 1 atm or 760 torr.

[b] The superscript indicates the temperature at which the density was measured.

[c] The index of refraction is a measure of the ability of the alkane to bend (refract) light rays. The values reported are for light of the D line of the sodium spectrum (n_D).

4.3 IUPAC NOMENCLATURE OF ALKANES, ALKYL HALIDES, AND ALCOHOLS

The development of a formal system for naming organic compounds did not come about until near the end of the nineteenth century. Prior to that time many organic compounds had already been discovered. The names given these compounds sometimes reflected a source of the compound. Acetic acid, for example, can be obtained from vinegar; it got its name from the Latin word for vinegar, *acetum*. Formic acid can be obtained from some ants; it got its name from the Latin word for ants, *formicae*. Ethanol (or ethyl alcohol) was at one time called grain alcohol because it was obtained by the fermentation of grains.

TABLE 4.3   Number of alkane isomers

MOLECULAR FORMULA	POSSIBLE NUMBER OF CONSTITUTIONAL ISOMERS
C_4H_{10}	2
C_5H_{12}	3
C_6H_{14}	5
C_7H_{16}	9
C_8H_{18}	18
C_9H_{20}	35
$C_{10}H_{22}$	75
$C_{15}H_{32}$	4,347
$C_{20}H_{42}$	366,319
$C_{30}H_{62}$	4,111,846,763
$C_{40}H_{82}$	62,481,801,147,341

These older names for organic compounds are now called "common" or "trivial" names. Many of these names are still widely used by chemists, biochemists, and in commerce. (Many are even written into laws.) For this reason it is still necessary to learn the common names for some of the common compounds. We shall point out these common names as we go along, and we shall use them occasionally. Most of the time, however, the names that we shall use will be those called IUPAC names.

The formal system of nomenclature used today is one proposed by the International Union of Pure and Applied Chemistry (IUPAC). This system was first developed in 1892 and has been revised at irregular intervals to keep it up to date. Underlying the IUPAC system of nomenclature for organic compounds is a fundamental principle: *Each different compound should have a different name.* Thus, through a systematic set of rules, the IUPAC system provides different names for the more than 6 million known organic compounds, and names can be devised for any one of millions of other compounds yet to be synthesized. In addition, the IUPAC system is simple enough to allow any chemist familiar with the rules (or with the rules at hand) to write the name for any compound that might be encountered. In the same way, one is also able to derive the structure of a given compound from its IUPAC name.

The IUPAC system for naming alkanes is not difficult to learn, and the principles involved are used in naming compounds in other families as well. For these reasons we begin our study of the IUPAC system with the rules for naming alkanes, and then study the rules for alkyl halides, and alcohols.

The names for several of the unbranched alkanes are listed in Table 4.4. The ending for all of the names of alkanes is *-ane.* The stems of the names of most of the alkanes (above C_4) are of Greek and Latin origin. Learning the stems is like learning to count in organic chemistry. Thus, one, two, three, four, five, becomes meth- , eth- , prop- , but- , pent- .

TABLE 4.4 The unbranched alkanes

NAME	NUMBER OF CARBON ATOMS	STRUCTURE	NAME	NUMBER OF CARBON ATOMS	STRUCTURE
Methane	1	CH_4	Heptadecane	17	$CH_3(CH_2)_{15}CH_3$
Ethane	2	CH_3CH_3	Octadecane	18	$CH_3(CH_2)_{16}CH_3$
Propane	3	$CH_3CH_2CH_3$	Nonadecane	19	$CH_3(CH_2)_{17}CH_3$
Butane	4	$CH_3(CH_2)_2CH_3$	Eicosane	20	$CH_3(CH_2)_{18}CH_3$
Pentane	5	$CH_3(CH_2)_3CH_3$	Heneicosane	21	$CH_3(CH_2)_{19}CH_3$
Hexane	6	$CH_3(CH_2)_4CH_3$	Docosane	22	$CH_3(CH_2)_{20}CH_3$
Heptane	7	$CH_3(CH_2)_5CH_3$	Tricosane	23	$CH_3(CH_2)_{21}CH_3$
Octane	8	$CH_3(CH_2)_6CH_3$	Triacontane	30	$CH_3(CH_2)_{28}CH_3$
Nonane	9	$CH_3(CH_2)_7CH_3$	Hentriacontane	31	$CH_3(CH_2)_{29}CH_3$
Decane	10	$CH_3(CH_2)_8CH_3$	Tetracontane	40	$CH_3(CH_2)_{38}CH_3$
Undecane	11	$CH_3(CH_2)_9CH_3$	Pentacontane	50	$CH_3(CH_2)_{48}CH_3$
Dodecane	12	$CH_3(CH_2)_{10}CH_3$	Hexacontane	60	$CH_3(CH_2)_{58}CH_3$
Tridecane	13	$CH_3(CH_2)_{11}CH_3$	Heptacontane	70	$CH_3(CH_2)_{68}CH_3$
Tetradecane	14	$CH_3(CH_2)_{12}CH_3$	Octacontane	80	$CH_3(CH_2)_{78}CH_3$
Pentadecane	15	$CH_3(CH_2)_{13}CH_3$	Nonacontane	90	$CH_3(CH_2)_{88}CH_3$
Hexadecane	16	$CH_3(CH_2)_{14}CH_3$	Hectane	100	$CH_3(CH_2)_{98}CH_3$

4.3A NOMENCLATURE OF UNBRANCHED ALKYL GROUPS

If we remove one hydrogen atom from an alkane, we obtain what is called **an alkyl group.** These alkyl groups have names that end in **-yl.** When the alkane is **unbranched,** and the hydrogen atom that is removed is a **terminal** hydrogen atom, the names are straightforward:

Alkane		*Alkyl Group*	*Abbreviation*
CH_3—H **Methane**	becomes	CH_3— **Methyl**	Me—
CH_3CH_2—H **Ethane**	becomes	CH_3CH_2— **Ethyl**	Et—
$CH_3CH_2CH_2$—H **Propane**	becomes	$CH_3CH_2CH_2$— **Propyl**	Pr—
$CH_3CH_2CH_2CH_2$—H **Butane**	becomes	$CH_3CH_2CH_2CH_2$— **Butyl**	Bu—

4.3B NOMENCLATURE OF BRANCHED-CHAIN ALKANES

Branched-chain alkanes are named according to the following rules:

1. **Locate the longest continuous chain of carbon atoms; this chain determines the parent name for the alkane.**

We designate the following compound, for example, as a *hexane* because the longest continuous chain contains six carbon atoms.

$$CH_3CH_2CH_2CH_2\underset{\underset{CH_3}{|}}{CH}CH_3$$

The longest continuous chain may not always be obvious from the way the formula is written. Notice, for example, that the following alkane is designated as a *heptane* because the longest chain contains seven carbon atoms.

$$CH_3CH_2CH_2CH_2\underset{\underset{\underset{CH_3}{|}}{CH_2}}{CH}{-}CH_3$$

2. **Number the longest chain beginning with the end of the chain nearer the substituent.**

   Applying this rule, we number the two alkanes that we illustrated previously in the following way.

   Substituent

   $$\overset{6}{C}H_3\overset{5}{C}H_2\overset{4}{C}H_2\overset{3}{C}H_2\overset{2}{\underset{\underset{CH_3}{|}}{C}H}\overset{1}{C}H_3 \qquad \overset{7}{C}H_3\overset{6}{C}H_2\overset{5}{C}H_2\overset{4}{C}H_2\overset{3}{\underset{\underset{\underset{^1CH_3}{|}}{^2CH_2}}{C}H}CH_3$$

   Substituent

3. **Use the numbers obtained by application of rule 2 to designate the location of the substituent group.** The parent name is placed last, and the substituent group, preceded by the number designating its location on the chain, is placed first. Numbers are separated from words by a hyphen. Our two examples are 2-methylhexane and 3-methylheptane, respectively.

   $$\overset{6}{C}H_3\overset{5}{C}H_2\overset{4}{C}H_2\overset{3}{C}H_2\overset{2}{\underset{\underset{CH_3}{|}}{C}H}\overset{1}{C}H_3 \qquad \overset{7}{C}H_3\overset{6}{C}H_2\overset{5}{C}H_2\overset{4}{C}H_2\overset{3}{\underset{\underset{\underset{^1CH_3}{|}}{^2CH_2}}{C}H}CH_3$$

   2-Methylhexane   3-Methylheptane

4. **When two or more substituents are present, give each substituent a number corresponding to its location on the longest chain.** For example, we designate the following compound as 4-ethyl-2-methylhexane.

   $$CH_3\underset{\underset{CH_3}{|}}{CH}{-}CH_2{-}\underset{\underset{\underset{CH_3}{|}}{CH_2}}{CH}CH_2CH_3$$

   4-Ethyl-2-methylhexane

   The substituent groups should be listed *alphabetically* (i.e., ethyl before methyl).* In deciding on alphabetical order disregard multiplying prefixes such as "di" and "tri."

---

*Some handbooks also list the groups in order of increasing size or complexity (i.e., methyl before ethyl). Alphabetical listing, however, is now by far the most widely used system.

5. **When two substituents are present on the same carbon atom, use that number twice.**

$$CH_3CH_2-\overset{\overset{\displaystyle CH_3}{|}}{\underset{\underset{\displaystyle CH_3}{|}}{\underset{CH_2}{|}}{C}}-CH_2CH_2CH_3$$

3-Ethyl-3-methylhexane

6. **When two or more substituents are identical, indicate this by the use of the prefixes di-, tri-, tetra-, and so on.** Then make certain that each and every substituent has a number. Commas are used to separate numbers from each other.

$$CH_3CH\!-\!\!-\!\!-\!CHCH_3 \qquad CH_3\overset{\overset{\displaystyle CH_3}{|}}{CH}CHCHCH_3 \qquad CH_3\overset{\overset{\displaystyle CH_3}{|}}{C}CH_2\overset{\overset{\displaystyle CH_3}{|}}{C}CH_3$$

      $\underset{CH_3}{|}\qquad\underset{CH_3}{|}$ $\underset{CH_3}{|}\quad\underset{CH_3}{|}$ $\underset{CH_3}{|}\quad\underset{CH_3}{|}$

2,3-Dimethylbutane   **2,3,4-Trimethylpentane**   **2,2,4,4-Tetramethylpentane**

Application of these six rules allows us to name most of the alkanes that we shall encounter. Two other rules, however, may be required occasionally.

7. **When two chains of equal length compete for selection as the parent chain, choose the chain with the greater number of substituents.**

$$\overset{7}{C}H_3\overset{6}{C}H_2-\overset{5}{C}H-\overset{4}{C}H-\overset{3}{C}H-\overset{2}{C}H-\overset{1}{C}H_3$$

$$\underset{CH_3}{|}\quad\underset{CH_2}{|}\quad\underset{CH_3}{|}\quad\underset{CH_3}{|}$$

$$\underset{CH_3}{|}$$

2,3,5-Trimethyl-4-propylheptane
(four substituents)
(*not* 4-*sec*-butyl-2,3-dimethylheptane)
(three substituents)

8. **When branching first occurs at an equal distance from either end of the longest chain, choose the name that gives the lower number at the first point of difference.**

$$\overset{6}{C}H_3-\overset{5}{C}H-\overset{4}{C}H_2-\overset{3}{C}H\!-\!\!-\!\!-\!\overset{2}{C}H-\overset{1}{C}H_3$$

$$\underset{CH_3}{|}\qquad\quad\underset{CH_3}{|}\quad\underset{CH_3}{|}$$

2,3,5-Trimethylhexane
(*not* 2,4,5-trimethylhexane)

4.3C NOMENCLATURE OF BRANCHED ALKYL GROUPS

In Section 4.3A you learned the names for the unbranched alkyl groups such as methyl, ethyl, propyl, butyl, and so on, groups derived by removing a terminal hydrogen from an alkane. For alkanes with more than two carbon atoms, more than one derived group is possible. Two groups can be derived from propane, for example; the **propyl group,** is derived by removal of a terminal hydrogen, and the **1-methylethyl** or **isopropyl group,** is derived by removal of a hydrogen from the central carbon:

4.3 IUPAC NOMENCLATURE

Three-Carbon Groups

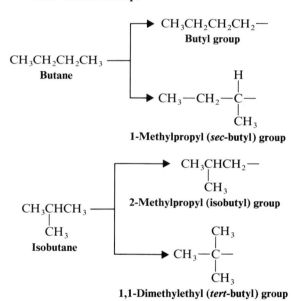

1-Methylethyl is the systematic name for this group, isopropyl is a common name. Systematic nomenclature for alkyl groups is similar to that for branched-chain alkanes, with the provision that *numbering always begins at the point where the group is attached to the main chain.* There are four C-4 groups. Two are derived from butane and two are derived from isobutane.*

Four-Carbon Groups

The following examples show how the names of these groups are employed.

CH₃CH₂CH₂CHCH₂CH₂CH₃
                 |
         CH₃—CH
              |
              CH₃

4-(1-Methylethyl)heptane or 4-isopropylheptane

CH₃CH₂CH₂CHCH₂CH₂CH₂CH₃
                 |
          CH₃—C—CH₃
               |
               CH₃

4-(1,1-Dimethylethyl)octane or 4-*tert*-butyloctane

* Isobutane is a common name for 2-methylpropane that is approved by the IUPAC.

CHAPTER 4. ALKANES AND CYCLOALKANES: CONFORMATIONS OF MOLECULES

The common names, **isopropyl, isobutyl, *sec*-butyl,** and ***tert*-butyl** are approved by the IUPAC for the unsubstituted groups, and they are still very frequently used. You should memorize these groups so well that you will recognize them anyway that they are written. In deciding on alphabetical order for these groups you should disregard structure defining prefixes that are written in italics and separated from the name by a hyphen. Thus *tert*-butyl precedes ethyl, but ethyl precedes isobutyl.

There is one five-carbon group with an IUPAC approved common name that you should also know: the 2,2-dimethylpropyl group, commonly called the **neopentyl group.**

$$
\begin{array}{c}
\quad\quad CH_3 \\
\quad\quad | \\
CH_3{-}C{-}CH_2{-} \\
\quad\quad | \\
\quad\quad CH_3
\end{array}
$$

2,2-Dimethylpropyl or neopentyl group

Problem 4.2

(a) Give correct IUPAC names for all the C_6H_{14} isomers in Table 4.2.
(b) Write structural formulas for the nine isomers of C_7H_{16} and give IUPAC names for each. (*Hint:* You may find it helpful to name each compound as you write its structure. This will help you to decide whether or not two structures are really different. If their IUPAC names are different then so are the structures.)

4.3D CLASSIFICATION OF HYDROGEN ATOMS

The hydrogen atoms of an alkane are classified on the basis of the carbon atom to which they are attached. A hydrogen atom attached to a primary carbon atom is a primary hydrogen atom, and so forth. The following compound, 2-methylbutane, has primary, secondary, and tertiary hydrogen atoms.

$$
\begin{array}{c}
1°\ \text{Hydrogen atoms} \\
CH_3 \\
| \\
CH_3{-}CH{-}CH_2{-}CH_3 \\
3°\ \text{Hydrogen atom} \quad\quad 2°\ \text{Hydrogen atoms}
\end{array}
$$

On the other hand, 2,2-dimethylpropane, a compound that is often called **neopentane,** has only primary hydrogen atoms.

$$
\begin{array}{c}
\quad\quad CH_3 \\
\quad\quad | \\
CH_3{-}C{-}CH_3 \\
\quad\quad | \\
\quad\quad CH_3
\end{array}
$$

2,2-Dimethylpropane
(neopentane)

4.3E NOMENCLATURE OF ALKYL HALIDES

Alkanes bearing halogen substituents are named in the IUPAC substitutive system as haloalkanes:

$$CH_3CH_2Cl \qquad CH_3CH_2CH_2F \qquad CH_3CHBrCH_3$$

Chloroethane   **1-Fluoropropane**   **2-Bromopropane**

When the parent chain has both a halo and an alkyl substituent attached to it, number the chain from the end nearer the first substituent, regardless of whether it is halo or alkyl. If two substituents are of equal distance from the end of the chain, then number the chain from the end nearer the substituent that has alphabetical precedence.

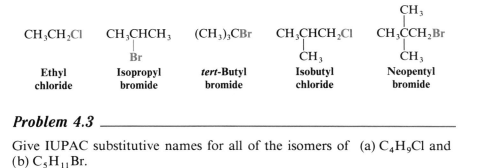

2-Chloro-3-methylpentane   2-Chloro-4-methylpentane

Common names for many simple haloalkanes are still widely used, however. In this common nomenclature system, called *radicofunctional nomenclature,* haloalkanes are named as alkyl halides. (The following names are also accepted by the IUPAC.)

Ethyl chloride	Isopropyl bromide	*tert*-Butyl bromide	Isobutyl chloride	Neopentyl bromide

CH_3CH_2Cl CH_3CHCH_3 (Br) $(CH_3)_3CBr$ CH_3CHCH_2Cl (CH_3) CH_3CCH_2Br (CH_3)(CH_3)

Problem 4.3

Give IUPAC substitutive names for all of the isomers of (a) C_4H_9Cl and (b) $C_5H_{11}Br$.

4.3F NOMENCLATURE OF ALCOHOLS

In what is called IUPAC **substitutive nomenclature** a name may have as many as four features: **locants, prefixes, parent compound,** and **one suffix.** Consider the following compound as an illustration without, for the moment, being concerned as to how the name arises.

$$CH_3CH_2CHCH_2CH_2CH_2OH$$
$$|$$
$$CH_3$$

4-Methyl-1-hexanol

locant   prefix   locant   parent   suffix

The *locant* **4-** tells that the substituent **methyl** group, named as a *prefix,* is attached to the *parent compound* at C-4. The *parent compound* contains six carbon atoms and no multiple bonds, hence the parent name **hexane,** and it is an alcohol, therefore it has the *suffix* **-ol.** The locant **1-,** tells that C-1 bears the hydroxyl group. **In general, numbering of the chain always begins at the end nearer the group named as a suffix.**

The following procedure should be followed in giving alcohols IUPAC substitutive names:

1. Select the longest continuous carbon chain *to which the hydroxyl is directly attached.* Change the name of the alkane corresponding to this chain by dropping the final *e* and adding the suffix *ol.*

2. Number the longest continuous carbon chain so as to give the carbon atom bearing the hydroxyl group the lower number. Indicate the position of the hydroxyl group by using this number as a locant; indicate the positions of other substituents (as prefixes) by using the numbers corresponding to their positions along the carbon chain as locants.

The following examples show how these rules are applied.

$$\overset{3}{C}H_3\overset{2}{C}H_2\overset{1}{C}H_2OH \qquad \overset{1}{C}H_3\overset{2}{C}H\overset{3}{C}H_2\overset{4}{C}H_3 \qquad \overset{5}{C}H_3\overset{4}{C}H\overset{3}{C}H_2\overset{2}{C}H_2\overset{1}{C}H_2OH$$

$$\qquad\qquad\qquad\qquad OH \qquad\qquad\qquad CH_3$$

1-Propanol   **2-Butanol**   **4-Methyl-1-pentanol**
(*not* 2-methyl-5-pentanol)

$$\qquad\qquad\qquad\qquad\qquad\qquad\qquad\qquad\qquad\qquad CH_3$$

$$Cl\overset{3}{C}H_2\overset{2}{C}H_2\overset{1}{C}H_2OH \qquad\qquad \overset{1}{C}H_3\overset{2}{C}H\overset{3}{C}H_2\overset{4}{C}\overset{5}{C}H_3$$

$$\qquad\qquad\qquad\qquad\qquad\qquad\qquad OH \quad CH_3$$

3-Chloro-1-propanol   **4,4-Dimethyl-2-pentanol**

Problem 4.4

Give IUPAC substitutive names for all of the isomeric alcohols with the formulas (a) $C_4H_{10}O$ and (b) $C_5H_{12}O$.

Simple alcohols are often called by *common* radicofunctional names that are also approved by the IUPAC. We have seen several examples already (Section 2.10). In addition to *methyl alcohol, ethyl alcohol,* and *isopropyl alcohol,* there are several others including the following:

$$CH_3CH_2CH_2OH \qquad CH_3CH_2CH_2CH_2OH \qquad CH_3CH_2CHCH_3$$

$$\qquad\qquad\qquad\qquad\qquad\qquad\qquad\qquad\qquad\qquad OH$$

Propyl alcohol   **Butyl alcohol**   *sec*-**Butyl alcohol**

$$\qquad\quad CH_3 \qquad\qquad\quad CH_3 \qquad\qquad\quad CH_3$$

$$CH_3-\underset{|}{\overset{|}{C}}-OH \qquad CH_3CHCH_2OH \qquad CH_3CCH_2OH$$

$$\qquad\quad CH_3 \qquad\qquad\qquad\qquad\qquad\qquad CH_3$$

tert-**Butyl alcohol**   **Isobutyl alcohol**   **Neopentyl alcohol**

Alcohols containing two hydroxyl groups are commonly called glycols. In the IUPAC substitutive system they are named as **diols.**

	CH_2-CH_2	CH_3CH-CH_2	$CH_2CH_2CH_2$
	$\quad\quad\quad$ OH $\quad$ OH	$\quad\quad\quad$ OH $\quad$ OH	$\quad\quad$ OH $\quad\quad$ OH
Common	**Ethylene glycol**	**Propylene glycol**	**Trimethylene glycol**
Substitutive	**1,2-Ethanediol**	**1,2-Propanediol**	**1,3-Propanediol**

4.4 NOMENCLATURE OF CYCLOALKANES

4.4A MONOCYCLIC COMPOUNDS

Cycloalkanes with only one ring are named by attaching the prefix cyclo to the names of the alkanes possessing the same number of carbon atoms. For example,

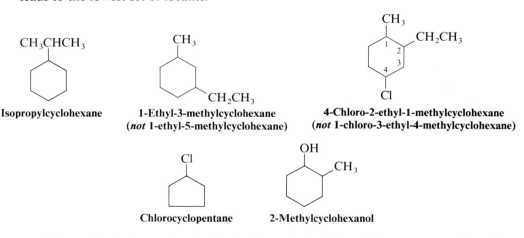

Cyclopropane   **Cyclopentane**

Naming substituted cycloalkanes is straightforward: We name them as *alkylcycloalkanes, halocycloalkanes, alkylcycloalkanols,* and so on. If only one substituent is present, it is not necessary to designate its position. When two substituents are present, we number the ring *beginning with the substituent* first in the alphabet, and number in the direction that gives the next substituent the lower number possible. When three or more substituents are present, we begin at the substituent that leads to the lowest set of locants.

CH_3CHCH_3

Isopropylcyclohexane

CH_3

CH_2CH_3

1-Ethyl-3-methylcyclohexane
(*not* 1-ethyl-5-methylcyclohexane)

CH_3

CH_2CH_3

Cl

4-Chloro-2-ethyl-1-methylcyclohexane
(*not* 1-chloro-3-ethyl-4-methylcyclohexane)

Cl

Chlorocyclopentane

OH

CH_3

2-Methylcyclohexanol

When a single ring system is attached to a single chain with a greater number of carbon atoms, or when more than one ring system is attached to a single chain, then it is appropriate to name the compounds as *cycloalkylalkanes.* For example:

$-CH_2CH_2CH_2CH_2CH_3$

1-Cyclobutylpentane

1,3-Dicyclohexylpropane

Problem 4.5

Give names for the following substituted cycloalkanes:

(a)

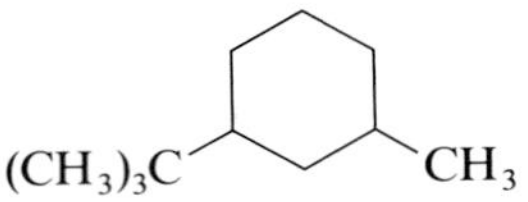

$(CH_3)_3C$ — CH_3

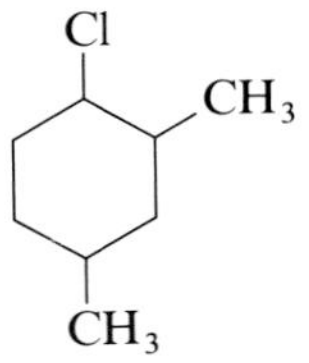

(b) 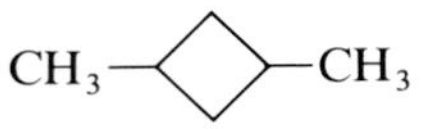 CH_3 — ◇ — CH_3

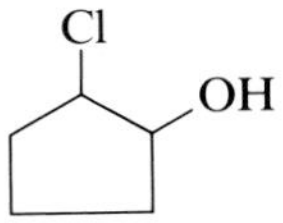

(c) 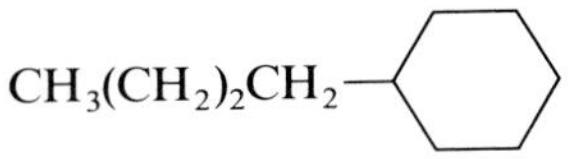 $CH_3(CH_2)_2CH_2$ —

(d) Cl, CH_3, CH_3

(e) Cl, OH

(f) 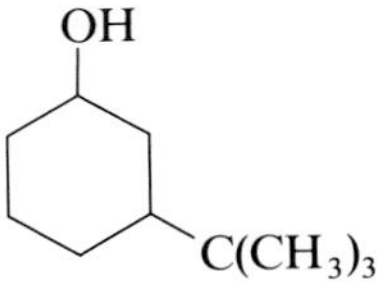 OH, $C(CH_3)_3$

4.4B BICYCLIC COMPOUNDS

We name compounds containing two fused or bridged rings as **bicycloalkanes** and we use the name of the alkane corresponding to the total number of carbon atoms in the rings as the parent name. The following compound, for example, contains seven carbon atoms and is, therefore, a bicycloheptane. The carbon atoms common to both rings are called bridgeheads, and each bond, or chain of atoms connecting the bridgehead atoms, is called a bridge.

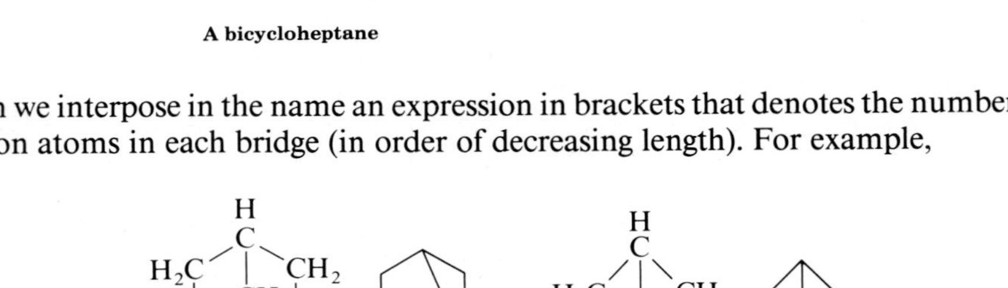

One-carbon bridge — Bridgehead — CH

Two-carbon bridge — CH$_2$ — CH$_2$ — CH$_2$ — CH$_2$ — CH$_2$ — Two-carbon bridge — CH — Bridgehead

A bicycloheptane

Then we interpose in the name an expression in brackets that denotes the number of carbon atoms in each bridge (in order of decreasing length). For example,

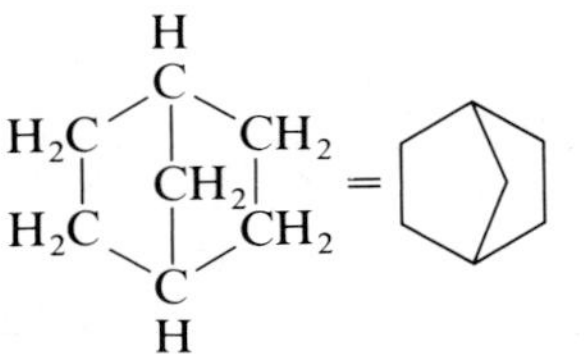

Bicyclo[2.2.1]heptane
(also called *norbornane*)

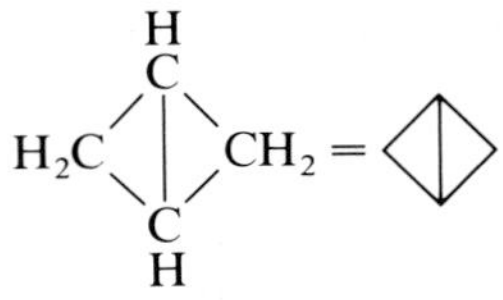

Bicyclo[1.1.0]butane

If substituents are present, we number the bridged ring system beginning at one bridgehead, proceeding first along the longest bridge to the other bridgehead, then along the next longest bridge back to the first bridgehead: The shortest bridge is numbered last.

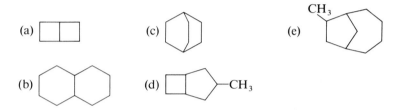

8-Methylbicyclo[3.2.1]octane   **8-Methylbicyclo[4.3.0]nonane**

Problem 4.6

Give names for each of the following bicyclic alkanes:

(a)   (c)   (e)

(b)   (d) ─CH₃

(f) Write the structure of a bicyclic compound that is an isomer of bicyclo-[2.2.1]heptane and give its name.

4.5 PHYSICAL PROPERTIES
OF ALKANES AND CYCLOALKANES

If we examine the unbranched alkanes in Table 4.4 we notice that each alkane differs from the preceding one by one $-CH_2-$ group. Butane, for example, is $CH_3(CH_2)_2CH_3$ and pentane is $CH_3(CH_2)_3CH_3$. A series of compounds like this, where each member differs from the next member by a constant unit, is called a **homologous series**. Members of a homologous series are called **homologs**.

At room temperature (25 °C) and 1-atm pressure the first four members of the homologous series of unbranched alkanes (Table 4.5) are gases; the C_5-C_{17} unbranched alkanes (pentane to heptadecane) are liquids; and the unbranched alkanes with 18 and more carbon atoms are solids.

Boiling Points The boiling points of the unbranched alkanes show a regular increase with increasing molecular weight (Fig. 4.3). Branching of the alkane chain, however, lowers the boiling point. As examples consider the C_6H_{14} isomers in Table 4.2. Hexane boils at 68 °C, and 2-methylpentane and 3-methylpentane, each having one branch, boil lower at 60.3 and 63.3 °C, respectively. 2,3-Dimethylbutane and 2,2-dimethylbutane, each with two branches, boil lower still at 58 and 49.7 °C, respectively.

CHAPTER 4. ALKANES AND CYCLOALKANES: CONFORMATIONS OF MOLECULES

TABLE 4.5   Physical constants of unbranched alkanes

NUMBER OF CARBON ATOMS	NAME	bp (°C) (1 atm)	mp (°C)	DENSITY d^{20} (g mL^{-1})
1	Methane	−161.5	−182	
2	Ethane	−88.6	−183	
3	Propane	−42.1	−188	
4	Butane	−0.5	−138	
5	Pentane	36.1	−130	0.626
6	Hexane	68.7	−95	0.659
7	Heptane	98.4	−91	0.684
8	Octane	125.7	−57	0.703
9	Nonane	150.8	−54	0.718
10	Decane	174.1	−30	0.730
11	Undecane	195.9	−26	0.740
12	Dodecane	216.3	−10	0.749
13	Tridecane	235.4	−5.5	0.756
14	Tetradecane	253.5	6	0.763
15	Pentadecane	270.5	10	0.769
16	Hexadecane	287	18	0.773
17	Heptadecane	303	22	0.778
18	Octadecane	316.7	28	0.777
19	Nonadecane	330	32	0.777
20	Eicosane	343	36.8	0.789

Part of the explanation for these effects lies in the van der Waals forces that we studied in Section 2.16D. With unbranched alkanes, as molecular weight increases, so too does molecular size, and even more importantly molecular surface areas. With increasing surface area, the van der Waals forces between molecules increase, therefore, more energy (a higher temperature) is required to separate molecules from one another and produce boiling. Chain branching, on the other hand, makes a molecule more compact, reducing its surface area, and with it the strength of the van der Waals forces operating between it and adjacent molecules; this has the effect of lowering the boiling point.

Melting Points   The unbranched alkanes do not show the same smooth increase in melting points with increasing molecular weight (black line Fig. 4.4) that they show in their boiling points. There is an alternation as one progresses from an unbranched alkane with an even number of carbon atoms to the next one with an odd number of carbon atoms. For example, propane (mp, −188 °C) melts lower than ethane (mp, −183 °C) and also lower than methane (mp, −182 °C). Butane, (mp, −138 °C) melts 53 °C higher than propane and only 5 °C lower than pentane (mp, −130 °C). If, however, the even- and odd-numbered alkanes are plotted on *separate* curves (white and red lines in Fig. 4.4), there *is* a smooth increase in melting point with increasing molecular weight.

4.5 PHYSICAL PROPERTIES OF ALKANES AND CYCLOALKANES

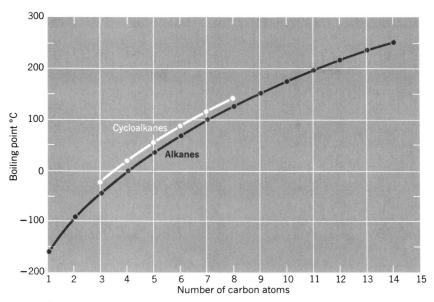

FIGURE 4.3 Boiling points of unbranched alkanes (in red) and cycloalkanes (in white).

X-ray diffraction studies, which provide information about molecular structure, have revealed the reason for this apparent anomaly. Alkane chains with an even number of carbon atoms pack more closely in the crystalline state. As a result, attractive forces between individual chains are greater and melting points are higher.

The effect of chain branching on the melting points of alkanes is more difficult to predict. Generally, however, branching that produces highly symmetrical structures results in abnormally high melting points. The compound 2,2,3,3-tetramethyl-butane, for example, melts at 100.7 °C. Its boiling point is only six degrees higher, 106.3 °C.

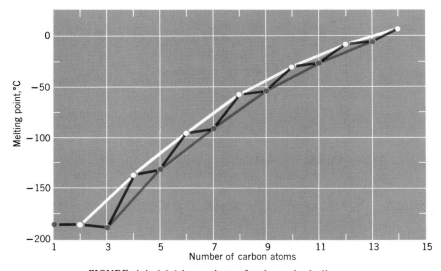

FIGURE 4.4 Melting points of unbranched alkanes.

TABLE 4.6   Physical constants of cycloalkanes

NUMBER OF CARBON ATOMS	NAME	bp (°C) (1 atm)	mp (°C)	DENSITY d^{20} (g mL^{-1})	REFRACTIVE INDEX (n_D^{20})
3	Cyclopropane	−33	−126.6		
4	Cyclobutane	13	−90		1.4260
5	Cyclopentane	49	−94	0.751	1.4064
6	Cyclohexane	81	6.5	0.779	1.4266
7	Cycloheptane	118.5	−12	0.811	1.4449
8	Cyclooctane	149	13.5	0.834	

$$\begin{array}{ccc} & CH_3 & CH_3 \\ & | & | \\ CH_3-&C-\!\!-\!\!-C&-CH_3 \\ & | & | \\ & CH_3 & CH_3 \end{array}$$

2,2,3,3-Tetramethylbutane

Cycloalkanes also have much higher melting points than their open-chain counterparts (Table 4.6). Because of their greater symmetry they pack more tightly into a crystal lattice.

Density   As a class, the alkanes and cycloalkanes are the least dense of all groups of organic compounds. All alkanes and cycloalkanes have densities considerably less than 1.00 g mL^{-1} (the density of water at 4 °C). As a result, petroleum (a mixture of hydrocarbons rich in alkanes) floats on water.

Solubility   Alkanes and cycloalkanes are almost totally insoluble in water because of their very low polarity and their inability to form hydrogen bonds. Liquid alkanes and cycloalkanes are soluble in one another, and they generally dissolve in solvents of low polarity. Good solvents for them are benzene, carbon tetrachloride, chloroform, and other hydrocarbons.

4.6 SIGMA BONDS AND BOND ROTATION

Groups bonded only by a sigma bond (i.e., by a single bond) can undergo rotation about that bond with respect to each other. The temporary molecular shapes that result from rotations of groups about single bonds are called **conformations** of the molecule. An analysis of the energy changes that a molecule undergoes as groups rotate about single bonds is called a **conformational analysis.***

Let us consider the ethane molecule as an example. Obviously an infinite number of different conformations could result from rotations of the CH$_3$ groups about the carbon–carbon bond. These different conformations, however, are not all of equal stability. The conformation (Fig. 4.5) in which the hydrogen atoms attached to

---

*Conformational analysis owes its modern origins largely to the work of O. Hassel of Norway and D. H. R. Barton of Great Britain. Hassel and Barton won the Nobel Prize in 1969, mainly for their contributions in this area. The idea that certain conformations of molecules will be favored, however, originated from the work of van't Hoff.

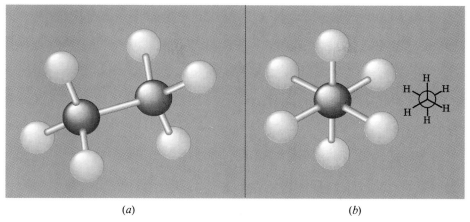

FIGURE 4.5 (*a*) The staggered conformation of ethane. (*b*) The Newman projection formula for the staggered conformation.

each carbon atom are perfectly staggered when viewed from one end of the molecule along the carbon–carbon bond axis is the *most stable* conformation (i.e., it is the conformation of *lowest potential energy*). This is easily explained in terms of repulsive interactions between bonding pairs of electrons. The staggered conformation allows the maximum possible separation of the electron pairs of the six carbon–hydrogen bonds and therefore it has the lowest energy.

In Fig. 4.5*b* we have drawn what is called a **Newman projection formula*** for ethane. In writing a Newman projection we imagine ourselves viewing the molecule from one end directly along the carbon–carbon bond axis. The bonds of the front carbon atom are represented as $\curlyvee$ and those of the back atom as $\curlyvee$.

The least stable conformation of ethane is the **eclipsed conformation** (Fig. 4.6). When viewed from one end along the carbon–carbon bond axis, the hydrogen atoms

*These formulas are named after their inventor Melvin S. Newman of The Ohio State University.

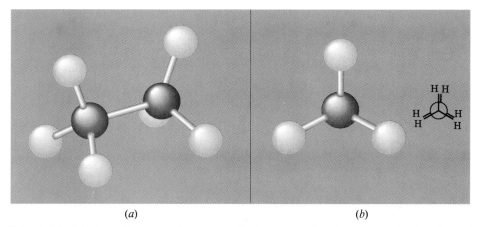

FIGURE 4.6 (*a*) The eclipsed conformation of ethane. (*b*) The Newman projection formula for the eclipsed conformation.

attached to each carbon atom in the eclipsed conformation are in direct opposition to each other. This conformation requires the maximum repulsive interaction between the electrons of the six carbon–hydrogen bonds. It is, therefore, of highest energy and has the least stability.

We represent this situation graphically by plotting the energy of an ethane molecule as a function of rotation about the carbon–carbon bond. The energy changes that occur are illustrated in Fig. 4.7.

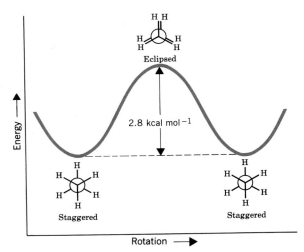

FIGURE 4.7 Potential energy changes that accompany rotation of groups about the carbon–carbon bond of ethane.

In ethane the difference in energy between the staggered and eclipsed conformations is 2.8 kcal mol^{-1} (12 kJ mol^{-1}). This small barrier to rotation is called the **torsional barrier** of the single bond. Unless the temperature is extremely low (-250 °C) many ethane molecules (at any given moment) will have enough energy to surmount this barrier. Some molecules will wag back and forth with their atoms in staggered or nearly staggered conformations. The more energetic ones, however, will rotate through eclipsed conformations to other staggered conformations.

What does all this mean about ethane? We can answer this question in two different ways. If we consider a single molecule of ethane, we can say, for example, that it will spend most of its time in the lowest energy, staggered conformation, or in a conformation very close to being staggered. Many times every second, however, it will acquire enough energy through collisions with other molecules to surmount the torsional barrier and it will rotate through an eclipsed conformation. If we speak in terms of a large number of ethane molecules (a more realistic situation), we can say that at any given moment most of the molecules will be in staggered or nearly staggered conformations.

If we consider substituted ethanes (G is a group or atom other than hydrogen) such as GCH_2CH_2G, the barriers to rotation are somewhat larger but they are still far too small to allow isolation of the different staggered conformations or **conformers** (see following figure), even at temperatures considerably below room temperature.

**These conformers cannot be
isolated except at extremely
low temperatures**

4.7 CONFORMATIONAL ANALYSIS OF BUTANE

When we concern ourselves with *the three-dimensional aspects of molecular structure,* we are involved in the field of study called **stereochemistry.** We have already had some experience with stereochemistry because we began considering the shapes of molecules as early as Chapter 1. In this chapter, however, we begin our study in earnest as we take a detailed look at the *conformations* of alkanes and cycloalkanes. In many of the chapters that follow we shall see some of the consequences of this stereochemistry in the reactions that these molecules undergo. In Chapter 5, we shall see further basic principles of stereochemistry when we examine the properties of molecules that, because of their shape, are said to possess "handedness" or **chirality.** Let us begin, however, with a relatively simple molecule, butane, and study its conformations and their relative energies.

4.7A A CONFORMATIONAL ANALYSIS OF BUTANE

The study of the energy changes that occur in a molecule when groups rotate about single bonds is called *conformational analysis.* We saw the results of such a study for ethane in Section 4.6. Ethane has a slight barrier (2.8 kcal mol^{-1}) to free rotation about the carbon–carbon single bond. This barrier causes the potential energy of the ethane molecule to rise to a maximum when rotation brings the hydrogen atoms into an eclipsed conformation. This barrier to free rotation in ethane is called the **torsional strain** of an eclipsed conformation of the molecule.

If we consider rotation about the C-2—C-3 bond of butane, torsional strain plays a part, too. There are, however, additional factors. To see what these are, we should look at the important conformations of butane **I–VI.**

I	II	III
An *anti* conformation	An eclipsed conformation	A *gauche* conformation

IV	V	VI
An eclipsed conformation	A *gauche* conformation	An eclipsed conformation

The **anti conformation (I)** does not have torsional strain because the groups are staggered and the methyl groups are far apart. Therefore, the *anti* conformation is the most stable. The methyl groups in the **gauche conformations** are close enough to each other that the van der Waals forces between them are *repulsive;* the electron clouds of the two groups are so close that they repel each other. This repulsion causes the *gauche* conformations to have approximately 0.9 kcal mol^{-1} (3.7 kJ mol^{-1}) more energy than the *anti* conformation.

The eclipsed conformations (**II, IV,** and **VI**) represent energy maxima in the potential energy diagram (Fig. 4.8). Eclipsed conformations **II** and **VI** not only have torsional strain, they have additional van der Waals repulsions arising from the eclipsed methyl groups and hydrogen atoms. Eclipsed conformation **IV** has the greatest energy of all because, in addition to torsional strain, there is the added large van der Waals repulsive force between the eclipsed methyl groups.

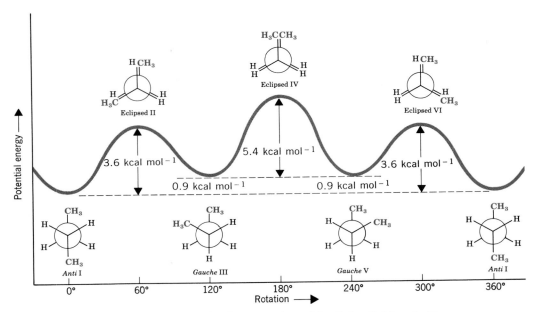

FIGURE 4.8 Energy changes that arise from rotation of the C-2—C-3 bond of butane.

While the barriers to rotation in a butane molecule are larger than those of an ethane molecule (Section 4.6), they are still far too small to permit isolation of the *gauche* and *anti* conformations at normal temperatures. Only at extremely low temperatures would the molecules have insufficient energies to surmount these barriers.

We saw earlier that van der Waals forces can be *attractive*. Here, however, we find that they can also be *repulsive*. Whether or not van der Waals interactions lead to attraction or repulsion depends on the distance that separates the two groups. As two nonpolar groups are brought closer and closer together, the first effect is one in which a momentarily unsymmetrical distribution of electrons in one group induces an opposite polarity in the other. The opposite charges induced in those portions of the two groups that are in closest proximity lead to attraction between them. This attraction increases to a maximum as the internuclear distance of the two groups decreases. The internuclear distance at which the attractive force is at a maximum is equal to the sum of what are called the *van der Waals radii* of the two groups. The van der Waals radius of a group is, in effect, a measure of its size. If the two groups are brought still closer—closer than the sum of their van der Waals radii—the interaction between them becomes repulsive: Their electron clouds begin to penetrate each other, and strong electron–electron interactions begin to occur.

Problem 4.7

Sketch a curve similar to that in Fig. 4.8 showing in general terms the energy changes that occur when the groups rotate about one carbon–carbon bond of propane. You need not concern yourself with the actual numerical values of the energy changes, but you should label all maxima and minima with the appropriate conformations.

4.8 THE RELATIVE STABILITIES OF CYCLOALKANES: RING STRAIN

Cycloalkanes do not all have the same relative stability. Data from heats of combustion (Section 4.8A) show that cyclohexane is the most stable cycloalkane and cyclopropane and cyclobutane are much less stable. The relative instability of cyclopropane and cyclobutane is a direct consequence of their cyclic structures and for this reason their molecules are said to possess **ring strain.** To see how this can be demonstrated experimentally, we need to examine the relative heats of combustion of cycloalkanes.

4.8A HEATS OF COMBUSTION

The **heat of combustion** of a compound is the enthalpy change for the complete oxidation of the compound.

For a hydrocarbon complete oxidation means converting it to carbon dioxide and water. This can be accomplished experimentally, and the amount of heat evolved can be accurately measured in a device called a calorimeter. For methane, for example, the heat of combustion is -192 kcal mol^{-1} (-803 kJ mol^{-1}).

$$CH_4 + 2\,O_2 \longrightarrow CO_2 + 2\,H_2O \qquad \Delta H° = -192 \text{ kcal mol}^{-1} \quad (-803 \text{ kJ mol}^{-1})$$

For isomeric hydrocarbons, complete combustion of 1 mol of each will require the same amount of oxygen and will yield the same number of moles of carbon dioxide and water. We can, therefore, use heats of combustion to measure the relative stabilities of the isomers.

Consider, as an example, the combustion of butane and isobutane:

$$CH_3CH_2CH_2CH_3 + 6\tfrac{1}{2}\,O_2 \longrightarrow 4\,CO_2 + 5\,H_2O \qquad \Delta H° = -687.5 \text{ kcal mol}^{-1}$$
$$(C_4H_{10}) \qquad\qquad\qquad\qquad\qquad\qquad\qquad\qquad (-2877 \text{ kJ mol}^{-1})$$

$$CH_3CHCH_3 + 6\tfrac{1}{2}\,O_2 \longrightarrow 4\,CO_2 + 5\,H_2O \qquad \Delta H° = -685.5 \text{ kcal mol}^{-1}$$
$$\overset{|}{CH_3} \qquad\qquad\qquad\qquad\qquad\qquad\qquad\qquad (-2868 \text{ kJ mol}^{-1})$$
$$(C_4H_{10})$$

Since butane liberates more heat on combustion than isobutane, it must contain relatively more potential energy. Isobutane, therefore, must be *more stable.* Figure 4.9 illustrates this comparison.

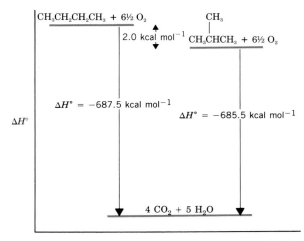

FIGURE 4.9 Heats of combustion show that isobutane is more stable than butane by 2.0 kcal mol^{-1} (8.4 kJ mol^{-1}).

4.8B HEATS OF COMBUSTION OF CYCLOALKANES

The cycloalkanes constitute a *homologous series;* each member of the series differs from the one immediately preceding it by the constant amount of one —CH_2— group. Thus, the general equation for combustion of a cycloalkane can be formulated as follows:

$$(CH_2)_n + \tfrac{3}{2}\, n\, O_2 \longrightarrow n\, CO_2 + n\, H_2O + \text{heat}$$

Because the cycloalkanes are not isomeric, their heats of combustion cannot be compared directly. However, we can calculate the amount of heat evolved *per CH$_2$ group.* On this basis, the stabilities of the cycloalkanes become directly comparable. The results of such an investigation are given in Table 4.7.

TABLE 4.7 Heats of combustion of cycloalkanes

CYCLOALKANE (CH$_2$)$_n$	n	HEAT OF COMBUSTION (kcal mol^{-1})	(kJ mol^{-1})	HEAT OF COMBUSTION PER CH$_2$ GROUP (kcal mol^{-1})	(kJ mol^{-1})
Cyclopropane	3	499.8	2091	166.6	697.5
Cyclobutane	4	655.9	2744	164.0	686.2
Cyclopentane	5	793.5	3220	158.7	664.0
Cyclohexane	6	944.5	3952	157.4	658.6
Cycloheptane	7	1108.2	4636.7	158.3	662.3
Cyclooctane	8	1269.2	5310.3	158.6	663.6
Cyclononane	9	1429.5	5981.0	158.8	664.4
Cyclodecane	10	1586.0	6635.8	158.6	663.6
Cyclopentadecane	15	2362.5	9984.7	157.5	659.0
Unbranched alkane				157.4	658.6

TABLE 4.8   Ring strain of cycloalkanes

| | RING STRAIN | |
CYCLOALKANE	(kcal mol^{-1})	(kJ mol^{-1})
Cyclopropane	27.6	115
Cyclobutane	26.3	110
Cyclopentane	6.5	27
Cyclohexane	0	0
Cycloheptane	6.4	27
Cyclooctane	10.0	42
Cyclononane	12.9	54
Cyclodecane	12.0	50
Cyclopentadecane	1.5	6

Several observations emerge from a consideration of these results.

1. Cyclohexane has the lowest heat of combustion per CH_2 group (157.4 kcal mol^{-1}). This amount does not differ from that of unbranched alkanes, which, having no ring, can have no ring strain. We can assume, therefore, that cyclohexane has no ring strain and that it can serve as our standard for comparison with other cycloalkanes. We can calculate ring strain for the other cycloalkanes (Table 4.8) by multiplying 157.4 kcal mol^{-1} by n and then subtracting the result from the heat of combustion of the cycloalkane.

2. The combustion of cyclopropane evolves the greatest amount of heat per CH_2 group. Therefore, molecules of cyclopropane must have the greatest ring strain (27.6 kcal mol^{-1}, cf. Table 4.8). Since cyclopropane molecules evolve the greatest amount of heat energy per CH_2 group on combustion, they must contain the greatest amount of potential energy per CH_2 group. Thus what we call ring strain is a form of potential energy that the cyclic molecule contains. The more ring strain a molecule possesses, the more potential energy it has and the less stable it is compared to its ring homologs.

3. The combustion of cyclobutane evolves the second largest amount of heat per CH_2 group and, therefore, cyclobutane has the second largest amount of ring strain (26.3 kcal mol^{-1}).

4. While other cycloalkanes possess ring strain to varying degrees, the relative amounts are not large. Cyclopentane and cycloheptane have about the same modest amount of ring strain. Rings of 8, 9, and 10 members have slightly larger amounts of ring strain and then the amount falls off. A 15-membered ring has only a very slight amount of ring strain.

4.9 THE ORIGIN OF RING STRAIN IN CYCLOPROPANE AND CYCLOBUTANE: ANGLE STRAIN AND TORSIONAL STRAIN

The carbon atoms of alkanes are sp^3 hybridized. The normal tetrahedral bond angle of an sp^3-hybridized atom is 109.5°. In cyclopropane (a molecule with the shape of a regular triangle) the internal angles must be 60° and therefore they must depart from this ideal value by a very large amount — by 49.5°.

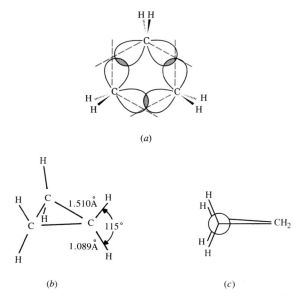

This compression of the internal bond angle causes what chemists call **angle strain.** Angle strain exists in a cyclopropane ring because the sp^3 orbitals of the carbon atoms cannot overlap as effectively (Fig. 4.10a) as they do in alkanes (where perfect end-on overlap is possible). The carbon–carbon bonds of cyclopropane are often described as being "bent." Orbital overlap is less effective. (The orbitals used for these bonds are not purely sp^3, they contain more p character). The carbon–carbon bonds of cyclopropane are weaker, and as a result, the molecule has greater potential energy.

(a)

(b)   (c)

FIGURE 4.10 (a) Orbital overlap in the carbon–carbon bonds of cyclopropane cannot occur perfectly end-on. This leads to weaker "bent" bonds and to angle strain. (b) Bond distances and angles in cyclopropane. (c) A Newman projection formula as viewed along one carbon–carbon bond shows the eclipsed hydrogens. (Viewing along either of the other two bonds would show the same picture.)

While angle strain accounts for most of the ring strain in cyclopropane, it does not account for it all. Because the ring is (of necessity) planar, the hydrogen atoms of the ring are all *eclipsed* (Fig. 4.10b and c), and the molecule has torsional strain as well.

Cyclobutane also has considerable angle strain. The internal angles are 88° — a departure of more than 21° from the normal tetrahedral bond angle. The cyclobutane ring is not planar but is slightly "folded" (Fig. 4.11a). If the cyclobutane ring were planar, the angle strain would be somewhat less (the internal angles would be 90° instead of 88°), but torsional strain would be considerably larger because all eight hydrogen atoms would be eclipsed. By folding or bending slightly the cyclobutane ring relieves more of its torsional strain than it gains in the slight increase in its angle strain.

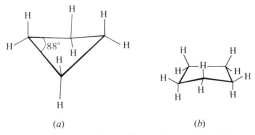

(a)   (b)

FIGURE 4.11 (a) The "folded" or "bent" conformation of cyclobutane. (b) The "bent" or "envelope" form of cyclopentane. In this structure the front carbon atom is bent upwards. In actuality, the molecule is flexible and shifts conformations constantly.

4.9A CYCLOPENTANE

The internal angles of a regular pentagon are 108°, a value very close to the normal tetrahedral bond angles of 109.5°. Therefore, if cyclopentane molecules were planar, they would have very little angle strain. Planarity, however, would introduce considerable torsional strain because all 10 hydrogen atoms would be eclipsed. Consequently, like cyclobutane, cyclopentane assumes a slightly bent conformation in which one or two of the atoms of the ring are out of the plane of the others (Fig. 4.11b). This relieves some of the torsional strain. Slight twisting of carbon–carbon bonds can occur with little change in energy, and causes the out-of-plane atoms to move into plane and causes others to move out. Therefore, the molecule is flexible and shifts rapidly, from one conformation to another. With little torsional strain and angle strain, cyclopentane is almost as stable as cyclohexane.

4.10 CONFORMATIONS OF CYCLOHEXANE

There is considerable evidence that the most stable conformation of the cyclohexane ring is the "chair" conformation illustrated in Fig. 4.12.* In this nonplanar structure the carbon–carbon bond angles are all 109.5° and are thereby free of angle strain. The chair conformation is free of torsional strain as well. When viewed along any carbon–carbon bond (viewing the structure from an end, Fig. 4.13), the atoms are seen to be perfectly staggered. Moreover, the hydrogen atoms at opposite corners of the cyclohexane ring are maximally separated.

By simple rotations about the carbon–carbon single bonds of the ring, the chair conformation can assume another shape called the "boat" conformation (Fig. 4.14). The boat conformation is like the chair conformation in that it is also free of angle strain.

*An understanding of this and subsequent discussions of conformational analysis can be aided immeasurably through the use of a molecular model.

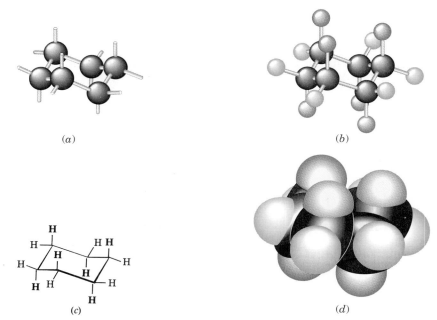

FIGURE 4.12 Representations of the chair conformation of cyclohexane: (*a*) carbon skeleton only; (*b*) carbon and hydrogen atoms; (*c*) line drawing; (*d*) space-filling model of cyclohexane. Notice that there are two types of hydrogen substituents—those that project up or down (shown in red) and those that lie generally in the plane of the ring (shown black or gray). We shall discuss this further in Section 4.11.

The boat conformation, however, is not free of torsional strain. When a model of the boat conformation is viewed down carbon-carbon bond axes along either side (Fig. 4.15*a*), the hydrogen substituents at those carbon atoms, are found to be eclipsed. Additionally, two of the hydrogen atoms on C-1 and C-4 are close enough to each other to cause van der Waals repulsion (Fig. 4.15*b*). This latter effect has been called the "flagpole" interaction of the boat conformation. Torsional strain and flagpole interactions cause the boat conformation to have considerably higher energy than the chair conformation.

Although it is more stable, the chair conformation is much more rigid than the boat conformation. The boat conformation is quite flexible. By flexing to a new form—the twist conformation (Fig. 4.16)—the boat conformation can relieve some of its torsional strain and, at the same time, reduce the flagpole interactions. Thus, the twist conformation has a lower energy than the boat conformation. *The stability*

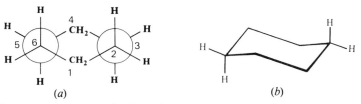

FIGURE 4.13 (*a*) A Newman projection of the chair conformation of cyclohexane. (Comparison with an actual molecular model will make this formulation clearer and will show that similar staggered arrangements are seen when other carbon–carbon bonds are chosen for sighting.) (*b*) Illustration of large separation between hydrogen atoms at opposite corners of the ring (designated C-1 and C-4) when the ring is in the chair conformation.

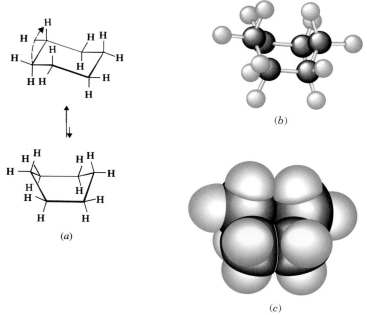

FIGURE 4.14 (*a*) The boat conformation of cyclohexane is formed by "flipping" one end of the chair form up (or down). This flip requires only rotations about carbon–carbon single bonds. (*b*) Ball-and-stick model of the boat conformation. (*c*) A space-filling model.

FIGURE 4.15 (*a*) Illustration of the eclipsed conformation of the boat conformation of cyclohexane. (*b*) Flagpole interaction of the C-1 and C-4 hydrogen atoms of the boat conformation.

gained by flexing is insufficient, however, to cause the twist conformation of cyclohexane to be more stable than the chair conformation. The chair conformation is estimated to be lower in energy than the twist conformation by approximately 5 kcal mol^{-1} (21 kJ mol^{-1}).

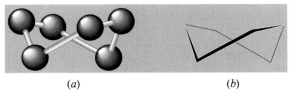

FIGURE 4.16 (*a*) Carbon skeleton and (*b*) line drawing of the twist conformation of cyclohexane.

The energy barriers between the chair, boat, and twist conformations of cyclohexane are low enough (Fig. 4.17) to make their separation impossible at room temperature. At room temperature the thermal energies of the molecules are great enough to cause approximately 1 million interconversions to occur each second and, *because of its greater stability, more than 99% of the molecules are estimated to be in a chair conformation at any given moment.*

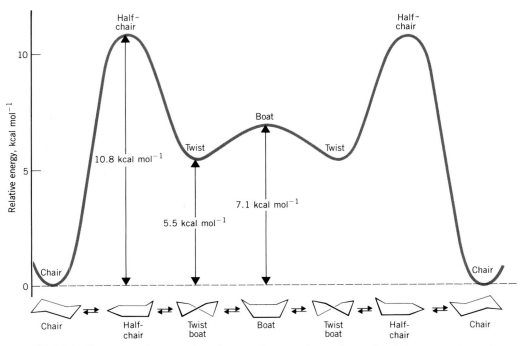

FIGURE 4.17 The relative energies of the various conformations of cyclohexane. The positions of maximum energy are conformations called half-chair conformations, in which the carbon atoms of one end of the ring have become coplanar.

4.10A CONFORMATIONS OF HIGHER CYCLOALKANES

Cycloheptane, cyclooctane, and cyclononane and other higher cycloalkanes also exist in nonplanar conformations. The small instabilities of these higher cycloalkanes (Table 4.7) appear to be caused primarily by torsional strain and van der Waals repulsions between hydrogen atoms across rings, called *transannular strain.* The nonplanar conformations of these rings, however, are essentially free of angle strain.

X-ray crystallographic studies of cyclodecane reveal that the most stable conformation has carbon–carbon–carbon bond angles of 117°. This indicates some angle strain. The wide bond angles apparently allow the molecule to expand and thereby minimize unfavorable repulsions between hydrogen atoms across the ring.

There is very little free space in the center of a cycloalkane unless the ring is quite large. Calculations indicate that cyclooctadecane, for example, is the smallest ring through which a $-CH_2CH_2CH_2-$ chain can be threaded. Molecules have been synthesized, however, which have large rings threaded on chains and which have large rings that are interlocked like links in a chain. These latter molecules are called **catenanes.**

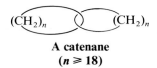

$$(CH_2)_n \qquad (CH_2)_n$$

A catenane
($n \geqslant 18$)

4.11 SUBSTITUTED CYCLOHEXANES: AXIAL AND EQUATORIAL HYDROGEN ATOMS

The six-membered ring is the most common ring found among nature's organic molecules. For this reason, we shall give it special attention. We have already seen that the chair conformation of cyclohexane is the most stable one and that it is the predominant conformation of the molecules in a sample of cyclohexane. With this fact in mind, we are in a position to undertake a limited analysis of the conformations of substituted cyclohexanes.

If we look carefully at the chair conformation of cyclohexane (Fig. 4.18), we can see that there are only two different kinds of hydrogen atoms. One hydrogen atom attached to each of the six carbon atoms lies in a plane generally defined by the ring of carbon atoms. These hydrogen atoms, by analogy with the equator of the earth, are called **equatorial** hydrogen atoms. Six other hydrogen atoms, one on each carbon, are oriented in a direction that is generally perpendicular to the average plane of the ring. These hydrogen atoms, again by analogy with the earth, are called **axial** hydrogen atoms. There are three axial hydrogen atoms on each face of the cyclohexane ring and their orientation (up or down) alternates from one carbon atom to the next.

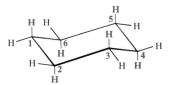

FIGURE 4.18 The chair conformation of cyclohexane. The axial hydrogen atoms are shown in color.

STUDY AID

You should now learn how to draw the important chair conformation. Notice (Fig. 4.19) the sets of parallel lines that constitute the bonds of the ring and the equatorial hydrogen atoms. Notice, too, that when drawn this way, the axial bonds are all vertical, and when the vertex of the ring points up, the axial bond is up; when the vertex is down, the axial bond is down.

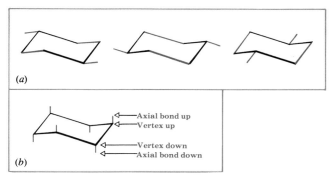

FIGURE 4.19 (a) Sets of parallel lines that constitute the ring and equatorial C—H bonds of the chair conformation. (b) The axial bonds are all vertical. When the vertex of the ring points up, the axial bond is up and vice versa.

We saw in Section 4.10 (and Fig. 4.17) that at room temperature, the cyclohexane ring rapidly flips back and forth between two *equivalent* chain conformations. An important thing to notice now is that **when the ring flips all of the bonds that were axial become equatorial and vice versa:**

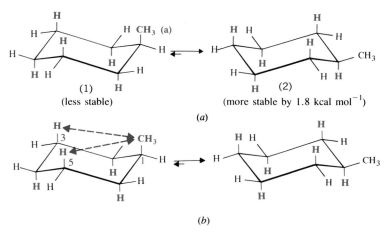

The question one might next ask is what is the most stable conformation of a cyclohexane derivative *in which one hydrogen atom has been replaced by a substituent?* That is, what is the most stable conformation of a monosubstituted cyclohexane? We can answer this question by considering methylcyclohexane as an example.

Methylcyclohexane has two possible chair conformations (Fig. 4.20), and these are interconvertible through the partial rotations that constitute a ring flip. In one conformation (Fig. 4.20a) the methyl group occupies an *axial* position, and in the other the methyl group occupies an *equatorial* position. Studies indicate that the conformation with the methyl group equatorial is more stable than the conformation with the methyl group axial by about 1.8 kcal mol^{-1}. Thus, in the equilibrium mixture, the conformation with the methyl group in the equatorial position is the predominant one. Calculations show that it constitutes about 95% of the equilibrium mixture (Table 4.9.).

FIGURE 4.20 (*a*) The conformations of methylcyclohexane with the methyl group axial (1) and equatorial (2). (*b*) 1,3-Diaxial interactions between the two axial hydrogen atoms and the axial methyl group in the axial conformation of methylcyclohexane. Less crowding occurs in the equatorial conformation.

The greater stability of methylcyclohexane with an equatorial methyl group can be understood through an inspection of the two forms as they are shown in Fig. 4.20*b* and *c*.

Studies done with scale models of the two conformations show that when the methyl group is axial, it is so close to the two axial hydrogen atoms on the same side of

TABLE 4.9   Relationship between free-energy difference and isomer percentages for isomers at equilibrium at 25 °C

FREE-ENERGY DIFFERENCE, $\Delta G°$ (kcal mol^{-1})	MORE STABLE ISOMER (%)	LESS STABLE ISOMER (%)
0	50	50
0.41	67	33
0.65	75	25
0.82	80	20
0.95	83	17
1.4	91	9
1.8	95	5
2.7	99	1
4.1	99.9	0.1
5.5	99.99	0.01

the molecule (attached to C-3 and C-5 atoms) that the van der Waals forces between them are repulsive. This type of steric strain, because it arises from an interaction between axial groups on carbon atoms 1 and 3 (or 5) is called a **1,3-diaxial interaction.** Similar studies with other substituents indicate that *there is generally less repulsive interaction when the groups are equatorial rather than axial.*

The strain caused by a 1,3-diaxial interaction in methylcyclohexane is the same as the strain caused by the close proximity of the hydrogen atoms of methyl groups in the *gauche* form of butane (Section 4.7A). Recall that the interaction in *gauche*-butane (called, for convenience, a *gauche interaction*) causes *gauche*-butane to be less stable than *anti*-butane by 0.9 kcal mol^{-1}. The following Newman projections will help you to see that the two steric interactions are the same. In the second projection we view axial methylcyclohexane along the C-1—C-2 bond and see that what we call a 1,3-diaxial interaction is simply a *gauche* interaction between the hydrogen atoms of the methyl group and the hydrogen atom at C-3.

gauche-**Butane**
(0.9 kcal mol^{-1} steric strain)

Axial methylcyclohexane
(two *gauche* interactions =
1.8 kcal mol^{-1} steric strain)

Equatorial methylcyclohexane

Viewing methylcyclohexane along the C-1–C-6 bond (do this with a model) shows that it has a second *gauche* interaction between the hydrogen atoms of the methyl group and the hydrogen atom at C-5. The methyl group of *axial*-methylcyclohexane, therefore, has two *gauche* interactions and, consequently, it has $2 \times 0.9 = 1.8$ kcal mol^{-1} of strain. The methyl group of equatorial methylcyclohexane does not have a *gauche* interaction because it is *anti* to C-3 and C-5.

In cyclohexane derivatives with larger alkyl substituents, the strain caused by 1,3-diaxial interactions is even more pronounced. The conformation of *tert*-butylcyclohexane with the *tert*-butyl group equatorial is estimated to be more than 5 kcal mol^{-1} more stable than the axial form (Fig. 4.21). This large energy difference between the two conformations means that, at room temperature, virtually 100% of the molecules of *tert*-butylcyclohexane have the *tert*-butyl group in the equatorial position.

Equatorial *tert*-butylcyclohexane
(~100%)

ring flip

Axial *tert*-butylcyclohexane
(~0%)

FIGURE 4.21 Diaxial interactions with the large *tert*-butyl group axial cause the conformation with the *tert*-butyl group equatorial to be present almost exclusively.

4.12 DISUBSTITUTED CYCLOALKANES: CIS-TRANS ISOMERISM

The presence of two substituents on the ring of a molecule of any cycloalkane allows for the possibility of cis–trans isomerism. We can see this most easily if we begin by examining cyclopentane derivatives because the cyclopentane ring is essentially planar. (At any given moment the ring of cyclopentane is, of course, slightly bent, but we know that the various bent conformations are rapidly interconverted. Over a period of time, the average conformation of the cyclopentane ring is planar.) Since the planar representation is much more convenient for an initial presentation of cis–trans isomerism in cycloalkanes, we shall use it here.

Let us consider 1,2-dimethylcyclopentane as an example. We can write the structures shown in Fig. 4.22. In the first structure the methyl groups are on the same side of the ring, that is, they are cis. In the second structure the methyl groups are on opposite sides of the ring; they are trans.

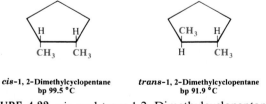

cis-1, 2-Dimethylcyclopentane
bp 99.5 °C

trans-1, 2-Dimethylcyclopentane
bp 91.9 °C

FIGURE 4.22 *cis*- and *trans*-1,2- Dimethylcyclopentanes.

The *cis*- and *trans*-1,2-dimethylcyclopentanes are stereoisomers: They differ from each other only in the arrangement of the atoms in space. The two forms cannot be interconverted without breaking carbon–carbon bonds. As a result, the cis and trans forms can be separated, placed in separate bottles, and kept indefinitely.

1,3-Dimethylcyclopentanes show cis–trans isomerism as well:

cis-1, 3-Dimethylcyclohexane   trans-1, 3-Dimethylcyclohexane

The physical properties of cis–trans isomers are different; they have different melting points, boiling points, and so on. Table 4.10 lists these physical constants of the dimethylcyclohexanes.

TABLE 4.10   Physical constants of *cis-* and *trans-* disubstituted cyclohexane derivatives

SUBSTITUENTS	ISOMER	mp (°C)	bp (°C)[a]
1,2-Dimethyl-	cis	-50.1	130.04^{760}
1,2-Dimethyl-	trans	-89.4	123.7^{760}
1,3-Dimethyl-	cis	75.6	120.1^{760}
1,3-Dimethyl-	trans	-90.1	123.5^{760}
1,2-Dichloro-	cis	-6	93.5^{22}
1,2-Dichloro-	trans	-7	74.7^{16}

[a]The pressures (in units of torr) at which the boiling points were measured are given as superscripts.

Problem 4.8

Write structures for the cis and trans isomers of (a) 1,2-dimethylcyclopropane and (b) 1,2-dibromocyclobutane.

The cyclohexane ring is, of course, not planar. A "time average" of the various interconverting chair conformations would, however, be planar and, as with cyclopentane, this planar representation is convenient for introducing the topic of cis–trans isomerism of cyclohexane derivatives. The planar representations of the 1,2-, 1,3-, and 1,4-dimethylcyclohexane isomers follow:

cis-1, 2-Dimethylcyclohexane   trans-1, 2-Dimethylcyclohexane

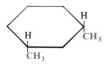
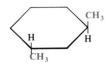

cis-1, 3-Dimethylcyclohexane   trans-1, 3-Dimethylcyclohexane cis-1, 4-Dimethylcyclohexane   trans-1, 4-Dimethylcyclohexane

4.12A CIS – TRANS ISOMERISM AND CONFORMATIONAL STRUCTURES

If we consider the *actual* conformations of these isomers, the structures are somewhat more complex. Beginning with *trans*-1,4-dimethylcyclohexane, because it is easiest to visualize, we find there are two possible chair conformations (Fig. 4.23). In one conformation both methyl groups are axial; in the other both are equatorial. The diequatorial conformation is, as we would expect it to be, the more stable conformation, and it represents the structure of at least 99% of the molecules at equilibrium.

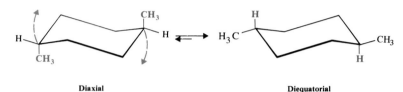

Diaxial   Diequatorial

FIGURE 4.23 The two chair conformations of *trans*-1,4-dimethylcyclohexane. (*Note:* all other C—H bonds have been omitted for clarity.)

That the diaxial form of *trans*-1,4-dimethylcyclohexane is a trans isomer is easy to see; the two methyl groups are clearly on opposite sides of the ring. The trans relationship of the methyl groups in the diequatorial form is not as obvious, however. The trans relationship of the methyl groups becomes more apparent if we imagine ourselves "flattening" the molecule by turning one end up and the other down.

A second *and general* way to recognize a *trans*-disubstituted cyclohexane is to notice that one group is attached by the *upper* bond (of the two to its carbon) and one by the *lower* bond.

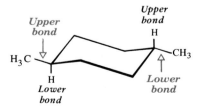

Upper bond

Upper bond

Lower bond

Lower bond

trans-1, 4-Dimethylcyclohexane

In a *cis*-disubstituted cyclohexane both groups will be attached by an upper bond or both by a lower bond. For example,

4.12 DISUBSTITUTED CYCLOALKANES: CIS–TRANS ISOMERISM

cis-1, 4-Dimethylcyclohexane

cis-1,4-Dimethylcyclohexane actually exists in two *equivalent* chair conformations (Fig. 4.24). The cis relationship of the methyl groups, however, precludes the possibility of a structure with both groups in an equatorial position. One group is axial in either conformation.

Equatorial-axial   Axial-equatorial

FIGURE 4.24   Equivalent conformations of *cis*-1,4-dimethylcyclohexane.

Sample Problem

Consider each of the following conformational structures and tell whether each is cis or trans.

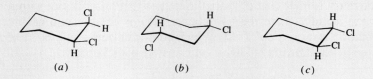

(*a*)   (*b*)   (*c*)

Answer:
(a) Each chlorine atom is attached by the upper bond at its carbon; therefore, both chlorine atoms are on the same side of the molecule and this is a cis isomer. This is *cis*-1,2-dichlorocyclohexane.   (b) Here both chlorine atoms are attached by a lower bond; therefore, in this example, too, both chlorine atoms are on the same side of the molecule and this, too, is a cis isomer. It is *cis*-1,3-dichlorocyclohexane.   (c) Here one chlorine atom is attached by a lower bond and one by an upper bond. The two chlorine atoms, therefore, are on opposite sides of the molecule, and this is a trans isomer. It is *trans*-1,2-dichlorocyclohexane.

Problem 4.9

(a) Write structural formulas for the two chair conformations of *cis*-1-*tert*-butyl-4-methylcyclohexane.   (b) Are these two conformations equivalent? (c) If not, which would be more stable?   (d) Which would be the preferred conformation at equilibrium?

trans-1,3-Dimethylcyclohexane is like the *cis*-1,4-compound in that no chair conformation is possible with both methyl groups in the favored equatorial position. The following two conformations are of equal energy and are equally populated at equilibrium.

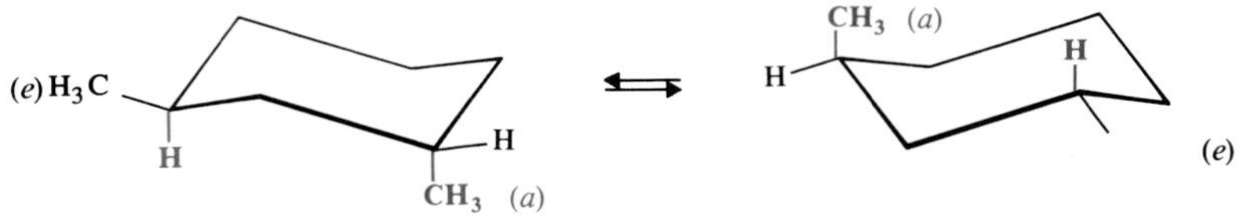

trans-1, 3-Dimethylcyclohexane

If, however, we consider some other *trans*-1,3-disubstituted cyclohexane in which one group is larger than the other, the conformation of lower energy is the one having the larger group in the equatorial position. For example, the more stable conformation of *trans*-1-*tert*-butyl-3-methylcyclohexane, shown here, has the large *tert*-butyl group occupying the equatorial position.

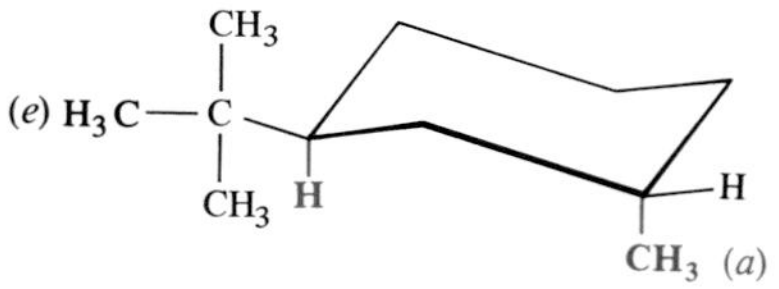

Problem 4.10

(a) Write chair conformations for *cis*- and *trans*-1,2-dimethylcyclohexane. (b) For which isomer (cis or trans) are the two conformations equivalent? (c) For the isomer where the two conformations are not equivalent, which conformation is more stable? (d) Which conformation would be more highly populated at equilibrium? (Check your answer with Table 4.11.)

The different conformations of the dimethylcyclohexanes are summarized in Table 4.11. The more stable conformation, where one exists, is set in heavy type.

4.13 BICYCLIC AND POLYCYCLIC ALKANES

Many of the molecules that we encounter in our study of organic chemistry contain more than one ring (Section 4.4B). One of the most important bicyclic systems

TABLE 4.11   Conformations of dimethylcyclohexanes

COMPOUND	cis ISOMER			trans ISOMER		
1,2-Dimethyl-	*a,e*	or	*e,a*	***e,e***	or	*a,a*
1,3-Dimethyl-	***e,e***	or	*a,a*	*a,e*	or	*e,a*
1,4-Dimethyl-	*a,e*	or	*e,a*	***e,e***	or	*a,a*

4.13 BICYCLIC AND POLYCYCLIC ALKANES

is bicyclo[4.4.0]decane, a compound that is usually called by its common name, *decalin.*

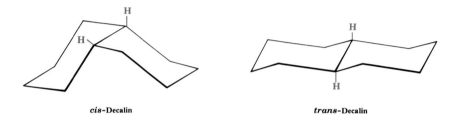

Decalin (bicyclo[4.4.0]decane)
(carbon atoms 1 and 6 are bridgehead carbon atoms)

Decalin shows cis–trans isomerism:

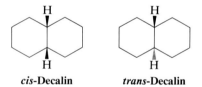

cis-Decalin   *trans*-Decalin

In *cis*-decalin the two hydrogen atoms attached to the bridgehead atoms lie on the same side of the ring; in *trans*-decalin they are on opposite sides. We often indicate this by writing their structures in the following way:

cis-Decalin   *trans*-Decalin

Simple rotations of groups about carbon–carbon bonds do not interconvert *cis*- and *trans*-decalins. In this respect they resemble the isomeric *cis*- and *trans*-disubstituted cyclohexanes. (We can, in fact, regard them as being *cis*- or *trans*-1,2-disubstituted cyclohexanes in which the 1,2-substituents are the two ends of a four-carbon bridge, that is, $-CH_2CH_2CH_2CH_2-$.)

The *cis*- and *trans*-decalins can be separated. *cis*-Decalin boils at 195 °C (at 760 torr) and *trans*-decalin boils at 185.5 °C (at 760 torr).

Adamantane (see the following figure) is a tricyclic system that contains a three-dimensional array of cyclohexane rings, all of which are in the chair form. Extending the structure of adamantane in three dimensions gives the structure of diamond. The great hardness of diamond results from the fact that the entire diamond crystal is actually one very large molecule—a molecule that is held together by millions of strong covalent bonds.*

---

* There are five known allotropic forms of carbon—graphite, diamond, Wurzite carbon [with a structure related to Wurzite (ZnS)], a C_{60}, called "buckminsterfullerene" with the structure of a soccer ball, and a C_{70}. See *Chem. Eng. News,* Oct 29, **1990,** 22–25.

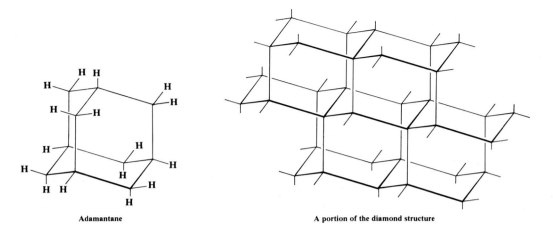

Adamantane

A portion of the diamond structure

One goal of research in recent years has been the synthesis of unusual, and sometimes highly strained, cyclic hydrocarbons. Among those that have been prepared are the compounds that follow:

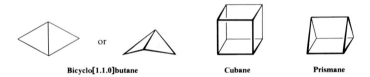

Bicyclo[1.1.0]butane

Cubane

Prismane

In 1982, Leo A. Paquette and his co-workers at The Ohio State University announced the successful synthesis of the "most complex, symmetric, and aesthetically appealing" molecule called dodecahedrane.

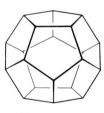

Dodecahedrane

4.14 CHEMICAL REACTIONS OF ALKANES

Alkanes, as a class, are characterized by a general inertness to many chemical reagents. Carbon–carbon and carbon–hydrogen bonds are quite strong; they do not break unless alkanes are heated to very high temperatures. Because carbon and hydrogen atoms have nearly the same electronegativity, the carbon–hydrogen bonds of alkanes are only slightly polarized. As a consequence, they are generally unaffected by most bases. Molecules of alkanes have no unshared electrons to offer sites for attack by acids. This low reactivity of alkanes toward many reagents accounts for the fact that alkanes were originally called *paraffins* (Latin: *parum affinis,* little affinity).

The term paraffin, however, is probably not an appropriate one. We all know that alkanes react vigorously with oxygen when an appropriate mixture is ignited.

This combustion occurs in the cylinders of automobiles, and in oil furnaces, for example. When heated, alkanes also react with chlorine and bromine, and they react explosively with fluorine. We shall study these reactions in Chapter 7.

4.15 SYNTHESIS OF ALKANES AND CYCLOALKANES

Mixtures of alkanes as they are obtained from petroleum are suitable as fuels. However, in our laboratory work we often have the need for a pure sample of a particular alkane. For these purposes, the chemical preparation — or synthesis — of that particular alkane is often the most reliable way of obtaining it. The preparative method that we choose should be one that will lead to the desired product alone or, at least, to products that can be easily and effectively separated.

Several such methods are available, and three are outlined here. In subsequent chapters we shall encounter others.

4.15A HYDROGENATION OF ALKENES

Alkenes react with hydrogen in the presence of metal catalysts such as nickel and platinum to produce alkanes. The general reaction is one in which the atoms of the hydrogen molecule add to each atom of the carbon–carbon double bond of the alkene. This converts the alkene to an alkane.

General Reaction

$$
\begin{array}{c}
\diagdown \diagup \\
\mathrm{C} \\
\| \\
\mathrm{C} \\
\diagup \diagdown
\end{array}
\ +\
\begin{array}{c}
\mathrm{H} \\
| \\
\mathrm{H}
\end{array}
\ \xrightarrow[\text{solvent}]{\text{Pt or Ni}}\
\begin{array}{c}
| \\
-\mathrm{C}-\mathrm{H} \\
| \\
-\mathrm{C}-\mathrm{H} \\
|
\end{array}
$$

Alkene   Alkane

The reaction is usually carried out by dissolving the alkene in a solvent such as ethyl alcohol (C_2H_5OH), adding the metal catalyst, and then exposing the mixture to hydrogen gas under pressure in a special apparatus. (We shall have much more to say about this reaction — called hydrogenation — in Chapter 8.)

Specific Examples

$$CH_3CH{=}CH_2 + H{-}H \xrightarrow[\substack{C_2H_5OH \\ (25\ ^\circ C,\ 50\ atm)}]{Ni} CH_3CH{-}CH_2$$

Propene   Propane

$$
\begin{array}{c}
\quad\ CH_3 \\
\quad\ | \\
CH_3{-}C{=}CH_2 + H_2
\end{array}
\xrightarrow[\substack{C_2H_5OH \\ (25\ ^\circ C,\ 50\ atm)}]{Ni}
\begin{array}{c}
CH_3 \\
| \\
CH_3{-}C{-}CH_2 \\
|\ \ \ | \\
H\ \ H
\end{array}
$$

2-Methylpropene   Isobutane

$$\bigcirc\!\!\!| \ +\ H_2 \xrightarrow[\substack{C_2H_5OH \\ (25\ ^\circ C,\ 1\ atm)}]{Pt} \bigcirc$$

Cyclohexene   Cyclohexane

Problem 4.11

Three different alkenes will react with hydrogen in the presence of a platinum or nickel catalyst to yield butane. What are their structures? Show the reactions.

4.15B REDUCTION OF ALKYL HALIDES

Most alkyl halides react with zinc and aqueous acid to produce an alkane. In this reaction zinc acts as a reducing agent and causes the halogen of the alkyl halide to be replaced by hydrogen. (Since hydrogen is less electronegative than a halogen, the alkyl halide is said to be **reduced**.) The general reaction is as follows:

General Reaction

$$2\ R{-}X + Zn + 2\ H^+ \longrightarrow 2\ R{-}H + ZnX_2$$

$$\text{or*}\quad R{-}X \xrightarrow[(-ZnX_2)]{Zn,\ H^+} R{-}H$$

Specific Examples

$$2\ CH_3CH_2CHCH_3 \xrightarrow[Zn]{H^+} 2\ CH_3CH_2CHCH_3 + ZnBr_2$$
$$\qquad\qquad\ \ |\qquad\qquad\qquad\qquad\qquad\qquad |$$
$$\qquad\qquad\ \ Br \qquad\qquad\qquad\qquad\qquad\qquad H$$

sec-Butyl bromide   Butane
(2-bromobutane)

$$\qquad\qquad CH_3 \qquad\qquad\qquad\qquad\qquad CH_3$$
$$\qquad\qquad\ |\qquad\qquad\qquad\qquad\qquad\qquad |$$
$$2\ CH_3CHCH_2CH_2{-}Br \xrightarrow[Zn]{H^+} 2\ CH_3CHCH_2CH_2{-}H + ZnBr_2$$

Isopentyl bromide   Isopentane
(1-bromo-3-methylbutane)   (2-methylbutane)

Problem 4.12

In addition to isopentyl bromide (just cited), three other alkyl halides will yield isopentane when they are treated with zinc and aqueous acid. What are their structures? Show the reactions.

4.15C LITHIUM DIALKYLCUPRATES: THE COREY-POSNER, WHITESIDES-HOUSE SYNTHESIS

A highly versatile method for the synthesis of alkanes and other hydrocarbons from organic halides has been developed by E. J. Corey† (Harvard University) and G. H. Posner (The Johns Hopkins University) and by G. M. Whitesides (MIT) and H. O.

---

*This illustrates the way organic chemists often write abbreviated equations for chemical reactions. The organic reactant is shown on the left and the organic product on the right. The reagents necessary to bring about the transformation are written over (or under) the arrow. The equations are often left unbalanced and sometimes byproducts (in this case, ZnX_2) are either omitted or are placed under the arrow in parentheses with a minus sign, for example, $(-ZnX_2)$.

† Corey was awarded the Nobel Prize for Chemistry in 1990, for finding new ways of synthesizing organic compounds, which, in the words of the Nobel committee "have contributed to the high standards of living and health enjoyed . . . in the Western world."

4.15 SYNTHESIS OF ALKANES AND CYCLOALKANES

House (Georgia Institute of Technology). The overall synthesis provides, for example, a way for coupling the alkyl groups of two alkyl halides to produce an alkane:

$$R-X + R'-X \xrightarrow[\substack{\text{several} \\ \text{steps} \\ (-2\,X)}]{} R-R'$$

In order to accomplish this coupling, we must transform one alkyl halide into a lithium dialkylcuprate (R_2CuLi). This transformation requires two steps. First, the alkyl halide is treated with lithium metal in an ether solvent to convert the alkyl halide into an alkyllithium, RLi (Section 3.8).

$$R-X + 2\,Li \xrightarrow[\text{ether}]{\text{diethyl}} \underset{\textbf{Alkyllithium}}{RLi} + LiX$$

Then the alkyllithium is treated with cuprous iodide (CuI). This converts it to the lithium dialkylcuprate.

$$2\,RLi + CuI \longrightarrow \underset{\substack{\textbf{Lithium} \\ \textbf{dialkylcuprate}}}{R_2CuLi} + LiI$$
$$\underset{\textbf{Alkyllithium}}{}$$

When the lithium dialkylcuprate is treated with the second alkyl halide ($R'-X$), coupling takes place between one alkyl group of the lithium dialkylcuprate and the alkyl group of the alkyl halide, $R'-X$.

$$\underset{\substack{\textbf{Lithium} \\ \textbf{dialkylcuprate}}}{R_2CuLi} + \underset{\textbf{Alkyl halide}}{R'-X} \longrightarrow \underset{\textbf{Alkane}}{R-R'} + RCu + LiX$$

For the last step to give a good yield of the alkane, the alkyl halide $R'-X$ must be either a methyl halide, a primary alkyl halide, or a secondary cycloalkyl halide. The alkyl groups of the lithium dialkylcuprate may be methyl, 1°, 2°, or 3°.* Moreover, the two alkyl groups being coupled need not be different.

The overall scheme for this alkane synthesis is given in Fig. 4.25.

* Special techniques, which we shall not discuss here, are required when R is tertiary. For an excellent review of these reactions see Gary H. Posner, "Substitution Reactions Using Organocopper Reagents," *Organic Reactions,* Vol. 22, Wiley, New York, 1975.

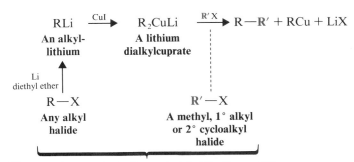

These are the organic starting materials. The R— and R'— groups need not be different.

FIGURE 4.25 A scheme outlining the synthesis of alkanes via the Corey–Posner, Whitesides–House method.

Consider the following two examples: the synthesis of hexane from methyl iodide and pentyl iodide, and the synthesis of nonane from butyl bromide and pentyl bromide:

$$CH_3-I \xrightarrow[\text{diethyl ether}]{Li} CH_3Li \xrightarrow{CuI} (CH_3)_2CuLi \xrightarrow{CH_3CH_2CH_2CH_2CH_2I}$$

$$CH_3-CH_2CH_2CH_2CH_2CH_3$$

Hexane
(98%)

$$CH_3CH_2CH_2CH_2Br \xrightarrow[\text{diethyl ether}]{Li} CH_3CH_2CH_2CH_2Li \xrightarrow{CuI}$$

$$(CH_3CH_2CH_2CH_2)_2CuLi \xrightarrow{CH_3CH_2CH_2CH_2CH_2Br} CH_3CH_2CH_2CH_2-CH_2CH_2CH_2CH_2CH_3$$

Nonane
(98%)

Lithium dialkylcuprates couple with other organic groups. Coupling reactions of lithium dimethylcuprate with two cycloalkyl halides are shown here.

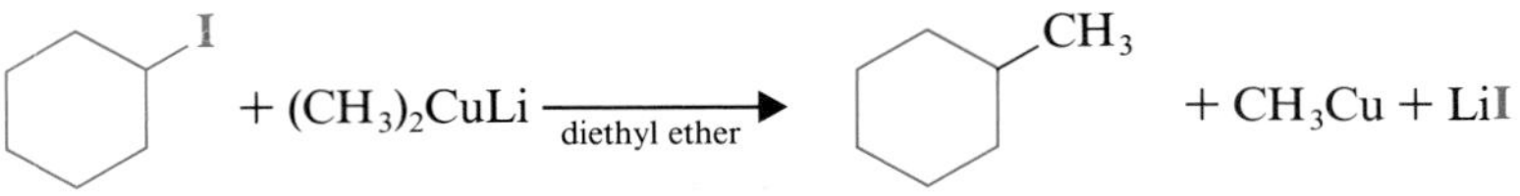

Methylcyclohexane
(75%)

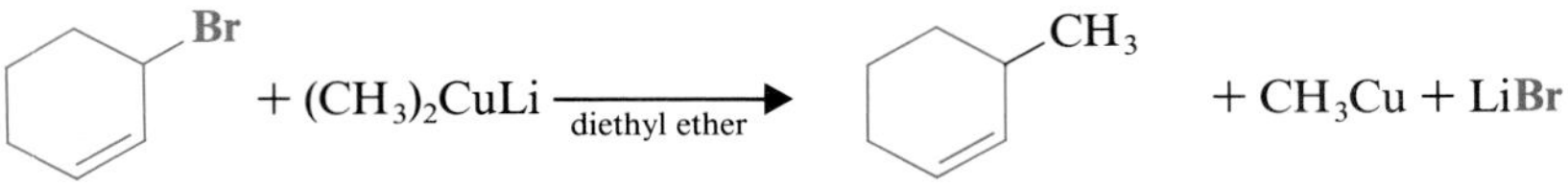

3-Methylcyclohexene
(75%)

Lithium dialkylcuprates also couple with phenyl halides. An example is the following synthesis of butyl benzene.

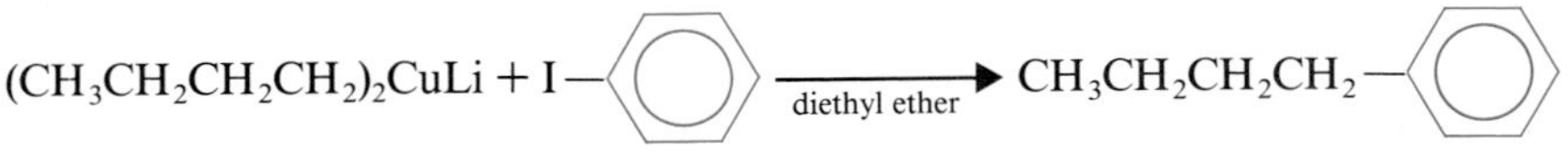

Butylbenzene
(75%)

The following scheme summarizes the coupling reactions of lithium dialkylcuprates.

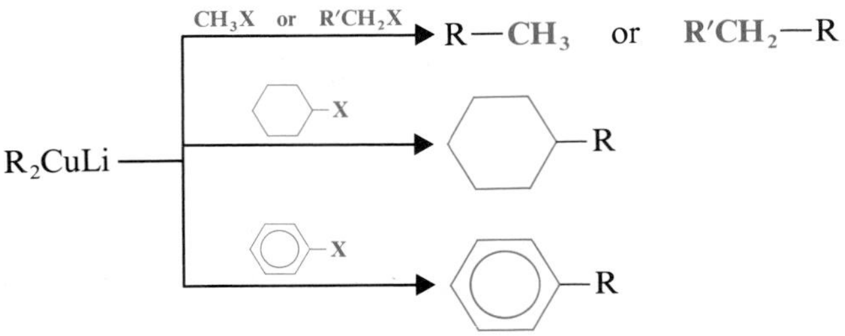

4.16 PLANNING ORGANIC SYNTHESES

Most of the more than 6 million organic compounds that are now known have come about because organic chemists have synthesized them. Only a small fraction of these compounds have been isolated from natural sources. Even then, in the isolation of a naturally occurring compound, the final proof of its structure is the synthesis of the compound by an unambiguous route from simpler molecules.

Syntheses are carried out for many reasons. We may need a particular compound to test some hypothesis about a reaction mechanism or about how a certain organism metabolizes the compound. In cases like these, we will need a particular compound, and we may need it with a "labeled" atom (e. g., deuterium or tritium) at a particular position.

The syntheses that you are asked to design in this text have a teaching purpose. At first, you will be asked to design syntheses of relatively simple compounds that are, in most instances, commercially available. Nevertheless, successfully planning these syntheses can offer an intellectual challenge and reward.

In planning syntheses we are required to think backward, to work our way backwards from relatively complex molecules to simpler ones that will act as the precursor (or precursors if two molecules are combined) for our target molecule. We carry out what is called a retrosynthetic analysis, and we represent this reasoning process in the following way:

Target Molecule $\Longrightarrow$ Precursors

The open arrow is a symbol that relates the target molecule to its most immediate precursors.*

In most instances more than one step will be required to bring about a synthesis. We then repeat the analytical process: The precursors become our target molecules, and we reason backward to another level of precursors, and so on, until we reach the level of the compounds that we have available as starting materials.

Target Molecule $\Longrightarrow$ 1st Precursor $\Longrightarrow$ 2nd Precursor $\Longrightarrow$ $\Longrightarrow$ Starting Compound

There will almost always be more than one way to carry out a synthesis. We usually face the sort of situation given in Fig. 4.26.

Often more than one route will give the desired product in a reasonable percentage yield. However, not all pathways will be available to us because of restrictions brought about by the reactions that we wish to use. If a step, for example, involves coupling of a lithium dialkylcuprate with an alkyl halide, we should not try to couple the lithium dialkylcuprate with a 2° or 3° alkyl halide, because the yields for this type of coupling are generally very low (Section 4.15C).

Let us consider an example: the synthesis of 2-methylpentane. One way to disclose retrosynthetic pathways is to look for **disconnections** in the target molecule. We might, for example, imagine the following disconnection, which discloses two

---

* Although organic chemists have used this approach intuitively for many years, E. J. Corey originated the term *retrosynthetic analysis,* and was the first person to state its principles formally. His studies, dating from the 1960s, have made the designing of organic syntheses systematic enough to be aided by computers. You may want to read the book: E. J. Corey and Xue-Min Chen, *The Logic of Chemical Synthesis,* Wiley, New York, 1989.

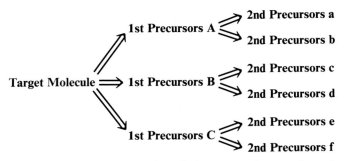

FIGURE 4.26 The retroanalytic process often discloses several routes from the target molecule back to varied precursors.

possible syntheses using lithium dialkylcuprates. Only the second synthesis is likely to give a good yield, however.

Analysis

$$CH_3 \overset{CH_3}{\underset{|}{\overset{|}{C}}}H-CH_2-CH_3 \nearrow (CH_3)_2CuLi + X-\overset{CH_3}{\underset{|}{\overset{|}{C}}}HCH_2CH_3$$

$$\searrow CH_3-X + LiCu\left(\overset{CH_3}{\underset{|}{\overset{|}{C}}}HCH_2CH_3\right)_2$$

Syntheses

$$(CH_3)_2CuLi + X-\overset{CH_3}{\underset{|}{\overset{|}{C}}}HCH_2CH_3 \xrightarrow{\text{ether}} CH_3\overset{CH_3}{\underset{|}{\overset{|}{C}}}HCH_2CH_3 \quad \begin{array}{l}\textbf{Poor yield because}\\ \textbf{the alkyl halide is 2°}\end{array}$$

$$CH_3-X + LiCu\left(\overset{CH_3}{\underset{|}{\overset{|}{C}}}HCH_2CH_3\right)_2 \xrightarrow{\text{ether}} CH_3\overset{CH_3}{\underset{|}{\overset{|}{C}}}HCH_2CH_3$$

Other disconnections and the syntheses that they reveal are the following:

Analysis

$$CH_3-\overset{CH_3}{\underset{|}{\overset{|}{C}}}H \overset{\vdots}{=} CH_2-CH_3 \nearrow \left(CH_3\overset{CH_3}{\underset{|}{\overset{|}{C}}}H\right)_2CuLi + CH_3CH_2-X$$

$$\searrow CH_3\overset{CH_3}{\underset{|}{\overset{|}{C}}}H-X + (CH_3CH_2)_2CuLi$$

Syntheses

$$\left(CH_3\overset{CH_3}{\underset{|}{\overset{|}{C}}}H\right)_2CuLi + CH_3CH_2-X \xrightarrow{\text{ether}} CH_3\overset{CH_3}{\underset{|}{\overset{|}{C}}}HCH_2CH_3$$

$$CH_3\overset{CH_3}{\underset{|}{\overset{|}{C}}}H-X + (CH_3CH_2)_2CuLi \xrightarrow{\text{ether}} CH_3\overset{CH_3}{\underset{|}{\overset{|}{C}}}HCH_2CH_3 \quad \begin{array}{l}\textbf{Poor yield because}\\ \textbf{the alkyl halide is 2°}\end{array}$$

Analysis

$$CH_3-\overset{\overset{\displaystyle CH_3}{|}}{CH}-CH_2 \overset{+}{\rightleftharpoons} CH_3$$

$$\left(CH_3\overset{\overset{\displaystyle CH_3}{|}}{CH}CH_2\right)_2 CuLi + CH_3-X \xrightarrow[\text{ether}]{\text{diethyl}} CH_3\overset{\overset{\displaystyle CH_3}{|}}{CH}CH_2CH_3$$

$$CH_3\overset{\overset{\displaystyle CH_3}{|}}{CH}CH_2-X + (CH_3)_2CuLi \xrightarrow[\text{ether}]{\text{diethyl}} CH_3\overset{\overset{\displaystyle CH_3}{|}}{CH}CH_2CH_3$$

Syntheses

$$\left(CH_3\overset{\overset{\displaystyle CH_3}{|}}{CH}CH_2\right)_2 CuLi + CH_3-X \xrightarrow[\text{ether}]{} CH_3\overset{\overset{\displaystyle CH_3}{|}}{CH}CH_2CH_3$$

$$CH_3\overset{\overset{\displaystyle CH_3}{|}}{CH}CH_2-X + (CH_3)_2CuLi \xrightarrow[\text{ether}]{} CH_3\overset{\overset{\displaystyle CH_3}{|}}{CH}CH_2CH_3$$

Problem 4.13

Outline a synthesis of each of the following alkanes from appropriate alkyl halides using the Corey–Posner, Whitesides–House method:

(a) Propane   (d) 2,7-Dimethyloctane   (f) Isopropylcyclopentane

(b) Butane   (e) Ethylcyclohexane   (g) 3-Methylcyclopentene

(c) 2-Methylpropane

Problem 4.14

Outline methods showing how hexane could be prepared starting with:

(a) A bromopropane   (c) A bromopentane   (e) A hexene

(b) A bromobutane   (d) A bromohexane

4.17 SOME IMPORTANT TERMS AND CONCEPTS

Alkanes are hydrocarbons with the general formula C_nH_{2n+2}. Molecules of alkanes have no rings (i.e., they are **acyclic**) and they have only single bonds between carbon atoms. Their carbon atoms are sp^3 hybridized.

Cycloalkanes are hydrocarbons whose molecules have their carbon atoms arranged into one or more rings. They have only single bonds between carbon atoms, and their carbon atoms are sp^3 hybridized. Cycloalkanes with only one ring have the general formula C_nH_{2n}.

Conformational analysis is a study of the energy changes that occur in a molecule when groups rotate about single bonds.

Torsional strain refers to a small barrier to free rotation about the carbon–carbon single bond that is associated with the eclipsed conformation. For ethane this barrier is 2.8 kcal mol^{-1} (11.7 kJ mol^{-1}).

CHAPTER 4. ALKANES AND CYCLOALKANES: CONFORMATIONS OF MOLECULES

van der Waals forces are weak forces that act between nonpolar molecules or between parts of the same molecule. Bringing two groups together first results in an *attractive* van der Waals force between them because a temporary unsymmetrical distribution of electrons in one group induces an opposite polarity in the other. When the groups are brought closer than their *van der Waals radii,* the force between them becomes repulsive because their electron clouds begin to interpenetrate each other. The methyl groups of the *gauche* form of butane, for example, are close enough for the van der Waals forces to be repulsive.

Ring strain. Certain cycloalkanes have greater potential energy than open-chain compounds. This extra potential energy is called ring strain. The principal sources of ring strain are *torsional strain* and *angle strain.*

Angle strain is introduced into a molecule because some factor (e.g., ring size) causes the bond angles of its atoms to deviate from the normal bond angle. The normal bond angles of an sp^3 carbon are $109.5°$, but in cyclopropane, for example, one pair of bonds at each carbon atom is constrained to a much smaller angle. This introduces considerable angle strain into the molecule, causing molecules of cyclopropane to have greater potential energy per CH_2 group than cycloalkanes with less (or no) angle strain.

cis – trans Isomerism is a type of stereoisomerism that occurs with certain alkenes (Section 2.4B) and with disubstituted cycloalkanes. cis–trans Isomers of 1,2-dimethylcyclopropane are shown here.

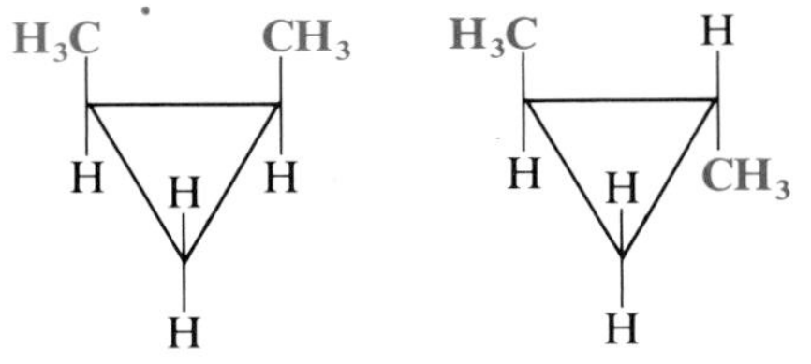

These two isomers can be separated and they have different physical properties. The two forms cannot be interconverted without breaking carbon–carbon bonds.

Conformations of molecules of cyclohexane. The most stable conformation is a chair conformation. Twist conformations and boat conformations have greater potential energy. These conformations (chair, boat, and twist) can be interconverted by rotations of single bonds. In a sample of cyclohexane more than 99% of the molecules are in a chair conformation at any given moment. A group attached to a carbon atom of a molecule of cyclohexane in a chair conformation can assume either of two positions: *axial* or *equatorial,* and these are interconverted when the ring flips from one chair conformation to another. A group has more room when it is equatorial; thus most of the molecules of substituted cyclohexanes at any given moment will be in the chair conformation that has the largest group (or groups) equatorial.

Additional Problems

4.15 Write a structural formula for each of the following compounds:

(a) 2,3-Dichloropentane   (b) *tert*-Butyl iodide

ADDITIONAL PROBLEMS

(c) 3-Ethylpentane

(d) 2,3,4-Trimethyldecane

(e) 4-Isopropylnonane

(f) 1,1-Dimethylcyclopropane

(g) *cis*-1,2-Dimethylcyclobutane

(h) *trans*-1,3-Dimethylcyclobutane

(i) Isopropylcyclohexane
(most stable conformation)

(j) *trans*-1-Isopropyl-3-methylcyclohexane
(most stable conformation)

(k) 1-Chloro-4-methylpentane

(l) 2,2,4-Tetramethyloctane

(m) Neopentyl chloride

(n) 1-Chloro-3-methylbutane

4.16   Name each of the following compounds by the IUPAC system:

(a) $CH_3CH(C_2H_5)CH(CH_3)CH_2CH_3$

(b) $CH_3CH(CH_3)CH_2CH_3$

(c)
$$H_3C \diagdown CH_3$$
$$CH-CH_2-CH$$
$$H_3C \diagup CH_3$$

(d) $CH_3CH_2CH(C_2H_5)CH_3$

(e) $CH_3CH_2-\langle hexagon \rangle$

(f)

(g) $CH_3CH_2CH_2CH_2CHCH_2CH_2CH_2CHCH_3$

with substituents:
$$\overset{CH_3}{\underset{}{|}}$$ (on the right carbon)
$$\underset{CH_2}{|}$$
$$\underset{CH}{|}$$
$$H_3C \diagup \diagdown CH_3$$

4.17   Write the structure and give the IUPAC name of an alkane or cycloalkane with the formula: (a) C_5H_{12} that has only primary hydrogen atoms (i.e., hydrogen atoms attached to primary carbon atoms),   (b) C_5H_{12} that has only one tertiary hydrogen atom,   (c) C_5H_{12} that has only primary and secondary hydrogen atoms,   (d) C_5H_{10} that has only secondary hydrogen atoms, and   (e) C_6H_{14} that has only primary and tertiary hydrogen atoms.

4.18   Three different alkenes yield 2-methylbutane when they are hydrogenated in the presence of a metal catalyst. Give their structures and write equations for the reactions involved.

4.19   An alkane with the formula C_6H_{14} can be synthesized by treating (in separate reactions) five different alkyl chlorides ($C_6H_{13}Cl$) with zinc and aqueous acid. Give the structure of the alkane and the structures of the alkyl chlorides.

4.20   An alkane with the formula C_6H_{14} can be prepared by reduction (with Zn and H^+) of only two alkyl chlorides ($C_6H_{13}Cl$) and by the hydrogenation of only two alkenes (C_6H_{12}). Write the structure of this alkane, give its IUPAC name, and show the reactions.

4.21   Four different cycloalkenes will all yield methylcyclopentane when subjected to catalytic hydrogenation. What are their structures? Show the reactions.

4.22   The heats of combustion of three pentane (C_5H_{12}) isomers are $CH_3(CH_2)_3CH_3$, 845.2 kcal mol^{-1}; $CH_3CH(CH_3)CH_2CH_3$, 843.4 kcal mol^{-1}; and $(CH_3)_3CCH_3$, 840.0 kcal mol^{-1}. Which isomer is most stable? Construct a diagram such as that in Fig. 4.9 showing the relative potential energies of the three compounds.

4.23   Tell what is meant by a homologous series and illustrate your answer by writing a homologous series of alkyl halides.

4.24   Write the structures of two chair conformations of 1-*tert*-butyl-1-methylcyclohexane. Which conformation is more stable? Explain your answer.

4.25   Ignoring compounds with double bonds, write structural formulas and give names for all of the isomers with the formula C_5H_{10}.

4.26   Write structures for the following bicyclic alkanes.

(a) Bicyclo[1.1.0]butane   (c) 2-Chlorobicyclo[3.2.0]heptane

(b) Bicyclo[2.1.0]pentane   (d) 7-Methylbicyclo[2.2.1]heptane

4.27   The carbon–carbon bond angles of isobutane are about 111.5°. These angles are larger than those expected from regular (or undistorted) tetrahedral carbon (i.e., 109.5°). Explain.

4.28   Sketch approximate potential energy diagrams for rotations about   (a) the C-2—C-3 bond of 2,3-dimethylbutane,   (b) the C-2—C-3 bond of 2,2,3,3-tetramethylbutane, and (c) the C-2—C-3 bond of 2-methylbutane.

4.29   Without referring to tables, decide which member of each of the following pairs has the higher boiling point. Explain your answers.

(a) Hexane or isohexane   (d) Ethane or chloroethane

(b) Hexane or pentane   (e) Propane or ethanol

(c) Pentane or neopentane

4.30   *cis*-1,2-Dimethylcyclopropane has a larger heat of combustion than *trans*-1,2-dimethylcyclopropane. (a) Which compound is more stable? (b) Give a reason that would explain your answer to part (a).

4.31   Write structural formulas for   (a) the two chair conformations of *cis*-1-isopropyl-3-methylcyclohexane,   (b) the two chair conformations of *trans*-1-isopropyl-3-methylcyclohexane, and   (c) designate which conformation in parts (a) and (b) is more stable.

4.32   Which member of each of the following pairs of compounds would be more stable? (a) *cis*- or *trans*-1,2-Dimethylcyclohexane,   (b) *cis*- or *trans*-1,3-dimethylcyclohexane, and (c) *cis*- or *trans*-1,4-dimethylcyclohexane.

4.33   Norman L. Allinger of the University of Georgia has obtained evidence indicating that, while *cis*-1,3-di-*tert*-butylcyclohexane exists predominantly in a chair conformation, *trans*-1,3-di-*tert*-butylcyclohexane adopts a twist–boat conformation. Explain.

4.34   The important sugar glucose exists in the following cyclic form:

$$
\begin{array}{c}
CH_2OH \\
| \\
CH \\
HOCH \qquad O \\
| \qquad | \\
HOCH \qquad CHOH \\
CH \\
| \\
OH
\end{array}
$$

The six-membered ring of glucose has the chair conformation. In one isomer, *β*-glucose, all of the secondary —OH groups and the —CH₂OH group are equatorial. Write a structure for *β*-glucose.

ADDITIONAL PROBLEMS

*4.35 When 1,2-dimethylcyclohexene (below) is allowed to react with hydrogen in the presence of a platinum catalyst, the product of the reaction is a cycloalkane that has a melting point of -50 °C and a boiling point of 130 °C (at 760 torr). (a) What is the structure of the product of this reaction? (b) Consult an appropriate table and tell which stereoisomer it is. (c) What does this experiment suggest about the mode of addition of hydrogen to the double bond?

1,2-Dimethylcyclohexene

*4.36 When cyclohexene is dissolved in an appropriate solvent and allowed to react with chlorine, the product of the reaction, $C_6H_{10}Cl_2$, has a melting point of -7 °C and a boiling point (at 16 torr) of 74 °C. (a) Which stereoisomer is this? (b) What does this experiment suggest about the mode of addition of chlorine to the double bond?

*An asterisk beside a problem indicates that it is somewhat more challenging. Your instructor may tell you that these problems are optional.

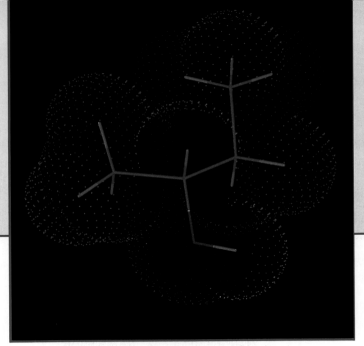

A 2-butanol enantiomer (see Section 5.2).

CHAPTER

5

STEREOCHEMISTRY: CHIRAL MOLECULES

5.1 ISOMERISM: CONSTITUTIONAL ISOMERS AND STEREOISOMERS

Isomers are different compounds that have the same molecular formula. In our study of carbon compounds, thus far, most of our attention has been directed toward those isomers that we have called constitutional isomers.

Constitutional isomers are isomers that differ because their atoms are connected in a different order. They are said to have a different **connectivity**. Several examples of constitutional isomers are the following:

Molecular Formula	Constitutional Isomers		
C_4H_{10}	$CH_3CH_2CH_2CH_3$ **Butane**	and	$CH_3\overset{\overset{\displaystyle CH_3}{\vert}}{C}HCH_3$ **Isobutane**

5.1 ISOMERISM: CONSTITUTIONAL ISOMERS AND STEREOISOMERS

C_3H_7Cl $CH_3CH_2CH_2Cl$ and CH_3CHCH_3

                                                 Cl

           1-Chloropropane   **2-Chloropropane**

C_2H_6O CH_3CH_2OH and CH_3OCH_3

               Ethanol   **Dimethyl ether**

Stereoisomers are not constitutional isomers—they have their constituent atoms connected in the same way. ***Stereoisomers differ only in arrangement of their atoms in space.*** The cis and trans isomers of alkenes are stereoisomers (Section 2.4B); we can see that this is true if we examine the *cis*- and *trans*-1,2-dichloroethenes shown here.

cis-1,2-Dichloroethene   **trans-1,2-Dichloroethene**
       $(C_2H_2Cl_2)$ **$(C_2H_2Cl_2)$**

cis-1,2-Dichloroethene and *trans*-1,2-dichloroethene are isomers because both compounds have the same molecular formula ($C_2H_2Cl_2$) but they are different. They cannot be easily interconverted because of the large barrier to rotation of the carbon–carbon double bond. Stereoisomers are *not* constitutional isomers, because the order of connections of the atoms in both compounds is the same. Both compounds have two central carbon atoms joined by a double bond, and both compounds have one chlorine atom and one hydrogen atom attached to the two central atoms. The *cis*-1,2-dichloroethene and *trans*-1,2-dichloroethene isomers differ only in the arrangement of their atoms in space. In *cis*-1,2-dichloroethene the hydrogen atoms are on the same side of the molecule, and in *trans*-1,2-dichloroethene the hydrogen atoms are on opposite sides. Thus, *cis*-1,2-dichloroethene and *trans*-1,2-dichloroethene are stereoisomers (see Section 2.4B).

Stereoisomers can be subdivided into two general categories: **enantiomers** and **diastereomers.** Enantiomers are stereoisomers whose molecules *are mirror images of each other.* Diastereomers are stereoisomers whose molecules *are not mirror images of each other.*

Molecules of *cis*-1,2-dichloroethene and *trans*-1,2-dichloroethene *are not* mirror images of each other. If one holds a model of *cis*-1,2-dichloroethene up to a mirror, the model that one sees in the mirror is not *trans*-1,2-dichloroethene. But *cis*-1,2-dichloroethene and *trans*-1,2-dichloroethene *are* stereoisomers and, since they are not related to each other as an object and its mirror image, they are diastereomers.

Cis and trans isomers of cycloalkanes furnish us with another example of stereoisomers that are diastereomers of each other. Consider the following two compounds.

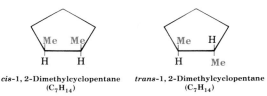

    cis-1, 2-Dimethylcyclopentane   *trans*-1, 2-Dimethylcyclopentane
         (C_7H_{14}) (C_7H_{14})

These two compounds are isomers of each other *because they are different compounds* that are *not* interconvertible, and *because they have the same molecular formula* (C_7H_{14}). They are not constitutional isomers because their atoms are joined in the same way. They are, therefore, *stereoisomers. They differ only in the arrangement of their atoms in space.* They are not enantiomers because their molecules are not mirror images of each other. They are, therefore, *diastereomers.* (In Section 5.12 we shall find that the *trans*-1,2-dimethylcyclopentane also has an enantiomer.)

cis–trans Isomers are not the only kind of diastereomers that we will encounter. In Section 5.9 we shall study diastereomers that are not cis–trans isomers. The essential requirements that must be fulfilled for two compounds to be diastereomers of each other are that the two compounds be stereoisomers of each other, and that they not be mirror images of each other.

SUBDIVISION OF ISOMERS

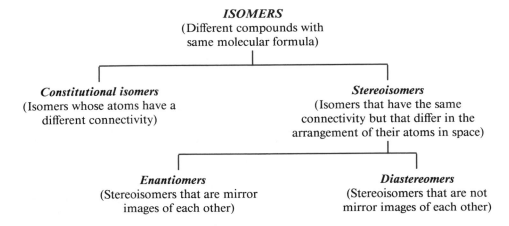

ISOMERS
(Different compounds with same molecular formula)

Constitutional isomers
(Isomers whose atoms have a different connectivity)

Stereoisomers
(Isomers that have the same connectivity but that differ in the arrangement of their atoms in space)

Enantiomers
(Stereoisomers that are mirror images of each other)

Diastereomers
(Stereoisomers that are not mirror images of each other)

5.2 ENANTIOMERS AND CHIRAL MOLECULES

Enantiomers occur only with those compounds whose molecules are **chiral. A chiral molecule is defined as one that is not superposable* on its mirror image.** The chiral molecule and its mirror image are enantiomers, and the relationship between the chiral molecule and its mirror image is defined as enantiomeric.

The word chiral comes from the Greek word *cheir,* meaning "hand." Chiral objects (including molecules) are said to possess "handedness." The term chiral is used to describe molecules of enantiomers because they are related to each other in the same way that a left hand is related to a right hand. When you view your left hand in a mirror, the mirror image of your left hand is a right hand (Fig. 5.1). Your left and right hands, moreover, are not superposable (Fig. 5.2). (This fact becomes obvious when one attempts to put a "left-handed" glove on a right hand or vice versa.)

Many familiar objects are chiral and the chirality of some of these objects is clear because we normally speak of them as having "handedness." We speak, for example, of nuts and bolts as having right- or left-handed threads or of a propeller as having a right- or left-handed pitch. The chirality of many other objects is not obvious in this

*Remember: To be *superposable* means that we can place one thing on top of the other *so that all parts of each coincide* (cf. Section 2.4B).

5.2 ENANTIOMERS AND CHIRAL MOLECULES

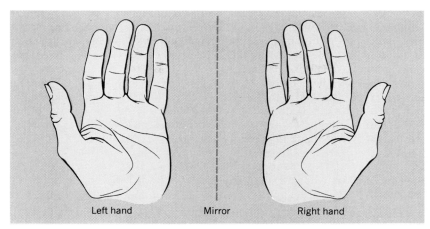

Left hand Mirror Right hand

FIGURE 5.1 The mirror image of a left hand is a right hand.

sense, but becomes obvious when we apply the test of nonsuperposability of the object and its mirror image.

Objects (and molecules) that *are* superposable on their mirror images are **achiral.** Most socks, for example, are achiral whereas gloves are chiral.

Chirality is a phenomenon that pervades the world we live in. The human body is structurally chiral with the heart lying to the left of center, and the liver to the right. For evolutionary reasons, far from understood, most people are right handed. Helical sea-shells are chiral, and most spiral like a right-handed screw. Many plants show chirality in the way they wind around supporting structures. The honeysuckle, *Lonicera sempervir-ens,* winds as a left-handed helix; bindweed, *Convolvulus arvensi,* winds in a right-handed way. Most of the molecules that make up plants and animals are chiral, and almost always only one form of the chiral molecule occurs naturally. All but one of the 20 amino acids that make up naturally occurring proteins are chiral, and all of them are classified as being left handed. The molecules of natural sugars are almost all classified as being right handed, including the sugar that occurs in DNA. Chiral molecules can show their different handed-

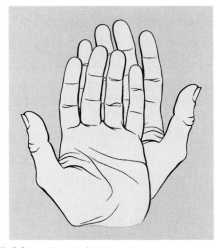

FIGURE 5.2 Left and right hands are not superposable.

ness in many ways including the way they affect human beings. One enantiomeric form of a compound called limonene (Section 23.3) smells like oranges, the other enantiomer smells like lemons. One enantiomer of a compound called carvone smells like caraway, the other has the odor of spearmint. Differences in chirality can have much more dramatic, indeed tragic effects, on humans. In 1963, the drug thalidomide, given to pregnant women to alleviate the symptoms of morning sickness, was found to have been responsible for horrible birth defects in many of the children born subsequent to the use of the drug. It was found later that while one of the thalidomide enantiomers has the intended effect of curing morning sickness, the other enantiomer, also present in the drug, causes birth defects. (For an interesting recent article, see R. A. Hegstrum and D. K. Kondepudi, "The Handedness of the Universe," *Sci. Am.,* **1990,** *262,* 98–105.)

Problem 5.1

Classify the following objects as to whether they are chiral or achiral.

(a) Screw   (c) Fork   (e) Foot   (g) Shoe

(b) Plain spoon   (d) Cup   (f) Ear   (h) Spiral staircase

The chirality of molecules can be demonstrated with relatively simple compounds. Consider, for example, 2-butanol.

$$CH_3CHCH_2CH_3$$
$$|$$
$$OH$$
2-Butanol

Until now, we have presented the formula just written as though it represented only one compound and we have not mentioned that molecules of 2-butanol are chiral. Because they are, there are actually two different 2-butanols and these two 2-butanols are enantiomers. We can understand this if we examine the drawings and models in Fig. 5.3.

If model **I** is held before a mirror, model **II** is seen in the mirror and vice versa. Models **I** and **II** are not superposable on each other; therefore they represent different, but isomeric, molecules. *Because models I and II are nonsuperposable mirror images of each other, the molecules that they represent are enantiomers.*

Problem 5.2

(a) If models are available, construct the 2-butanols represented in Fig. 5.3 and demonstrate for yourself that they are not mutually superposable. (b) Make similar models of 2-propanol ($CH_3CHOHCH_3$). Are they superposable? (c) Is 2-propanol chiral? (d) Would you expect to find enantiomeric forms of 2-propanol?

How do we know when to expect the possibility of enantiomers? One way (but not the only way) is to recognize that a pair of enantiomers is always possible for molecules that contain **one tetrahedral atom with four different groups attached to**

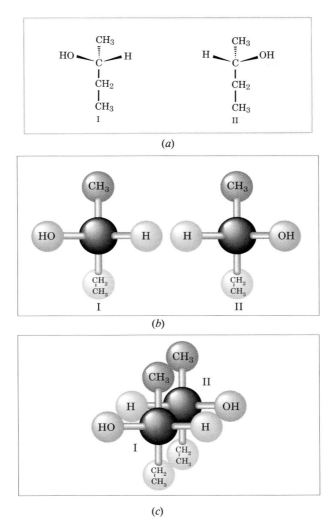

FIGURE 5.3 (*a*) Three-dimensional drawings of the 2-butanol enantiomers **I** and **II**. (*b*) Models of the 2-butanol enantiomers. (*c*) An unsuccessful attempt to superpose models of **I** and **II**.

it.* In 2-butanol (Fig. 5.4) this atom is C-2. The four different groups that are attached to C-2 are a hydroxyl group, a hydrogen atom, a methyl group, and an ethyl group.

An important property of enantiomers such as these is that *interchanging any two groups at the tetrahedral atom that bears four different groups converts one enantiomer into the other.* In Fig. 5.3*b* it is easy to see that interchanging the hydroxyl group and the hydrogen atom converts one enantiomer into the other. You should now convince yourself with models that interchanging any other two groups has the same result.

---

* We shall see later that enantiomers are also possible for molecules that contain more than one tetrahedral atom with four different groups attached to it, but some of these molecules (Section 5.9A) do not exist as enantiomers.

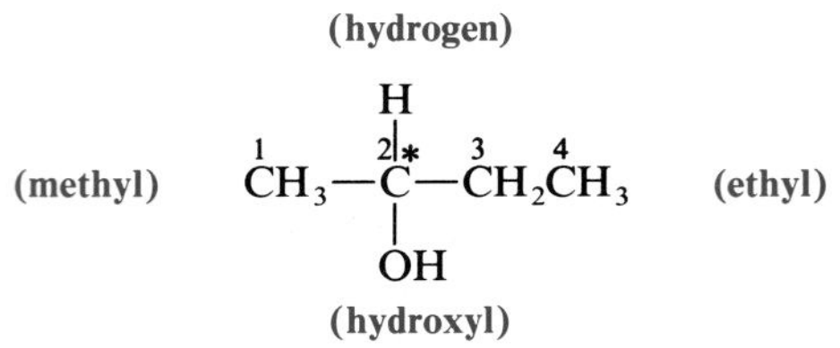

CHAPTER 5. STEREOCHEMISTRY: CHIRAL MOLECULES

(hydrogen)

$$
\text{(methyl)} \quad \overset{1}{C}H_3 - \overset{H}{\underset{\underset{OH}{|}}{\overset{2}{C}}} \overset{*}{\underset{}{-}} \overset{3}{C}H_2 \overset{4}{C}H_3 \quad \text{(ethyl)}
$$

(hydroxyl)

FIGURE 5.4 The tetrahedral carbon atom of 2-butanol that bears four different groups. [By convention such atoms are often designated with an asterisk (*).]

Because interchanging two groups at C-2 converts one stereoisomer into another, C-2 is an example of what is called a ***stereocenter.*** A ***stereocenter*** is defined as ***an atom bearing groups of such nature that an interchange of any two groups will produce a stereoisomer.*** Carbon-2 of 2-butanol is an example of a ***tetrahedral stereocenter.*** Not all stereocenters are tetrahedral, however. The carbon atoms of *cis-* and *trans-*1,2-dichloroethene (Section 5.2) are examples of *trigonal planar stereocenters* because an interchange of groups at either atom also produces a stereoisomer (a diastereomer). In this chapter, however, we shall concern ourselves primarily with tetrahedral stereocenters.

When we discuss interchanging groups like this, we must take care to notice that what we are describing is *something we do to a molecular model* or *something we do on paper.* An interchange of groups in a real molecule, if it can be done, requires breaking covalent bonds, and this is something that requires a large input of energy. This means that enantiomers such as the 2-butanol enantiomers ***do not interconvert*** spontaneously.

> Prior to 1984, *tetrahedral atoms* with four different groups were called *chiral atoms* or *asymmetric atoms.* Then, in an important publication, K. Mislow (of Princeton University) and J. Siegel (now at the University of California, San Diego) pointed out that the use of terms like this has represented a source of conceptual confusion in stereochemistry that has existed from the time of van't Hoff (Section 5.3A). Chirality is a geometric property that pervades and affects all parts of a chiral molecule. All of the atoms of 2-butanol, for example, are in a chiral environment and, therefore, all are said to be *chirotopic.* When we consider an atom such as C-2 of 2-butanol in the way that we describe here, however, we are considering it as a *stereocenter* and, therefore, we should designate it as such, and not as a "chiral atom." Further consideration of these issues is beyond our scope here, but those interested may wish o read the original paper; cf. K. Mislow and J. Siegel, *J. Am. Chem. Soc.,* **1984,** *106,* 3319–3328.

Figure 5.5 demonstrates the validity of the generalization that enantiomeric compounds necessarily result whenever a molecule contains a single tetrahedral stereocenter.

Problem 5.3

Demonstrate the validity of what we have represented in Fig. 5.5 by constructing models. Arrange four different colored atoms at each corner of a tetrahedral carbon atom. Demonstrate for yourself that **III** and **IV** are related as an object and its mirror image *and that they are not superposable* (i.e., that **III** and **IV** are chiral molecules and are enantiomers). (a) Replace one atom on each model

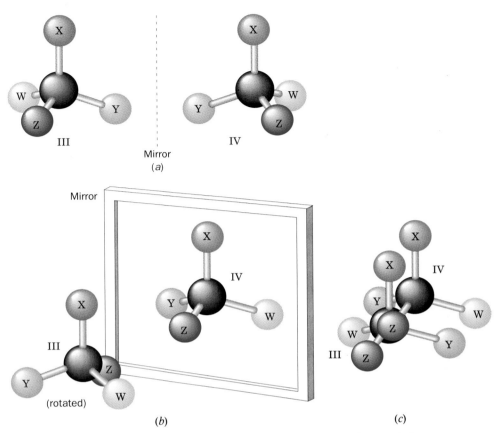

FIGURE 5.5 A demonstration of chirality of a generalized molecule containing one tetrahedral stereocenter. (*a*) The four different groups around the carbon atom in **III** and **IV** are arbitrary. (*b*) **III** is rotated and placed in front of a mirror. **III** and **IV** are found to be related as an object and its mirror image. (*c*) **III** and **IV** are not superposable; therefore, the molecules that they represent are chiral and are enantiomers.

so that each model has two atoms of the same color arranged around the central carbon atom. Are the molecules that these models represent mirror images of each other? (b) Are they superposable? (c) Are they chiral? (d) Are they enantiomers?

If all of the tetrahedral atoms in a molecule have two or more groups attached that *are the same* the molecule does not have a stereocenter. The molecule is superposable on its mirror image and is **achiral**. An example of a molecule of this type is 2-propanol; carbon atoms 1 and 3 bear three identical hydrogen atoms and the central atom bears two identical methyl groups. If we write three-dimensional formulas for 2-propanol, we find (Fig. 5.6) that one structure can be superposed on its mirror image.

Thus, we would not predict the existence of enantiomeric forms of 2-propanol, and experimentally only one form of 2-propanol has ever been found.

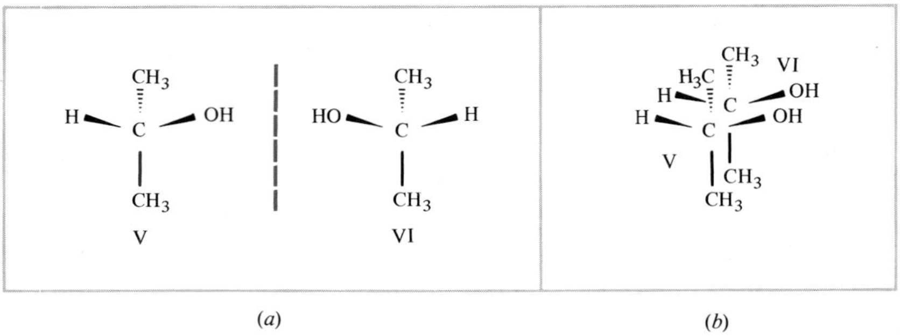

(a) (b)

FIGURE 5.6 (a) 2-Propanol (**V**) and its mirror image (**VI**). (b) When either one is rotated, the two structures are superposable and thus do not represent enantiomers. They represent two molecules of the same compound. 2-Propanol does not have a stereocenter.

Problem 5.4

Some of the molecules listed here have stereocenters; some do not. Write three-dimensional formulas for the enantiomers of those molecules that do have stereocenters.

(a) 1-Chloropropane   (e) 2-Bromobutane

(b) Bromochloroiodomethane   (f) 1-Chloropentane

(c) 1-Chloro-2-methylpropane   (g) 2-Chloropentane

(d) 2-Chloro-2-methylpropane   (h) 3-Chloropentane

5.3 HISTORICAL ORIGIN OF STEREOCHEMISTRY

In 1877, Hermann Kolbe (of the University of Leipzig), one of the most eminent organic chemists of the time, wrote the following:

> Not long ago, I expressed the view that the lack of general education and of thorough training in chemistry was one of the causes of the deterioration of chemical research in Germany. . . . Will anyone to whom my worries seem exaggerated please read, if he can, a recent memoir by a Herr van't Hoff on 'The Arrangements of Atoms in Space,' a document crammed to the hilt with the outpourings of a childish fantasy. . . . This Dr. J. H. van't Hoff, employed by the Veterinary College at Utrecht, has, so it seems, no taste for accurate chemical research. He finds it more convenient to mount his Pegasus (evidently taken from the stables of the Veterinary College) and to announce how, on his bold flight to Mount Parnassus, he saw the atoms arranged in space.

Kolbe, nearing the end of his career, was reacting to a publication of a 22-year-old Dutch scientist. This publication had appeared 2 years earlier in September 1874, and in it, van't Hoff had argued that the spatial arrangement of four groups around a central carbon atom is tetrahedral. A young French scientist, J. A. Le Bel, had independently advanced the same idea in a publication in November 1874. Within 10 years after Kolbe's comments, however, abundant evidence had accumulated that substantiated the "childish fantasy" of van't Hoff. Later in his career (in 1901), and for other work, van't Hoff was named the first recipient of the Nobel Prize for chemistry.

Together, the publications of van't Hoff and Le Bel marked an important turn in a field of study that is concerned with the structures of molecules in three dimensions: *stereochemistry.* Stereochemistry, as we shall see in Section 5.14, had been founded earlier by Louis Pasteur.

It was reasoning based on many observations such as those we presented earlier in this section that led van't Hoff and Le Bel to the conclusion that the spatial orientation of groups around carbon atoms is tetrahedral when a carbon atom is bonded to four other atoms. The following information was available to van't Hoff and Le Bel.

1. Only one compound with the general formula CH_3X is ever found.
2. Only one compound with the formula CH_2X_2 or CH_2XY is ever found.
3. Two enantiomeric compounds with the formula CHXYZ are found.

By working Problem 5.5 you can see more about the reasoning of van't Hoff and Le Bel.

Problem 5.5 ———————————————————————

(a) Prove to yourself the correctness of the reasoning of van't Hoff and Le Bel by writing tetrahedral representations for carbon compounds of the three types given previously. (b) How many isomers would be possible in each instance if the carbon atom were at the center of a square? (c) At the center of a rectangle? (d) At one corner of a regular pyramid?

5.4 TESTS FOR CHIRALITY: PLANES OF SYMMETRY

The ultimate way to test for molecular chirality is to construct models of the molecule and its mirror image and then determine whether they are superposable. If the two models are superposable, the molecule that they represent is achiral. If the models are not superposable, then the molecules that they represent are chiral. We can apply this test with actual models, as we have just described, or we can apply it by drawing three-dimensional structures and attempting to superpose them in our minds.

There are other aids, however, that will assist us in recognizing chiral molecules. We have mentioned one already: the presence of a *single* tetrahedral stereocenter. The other aids are based on the absence in the molecule of certain symmetry elements. A molecule **will not be chiral,** for example, if it possesses **a plane of symmetry.**

A plane of symmetry (also called a **mirror plane**) is defined as *an imaginary plane that bisects a molecule in such a way that the two halves of the molecule are mirror images of each other.* The plane may pass through atoms, between atoms, or both. For example, 2-chloropropane has a plane of symmetry (Fig. 5.7*a*), while 2-chlorobutane does not (Fig. 5.7*b*). **All molecules with a plane of symmetry are achiral.**

Problem 5.6 ———————————————————————

Which of the objects listed in Problem 5.1 possess a plane of symmetry and are, therefore, achiral?

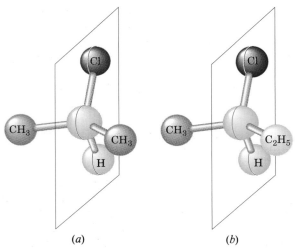

FIGURE 5.7 (a) 2-Chloropropane has a plane of symmetry and is achiral. (b) 2-Chlorobutane does not possess a plane of symmetry and is chiral.

Problem 5.7 _____

Write three-dimensional formulas and designate a plane of symmetry for all of the achiral molecules in Problem 5.4. (In order to be able to designate a plane of symmetry you may have to write the molecule in an appropriate conformation. This is permissible with all of these molecules because they have only single bonds and groups joined by single bonds are capable of essentially free rotation at room temperature. We discuss this matter further in Section 5.8.)

5.5 NOMENCLATURE OF ENANTIOMERS: THE (*R–S*) SYSTEM

The two enantiomers of 2-butanol are the following:

$$
\begin{array}{cc}
\text{CH}_3 & \text{CH}_3 \\
\text{HO}{\diagdown}\overset{\vdots}{\underset{\text{C}}{}}{\diagup}\text{H} & \text{H}{\diagdown}\overset{\vdots}{\underset{\text{C}}{}}{\diagup}\text{OH} \\
| & | \\
\text{CH}_2 & \text{CH}_2 \\
| & | \\
\text{CH}_3 & \text{CH}_3 \\
\\
\textbf{I} & \textbf{II}
\end{array}
$$

If we name these two enantiomers using only the IUPAC system of nomenclature that we have learned so far, both enantiomers will have the same name — 2-butanol (or *sec*-butyl alcohol) (Section 4.3F). This is undesirable because *each compound must have its own distinct name.* Moreover, the name that is given a compound should allow a chemist who is familiar with the rules of nomenclature to write the structure of the compound from its name alone. Given the name 2-butanol, a chemist could write either structure **I** or structure **II**.

5.5 NOMENCLATURE OF ENANTIOMERS: THE (R-S) SYSTEM

Three chemists, R. S. Cahn (England), C. K. Ingold (England), and V. Prelog (Switzerland), devised a system of nomenclature that, when added to the IUPAC system, solves both of these problems. This system, called the $(R-S)$ system, or the Cahn–Ingold–Prelog system, is now widely used and is part of the IUPAC rules.

According to this system, one enantiomer of 2-butanol should be designated (R)-2-butanol and the other enantiomer should be designated (S)-2-butanol. [(R) and (S) are from the Latin words *rectus* and *sinister,* meaning right and left, respectively.]

The (R) and (S) designations are assigned on the basis of the following procedure. You should use models as you follow the steps.

1. Each of the four groups attached to the stereocenter is assigned a **priority** or **preference** a, b, c, or d. Priority is first assigned on the basis of the **atomic number** of the atom that is directly attached to the stereocenter. The group with the lowest atomic number is given the lowest priority, d; the group with next higher atomic number is given the next higher priority, c; and so on. (In the case of isotopes, the isotope of greatest atomic mass has highest priority.)

We can illustrate the application of this rule with the 2-butanol enantiomer, **I**.

$$
\text{(a)} \quad \text{HO} \diagdown \underset{\displaystyle |}{\overset{\displaystyle CH_3 \text{ (b or c)}}{C}} \diagup \text{H (d)}
$$

$$
\begin{array}{c}
CH_2 \text{ (b or c)} \\
| \\
CH_3
\end{array}
$$

I

Oxygen has the highest atomic number of the four atoms attached to the stereocenter and is assigned the highest priority, a. Hydrogen has the lowest atomic number and is assigned the lowest priority, d. A priority cannot be assigned for the methyl group and the ethyl group by this approach because the atom that is directly attached to the stereocenter is a carbon atom in both groups.

2. When a priority cannot be assigned on the basis of the atomic number of the atoms that are directly attached to the stereocenter, then the next set of atoms in the unassigned groups are examined. This process is continued until a decision can be made. *We assign a priority at the first point of difference.**

When we examine the methyl group of enantiomer **I**, we find that the next set of atoms consists of three hydrogen atoms (**H, H, H**). In the ethyl group of **I** the next set of atoms consists of one carbon atom and two hydrogen atoms (**C, H, H**). Carbon has a higher atomic number than hydrogen so we assign the ethyl group the higher priority, b, and the methyl group the lower priority, c.

---

* The rules for a branched chain require that we follow the chain with the highest priority atoms.

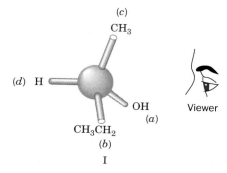

H
| (c) (H, H, H)
H— C —H
(a)   HO⁀C⁀H (d) (C, H, H) > (H, H, H)
|
H— C —H
| (b) (C, H, H)
H— C —H
|
H

I

3. We now rotate the formula (or model) so that the group with lowest priority (*d*) is directed away from us.

Then we trace a path from *a* to *b* to *c*. If, as we do this, the direction of our finger (or pencil) is *clockwise,* the enantiomer is designated (*R*). If the direction is *counterclockwise,* the enantiomer is designated (*S*). On this basis the 2-butanol enantiomer **I** is (*R*)-2-butanol.

Arrows are clockwise

Problem 5.8

Apply the procedure just given to the 2-butanol enantiomer **II** and show that it is (*S*)-2-butanol.

Problem 5.9

Give (*R*) and (*S*) designations for each pair of enantiomers given as answers to Problem 5.4.

5.5 NOMENCLATURE OF ENANTIOMERS: THE (R–S) SYSTEM

The first three rules of the Cahn–Ingold–Prelog system allow us to make an (R) or (S) designation for most compounds containing single bonds. For compounds containing multiple bonds one other rule is necessary.

4. Groups containing double or triple bonds are assigned priorities as if both atoms were duplicated or triplicated, that is,

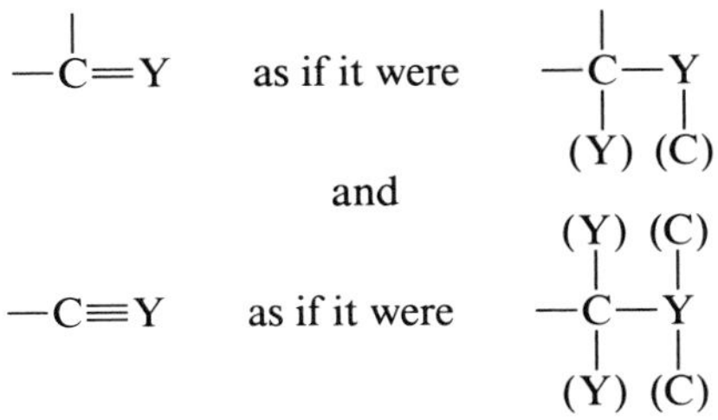

$$-\overset{|}{\underset{}{C}}{=}Y \quad \text{as if it were} \quad -\overset{|}{\underset{(Y)\ (C)}{C}}{-}\overset{|}{Y}$$

and

$$-C{\equiv}Y \quad \text{as if it were} \quad -\overset{(Y)\ (C)}{\underset{(Y)\ (C)}{C}}{-}Y$$

where the symbols in parentheses are duplicate or triplicate representations of the atoms at the other end of the double bond.

Thus, the vinyl group, $-CH{=}CH_2$, is of higher priority than the isopropyl group, $-CH(CH_3)_2$.

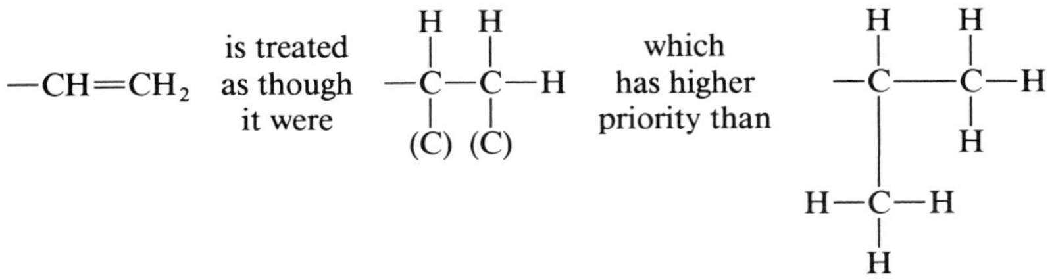

$$-CH{=}CH_2 \quad \begin{matrix}\text{is treated}\\\text{as though}\\\text{it were}\end{matrix} \quad \overset{H\ \ H}{\underset{(C)\ (C)}{-C-C-H}} \quad \begin{matrix}\text{which}\\\text{has higher}\\\text{priority than}\end{matrix} \quad \overset{H\ \ \ \ H}{-C-\!\!-\!\!-C-H}$$

because at the third set of atoms out, the vinyl group (see following structure) is C, H, H, whereas the isopropyl group along either branch is H, H, H. (At the first and second set of atoms both groups are the same: C, then C, C, H.)

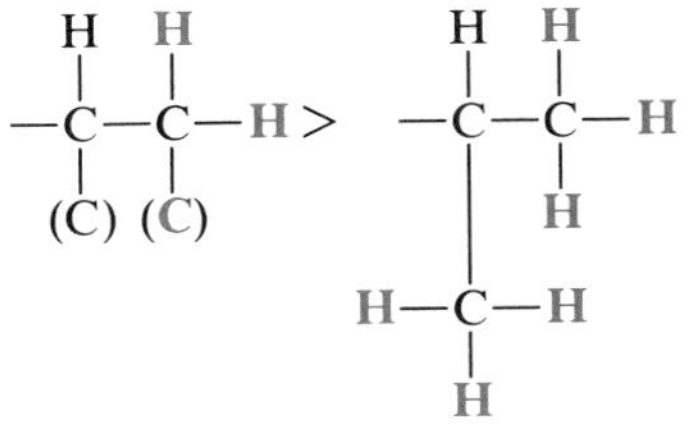

$$\overset{H\ \ H}{\underset{(C)\ (C)}{-C-C-H}} > \overset{H\ \ H}{-C-C-H}$$

C, H, H	>	H, H, H
Vinyl group		**Isopropyl group**

Other rules exist for more complicated structures, but we shall not study them here.

Problem 5.10

An important compound in stereochemistry and biology is the compound glyceraldehyde (see the following structure). Write three-dimensional formulas for the glyceraldehyde enantiomers and give each its proper $(R–S)$ designation.

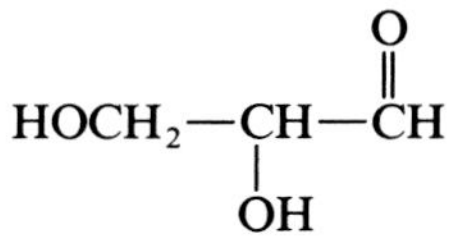

$$HOCH_2\!-\!\overset{\displaystyle \underset{|}{OH}}{CH}\!-\!\overset{\displaystyle \overset{O}{\|}}{CH}$$

Glyceraldehyde

Problem 5.11

Assign (R) or (S) designations to each of the following compounds:

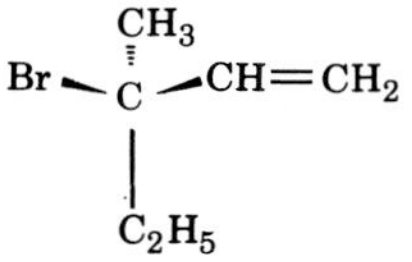

$$Br\!\diagdown\!\underset{|}{\overset{\displaystyle CH_3}{C}}\!\diagup\!CH\!=\!CH_2 \qquad \qquad$$
$$C_2H_5$$

$$F\!\diagdown\!\underset{|}{\overset{\displaystyle H}{C}}\!\diagup\!CH\!=\!CH_2$$
$$CH$$
$$H_3C \diagdown \quad \diagup CH_3$$

$$H_3C\!\diagdown\!\underset{|}{\overset{\displaystyle H}{C}}\!\diagup\!C\!\equiv\!CH$$
$$CH$$
$$H_3C \diagdown \quad \diagup CH_3$$

(a) 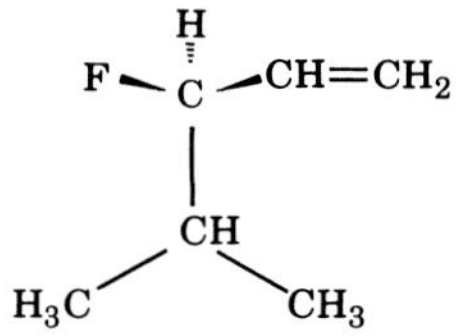   (b) 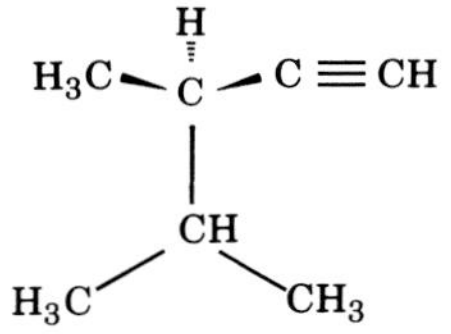   (c)

Sample Problem

Consider the following pair of structures and tell whether they represent enantiomers or two molecules of the same compound in different orientations.

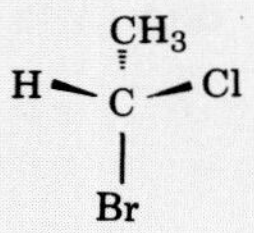

$$H\!\diagdown\!\underset{|}{\overset{\displaystyle CH_3}{C}}\!\diagup\!Cl \qquad Br\!\diagdown\!\underset{|}{\overset{\displaystyle Cl}{C}}\!\diagup\!CH_3$$
$$Br \qquad\qquad\qquad H$$
$$\textbf{A} \qquad\qquad\qquad \textbf{B}$$

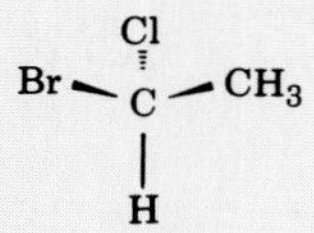

Answer:

One way to approach this kind of problem is to take one structure and in your mind, hold it by one group. Then rotate the other groups until at least one group is in the same place as it is in the other structure. (Until you can do this easily in your mind, practice with models.) By a series of rotations like this you will be able to convert the structure you are manipulating into one that is either identical with, or the mirror image of the other. For example, take **B**, hold it by the Cl atom and then rotate the other groups about the C*—Cl bond until the bromine is at the bottom (as it is in **A**). Then hold it by the Br and rotate the other groups about the C*—Br bond. This will make **B** identical with **A**.

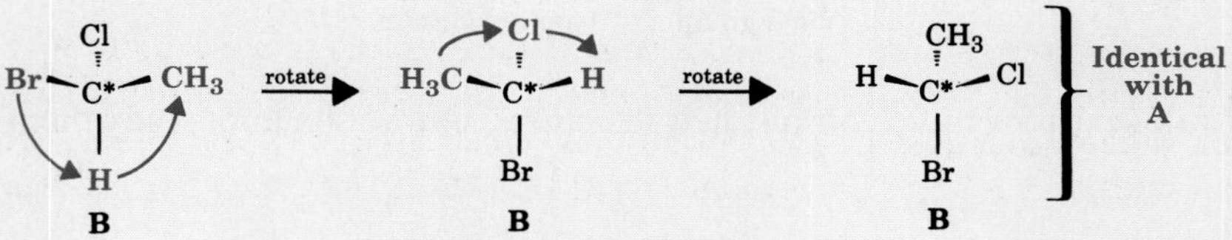

$$Br\!\diagdown\!\underset{\displaystyle H}{\overset{\displaystyle Cl}{C*}}\!\diagup\!CH_3 \quad \xrightarrow{\text{rotate}} \quad H_3C\!\diagdown\!\underset{\displaystyle Br}{\overset{\displaystyle Cl}{C*}}\!\diagup\!H \quad \xrightarrow{\text{rotate}} \quad H\!\diagdown\!\underset{\displaystyle Br}{\overset{\displaystyle CH_3}{C*}}\!\diagup\!Cl$$
$$\textbf{B} \qquad\qquad\qquad\qquad \textbf{B} \qquad\qquad\qquad\qquad \textbf{B}$$

Identical with **A**

    Another approach is to recognize that exchanging two groups at the stereocenter *inverts the configuration of* that carbon atom and converts a structure *with only one stereocenter* into its enantiomer; a second exchange recreates the original molecule. So we proceed this way, keeping track of how many exchanges are required to convert **B** into **A**. In this instance we find that two exchanges are required, and, again, we conclude that **A** and **B** are the same.

A useful check is to name each compound including its $(R-S)$ designation. If the names are the same, then the structures are the same. In this instance both structures are (R)-1-bromo-1-chloroethane.

Problem 5.12

Tell whether the two structures in each pair represent enantiomers or two molecules of the same compound in different orientations.

5.6 PROPERTIES OF ENANTIOMERS: OPTICAL ACTIVITY

The molecules of enantiomers are not superposable one on the other, and on this basis alone, we have concluded that enantiomers are different compounds. How are they different? Do enantiomers resemble constitutional isomers and diastereomers in having different melting and boiling points? The answer is *no*. Enantiomers have *identical* melting and boiling points. Do enantiomers have different indexes of refraction, different solubilities in common solvents, different infrared spectra, and different rates of reaction with ordinary reagents? The answer to each of these questions is also no.

Many of these properties (e. g., boiling points, melting points, and solubilities) are dependent on the magnitude of the intermolecular forces operating between the molecules (Section 2.16), and for molecules that are mirror images of each other these forces will be identical.

CHAPTER 5. STEREOCHEMISTRY: CHIRAL MOLECULES

TABLE 5.1   Physical properties of (*R*)- and (*S*)-2-butanol

PHYSICAL PROPERTY	(*R*)-2-BUTANOL	(*S*)-2-BUTANOL
Boiling point (1 atm)	99.5 °C	99.5 °C
Density (g mL^{-1} at 20 °C)	0.808	0.808
Index of refraction (20 °C)	1.397	1.397

We can see examples if we examine Table 5.1 where some of the physical properties of the 2-butanol enantiomers are listed.

Enantiomers show different behavior only when they interact with other chiral substances. Enantiomers show different rates of reaction toward other chiral molecules — that is, toward reagents that consist of a single enantiomer or an excess of a single enantiomer. Enantiomers also show different solubilities in solvents that consist of a single enantiomer or an excess of a single enantiomer.

One easily observable way in which enantiomers differ is in *their behavior toward plane-polarized light.* When a beam of plane-polarized light passes through an enantiomer, the plane of polarization **rotates.** Moreover, separate enantiomers rotate the plane of plane-polarized light equal amounts *but in opposite directions.* Because of their effect on plane-polarized light, separate enantiomers are said to be **optically active compounds.**

In order to understand this behavior of enantiomers we need to understand the nature of plane-polarized light. We also need to understand how an instrument called a **polarimeter** operates.

5.6A PLANE-POLARIZED LIGHT

Light is an electromagnetic phenomenon. A beam of light consists of two mutually perpendicular oscillating fields: an oscillating electric field and an oscillating magnetic field (Fig. 5.8).

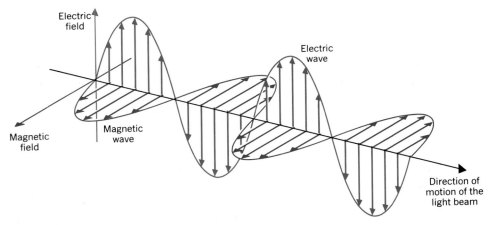

FIGURE 5.8 The oscillating electric and magnetic fields of a beam of ordinary light in one plane. The waves depicted here occur in all possible planes in ordinary light.

5.6 PROPERTIES OF ENANTIOMERS: OPTICAL ACTIVITY

If we were to view a beam of ordinary light from one end, and if we could actually see the planes in which the electrical oscillations were occurring, we would find that oscillations of the electric field were occurring in all possible planes perpendicular to the direction of propagation (Fig. 5.9). (The same would be true of the magnetic field.)

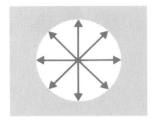

FIGURE 5.9 Oscillation of the electrical field of ordinary light occurs in all possible planes perpendicular to the direction of propagation.

When ordinary light is passed through a polarizer, the polarizer interacts with the electrical field so that the electrical field of the light that emerges from the polarizer (and the magnetic field perpendicular to it) is oscillating only in one plane. Such light is called plane-polarized light (Fig. 5.10).

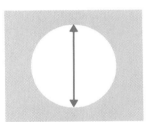

FIGURE 5.10 The plane of oscillation of the electrical field of plane-polarized light. In this example the plane of polarization is vertical.

The lenses of Polaroid sunglasses have this effect. You can demonstrate for yourself that this is true with two pairs of Polaroid sunglasses. If two lenses are placed one on top of the other so that the axes of polarization coincide, then light passes through both normally. Then if one lens is rotated 90° with respect to the other, no light passes through.

5.6B THE POLARIMETER

The device that is used for measuring the effect of plane-polarized light on optically active compounds is a polarimeter. A sketch of a polarimeter is shown in Fig. 5.11. The principal working parts of a polarimeter are (1) a light source (usually a sodium lamp), (2) a polarizer, (3) a tube for holding the optically active substance (or solution) in the light beam, (4) an analyzer, and (5) a scale for measuring the number of degrees that the plane of polarized light has been rotated.

CHAPTER 5. STEREOCHEMISTRY: CHIRAL MOLECULES

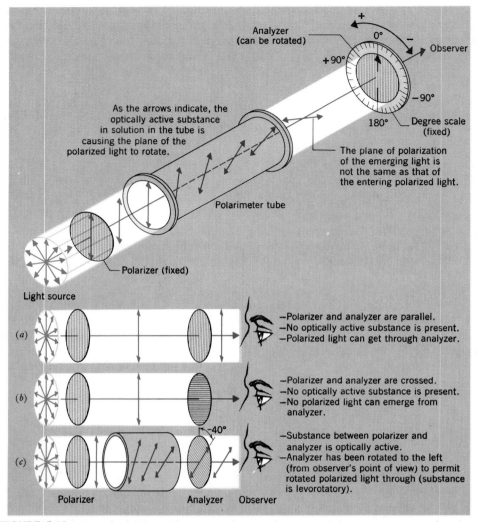

FIGURE 5.11 The principal working parts of a polarimeter and the measurement of optical rotation. (From John R. Holum, *Organic Chemistry: A Brief Course,* Wiley, New York, 1975, p. 316.)

The analyzer of a polarimeter (Fig. 5.11) is nothing more than another polarizer. If the tube of the polarimeter is empty, or if an optically *inactive* substance is present, the axes of the plane-polarized light and the analyzer will be exactly parallel when the instrument reads 0°, and the observer will detect the maximum amount of light passing through. If, by contrast, the tube contains an optically active substance, a solution of one enantiomer, for example, the plane of polarization of the light will be rotated as it passes through the tube. In order to detect the maximum brightness of light the observer will have to rotate the axis of the analyzer in either a clockwise or counterclockwise direction. If the analyzer is rotated in a clockwise direction, the rotation, α (measured in degrees), is said to be positive (+). If the rotation is counterclockwise, the rotation is said to be negative (−). A substance that rotates plane-polarized light in the clockwise direction is also said to be **dextrorotatory,** and one that rotates plane-polarized light in a counterclockwise direction is said to be **levorotatory** (from the Latin: *dexter,* right and *laevus,* left).

5.6C SPECIFIC ROTATION

The number of degrees that the plane of polarization is rotated as the light passes through a solution of an enantiomer depends on the number of chiral molecules that it encounters. This, of course, depends on the length of the tube and the concentration of the enantiomer. In order to place measured rotations on a standard basis, chemists calculate a quantity called the **specific rotation, $[\alpha]$,** by the following equation:

$$[\alpha] = \frac{\alpha}{c \cdot l}$$

where $[\alpha]$ = the specific rotation

α = the observed rotation

c = the concentration of the solution in grams per milliliter of solution (or density in g mL^{-1} for neat liquids)

l = the length of the tube in decimeters (1 dm = 10 cm)

The specific rotation also depends on the temperature and the wavelength of light that is employed. Specific rotations are reported so as to incorporate these quantities as well. A specific rotation might be given as follows:

$$[\alpha]_D^{25} = +3.12°$$

This means that, the D line of a sodium lamp ($\lambda = 599.6$ nm) was used for the light, that a temperature of 25 °C was maintained, and that a sample containing 1.00 g mL^{-1} of the optically active substance, in a 1-dm tube, produced a rotation of 3.12° in a clockwise direction.*

The specific rotations of (R)-2-butanol and (S)-2-butanol are given here.

(R)-2-Butanol
$[\alpha]_D^{25} = -13.52°$

(S)-2-Butanol
$[\alpha]_D^{25} = +13.52°$

The direction of rotation of plane-polarized light is often incorporated into the names of optically active compounds. The following two sets of enantiomers show how this is done.

---

* The magnitude of rotation is dependent on the solvent when solutions are measured. This is the reason the solvent is specified when a rotation is reported in the chemical literature.

$$HOCH_2 - C \langle \begin{array}{c} CH_3 \\ H \end{array}$$

(R)-(+)-2-Methyl-1-butanol
$[\alpha]_D^{25} = +5.756°$

$$H - C \langle \begin{array}{c} CH_3 \\ CH_2OH \end{array}$$

(S)-(−)-2-Methyl-1-butanol
$[\alpha]_D^{25} = +5.756°$

$$ClCH_2 - C \langle \begin{array}{c} CH_3 \\ H \end{array}$$

(R)-(−)-1-Chloro-2-methylbutane
$[\alpha]_D^{25} = -1.64°$

$$H - C \langle \begin{array}{c} CH_3 \\ CH_2Cl \end{array}$$

(S)-(+)-1-Chloro-2-methylbutane
$[\alpha]_D^{25} = +1.64°$

The previous compounds also illustrate an important principle: *No obvious correlation exists between the configurations of enantiomers and the direction [(+) or (−)] in which they rotate plane-polarized light.*

(R)-(+)-2-Methyl-1-butanol and (R)-(−)-1-chloro-2-methylbutane have the same *configuration,* that is, they have the same general arrangement of their atoms in space. They have, however, an opposite effect on the direction of rotation of the plane of plane-polarized light.

$$HOCH_2 - C \langle \begin{array}{c} CH_3 \\ H \end{array} \qquad \text{Same configuration} \qquad ClCH_2 - C \langle \begin{array}{c} CH_3 \\ H \end{array}$$

(R)-(+)-2-Methyl-1-butanol (R)-(−)-1-Chloro-2-methylbutane

These same compounds also illustrate a second important principle: *No necessary correlation exists between the (R) and (S) designation and the direction of rotation of plane-polarized light.* (R)-2-Methyl-1-butanol is dextrorotatory (+), and (R)-1-chloro-2-methylbutane is levorotatory (−).

A method based on the measurement of optical rotation measured at many different wavelengths, called optical rotatory dispersion, has been used to correlate configurations of chiral molecules. A discussion of the technique of optical rotatory dispersion, however, is beyond the scope of this text.

5.7 THE ORIGIN OF OPTICAL ACTIVITY

It is not possible to give a complete, condensed account of the origin of the optical activity observed for separate enantiomers. An insight into the source of this phenomenon can be obtained, however, by comparing what occurs when a beam of plane-polarized light passes through a solution of *achiral* molecules with what occurs when a beam of plane-polarized light passes through a solution of *chiral* molecules.

Almost all *individual* molecules, whether chiral or achiral, are theoretically capable of producing a slight rotation of the plane of plane-polarized light. The direction and magnitude of the rotation produced by an individual molecule depends, in part, on its orientation at the precise moment that it encounters the beam. In a solution, of course, billions of molecules are in the path of the light beam and at any given moment these molecules will be present in all possible orientations. If the beam of plane-polarized light passes through a solution of the achiral compound 2-propanol, for example, it should encounter at least two molecules in the exact orientations shown in Fig. 5.12. The effect of the first encounter might be to produce a very slight rotation of the plane of polarization to the right. Before the beam emerges from the solution, however, it should encounter at least one molecule of 2-propanol that is in exactly the mirror-image orientation of the first. The effect of this second encounter will be to produce an equal and opposite rotation of the plane: a rotation that exactly cancels the first rotation. The beam, therefore, emerges with no net rotation.

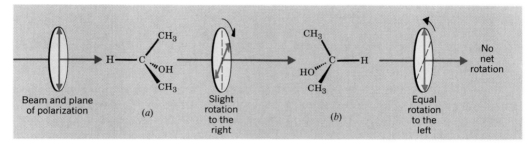

FIGURE 5.12 A beam of plane-polarized light encountering a molecule of 2-propanol (an achiral molecule) in orientation (*a*) and then a second molecule in the mirror-image orientation (*b*). The beam emerges from these two encounters with no net rotation of its plane of polarization.

What we have just described for the two encounters shown in Fig. 5.12 can be said of all possible encounters of the beam with molecules of 2-propanol. Because so many molecules are present, it is statistically certain that *for each encounter with a particular orientation there will be an encounter with a molecule that is in a mirror-image orientation.* The result of all of these encounters will be such that all of the rotations produced by individual molecules will be canceled and 2-propanol will be found to be **optically inactive.**

What, then, is the situation when a beam of plane-polarized light passes through a solution of one enantiomer of a chiral compound? We can answer this question by considering what might occur when plane-polarized light passes through a solution of pure (*R*)-2-butanol. Figure 5.13 illustrates one possible encounter of a beam of plane-polarized light with a molecule of (*R*)-2-butanol.

When a beam of plane-polarized light passes through a solution of (*R*)-2-butanol, *no molecule is present that can ever be exactly oriented as a mirror image of any given orientation of an (R)-2-butanol molecule.* The only molecules that could do this would be molecules of (*S*)-2-butanol, and they are not present. Exact cancellation of the rotations produced by all of the encounters of the beam with random orientations of (*R*)-2-butanol does not happen and, as a result, a net rotation of the plane of polarization is observed. (*R*)-2-Butanol is found to be *optically active.*

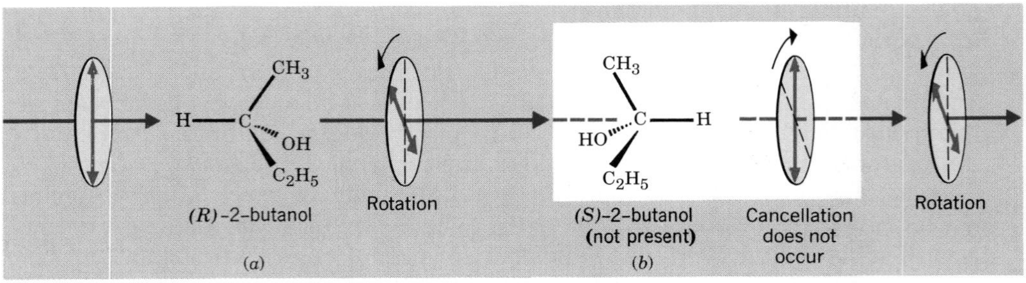

FIGURE 5.13 (a) A beam of plane-polarized light encounters a molecule of (R)-2-butanol (a chiral molecule) in a particular orientation. This encounter produces a slight rotation of the plane of polarization. (b) Exact cancellation of this rotation requires that a second molecule be oriented as an exact mirror image. This cancellation does not occur because the only molecule that could ever be oriented as an exact mirror image at the first encounter is a molecule of (S)-2-butanol, which is not present. As a result, a net rotation of the plane of polarization occurs.

5.7A RACEMIC FORMS

The net rotation of the plane of polarization that we observe for a solution consisting of molecules of (R)-2-butanol alone would not be observed if we passed the beam through a solution that contained equimolar amounts of (R)-2-butanol and (S)-2-butanol. In the latter instance, molecules of (S)-2-butanol would be present in a quantity equal to those of (R)-2-butanol and for every possible orientation of one enantiomer, a molecule of the other enantiomer would be in a mirror-image orientation. Exact cancellations of all rotations would occur, and the solution of the equimolar mixture of enantiomers would be *optically inactive.*

An equimolar mixture of two enantiomers is called a **racemic form** (either a **racemate** or a **racemic mixture**). A racemic form shows no rotation of plane-polarized light; as such, it is often designated as being (±). A racemic form of (R)-(−)-2-butanol and (S)-(+)-2-butanol might be indicated as

$$(\pm)\text{-2-Butanol} \qquad \text{or as} \qquad (\pm)\text{-CH}_3\text{CH}_2\text{CHOHCH}_3$$

5.7B ENANTIOMERIC PURITY, OPTICAL PURITY, AND ENANTIOMERIC EXCESS

A sample of an optically active substance that consists of a single enantiomer is said to be **enantiomerically pure.** An enantiomerically pure sample of (S)-(+)-2-butanol shows a specific rotation of +13.52° ($[\alpha]_D^{25} = +13.52°$). On the other hand, a sample of (S)-(+)-2-butanol that contains less than an equimolar amount of (R)-(−)-2-butanol will show a specific rotation that is less than +13.52° but greater than 0°. Such a sample is said to have an *enantiomeric purity* less than 100%. The **percent enantiomeric purity** is defined as follows:

Percent enantiomeric purity

$$= \frac{\text{moles of one enantiomer} - \text{moles of other enantiomer}}{\text{moles of both enantiomers}} \times 100$$

The percent enantiomeric purity is also often called the **enantiomeric excess (ee)** and it is equal to *the percent optical purity.* The percent optical purity is defined in terms of specific rotations:

$$\text{Percent optical purity*} = \frac{\text{observed specific rotation}}{\text{specific rotation of the pure enantiomer}} \times 100$$

Let us suppose, for example, that the sample showed a specific rotation of +6.76°. We would then say that the optical purity of the (S)-(+)-2-butanol is 50%.

$$\text{Optical purity} = \frac{+6.76°}{+13.52°} \times 100 = 50\%$$

When we say the optical purity of this mixture is 50%, we also mean that 50% of the mixture consists of the racemic form, (±)-2-butanol, and the other 50% consists of the enantiomer, (S)-(+)-2-butanol. Therefore, we can say that the enantiomeric excess of the mixture is 50%.

Problem 5.13

What relative molar proportions of (S)-(+)-2-butanol and (R)-(−)-2-butanol would give a specific rotation, $[\alpha]_D^{25}$, equal to +6.76°?

5.8 THE SYNTHESIS OF ENANTIOMERS

Many times in the course of working in the organic laboratory a reaction carried out with reactants whose molecules are achiral results in the formation of products whose molecules are chiral. In the absence of any chiral influence (from the solvent or a catalyst), the outcome of such a reaction is the formation of a racemic form. The reason: The chiral molecules of the product are obtained as a 50:50 mixture of enantiomers.

An example is the synthesis of 2-butanol by the nickel-catalyzed hydrogenation of 2-butanone. In this reaction the hydrogen molecule adds across the carbon–oxygen double bond in much the same way that it adds to a carbon–carbon double bond (Section 4.15A).

$$\underset{\substack{\text{2-Butanone} \\ \text{(achiral} \\ \text{molecules)}}}{\text{CH}_3\text{CH}_2\overset{\displaystyle O}{\underset{\displaystyle \|}{\text{C}}}\text{CH}_3} + \underset{\substack{\text{Hydrogen} \\ \text{(achiral} \\ \text{molecules)}}}{\text{H—H}} \xrightarrow{\text{Ni}} \underset{\substack{(\pm)\text{-2-Butanol} \\ \text{[chiral molecules} \\ \text{but 50:50 mixture } (R) \text{ and } (S)]}}{(\pm)\ \text{CH}_3\text{CH}_2\overset{*}{\underset{\displaystyle \text{OH}}{\text{CH}}}\text{CH}_3}$$

Molecules of neither reactant (2-butanone nor hydrogen) are chiral. The molecules of the product (2-butanol) are chiral. The product, however, is obtained as a racemic form because the two enantiomers, (R)-(−)-2-butanol and (S)-(+)-2-butanol, are obtained in equal amounts.

---

* The term *optical purity* is applied to a single enantiomer or to mixtures of enantiomers only. It should not be applied to mixtures in which some other compound is present.

This is not the result if reactions like this are carried out in the presence of a chiral influence such as an optically active solvent or, as we shall see later, an enzyme. The nickel catalyst used in this reaction does not exert a chiral influence.

Figure 5.14 shows why a racemic form of 2-butanol is obtained. Hydrogen, adsorbed on the surface of the nickel catalyst, adds with equal facility at either face of 2-butanone. Reaction at one face produces one enantiomer; reaction at the other face produces the other enantiomer, and the two reactions occur at the same rate.

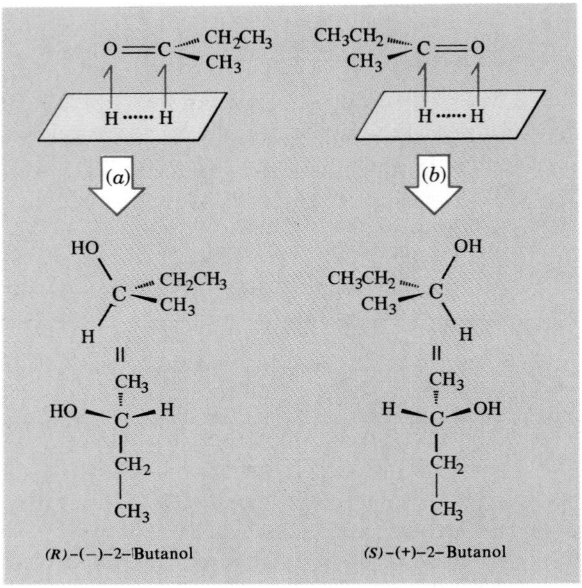

FIGURE 5.14 The reaction of 2-butanone with hydrogen in the presence of a nickel catalyst. The reaction rate by path (a) is equal to that by path (b). (R)-(−)-2-butanol and (S)-(+)-2-butanol are produced in equal amounts, as a racemic form.

5.9 MOLECULES WITH MORE THAN ONE STEREOCENTER

Thus far all of the chiral molecules that we have considered have contained only one stereocenter. Many organic molecules, especially those important in biology, contain more than one stereocenter. Cholesterol (Section 23.4B), for example, contains eight stereocenters. (Can you locate them?) We can begin, however, with simpler molecules. Let us consider 2,3-dibromopentane shown here—a structure that has two stereocenters.

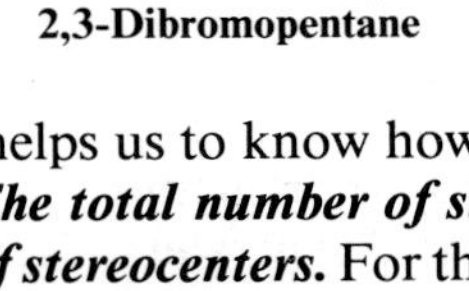

$$CH_3\overset{*}{C}H\overset{*}{C}HCH_2CH_3$$
$$\underset{Br\ \ \ Br}{|\ \ \ |}$$

2,3-Dibromopentane

There is a useful rule that helps us to know how many stereoisomers to expect from structures like this one. **The total number of stereoisomers will not exceed 2^n where n is equal to the number of stereocenters.** For this structural formula we should not expect more than four stereoisomers ($2^2 = 4$).

5.9 MOLECULES WITH MORE THAN ONE STEREOCENTER

Our next task is to write three-dimensional formulas for the stereoisomers of the compound. We begin by writing a three-dimensional formula for one stereoisomer and then by writing the formula for *its* mirror image.

$$
\begin{array}{cc}
\text{CH}_3 & \text{CH}_3 \\
\text{H} \diagdown \!\! \text{C} \!\! \diagup \text{Br} \quad & \text{Br} \diagdown \!\! \text{C} \!\! \diagup \text{H} \\
\mid & \mid \\
\text{H} \diagup \!\! \text{C} \!\! \diagdown \text{Br} \quad & \text{Br} \diagup \!\! \text{C} \!\! \diagdown \text{H} \\
\text{C}_2\text{H}_5 & \text{C}_2\text{H}_5 \\
\mathbf{1} & \mathbf{2}
\end{array}
$$

It is helpful to follow certain conventions when we write these three-dimensional formulas. For example, we usually write our structures in eclipsed conformations. When we do this we do not mean to imply that eclipsed conformations are the most stable ones — they most certainly are not. We write eclipsed conformations because, as we shall see later, they make it easy for us to recognize planes of symmetry when they are present. We also write the longest carbon chain in a generally vertical orientation on the page; this makes the structures that we write directly comparable. As we do these things, however, *we must remember that molecules can rotate in their entirety* and that *at normal temperatures rotations about all single bonds are also possible.* If rotations of the structure itself or rotations of groups joined by single bonds make one structure superposable with another, then *the structures do not represent different compounds;* instead, they represent different orientations or different conformations of two molecules of the same compound.

Since structures **1** and **2** are not superposable, they represent different compounds. Since structures **1** and **2** differ *only* in the arrangement of their atoms in space, they represent stereoisomers. Structures **1** and **2** are also mirror images of each other, thus **1** and **2** represent enantiomers.

Structures **1** and **2** are not the only possible structures, however. We find that we can write a structure **3** that is different from either **1** or **2**, and we can write a structure **4** that is a nonsuperposable mirror image of structure **3**.

$$
\begin{array}{cc}
\text{CH}_3 & \text{CH}_3 \\
\text{Br} \diagdown \!\! \text{C} \!\! \diagup \text{H} \quad & \text{H} \diagdown \!\! \text{C} \!\! \diagup \text{Br} \\
\mid & \mid \\
\text{H} \diagup \!\! \text{C} \!\! \diagdown \text{Br} \quad & \text{Br} \diagup \!\! \text{C} \!\! \diagdown \text{H} \\
\text{C}_2\text{H}_5 & \text{C}_2\text{H}_5 \\
\mathbf{3} & \mathbf{4}
\end{array}
$$

Structures **3** and **4** correspond to another pair of enantiomers. Structures **1 – 4** are all different, so there are, in total, four stereoisomers of 2,3-dibromopentane. At this point you should convince yourself that there are no other stereoisomers by writing other structural formulas. You will find that rotation of the single bonds (or of the entire structure) of any other arrangement of the atoms will cause the structure to become superposable with one of the structures that we have written here. Better yet, using different-colored balls, make molecular models as you work this out.

The compounds represented by structures **1 – 4** are all optically active compounds. Any one of them, if placed separately in a polarimeter, would show optical activity.

The compounds represented by structures **1** and **2** are enantiomers. The compounds represented by structures **3** and **4** are also enantiomers. But what is the isomeric relation between the compounds represented by **1** and **3**?

We can answer this question by observing that **1** and **3** *are stereoisomers* and that they *are not mirror images of each other*. They are, therefore, *diastereomers*. **Diastereomers have different physical properties**—different melting points and boiling points, different solubilities, and so forth. In this respect these diastereomers are just like diastereomeric alkenes such as *cis-* and *trans-*2-butene.

Problem 5.14 ———————————————————————

(a) What is the stereoisomeric relation between compounds **2** and **3**? (b) Between **1** and **4**? (c) Between **2** and **4**? (d) Make a table showing all of the stereoisomeric relations between all possible pairs of compounds **1–4**. (e) Would compounds **1** and **2** have the same boiling point? (f) Would compounds **1** and **3**?

5.9A MESO COMPOUNDS

A structure with two stereocenters will not always have four possible stereoisomers. Sometimes there are only *three*. This happens because some molecules with stereocenters are, overall, *achiral*.

To understand this, let us write stereochemical formulas for 2,3-dibromobutane shown here.

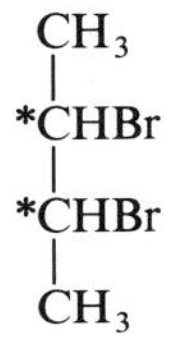

$$CH_3$$
$$|$$
$$*CHBr$$
$$|$$
$$*CHBr$$
$$|$$
$$CH_3$$

2,3-Dibromobutane

We begin in the same way as we did before. We write the formula for one stereoisomer and for its mirror image.

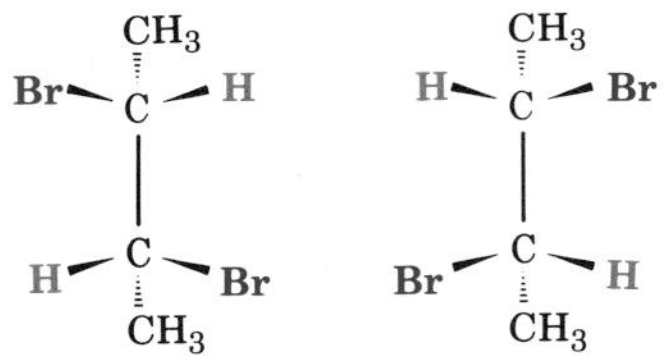

A   **B**

Structures **A** and **B** are nonsuperposable and represent a pair of enantiomers.

When we write structure **C** (see the following structure) and its mirror image **D**, however, the situation is different. *The two structures are superposable.* This means that **C** and **D** do not represent a pair of enantiomers. Formulas **C** and **D** represent two different orientations of the same compound.

5.9 MOLECULES WITH MORE THAN ONE STEREOCENTER

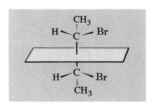

The molecule represented by structure **C** (or **D**) is not chiral even though it contains tetrahedral atoms with four different attached groups. Such molecules are called *meso compounds.* Meso compounds, *because they are achiral,* are optically inactive.

The ultimate test for molecular chirality is to construct a model (or write the structure) of the molecule and then test whether or not the model (or structure) is superposable on its mirror image. If it is, the molecule is achiral: If it *is not,* the molecule is chiral.

We have already carried out this test with structure **C** and found that it is achiral. We can also demonstrate that **C** is achiral in another way. Figure 5.15 shows that structure **C** *has a plane of symmetry* (Section 5.4).

FIGURE 5.15 The plane of symmetry of *meso*-2,3-dibromobutane. This plane divides the molecule into halves that are mirror images of each other.

Problem 5.15

Which of the following would be optically active?

(a) **A** alone   (c) **C** alone

(b) **B** alone   (d) An equimolar mixture of **A** and **B**

Problem 5.16

Shown here are formulas for compounds **A**, **B**, or **C** written in noneclipsed conformations. In each instance tell which compound (**A**, **B**, or **C**) each formula represents.

CH$_3$
Br — C — H
        |
    H — C — Br
  H$_3$C
(1)

CH$_3$
Br — C — H
        |
 H$_3$C — C — Br
        H
(2)

H$_3$C
H — C — Br
        |
 Br — C — CH$_3$
        H
(3)

Problem 5.17

Write three-dimensional formulas for all of the stereoisomers of each of the following compounds.

(a) CH$_3$CHClCHClCH$_3$

(b) CH$_3$CHBrCHClCH$_3$

(c) CH$_3$CHBrCHBrCH$_2$Br

(d) CH$_2$BrCHBrCHBrCH$_2$Br

(e) CH$_3$CHClCHClCHClCH$_3$

(f) In answers to parts (a)–(e) label pairs of enantiomers and meso compounds.

5.10 NAMING COMPOUNDS WITH MORE THAN ONE STEREOCENTER

If a compound has more than one tetrahedral stereocenter, we analyze each center separately and decide whether it is (R) or (S). Then, using numbers, we tell which designation refers to which carbon atom.

Consider the stereoisomer **A** of 2,3-dibromobutane.

$_1$CH$_3$
Br — $_2$C — H
        |
   H — $_3$C — Br
      $_4$CH$_3$

A
2,3-Dibromobutane

When this formula is rotated so that the group of lowest priority attached to C-2 is directed away from the viewer it resembles the following.

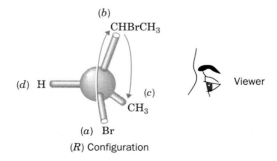

(b) CHBrCH$_3$

(d) H

(c) CH$_3$

(a) Br

(R) Configuration

Viewer

The order of progression from the group of highest priority to that of next highest priority (from —Br, to —CHBrCH$_3$, to —CH$_3$) is clockwise. So C-2 has the (R) configuration.

When we repeat this procedure with C-3 we find that C-3 also has the (R) configuration.

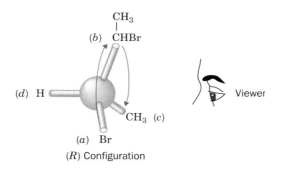

(R) Configuration

Compound **A**, therefore, is $(2R, 3R)$-2,3-dibromobutane.

Problem 5.18

Give names that include (R) and (S) designations for compounds **B** and **C** in Section 5.9.

Problem 5.19

Give names that include (R) and (S) designations for your answers to Problem 5.17, parts (a) and (b).

5.11 FISCHER PROJECTION FORMULAS

In writing structures for chiral molecules thus far, we have used only three-dimensional formulas, and we shall continue to do so until we study carbohydrates in Chapter 22. The reason: Three-dimensional formulas are unambiguous and can be manipulated on paper in any way that we wish, as long as we do not break bonds. Their use, moreover, teaches us to see molecules (in our mind's eye) in three dimensions, and this ability will serve us well.

Chemists sometimes represent structures for chiral molecules with *two-dimensional formulas* called **Fischer projection formulas.** These two-dimensional formulas are especially useful for compounds with several stereocenters because they save space and are easy to write. Their use, however, requires a rigid adherence to certain conventions. ***Used carelessly, these projection formulas can easily lead to incorrect conclusions.***

The Fischer projection formula for $(2R, 3R)$-2,3-dibromobutane is written as follows:

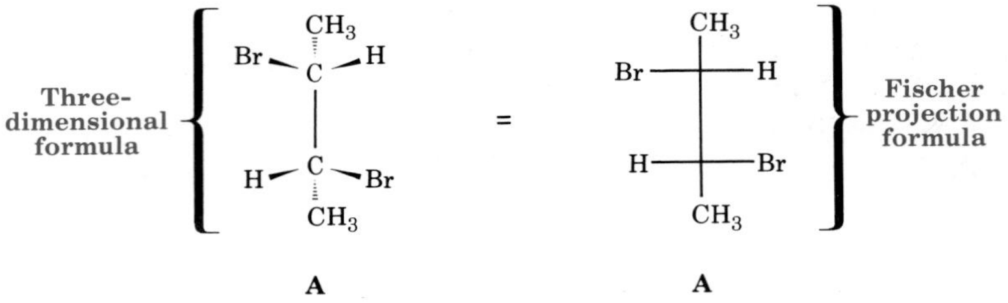
Three-dimensional formula
CH3
Br
C
H
H
C
Br
CH3
A
=
CH3
Br
H
H
Br
CH3
A
Fischer projection formula

By convention, Fischer projections are written with the main carbon chain extending from top to bottom and with all groups eclipsed. ***Vertical lines represent bonds that project behind the plane of the paper (or that lie in it). Horizontal lines represent bonds that project out of the plane of the paper.*** The intersection of vertical and horizontal lines represents a carbon atom, usually one that is a stereocenter.

In using Fischer projections to test the superposability for two structures, we are permitted to rotate them in the plane of the paper by 180° *but by no other angle.* We must always keep them in the plane of the paper, and ***we are not allowed to flip them over.***

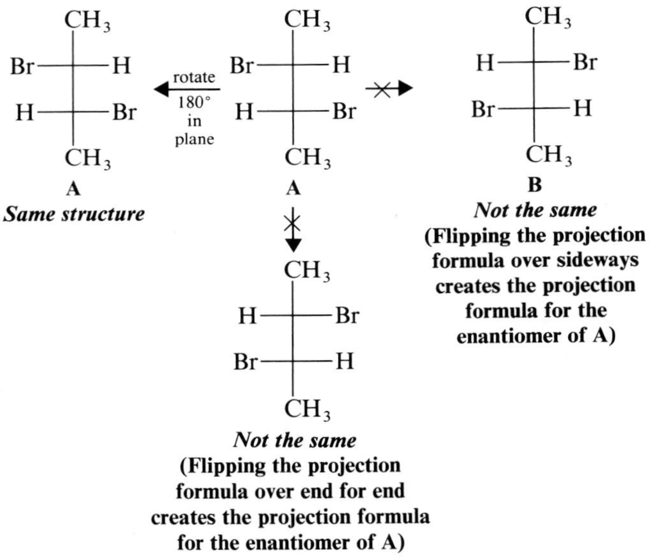
CH3
Br
H
H
Br
CH3
A
Same structure
rotate
180°
in
plane
CH3
Br
H
H
Br
CH3
A
CH3
H
Br
Br
H
CH3
B
Not the same
(Flipping the projection formula over sideways creates the projection formula for the enantiomer of A)
CH3
H
Br
Br
H
CH3
Not the same
(Flipping the projection formula over end for end creates the projection formula for the enantiomer of A)

Your instructor will advise you about the use you are to make of Fischer projections.

5.12 STEREOISOMERISM OF CYCLIC COMPOUNDS

Because the cyclopentane ring is essentially planar, cyclopentane derivatives offer a convenient starting point for a discussion of the stereoisomerism of cyclic compounds. For example, 1,2-dimethylcyclopentane has two stereocenters and exists in three stereoisomeric forms **5**, **6**, and **7**.

5.12 STEREOISOMERISM OF CYCLIC COMPOUNDS

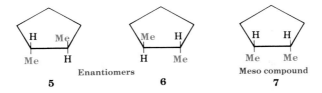

	Enantiomers	
H Me	Me H	H H
Me H	H Me	Me Me
		Meso compound
5	**6**	**7**

The trans compound exists as a pair of enantiomers **5** and **6**. *cis*-1,2-Dimethyl-cyclopentane is a meso compound. It has a plane of symmetry that is perpendicular to the plane of the ring.

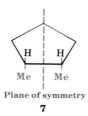

H : H
Me : Me

Plane of symmetry

7

Problem 5.20

(a) Is the *trans*-1,2-dimethylcyclopentane (**5**) superposable on its mirror image (i.e., on compound **6**)? (b) Is the *cis*-1,2-dimethylcyclopentane (**7**) superposable on its mirror image? (c) Is the *cis*-1,2-dimethylcyclopentane a chiral molecule? (d) Would *cis*-1,2-dimethylcyclopentane show optical activity? (e) What is the stereoisomeric relation between **5** and **7**? (f) Between **6** and **7**?

Problem 5.21

Write structural formulas for all of the stereoisomers of 1,3-dimethylcyclopentane. Label pairs of enantiomers and meso compounds if they exist.

5.12A CYCLOHEXANE DERIVATIVES

1,4-Dimethylcyclohexanes. If we examine a formula of 1,4-dimethylcyclohexane we find that it does not contain any tetrahedral atoms with four different groups. However, we learned in Section 4.12 that 1,4-dimethylcyclohexane exists as cis–trans isomers. The cis and trans forms (Fig. 5.16) are *diastereomers*. Neither compound is chiral and, therefore, neither is optically active. Notice that both the cis and trans forms of 1,4-dimethylcyclohexane have a plane of symmetry.

1,3-Dimethylcyclohexanes. A 1,3-dimethylcyclohexane has two stereocenters; we can, therefore, expect as many as four stereoisomers ($2^2 = 4$). In reality there are only three. *cis*-1,3-Dimethylcyclohexane has a plane of symmetry (Fig. 5.17) and is achiral. *trans*-1,3-Dimethylcyclohexane does not have a plane of symmetry and exists as a pair of enantiomers (Fig. 5.18). You may want to make models of the *trans*-1,3-dimethylcyclohexane enantiomers. Having done so, convince yourself that

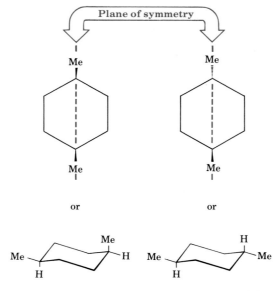

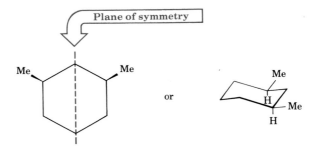

FIGURE 5.16 The cis and trans forms of 1,4-dimethylcyclohexane are diastereomers of each other. Both compounds are achiral.

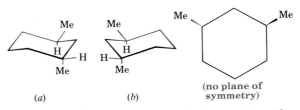

FIGURE 5.17 *cis*-1,3-Dimethylcyclohexane has a plane of symmetry and is, therefore, achiral.

FIGURE 5.18 *trans*-1,3-Dimethylcyclohexane does not have a plane of symmetry and exists as a pair of enantiomers. The two structures (*a*) and (*b*) shown here are not superposable as they stand, and flipping the ring of either structure does not make it superposable on the other.

5.12 STEREOISOMERISM OF CYCLIC COMPOUNDS

they cannot be superposed as they stand, and that they cannot be superposed after one enantiomer has undergone a ring flip.

1,2-Dimethylcyclohexanes. A 1,2-dimethylcyclohexane also has two stereocenters and again we might expect as many as four stereoisomers. However, again we find that there are only three. *trans*-1,2-Dimethylcyclohexane (Fig. 5.19) exists as a pair of enantiomers. Its molecules do not have a plane of symmetry.

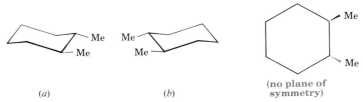

(a)   (b)   (no plane of symmetry)

FIGURE 5.19 *trans*-1,2-Dimethylcyclohexane has no plane of symmetry and exists as a pair of enantiomers (a) and (b). [Notice that we have written the most stable conformations for (a) and (b). A ring flip of either (a) or (b) would cause both methyl groups to become axial.]

With *cis*-1,2-dimethylcyclohexane, the situation is somewhat more complex. If we consider the two conformational structures (a) and (b) shown in Fig. 5.20 we find that these two mirror-image structures are not superposable one on the other, *but they are interconvertible by a ring flip.* (You should prove this to yourself with models.) Therefore, while the two structures represent enantiomers *they cannot be separated* because at temperatures even considerably below room temperature they interconvert rapidly. They simply represent *different conformations of the same compound.* If we consider the structure for *cis*-1,2-dimethylcyclohexane with a planar ring shown in Fig. 5.20 (and a time average of the ring of the two chair conformations is planar) we find that the structure has a plane of symmetry. On this basis we would not expect to find a pair of separable enantiomers.

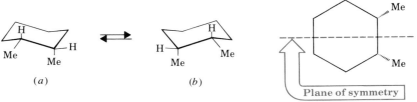

(a)   (b)   Plane of symmetry

FIGURE 5.20 *cis*-1,2-Dimethylcyclohexane exists as two rapidly interconvertible chair conformations (a) and (b). A planar representation of the ring has a plane of symmetry.

Problem 5.22

Write formulas for all of the isomers of each of the following. Designate pairs of enantiomers and achiral compounds where they exist.

(a) 1-Bromo-2-chlorocyclohexane   (c) 1-Bromo-4-chlorocyclohexane

(b) 1-Bromo-3-chlorocyclohexane

Problem 5.23

Give the $(R-S)$ designation for each compound given as an answer to Problem 5.22.

5.13 RELATING CONFIGURATIONS THROUGH REACTIONS IN WHICH NO BONDS TO THE STEREOCENTER ARE BROKEN

If a reaction takes place in a way so that no bonds to the stereocenter are broken, the product will of necessity have the same general configuration of groups around the stereocenter as the reactant. Such a reaction is said **to proceed with retention of configuration.** Consider as an example the reaction that takes place when (S)-$(-)$-2-methyl-1-butanol is heated with concentrated hydrochloric acid.

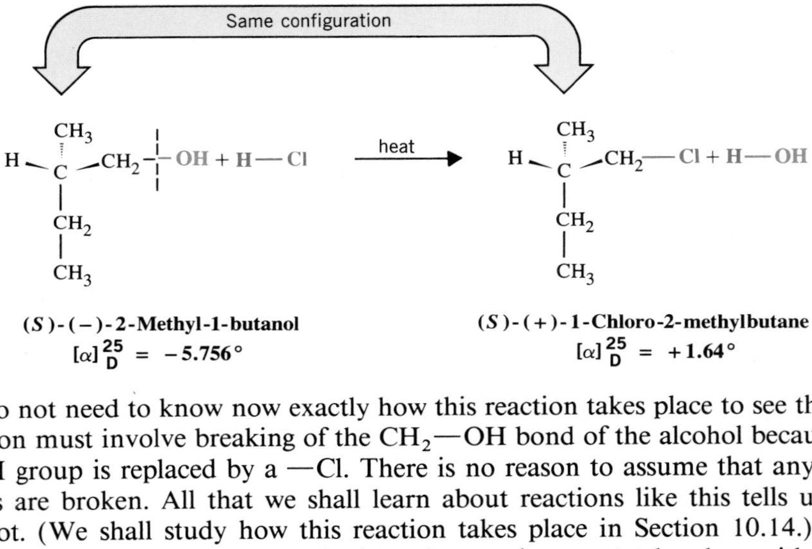

Same configuration

$$H \sim \underset{C}{\overset{CH_3}{|}} \sim CH_2 - OH + H - Cl \xrightarrow{\text{heat}} H \sim \underset{C}{\overset{CH_3}{|}} \sim CH_2 - Cl + H - OH$$

(S)-$(-)$-**2-Methyl-1-butanol**

$[\alpha]_D^{25} = -5.756°$

(S)-$(+)$-**1-Chloro-2-methylbutane**

$[\alpha]_D^{25} = +1.64°$

We do not need to know now exactly how this reaction takes place to see that the reaction must involve breaking of the CH_2—OH bond of the alcohol because the —OH group is replaced by a —Cl. There is no reason to assume that any other bonds are broken. All that we shall learn about reactions like this tells us they are not. (We shall study how this reaction takes place in Section 10.14.) Since no bonds to the stereocenter are broken, the reaction must take place with retention of configuration, and the product of the reaction *must have the same configuration of groups around the stereocenter that the reactant had.* By saying that the two compounds have the same configuration we simply mean that comparable or identical groups in the two compounds occupy the same relative positions in space around the stereocenter. (In this instance the —CH_2OH group and the —CH_2Cl are comparable and they occupy the same relative position in both compounds; all the other groups are identical and they occupy the same positions.)

Notice that in this example while the $(R-S)$ designation *does not change* [both reactant and product are (S)] the direction of optical rotation *does change* [the reactant is $(-)$ and the product is $(+)$]. Neither occurrence is a necessity when a reaction proceeds with retention of configuration. In the next section we shall see examples of reactions in which configurations are retained and where the direction of optical rotation does not change. The following reaction is an example of a reaction that proceeds with retention of configuration but involves a change in $(R-S)$ designation.

$$
\begin{array}{ccc}
\text{CH}_2\text{—Br} & & \text{CH}_2\text{—H} \\
\text{H} \diagdown \underset{\text{C}}{} \diagup \text{OH} & \xrightarrow[\text{retention of configuration}]{\text{Zn, H}^+ \, (-\text{ZnCl}_2)} & \text{H} \diagdown \underset{\text{C}}{} \diagup \text{OH} \\
\text{CH}_2 & & \text{CH}_2 \\
\text{CH}_3 & & \text{CH}_3 \\
\textbf{(R)-1-Bromo-2-butanol} & & \textbf{(S)-2-Butanol}
\end{array}
$$

In this example the $(R-S)$ designation changes because the $-\text{CH}_2\text{Br}$ group of the reactant ($-\text{CH}_2\text{Br}$ has a higher priority than $-\text{CH}_2\text{CH}_3$) changes to a $-\text{CH}_3$ group in the product ($-\text{CH}_3$ has a lower priority than $-\text{CH}_2\text{CH}_3$).

5.13A RELATIVE AND ABSOLUTE CONFIGURATIONS

Reactions in which no bonds to the stereocenter are broken are useful in relating configurations of chiral molecules. That is, they allow us to demonstrate that certain compounds have the same **relative configuration.** In each of the examples that we have just cited, the products of the reactions have the same *relative configurations* as the reactants.

Before 1951 only relative configurations of chiral molecules were known. No one prior to that time had been able to demonstrate with certainty what the actual spatial arrangement of groups was in any chiral molecule. To say this another way, no one had been able to determine the **absolute configuration** of an optically active compound.

Configurations of chiral molecules were related to each other *through reactions of known stereochemistry.* Attempts were also made to relate all configurations back to a single compound that had been chosen arbitrarily to be the standard. This standard compound was glyceraldehyde.

$$
\begin{array}{c}
\text{O} \\
\parallel \\
\text{CH} \\
| \\
\text{*CHOH} \\
| \\
\text{CH}_2\text{OH} \\
\textbf{Glyceraldehyde}
\end{array}
$$

Glyceraldehyde molecules have one tetrahedral stereocenter; therefore, glyceraldehyde exists as a pair of enantiomers.

$$
\begin{array}{ccc}
\text{O} & & \text{O} \\
\parallel & & \parallel \\
\text{C—H} & & \text{C—H} \\
\text{H} \diagdown \underset{\text{C}}{} \diagup \text{OH} & \text{and} & \text{HO} \diagdown \underset{\text{C}}{} \diagup \text{H} \\
\text{CH}_2\text{OH} & & \text{CH}_2\text{OH} \\
\textit{(R)}\text{-Glyceraldehyde} & & \textit{(S)}\text{-Glyceraldehyde}
\end{array}
$$

In the older system for designating configurations (R)-glyceraldehyde was called D-glyceraldehyde and (S)-glyceraldehyde was called L-glyceraldehyde. This system of nomenclature is still widely used in biochemistry.

One glyceraldehyde enantiomer is dextrorotatory (+) and the other, of course, is levorotatory (−). Before 1951 no one could be sure, however, which configuration belonged to which enantiomer. Chemists decided arbitrarily to assign the (R) configuration to the (+)-enantiomer. Then configurations of other molecules were related to one glyceraldehyde enantiomer or the other through reactions of known stereochemistry.

For example, the configuration of (−)-lactic acid can be related to (+)-glyceraldehyde through the following sequence of reactions.

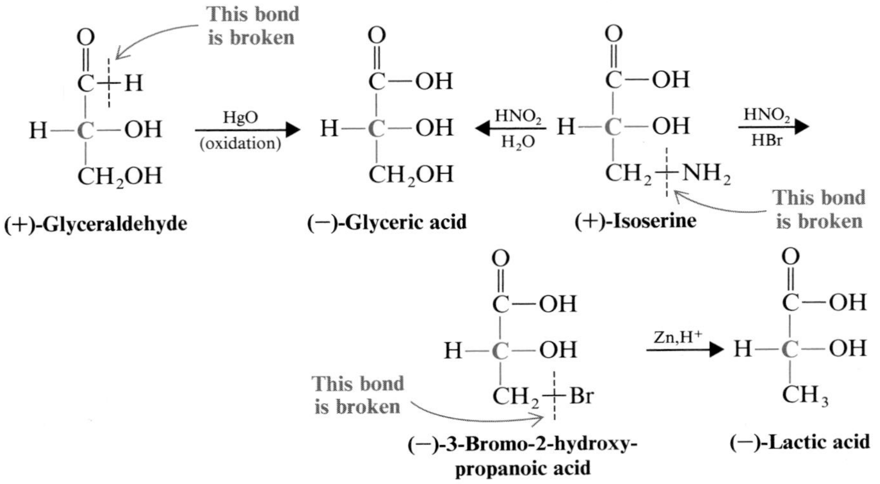

(+)-Glyceraldehyde   (−)-Glyceric acid   (+)-Isoserine

(−)-3-Bromo-2-hydroxy-
propanoic acid   (−)-Lactic acid

The stereochemistry of all of these reactions is known. Because bonds to the stereocenter (shown in red) are not broken in any of them, they all proceed with retention of configuration. If the assumption is made that the configuration of (+)-glyceraldehyde is as follows:

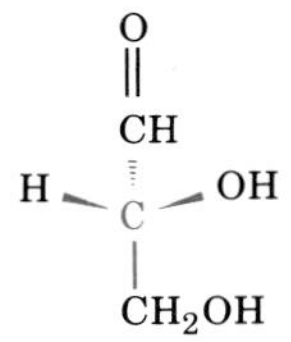

(R)-(+)-Glyceraldehyde

then the configuration of (−)-lactic acid is

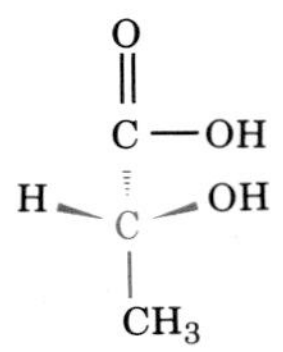

(R)-(−)-Lactic acid

Problem 5.24

(a) Write three-dimensional structures for the relative configurations of (−)-glyceric acid and (−)-3-bromo-2-hydroxypropanoic acid. (b) What is the (R–S) designation of (−)-glyceric acid? (c) Of (+)-isoserine? (d) Of (−)-3-bromo-2-hydroxypropanoic acid?

The configuration of (−)-glyceraldehyde was also related through reactions of known stereochemistry to (+)-tartaric acid.

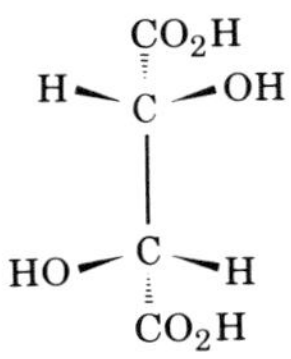

$$
\begin{array}{c}
CO_2H \\
H - C - OH \\
| \\
HO - C - H \\
CO_2H
\end{array}
$$

(+)-Tartaric acid

In 1951 J. M. Bijvoet, the director of the van't Hoff Laboratory of the University of Utrecht in Holland, using a special technique of X-ray diffraction, was able to show conclusively that (+)-tartaric acid had the absolute configuration shown above. This meant that the original arbitrary assignment of the configurations of (+)- and (−)-glyceraldehyde was also correct. It also meant that the configurations of all of the compounds that had been related to one glyceraldehyde enantiomer or the other were now known with certainty and were now **absolute configurations.**

5.14 SEPARATION OF ENANTIOMERS: RESOLUTION

So far we have left unanswered an important question about optically active compounds and racemic forms: How are enantiomers separated? Enantiomers have identical solubilities in ordinary solvents, and they have identical boiling points. Consequently, the conventional methods for separating organic compounds such as crystallization and distillation fail when applied to a racemic form.

It was, in fact, Louis Pasteur's separation of a racemic form of a salt of tartaric acid in 1848 that led to the discovery of the phenomenon called enantiomerism. Pasteur, consequently, is often considered to be the founder of the field of stereochemistry.

(+)-Tartaric acid is one of the byproducts of wine making (nature usually only synthesizes one enantiomer of a chiral molecule). Pasteur had obtained a sample of racemic tartaric acid from the owner of a chemical plant. In the course of his investigation Pasteur began examining the crystal structure of the sodium ammonium salt of racemic tartaric acid. He noticed that two types of crystals were present. One was identical with crystals of the sodium ammonium salt of (+)-tartaric acid that had been discovered earlier and had been shown to be dextrorotatory. Crystals of the other type were *non*superposable mirror images of the first kind. The two types of crystals were actually chiral. Using tweezers and a magnifying glass, Pasteur separated the two kinds of crystals, dissolved them in water, and placed the solutions in a polarimeter. The solution of crystals of the first type was dextrorotatory, and the crystals themselves proved to be identical with the sodium ammonium salt of (+)-tartaric acid that was already known. The solution of crystals of the second type was levorotatory; it rotated plane-polarized light in the opposite direction and by an equal amount. The crystals of the second type were the sodium ammonium salt of (−)-tartaric acid. The chirality of the crystals themselves disappeared, of course, as the crystals dissolved into their solutions *but the optical activity* remained. Pasteur reasoned, therefore, that the molecules themselves must be chiral.

Pasteur's discovery of enantiomerism and his demonstration that the optical activity of the two forms of tartaric acid was a property of the molecules themselves led, in 1874, to the proposal of the tetrahedral structure of carbon by van't Hoff and Le Bel.

Unfortunately, few organic compounds give chiral crystals as do the (+)- and (−)-tartaric acid salts. Few organic compounds crystallize into separate crystals (containing separate enantiomers) that are visibly chiral like the crystals of the sodium ammonium salt of tartaric acid. Pasteur's method, therefore, is not one that is generally applicable.

The most useful procedure for separating enantiomers is based on allowing a racemic form to react with a single enantiomer of some other compound. This changes a *racemic form into a mixture of diastereomers;* and **diastereomers, because they have different melting points, different boiling points, and different solubilities, can be separated by conventional means.** We shall see how this is done in Chapter 20. The separation of the enantiomers of a racemic form is called **resolution.**

5.15 COMPOUNDS WITH STEREOCENTERS OTHER THAN CARBON

Any tetrahedral atom with four different groups attached to it is a stereocenter. Listed here are general formulas of compounds whose molecules contain stereocenters other than carbon. Silicon and germanium are in the same group of the periodic table as carbon. They form tetrahedral compounds as carbon does. When four different groups are situated around the central atom in silicon, germanium, and nitrogen compounds, the molecules are chiral and the enantiomers can be separated.

$$R_4 \diagdown \underset{\underset{R_3}{|}}{\overset{\overset{R_1}{\vdots}}{Si}} \diagup R_2 \qquad R_4 \diagdown \underset{\underset{R_3}{|}}{\overset{\overset{R_1}{\vdots}}{Ge}} \diagup R_2 \qquad R_4 \diagdown \underset{\underset{R_3}{|}}{\overset{\overset{R_1}{\vdots}}{N^+}} \diagup R_2 \qquad X^-$$

5.16 CHIRAL MOLECULES THAT DO NOT POSSESS A TETRAHEDRAL ATOM WITH FOUR DIFFERENT GROUPS

A molecule is chiral if it is not superposable on its mirror image. The presence of a tetrahedral atom with four different groups is only one focus that will confer chirality on a molecule. Most of the molecules that we shall encounter do have such stereocenters. Many chiral molecules are known, however, that do not. An example is 1,3-dichloroallene.

Allenes are compounds whose molecules contain the following double bond sequence.

$$\underset{\diagup}{\overset{\diagdown}{}} C = C = C \overset{\diagup}{\underset{\diagdown}{}}$$

The planes of the π bonds of allenes are perpendicular to each other.

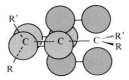

This geometry of the π bonds causes the groups attached to the end carbon atoms to lie in perpendicular planes and, because of this, allenes with different substituents on the end carbon atoms are chiral (Fig. 5.21). (Allenes do not show cis–trans isomerism.)

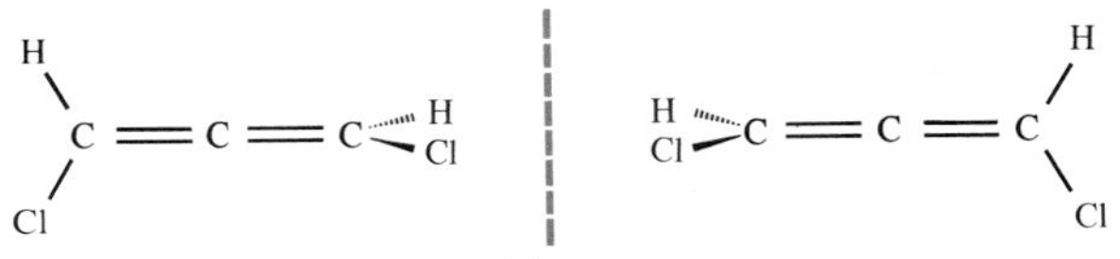

Mirror

FIGURE 5.21 Enantiomeric forms of 1,3-dichloroallene. These two molecules are nonsuperposable mirror images of each other and are, therefore, chiral. They do not possess a tetrahedral atom with four different groups, however.

5.17 SOME IMPORTANT TERMS AND CONCEPTS

Stereochemistry. Chemical studies that take into account the spatial aspects of molecules.

Isomers are different compounds that have the same molecular formula. All isomers fall into either of two groups: *constitutional* isomers or *stereoisomers.*

Constitutional isomers are isomers that have their atoms connected in a different order.

Stereoisomers have their atoms joined in the same order but differ in the way their atoms are arranged in space. Stereoisomers can be subdivided into two categories: *enantiomers* and *diastereomers.*

Enantiomers are stereoisomers that are related as an object and its mirror image. Enantiomers occur only with compounds whose molecules are chiral, that is, with molecules that are *not* superposable on their mirror images. Separate enantiomers rotate the plane of plane polarized light and are said to be *optically active.* They have equal but opposite specific rotation.

Diastereomers are stereoisomers that are not enantiomers, that is, they are stereoisomers that are not related as an object and its mirror image.

Chirality is equivalent to "handedness." A chiral molecule is one that is not superposable on its mirror image. An *achiral* molecule is one that can be superposed on its mirror image. Any tetrahedral atom that has four different attached groups is a **stereocenter.** A pair of enantiomers is possible for all molecules that contain a single tetrahedral stereocenter. For molecules with more than one stereocenter, the number of stereoisomers will not exceed 2^n where n is the number of stereocenters.

Plane of symmetry. An imaginary plane that bisects a molecule in such a way that the two halves of the molecule are mirror images of each other. Any molecule that has a plane of symmetry will be achiral.

Configuration. The particular arrangement of atoms (or groups) in space that is characteristic of a given stereoisomer. The configuration at each stereocenter can be designated as (R) or (S) by using the rules given in Section 5.5.

Racemic form (racemate or racemic mixture). An equimolar mixture of enantiomers.

Meso compound. An optically inactive compound whose molecules are achiral even though they contain tetrahedral atoms with four different attached groups.

Resolution. The separation of the enantiomers of a racemic form.

Additional Problems

5.25 Give definitions of each of the following terms and examples that illustrate their meaning:

(a) Isomers	(f) Meso compound	(k) Achiral molecule
(b) Constitutional isomers	(g) Racemic form	(l) Optical activity
(c) Stereoisomers	(h) Plane of symmetry	(m) Dextrorotatory
(d) Diastereomers	(i) Stereocenter	(n) Retention of configuration
(e) Enantiomers	(j) Chiral molecule	

5.26 Consider the following pairs of structures. Identify the relation between them by describing them as representing enantiomers, diastereomers, constitutional isomers, or two molecules of the same compound.

(e)

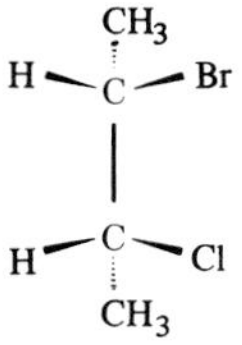

CH_3
H — C — Br

H — C — Cl
CH_3

and

Cl
H — C — CH_3

H — C — CH_3
Br

(f)

CH_3
H — C — Cl
CH_3

and

CH_3
H — C — H
CH_2Cl

(g)

CH_3
H — C — Cl
CH_3

and

CH_3
Cl — C — H
CH_3

(h)

H_3C H

H CH_3

and

H   H

H_3C CH_3

(i) H_3C ⸺ CH_3 and H_3C ⸺ CH_3

(j) ⸺ CH_3 / CH_3 and H_3C / H_3C

(k)

HO   OH
H   H

and

H   H
HO   OH

(l)

Cl   H
H   Cl

and

H   Cl
Cl   H

(m)

Cl   H
H   Cl

and

H   Cl
Cl   H

(n)

△ CH_3 and   ☐

(o)

H_3C H
C = C
H_3C Cl

and

H_3C Cl
C = C
H_3C H

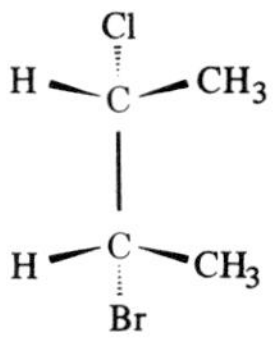

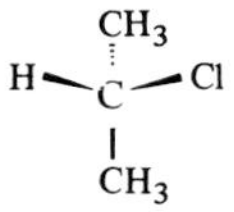

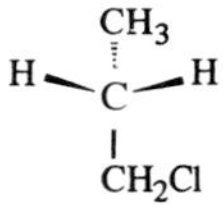

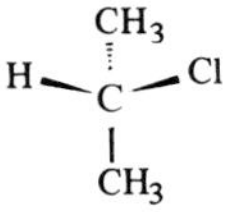

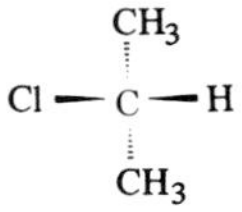

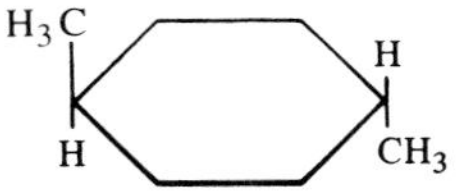

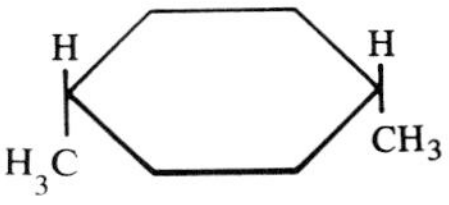

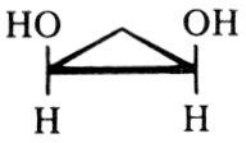

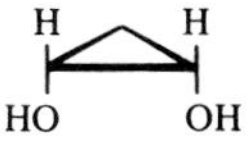

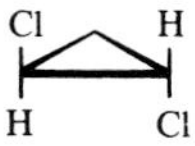

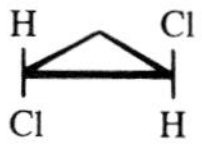

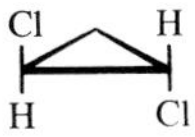

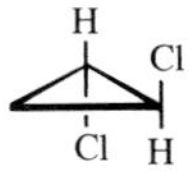

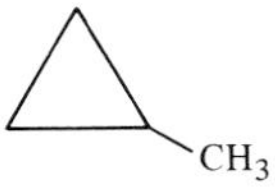

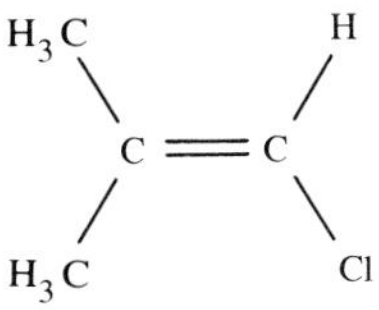

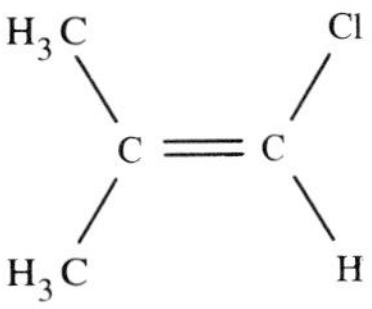

(p)

$$H_3C \quad\quad H$$
$$C = C$$
$$Cl \quad\quad CH_3$$

and

$$H_3C \quad\quad CH_3$$
$$C = C$$
$$Cl \quad\quad H$$

(q)

$$H$$
$$C = C = C \overset{\cdots H}{\underset{CH_3}{}}$$
$$H_3C$$

and

$$H \cdots C = C = C \overset{H}{}$$
$$H_3C \quad\quad\quad\quad CH_3$$

5.27   There are four dimethylcyclopropane isomers. (a) Write three-dimensional formulas for them. (b) Which dimethylcyclopropane isomers would, if taken separately, show optical activity? (c) If a mixture consisting of 1 mol of each of the four dimethylcyclopropane isomers were subjected to fractional distillation, how many fractions would be obtained? (d) How many of these fractions would show optical activity?

5.28   (Use models to solve this problem.) (a) Write a conformational structure for the most stable conformation of *trans*-1,2-cyclohexanediol and write its mirror image. (b) Are these two molecules superposable? (c) Are they interconvertible through a ring "flip"? (d) Repeat the process in part (a) with *cis*-1,2-cyclohexanediol. (e) Are these structures superposable? (f) Are they interconvertible?

5.29   (Use models to solve this problem.) (a) Write a conformational structure for the most stable conformation of *trans*-1,4-cyclohexanediol and for its mirror image. (b) Are these structures superposable? (c) Do they represent enantiomers? (d) Does *trans*-1,4-cyclohex-anediol have a stereoisomer, and if so, what is it? (e) Is this stereoisomer chiral?

5.30   (Use models to solve this problem.) Write conformational structures for all of the stereoisomers of 1,3-cyclohexanediol. Label pairs of enantiomers and meso compounds if they exist.

5.31   Tartaric acid [$HO_2CCH(OH)CH(OH)CO_2H$] was an important compound in the history of stereochemistry. Two naturally occurring forms of tartaric acid are optically inactive. One form has a melting point of 206 °C, the other a melting point of 140 °C. The inactive tartaric acid with a melting point of 206 °C can be separated into two optically active forms of tartaric acid with the same melting point (170 °C). One optically active tartaric acid has $[\alpha]_D^{25} = +12°$, the other $[\alpha]_D^{25} = -12°$. All attempts to separate the other inactive tartaric acid (melting point 140 °C) into optically active compounds fail. (a) Write the three-dimensional structure of the tartaric acid with melting point 140 °C. (b) What are possible structures for the optically active tartaric acids with melting points of 170 °C? (c) Can you be sure which tartaric acid in (b) has a positive rotation and which has a negative rotation? (d) What is the nature of the form of tartaric acid with a melting point of 206 °C?

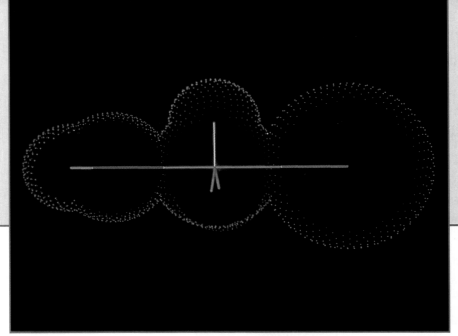

Transition state for an S_N2 reaction (Section 6.8).

6

IONIC REACTIONS—NUCLEOPHILIC SUBSTITUTION AND ELIMINATION REACTIONS OF ALKYL HALIDES

6.1 INTRODUCTION

The halogen atom of an alkyl halide is attached to an sp^3-hybridized carbon. The arrangement of groups around the carbon atom, therefore, is generally tetrahedral. Because halogen atoms are more electronegative than carbon, the carbon–halogen bond of alkyl halides is *polarized;* the carbon atom bears a partial positive charge, the halogen atom a partial negative charge.

$$\overset{\backslash}{\underset{/}{C}}\overset{\delta^+}{}\!\!\longrightarrow\overset{\delta^-}{X}$$

The size of the halogen atom increases as we go down the periodic table: fluorine atoms are the smallest and iodine atoms the largest. Consequently, the carbon–halogen bond length (Table 6.1) also increases as we go down the periodic table.

In the laboratory and in industry, alkyl halides are used as solvents for relatively nonpolar compounds, and they are used as the starting materials for the synthesis of

207

TABLE 6.1 Carbon – halogen
bond lengths

BOND	BOND LENGTH (Å)
CH_3—F	1.39
CH_3—Cl	1.78
CH_3—Br	1.93
CH_3—I	2.14

many compounds. As we shall learn in this chapter, the halogen atom of an alkyl halide can be easily replaced by other groups, and the presence of a halogen atom on a carbon chain also affords us the possibility of introducing a multiple bond.

Compounds in which a halogen atom is bonded to an sp^2-hybridized carbon are called **vinylic halides** or **phenyl halides**. The compound CH_2=CHCl has the common name **vinyl chloride** and the group, CH_2=CH—, is commonly called the **vinyl group.** A *vinylic halide,* therefore, is a general term that refers to a compound in which a halogen is attached to a carbon atom that is also forming a double bond to another carbon atom. *Phenyl halides* are compounds in which a halogen is attached to a benzene ring (Section 2.7). Phenyl halides belong to a larger group of compounds that we shall study later, called **aryl halides.**

A vinylic halide   **A phenyl halide or aryl halide**

Together with alkyl halides, these compounds comprise a larger group of compounds known simply as **organic halides** or **organohalogen compounds.** The chemistry of vinylic and aryl halides is, as we shall also learn later, quite different from alkyl halides, and it is on alkyl halides that we shall focus most of our attention in this chapter.

6.2 PHYSICAL PROPERTIES OF ORGANIC HALIDES

Most alkyl and aryl halides have very low solubilities in water, but as we might expect, they are miscible with each other and with other relatively nonpolar solvents. Dichloromethane (CH_2Cl_2, also called *methylene chloride*), trichloromethane ($CHCl_3$, also called *chloroform*), and tetrachloromethane (CCl_4, also called *carbon tetrachloride*) are often used as solvents for nonpolar and moderately polar compounds. Many chloroalkanes including $CHCl_3$ and CCl_4 have a cumulative toxicity and are carcinogenic, however, and should, therefore, be used only in fume hoods and with great care.

Methyl iodide (bp, 42 °C) is the only monohalomethane that is a liquid at room temperature and 1-atm pressure. Ethyl bromide (bp, 38 °C) and ethyl iodide (bp, 72 °C) are both liquids but ethyl chloride (bp, 13 °C) is a gas. The propyl chlorides, bromides, and iodides are all liquids. In general alkyl chlorides, bromides, and iodides are all liquids and tend to have boiling points near those of alkanes of similar molecular weights.

Polyfluoroalkanes, however, tend to have unusually low boiling points (Section 2.16D). Hexafluoroethane boils at $-79\ °C$, even though its molecular weight (MW = 138) is near that of decane (MW = 144; bp, 174 $°C$).

Table 6.2 lists the physical properties of some common organic halides.

6.3 REACTION MECHANISMS

In this chapter we shall begin to look at some of the important reactions that alkyl halides undergo. As we examine these reactions we shall not only want to know what the products are, we shall also be interested in *how the reaction takes place.* We shall be interested in what chemists call the ***mechanism of the reaction — the events that are postulated to take place at the molecular level as reactants become products.*** If the reaction takes place in more than one step, then what are these steps, and what kinds of **intermediates** intervene between reactants and products?

6.3A HOMOLYSIS AND HETEROLYSIS OF COVALENT BONDS

Reactions of organic compounds almost inevitably involve the making and breaking of covalent bonds. If we consider a hypothetical molecule A∶B, its covalent bond may break in three possible ways:

$$
A∶B
\begin{cases}
\xrightarrow{(1)} & A\cdot\ +\cdot B \quad \text{Homolysis} \\
\xrightarrow{(2)} & A∶^-\ +\ B^+ \\
\xrightarrow{(3)} & A^+\ +∶B^-
\end{cases}
\Bigg\} \text{Heterolysis}
$$

In (1) above the bond breaks so that A and B each retain one of the electrons of the bond, and cleavage leads to the neutral fragments A· and B·. This type of bond breaking is called **homolysis** (Gr: *homo-*, the same, + *lysis,* loosening or cleavage); the bond is said to have broken *homolytically.* The neutral fragments A· and B· are called **radicals,** or sometimes **free radicals.** Radicals always contain unpaired electrons.

In (2) and (3) bond cleavage leads to charged fragments or **ions** (A∶⁻ and B⁺ or A⁺ and ∶B⁻). This kind of bond cleavage is called **heterolysis** (Gr: *hetero-*, different, + *lysis*); the bond is said to have broken *heterolytically.*

6.3B REACTIVE INTERMEDIATES IN ORGANIC CHEMISTRY

Organic reactions that take place in more than one step involve the formation of an *intermediate* — one that results from either homolysis or heterolysis of a bond. Homolysis of a bond to carbon leads to an intermediate known as a carbon *radical* (or free radical).

$$
-\overset{|}{\underset{|}{C}}∶Z \xrightarrow{\text{homolysis}} -\overset{|}{\underset{|}{C}}\cdot\ +\ Z\cdot
$$

Carbon radical
(or *free* radical)

TABLE 6.2 Organic halides

GROUP	FLUORIDE		CHLORIDE		BROMIDE		IODIDE	
	bp (°C)	DENSITY (g mL⁻¹)	bp (°C)	DENSITY (g mL⁻¹)	bp (°C)	DENSITY (g mL⁻¹)	bp (°C)	DENSITY (g mL⁻¹)
Methyl	−78.4	0.84[−60]	−23.8	0.92[20]	3.6	1.73[0]	42.5	2.28[20]
Ethyl	−37.7	0.72[20]	13.1	0.91[15]	38.4	1.46[20]	72	1.95[20]
Propyl	−2.5	0.78[−3]	46.6	0.89[20]	70.8	1.35[20]	102	1.74[20]
Isopropyl	−9.4	0.72[20]	34	0.86[20]	59.4	1.31[20]	89.4	1.70[20]
Butyl	32	0.78[20]	78.4	0.89[20]	101	1.27[20]	130	1.61[20]
sec-Butyl			68	0.87[20]	91.2	1.26[20]	120	1.60[20]
Isobutyl			69	0.87[20]	91	1.26[20]	119	1.60[20]
tert-Butyl	12	0.75[12]	51	0.84[20]	73.3	1.22[20]	100 dec[a]	1.57[0]
Pentyl	62	0.79[20]	108.2	0.88[20]	129.6	1.22[20]	155[740]	1.52[20]
Neopentyl			84.4	0.87[20]	105	1.20[20]	127 dec[a]	1.53[13]
CH$_2$=CH—	−72	0.68[26]	−13.9	0.91[20]	16	1.52[14]	56	2.04[20]
CH$_2$=CHCH$_2$—	−3		45	0.94[20]	70	1.40[20]	102–103	1.84[22]
C$_6$H$_5$—	85	1.02[20]	132	1.10[20]	155	1.52[20]	189	1.82[20]
C$_6$H$_5$CH$_2$—	140	1.02[25]	179	1.10[25]	201	1.44[22]	93[10]	1.73[25]

[a] Decompose is abbreviated as dec.

Heterolysis of a bond to carbon can lead either to a trivalent carbon cation or carbon anion.

$$-\overset{\displaystyle |}{\underset{\displaystyle |}{C}}{:}Z \xrightarrow{\text{heterolysis}} \begin{cases} -\overset{\displaystyle |}{\underset{\displaystyle |}{C}}{}^{+} \quad + :Z^{-} \\ \textbf{Carbocation} \\ \textbf{(or \textit{carbenium ion})} \\ \\ -\overset{\displaystyle |}{\underset{\displaystyle |}{C}}{:}^{-} + Z^{+} \\ \textbf{Carbanion} \end{cases}$$

Trivalent carbon cations are called either **carbocations** or **carbenium ions.*** The term *carbocation* has a clear and distinct meaning. The newer term *carbenium ion* has not yet found wide usage. Because of this, we shall always refer to trivalent, positively charged species such as $-\overset{\displaystyle |}{\underset{\displaystyle |}{C}}{}^{+}$ as carbocations.

Carbon anions are called **carbanions.**

Carbon radicals and carbocations are electron-deficient species. A carbon radical has seven electrons in its valence shell; a carbocation has only six and is positively charged. As a consequence, both species are **electron-seeking reagents** called **electrophiles.** *In their reactions they seek the extra electron or electrons that will give them a stable octet.*

Carbanions are usually strong **bases** and strong **nucleophiles.** *Nucleophiles are Lewis bases — they are electron-pair donors. Carbanions, therefore seek either a proton or some other positively charged center to neutralize their negative charge.*

Carbon radicals, carbocations, and carbanions are usually highly reactive species. In most instances they exist only as short-lived intermediates in an organic reaction. Under certain conditions, however, these species may exist long enough for chemists to study them using special techniques.

A few carbon radicals, carbocations, and carbanions are stable enough to be isolated. This only happens, however, when special groups are attached to the central carbon atom that allow the charge or the odd electron to be stabilized.

6.3C IONIC REACTIONS AND RADICAL REACTIONS

Most reactions of organic compounds can be placed into either of two broad categories: **ionic reactions** or **radical reactions.** As these names suggest, these categories arise from the kinds of reagents that are used to bring about the reactions and from the kinds of reactive intermediates that form in them. In ionic reactions the bonds of the reacting molecules undergo **heterolysis;** in radical reactions, they undergo *homolysis.*

We shall discuss radical reactions in detail in Chapter 7. In this chapter we concern ourselves only with ionic reactions.

---

*An older term, *carbonium ion,* is no longer used because it has taken on a different meaning.

6.4 NUCLEOPHILIC SUBSTITUTION REACTIONS

There are many reactions of the general type shown here.

$$Nu:^- \quad + \quad R-\ddot{X}: \longrightarrow R-Nu + \quad :\ddot{X}:^-$$

| Nucleophile | Alkyl halide (substrate) | Product | Halide ion |

Following are some examples:

$$H\ddot{O}:^- + CH_3-\ddot{C}l: \longrightarrow CH_3-\ddot{O}H + :\ddot{C}l:^-$$

$$CH_3\ddot{O}:^- + CH_3CH_2-\ddot{B}r: \longrightarrow CH_3CH_2-\ddot{O}CH_3 + :\ddot{B}r:^-$$

$$:\ddot{I}:^- + CH_3CH_2CH_2-\ddot{C}l: \longrightarrow CH_3CH_2CH_2-\ddot{I}: + :\ddot{C}l:^-$$

In this type of reaction a **nucleophile, a species with an unshared electron pair,** reacts with an alkyl halide (called the **substrate**) by replacing the halogen substituent. A *substitution reaction* takes place and the halogen substituent, called the leaving group, departs as a halide ion. Because the substitution reaction is initiated by a nucleophile, it is called a **nucleophilic substitution reaction.**

In nucleophilic substitution reactions the carbon–halogen bond of the substrate undergoes *heterolysis,* and the unshared pair of the nucleophile is used to form a new bond to the carbon atom:

$$Nu:^- + \quad R\,\vdots\,\ddot{X}: \longrightarrow Nu:R + :\ddot{X}:^-$$

Leaving group

Nucleophile

Heterolysis occurs here

One of the questions we shall want to address later in this chapter is, when does the carbon–halogen bond break? Does it break at the same time that the new bond between the nucleophile and the carbon forms?

$$Nu:^- + R:\ddot{X}: \longrightarrow \overset{\delta-}{Nu}---R---\overset{\delta-}{\ddot{X}:} \longrightarrow Nu:R + :\ddot{X}:^-$$

Or does the carbon–halogen bond break first?

$$R:\ddot{X}: \longrightarrow R^+ + :\ddot{X}:^-$$

then

$$Nu:^- + R^+ \longrightarrow Nu:R$$

We shall find that the answer depends primarily on the structure of the alkyl halide.

6.5 NUCLEOPHILES

A nucleophile is a reagent that seeks a positive center. (The word nucleophile comes from nucleus, the positive part of an atom plus *phile* from the Greek word *philein* meaning to love.) When a nucleophile reacts with an alkyl halide, the positive center that the nucleophile seeks is the carbon atom that bears the halogen atom. This carbon atom carries a partial positive charge because the electronegative halogen pulls the electrons of the carbon–halogen bond in its direction (see Section 1.19).

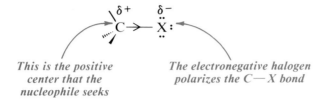

This is the positive center that the nucleophile seeks

The electronegative halogen polarizes the C—X bond

A nucleophile is any negative ion or any neutral molecule that has an unshared electron pair. For example, both hydroxide ions and water molecules can act as nucleophiles by reacting with alkyl halides to produce alcohols.

General Reaction

$$\text{H}-\ddot{\text{O}}\!:^- \;+\; \text{R}-\ddot{\text{X}}\!: \;\longrightarrow\; \text{R}-\ddot{\text{O}}-\text{H} \;+\; :\ddot{\text{X}}\!:^-$$

Nucleophile   **Alkyl halide**   **Alcohol**   **Leaving group**

Specific Example

$$\text{H}-\ddot{\text{O}}\!:^- \;+\; \text{CH}_3\text{CH}_2-\ddot{\text{Br}}\!: \;\longrightarrow\; \text{CH}_3\text{CH}_2-\ddot{\text{O}}-\text{H} \;+\; :\ddot{\text{Br}}\!:^-$$

Nucleophile   **Alkyl halide**   **Alcohol**   **Leaving group**

General Reaction

$$\text{R}-\ddot{\text{X}}\!: \;+\; \underset{\underset{\text{H}}{|}}{\text{H}-\ddot{\text{O}}\!:} \;\longrightarrow\; \text{R}-\underset{\underset{\text{H}}{|}}{\overset{\pm}{\ddot{\text{O}}}}\!-\text{H} \;+\; :\ddot{\text{X}}\!:^-$$

Alkyl   **Nucleophile**   **Alkyloxonium**
halide   **ion**

$$\text{H}_2\text{O} \Big\updownarrow$$

$$\text{R}-\text{OH} + \text{H}_3\text{O}^+ + :\ddot{\text{X}}\!:^-$$

Specific Example

$$(\text{CH}_3)_3\text{C}-\ddot{\text{Cl}}\!: \;+\; \text{H}-\ddot{\text{O}}\!: \;\longrightarrow\; (\text{CH}_3)_3\text{C}-\underset{\underset{\text{H}}{|}}{\overset{\pm}{\ddot{\text{O}}}}\!-\text{H} \;+\; :\ddot{\text{Cl}}\!:^-$$

$$\text{H}_2\text{O} \Big\updownarrow$$

$$(\text{CH}_3)_3\text{C}-\text{OH} + \text{H}_3\text{O}^+ + :\ddot{\text{Cl}}^-$$

In this last reaction the first product is an alkyloxonium ion, $\text{R}-\overset{\pm}{\underset{\underset{\text{H}}{|}}{\text{O}}}-\text{H}$, which

then loses a proton to a water molecule to form an alcohol. Alkyloxonium ions are

like hydronium ions, H—O$\overset{+}{-}$H, and just as hydronium ions can donate protons to
                 |
                 H
bases, so too can alkyloxonium ions. Just as hydronium ions are "protonated" water
molecules, alkyloxonium ions of the type R—O$\overset{+}{-}$H are often called "protonated
                         |
                         H
alcohols." Both hydronium ions and alkyloxonium ions are strong Brønsted acids.

Problem 6.1

Write an electron dot structure for each of the following molecules and ions
showing that each is a potential nucleophile:

(a) Ethanol, C_2H_5OH (g) Acetate ion, $CH_3CO_2^-$

(b) Ethoxide ion, $C_2H_5O^-$ (h) Formic acid, HCO_2H

(c) Ammonia, NH_3 (i) Formate ion, HCO_2^-

(d) Methylamine, CH_3NH_2 (j) Ethanethiol, C_2H_5SH

(e) Cyanide ion, CN^- (k) Ethanethiolate ion, $C_2H_5S^-$

(f) Acetic acid, CH_3CO_2H (l) Azide ion, N_3^-

6.5A LEAVING GROUPS

Alkyl halides are not the only substances that can act as substrates in nucleophilic
substitution reactions. We shall see later that other compounds can also react in the
same way. To be reactive — that is, to be able to act as the substrate in a nucleophilic
substitution reaction — a molecule must have a good **leaving group** (or **nucleofuge**).
In alkyl halides the leaving group is the halogen substituent — it leaves as a halide ion.
***To be a good leaving group the substituent must be able to leave as a relatively stable,
weakly basic molecule or ion.*** (We shall see why in Section 6.15E.) Because halide
ions are relatively stable and are very weak bases, they are good leaving groups. Other
groups can function as good leaving groups as well. We can write more general
equations for nucleophilic substitution reactions using L to represent a leaving group.

$$\text{Nu:}^- + \text{R—L} \longrightarrow \text{R—Nu} + \text{:L}^-$$

or

$$\text{Nu:} + \text{R—L} \longrightarrow \text{R—Nu}^+ + \text{:L}^-$$

Specific Examples

$$\text{H}\ddot{\text{O}}\text{:}^- + \text{CH}_3\text{—}\ddot{\text{C}}\text{l:} \longrightarrow \text{CH}_3\text{—}\ddot{\text{O}}\text{H} + \text{:}\ddot{\text{C}}\text{l:}^-$$

$$\text{H}_3\text{N:} + \text{CH}_3\text{—}\ddot{\text{B}}\text{r:} \longrightarrow \text{CH}_3\text{—}\text{NH}_3^+ + \text{:}\ddot{\text{B}}\text{r:}^-$$

Later we shall also see reactions where the substrate bears a positive charge and a
reaction like the following takes place:

$$\text{Nu:} + \text{R—L}^+ \longrightarrow \text{R—Nu}^+ + \text{:L}$$

Specific Example

$$CH_3-\overset{..}{O}: + CH_3-\overset{..}{O}{}^{\pm}-H \longrightarrow CH_3-\overset{..}{O}{}^{\pm}-CH_3 + :\overset{..}{O}-H$$
$$\qquad\quad | \qquad\qquad | \qquad\qquad\qquad | \qquad\qquad |$$
$$\qquad\quad H \qquad\qquad H \qquad\qquad\qquad H \qquad\qquad H$$

Nucleophilic substitution reactions will be more understandable and useful if we know something about their mechanisms. How does the nucleophile replace the leaving group? Does the reaction take place in one step, or is more than one step involved? If more than one step is involved, what kinds of intermediates are formed? Which steps are fast and which are slow? In order to answer these questions we need to know something about the rates of chemical reactions.

6.6 THERMODYNAMICS AND KINETICS OF CHEMICAL REACTIONS

With a chemical reaction we are usually concerned with two features: *the extent* to which it takes place and *the rate* of the reaction. By the extent of the reaction, we mean how completely will the reactants be converted to products when an equilibrium is established between them. By the rate of the reaction (also called the *kinetics* of the reaction) we mean how rapidly will the reactants be converted to products. In simpler terms then, with chemical reactions we are concerned with "how far" and "how fast."

We saw in Section 3.6 that the extent to which a reaction takes place can be expressed by an equilibrium constant, K_{eq}, and that the equilibrium constant is related to the change in the standard free energy for the reaction, $\Delta G°$:

$$\Delta G° = -2.303\ RT \log K_{eq}$$

This relationship means that a large negative value of $\Delta G°$ will ensure that the reaction *proceeds to completion;* — that the reactants, for all practical purposes will be completely converted to products when equilibrium is reached. If a reaction, on reaching equilibrium, is capable of producing several products, the major product will be the one for which the value of $\Delta G°$ is most favorable (most negative), that is, **reactions that reach equilibrium will lead to the most stable product or products.** Such reactions are said to be under **thermodynamic control** or **equilibrium control.**

The value of $\Delta G°$, however, tells us nothing about how rapidly the reaction will take place — about how long it will take for equilibrium to be reached. The reaction of hydrogen with oxygen to produce water, for example,

$$2\ H_2 + O_2 \longrightarrow 2\ H_2O$$

has a very large negative free-energy change. However, in the absence of a catalyst or a flame, the reaction takes place so slowly as to be imperceptible.

For many other reactions (Fig. 6.1), pathways to several different products may have favorable free-energy changes, but equilibrium is never reached, and **the product that we actually obtain in greatest amount is the one that comes from the reaction that occurs most rapidly.** These reactions are said to be under **kinetic control** or **rate control.** We can see from this that a knowledge of the factors that determine reaction rates is of considerable importance as well.

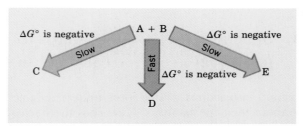

FIGURE 6.1 The hypothetical reaction of A and B to form different products, C, D, and E. All of the reactions have favorable free-energy changes. Compound D is the product that is mainly obtained, however, because it is produced by the reaction that proceeds most rapidly. Compounds E and C are not isolated in appreciable amounts because the reactions by which they are formed are slow.

6.7 KINETICS OF A NUCLEOPHILIC SUBSTITUTION REACTION: AN S_N2 REACTION

To understand how the rate of a reaction might be measured let us consider an actual example: the reaction that takes place between methyl chloride with hydroxide ion in aqueous solution.

$$CH_3\!-\!Cl + OH^- \xrightarrow[H_2O]{60\ °C} CH_3\!-\!OH + Cl^-$$

Although methyl chloride is not highly soluble in water, it is soluble enough to allow us to carry out our kinetic study. The presence of hydroxide ion in the aqueous solution can be assured by simply adding sodium hydroxide. We carry out the reaction at a specific temperature because reaction rates are known to be temperature dependent (Section 6.9).

The rate of the reaction can be determined experimentally by measuring the rate at which methyl chloride or hydroxide ion *disappears* from the solution, or the rate at which methanol or chloride ion *appears* in the solution. We can make any of these measurements by withdrawing a small sample from the reaction mixture soon after the reaction begins and analyzing it for the concentrations of CH_3Cl or OH^- and CH_3OH or Cl^-. We are interested in what are called *initial rates,* because as time passes the concentrations of the reactants change. Since we will also know the initial concentrations of reactants (because we measured them when we made up the solution), it will be easy to calculate the rate at which the reactants are disappearing from the solution or the products are appearing in solution.

We perform several such experiments keeping the temperature the same, but varying the initial concentrations of the reactants. The results that we might get are shown in Table 6.3.

Notice that the experiments show that the rate depends on the concentration of methyl chloride *and* on the concentration of hydroxide ion. When we doubled the concentration of methyl chloride in experiment 2, the rate *doubled.* When we doubled the concentration of hydroxide ion in experiment 3, the rate *doubled.* When we doubled both concentrations in experiment 4 the rate increased by *four times.*

We can express these results as a proportionality,

$$\text{Rate} \propto [CH_3Cl]\,[OH^-]$$

TABLE 6.3   Rate study of reaction of CH_3Cl with OH^- at 60 °C

EXPERIMENT NUMBER	INITIAL $[CH_3Cl]$	INITIAL $[OH^-]$	INITIAL RATE (mol L^{-1} s^{-1})
1	0.0010	1.0	4.9×10^{-7}
2	0.0020	1.0	9.8×10^{-7}
3	0.0010	2.0	9.8×10^{-7}
4	0.0020	2.0	19.6×10^{-7}

and this proportionality can be expressed as an equation through the introduction of a proportionality constant (k) called the rate constant:

$$Rate = k[CH_3Cl]\,[OH^-]$$

For this reaction at this temperature we find that $k = 4.9 \times 10^{-4}$ L mol^{-1} s^{-1}. (Verify this for yourself by doing the calculation.)

This reaction is said to be **second order overall.*** It is reasonable to conclude, therefore, that *for the reaction to take place a hydroxide ion and a methyl chloride molecule must collide.* We also say that the reaction is **bimolecular.** (By *bimolecular* we mean that two species are involved in the step whose rate is being measured.) We call this kind of reaction an S_N2 reaction, meaning **Substitution, Nucleophilic, bimolecular.**

6.8 A MECHANISM FOR THE S_N2 REACTION

A modern mechanism for the S_N2 reaction—one based on ideas proposed by Edward D. Hughes and Sir Christopher Ingold in 1937†—is outlined below.

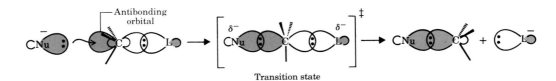

Transition state

According to this mechanism, the nucleophile approaches the carbon bearing the leaving group from the **backside,** that is, from the side directly opposite the leaving group. The orbital that contains the electron pair of the nucleophile begins to overlap with an empty (antibonding) orbital of the carbon atom bearing the leaving group. As

---

* In general the overall order of a reaction is equal to the sum of the exponents a and b in the rate equation.

$$Rate = k[A]^a\,[B]^b$$

If in some other reaction, for example, we found that the

$$Rate = k[A]^2\,[B]$$

then we would say that the reaction is second order with respect to [A], first order with respect to [B], and third order overall.

† Ingold and Hughes, of the University College, London, were pioneers in this field. Their work provided the foundation on which our modern understanding of nucleophilic substitution and elimination is built.

the reaction progresses the bond between the nucleophile and the carbon atom grows, and the bond between the carbon atom and the leaving group weakens. As this happens, the carbon atom has its configuration turned inside out, it becomes *inverted,** and the leaving group is pushed away. The formation of the bond between the nucleophile and the carbon atom provides most of the energy necessary to break the bond between the carbon atom and the leaving group. We can represent this mechanism with methyl chloride and hydroxide ion in the following way:

S_N2 Reaction

Transition state

The Hughes–Ingold mechanism for the S_N2 reaction involves only one step. There are no intermediates. The reaction proceeds through the formation of an unstable arrangement of atoms called the **transition state.**

Transition state

The transition state is a fleeting arrangement of the atoms in which the nucleophile and the leaving group are both partially bonded to the carbon atom undergoing attack. Because the transition state involves both the nucleophile (e. g., a hydroxide ion) and the substrate (e. g., a molecule of methyl chloride), this mechanism accounts for the second-order reaction kinetics that we observe. (Because bond formation and bond breaking occur in a single transition state, the S_N2 reaction is an example of what is called a concerted reaction.)

The transition state has an extremely brief existence. It lasts only as long as the time required for one molecular vibration, about 10^{-12} s. The energy and structure of the transition state are highly important aspects of any chemical reaction. We shall, therefore, examine this subject further in Section 6.9.

6.9 TRANSITION STATE THEORY: FREE-ENERGY DIAGRAMS

A reaction that proceeds with a negative free-energy change is said to be **exergonic;** one that proceeds with a positive free-energy change is said to be **endergonic.** The reaction between methyl chloride and hydroxide ion in aqueous solution is highly

---

* Considerable evidence had appeared in the years prior to Hughes and Ingold's 1937 publication indicating that in reactions like this an inversion of configuration of the carbon bearing the leaving group takes place. The first observation of such an inversion was made by the Latvian chemist Paul Walden in 1896, and such inversions are called **Walden inversions** in his honor. We shall study this aspect of the S_N2 reaction further in Section 6.10.

exergonic; at 60 °C (333 K), $\Delta G° = -24$ kcal mol^{-1}. (The reaction is also exothermic, $\Delta H° = -18$ kcal mol^{-1}).

$$CH_3—Cl + OH^- \longrightarrow CH_3—OH + Cl^- \qquad \Delta G° = -24 \text{ kcal mol}^{-1}$$

The equilibrium constant for the reaction is extremely large:

$$\Delta G° = -2.303 \, RT \log K_{eq}$$

$$\log K_{eq} = \frac{-\Delta G°}{2.303 \, RT}$$

$$\log K_{eq} = \frac{-(-24 \text{ kcal mol}^{-1})}{2.303 \times 0.001987 \text{ kcal K}^{-1} \text{ mol}^{-1} \times 333 \text{ K}}$$

$$\log K_{eq} = 15.75$$

$$K_{eq} = 5.6 \times 10^{15}$$

An equilibrium constant as large as this means that the reaction goes to completion.

Because the free-energy change is negative, we can say that in energy terms the reaction goes **downhill.** The products of the reaction are at a lower level of free energy than the reactants.

However, considerable experimental evidence exists showing that **if covalent bonds are broken in a reaction, the reactants must go up an energy hill first,** before they can go downhill. This will be true even if the reaction is exergonic.

We can represent this graphically by plotting the free energy of the reacting particles against the reaction coordinate. Such a graph is given in Fig. 6.2. We have chosen as our example a generalized S_N2 reaction.

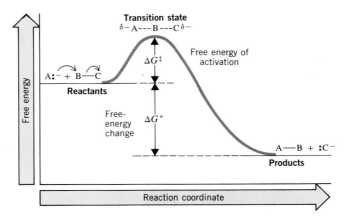

FIGURE 6.2 A free-energy diagram for a hypothetical S_N2 reaction that takes place with a negative $\Delta G°$.

The reaction coordinate is a quantity that measures the progress of the reaction. It represents the changes in bond orders and bond distances that must take place as the reactants are converted to products. In this instance the B—C distance could be used as the reaction coordinate because as the reaction progresses the B—C distance becomes longer.

In our illustration (Fig. 6.2), we can see that **an energy barrier** exists between the reactants and products. The height of this barrier (in kilocalories per mole) above the level of reactants is called **the free energy of activation, $\Delta G^{\ddagger}$.**

The top of the energy hill corresponds to the **transition state.** *The difference in free energy between the reactants and the transition state is the free energy of activation, $\Delta G^{\ddagger}$. The difference in free energy between the reactants and products is the free-energy change for the reaction, $\Delta G°$.* For our example, the free-energy level of the products is lower than that of the reactants. In terms of our analogy, we can say that the reactants in one energy valley must traverse an energy hill (the transition state) in order to reach the lower energy valley of the products.

If a reaction in which covalent bonds are broken proceeds with a positive free-energy change (Fig. 6.3), there will still be a free energy of activation. That is, if the products have greater free energy than reactants, the transition state will have a free energy even higher. ($\Delta G^{\ddagger}$ will be larger than $\Delta G°$.) In other words, in the **uphill** (endergonic) reaction an even larger energy hill lies between the reactants in one valley and the products in a higher one.

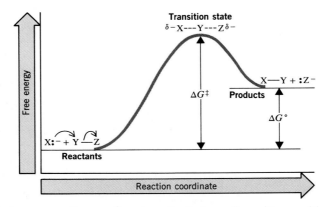

FIGURE 6.3 A free-energy diagram for a hypothetical reaction with a positive free-energy change.

Just as the overall free-energy change for a reaction contains enthalpy and entropy components (Section 3.6):

$$\Delta G° = \Delta H° - T\Delta S°$$

The free energy of activation has similar components:

$$\Delta G^{\ddagger} = \Delta H^{\ddagger} - T\Delta S^{\ddagger}$$

The enthalpy of activation ($\Delta H^{\ddagger}$) is the difference in bond energies between the reactants and the transition state. It is, in effect, the energy necessary to bring about the partial breaking of bonds that must happen in the transition state. Some of this energy may be furnished by the bonds that are partially formed. Not all will be, however, because bond breaking and bond formation are not perfectly synchronized; bond formation lags behind. The entropy of activation ($\Delta S^{\ddagger}$) is the difference in entropy between the reactants and the transition state. Most reactions require the reactants to come together with a particular orientation. (Consider, e. g., the specific orientation required in the S_N2 reaction.) This requirement for a particular orientation means that the transition state must be

6.9 TRANSITION STATE THEORY: FREE-ENERGY DIAGRAMS

more ordered than the reactants and that $\Delta S^{\ddagger}$ will be negative. The more highly ordered the transition state, the more negative $\Delta S^{\ddagger}$ will be. When a three-dimensional plot of free energy versus the reaction coordinate is made, the transition state is found to resemble a mountain pass or *col* (Fig. 6.4) rather than the top of an energy hill as we have shown in Figs. 6.2 and 6.3. (A plot such as that seen in Figs. 6.2 or 6.3 is simply a two-dimensional slice through the three-dimensional energy surface for the reaction.) That is, the reactants and products appear to be separated by an energy barrier resembling a mountain range. While an infinite number of possible routes lead from reactants to products, the transition state lies at the top of the route that requires the lowest energy climb. Whether or not the pass is a wide or narrow one depends on $\Delta S^{\ddagger}$. A wide pass means that there is a relatively large number of orientations of reactants that allow a reaction to take place. A narrow pass means just the opposite.

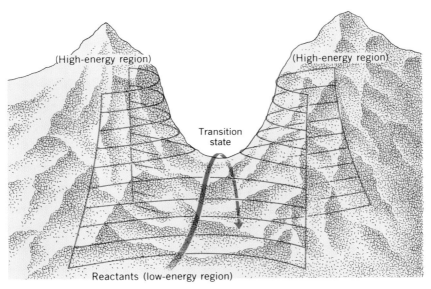

FIGURE 6.4 Mountain pass or col analogy for the transition state. (Adapted with permission from J. E. Leffler and E. Grunwald, *Rates and Equilibria of Organic Reactions,* Wiley, New York, 1963, p. 6.)

The existence of an activation energy ($\Delta G^{\ddagger}$) explains why most chemical reactions occur much more rapidly at higher temperatures. *For many reactions taking place near room temperature, a 10 °C increase in temperature will cause the reaction rate to double.*

This dramatic increase in reaction rate results from a large increase in the number of collisions between reactants that together have sufficient energy to surmount the barrier at the higher temperature. The kinetic energies of molecules at a given temperature are not all the same. Figure 6.5 shows the distribution of energies brought to collisions at two temperatures (that do not differ greatly), labeled T_1 and T_2. Because of the way energies are distributed at different temperatures (as indicated by the shapes of the curves), increasing the temperature by only a small amount causes a large increase in the number of collisions with larger energies. In Fig. 6.5 we have designated a particular minimal free energy as being required to bring about a reaction between colliding molecules. The number of collisions having sufficient energy to allow reaction to take place at a given temperature is proportional to the area under that portion of the curve that represents free energies greater than or equal to $\Delta G^{\ddagger}$. At the lower temperature (T_1) this number is relatively small. At the higher temperature (T_2), however, the number of collisions that take place with enough energy to react is very much larger. Consequently, a modest temperature increase produces a large increase in the number of collisions with energy sufficient to lead to a reaction.

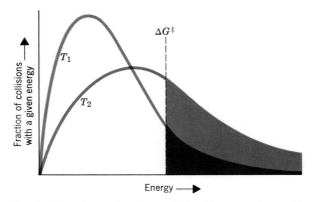

FIGURE 6.5 The distribution of energies at two different temperatures, T_1 and T_2 $(T_2 > T_1)$. The number of collisions with energies greater than the free energy, of activation is indicated by the appropriately shaded area under each curve.

There is also an important relationship between the rate of a reaction and the magnitude of the free energy of activation. The relationship between the rate constant (k) and $\Delta G^{\ddagger}$ is an *exponential one*.

$$k = k_0 e^{-\Delta G^{\ddagger}/RT}$$

In this equation, e is 2.718, the base of natural logarithms, and k_0 is the absolute rate constant, which equals the rate at which all transition states proceed to products. At

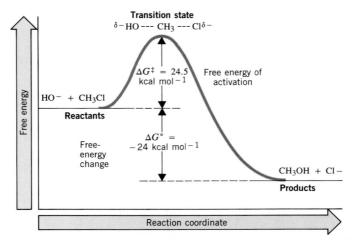

FIGURE 6.6 A potential energy diagram for the reaction of methyl chloride with hydroxide ion.

25 °C, $k_0 = 6.2 \times 10^{12}$ s^{-1}. Because of this exponential relationship, **a reaction with a lower free energy of activation will occur very much faster than a reaction with a higher one.**

Generally speaking, if a reaction has a $\Delta G^{\ddagger}$ less than 20 kcal mol^{-1}, it will take place readily at room temperature or below. If $\Delta G^{\ddagger}$ is greater than 20 kcal mol^{-1} heating will be required to cause the reaction to occur at a reasonable rate.

A free-energy diagram for the reaction of methyl chloride with hydroxide ion is shown in Fig. 6.6. At 60 °C, $\Delta G^{\ddagger} = 24.5$ kcal mol^{-1}, which means that at this temperature, the reaction will reach completion in a matter of a few hours.

6.10 THE STEREOCHEMISTRY OF S_N2 REACTIONS

As we learned earlier (Section 6.8), in an S_N2 reaction *the nucleophile attacks from the backside, that is, from the side directly opposite the leaving group.* This mode of attack (see following figure) causes **a change in the configuration** of the carbon atom that is the object of nucleophilic attack. (The configuration of an atom *is the particular arrangement of groups around that atom in space,* Section 5.6C) As the displacement takes place, the configuration of the carbon atom under attack **inverts** — it is turned inside out in much the same way that an umbrella is turned inside out, or inverts, when caught in a strong wind.

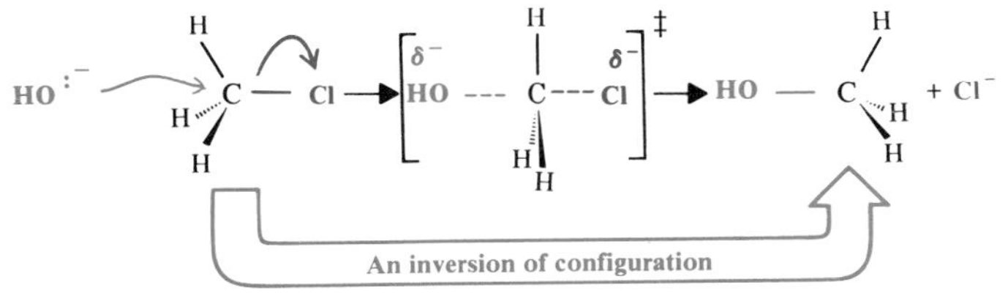

An inversion of configuration

With a molecule like methyl chloride, however, there is no way to prove that attack by the nucleophile inverts the configuration of the carbon atom because one form of methyl chloride is identical to its inverted form. With a cyclic molecule like *cis*-1-chloro-3-methylcyclopentane, however, we can observe the results of a *configuration inversion.* When *cis*-1-chloro-3-methylcyclopentane reacts with hydroxide ion in an S_N2 reaction the product is *trans*-3-methylcyclopentanol. *The hydroxide ion ends up being bonded on the opposite side of the ring from the chloride it replaces:*

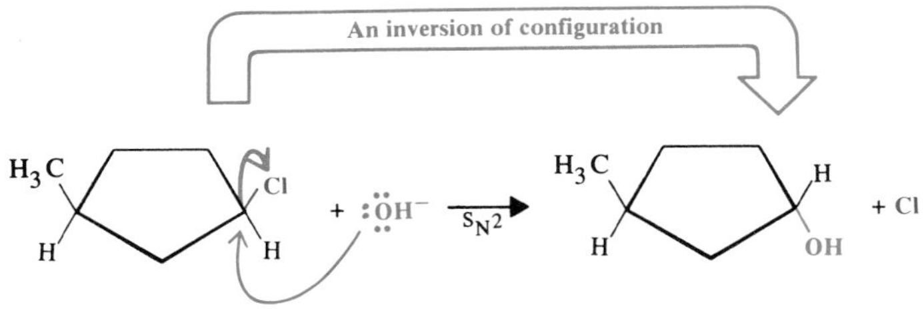

An inversion of configuration

cis-1-Chloro-3-
methylcyclopentane

trans-3-Methylcyclopentanol

Presumably, the transition state for this reaction is like that shown here.

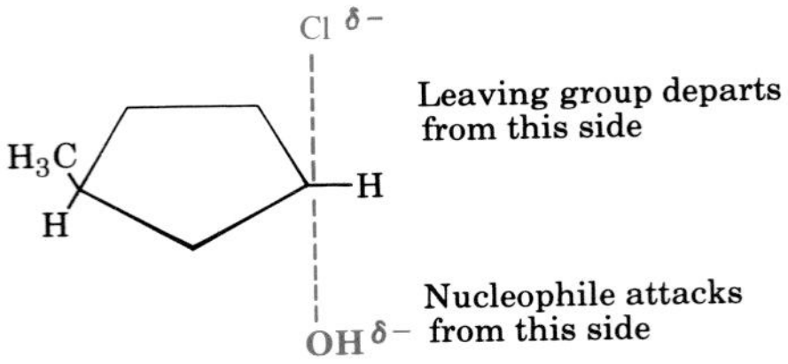

Cl $\delta-$

Leaving group departs
from this side

H$_3$C

H

H

Nucleophile attacks
OH $\delta-$ from this side

Problem 6.2

What product would result from the reaction just given, if attack by the hydroxide ion had occurred from the same side as the leaving group—that is, what product would have been formed if retention of configuration had taken place?

We can also observe an inversion of configuration with an acyclic molecule *when the S_N2 reaction takes place at a stereocenter.* Here, too, we find that *S_N2 reactions always lead to inversion of configuration.*

A compound that contains one stereocenter and, therefore, exists as a pair of enantiomers is 2-bromooctane. These enantiomers have been obtained separately and are known to have the configurations and rotations shown here.

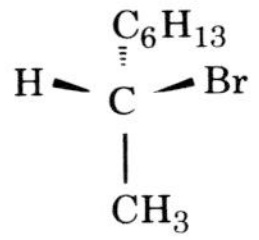

C$_6$H$_{13}$
H— C —Br

CH$_3$

(R)-(−)-2-Bromooctane
$[\alpha]_D^{25} = -34.25°$

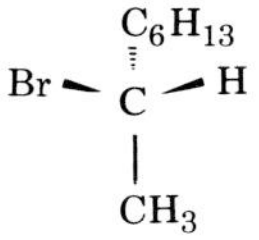

C$_6$H$_{13}$
Br— C —H

CH$_3$

(S)-(+)-2-Bromooctane
$[\alpha]_D^{25} = +34.25°$

The alcohol 2-octanol is also chiral. The configurations and rotations of the 2-octanol enantiomers have also been determined:

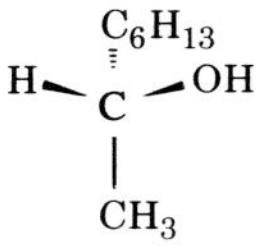

C$_6$H$_{13}$
H— C —OH

CH$_3$

(R)-(−)-2-Octanol
$[\alpha]_D^{25} = -9.90°$

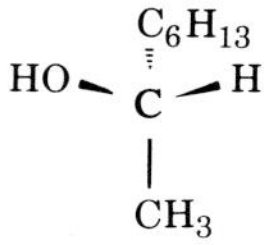

C$_6$H$_{13}$
HO— C —H

CH$_3$

(S)-(+)-2-Octanol
$[\alpha]_D^{25} = +9.90°$

When (R)-(−)-2-bromooctane reacts with sodium hydroxide, the only substitution product that is obtained from the reaction is (S)-(+)-2-octanol. The following reaction is S$_N$2 and takes place with *complete inversion of configuration.*

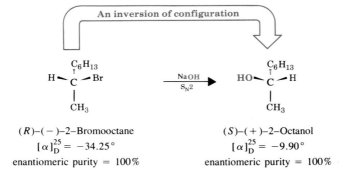

(R)–(−)–2–Bromooctane

$[\alpha]_D^{25} = -34.25°$

enantiomeric purity = 100%

(S)–(+)–2–Octanol

$[\alpha]_D^{25} = -9.90°$

enantiomeric purity = 100%

Problem 6.3

S$_N$2 reactions that involve breaking a bond to a stereocenter can be used to relate configurations of molecules because the *stereochemistry* of the reaction is known. (a) Illustrate how this is true by assigning configurations to the 2-chlorobutane enantiomers based on the following data. [The configuration of (−)-2-butanol is given in Section 5.6C.]

$$(+)\text{-2-Chlorobutane} \xrightarrow[\text{S}_\text{N}2]{\text{OH}^-} (-)\text{-2-Butanol}$$

$[\alpha]_D^{25} = +36.00°$ $[\alpha]_D^{25} = -13.52°$

enantiomerically pure   **enantiomerically pure**

(b) When optically pure (+)-2-chlorobutane is allowed to react with potassium iodide in acetone in an S$_N$2 reaction, the 2-iodobutane that is produced has a minus rotation. What is the configuration of (−)-2-iodobutane? Of (+)-2-iodobutane?

6.11 THE REACTION OF *TERT*-BUTYL CHLORIDE WITH HYDROXIDE ION: AN S$_N$1 REACTION

When *tert*-butyl chloride reacts with sodium hydroxide in a mixture of water and acetone, the kinetic results are quite different. The rate of formation of *tert*-butyl alcohol is dependent on the concentration of *tert*-butyl chloride, but it is *independent of the concentration of hydroxide ion.* Doubling the *tert*-butyl chloride concentration *doubles* the rate of the reaction, but changing the hydroxide ion concentration (within limits) has no appreciable effect. *tert*-Butyl chloride reacts by substitution at virtually the same rate in pure water (where the hydroxide ion is 10^{-7} M) as it does in 0.05 M aqueous sodium hydroxide (where the hydroxide ion concentration is 500,000 times larger). (We shall see in Section 6.10 that the important nucleophile in this reaction is a molecule of water.)

Thus the rate equation for this substitution reaction is first order with respect to *tert*-butyl chloride and *first order overall.*

$$(CH_3)_3C-Cl + OH^- \xrightarrow[\text{H}_2\text{O}]{\text{acetone}} (CH_3)_3C-OH + Cl^-$$

$$\text{Rate} \propto [(CH_3)_3CCl]$$

$$\text{Rate} = k[(CH_3)_3CCl]$$

We can conclude, therefore, that hydroxide ions do not participate in the transition state of the step that controls the rate of the reaction, and that only molecules of *tert*-butyl chloride are involved. This reaction is said to be **unimolecular.** We call this type of reaction an S_N1 reaction **(Substitution, Nucleophilic, unimolecular).**

How can we explain an S_N1 reaction in terms of a mechanism? To do so we shall need to consider the possibility that the mechanism involves more than one step. But what kind of kinetic results should we expect from a multistep reaction? Let us consider this point further.

6.11A MULTISTEP REACTIONS AND THE RATE-DETERMINING STEP

If a reaction takes place in a series of steps, and if the first step is intrinsically slower than all the others, then the rate of the overall reaction will be essentially the same as the rate of this slow step. This slow step, consequently, is called the **rate-limiting step** or the **rate-determining step.**

Consider a multistep reaction such as the following:

Step 1   Reactant $\xrightarrow{\text{slow}}$ intermediate-1

Step 2   Intermediate-1 $\xrightarrow{\text{fast}}$ intermediate-2

Step 3   Intermediate-2 $\xrightarrow{\text{fast}}$ product

When we say that the first step is intrinsically slow, we mean that the rate constant for step 1 is very much smaller than the rate constant for step 2 or for step 3:

Step 1   Rate = k_1 [Reactant]

Step 2   Rate = k_2 [Intermediate-1]

Step 3   Rate = k_3 [Intermediate-2]

$$k_1 \ll k_2 \quad \text{or} \quad k_3$$

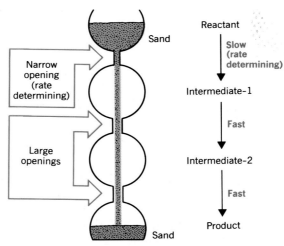

FIGURE 6.7 A modified hourglass that serves as an analogy for a multistep reaction. The overall rate is limited by the rate of the slow step.

When we say that steps 2 and 3 are *fast,* we mean that because their rate constants are larger, they could (in theory) take place rapidly if the concentrations of the two intermediates ever became high. In actuality, the concentrations of the intermediates are always very small because of the slowness of step 1, and steps 2 and 3 actually occur at the same rate as step 1.

An analogy may help clarify this. Imagine an hourglass modified in the way shown in Fig. 6.7. The opening between the top chamber and the one just below is considerably smaller than the other two. The overall rate at which sand falls from the top to the bottom of the hourglass is limited by the rate at which sand passes through this small orifice. This step, in the passage of sand, is analogous to the rate-determining step of the multistep reaction.

6.12 A MECHANISM FOR THE S_N1 REACTION

The mechanism for the reaction of *tert*-butyl chloride with water (Section 6.8) apparently involves three steps. Two distinct **intermediates** are formed. The first step is the slow step—it is the rate-determining step. In it a molecule of *tert*-butyl chloride ionizes and becomes a *tert*-butyl cation and a chloride ion. Carbocation formation in general takes place slowly because it is usually a highly endothermic process and is uphill in terms of free energy.

$$
\textit{Step 1} \quad
CH_3-\underset{\underset{CH_3}{|}}{\overset{\overset{CH_3}{|}}{C}}-Cl
\xrightarrow[\text{(rate-determining step)}]{\text{slow}}
CH_3-\underset{\underset{CH_3}{|}}{\overset{\overset{CH_3}{|}}{C}}{}^+ + Cl^-
$$

The next two steps are the following:

$$
\textit{Step 2} \quad
CH_3-\underset{\underset{CH_3}{|}}{\overset{\overset{CH_3}{|}}{C}}{}^+ + :\overset{..}{O}H_2
\xrightleftharpoons{\text{fast}}
CH_3-\underset{\underset{CH_3}{|}}{\overset{\overset{CH_3}{|}}{C}}-\overset{+}{O}H_2
$$

$$
\textit{Step 3} \quad
CH_3-\underset{\underset{CH_3}{|}}{\overset{\overset{CH_3}{|}}{C}}-OH_2{}^+ + H_2\overset{..}{O}:
\xrightleftharpoons{\text{fast}}
CH_3-\underset{\underset{CH_3}{|}}{\overset{\overset{CH_3}{|}}{C}}-OH + H_3O^+
$$

In the second step the intermediate *tert*-butyl cation reacts rapidly with water to produce a *tert*-butyloxonium ion (another intermediate) which, in the third step, rapidly transfers a proton to a molecule of water producing *tert*-butyl alcohol.

The first step requires heterolytic cleavage of the carbon–chlorine bond. Because no other bonds are formed in this step, it should be highly endothermic and it should have a high free energy of activation. That it takes place at all is largely because of the ionizing ability of the solvent, water. Experiments indicate that in the gas phase (i.e., in the absence of a solvent), the free energy of activation is about 150 kcal mol^{-1}! In aqueous solution, however, the free energy of activation is much lower—about 20 kcal mol^{-1}. Water molecules surround and stabilize the cation and anion that are produced (cf. Section 2.16E).

Even though the *tert*-butyl cation produced in step 1 is stabilized by solvation, it is still a highly reactive species. Almost immediately after it is formed, it reacts with one of the surrounding water molecules to form the *tert*-butyloxonium ion, $(CH_3)_3COH_2^+$. (It may also occasionally react with a hydroxide ion, but water molecules are far more plentiful.)

A free-energy diagram for the S_N1 reaction of *tert*-butyl chloride and water is given in Fig. 6.8.

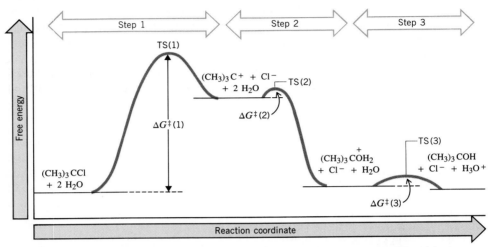

FIGURE 6.8 A Free-energy diagram for the S_N1 reaction of *tert*-butyl chloride with water. The free energy of activation for the first step, $\Delta G^{\ddagger}(1)$, is much larger than $\Delta G^{\ddagger}(2)$ or $\Delta G^{\ddagger}(3)$. TS(1) represents transition state (1), and so on.

The important transition state for the S_N1 reaction is the transition state of the rate-determining step [TS(1)]. In it the carbon–chlorine bond of *tert*-butyl chloride is largely broken and ions are beginning to develop:

$$CH_3-\overset{\overset{\displaystyle CH_3}{|}}{\underset{\underset{\displaystyle CH_3}{|}}{C}}{}^{\delta+}-Cl^{\delta-}$$

The solvent (water) stabilizes these developing ions by solvation.

6.13 CARBOCATIONS

Beginning in the 1920s much evidence began to accumulate implicating simple alkyl cations as intermediates in a variety of ionic reactions. However, because alkyl cations are highly unstable and highly reactive, they were in all instances studied prior to 1962 very short lived, transient species that could not be observed directly.* However, in 1962 George A. Olah (now at the University of Southern California) and his co-workers published the first of a series of papers describing experiments in

---

* As we shall learn later, carbocations bearing aromatic groups can be much more stable; one of these had been studied as early as 1901.

which alkyl cations were prepared in an environment in which they were reasonably stable and in which they could be observed by a number of spectroscopic techniques. We shall see the results of some of these spectroscopic studies in Chapter 14.

6.13A THE STRUCTURE OF CARBOCATIONS

Considerable experimental evidence indicates that the structure of carbocations is **trigonal planar** like that of BH_3 (Section 1.14). Just as the trigonal planar structure of BH_3 can be accounted for on the basis of sp^2 hybridization so, too (Fig. 6.9), can the trigonal planar structure of carbocations.

The central carbon atom in a carbocation is electron deficient; it has only six electrons in its outside energy level. In our model (Fig. 6.9) these six electrons are used to form sigma covalent bonds to hydrogen atoms (or to alkyl groups). The p orbital contains no electrons.

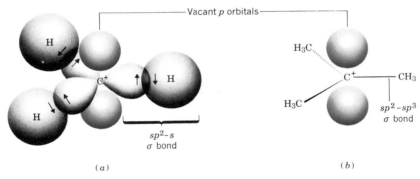

(a) (b)

FIGURE 6.9 (*a*) Orbital structure of the methyl cation. The bonds are sigma bonds (σ) formed by overlap of the carbon atom's three sp^2 orbitals with the $1s$ orbitals of the hydrogen atoms. The p orbital is vacant. (*b*) A dash-line-wedge representation of the *tert*-butyl cation. The bonds between carbon atoms are formed by overlap of sp^3 orbitals of the methyl groups with sp^2 orbitals of the central carbon atom.

6.13B THE RELATIVE STABILITIES OF CARBOCATIONS

A large body of experimental evidence indicates that the relative stabilities of carbocations are related to the number of alkyl groups attached to the positively charged trivalent carbon atom. Tertiary carbocations are the most stable, and the methyl cation is the least stable. The overall order of stability is as follows:

$$
\underset{\substack{3° \\ \text{(most} \\ \text{stable)}}}{\overset{\text{R}}{\underset{\text{R}}{\text{R}-\overset{|}{\underset{|}{\text{C}}}{}^{+}}}} > \underset{2°}{\overset{\text{R}}{\underset{\text{H}}{\text{R}-\overset{|}{\underset{|}{\text{C}}}{}^{+}}}} > \underset{1°}{\overset{\text{H}}{\underset{\text{H}}{\text{R}-\overset{|}{\underset{|}{\text{C}}}{}^{+}}}} > \underset{\substack{\text{Methyl} \\ \text{(least} \\ \text{stable)}}}{\overset{\text{H}}{\underset{\text{H}}{\text{H}-\overset{|}{\underset{|}{\text{C}}}{}^{+}}}}
$$

This order of stability of carbocations can be explained on the basis of a law of physics that states that *a charged system is stabilized when the charge is dispersed or delocalized.* Alkyl groups, when compared to hydrogen atoms, are **electron releasing.**

This means that alkyl groups will shift electron density toward a positive charge. Through electron release, *alkyl groups* attached to the positive carbon atom of a carbocation **delocalize** the positive charge. In doing so, the attached alkyl groups assume part of the positive charge themselves and thus *stabilize* the carbocation. We can see how this occurs by inspecting Fig. 6.10.

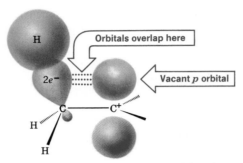

FIGURE 6.10 *How a methyl group helps stabilize the positive charge of a carbocation.* Electron density from one of the carbon–hydrogen sigma bonds of the methyl group flows into the vacant p orbital of the carbocation because the orbitals can partly overlap. Shifting electron density in this way makes the sp^2-hybridized carbon of the carbocation somewhat less positive and the hydrogens of the methyl group assume some of the positive charge. Delocalization (dispersal) of the charge in this way leads to greater stability.

In the *tert*-butyl cation (see the following structure) three electron-releasing methyl groups surround the central carbon atom and assist in delocalizing the positive charge. In the isopropyl cation there are only two attached methyl groups that can serve to delocalize the charge. In the ethyl cation there is only one attached methyl group, and in the methyl cation there is none at all. As a result, *the delocalization of charge and the order of stability of the carbocations parallel the number of attached methyl groups.*

$\delta+$ $\overset{\downarrow}{CH_3}$ $\delta+CH_3 \rightarrow \overset{\uparrow}{\underset{\overset{\uparrow}{CH_3}}{\overset{\delta+}{C}}}\,^{\delta+}$ $\delta+$	is more stable than	$\delta+$ $\overset{\downarrow}{CH_3}$ $\delta+CH_3 \rightarrow \overset{\delta+}{\underset{H}{C}}$	is more stable than
tert-Butyl cation (3°) (most stable)		Isopropyl cation (2°)	

H $\delta+CH_3 \rightarrow \overset{\delta+}{\underset{H}{C}}$ H	is more stable than	H $H—\overset{+}{\underset{H}{C}}$ H	
Ethyl cation (1°)		Methyl cation (least stable)	

The relative stability of carbocations is 3° > 2° > 1° > methyl

6.14 THE STEREOCHEMISTRY OF S_N1 REACTIONS

Because the carbocation formed in the first step of an S_N1 reaction has a trigonal planar structure (Section 6.13A) when it reacts with a nucleophile, it may do so from either the frontside or backside (see following illustration). With the *tert*-butyl cation this makes no difference because the same product is formed by either mode of attack.

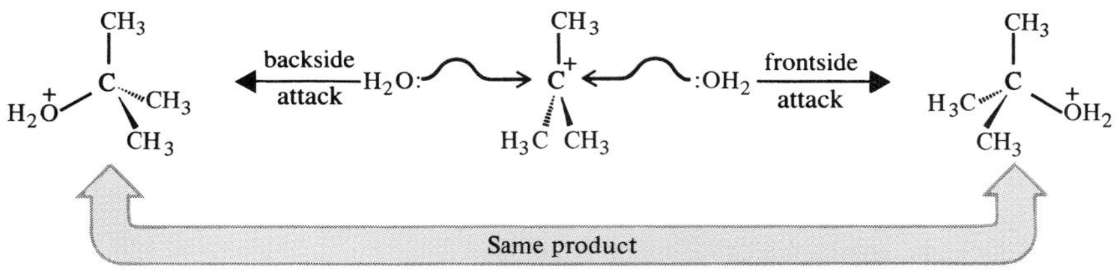

6.14 THE STEREOCHEMISTRY OF S$_N$1 REACTIONS

With some cations, however, *different products arise from the two reaction possibilities.* We shall study this point next.

6.14A REACTIONS THAT INVOLVE RACEMIZATION

A reaction that transforms an optically active compound into a racemic form is said to proceed with **racemization.** If the original compound loses all of its optical activity in the course of the reaction, chemists describe the reaction as having taken place with *complete* racemization. If the original compound loses only part of its optical activity, as would be the case if an enantiomer were only partially converted to a racemic form, then chemists describe this as proceeding with *partial* racemization.

Racemization will take place *whenever the reaction causes chiral molecules to be converted to an achiral intermediate.*

Examples of this type of reaction are S$_N$1 reactions in which the leaving group departs from a stereocenter. These reactions almost always result in extensive and sometimes complete racemization. For example, heating optically active (*S*)-3-bromo-3-methylhexane with aqueous acetone results in the formation of 3-methyl-3-hexanol as a racemic form.

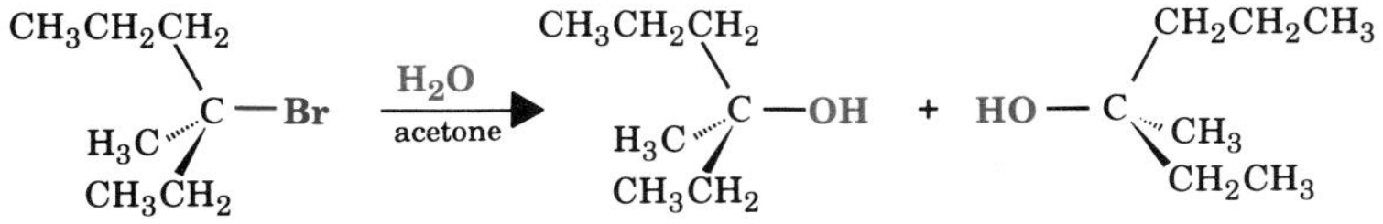

The reason: The S$_N$1 reaction proceeds through the formation of an intermediate carbocation (Fig. 6.11) and the carbocation, because of its trigonal planar configuration, *is achiral.* It reacts with water with equal rates from either side to form the enantiomers of 3-methyl-3-hexanol in equal amounts.

Problem 6.4

Keeping in mind that carbocations have a trigonal planar structure, (a) write a structure for the carbocation intermediate and (b) write structures for the alcohol (or alcohols) you would expect from the following reaction:

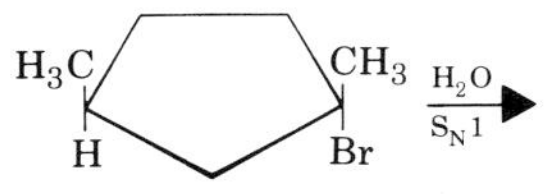

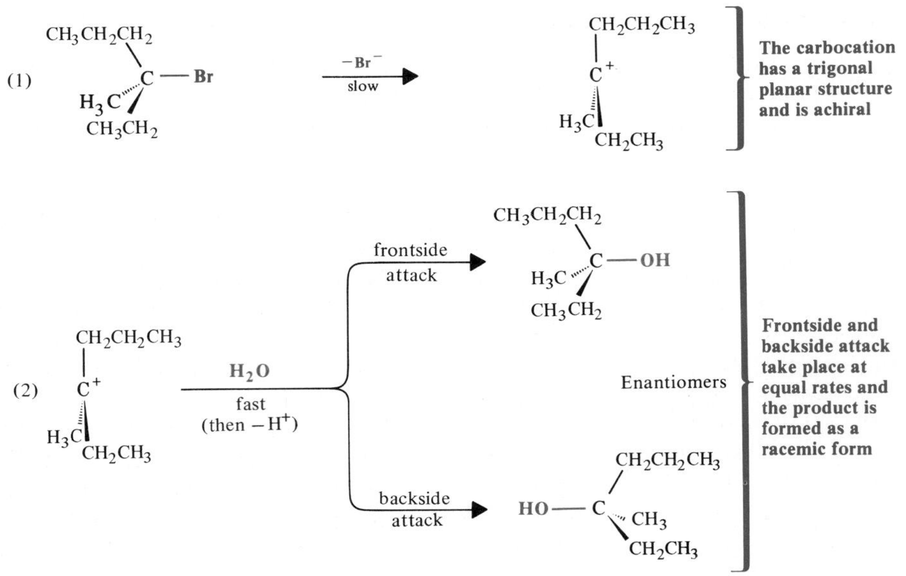

FIGURE 6.11 The S_N1 reaction of 3-bromo-3-methylhexane proceeds with racemization because the intermediate carbocation is achiral.

6.14B SOLVOLYSIS

The S_N1 reaction of an alkyl halide with water is an example of **solvolysis.** A solvolysis is a nucleophilic substitution in which *the nucleophile is a molecule of the solvent* (*solvent + lysis:* cleavage by the solvent). Since the solvent in this instance is water, we could also call the reaction a **hydrolysis.** If the reaction had taken place in methanol we would call the reaction a **methanolysis.**

Examples of Solvolysis

$$(CH_3)_3C—Br + H_2O \longrightarrow (CH_3)_3C—OH + HBr$$

$$(CH_3)_3C—Cl + CH_3OH \longrightarrow (CH_3)_3C—OCH_3 + HCl$$

$$(CH_3)_3C—Cl + H\overset{O}{\overset{\|}{C}}OH \longrightarrow (CH_3)_3C—O\overset{O}{\overset{\|}{C}}H + HCl$$

These reactions all involve the initial formation of a carbocation and the subsequent reaction of that cation with a molecule of the solvent. In the last example the solvent is formic acid (HCO_2H) and the following steps take place:

Step 1 $(CH_3)_3C—Cl \xrightarrow{\text{slow}} (CH_3)_3C^+ + Cl^-$

Step 2 $(CH_3)_3C^+ + H\ddot{O}—\overset{O}{\overset{\|}{C}}H \xrightarrow{\text{fast}} (CH_3)_3C—\underset{\underset{H}{|}}{O^{\pm}}—\overset{O}{\overset{\|}{C}}H$

Step 3 $(CH_3)_3C—\underset{\underset{H}{|}}{O^{\pm}}—\overset{O}{\overset{\|}{C}}H \xrightarrow{\text{fast}} (CH_3)_3C—O—\overset{O}{\overset{\|}{C}}H + H^+$

Problem 6.5

(a) What product would be obtained from the ethanolysis of *tert*-butyl chloride?   (b) Outline the steps of this S_N1 reaction.

6.15 FACTORS AFFECTING THE RATES OF S_N1 AND S_N2 REACTIONS

Now that we have an understanding of the mechanisms of S_N2 and S_N1 reactions, our next task is to explain why methyl chloride reacts by an S_N2 mechanism and *tert*-butyl chloride by an S_N1 mechanism. We would also like to be able to predict which pathway — S_N1 or S_N2 — would be followed by the reaction of any alkyl halide with any nucleophile under varying conditions.

The answer to this kind of question is to be found in the *relative rates of the reactions that occur.* If a given alkyl halide and nucleophile react *rapidly* by an S_N2 mechanism but *slowly* by an S_N1 mechanism under a given set of conditions, then an S_N2 pathway will be followed by most of the molecules. On the other hand another alkyl halide and another nucleophile may react very slowly (or not at all) by an S_N2 pathway. If they react rapidly by an S_N1 mechanism, then the reactants will follow an S_N1 pathway.

Experiments have shown that a number of factors affect the relative rates of S_N1 and S_N2 reactions. The most important factors are

1. The structure of the substrate.
2. The concentration and reactivity of the nucleophile (for bimolecular reactions only).
3. The effect of the solvent.
4. The nature of the leaving group.

6.15A THE EFFECT OF THE STRUCTURE OF THE SUBSTRATE

S_N2 Reactions.   Simple alkyl halides show the following general order of reactivity in S_N2 reactions:

$$\text{methyl} > \text{primary} > \text{secondary} > \text{(tertiary)}$$

Methyl halides react most rapidly and tertiary halides react so slowly as to be unreactive by the S_N2 mechanism. Table 6.4 gives the relative rates of typical S_N2 reactions.

TABLE 6.4   Relative rates of reactions of alkyl halides in S_N2 reactions

SUBSTITUENT	COMPOUND	RELATIVE RATE
Methyl	CH_3-X	30
1°	CH_3CH_2-X	1
2°	$(CH_3)_2CHX$	0.02
Neopentyl	$(CH_3)_3CCH_2X$	0.00001
3°	$(CH_3)_3CX$	~0

Neopentyl halides, even though they are primary halides, are very unreactive.

$$CH_3-\underset{\underset{CH_3}{|}}{\overset{\overset{CH_3}{|}}{C}}-CH_2-X$$

A neopentyl halide

The important factor behind this order of reactivity is a **steric effect.** A steric effect is an effect on relative rates caused by the space-filling properties of those parts of a molecule attached at or near the reacting site. One kind of steric effect — the kind that is important here — is called **steric hindrance.** By this we mean that the spatial arrangement of the atoms or groups at or near the reacting site of a molecule hinders or retards a reaction.

For particles (molecules and ions) to react, their reactive centers must be able to come within bonding distance of each other. Although most molecules are reasonably flexible, very large and bulky groups can often hinder the formation of the required transition state. In some cases they can prevent its formation altogether.

An S_N2 reaction requires an approach by the nucleophile to a distance within bonding range of the carbon atom bearing the leaving group. Because of this, bulky substituents on *or near* that carbon atom have a dramatic inhibiting effect (Fig. 6.12). They cause the potential energy of the required transition state to be increased and, consequently, they increase the free energy of activation for the reaction. Of the simple alkyl halides, methyl halides react most rapidly in S_N2 reactions because only three small hydrogen atoms interfere with the approaching nucleophile. Neopentyl and tertiary halides are the least reactive because bulky groups present a strong hindrance to the approaching nucleophile. (Tertiary substrates, for all practical purposes, do not react by an S_N2 mechanism.)

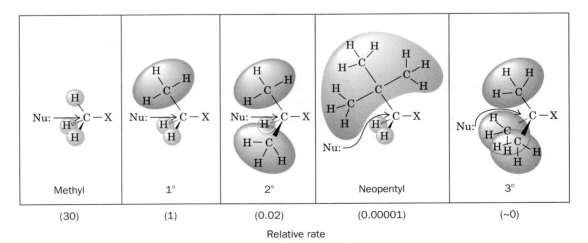

Methyl	1°	2°	Neopentyl	3°
(30)	(1)	(0.02)	(0.00001)	(~0)

Relative rate

FIGURE 6.12 Steric effects in the S_N2 reaction.

S_N1 Reactions. **The primary factor that determines the reactivity of organic substrates in an S_N1 reaction is the relative stability of the carbocation that is formed.**

6.15 FACTORS AFFECTING THE RATES OF S_N1 AND S_N2 REACTIONS

Except for those reactions that take place in strong acids, which we shall study later, the only organic compounds that undergo reaction by an S_N1 path at a reasonable rate are *those that are capable of forming relatively stable carbocations.* Of the simple alkyl halides that we have studied so far, this means (for all practical purposes) that only tertiary halides react by an S_N1 mechanism. (Later we shall see that certain organic halides, called *allylic halides* and *benzylic halides,* can also react by an S_N1 mechanism because they can form relatively stable carbocations, cf. Section 13.11.)

Tertiary carbocations are stabilized because three alkyl groups release electrons to the positive carbon atom and thereby disperse its charge (see Section 6.13B).

Formation of a relatively stable carbocation is important in an S_N1 reaction because it means that the free energy of activation for the slow step for the reaction (i. e., $R-X \longrightarrow R^+ + X^-$) will be low enough for the overall reaction to take place at a reasonable rate. If you examine Fig. 6.8 again, you will see this step (step 1) is *uphill in terms of free energy* ($\Delta G°$ for this step is positive). It is also uphill in terms of enthalpy ($\Delta H°$ is also positive), and, therefore, this step is *endothermic.* According to a postulate made by G. S. Hammond (then at the California Institute of Technology) and J. E. Leffler (Florida State University) **the transition state for a step that is uphill in energy should show a strong resemblance to the product of that step.*** Since the product of this step (actually an intermediate in the overall reaction) is a carbocation, any factor that stabilizes it—such as dispersal of the positive charge by electron-releasing groups—should also stabilize the transition state in which the positive charge is developing.

Step (1)

Reactant

Transition state
*resembles product of step
because $\Delta G°$ is positive*

Product of step
stabilized by three
electron-releasing
groups

For a methyl, primary, or secondary halide to react by an S_N1 mechanism it would have to ionize to form a methyl, primary, or secondary carbocation. These carbocations, however, are much higher in energy than a tertiary carbocation, and the transition states leading to these carbocations are even higher in energy. The activation energy for an S_N1 reaction of a simple methyl, primary or secondary halide, consequently, is so large (the reaction is so slow) that, for all practical purposes, an S_N1 reaction does not compete with the corresponding S_N2 reaction.

6.15B THE EFFECT OF THE CONCENTRATION AND STRENGTH OF THE NUCLEOPHILE

Since the nucleophile does not participate in the rate-determining step of an S_N1 reaction, the rates of S_N1 reactions are unaffected by either the concentration or the identity of the nucleophile. The rates of S_N2 reactions, however, depend on *both* the concentration *and* the identity of the attacking nucleophile. We saw in Section 6.7 how increasing the concentration of the nucleophile increases the rate of an S_N2

---

* We shall study the Hammond–Leffler postulate further in Section 7.7A.

reaction. We can now examine how the rate of an S_N2 reaction depends on the identity of the nucleophile.

We describe nucleophiles as being *strong* or *weak*. When we do this we are really describing their relative reactivities in S_N2 reactions. A strong nucleophile is one that reacts rapidly with a given substrate. A weak nucleophile is one that reacts slowly with the same substrate under the same reaction conditions.

The methoxide ion, for example, is a strong nucleophile. It reacts relatively rapidly with methyl iodide to produce dimethyl ether.

$$CH_3O^- + CH_3I \xrightarrow{\text{rapid}} CH_3OCH_3 + I^-$$

Methanol, on the other hand, is a weak nucleophile. Under the same conditions it reacts very slowly with methyl iodide.

$$CH_3OH + CH_3I \xrightarrow{\text{very slow}} CH_3\overset{+}{\underset{\underset{H}{|}}{O}}CH_3 + I^-$$

The relative strengths of nucleophiles can be correlated with two structural features:

1. **A negatively charged nucleophile is always a stronger nucleophile than its conjugate acid.** Thus HO^- is a stronger nucleophile than H_2O and RO^- is stronger than ROH.

2. **In a group of nucleophiles in which the nucleophilic atom is the same, nucleophilicities parallel basicities.** Oxygen compounds, for example, show the following order of reactivity:

$$RO^- > HO^- \gg RCO_2^- > ROH > H_2O$$

This is also their order of basicity. An alkoxide ion (RO^-) is a slightly stronger base than a hydroxide ion (HO^-), a hydroxide ion is a much stronger base than a carboxylate ion (RCO_2^-), and so on.

6.15C SOLVENT EFFECTS ON S_N2 REACTIONS. POLAR PROTIC AND APROTIC SOLVENTS

The relative strengths of nucleophiles do not always parallel their basicities *when the nucleophilic atoms are not the same.* When we examine the relative nucleophilicity of compounds within the same group of the periodic table, we find that *in hydroxylic solvents such as alcohols and water* the nucleophile with the larger nucleophilic atom is stronger. Thiols (R—SH) are stronger nucleophiles than alcohols (ROH); RS^- ions are stronger than RO^- ions; and the halide ions show the following order:

$$I^- > Br^- > Cl^- > F^-$$

This effect is related to the strength of the interactions between the nucleophile and its surrounding layer of solvent molecules. A molecule of a solvent such as water or an alcohol—called a **protic solvent** (Section 3.7)—*has a hydrogen atom attached to an atom of a strongly electronegative element (oxygen).* Molecules of protic solvents can, therefore, form hydrogen bonds to nucleophiles in the following way:

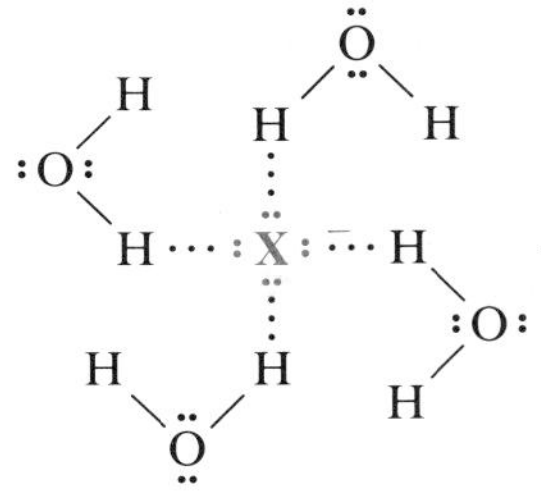

Molecules of the protic solvent, water, solvate a halide ion by forming hydrogen bonds to it

A small nucleophile, such as a fluoride ion, because its charge is more concentrated, is more strongly solvated than a larger one. Hydrogen bonds to a small atom are stronger than those to a large atom. For a nucleophile to react, it must shed some of its solvent molecules because it must closely approach the carbon bearing the leaving group. A large ion, because the hydrogen bonds between it and the solvent are weaker, can shed some of its solvent molecules more easily and thus it will be more nucleophilic.

The greater reactivity of nucleophiles with large nucleophilic atoms is not entirely related to solvation. Larger atoms are more **polarizable** (their electron clouds are more easily distorted), therefore, a larger nucleophilic atom can donate a greater degree of electron density to the substrate than a smaller nucleophile whose electrons are more tightly held.

While nucleophilicity and basicity are related, they are not measured in the same way. Basicity, as expressed by K_a, is measured *by the position of an equilibrium* involving an electron-pair donor (base), a proton, the conjugate acid, and the conjugate base. Nucleophilicity is measured *by relative rates of reaction,* by how rapidly an electron-pair donor reacts at an atom (usually carbon) bearing a leaving group. For example, the hydroxide ion (OH^-) is a stronger base than a cyanide ion (CN^-); at equilibrium it has the greater affinity for a proton (the pK_a of H_2O is ~ 16, while the pK_a of HCN is ~ 10). Nevertheless, cyanide ion is a stronger nucleophile, it reacts more rapidly with a carbon bearing a leaving group than a hydroxide ion.

The relative nucleophilicities of some common nucleophiles in protic solvents are as follows:

Relative Nucleophilicity in Protic Solvents

$$SH^- > CN^- > I^- > OH^- > N_3^- > Br^- > CH_3CO_2^- > Cl^- > F^- > H_2O$$

Polar Aprotic Solvents

Aprotic solvents are those solvents whose molecules do not have a hydrogen atom that is attached to an atom of a strongly electronegative element. Most aprotic solvents (benzene, the alkanes, etc.) are relatively nonpolar, and they do not dissolve most ionic compounds. (In Section 10.22 we shall see how they can be induced to do so, however.) In recent years a number of **polar aprotic solvents** have come into wide use by chemists; *they are especially useful in S_N2 reactions.* Several examples *are shown here.*

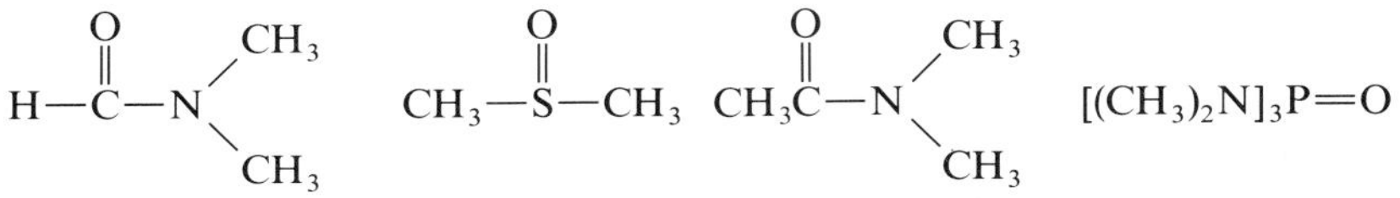

N,N-Dimethylformamide (DMF)   Dimethyl sulfoxide (DMSO)   Dimethylacetamide (DMA)   Hexamethylphosphoric triamide (HMPT)

All of these solvents (DMF, DMSO, DMA, and HMPT) dissolve ionic compounds, and they solvate cations very well. They do so in the same way that protic solvents solvate cations: by orienting their negative ends around the cation and by donating unshared electron pairs to vacant orbitals of the cation:

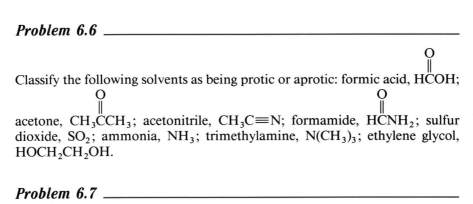

A sodium ion solvated by molecules of the protic solvent water

A sodium ion solvated by molecules of the aprotic solvent dimethyl sulfoxide

However, because they cannot form hydrogen bonds, *aprotic solvents do not solvate anions to any appreciable extent.* In these solvents anions are unencumbered by a layer of solvent molecules and, therefore, they are poorly stabilized by solvation. These "naked" anions are highly reactive both *as bases and nucleophiles.* In DMSO, for example, the relative order of reactivity of halide ions is the same as their relative basicity:

$$F^- > Cl^- > Br^- > I^-$$

This is the opposite of their strength as nucleophiles in alcohol or water solutions:

$$I^- > Br^- > Cl^- > F^-$$

The rates of S_N2 reactions generally are vastly increased when they are carried out in polar aprotic solvents. The increase in rate can be as large as a millionfold.

Problem 6.6

Classify the following solvents as being protic or aprotic: formic acid, $HCOH$; acetone, CH_3CCH_3; acetonitrile, $CH_3C{\equiv}N$; formamide, $HCNH_2$; sulfur dioxide, SO_2; ammonia, NH_3; trimethylamine, $N(CH_3)_3$; ethylene glycol, $HOCH_2CH_2OH$.

Problem 6.7

Would you expect the reaction of propyl bromide with sodium cyanide (NaCN), that is,

6.15 FACTORS AFFECTING THE RATES OF S_N1 AND S_N2 REACTIONS

$$CH_3CH_2CH_2Br + NaCN \longrightarrow CH_3CH_2CH_2CN + NaBr$$

to occur faster in DMF or in ethanol? Explain your answer.

Problem 6.8

Which would you expect to be the stronger nucleophile in a protic solvent:
(a) the amide ion (NH_2^-) or ammonia? (b) RS^- or RSH? (c) PH_3 or NH_3?

6.15D SOLVENT EFFECTS ON S_N1 REACTIONS. THE IONIZING ABILITY OF THE SOLVENT

Because of its ability to solvate cations *and* anions so effectively, the use of a **polar protic solvent** will greatly increase the rate of ionization of an alkyl halide *in any S_N1 reaction.* It does this because solvation stabilizes the transition state leading to the intermediate carbocation and halide ion more than it does the reactants; thus the free energy of activation is lower. The transition state for this endothermic step is one in which separated charges are developing and thus it resembles the ions that are ultimately produced.

$$(CH_3)_3C\!-\!Cl \longrightarrow \left[(CH_3)_3\overset{\delta+}{C}\cdots\overset{\delta-}{Cl}\right] \longrightarrow (CH_3)_3C^+ + Cl^-$$

Reactant   **Transition state**   **Products**

Separated charges are developing

A rough indication of a solvent's polarity is a quantity called the **dielectric constant.** The dielectric constant is a measure of the solvent's ability to insulate opposite charges from each other. Electrostatic attractions and repulsions between ions are smaller in solvents with higher dielectric constants. Table 6.5 gives the dielectric constants of some common solvents.

Water is the most effective solvent for promoting ionization, but most organic compounds do not dissolve appreciably in water. They usually dissolve, however, in alcohols, and quite often mixed solvents are used. Methanol–water and ethanol–water are common mixed solvents for nucleophilic substitution reactions.

Problem 6.9

When *tert*-butyl bromide undergoes solvolysis in a mixture of methanol and water, the rate of solvolysis (measured by the rate at which bromide ions form in the mixture) *increases* when the percentage of water in the mixture is increased. (a) Explain this occurrence. (b) Provide an explanation for the observation that the rate of the S_N2 reaction of ethyl chloride with potassium iodide in methanol and water *decreases* when the percentage of water in the mixture is increased.

TABLE 6.5 Dielectric constants of common solvents

	SOLVENT	FORMULA	DIELECTRIC CONSTANT
	Water	H_2O	80
	Formic acid	$\overset{\displaystyle O}{\overset{\|}{HCOH}}$	59
	Dimethyl sulfoxide (DMSO)	$\overset{\displaystyle O}{\overset{\|}{CH_3SCH_3}}$	49
	N,N-Dimethylformamide (DMF)	$\overset{\displaystyle O}{\overset{\|}{HCN(CH_3)_2}}$	37
	Acetonitrile	$CH_3C{\equiv}N$	36
	Methanol	CH_3OH	33
	Hexamethylphosphoric triamide (HMPT)	$[(CH_3)_2N]_3P{=}O$	30
	Ethanol	CH_3CH_2OH	24
	Acetone	$\overset{\displaystyle O}{\overset{\|}{CH_3CCH_3}}$	21
	Acetic acid	$\overset{\displaystyle O}{\overset{\|}{CH_3COH}}$	6

Increasing solvent polarity

6.15E THE NATURE OF THE LEAVING GROUP

The best leaving groups are those that become the most stable ions after they depart. Since most leaving groups leave as a negative ion, the best leaving groups are those ions that stabilize a negative charge most effectively. Because weak bases do this best, the best leaving groups are weak bases. The reason that stabilization of the negative charge is important can be understood by considering the structure of the transition states. In either an S_N1 or S_N2 reaction the leaving group begins to acquire a negative charge as the transition state is reached.

S_N1 Reaction (rate-limiting step)

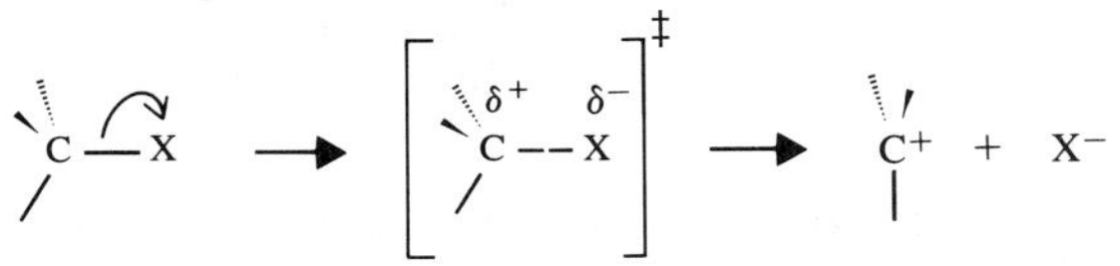

Transition state

S_N2 Reaction

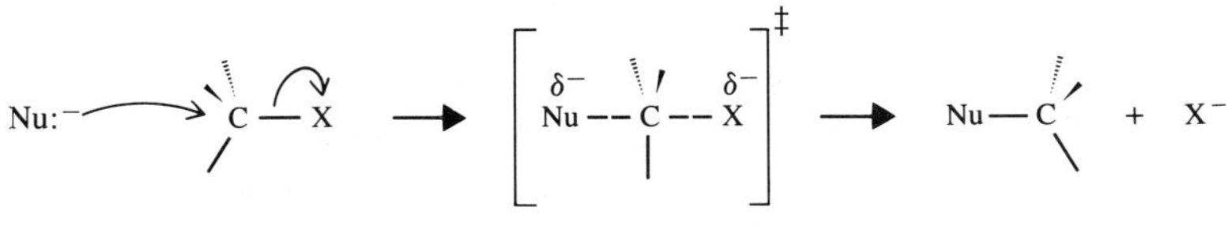

Transition state

6.15 FACTORS AFFECTING THE RATES OF S_N1 AND S_N2 REACTIONS

Stabilization of this developing negative charge by the leaving group stabilizes the transition state (lowers its potential energy); this lowers the energy of activation, and thereby increases the rate of the reaction. Of the halogens, an iodide ion is the best leaving group and a fluoride ion is the poorest:

$$I^- > Br^- > Cl^- \gg F^-$$

The order is the opposite of the basicity:

$$F^- \gg Cl^- > Br^- > I^-$$

Other weak bases that are good leaving groups that we shall study later, are alkanesulfonate ions, alkyl sulfate ions, and the *p*-toluenesulfonate ion.

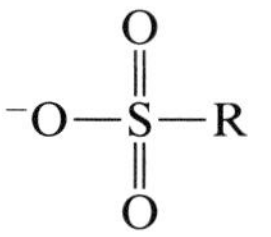

An alkanesulfonate ion 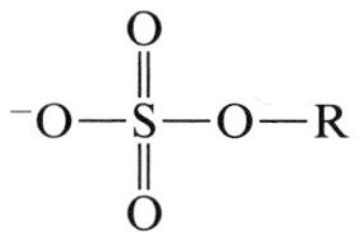   **An alkyl sulfate ion** 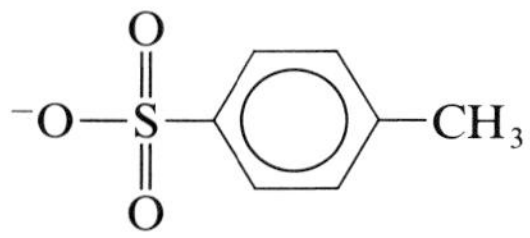   ***p*-Toluenesulfonate ion**

These anions are all the conjugate bases of very strong acids.

The trifluoromethanesulfonate ion ($CF_3SO_3^-$, commonly called the **triflate ion**) is one of the best leaving groups known to chemists. It is the anion of CF_3SO_3H, an exceedingly strong acid — one that is much stronger than sulfuric acid.

$$CF_3SO_3^-$$
Triflate ion
(a "super" leaving group)

Strongly basic ions rarely act as leaving groups. The hydroxide ion, for example, is a strong base and thus reactions like the following do not take place:

This reaction does not take place because the leaving group is a strongly basic hydroxide ion

However, when an alcohol is dissolved in a strong acid it can react with a halide ion. Because the acid protonates the —OH group of the alcohol, the leaving group no longer needs to be a hydroxide ion; it is now a molecule of water — a much weaker base than a hydroxide ion.

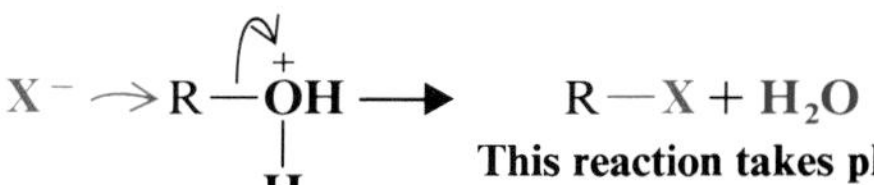

This reaction takes place because the leaving group is a weak base

Problem 6.10

The reaction of methyl chloride with aqueous sodium hydroxide to produce methanol and sodium chloride is essentially irreversible—the reaction proceeds virtually to completion. What factors account for this?

Very powerful bases such as hydride ions ($H:^-$) and alkanide ions ($R:^-$) never act as leaving groups. Therefore, reactions such as the following never take place:

$$Nu:^- + CH_3CH_2{-}H \xrightarrow{\times} CH_3CH_2{-}Nu + H:^-$$

$$\text{or} \quad Nu:^- + CH_3{-}CH_3 \xrightarrow{\times} CH_3{-}Nu + CH_3:^-$$

These are not leaving groups

6.15F SUMMARY: S_N1 VERSUS S_N2

Reactions of alkyl halides by an S_N1 mechanism are favored by the use of substrates that can form relatively stable carbocations, by the use of weak nucleophiles, and by the use of highly ionizing solvents. S_N1 mechanisms, therefore, are important in solvolysis reactions of tertiary halides, especially when the solvent is highly polar. In a solvolysis the nucleophile is weak because it is a neutral molecule (of the solvent) rather than an anion.

If we want to favor the reaction of an alkyl halide by an S_N2 mechanism, we should use a relatively unhindered alkyl halide, a strong nucleophile, a polar aprotic solvent, and a high concentration of the nucleophile. For substrates, the order of reactivity in S_N2 reactions is

$$CH_3{-}X > C{-}CH_2{-}X > C{-}\overset{\overset{\displaystyle C}{|}}{C}H{-}X$$
$$\text{Methyl} > \quad 1° \quad > \quad 2°$$

Tertiary halides do not react by an S_N2 mechanism.

The effect of the leaving group is the same in both S_N1 and S_N2 reactions: alkyl iodides react fastest; fluorides react slowest. (Because alkyl fluorides react so slowly, they are seldom used in nucleophilic substitution reactions.)

$$R{-}I > R{-}Br > R{-}Cl \quad S_N1 \text{ or } S_N2$$

6.16 ORGANIC SYNTHESIS: FUNCTIONAL GROUP TRANSFORMATIONS USING S_N2 REACTIONS

The process of making one compound from another is called **synthesis**. When, for one reason or another, we find ourselves in need of an organic compound that is not available in the stockroom, or perhaps even of one that has never been made before, the task of synthesis starts. We shall have the job of making the compound we need from other compounds that are available.

S_N2 reactions are highly useful in organic synthesis because they enable us to convert one functional group into another—a process that is called a **functional**

6.16 ORGANIC SYNTHESIS: FUNCTIONAL GROUP TRANSFORMATIONS USING S$_N$2 REACTIONS

group transformation or a **functional group interconversion.** With the S$_N$2 reactions shown in Fig. 6.13, the functional group of a methyl, primary, or secondary alkyl halide can be transformed into that of an alcohol, ether, thiol, thioether, nitrile, ester, and so on. (*Note:* The use of the prefix *thio* in a name means that a sulfur atom has replaced an oxygen atom in the compound.)

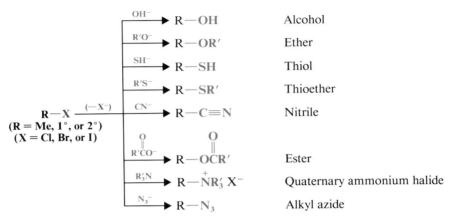

FIGURE 6.13 Functional group interconversions of methyl, primary, and secondary alkyl halides using S$_N$2 reactions.

Alkyl chlorides and bromides are also easily converted to alkyl iodides by nucleophilic substitution reactions.

$$R-Cl \atop R-Br \Big\} \xrightarrow{I^-} R-I \quad (+ Cl^- \text{ or } Br^-)$$

One other aspect of the S$_N$2 reaction that is of great importance in synthesis is its **stereochemistry** (Section 6.10). S$_N$2 reactions always occur **with inversion of configuration** at the atom that bears the leaving group. This means that when we use S$_N$2 reactions in syntheses we can be sure of the configuration of our product if we know the configuration of our reactant. For example, suppose we need a sample of the nitrile shown here with the (*S*) configuration.

$$:N \equiv C - C \overset{CH_3}{\underset{CH_2CH_3}{\overset{|}{<}}} H$$

(*S*)–2–Methylbutanenitrile

If we have available (*R*)-2-bromobutane, we can carry out the following synthesis:

$$:N \equiv C:^- \; + \; \overset{CH_3}{\underset{CH_3CH_2}{\overset{\backslash}{C}}} - Br \; \xrightarrow[\text{(inversion)}]{S_N2} \; :N \equiv C - C \overset{CH_3}{\underset{CH_2CH_3}{\overset{/}{<}}} H \; + \; Br^-$$

(*R*)–2–Bromobutane   (*S*)–2–Methylbutanenitrile

Problem 6.11

Starting with (*S*)-2-bromobutane, outline syntheses of each of the following compounds:

(a) (*R*)-CH₃CHCH₂CH₃
 |
 OCH₂CH₃

(b) (*R*)-CH₃CHCH₂CH₃
 |
 OCCH₃
 ‖
 O

(c) (*R*)-CH₃CHCH₂CH₃
 |
 SH

(d) (*R*)-CH₃CHCH₂CH₃
 |
 SCH₃

6.16A THE UNREACTIVITY OF VINYLIC AND PHENYL HALIDES

As we learned in Section 6.1, compounds that have a halogen atom attached to one carbon atom of a double bond are called **vinylic halides;** those that have a halogen atom attached to a benzene ring are called **phenyl halides.**

A vinylic halide   **Phenyl halide**

Vinylic halides and phenyl halides are generally unreactive in S_N1 or S_N2 reactions. Vinylic and phenyl cations are relatively unstable and do not form readily. This explains the unreactivity of vinylic and phenyl halides in S_N1 reactions. The carbon–halogen bond of a vinylic or phenyl halide is stronger than that of an alkyl halide (we shall see why later) and the electrons of the double bond or benzene ring repel the approach of a nucleophile from the backside. These factors explain the unreactivity of a vinylic or phenyl halide in an S_N2 reaction.

6.17 ELIMINATION REACTIONS OF ALKYL HALIDES

Another characteristic of alkyl halides is that they undergo elimination reactions. In an elimination reaction the fragments of some molecule (YZ) are removed (eliminated) from adjacent atoms of the reactant. This elimination leads to the introduction of a multiple bond:

6.17A DEHYDROHALOGENATION

A widely used method for synthesizing alkenes is the elimination of HX from adjacent atoms of an alkyl halide. Heating the alkyl halide with a strong base causes the reaction to take place. The following are two examples:

$$CH_3CHCH_3 \xrightarrow[C_2H_5OH, 55 \,°C]{C_2H_5ONa} CH_2{=}CH{-}CH_3 + NaBr + C_2H_5OH$$
$$\underset{Br}{|}$$

(79%)

$$CH_3{-}\underset{\underset{CH_3}{|}}{\overset{\overset{CH_3}{|}}{C}}{-}Br \xrightarrow[C_2H_5OH, 25\,°C]{C_2H_5ONa} CH_3{-}\underset{CH_3}{\overset{CH_3}{|}}{C}{=}CH_2 + NaBr + C_2H_5OH$$

(91%)

Reactions like these are not limited to the elimination of hydrogen bromide. Chloroalkanes also undergo the elimination of hydrogen chloride, iodoalkanes undergo the elimination of hydrogen iodide and, in all cases, alkenes are produced. When the elements of a hydrogen halide are eliminated from a haloalkane in this way, the reaction is often called **dehydrohalogenation.**

$$-\overset{H}{\underset{|}{\overset{|}{C}}}{}^\beta{-}\overset{|}{\underset{X}{\overset{|}{C}}}{}^\alpha + \;:B^- \longrightarrow \;\overset{\diagdown}{\diagup}C{=}C\overset{\diagup}{\diagdown} + H{:}B + :X^-$$

A base

Dehydrohalogenation

In these eliminations, as in S_N1 and S_N2 reactions, there is a leaving group and an attacking particle (the base) that possesses an electron pair.

Chemists often call the carbon atom that bears the substituent (e. g., the halogen atom in the previous reaction) the **alpha (α) carbon atom** and any carbon atom adjacent to it a **beta (β) carbon atom.** A hydrogen atom attached to the β carbon atom is called a β **hydrogen atom.** Since the hydrogen atom that is eliminated in dehydrohalogenation is from the β carbon atom, these reactions are often called β **eliminations.** They are also often referred to as **1,2 eliminations.**

We shall have more to say about dehydrohalogenation in Chapter 8, but we can examine several important aspects here.

6.17B BASES USED IN DEHYDROHALOGENATION

Various strong bases have been used for dehydrohalogenations. Potassium hydroxide dissolved in ethanol is a reagent sometimes used, but the sodium salts of alcohols often offer distinct advantages.

The sodium salt of an alcohol (a sodium alkoxide) can be prepared by treating an alcohol with sodium metal:

$$2\,R{-}\overset{..}{\underset{..}{O}}H + 2\,Na \longrightarrow 2\,R{-}\overset{..}{\underset{..}{O}}{:}^-Na^+ + H_2$$

Alcohol   **Sodium**
                                          alkoxide

This reaction involves the displacement of hydrogen from the alcohol and is, thus, an **oxidation–reduction reaction.** Sodium, an alkali metal, is a very powerful reducing agent and always displaces hydrogen atoms that are bonded to oxygen atoms. The vigorous (at times explosive) reaction of sodium with water is of the same type.

$$2\ H\ddot{O}H + 2\ Na \longrightarrow 2\ H\ddot{O}\!:^- Na^+ + H_2$$

Sodium hydroxide

Sodium alkoxides can also be prepared by allowing an alcohol to react with sodium hydride (NaH). The hydride ion ($H\!:^-$) is a very strong base.

$$R\!-\!\ddot{O}H + Na^+\!:\!H^- \longrightarrow R\!-\!\ddot{O}\!:^- Na^+ + H_2$$

Sodium (and potassium) alkoxides are usually prepared by using an excess of the alcohol, and the excess alcohol becomes the solvent for the reaction. Sodium ethoxide is frequently employed in this way.

$$2\ CH_3CH_2OH + 2\ Na \longrightarrow 2\ CH_3CH_2O^-Na^+ + H_2$$

Ethanol   **Sodium ethoxide**
(excess)

Potassium *tert*-butoxide is another highly effective dehydrohalogenating reagent.

$$
\begin{array}{ccc}
\quad CH_3 & & \quad CH_3 \\
\quad | & & \quad | \\
2\ CH_3C\!-\!\ddot{O}H + 2\ K \longrightarrow & 2\ CH_3C\!-\!\ddot{O}\!:^- K^+ & +\ H_2 \\
\quad | & & \quad | \\
\quad CH_3 & & \quad CH_3
\end{array}
$$

tert-**Butyl alcohol**   **Potassium *tert*-butoxide**
(excess)

6.17C MECHANISMS OF DEHYDROHALOGENATIONS

Elimination reactions occur by a variety of mechanisms. With alkyl halides, two mechanisms are especially important because they are closely related to the S_N2 and S_N1 reactions that we have just studied. One mechanism is a bimolecular mechanism called the E2 reaction; the other is a unimolecular mechanism called the E1 reaction.

6.18 THE E2 REACTION

When isopropyl bromide is heated with sodium ethoxide in ethanol to form propene, the reaction rate depends on the concentration of isopropyl bromide and on the concentration of ethoxide ion. The rate equation is first order in each reactant and second order overall.

$$\text{Rate} \propto [CH_3CHBrCH_3]\,[C_2H_5O^-]$$

$$\text{Rate} = k[CH_3CHBrCH_3]\,[C_2H_5O^-]$$

From this we infer that the transition state for the rate-determining step must involve both the alkyl halide and the alkoxide ion. The reaction must be bimolecular.

Considerable experimental evidence indicates that the reaction takes place in the following way:

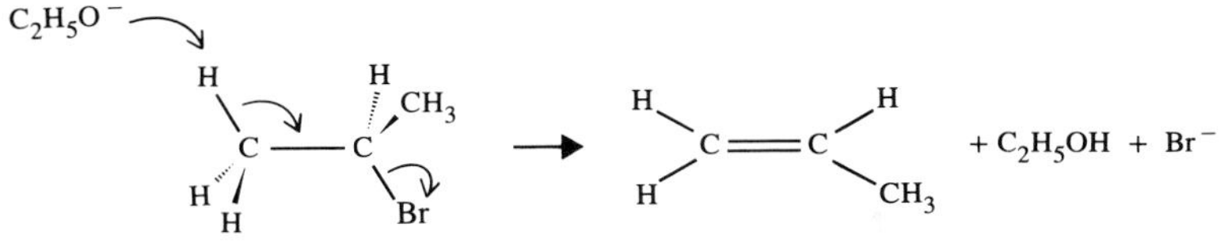

The ethoxide ion, using its electron pair, acts as a base and begins to remove one of the β hydrogen atoms by forming a covalent bond to it. At the same time the electron pair that had joined the β hydrogen atom to its carbon atom moves in to become the second bond of the double bond, and the bromine atom begins to depart with its electron pair (as a solvated bromide ion). The transition state (see following diagram) is one in which partial bonds exist between the ethoxide ion and the β hydrogen atom, between the β hydrogen atom and the β carbon atom, and between the α carbon atom and the bromine atom. The carbon–carbon bond has also begun to develop some double-bond character.

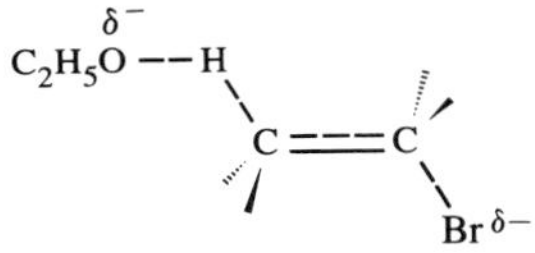

Transition state for an E2 reaction

When we study the E2 reaction further in Section 8.12C, we shall find that the orientation of the hydrogen atom being removed and the leaving group is not arbitrary and that the orientation shown above is required.

6.19 THE E1 REACTION

Eliminations may take a different pathway from that given in Section 6.18. Treating *tert*-butyl chloride with 80% aqueous ethanol at 25 °C, for example, gives *substitution products* in 83% yield and an elimination product (2-methylpropene) in 17% yield.

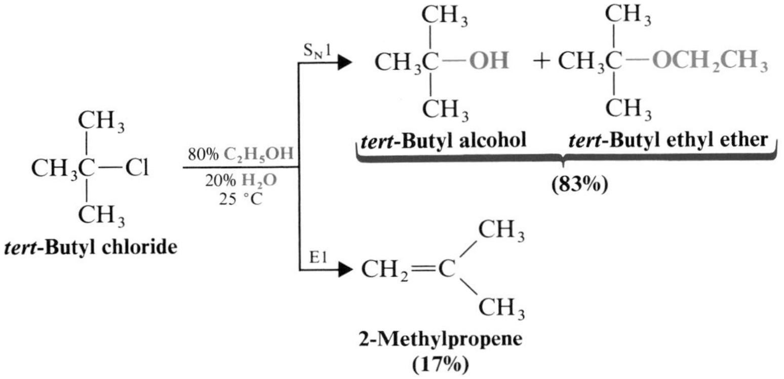

The initial step for both reactions is the formation of a *tert*-butyl cation. This is also the rate-determining step for both reactions; thus both reactions are unimolecular.

$$CH_3-\underset{\underset{CH_3}{|}}{\overset{\overset{CH_3}{|}}{C}}-\ddot{C}l: \xrightarrow{slow} \underset{\underset{CH_3}{|}}{\overset{\overset{CH_3}{|}}{CH_3C^+}} + \ :\ddot{\underset{..}{C}}l:^-$$

(solvated)   (solvated)

Whether substitution or elimination takes place depends on the next step (the fast step). If a solvent molecule reacts as a nucleophile at the positive carbon atom of the *tert*-butyl cation, the product is *tert*-butyl alcohol or *tert*-butyl ethyl ether and the reaction is S_N1.

$$\underset{\underset{CH_3}{|}}{\overset{\overset{CH_3}{|}}{CH_3C^+}} \ Sol-\ddot{O}H \xrightarrow{fast} \underset{\underset{CH_3}{|}}{\overset{\overset{CH_3}{|}}{CH_3C}}\overset{Sol}{\underset{H}{\pm}}\ddot{O}: \ \rightleftharpoons \underset{\underset{CH_3}{|}}{\overset{\overset{CH_3}{|}}{CH_3C}}-O-Sol + H^+ \left.\right\} \begin{array}{c} S_N1 \\ \textbf{reaction} \end{array}$$

$(Sol = H-$ or $CH_3CH_2-)$

If, however, a solvent molecule acts as a base and abstracts one of the β hydrogen atoms as a proton, the product is 2-methylpropene and the reaction is E1.

E1 reactions almost always accompany S_N1 reactions.

$$Sol-\ddot{O}: \rightarrow H-CH_2-\underset{\underset{CH_3}{|}}{\overset{\overset{CH_3}{|}}{C^+}} \xrightarrow{fast} Sol-\ddot{O}\overset{\pm}{\underset{H}{}}H + CH_2=C\overset{CH_3}{\underset{CH_3}{}} \left.\right\} \begin{array}{c} E1 \\ \textbf{reaction} \end{array}$$

2-Methylpropene

6.20 SUBSTITUTION VERSUS ELIMINATION

Because the reactive part of a nucleophile or a base is an unshared electron pair, all nucleophiles are potential bases and all bases are potential nucleophiles. It should not be surprising, then, that nucleophilic substitution reactions and elimination reactions often compete with each other.

6.20A S_N2 VERSUS E2

Since eliminations occur best by an E2 path when carried out with a high concentration of a strong base (and thus a high concentration of a strong nucleophile), substitution reactions by an S_N2 path often compete with the elimination reaction. When the nucleophile (base) attacks a β hydrogen atom, elimination occurs. When the nucleophile attacks the carbon atom bearing the leaving group, substitution results.

6.20 SUBSTITUTION VERSUS ELIMINATION

$$\text{Nu:}^- \underset{(b)}{\overset{(a)}{\rightleftharpoons}} \begin{array}{c} H-C- \\ | \\ C-X \\ | \end{array} \longrightarrow$$

(a) elimination E2

$$\begin{array}{c} \diagdown \diagup \\ C \\ \| \\ C \\ \diagup \diagdown \end{array} + \text{Nu}-H + :X^-$$

(b) substitution $S_N 2$

$$\begin{array}{c} H-C- \\ | \\ \text{Nu}-C- \\ | \end{array} + X:^-$$

When the substrate is a primary halide and the base is ethoxide ion, substitution is highly favored.

$$CH_3CH_2O^-Na^+ + CH_3CH_2Br \xrightarrow[\substack{55\ °C \\ (-NaBr)}]{C_2H_5OH} CH_3CH_2OCH_2CH_3 + CH_2{=}CH_2$$

	$S_N 2$	E2
	(90%)	(10%)

With secondary halides, however, the elimination reaction is favored.

$$C_2H_5O^-Na^+ + CH_3\underset{\underset{Br}{|}}{CH}CH_3 \xrightarrow[\substack{55\ °C \\ (-NaBr)}]{C_2H_5OH} CH_3\underset{\underset{\underset{C_2H_5}{|}}{O}}{CH}CH_3 + CH_2{=}CHCH_3$$

$$S_N 2 \qquad\qquad E2$$
$$(21\%) \qquad\qquad (79\%)$$

With tertiary halides an $S_N 2$ reaction cannot take place and thus the elimination reaction is highly favored, especially when the reaction is carried out at higher temperatures. Any substitution that occurs probably takes place through an $S_N 1$ mechanism.

$$C_2H_5O^-Na^+ + CH_3\underset{\underset{Br}{|}}{\overset{\overset{CH_3}{|}}{C}}CH_3 \xrightarrow[\substack{25\ °C \\ (-NaBr)}]{C_2H_5OH} CH_3\underset{\underset{\underset{C_2H_5}{|}}{O}}{\overset{\overset{CH_3}{|}}{C}}CH_3 + CH_2{=}\overset{\overset{CH_3}{|}}{C}CH_3$$

$$S_N 1 \qquad\qquad \text{Mainly E2}$$
$$(9\%) \qquad\qquad (91\%)$$

$$C_2H_5O^-Na^+ + CH_3\underset{\underset{Br}{|}}{\overset{\overset{CH_3}{|}}{C}}CH_3 \xrightarrow[\substack{55\ °C \\ (-NaBr)}]{C_2H_5OH} CH_2{=}\overset{\overset{CH_3}{|}}{C}CH_3 + C_2H_5OH$$

$$E2 + E1$$
$$(100\%)$$

Increasing the temperature favors eliminations (E1 and E2) over substitutions. The reason: Eliminations have higher energies of activation than substitutions because eliminations have a greater change in bonding (more bonds are broken and formed). By giving more molecules enough energy to surmount the energy barriers, increasing the temperature increases the rates of both substitutions and eliminations, however, because the energy barriers for eliminations are higher, the proportion of molecules able to cross them is significantly higher.

Increasing the reaction temperature is one way of favorably influencing an elimination reaction of an alkyl halide. Another way is to use a strong sterically hindered base such as the *tert*-butoxide ion. The bulky methyl groups of the *tert*-butoxide ion appear to inhibit its reacting by substitution, so elimination reactions take precedence. We can see an example of this effect in the following two reactions. The relatively unhindered methoxide ion reacts with octadecyl bromide primarily by *substitution;* the bulky *tert*-butoxide ion gives mainly *elimination.*

$$CH_3O^- + CH_3(CH_2)_{15}CH_2CH_2\text{—Br} \xrightarrow[\text{65 °C}]{\text{CH}_3\text{OH}}$$

$$CH_3(CH_2)_{15}CH\text{=}CH_2 + CH_3(CH_2)_{15}CH_2CH_2OCH_3$$

E2   S$_N$2
(1%)   (99%)

$$\underset{\underset{CH_3}{|}}{\overset{\overset{CH_3}{|}}{CH_3\text{—C—}O^-}} + CH_3(CH_2)_{15}CH_2CH_2\text{—Br} \xrightarrow[\text{40 °C}]{(CH_3)_3COH}$$

$$CH_3(CH_2)_{15}CH\text{=}CH_2 + CH_3(CH_2)_{15}CH_2CH_2\text{—O—}\underset{\underset{CH_3}{|}}{\overset{\overset{CH_3}{|}}{C}}\text{—CH}_3$$

E2   S$_N$2
(85%)   (15%)

Another factor that affects the relative rates of E2 and S$_N$2 reactions is the relative basicity and polarizability of the base/nucleophile. Use of a strong, slightly polarizable base such as amide ion (NH_2^-) or alkoxide ion (especially a hindered one) tends to increase the likelihood of elimination (E2). Use of a weakly basic ion such as a chloride ion (Cl^-) or an acetate ion ($CH_3CO_2^-$) or a weakly basic and highly polarizable one such as Br^-, I^-, or RS^- increases the likelihood of substitution (S$_N$2). Acetate ion, for example, reacts with isopropyl bromide almost exclusively by the S$_N$2 path:

$$\underset{}{\overset{\overset{O}{\|}}{CH_3C}}\text{—}O^- + \underset{}{\overset{\overset{CH_3}{|}}{CH_3CH}}\text{—Br} \longrightarrow \overset{\overset{O}{\|}}{CH_3C}\text{—}O\text{—}\overset{\overset{CH_3}{|}}{CH}CH_3 + Br^-$$

S$_N$2
(~100%)

The more strongly basic ethoxide ion (Section 6.17B) reacts with the same compound mainly by an E2 mechanism.

6.20B TERTIARY HALIDES: S$_N$1 VERSUS E1

Because the E1 reaction and the S$_N$1 reaction proceed through the formation of a common intermediate, the two types respond in similar ways to factors affecting reactivities. E1 reactions are favored with substrates that can form stable carbocations (i.e., tertiary halides); they are also favored by the use of weak nucleophiles (bases) and they are generally favored by the use of polar solvents.

It is usually difficult to influence the relative partition between S_N1 and E1 products because the energy of activation for either reaction of the carbocation (loss of a proton or combination with a molecule of the solvent) is very small.

In most unimolecular reactions the S_N1 reaction is favored over the E1 reaction, especially at lower temperatures. *In general, however, substitution reactions of tertiary halides are not very useful as synthetic methods. Such halides undergo eliminations much too easily.*

Increasing the temperature of the reaction favors reaction by the E1 mechanism at the expense of the S_N1 mechanism. *If the elimination product is desired, however, it is more convenient to add a strong base and force an E2 reaction to take place instead.*

6.21 OVERALL SUMMARY

The most important reaction pathways for the substitution and elimination reactions of alkyl halides can be summarized in the way shown in Table 6.6.

TABLE 6.6   Overall summary of S_N1, S_N2, E1, and E2 reactions

CH_3X	RCH_2X	R | $RCHX$	R | $R-C-X$ | R
Methyl	**1°**	**2°**	**3°**
	Bimolecular reactions only		$S_N1/E1$ or E2
Gives S_N2 reactions	Gives mainly S_N2 except with a hindered strong base [e.g., $(CH_3)_3CO^-$] and then gives mainly E2	Gives mainly S_N2 with weak bases (e.g., I^-, CN^-, RCO_2^-) and mainly E2 with strong bases (e.g., RO^-)	No S_N2 reaction. In solvolysis gives $S_N1/E1$, and at lower temperatures S_N1 is favored. When a strong base (e.g., RO^-) is used, E2 predominates

Let us examine several sample exercises that will illustrate how the information in Table 6.6 can be used.

Sample Problem

Give the product (or products) that you would expect to be formed in each of the following reactions. In each case give the mechanism (S_N1, S_N2, E1, or E2) by which the product is formed and predict the relative amount of each (i.e., would the product be the only product, the major product, or a minor product?).

(a) $CH_3CH_2CH_2Br + CH_3O^- \xrightarrow[CH_3OH]{50\ °C}$

(b) $CH_3CH_2CH_2Br + (CH_3)_3CO^- \xrightarrow[(CH_3)_3COH]{50\ °C}$

(c)
$$\underset{CH_3CH_2}{\overset{CH_3}{\diagdown}}C\text{—Br} + HS^- \xrightarrow[CH_3OH]{50\ ^\circ C}$$

(d) $(CH_3CH_2)_3CBr + OH^- \xrightarrow[CH_3OH]{50\ ^\circ C}$

(e) $(CH_3CH_2)_3CBr \xrightarrow[CH_3OH]{25\ ^\circ C}$

Answer:

(a) The substrate is a 1° halide. The base/nucleophile is CH_3O^-, a strong base (but not a hindered one) and a good nucleophile. According to Table 6.6 we should expect an S_N2 reaction mainly, and that the major product would be $CH_3CH_2CH_2OCH_3$. A minor product might be $CH_3CH\text{=}CH_2$ by an E2 pathway.

(b) Again the substrate is a 1° halide, but the base/nucleophile, $(CH_3)_3CO^-$, is a strong hindered base. We should expect, therefore, that the major product would be $CH_3CH\text{=}CH_2$ by an E2 pathway, and that a minor product would be $CH_3CH_2CH_2OC(CH_3)_3$ by an S_N2 pathway.

(c) The reactant is (S)-2-bromobutane, a 2° halide, and one in which the leaving group is attached to a stereocenter. The base/nucleophile is HS^-, a strong nucleophile, but a weak base. We should expect mainly an S_N2 reaction, causing an inversion of configuration at the stereocenter, and producing the (R)-stereoisomer below

$$\underset{\overset{|}{H}}{\overset{\overset{CH_3}{\diagup}}{HS\text{—}C}}\text{''''}CH_2CH_3$$

(d) The base/nucleophile is OH^-, a strong base and a strong nucleophile. However, the substrate is a 3° halide, therefore, we should not expect an S_N2 reaction. The major product should be $CH_3CH\text{=}C(CH_2CH_3)_2$ via an E2 reaction. At this higher temperature, and in the presence of a strong base, we should not expect an appreciable amount of the S_N1 product, $CH_3OC(CH_2CH_3)_3$.

(e) This is solvolysis; the only base/nucleophile is the solvent, CH_3OH, which is a weak base (therefore, no E2 reaction) and a weak nucleophile. The substrate is tertiary (therefore, no S_N2 reaction). At this lower temperature we should expect mainly an S_N1 pathway leading to $CH_3OC(CH_2CH_3)_3$. A minor product, by an E1 pathway would be $CH_3CH\text{=}C(CH_2CH_3)_2$.

6.22 SOME IMPORTANT TERMS AND CONCEPTS

Carbocation. A positive ion formed by heterolysis of a bond to a carbon atom as follows:

$$-\overset{|}{\underset{|}{C}}-X \longrightarrow -\overset{|}{\underset{|}{C}}{}^+ + :X^-$$

6.22 SOME IMPORTANT TERMS AND CONCEPTS

Carbocations show the relative stabilities:

$$3° > 2° > 1° > \text{methyl}$$

Nucleophile. A negative ion or a molecule that has an unshared pair of electrons. In a chemical reaction a nucleophile attacks a positive center of some other molecule or positive ion.

Nucleophilic substitution reaction (abbreviated as S_N reaction). A substitution reaction brought about when a nucleophile reacts with a *substrate* that bears a *leaving group*.

S_N2 **reaction.** A nucleophilic substitution reaction for which the rate-determining step is *bimolecular* (i.e., the transition state involves two species). The reaction of methyl chloride with hydroxide ion is an S_N2 reaction. According to the Ingold mechanism it takes place in a *single step* as follows:

$$HO^- + CH_3 - Cl \longrightarrow \left[\overset{\delta-}{HO} \cdots CH_3 \cdots \overset{\delta-}{Cl} \right] \longrightarrow HO - CH_3 + Cl^-$$
$$\text{Transition state}$$

The order of reactivity of alkyl halides in S_N2 reactions is

$$CH_3 - X > RCH_2X > R_2CHX$$
$$\textbf{Methyl} \quad \quad \textbf{1°} \quad \quad \textbf{2°}$$

S_N1 **reaction.** A nucleophilic substitution reaction for which the rate-determining step is *unimolecular*. The hydrolysis of *tert*-butyl chloride is an S_N1 reaction that takes place in three steps as follows. The rate-determining step is step 1.

Step 1 $\quad (CH_3)_3CCl \xrightarrow{\text{slow}} (CH_3)_3C^+ + Cl^-$

Step 2 $\quad (CH_3)_3C^+ + H_2O \xrightarrow{\text{fast}} (CH_3)_3C\overset{+}{O}H_2$

Step 3 $\quad (CH_3)_3C\overset{+}{O}H_2 + H_2O \xrightarrow{\text{fast}} (CH_3)_3COH + H_3O^+$

S_N1 reactions are important with tertiary halides and with other substrates that can form relatively stable carbocations.

Solvolysis. A nucleophilic substitution reaction in which the nucleophile is a molecule of the solvent.

Steric effect. An effect on relative reaction rates caused by the space-filling properties of those parts of a molecule attached at or near the reacting site. *Steric hindrance* is an important effect in S_N2 reactions. It explains why methyl halides are most reactive and tertiary halides are least reactive.

Elimination reaction. A reaction in which the fragments of some molecule are eliminated from adjacent atoms of the reactant to give a multiple bond. Dehydrohalogenation is an elimination reaction in which HX is eliminated from an alkyl halide, leading to the formation of an alkene.

$$\underset{X}{\overset{H}{-\underset{|}{\overset{|}{C}}-\underset{|}{\overset{|}{C}}-}} + :B^- \longrightarrow ^{\diagdown}C{=}C^{\diagup} + H:B + :X^-$$

E1 reaction. A unimolecular elimination. The first step of an E1 reaction, formation of a carbocation, is the same as that of an S_N1 reaction, consequently E1 and S_N1 reactions compete with each other. E1 reactions are important when tertiary halides are subjected to solvolysis in polar solvents especially at higher temperatures. The steps in the E1 reaction of *tert*-butyl chloride are the following:

Step 1

$$CH_3-\underset{\underset{CH_3}{|}}{\overset{\overset{CH_3}{|}}{C}}-Cl \xrightarrow{\text{slow}} CH_3-\underset{\underset{CH_3}{|}}{\overset{\overset{CH_3}{|}}{C^+}} + Cl^-$$

Step 2

$$Sol-\ddot{O}H + H-CH_2-\underset{\underset{CH_3}{|}}{\overset{\overset{CH_3}{|}}{C^+}} \longrightarrow CH_2=C\overset{CH_3}{\underset{CH_3}{\diagup}} + Sol-\overset{+}{O}H_2$$

E2 reaction. A bimolecular elimination that often competes with S_N2 reactions. E2 reactions are favored by the use of a high concentration of a strong, bulky, and slightly polarizable base. The order of reactivity of alkyl halides toward E2 reactions is $3° \gg 2° > 1°$. The mechanism of the E2 reaction involves a single step:

$$B:^- + -\overset{\overset{H}{|}}{C}-\overset{|}{\underset{X}{C}}- \longrightarrow B-H + \diagdown C=C \diagup + X^-$$

Additional Problems

6.12   Show how you might use a nucleophilic substitution reaction of propyl bromide to synthesize each of the following compounds. (You may use any other compounds that are necessary.)

(a) $CH_3CH_2CH_2OH$

(b) $CH_3CH_2CH_2I$

(c) $CH_3CH_2OCH_2CH_2CH_3$

(d) $CH_3CH_2CH_2-S-CH_3$

(e) $CH_3\overset{\overset{O}{\|}}{C}OCH_2CH_2CH_3$

(f) $CH_3CH_2CH_2N_3$

(g) $CH_3-\underset{\underset{CH_3}{|}}{\overset{\overset{CH_3}{|}}{N^+}}-CH_2CH_2CH_3 \; Br^-$

(h) $CH_3CH_2CH_2CN$

(i) $CH_3CH_2CH_2SH$

6.13   Which alkyl halide would you expect to react more rapidly by an S_N2 mechanism? Explain your answer.

(a) $CH_3CH_2CH_2CH_2Br$ or $CH_3CH_2\underset{\underset{Br}{|}}{CH}CH_3$

(b) $CH_3CH_2\underset{\underset{Br}{|}}{CH}CH_3$ or $CH_3\underset{\underset{Br}{|}}{\overset{\overset{CH_3}{|}}{C}}CH_3$

(c) $CH_3CH_2CH_2Cl$ or $CH_3CH_2CH_2Br$

ADDITIONAL PROBLEMS

(d) $CH_3CHCH_2CH_2Br$ or $CH_3CH_2CHCH_2Br$
    $\quad\ \ |$ $\qquad\qquad\ |$
    $\quad\ \ CH_3$ $\qquad\qquad\ CH_3$

(e) CH_3CH_2Cl or $CH_2{=}CHCl$

6.14 Which S_N2 reaction of each pair would you expect to take place more rapidly in a protic solvent? Explain your answer.

(a) $CH_3CH_2CH_2Br + CH_3OH \longrightarrow CH_3CH_2CH_2OCH_3 + HBr$
    or
    $CH_3CH_2CH_2Br + CH_3O^- \longrightarrow CH_3CH_2CH_2OCH_3 + Br^-$

(b) $CH_3CH_2I + OH^- \longrightarrow CH_3CH_2OH + I^-$
    or
    $CH_3CH_2I + SH^- \longrightarrow CH_3CH_2SH + I^-$

(c) $CH_3Br + CH_3OH \longrightarrow CH_3OCH_3 + HBr$
    or
    $CH_3Br + CH_3SH \longrightarrow CH_3SCH_3 + HBr$

(d) $CH_3CH_2I(1.0\ M) + CH_3S^-\ (1.0\ M) \longrightarrow CH_3CH_2SCH_3 + I^-$
    or
    $CH_3CH_2I(1.0\ M) + CH_3S^-\ (2.0\ M) \longrightarrow CH_3CH_2SCH_3 + I^-$

6.15 Which S_N1 reaction would you expect to take place more rapidly? Explain your answer.

(a) $(CH_3)_3CI + CH_3OH \longrightarrow (CH_3)_3COCH_3 + HI$
    or
    $(CH_3)_3CCl + CH_3OH \longrightarrow (CH_3)_3COCH_3 + HCl$

(b) $(CH_3)_3CBr + H_2O \longrightarrow (CH_3)_3COH + HBr$
    or
    $(CH_3)_3CBr + CH_3OH \longrightarrow (CH_3)_3COCH_3 + HBr$

(c) $(CH_3)_3CCl(1.0\ M) + CH_3O^-(0.01\ M) \xrightarrow[CH_3OH]{} (CH_3)_3COCH_3 + Cl^-$
    or
    $(CH_3)_3CCl(1.0\ M) + CH_3O^-(0.001\ M) \xrightarrow[CH_3OH]{} (CH_3)_3COCH_3 + Cl^-$

(d) $(CH_3)_3CCl + H_2O \longrightarrow (CH_3)_3COH + HCl$
    or
    $(CH_3)_2C{=}CHCl + H_2O \longrightarrow (CH_3)_2C{=}CHOH + HCl$

6.16 With methyl, ethyl, or cyclopentyl halides as your organic starting materials and using any needed solvents or inorganic reagents, outline syntheses of each of the following. More than one step may be necessary and you need not repeat steps carried out in earlier parts of this problem.

(a) CH_3I (d) CH_3CH_2OH (g) CH_3CN (j) $CH_3OCH_2CH_3$

(b) CH_3CH_2I (e) CH_3SH (h) CH_3CH_2CN (k) Cyclopentene

(c) CH_3OH (f) CH_3CH_2SH (i) CH_3OCH_3

6.17 Listed here are several hypothetical nucleophilic substitution reactions. None is synthetically useful because the product indicated is *not* formed at an appreciable rate. In each case account for the failure of the reaction to take place.

(a) $HO^- + CH_3CH_3 \xrightarrow{\times} CH_3CH_2OH + H{:}^-$

(b) $HO^- + CH_3CH_2CH_3 \xrightarrow{\times} CH_3CH_2OH + CH_3{:}^-$

(c) ⬠ $+ H_2O \xrightarrow{\times} CH_3CH_2CH_2CH_2CH_2OH$

(d) $CN^- + (CH_3)_3CBr \not\longrightarrow (CH_3)_3C—CN + Br^-$

(e) $CH_3CH{=}CHBr + CH_3S^- \not\longrightarrow CH_3CH{=}CHSCH_3 + Br^-$

(f) $Cl^- + CH_3OCH_3 \not\longrightarrow CH_3Cl + CH_3O^-$

(g) $NH_3 + CH_3CH_2\overset{+}{O}H_2 \not\longrightarrow CH_3CH_2NH_3^+ + H_2O$

(h) $CH_3{:}^- + CH_3CH_2OH \not\longrightarrow CH_3CH_2CH_3 + OH^-$

6.18   You are given the task of preparing propene by dehydrohalogenating one of the halopropanes (i.e., $CH_3CH_2CH_2Br$ or $CH_3CHBrCH_3$). Which halide would you choose to give the alkene in maximum yield? Why?

6.19   Your task is to prepare isopropyl methyl ether, $CH_3OCH(CH_3)_2$, by one of the following reactions. Which reaction would give the better yield? Explain your choice.

(1) $CH_3ONa + (CH_3)_2CHI \longrightarrow CH_3OCH(CH_3)_2$

(2) $(CH_3)_2CHONa + CH_3I \longrightarrow CH_3OCH(CH_3)_2$

6.20   Which product (or products) would you expect to obtain from each of the following reactions? In each case give the mechanism (S_N1, S_N2, E1, or E2) by which each product is formed and predict the relative amount of each (i.e., would the product be the only product, the major product, a minor product, etc.?).

(a) $CH_3CH_2CH_2CH_2Br + CH_3O^- \xrightarrow[CH_3OH]{50\ °C}$

(b) $CH_3CH_2CH_2CH_2Br + (CH_3)_3CO^- \xrightarrow[(CH_3)_3COH]{50\ °C}$

(c) $(CH_3)_3CO^- + CH_3I \xrightarrow[(CH_3)_3COH]{50\ °C}$

(d) $(CH_3)_3CI + CH_3O^- \xrightarrow[CH_3OH]{50\ °C}$

(e)

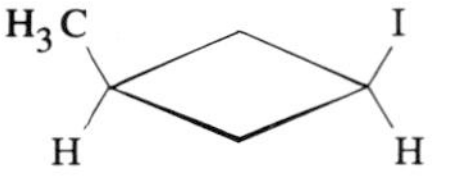

$+ \ CH_3O^- \xrightarrow[CH_3OH]{50\ °C}$

(f)

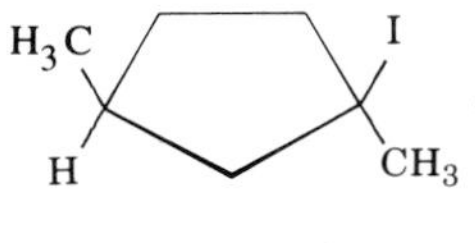

$\xrightarrow[CH_3OH]{25\ °C}$

(g) $CH_3CH_2\underset{\underset{Br}{|}}{C}HCH_2CH_3 + C_2H_5O^- \xrightarrow[C_2H_5OH]{50\ °C}$

(h) $(CH_3)_3CO^- + CH_3\underset{\underset{Br}{|}}{C}HCH_3 \xrightarrow[(CH_3)_3COH]{50\ °C}$

(i) $HO^- + (R)\text{-2-bromobutane} \xrightarrow{25\ °C}$

(j) $(S)\text{-3-bromo-3-methylhexane} \xrightarrow[CH_3OH]{25\ °C}$

(k) $(S)\text{-2-bromooctane} + I^- \xrightarrow[CH_3OH]{50\ °C}$

6.21   Write conformational structures for the substitution products of the following deuterium-labeled compounds:

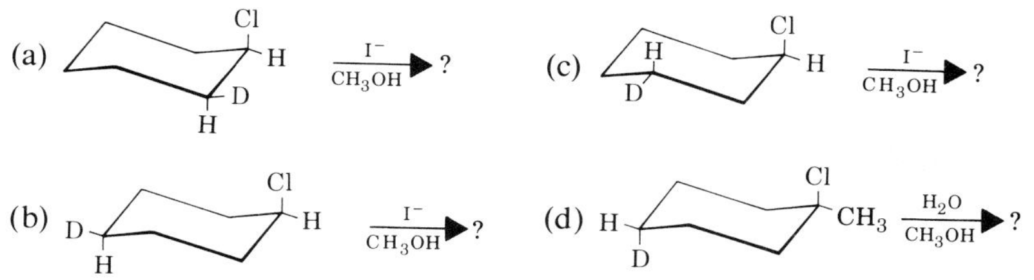

(a) $\xrightarrow[CH_3OH]{I^-}$? (c) $\xrightarrow[CH_3OH]{I^-}$?

(b) $\xrightarrow[CH_3OH]{I^-}$? (d) $\xrightarrow[CH_3OH]{H_2O}$?

6.22 Although ethyl bromide and isobutyl bromide are both primary halides, ethyl bromide undergoes S_N2 reactions more than 10 times faster than isobutyl bromide. When each compound is treated with a strong base/nucleophile ($CH_3CH_2O^-$), isobutyl bromide gives a greater yield of elimination products than substitution products, whereas with ethyl bromide this behavior is reversed. What factor accounts for these results?

6.23 Consider the reaction of I^- with CH_3CH_2Cl. (a) Would you expect the reaction to be S_N1 or S_N2? The rate constant for the reaction at 60 °C is 5×10^{-5} L mol^{-1} s^{-1}. (b) What is the reaction rate if $[I^-] = 0.1$ mol L^{-1} and $[CH_3CH_2Cl] = 0.1$ mol L^{-1}? (c) If $[I^-] = 0.1$ mol L^{-1} and $[CH_3CH_2Cl] = 0.2$ mol L^{-1}? (d) If $[I^-] = 0.2$ mol L^{-1} and $[CH_3CH_2Cl] = 0.1$ mol L^{-1}? (e) If $[I^-] = 0.2$ mol L^{-1} and $[CH_3CH_2Cl] = 0.2$ mol L^{-1}?

6.24 Which reagent in each pair listed here would be the stronger nucleophile in a protic solvent?

(a) CH_3NH^- or CH_3NH_2 (e) H_2O or H_3O^+

(f) NH_3 or NH_4^+

(b) CH_3O^- or $CH_3\overset{\displaystyle O}{\overset{\|}{C}}O^-$ (g) H_2S or HS^-

(c) CH_3SH or CH_3OH

(d) $(C_6H_5)_3N$ or $(C_6H_5)_3P$ (h) $CH_3\overset{\displaystyle O}{\overset{\|}{C}}O^-$ or OH^-

6.25 Write mechanisms that account for the products of the following reactions:

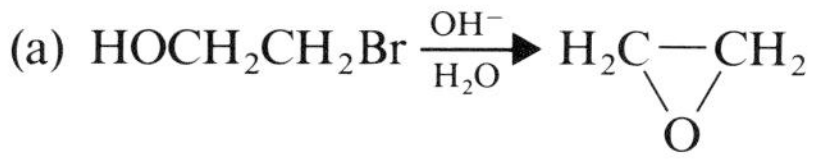

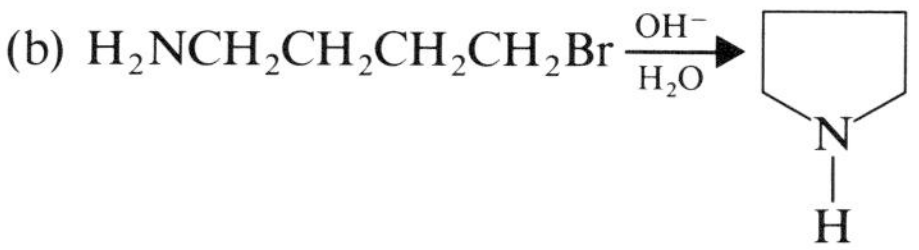

(a) $HOCH_2CH_2Br \xrightarrow[H_2O]{OH^-} H_2C\overset{\displaystyle }{\underset{\displaystyle O}{\diagdown\diagup}}CH_2$

(b) $H_2NCH_2CH_2CH_2CH_2Br \xrightarrow[H_2O]{OH^-}$

6.26 Many S_N2 reactions of alkyl chlorides and alkyl bromides are catalyzed by the addition of sodium or potassium iodide. For example, the hydrolysis of methyl bromide takes place much faster in the presence of sodium iodide. Explain.

6.27 When *tert*-butyl chloride undergoes hydrolysis (Section 6.12) in aqueous sodium hydroxide, the rate of formation of *tert*-butyl alcohol does not increase appreciably as the hydroxide ion concentration is increased. Increasing hydroxide ion concentration, however, causes a marked increase in the rate of disappearance of *tert*-butyl chloride. Explain.

6.28 (a) Consider the general problem of converting a tertiary alkyl halide to an alkene, for example, the conversion of *tert*-butyl chloride to 2-methylpropene. What experimental conditions would you choose to insure that elimination is favored over substitution? (b) Consider the opposite problem, that of carrying out a substitution reaction on a tertiary alkyl halide. Use as your example the conversion of *tert*-butyl chloride to *tert*-butyl ethyl ether. What experimental conditions would you employ to insure the highest possible yield of the ether?

6.29 Bridged cyclic compounds like those shown here are extremely *unreactive* in S_N2 reactions.

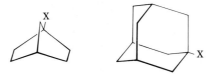

(a) Give a reason that will explain this. (b) How can you explain the fact that compounds of this type are also less reactive in S_N1 reactions than similar noncyclic compounds? (Consider the fact that carbocations are generally sp^2 hybridized.)

6.30 When CH_3Br reacts with CN^- the major product is CH_3CN, but some CH_3NC is formed as well. Write the Lewis structure for both products and explain.

*6.31 The relative rates of ethanolysis of several primary alkyl halides are as follows: CH_3CH_2Br, 1.0; $CH_3CH_2CH_2Br$, 0.28; $(CH_3)_2CHCH_2Br$, 0.030; $(CH_3)_3CCH_2Br$, 0.0000042. (a) Are these reactions S_N1 or S_N2? (b) What factor will account for these relative reactivities?

*6.32 In contrast to S_N2 reactions, S_N1 reactions show relatively little nucleophile selectivity. That is, when more than one nucleophile is present in the reaction medium, S_N1 reactions show only a slight tendency to discriminate between weak nucleophiles and strong nucleophiles, whereas S_N2 reactions show a marked tendency to discriminate. (a) Provide an explanation for this behavior. (b) Show how your answer accounts for the fact that $CH_3CH_2CH_2CH_2Cl$ reacts with 0.01 M NaCN in ethanol to yield primarily $CH_3CH_2CH_2CH_2CN$, whereas under the same conditions, $(CH_3)_3CCl$ reacts to give primarily $(CH_3)_3COCH_2CH_3$.

*6.33 When *tert*-butyl bromide undergoes S_N1 hydrolysis, adding a "common ion" (e.g., NaBr) to the aqueous solution has no effect on the rate. On the other hand when $(C_6H_5)_2CHBr$ undergoes S_N1 hydrolysis, adding NaBr retards the reaction. Given that the $(C_6H_5)_2CH^+$ cation is known to be much more stable than the $(CH_3)_3C^+$ cation (and we shall see why in Section 15.12B), provide an explanation for the different behavior of the two compounds.

*6.34 When the alkyl bromides (listed here) were subjected to hydrolysis in a mixture of ethanol and water (80% C_2H_5OH/20% H_2O) at 55 °C, the rates of the reaction showed the following order:

$$(CH_3)_3CBr > CH_3Br > CH_3CH_2Br > (CH_3)_2CHBr$$

Provide an explanation for this order of reactivity.

SPECIAL TOPIC

A

A BIOLOGICAL NUCLEOPHILIC SUBSTITUTION REACTION: BIOLOGICAL METHYLATION

The cells of living organisms synthesize many of the compounds they need from smaller molecules. Often these biosyntheses resemble the syntheses organic chemists carry out in their laboratories. Let us examine one example now.

Many reactions take place in the cells of plants and animals that involve the transfer of a methyl group from an amino acid called methionine to some other compound. That this transfer takes place can be demonstrated experimentally by feeding a plant or animal methionine containing a radioactive carbon atom (^{14}C) in its methyl group. Later, other compounds containing the "labeled" methyl group can be isolated from the organism. Some of the compounds that get their methyl groups from methionine are the following. The radioactively labeled carbon atom is shown in color.

Choline is important in the transmission of nerve impulses, adrenaline causes blood pressure to increase, and nicotine is the compound contained in tobacco that makes smoking tobacco addictive. (In larger doses nicotine is poisonous.)

The transfer of the methyl group from methionine to these other compounds does not take place directly. The actual methylating agent is not methionine; it is

S-adenosylmethionine,* a compound that results when methionine reacts with adenosine triphosphate (ATP):

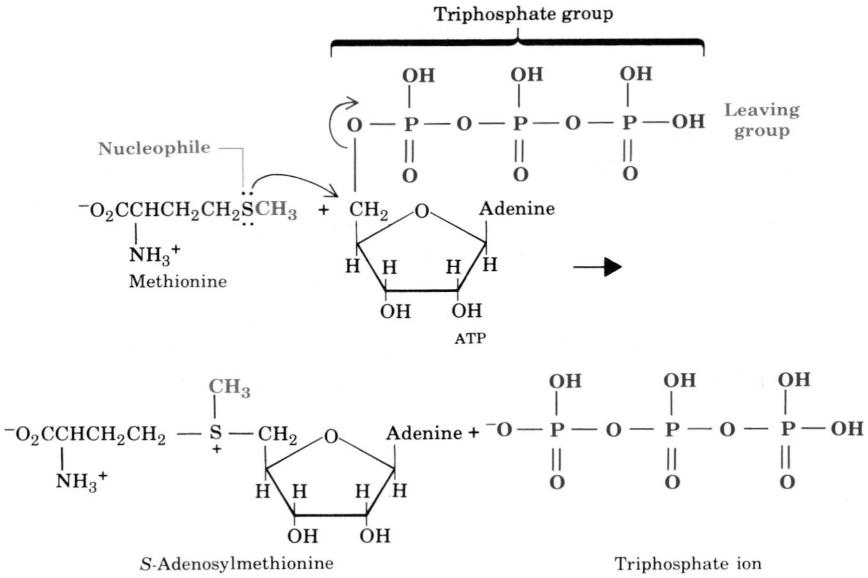

ATP

S-Adenosylmethionine

Triphosphate ion

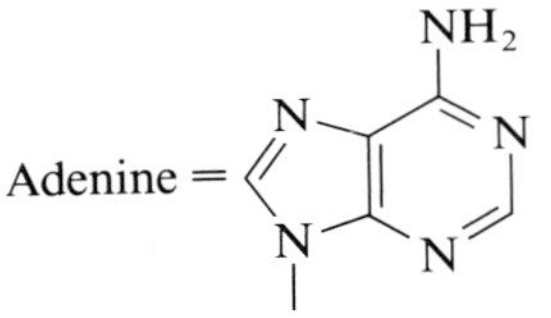

Adenine =

This reaction is a nucleophilic substitution reaction. The nucleophilic atom is the sulfur atom of methionine. The leaving group is the weakly basic triphosphate group of adenosine triphosphate. The product, *S*-adenosylmethionine, contains a methyl-sulfonium group, $CH_3—\overset{|}{\underset{}{S^{\pm}}}$.

S-Adenosylmethionine then acts as the substrate for other nucleophilic substitution reactions. In the biosynthesis of choline, for example, it transfers its methyl group to a nucleophilic nitrogen atom of 2-(*N*,*N*-dimethylamino)ethanol:

2–(*N*–Dimethylamino)ethanol

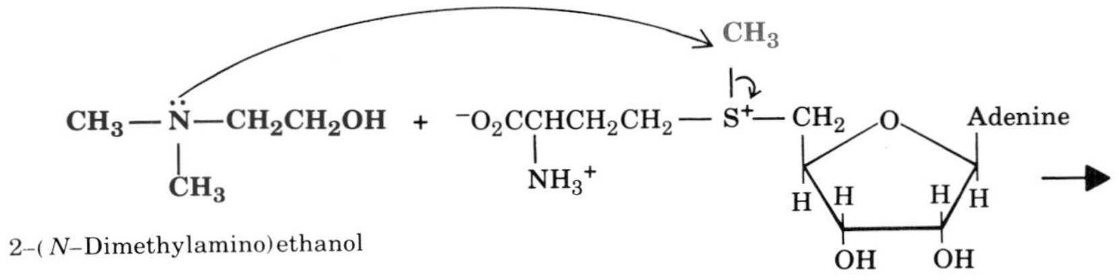

*The prefix *S* is a locant meaning "on the sulfur atom" and should not be confused with the (*S*) used to define absolute configuration. Another example of this kind of locant is *N* meaning "on the nitrogen atom."

$$CH_3-N^+-CH_2CH_2OH \;+\; ^-O_2CCHCH_2CH_2-\ddot{S}-CH_2$$

(structure with Choline labeled below the first group, NH_3^+ below the second group, and a ribose ring bearing Adenine, with $H\,H$, H/H positions and OH OH below)

These reactions appear complicated only because the structures of the nucleophiles and substrates are complex. Yet conceptually they are simple and they illustrate many of the principles we have encountered in Chapter 6. In them we see how nature makes use of the high nucleophilicity of sulfur atoms. We also see how a weakly basic group (e.g., the triphosphate group of ATP) functions as a leaving group. In the reaction of 2-(N, N-dimethylamino)ethanol we see that the more basic $(CH_3)_2N-$ group acts as the nucleophile rather than the less basic —OH group. And when a nucleophile attacks S-adenosylmethionine, we see that the attack takes place at the less hindered CH_3- group rather than at one of the more hindered $-CH_2-$ groups.

Problem A.1

(a) What is the leaving group when 2-(N, N-dimethylamino)ethanol reacts with S-adenosylmethionine? (b) What would the leaving group have to be if methionine itself were to react with 2-(N, N-dimethylamino)ethanol? (c) Of what special significance is this difference?

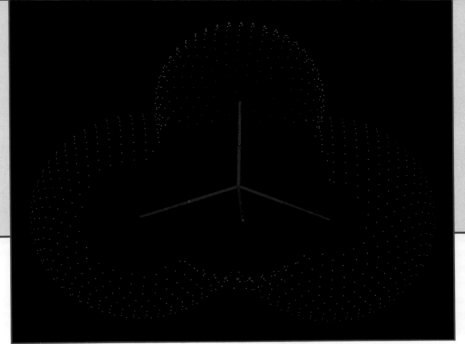

A freon (see Section 7.10C).

CHAPTER
7
RADICAL REACTIONS

7.1 INTRODUCTION

Thus far all of the reactions whose mechanisms we have studied have been **ionic reactions.** Ionic reactions are those in which covalent bonds break **heterolytically,** and in which ions are involved as reactants, intermediates, or products.

Another broad category of reactions have mechanisms that involve **homolysis** of covalent bonds with the production of intermediates possessing unpaired electrons called **radicals** (or **free radicals**).

$$A : B \xrightarrow{\text{homolysis}} A\cdot + \cdot B$$
$$\textbf{Radicals}$$

This simple example also illustrates another way curved arrows are used in writing reaction mechanisms. Here we show the movement of **a single electron** (not of an electron pair as we have done earlier) so we use **single-barbed arrows.** In this instance, each group, A and B, comes away with one of the electrons of the covalent bond that joined them.

Production of Radicals. Energy must be supplied to cause homolysis of covalent bonds (Section 7.2) and this is usually done in two ways: by heating or by irradiation with light. For example, compounds with an oxygen–oxygen single bond, called **peroxides,** undergo homolysis readily when heated, because the oxygen–oxygen bond is weak. The products are two radicals, called alkoxyl radicals.

$$R-\overset{..}{\underset{..}{O}}:\overset{..}{\underset{..}{O}}-R \xrightarrow{\ heat\ } 2\ R-\overset{..}{\underset{..}{O}}\cdot$$

Dialkyl peroxide   **Alkoxyl radicals**

Halogen molecules (X_2) also contain a relatively weak bond. As we shall soon see, halogens undergo homolysis readily when heated, or when irradiated with light of a wavelength that can be absorbed by the halogen molecule.

$$:\overset{..}{\underset{..}{X}}:\overset{..}{\underset{..}{X}}: \xrightarrow[\text{heat or light}]{\text{homolysis}} 2:\overset{..}{\underset{..}{X}}\cdot$$

The products of this homolysis are halogen atoms, and because halogen atoms contain an unpaired electron, they are radicals.

Reactions of Radicals. Almost all small radicals are short-lived, highly reactive species. When they collide with other molecules they tend to react in a way that leads to pairing of their unpaired electron. One way they can do this is by abstracting an atom from another molecule. For example, a halogen atom might abstract a hydrogen atom from an alkane. This hydrogen abstraction gives the halogen atom an electron (from the hydrogen atom) to pair with its unpaired electron. Notice, however, that the other product of this abstraction *is another radical,* in this case, an alkyl radical, $R\cdot$.

General Reaction

$$:\overset{..}{\underset{..}{X}}\cdot + H:R \longrightarrow H:\overset{..}{\underset{..}{X}}: + R\cdot$$

          Alkane   **Alkyl
                                                    radical**

Specific Example

$$:\overset{..}{\underset{..}{Cl}}\cdot + H:CH_3 \longrightarrow H:\overset{..}{\underset{..}{Cl}}: + CH_3\cdot$$

          Methane   **Methyl
                                                    radical**

This behavior is characteristic of radical reactions. Consider another example, one that shows another way that radicals can react: They can combine with a compound containing a multiple bond to produce a new, larger radical. (We shall study reactions of this type in Section 9.10.)

$$R\cdot \overset{\displaystyle R}{\underset{\displaystyle}{}} $$

$$-\overset{|}{C}=\overset{|}{C}- \longrightarrow -\overset{\displaystyle R}{\underset{|}{\overset{|}{C}}}-\overset{\displaystyle \cdot}{\underset{|}{C}}-$$

          Alkene   **New radical**

Radicals in Industry. Radical reactions are important in many industrial processes. We shall learn later, for example (Section 9.11 and Special Topic B), how radical reactions are used to produce a whole class of useful "plastics" or *polymers* such as polyethylene, Teflon, polystyrene, and so on. Radical reactions are also central in the "cracking" process by which gasoline and other fuels are made from petroleum. And, the combustion process by which these fuels are converted to energy, involves radical reactions (Section 7.10A).

Radicals in Biology and Medicine. Radical reactions are of vital importance in biology and medicine. Radical reactions are ubiquitous in living things, because radicals are produced in the normal course of metabolism. However, because radicals are highly reactive, they are also capable of randomly damaging all components of the body. Accordingly, they are believed to be important in the "aging process" in the sense that radicals are involved in the development of the chronic diseases that are life limiting. For example, there is steadily growing evidence that radical reactions are important in the development of cancers and in the development of atherosclerosis. Radicals in cigarette smoke have been implicated in inactivation of an antiprotease in the lungs, an inactivation that leads to the development of emphysema.

In Section 7.10B, we shall learn how radicals produced in the upper atmosphere from chlorofluorocarbons, are causing the depletion of the ozone layer that protects living organisms from highly damaging ultraviolet (UV) radiation.

Before exploring radical chemistry further it will be useful to examine the energy changes that occur when covalent bonds break homolytically. We shall see that these changes provide us with information about an important aspect of radicals that will help us to understand their reactions: their relative stability.

7.2 HOMOLYTIC BOND DISSOCIATION ENERGIES

When atoms combine to form molecules, energy is released as covalent bonds form. The molecules of the products have lower enthalpy than the separate atoms. When hydrogen atoms combine to form hydrogen molecules, for example, the reaction is *exothermic;* it evolves 104 kcal of heat for every mole of hydrogen that is produced. Similarly, when chlorine atoms combine to form chlorine molecules, the reaction evolves 58 kcal mol^{-1} of chlorine produced.

$$H\cdot + H\cdot \longrightarrow H-H \qquad \Delta H° = -104 \text{ kcal mol}^{-1}$$
$$Cl\cdot + Cl\cdot \longrightarrow Cl-Cl \qquad \Delta H° = -58 \text{ kcal mol}^{-1}$$

Bond formation is an exothermic process

To break covalent bonds, energy must be supplied. Reactions in which only bond breaking occurs are always endothermic. The energy required to break the covalent bonds of hydrogen or chlorine homolytically is exactly equal to that evolved when the separate atoms combine to form molecules. In the bond cleavage reaction, however, $\Delta H°$ is positive.

$$H-H \longrightarrow H\cdot + H\cdot \qquad \Delta H° = +104 \text{ kcal mol}^{-1}$$
$$Cl-Cl \longrightarrow Cl\cdot + Cl\cdot \qquad \Delta H° = +58 \text{ kcal mol}^{-1}$$

The energies required to break covalent bonds homolytically have been determined experimentally for many types of covalent bonds. These energies are called **homolytic bond dissociation energies,** and they are usually abbreviated by the symbol

$DH°$. The homolytic bond dissociation energies of hydrogen and chlorine, for example, might be written in the following way.

$$\text{H—H} \qquad\qquad \text{Cl—Cl}$$
$$(DH° = 104 \text{ kcal mol}^{-1}) \qquad (DH° = 58 \text{ kcal mol}^{-1})$$

The homolytic bond dissociation energies of a variety of covalent bonds are listed in Table 7.1.

7.2A HOMOLYTIC BOND DISSOCIATION ENERGIES AND HEATS OF REACTION

Bond dissociation energies have, as we shall see, a variety of uses. They can be used, for example, to calculate the enthalpy change ($\Delta H°$) for a reaction. To make such a calculation (see following reaction) we must remember that for bond breaking $\Delta H°$ is positive and for bond formation $\Delta H°$ is negative. Let us consider, for example, the reaction of hydrogen and chlorine to produce 2 mol of hydrogen chloride. From Table 7.1 we get the following values of $DH°$.

$$\text{H—H} \quad + \quad \text{Cl—Cl} \longrightarrow \qquad 2 \text{ H—Cl}$$

$(DH° = 104)$ $(DH° = 58)$	$(DH° = 103) \times 2$
$+162$ kcal mol^{-1} is required for bond cleavage	-206 kcal mol^{-1} is evolved in bond formation

Overall, the reaction is exothermic:

$$\Delta H° = (-206 \text{ kcal mol}^{-1} + 162 \text{ kcal mol}^{-1}) = -44 \text{ kcal mol}^{-1}$$

For the purpose of our calculation, we have assumed a particular pathway, that amounts to:

$$\text{H—H} \longrightarrow 2 \text{ H·}$$
and
$$\text{Cl—Cl} \longrightarrow 2 \text{ Cl·}$$
then
$$2 \text{ H·} + 2 \text{ Cl·} \longrightarrow 2 \text{ H—Cl}$$

This is not the way the reaction actually occurs. Nonetheless, the heat of reaction, $\Delta H°$, is a thermodynamic quantity that is dependent *only* on the initial and final states of the reacting molecules. $\Delta H°$ is independent of the path followed and, for this reason, our calculation is valid.

Problem 7.1

Calculate the heat of reaction, $\Delta H°$, for the following reactions:

(a) $H_2 + Br_2 \longrightarrow 2 \text{ HBr}$

(b) $CH_3CH_3 + F_2 \longrightarrow CH_3CH_2F + HF$

(c) $CH_3CH_3 + I_2 \longrightarrow CH_3CH_2I + HI$

(d) $CH_4 + Cl_2 \longrightarrow CH_3Cl + HCl$

(e) $(CH_3)_3CH + Cl_2 \longrightarrow (CH_3)_3CCl + HCl$

(f) $(CH_3)_3CH + Br_2 \longrightarrow (CH_3)_3CBr + HBr$

(g) $CH_3CH_2CH_3 \longrightarrow CH_3CH_2· + CH_3·$

(h) $2 \text{ } CH_3CH_2· \longrightarrow CH_3CH_2CH_2CH_3$

TABLE 7.1   Single-bond homolytic dissociation energies $DH°$ at 25 °C

$$A : B \longrightarrow A\cdot + B\cdot$$

BOND BROKEN (shown in red)	kcal mol^{-1}	kJ mol^{-1}	BOND BROKEN (shown in red)	kcal mol^{-1}	kJ mol^{-1}
H—H	104	435	$(CH_3)_2CH$—H	94.5	395
D—D	106	444	$(CH_3)_2CH$—F	105	439
F—F	38	159	$(CH_3)_2CH$—Cl	81	339
Cl—Cl	58	243	$(CH_3)_2CH$—Br	68	285
Br—Br	46	192	$(CH_3)_2CH$—I	53	222
I—I	36	151	$(CH_3)_2CH$—OH	92	385
H—F	136	569	$(CH_3)_2CH$—OCH_3	80.5	337
H—Cl	103	431	$(CH_3)_2CHCH_2$—H	98	410
H—Br	87.5	366	$(CH_3)_3C$—H	91	381
H—I	71	297	$(CH_3)_3C$—Cl	78.5	328
CH_3—H	104	435	$(CH_3)_3C$—Br	63	264
CH_3—F	108	452	$(CH_3)_3C$—I	49.5	207
CH_3—Cl	83.5	349	$(CH_3)_3C$—OH	90.5	379
CH_3—Br	70	293	$(CH_3)_3C$—OCH_3	78	326
CH_3—I	56	234	$C_6H_5CH_2$—H	85	356
CH_3—OH	91.5	383	$CH_2{=}CHCH_2$—H	85	356
CH_3—OCH_3	80	335	$CH_2{=}CH$—H	108	452
CH_3CH_2—H	98	410	C_6H_5—H	110	460
CH_3CH_2—F	106	444	$HC{\equiv}C$—H	125	523
CH_3CH_2—Cl	81.5	341	CH_3—CH_3	88	368
CH_3CH_2—Br	69	289	CH_3CH_2—CH_3	85	356
CH_3CH_2—I	53.5	224	$CH_3CH_2CH_2$—CH_3	85	356
CH_3CH_2—OH	91.5	383	CH_3CH_2—CH_2CH_3	82	343
CH_3CH_2—OCH_3	80	335	$(CH_3)_2CH$—CH_3	84	351
			$(CH_3)_3C$—CH_3	80	335
$CH_3CH_2CH_2$—H	98	410	HO—H	119	498
$CH_3CH_2CH_2$—F	106	444	HOO—H	90	377
$CH_3CH_2CH_2$—Cl	81.5	341	HO—OH	51	213
$CH_3CH_2CH_2$—Br	69	289	CH_3CH_2O—OCH_3	44	184
$CH_3CH_2CH_2$—I	53.5	224	CH_3CH_2O—H	103	431
$CH_3CH_2CH_2$—OH	91.5	383	$CH_3\overset{\displaystyle O}{\overset{\|}{C}}$—H	87	364
$CH_3CH_2CH_2$—OCH_3	80	335			

7.2B HOMOLYTIC BOND DISSOCIATION ENERGIES AND THE RELATIVE STABILITIES OF RADICALS

Homolytic bond dissociation energies also provide us with a convenient way to estimate the relative stabilities of radicals. If we examine the data given in Table 7.1, we find the following values of $DH°$ for the primary and secondary C—H bonds of propane:

$$CH_3CH_2CH_2—H \qquad (CH_3)_2CH—H$$
$$(DH° = 98 \text{ kcal mol}^{-1}) \qquad (DH° = 94.5 \text{ kcal mol}^{-1})$$

This means that for the reaction in which the designated C—H bonds are broken homolytically, the values of $\Delta H°$ are those given here.

$$CH_3CH_2CH_2—H \longrightarrow CH_3CH_2CH_2\cdot + H\cdot \qquad \Delta H° = +98 \text{ kcal mol}^{-1}$$

Propyl radical
(a 1° radical)

$$CH_3\underset{|}{\overset{}{C}}HCH_3 \longrightarrow CH_3\overset{.}{C}HCH_3 + H\cdot \qquad \Delta H° = +94.5 \text{ kcal mol}^{-1}$$
$$H$$

Isopropyl radical
(a 2° radical)

These reactions resemble each other in two respects: They both begin with the same alkane (propane), and they both produce an alkyl radical and a hydrogen atom. They differ, however, in the amount of energy required and in the type of carbon radical being produced.* These two differences are related to each other.

More energy must be supplied to produce a primary alkyl radical (the propyl radical) from propane than is required to produce a secondary carbon radical (the isopropyl radical) from the same compound. This must mean that the primary radical has absorbed more energy and thus has greater *potential energy*. Because the relative stability of a chemical species is inversely related to its potential energy, the secondary radical must be the *more stable* radical (Fig. 7.1*a*). In fact, the secondary isopropyl radical is more stable than the primary propyl radical by 3.5 kcal mol^{-1}.

We can use the data in Table 7.1 to make a similar comparison of the *tert*-butyl radical (a 3° radical) and the isobutyl radical (a 1° radical) relative to isobutane.

$$CH_3-\underset{\underset{H}{|}}{\overset{\overset{CH_3}{|}}{C}}-CH_2-H \longrightarrow CH_3\overset{\overset{CH_3}{|}}{\underset{}{C}}CH_3 + H\cdot \qquad \Delta H° = +91 \text{ kcal mol}^{-1}$$

***tert*-Butyl**
radical
(a 3° radical)

$$CH_3-\underset{\underset{H}{|}}{\overset{\overset{CH_3}{|}}{C}}-CH_2-H \longrightarrow CH_3\overset{\overset{CH_3}{|}}{\underset{}{C}}HCH_2\cdot + H\cdot \qquad \Delta H° = +98 \text{ kcal mol}^{-1}$$

Isobutyl radical
(a 1° radical)

*Alkyl radicals are classified as being 1°, 2°, or 3° on the basis of the carbon atom that has the unpaired electron.

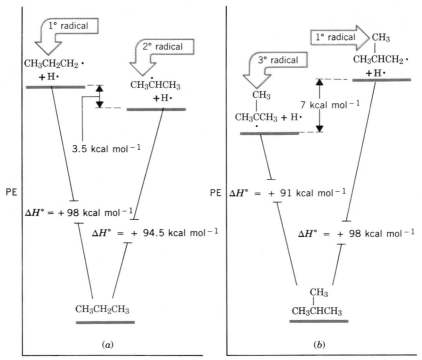

FIGURE 7.1 (*a*) A comparison of the potential energies of the propyl radical (+H ·) and the isopropyl radical (+H ·) relative to propane. The isopropyl radical—a 2° radical—is more stable than the 1° radical by 3.5 kcal mol⁻¹. (*b*) A comparison of the potential energies of the *tert*-butyl radical (+H ·) and the isobutyl radical (+H ·) relative to isobutane. The 3° radical is more stable than the 1° radical by 7 kcal mol⁻¹.

Here we find (Fig. 7.1*b*) that the difference in stability of the two radicals is even larger. The tertiary radical is more stable than the primary radical by 7 kcal mol⁻¹.

The kind of pattern that we find in these examples is found with alkyl radicals generally; overall their relative stabilities are the following:

Tertiary > Secondary > Primary > Methyl

$$ \underset{\overset{|}{C}}{\overset{\overset{C}{|}}{C-C\cdot}} > \underset{\overset{|}{H}}{\overset{\overset{C}{|}}{C-C\cdot}} > \underset{\overset{|}{H}}{\overset{\overset{H}{|}}{C-C\cdot}} > \underset{\overset{|}{H}}{\overset{\overset{H}{|}}{H-C\cdot}} $$

The order of stability of alkyl radicals is the same as for carbocations (Section 6.13B), and the reasons are similar. Although alkyl radicals are uncharged, the carbon that bears the odd electron is *electron deficient*. Therefore, electron-releasing alkyl groups attached to this carbon provide a stabilizing effect, and the more alkyl groups that are attached to this carbon the more stable the radical is.

Problem 7.2

(a) Sketch diagrams similar to those in Fig. 7.1 showing the potential energy of $(CH_3)_2CH \cdot + H \cdot$ relative to propane and the potential energy of

$CH_3CH_2\cdot + H\cdot$ relative to ethane. Align the two diagrams so that the potential energy of the alkane is the same in each. What does this indicate about the stability of an ethyl radical and an isopropyl radical relative to the alkane from which each is derived? (b) Repeat this process by drawing potential energy diagrams showing the energy of $CH_3CH_2\cdot + H\cdot$ relative to ethane and of $CH_3\cdot + H\cdot$ relative to methane. What do these graphs indicate about the relative stabilities of an ethyl radical and a methyl radical? (c) Make similar sketches that compare an ethyl radical with a propyl radical. (d) Account for the similarity of the potential energy diagrams in part (c).

Problem 7.3

One can also estimate the relative stabilities of alkyl radicals by comparing the homolytic bond dissociation energies of the C—X bonds of haloalkanes. Show how this can be done with CH_3—Cl, CH_3CH_2—Cl, $(CH_3)_2CH$—Cl, and $(CH_3)_3C$—Cl.

7.3 THE REACTIONS OF ALKANES WITH HALOGENS

Methane, ethane, and other alkanes react with the first three members of the halogen family: fluorine, chlorine, and bromine. Alkanes do not react appreciably with iodine. With methane the reaction produces a mixture of halomethanes and a hydrogen halide.

X = F, Cl, or Br

The reaction of an alkane with a halogen is called **halogenation.** The general reaction to produce a monohaloalkane can be written as follows:

$$R—H + X_2 \longrightarrow R—X + HX$$

In these reactions a halogen atom replaces one or more of the hydrogen atoms of the alkane. Reactions of this type, *in which one atom or group replaces another,* are called **substitution reactions.**

$$-\overset{|}{\underset{|}{C}}-H + Cl_2 \longrightarrow -\overset{|}{\underset{|}{C}}-Cl + H—Cl \qquad \textbf{A substitution reaction}$$

7.3A HALOGENATION REACTIONS

One complicating characteristic of alkane halogenations is that multiple substitution reactions almost always occur. As we saw at the beginning of this section, the halogenation of methane produces a mixture of monohalomethane, dihalomethane, trihalomethane, and tetrahalomethane.

This happens because all hydrogen atoms attached to carbon are capable of reacting with fluorine, chlorine, or bromine.

Let us consider the reaction that takes place between chlorine and methane as an example. If we mix methane and chlorine (both substances are gases at room temperature) and then either heat the mixture or irradiate it with light, a reaction begins to occur vigorously. At the outset, the only compounds that are present in the mixture are chlorine and methane, and the only reaction that can take place is one that produces chloromethane and hydrogen chloride.

$$\underset{\substack{|\\H}}{\overset{\substack{H\\|}}{H-C-H}} + Cl_2 \longrightarrow \underset{\substack{|\\H}}{\overset{\substack{H\\|}}{H-C-Cl}} + H-Cl$$

As the reaction progresses, however, the concentration of chloromethane in the mixture increases, and a second substitution reaction begins to occur. Chloromethane reacts with chlorine to produce dichloromethane.

$$\underset{\substack{|\\H}}{\overset{\substack{H\\|}}{H-C-Cl}} + Cl_2 \longrightarrow \underset{\substack{|\\H}}{\overset{\substack{Cl\\|}}{H-C-Cl}} + H-Cl$$

Dichloromethane can then produce trichloromethane,

$$\underset{\substack{|\\H}}{\overset{\substack{Cl\\|}}{H-C-Cl}} + Cl_2 \longrightarrow \underset{\substack{|\\Cl}}{\overset{\substack{Cl\\|}}{H-C-Cl}} + H-Cl$$

and trichloromethane, as it accumulates in the mixture, can react with chlorine to produce tetrachloromethane.

$$\underset{\substack{|\\Cl}}{\overset{\substack{Cl\\|}}{H-C-Cl}} + Cl_2 \longrightarrow \underset{\substack{|\\Cl}}{\overset{\substack{Cl\\|}}{Cl-C-Cl}} + H-Cl$$

Each time a substitution of —Cl for —H takes place a molecule of H—Cl is produced.

Sample Problem

If the goal of a synthesis is to prepare chloromethane (CH_3Cl), its formation can be maximized and the formation of CH_2Cl_2, $CHCl_3$, and CCl_4 minimized by using a large excess of methane in the reaction mixture. Explain why this is possible.

Answer:

The use of a large excess of methane maximizes the probability that chlorine will attack methane molecules because the concentration of methane in the mixture will always be relatively large. It also minimizes the probability that chlorine will attack molecules of CH_3Cl, CH_2Cl_2, and $CHCl_3$, because their concentrations will always be relatively small. After the reaction is over, the unreacted excess methane can be recovered and recycled.

When ethane and chlorine react, similar substitution reactions occur. Ultimately all six hydrogen atoms of ethane may be replaced. We notice in the following diagram that the second substitution reaction of ethane results in the formation of two different molecules: 1,1-dichloroethane and 1,2-dichloroethane. These two molecules have the same molecular formula ($C_2H_4Cl_2$) but these atoms are connected in a different way. They are, therefore, **constitutional isomers.**

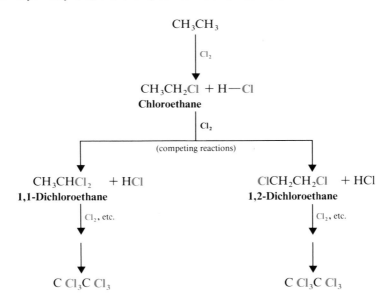

Chlorination of most alkanes whose molecules contain three carbon atoms or more gives a mixture of isomeric monochloro products as well as more highly halogenated compounds. Chlorine is relatively **unselective;** it does not discriminate greatly among the different types of hydrogen atoms (primary, secondary, and tertiary) in an alkane. An example is the light-promoted chlorination of isobutane.

Because alkane chlorinations usually yield a complex mixture of products, they are not generally useful as synthetic methods when our goal is the preparation of a specific alkyl chloride. An exception is the halogenation of an alkane (or cycloalkane) whose hydrogen atoms *are all equivalent*.* Neopentane, for example, can form only one monohalogenation product, and the use of a large excess of neopentane minimizes polychlorination.

$$CH_3-\underset{\underset{CH_3}{|}}{\overset{\overset{CH_3}{|}}{C}}-CH_3 + Cl_2 \xrightarrow[\text{or light}]{\text{heat}} CH_3-\underset{\underset{CH_3}{|}}{\overset{\overset{CH_3}{|}}{C}}-CH_2Cl + HCl$$

Neopentane   **Neopentyl chloride**
(excess)

In a similar way cyclobutane yields cyclobutyl chloride.

$$\square + Cl_2 \xrightarrow[\text{or light}]{\text{heat}} \square^{Cl} + HCl$$

(excess)

Bromine is generally less reactive toward alkanes than chlorine, and bromine is *more selective* in the site of attack when it does react. We shall examine this topic further in Section 7.7A.

7.4 CHLORINATION OF METHANE: MECHANISM OF REACTION

The *halogenation* reactions of alkanes take place by a radical mechanism. Let us begin our study of them by examining a simple example of an alkane halogenation: the reaction of methane with chlorine that takes place in the gas phase.

Several important experimental observations can be made about this reaction:

$$CH_4 + Cl_2 \longrightarrow CH_3Cl + HCl\ (+ CH_2Cl_2, CHCl_3, \text{ and } CCl_4)$$

1. **The reaction is promoted by heat or light.** At room temperature methane and chlorine do not react at a perceptible rate as long as the mixture is kept away from light. Methane and chlorine do react, however, at room temperature if the gaseous reaction mixture is irradiated with UV light, and methane and chlorine do react in the dark, if the gaseous mixture is heated to temperatures greater than 100 °C.
2. **The light-promoted reaction is highly efficient.** A relatively small number of light photons permits the formation of relatively large amounts of chlorinated product.

A mechanism that is consistent with these observations has several steps. The first step involves the fragmentation of a chlorine molecule, by heat or light, into two chlorine atoms.

---

*Equivalent hydrogen atoms are defined as those which on replacement by some other group (e.g., chlorine) yield the same compound.

7.4 CHLORINATION OF METHANE: MECHANISM OF REACTION

Step 1 $\quad$:Cl : Cl : $\xrightarrow[\text{or light}]{\text{heat}}$ 2 :Cl·

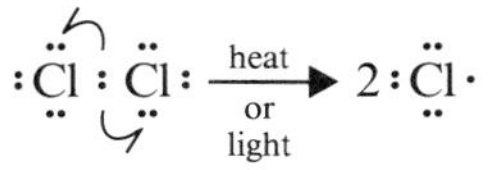

Chlorine is known, from other evidence, to undergo such reactions. It can be shown, moreover, that the frequency of light that promotes the chlorination of methane is a frequency that is absorbed by chlorine molecules and not by methane molecules.

The second and third steps of the mechanism are as follows:*

Step 2 $\quad$:Cl· + H:C—H $\longrightarrow$ H:Cl: + ·C—H

Step 3 $\quad$ H—C· + :Cl:Cl: $\longrightarrow$ H—C:Cl: + ·Cl:

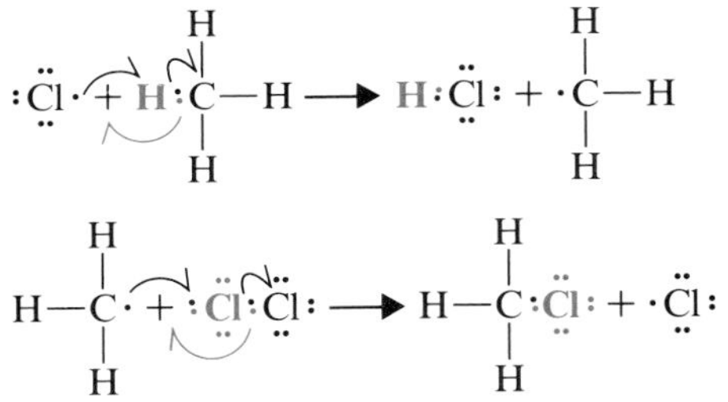

Step 2 is the abstraction of a hydrogen atom from the methane molecule by a chlorine atom. This step results in the formation of a molecule of hydrogen chloride and a methyl radical.

In step 3 the highly reactive methyl radical reacts with a chlorine molecule by abstracting a chlorine atom. This results in the formation of a molecule of chloromethane (one of the ultimate products of the reaction) and a *chlorine atom.* This latter product is particularly significant, for the chlorine atom formed in step 3 can attack another methane molecule and cause a repetition of step 2. Then, step 3 is repeated, and so forth, for hundreds or thousands of times. (With each repetition of step 3 a molecule of chloromethane is produced.) This type of sequential, stepwise mechanism, in which each step generates the reactive intermediate that causes the next step to occur, is called a **chain reaction.**

Step 1 is called the **chain-initiating step.** In the chain-initiating step *radicals are created.* Steps 2 and 3 are called **chain-propagating steps.** In chain-propagating steps *one radical generates another.*

Chain Initiation

Step 1 $\quad$ $Cl_2 \xrightarrow[\text{light}]{\text{heat}}$ 2 Cl·

Chain Propagation

Step 2 $\quad$ $CH_4 + Cl· \longrightarrow$ H—Cl + $CH_3·$

Step 3 $\quad$ $CH_3· + Cl_2· \longrightarrow CH_3Cl + Cl·$

The chain nature of the reaction accounts for the observation that the light-promoted reaction is highly efficient. The presence of a relatively few atoms of chlorine at any given moment is all that is needed to cause the formation of many thousands of molecules of chloromethane.

Remember: These conventions are used in illustrating reaction mechanisms in this text.

1. Arrows ⌢ or ⌢ always show the direction of movement of electrons.
2. Single-barbed arrows ⌢ show the attack (or movement) of an unpaired electron.
3. Double-barbed arrows ⌢ show the attack (or movement) of an electron pair.

What causes the chains to terminate? Why does one photon of light not promote the chlorination of all of the methane molecules present? We know that this does not happen because we find that at low temperatures, continuous irradiation is required or the reaction slows and stops. The answer to these questions is the existence of **chain-terminating steps:** steps that occur infrequently, but occur often enough to *use up one or both of the reactive intermediates.* The continuous replacement of intermediates used up by chain-terminating steps requires continuous irradiation. Plausible chain-terminating steps are

Chain Termination

$$H-\overset{\overset{\displaystyle H}{|}}{\underset{\underset{\displaystyle H}{|}}{C}}\cdot + \cdot\ddot{C}l\colon \longrightarrow H-\overset{\overset{\displaystyle H}{|}}{\underset{\underset{\displaystyle H}{|}}{C}}\cdot\ddot{C}l\colon$$

$$H-\overset{\overset{\displaystyle H}{|}}{\underset{\underset{\displaystyle H}{|}}{C}}\cdot + \cdot\overset{\overset{\displaystyle H}{|}}{\underset{\underset{\displaystyle H}{|}}{C}}-H \longrightarrow H-\overset{\overset{\displaystyle H}{|}}{\underset{\underset{\displaystyle H}{|}}{C}}\colon\overset{\overset{\displaystyle H}{|}}{\underset{\underset{\displaystyle H}{|}}{C}}-H$$

and
$$\colon\!\ddot{C}l\cdot + \cdot\ddot{C}l\colon \longrightarrow \colon\!\ddot{C}l\colon\!\ddot{C}l\colon$$

This last step probably occurs least frequently. The two chlorine atoms are highly energetic; as a result, the simple diatomic chlorine molecule that is formed has to dissipate its excess energy rapidly by colliding with some other molecule or the walls of the container. Otherwise it simply flies apart again. By contrast, chloromethane and ethane, formed in the other two chain-terminating steps, can dissipate their excess energy through vibrations of their C—H bonds.

Our radical mechanism also explains how the reaction of methane with chlorine produces the more highly halogenated products, CH_2Cl_2, $CHCl_3$, and CCl_4 (as well as additional HCl). As the reaction progresses, chloromethane (CH_3Cl) accumulates in the mixture and its hydrogen atoms, too, are susceptible to abstraction by chlorine. Thus chloromethyl radicals are produced that lead to dichloromethane (CH_2Cl_2)

Step 2a
$$Cl\cdot + H\overset{\overset{\displaystyle Cl}{|}}{\underset{\underset{\displaystyle H}{|}}{C}}-H \longrightarrow H\colon\!Cl + \cdot\overset{\overset{\displaystyle Cl}{|}}{\underset{\underset{\displaystyle H}{|}}{C}}-H$$

Step 3a
$$H-\overset{\overset{\displaystyle Cl}{|}}{\underset{\underset{\displaystyle H}{|}}{C}}\cdot + Cl\colon\!Cl \longrightarrow H-\overset{\overset{\displaystyle Cl}{|}}{\underset{\underset{\displaystyle H}{|}}{C}}\colon\!Cl + Cl\cdot$$

Then step 2a is repeated, then step 3a is repeated, and so on. Each repetition of step 2a yields a molecule of HCl, and each repetition of step 3a yields a molecule of CH_2Cl_2.

Problem 7.4

Write mechanisms showing how $CHCl_3$ and CCl_4 might be formed in the reaction mixture when methane is chlorinated.

Problem 7.5 ――――――――――――――――――――――――――

When methane is chlorinated, among the products are found traces of chloro-ethane. How is it formed? Of what significance is its formation?

Problem 7.6 ――――――――――――――――――――――――――

If our goal is to synthesize CCl_4 in maximum yield, this can be accomplished by using a large excess of chlorine. Explain.

7.5 CHLORINATION OF METHANE: ENERGY CHANGES

We saw in Section 7.2A that we can calculate the overall heat of reaction from bond dissociation energies. We can also calculate the heat of reaction for each individual step of a mechanism.

Chain Initiation

Step 1 $Cl—Cl \longrightarrow 2\ Cl\cdot$ $\Delta H° = +58$ kcal mol^{-1}
         $(DH° = 58)$

Chain Propagation

Step 2 $CH_3—H + Cl\cdot \longrightarrow H—Cl + CH_3\cdot$ $\Delta H° = +1$ kcal mol^{-1}
         $(DH° = 104)$ $(DH° = 103)$

Step 3 $CH_3\cdot + Cl—Cl \longrightarrow CH_3—Cl + Cl\cdot$ $\Delta H° = -25.5$ kcal mol^{-1}
         $(DH° = 58)$ $(DH° = 83.5)$

Chain Termination

         $CH_3\cdot + Cl\cdot \longrightarrow CH_3—Cl$ $\Delta H° = -83.5$ kcal mol^{-1}
                   $(DH° = 83.5)$

         $CH_3\cdot + \cdot CH_3 \longrightarrow CH_3—CH_3$ $\Delta H° = -88$ kcal mol^{-1}
                   $(DH° = 88)$

         $Cl\cdot + Cl\cdot \longrightarrow Cl—Cl$ $\Delta H° = -58$ kcal mol^{-1}
                   $(DH° = 58)$

In the chain-initiating step only one bond is broken — the bond between two chlorine atoms — and no bonds are formed. The heat of reaction for this step is simply the bond dissociation energy for a chlorine molecule, and it is highly endothermic.

In the chain-terminating steps bonds are formed, but no bonds are broken. As a result, all of the chain-terminating steps are highly exothermic.

Each of the chain-propagating steps, on the other hand, requires the breaking of one bond and the formation of another. The value of $\Delta H°$ for each of these steps is the difference between the bond dissociation energy of the bond that is broken and the bond dissociation energy for the bond that is formed. The first chain-propagating step is slightly endothermic ($\Delta H° = +1$ kcal mol^{-1}), but the second is exothermic by a large amount ($\Delta H° = -25.5$ kcal mol^{-1}).

Problem 7.7

Assuming the same mechanism occurs, calculate $\Delta H°$ for the chain-initiating, chain-propagating, and chain-terminating steps involved in the bromination of methane.

The addition of the chain-propagating steps yields the overall equation for the chlorination of methane:

$$Cl\cdot + CH_3{-}H \longrightarrow CH_3\cdot + H{-}Cl \qquad \Delta H° = +\ 1\quad kcal\ mol^{-1}$$
$$\underline{CH_3\cdot + Cl{-}Cl \longrightarrow CH_3{-}Cl + Cl\cdot \qquad \Delta H° = -25.5\ kcal\ mol^{-1}}$$
$$CH_3{-}H + Cl{-}Cl \longrightarrow CH_3{-}Cl + H{-}Cl \qquad \Delta H° = -24.5\ kcal\ mol^{-1}$$

and the addition of the values of $\Delta H°$ for the individual chain-propagating steps yields the overall value of $\Delta H°$ for the reaction.

Problem 7.8

Why would it be incorrect to include the chain-initiating and chain-terminating steps in the calculation of the overall value of $\Delta H°$ given previously?

7.5A THE OVERALL FREE-ENERGY CHANGE

For many reactions the entropy change is so small that the term $T\Delta S°$ in the expression

$$\Delta G° = \Delta H° - T\Delta S°$$

is almost zero, and $\Delta G°$ is approximately equal to $\Delta H°$. This happens when the reaction is one in which the relative order of reactants and products is about the same. Recall (Section 3.6) that entropy measures the relative disorder or randomness of a system. For a chemical system the relative disorder of the molecules can be related to the number of *degrees of freedom* available to the molecules and their constituent atoms. Degrees of freedom are associated with ways in which *movement or changes in relative position can occur.* Molecules have three sorts of degrees of freedom: translational degrees of freedom associated with movements of the whole molecule through space, rotational degrees of freedom associated with the tumbling motions of the molecule, and vibrational degrees of freedom associated with the stretching and bending motion of atoms about the bonds that connect them (Fig. 7.2). If the atoms of the products of a reaction have more degrees of freedom available than they did as reactants, the entropy change ($\Delta S°$) for the reaction will be positive. If, on the other hand, the atoms of the products are more constrained (have fewer degrees of freedom) than the reactants, a negative $\Delta S°$ will result.

Consider the reaction of methane with chlorine.

$$CH_4 + Cl_2 \longrightarrow CH_3Cl + HCl$$

Here, 2 mol of the products are formed from the same number of moles of the reactants. Thus the number of translational degrees of freedom available to products

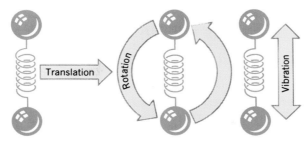

FIGURE 7.2 Translational, rotational, and vibrational degrees of freedom for a simple diatomic molecule.

and reactants will be the same. Furthermore, CH_3Cl is a tetrahedral molecule like CH_4, and HCl is a diatomic molecule like Cl_2. This means that vibrational and rotational degrees of freedom available to products and reactants should also be approximately the same. The actual entropy change for this reaction is quite small, $\Delta S° = +0.67$ cal K^{-1} mol^{-1}. Therefore, at room temperature (298 K) the $T\Delta S°$ term is 0.2 kcal mol^{-1}. The enthalpy change for the reaction and the free-energy change are almost equal, $\Delta H° = -24.5$ kcal mol^{-1}, and $\Delta G° = -24.7$ kcal mol^{-1}.

In situations like this one it is often convenient to make predictions about whether or not a reaction will proceed to completion on the basis of $\Delta H°$ rather than $\Delta G°$ since $\Delta H°$ values are readily obtained from bond dissociation energies.

7.5B ACTIVATION ENERGIES

For many reactions that we shall study in which entropy changes are small, it is also often convenient to base our estimates of reaction rates on what are called simply **energies of activation, E_{act}**, rather than on free energies of activation, $\Delta G^{\ddagger}$. Without going into detail, suffice it to say, that these two quantities are closely related, and that **both measure the difference in potential energy between the reactants and the transition state.** Therefore, a low energy of activation means a reaction will take place rapidly; a high energy of activation means that a reaction will take place slowly.

Having seen earlier in this section how to calculate $\Delta H°$ for each step in the chlorination of methane, let us consider the energy of activation for each step. These values are as follows:

Chain Initiation

  Step 1 $Cl_2 \longrightarrow 2\ Cl\cdot$ $\qquad\qquad\qquad$ $E_{act} = +58$ kcal mol^{-1}

Chain Propagation

  Step 2 $Cl\cdot + CH_4 \longrightarrow HCl + CH_3\cdot$ $\quad$ $E_{act} = +3.8$ kcal mol^{-1}

  Step 3 $CH_3\cdot + Cl_2 \longrightarrow CH_3Cl + Cl\cdot$ $\quad$ $E_{act} = \sim 2$ kcal mol^{-1}

How does one know what the energy of activation for a reaction will be? Could we, for example, have predicted from bond dissociation energies that the energy of activation for the reaction, $Cl\cdot + CH_4 \longrightarrow HCl + CH_3\cdot$, would be precisely 3.8 kcal mol^{-1}? The answer is *no*. The energy of activation must be determined from other experimental data. It cannot be directly measured—it is calculated. Certain principles can be established, however, that enable one to arrive at estimates of energies of activation:

CHAPTER 7. RADICAL REACTIONS

1. Any reaction in which *bonds are broken* will have an energy of activation greater than zero. This will be true even if a stronger bond is formed and the reaction is exothermic. The reason: Bond formation and bond breaking do not occur simultaneously in the transition state. Bond formation lags behind, and its energy is not all available for bond breaking.

2. Activation energies of *endothermic reactions that involve both bond formation and bond rupture will be greater than the heat of reaction, $\Delta H°$.* Two examples illustrate this principle: the first chain-propagating step in the chlorination of methane and the corresponding step in the bromination of methane:

$$Cl\cdot \ + \ CH_3{-}H \ \longrightarrow \ H{-}Cl \ + CH_3\cdot \qquad \Delta H° = +1 \text{ kcal mol}^{-1}$$
$$(DH° = 104) \qquad (DH° = 103) \qquad\qquad E_{act} = +3.8 \text{ kcal mol}^{-1}$$

$$Br\cdot \ + \ CH_3{-}H \ \longrightarrow \ H{-}Br \ + CH_3\cdot \qquad \Delta H° = +16.5 \text{ kcal mol}^{-1}$$
$$(DH° = 104) \qquad (DH° = 87.5) \qquad\qquad E_{act} = +18.6 \text{ kcal mol}^{-1}$$

In both of these reactions the energy released in bond formation is less than that required for bond rupture; both reactions are, therefore, endothermic. We can easily see why the energy of activation for each reaction is greater than the heat of reaction by looking at the potential energy diagrams in Fig. 7.3. In each case the path from reactants to products is from a lower energy plateau to a higher one. In each case the intervening energy hill is higher still, and since the energy of

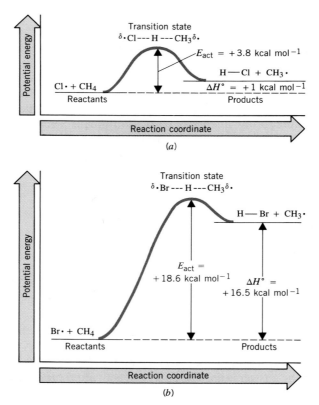

FIGURE 7.3 Potential Energy diagrams for (*a*) the reaction of a chlorine atom with methane and (*b*) for the reaction of a bromine atom with methane.

activation is the vertical (energy) distance between the plateau of reactants and the top of this hill the energy of activation exceeds the heat of reaction.

3. **The energy of activation of a gas-phase reaction where bonds are broken homolytically but no bonds are formed is equal to $\Delta H°$.*** An example of this type of reaction is the chain-initiating step in the chlorination of methane: the dissociation of chlorine molecules into chlorine atoms.

$$\text{Cl—Cl} \longrightarrow 2\ \text{Cl·} \qquad \Delta H° = +58 \text{ kcal mol}^{-1}$$
$$(DH° = 58) \qquad\qquad E_{act} = +58 \text{ kcal mol}^{-1}$$

The potential energy diagram for this reaction is shown in Fig. 7.4.

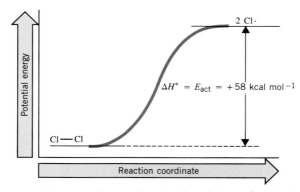

FIGURE 7.4 The potential energy diagram for the dissociation of a chlorine molecule into chlorine atoms.

4. The energy of activation for a **gas-phase** reaction in which **small radicals combine to form molecules is usually zero.** In reactions of this type the problem of nonsimultaneous bond formation and bond rupture does not exist; only one process occurs: that of bond formation. All of the chain-terminating steps in the chlorination of methane fall into this category. An example is the combination of two methyl radicals to form a molecule of ethane.

$$2\ \text{CH}_3\cdot \longrightarrow \text{CH}_3\text{—CH}_3 \qquad \Delta H° = -88 \text{ kcal mol}^{-1}$$
$$(DH° = 88) \qquad\qquad E_{act} = 0$$

Figure 7.5 illustrates the potential energy changes that occur in this reaction.

In Section 7.7 we shall see how we can estimate energies of activation by taking advantage of the fact that the transition states of reactions resemble the reactants and products.

Problem 7.9

When gaseous ethane is heated to a very high temperature, radical reactions take place that produce (among other products) methane and butane. This type

---

*This rule applies only to radical reactions taking place in the gas phase. It does not apply to reactions taking place in solution, especially where ions are involved, because solvation energies are also important.

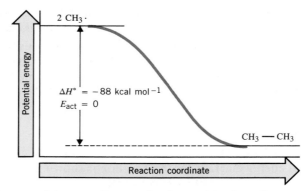

FIGURE 7.5 The potential energy diagram for the combination of two methyl radicals to form a molecule of thane.

of change is called thermal cracking. Among the reactions that take place when ethane undergoes thermal cracking are the following:

(1) $CH_3CH_3 \longrightarrow 2\ CH_3\cdot$

(2) $CH_3\cdot + CH_3CH_3 \longrightarrow CH_4 + CH_3CH_2\cdot$

(3) $2\ CH_3CH_2\cdot \longrightarrow CH_3CH_2CH_2CH_3$

(4) $CH_3CH_2\cdot \longrightarrow CH_2{=}CH_2 + H\cdot$

(5) $CH_3\cdot + H\cdot \longrightarrow CH_4$

(a) For which reaction(s) would you expect E_{act} to equal zero? (b) For which would you expect E_{act} to be greater than zero? (c) For which would you expect E_{act} to equal $\Delta H°$?

Problem 7.10 _____

Sketch potential energy diagrams for the following reactions. Label the heat of reaction ($\Delta H°$) and the energy of activation (E_{act}) in each case. [Notice that the reactions in (1) and (2) are the reverse of those shown in Fig. 7.3.]

(1) $CH_3\cdot + HCl \longrightarrow CH_3{-}H + Cl\cdot$

(2) $CH_3\cdot + HBr \longrightarrow CH_3{-}H + Br\cdot$

(3) $CH_3{-}CH_3 \longrightarrow 2\ CH_3\cdot$

(4) $Br{-}Br \longrightarrow 2\ Br\cdot$

(5) $2\ Cl\cdot \longrightarrow Cl{-}Cl$

7.6 REACTION OF METHANE WITH OTHER HALOGENS

The *reactivity* of one substance toward another is measured by the *rate* at which the two substances react. A reagent that reacts very rapidly with a particular substance is said to be highly reactive toward that substance. One that reacts slowly or not at all under the same experimental conditions (e.g., concentration, pressure, and temperature) is said to have a low relative reactivity or to be unreactive. The reactions of the halogens (fluorine, chlorine, bromine, and iodine) with methane show a wide spread of relative reactivities. Fluorine is most reactive — so reactive, in fact, that without special precautions mixtures of fluorine and methane explode. Chlorine is the next most reactive. However, the chlorination of methane is easily controlled by the judicious control of heat and light. Bromine is much less reactive toward methane than chlorine, and iodine is so unreactive that for all practical purposes we can say that no reaction takes place at all.

If the mechanisms for fluorination, bromination, and iodination of methane are the same as for its chlorination, we can explain the wide variation in reactivity of the halogens by a careful examination of $\Delta H°$ and E_{act} for each step.

FLUORINATION

	$\Delta H°(\text{kcal mol}^{-1})$	$E_{act}(\text{kcal mol}^{-1})$

Chain Initiation

$$F_2 \longrightarrow 2\,F\cdot \qquad\qquad +38 \qquad\qquad +38$$

Chain Propagation

$$F\cdot + CH_4 \longrightarrow HF + CH_3\cdot \qquad -32 \qquad\qquad +1.2$$
$$CH_3\cdot + F_2 \longrightarrow CH_3F + F\cdot \qquad -70 \qquad\qquad \text{small}$$
$$\text{Overall } \Delta H° = -102$$

The chain-initiating step in fluorination is highly endothermic and thus has a high energy of activation.

If we did not know otherwise, we might carelessly conclude from the energy of activation of the chain-initiating step alone that fluorine would be quite unreactive toward methane. (If we then proceeded to try the reaction, as a result of this careless assessment, the results would be literally disastrous.) We know, however, that the chain-initiating step occurs only infrequently relative to the chain-propagating steps. One initiating step is able to produce thousands of fluorination reactions. As a result, the high activation energy for this step is not an impediment to the reaction.

Chain-propagating steps, by contrast, cannot afford to have high energies of activation. If they do, the highly reactive intermediates are consumed by chain-terminating steps before the chains progress very far. Both of the chain-propagating steps in fluorination have very small energies of activation. This allows a relatively large fraction of energetically favorable collisions even at room temperature. Moreover, the overall heat of reaction, $\Delta H°$, is very large. This means that as the reaction occurs, a large quantity of heat is evolved. This heat may accumulate in the mixture faster than it dissipates to the surroundings, causing the temperature to rise and with it a rapid increase in the frequency of additional chain-initiating steps that would generate additional chains. These two factors, the low energy of activation for the chain-propagating steps, and the large overall heat of reaction, account for the high reactivity of fluorine toward methane.*

---

*Fluorination reactions can be controlled. This is usually accomplished by diluting both the hydrocarbon and the fluorine with an inert gas such as helium before bringing them together. The reaction is also carried out in a reactor packed with copper shot. The copper, by absorbing the heat produced, moderates the reaction.

CHLORINATION

	$\Delta H°$(kcal mol^{-1})	E_{act}(kcal mol^{-1})

Chain Initiation

$$Cl_2 \longrightarrow 2Cl\cdot \qquad\qquad +58 \qquad\qquad\qquad +58$$

Chain Propagation

$$Cl\cdot + CH_4 \longrightarrow HCl + CH_3\cdot \qquad\qquad +1 \qquad\qquad +3.8$$
$$CH_3\cdot + Cl_2 \longrightarrow CH_3Cl + Cl\cdot \qquad\qquad -25.5 \qquad\qquad \text{small}$$
$$\text{Overall } \Delta H° = -24.5$$

The higher energy of activation of the first chain-propagating step (the hydrogen abstraction step) in chlorination of methane ($+3.8$ kcal mol^{-1}), versus the lower energy of activation ($+1.2$ kcal mol^{-1}) in fluorination, partly explains the lower reactivity of chlorine. The greater energy required to break the chlorine–chlorine bond in the initiating step ($+58$ kcal mol^{-1} for Cl_2 versus $+38$ kcal mol^{-1} for F_2) has some effect, too. However, the much greater overall heat of reaction in fluorination probably plays the greatest role in accounting for the much greater reactivity of fluorine.

BROMINATION

	$\Delta H°$(kcal mol^{-1})	E_{act}(kcal mol^{-1})

Chain Initiation

$$Br_2 \longrightarrow 2Br\cdot \qquad\qquad +46 \qquad\qquad\qquad +46$$

Chain Propagation

$$Br\cdot + CH_4 \longrightarrow HBr + CH_3\cdot \qquad\qquad +16.5 \qquad\qquad +18.6$$
$$CH_3\cdot + Br_2 \longrightarrow CH_3Br + Br\cdot \qquad\qquad -24 \qquad\qquad \text{small}$$
$$\text{Overall } \Delta H° = -7.5$$

In contrast to chlorination, the hydrogen-atom abstraction step in bromination has a very high energy of activation ($E_{act} = 18.6$ kcal mol^{-1}). This means that only a very tiny fraction of all of the collisions between bromine atoms and methane molecules will be energetically effective even at a temperature of 300 °C. Bromine, as a result, is much less reactive toward methane than chlorine even though the net reaction is slightly exothermic.

IODINATION

	$\Delta H°$(kcal mol^{-1})	E_{act}(kcal mol^{-1})

Chain Initiation

$$I_2 \longrightarrow 2I\cdot \qquad\qquad +36 \qquad\qquad\qquad +36$$

Chain Propagation

$$I\cdot + CH_4 \longrightarrow HI + CH_3\cdot \qquad\qquad +33 \qquad\qquad +33.5$$
$$CH_3\cdot + I_2 \longrightarrow CH_3I + I\cdot \qquad\qquad -20 \qquad\qquad \text{small}$$
$$\text{Overall } \Delta H° = +13$$

The thermodynamic quantities for iodination of methane make it clear that the chain-initiating step is not responsible for the observed order of reactivities: $F_2 >$ $Cl_2 > Br_2 > I_2$. The iodine–iodine bond is even weaker than the fluorine–fluorine bond. On this basis alone, one would predict that iodine would be the most reactive of the halogens. This clearly is not the case. Once again, it is the hydrogen-atom abstraction step that correlates with the experimentally determined order of reactivities. The energy of activation of this step in the iodine reaction (33.5 kcal mol^{-1}) is so large that only two collisions out of every 10^{12} have sufficient energy to produce reactions at 300 °C. As a result, iodination is not a feasible reaction experimentally.

Before we leave this topic, one further point needs to be made. We have given explanations of the relative reactivities of the halogens toward methane that have been based on energy considerations alone. This has been possible *only because the reactions are quite similar and thus have similar entropy changes.* Had the reactions been of different types, this kind of analysis would not have been proper and might have given incorrect explanations.

7.7 HALOGENATION OF HIGHER ALKANES

Higher alkanes react with halogens by the same kind of chain mechanisms as those that we have just seen. Ethane, for example, reacts with chlorine to produce chloroethane (ethyl chloride). The mechanism is as follows:

Chain Initiation

Step 1 $Cl_2 \xrightarrow[\text{or heat}]{\text{light}} 2\,Cl\cdot$

Chain Propagation

Step 2 $CH_3CH_2\!:\!H + \cdot Cl \longrightarrow CH_3CH_2\cdot + H\!:\!Cl$

Step 3 $CH_3CH_2\cdot + Cl\!:\!Cl \longrightarrow CH_3CH_2\!:\!Cl + Cl\cdot$

Then steps 2, 3, 2, 3, and so on.

Chain Termination

$$CH_3CH_2\cdot + \cdot Cl \longrightarrow CH_3CH_2\!:\!Cl$$

$$CH_3CH_2\cdot + \cdot CH_2CH_3 \longrightarrow CH_3CH_2\!:\!CH_2CH_3$$

$$Cl\cdot + \cdot Cl \longrightarrow Cl\!:\!Cl$$

Problem 7.11

The energy of activation for the hydrogen-atom abstraction step in the chlorination of ethane is 1.0 kcal mol^{-1}. (a) Use the homolytic bond dissociation energies in Table 7.1 to calculate $\Delta H°$ for this step. (b) Sketch a potential energy diagram for the hydrogen-atom abstraction step in the chlorination of ethane similar to that for the chlorination of methane shown in Fig. 7.3a.

(c) When an equimolar mixture of methane and ethane is chlorinated, the reaction yields far more ethyl chloride than methyl chloride (~ 400 molecules of ethyl chloride for every molecule of methyl chloride). Explain this greater yield of ethyl chloride.

Problem 7.12

When ethane is chlorinated 1,1-dichloroethane and 1,2-dichloroethane as well as more highly chlorinated ethanes are formed in the mixture (cf. Section 7.3A). Write chain mechanisms accounting for the formation of 1,1-dichloroethane and 1,2-dichloroethane.

Chlorination of most alkanes whose molecules contain more than two carbon atoms gives a mixture of isomeric monochloro products (as well as more highly chlorinated compounds). Several examples follow. The percentages given are based on the total amount of monochloro products formed in each reaction.

$$CH_3CH_2CH_3 \xrightarrow[\text{light, 25 °C}]{Cl_2} CH_3CH_2CH_2Cl + CH_3CHCH_3$$
$$\underset{|}{} \underset{Cl}{}$$

Propane	**Propyl chloride**	**Isopropyl chloride**
	(45%)	**(55%)**

$$\underset{\underset{CH_3CHCH_3}{|}}{CH_3} \xrightarrow[\substack{\text{light} \\ 25 °C}]{Cl_2} \underset{\underset{CH_3CHCH_2Cl}{|}}{CH_3} + \underset{\underset{CH_3CCH_3}{|}}{\overset{CH_3}{}}$$

Isobutane   **Isobutyl chloride**   *tert*-**Butyl chloride**

(63%)   (37%)

$$\underset{\underset{H}{|}}{\overset{CH_3}{\underset{|}{}}}CH_3CCH_2CH_3 \xrightarrow[300 °C]{Cl_2} ClCH_2CHCH_2CH_3 + CH_3CCH_2CH_3$$

2-Methylbutane   **1-Chloro-2-methyl-butane (30%)**   **2-Chloro-2-methyl-butane (22%)**

$$+ CH_3CHCHCH_3 + CH_3CHCH_2CH_2Cl$$

2-Chloro-3-methyl-butane (33%)   **1-Chloro-3-methyl-butane (15%)**

The ratios of products that we obtain from chlorination reactions of higher alkanes are not identical with what we would expect if all the hydrogen atoms of the alkane were equally reactive. We find that there is a correlation between reactivity of different hydrogen atoms and the type of hydrogen atom (1°, 2°, or 3°) being replaced. The tertiary hydrogen atoms of an alkane are most reactive, secondary hydrogen atoms are next most reactive, and primary hydrogen atoms are the least reactive (see Problem 7.13).

Problem 7.13

If we examine just the monochloro products of the reaction of isobutane with chlorine just given, we find that isobutyl chloride represents 63% of the mono-chlorinated product, while *tert*-butyl chloride represents 37%. Explain how this demonstrates that the tertiary hydrogen atom is more reactive. (*Hint:* Consider what percentages of the butyl chlorides would be obtained if the nine primary hydrogen atoms and the single tertiary hydrogen atom were all equally reactive.)

We can account for the relative reactivities of the primary, secondary, and tertiary hydrogen atoms in a chlorination reaction on the basis of the homolytic bond dissociation energies we saw earlier (Table 7.1). Of the three types, breaking a tertiary C—H bond requires the least energy, and breaking a primary C—H bond requires the most. Since the step in which the C—H bond is broken (i.e., the hydrogen-atom abstraction step) determines the location or orientation of the chlorination, we would expect the E_{act} for abstracting a tertiary hydrogen atom to be least and E_{act} for abstracting a primary hydrogen atom to be greatest. Thus tertiary hydrogen atoms should be most reactive, secondary hydrogen atoms should be the next most reactive, and primary hydrogen atoms should be the least reactive.

The differences in the rates with which primary, secondary, and tertiary hydrogen atoms are replaced by chlorine are not large, however. Chlorine, as a result, does not discriminate among the different types of hydrogen atoms in a way that makes chlorination of higher alkanes a generally useful laboratory synthesis. (Alkane chlorinations do find use in some industrial processes, especially in those instances where mixtures of alkyl chlorides can be used.)

Problem 7.14

Chlorination reactions of certain higher alkanes can be used for laboratory preparations. Examples are the preparation of neopentyl chloride from neopentane and cyclopentyl chloride from cyclopentane. What structural feature of these molecules makes this possible?

Problem 7.15

The hydrogen-atom abstraction steps for most alkane chlorinations are exothermic. Show that this is true by calculating $\Delta H°$ for the reaction where Cl· abstracts (a) a primary hydrogen of ethane, (b) a secondary hydrogen of propane, and (c) a primary hydrogen of propane.

7.7A SELECTIVITY OF BROMINE

Bromine is less reactive toward alkanes in general than chlorine, but bromine is more *selective* in the site of attack when it does react. Bromine shows a much greater ability to discriminate among the different types of hydrogen atoms. The reaction of isobutane and bromine, for example, gives almost exclusive replacement of the tertiary hydrogen atom.

$$CH_3-\underset{\underset{H}{|}}{\overset{\overset{CH_3}{|}}{C}}-CH_3 \xrightarrow[\text{light, 127 °C}]{Br_2} CH_3-\underset{\underset{Br}{|}}{\overset{\overset{CH_3}{|}}{C}}-CH_3 + CH_3-\underset{\underset{H}{|}}{\overset{\overset{CH_3}{|}}{C}}-CH_2Br$$

(> 99%)   (trace)

A very different result is obtained when isobutane reacts with chlorine.

$$CH_3\underset{\underset{}{}}{\overset{\overset{CH_3}{|}}{C}HCH_3} \xrightarrow[\text{25 °C}]{Cl_2, \, hv} CH_3\underset{\underset{Cl}{|}}{\overset{\overset{CH_3}{|}}{C}CH_3} + CH_3\overset{\overset{CH_3}{|}}{C}HCH_2Cl$$

(37%)   (63%)

The greater selectivity of bromine can be explained in terms of transition state theory, and bromine's greater selectivity is directly related to its lower reactivity.* According to the Hammond–Leffler postulate (Section 6.15A) *the structure of the transition state of an endothermic step of a reaction resembles the products of that step more than it does the reactants. For an exothermic step the structure of the transition state is more like the reactants than the products.*

The Hammond–Leffler Postulate can be better understood through considera-tion of the potential energy versus reaction coordinate diagrams given in Fig. 7.6.

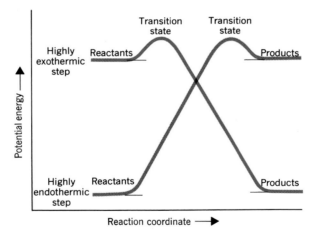

FIGURE 7.6 Energy diagrams for highly exothermic and highly endothermic steps of reac-tions. (From William A. Pryor, *Introduction to Free Radical Chemistry* © 1966. Reprinted by permission of Prentice–Hall, Inc., Englewood Cliffs, NJ, p. 53.)

In a highly exothermic step the energy levels of the reactants and the transition state are close to each other. The transition state also lies close to the reactants along the *reaction coordinate.* This means that in the highly exothermic step, bond breaking has not proceeded very far when the transition state is reached. In the exothermic reactions of isobutane molecules with chlorine atoms, for example, relatively little carbon–hydrogen bond breaking has developed in the transition states. The transi-tion states for the two hydrogen-atom abstraction steps might resemble those shown here.

*While reactivity and selectivity are inversely related in these alkane halogenations, they are not necessar-ily related in other reactions.

$$CH_3CHCH_3 + Cl\cdot \longrightarrow \left[CH_3\overset{CH_3}{\underset{\delta\cdot}{C}}HCH_2\text{---}H\text{------}\overset{\delta\cdot}{Cl} \right] \longrightarrow CH_3\overset{CH_3}{C}HCH_2\cdot + HCl$$

Reactantlike transition state

1° Radical

$$\xrightarrow{Cl_2}$$

$$CH_3\overset{CH_3}{C}HCH_2Cl + Cl\cdot$$

Isobutyl chloride

$$CH_3\overset{CH_3}{\underset{CH_3}{C}}\text{---}H + Cl\cdot \longrightarrow \left[CH_3\overset{CH_3}{\underset{CH_3}{\overset{\delta\cdot}{C}}}\text{---}H\text{------}\overset{\delta\cdot}{Cl} \right] \longrightarrow CH_3\overset{CH_3}{\underset{CH_3}{C}}\cdot + HCl$$

Reactantlike transition state

3° Radical

$$\xrightarrow{Cl_2}$$

$$CH_3\overset{CH_3}{\underset{CH_3}{C}}\text{---}Cl + Cl\cdot$$

***tert*-Butyl chloride**

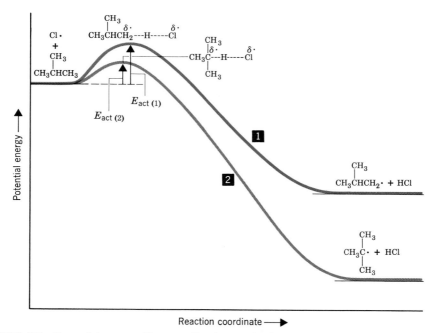

FIGURE 7.7 Potential energy diagrams for the two hydrogen-atom abstraction steps in the reaction of isobutane with Cl · . Both steps are exothermic and both transition states resemble the reactants. The activation energies are similar, but because 3° C—H bonds are broken more easily than 1° C—H bonds, reaction (2) has a lower activation energy and proceeds at a somewhat faster rate.

Because the transition states in both cases are reactantlike in both structure and energy, they show relatively little resemblance to the products of the hydrogen-atom abstraction step, a 1° radical and a 3° radical. And because the reactants in both cases are the same, the exact type of C—H bond being broken (primary or tertiary) has a relatively small influence on the relative rates of the reactions. The two reactions proceed with similar (but not identical) rates because their respective activation energies are quite similar (Fig. 7.7).

The transition states of highly endothermic steps, on the other hand, lie close to the products on the potential energy coordinate and *along the reaction coordinate.* In highly endothermic steps the bond has broken to a considerable extent by the time the transition state is reached. The two hydrogen-atom abstraction steps in the reaction of isobutane with bromine are both highly endothermic. In these reactions considerable carbon–hydrogen bond breaking has occurred when the transition state is reached. These transition states might be depicted in the following way:

$$\underset{\substack{| \\ CH_3}}{\overset{\substack{CH_3 \\ |}}{CH_3CHCH_3}} + Br\cdot \longrightarrow \left[\underset{\substack{| \\ CH_3}}{\overset{\substack{CH_3 \\ |}}{CH_3CHCH_2}} \overset{\delta\cdot}{-\!-\!-\!-\!-} H \overset{\delta\cdot}{-\!-\!-} Br \right] \longrightarrow \underset{\substack{| \\ CH_3}}{\overset{\substack{CH_3 \\ |}}{CH_3CHCH_2}}\cdot + HBr$$

Productlike transition state   1° Radical

$$\downarrow Br_2$$

$$\underset{\substack{| \\ CH_3}}{\overset{\substack{CH_3 \\ |}}{CH_3CHCH_2Br}} + Br\cdot$$

Isobutyl bromide

$$\underset{\substack{| \\ CH_3}}{\overset{\substack{CH_3 \\ |}}{CH_3C}}{-}H + Br\cdot \longrightarrow \left[\underset{\substack{| \\ CH_3}}{\overset{\substack{CH_3 \\ |\delta\cdot}}{CH_3C}} {-\!-\!-\!-\!-\!-} H \overset{\delta\cdot}{-\!-\!-} Br \right] \longrightarrow \underset{\substack{| \\ CH_3}}{\overset{\substack{CH_3 \\ |}}{CH_3C}}\cdot \ + HBr$$

Productlike transition state   3° Radical

$$\downarrow Br_2$$

$$\underset{\substack{| \\ CH_3}}{\overset{\substack{CH_3 \\ |}}{CH_3C}}{-}Br + Br\cdot$$

tert-Butyl bromide

Because the transition states for both steps in bromination are productlike in structure and energy, and because the products of each hydrogen-atom abstraction step are, in fact, quite different (a 1° radical vs a 3° radical), the type of C—H bond being broken will have a marked influence on the relative rates of the reactions. In fact, they proceed with very different rates. Abstraction of the 3° hydrogen takes place much faster. Bromine, as a result, discriminates more effectively between the primary and tertiary hydrogen atoms. A comparison of potential energy diagrams for the abstraction of the primary and tertiary hydrogen atoms by bromine is given in Fig. 7.8.

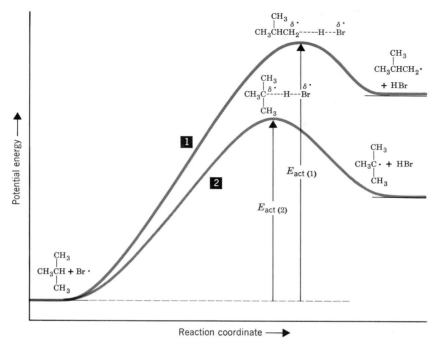

FIGURE 7.8 Potential energy diagrams for the two hydrogen-atom abstraction steps in the reaction of isobutane with Br · . Both steps are highly endothermic and, in both, the transition states resemble the products. Since the products—a 3° radical and a 1° radical—have quite different potential energies (stabilities), the transition states for the two steps are also quite different. The transition state for reaction (1) resembles a 1° radical. It occurs at a much higher potential energy than the transition state for reaction (2) because the transition state for reaction (2) resembles a much more stable 3° radical. The activation energy for reaction (2) is much lower than that for reaction (1). Reaction (2), consequently, proceeds at a much faster rate. The ultimate product that arises from reaction (2) is *tert*-butyl bromide, and this is the predominant product of the reaction.

Problem 7.16

Fluorine is far less selective than bromine and is even less selective than chlorine. The products that one obtains from alkane fluorinations are, in fact, almost those that one would expect if the different types of hydrogen were equally reactive. Explain.

7.8 THE GEOMETRY OF ALKYL RADICALS

Experimental evidence indicates that the geometrical structure of most alkyl radicals is trigonal planar at the carbon having the unpaired electron. This structure can be accommodated by an sp^2-hybridized central carbon. In an alkyl radical, the p orbital contains the unpaired electron (Fig. 7.9).

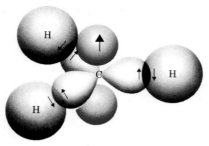

FIGURE 7.9 sp^2-Hybridized carbon atom at the center of a methyl radical showing the odd electron in one lobe of the half-filled p orbital. It could be shown in the other lobe.

7.9 REACTIONS THAT GENERATE TETRAHEDRAL STEREOCENTERS

When achiral molecules react to produce a compound with a single tetrahedral stereocenter, the product will be obtained as a racemic form. This will always be true in the absence of any chiral influence on the reaction such as an enzyme or the use of a chiral solvent.

Let us examine a reaction that illustrates this principle, the radical chlorination of pentane.

$$CH_3CH_2CH_2CH_2CH_3 \xrightarrow[\text{(achiral)}]{Cl_2} CH_3CH_2CH_2CH_2CH_2Cl$$

Pentane　　　　　　　　　　　　　**1-Chloropentane**
(achiral)　　　　　　　　　　　　　**(achiral)**

$$+ CH_3CH_2CH_2\overset{*}{C}HClCH_3 + CH_3CH_2CHClCH_2CH_3$$

(±)-2-Chloropentane　　　　**3-Chloropentane**
(a racemic form)　　　　　　**(achiral)**

The reaction will lead to the products shown here, as well as more highly chlorinated products. (We can use an excess of pentane to minimize multiple chlorinations.)

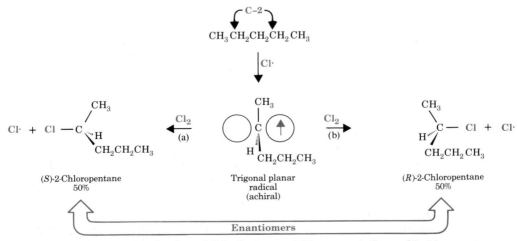

FIGURE 7.10 How chlorination of C-2 of pentane yields a racemic form of 2-chloropentane.

Neither 1-chloropentane nor 3-chloropentane contains a stereocenter, but 2-chloropentane does, and it is *obtained as a racemic form*. If we examine the mechanism in Fig. 7.10 we shall see why.

Abstraction of a hydrogen atom from C-2 produces a trigonal planar radical that is achiral. This radical then reacts with chlorine at either face [by path (a) or (b)]. Because the radical is achiral the probability of reaction by either path is the same, therefore, the two enantiomers are produced in equal amounts.

7.9A GENERATION OF A SECOND STEREOCENTER IN A RADICAL HALOGENATION

Let us now examine what happens when a chiral molecule (containing one stereocenter) reacts so as to yield a product with a second stereocenter. As an example consider what happens when (S)-2-chloropentane undergoes chlorination at C-3 (other products are formed, of course by chlorination at other carbon atoms). The results of chlorination at C-3 are shown in Fig. 7.11.

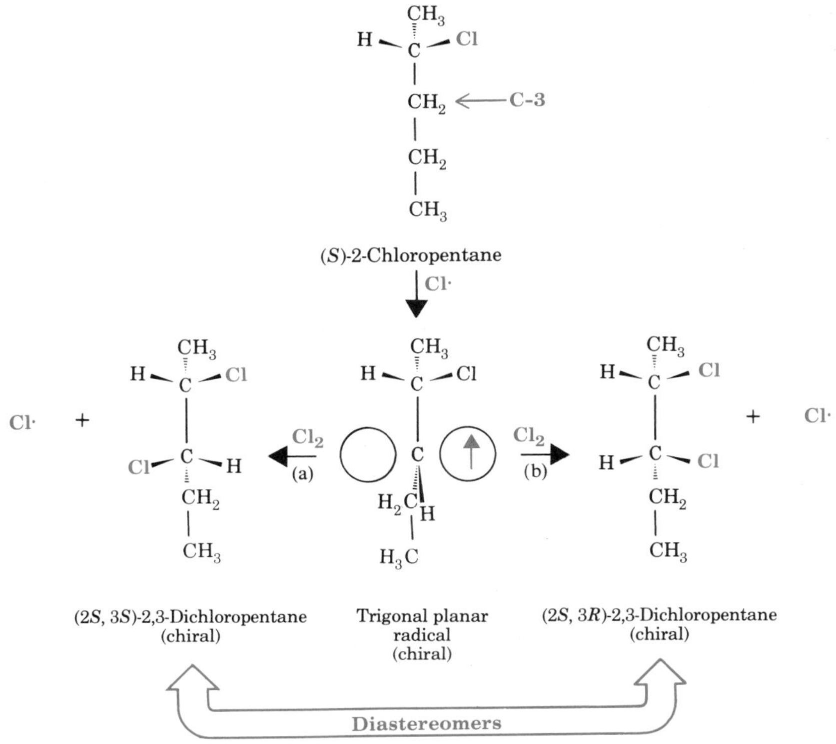

FIGURE 7.11 Chlorination of (S)-2-chloropentane at C-3. Abstraction of a hydrogen atom from C-3 produces a radical that is chiral (it contains a stereocenter at C-2). This chiral radical can then react with chlorine at one face [path (a)] to produce (2S, 3S)-2,3-dichloropentane and at the other face [path (b)] to yield (2S,3R)-2,3-dichloropentane. These two compounds are diastereomers and they are not produced in equal amounts. Each product is chiral and each alone would be optically active.

The products of the reactions are (2S,3S)-2,3-dichloropentane and (2S,3R)-2,3-dichloropentane. These two compounds are **diastereomers.** (They are stereoisomers but they are not mirror images of each other.) The two diastereomers are *not* produced in equal amounts. Because the intermediate radical itself is chiral, reactions at the two faces are not equally likely. The radical will react with chlorine to a greater extent at one face than the other (although we cannot easily predict which). That is, the presence of a stereocenter in the radical (at C-2) influences the reaction that introduces the new stereocenter (at C-3).

Both of the 2,3-dichloropentane diastereomers are chiral, and therefore, each would exhibit optical activity. Moreover, because the two compounds are *diastereomers,* they will have different physical properties (e.g., different melting points and boiling points) and will be separable by conventional means (by gas–liquid chromatography or by careful fractional distillation).

Problem 7.17

Consider the chlorination of (*S*)-2-chloropentane at C-4. (a) Write stereochemical structures for the products that would be obtained and give each its proper (*R–S*) designation. (b) What is the stereoisomeric relationship between these products? (c) Are both products chiral? (d) Are both optically active? (e) Could the products be separated by conventional means? (f) What other dichloropentanes would be obtained by chlorination of (*S*)-2-chloropentane? (g) Which of these are optically active?

Problem 7.18

Consider the chlorination of pentane itself using sufficient chlorine to cause dichlorination. After the reaction is over you isolate all of the isomers with the molecular formula $C_5H_{10}Cl_2$ and subject this mixture to careful fractional distillation. (a) Tell how many fractions you would obtain, and what each fraction would contain. (b) Which (if any) of these fractions would show optical activity?

Problem 7.19

We show the chlorination of 2-methylbutane yielding 1-chloro-2-methylbutane, 2-chloro-2-methylbutane, 2-chloro-3-methylbutane, and 1-chloro-3-methylbutane on page 284. (a) Assuming that these compounds were separated after the reaction by fractional distillation, tell whether any fractions would show optical activity. (b) Would any of these fractions be resolvable into enantiomers?

7.10 OTHER IMPORTANT RADICAL CHAIN REACTIONS

Radical chain mechanisms are important in understanding many other organic reactions. We shall see other examples in later chapters, but let us examine three here: the combustion of alkanes, autoxidation, and some reactions of chlorofluoromethanes that have threatened the protective layer of ozone in the stratosphere.

7.10A COMBUSTION OF ALKANES

When alkanes react with oxygen (e.g., in oil furnaces and in internal combustion engines) a complex series of reactions takes place ultimately converting the alkane to carbon dioxide and water (Section 4.8A). Although our understanding of the detailed mechanism of combustion is incomplete, we do know that the important reactions occur by radical chain mechanisms with chain-initiating and chain-propagating steps like the following reactions.

$$RH + O_2 \longrightarrow R\cdot + \cdot OOH \qquad \text{Initiating}$$
$$R\cdot + O_2 \longrightarrow R\text{—}OO\cdot$$
$$R + OO\cdot + R\text{—}H \longrightarrow R\text{—}OOH + R\cdot \Big\} \text{ Propagating}$$

One product of the second step is R—OOH, called an alkyl hydroperoxide. The oxygen–oxygen bond of an alkyl hydroperoxide is quite weak, and it can break and produce radicals that can initiate other chains:

$$RO\text{—}OH \longrightarrow RO\cdot + HO\cdot$$

7.10B AUTOXIDATION

Linoleic acid is an example of a *polyunsaturated fatty acid,* the kind of polyunsaturated acid that occurs as an ester in **polyunsaturated fats** (Section 8.5 and Chapter 23). By polyunsaturated, we mean that the compound contains two or more double bonds.

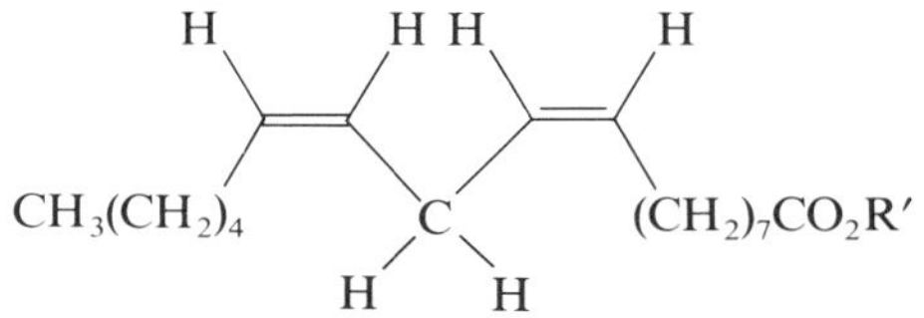

Linoleic acid
(as an ester)

Polyunsaturated fats occur widely in the fats and oils that are components of our diets. They are also widespread in the tissues of the body where they perform numerous vital functions.

The hydrogen atoms of the —CH_2— group located between the two double bonds of linoleic acid are especially susceptible to abstraction by radicals (we shall see why in Chapter 12). Abstraction of one of these hydrogen atoms produces a new radical that can react with oxygen in a chain reaction that belongs to a general type of reaction called **autoxidation** (Fig. 7.12). The result of autoxidation is the formation of a hydroperoxide. Autoxidation is a process that occurs in many substances; for example, autoxidation is responsible for the development of the rancidity that occurs when fats and oils spoil. Autoxidation also occurs in the body, and here it may cause irreversible damage. Autoxidation is inhibited when compounds are present that can rapidly "trap" peroxyl radicals by reacting with them to give stabilized radicals that do not continue the chain.

$$L\text{—}O\text{—}O\cdot + In\text{—}H \longrightarrow L\text{—}O\text{—}OH + In\cdot$$

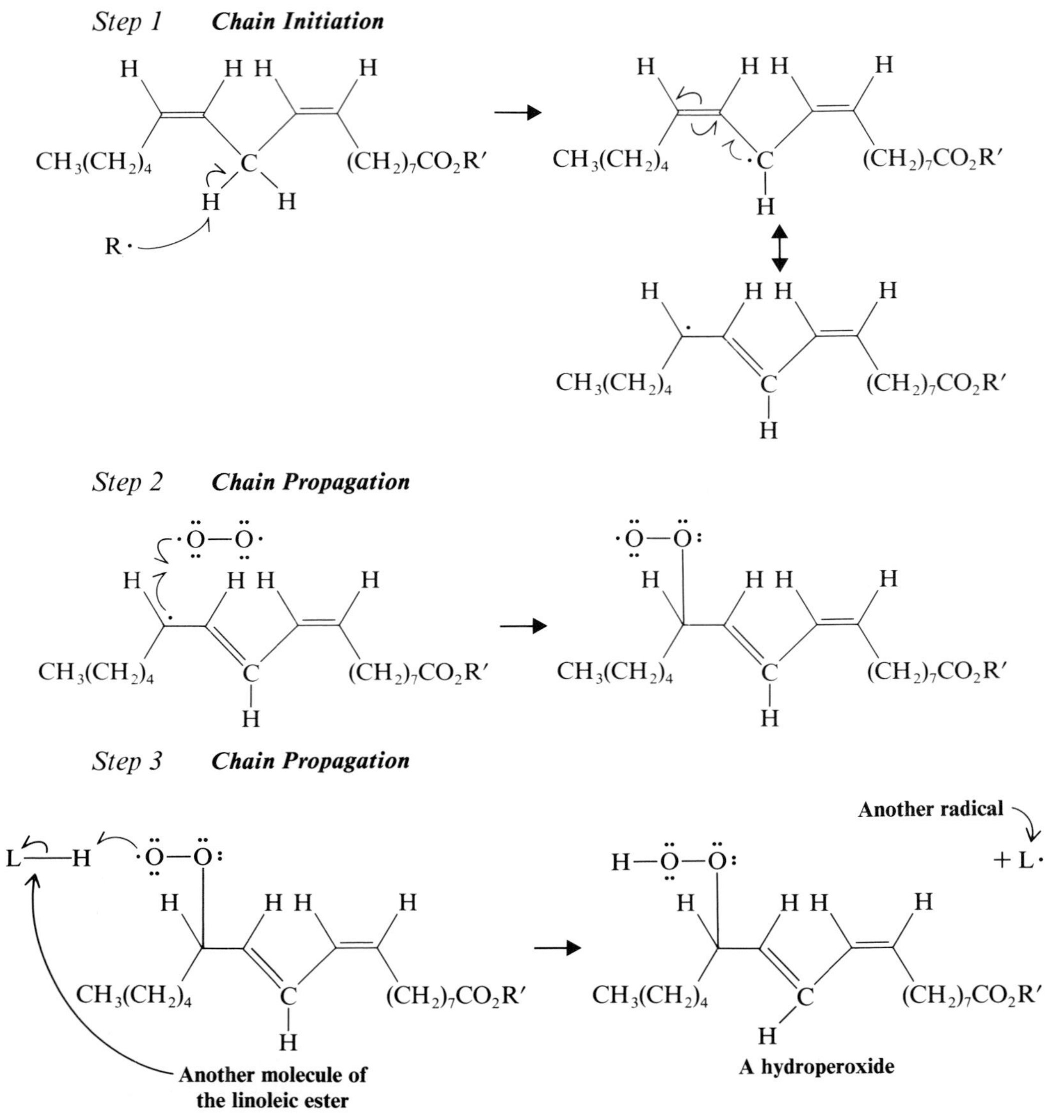

Step 1   ***Chain Initiation***

Step 2   ***Chain Propagation***

Step 3   ***Chain Propagation***

FIGURE 7.12 Autoxidation of a linoleic acid ester. In step 1 the reaction is initiated by the attack of a radical on one of the hydrogen atoms of the $-CH^2-$ group between the two double bonds; this hydrogen abstraction produces a radical that is a resonance hybrid. In step 2 this radical reacts with oxygen in the first of two chain-propagating steps to produce an oxygen-containing radical, which in step 3 can abstract a hydrogen from another molecule of the linoleic ester. The result of this second chain-propagating step is the formation of a hydroperoxide and a radical, ($L\cdot$) that can bring about a repetition of step 2.

Vitamin E (α-tocopherol) is capable of acting as a radical trap in this way, and one of the important roles that vitamin E plays in the body may be in inhibiting radical reactions that could cause cell damage. Compounds like BHT are added to foods to prevent autoxidation. BHT is also known to trap radicals.

7.10 OTHER IMPORTANT RADICAL CHAIN REACTIONS

Vitamin E
(α-tocopherol)

BHT

7.10C FREONS AND OZONE DEPLETION

In the stratosphere at altitudes of about 25 km, very high-energy (very short wavelength) UV light converts diatomic oxygen (O_2) into ozone (O_3). The reactions that take place may be represented as follows:

Step 1 $O_2 + hv \longrightarrow O + O$

Step 2 $O + O_2 + M \longrightarrow O_3 + M + \text{heat}$

where M is some other particle that can absorb some of the energy released in the second step.

The ozone produced in step 2 can also interact with high-energy UV light in the following way.

Step 3 $O_3 + hv \longrightarrow O_2 + O + \text{heat}$

The oxygen atom formed in step 3 can cause a repetition of step 2, and so forth. The net result of these steps is to convert highly energetic UV light into heat. This is important because the existence of this cycle shields the earth from radiation that is destructive to living organisms. This shield makes life possible on the earth's surface. Even a relatively small increase in high-energy UV radiation at the earth's surface would cause a large increase in the incidence of skin cancers.

Production of chlorofluoromethanes (and of chlorofluoroethanes) called *Freons* began in 1930. These compounds have been used as refrigerants, solvents, and propellants in aerosol cans. Typical Freons are trichlorofluoromethane, $CFCl_3$ (called Freon-11), and dichlorodifluoromethane, CF_2Cl_2 (called Freon-12).

By 1974 world Freon production was about 2 billion pounds annually. Most Freon, even that used in refrigeration, eventually makes its way into the atmosphere where it diffuses unchanged into the stratosphere. In June 1974 F. S. Rowland and M. J. Molina published an article indicating, for the first time, that in the stratosphere Freon is able to initiate radical chain reactions that can upset the natural ozone balance. The reactions that take place are the following. (Freon-12 is used as an example.)

Chain Initiation

    Step 1 $CF_2Cl_2 + hv \longrightarrow CF_2Cl\cdot + Cl\cdot$

Chain Propagation

    Step 2 $Cl\cdot + O_3 \longrightarrow ClO\cdot + O_2$

    Step 3 $ClO\cdot + O \longrightarrow O_2 + Cl\cdot$

In the chain-initiating step, UV light causes homolytic cleavage of one C—Cl bond of the Freon. The chlorine atom, thus produced, is the real villain; it can set off a chain reaction that destroys thousands of molecules of ozone before it diffuses out of the stratosphere or reacts with some other substance.

In 1975 a study by the National Academy of Science supported the predictions of Rowland and Molina and since January 1978 the use of Freons in aerosol cans in the United States has been banned. Many other countries still allow this use of Freons, however.

In 1985 a hole was discovered in the ozone layer above Antarctica. Studies done since then strongly suggest that chlorine atom destruction of the ozone is a factor in the formation of the hole. This ozone hole has continued to grow in size and such a hole has also been discovered in the Arctic ozone layer. Should the ozone layer be depleted, more of the Sun's damaging rays would penetrate to the surface of the earth.

Recognizing the global nature of the problem, in 1987, 24 nations signed the "Montreal Protocol," which among other things, requires these nations to reduce their consumption of chlorofluorocarbons by 50% before the turn of the century.

7.11 SOME IMPORTANT TERMS AND CONCEPTS

Radicals (or free radicals) are reactive intermediates that have an unpaired electron. The relative stability of alkyl radicals is as follows:

$$\underset{\overset{|}{C}}{\overset{\overset{C}{|}}{C-C\cdot}} > \underset{\overset{|}{H}}{\overset{\overset{C}{|}}{C-C\cdot}} > \underset{\overset{|}{H}}{\overset{\overset{H}{|}}{C-C\cdot}} > \underset{\overset{|}{H}}{\overset{\overset{H}{|}}{H-C\cdot}}$$

    3°   >   2°   >   1°   > Methyl

Bond dissociation energy (abbreviated $DH°$) is the amount of energy required for homolysis of a covalent bond.

Halogenations of alkanes are substitution reactions in which a halogen replaces one (or more) of the alkane's hydrogen atoms.

$$RH + X_2 \longrightarrow RX + HX$$

The reactions occur by a radical mechanism.

Chain Initiation

    Step 1 $X_2 \longrightarrow 2X\cdot$

Chain Propagation

    Step 2 $RH + X\cdot \longrightarrow R\cdot + HX$

Step 3   R· + X$_2$ ⟶ RX + X·

Chain reactions are reactions whose mechanisms involve a series of steps with each step producing a reactive intermediate that causes the next step to occur. The halogenation of an alkane is a chain reaction.

Additional Problems

7.20   The radical reaction of propane with chlorine yields (in addition to more highly halogenated compounds) 1-chloropropane and 2-chloropropane. Write chain-initiating and chain-propagating steps showing how each compound is formed.

7.21   In addition to more highly chlorinated products, chlorination of butane yields a mixture of compounds with the formula C$_4$H$_9$Cl. (a) Taking stereochemistry into account, how many different isomers with the formula C$_4$H$_9$Cl would you expect to be produced? (b) If the mixture of C$_4$H$_9$Cl isomers were subjected to fractional distillation how many fractions would you expect to obtain?   (c) Which fractions would be optically inactive? (d) Which would you be able to resolve into enantiomers?

7.22   Chlorination of (R)-2-chlorobutane yields a mixture of isomers with the formula C$_4$H$_8$Cl$_2$. (a) How many different isomers would you expect to be produced? Write their structures.   (b) If the mixture of C$_4$H$_8$Cl$_2$ isomers were subjected to fractional distillation how many fractions would you expect to obtain?   (c) Which of these fractions would be optically active?

7.23   Peroxides are often used to initiate radical chain reactions such as alkane halogenations. (a) Examine the bond energies in Table 7.1 and give reasons that will explain why peroxides are especially effective as radical initiators.   (b) Illustrate your answer by outlining how di-*tert*-butyl peroxide, (CH$_3$)$_3$CO—OC(CH$_3$)$_3$, might initiate an alkane halogenation.

7.24   Radical fluorination of methane occurs in the absence of light. A mechanism that has been proposed for the dark reaction is

$$CH_4 + F_2 \xrightarrow{\text{slow}} CH_3\cdot\ + HF + F\cdot$$

$$CH_3\cdot\ + F\cdot \xrightarrow{\text{fast}} CH_3F$$

(a) Basing your answer on bond dissociation energies, assess the likelihood of the reaction occurring by this mechanism.   (b) What is the likelihood of a similar mechanism occurring when a mixture of methane and chlorine is heated in the dark?

7.25   Use bond dissociation energies in Table 7.1 to account for the following: (a) Thermal cracking of a C—H bond of methane requires a higher temperature (~ 1200 °C) than does a similar breaking of a C—H bond of ethane (500–600 °C).   (b) When ethane undergoes homolysis at high temperatures, the C—C bond breaks more readily than the C—H bonds. (c) When butane "cracks" the reaction CH$_3$CH$_2$CH$_2$CH$_3$ ⟶ 2 CH$_3$CH$_2$· occurs more readily than the reaction CH$_3$CH$_2$CH$_2$CH$_3$ ⟶ CH$_3$CH$_2$CH$_2$· + CH$_3$· .

7.26   When propane is heated to a very high temperature, it undergoes thermal cracking through homolysis of C—C and C—H bonds. The major products of the reaction are methane and ethene. A chain mechanism has been proposed for this reaction.   (a) Which of the following reactions is most likely to be the major chain-initiating step? Explain your answer by estimating activation energies for each reaction.

$$CH_3CH_2CH_3 \longrightarrow CH_3CH_2\cdot + CH_3\cdot$$

$$CH_3CH_2CH_3 \longrightarrow CH_3CH_2CH_2\cdot + H\cdot$$

$$CH_3CH_2CH_3 \longrightarrow CH_3\dot{C}HCH_3 + H\cdot$$

Possible chain-propagating steps are

Step 1 $CH_3\cdot + CH_3CH_2CH_3 \longrightarrow CH_4 + \cdot CH_2CH_2CH_3$

Step 2 $\cdot CH_2\!-\!CH_2\!:\!CH_3 \longrightarrow CH_2{=}CH_2 + \cdot CH_3$

(b) Both reactions have reasonably low activation energies (low enough to occur at very high temperatures). Show that this is likely for step 1 by calculating $\Delta H°$ for step 1.   (c) An alternative to step 1 is

$$CH_3\cdot + CH_3CH_2CH_3 \longrightarrow CH_4 + CH_3\dot{C}HCH_3$$

Comment on the likelihood of this reaction occurring in terms of energy and probability factors.

7.27   The following reactions show comparisons between two sets of similar reactions. In each set we compare reactions in which a hydrogen atom is abstracted from methane and from ethane. In the first set (**A**) the abstracting agent is a methyl radical; in the second set (**B**) it is a bromine atom.   (a) Sketch energy diagrams for each set of reactions taking the Hammond–Leffler postulate into account. Take care to locate each transition state properly not only along the energy axis but along the reaction coordinate as well. For convenience in making comparisons, you should align the curves so that the potential energies of the reactants are the same.
(b) For which reaction will bond breaking have occurred to the *least* extent when the transition state is reached?   (c) To the *greatest* extent?   (d) To what approximate extent will bond breaking have occurred in reaction **A** step 1?   (e) For which set of reactions will the transition states more resemble products?   (f) Notice that the difference in $\Delta H°$ for the two sets of reactions is the same (6 kcal mol^{-1}). Why is this so?   (g) The difference in E_{act} for the first set of reactions is relatively small (2.8 kcal mol^{-1}). For the second set of reactions, however, the difference in E_{act} is large (5.0 kcal mol^{-1}); it is nearly as large as the difference in $\Delta H°$. Explain.

		$\Delta H°$ (kcal mol^{-1})	E_{act} (kcal mol^{-1})
(A)			
Step 1	$CH_3\cdot + H{-}CH_3 \longrightarrow CH_3{-}H + \cdot CH_3$	0	14.5
Step 2	$CH_3\cdot + H{-}CH_2CH_3 \longrightarrow CH_3{-}H + \cdot CH_2CH_3$	-6.0	11.7
	Difference	6.0	2.8
(B)			
Step 1	$Br\cdot + H{-}CH_3 \longrightarrow Br{-}H + \cdot CH_3$	16.5	18.6
Step 2	$Br\cdot + H{-}CH_2CH_3 \longrightarrow Br{-}H + \cdot CH_2CH_3$	10.5	13.6
	Difference	6.0	5.0

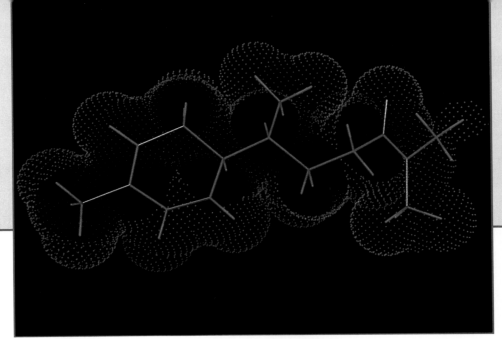

Zingiberene (see Problem 8.6).

CHAPTER

8

ALKENES AND ALKYNES I. PROPERTIES AND SYNTHESIS

8.1 INTRODUCTION

Alkenes are hydrocarbons whose molecules contain the carbon–carbon double bond. An old name for this family of compounds that is still often used is the name *olefins*. Ethene, the simplest olefin (alkene), was called olefiant gas (Latin: *oleum,* oil + *facere,* to make) because gaseous ethene (C_2H_4) reacts with chlorine to form $C_2H_4Cl_2$, a liquid (oil).

Hydrocarbons whose molecules contain the carbon–carbon triple bond are called alkynes. The common name for this family is *acetylenes,* after the first member, $HC\equiv CH$.

8.2 NOMENCLATURE OF ALKENES AND CYCLOALKENES

Many older names for alkenes are still in common use. Propene is often called propylene, and 2-methylpropene frequently bears the name isobutylene.

$$CH_2{=}CH_2 \qquad CH_3CH{=}CH_2 \qquad CH_3{-}\underset{\underset{\displaystyle CH_3}{|}}{C}{=}CH_2$$

IUPAC: Ethene   **IUPAC: Propene**   **IUPAC: 2-Methylpropene**
or ethylene*   **or propylene***   **Common: Isobutylene**

The IUPAC rules for naming alkenes are similar in many respects to those for naming alkanes:

1. **Determine the base name by selecting the longest chain that contains the double bond and change the ending of the name of the alkane of identical length from ane to ene.** Thus, if this longest chain contains five carbon atoms, the base name for the alkene is *pentene;* if it contains six carbon atoms, the base name is *hexene,* and so on.

2. **Number the chain so as to include both carbon atoms of the double bond, and begin numbering at the end of the chain nearer the double bond. Designate the location of the double bond by using the number of the first atom of the double bond as a prefix:**

$$\overset{1}{C}H_2{=}\overset{2}{C}H\overset{3}{C}H_2\overset{4}{C}H_3 \qquad\qquad CH_3CH{=}CHCH_2CH_2CH_3$$

      1-Butene   **2-Hexene**
   (*not* 3-butene)   (*not* 4-hexene)

3. **Indicate the locations of the substituent groups by the numbers of the carbon atoms to which they are attached.**

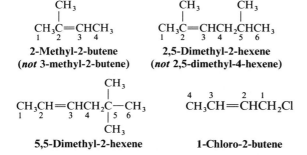

   2-Methyl-2-butene   **2,5-Dimethyl-2-hexene**
(*not* 3-methyl-2-butene)   (*not* 2,5-dimethyl-4-hexene)

     5,5-Dimethyl-2-hexene   **1-Chloro-2-butene**

4. **Number substituted cycloalkenes in the way that gives the carbon atoms of the double bond the 1- and 2- positions and that also gives the substituent groups the lower numbers at the first point of difference.** With substituted cycloalkenes it is not necessary to specify the position of the double bond since it will always begin with C-1 and C-2. The two examples listed here illustrate the application of these rules.

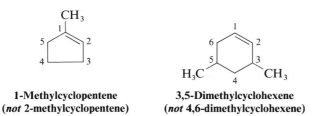

    1-Methylcyclopentene   **3,5-Dimethylcyclohexene**
(*not* 2-methylcyclopentene)   (*not* 4,6-dimethylcyclohexene)

*The IUPAC system also retains the names ethylene and propylene when no substituents are present.

5. Two frequently encountered alkenyl groups are the *vinyl group* and the *allyl group.*

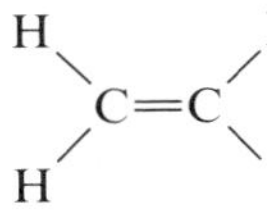

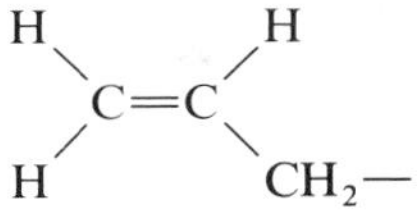

CH$_2$=CH—   CH$_2$=CHCH$_2$—
The vinyl group   The allyl group

The following examples illustrate how these names are employed:

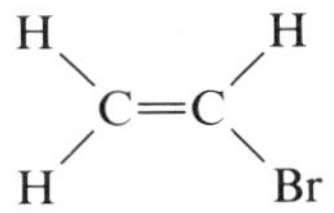

Bromoethene   3-Chloropropene
or   or
vinyl bromide   allyl chloride
(common)   (common)

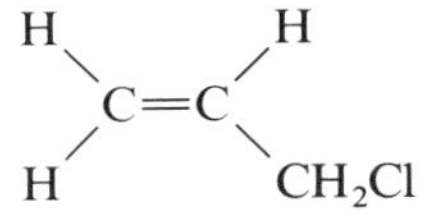

6. Designate the geometry of a double bond of a disubstituted alkene with the prefixes *cis-* and *trans-*. If two identical groups (usually hydrogen atoms) are on the same side of the double bond, it is **cis;** if they are on opposite sides, it is **trans.**

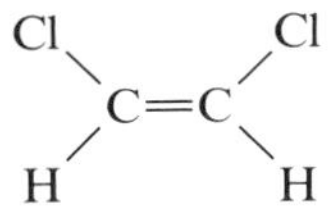

cis-1,2-Dichloroethene 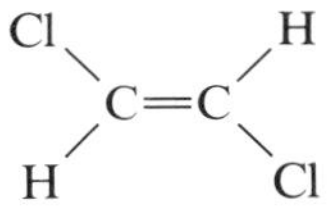   *trans*-1,2-Dichloroethene

In Section 8.2A we shall see another method for designating the geometry of the double bond.

Problem 8.1

Give IUPAC names for the following alkenes:

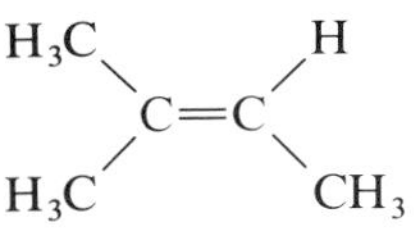

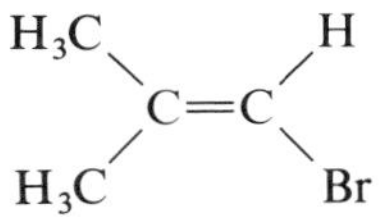

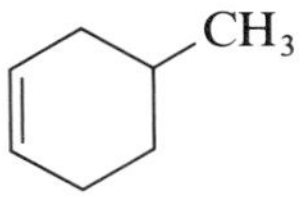

Problem 8.2

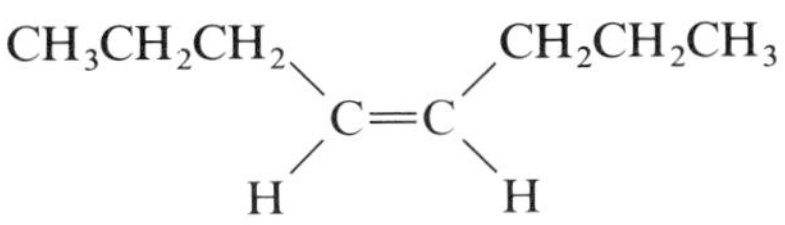

Write structural formulas for

(a) *cis*-3-Hexene

(b) *trans*-2-Pentene

(c) 3-Ethylcyclohexene

(d) Vinylcyclohexane

(e) 4,4-Dimethyl-1-hexene   (h) 1,2-Dimethylcyclohexene

(f) 3-Methylcyclopentene   (i) 1,3-Dimethylcyclopentene

(g) 3-Chloro-1-octene   (j) 1,5-Dibromocyclohexene

8.2A THE (E)-(Z) SYSTEM FOR DESIGNATING ALKENE DIASTEREOMERS

The terms cis and trans, when used to designate the stereochemistry of alkene diastereomers, are unambiguous only when applied to disubstituted alkenes. If the alkene is trisubstituted or tetrasubstituted, the terms cis and trans are either ambiguous or do not apply at all. Consider the following alkene as an example.

$$
\begin{array}{ccc}
\text{Br} & & \text{Cl} \\
\diagdown & & \diagup \\
& \text{C}=\text{C} & \\
\diagup & & \diagdown \\
\text{H} & & \text{F}
\end{array}
$$

A

It is impossible to decide whether **A** is cis or trans since no two groups are the same.

    A newer system is based on the priorities of groups in the Cahn–Ingold–Prelog convention (Section 5.5). This system, called the (E)–(Z) system, applies to alkene diastereomers of all types. In the (E)–(Z) system, we examine the two groups attached to one carbon atom of the double bond and decide which has higher priority. Then we repeat that operation at the other carbon atom.

Higher priority → Cl   F   F   Cl ← Higher priority   Cl > F

Higher priority → Br   H (Z)   Higher priority → Br   H (E)   Br > H

We take the group of higher priority on one carbon atom and compare it with the group of higher priority on the other carbon atom. If the two groups of higher priority are on the same side of the double bond, the alkene is designated (Z) (from the German word *zusammen,* meaning together). If the two groups of higher priority are on opposite sides of the double bond, the alkene is designated (E) (from the German word *entgegen,* meaning opposite). The following examples illustrate this:

CH₃ > H

(Z)-2-Butene
(cis-2-butene)

(E)-2-Butene
(trans-2-butene)

Cl > H
Br > Cl

(E)-1-Bromo-1,2-dichloroethene

(Z)-1-Bromo-1,2-dichloroethene

Problem 8.3

Using (E)–(Z) designation [and in parts (e) and (f) the (R)–(S) designation as well] give names for each of the following:

(a) 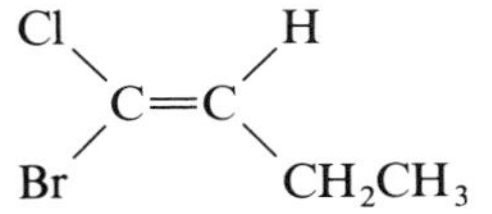
$$
\begin{array}{c}
Cl \quad\quad H \\
C=C \\
Br \quad\quad CH_2CH_3
\end{array}
$$

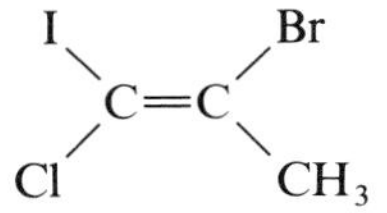

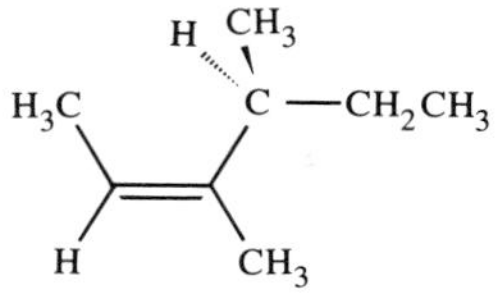

(b)
$$
\begin{array}{c}
I \quad\quad Br \\
C=C \\
Cl \quad\quad CH_3
\end{array}
$$

(c)
$$
\begin{array}{c}
H_3C \quad\quad CH_2CH_3 \\
C=C \\
H \quad\quad CH(CH_3)_2
\end{array}
$$

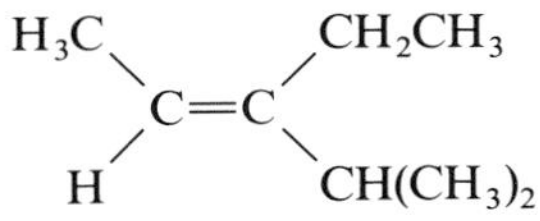

(d) 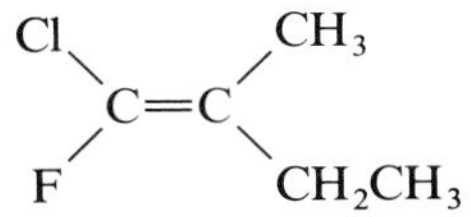
$$
\begin{array}{c}
Cl \quad\quad CH_3 \\
C=C \\
F \quad\quad CH_2CH_3
\end{array}
$$

(e)
$$
\begin{array}{c}
H \quad CH_3 \\
H_3C \quad\quad C-CH_2CH_3 \\
C=C \\
H \quad\quad CH_3
\end{array}
$$

(f)
$$
\begin{array}{c}
Br \quad\quad Cl \\
C=C \\
H \quad\quad C-CH_2CH_2CH_3 \\
H_3C\ H
\end{array}
$$

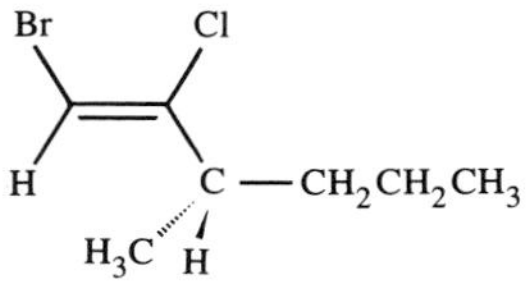

8.3 NOMENCLATURE OF ALKYNES

8.3A IUPAC NOMENCLATURE

Alkynes are named in much the same way as alkenes. Unbranched alkynes, for example, are named by replacing the **-ane** of the name of the corresponding alkane with the ending **-yne**. The chain is numbered in order to give the carbon atoms of the triple bond the lower possible numbers. The lower number of the two carbon atoms of the triple bond is used to designate the location of the triple bond. The IUPAC names of three unbranched alkynes are shown here.

$$H-C\equiv C-H \quad\quad CH_3CH_2C\equiv CCH_3 \quad\quad H-C\equiv CCH_2CH=CH_2$$

Ethyne or acetylene*   **2-Pentyne**   **1-Penten-4-yne†**

The locations of substituent groups of branched alkynes and substituted alkynes are also indicated with numbers.

$$\overset{3}{Cl}-\overset{2}{CH_2}\overset{1}{C}\equiv CH \quad\quad \overset{4}{CH_3}\overset{3}{C}\equiv \overset{2}{C}\overset{1}{CH_2}Cl$$

3-Chloropropyne   **1-Chloro-2-butyne**

$$\overset{6}{CH_3}\overset{5}{CH}\overset{4}{CH_2}\overset{3}{CH_2}\overset{2}{C}\equiv \overset{1}{CH} \quad\quad CH_3\overset{CH_3}{\underset{CH_3}{C}}CH_2C\equiv CH$$

5-Methyl-1-hexyne   **4,4-Dimethyl-1-pentyne**

*The name acetylene is retained by the IUPAC system for the compound $HC\equiv CH$ and is used frequently.
†Where there is a choice the double bond is given the lower number.

Problem 8.4

Give the IUPAC names of all of the alkyne isomers of (a) C_4H_6, (b) C_5H_8, and (c) C_6H_{10}.

Monosubstituted acetylenes or 1-alkynes are called **terminal alkynes,** and the hydrogen attached to the carbon of the triple bond is called the acetylenic hydrogen.

$$R-C\equiv C-H \qquad \swarrow \text{Acetylenic hydrogen}$$

A terminal alkyne

The anion obtained when the acetylenic hydrogen is removed is known as *an alkynide ion* or an acetylide ion.

$$R-C\equiv C:^- \qquad CH_3C\equiv C:^-$$

An alkynide ion　　**The propynide ion**
(an acetylide ion)

8.4 PHYSICAL PROPERTIES OF ALKENES AND ALKYNES

Alkenes and alkynes have physical properties similar to those of corresponding alkanes. The lower molecular weight alkenes and alkynes (Tables 8.1 and 8.2) are gases at room temperature. Being relatively nonpolar themselves, alkenes and alkynes dissolve in nonpolar solvents or in solvents of low polarity. Alkenes and alkynes are only *very slightly soluble* in water (with alkynes being slightly more soluble than alkenes). The densities of alkenes and alkynes are less than that of water.

TABLE 8.1　Physical constants of alkenes

NAME	FORMULA	mp (°C)	bp (°C)	DENSITY d_4^{20}(g mL^{-1})
Ethene	$CH_2=CH_2$	−169	−104	0.384[a]
Propene	$CH_3CH=CH_2$	−185	−47	0.514
1-Butene	$CH_3CH_2CH=CH_2$	−185	−6.3	0.595
(Z)-2-Butene	$CH_3CH=CHCH_3$ (cis)	−139	3.7	0.621
(E)-2-Butene	$CH_3CH=CHCH_3$ (trans)	−106	0.9	0.604
1-Pentene	$CH_3(CH_2)_2CH=CH_2$	−165	30	0.641
2-Methyl-1-butene	$CH_2=C(CH_3)CH_2CH_3$	−138	31	0.650
1-Hexene	$CH_3(CH_2)_3CH=CH_2$	−140	63	0.673
1-Heptene	$CH_3(CH_2)_4CH=CH_2$	−119	94	0.697

[a]Density at −10 °C.

TABLE 8.2   Physical constants of alkynes

NAME	FORMULA	mp (°C)	bp (°C)	DENSITY d_4^{20}(g mL^{-1})
Ethyne	HC≡CH	− 80.8	− 84.0$_{(sub)}^{760}$	
Propyne	CH$_3$C≡CH	− 101.51	− 23.2	
1-Butyne	CH$_3$CH$_2$C≡CH	− 125.7	8.1	
2-Butyne	CH$_3$C≡CCH$_3$	− 32.3	27	0.691
1-Pentyne	CH$_3$(CH$_2$)$_2$C≡CH	− 90	39.3	0.695
2-Pentyne	CH$_3$CH$_2$C≡CCH$_3$	− 101	55.5	0.714
1-Hexyne	CH$_3$(CH$_2$)$_3$C≡CH	− 132	71	0.715
2-Hexyne	CH$_3$(CH$_2$)$_2$C≡CCH$_3$	− 88	84	0.730
3-Hexyne	CH$_3$CH$_2$C≡CCH$_2$CH$_3$	− 101	81.8	0.724

8.5 HYDROGENATION OF ALKENES

Alkenes react with hydrogen in the presence of a variety of finely divided metal catalysts (cf. Section 4.15). The reaction that takes place is an **addition reaction;** one atom of hydrogen *adds* to each carbon atom of the double bond. Without a catalyst the reaction does not take place at an appreciable rate. (We shall see how the catalyst functions in Section 8.6.)

$$CH_2=CH_2 + H_2 \xrightarrow[\substack{\text{or Pt} \\ 25\ °C}]{\text{Ni, Pd}} CH_3-CH_3$$

$$CH_3CH=CH_2 + H_2 \xrightarrow[\substack{\text{or Pt} \\ 25\ °C}]{\text{Ni, Pd}} CH_3CH_2-CH_3$$

The product that results from the addition of hydrogen to an alkene is an alkane. Alkanes have only single bonds and contain the maximum number of hydrogen atoms that a hydrocarbon can possess. For this reason, alkanes are said to be **saturated compounds.** Alkenes, because they contain a double bond and possess fewer than the maximum number of hydrogen atoms, are capable of adding hydrogen and are said to be **unsaturated.** The process of adding hydrogen to an alkene is sometimes described as being one of **reduction.** Most often, however, the term used to describe the addition of hydrogen is **catalytic hydrogenation.**

This addition of hydrogen is often done when liquid vegetable oils are converted to solid fats in making margarine and solid cooking fats. (Examine the labels of many prepared foods and you will find that they contain "partially hydrogenated vegetable oils.") As you may also know, the ratio of saturated to unsaturated fat in the diet is an important consideration. Our bodies are incapable of making polyunsaturated fats, and, therefore, they must be present in our diets in moderate amounts in order to maintain health. Saturated fats can be made in our cells from other food sources, for example, from carbohydrates (i. e., from sugars and starches). For this reason saturated fats in our diet are not absolutely necessary, and indeed, too much saturated fat has been implicated in the development of cardiovascular disease.

8.6 HYDROGENATION: THE FUNCTION OF THE CATALYST

Hydrogenation of an alkene is an exothermic reaction ($\Delta H^\circ \cong -30$ kcal mol^{-1}).

$$R-CH=CH-R + H_2 \xrightarrow{\text{hydrogenation}} R-CH_2-CH_2-R + \text{heat}$$

Hydrogenation reactions usually have high free energies of activation. The reaction of an alkene with molecular hydrogen does not take place at room temperature in the absence of a catalyst, but often *does* take place at room temperature when a metal catalyst is added. The catalyst provides a new pathway for the reaction with a *lower free energy of activation* (Fig. 8.1).

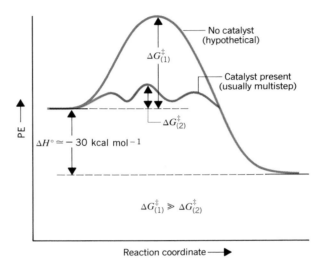

FIGURE 8.1   Potential energy diagram for the hydrogenation of an alkene in the presence of a catalyst and the hypothetical reaction in the absence of a catalyst. The energy of activation for the uncatalyzed reaction [$\Delta G^\ddagger_{(1)}$] is very much larger than the largest energy of activation for the catalyzed reaction [$\Delta G^\ddagger_{(2)}$].

The most commonly used catalysts for hydrogenation (finely divided platinum, nickel, palladium, rhodium, and ruthenium) apparently serve to adsorb hydrogen molecules on their surfaces. This adsorption of hydrogen is essentially a chemical reaction; unpaired electrons on the surface of the metal *pair* with the electrons of hydrogen (Fig. 8.2a) and bind the hydrogen to the surface. The collision of an alkene with the surface bearing adsorbed hydrogen causes adsorption of the alkene as well (Fig. 8.2b). A stepwise transfer of hydrogen atoms takes place, and this produces an alkane before the organic molecule leaves the catalyst surface (Fig. 8.2c and d). As a consequence, *both hydrogen atoms usually add from the same side of the molecule.* This mode of addition is called a **syn** addition (Section 8.6A).

Catalytic hydrogenation is a syn addition

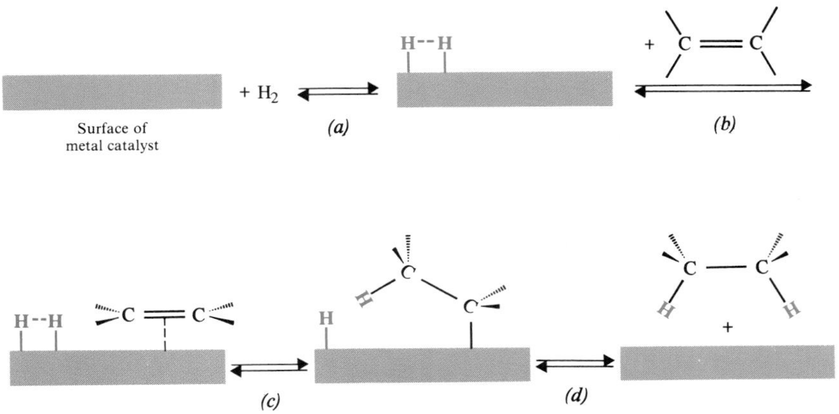

FIGURE 8.2 The mechanism for the hydrogenation of an alkene as catalyzed by finely divided platinum metal. Notice that both hydrogen atoms add from the same side of the double bond.

8.6A SYN AND ANTI ADDITIONS

An addition that places the parts of the adding reagent on the same side (or face) of the reactant is called a **syn addition.** We have just seen that the platinum-catalyzed addition of hydrogen ($X = Y = H$) is a syn addition.

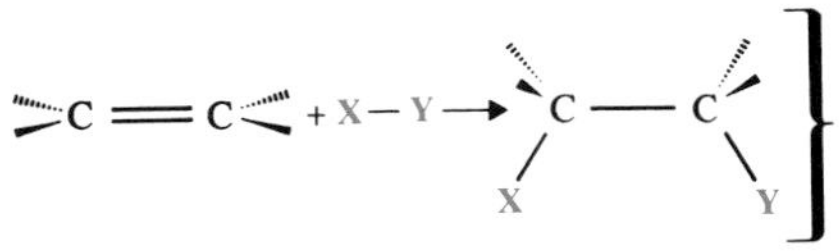

A syn addition

The opposite of a syn addition is an **anti addition.** An anti addition places the parts of the adding reagent on opposite faces of the reactant.

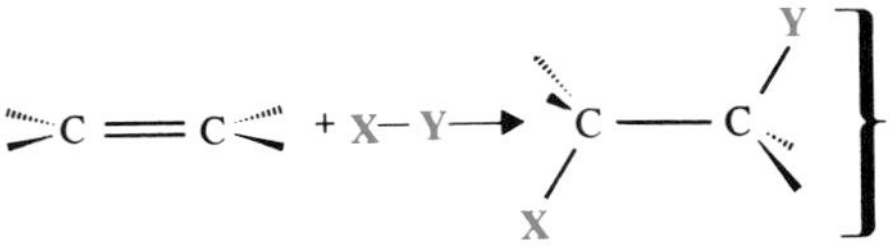

An anti addition

In Chapter 9 we shall study a number of important syn and anti additions.

8.7 HYDROGENATION OF ALKYNES

Depending on the conditions and the catalyst employed, one or two molar equivalents of hydrogen will add to a carbon–carbon triple bond. When a platinum catalyst is used, the alkyne generally reacts with two molar equivalents of hydrogen to give an alkane.

$$CH_3C{\equiv}CCH_3 \xrightarrow[H_2]{Pt} [CH_3CH{=}CHCH_3] \xrightarrow[H_2]{Pt} CH_3CH_2CH_2CH_3$$

However, hydrogenation of an alkyne to an alkene can be accomplished through the use of special catalysts or reagents. Moreover, these special methods allow the preparation of either (*E*) or (*Z*) alkenes from disubstituted alkynes.

8.7A SYN ADDITION OF HYDROGEN: SYNTHESIS OF *CIS*-ALKENES

A catalyst that permits hydrogenation of an alkyne to an alkene is the nickel boride compound called P-2 catalyst. This catalyst can be prepared by the reduction of nickel acetate with sodium borohydride.

$$Ni\left(\overset{\overset{\displaystyle O}{\|}}{OCCH_3}\right)_2 \xrightarrow[C_2H_5OH]{NaBH_4} Ni_2B \ (P\text{-}2)$$

Hydrogenation of alkynes in the presence of P-2 catalyst causes **syn addition of hydrogen** to take place and the alkene that is formed from an alkyne with an internal triple bond has the (*Z*) or cis configuration. The hydrogenation of 3-hexyne (see Section 8.7B) illustrates this method. The reaction takes place on the surface of the catalyst (Section 8.6) accounting for the syn addition.

$$CH_3CH_2C{\equiv}CCH_2CH_3 \xrightarrow[\text{(syn addition)}]{H_2/Ni_2B \ (P\text{-}2)} \underset{\substack{H \qquad\qquad H}}{\overset{\substack{CH_3CH_2 \qquad\qquad CH_2CH_3}}{C{=}C}}$$

3-Hexyne

(*Z*)-**3-Hexene**
(*cis*-**3-hexene**)
(**97%**)

Other specially conditioned catalysts can be used to prepare *cis*-alkenes from disubstituted alkynes. Metallic palladium deposited on calcium carbonate can be used in this way after it has been conditioned with lead acetate and quinoline (Section 19.1B). This special catalyst is known as Lindlar's catalyst.

$$R{-}C{\equiv}C{-}R \xrightarrow[\substack{\text{quinoline}\\ \text{(syn addition)}}]{\substack{H_2, \ Pd/CaCO_3\\ \text{(Lindlar's catalyst)}}} \underset{\substack{H \qquad\qquad H}}{\overset{\substack{R \qquad\qquad R}}{C{=}C}}$$

8.7B ANTI ADDITION OF HYDROGEN: SYNTHESIS OF *TRANS*-ALKENES

An **anti addition** of hydrogen atoms to the triple bond occurs when alkynes are reduced with lithium or sodium metal in ammonia or ethylamine at low temperatures. This reaction called a **dissolving metal reduction** produces an (*E*) or *trans*-alkene.

$$CH_3(CH_2)_2{-}C{\equiv}C{-}(CH_2)_2CH_3 \xrightarrow[\text{(2) NH}_4\text{Cl}]{\text{(1) Li, C}_2\text{H}_5\text{NH}_2, \ -78 \ °C} \underset{\substack{H \qquad\qquad (CH_2)_2CH_3}}{\overset{\substack{CH_3(CH_2)_2 \qquad\qquad H}}{C{=}C}}$$

4-Octyne

(*E*)-**4-Octene**
(*trans*-**4-octene**)
(**52%**)

The mechanism for this reduction is shown in the following outline. It involves successive electron transfers from the lithium (or sodium) atom and proton transfers from the amine (or ammonia). In the first step, the lithium atom transfers an electron to the alkyne to produce an intermediate that bears a negative charge and has an unpaired electron, called a **radical anion.** In the second step, the amine transfers a proton to produce a **vinylic radical.** Then, transfer of another electron gives a **vinylic anion.** It is this step that determines the stereochemistry of the reaction. The *trans*-vinylic anion is formed preferentially because it is more stable; the bulky alkyl groups are farther apart. Protonation of the *trans*-vinylic anion leads to the *trans*-alkene.

Radical anion   Vinylic radical

trans-Vinylic anion   *trans*-Alkene

8.8 MOLECULAR FORMULAS OF HYDROCARBONS: THE INDEX OF HYDROGEN DEFICIENCY

Alkenes whose molecules contain only one double bond have the general formula C_nH_{2n}. They are isomeric with cycloalkanes. For example, 1-hexene and cyclohexane have the same molecular formula (C_6H_{12}):

$$CH_2=CHCH_2CH_2CH_2CH_3$$

1-Hexene   **Cyclohexane**
(C_6H_{12})   **(C_6H_{12})**

Cyclohexane and 1-hexene are constitutional isomers.

Alkynes and alkenes with two double bonds (alkadienes) have the general formula C_nH_{2n-2}. Hydrocarbons with one triple bond and one double bond (alkenynes) and alkenes with three double bonds (alkatrienes) have the general formula C_nH_{2n-4}, and so forth.

$$CH_2=CH-CH=CH_2 \qquad CH_2=CH-CH=CH-CH=CH_2$$

1,3-Butadiene   **1,3,5-Hexatriene**
(C_4H_6)   **(C_6H_8)**

A chemist working with an unknown hydrocarbon can obtain considerable information about its structure from its molecular formula and its **index of hydrogen deficiency.** The index of hydrogen deficiency is defined as the number of *pairs* of hydrogen atoms that must be subtracted from the molecular formula of the corresponding alkane to give the molecular formula of the compound under considera-tion.*

For example, both cyclohexane and 1-hexene have an index of hydrogen defi-ciency equal to one (meaning one *pair* of hydrogen atoms). The corresponding alkane (i.e., the alkane with the same number of carbon atoms) is hexane.

C_6H_{14} = formula of corresponding alkane (hexane)
C_6H_{12} = formula of compound (1-hexene or cyclohexane)
H_2 = difference = 1 pair of hydrogen atoms

Index of hydrogen deficiency = 1

The index of hydrogen deficiency of acetylene or of 1,3-butadiene equals 2; the index of hydrogen deficiency of 1,3,5-hexatriene equals 3. (Do the calculations.)

Determining the number of rings present in a given compound is easily done experimentally. Molecules with double bonds and triple bonds add hydrogen readily at room temperature in the presence of a platinum catalyst. **Each double bond consumes one molar equivalent of hydrogen; each triple bond consumes two. Rings are not affected by hydrogenation at room temperature.** Hydrogenation, therefore, allows us to distinguish between rings on the one hand and double or triple bonds on the other. Consider as an example two compounds with the molecular formula C_6H_{12}: 1-hexene and cyclohexane. 1-Hexene reacts with one molar equivalent of hydrogen to yield hexane; under the same conditions cyclohexane does not react.

$$CH_2{=}CH(CH_2)_3CH_3 + H_2 \xrightarrow[25\ °C]{Pt} CH_3(CH_2)_4CH_3$$

$$\bigcirc + H_2 \xrightarrow[25\ °C]{Pt} \text{no reaction}$$

Or consider another example. Cyclohexene and 1,3-hexadiene have the same molecular formula (C_6H_{10}). Both compounds react with hydrogen in the presence of a catalyst, but cyclohexene, because it has a ring and only one double bond, reacts with only one molar equivalent. 1,3-Hexadiene adds two molar equivalents.

$$\bigcirc + H_2 \xrightarrow[25\ °C]{Pt} \bigcirc$$

Cyclohexene

$$CH_2{=}CHCH{=}CHCH_2CH_3 + 2\,H_2 \xrightarrow[25\ °C]{Pt} CH_3(CH_2)_4CH_3$$

1,3-Hexadiene

Problem 8.5

(a) What is the index of hydrogen deficiency of 2-hexene? (b) Of methylcyclo-pentane? (c) Does the index of hydrogen deficiency reveal anything about the location of the double bond in the chain? (d) About the size of the ring? (e) What is the index of hydrogen deficiency of 2-hexyne? (f) In general terms,

*Some organic chemists refer to the index of hydrogen deficiency as the "degree of unsaturation" or "the number of double-bond equivalencies."

what structural possibilities exist for a compound with the molecular formula $C_{10}H_{16}$?

Problem 8.6

Zingiberene, a fragrant compound isolated from ginger, has the molecular formula $C_{15}H_{24}$ and is known not to contain any triple bonds. (a) What is the index of hydrogen deficiency of zingiberene? (b) When zingiberene is subjected to catalytic hydrogenation using an excess of hydrogen, 1 mol of zingiberene absorbs 3 mol of hydrogen and produces a compound with the formula $C_{15}H_{30}$. How many double bonds does a molecule of zingiberene have? (c) How many rings?

OPTIONAL MATERIAL

More on Calculating the Index of Hydrogen Deficiency (IHD)

Calculating the index of hydrogen deficiency (IHD) for compounds other than hydrocarbons is relatively easy.

For compounds containing halogen atoms we simply count the halogen atoms as though they were hydrogen atoms. Consider a compound with the formula $C_4H_6Cl_2$. To calculate the IHD, we change the two chlorine atoms to hydrogen atoms, considering the formula as though it were C_4H_8. This formula has two hydrogen atoms fewer than the formula for a saturated alkane (C_4H_{10}), and this tells us that the compound has an IHD = 1. It could, therefore, have either one ring or one double bond. [We could tell which it has from a hydrogenation experiment: If the compound adds one molar equivalent of hydrogen (H_2) on catalytic hydrogenation at room temperature, then it must have a double bond; if it does not add hydrogen, then it must have a ring.]

For compounds containing oxygen we simply ignore the oxygen atoms and calculate the IHD from the remainder of the formula. Consider as an example a compound with the formula C_4H_8O. For the purposes of our calculation we consider the compound to be simply C_4H_8 and we calculate an IHD = 1. Again, this means that the compound contains either a ring or a double bond. Some structural possibilities for this compound are shown next. Notice that the double bond may be present as a carbon–oxygen double bond.

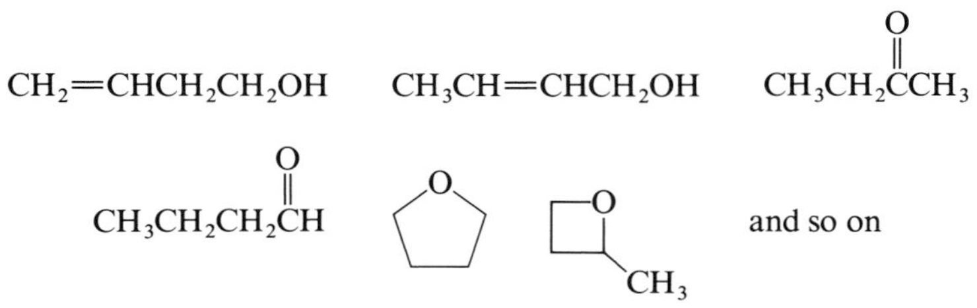

$$CH_2=CHCH_2CH_2OH \qquad CH_3CH=CHCH_2OH \qquad CH_3CH_2\overset{\overset{\displaystyle O}{\|}}{C}CH_3$$

$$CH_3CH_2CH_2\overset{\overset{\displaystyle O}{\|}}{C}H$$

and so on

For compounds containing nitrogen atoms we subtract one hydrogen for each nitrogen atom, and then we ignore the nitrogen atoms. For example, we treat a compound with the formula C_4H_9N as though it were C_4H_8, and again we get an IHD = 1. Some structural possibilities are the following:

$$CH_2{=}CHCH_2CH_2NH_2 \qquad CH_3CH{=}CHCH_2NH_2 \qquad CH_3CH_2\overset{\overset{\displaystyle NH}{\|}}{C}CH_3$$

$$CH_3CH_2CH_2CH{=}NH \qquad \qquad \text{and so on}$$

8.9 RELATIVE STABILITIES OF ALKENES

8.9A HEATS OF HYDROGENATION

Hydrogenation also provides a way to measure the relative stabilities of certain alkenes. The reaction of an alkene with hydrogen is an exothermic reaction; the enthalpy change involved is called **the heat of hydrogenation.** Most alkenes have heats of hydrogenation near -30 kcal mol^{-1}. Individual alkenes, however, have heats of hydrogenation that may differ from this value by more than 2 kcal mol^{-1}.

$$\ce{>C=C< + H-H ->[Pt] -\underset{H}{\overset{|}{C}}-\underset{H}{\overset{|}{C}}-} \qquad \Delta H° \simeq -30 \text{ kcal mol}^{-1}$$

These differences permit the measurement of the relative stabilities of alkene isomers *when hydrogenation converts them to the same product.*

Consider, as examples, the three butene isomers that follow:

$$\underset{\substack{\textbf{1-Butene} \\ \textbf{(C}_4\textbf{H}_8\textbf{)}}}{CH_3CH_2CH{=}CH_2} + H_2 \xrightarrow{Pt} \underset{\textbf{Butane}}{CH_3CH_2CH_2CH_3} \qquad \Delta H° = -30.3 \text{ kcal mol}^{-1}$$

$$\underset{\substack{\textbf{\textit{cis}-2-Butene} \\ \textbf{(C}_4\textbf{H}_8\textbf{)}}}{\ce{H3C\\ /CH3 \\ C=C \\ H/ \\H}} + H_2 \xrightarrow{Pt} \underset{\textbf{Butane}}{CH_3CH_2CH_2CH_3} \qquad \Delta H° = -28.6 \text{ kcal mol}^{-1}$$

$$\underset{\substack{\textbf{\textit{trans}-2-Butene} \\ \textbf{(C}_4\textbf{H}_8\textbf{)}}}{\ce{H3C\\ /H \\ C=C \\ H/ \\CH3}} + H_2 \xrightarrow{Pt} \underset{\textbf{Butane}}{CH_3CH_2CH_2CH_3} \qquad \Delta H° = -27.6 \text{ kcal mol}^{-1}$$

In each reaction the product (butane) is the same. In each case, too, one of the reactants (hydrogen) is the same. A different amount of *heat* is evolved in each reaction, however, and these differences must be related to different relative stabilities (different heat contents) of the individual butenes. 1-Butene evolves the greatest amount of heat when hydrogenated, and *trans*-2-butene evolves the least. Therefore 1-butene must have the greatest potential energy and be the least stable isomer.

trans-2-Butene must have the lowest potential energy and be the most stable isomer. The potential energy (and stability) of *cis*-2-butene falls in between. The order of stabilities of the butenes is easier to see if we examine the potential energy diagram in Fig. 8.3.

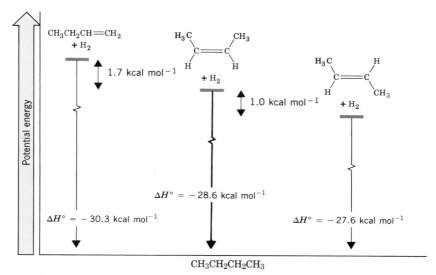

FIGURE 8.3   A potential energy diagram for the three butene isomers. The order of stability is *trans*-2-butene > *cis*-2-butene > 1-butene.

The greater stability of the *trans*-2-butene when compared to *cis*-2-butene illustrates a general pattern found in cis–trans alkene pairs. The 2-pentenes, for example, show the same stability relationship: **trans isomer > cis isomer.**

$$CH_3CH_2\underset{H}{\overset{}{C}}=\underset{H}{\overset{CH_3}{C}} \quad + H_2 \xrightarrow{Pt} CH_3CH_2CH_2CH_2CH_3 \quad \Delta H° = -28.6 \text{ kcal mol}^{-1}$$

cis-2-Pentene   **Pentane**

$$CH_3CH_2\underset{H}{\overset{}{C}}=\underset{CH_3}{\overset{H}{C}} \quad + H_2 \xrightarrow{Pt} CH_3CH_2CH_2CH_2CH_3 \quad \Delta H° = -27.6 \text{ kcal mol}^{-1}$$

trans-2-Pentene   **Pentane**

The greater potential energy of cis isomers can be attributed to strain caused by the crowding of two alkyl groups on the same side of the double bond (Fig. 8.4).

8.9B RELATIVE STABILITIES FROM HEATS OF COMBUSTION

When hydrogenation of isomeric alkenes does not yield the same alkane, *heats of combustion can be used to measure their relative stabilities.* For example, 2-methylpropene cannot be compared directly with the other butene isomers (1-butene, *cis*-,

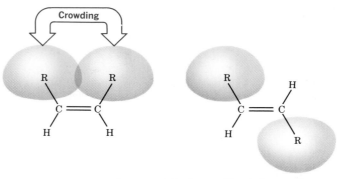

FIGURE 8.4 *cis-* and *trans-*Alkene isomers. The less stable cis isomer has greater strain.

and *trans*-2-butene) because on hydrogenation 2-methylpropene yields isobutane, *not butane:*

$$CH_3\underset{\underset{\displaystyle CH_3}{|}}{C}=CH_2 \ + H_2 \xrightarrow{Pt} CH_3\underset{\underset{\displaystyle CH_3}{|}}{C}HCH_3$$

2-Methylpropene   **Isobutane**

Isobutane and butane do not have the same potential energy so a direct comparison of heats of hydrogenation is not possible.

However, when 2-methylpropene is subjected to complete combustion, the products are the same as those produced by the other butene isomers. Each isomer consumes six molar equivalents of oxygen and *produces four molar equivalents of CO₂ and four molar equivalents of H₂O.* Comparison of the heats of combustion shows that 2-methylpropene is the most stable of the four isomers because it evolves the least heat.

$$CH_3CH_2CH=CH_2 + 6\,O_2 \longrightarrow 4\,CO_2 + 4\,H_2O \qquad \Delta H° = -649.8 \text{ kcal mol}^{-1}$$

$$\underset{H}{\overset{H_3C}{\diagdown}}C=C\underset{H}{\overset{CH_3}{\diagup}} + 6\,O_2 \longrightarrow 4\,CO_2 + 4\,H_2O \qquad \Delta H° = -648.1 \text{ kcal mol}^{-1}$$

$$\underset{H}{\overset{H_3C}{\diagdown}}C=C\underset{CH_3}{\overset{H}{\diagup}} + 6\,O_2 \longrightarrow 4\,CO_2 + 4\,H_2O \qquad \Delta H° = -647.1 \text{ kcal mol}^{-1}$$

$$CH_3\underset{\underset{\displaystyle CH_3}{|}}{C}=CH_2 + 6\,O_2 \longrightarrow 4\,CO_2 + 4\,H_2O \qquad \Delta H° = -646.1 \text{ kcal mol}^{-1}$$

The heat evolved by each of the other three isomers, moreover, confirms the order of stability measured by heats of hydrogenation. Therefore, the stability of the butene isomers overall is

$$CH_3\underset{\underset{\displaystyle CH_3}{|}}{C}=CH_2 > trans\text{-}CH_3CH=CHCH_3 > cis\text{-}CH_3CH=CHCH_3 > CH_3CH_2CH=CH_2$$

8.9C OVERALL RELATIVE STABILITIES OF ALKENES

Studies of numerous alkenes reveal a pattern of stabilities that is related to the number of alkyl groups attached to the carbon atoms of the double bond. **The greater the number of attached alkyl groups, (i.e., the more highly substituted the carbon atoms of the double bond) the greater is the alkene's stability.** This order of stabilities can be given in general terms as follows:*

Relative Stabilities of Alkenes

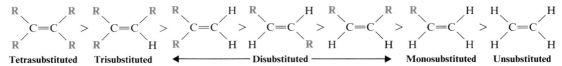

| Tetrasubstituted | Trisubstituted | ◄——————— Disubstituted ———————► | Monosubstituted | Unsubstituted |

Problem 8.7

Heats of hydrogenation of three alkenes are as follows:

$$\text{2-methyl-1-butene } (-28.5 \text{ kcal mol}^{-1})$$

$$\text{3-methyl-1-butene } (-30.3 \text{ kcal mol}^{-1})$$

$$\text{2-methyl-2-butene } (-26.9 \text{ kcal mol}^{-1})$$

(a) Write the structure of each alkene and classify it as to whether its doubly bonded atoms are monosubstituted, disubstituted, trisubstituted, and so on. (b) Write the product formed when each alkene is hydrogenated. (c) Can heats of hydrogenation be used to relate the relative stabilities of these three alkenes? (d) If so, what is the predicted order of stability? If not, why not? (e) What other alkene isomers are possible for these alkenes? Write their structures. (f) What data would be necessary to relate the stabilities of all of these isomers?

Problem 8.8

Predict the more stable alkene of each pair. (a) 1-Heptene or *cis*-2-heptene, (b) *cis*-2-heptene or *trans*-2-heptene, (c) *trans*-2-heptene or 2-methyl-2-hexene, and (d) 2-methyl-2-hexene or 2,3-dimethyl-2-pentene.

Problem 8.9

Reconsider the pairs of alkenes given in Problem 8.8. For which pairs could you use heats of hydrogenation to determine their relative stabilities? For which pairs would you be required to use heats of combustion?

---

*This order of stabilities may seem contradictory when compared with the explanation given for the relative stabilities of cis and trans isomers. Although a detailed explanation of the trend given here is beyond our scope, the relative stabilities of substituted alkenes can be rationalized. Part of the explanation can be given in terms of the electron-releasing effect of alkyl groups, an effect that satisfies the electron-withdrawing properties of the sp^2-hybridized carbon atoms of the double bond.

8.10 CYCLOALKENES

The rings of cycloalkenes containing five carbon atoms or fewer exist only in the cis form (Fig. 8.5). The introduction of a trans double bond into rings this small would, if it were possible, introduce greater strain than the bonds of the ring atoms could accommodate. *trans*-Cyclohexene might resemble the structure shown in Fig. 8.6. There is evidence that it can be formed as a very reactive short-lived intermediate in some chemical reactions.

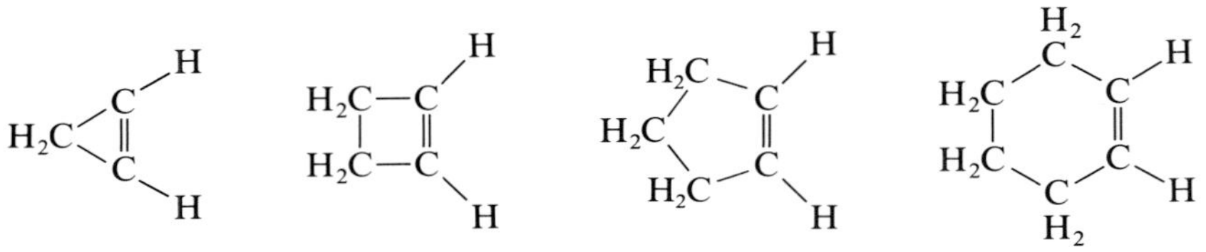

| Cyclopropene | Cyclobutene | Cyclopentene | Cyclohexene |

FIGURE 8.5 *cis*-Cycloalkenes.

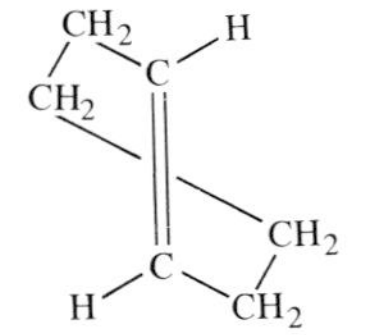

FIGURE 8.6 Hypothetical *trans*-cyclohexene. This molecule is apparently too highly strained to exist at room temperature.

trans-Cycloheptene has been observed with instruments called spectrometers, but it is a substance with a very short lifetime and has not been isolated.

trans-Cyclooctene (Fig. 8.7) has been isolated, however. Here the ring is large enough to accommodate the geometry required by a trans double bond and still be stable at room temperature. *trans*-Cyclooctene is chiral and exists as a pair of enantiomers.

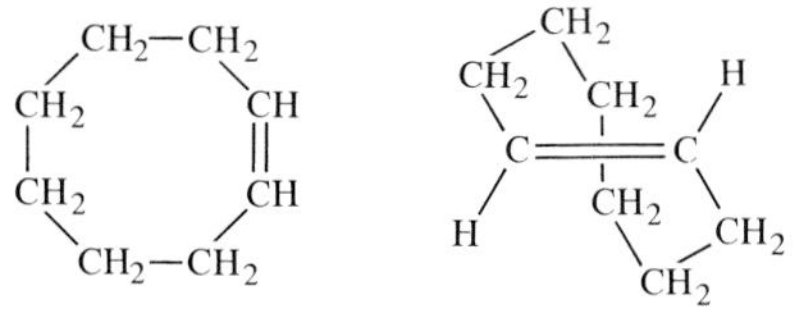

cis-Cyclooctene   *trans*-Cyclooctene

FIGURE 8.7 The cis and trans forms of cyclooctene.

8.11 SYNTHESIS OF ALKENES VIA ELIMINATION REACTIONS

Because an elimination reaction can introduce a double bond into a molecule, eliminations are widely used for synthesizing alkenes. In this chapter we shall study three methods based on eliminations. The following examples of each of these methods are given using a simple two-carbon starting reagent.

Dehydrohalogenation of Alkyl Halides (Sections 6.17, 6.18, and 8.12)

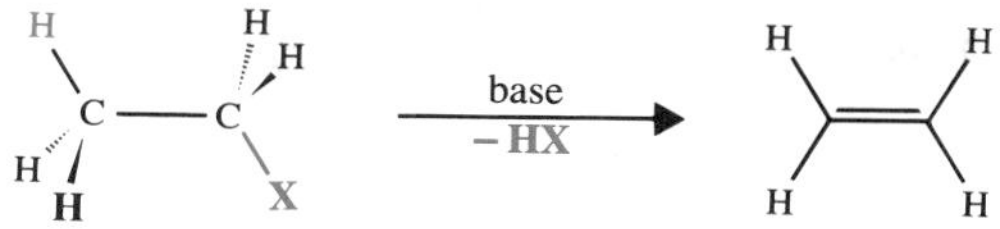

Dehydration of Alcohols (Sections 8.13–8.15)

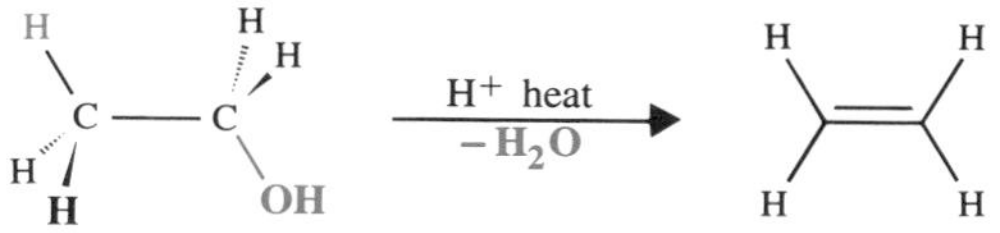

Debromination of vic-Dibromides (Section 8.16)

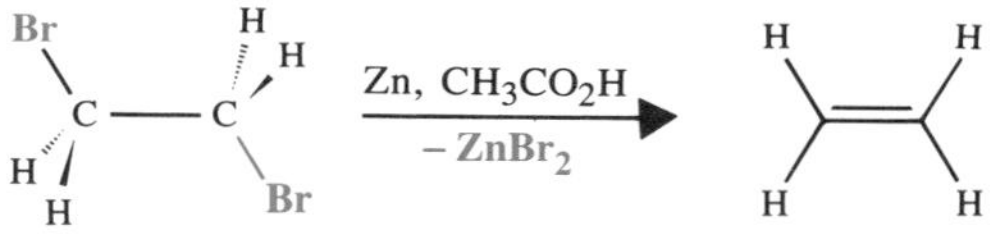

8.12 DEHYDROHALOGENATION OF ALKYL HALIDES

Synthesis of an alkene by dehydrohalogenation is almost always better achieved by an E2 reaction:

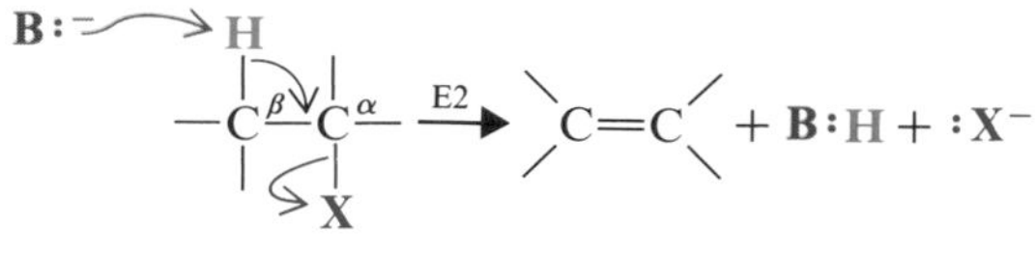

The reason for this choice is that dehydrohalogenation by an E1 mechanism is too variable. Too many competing events are possible, one being rearrangement of the carbon skeleton (Section 8.15). In order to bring about an E2 reaction, use a secondary or tertiary alkyl halide if possible. (If the synthesis must begin with a primary halide, then use a bulky base.) To try to avoid E1 conditions use a high concentration of a strong, relatively nonpolarizable base such as an alkoxide ion, and use a relatively nonpolar solvent such as an alcohol. To favor elimination generally, use a relatively high temperature. The typical reagents for dehydrohalogenation are sodium ethoxide in ethanol and potassium *tert*-butoxide in *tert*-butyl alcohol. Potassium hydroxide in ethanol is also used sometimes; in this reagent the reactive bases probably include the ethoxide ion formed by the following equilibrium.

$$OH^- + C_2H_5OH \rightleftharpoons H_2O + C_2H_5O^-$$

8.12A E2 REACTIONS: THE ORIENTATION OF THE DOUBLE BOND IN THE PRODUCT. ZAITSEV'S RULE

In earlier examples of dehydrohalogenations (Sections 6.17–6.19) only a single elimination product was possible. For example:

$$CH_3CHCH_3 \ \underset{\substack{C_2H_5OH \\ 55\ °C}}{\overset{C_2H_5O^-Na^+}{\longrightarrow}} \ CH_2{=}CHCH_3$$
$$\underset{Br}{|} \qquad\qquad\qquad (79\%)$$

$$\underset{\underset{Br}{|}}{\overset{\overset{CH_3}{|}}{CH_3CCH_3}} \ \underset{\substack{C_2H_5OH \\ 55\ °C}}{\overset{C_2H_5O^-Na^+}{\longrightarrow}} \ \overset{\overset{CH_3}{|}}{CH_2{=}C{-}CH_3}$$
$$(100\%)$$

$$CH_3(CH_2)_{15}CH_2CH_2Br \ \underset{\substack{(CH_3)_3COH \\ 40\ °C}}{\overset{(CH_3)_3CO^-K^+}{\longrightarrow}} \ CH_3(CH_2)_{15}CH{=}CH_2$$
$$(85\%)$$

Dehydrohalogenation of most alkyl halides, however, yields more than one product. For example, dehydrohalogenation of 2-bromo-2-methylbutane can yield two products: 2-methyl-2-butene or 2-methyl-1-butene.

2-Bromo-2-methylbutane

2-Methyl-2-butene

2-Methyl-1-butene

If we use a base such as ethoxide ion or hydroxide ion, the major product of the reaction will be **the more stable alkene.** The more stable alkene, as we know from Section 8.9, has the more highly substituted double bond.

$$CH_3CH_2O^- + \underset{\underset{Br}{|}}{\overset{\overset{CH_3}{|}}{CH_3CH_2C{-}CH_3}} \ \underset{CH_3CH_2OH}{\overset{70\ °C}{\longrightarrow}} \ CH_3CH{=}C{\overset{CH_3}{\underset{CH_3}{}}} + CH_3CH_2C{\overset{CH_2}{\underset{CH_3}{}}}$$

2-Methyl-2-butene	2-Methyl-1-butene
(69%)	(31%)
(more stable)	(less stable)

2-Methyl-2-butene is a trisubstituted alkene (three methyl groups are attached to carbon atoms of the double bond), whereas 2-methyl-1-butene is only disubstituted. 2-Methyl-2-butene is the major product.

    The reason for this behavior appears to be related to the double-bond character that develops in the transition state (cf. Section 6.18) for each reaction:

8.12 DEHYDROHALOGENATION OF ALKYL HALIDES

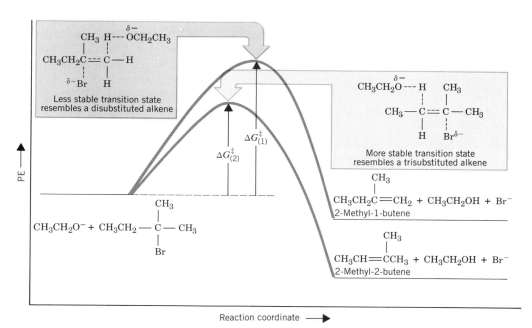

Transition state for an E2 reaction
*The carbon–carbon bond has some of the
character of a double bond*

The transition state for the reaction leading to 2-methyl-2-butene (Fig. 8.8) resembles the product of the reaction: a trisubstituted alkene. The transition state for the reaction leading to 2-methyl-1-butene resembles its product: a disubstituted alkene. Because the transition state leading to 2-methyl-2-butene resembles a more stable alkene, this transition state is more stable. Because this transition state is more stable (occurs at lower potential energy), the free energy of activation for this reaction is lower and 2-methyl-2-butene is formed faster. This explains why 2-methyl-2-butene is the major product. These reactions are known to be under kinetic control (Section 6.6).

FIGURE 8.8 Reaction (2) leading to the more stable alkene occurs faster than reaction (1) leading to the less stable alkene; $\Delta G^{\ddagger}_{(2)}$ is less than $\Delta G^{\ddagger}_{(2)}$.

Whenever an elimination occurs to give the most stable, most highly substituted alkene, chemists say that the elimination follows the **Zaitsev rule,** named for the nineteenth-century Russian chemist A. N. Zaitsev (1841–1910) who formulated it. (Zaitsev's name is also transliterated as Zaitzev, Saytzeff, Saytseff, or Saytzev.)

Problem 8.10

Dehydrohalogenation of 2-bromobutane with potassium hydroxide in ethanol yields a mixture of 2-butene and 1-butene. (a) Which butene would you expect to predominate? (b) The 2-butene formed in the reaction is a mixture of *cis*-2-butene and *trans*-2-butene. Which 2-butene would you expect to predominate?

8.12B AN EXCEPTION TO ZAITSEV'S RULE

Carrying out dehydrohalogenations with a base such as potassium *tert*-butoxide in *tert*-butyl alcohol favors the formation of **the less substituted alkene:**

$$CH_3-\underset{\underset{CH_3}{|}}{\overset{\overset{CH_3}{|}}{C}}-O^- + CH_3CH_2-\underset{\underset{CH_3}{|}}{\overset{\overset{CH_3}{|}}{C}}-Br \xrightarrow[\text{(CH}_3\text{)}_3\text{COH}]{75\ °C} CH_3CH=C\overset{CH_3}{\underset{CH_3}{}} + CH_3CH_2C\overset{CH_2}{\underset{CH_3}{}}$$

2-Methyl-2-butene	2-Methyl-1-butene
(27.5%)	(72.5%)
(more substituted)	(less substituted)

The reasons for this behavior are complicated but seem to be related in part to the steric bulk of the base and to the fact that in *tert*-butyl alcohol the base is associated with solvent molecules and thus made even larger. The large *tert*-butoxide ion appears to have difficulty removing one of the internal (2°) hydrogen atoms because of greater crowding at that site in the transition state. It removes one of the more exposed (1°) hydrogen atoms of the methyl group instead. When an elimination yields the less substituted alkene, we say that it follows the **Hofmann rule** (see Section 19.13A).

8.12C THE STEREOCHEMISTRY OF E2 REACTIONS: THE ORIENTATION OF GROUPS IN THE TRANSITION STATE

Considerable experimental evidence indicates that the five atoms involved in the transition state of an E2 reaction (including the base) must lie in the same plane. The requirement for coplanarity of the H—C—C—L unit arises from a need for proper overlap of orbitals in the developing π bond of the alkene that is being formed. There are two ways that this can happen:

anti Periplanar
transition state
(preferred)

syn Periplanar
transition state
(only with certain
rigid molecules)

Evidence also indicates that of these two arrangements for the transition state, the arrangement called the **anti periplanar** conformation is the preferred one. The **syn periplanar** transition state occurs only with rigid molecules that are unable to assume the anti arrangement. The reason: The antiperiplanar transition state is staggered (and therefore of lower energy), while the syn periplanar transition state is eclipsed.

8.12 DEHYDROHALOGENATION OF ALKYL HALIDES

Problem 8.11

Consider a simple molecule such as ethyl bromide and show with Newman projection formulas how the anti periplanar transition state would be favored over the syn periplanar one.

Part of the evidence for the preferred anti periplanar arrangement of groups comes from experiments done with cyclic molecules. As examples, let us consider the different behavior shown in E2 reactions by two compounds containing cyclohexane rings that have the common names *neomenthyl chloride* and *menthyl chloride*.

H_3C⬩⬠⬩⬩CH(CH$_3$)$_2$ H_3C⬩⬠⬩⬩CH(CH$_3$)$_2$

Cl   Cl

Neomenthyl chloride   **Menthyl chloride**

The β hydrogen and the leaving group on a cyclohexane ring can assume an anti periplanar conformation **only when they are both axial:**

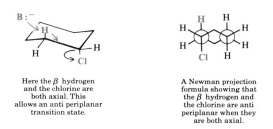

Here the β hydrogen
and the chlorine are
both axial. This
allows an anti periplanar
transition state.

A Newman projection
formula showing that
the β hydrogen and
the chlorine are anti
periplanar when they
are both axial.

Neither an axial–equatorial nor an equatorial–equatorial orientation of the groups allows the formation of an anti periplanar transition state.

In the more stable conformation of neomenthyl chloride (see following figure), the alkyl groups are both equatorial and the chlorine is axial. There are also axial hydrogen atoms on both C-2 and C-4. The base can attack either of these hydrogen atoms and achieve an anti periplanar transition state for an E2 reaction. Products corresponding to each of these transition states (2-menthene and 3-menthene) are formed rapidly. In accordance with Zaitsev's rule, 3-menthene (with the more highly substituted double bond) is the major product.

H_3C ... CH(CH$_3$)$_2$ $\xrightarrow[\substack{CH_3CH_2OH \\ fast}]{CH_3CH_2O^-}$ H_3C ⬡ CH(CH$_3$)$_2$

Neomenthyl chloride (both
red hydrogens are anti
to the chlorine in this the
more stable conformation).

3−Menthene
(78%)

$+ H_3C$ ⬡ CH(CH$_3$)$_2$

2−Menthene
(22%)

On the other hand, the more stable conformation of menthyl chloride has all three groups (including the chlorine) equatorial. For the chlorine to become axial, menthyl chloride has to assume a conformation in which the large isopropyl group and the methyl group are also axial. This conformation is of much higher energy, and the activation energy for the reaction is large because it includes the energy necessary for the conformational change. Consequently, menthyl chloride undergoes an E2 reaction very slowly, and the product is entirely 2-menthene (contrary to Zaitsev's Rule). This product (or any resulting from an elimination to yield the less-substituted alkene) is sometimes called *the Hofmann product* (Section 19.13A).

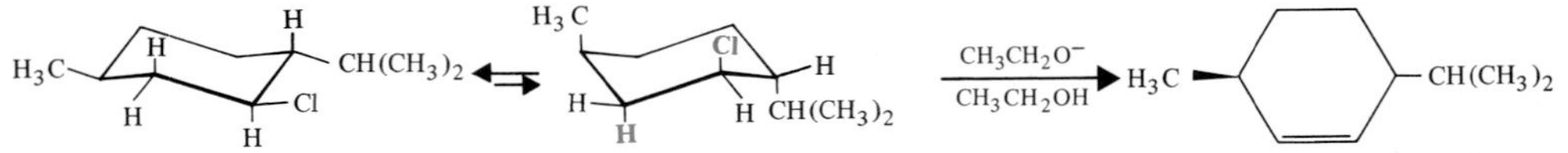

Menthyl chloride
more stable
conformation (anti
elimination is
not possible.)

Menthyl chloride
less stable
conformation
(red H and Cl
are axial and
can undergo
elimination.)

2—Menthene
(100%)

Problem 8.12

When *cis*-1-bromo-4-*tert*-butylcyclohexane is treated with sodium ethoxide in ethanol, it reacts rapidly; the product is 4-*tert*-butylcyclohexene. Under the same conditions, *trans*-1-bromo-4-*tert*-butylcyclohexane reacts very slowly. Write conformational structures and explain the difference in reactivity of these cis–trans isomers.

Problem 8.13

(a) When *cis*-1-bromo-2-methylcyclohexane undergoes an E2 reaction, two products (cycloalkenes) are formed. What are these two cycloalkenes, and which would you expect to be the major product? Write conformational structures showing how each is formed. (b) When *trans*-1-bromo-2-methylcyclohexane reacts in an E2 reaction, only one cycloalkene is formed. What is this product? Write conformational structures showing why it is the only product.

8.13 DEHYDRATION OF ALCOHOLS

Heating most alcohols with a strong acid causes them to lose a molecule of water (to **dehydrate**) and form an alkene:

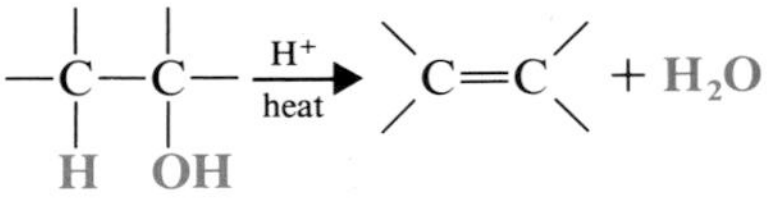

The reaction is an **elimination** and is favored at higher temperatures (Section 6.20). The most commonly used acids in the laboratory are Brønsted acids — proton donors such as sulfuric acid and phosphoric acid. Lewis acids such as alumina (Al_2O_3) are often used in industrial, gas-phase dehydrations.

8.13 DEHYDRATION OF ALCOHOLS

Dehydration reactions of alcohols show several important characteristics, which we shall soon explain.

1. **The experimental conditions — temperature and acid concentration — that are required to bring about dehydration are closely related to the structure of the individual alcohol.** Alcohols in which the hydroxyl group is attached to a primary carbon (primary alcohols) are the most difficult to dehydrate. Dehydration of ethanol, for example, requires concentrated sulfuric acid and a temperature of 180 °C.

$$H-\underset{\underset{H}{|}}{\overset{\overset{H}{|}}{C}}-\underset{\underset{O-H}{|}}{\overset{\overset{H}{|}}{C}}-H \xrightarrow[\substack{180\ °C}]{\substack{\text{concd.}\\ H_2SO_4}} H-\overset{\overset{H}{|}}{C}=\overset{\overset{H}{|}}{C}-H + H_2O$$

Ethanol
(a 1° alcohol)

Secondary alcohols usually dehydrate under milder conditions. Cyclohexanol, for example, dehydrates in 85% phosphoric acid at 165–170 °C.

Cyclohexanol $\xrightarrow[\substack{165-170\ °C}]{\substack{85\%\ H_3PO_4}}$ **Cyclohexene** $+ H_2O$
(80%)

Tertiary alcohols are usually so easily dehydrated that extremely mild conditions can be used. *tert*-Butyl alcohol, for example, dehydrates in 20% aqueous sulfuric acid at a temperature of 85 °C.

$$CH_3-\underset{\underset{CH_3}{|}}{\overset{\overset{CH_3}{|}}{C}}-OH \xrightarrow[\substack{85\ °C}]{\substack{20\%\ H_2SO_4}} CH_3-\underset{\overset{\|}{CH_2}}{\overset{\overset{CH_3}{|}}{C}} + H_2O$$

tert-**Butyl**   **2-Methylpropene**
alcohol   **(84%)**

Thus, overall, the relative ease with which alcohols undergo dehydration is in the following order:

Ease of Dehydration

$$\underset{\underset{\underset{3°\ Alcohol}{}}{R}}{\overset{\overset{R}{|}}{R}}-\overset{|}{\underset{|}{C}}-OH > \underset{\underset{\underset{2°\ Alcohol}{}}{H}}{\overset{\overset{R}{|}}{R}}-\overset{|}{\underset{|}{C}}-OH > \underset{\underset{\underset{1°\ Alcohol}{}}{H}}{\overset{\overset{H}{|}}{R}}-\overset{|}{\underset{|}{C}}-OH$$

This behavior, as we shall see in Section 8.14, is related to the stability of the carbocation formed in each reaction.

2. **Some primary and secondary alcohols also undergo rearrangements of their carbon skeleton during dehydration.** Such a rearrangement occurs in the dehydration of 3,3-dimethyl-2-butanol.

$$CH_3-\underset{\underset{OH}{|}}{\overset{\overset{CH_3}{|}}{C}}-\underset{\underset{CH_3}{}}{CH}-CH_3 \xrightarrow[80\ ^\circ C]{85\%\ H_3PO_4} CH_3-\overset{\overset{CH_3}{|}}{C}=\overset{\overset{CH_3}{|}}{C}-CH_3 + CH_2=\overset{\overset{CH_3}{|}}{C}-CHCH_3$$

3,3-Dimethyl-2-butanol   **2,3-Dimethyl-2-butene**   **2,3-Dimethyl-1-butene**

(80%)   (20%)

Notice that the carbon skeleton of the reactant is

$$C-\underset{\underset{C}{|}}{\overset{\overset{C}{|}}{C}}-C-C \qquad \text{while that of the products is} \qquad C-\underset{}{\overset{\overset{C\ \ C}{|\ \ |}}{C}}-C-C$$

We shall see in Section 8.15 that this reaction involves the migration of a methyl group from one carbon to the next.

8.13A MECHANISM OF ALCOHOL DEHYDRATION: AN E1 REACTION

Explanations for all of these observations can be based on a step-wise mechanism originally proposed by F. Whitmore (of the Pennsylvania State University). The mechanism is *an E1 reaction in which the substrate is a protonated alcohol (or an alkyloxonium ion,* see Section 6.5A). Consider the dehydration of *tert*-butyl alcohol as an example.

Step 1

$$CH_3-\underset{\underset{CH_3}{|}}{\overset{\overset{CH_3}{|}}{C}}-\overset{..}{O}-H + H-\overset{+}{\underset{\underset{H}{|}}{O}}\!: \rightleftharpoons CH_3-\underset{\underset{CH_3}{|}}{\overset{\overset{CH_3}{|}}{C}}-\overset{\overset{H}{|}}{\underset{..}{O^+}}-H + H\!:\!\overset{..}{O}-H$$

**Protonated alcohol
or alkyloxonium ion**

In this step, an acid–base reaction, a proton is rapidly transferred from the acid to one of the unshared electron pairs of the alcohol. In dilute sulfuric acid the acid is a hydronium ion; in concentrated sulfuric acid the proton donor is sulfuric acid itself. This step is characteristic of all reactions of an alcohol with a strong acid.

The presence of the positive charge on the oxygen of the protonated alcohol weakens all bonds from oxygen including the carbon–oxygen bond, and in step 2 the carbon–oxygen bond breaks. The leaving group is a molecule of water:

Step 2

$$CH_3-\underset{\underset{CH_3}{|}}{\overset{\overset{CH_3}{|}}{C}}-\overset{\overset{H}{|}}{\underset{..}{O^+}}-H \rightleftharpoons CH_3-\underset{\underset{CH_3}{|}}{\overset{\overset{CH_3}{|}}{C^+}} + \ :\!\overset{}{O}-H$$

A carbocation

The carbon–oxygen bond breaks **heterolytically.** The bonding electrons depart with the water molecule and leave behind a carbocation. The carbocation is, of course, highly reactive because the central carbon atom has only six electrons in its valence level, not eight.

Finally, in step 3, the carbocation transfers a proton to a molecule of water. The result is the formation of a hydronium ion and an alkene.

$$\text{Step 3} \qquad \underset{\underset{\text{CH}_3}{|}}{\overset{\overset{\displaystyle H}{|}}{\text{CH}_3{-}\overset{}{\text{C}}{}^+}} \quad \overset{H{-}C{-}H}{\underset{}{}} \quad +:\overset{\overset{H}{|}}{\underset{\cdot\cdot}{O}}{-}H \rightleftharpoons \underset{\underset{\text{CH}_3}{|}}{\text{CH}_3{-}\overset{\overset{\displaystyle \text{CH}_2}{\|}}{\text{C}}} \quad +\; H{-}\overset{\overset{H}{|}}{\underset{\cdot\cdot}{O}}{}^{\pm}{-}H$$

2-Methylpropene

In step 3, also an acid – base reaction, any one of the nine protons available at the three methyl groups can be transferred to a molecule of water. The electron pair that bonded the hydrogen atom to the carbon atom in the carbocation becomes the second bond of the double bond of the alkene. Notice that this step restores an octet of electrons to the central carbon atom.

Problem 8.14

(a) What would the leaving group have to be for the alcohol itself (rather than the protonated alcohol) to undergo dehydration? (b) How does your answer explain the requirement for an acid catalyst in alcohol dehydrations?

By itself, the Whitmore mechanism does not explain the observed order of reactivity of alcohols: **tertiary > secondary > primary.** Taken alone, it does not explain the formation of more than one product in the dehydration of certain alcohols nor the occurrence of a rearranged carbon skeleton in the dehydration of others. But when coupled with what is known about *the stability of carbocations,* the Whitmore mechanism *does* eventually account for all of these observations.

8.14 CARBOCATION STABILITY AND THE TRANSITION STATE

We saw in Section 6.13 that the order of stability of carbocations is tertiary > secondary > primary > methyl:

$$\underset{\underset{\text{R}}{|}}{\overset{\overset{\text{R}}{|}}{\text{R}{-}\text{C}{}^+}} > \underset{\underset{\text{R}}{|}}{\overset{\overset{\text{H}}{|}}{\text{R}{-}\text{C}{}^+}} > \underset{\underset{\text{H}}{|}}{\overset{\overset{\text{H}}{|}}{\text{R}{-}\text{C}{}^+}} > \underset{\underset{\text{H}}{|}}{\overset{\overset{\text{H}}{|}}{\text{H}{-}\text{C}{}^+}}$$

$$\text{3}^\circ \quad > \quad \text{2}^\circ \quad > \quad \text{1}^\circ \quad > \text{ Methyl}$$

In the dehydration of alcohols (i.e., following steps 1 – 3 in the forward direction) the slowest step is step 2 because as we shall see, it is *a highly endothermic step:* the formation of the carbocation from the protonated alcohol. The first and third steps are simple acid – base reactions. Proton-transfer reactions of this type occur very rapidly.

General Mechanism for the Acid-Catalyzed Dehydration of an Alcohol

$$\text{Step 1} \qquad \underset{\underset{H}{|}}{\overset{\overset{|}{|}}{{-}\text{C}{-}}}\overset{|}{\underset{}{\text{C}}}{-}\overset{\cdot\cdot}{\underset{\cdot\cdot}{O}}H + H_3O:^+ \rightleftharpoons \underset{\underset{H}{|}}{\overset{\overset{|}{|}}{{-}\text{C}{-}}}\overset{|}{\underset{}{\text{C}}}{-}\overset{\overset{H}{|}}{\underset{\cdot\cdot}{O}}{}^{\pm}H + H_2\overset{\cdot\cdot}{O}: \qquad \text{Fast}$$

Step 2 $-\overset{\displaystyle |}{\underset{\displaystyle |}{C}}-\overset{\displaystyle |}{\underset{\displaystyle \underset{\textstyle H}{|}}{C}}-\overset{\displaystyle \overset{\textstyle H}{|}}{\underset{\displaystyle ..}{O}}{}^{\pm}\!-H \rightleftharpoons -\overset{\displaystyle |}{\underset{\displaystyle |}{C}}-\overset{\displaystyle |}{\underset{\displaystyle \underset{\textstyle H}{|}}{\overset{+}{C}}}- + H_2\ddot{O}:$ Slow (rate determining)

Step 3 $-\overset{\displaystyle |}{\underset{\displaystyle \underset{\textstyle H}{|}}{C}}\!\!-\!\!\overset{\displaystyle |}{\underset{\displaystyle +}{C}}- + H_2\ddot{O}: \rightleftharpoons -\overset{\displaystyle |}{C}=\overset{\displaystyle |}{C}- + H_3O:^{+}$ Fast

Because step 2 is, then, the rate-determining step, it is the step that determines the reactivity of alcohols toward dehydration. With this in mind, we can now understand why tertiary alcohols are the most easily dehydrated. The formation of a tertiary carbocation is easiest because the free energy of activation for step 2 of a reaction leading to a tertiary carbocation is lowest (see Fig. 8.9).

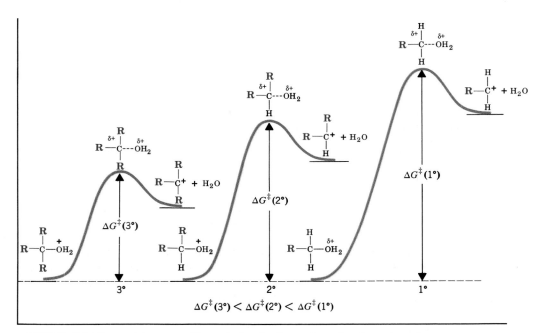

FIGURE 8.9   Potential energy diagrams for the formation of carbocations from protonated tertiary, secondary, and primary alcohols. The relative free energies of activation are tertiary < secondary < primary.

The reactions by which carbocations are formed from protonated alcohols are all highly *endothermic.* According to the Hammond–Leffler postulate (Sections 6.15A and 7.7A), there should be a strong resemblance between the transition state and the product in each case. Of the three, ***the transition state that leads to the tertiary carbocation is lowest in potential energy because it resembles the most stable product.*** By contrast, the transition state that leads to the primary carbocation occurs at highest potential energy because it resembles the least stable product. In each instance, moreover, the same factor stabilizes the transition state that stabilizes the carbocation itself: **delocalization of the charge.** We can understand this if we examine the process by which the transition state is formed.

$$-\overset{|}{\underset{|}{C}}\overset{H}{\overset{|}{O}}\!\pm\!H \rightleftharpoons \left[-\overset{|}{\underset{|}{C}}{}^{\delta\pm}\overset{H}{\overset{|}{O}}{}^{\delta\pm}H \right] \rightleftharpoons -\overset{|}{\underset{|}{C}}{}^{+} \quad + \; :\overset{H}{\overset{|}{O}}\!-\!H$$

Protonated　　　　**Transition**　　　**Carbocation**
alcohol　　　　　　**state**

The oxygen atom of the protonated alcohol bears a full positive charge. As the transition state develops this oxygen atom begins to separate from the carbon atom to which it is attached. The carbon atom, because it is losing the electrons that bonded it to the oxygen atom, begins to develop a partial positive charge. This developing positive charge *is most effectively delocalized in the transition state leading to a tertiary carbocation because of the presence of three electron-releasing alkyl groups.* The positive charge is less effectively delocalized in the transition state leading to a secondary carbocation (*two* electron-releasing groups) and is least effectively delocalized in the transition state leading to a primary carbocation (*one* electron-releasing group).

Transition state leading　　**Transition state leading**　　**Transition state leading**
to 3° carbocation　　　　　**to 2° carbocation**　　　　　**to 1° carbocation**
(most stable)　　　　　　　　　　　　　　　　　　　　**(least stable)**

8.15 CARBOCATION STABILITY AND THE OCCURRENCE OF MOLECULAR REARRANGEMENTS

With an understanding of carbocation stability and its effect on transition states behind us, we now proceed to explain the rearrangements of carbon skeletons that occur in some alcohol dehydrations. For example, let us consider again the rearrangement that occurs when 3,3-dimethyl-2-butanol is dehydrated.

$$CH_3-\overset{CH_3}{\underset{CH_3}{\overset{|}{\underset{|}{C}}}}-\overset{OH}{\underset{|}{\overset{|}{C}H}}-CH_3 \xrightarrow[\text{heat}]{85\%\ H_3PO_4} CH_3-\overset{CH_3}{\overset{|}{C}}=\overset{CH_3}{\overset{|}{C}}-CH_3 + CH_2=\overset{CH_3}{\overset{|}{C}}-CHCH_3$$

3,3-Dimethyl-2-butanol　　　　**2,3-Dimethyl-2-butene**　　**2,3-Dimethyl-1-butene**
　　　　　　　　　　　　　　　　(major product)　　　　　**(minor product)**

The first step of this dehydration is the formation of the protonated alcohol in the usual way:

Step 1　　$CH_3-\overset{CH_3}{\underset{:\overset{..}{O}-H}{\overset{|}{\underset{|}{C}}}}-CH-CH_3 + H-\overset{H}{\underset{H}{\overset{|}{O}}}:^+ \rightleftharpoons CH_3-\overset{CH_3}{\underset{:\overset{..}{O}H_2}{\overset{|}{\underset{|}{\overset{|}{C}}}}}-CHCH_3 + H_2\overset{..}{O}:$

Protonated alcohol

In the second step the protonated alcohol loses water and a secondary carbocation forms:

$$Step\ 2 \quad CH_3-\underset{\underset{+}{\overset{|}{CH_3\ :OH_2}}}{\overset{\overset{CH_3}{|}}{C}}-CH-CH_3 \rightleftharpoons CH_3-\underset{\overset{|}{CH_3}}{\overset{\overset{CH_3}{|}}{C}}-\underset{+}{C}HCH_3 + H_2\ddot{O}:$$

A 2° carbocation

Now the rearrangement occurs. ***The less stable, secondary carbocation rearranges to a more stable tertiary carbocation.***

$$Step\ 3 \quad CH_3-\underset{\overset{|}{CH_3}}{\overset{\overset{CH_3}{|}}{C}}-\underset{+}{C}HCH_3 \longrightarrow \left[CH_3-\underset{\overset{|}{CH_3}}{\overset{\overset{CH_3}{\overset{\delta+}{|}}}{C}}\cdots\overset{\delta+}{C}HCH_3\right] \longrightarrow CH_3-\underset{\overset{|}{CH_3}}{\overset{\overset{CH_3}{\overset{+}{|}}}{C}}-CH-CH_3$$

| **2° Carbocation** | **Transition state** | **3° Carbocation** |
| **(less stable)** | | **(more stable)** |

The rearrangement occurs through the migration of an alkyl group (methyl) from the carbon atom adjacent to the one with the positive charge. The methyl group migrates **with its pair of electrons,** that is, as a methyl anion, $^-:CH_3$ (called a methanide ion). After the migration is complete, the carbon atom that the methyl anion left has become a carbocation, and the positive charge on the carbon atom to which it migrated has been neutralized. Because a group migrates from one carbon to the next, this kind of rearrangement is often called **a 1,2-shift.**

In the transition state the shifting methyl is partly bonded to both carbon atoms by the pair of electrons with which it migrates. It never leaves the carbon skeleton.

The final step of the reaction is the loss of proton from the new carbocation and the formation of an alkene. This step, however, can occur in two ways.

$$Step\ 4 \quad H-\overset{(a)}{\frown}CH_2-\underset{\overset{|}{CH_3}}{\overset{+}{C}}-\overset{\overset{H\ (b)}{|}}{\underset{\overset{|}{CH_3}}{C}}-CH_3-$$

(a) → $CH_2{=}\underset{\overset{|}{CH_3}}{C}{-}\underset{\overset{|}{CH_3}}{C}HCH_3$ **Less stable alkene**

(minor product)

(b) → $CH_3{-}\underset{\overset{|}{CH_3}}{C}{=}\underset{\overset{|}{CH_3}}{C}{-}CH_3$ **More stable alkene**

(major product)

The more favored route is dictated by the type of alkene being formed. Path (b) leads to the highly stable tetrasubstituted alkene, and this is the path followed by most of the carbocations. Path (a), on the other hand, leads to a less stable, disubstituted alkene and produces the minor product of the reaction. ***The formation of the more stable alkene is the general rule (Zaitsev's rule) in the acid-catalyzed dehydration reactions of alcohols.***

Studies of thousands of reactions involving carbocations show that rearrangements like those just described are general phenomena. ***They occur almost invariably when the migration of an alkyl alkanide ion or hydride ion can lead to a more stable carbocation.*** The following are examples:

$$CH_3-\overset{\overset{\displaystyle CH_3}{|}}{\underset{\underset{\displaystyle CH_3}{|}}{C}}-\overset{+}{C}H-CH_3 \xrightarrow[\text{migration}]{\text{methanide}} CH_3-\overset{\overset{\displaystyle CH_3}{|}}{\underset{\underset{\displaystyle CH_3}{|}}{\overset{+}{C}}}-CH-CH_3$$

2° Carbocation   3° Carbocation

$$CH_3-\overset{\overset{\displaystyle H}{|}}{\underset{\underset{\displaystyle CH_3}{|}}{C}}-\overset{+}{C}H-CH_3 \xrightarrow[\text{migration}]{\text{hydride}} CH_3-\overset{\overset{\displaystyle H}{|}}{\underset{\underset{\displaystyle CH_3}{|}}{\overset{+}{C}}}-CH-CH_3$$

2° Carbocation   3° Carbocation

$$CH_3-\overset{\overset{\displaystyle CH_3}{|}}{\underset{\underset{\displaystyle CH_3}{|}}{C}}-\overset{+}{C}H_2 \xrightarrow[\text{migration}]{\text{methanide}} CH_3-\overset{\overset{\displaystyle +}{}}{\underset{\underset{\displaystyle CH_3}{|}}{C}}-CH_2-CH_3$$

1° Carbocation   3° Carbocation

Rearrangements of carbocations can also lead to a change in ring size, as the following example shows:

2° Carbocation

3° Carbocation

Problem 8.15

Acid-catalyzed dehydration of neopentyl alcohol, $(CH_3)_3CCH_2OH$, yields 2-methyl-2-butene as the major product. Outline a mechanism showing all steps in its formation.

Problem 8.16

Heating neopentyl iodide, $(CH_3)_3CCH_2I$, in formic acid (a solvent of very high ionizing ability) slowly leads to the formation of 2-methyl-2-butene as the major product. Propose a mechanism for this reaction.

Problem 8.17

When the compound called *isoborneol* (p. 330) is heated with 50% sulfuric acid, the product of the reaction is the compound called camphene and not bornylene as one might expect. Using models to assist you, write a step-by-step mechanism showing how camphene is formed.

HO $\xrightarrow[\text{heat}]{\text{H}_3\text{O}^+}$ CH$_2$ not

Isoborneol   Camphene   Bornylene

8.16 ALKENES BY DEBROMINATION OF VICINAL DIBROMIDES

Vicinal (or **vic**) dihalides are dihalo compounds in which the halogens are situated on adjacent carbon atoms. The name **geminal** (or **gem**) dihalide is used for those dihalides where both halogen atoms are attached to the same carbon atom.

$$-\overset{|}{\underset{X}{C}}-\overset{|}{\underset{X}{C}}- \qquad -\overset{|}{\underset{|}{\underset{X}{C}}}-\overset{\overset{X}{|}}{\underset{|}{C}}-$$

A *vic*-dihalide   **A *gem*-dihalide**

vic-Dibromides undergo **debromination** when they are treated with a solution of sodium iodide in acetone or with a mixture of zinc dust in acetic acid (or ethanol).

$$-\overset{|}{\underset{Br}{C}}-\overset{|}{\underset{Br}{C}}- + 2NaI \xrightarrow{\text{acetone}} \overset{\diagdown}{\diagup}C=C\overset{\diagup}{\diagdown} + I_2 + 2NaBr$$

$$-\overset{|}{\underset{Br}{C}}-\overset{|}{\underset{Br}{C}}- + Zn \xrightarrow[\underset{CH_3CH_2OH}{\text{or}}]{CH_3CO_2H} \overset{\diagdown}{\diagup}C=C\overset{\diagup}{\diagdown} + ZnBr_2$$

Debromination by sodium iodide takes place by an E2 mechanism similar to that for dehydrohalogenation.

$$I:^- + \overset{\overset{Br}{|}}{\underset{\underset{Br}{|}}{C}}-C \longrightarrow \overset{\diagdown}{\diagup}C=C\overset{\diagup}{\diagdown} + IBr + :Br^-$$

then $I^- + IBr \longrightarrow I_2 + Br^-$

Debromination by zinc takes place on the surface of the metal and the mechanism is uncertain. Other electropositive metals (e.g., Na, Ca, and Mg) also cause debromination of *vic*-dibromides.

vic-Dibromides are usually prepared by the addition of bromine to an alkene (cf. Section 9.6). Consequently, dehalogenation of a *vic*-dibromide is of little use as a general preparative reaction. Bromination followed by debromination is useful, however, in the purification of alkenes (see Problem 8.42) and in "protecting" the double bond. We shall see an example of this later.

8.17 SUMMARY OF METHODS FOR THE PREPARATION OF ALKENES

In this chapter we described four general methods for the preparation of alkenes.

1. **Dehydrohalogenation of alkyl halides (Section 8.12)**

General Reaction

$$-\overset{|}{\underset{H}{C}}-\overset{|}{\underset{X}{C}}- \xrightarrow[\text{heat}]{\substack{\text{base} \\ (-\text{HX})}} \overset{\diagdown}{\diagup}C=C\overset{\diagup}{\diagdown}$$

Specific Examples

$$CH_3CH_2\underset{\underset{Br}{|}}{C}HCH_3 \xrightarrow[C_2H_5OH]{C_2H_5ONa} CH_3CH=CHCH_3 + CH_3CH_2CH=CH_2$$
$$\text{(cis and trans, 81\%)} \qquad \text{(19\%)}$$

$$CH_3CH_2\underset{\underset{Br}{|}}{C}HCH_3 \xrightarrow[70\,°C]{(CH_3)_3COK} CH_3CH=CHCH_3 + CH_3CH_2CH=CH_2$$
$$\text{Disubstituted alkenes} \qquad \text{Monosubstituted alkene}$$
$$\text{(cis and trans, 47\%)} \qquad \text{(53\%)}$$

2. **Dehydration of alcohols (Sections 8.13–8.15)**

General Reaction

$$-\overset{|}{\underset{H}{C}}-\overset{|}{\underset{OH}{C}}- \xrightarrow[\text{heat}]{\text{acid}} \overset{\diagdown}{\diagup}C=C\overset{\diagup}{\diagdown} + H_2O$$

Specific Examples

$$CH_3CH_2OH \xrightarrow[180\,°C]{\text{concd } H_2SO_4} CH_2=CH_2 + H_2O$$

$$CH_3\overset{\overset{\displaystyle CH_3}{|}}{\underset{\underset{\displaystyle CH_3}{|}}{C}}-OH \xrightarrow[85\,°C]{20\%\ H_2SO_4} CH_3\overset{\overset{\displaystyle CH_3}{|}}{C}=CH_2 + H_2O$$
$$\text{(83\%)}$$

3. **Dehalogenation of *vic*-dibromides (Section 8.16)**

General Reaction

$$-\overset{|}{\underset{Br}{C}}-\overset{|}{\underset{Br}{C}}- \xrightarrow[CH_3CO_2H]{Zn} \overset{\diagdown}{\diagup}C=C\overset{\diagup}{\diagdown} + ZnBr_2$$

4. Hydrogenation of alkynes (Section 8.7B)

General Reaction

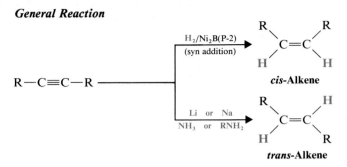

In subsequent chapters we shall see a number of other methods for alkene synthesis.

8.18 SYNTHESIS OF ALKYNES BY ELIMINATION REACTIONS

Alkynes can also be synthesized from alkenes. In this method an alkene is first treated with bromine to form a *vic*-dibromo compound.

$$
RCH{=}CHR + Br_2 \longrightarrow R-\underset{\underset{Br}{|}}{\overset{\overset{H}{|}}{C}}-\underset{\underset{Br}{|}}{\overset{\overset{H}{|}}{C}}-R
$$

vic-Dibromide

Then the *vic* dibromide is dehydrohalogenated through its reaction with a strong base. The dehydrohalogenation occurs in two steps. The first step yields a bromo-alkene.

Step 1 $R-\overset{H}{\underset{Br}{C}}-\overset{H}{\underset{Br}{C}}-R + {:}NH_2^- \longrightarrow R-\overset{H}{C}{=}\overset{}{\underset{Br}{C}}-R + NH_3 + Br^-$

vic-Dibromide   Strong base   Bromoalkene

The second step is more difficult; it yields an alkyne.

Step 2 $H_2\ddot{N}{:}^- + R-\overset{H}{C}{=}\overset{}{\underset{Br}{C}}-R \longrightarrow R-C{\equiv}C-R + NH_3 + Br^-$

Strong base   Alkyne

Depending on the conditions, these two dehydrohalogenations may be carried out as separate reactions or they may be carried out consecutively in a single mixture. The strong base, sodium amide, is capable of effecting both dehydrohalogenations in a single reaction mixture. (At least two molar equivalents of sodium amide per mole of the dihalide must be used, and if the product is a terminal alkyne, three molar equivalents must be used because the terminal alkyne will react with sodium amide as it is formed in the mixture.) Dehydrohalogenations with sodium amide are usually carried out in liquid ammonia or in an inert medium such as mineral oil.

The following example illustrates this method.

$$CH_3CH_2CH=CH_2 \xrightarrow[CCl_4]{Br_2} CH_3CH_2CHCH_2Br \underset{\underset{110-160\,°C}{\text{mineral oil}}}{\xrightarrow{NaNH_2}}$$

with Br below the CHCH_2Br carbon.

$$\begin{bmatrix} CH_3CH_2CH=CHBr \\ + \\ CH_3CH_2C=CH_2 \\ | \\ Br \end{bmatrix} \underset{\underset{110-160\,°C}{\text{mineral oil}}}{\xrightarrow{NaNH_2}} [CH_3CH_2C\equiv CH] \xrightarrow{NaNH_2}$$

$$CH_3CH_2C\equiv C\!:^-Na^+ \xrightarrow{NH_4Cl} CH_3CH_2C\equiv CH + NH_3 + NaCl$$

Ketones can be converted to *gem*-dichlorides through their reaction with phosphorus pentachloride, and these can also be used to synthesize alkynes.

Methyl cyclohexyl ketone → **A gem-dichloride (70–80%)** → **Cyclohexylacetylene (46%)**

PCl$_5$, 0 °C (− POCl$_3$); (1) 3NaNH$_2$, mineral oil, heat, (2) H$^+$

Problem 8.18

Outline all steps in a synthesis of propyne from each of the following:

(a) CH_3COCH_3 (c) $CH_3CHBrCH_2Br$

(b) $CH_3CH_2CHBr_2$ (d) $CH_3CH=CH_2$

8.19 THE ACIDITY OF TERMINAL ALKYNES

The hydrogen atoms of ethyne are considerably more acidic than those of ethene or ethane (Section 3.5A).

$$H-C\equiv C-H \qquad C=C \qquad H-C-C-H$$

$$pK_a = 25 \qquad pK_a = 44 \qquad pK_a = 50$$

The order of basicities of the anions is opposite the relative acidity of the hydrocarbons. The ethanide ion is the most basic and the ethynide ion is the least basic.

Relative Basicity

$$CH_3CH_2\!:^- > CH_2=CH\!:^- > HC\equiv C\!:^-$$

What we have said about ethyne and ethynide ions is true of any terminal alkyne $(RC{\equiv}CH)$ and any alkynide ion $(RC{\equiv}C:^-)$. If we include other hydrogen compounds of the first-row elements of the periodic table, we can write the following orders of relative acidities and basicities:

Relative Acidity

$$H-\ddot{O}H > H-\ddot{O}R > H-C{\equiv}CR > H-\ddot{N}H_2 > H-CH{=}CH_2 > H-CH_2CH_3$$

pK_a 15.8   16–17   25   38   44   50

Relative Basicity

$$^-{:}\ddot{O}H < ^-{:}\ddot{O}R < ^-{:}C{\equiv}CR < ^-{:}\ddot{N}H_2 < ^-{:}CH{=}CH_2 < ^-{:}CH_2CH_3$$

We see from the order just given that while terminal alkynes are more acidic than ammonia, they are less acidic than alcohols and are less acidic than water.

> The arguments just made apply only to acid–base reactions that take place in solution. In the gas phase, acidities and basicities are very much different. For example, in the gas phase the hydroxide ion is a stronger base than the acetylide ion. The explanation for this shows us again the important roles solvents play in reactions that involve ions (cf. Section 6.15). In solution, smaller ions (e.g., hydroxide ions) are more effectively solvated than larger ones (e.g., ethynide ions). Because they are more effectively solvated, smaller ions are more stable and are therefore less basic. In the gas phase, large ions are stabilized by polarization of their bonding electrons and the bigger a group is the more polarizable it will be. Thus in the gas phase larger ions are less basic.

Problem 8.19

Predict the products of the following acid–base reactions. If the equilibrium would not result in the formation of appreciable amounts of products, you should so indicate. In each case label the stronger acid, the stronger base, the weaker acid, and the weaker base.

(a) $H-C{\equiv}C-H + NaNH_2 \longrightarrow$

(b) $CH_2{=}CH_2 + NaNH_2 \longrightarrow$

(c) $CH_3CH_3 + NaNH_2 \longrightarrow$

(d) $H-C{\equiv}C:^-Na^+ + CH_3CH_2OH \longrightarrow$

(e) $H-C{\equiv}C:^-Na^+ + H_2O \longrightarrow$

8.20 REPLACEMENT OF THE ACETYLENIC HYDROGEN ATOM OF TERMINAL ALKYNES

Sodium ethynide and other sodium alkynides can be prepared by treating terminal alkynes with sodium amide in liquid ammonia.

$$H-C{\equiv}C-H + NaNH_2 \xrightarrow{\text{liq. NH}_3} H-C{\equiv}C:^-Na^+ + NH_3$$

$$CH_3C{\equiv}C-H + NaNH_2 \xrightarrow{\text{liq. NH}_3} CH_3C{\equiv}C:^-Na^+ + NH_3$$

8.20 REPLACEMENT OF THE ACETYLENIC HYDROGEN ATOM OF TERMINAL ALKYNES

These are acid–base reactions. The amide ion, by virtue of its being the anion of the very weak acid, ammonia ($pK_a = 38$), is able to remove the acetylenic protons of terminal alkynes ($pK_a = 25$). These reactions, for all practical purposes, go to completion.

Sodium alkynides are useful intermediates for the synthesis of other alkynes. These syntheses can be accomplished by treating the sodium alkynide with a primary alkyl halide.

$$R-C{\equiv}C{:}^-Na^+ + R'CH_2{-}Br \longrightarrow R-C{\equiv}C-CH_2R' + NaBr$$

| Sodium alkynide | Primary alkyl halide | Mono- or disubstituted acetylene |

(R or R′ or both may be hydrogen)

The following examples illustrate this synthesis of alkynes:

$$HC{\equiv}C{:}^-Na^+ + CH_3{-}Br \xrightarrow[5\ h]{liq.\ NH_3} H-C{\equiv}C-CH_3 + NaBr$$

Propyne
(84%)

$$CH_3CH_2C{\equiv}C{:}^-Na^+ + CH_3CH_2{-}Br \xrightarrow[6\ h]{liq.\ NH_3} CH_3CH_2C{\equiv}CCH_2CH_3 + NaBr$$

3-Hexyne
(75%)

In all of these examples the alkynide ion acts as a nucleophile and displaces a halide ion from the primary alkyl halide. The result is **an S_N2 reaction** (Section 6.7).

$$RC{\equiv}C{:}^- \quad \overset{R'}{\underset{H}{\overset{|}{C}}}{-}\overset{..}{\underset{..}{Br}}{:} \xrightarrow[S_N2]{nucleophilic\ substitution} RC{\equiv}C-CH_2R' + NaBr$$

| Sodium alkynide | 1° Alkyl halide |

The unshared electron pair of the alkynide ion attacks the backside of the carbon atom that bears the halogen atom and forms a bond to it. The halogen atom departs as a halide ion.

When secondary or tertiary halides are used, the alkynide ion acts as a base rather than as a nucleophile, and the major result is an **E2 elimination** (Section 6.18). The products of the elimination are an alkene and the alkyne from which the sodium alkynide was originally formed.

$$RC{\equiv}C{:}^- \quad H{-}\overset{R'}{\underset{\underset{R''}{C}{-}Br}{\overset{H}{C}}} \xrightarrow{E2} RC{\equiv}CH + R'CH{=}CHR'' + Br^-$$

2° Alkyl halide

Problem 8.20

In addition to sodium amide and liquid ammonia, assume that you have the following four compounds available and want to carry out a synthesis of 2,2-dimethyl-3-hexyne. Which synthetic route would you choose?

$$CH_3CH_2C\equiv CH \qquad CH_3-\underset{\underset{\displaystyle CH_3}{|}}{\overset{\overset{\displaystyle CH_3}{|}}{C}}-C\equiv CH \qquad CH_3CH_2Br \qquad CH_3-\underset{\underset{\displaystyle CH_3}{|}}{\overset{\overset{\displaystyle CH_3}{|}}{C}}-Br$$

8.21 OTHER METAL ACETYLIDES

Ethyne and terminal alkynes also form metal derivatives with silver and copper(I) ions.

$$RC\equiv CH + Cu(NH_3)_2^+ + OH^- \xrightarrow{H_2O} R-C\equiv CCu + H_2O + 2\,NH_3$$

$$RC\equiv CH + Ag(NH_3)_2^+ + OH^- \xrightarrow{H_2O} RC\equiv CAg + H_2O + 2NH_3$$

Silver and copper alkynides differ from sodium alkynides in several ways. The metal–carbon bond in silver and copper alkynides is largely covalent. As a result, silver and copper alkynides are poor bases and poor nucleophiles. Silver and copper alkynides can be prepared in water, whereas sodium alkynides react vigorously with water.

$$R-C\equiv CNa + H_2O \longrightarrow R-C\equiv CH + NaOH$$

Silver and copper alkynides are also quite insoluble in water and precipitate when they are prepared. This is the basis for an old and still convenient test for terminal alkynes as well as a method for separating terminal alkynes from alkynes that have an internal triple bond.

$$R-C\equiv C-R + Ag(NH_3)_2{}^+OH^- \longrightarrow \text{no precipitate}$$

$$R-C\equiv CH + Ag(NH_3)_2{}^+OH^- \longrightarrow RC\equiv CAg\downarrow$$

Once a separation has been carried out, the terminal alkyne can be regenerated by treating the alkynide with sodium cyanide (or with a strong acid).

$$R-C\equiv CAg + 2\,CN^- + H_2O \longrightarrow R-C\equiv CH + Ag(CN)_2{}^- + OH^-$$

Silver and copper alkynides must be handled cautiously; when dry they are likely to explode.

Additional Problems

8.21 Each of the following names is incorrect. Tell how and give the correct name.

(a) *cis*-3-Pentene   (c) 2-Methylcycloheptene   (e) 3-Methyl-2-butene

(b) 1,1,2,2-Tetramethylethene   (d) 1-Methyl-1-heptene   (f) 4,5-Dichlorocyclopentene

ADDITIONAL PROBLEMS

8.22 Write a structural formula for each of the following:

(a) 1-Methylcyclobutene   (e) (*Z*)-3-Heptene   (i) 4-Cyclopentyl-1-pentene

(b) 3-Methylcyclopentene   (f) 3,3,3-Trichloropropene   (j) Cyclopropylethene

(c) 2,3-Dimethyl-2-pentene   (g) Isobutylene   (k) 4-Methyl-2-hexyne

(d) (*E*)-2-Hexene   (h) Propylene   (l) (*Z*)-3-Methyl-2-hexen-5-yne

8.23 Write structural formulas and give IUPAC names for all alkene isomers of (a) C_5H_{10} and (b) C_6H_{12}. (c) What other isomers are possible for C_5H_{10} and C_6H_{12}? Write their structures.

8.24 Give the IUPAC names for each of the following:

(a)

CH_3

CH_3

(b) CH_2=CCH_2CH_3

        $CH_2CH_2CH_3$

(c)

CH_3CH_2
$CH_3CH_2CH_2$ C=CH_2

(d)

CH_3

CH_2CH_3

(e) $CH_3CH_2CCH_2C$≡CCH_3

        CH_3 (top) CH_3 (bottom)

(f) HC≡$CCHCH_2CH$=CH_2

        CH_3

8.25 Outline a synthesis of propene from each of the following:

(a) Propyl chloride   (d) Isopropyl alcohol

(b) Isopropyl chloride   (e) 1,2-Dibromopropane

(c) Propyl alcohol   (f) Propyne

8.26 Outline a synthesis of cyclopentene from each of the following:

(a) Bromocyclopentane

(b) 1,2-Dichlorocyclopentane

(c) Cyclopentanol [i.e., $(CH_2)_4CHOH$]

8.27 Starting with ethyne outline syntheses of each of the following. You may use any other needed reagents, and you need not show the synthesis of compounds prepared in earlier parts of this problem.

(a) Propyne   (h) (*Z*)-2-hexene

(b) 1-Butyne   (i) (*E*)-2-Hexene

(c) 2-Butyne   (j) 3-Hexyne

(d) *cis*-2-Butene   (k) CH_3CH_2C≡CD

(e) *trans*-2-Butene   (l) H_3C CH_3

(f) 1-Pentyne C=C

(g) 2-Hexyne D D

8.28 Starting with 1-methylcyclohexene and using any other needed reagents, outline a synthesis of the following deuterium-labeled compound.

D

CH_3

D

H

8.29   When *trans*-2-methylcyclohexanol (see following reaction) is subjected to acid-catalyzed dehydration, the major product is 1-methylcyclohexene:

$$\text{(CH}_3\text{, OH cyclohexane)} \xrightarrow[\text{heat}]{\text{H}^+} \text{(CH}_3\text{ cyclohexene)}$$

However, when *trans*-1-bromo-2-methylcyclohexane is subjected to dehydrohalogenation, the major product is 3-methylcyclohexene:

$$\text{(CH}_3\text{, Br cyclohexane)} \xrightarrow[\substack{\text{CH}_3\text{CH}_2\text{OH}\\\text{heat}}]{\text{CH}_3\text{CH}_2\text{O}^-} \text{(CH}_3\text{ cyclohexene)}$$

Account for the different products of these two reactions.

8.30   Write structural formulas for the products of the following reactions. If more than one product is possible, tell which one would be the major product.

(a) $\underset{\underset{\text{Cl}}{|}}{\overset{\overset{\text{CH}_3}{|}}{\text{CH}_3\text{C}}}\text{CH}_2\text{CH}_2\text{CH}_3 \xrightarrow[\text{C}_2\text{H}_5\text{OH}]{\text{KOH}}$

(b) $\underset{\underset{\text{Cl}}{|}}{\text{CH}_3\text{CH}}\text{CH}_2\text{CH}_2\text{CH}_3 \xrightarrow[\text{C}_2\text{H}_5\text{OH}]{\text{C}_2\text{H}_5\text{ONa}}$

(c) $\underset{\underset{\text{OH}}{|}}{\overset{\overset{\text{CH}_3}{|}}{\text{CH}_3\text{C}}}\text{CH}_2\text{CH}_2\text{CH}_3 \xrightarrow[\text{heat}]{\text{H}_3\text{PO}_4}$

(d)  $\xrightarrow[\text{(CH}_3)_3\text{COH}]{\text{(CH}_3)_3\text{COK}} ? \xrightarrow{\text{Br}_2} \text{(e)} \xrightarrow[\text{acetone}]{\text{NaI}} \text{(f)} \xrightarrow[\text{Pt}]{\text{H}_2} \text{(g)}$

8.31   Cyclohexane and 1-hexene have the same molecular formula. Suggest a simple chemical reaction that will distinguish one from the other.

8.32   For which of the following compounds is cis–trans isomerism possible? Where cis–trans isomerism is possible, write structural formulas for the isomeric compounds.

(a) 1-Butene
(b) 2-Methylpropene
(c) 2-Heptene
(d) 2-Methyl-2-heptene
(e) 1-Chloro-1-butene
(f) 1,1-Dichloro-1-butene

(g) (cyclopentene with CH₃)

(h) (cyclopropane with CH₂ and CH₃)

(i) (cyclopropane with CHCH₃ and CH₃)

8.33   (a) Arrange the following alkenes in order of their relative stabilities:

   trans-3-hexene   1-hexene   2-methyl-2-pentene   *cis*-2-hexene   2,3-dimethyl-2-butene

(b) For which of the alkenes listed in part (a) could comparative heats of hydrogenation be used to measure their relative stabilities?

8.34 Which compound would you expect to have the larger heat of hydrogenation (in kilocalories per mole): *cis*-cyclooctene or *trans*-cyclooctene? Explain.

8.35 When *cis*-2-butene is heated to a temperature greater than 300 °C, a mixture of two isomeric 2-butenes results. (a) What chemical change takes place? (b) Which butene isomer would you expect to predominate in the mixture when equilibrium is established between them?

8.36 Write the structural formulas for the alkenes that could be formed when each of the following alkyl halides is subjected to dehydrohalogenation by the action of ethoxide ion in ethanol. When more than one product results, designate the major product. (Neglect cis–trans isomerism in this problem.)

(a) $CH_3CHBrCH(CH_3)CH_3$

(b) $CH_3CH_2CH(CH_3)CH_2Br$

(c) $CH_3CH_2CHBrCH_2CH_3$

(d) $CH_3CHBrCH_2CH_2CH_3$

(e) 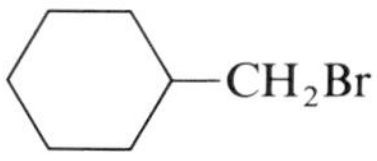 ⬡—CH_2Br

(f) 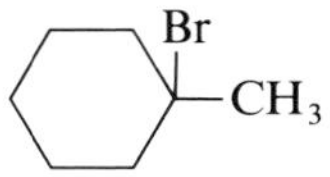 ⬡—CH_3 (with Br)

8.37 Starting with an appropriate alkyl halide and base, outline syntheses that would yield each of the following alkenes as the major (or only) product.

(a) 1-Pentene

(b) 3-Methyl-1-butene

(c) 2,3-Dimethyl-1-butene

(d) 4-Methylcyclohexene

(e) 1-Methylcyclopentene

8.38 Give structural formulas for the alcohol or alcohols that, on dehydration, would yield each of the following alkenes as the major product.

(a) 2-Methylpropene

(b) 2,3-Dimethyl-2-butene

(c) Cyclopentene

(d) Cyclohexene

(e) *trans*-2-Butene

(f) 1-Methylcyclopentene

8.39 Arrange the following alcohols in order of their reactivity toward acid-catalyzed dehydration and explain your reasoning:

$$CH_3CHCH_2CH_2OH \qquad CH_3\overset{\underset{\displaystyle |}{OH}}{C}CH_2CH_3 \qquad CH_3\overset{\underset{\displaystyle |}{OH}}{C}HCHCH_3$$
$$\underset{\displaystyle CH_3}{|} \qquad\qquad\quad \underset{\displaystyle CH_3}{|} \qquad\qquad\quad \underset{\displaystyle CH_3}{|}$$

8.40 (a) When 1,2-dimethylcyclopentene reacts with hydrogen in the presence of finely divided platinum, only one of the isomeric 1,2-dimethylcyclopentanes forms in appreciable amounts. Which is it? (Assume a mechanism similar to that in Fig. 8.2.) (b) What predominant product would you expect from a similar hydrogenation of 1,2-dimethylcyclohexene? Write a conformational formula for this product.

8.41 Write step-by-step mechanisms that account for each product of the following reactions and explain the relative proportions of the isomers obtained in each instance.

(a) 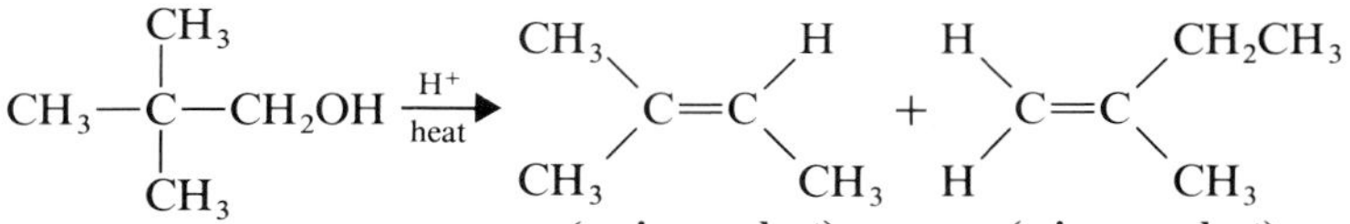 $CH_3-\overset{\underset{\displaystyle CH_3}{\displaystyle |}}{\overset{\displaystyle CH_3}{\underset{\displaystyle |}{C}}}-CH_2OH \xrightarrow[\text{heat}]{H^+}$
$$\overset{CH_3}{\underset{CH_3}{}}C=C\overset{H}{\underset{CH_3}{}} \quad + \quad \overset{H}{\underset{H}{}}C=C\overset{CH_2CH_3}{\underset{CH_3}{}}$$

(major product)   **(minor product)**

(b)

(95%)   (5%)

(c)

(major product)   (minor products)

8.42   Cholesterol is an important steroid found in nearly all body tissues; it is also the major component of gallstones. Impure cholesterol can be obtained from gallstones by extracting them with an organic solvent. The crude cholesterol thus obtained can be purified by (a) treatment with Br_2 in $CHCl_3$, (b) careful crystallization of the product, and (c) treatment of the latter with zinc in ethanol. What reactions are involved in this procedure?

Cholesterol

8.43   Caryophyllene, a compound found in oil of cloves, has the molecular formula $C_{15}H_{24}$ and has no triple bonds. Reaction of caryophyllene with an excess of hydrogen in the presence of a platinum catalyst produces a compound with the formula $C_{15}H_{28}$. How many (a) double bonds, and (b) rings does a molecule of caryophyllene have?

8.44   Squalene, an important intermediate in the biosynthesis of steroids, has the molecular formula $C_{30}H_{50}$ and has no triple bonds. (a) What is the index of hydrogen deficiency of squalene? (b) Squalene undergoes catalytic hydrogenation to yield a compound with the molecular formula $C_{30}H_{62}$. How many double bonds does a molecule of squalene have? (c) How many rings?

8.45   Reconsider the interconversion of *cis*-2-butene and *trans*-2-butene given in Problem 8.35. (a) What is the value of $\Delta H°$ for the reaction, *cis*-2-butene ⟶ *trans*-2-butene? (b) What minimum value of E_{act} would you expect for this reaction? (c) Sketch a potential energy diagram for the reaction and label $\Delta H°$ and E_{act}.

8.46   Propose structures for compounds **E–H**. (a) Compound **E** has the molecular formula C_5H_8 and is optically active. On catalytic hydrogenation **E** yields **F**. Compound **F** has the molecular formula C_5H_{10}, is optically inactive, and cannot be resolved into separate enantiomers. (b) Compound **G** has the molecular formula C_6H_{10} and is optically active. Compound **G** contains no triple bonds. On catalytic hydrogenation **G** yields **H**. Compound **H** has the molecular formula C_6H_{14}, is optically inactive, and cannot be resolved into separate enantiomers.

ADDITIONAL PROBLEMS

8.47 Compounds **I** and **J** both have the molecular formula C_7H_{14}. Compounds **I** and **J** are both optically active and both rotate plane-polarized light in the same direction. On catalytic hydrogenation **I** and **J** yield the same compound **K**(C_7H_{16}). Compound **K** is optically active. Propose possible structures for **I**, **J**, and **K**.

8.48 Compounds **L** and **M** have the molecular formula C_7H_{14}. Compounds **L** and **M** are optically inactive, are nonresolvable, and are diastereomers of each other. Catalytic hydrogenation of either **L** or **M** yields **N**. Compound **N** is optically inactive but can be resolved into separate enantiomers. Propose possible structures for **L**, **M**, and **N**.

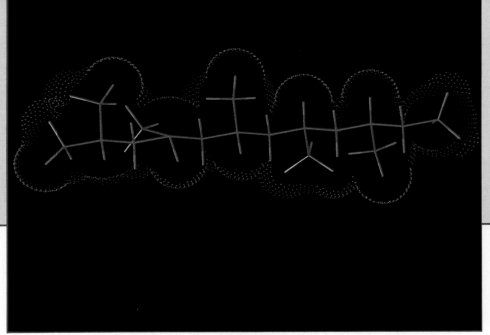

Atactic polypropylene (see Section 9.10 and Special Topic B).

9

ALKENES AND ALKYNES II. ADDITION REACTIONS

9.1 INTRODUCTION: ADDITIONS TO ALKENES

A characteristic reaction of compounds with a carbon–carbon double bond is an **addition**—a reaction of the general type shown below.

$$\underset{/}{\overset{\backslash}{}}C{=}C\underset{\backslash}{\overset{/}{}} + A{-}B \xrightarrow{\text{addition}} A{-}\overset{|}{\underset{|}{C}}{-}\overset{|}{\underset{|}{C}}{-}B$$

We saw in Section 8.5 that alkenes undergo the addition of hydrogen. In this chapter we shall study other examples of additions to the double bonds of alkenes. We begin with the additions of hydrogen halides, sulfuric acid, water (in the presence of an acid catalyst), and halogens.

9.1 INTRODUCTION: ADDITIONS TO ALKENES

$$\text{Alkene} \quad \text{C}{=}\text{C}$$

- H—X → H—C—C—X **Alkyl halide** (Sections 9.2, 9.3, and 9.9)
- H—OSO₃H → H—C—C—OSO₃H **Alkyl hydrogen sulfate** (Section 9.4)
- H—OH → H—C—C—OH **Alcohol** (Section 9.5)
- X—X → X—C—C—X **Dihaloalkane** (Sections 9.6–9.8)

Two characteristics of the double bond help us understand why these addition reactions occur:

1. An addition reaction results in the conversion of one π bond (Section 2.4) and one σ bond into two σ bonds. The result of this change is usually energetically favorable. The heat evolved in making two σ bonds exceeds that needed to break one σ bond and one π bond (because π bonds are weaker), and, therefore, addition reactions are usually exothermic.

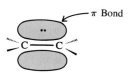

| π bond σ bond   2 σ bonds |
| Bonds broken   Bonds formed |

2. The electrons of the π bond are exposed. Because the π bond results from overlapping p orbitals, the π electrons lie above and below the plane of the double bond:

π Bond

The π bond is particularly susceptible to electron-seeking reagents. Such reagents are said to be **electrophilic** (electron seeking) and are called **electrophiles**. Electrophiles include positive reagents such as protons (H^+), neutral reagents such as bromine (because it can be polarized so that one end is positive), and the Lewis acids BF_3 and $AlCl_3$. Metal ions that contain vacant orbitals—the silver ion (Ag^+), the mercuric ion (Hg^{2+}), and the platinum ion (Pt^{2+}), for example—also act as electrophiles.

Hydrogen halides, for example, react with alkenes by donating a proton to the π bond. The proton uses the two electrons of the π bond to form a σ bond to one of the carbon atoms. This leaves a vacant p orbital and a + charge on the other carbon. The overall result is the formation of a carbocation and a chloride ion from the alkene and HCl:

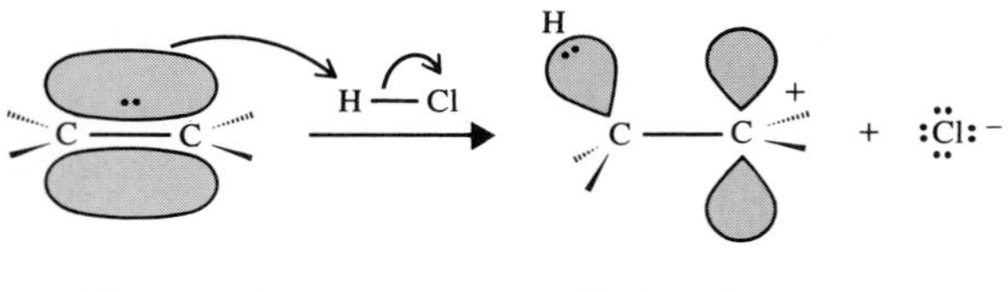

Alkene **Carbocation**

Being highly reactive, the carbocation then combines with the chloride ion by accepting one of its electron pairs:

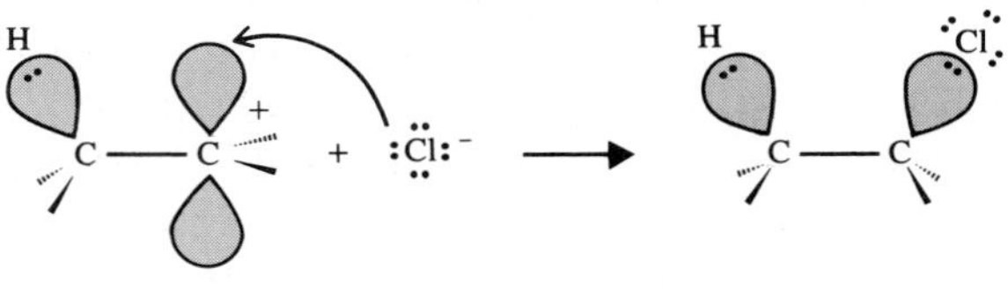

Electrophiles are Lewis acids. They are molecules or ions that can accept an electron pair. Nucleophiles are molecules or ions that can furnish an electron pair (i.e., Lewis bases). Any reaction of an electrophile also involves a nucleophile. In the protonation of an alkene the electrophile is the proton donated by an acid; the nucleophile is the alkene.

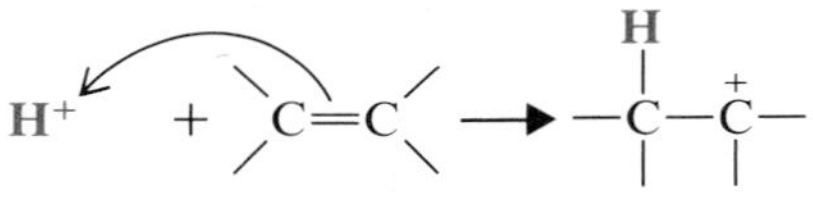

Electrophile   Nucleophile

In the next step, the reaction of the carbocation with a chloride ion, the carbocation is the electrophile and the chloride ion is the nucleophile.

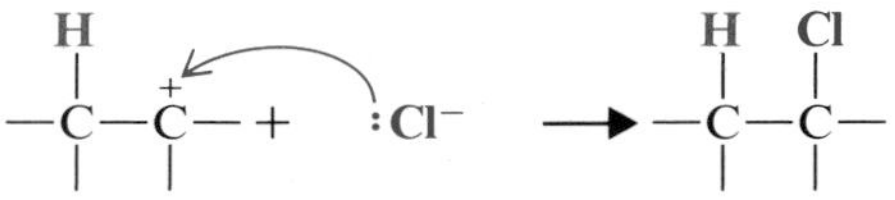

Electrophile   Nucleophile

9.2 ADDITION OF HYDROGEN HALIDES TO ALKENES: MARKOVNIKOV'S RULE

Hydrogen halides (HF, HCl, HBr, and HI) add readily to the double bond of alkenes:

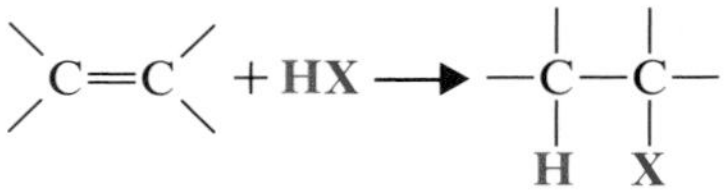

Two examples are shown here.

9.2 ADDITION OF HYDROGEN HALIDES TO ALKENES: MARKOVNIKOV'S RULE

$$CH_3CH=CHCH_3 + HCl \longrightarrow CH_3CH_2\underset{\underset{Cl}{|}}{C}HCH_3$$

2-Butene
(cis or trans)

2-Chlorobutane

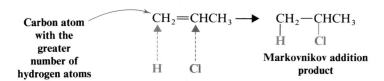

Cyclohexene   + HBr ⟶   **Cyclohexyl bromide**

In carrying out these reactions, the hydrogen halide may be dissolved in acetic acid and mixed with the alkene, or gaseous hydrogen halide may be bubbled directly into the alkene with the alkene, itself, being used as the solvent.

The addition of HX to an unsymmetrical alkene could conceivably occur in two ways. In practice, however, one product usually predominates. The addition of HCl to propene, for example, could conceivably lead to either 1-chloropropane or 2-chloropropane. The actual product, however, is 2-chloropropane.

$$CH_2=CHCH_3 + HCl \longrightarrow CH_3\underset{\underset{Cl}{|}}{C}HCH_3 \qquad (not\ ClCH_2CH_2CH_3)$$

2-Chloropropane   **1-Chloropropane**

When 2-methylpropene reacts with HCl, the product is *tert*-butyl chloride, not isobutyl chloride.

$$\underset{H_3C}{\overset{H_3C}{\diagdown}}C=CH_2 + HCl \longrightarrow CH_3-\underset{\underset{Cl}{|}}{\overset{\overset{CH_3}{|}}{C}}-CH_3 \qquad \left(not\ CH_3-\underset{\overset{CH_3}{|}}{\overset{\overset{CH_3}{|}}{C}}H-CH_2-Cl\right)$$

2-Methylpropene   *tert*-**Butyl chloride**   **Isobutyl chloride**
(isobutylene)

Consideration of many examples like this led the Russian chemist Vladimir Markovnikov in 1870 to formulate what is now known as **Markovnikov's rule.** One way to state this rule is to say that ***in the addition of HX to an alkene, the hydrogen atom adds to the carbon atom of the double bond that already has the greater number of hydrogen atoms.**** The addition of HCl to propene is an illustration.

Carbon atom
with the
greater
number of
hydrogen atoms

$$CH_2=CHCH_3 \longrightarrow CH_2-CHCH_3$$
$$H \qquad Cl$$

H   Cl

Markovnikov addition product

Reactions that illustrate Markovnikov's rule are said to be *Markovnikov additions.*

A mechanism for addition of a hydrogen halide to an alkene involves the following two steps:

* In his original publication, Markovnikov described the rule in terms of the point of attachment of the halogen atom, stating that "if an unsymmetrical alkene combines with a hydrogen halide, the halide ion adds to the carbon atom with the fewer hydrogen atoms."

Step 1

Step 2

The important step — because it is the **rate-determining step** — is step 1. In step 1 the alkene accepts a proton from the hydrogen halide and forms a carbocation. This step (Fig. 9.1) is highly endothermic and has a high free energy of activation. Consequently, it takes place slowly. In step 2 the highly reactive carbocation stabilizes itself by combining with a halide ion. This exothermic step has a very low free energy of activation and takes place very rapidly.

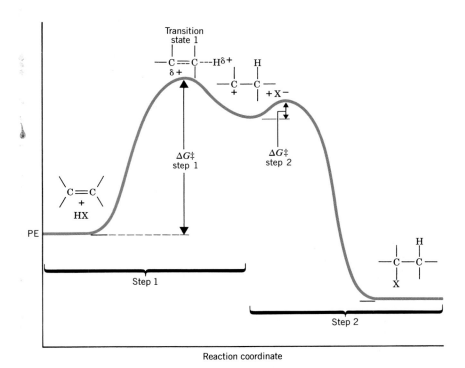

FIGURE 9.1 Potential energy diagram for the addition of HX to an alkene. The free energy of activation for step 1 is much larger than for step 2.

9.2A THEORETICAL EXPLANATION OF MARKOVNIKOV'S RULE

If the alkene that undergoes addition of a hydrogen halide is an unsymmetrical alkene such as propene, then step 1 could conceivably lead to two different carbocations:

$$CH_3CH = CH_2 + H^+ \longrightarrow CH_3\overset{H}{\underset{}{C}}H - \overset{+}{C}H_2$$

1° Carbocation
(less stable)

9.2 ADDITION OF HYDROGEN HALIDES TO ALKENES: MARKOVNIKOV'S RULE

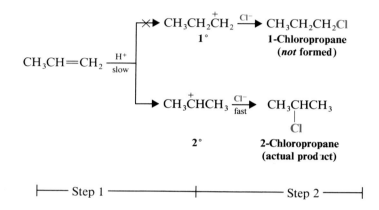

$$CH_3CH{=}CH_2 + \overset{}{H^+} \longrightarrow CH_3\overset{+}{C}H{-}CH_2{-}H$$

2° Carbocation
(more stable)

These two carbocations are not of equal stability, however. The secondary carbocation is *more stable,* and it is the greater stability of the secondary carbocation that accounts for the correct prediction of the overall addition by Markovnikov's rule. In the addition of HCl to propene, for example, the reaction takes the following course:

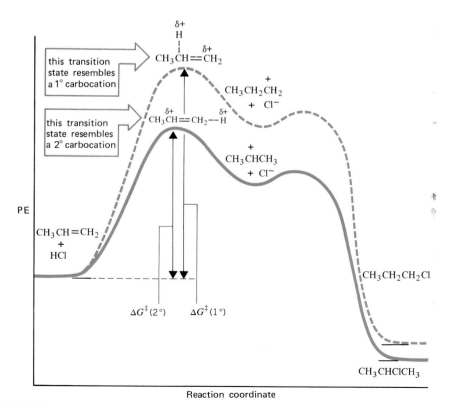

FIGURE 9.2 Potential energy diagram for the addition of HCl to propene. $\Delta G^\ddagger$ (2°) is less than $\Delta G^\ddagger$ (1°).

The ultimate product of the reaction is 2-chloropropane because the more stable secondary carbocation is formed preferentially in the first step.

The more stable carbocation predominates because it is formed faster. We can understand why this is true if we examine the potential energy diagrams in Fig. 9.2.

The reaction (Fig. 9.2) leading to the secondary carbocation (and ultimately to 2-chloropropane) has the lower free energy of activation. That is reasonable because its transition state resembles the more stable carbocation. The reaction leading to the primary carbocation (and ultimately to 1-chloropropane) has a higher free energy of activation because its transition state resembles a less stable primary carbocation. This second reaction is much slower and does not compete with the first reaction.

The reaction of HCl with 2-methylpropene produces only *tert*-butyl chloride, and for the same reason. Here, in the first step (i.e., the attachment of the proton) the choice is even more pronounced — between a tertiary carbocation and a primary carbocation.

Thus, isobutyl chloride is *not* obtained as a product of the reaction because its formation would require the formation of a primary carbocation. Such a reaction would have a much higher free energy of activation than that leading to a tertiary carbocation.

$$
\begin{array}{c}
\underset{H_3C}{\overset{H_3C}{\diagdown}}C=C\underset{H}{\overset{H}{\diagup}} \\
\textbf{2-Methylpropene}
\end{array}
$$

HCl

$$
\underset{+}{CH_3-\overset{\overset{\displaystyle CH_3}{|}}{C}-CH_2-H}
$$

3° Carbocation

Cl⁻

$$
CH_3-\overset{\overset{\displaystyle CH_3}{|}}{\underset{\underset{\displaystyle Cl}{|}}{C}}-CH_2-H
$$

***tert*-Butyl chloride**
(actual product)

$$
CH_3-\overset{\overset{\displaystyle CH_3}{|}}{\underset{\underset{\displaystyle H}{|}}{C}}-\overset{+}{CH_2}
$$

1° Carbocation

Cl⁻

$$
CH_3-\overset{\overset{\displaystyle CH_3}{|}}{\underset{\underset{\displaystyle H}{|}}{C}}-CH_2-Cl
$$

Isobutyl chloride
(not formed)

Because carbocations are formed in the addition of HX to an alkene, rearrangements invariably occur when the carbocation initially formed can rearrange to a more stable one (see Problem 9.3).

9.2B MODERN STATEMENT OF MARKOVNIKOV'S RULE

With this understanding of the mechanism for the ionic addition of hydrogen halides to alkenes behind us, we are now in a position to give the following modern statement of Markovnikov's rule: ***In the ionic addition of an unsymmetrical reagent to a double*** *bond, the positive portion of the adding reagent attaches itself to a carbon atom of the double bond so as to yield the more stable carbocation as an intermediate.* Because this is the step that occurs first (prior to the addition of the negative portion of the adding reagent), it is the step that determines the overall orientation of the reaction.

Notice that this formulation of Markovnikov's rule allows us to predict the outcome of the addition of a reagent such as ICl. Because of the greater electronegativity of chlorine, the positive portion of this molecule is iodine. The addition of ICl to 2-methylpropene takes place in the following way and produces 2-chloro-1-iodo-2-methylpropane.

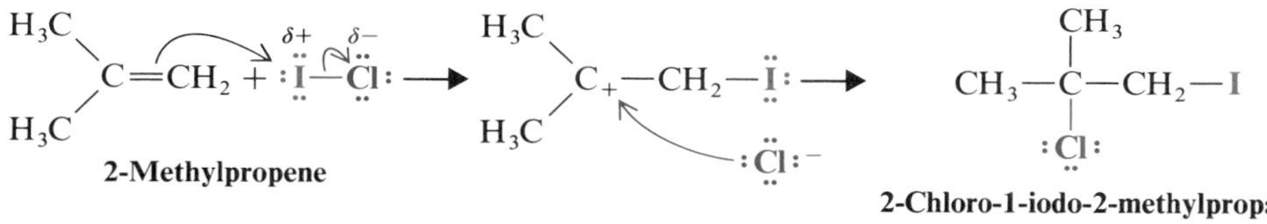

2-Methylpropene

2-Chloro-1-iodo-2-methylpropane

Problem 9.1

Give the structure and name of the product that would be obtained from the ionic addition of ICl to propene.

Problem 9.2

Outline mechanisms for the ionic additions (a) of HI to 1-butene, (b) of IBr to 2-methyl-2-butene, and (c) of HCl to 1-methylcyclohexene.

Problem 9.3

The addition of hydrogen chloride to 3,3-dimethyl-1-butene (see following reaction) yields two products: 3-chloro-2,2-dimethylbutane and 2-chloro-2,3-dimethylbutane. Write mechanisms that account for the formation of each product.

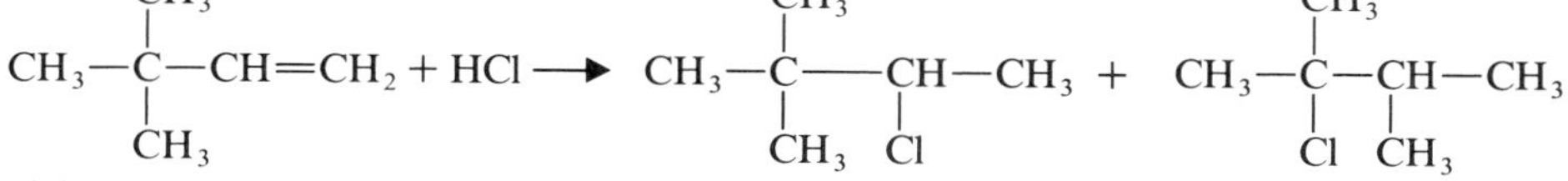

3,3-Dimethyl-1-butene

3-Chloro-2,2-dimethylbutane

2-Chloro-2,3-dimethylbutane

9.2C REGIOSELECTIVE REACTIONS

Chemists describe reactions like the Markovnikov additions of hydrogen halides to alkenes as being *regioselective. Regio* comes from the Latin word *regionem* meaning direction. When a reaction *that can potentially yield two or more constitutional isomers actually produces only one* (or a predominance of one), the reaction is said to be *regioselective.* The addition of HX to an unsymmetrical alkene such as propene could conceivably yield two constitutional isomers, for example. However, as we have seen, the reaction yields only one, and therefore it is regioselective.

9.2D AN EXCEPTION TO MARKOVNIKOV'S RULE

In Section 9.9 we shall study an exception to Markovnikov's rule. This exception concerns the addition of HBr to alkenes **when the addition is carried out in the presence of peroxides** (i.e., compounds with the general formula ROOR). When alkenes are treated with HBr in the presence of peroxides the addition occurs in an anti-Markovnikov manner in the sense that the hydrogen atom becomes attached to the carbon atom with the fewer hydrogen atoms. With propene, for example, the addition takes place as follows:

$$CH_3CH{=}CH_2 + HBr \xrightarrow{ROOR} CH_3CH_2CH_2Br$$

In Section 9.9 we shall find that this addition occurs by *a radical mechanism,* and not by the ionic mechanism given in Section 9.2. This anti-Markovnikov addition occurs *only when HBr is used in the presence of peroxides* and does not occur significantly with HF, HCl, and HI even when peroxides are present.

9.3 STEREOCHEMISTRY OF THE IONIC ADDITION TO AN ALKENE

Consider the following addition of HCl to 1-butene and notice that the reaction leads to the formation of a product, 2-chlorobutane, that contains a stereocenter.

$$CH_3CH_2CH{=}CH_2 + HCl \longrightarrow CH_3CH_2\overset{*}{C}HCH_3$$
$$\underset{\displaystyle Cl}{|}$$

The product, therefore, can exist as a pair of enantiomers. The question now arises as to how these enantiomers will be formed. Will one enantiomer be formed in greater amount than the other? The answer is *no;* the carbocation that is formed in the first step of the addition (see following figure) is trigonal planar and *is achiral* (a model will show that it has a plane of symmetry). When the chloride ion reacts with this achiral carbocation in the second step, *reaction is equally likely at either face.* The reactions leading to the two enantiomers occur at the same rate, and the enantiomers, therefore, are produced in equal amounts *as a racemic form.*

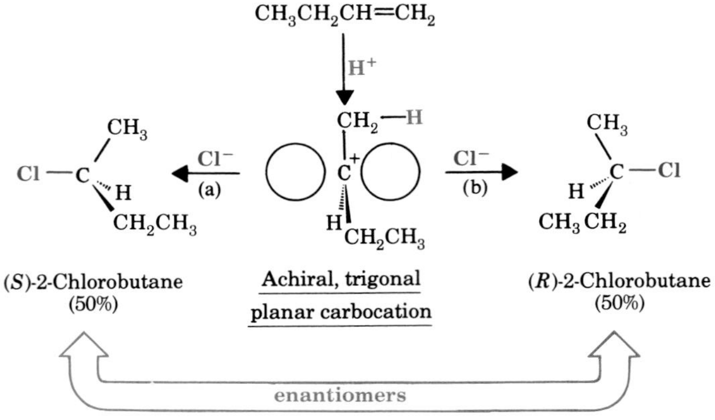

(S)-2-Chlorobutane (50%)   Achiral, trigonal planar carbocation   (R)-2-Chlorobutane (50%)

enantiomers

9.4 ADDITION OF SULFURIC ACID TO ALKENES

When alkenes are treated with **cold** concentrated sulfuric acid, *they dissolve* because they react by addition to form alkyl hydrogen sulfates. The mechanism is similar to that for the addition of HX. In the first step of this reaction the alkene accepts a proton from sulfuric acid to form a carbocation; in the second step the carbocation reacts with a hydrogen sulfate ion to form an alkyl hydrogen sulfate:

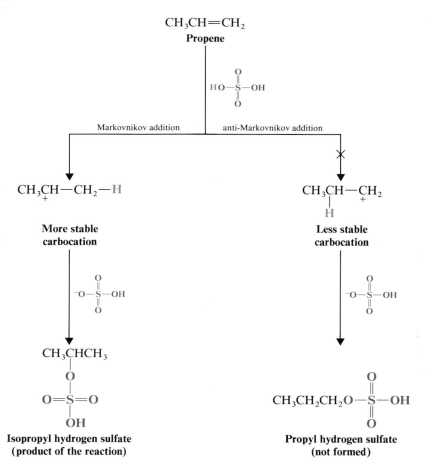

| | Alkene | Sulfuric acid | Carbocation | Hydrogen sulfate ion | Alkyl hydrogen sulfate |

Soluble in sulfuric acid

The addition of sulfuric acid is also regioselective, and it follows Markovnikov's rule. Propene, for example, reacts to yield isopropyl hydrogen sulfate rather than propyl hydrogen sulfate.

CH₃CH=CH₂
Propene

Markovnikov addition — anti-Markovnikov addition

CH₃CH—CH₂—H
More stable carbocation

CH₃CH—CH₂ H
Less stable carbocation

CH₃CHCH₃
Isopropyl hydrogen sulfate
(**product of the reaction**)

CH₃CH₂CH₂O—S—OH
Propyl hydrogen sulfate
(**not formed**)

9.4A ALCOHOLS FROM ALKYL HYDROGEN SULFATES

Alkyl hydrogen sulfates can be easily hydrolyzed to alcohols by **heating** them with water. The overall result of the addition of sulfuric acid to an alkene followed by hydrolysis is the Markovnikov addition of H— and —OH.

$$CH_3CH{=}CH_2 \xrightarrow[H_2SO_4]{cold} \underset{\underset{OSO_3H}{\vert}}{CH_3CHCH_3} \xrightarrow{H_2O,\ heat} \underset{\underset{OH}{\vert}}{CH_3CHCH_3} + H_2SO_4$$

Problem 9.4

In one industrial synthesis of ethanol, ethene is first dissolved in 95% sulfuric acid. In a second step water is added and the mixture is heated. Outline the reactions involved.

9.5 ADDITION OF WATER TO ALKENES: ACID-CATALYZED HYDRATION

The acid-catalyzed addition of water to the double bond of an alkene (hydration of an alkene) is a method for the preparation of low molecular weight alcohols that has its greatest utility in large-scale industrial processes. The acids most commonly used to catalyze the hydration of alkenes are sulfuric acid and phosphoric acid. These reactions, too, are usually regioselective, and the addition of water to the double bond follows Markovnikov's rule. In general the reaction takes the form that follows:

$$\overset{\diagdown}{\underset{\diagup}{}}C{=}C\overset{\diagup}{\underset{\diagdown}{}} + HOH \xrightarrow{H^+} \underset{\underset{H}{\vert}}{-\overset{\vert}{C}} \underset{\underset{OH}{\vert}}{-\overset{\vert}{C}-}$$

An example is the hydration of 2-methylpropene.

$$\underset{\underset{}{}}{CH_3-\overset{\overset{CH_3}{\vert}}{C}{=}CH_2} + HOH \xrightarrow{H^+}_{25\ °C} CH_3-\overset{\overset{CH_3}{\vert}}{\underset{\underset{OH}{\vert}}{C}}-CH_2{-}H$$

2-Methylpropene　　　　　　　　　　*tert*-**Butyl alcohol**
(isobutylene)

Because the reactions follow Markovnikov's rule, acid-catalyzed hydrations of alkenes do not yield primary alcohols except in the special case of the hydration of ethene.

$$CH_2{=}CH_2 + HOH \xrightarrow[300\ °C]{H_3PO_4} CH_3CH_2OH$$

The mechanism for the hydration of an alkene is simply the reverse of the mechanism for the dehydration of an alcohol. We can illustrate this by giving the mechanism for the **hydration** of 2-methylpropene and by comparing it with the mechanism for the **dehydration** of *tert*-butyl alcohol given in Section 8.13.

9.5 ADDITION OF WATER TO ALKENES: ACID-CATALYZED HYDRATION

Step 1

$$CH_3-\overset{\overset{\displaystyle CH_2}{\|}}{\underset{\underset{\displaystyle CH_3}{|}}{C}} + H-\overset{+}{O}-H \underset{slow}{\rightleftharpoons} CH_3-\overset{\overset{\displaystyle CH_2-H}{|}}{\underset{\underset{\displaystyle CH_3}{|}}{C^+}} + :\overset{\overset{\displaystyle H}{|}}{O}-H$$

Step 2

$$CH_3-\overset{\overset{\displaystyle CH_3}{|}}{\underset{\underset{\displaystyle CH_3}{|}}{C^+}} + :\overset{\overset{\displaystyle H}{|}}{O}-H \underset{fast}{\rightleftharpoons} CH_3-\overset{\overset{\displaystyle CH_3}{|}}{\underset{\underset{\displaystyle CH_3}{|}}{C}}-\overset{+}{O}-H$$

Step 3

$$CH_3-\overset{\overset{\displaystyle CH_3}{|}}{\underset{\underset{\displaystyle CH_3}{|}}{C}}-\overset{+}{O}-H + :\overset{\overset{\displaystyle H}{|}}{O}-H \underset{fast}{\rightleftharpoons} CH_3-\overset{\overset{\displaystyle CH_3}{|}}{\underset{\underset{\displaystyle CH_3}{|}}{C}}-\ddot{O}-H + H-\overset{\overset{\displaystyle H}{|}}{\underset{+}{O}}-H$$

The rate-determining step in the *hydration* mechanism is step 1: the formation of the carbocation. It is this step, too, that accounts for the Markovnikov addition of water to the double bond. The reaction produces *tert*-butyl alcohol because step 1 leads to the formation of the more stable *tert*-butyl cation rather than the much less stable isobutyl cation:

$$CH_3-\overset{\overset{\displaystyle CH_2}{\|}}{\underset{\underset{\displaystyle CH_3}{|}}{C}} + H-\overset{+}{O}-H \underset{\underset{\displaystyle slow}{}}{\overset{\displaystyle very}{\rightleftharpoons}} CH_3\overset{\overset{\displaystyle CH_2{}^+}{|}}{\underset{\underset{\displaystyle CH_3}{|}}{C}}-H + :\overset{\overset{\displaystyle H}{|}}{O}-H$$

For all practical purposes this reaction does not take place because it produces a 1° carbocation

The reactions whereby *alkenes are hydrated or alcohols are dehydrated* are reactions in which the ultimate product is governed by the position of an equilibrium. Therefore, in the *dehydration of an alcohol* it is best to use a concentrated acid so that the concentration of water is low. (The water can be removed as it is formed, and it helps to use a high temperature.) In the *hydration of an alkene* it is best to use dilute acid so that the concentration of water is high. (It also usually helps to use a lower temperature.)

Problem 9.5

(a) Show all steps in the acid-catalyzed hydration of propene. (b) Account for the fact that the product of the reaction is isopropyl alcohol (in accordance with Markovnikov's rule) and not propyl alcohol, that is,

$$H_2O + CH_3-CH=CH_2 \xrightarrow{H^+} CH_3\underset{\underset{\displaystyle OH}{|}}{C}HCH_3 \quad (not\ CH_3CH_2CH_2OH)$$

Isopropyl alcohol   Propyl alcohol

One complication associated with alkene hydrations is the occurrence of **rearrangements.** Because the reaction involves the formation of a carbocation in the first step, the carbocation formed initially invariably rearranges to a more stable one if such a rearrangement is possible. An illustration is the formation of 2,3-dimethyl-2-butanol as the major product when 3,3-dimethyl-1-butene is hydrated:

$$CH_3-\underset{\underset{CH_3}{|}}{\overset{\overset{CH_3}{|}}{C}}-CH=CH_2 \xrightarrow[H_2O]{H_2SO_4} CH_3-\underset{\underset{CH_3}{|}}{\overset{\overset{OH}{|}}{C}}-\underset{\underset{CH_3}{|}}{CH}-CH_3$$

3,3-Dimethyl-1-butene   2,3-Dimethyl-2-butanol
                                       (major product)

Problem 9.6

Outline all steps in a mechanism showing how 2,3-dimethyl-2-butanol is formed in the acid-catalyzed hydration of 3,3-dimethyl-1-butene.

Problem 9.7

The following order of reactivity is observed when the following alkenes are subjected to acid-catalyzed hydration.

$$(CH_3)_2C=CH_2 > CH_3CH=CH_2 > CH_2=CH_2$$

Explain this order of reactivity.

Problem 9.8

When 2-methylpropene (isobutylene) is dissolved in methanol containing a strong acid, a reaction takes place to produce *tert*-butyl methyl ether, $CH_3OC(CH_3)_3$. Write a mechanism that accounts for this.

The occurrence of carbocation rearrangements limits the utility of alkene hydrations as a laboratory method for preparing alcohols. In Chapter 10 we shall study two very useful laboratory syntheses. One, called **oxymercuration–demercuration,** allows the Markovnikov addition of H— and —OH *without rearrangements.* Another, called **hydroboration–oxidation,** permits the *anti-Markovnikov* and *syn addition* of H— and —OH.

9.6 ADDITION OF BROMINE AND CHLORINE TO ALKENES

In the absence of light, *alkanes* do not react appreciably with chlorine or bromine at room temperature (Section 7.4). If we add an alkane to a solution of bromine in carbon tetrachloride, the red-brown color of the bromine will persist in the solution as long as we keep the mixture away from sunlight and as long as the solution is not heated.

$$\underset{\underset{\text{(colorless)}}{\text{Alkane}}}{R-H} + \underset{\underset{\text{(red brown)}}{\text{Bromine}}}{Br_2} \xrightarrow[\text{in the dark, CCl}_4]{\text{room temperature}} \text{no appreciable reaction}$$

On the other hand, if we expose the reactants to sunlight, the bromine color will fade slowly. If we now place a small piece of moist blue litmus paper in the region above the liquid, the litmus paper will turn red because of the hydrogen bromide that evolves as the alkane and bromine react. (Hydrogen bromide is not very soluble in carbon tetrachloride.)

$$R\text{---}H \ + \ Br_2 \ \xrightarrow[\text{sunlight, CCl}_4]{\text{room temperature}} \ R\text{---}Br \ + \ HBr$$

Alkane	Bromine		Alkyl halide	Hydrogen bromide
(colorless)	(red brown)		(colorless)	(detected by moist blue litmus)

The behavior of **alkenes** toward bromine in carbon tetrachloride contrasts markedly with that of alkanes *and is a useful test for carbon–carbon multiple bonds.* Alkenes react rapidly with bromine at room temperature and in the *absence of light.* If we add bromine to an alkene, the red-brown color of the bromine disappears almost instantly as long as the alkene is present in excess. If we test the atmosphere above the solution with moist blue litmus paper, we shall find that no hydrogen bromide is present. The reaction is one of addition. (Alkynes, as we shall see in Section 9.14, also undergo addition of bromine.)

$$\diagdown\!\!\!C\!=\!\!C\!\diagup + \ Br_2 \ \xrightarrow[\text{in the dark, CCl}_4]{\text{room temperature}} \ \underset{\underset{Br \ \ Br}{|\quad|}}{-\overset{|}{C}-\overset{|}{C}-}$$

Rapid decolorization of Br$_2$/CCl$_4$ is a test for alkenes and alkynes

An alkene	*vic*-Dibromide
(colorless)	(colorless)

The addition reaction between alkenes and chlorine or bromine is a general one. The products are vicinal dihalides.

$$CH_3CH\!=\!CHCH_3 + Cl_2 \ \xrightarrow{-9\,°C} \ \underset{\underset{Cl \quad Cl}{|\quad\;\;|}}{CH_3CH\!-\!CHCH_3} \qquad (100\%)$$

$$CH_3CH_2CH\!=\!CH_2 + Cl_2 \ \xrightarrow{-9\,°C} \ \underset{\underset{Cl \quad Cl}{|\quad\;\;|}}{CH_3CH_2CH\!-\!CH_2} \qquad (97\%)$$

$$\bigcirc\!\!| + Br_2 \ \xrightarrow[\text{CCl}_4/\text{C}_2\text{H}_5\text{OH}]{-5\,°C} \qquad + \text{ enantiomer} \qquad (95\%)$$

trans-1,2-Dibromocyclohexane
(as a racemic form)

9.6A MECHANISM OF HALOGEN ADDITION

One mechanism that has been proposed for halogen addition is **an ionic mechanism.*** In the first step the exposed electrons of the π bond of the alkene attack the halogen in the following way:

---

*There is evidence that in the absence of oxygen some reactions between alkenes and chlorine proceed through a radical mechanism. We shall not discuss this mechanism here, however.

Bromonium ion   **Bromide ion**

As the π electrons of the alkene approach the bromine molecule, the electrons of the bromine–bromine bond drift in the direction of the bromine atom more distant from the approaching alkene. The bromine molecule becomes *polarized* as a result. The more distant bromine develops a partial negative charge; the nearer bromine becomes partially positive. Polarization weakens the bromine–bromine bond, causing it to *break heterolytically*. A bromide ion departs, and a *bromonium ion* forms. In the bromonium ion a positively charged bromine atom is bonded to two carbon atoms by *two pairs of electrons:* one pair from the π bond of the alkene, the other pair from the bromine atom (one of its unshared pairs).

In the second step, one of the bromide ions produced in step 1 attacks one of the carbon atoms of the bromonium ion. The nucleophilic attack results in the formation of a *vic*-dibromide by opening the three-membered ring.

vic-Dibromide

This ring opening (see preceding figure) is an S_N2 reaction. The bromide ion, acting as a nucleophile, uses a pair of electrons to form a bond to one carbon atom of the bromonium ion while the positive bromine of the bromonium ion acts as a leaving group.

9.7 STEREOCHEMISTRY OF THE ADDITION OF HALOGENS TO ALKENES

The addition of bromine to cyclopentene provides additional evidence for bromonium ion intermediates in bromine additions. When cyclopentene reacts with bromine in carbon tetrachloride, **anti addition** occurs, and the products of the reaction are *trans*-1,2-dibromocyclopentane enantiomers (as a racemate).

+ enantiomer

trans-1, 2-Dibromo-
cyclopentane

This anti addition of bromine to cyclopentene can be explained by a mechanism that involves the formation of a bromonium ion in the first step. In the second step, a bromide ion attacks a carbon atom of the ring from the side opposite that of the bromonium ion. The reaction is an S_N2 reaction. Nucleophilic attack by the bromide ion causes *inversion of the configuration of the carbon being attacked* (Section 6.10). This inversion of configuration at one carbon atom of the ring leads to the formation of one *trans*-1,2-dibromocyclopentane enantiomer. (The other enantiomer results from attack of the bromide ion at the other carbon of the bromonium ion.).

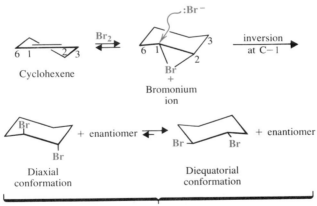

Bromonium
ion

trans-1, 2-Dibromo-
cyclopentane

When cyclohexene undergoes addition of bromine, the product is a racemate of the *trans*-1,2-dibromocyclohexane enantiomers (Section 9.6). In this instance, too, *anti* addition results from the intermediate formation of a bromonium ion followed by S_N2 attack by a bromide ion. The reaction shown here illustrates the formation of one enantiomer. (The other enantiomer is formed when the bromide ion attacks the other carbon of the bromonium ion.)

Cyclohexene

Bromonium
ion

Diaxial
conformation

Diequatorial
conformation

trans-1, 2-Dibromocyclohexane

Notice that the initial product of the reaction is the *diaxial conformer*. This rapidly converts into the diequatorial form, and when equilibrium is reached the diequatorial form predominates. We saw earlier (Section 8.12C) that when cyclohexane derivatives undergo elimination, the required conformation is the diaxial one. Here we find that when cyclohexene undergoes addition (the opposite of elimination), the initial product is also diaxial.

9.7A STEREOSPECIFIC REACTIONS

The anti addition of a halogen to an alkene provides us with an example of what is called a **stereospecific reaction.**

A reaction is *stereospecific* when *a particular stereoisomeric form of the starting material reacts in such a way that it gives a specific stereoisomeric form of the product.* It does this because the reaction mechanism requires that the configurations of the atoms involved change in a characteristic way.

Consider the reactions of *cis-* and *trans*-2-butene with bromine shown below. When *trans*-2-butene adds bromine, the product is the meso compound, (2R,3S)-2,3-dibromobutane. When *cis*-2-butene adds bromine, the product is a *racemic form* of (2R,3R)-2,3-dibromobutane and (2S,3S)-2,3-dibromobutane.

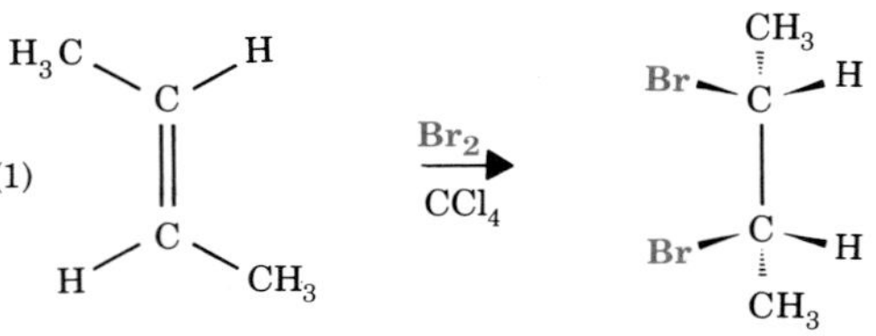

trans–2–Butene

(2R, 3S)–2,3–Dibromobutane
(a meso compound)

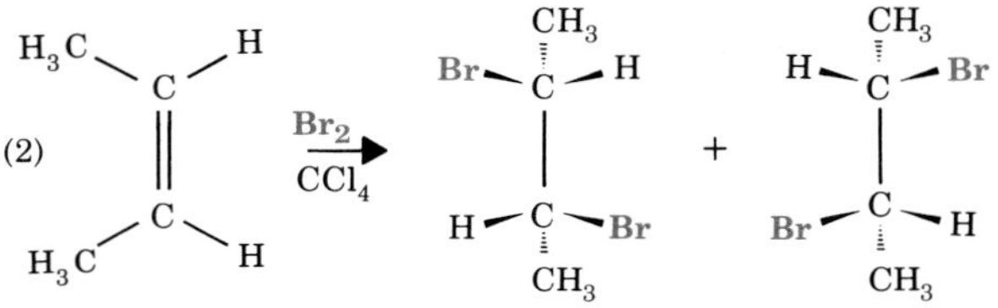

cis–2–Butene

(2R, 3R)

(2S, 3S)

The reactants *cis*-2-butene and *trans*-2-butene are stereoisomers; they are *diastereomers*. The product of reaction (1), (2R,3S)-2,3-dibromobutane, is a meso compound, and it is a stereoisomer of either of the products of reaction (2), (the enantiomeric 2,3-dibromobutanes). Thus, by definition, both reactions are stereospecific. One stereoisomeric form of the reactant (e.g., *trans*-2-butene) gives one product (the meso compound) while the other stereoisomeric form of the reactant (*cis*-2-butene) gives a stereoisomerically different product (the enantiomers).

We can better understand the results of these two reactions if we examine their mechanisms.

Figure 9.3 shows how *cis*-2-butene adds bromine to yield intermediate bromonium ions that are achiral. (The bromonium ion has a plane of symmetry. Can you find it?) These bromonium ions can then react with bromide ions by either path (a) or by path (b). Reaction by path (a) yields one 2,3-dibromobutane enantiomer; reaction by path (b) yields the other enantiomer. Reaction occurs at the same rate by either path; therefore the two enantiomers are produced in equal amounts (as a racemic form).

Figure 9.4 shows how *trans*-2-butene reacts at the bottom face to yield an intermediate bromonium ion that is chiral. (Reaction at the other face would produce the enantiomeric bromonium ion.) Reaction of this chiral bromonium ion (or its enantiomer) with a bromide ion either by path (a) or by path (b) yields the same compound, the *meso*-2,3-dibromobutane.

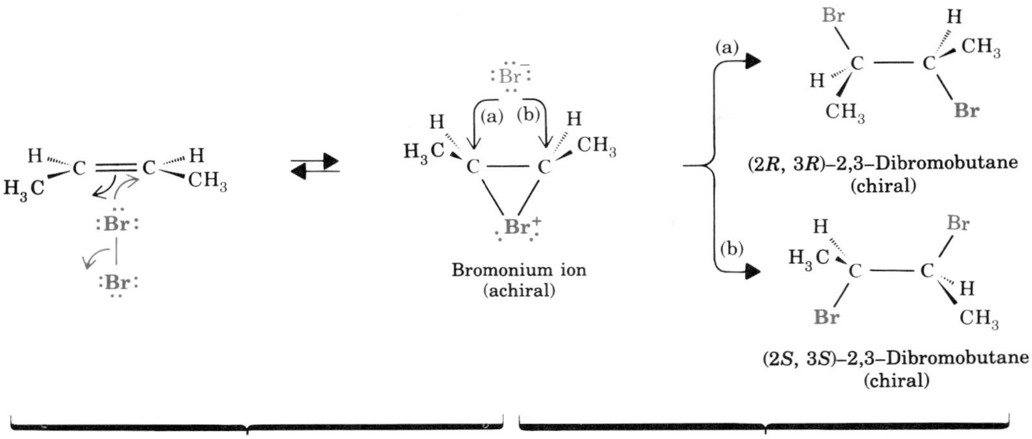

9.7 STEREOCHEMISTRY OF THE ADDITION OF HALOGENS TO ALKENES

FIGURE 9.3 A mechanism showing how *cis*-2-butene reacts with bromine to yield the enantiomeric 2,3-dibromobutanes.

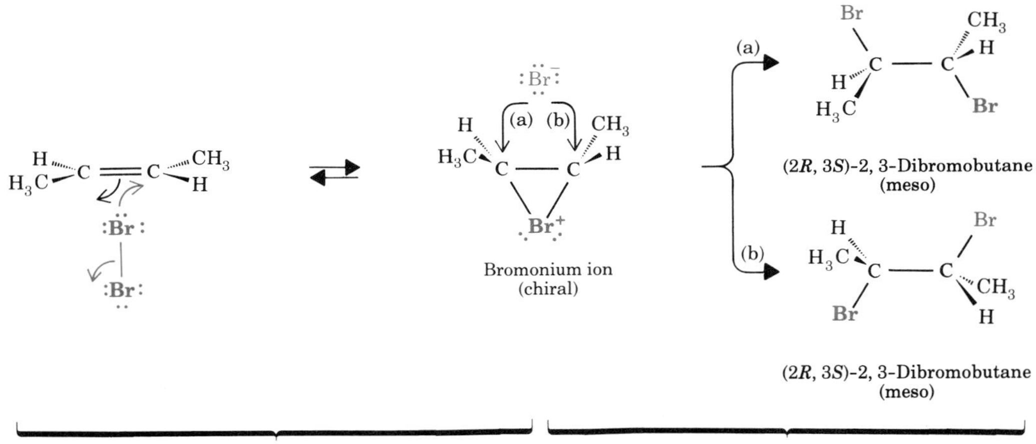

cis-2-Butene reacts with bromine to yield achiral bromonium ions and bromide ions. [Reaction at the other face of the alkene (top) would yield the same bromonium ions.]

The bromonium ions react with the bromide ions at equal rates by paths (a) and (b) to yield the two enantiomers in equal amounts (*i.e.*, as the racemic form).

trans-2-Butene reacts with bromine to yield chiral bromonium ions and bromide ions. [Reaction at the other face (top) would yield the enantiomer of the bromonium ion as shown here.]

When the bromonium ions react by either path *(a)* or *(b)*, they yield the same achiral meso compound. [Reaction of the enantiomer of the intermediate bromonium ion would produce the same result.]

FIGURE 9.4 A mechanism showing how *trans*-2-butene reacts with bromine to yield *meso*-2,3-dibromobutane.

Problem 9.9

In Section 9.7 you studied a mechanism for the formation of one enantiomer of *trans*-1,2-dibromocyclopentane when bromine adds to cyclopentene. You should now write a mechanism showing how the other enantiomer forms.

9.8 HALOHYDRIN FORMATION

If the halogenation of an alkene is carried out in aqueous solution (rather than in carbon tetrachloride), the major product of the overall reaction is not a *vic*-dihalide, but rather it is a **halo alcohol** called a **halohydrin.** In this case, molecules of the solvent become reactants, too.

$$\text{C=C} + \text{X}_2 + \text{H}_2\text{O} \longrightarrow -\overset{|}{\underset{X}{C}}-\overset{|}{\underset{OH}{C}}- + -\overset{|}{\underset{X}{C}}-\overset{|}{\underset{X}{C}}- + \text{HX}$$

X = Cl or Br   Halohydrin   *vic*-Dihalide

Halohydrin formation can be explained by the following mechanism:

Step 1 $\text{C=C} + \text{X}-\text{X} \rightleftharpoons -\overset{|}{C}-\overset{|}{C}- + \text{X}^-$ with $\overset{+}{\underset{..}{X}}$

Step 2 $-\overset{|}{\underset{\overset{+}{X}}{C}}-\overset{|}{C}- + \text{H}_2\overset{..}{\text{O}}: \longrightarrow -\overset{|}{C}-\overset{\overset{+}{\text{OH}_2}}{\underset{X}{C}}- \xrightarrow{-\text{H}^+} -\overset{|}{C}-\overset{\text{OH}}{\underset{X}{C}}-$

The first step is the same as that for halogen addition. In the second step, however, the two mechanisms differ. In halohydrin formation, water acts as the nucleophile and attacks one carbon atom of the halonium ion. The three-membered ring opens, and a protonated halohydrin is produced. Loss of a proton then leads to the formation of the halohydrin itself.

Water, because of its unshared electron pairs, acts as a nucleophile in this and in many other reactions. In this instance water molecules far outnumber halide ions because water is the solvent for the reactants. This accounts for the halohydrin being the major product.

Problem 9.10 ———————————————————————————————

Outline a mechanism that accounts for the formation of *trans*-2-chlorocyclo-pentanol from cyclopentene and chlorine in aqueous solution.

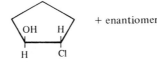

+ enantiomer

trans-2-Chlorocyclopentanol

If the alkene is unsymmetrical, the halogen ends up on the carbon atom with the greater number of hydrogen atoms. Bonding in the intermediate bromonium ion (next page) is apparently *unsymmetrical.* The more highly substituted carbon atom bears the greater positive charge because it resembles the more stable carbocation.

Consequently, water attacks this carbon atom preferentially. The greater positive charge on the tertiary carbon permits a pathway with a lower free energy of activation even though attack at the primary carbon atom is less hindered.

$$H_3C \overset{H_3C}{\underset{H_3C}{\diagup}} C=CH_2 \underset{Br_2}{\rightleftharpoons} CH_3 - \overset{\delta+}{\underset{\underset{\delta+}{Br}}{C}} \overset{\frown}{\underset{}{CH_2}} \overset{:\ddot{O}H_2}{\longrightarrow} CH_3 - \overset{\overset{+}{O}H_2}{\underset{CH_3}{C}} - CH_2Br \overset{-H^+}{\longrightarrow} CH_3 - \overset{OH}{\underset{CH_3}{C}} - CH_2Br$$

(73%)

Problem 9.11

When ethene gas is passed into an aqueous solution containing bromine and sodium chloride, the products of the reaction are $BrCH_2CH_2Br$, $BrCH_2CH_2OH$, *and* $BrCH_2CH_2Cl$. Write mechanisms showing how each product is formed.

9.9 RADICAL ADDITION TO ALKENES: THE ANTI-MARKOVNIKOV ADDITION OF HYDROGEN BROMIDE

Before 1933, the orientation of the addition of hydrogen bromide to alkenes was the subject of much confusion. At times addition occurred in accordance with Markovnikov's rule; at other times it occurred in just the opposite manner. Many instances were reported where, under what seemed to be the same experimental conditions, Markovnikov additions were obtained in one laboratory and anti-Markovnikov additions in another. At times even the same chemist would obtain different results using the same conditions but on different occasions.

The mystery was solved in 1933 by the research of M. S. Kharasch and F. R. Mayo (of the University of Chicago). The explanatory factor turned out to be organic peroxides present in the alkenes—peroxides that were formed by the action of atmospheric oxygen on the alkenes (Section 7.10B). Kharasch and Mayo found that when alkenes that contained peroxides or hydroperoxides reacted with hydrogen bromide, anti-Markovnikov addition of hydrogen bromide occurred.

$$R - \ddot{O} - \ddot{O} - R \qquad R - \ddot{O} - \ddot{O} - H$$

An organic peroxide   **An organic hydroperoxide**

Under these conditions, for example, propene yields 1-bromopropane. In the absence of peroxides, or in the presence of compounds that would "trap" radicals, normal Markovnikov addition occurs.

$$CH_3CH=CH_2 + HBr \xrightarrow{ROOR} CH_3CH_2CH_2Br \qquad \text{Anti-Markovnikov addition}$$

$$CH_3CH=CH_2 + HBr \xrightarrow[\text{peroxides}]{\text{no}} CH_3\underset{\underset{Br}{|}}{CH}CH_3 \qquad \text{Markovnikov addition}$$

2-Bromopropane

Hydrogen fluoride, hydrogen chloride, and hydrogen iodide *do not* give anti-Markovnikov addition even when peroxides are present.

According to Kharasch and Mayo, the mechanism for anti-Markovnikov addition of hydrogen bromide is a *radical chain reaction* initiated by peroxides:

Chain Initiation

Step 1 $R—\ddot{O}\!:\!\ddot{O}—R \xrightarrow{\text{heat}} 2\,R—\ddot{O}\cdot$

Step 2 $R—\ddot{O}\cdot + H\!:\!\ddot{B}r\!: \longrightarrow R—\ddot{O}\!:\!H + :\!\ddot{B}r\cdot$

Chain Propagation

Step 3 $:\!\ddot{B}r\cdot + CH_2\!:\!:\!CHCH_3 \longrightarrow :\!\ddot{B}r\!:\!CH_2CHCH_3$

   2° Radical

Step 4 $:\!\ddot{B}r—CH_2CHCH_3 + H\!:\!\ddot{B}r\!: \longrightarrow BrCH_2CHCH_3 + \cdot\ddot{B}r\!:$

   $\underset{H}{|}$

   1-Bromopropane

Step 1 is the simple homolytic cleavage of the peroxide molecule to produce two alkoxyl radicals. The oxygen–oxygen bond of peroxides is weak and such reactions are known to occur readily.

$$R—\ddot{O}\!:\!\ddot{O}—R \longrightarrow 2\,R—\ddot{O}\cdot \qquad \Delta H° \cong +35 \text{ kcal mol}^{-1}$$

   Peroxide   **Alkoxyl radical**

Step 2 of the mechanism, abstraction of a hydrogen atom by the radical, is exothermic and has a low free energy of activation.

$$R—\ddot{O}\cdot + H\!:\!\ddot{B}r\!: \longrightarrow R—\ddot{O}\!:\!H + :\!\ddot{B}r\cdot \qquad \begin{array}{l} \Delta H° \cong -23 \text{ kcal mol}^{-1} \\ \Delta G^{\ddagger} \text{ is low} \end{array}$$

Step 3 of the mechanism determines the final orientation of bromine in the product. It occurs as it does because a *more stable secondary radical* is produced and because *attack at the primary carbon atom is less hindered.* Had the bromine attacked propene at the secondary carbon atom, a less stable, primary radical would have been the result,

$$Br\cdot + CH_2{=}CHCH_3 \xrightarrow{} \cdot CH_2CHCH_3$$

   $\underset{Br}{|}$

   1° Radical
   (less stable)

and attack at the secondary carbon atom would have been more hindered.

Step 4 of the mechanism is simply the abstraction of a hydrogen atom from hydrogen bromide by the radical produced in step 3. This hydrogen-atom abstraction produces a bromine atom that can bring about step 3 again, then step 4 occurs again — a chain reaction.

We can now see the contrast between the two ways that HBr can add to an alkene. In the absence of peroxides, the reagent that attacks the double bond is a proton.

Because a proton is small, steric effects are unimportant. It attaches itself to a carbon atom in the way that yields the more stable carbocation. The result is Markovnikov addition.

Ionic Addition

$$CH_3CH{=}CH_2 \xrightarrow{\ H^+\ } CH_3\overset{+}{C}HCH_3 \xrightarrow{\ Br^-\ } CH_3CHCH_3$$

with Br attached below the central carbon (Br)

| More stable carbocation | Markovnikov product |

In the presence of peroxides, the reagent that attacks the double bond is a larger bromine atom. It attaches itself to the less-hindered carbon atom in the way that yields the more stable radical. The result is anti-Markovnikov addition.

Radical Addition

$$CH_3CH{=}CH_2 \xrightarrow{\ Br\cdot\ } CH_3\dot{C}HCH_2Br \xrightarrow{\ HBr\ } CH_3CH_2CH_2Br + Br\cdot$$

| More stable radical | Anti-Markovnikov product |

9.9A OTHER RADICAL ADDITIONS TO ALKENES

Many molecules, other than hydrogen bromide, add to alkenes under the influence of a peroxide initiator. Tetrabromomethane, for example, reacts with 1-octene to yield 1,1,1,3-tetrabromononane.

$$CH_3(CH_2)_5CH{=}CH_2 + CBr_4 \xrightarrow{\ ROOR\ } CH_3(CH_2)_5CHCH_2CBr_3$$

with Br attached below carbon (Br)

1-Octene   **1,1,1,3-Tetrabromononane**

The mechanism for this reaction is as follows:

Chain Initiation

    Step 1 $RO{-}OR \longrightarrow 2\,RO\cdot$

    Step 2 $RO\cdot + Br{-}CBr_3 \longrightarrow ROBr + \cdot CBr_3$

Chain Propagation

    Step 3 $CH_3(CH_2)_5CH{=}CH_2 + \cdot CBr_3 \longrightarrow CH_3(CH_2)_5\dot{C}HCH_2{-}CBr_3$

    Step 4 $CH_3(CH_2)_5\dot{C}HCH_2{-}CBr_3 + Br{-}CBr_3 \longrightarrow$

$$CH_3(CH_2)_5CHCH_2{-}CBr_3 + \cdot CBr_3$$

with Br attached below carbon (Br)

Other examples of radical additions to alkenes are the following:

$$CH_3CH_2CH_2CH{=}CH_2 + HCCl_3 \xrightarrow{\ peroxides\ } CH_3CH_2CH_2CH_2CH_2{-}CCl_3$$

1,1,1-Trichlorohexane

$$CH_3-\underset{\underset{CH_3}{|}}{C}=CH_2 + CH_3CH_2SH \xrightarrow{\text{peroxides}} CH_3-\underset{\underset{CH_3}{|}}{CH}-CH_2-S-CH_2CH_3$$

$$CH_3CH_2-\underset{\underset{CH_3}{|}}{C}=CH_2 + CCl_4 \xrightarrow{\text{peroxides}} CH_3CH_2-\underset{\underset{Cl}{|}}{\overset{\overset{CH_3}{|}}{C}}-CH_2-CCl_3$$

1,1,1,3-Tetrachloro-3-methylpentane

Problem 9.12

Write radical, chain-reaction mechanisms that account for the products formed in each of the reactions listed here.

Radicals also cause alkenes to add to each other to form large molecules called addition polymers. These reactions are described in Section 9.10.

9.10 RADICAL POLYMERIZATION OF ALKENES: ADDITION POLYMERS

Polymers are substances that consist of very large molecules called **macromolecules** that are made up of many repeating subunits. The molecular subunits that are used to synthesize polymers are called **monomers,** and the reactions by which momomers are joined together are called **polymerizations.** Many polymerizations can be initiated by radicals.

Ethylene, for example, is the monomer that is used to synthesize the familiar polymer called *polyethylene.*

$$m\,CH_2{=}CH_2 \xrightarrow{\text{polymerization}} -CH_2CH_2{+}CH_2CH_2{+}_n CH_2CH_2-$$

Monomeric units

Ethylene	Polyethylene
monomer	*polymer*

(*m* and *n* are large numbers)

Because polymers such as polyethylene are made by addition reactions, they are often called **addition polymers.** Let us now examine in some detail how polyethylene is made.

Ethylene polymerizes by a radical mechanism when it is heated at a pressure of 1000 atm with a small amount of an organic peroxide (called a diacylperoxide). The diacylperoxide dissociates to produce radicals, which in turn initiate chains.

Chain Initiation

$$Step\ 1 \quad R-\underset{\overset{\|}{O}}{C}-O{:}O-\underset{\overset{\|}{O}}{C}-R \longrightarrow 2\,R{:}\underset{\overset{\|}{O}}{C}-O\cdot \longrightarrow 2\,CO_2 + 2\,R\cdot$$

Diacylperoxide

Step 2 $R\cdot + CH_2=CH_2 \longrightarrow R:CH_2-CH_2\cdot$

Chain Propagation

Step 3 $R-CH_2CH_2\cdot + n\ CH_2=CH_2 \longrightarrow R(CH_2CH_2)_n CH_2CH_2\cdot$

Chains propagate by adding successive ethylene units, until their growth is stopped by combination or disproportionation.

Chain Termination

Step 4 $2\ R(CH_2CH_2)_n CH_2CH_2\cdot$

combination $\longrightarrow [R(CH_2CH_2)_n CH_2CH_2]_2$

disproportionation $\longrightarrow R(CH_2CH_2)_n CH=CH_2 + R(CH_2CH_2)_n CH_2CH_3$

The radical at the end of the growing polymer chain can also abstract a hydrogen atom from itself by what is called "back biting." This leads to chain branching.

Chain Branching

The polyethylene produced by radical polymerization is not generally useful unless it has a molecular weight of nearly 1,000,000. Very high molecular weight polyethylene can be obtained by using a low concentration of the initiator. This initiates the growth of only a few chains and ensures that each chain will have a large excess of the monomer available. More initiator may be added as chains terminate during the polymerization and, in this way, new chains are begun.

Polyethylene has been produced commercially since 1943. It is used in manufacturing flexible bottles, films, sheets, and insulation for electric wires. Polyethylene produced by radical polymerization has a softening point of about 110 °C.

Polyethylene can be produced in a different way using catalysts called **Ziegler–Natta catalysts** that are organometallic complexes of transition metals. In this process no radicals are produced, no back biting occurs, and, consequently, there is no chain branching. The polyethylene that is produced is of higher density, has a higher melting point, and has greater strength. (Ziegler–Natta catalysts are discussed in greater detail in Special Topic B.)

Another familiar polymer is *polystyrene.* The monomer used in making polystyrene is phenylethene, a compound commonly known as *styrene.*

$$m\ CH_2{=}CH \xrightarrow{\text{polymerization}} {-}CH_2CH{\left(CH_2CH\right)_n}CH_2CH{-}$$

Styrene   **Polystyrene**

Addition polymers are discussed in much more detail in Special Topic B. Table 9.1 lists several other common addition polymers.

TABLE 9.1   Other common addition polymers

MONOMER	POLYMER	NAMES
$CH_2{=}CHCH_3$	$\left(CH_2{-}CH\right)_n$ $\vert$ CH_3	Polypropylene
$CH_2{=}CHCl$	$\left(CH_2{-}CH\right)_n$ $\vert$ Cl	Poly(vinyl chloride), PVC
$CH_2{=}CHCN$	$\left(CH_2{-}CH\right)_n$ $\vert$ CN	Polyacrylonitrile, Orlon
$CF_2{=}CF_2$	$\left(CF_2{-}CF_2\right)_n$	Polytetrafluoroethene, Teflon
CH_3 $\vert$ $CH_2{=}CCO_2CH_3$	CH_3 $\vert$ $\left(CH_2{-}C\right)_n$ $\vert$ CO_2CH_3	Poly(methyl methacrylate), Lucite, Plexiglas, Perspex

9.11 OXIDATIONS OF ALKENES: SYN HYDROXYLATION

Alkenes undergo a number of reactions in which the carbon–carbon double bond is oxidized. Potassium permanganate or osmium tetroxide, for example, can be used to oxidize alkenes to **1,2-diols** called **glycols.**

$$CH_2{=}CH_2 + KMnO_4 \xrightarrow[\text{OH}^-]{\text{cold}} \underset{\underset{\text{OH OH}}{\vert\ \ \vert}}{H_2C{-}CH_2}$$

Ethene   **1,2-Ethanediol (ethylene glycol)**

$$CH_3CH{=}CH_2 \xrightarrow[\text{(2) } Na_2SO_3 \ \text{or} \ NaHSO_3/H_2O]{\text{(1) } OsO_4} \underset{\underset{\text{OH   OH}}{\vert\ \ \ \vert}}{CH_3CH{-}CH_2}$$

Propene   **1,2-Propanediol (propylene glycol)**

9.11A SYN HYDROXYLATION OF ALKENES

The mechanisms for the formation of glycols by permanganate ion and osmium tetroxide oxidations first involve the formation of cyclic intermediates. Then in several steps cleavage at the oxygen – metal bond takes place (at the dashed lines in the following reactions) ultimately producing the glycol and MnO_2 or osmium metal.

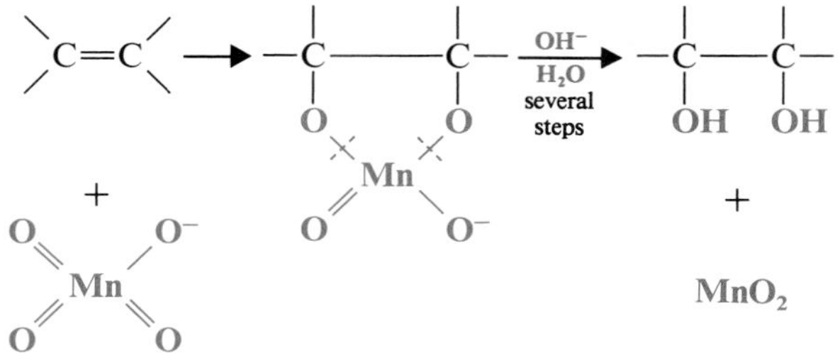

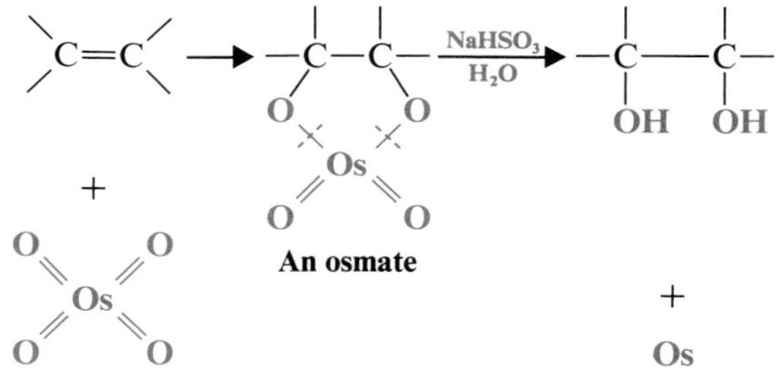

The course of these reactions is **syn hydroxylation.** This can be seen, readily, when cyclopentene reacts with cold dilute potassium permanganate (in base) or with osmium tetroxide (followed by treatment with $NaHSO_3$ or Na_2SO_3). The product in either case is *cis*-1,2-cyclopentanediol. (*cis*-1,2-Cyclopentanediol is a meso compound.)

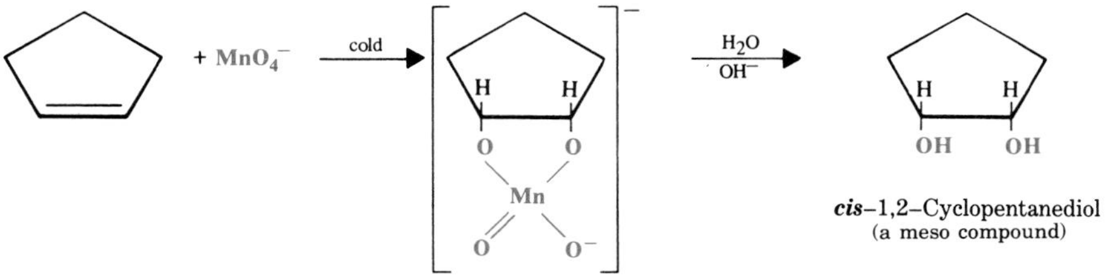

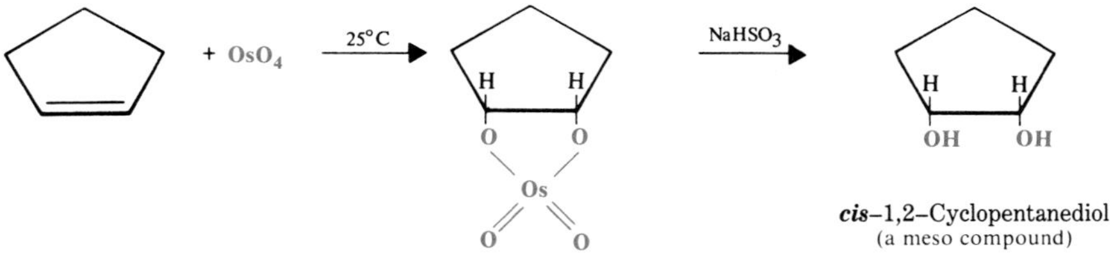

Of the two reagents used for syn hydroxylation, osmium tetroxide gives the higher yields. However, osmium tetroxide is highly toxic and is very expensive. For this reason, methods have been developed that permit OsO_4 to be used catalytically in conjunction with a cooxidant. (We shall not discuss these methods further here, however.) Potassium permanganate is a very powerful oxidizing agent and, as we shall see in Section 9.12, *it is easily capable of causing further oxidation of the glycol.* Limiting the reaction to hydroxylation alone is often difficult, but is usually attempted by using cold, dilute, and basic solutions of potassium permanganate. Even so, yields are sometimes very low.

Problem 9.13

(a) What product(s) would you expect from syn hydroxylation of *cis*-2-butene? (b) Of *trans*-2-butene? (c) Are these reactions stereospecific? Explain your answer.

9.12 OXIDATIVE CLEAVAGE OF ALKENES

Alkenes are oxidatively cleaved to salts of carboxylic acids *by hot permanganate solutions.* We can illustrate this reaction with the oxidative cleavage of either *cis*- or *trans*-2-butene to two molar equivalents of acetate ion. The intermediate in this reaction may be a glycol that is oxidized further with cleavage at the carbon–carbon bond.

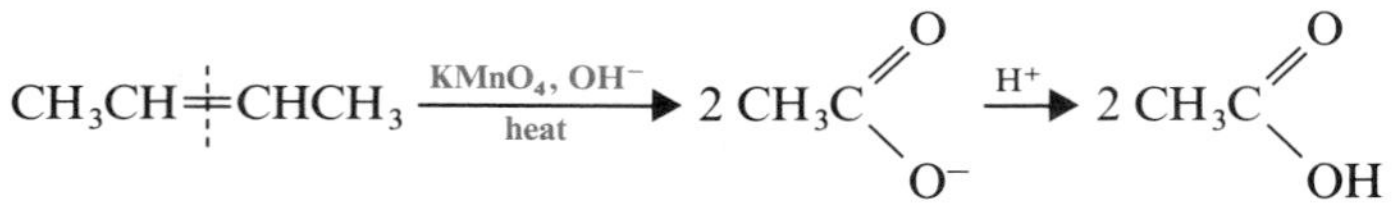

$$CH_3CH{=}CHCH_3 \xrightarrow[\text{heat}]{KMnO_4,\ OH^-} 2\ CH_3C\overset{O}{\underset{O^-}{\diagdown}} \xrightarrow{H^+} 2\ CH_3C\overset{O}{\underset{OH}{\diagdown}}$$

(cis or trans)   **Acetate ion**   **Acetic acid**

Acidification of the mixture, after the oxidation is complete, produces 2 mol of acetic acid for each mole of 2-butene.

The terminal CH_2 group of a 1-alkene is completely oxidized to carbon dioxide and water by hot permanganate. A disubstituted carbon atom of a double bond becomes the $\diagup^{\diagup}C{=}O$ group of a ketone (Section 2.13).

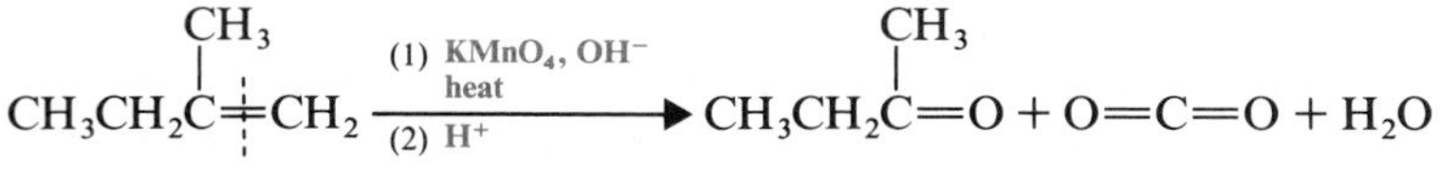

$$CH_3CH_2\overset{CH_3}{\underset{|}{C}}{=}CH_2 \xrightarrow[\text{(2) } H^+]{\text{(1) } KMnO_4,\ OH^- \text{ heat}} CH_3CH_2\overset{CH_3}{\underset{|}{C}}{=}O + O{=}C{=}O + H_2O$$

The oxidative cleavage of alkenes has frequently been used to prove the location of the double bond in an alkene chain or ring. The reasoning process requires us to think backward much as we do with retrosynthetic analysis. Here we are required to work backward from the products to the reactant that might have led to those products. We can see how this might be done with the following examples:

Example A

An unknown alkene with the formula C_8H_{16} was found, on oxidation with hot basic permanganate, to yield a three-carbon carboxylic acid (propanoic acid) and a five-carbon carboxylic acid (pentanoic acid).

$$C_8H_{16} \xrightarrow[\text{(2) H}^+]{\substack{\text{(1) KMnO}_4,\, \text{H}_2\text{O,}\\ \text{OH}^-,\, \text{heat}}} CH_3CH_2\overset{\displaystyle O}{\overset{\|}{C}}-OH + HO-\overset{\displaystyle O}{\overset{\|}{C}}CH_2CH_2CH_2CH_3$$

Propanoic acid   **Pentanoic acid**

Oxidative cleavage must have occurred as follows, and the unknown alkene must have been *cis-* or *trans-*3-octene.

Cleavage occurs here

$$CH_3CH_2CH\!=\!CHCH_2CH_2CH_3 \xrightarrow[\text{(2) H}^+]{\substack{\text{(1) KMnO}_4,\, \text{H}_2\text{O,}\\ \text{OH}^-,\, \text{heat}}} CH_3CH_2\overset{\displaystyle O}{\overset{\|}{C}}-OH + HO-\overset{\displaystyle O}{\overset{\|}{C}}CH_2CH_2CH_2CH_3$$

Unknown alkene
(either *cis-* or *trans-*3-octene)

Example B

An unknown alkene with the formula C_7H_{12} undergoes oxidation by hot basic $KMnO_4$ to yield, after acidification, *only one product:*

$$C_7H_{12} \xrightarrow[\text{(2) H}^+]{\substack{\text{(1) KMnO}_4,\, \text{H}_2\text{O,}\\ \text{OH}^-,\, \text{heat}}} CH_3\overset{\displaystyle O}{\overset{\|}{C}}CH_2CH_2CH_2CH_2\overset{\displaystyle O}{\overset{\|}{C}}-OH$$

Since the product contains the same number of carbon atoms as the reactant, the only reasonable explanation is that the reactant has a double bond contained in a ring. Oxidative cleavage of the double bond opens the ring.

$$\text{(1-methylcyclohexene)} \xrightarrow[\text{(2) H}^+]{\substack{\text{(1) KMnO}_4,\, \text{H}_2\text{O,}\\ \text{OH}^-,\, \text{heat}}} CH_3\overset{\displaystyle O}{\overset{\|}{C}}CH_2CH_2CH_2CH_2\overset{\displaystyle O}{\overset{\|}{C}}-OH$$

Unknown alkene
(1-methylcyclohexene)

9.12A OZONOLYSIS OF ALKENES

A more widely used method for locating the double bond of an alkene involves the use of ozone (O_3). Ozone reacts vigorously with alkenes to form unstable compounds called *initial ozonides,* which rearrange spontaneously to form compounds known as **ozonides.**

Initial ozonide   **Ozonide**

This rearrangement is thought to occur through dissociation of the initial ozonide into reactive fragments that recombine to yield the ozonide.

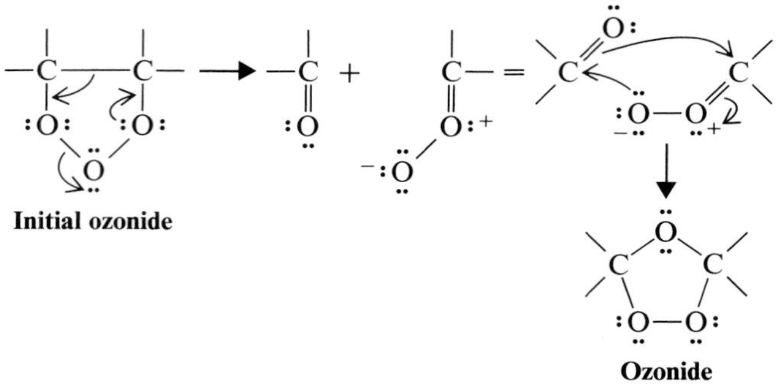

Initial ozonide

Ozonide

Ozonides, themselves, are very unstable compounds and low molecular weight ozonides often explode violently. Because of this property they are not usually isolated, but are reduced directly by treatment with zinc and water. The reduction produces carbonyl compounds (either aldehydes or ketones, see Section 2.13) that can be safely isolated and identified.

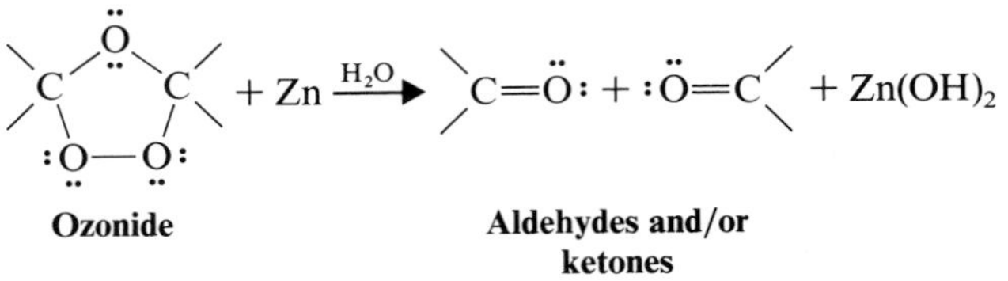

Ozonide

Aldehydes and/or ketones

The overall process of ozonolysis followed by reduction with zinc and water amounts to a disconnection of the carbon–carbon double bond in the following fashion.

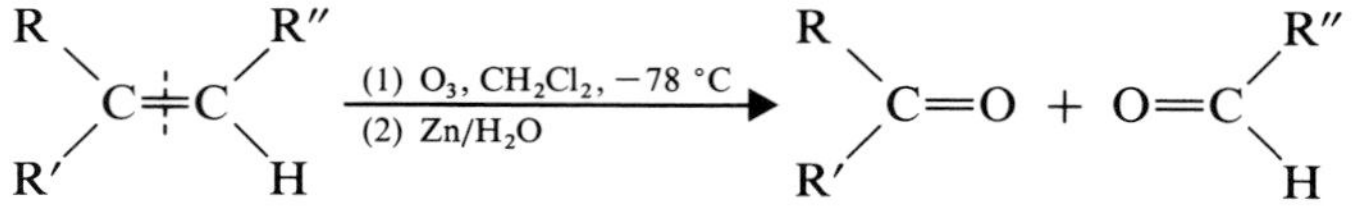

Notice that a —H attached to the double bond is not oxidized to —OH as it is with permanganate oxidations. Consider the following examples as illustrations of the overall process.

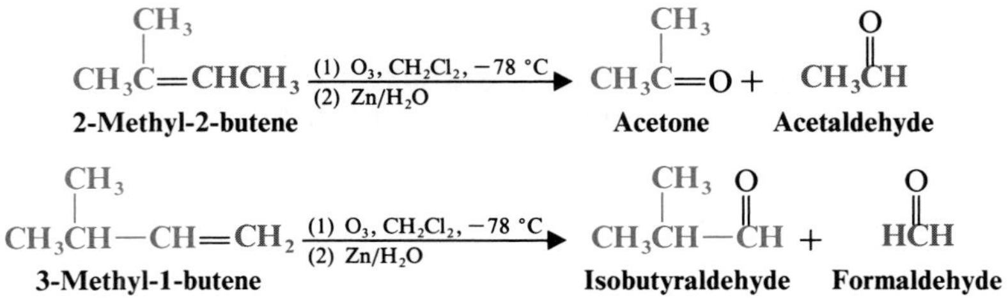

2-Methyl-2-butene

Acetone **Acetaldehyde**

3-Methyl-1-butene

Isobutyraldehyde **Formaldehyde**

Problem 9.14

Write the general structures of the alkenes that would produce the following products when treated with ozone and then with zinc and water.

(a) 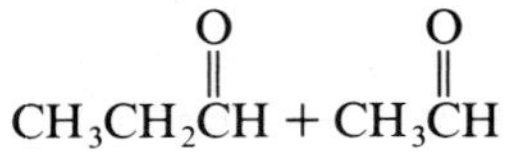 $CH_3CH_2CH + CH_3CH$ (with O double-bonded to each CH)

(b) CH$_3$—C=O   only (2 mol are produced from 1 mol of alkene)
        |
       CH$_3$

(c) CH$_3$CH$_2$CH—$\overset{\overset{\displaystyle O}{\|}}{C}$H + H$\overset{\overset{\displaystyle O}{\|}}{C}$H
          |
         CH$_3$

(d) H—$\overset{\overset{\displaystyle O}{\|}}{C}CH_2CH_2CH_2CH_2$$\overset{\overset{\displaystyle O}{\|}}{C}$—H   only

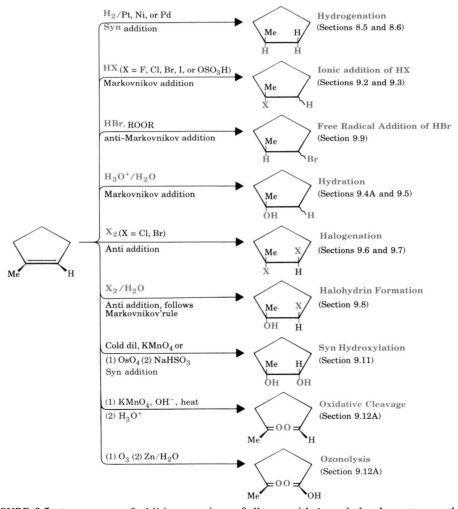

FIGURE 9.5 A summary of addition reactions of alkenes with 1-methylcyclopentene as the organic substrate. A bond designated ∿ means that the stereochemistry of the group is unspecified. For brevity we have shown the structure of only one enantiomer of the product even though racemic forms would be produced in all instances in which the product is chiral.

9.13 SUMMARY OF ADDITION REACTIONS OF ALKENES

The stereochemistry and regiospecificity (where appropriate) of the addition reactions of alkenes that we have studied thus far are summarized in Figure 9.5. We have used 1-methylcyclopentene as the starting alkene.

9.14 ADDITION OF BROMINE AND CHLORINE TO ALKYNES

Alkynes show the same kind of reactions toward chlorine and bromine that alkenes do: ***They react by addition.*** However, with alkynes the addition may occur once or twice, depending on the number of molar equivalents of halogen we employ.

$$-C\equiv C- \xrightarrow[\text{CCl}_4]{\text{Br}_2} \quad \overset{\backslash}{\underset{\text{Br}}{/}}C=C\overset{\text{Br}}{\underset{\backslash}{/}} \xrightarrow[\text{CCl}_4]{\text{Br}_2} \quad -\overset{\overset{\text{Br}}{|}}{\underset{\underset{\text{Br}}{|}}{C}}-\overset{\overset{\text{Br}}{|}}{\underset{\underset{\text{Br}}{|}}{C}}-$$

Dibromoalkene   **Tetrabromoalkane**

$$-C\equiv C- \xrightarrow[\text{CCl}_4]{\text{Cl}_2} \quad \overset{\backslash}{\underset{\text{Cl}}{/}}C=C\overset{\text{Cl}}{\underset{\backslash}{/}} \xrightarrow[\text{CCl}_4]{\text{Cl}_2} \quad -\overset{\overset{\text{Cl}}{|}}{\underset{\underset{\text{Cl}}{|}}{C}}-\overset{\overset{\text{Cl}}{|}}{\underset{\underset{\text{Cl}}{|}}{C}}-$$

Dichloroalkene   **Tetrachloroalkane**

It is usually possible to prepare a dihaloalkene by simply adding one molar equivalent of the halogen.

$$\text{CH}_3\text{CH}_2\text{CH}_2\text{CH}_2\text{C}\equiv\text{CCH}_2\text{OH} \xrightarrow[\substack{\text{CCl}_4 \\ 0\,°\text{C}}]{\text{Br}_2\text{ (1 mol)}} \text{CH}_3\text{CH}_2\text{CH}_2\text{CH}_2\text{CBr}=\text{CBrCH}_2\text{OH}$$
$$\text{(80\%)}$$

Most additions of chlorine and bromine to alkynes are anti additions and yield *trans*-dihaloalkenes. Addition of bromine to acetylenedicarboxylic acid, for example, gives the trans isomer in 70% yield.

$$\text{HO}_2\text{C}-\text{C}\equiv\text{C}-\text{CO}_2\text{H} \xrightarrow{\text{Br}_2} \quad \overset{\text{HO}_2\text{C}}{\underset{\text{Br}}{\diagdown}}C=C\overset{\text{Br}}{\underset{\text{CO}_2\text{H}}{\diagup}}$$

Acetylenedicarboxylic   **(70%)**
acid

Problem 9.15

Alkenes are more reactive than alkynes toward addition of electrophilic reagents (i.e., Br_2, Cl_2, or HCl). Yet when alkynes are treated with one molar equivalent of these same electrophilic reagents, it is easy to stop the addition at the "alkene stage." This appears to be a paradox and yet it is not. Explain.

9.15 ADDITION OF HYDROGEN HALIDES TO ALKYNES

Alkynes react with hydrogen chloride and hydrogen bromide to form haloalkenes or geminal dihalides depending, once again, on whether one or two molar equivalents of the hydrogen halide are used. **Both additions are regioselective and follow Markovnikov's rule:**

$$-C \equiv C- \xrightarrow{HCl} \underset{/}{\overset{H}{\diagdown}}C=C\underset{Cl}{\overset{/}{\diagup}} \xrightarrow{HCl} -\overset{\overset{H}{|}}{\underset{\underset{H}{|}}{C}}-\overset{\overset{Cl}{|}}{\underset{\underset{Cl}{|}}{C}}-$$

Chloroalkene   ***gem*-Dichloride**

$$-C \equiv C- \xrightarrow{HBr} \underset{/}{\overset{H}{\diagdown}}C=C\underset{Br}{\overset{/}{\diagup}} \xrightarrow{HBr} -\overset{\overset{H}{|}}{\underset{\underset{H}{|}}{C}}-\overset{\overset{Br}{|}}{\underset{\underset{Br}{|}}{C}}-$$

Bromoalkene   ***gem*-Dibromide**

The hydrogen atom of the hydrogen halide becomes attached to the carbon atom that has the greater number of hydrogen atoms. Propyne, for example, reacts with one molar equivalent of hydrogen chloride to yield 2-chloropropene and with two molar equivalents to yield 2,2-dichloropropane.

$$CH_3C \equiv CH \xrightarrow{HCl} CH_3-\underset{\underset{Cl}{|}}{C}=CH_2 \xrightarrow{HCl} CH_3-\overset{\overset{Cl}{|}}{\underset{\underset{Cl}{|}}{C}}-CH_3$$

2-Chloropropene   **2,2-Dichloropropane**

The initial addition of a hydrogen halide to an alkyne usually occurs in an **anti** manner. This is especially likely if an ionic halide corresponding to the halogen of the hydrogen halide is present in the mixture.

$$CH_3CH_2C \equiv CCH_2CH_3 + HCl \xrightarrow[\substack{CH_3CO_2H \\ 25\ °C}]{Cl^-} \underset{H}{\overset{CH_3CH_2}{\diagdown}}C=C\underset{CH_2CH_3}{\overset{Cl}{\diagup}}$$

(97%)

The mechanism of the addition of HX to an alkyne involves the formation of an intermediate **vinylic cation,** which subsequently reacts with the halide ion to produce the haloalkene. Vinylic cations are much less stable than corresponding alkyl cations.

$$R-C \equiv CH + H^+ \longrightarrow R-\overset{+}{C}=CH_2 \xrightarrow{:X^-} R-\overset{\overset{X}{|}}{C}=CH_2$$

Vinylic cation   **Haloalkene**

The haloalkene can react further to yield the *gem*-dihalide:

$$R-\overset{:\ddot{X}:}{C}=CH_2 + H^+ \longrightarrow R-\overset{\ddot{X}:^+}{C}-CH_3 \xrightarrow{:X^-} R-\overset{\overset{X}{|}}{\underset{\underset{X}{|}}{C}}-CH_3$$

In this step the electron pair of the halogen helps stabilize the intermediate cation.

Anti-Markovnikov addition of hydrogen bromide to alkynes occurs when peroxides are present in the reaction mixture. These reactions take place through a free radical mechanism (Section 9.9).

$$CH_3CH_2CH_2CH_2C\equiv CH \xrightarrow[\text{peroxides}]{\text{HBr}} CH_3CH_2CH_2CH_2CH=CHBr$$
$$\text{(74\%)}$$

9.16 OXIDATIVE CLEAVAGE OF ALKYNES

Treating alkynes with ozone or with basic potassium permanganate leads to cleavage at the carbon–carbon triple bond. The products are carboxylic acids.

$$R-C\equiv C-R' \xrightarrow[\text{(2) H}_2\text{O}]{\text{(1) O}_3} RCO_2H + R'CO_2H$$

or
$$R-C\equiv C-R' \xrightarrow[\text{(2) H}^+]{\text{(1) KMnO}_4, \text{ OH}^-} RCO_2H + R'CO_2H$$

Problem 9.16 _____

Give the name and structure of each of the following alkynes used in the following reactions.

(a) $C_7H_{12} \xrightarrow[\text{(2) H}_2\text{O}]{\text{(1) O}_3}$ CH$_3$CHCO$_2$H + CH$_3$CH$_2$CO$_2$H
$\qquad\qquad\qquad\qquad\quad |$
$\qquad\qquad\qquad\quad$ CH$_3$

(b) $C_8H_{12} \xrightarrow[\text{(2) H}_2\text{O}]{\text{(1) O}_3}$ HO$_2$C—(CH$_2$)$_6$—CO$_2$H $\qquad$ only

(c) $C_7H_{12} \xrightarrow[\text{Pt}]{\text{2 H}_2}$ CH$_3$CH$_2$CH$_2$CH$_2$CH$_2$CH$_2$CH$_3$

$\qquad\quad\vdash\xrightarrow[\text{OH}^-]{\text{Ag(NH}_3)_2^+}$ C$_7$H$_{11}$Ag↓

9.17 SUMMARY OF ADDITION REACTIONS OF ALKYNES

Figure 9.6 summarizes the addition reactions of alkynes.

9.18 SYNTHETIC STRATEGIES REVISITED

In planning a synthesis we often have to consider four interrelated aspects:

1. Construction of the carbon skeleton
2. Functional group interconversions
3. Control of regiochemistry
4. Control of stereochemistry

You have had some experience in the first two aspects of synthetic strategy in earlier sections. In Section 4.16 you were introduced to the ideas of *retrosynthetic*

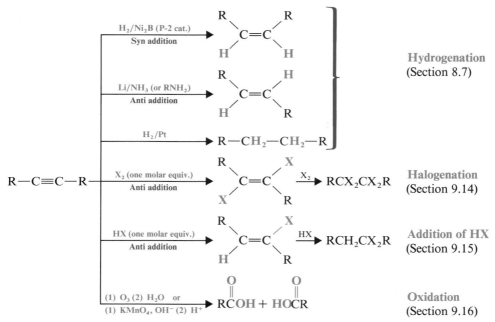

FIGURE 9.6 A summary of the addition reactions of alkynes.

analysis and how this kind of thinking could be applied to the construction of carbon skeletons of alkanes and cycloalkanes. In Section 6.16 you learned the meaning of a *functional group interconversion* and learned how nucleophilic substitution reactions could be used for this purpose. In other sections, perhaps without realizing it, you have begun adding to your basic store of methods for construction of carbon skeletons, and for making functional group interconversions. This might be the time to begin keeping a notebook that lists all the reactions that you have learned, noting especially their applications to synthesis. This notebook will become your **Tool Kit for Organic Synthesis.**

Now is the time to look at some new examples and to see how we integrate all four aspects of synthesis into our planning.

Consider a problem in which we are asked to outline a synthesis of 1-bromobutane from compounds of two carbon atoms or fewer. This synthesis, as we shall see, involves construction of the carbon skeleton, functional group interconversion, and control of regiochemistry.

We begin by thinking backward. One way to make 1-bromobutane is by addition of bromine to 1-butene. The regiochemistry of this functional group interconversion must be anti-Markovnikov, however.

Analysis

$$CH_3CH_2CH_2CH_2Br \Longrightarrow CH_3CH_2CH=CH_2 + H-Br \qquad \text{Anti-Markovnikov addition}$$

Synthesis

$$CH_3CH_2CH=CH_2 + HBr \xrightarrow{ROOR} CH_3CH_2CH_2CH_2Br$$

Remember: The open arrow is a symbol used to show a retrosynthetic process that relates the target molecule to its precursors.

$$\text{Target molecule} \Longrightarrow \text{precursors}$$

Next we try to think of a way to synthesize 1-butene, keeping in mind that we have to construct the carbon skeleton from compounds with two carbon atoms or fewer. One retrosynthetic route might be

Analysis

$$CH_3CH_2CH{=}CH_2 \Longrightarrow CH_3CH_2C{\equiv}CH + H_2$$

$$CH_3CH_2C{\equiv}CH \Longrightarrow CH_3CH_2Br + NaC{\equiv}CH$$

$$NaC{\equiv}CH \Longrightarrow HC{\equiv}CH + NaNH_2$$

Synthesis

$$HC{\equiv}C{-}H + Na^+{}^-NH_2 \xrightarrow[-20\ °C]{\text{liq. NH}_3} HC{\equiv}C{:}^-\ Na^+$$

$$CH_3CH_2{-}Br + Na^+{}^-{:}C{\equiv}CH \xrightarrow[-33\ °C]{\text{liq. NH}_3} CH_3CH_2C{\equiv}CH$$

$$CH_3CH_2C{\equiv}CH + H_2 \xrightarrow{H_2,\ Ni_2B(P{-}2)} CH_3CH_2CH{=}CH_2$$

One approach to retrosynthetic analysis is to consider a retrosynthetic step as a "disconnection" of one of the bonds (Section 4.16).* For example, an important step in the synthesis that we have just given, is the one in which a new carbon–carbon bond is formed. Retrosynthetically, it can be shown in the following way:

$$CH_3CH_2{-}C{\equiv}CH \Longrightarrow CH_3\overset{+}{C}H_2 + {}^-{:}C{\equiv}CH$$

The fragments of this disconnection are an ethyl cation and an ethynide anion. These fragments are called **synthons.** Seeing these synthons may help us to reason as follows: "We could, in theory, synthesize a molecule of 1-butyne by combining an ethyl cation with an ethynide anion." We know, however, that bottles of carbocations and carbanions are not to be found on our laboratory shelves. What we need are the **synthetic equivalents** of these synthons. The synthetic equivalent of an ethynide ion is sodium ethynide, because sodium ethynide contains an ethynide ion (and a sodium cation). The synthetic equivalent of an ethyl cation is ethyl bromide. To understand how this is true, we reason as follows: If ethyl bromide were to react by an S_N1 reaction, it would produce an ethyl cation and a bromide ion. However, we know that being a primary halide, ethyl bromide is unlikely to react by an S_N1 reaction. Ethyl bromide, however, will react readily with a strong nucleophile such as sodium ethynide by an S_N2 reaction, and when it reacts, the product that is obtained is the same as the product that would have been obtained from the reaction of an ethyl cation with sodium ethynide. Thus, ethyl bromide, in this reaction, functions as the synthetic equivalent of an ethyl cation.

Consider another example, a synthesis that requires stereochemical control: the synthesis of the enantiomeric 2,3-butanediols, (2R,3R)-2,3-butanediol and (2S,3S)-2,3-butanediol, from compounds of two-carbon atoms or fewer.

---

* For an excellent detailed treatment of this approach you might want to read: Stuart Warren, *Organic Synthesis, The Disconnection Approach,* Wiley, New York, 1982, and Stuart Warren, *Workbook for Organic Synthesis, the Disconnection Approach,* Wiley, New York, 1982.

9.18 SYNTHETIC STRATEGIES REVISITED

Here (recall Problem 9.13) we see that a possible final step to the enantiomers is syn hydroxylation of *trans*-2-butene.

Analysis

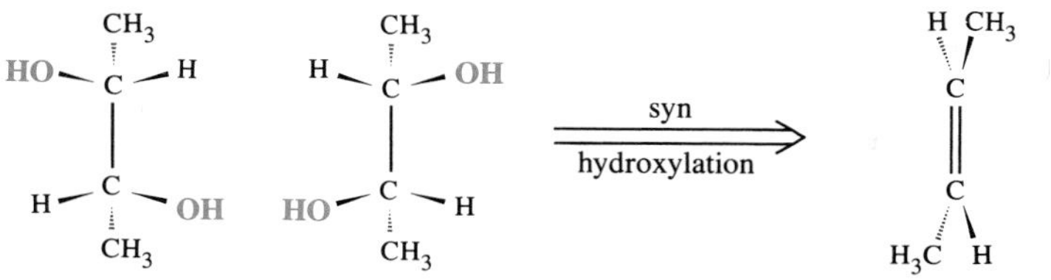

HO—C—H $\quad$ H—C—OH $\qquad\xrightarrow[\text{hydroxylation}]{\text{syn}}\qquad$ (*trans*-2-Butene)

(2R, 3R) $\qquad$ (2S, 3S)

Enantiomeric 2,3-butanediols

Synthesis

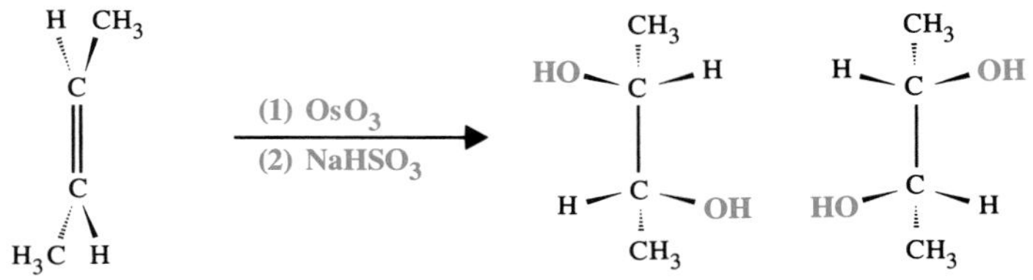

trans–2–Butene $\quad\xrightarrow[\text{(2) NaHSO}_3]{\text{(1) OsO}_3}\quad$ (2R, 3R) $\quad$ (2S, 3S)

Enantiomeric 2,3-butanediols

This reaction is stereospecific and will produce the desired enantiomeric 2,3-butanediols as a racemic form.

Next, a synthesis of *trans*-2-butene can be accomplished by treating 2-butyne with lithium in liquid ammonia. This is a reaction that is also stereospecific and the addition of hydrogen is anti giving us the trans product that we need.

Analysis

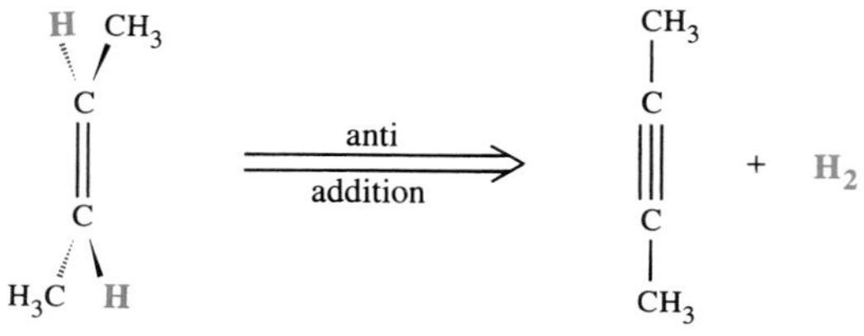

trans-2-Butene $\quad\xrightarrow[\text{addition}]{\text{anti}}\quad$ 2-Butyne $\;+\; H_2$

Synthesis

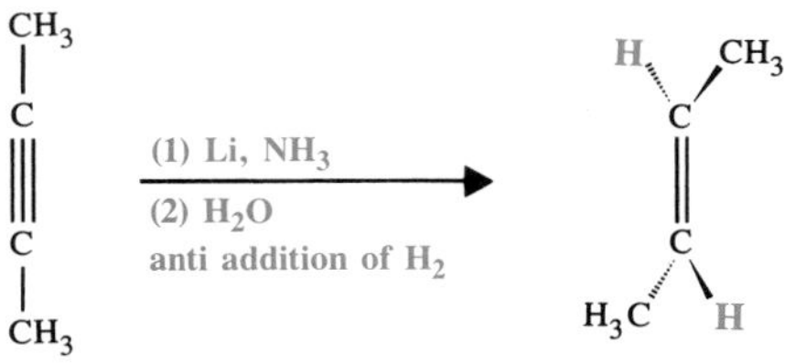

2-Butyne $\quad\xrightarrow[\substack{\text{(2) H}_2\text{O}\\ \text{anti addition of H}_2}]{\text{(1) Li, NH}_3}\quad$ *trans*-2-Butene

Finally, we can synthesize 2-butyne from propyne by first converting it to sodium propynide and then alkylating sodium propynide with methyl iodide:

Analysis

$$CH_3-C\equiv C\nmid CH_3 \Longrightarrow CH_3-C\equiv C:^-Na^+ + CH_3-I$$

$$CH_3-C\equiv C:^-Na^+ \Longrightarrow CH_3-C\equiv C-H + NaNH_2$$

Synthesis

$$CH_3-C\equiv C-H \xrightarrow[\text{(2) }CH_3I]{\text{(1) NaNH}_2/\text{liq. NH}_3} CH_3-C\equiv C-CH_3$$

Finally, we can synthesize propyne from ethyne:

Analysis

$$H-C\equiv C\nmid CH_3 \Longrightarrow H-C\equiv C:^-Na^+ + CH_3-I$$

Synthesis

$$H-C\equiv C-H \xrightarrow[\text{(2) }CH_3I]{\text{(1) NaNH}_2/\text{liq. NH}_3} CH_3-C\equiv C-H$$

Sample Problem

Illustrating a Stereospecific Multistep Synthesis

Starting with compounds of two carbon atoms or fewer, outline a stereospecific synthesis of *meso*-3,4-dibromohexane.

Answer:

We begin by working backward from the product. The addition of bromine to an alkene is stereospecifically anti. Therefore, adding bromine to *trans*-3-hexene will give *meso*-3,4-dibromohexane:

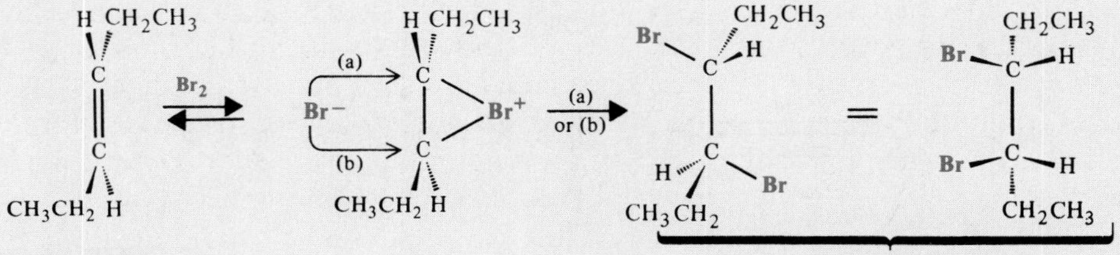

trans-3-Hexene   *meso*-3, 4-Dibromohexane

We can make *trans*-3-hexene in a stereospecific way from 3-hexyne by reducing it with lithium in ammonia (Section 8.7). Again the addition is anti.

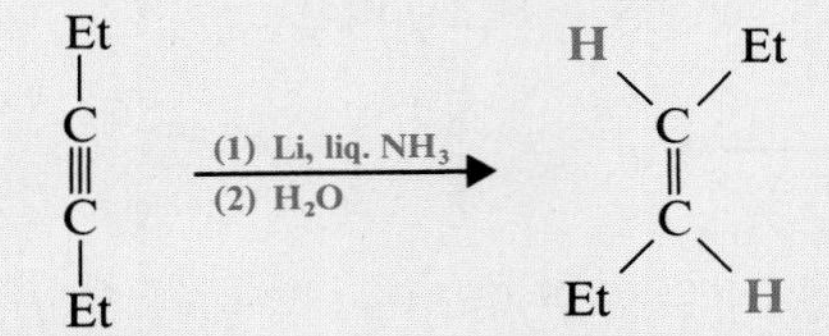

3-Hexyne   *trans*-3-Hexene

3-Hexyne can be made from acetylene and ethyl bromide by successive alkylations using sodium amide as a base:

$$H—C≡C—H \xrightarrow[\text{(2) } CH_3CH_2Br]{\text{(1) NaNH}_2}$$

$$CH_3CH_2C≡CH \xrightarrow[\text{(2) } CH_3CH_2Br]{\text{(1) NaNH}_2} CH_3CH_2C≡CCH_2CH_3$$

Problem 9.17

How would you modify the procedure given in the sample problem so as to synthesize a racemic form of (3R,4R)- and (3S,4S)-3,4-dibromohexane?

9.19 SIMPLE CHEMICAL TESTS FOR ALKANES, ALKENES, ALKYNES, ALKYL HALIDES, AND ALCOHOLS

Very often in the course of laboratory work we need to decide what functional groups are present in a compound that we have isolated. We may have isolated a compound from a synthesis, for example, and the presence of a particular functional group may tell us whether our synthesis has succeeded or failed. Or we may have isolated a compound from some natural material. Before we subject it to elaborate procedures for structure determination, it is often desirable to know something about the kind of compound we have.

Spectroscopic methods are available that will do all of these things for us, and we shall study these procedures in Chapter 14. Spectrometers are expensive instruments, however. It is helpful, therefore, to have simpler means to identify a particular functional group.

Very often this can be done by a simple chemical test. Such a test will often consist of a single reagent that, when mixed with the compound in question, will indicate the presence of a particular functional group. Not all reactions of a functional group serve as chemical tests, however. To be useful the reaction must proceed with a clear signal: a color change, the evolution of a gas, or the appearance of a precipitate.

9.19A CHEMICAL TESTS

A number of reagents that are used as tests for some of the functional groups that we have studied so far are summarized in the following sections. We are restricting our attention at this point to alkanes, alkenes, alkynes, alkyl halides, and alcohols.

9.19B CONCENTRATED SULFURIC ACID (SECTION 9.4)

Alkenes, alkynes, and alcohols are protonated and, therefore, dissolve when they are added to cold concentrated sulfuric acid. Alkanes and alkyl halides are insoluble in cold concentrated sulfuric acid.

9.19C BROMINE IN CARBON TETRACHLORIDE (SECTION 9.6)

Alkenes and alkynes both add bromine at room temperature and in the absence of light. Alkanes, alkyl halides, and alcohols do not react with bromine unless the reaction mixture is heated or exposed to strong irradiation. Thus, rapid decolorization of bromine in carbon tetrachloride at room temperature and in the absence of strong irradiation by light indicates the presence of a carbon–carbon double bond or a carbon–carbon triple bond.

9.19D COLD DILUTE POTASSIUM PERMANGANATE (SECTION 9.10)

Alkenes and alkynes are oxidized by cold dilute solutions of potassium permanganate. If the alkene or alkyne is present in excess, the deep-purple color of the permanganate solution disappears and is replaced by the brown color of precipitated manganese dioxide.

Alkanes, alkyl halides, and pure alcohols do not react with cold dilute potassium permanganate. When these compounds are tested, the purple color is not discharged and a precipitate of manganese dioxide does not appear. (Impure alcohols often contain aldehydes and aldehydes give a positive test with cold dilute potassium permanganate.)

Cold dilute potassium permanganate is often called Baeyer's reagent.

9.19E ALCOHOLIC SILVER NITRATE

Alkyl and allylic halides (Section 12.2) react with silver ion to form a precipitate of silver halide. Ethanol is a convenient solvent because it dissolves silver nitrate and the alkyl halide. It does not dissolve the silver halide.

$$\underset{\substack{\textbf{Alkyl}\\\textbf{halide}}}{\text{R—X}} + \text{AgNO}_3 \xrightarrow{\text{alcohol}} \text{AgX} \downarrow + \text{R}^+ \longrightarrow \text{other products}$$

$$\underset{\textbf{An allylic halide}}{\text{R—CH=CHCH}_2\text{X}} + \text{AgNO}_3 \xrightarrow{\text{alcohol}} \text{AgX} \downarrow + \text{RCH=CH}\overset{+}{\text{CH}}_2 \longrightarrow \text{other products}$$

Vinylic halides and phenyl halides (Section 6.16A) do not give a silver halide precipitate when treated with silver nitrate in alcohol because vinylic cations and phenyl cations are very unstable and, therefore, do not form readily.

9.19F SILVER NITRATE IN AMMONIA

Silver nitrate reacts with aqueous ammonia to give a solution containing $\text{Ag(NH}_3)_2\text{OH}$. This reacts with terminal alkynes to form a precipitate of the silver alkynide (Section 8.21).

$$\text{R—C}\equiv\text{CH} + \text{Ag(NH}_3)_2{}^+ + \text{OH}^- \longrightarrow \text{R—C}\equiv\text{CAg} \downarrow + \text{HOH} + 2\,\text{NH}_3$$

Nonterminal alkynes do not give a precipitate. *Silver alkynides can be distinguished from silver halides on the basis of their solubility in nitric acid; silver alkynides dissolve, whereas silver halides do not.*

Additional Problems

9.18 Write structural formulas for the products that form when 1-pentene reacts with each of the following reagents:

(a) HCl

(b) Br_2 in CCl_4, room temperature

(c) H_3O^+, H_2O, heat

(d) Cold concentrated H_2SO_4

(e) Cold concentrated H_2SO_4, then H_2O and heat

(f) HBr

(g) HI

(h) H_2, Pt

(i) Br_2 in CCl_4, then KI in acetone

(j) Dilute $KMnO_4$, OH^-, cold

(k) OsO_4, then $NaHSO_3/H_2O$

(l) $KMnO_4$, OH^-, heat, then H^+

(m) O_3, then Zn, H_2O

(n) Br_2 in H_2O

(o) HBr, peroxides

9.19 Repeat Problem 9.18 using cyclopentene instead of 1-pentene.

9.20 In the presence of peroxides, 1-octene reacts with each of the following compounds to yield the product indicated. Write mechanisms for each reaction.

(a) 1-Octene + $CBrCl_3$ $\xrightarrow{ROOR}$ $CH_3(CH_2)_5CHCH_2CCl_3$
$$\qquad\qquad\qquad\qquad\qquad\qquad \underset{Br}{|}$$

(b) 1-Octene + $CHCl_3$ $\xrightarrow{ROOR}$ $CH_3(CH_2)_7CCl_3$

(c) 1-Octene + CCl_4 $\xrightarrow{ROOR}$ $CH_3(CH_2)_5CHCH_2CCl_3$
$$\qquad\qquad\qquad\qquad\qquad\qquad \underset{Cl}{|}$$

9.21 Give the structure of the products that you would expect from the reaction of 1-pentyne with:

(a) One molar equivalent of Br_2

(b) One molar equivalent of HCl

(c) Two molar equivalents of HCl

(d) One molar equivalent of HBr and peroxides

(e) H_2O, H^+, Hg^{2+}

(f) H_2, Ni_2B(P-2)

(g) $NaNH_2$ in liq. NH_3

(h) $NaNH_2$ in liq. NH_3, then CH_3I

(i) $Ag(NH_3)_2OH$

(j) $Cu(NH_3)_2OH$

9.22 Give the structure of the products you would expect from the reaction (if any) of 3-hexyne with:

(a) One molar equivalent of HCl

(b) Two molar equivalents of HCl

(c) One molar equivalent of Br_2

(d) Two molar equivalents of Br_2

(e) Ni_2B(P-2), H_2

(f) One molar equivalent of HBr

(g) Li/liq. NH_3

(h) H_2O, H^+, Hg^{2+}

(i) $Ag(NH_3)_2OH$

(j) Two molar equivalents of H_2, Pt

(k) $KMnO_4$, OH^-, then H^+

(l) O_3, H_2O

(m) $NaNH_2$, liq. NH_3

9.23 Show how each of the following compounds might be transformed into 1-pentyne:

(a) 1-Pentene

(b) 1-Chloropentane

(c) 1-Chloro-1-pentene

(d) 1,1-Dichloropentane

(e) 1-Bromopropane and acetylene

9.24 Starting with 2-methylpropene (isobutylene) and using any other needed reagents, outline a synthesis of each of the following:

(a) $(CH_3)_3COH$

(b) $(CH_3)_3CCl$

(c) $(CH_3)_3CBr$

(d) $(CH_3)_2CHCH_2Br$

(e) $(CH_3)_2CHCH_2I$

(f) $(CH_3)_2CHCH_2CN$

(g) $(CH_3)_3CF$

(h) $(CH_3)_2C(OH)CH_2Cl$

(i) Polyisobutylene

9.25 Myrcene, a fragrant compound found in bayberry wax, has the formula $C_{10}H_{16}$ and is known not to contain any triple bonds. (a) What is the index of hydrogen deficiency of myrcene? When treated with excess hydrogen and a platinum catalyst, myrcene is converted to a compound **(A)** with the formula $C_{10}H_{22}$. (b) How many rings does myrcene contain? (c) How many double bonds? Compound **A** can be identified as 2,6-dimethyloctane. Ozonolysis of myrcene followed by treatment with zinc and water yields 2 mol of formaldehyde (HCHO), 1 mol of acetone (CH_3COCH_3), and a third compound **(B)** with the formula $C_5H_6O_3$. (d) What is the structure of myrcene? (e) Of compound **B**?

9.26 When either *cis*- or *trans*-2-butene is treated with hydrogen chloride in ethanol, one of the products of the reaction is *sec*-butyl ethyl ether. Write a mechanism that accounts for the formation of this product.

9.27 When alkenes add HX, the relative rates of reaction are $R_2C=CH_2 > RCH=CH_2 > CH_2=CH_2$. What factor accounts for this?

9.28 Write the products and show how many molar equivalents of each would be formed when squalene is subjected to ozonolysis and the ozonide is subsequently treated with zinc and water.

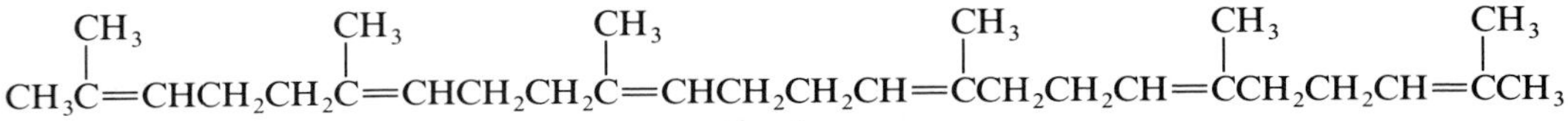

$$CH_3\underset{\underset{\displaystyle CH_3}{|}}{C}=CHCH_2CH_2\underset{\underset{\displaystyle CH_3}{|}}{C}=CHCH_2CH_2\underset{\underset{\displaystyle CH_3}{|}}{C}=CHCH_2CH_2CH=\underset{\underset{\displaystyle CH_3}{|}}{C}CH_2CH_2CH=\underset{\underset{\displaystyle CH_3}{|}}{C}CH_2CH_2CH=\underset{\underset{\displaystyle CH_3}{|}}{C}CH_3$$

Squalene

9.29 Arrange the following alkenes in order of their reactivity toward acid-catalyzed hydration and explain your reasoning:

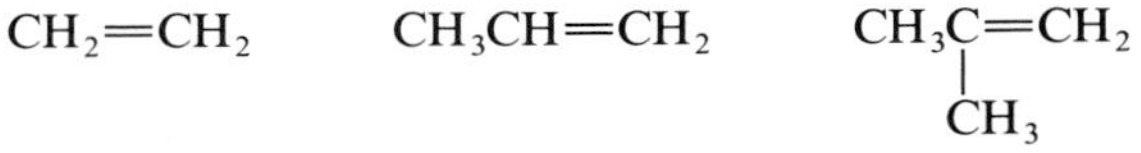

$$CH_2=CH_2 \qquad CH_3CH=CH_2 \qquad CH_3\underset{\underset{\displaystyle CH_3}{|}}{C}=CH_2$$

9.30 (a) When treated with strong acid at 25 °C, either *cis*-2-butene or *trans*-2-butene is converted to a mixture of *trans*-2-butene, *cis*-2-butene, and 1-butene. *trans*-2-Butene predominates in the mixture. (The mixture contains 74% *trans*-2-butene, 23% *cis*-2-butene, and 3% 1-butene.) Write mechanisms for the reactions that occur, and account for the relative amounts of the alkene isomers that are formed. (b) When treated with strong acid, 1-butene is converted to the same mixture of alkenes referred to in part (a). How can you explain this? (c) Can you also explain why 2-methylpropene is *not* formed in either of the reactions referred to in parts (a) or (b) even through 2-methylpropene is more stable than 1-butene?

9.31 Write a mechanism that explains the course of the following reaction:

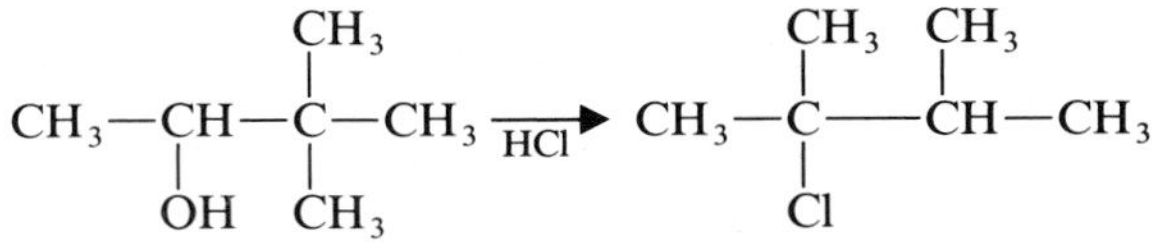

$$CH_3-\underset{\underset{\displaystyle OH}{|}}{CH}-\underset{\overset{\displaystyle CH_3}{|}}{\underset{\underset{\displaystyle CH_3}{|}}{C}}-CH_3 \xrightarrow{HCl} CH_3-\underset{\overset{\displaystyle CH_3}{|}}{\underset{\underset{\displaystyle Cl}{|}}{C}}-\overset{\displaystyle CH_3}{\overset{|}{CH}}-CH_3$$

ADDITIONAL PROBLEMS

9.32 A cycloalkene reacts with hydrogen and a catalyst to yield methylcyclohexane. On vigorous oxidation with potassium permanganate the cycloalkene yields only

$$CH_2CO_2H$$
$$|$$
$$CH_3CHCH_2CH_2CO_2H$$

What is the structure of the cycloalkene?

9.33 Outline all steps in a laboratory synthesis of each of the following compounds. You should begin with the organic compound indicated, and you may use any needed solvents or inorganic compounds. These syntheses may require more than one step and should be designed to give reasonably good yields of reasonably pure products.

(a) Propene from propane

(b) 2-Bromopropane from propane

(c) 1-Bromopropane from propane

(d) 2-Methylpropene from 2-methylpropane

(e) *tert*-Butyl alcohol from 2-methylpropane

(f) 1,2-Dichlorobutane from 1-chlorobutane

(g) 2-Bromoethanol from ethyl bromide

(h) 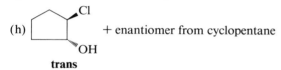 + enantiomer from cyclopentane

(i) 2-Bromobutane from 1-bromobutane

9.34 The green peach aphid is repelled by its own defensive pheromone. (It is also repelled by other squashed aphids.) This alarm pheromone has been isolated and has been shown to have the molecular formula $C_{15}H_{24}$. On catalytic hydrogenation it absorbs 4 mol of hydrogen and yields 2,6,10-trimethyldodecane, that is,

$$CH_3 \qquad\qquad CH_3 \qquad\qquad CH_3$$
$$| \qquad\qquad\quad | \qquad\qquad\quad |$$
$$CH_3CHCH_2CH_2CH_2CHCH_2CH_2CH_2CHCH_2CH_3$$

When subjected to ozonolysis followed by treatment with zinc and water, 1 mol of the alarm pheromone produces: 2 mol of formaldehyde, $H-\overset{\overset{\displaystyle O}{\|}}{C}-H$; 1 mol of acetone,

$CH_3\overset{\overset{\displaystyle O}{\|}}{C}CH_3$; 1 mol of $CH_3\overset{\overset{\displaystyle O}{\|}}{C}CH_2CH_2\overset{\overset{\displaystyle O}{\|}}{C}H$; and 1 mol of $H\overset{\overset{\displaystyle O}{\|}}{C}CH_2CH_2\overset{\overset{\displaystyle O}{\|}}{C}-\overset{\overset{\displaystyle O}{\|}}{C}H$.

Neglecting cis–trans isomerism, propose a structure for the green peach aphid alarm pheromone.

9.35 (a) What product would you expect to form when isobutyl bromide is heated with $(CH_3)_3COK/(CH_3)_3COH$? (b) Can you suggest a method for the conversion of isobutyl bromide into *tert*-butyl bromide?

9.36 When cyclopentene is allowed to react with bromine in an aqueous solution of sodium chloride, the products of the reaction are *trans*-1,2-dibromocyclopentane, the *trans*-bromohydrin of cyclopentene, *and trans-1-bromo-2-chlorocyclopentane.* Write a mechanism that explains the formation of this last product.

9.37 Wri: e stereochemical formulas for all of the products that you would expect from each of the following reactions. (You may find models helpful.)

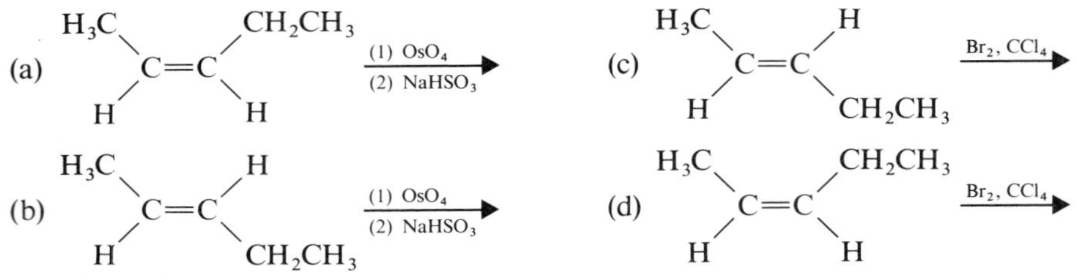

(a)
$$\underset{H}{\overset{H_3C}{>}}C=C\underset{H}{\overset{CH_2CH_3}{<}} \quad \xrightarrow[\text{(2) NaHSO}_3]{\text{(1) OsO}_4}$$

(c)
$$\underset{H}{\overset{H_3C}{>}}C=C\underset{CH_2CH_3}{\overset{H}{<}} \quad \xrightarrow{\text{Br}_2,\ \text{CCl}_4}$$

(b)
$$\underset{H}{\overset{H_3C}{>}}C=C\underset{CH_2CH_3}{\overset{H}{<}} \quad \xrightarrow[\text{(2) NaHSO}_3]{\text{(1) OsO}_4}$$

(d)
$$\underset{H}{\overset{H_3C}{>}}C=C\underset{H}{\overset{CH_2CH_3}{<}} \quad \xrightarrow{\text{Br}_2,\ \text{CCl}_4}$$

9.38 Give $(R-S)$ designations for each different compound given as an answer to Problem 9.37.

9.39 Describe with equations a simple test that would distinguish between the members of the following pairs of compounds. (In each case tell what you would see.)

(a) Propane and propyne

(b) Propene and propyne

(c) 1-Bromopropene and 2-bromopropane

(d) 2-Bromo-2-butene and 1-butyne

(e) 1-Butyne and 2-butyne

(f) 2-Butyne and butyl alcohol

(g) 2-Butyne and 2-bromobutane

(h) $CH_3C{\equiv}CCH_2OH$ and $CH_3CH_2CH_2CH_2OH$

(i) $CH_3CH{=}CHCH_2OH$ and $CH_3CH_2CH_2CH_2OH$

9.40 Three compounds **A**, **B**, and **C** all have the formula C_5H_8. All three compounds rapidly decolorize bromine in CCl_4, all three give a positive test with dilute $KMnO_4$, and all three are soluble in cold concentrated sulfuric acid. Compound **A** gives a precipitate when treated with ammoniacal silver nitrate, but compounds **B** and **C** do not. Compounds **A** and **B** both yield pentane (C_5H_{12}) when they are treated with excess hydrogen in the presence of a platinum catalyst. Under these same conditions, compound **C** absorbs only 1 mol of hydrogen and gives a product with the formula C_5H_{10}. (a) Suggest possible structures for **A**, **B**, and **C**. (b) Are other structures possible for **B** and **C**? (c) Oxidative cleavage of **B** with hot, basic $KMnO_4$ gives, after acidification, acetic acid and $CH_3CH_2CO_2H$. What is the structure of **B**? (d) Cleavage of **C** with ozone gives $OHCCH_2CH_2CH_2CHO$. What is the structure of **C**?

9.41 Starting with 3-methyl-1-butyne and any inorganic reagents, show how the following compounds could be synthesized:

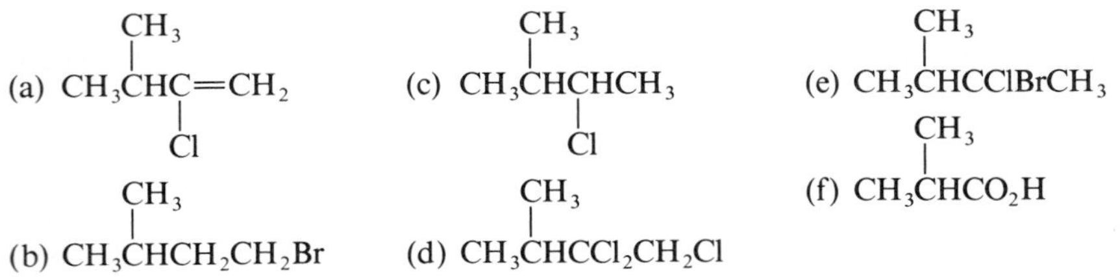

(a) $CH_3\overset{\overset{\displaystyle CH_3}{|}}{C}HC{=}CH_2$
$\underset{|}{\overset{}{Cl}}$

(c) $CH_3\overset{\overset{\displaystyle CH_3}{|}}{C}HCHCH_3$
$\underset{|}{\overset{}{Cl}}$

(e) $CH_3\overset{\overset{\displaystyle CH_3}{|}}{C}HCClBrCH_3$
$\underset{\overset{|}{CH_3}}{}$

(b) $CH_3\overset{\overset{\displaystyle CH_3}{|}}{C}HCH_2CH_2Br$

(d) $CH_3\overset{\overset{\displaystyle CH_3}{|}}{C}HCCl_2CH_2Cl$

(f) $CH_3\overset{\overset{\displaystyle CH_3}{|}}{C}HCO_2H$

9.42 Ricinoleic acid, a compound that can be isolated from castor oil, has the structure $CH_3(CH_2)_5CHOHCH_2CH{=}CH(CH_2)_7CO_2H$. (a) How many stereoisomers of this structure are possible? (b) Write these structures.

ADDITIONAL PROBLEMS

9.43　There are two dicarboxylic acids with the general formula $HO_2CCH{=}CHCO_2H$. One dicarboxylic acid is called maleic acid; the other is called fumaric acid. In 1880, Kekulé found that on treatment with cold dilute $KMnO_4$, maleic acid yields *meso*-tartaric acid and that fumaric acid yields (±)-tartaric acid. Show how this information allows one to write stereochemical formulas for maleic acid and fumaric acid.

9.44　Use your answers to the preceding problem to predict the stereochemical outcome of the addition of bromine to maleic acid and to fumaric acid.　(a) Which dicarboxylic acid would add bromine to yield a meso compound?　(b) Which would yield a racemic form?

9.45　An optically active compound A (assume that it is dextrorotatory) has the molecular formula $C_7H_{11}Br$. A reacts with hydrogen bromide, in the absence of peroxides, to yield isomeric products, B and C, with molecular formula $C_7H_{12}Br_2$. Compound B is optically active; C is not. Treating B with 1 mol of potassium *tert*-butoxide yields (+)A. Treating C with 1 mol of potassium *tert*-butoxide yields (±)A. Treating A with potassium *tert*-butoxide yields D (C_7H_{10}). Subjecting 1 mol of D to ozonolysis followed by treatment with zinc and water yields 2 mol of formaldehyde and 1 mol of 1,3-cyclopentanedione.

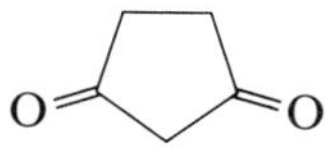

1,3-Cyclopentanedione

Propose stereochemical formulas for A, B, C, and D and outline the reactions involved in these transformations.

9.46　A naturally occurring antibiotic called mycomycin has the structure shown here. Mycomycin is optically active. Explain this by writing structures for the enantiomeric forms of mycomycin.

$$HC{\equiv}C{-}C{\equiv}C{-}CH{=}C{=}CH{-}(CH{=}CH)_2CH_2CO_2H$$

Mycomycin

9.47　An optically active compound D has the molecular formula C_6H_{10}. The compound gives a precipitate when treated with a solution containing $Ag(NH_3)_2OH$. On catalytic hydrogenation D yields E(C_6H_{14}). Compound E is optically inactive and cannot be resolved. Propose structures for D and E.

SPECIAL TOPIC

B

ADDITION POLYMERS FROM ALKENES

The names *Orlon, Plexiglas, Lucite, polyethylene,* and *Teflon* are now familiar names to most of us. These "plastics" or polymers are used in the construction of many objects around us—from the clothing we wear to portions of the houses we live in. Yet all of these compounds were unknown 60 years ago. The development of the processes by which synthetic polymers are made, more than any other single factor, has been responsible for the remarkable growth of the chemical industry in this century.

At the same time, some scientists are now expressing concern about the reliance we have placed on these synthetic materials. Because they are the products of laboratory and industrial processes rather than processes that occur in nature, nature often has no way of disposing of many of them. Although progress has been made in the development of "biodegradable plastics" in recent years, many materials are still used that are not biodegradable. Although most of these objects are combustible, incineration is not always a feasible method of disposal because of attendant air pollution.

Not all polymers are synthetic. Many naturally occurring compounds are polymers as well. Silk and wool are polymers that we call proteins. The starches of our diet are polymers and so is the cellulose of cotton and wood.

Polymers are compounds that consist of very large molecules made up of many repeating subunits. The molecular subunits that are used to synthesize polymers are called *monomers,* and the reactions by which monomers are joined together are called polymerization reactions.

Propylene, for example, can be polymerized to form *polypropylene.* This polymerization occurs by an addition reaction and, as a consequence, polymers such as polypropylene are called *addition polymers.*

$$CH_2{=}CH \xrightarrow{\text{polymerization}} -CH_2CH{\left(CH_2CH\right)}_n CH_2CH-$$

$$\qquad\quad | \qquad\qquad\qquad\qquad | \qquad\quad | \qquad\quad |$$

$$\qquad\quad CH_3 \qquad\qquad\qquad\quad CH_3 \quad\; CH_3 \qquad CH_3$$

Propylene   **Polypropylene**

As we might expect, alkenes are convenient starting materials for the preparation of addition polymers. The addition reactions occur through radical, cationic, or anionic mechanisms depending on how they are initiated. The following examples illustrate these mechanisms. All of these reactions are chain reactions.

Radical Polymerization

$$R\cdot + \;\overset{}{\underset{}{C}}{:}\overset{}{\underset{}{C} \longrightarrow} R{:}\overset{|}{\underset{|}{C}}{-}\overset{|}{\underset{|}{C}}\cdot \xrightarrow{\;C{=}C\;} R{-}\overset{|}{\underset{|}{C}}{-}\overset{|}{\underset{|}{C}}{-}\overset{|}{\underset{|}{C}}{-}\overset{|}{\underset{|}{C}}\cdot \longrightarrow \text{etc.}$$

Cationic Polymerization

$$R^+ + \quad \begin{array}{c} \\ / \end{array}C{=}C\begin{array}{c} \diagup \\ \diagdown \end{array} \longrightarrow R{-}\overset{|}{\underset{|}{C}}{-}\overset{|}{\underset{|}{C}}^+ \xrightarrow{\quad C{=}C \quad} R{-}\overset{|}{\underset{|}{C}}{-}\overset{|}{\underset{|}{C}}{-}\overset{|}{\underset{|}{C}}{-}\overset{|}{\underset{|}{C}}^+ \xrightarrow{\quad C{=}C \quad} \text{etc.}$$

Anionic Polymerization

$$Z\mathord{:}^- + \quad \begin{array}{c} \\ / \end{array}C{=}C\begin{array}{c} \diagup \\ \diagdown \end{array} \longrightarrow Z{-}\overset{|}{\underset{|}{C}}{-}\overset{|}{\underset{|}{C}}\mathord{:}^- \xrightarrow{\quad C{=}C \quad} Z{-}\overset{|}{\underset{|}{C}}{-}\overset{|}{\underset{|}{C}}{-}\overset{|}{\underset{|}{C}}{-}\overset{|}{\underset{|}{C}}\mathord{:}^- \xrightarrow{\quad C{=}C \quad} \text{etc.}$$

Radical polymerization of chloroethene (vinyl chloride) produces a polymer called poly(vinyl chloride) also known as **PVC.**

$$n\ CH_2{=}\underset{\underset{Cl}{|}}{CH} \longrightarrow \left(CH_2{-}\underset{\underset{Cl}{|}}{CH} \right)_n$$

Vinyl chloride   **Poly(vinyl chloride)**
(PVC)

This reaction produces a polymer that has a molecular weight of about 1,500,000 and that is a hard, brittle, and rigid material. In this form it is often used to make pipes, rods, and phonograph records. Poly(vinyl chloride) can be softened by mixing it with esters (called plasticizers). The softer material is used for making "vinyl leather," plastic raincoats, shower curtains, and garden hoses.

Exposure to vinyl chloride has been linked to the development of a rare cancer of the liver called angiocarcinoma. This link was first noted in 1974 and 1975 among workers in vinyl chloride factories. Since that time, standards have been set to limit workers' exposure to less than one part per million average over an 8-h day. The Food and Drug Administration (FDA) has banned the use of PVC in packages for food. [There is evidence that poly(vinyl chloride) contains traces of vinyl chloride.]

Acrylonitrile ($CH_2{=}CHCN$) polymerizes to form polyacrylonitrile or Orlon. The initiator for the polymerization is a mixture of ferrous sulfate and hydrogen peroxide. These two compounds react to produce hydroxyl radicals ($\cdot OH$), which act as chain initiators.

$$n\ CH_2{=}\underset{\underset{CN}{|}}{CH} \xrightarrow[\text{H}-\text{O}-\text{O}-\text{H}]{\text{FeSO}_4} \left(CH_2{-}\underset{\underset{CN}{|}}{CH} \right)_n$$

Acrylonitrile   **Polyacrylonitrile**
(Orlon)

Polyacrylonitrile decomposes before it melts, thus melt spinning cannot be used for the production of fibers. Polyacrylonitrile, however, is soluble in *N,N*-dimethyl-formamide, and these solutions can be used to spin fibers. Fibers produced in this way are used in making carpets and clothing.

Teflon is made by polymerizing tetrafluoroethylene in aqueous suspension.

$$n\ CF_2{=}CF_2 \xrightarrow[\substack{H_2O_2 \\ H_2O}]{Fe^{2+}} \left(CF_2{-}CF_2 \right)_n$$

The reaction is highly exothermic and water helps dissipate the heat that is produced. Teflon has a melting point (327 °C) that is unusually high for an addition polymer. It is also highly resistant to chemical attack and has a low coefficient of friction. Because of these properties Teflon is used in greaseless bearings, in liners for pots and pans, and in many special situations that require a substance that is highly resistant to corrosive chemicals.

Vinyl alcohol is an unstable compound that rearranges spontaneously to acetaldehyde (cf. Section 17.2). Consequently, the water-soluble polymer, poly(vinyl alco-

$$CH_2=CH \rightleftharpoons CH_3-CH$$
$$\underset{\text{OH}}{|} \qquad \underset{\text{O}}{\|}$$

Vinyl alcohol   Acetaldehyde

hol), cannot be made directly. It can be made, however, by an indirect method that begins with the polymerization of vinyl acetate to poly(vinyl acetate). This is then hydrolyzed to poly(vinyl alcohol). Hydrolysis is rarely carried to completion, however, because the presence of a few ester groups helps confer water solubility on the product. The ester groups apparently help keep the polymer chains apart and this permits hydration of the hydroxyl groups. Poly(vinyl alcohol) in which 10% of the ester groups remain dissolves readily in water. Poly(vinyl alcohol) is used to manufacture water-soluble films and adhesives. Poly(vinyl acetate) is used as an emulsion in water-base paints.

**Vinyl acetate   Poly(vinyl   Poly(vinyl
                      acetate)   alcohol)**

A polymer with excellent optical properties can be made by the free radical polymerization of methyl methacrylate. Poly(methyl methacrylate) is marketed under the names Lucite, Plexiglas, and Perspex.

**Methyl methacrylate   Poly(methyl
                            methacrylate)**

A mixture of vinyl chloride and vinylidene chloride polymerizes to form what is known as a *copolymer*. The familiar *Saran Wrap* used in food packaging is made by polymerizing a mixture in which the vinylidene chloride predominates.

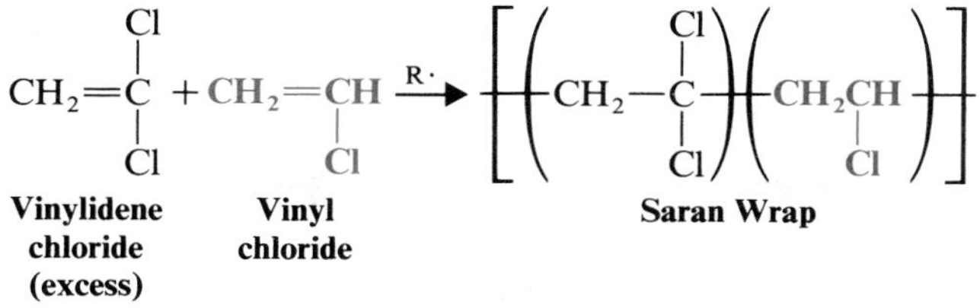

SPECIAL TOPIC B

$$CH_2{=}\underset{\underset{Cl}{|}}{\overset{\overset{Cl}{|}}{C}} + CH_2{=}\underset{\underset{Cl}{|}}{CH} \xrightarrow{R\cdot} \left[\left(CH_2{-}\underset{\underset{Cl}{|}}{\overset{\overset{Cl}{|}}{C}}\right)\left(CH_2CH\underset{\underset{Cl}{|}}{}\right)\right]$$

Vinylidene   **Vinyl**   **Saran Wrap**
chloride   **chloride**
(excess)

The subunits do not necessarily alternate regularly along the polymer chain.

Problem B.1

Can you suggest an explanation that accounts for the fact that the radical polymerization of propylene occurs in a head-to-tail fashion

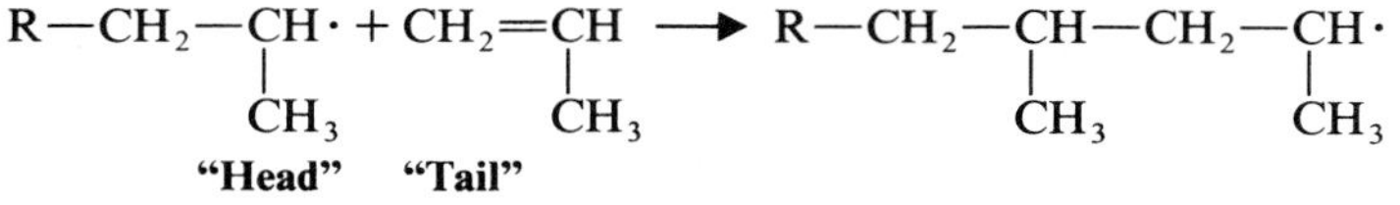

$$R{-}CH_2{-}\underset{\underset{CH_3}{|}}{CH}\cdot + CH_2{=}\underset{\underset{CH_3}{|}}{CH} \longrightarrow R{-}CH_2{-}\underset{\underset{CH_3}{|}}{CH}{-}CH_2{-}\underset{\underset{CH_3}{|}}{CH}\cdot$$

               "Head"   **"Tail"**

rather than the head-to-head manner, shown here?

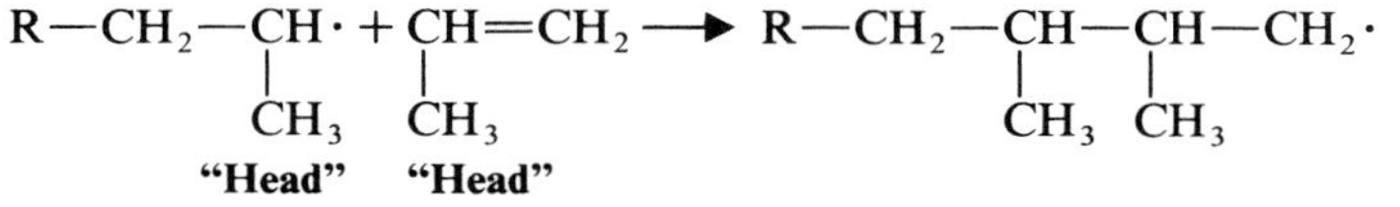

$$R{-}CH_2{-}\underset{\underset{CH_3}{|}}{CH}\cdot + \underset{\underset{CH_3}{|}}{CH}{=}CH_2 \longrightarrow R{-}CH_2{-}\underset{\underset{CH_3}{|}}{CH}{-}\underset{\underset{CH_3}{|}}{CH}{-}CH_2\cdot$$

               "Head"   **"Head"**

Problem B.2

Outline general methods for the synthesis of each of the following polymers by radical polymerization. Assume that the appropriate monomers are available.

(a) Poly(vinyl fluoride) (Tedlar), $\{CH_2CHF\}_n$

(b) Poly(chlorotrifluoroethylene) (Kel—F), $\{CF_2{-}CFCl\}_n$

(c) *Viton,* a copolymer of hexafluoropropene, $CF_2{=}CFCF_3$, and vinylidene fluoride ($CH_2{=}CF_2$).

Alkenes also polymerize when they are treated with strong acids. The growing chains in acid-catalyzed polymerizations are *cations* rather than radicals. The following reactions illustrate the cationic polymerization of isobutylene.

Step 1 $H_2O + BF_3 \rightleftharpoons H^+ + BF_3(OH)^-$

Step 2 $H^+ + CH_2{=}\underset{\underset{CH_3}{|}}{\overset{\overset{CH_3}{|}}{C}} \longrightarrow CH_3{-}\underset{\underset{CH_3}{|}}{\overset{\overset{CH_3}{|}}{C}}{}^+$

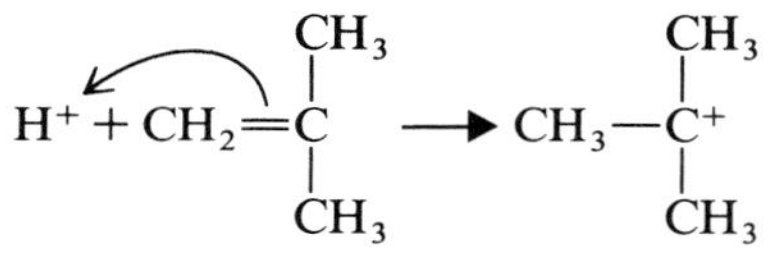

Step 3 $CH_3{-}\underset{\underset{CH_3}{|}}{\overset{\overset{CH_3}{|}}{C}}{}^+ + CH_2{=}\underset{\underset{CH_3}{|}}{\overset{\overset{CH_3}{|}}{C}} \longrightarrow CH_3{-}\underset{\underset{CH_3}{|}}{\overset{\overset{CH_3}{|}}{C}}{-}CH_2{-}\underset{\underset{CH_3}{|}}{\overset{\overset{CH_3}{|}}{C}}{}^+$

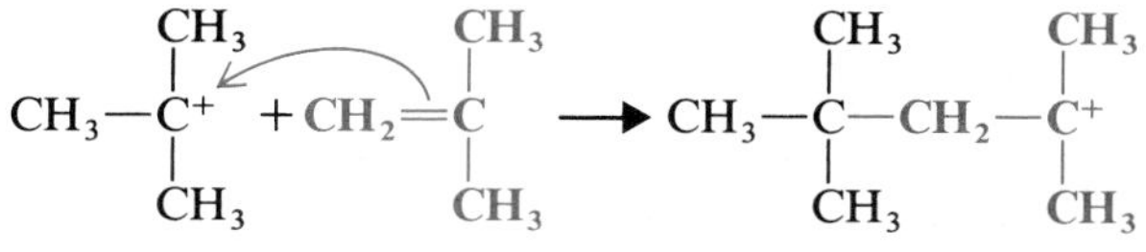

Step 4

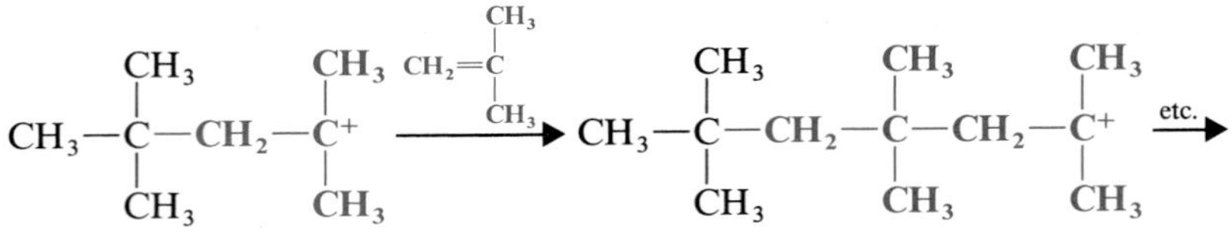

$$\underset{\underset{CH_3}{|}}{\overset{\overset{CH_3}{|}}{CH_3-\underset{|}{C}-CH_2-\overset{+}{C}}}\xrightarrow{\substack{CH_2=\overset{CH_3}{\underset{CH_3}{|}}{C}}}\underset{\underset{CH_3}{|}}{\overset{\overset{CH_3}{|}}{CH_3-\underset{|}{C}-CH_2-\underset{\underset{CH_3}{|}}{\overset{CH_3}{|}}{C}-CH_2-\overset{+}{C}}}\xrightarrow{\text{etc.}}$$

The catalysts used for cationic polymerizations are usually Lewis acids that contain a small amount of water. The polymerization of isobutylene illustrates how the catalyst (BF_3 and H_2O) functions to produce growing cationic chains.

Problem B.3

How can you account for the fact that isobutylene polymerizes in the way we indicated above, rather than in the manner shown here?

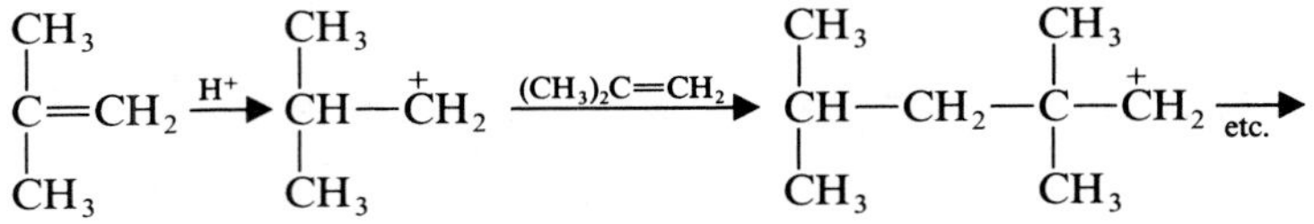

$$\underset{\underset{CH_3}{|}}{\overset{\overset{CH_3}{|}}{C}=CH_2}\xrightarrow{H^+}\underset{\underset{CH_3}{|}}{\overset{\overset{CH_3}{|}}{CH-\overset{+}{CH_2}}}\xrightarrow{(CH_3)_2C=CH_2}\underset{\underset{CH_3}{|}}{\overset{\overset{CH_3}{|}}{CH-CH_2-\underset{\underset{CH_3}{|}}{\overset{CH_3}{|}}{C}-\overset{+}{CH_2}}}\xrightarrow{\text{etc.}}$$

Alkenes containing electron-withdrawing groups polymerize in the presence of strong bases. Acrylonitrile, for example, polymerizes when it is treated with sodium amide ($NaNH_2$) in liquid ammonia. The growing chains in this polymerization are anions.

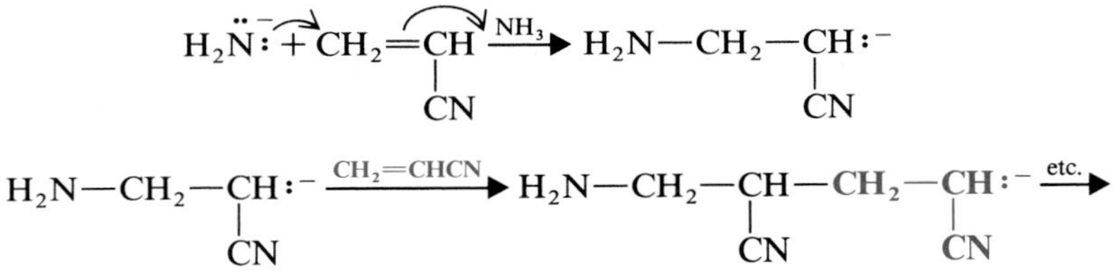

$$H_2\overset{..}{N}:^-+CH_2=\underset{\underset{CN}{|}}{CH}\xrightarrow{NH_3}H_2N-CH_2-\underset{\underset{CN}{|}}{CH}:^-$$

$$H_2N-CH_2-\underset{\underset{CN}{|}}{CH}:^-\xrightarrow{CH_2=CHCN}H_2N-CH_2-\underset{\underset{CN}{|}}{CH}-CH_2-\underset{\underset{CN}{|}}{CH}:^-\xrightarrow{\text{etc.}}$$

Anionic polymerization of acrylonitrile is less important in commercial production than the free radical process we illustrated earlier.

Problem B.4

If alkene monomers used in anionic polymerization are extremely pure, the chains continue growing until all of the monomer is consumed. Even then, however, most of the chain ends are still anions. These chains are said to be "living" chains. The "living" chains can be terminated—"killed"—by the addition of water. (a) How does water terminate the chain? (b) Speculate about what happens when one adds first ethylene oxide and then water to a "living" anionic polymer.

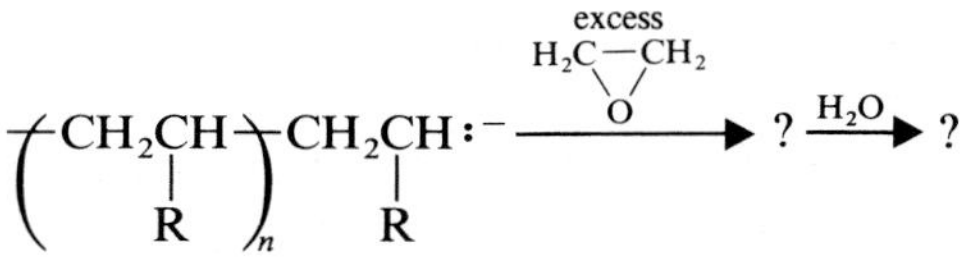

$$\left(\underset{\underset{R}{|}}{CH_2CH}\right)_n\underset{\underset{R}{|}}{CH_2CH}:^-\xrightarrow{\substack{\text{excess}\\H_2C-CH_2\\ \diagdown O\diagup}}?\xrightarrow{H_2O}?$$

HINT: Ethylene oxide, $H_2C\!-\!CH_2$, can also be polymerized by anions. The
reaction involves ring opening of the highly strained three-membered ring.

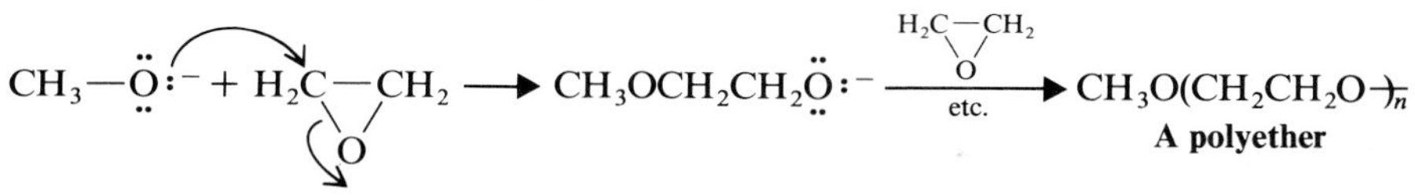

$$CH_3\!-\!\ddot{\text{O}}\!:^- + H_2C\!-\!CH_2 \longrightarrow CH_3OCH_2CH_2\ddot{\text{O}}\!:^- \xrightarrow[\text{etc.}]{\;\;} CH_3O(CH_2CH_2O)_n$$

A polyether

B.1 STEREOCHEMISTRY OF ADDITION POLYMERS

Head-to-tail polymerization of propylene produces a polymer in which every other
atom is a stereocenter. Many of the physical properties of the polypropylene produced in this way depend on the stereochemistry of these stereocenters.

$$CH_2\!=\!CH \xrightarrow[\text{(head to tail)}]{\text{polymerization}} -CH_2\overset{*}{C}HCH_2\overset{*}{C}HCH_2\overset{*}{C}HCH_2\overset{*}{C}H-$$
$$\underset{CH_3}{|} \qquad\qquad \underset{CH_3}{|}\;\; \underset{CH_3}{|}\;\; \underset{CH_3}{|}\;\; \underset{CH_3}{|}$$

There are three general arrangements of the methyl groups and hydrogen atoms
along the chain. These arrangements are described as being *atactic, syndiotactic,* and
isotactic.

If the stereochemistry at the stereocenters is random (Fig. B.1), the polymer is
said to be atactic (*a*, without + Greek: *taktikos,* order).

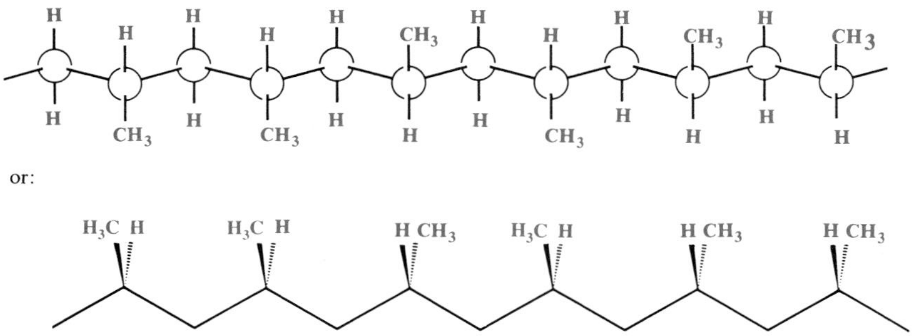

FIGURE B.1 Atactic polypropylene. (In this illustration a "stretched" carbon chain is used
for clarity.)

In atactic polypropylene the methyl groups are randomly disposed on either side
of the stretched carbon chain. If we were to arbitrarily designate one end of the chain
as having higher preference than the other, we could give $(R\!-\!S)$ designations (Section 5.5) to the stereocenters. In atactic polypropylene the sequence of $(R\!-\!S)$ designations along the chain is random.

Polypropylene produced by radical polymerization at high pressures is atactic.
Because the polymer is atactic, it is noncrystalline, has a low softening point, and has
poor mechanical properties.

A second possible arrangement of the groups along the carbon chain is that of
syndiotactic polypropylene. In syndiotactic polypropylene the methyl groups alter-

nate regularly from one side of the stretched chain to the other (Fig. B.2). If we were to arbitrarily designate one end of the chain of syndiotactic polypropylene as having higher preference, the configuration of the stereocenters would alternate, (R), (S), (R), (S), (R), (S), (R), (S), and so on.

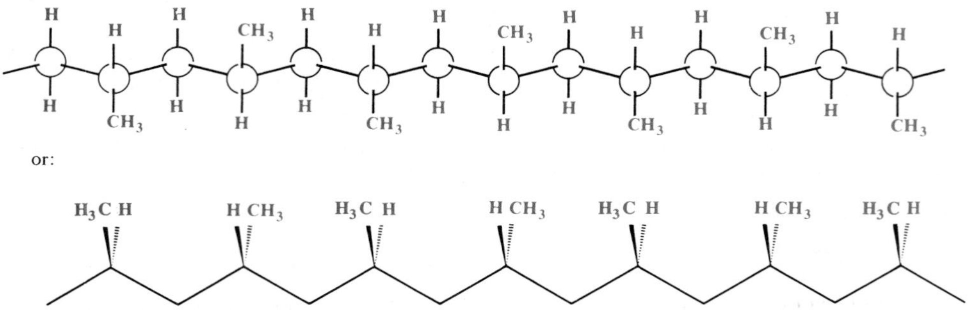

FIGURE B.2 Syndiotactic polypropylene.

The third possible arrangement of stereocenters is the *isotactic* arrangement shown in Fig. B.3. In the isotactic arrangement all of the methyl groups are on the same side of the stretched chain. The configurations of the stereocenters are either all (R) or all (S) depending on which end of the chain is assigned higher preference.

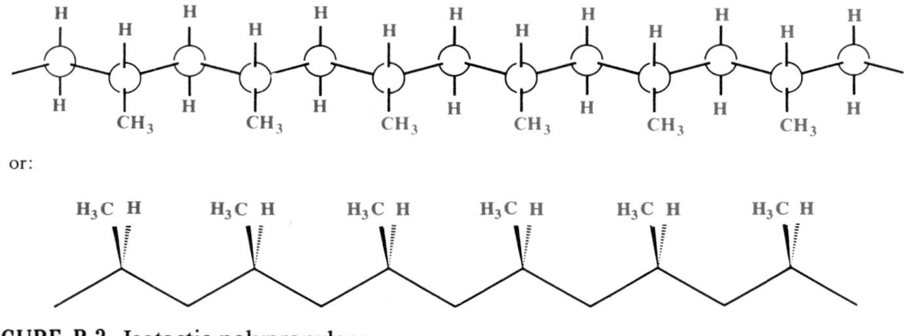

FIGURE B.3 Isotactic polypropylene.

The names isotactic and syndiotactic come from the Greek term *taktikos* (order) plus *iso* (same) and *syndyo* (two together).

Before 1953 isotactic and syndiotactic addition polymers were unknown. In that year, however, a German chemist, Karl Ziegler, and an Italian chemist, Giulio Natta, announced independently the discovery of catalysts that permit stereochemical control of polymerization reactions.* The Ziegler–Natta catalysts, as they are now called, are prepared from transition metal halides and a reducing agent. The catalysts most commonly used are prepared from titanium tetrachloride ($TiCl_4$) and a trialkylaluminum (R_3Al).

Ziegler–Natta catalysts are generally employed as suspended solids, and polymerization probably occurs at metal atoms on the surfaces of the particles. The

*Ziegler and Natta were awarded the Nobel Prize for their discoveries in 1963.

mechanism for the polymerization is an ionic mechanism, but its details are not fully understood. There is evidence that polymerization occurs through an insertion of the alkene monomer between the metal and the growing polymer chain.

Both syndiotactic and isotactic polypropylene have been made using Ziegler – Natta catalysts. The polymerizations occur at much lower pressures and the polymers that are produced are much higher melting than atactic polypropylene. Isotactic polypropylene, for example, melts at 175 °C. Isotactic and syndiotactic polymers are also much more crystalline than atactic polymers. The regular arrangement of groups along the chains allows them to fit together better in a crystal structure.

Atactic, syndiotactic, and isotactic forms of poly(methyl methacrylate) (p. 388) are known. The atactic form is a noncrystalline glass. The crystalline syndiotactic and isotactic forms melt at 160 and 200 °C, respectively.

Problem B.5

Write structural formulas for portions of the chain of: (a) Atactic poly(methyl methacrylate), (b) syndiotactic poly(methyl methacrylate), and (c) isotactic poly(methyl methacrylate).

SPECIAL TOPIC

C

DIVALENT CARBON COMPOUNDS: CARBENES

In recent years considerable research has been devoted to investigating the structures and reactions of a group of compounds in which carbon forms only *two bonds*. These neutral divalent carbon compounds are called *carbenes*.

Most carbenes are highly unstable compounds that are capable of only fleeting existence. Soon after carbenes are formed they usually react with another molecule. The reactions of carbenes are especially interesting because, in many instances, the reactions show a remarkable degree of stereospecificity. The reactions of carbenes are also of great synthetic use in the preparation of compounds that have three-membered rings.

C.1 STRUCTURE OF METHYLENE

The simplest carbene is the compound called methylene (CH_2). Methylene can be prepared by the decomposition of diazomethane* (CH_2N_2). This decomposition can be accomplished by heating diazomethane (thermolysis) or by irradiating it with light of a wavelength that it can absorb (photolysis).

$$:\overset{-}{C}H_2 - \overset{+}{N} \equiv N: \xrightarrow[\text{or light}]{\text{heat}} \quad :CH_2 \ + :N \equiv N:$$

Diazomethane **Methylene** **Nitrogen**

C.2 REACTIONS OF METHYLENE

Methylene reacts with alkenes by adding to the double bond to form cyclopropanes.

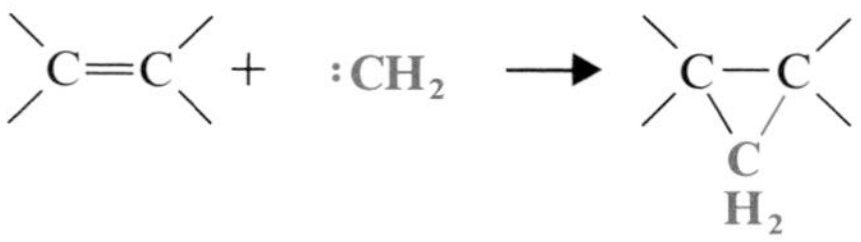

$$\overset{\diagdown}{\underset{\diagup}{C}} = \overset{\diagup}{\underset{\diagdown}{C}} \ + \ :CH_2 \ \longrightarrow \ \overset{\diagdown}{\underset{\diagup}{C}} - \overset{\diagup}{\underset{\diagdown}{C}}$$

Alkene **Methylene** **Cyclopropane**

* Diazomethane is a resonance hybrid of the three structures, **I**, **II**, and **III**, shown below.

$$:\overset{-}{C}H_2 - \overset{+}{N} \equiv N: \ \longleftrightarrow \ CH_2 = \overset{+}{N} = \overset{-}{N}: \ \longleftrightarrow \ :\overset{-}{C}H_2 - \overset{..}{N} = \overset{+}{N}:$$

I **II** **III**

We have chosen resonance structure **I** to illustrate the decomposition of diazomethane because with **I** it is readily apparent that heterolytic cleavage of the carbon–nitrogen bond results in the formation of methylene and molecular nitrogen.

C.3 REACTIONS OF OTHER CARBENES: DIHALOCARBENES

Dihalocarbenes are also frequently employed in the synthesis of cyclopropane derivatives from alkenes. Most reactions of dihalocarbenes are stereospecific.

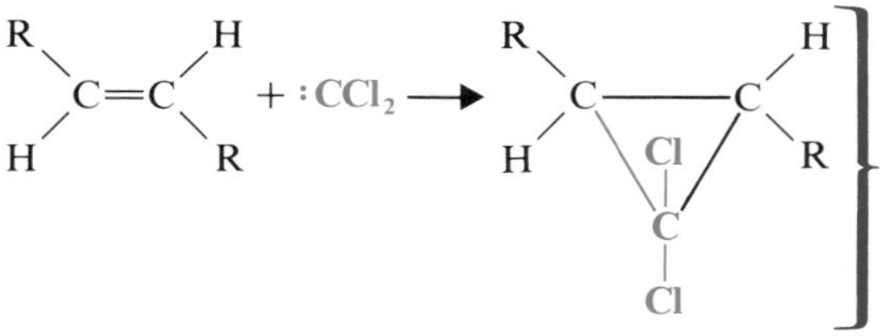

The addition of $:CX_2$ is stereospecific. If the R groups of the alkene are trans, they will be trans in the product

Dichlorocarbene can be synthesized by the *α elimination* of the elements of hydrogen chloride from chloroform. This reaction resembles the *β* elimination reactions by which alkenes are synthesized from alkyl halides (Section 6.17).

$$R-\ddot{O}:^-K^+ + H:CCl_3 \rightleftharpoons R-\ddot{O}:H + {}^-:CCl_3 + K^+ \xrightarrow{slow} :CCl_2 + :\ddot{C}l:^-$$

Dichlorocarbene

Compounds *with a β hydrogen* react by *β* elimination preferentially. Compounds with no *β* hydrogen but with an *α* hydrogen (such as chloroform) react by *α* elimination.

A variety of cyclopropane derivatives have been prepared by generating dichlorocarbene in the presence of alkenes. Cyclohexene, for example, reacts with dichlorocarbene generated by treating chloroform with potassium *tert*-butoxide to give a bicyclic product.

7,7-Dichlorobicyclo[4.1.0]heptane
(59%)

C.4 CARBENOIDS: THE SIMMONS–SMITH CYCLOPROPANE SYNTHESIS

A useful cyclopropane synthesis has been developed by H. E. Simmons and R. D. Smith of the du Pont Company. In this synthesis diiodomethane and a zinc–copper couple are stirred together with an alkene. The diiodomethane and zinc react to produce a carbenelike species called a *carbenoid*.

$$CH_2I_2 + Zn(Cu) \longrightarrow ICH_2ZnI$$

A carbenoid

The carbenoid then brings about the stereospecific addition of a CH_2 group directly to the double bond.

$$\underset{H}{\overset{R}{\diagdown}}C=C\underset{H}{\overset{R}{\diagup}} + ICH_2ZnI \longrightarrow \left[\underset{H}{\overset{R}{\diagdown}}C\!=\!\!C\underset{H}{\overset{R}{\diagup}} \underset{I}{\overset{C}{\underset{H_2}{\diagup}}}_{ZnI} \right] \longrightarrow \underset{H}{\overset{R}{\diagdown}}C\!-\!C\underset{H}{\overset{R}{\diagup}} + ZnI_2$$

This synthesis has been used widely. One example is the synthesis of methyl dihydrosterculate from methyl oleate.

$$\underset{H}{\overset{CH_3(CH_2)_7}{\diagdown}}C=C\underset{H}{\overset{(CH_2)_7CO_2CH_3}{\diagup}} \xrightarrow[\text{Zn(Cu)}]{CH_2I_2} \underset{H}{\overset{CH_3(CH_2)_7}{\diagdown}}C\!-\!C\underset{H}{\overset{(CH_2)_7CO_2CH_3}{\diagup}}$$

Methyl oleate   **Methyl dihydrosterculate**

Methyl dihydrosterculate is related to sterculic acid, an interesting compound that has been isolated from the kernel oil of the tropical tree *Sterculia foetida*. Sterculic acid was the first naturally occurring compound found to have the highly strained cyclopropene ring.

$$\underset{}{\overset{CH_3(CH_2)_7}{\diagdown}}C=C\overset{(CH_2)_7CO_2H}{\diagup}$$

Sterculic acid

Sterculic acid, itself, has been synthesized using the Simmons–Smith method.

$$CH_3(CH_2)_7C\!\equiv\!C(CH_2)_7CO_2H \xrightarrow[\substack{\text{diethyl ether}\\\text{reflux 9 h}}]{CH_2I_2/Zn(Cu)} \underset{}{\overset{CH_3(CH_2)_7}{\diagdown}}C=C\overset{(CH_2)_7CO_2H}{\diagup}$$

Stearolic acid   **(4%)**

This reaction illustrates the addition of a carbenoid to a carbon–carbon triple bond.

The zinc–copper couple used in the Simmons–Smith synthesis can also be prepared *in situ* (in the reaction mixture), as the following example illustrates.

$$\bigcirc\!\!\!| + CH_2I_2 \xrightarrow[\text{diethyl ether}]{\substack{Zn\\Cu_2Cl_2}}$$

Bicyclo[4.1.0]heptane
(92%)

Problem C.1

How might the following compounds be synthesized?

(a)

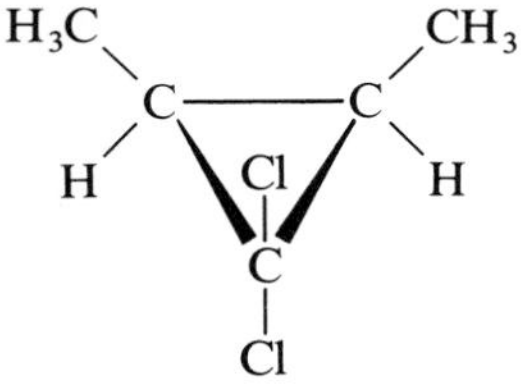

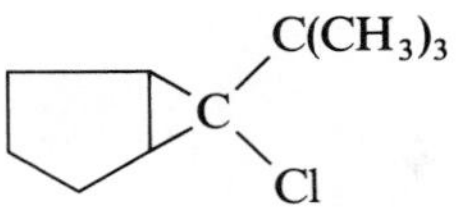

(b)

(c)

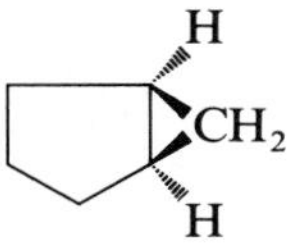

(d)

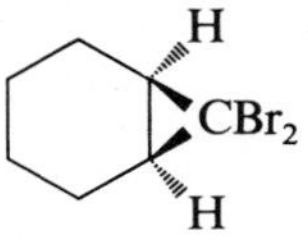

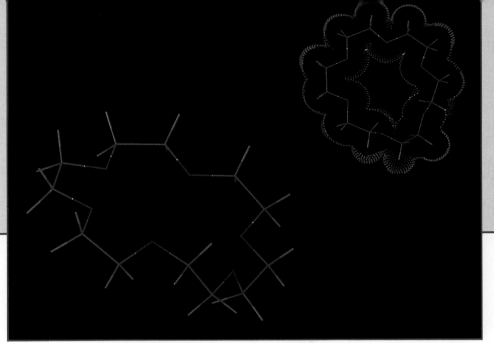

18-Crown-6 (see Section 10.22A).

10

ALCOHOLS AND ETHERS

10.1 STRUCTURE AND NOMENCLATURE

Alcohols are compounds whose molecules have a hydroxyl group attached to a *saturated* carbon atom.* The saturated carbon atom may be that of a simple alkyl group:

$$CH_3OH \qquad CH_3CH_2OH \qquad CH_3\underset{\underset{\displaystyle OH}{|}}{C}HCH_3 \qquad CH_3\underset{\underset{\displaystyle OH}{|}}{\overset{\overset{\displaystyle CH_3}{|}}{C}}CH_3$$

Methanol	**Ethanol**	**2-Propanol**	**2-Methyl-2-propanol**
(methyl alcohol)	**(ethyl alcohol)**	**(isopropyl alcohol)**	**(*tert*-butyl alcohol)**
	a 1° alcohol	*a 2° alcohol*	*a 3° alcohol*

The carbon atom may be a saturated carbon atom of an alkenyl or alkynyl group, or the carbon atom may be a saturated carbon atom that is attached to a benzene ring.

---

* Compounds in which a hydroxyl group is attached to an unsaturated carbon atom of a double bond (i.e., C=C) are called enols, cf. Section 17.2.

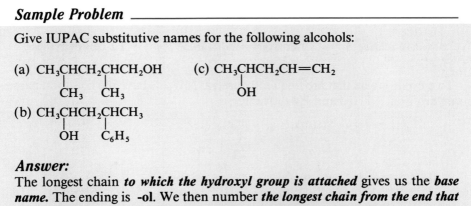

⬡—CH₂OH   CH₂=CHCH₂OH   H—C≡CCH₂OH

Benzyl alcohol   **2-Propenol**   **2-Propynol**

a benzylic alcohol   (allyl alcohol)   (propargyl alcohol)

an allylic alcohol

Compounds that have a hydroxyl group attached directly to a benzene ring are called *phenols*. (Phenols will be discussed in detail in Chapter 21.)

⬡—OH   H₃C—⬡—OH   Ar—OH

Phenol   *p*-**Methylphenol**   **General formula**

a substituted phenol   **for a phenol**

Ethers differ from alcohols in that the oxygen atom of an ether is bonded to two carbon atoms. The hydrocarbon groups may be alkyl, alkenyl, vinyl, alkynyl, or aryl. Several examples are shown here.

CH₃CH₂—O—CH₂CH₃   CH₂=CHCH₂—O—CH₃

Diethyl ether   **Allyl methyl ether**

CH₂=CH—O—CH=CH₂   ⬡—OCH₃

Divinyl ether   **Methyl phenyl ether**

10.1A NOMENCLATURE OF ALCOHOLS

We studied the IUPAC system of nomenclature for alcohols in Section 4.3F. As a review consider the following example.

Sample Problem

Give IUPAC substitutive names for the following alcohols:

(a) CH₃CHCH₂CHCH₂OH   (c) CH₃CHCH₂CH=CH₂
        | | |
        CH₃   CH₃   OH

(b) CH₃CHCH₂CHCH₃
        | |
        OH   C₆H₅

Answer:

The longest chain *to which the hydroxyl group is attached* gives us the *base name.* The ending is **-ol.** We then number *the longest chain from the end that gives the carbon bearing the hydroxyl group the lower number.* Thus, the names are

(a) CH₃CHCH₂CHCH₂OH   (b) CH₃CHCH₂CHCH₃
   5   4   3   2   1   1   2   3   4   5
       | | | |
       CH₃   CH₃   OH   C₆H₅

2,4-Dimethyl-1-pentanol   **4-Phenyl-2-pentanol**

(c) $\overset{1}{C}H_3\overset{2}{C}H\overset{3}{C}H_2\overset{4}{C}H=\overset{5}{C}H_2$
|
OH
    4-Penten-2-ol

The hydroxyl group [see example (c)] has precedence over double bonds and triple bonds in deciding which functional group to name as the suffix.

In common functional class nomenclature (Section 2.10) alcohols are called **alkyl alcohols** such as methyl alcohol, ethyl alcohol, and so on.

10.1B NOMENCLATURE OF ETHERS

Simple ethers are frequently given common radicofunctional names. One simply lists (in alphabetical order) both groups that are attached to the oxygen atom and adds the word *ether*.

$$CH_3OCH_2CH_3 \qquad CH_3CH_2OCH_2CH_3 \qquad C_6H_5O\overset{\overset{\displaystyle CH_3}{|}}{\underset{\underset{\displaystyle CH_3}{|}}{C}}-CH_3$$

Ethyl methyl ether **Diethyl ether** ***tert*-Butyl phenyl ether**

IUPAC substitutive names should be used for complicated ethers, however, and for compounds with more than one ether linkage. In this IUPAC style, ethers are named as alkoxyalkanes, alkoxyalkenes, and alkoxyarenes. The RO— group is an **alkoxy** group.

$$CH_3\overset{\overset{\displaystyle}{|}}{\underset{\underset{\displaystyle OCH_3}{|}}{C}}HCH_2CH_2CH_3 \qquad CH_3CH_2O-\underset{}{\bigcirc}-CH_3 \qquad CH_3OCH_2CH_2OCH_3$$

2-Methoxypentane **1-Ethoxy-4-methylbenzene** **1,2-Dimethoxyethane**

Two cyclic ethers that are frequently used as solvents have the common names tetrahydrofuran (THF) and 1,4-dioxane.

Tetrahydrofuran **1,4-Dioxane**
(oxacyclopentane) **(1,4-dioxacyclohexane)**

Problem 10.1

Give appropriate names for all of the alcohols and ethers with the formulas (a) C_3H_6O, (b) C_4H_8O, and (c) $C_5H_{12}O$.

10.2 PHYSICAL PROPERTIES OF ALCOHOLS AND ETHERS

The physical properties of a number of alcohols and ethers are given in Tables 10.1 and 10.2.

Ethers have boiling points that are roughly comparable with those of hydrocarbons of the same molecular weight. For example, the boiling point of diethyl ether (MW = 74) is 34.6 °C; that of pentane (MW = 72) is 36 °C. Alcohols, on the other hand, have much higher boiling points than comparable ethers or hydrocarbons. The boiling point of butyl alcohol (MW = 74) is 117.7 °C. We learned the reason for this behavior in Section 2.16C; the molecules of alcohols can associate with each other through **hydrogen bonding** while those of ethers and hydrocarbons cannot.

$$\begin{array}{ccc} R & & \\ \diagdown\,{}^{\delta-} & {}^{\delta+} & \cdot\cdot \\ :\!O: \cdots H\!-\!\ddot{O}^{\delta-} & \\ \diagup & & \diagdown \\ H & & R \end{array}$$

Hydrogen bonding between molecules of an alcohol

Ethers, however, *are* able to form hydrogen bonds with compounds such as water. Ethers, therefore, have solubilities in water that are similar to those of alcohols of the same molecular weight and that are very different from those of hydrocarbons.

Diethyl ether and 1-butanol, for example, have the same solubility in water, approximately 8 g per 100 mL at room temperature. Pentane, by contrast, is virtually insoluble in water.

Methanol, ethanol, both propyl alcohols, and *tert*-butyl alcohol are completely miscible with water (Table 10.2). The remaining butyl alcohols have solubilities in

TABLE 10.1 Physical properties of ethers

NAME	FORMULA	mp (°C)	bp (°C)	DENSITY d_4^{20} (g mL^{-1})
Dimethyl ether	CH_3OCH_3	-138	-24.9	0.661
Ethyl methyl ether	$CH_3OCH_2CH_3$		10.8	0.697
Diethyl ether	$CH_3CH_2OCH_2CH_3$	-116	34.6	0.714
Dipropyl ether	$(CH_3CH_2CH_2)_2O$	-122	90.5	0.736
Diisopropyl ether	$(CH_3)_2CHOCH(CH_3)_2$	-86	68	0.725
Dibutyl ether	$(CH_3CH_2CH_2CH_2)_2O$	-97.9	141	0.769
1,2-Dimethoxyethane	$CH_3OCH_2CH_2OCH_3$	-68	83	0.863
Tetrahydrofuran	$(CH_2)_4O$	-108	65.4	0.888
1,4-Dioxane	$O\!\!\bigcirc\!\!O$	11	101	1.033
Anisole (methoxybenzene)	$\bigcirc\!\!-OCH_3$	-37.3	158.3	0.994

TABLE 10.2   Physical properties of alcohols

COMPOUND	NAME	mp (°C)	bp (°C) (1 atm)	DENSITY d_4^{20} (g mL^{-1})	WATER SOLUBILITY (g 100 mL^{-1} H$_2$O)
Monohydroxy Alcohols					
CH_3OH	Methanol	− 97	64.7	0.792	∞
CH_3CH_2OH	Ethanol	−117	78.3	0.789	∞
$CH_3CH_2CH_2OH$	Propyl alcohol	−126	97.2	0.804	∞
$CH_3CH(OH)CH_3$	Isopropyl alcohol	− 88	82.3	0.786	∞
$CH_3CH_2CH_2CH_2OH$	Butyl alcohol	− 90	117.7	0.810	8.3
$CH_3CH(CH_3)CH_2OH$	Isobutyl alcohol	−108	108.0	0.802	10.0
$CH_3CH_2CH(OH)CH_3$	*sec*-Butyl alcohol	−114	99.5	0.808	26.0
$(CH_3)_3COH$	*tert*-Butyl alcohol	25	82.5	0.789	∞
$CH_3(CH_2)_3CH_2OH$	Pentyl alcohol	− 78.5	138.0	0.817	2.4
$CH_3(CH_2)_4CH_2OH$	Hexyl alcohol	− 52	156.5	0.819	0.6
$CH_3(CH_2)_5CH_2OH$	Heptyl alcohol	− 34	176	0.822	0.2
$CH_3(CH_2)_6CH_2OH$	Octyl alcohol	− 15	195	0.825	0.05
$CH_3(CH_2)_7CH_2OH$	Nonyl alcohol	− 5.5	212	0.827	
$CH_3(CH_2)_8CH_2OH$	Decyl alcohol	6	228	0.829	
$CH_2{=}CHCH_2OH$	Allyl alcohol	−129	97	0.855	∞
$(CH_2)_4CHOH$	Cyclopentanol	− 19	140	0.949	
$(CH_2)_5CHOH$	Cyclohexanol	24	161.5	0.962	3.6
$C_6H_5CH_2OH$	Benzyl alcohol	− 15	205	1.046	4
Diols and Triols					
CH_2OHCH_2OH	Ethylene glycol	− 12.6	197	1.113	∞
$CH_3CHOHCH_2OH$	Propylene glycol	− 59	187	1.040	∞
$CH_2OHCH_2CH_2OH$	Trimethylene glycol	− 30	215	1.060	∞
$CH_2OHCHOHCH_2OH$	Glycerol	18	290	1.261	∞

water between 8.3 and 26.0 g per 100 mL. The solubility of alcohols in water gradually decreases as the hydrocarbon portion of the molecule lengthens; long-chain alcohols are more "alkane-like" and are, therefore, less like water.

Problem 10.2

How can you account for the fact that the boiling point of ethylene glycol is much higher than that of either propyl alcohol or isopropyl alcohol even though all three compounds have roughly the same molecular weight?

10.3 IMPORTANT ALCOHOLS AND ETHERS

10.3A METHANOL

At one time, most methanol was produced by the destructive distillation of wood (i.e., heating wood to a high temperature in the absence of air). It was because of this method of preparation that methanol came to be called "wood alcohol." Today, most methanol is prepared by the catalytic hydrogenation of carbon monoxide. This reaction takes place under high pressure and at a temperature of 300–400 °C.

$$CO + 2 H_2 \xrightarrow[\substack{200-300 \text{ atm} \\ ZnO-Cr_2O_3}]{300-400 \text{ °C}} CH_3OH$$

Methanol is highly toxic. Ingestion of even small quantities of methanol can cause blindness; large quantities cause death. Methanol poisoning can also occur by inhalation of the vapors or by prolonged exposure to the skin.

10.3B ETHANOL

Ethanol can be made by the fermentation of sugars, and it is the alcohol of all alcoholic beverages. The synthesis of ethanol in the form of wine by the fermentation of the sugars of fruit juices was probably man's first accomplishment in the field of organic synthesis. Sugars from a wide variety of sources can be used in the preparation of alcoholic beverages. Often, these sugars are from grains, and it is this derivation that accounts for ethanol having the synonym "grain alcohol."

Fermentation is usually carried out by adding yeast to a mixture of sugars and water. Yeast contains enzymes that promote a long series of reactions that ultimately convert a simple sugar ($C_6H_{12}O_6$) to ethanol and carbon dioxide.

$$C_6H_{12}O_6 \xrightarrow{\text{yeast}} 2 CH_3CH_2OH + 2 CO_2$$
$$(\sim 95\% \text{ yield})$$

Fermentation alone does not produce beverages with an ethanol content greater than 12–15% because the enzymes of the yeast are deactivated at higher concentrations. To produce beverages of higher alcohol content the aqueous solution must be distilled. Brandy, whiskey, and vodka are produced in this way. The "proof" of an alcoholic beverage is simply twice the percentage of ethanol (by volume). One hundred proof whiskey is 50% ethanol. The flavors of the various distilled liquors result from other organic compounds that distill with the alcohol and water.

Distillation of a solution of ethanol and water will not yield ethanol more concentrated than 95%. A mixture of 95% ethanol and 5% water boils at a lower temperature (78.15 °C) than either pure ethanol (bp, 78.3 °C) or pure water (bp, 100 °C). Such a mixture is an example of an **azeotrope**.* Pure ethanol can be prepared by adding benzene to the mixture of 95% ethanol and water and then distilling this solution. Benzene forms a different azeotrope with ethanol and water that is 7.5% water. This azeotrope boils at 64.9 °C and allows removal of the water (along with some ethanol). Eventually pure ethanol distills over. Pure ethanol is called **absolute alcohol**.

Ethanol is quite cheap, but when it is used for beverages it is highly taxed. (The tax is greater than $20 per gallon in most states.) Federal law requires that some

*Azeotropes can also have boiling points that are higher than that of either of the pure components.

ethanol used for scientific and industrial purposes be adulterated or "denatured" to make it undrinkable. Various denaturants are used including methanol.

Ethanol is an important industrial chemical. Most ethanol for industrial purposes is produced by the acid-catalyzed hydration of ethene.

$$CH_2{=}CH_2 + H_2O \xrightarrow[\text{acid}]{} CH_3CH_2OH$$

Ethanol is a *hypnotic* (sleep producer). It depresses activity in the upper brain even though it gives the illusion of being a stimulant. Ethanol is also toxic, but it is much less toxic than methanol. In rats the lethal dose of ethanol is 13.7 g kg^{-1} of body weight. Abuse of ethanol is a major drug problem in most countries.

10.3C ETHYLENE GLYCOL

Ethylene glycol ($HOCH_2CH_2OH$) has a low molecular weight and a high-boiling point and is miscible with water. These properties make ethylene glycol an ideal automobile antifreeze. Much ethylene glycol is sold for this purpose under a variety of trade names.

10.3D DIETHYL ETHER

Diethyl ether is a very low-boiling, highly flammable liquid. Care should always be taken when diethyl ether is used in the laboratory, because open flames or sparks from light switches can cause explosive combustion of mixtures of diethyl ether and air.

Most ethers react slowly with oxygen by a radical process called **autoxidation** (see Section 7.10B) to form hydroperoxides and peroxides.

Step 1 $R\cdot + -\overset{\text{H}}{\underset{|}{C}}{-}OR' \longrightarrow R:H + -\overset{\cdot}{\underset{|}{C}}{-}OR'$

Step 2 $-\overset{\cdot}{\underset{|}{C}}{-}OR' + O_2 \longrightarrow -\overset{\overset{\displaystyle OO\cdot}{|}}{\underset{|}{C}}{-}OR'$

Step 3a $-\overset{\overset{\displaystyle OO\cdot}{|}}{\underset{|}{C}}{-}OR' + -\overset{\text{H}}{\underset{|}{C}}{-}OR' \longrightarrow -\overset{\overset{\displaystyle OOH}{|}}{\underset{|}{C}}{-}OR' + -\overset{\cdot}{\underset{|}{C}}{-}OR'$

A hydroperoxide

or

Step 3b $-\overset{\overset{\displaystyle OO\cdot}{|}}{\underset{|}{C}}{-}OR' + -\overset{\cdot}{\underset{|}{C}}{-}OR' \longrightarrow R'O{-}\overset{|}{\underset{|}{C}}{-}OO{-}\overset{|}{\underset{|}{C}}{-}OR'$

A peroxide

These hydroperoxides and peroxides, which often accumulate in ethers that have been left standing for long periods of time in contact with air (the air in the top of the bottle is enough), are dangerously explosive. They often detonate without warning when ether solutions are distilled to near dryness. Since ethers are used frequently in extractions, one should take care to test for and decompose any peroxides present in the ether before a distillation is carried out. (Consult a laboratory manual for instructions.)

Diethyl ether was first employed as a surgical anesthetic by C. W. Long of Jefferson, Georgia, in 1842. Long's use of diethyl ether was not published, but shortly thereafter, diethyl ether was introduced into surgical use at the Massachusetts General Hospital in Boston by J. C. Warren.

The most popular modern anesthetic is halothane ($CF_3CHBrCl$). Unlike diethyl ether, halothane is not flammable.

10.4 SYNTHESIS OF ALCOHOLS FROM ALKENES

We have already studied one method for the synthesis of alcohols from alkenes: **acid-catalyzed hydration** (or by the addition of sulfuric acid followed by hydrolysis, which amounts to the same thing).

10.4A HYDRATION OF ALKENES (DISCUSSED IN SECTION 9.5)

Alkenes add water in the presence of an acid catalyst. The addition follows Markovnikov's rule; thus, except for the hydration of ethylene, the reaction produces secondary and tertiary alcohols. The reaction is reversible and the mechanism for the hydration of an alkene is simply the reverse of that for the dehydration of an alcohol (Section 8.13).

$$\overset{\diagdown}{\diagup}C=C\overset{\diagup}{\diagdown} \underset{-H^+}{\overset{+H^+}{\rightleftharpoons}} -\overset{|}{\underset{H}{C}}-\overset{|}{\underset{+}{C}}- \underset{-H_2O}{\overset{+H_2O}{\rightleftharpoons}} -\overset{|}{\underset{H}{C}}-\overset{|}{\underset{^+OH_2}{C}}- \underset{+H^+}{\overset{-H^+}{\rightleftharpoons}} -\overset{|}{\underset{H}{C}}-\overset{|}{\underset{OH}{C}}-$$

Alkene   **Alcohol**

[*Remember:* Rearrangements occur whenever a less stable carbocation can rearrange (by a hydride or alkanide shift) to a more stable one.]

Problem 10.3

Show how you would prepare each of the following alcohols by acid-catalyzed hydration of the appropriate alkene.

(a) *tert*-Butyl alcohol   (c) Cyclopentanol
(b) 2-Hexanol   (d) 1-Methylcyclohexanol

Problem 10.4

When 3,3-dimethyl-1-butene is subjected to acid-catalyzed hydration the major product is 2,3-dimethyl-2-butanol. How can you explain this result?

In the sections that follow we shall study two new methods for synthesizing alcohols from alkenes. One of these methods, **oxymercuration–demercuration** (Section 10.5), complements acid-catalyzed hydration in that it gives us an additional method for **Markovnikov addition** of H— and —OH, **and one that is not complicated by rearrangements.** The other method, **hydroboration–oxidation** (Section 10.7), *gives us a method for the net anti-Markovnikov addition of H— and —OH.*

10.5 ALCOHOLS FROM ALKENES THROUGH OXYMERCURATION–DEMERCURATION

A highly useful laboratory procedure for synthesizing alcohols from alkenes is a two-step method called **oxymercuration–demercuration.**

Alkenes react with mercuric acetate in a mixture of THF and water to produce (hydroxyalkyl)mercury compounds. These (hydroxyalkyl)mercury compounds can be reduced to alcohols with sodium borohydride:

$$
-\overset{|}{C}=\overset{|}{C}- + H_2O + Hg\left(O\overset{\overset{O}{\|}}{C}CH_3\right)_2 \xrightarrow[\text{oxymercuration}]{\text{THF}} -\overset{|}{\underset{HO}{C}}-\overset{|}{\underset{Hg-O\overset{\overset{O}{\|}}{C}CH_3}{C}}- \;\;O + CH_3\overset{\overset{O}{\|}}{C}OH
$$

$$
-\overset{|}{\underset{HO}{C}}-\overset{|}{\underset{Hg-O\overset{\overset{O}{\|}}{C}CH_3}{C}}- \;\;O + OH^- + NaBH_4 \xrightarrow[\text{demercuration}]{} -\overset{|}{\underset{HO}{C}}-\overset{|}{\underset{H}{C}}- + Hg + CH_3\overset{\overset{O}{\|}}{C}O^-
$$

In the first step, **oxymercuration,** water and mercuric acetate add to the double bond in the second step, **demercuration,** sodium borohydride reduces the acetoxymercuri group and replaces it with hydrogen. (The acetate group is often abbreviated —OAc.)

Both steps can be carried out in the same vessel, and both reactions take place very rapidly at room temperature or below. The first step—oxymercuration—usually goes to completion within a period of 20 s–10 min. The second step—demercuration—normally requires less than an hour. The overall reaction gives alcohols in very high yields, usually greater than 90%.

Oxymercuration–demercuration is also highly regioselective. The net orientation of the addition of the elements of water, H— and —OH, *is in accordance with Markovnikov's rule.* The H— becomes attached to the carbon atom of the double bond with the greater number of hydrogen atoms:

$$
R-\overset{\overset{H}{|}}{C}=\overset{\overset{H}{|}}{C}-H \;\; \underset{(2)\; NaBH_4,\; OH^-}{\overset{(1)\; Hg(OAc)_2/THF-H_2O^*}{\longrightarrow}} \;\; R-\overset{\overset{H}{|}}{\underset{HO}{C}}-\overset{\overset{H}{|}}{\underset{H}{C}}-H
$$
$$
+
$$
$$
HO-H
$$

The following specific examples are illustrations:

---

*Writing reagents above and below the arrow like this $\xrightarrow[\text{(2) NaBH}_4,\; OH^-]{\text{(1) Hg(OAc)}_2/\text{THF}-\text{H}_2\text{O}}$ means that two steps are involved.

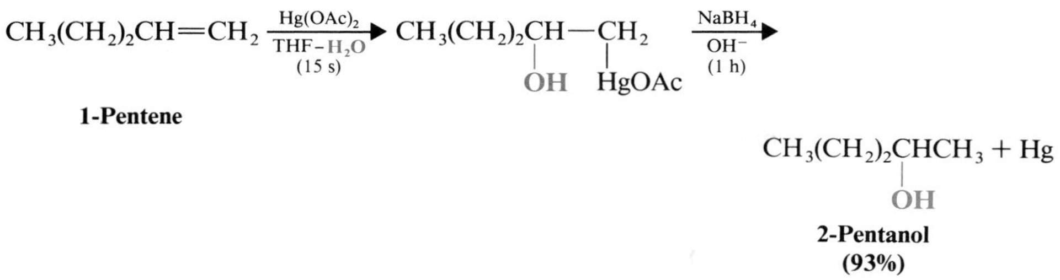

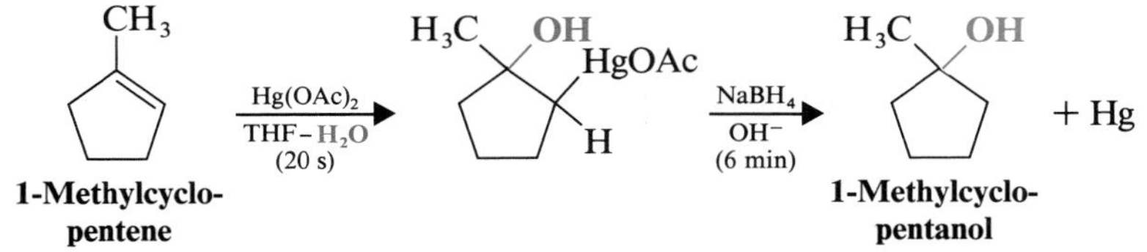

10.5 ALCOHOLS FROM ALKENES THROUGH OXYMERCURATION – DEMERCURATION

$$CH_3(CH_2)_2CH=CH_2 \xrightarrow[\substack{THF-H_2O \\ (15\ s)}]{Hg(OAc)_2} CH_3(CH_2)_2\underset{\underset{OH}{|}}{CH}-\underset{\underset{HgOAc}{|}}{CH_2} \xrightarrow[\substack{OH^- \\ (1\ h)}]{NaBH_4}$$

1-Pentene

$$CH_3(CH_2)_2\underset{\underset{OH}{|}}{CH}CH_3 + Hg$$

2-Pentanol
(93%)

1-Methylcyclo-
pentene

$\xrightarrow[\substack{THF-H_2O \\ (20\ s)}]{Hg(OAc)_2}$

$\xrightarrow[\substack{OH^- \\ (6\ min)}]{NaBH_4}$

$+ Hg$

1-Methylcyclo-
pentanol

Rearrangements of the carbon skeleton seldom occur in oxymercuration – demercuration. The following oxymercuration – demercuration of 3,3-dimethyl-1-butene is a striking example illustrating this feature.

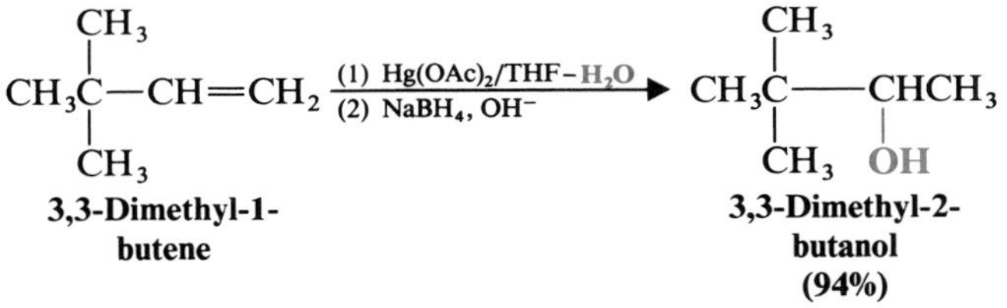

$$CH_3\underset{\underset{CH_3}{|}}{\overset{\overset{CH_3}{|}}{C}}-CH=CH_2 \xrightarrow[\text{(2) NaBH}_4,\ OH^-]{\text{(1) Hg(OAc)}_2/THF-H_2O} CH_3\underset{\underset{CH_3}{|}}{\overset{\overset{CH_3}{|}}{C}}\underset{\underset{OH}{|}}{-CHCH_3}$$

3,3-Dimethyl-1-
butene

3,3-Dimethyl-2-
butanol
(94%)

Analysis of the mixture of products by gas – liquid chromatography failed to reveal the presence of any 2,3-dimethyl-2-butanol. The acid-catalyzed hydration of 3,3-di-methyl-1-butene, by contrast, gives 2,3-dimethyl-2-butanol as the major product (Section 9.5).

A mechanism that accounts for the orientation of addition in the oxymercuration stage, and one that also explains the general lack of accompanying rearrangements, is shown below. According to this mechanism, the first step of the oxymercuration reaction is an electrophilic attack by the mercury species, $\overset{+}{Hg}OAc$, at the less substituted carbon of the double bond (i.e., at the carbon atom that bears the greater number of hydrogen atoms). We can illustrate this step using 3,3-dimethyl-1-butene as the example:

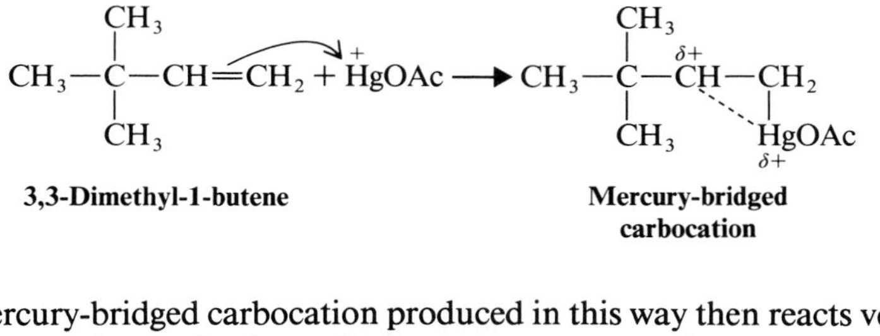

$$CH_3-\underset{\underset{CH_3}{|}}{\overset{\overset{CH_3}{|}}{C}}-CH=CH_2 + \overset{+}{Hg}OAc \longrightarrow CH_3-\underset{\underset{CH_3}{|}}{\overset{\overset{CH_3}{|}}{C}}-\overset{\delta+}{CH}\cdots\underset{\underset{\delta+}{|}}{\overset{|}{CH_2}}$$

3,3-Dimethyl-1-butene

Mercury-bridged
carbocation

The mercury-bridged carbocation produced in this way then reacts very rapidly with water to produce a (hydroxyalkyl)mercury compound.

$$CH_3-\overset{\overset{\displaystyle CH_3}{|}}{\underset{\underset{\displaystyle CH_3}{|}}{C}}-\overset{\delta+}{CH}-\overset{|}{\underset{\underset{\displaystyle HgOAc}{}}{CH_2}} \quad + \quad :\overset{\cdot\cdot}{O}-H \longrightarrow$$

Mercury-bridged
carbocation

$$CH_3-\overset{\overset{\displaystyle CH_3}{|}}{\underset{\underset{\displaystyle CH_3}{|}}{C}}-\overset{\displaystyle :\overset{+}{O}-H}{\underset{}{CH}}-\overset{|}{\underset{\underset{\displaystyle HgOAc}{}}{CH_2}} \quad \overset{\cdot\cdot}{O}-H \longrightarrow$$

$$CH_3-\overset{\overset{\displaystyle CH_3}{|}}{\underset{\underset{\displaystyle CH_3}{|}}{C}}-\overset{\overset{\displaystyle H}{|}}{\underset{}{\overset{\displaystyle :O:}{CH}}}-\overset{|}{\underset{\underset{\displaystyle HgOAc}{}}{CH_2}} \quad + \quad H-\overset{+}{\underset{\underset{\displaystyle H}{|}}{\overset{\cdot\cdot}{O}}}-H$$

(Hydroxyalkyl)mercury
compound

Calculations indicate that mercury-bridged carbocations like those formed in this reaction retain much of the positive charge on the mercury moiety. Only a small portion of the positive charge resides on the more substituted carbon atom. The charge is large enough to account for the observed Markovnikov addition, but it is too small to allow the usual rapid carbon-skeleton rearrangements that take place with more fully developed carbocations.

The mechanism for the replacement of the acetoxymercuri group by hydrogen is not well understood. Radicals are thought to be involved.

Problem 10.5

Starting with an appropriate alkene, show all steps in the synthesis of each of the following alcohols by oxymercuration–demercuration.

(a) *tert*-Butyl alcohol   (b) Isopropyl alcohol   (c) $CH_3\overset{\overset{\displaystyle OH}{|}}{\underset{\underset{\displaystyle CH_3}{|}}{C}}CH_2CH_3$

Problem 10.6

When an alkene is treated with mercuric trifluoroacetate, $Hg(O_2CCF_3)_2$, in THF containing an alcohol, ROH, the product is an (alkoxyalkyl)mercury compound. Treating this product with $NaBH_4/OH^-$ results in the formation of an ether. The overall process is called *solvomercuration–demercuration*.

$$\overset{\diagdown}{\diagup}C=C\overset{\diagup}{\diagdown} \quad \xrightarrow[\text{solvomercuration}]{Hg(O_2CCF_3)_2/THF-ROH} \quad -\overset{\overset{\displaystyle RO}{|}}{\underset{}{C}}-\overset{|}{\underset{\underset{\displaystyle HgO_2CCF_3}{}}{C}}- \quad \xrightarrow[\text{demercuration}]{NaBH_4,\ OH^-} \quad -\overset{\overset{\displaystyle RO}{|}}{\underset{}{C}}-\overset{|}{\underset{\underset{\displaystyle H}{|}}{C}}-$$

Alkene   (Alkoxyalkyl)mercuric   Ether
              trifluoroacetate

(a) Outline a likely mechanism for the solvomercuration step of this ether synthesis. (b) Show how you would use solvomercuration–demercuration to prepare *tert*-butyl methyl ether.

10.6 HYDROBORATION: SYNTHESIS OF ORGANOBORANES

The addition of a compound containing a hydrogen–boron bond, H—B (called a

boron hydride), to an alkene is the starting point for a number of highly useful synthetic procedures. This addition, called **hydroboration,** was discovered by Herbert C. Brown* (of Purdue University). In its simplest terms, hydroboration can be represented as follows:

$$\text{C}=\text{C} + \text{H}-\text{B} \xrightarrow{\text{hydroboration}} -\overset{|}{\underset{\text{H}}{\text{C}}}-\overset{|}{\underset{\text{B}-}{\text{C}}}-$$

| Alkene | Boron hydride | Organoborane |

Hydroboration can be carried out by using the boron hydride (B_2H_6) called **diborane.** It is much more convenient, however, to use a solution of diborane in THF. When diborane dissolves in THF each B_2H_6 dissociates to produce two molecules of a complex between BH_3 (called **borane**) and THF:

$$B_2H_6 + :O \longrightarrow O:BH_3$$

| Diborane | THF | THF:BH_3 |

BH_3 is a Lewis acid (because the boron has only six electrons in its valence shell). It accepts an electron pair from the oxygen atom of THF

Solutions containing the THF:BH_3 complex can be obtained commercially. Hydroboration reactions are usually carried out in ethers; either in diethyl ether, $(C_2H_5)_2O$, or in some higher molecular weight ether such as "diglyme," $(CH_3OCH_2CH_2)_2O$, *di*ethylene *gly*col *di*me*thyl ether.

> *Great care must be used in handling diborane and alkylboranes because they ignite spontaneously in air. The solution of THF:BH₃ is considerably less prone to spontaneous ignition but still must be used in an inert atmosphere and with care.*

10.6A MECHANISM OF HYDROBORATION

When a 1-alkene such as propene is treated with a solution containing the THF:BH_3 complex, the boron hydride adds successively to the double bonds of three molecules of the alkene to form a trialkylborane:

---

*Brown's discovery of hydroboration led to his being a co-winner of the Nobel Prize for Chemistry in 1979.

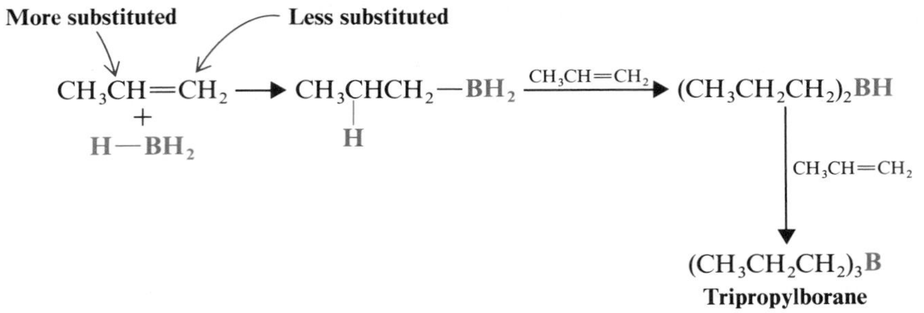

More substituted   Less substituted

$$CH_3CH{=}CH_2 \longrightarrow CH_3CHCH_2{-}BH_2 \xrightarrow{CH_3CH=CH_2} (CH_3CH_2CH_2)_2BH$$
$$+ \qquad\qquad\qquad |$$
$$H{-}BH_2 \qquad\qquad\qquad H$$

$$|\quad CH_3CH{=}CH_2$$

$$\downarrow$$

$$(CH_3CH_2CH_2)_3B$$
Tripropylborane

In each addition step *the boron atom becomes attached to the less substituted carbon atom of the double bond,* and a hydrogen atom is transferred from the boron atom to the other carbon atom of the double bond. Thus, hydroboration is regioselective and it is **anti-Markovnikov** (the hydrogen atom becomes attached to the carbon atom with **fewer** hydrogen atoms).

Other examples that illustrate this tendency for the boron atom to become attached to the less substituted carbon atom are shown here. The percentages designate where the boron atom becomes attached.

$$\underset{1\% \qquad\qquad 99\%}{CH_3CH_2\overset{\overset{\displaystyle CH_3}{|}}{C}{=}CH_2} \qquad\qquad \underset{2\% \qquad\qquad 98\%}{CH_3\overset{\overset{\displaystyle CH_3}{|}}{C}{=}CHCH_3}$$

Less substituted   Less substituted

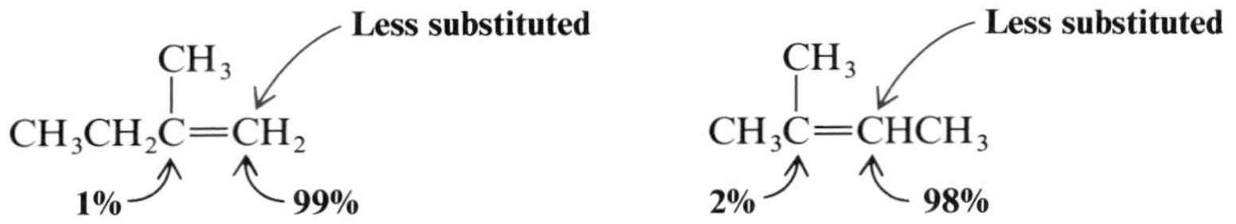

This observed attachment of boron to the less substituted carbon atom of the double bond seems to result in part from **steric factors** — the bulky boron-containing group can approach the less substituted carbon atom more easily.

A mechanism that has been proposed for the addition of BH_3 to the double bond begins with a donation of π electrons from the double bond to the vacant p orbital of BH_3 (Fig. 10.1). In the next step this complex becomes the addition product by passing through a transition state in which the boron atom is partially bonded to the less substituted carbon atom of the double bond and one hydrogen atom is partially bonded to the other carbon atom. As the transition state is approached, electrons shift in the direction of the boron atom and away from the more substituted carbon atom of the double bond. This makes the more substituted carbon atom develop a partial positive charge *and because it bears an electron-releasing alkyl group, it is better able to accommodate this positive charge.*

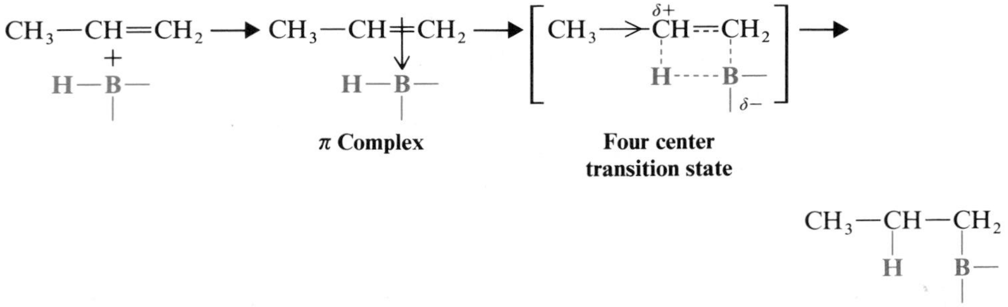

$$CH_3{-}CH{=}CH_2 \longrightarrow CH_3{-}CH{\overset{|}{=}}CH_2 \longrightarrow \left[CH_3{\rightarrow}\overset{\delta+}{CH}{=\!=\!=}CH_2 \right] \longrightarrow$$
$$+ \qquad\qquad\qquad \downarrow \qquad\qquad\qquad\quad \overset{\vdots}{H}{-----}\underset{|\;\delta-}{\overset{\vdots}{B}{-}}$$
$$H{-}B{-} \qquad\qquad H{-}B{-}$$

$$\pi \text{ Complex} \qquad\qquad \text{Four center}$$
$$\text{transition state}$$

$$CH_3{-}CH{-}CH_2$$
$$| \qquad |$$
$$H \qquad B{-}$$
$$|$$

FIGURE 10.1   A mechanism for the addition of a boron hydride to propene.

10.6B THE STEREOCHEMISTRY OF HYDROBORATION

The transition state for hydroboration requires that *the boron atom and the hydrogen atom add to the same face of the double bond* (look at Fig. 10.1 again). The addition, therefore, is a **syn** addition:

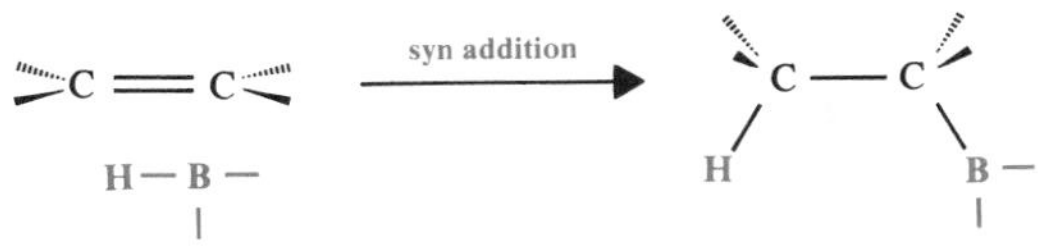

We can see the results of a syn addition in the hydroboration of 1-methylcyclopentene. (We also see again that the addition is anti-Markovnikov.)

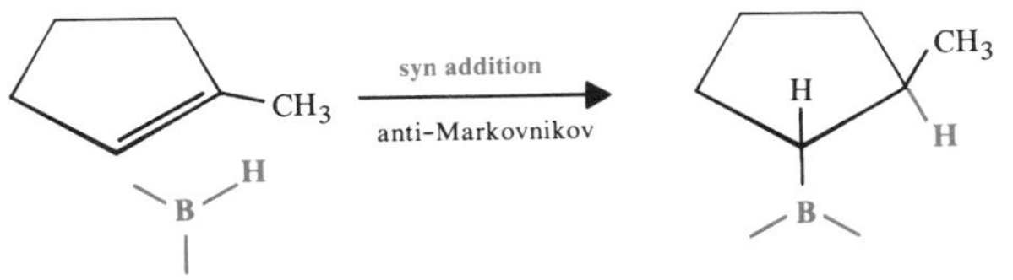

Problem 10.7

Starting with an appropriate alkene, show the synthesis of (a) tributylborane, (b) triisobutylborane, and (c) tri-*sec*-butylborane. (d) Show the stereochemistry involved in the hydroboration of 1-methylcyclohexene.

Problem 10.8

Treating a hindered alkene such as 2-methyl-2-butene with THF : BH_3 leads to the formation of a dialkylborane instead of a trialkylborane. When 2 mol of 2-methyl-2-butene add to 1 mol of BH_3, the product formed has the nickname "disiamylborane." Write its structure. (The name "disiamyl" comes from "*di-secondary-isoamyl*" a completely unsystematic and unacceptable name. The name "amyl" is an old common name for a five-carbon alkyl group.) Disiamylborane is a useful reagent in certain syntheses that require a sterically hindered borane.

10.7 ALCOHOLS FROM ALKENES THROUGH HYDROBORATION – OXIDATION

Addition of the elements of water to a double bond can also be achieved in the laboratory through the use of diborane or THF : BH_3. The addition of water is indirect and two reactions are involved. The first is the addition of borane to the double bond, **hydroboration**; the second is the **oxidation** and hydrolysis of the organoboron intermediate to an alcohol and boric acid. We can illustrate these steps with the hydroboration – oxidation of propene.

$$3\ CH_3CH{=}CH_2 \xrightarrow[\text{hydroboration}]{\text{THF : } BH_3} (CH_3CH_2CH_2)_3B \xrightarrow{H_2O_2/OH^-} 3\ CH_3CH_2CH_2OH$$

Propene   **Tripropylborane**   **Propyl alcohol**

The alkylboranes produced in the hydroboration step usually are not isolated. They are oxidized and hydrolyzed to alcohols in the same reaction vessel by the addition of hydrogen peroxide in an aqueous base.

$$R_3B \xrightarrow[\substack{NaOH,\ 25\ ^\circ C \\ oxidation}]{H_2O_2} 3\ R—OH + Na_3BO_3$$

The mechanism for the oxidation step begins with the addition of a hydroperoxide ion (HOO^-) to the electron-deficient boron atom.

$$R—B \overset{\displaystyle R}{\underset{\displaystyle R}{|}} +\ ^-O—OH \longrightarrow \left[R—B\overset{\displaystyle R}{\underset{\displaystyle R}{|}}—O—OH \right]^-$$

The resulting compound is unstable and loses a hydroxide ion. At the same time that this happens *an alkyl group migrates from the boron atom to the oxygen atom.*

$$\left[R—B\overset{\displaystyle R}{\underset{\displaystyle R}{|}}—O—OH \right]^- \longrightarrow R—B\overset{\displaystyle R}{\underset{\displaystyle R}{|}}—O—R + OH^-$$

This step *takes place with retention of configuration of the alkyl group.* Repetitions of these two steps occur until all of the alkyl groups have become attached to oxygen atoms. The result is the formation of a trialkyl borate, an ester, $B(OR)_3$. This ester then undergoes basic hydrolysis to produce three molecules of the alcohol and a borate ion.

$$B(OR)_3 + 3\ OH^- \xrightarrow{H_2O} 3\ ROH + BO_3{}^{3-}$$

Because hydroboration reactions are regioselective, the net result of hydroboration–oxidation is an apparent **anti-Markovnikov addition of water.** As a consequence, *hydroboration–oxidation gives us a method for the preparation of alcohols that cannot normally be obtained through the acid-catalyzed hydration of alkenes or by oxymercuration–demercuration.* For example, acid-catalyzed hydration (or oxymercuration–demercuration) of 1-hexene yields 2-hexanol:

$$CH_3CH_2CH_2CH_2CH{=}CH_2 \xrightarrow{H_3O^+,\ H_2O} CH_3CH_2CH_2CH_2\underset{\substack{| \\ OH}}{C}HCH_3$$

1-Hexene   **2-Hexanol**

Hydroboration–oxidation, by contrast, yields 1-hexanol:

$$CH_3CH_2CH_2CH_2CH{=}CH_2 \xrightarrow[\substack{(2)\ H_2O_2,\ OH^-}]{(1)\ THF:BH_3} CH_3CH_2CH_2CH_2CH_2CH_2OH$$

1-Hexene   **1-Hexanol (90%)**

Other examples of hydroboration–oxidation are the following:

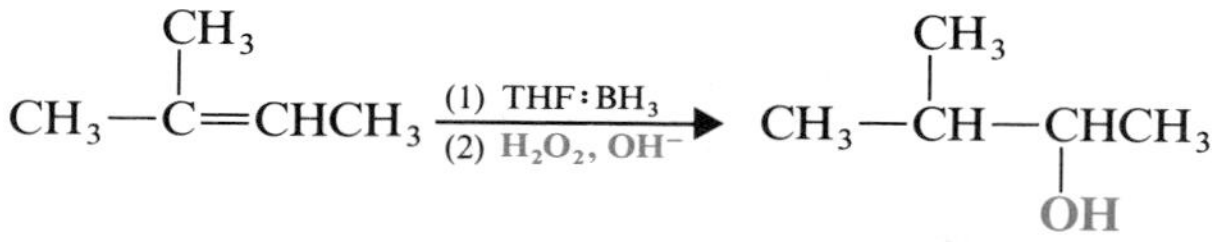

10.7 ALCOHOLS FROM ALKENES THROUGH HYDROBORATION-OXIDATION

$$CH_3-\underset{\underset{CH_3}{|}}{C}=CHCH_3 \xrightarrow[\text{(2) } H_2O_2,\ OH^-]{\text{(1) THF:}BH_3} CH_3-\underset{\underset{OH}{|}}{\overset{\overset{CH_3}{|}}{CH}}-CHCH_3$$

2-Methyl-2-butene   **3-Methyl-2-butanol (59%)**

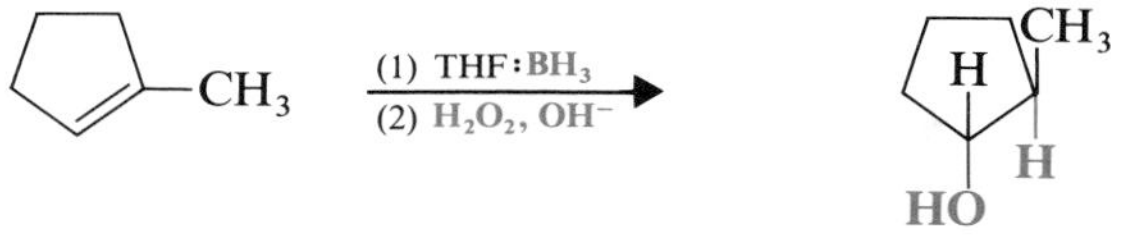

$$\text{⬠}-CH_3 \xrightarrow[\text{(2) } H_2O_2,\ OH^-]{\text{(1) THF:}BH_3}$$

1-Methylcyclopentene   ***trans*-2-Methylcyclopentanol (86%)**

10.7A THE STEREOCHEMISTRY OF THE OXIDATION OF ORGANOBORANES

Because the oxidation step in the hydroboration–oxidation synthesis of alcohols takes place with retention of configuration, ***the hydroxyl group replaces the boron atom where it stands in the organoboron compound.*** The net result of the two steps (hydroboration and oxidation) is the ***syn addition*** of —H and —OH. We can see this if we examine the hydroboration–oxidation of 1-methylcyclopentene (Fig. 10.2).

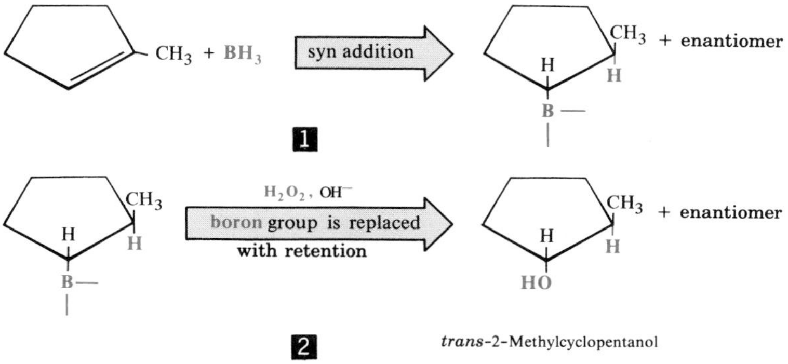

FIGURE 10.2 The hydroboration–oxidation of 1-methylcyclopentene. The first reaction is a syn addition of borane. (In this illustration we have shown the boron and hydrogen both entering from the bottom side of 1-methylcyclopentene. The reaction also takes place from the top side at an equal rate to produce the enantiomer.) In the second reaction the boron atom is replaced by a hydroxyl group with retention of configuration. The product is a trans compound (*trans*-2-methylcyclopentanol) and the overall result is the syn addition of —H and —OH.

Problem 10.9

Show how you might employ hydroboration–oxidation reactions to carry out the following syntheses.

(a) 1-Butene $\longrightarrow$ $CH_3CH_2CH_2CH_2OH$

(b) 2-Methyl-2-butene $\longrightarrow$ $CH_3\underset{\underset{OH}{|}}{\overset{\overset{CH_3}{|}}{CH}}CHCHCH_3$

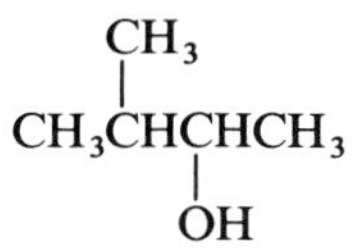

(c) 1-Methylcyclohexene ⟶

10.7B PROTONOLYSIS OF ORGANOBORANES

Heating an organoborane with acetic acid causes cleavage of the carbon–boron bond in the following way:

$$R-B- \xrightarrow[\text{heat}]{CH_3CO_2H} R-H + CH_3C-O-B-$$

Organoborane   **Alkane**

This reaction also takes place with retention of configuration, therefore, hydrogen replaces boron *where it stands* in the organoborane. The stereochemistry of this reaction, therefore, is like that of the oxidation of organoboranes, and it can be very useful in introducing deuterium or tritium in a specific way.

Problem 10.10 ——————————————————————

Starting with any alkene (or cycloalkene) you choose, and assuming you have deuterioacetic acid (CH_3CO_2D) available, outline syntheses of the following deuterium-labeled compounds.

(a) $CH_3\overset{\overset{\displaystyle CH_3}{|}}{C}HCH_2D$ (b) ⟨ ⟩—CH_2D (c)

(d) Assume you also have available $(BD_3)_2$ and CH_3CO_2T. Can you suggest a synthesis of the following?

10.8 REACTIONS OF ALCOHOLS

Our understanding of the reactions of alcohols will be aided by an initial examination of the electron distribution in the alcohol functional group, and of how this distribution affects its reactivity. The oxygen atom of an alcohol polarizes both the C—O bond and the O—H bond of an alcohol:

Polarization of the O—H bond makes the hydrogen partially positive and explains why alcohols are weak acids (Section 10.10). Polarization of the C—O bond makes the carbon atom partially positive and if it were not for the fact that OH⁻ is a strong base, and, therefore, a very poor leaving group, this carbon should be susceptible to nucleophilic attack.

The electron pairs on the oxygen atom make it both *basic* and *nucleophilic.* In the presence of strong acids alcohols act as bases and accept protons in the following way:

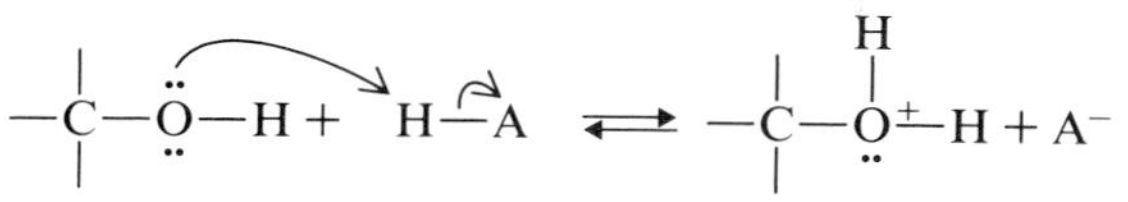

| **Alcohol** | **Strong acid** | **Protonated alcohol** |

Protonation of the alcohol converts a poor leaving group (OH⁻) into a good one (H_2O). It also makes the carbon atom even more positive (because $-OH_2^+$ is more electron withdrawing than $-OH$) and, therefore, even more susceptible to nucleophilic attack. Now S_N2 reactions become possible (Section 10.14).

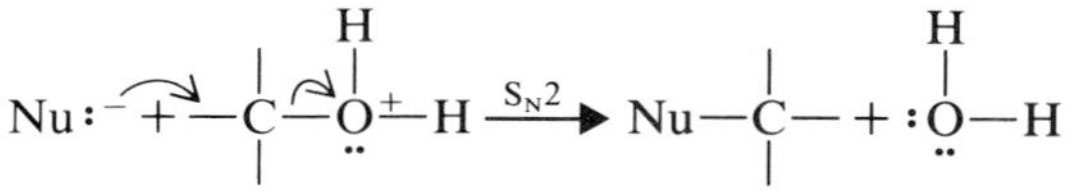

Protonated alcohol

Because alcohols are nucleophiles they, too, can react with protonated alcohols. This, as we shall see in Section 10.16, is an important step in the synthesis of ethers.

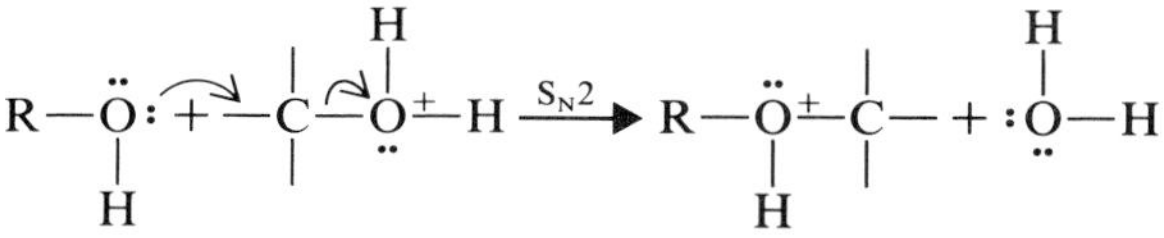

Protonated ether

At a high enough temperature, and in the absence of a good nucleophile, protonated alcohols are capable of undergoing E1 reactions. This is what happens in alcohol dehydrations (Section 8.13).

The nucleophilic nature of the oxygen atom of an alcohol also allows alcohols to combine with reagents (other than protons) that have the effect of converting the hydroxyl group into a good leaving group. For example, alcohols react with alkane-sulfonyl chlorides to become alkyl alkanesulfonates:

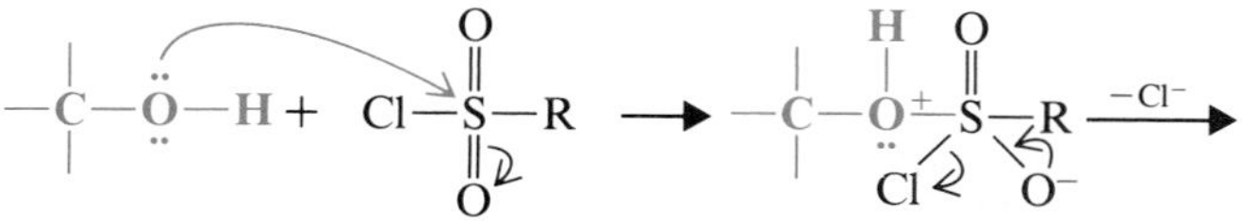

Alkanesulfonyl chloride

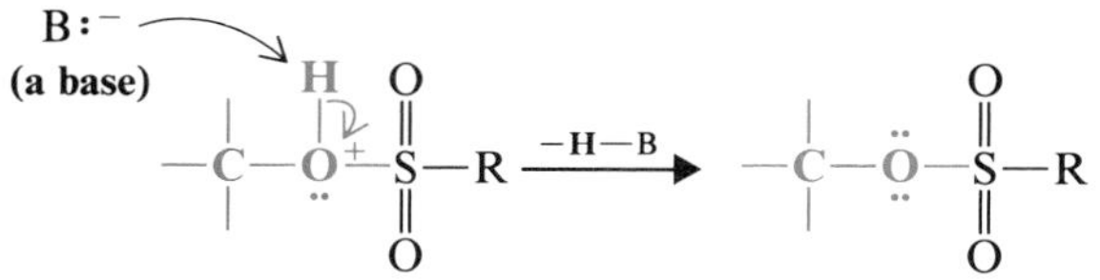

Alkyl alkanesulfonate

The alkanesulfonate group and other groups like it, are excellent leaving groups and, therefore, the synthesis of alkyl alkanesulfonates and other similar compounds (Section 10.11) offers an indirect method for replacing the —OH group of alcohols through S_N2 reactions.

$$Nu:^- + -\overset{|}{\underset{|}{C}}-\overset{..}{\underset{..}{O}}-\overset{\overset{O}{\|}}{\underset{\underset{O}{\|}}{S}}-R \xrightarrow{S_N2} Nu-\overset{|}{\underset{|}{C}}- + {}^-:\overset{..}{\underset{..}{O}}-\overset{\overset{O}{\|}}{\underset{\underset{O}{\|}}{S}}-R$$

Alkyl alkanesulfonate

Alcohols also react with PBr_3 and $SOCl_2$ to yield alkyl bromides and alkyl chlorides. These reactions, as we shall see in Section 10.15, are initiated by the alcohol using its unshared electron pairs to act as a nucleophile.

10.9 ALCOHOLS AS ACIDS

As we might expect, alcohols have acidities similar to that of water. Methanol is a slightly stronger acid than water ($pK_a = 15.7$) but most alcohols are somewhat weaker acids. Values of pK_a for several alcohols and other weak acids are listed in Table 10.3.

The reason sterically hindered alcohols such as *tert*-butyl alcohol are more acidic arises from solvation effects. With unhindered alcohols, water molecules are able to surround and solvate the negative oxygen of the alkoxide ion formed when an alcohol loses a proton. Solvation stabilizes the alkoxide ion and increases the acidity of the alcohol. (*Remember:* Any factor that stabilizes the conjugate base of an acid increases its acidity.)

$$R-\overset{..}{\underset{..}{O}}-H \quad :\overset{\overset{H}{|}}{\underset{..}{O}}-H \rightleftharpoons \quad R-\overset{..}{\underset{..}{O}}:^- \quad + H-\overset{\overset{H}{|}}{\underset{..}{O}}{}^{\pm}H$$

Alcohol   **Alkoxide ion**
                    (stabilized by solvation)

TABLE 10.3 pK_a Values for some weak acids

ACID	pK_a
CH_3OH	15.5
H_2O	15.74
CH_3CH_2OH	15.9
$(CH_3)_3COH$	18.0
$HC\equiv CH$	25
H_2	35
NH_3	38
CH_3CH_3	50

If the R— group of the alcohol is bulky, solvation of the alkoxide ion is hindered, and the alkoxide ion is not as effectively stabilized. The alcohol, consequently, is a weaker acid.

All alcohols, however, are much stronger acids than terminal alkynes, and are very much stronger acids than hydrogen, ammonia, and alkanes (see Table 10.3).

Relative Acidity

$$H_2O > ROH > RC\equiv CH > H_2 > NH_3 > RH$$

The conjugate base of an alcohol is an **alkoxide ion.** Sodium and potassium alkoxides can be prepared by treating alcohols with sodium or potassium metal or with the metal hydride (Section 6.17B). Because most alcohols are weaker acids than water, most alkoxide ions are stronger bases than the hydroxide ion.

Relative Basicity

$$R^- > NH_2^- > H^- > RC\equiv C^- > RO^- > OH^-$$

Problem 10.11 —————————————————————————

Write equations for the acid–base reactions that would occur if ethanol were added to each of the following compounds. In each equation label the stronger acid, the stronger base, and so on.

(a) $CH_3C\equiv CNa$ (b) $CH_3CH_2CH_2CH_2Li$ (c) NaH

Sodium and potassium alkoxides are often used as bases in organic syntheses (Section 6.17B). We use alkoxides such as ethoxide and *tert*-butoxide when we carry out reactions that require stronger bases than hydroxide ion, but do not require exceptionally powerful bases such as the amide ion or the anion of an alkane. We also use alkoxide ions when (for reasons of solubility) we need to carry out a reaction in an alcohol solvent rather than in water.

10.10 CONVERSION OF ALCOHOLS INTO MESYLATES AND TOSYLATES

Alcohols react with sulfonyl chlorides to form esters that are called **sulfonates.** Ethanol, for example, reacts with methanesulfonyl chloride to form ethyl methanesulfonate and with *p*-toluenesulfonyl chloride to form ethyl *p*-toluenesulfonate. These reactions involve cleavage of the O—H bond of the alcohol and not the C—O bond. [If the alcohol had been chiral no change of configuration would have occurred (see Section 10.11)].

$$\underset{\text{Methanesulfonyl chloride}}{CH_3\overset{\overset{O}{\|}}{\underset{\underset{O}{\|}}{S}}-Cl} + \underset{\text{Ethanol}}{H-OCH_2CH_3} \xrightarrow[(-\,HCl)]{\text{base}} \underset{\substack{\text{Ethyl methanesulfonate}\\\text{(ethyl mesylate)}}}{CH_3\overset{\overset{O}{\|}}{\underset{\underset{O}{\|}}{S}}-OCH_2CH_3}$$

$$CH_3-\text{⟨C₆H₄⟩}-\overset{\overset{O}{\|}}{\underset{\underset{O}{\|}}{S}}-Cl + H-OCH_2CH_3 \xrightarrow[(-HCl)]{\text{base}} CH_3-\text{⟨C₆H₄⟩}-\overset{\overset{O}{\|}}{\underset{\underset{O}{\|}}{S}}-OCH_2CH_3$$

<table>
<tr><td>*p*-Toluenesulfonyl
chloride</td><td>Ethanol</td><td>Ethyl *p*-toluenesulfonate
(ethyl tosylate)</td></tr>
</table>

The mechanism that follows (using methanesulfonyl chloride as the example) accounts for the fact that the C—O bond of the alcohol does not break.

$$Me-\overset{\overset{O}{\|}}{\underset{\underset{O}{\|}}{S}}-Cl \; + H-\ddot{O}-R \longrightarrow \left[Me-\overset{\overset{O^-}{\|}}{\underset{\underset{O}{\|}}{S}}-\overset{+}{O}\overset{R}{\underset{\underset{\text{Cl}}{}}{}} \; H \right] \longrightarrow$$

Methanesulfonyl   Alcohol
chloride

$$Me-\overset{\overset{O}{\|}}{\underset{\underset{O}{\|}}{S}}-\overset{+}{O}\overset{R}{\underset{H \quad :B}{}} \longrightarrow Me-\overset{\overset{O}{\|}}{\underset{\underset{O}{\|}}{S}}-O-R \; + H:B$$

      (a base)   Alkyl methanesulfonate

Problem 10.12

Suggest an experiment using an isotopically labeled alcohol that would prove that the formation of an alkyl sulfonate does not cause cleavage at the C—O bond of the alcohol.

Sulfonyl chlorides are usually prepared by treating sulfonic acids with phosphorus pentachloride. (We shall study syntheses of sulfonic acids in Chapter 15.)

$$CH_3-\text{⟨C₆H₄⟩}-\overset{\overset{O}{\|}}{\underset{\underset{O}{\|}}{S}}-OH + PCl_5 \longrightarrow CH_3-\text{⟨C₆H₄⟩}-\overset{\overset{O}{\|}}{\underset{\underset{O}{\|}}{S}}-Cl + POCl_3 + HCl$$

<table>
<tr><td>*p*-Toluenesulfonic
acid</td><td>*p*-Toluenesulfonyl chloride
(tosyl chloride)</td></tr>
</table>

Methanesulfonyl chloride and *p*-toluenesulfonyl chloride are used so often that organic chemists have shortened their rather long names to "mesyl chloride" and "tosyl chloride," respectively. The methanesulfonyl group is often called a "mesyl" group and the *p*-toluenesulfonyl group is called a "tosyl" group. Methanesulfonates are known as "mesylates" and *p*-toluenesulfonates are known as "tosylates."

$$CH_3-\overset{\overset{O}{\|}}{\underset{\underset{O}{\|}}{S}}- \quad \text{or} \quad Ms- \qquad\qquad CH_3-\text{⟨C₆H₄⟩}-\overset{\overset{O}{\|}}{\underset{\underset{O}{\|}}{S}}- \quad \text{or} \quad Ts-$$

     The mesyl group   The tosyl group

CH₃—S—OR or MsOR   CH₃—⟨◯⟩—S—OR or TsOR

An alkyl mesylate   **An alkyl tosylate**

Problem 10.13

Starting with *p*-toluenesulfonic acid or methanesulfonic acid and any necessary alcohols or inorganic reagents, show how you would prepare each of the following sulfonates: (a) Methyl *p*-toluenesulfonate, (b) isopropyl *p*-toluenesulfonate, and (c) *tert*-butyl methanesulfonate.

10.11 MESYLATES AND TOSYLATES IN S_N2 REACTIONS

Alkyl sulfonates are frequently used as substrates for nucleophilic substitution reactions because sulfonate ions are excellent leaving groups.

Nu:⁻ + RCH₂—O—S—R' ⟶ Nu—CH₂R +   ⁻O—S—R'

Alkyl sulfonate   **Sulfonate ion**
(tosylate, mesylate, etc.)   **(very weak base—**
                                   a good leaving group)

The trifluoromethanesulfonate ion ($CF_3SO_2O^-$) is one of the best of all known leaving groups. Alkyl trifluoromethanesulfonates—called *alkyl triflates*—react extremely rapidly in nucleophilic substitution reactions. The triflate ion is such a good leaving group that even vinylic triflates undergo S_N1 reactions and yield vinylic cations.

$$\underset{\substack{\text{Vinylic}\\\text{triflate}}}{\text{C=C}} \xrightarrow{\text{solvolysis}} \underset{\substack{\text{Vinylic}\\\text{cation}}}{\text{C=C}^{\pm}} + \underset{\substack{\text{Triflate}\\\text{ion}}}{^-OSO_2CF_3}$$

Alkyl sulfonates give us an indirect method for carrying out nucleophilic substitution reactions on alcohols. We first convert the alcohol to an alkyl sulfonate and then we allow the sulfonate to react with a nucleophile. When the carbon atom bearing the —OH is a stereocenter, the first step—sulfonate formation—proceeds with **retention of configuration** because no bonds to the stereocenter are broken. Only the O—H bond breaks. The second step—if the reaction is S_N2—proceeds with *inversion of configuration*.

Step 1

Step 2 Nu:⁻ + (structure: C bonded to R, H, R′, and O—Ts) —inversion, S_N2→ Nu—C (bonded to R, H, R′) + ⁻O—Ts

Alkyl sulfonates (tosylates, etc.) undergo all the nucleophilic substitution reactions that alkyl halides do.

Problem 10.14

Show the configurations of products formed when (a) (R)-2-butanol is converted to a tosylate, and (b) when this tosylate reacts with hydroxide ion by an S_N2 reaction. (c) Converting cis-4-methylcyclohexanol to a tosylate and then allowing the tosylate to react with LiCl (in an appropriate solvent) yields trans-1-chloro-4-methylcyclohexane. Outline the stereochemistry of these steps.

10.12 ALKYL PHOSPHATES

Alcohols react with phosphoric acid to yield alkyl phosphates:

$$\text{ROH} + \text{HO}-\overset{\overset{O}{\|}}{\underset{\underset{OH}{|}}{P}}-\text{OH} \xrightarrow[(-H_2O)]{} \text{RO}-\overset{\overset{O}{\|}}{\underset{\underset{OH}{|}}{P}}-\text{OH} \xrightarrow[(-H_2O)]{ROH}$$

Phosphoric acid　　　**Alkyl dihydrogen phosphate**

$$\text{RO}-\overset{\overset{O}{\|}}{\underset{\underset{OR}{|}}{P}}-\text{OH} \xrightarrow[(-H_2O)]{ROH} \text{RO}-\overset{\overset{O}{\|}}{\underset{\underset{OR}{|}}{P}}-\text{OR}$$

Dialkyl hydrogen phosphate　　　**Trialkyl phosphate**

When phosphoric acid is heated, it forms phosphoric *anhydrides* called diphosphoric acid and triphosphoric acid.

$$2\text{HO}-\overset{\overset{O}{\|}}{\underset{\underset{OH}{|}}{P}}-\text{OH} \xrightarrow[(-H_2O)]{} \text{HO}-\overset{\overset{O}{\|}}{\underset{\underset{OH}{|}}{P}}-\text{O}-\overset{\overset{O}{\|}}{\underset{\underset{OH}{|}}{P}}-\text{OH}$$

Anhydride linkage

Diphosphoric acid (pyrophosphoric acid)

$$3\text{HO}-\overset{\overset{O}{\|}}{\underset{\underset{OH}{|}}{P}}-\text{OH} \xrightarrow[(-2H_2O)]{} \text{HO}-\overset{\overset{O}{\|}}{\underset{\underset{OH}{|}}{P}}-\text{O}-\overset{\overset{O}{\|}}{\underset{\underset{OH}{|}}{P}}-\text{O}-\overset{\overset{O}{\|}}{\underset{\underset{OH}{|}}{P}}-\text{OH}$$

Anhydride linkages

Triphosphoric acid

These phosphoric acid anhydrides can also react with alcohols to form esters such as the following:

$$RO-\overset{\overset{\displaystyle O}{\|}}{\underset{\underset{\displaystyle OH}{|}}{P}}-O-\overset{\overset{\displaystyle O}{\|}}{\underset{\underset{\displaystyle OH}{|}}{P}}-OH \qquad RO-\overset{\overset{\displaystyle O}{\|}}{\underset{\underset{\displaystyle OH}{|}}{P}}-O-\overset{\overset{\displaystyle O}{\|}}{\underset{\underset{\displaystyle OH}{|}}{P}}-O-\overset{\overset{\displaystyle O}{\|}}{\underset{\underset{\displaystyle OH}{|}}{P}}-OH$$

An alkyl trihydrogen diphosphate   **An alkyl tetrahydrogen triphosphate**

Esters of phosphoric acids are extremely important in biochemical reactions. Especially important are triphosphate esters. Although hydrolysis of the ester group or of one of the anhydride linkages of an alkyl triphosphate is exothermic, these reactions occur very slowly in aqueous solutions. Near pH 7, these triphosphates exist as negatively charged ions and hence are much less susceptible to nucleophilic attack. Alkyl triphosphates are, consequently, relatively stable compounds in the aqueous medium of a living cell.

Ester linkage

Anhydride linkages

$$RO-\overset{O}{\overset{\|}{P}}-O-\overset{O}{\overset{\|}{P}}-O-\overset{O}{\overset{\|}{P}}-OH \xrightarrow[\text{slow}]{H_2O}$$

$$\longrightarrow ROH + HO-\overset{O}{\overset{\|}{P}}-O-\overset{O}{\overset{\|}{P}}-O-\overset{O}{\overset{\|}{P}}-OH$$

$$RO-\overset{O}{\overset{\|}{P}}-OH + HO-\overset{O}{\overset{\|}{P}}-O-\overset{O}{\overset{\|}{P}}-OH$$

$$\longrightarrow RO-\overset{O}{\overset{\|}{P}}-O-\overset{O}{\overset{\|}{P}}-OH + HO-\overset{O}{\overset{\|}{P}}-OH$$

Enzymes, on the other hand, are able to catalyze reactions of these triphosphates in which the energy made available when their anhydride linkages break helps the cell make other chemical bonds. We have more to say about this in Chapter 22 when we discuss the important triphosphate called adenosine triphosphate (or ATP).

10.13 CONVERSION OF ALCOHOLS INTO ALKYL HALIDES

Alcohols react with a variety of reagents to yield alkyl halides. The most commonly used reagents are hydrogen halides (HCl, HBr, or HI), phosphorus tribromide (PBr$_3$), and thionyl chloride (SOCl$_2$). Examples of the use of these reagents are the following. All of these reactions result in cleavage at the C—O bond of the alcohol.

$$CH_3-\overset{\overset{\displaystyle CH_3}{|}}{\underset{\underset{\displaystyle CH_3}{|}}{C}}-OH + HCl_{(concd)} \xrightarrow{25\,°C} CH_3-\overset{\overset{\displaystyle CH_3}{|}}{\underset{\underset{\displaystyle CH_3}{|}}{C}}-Cl + H_2O$$

(94%)

$$CH_3CH_2CH_2CH_2OH + HBr_{(concd)} \xrightarrow[\text{reflux}]{H_2SO_4} CH_3CH_2CH_2CH_2Br$$

(95%)

$$3(CH_3)_2CHCH_2OH + PBr_3 \xrightarrow[\text{4 h}]{-10 \text{ to } 0 \text{ °C}} 3(CH_3)_2CHCH_2Br + H_3PO_3$$
$$(55-60\%)$$

$$\text{(aryl)}-CH_2OH + SOCl_2 \xrightarrow[\text{pyridine}]{} \text{(aryl)}-CH_2Cl + SO_2 + HCl$$

OCH$_3$ OCH$_3$ (forms salt

(91%)   with pyridine)

10.14 ALKYL HALIDES FROM THE REACTIONS OF ALCOHOLS WITH HYDROGEN HALIDES

When alcohols react with a hydrogen halide, a substitution takes place producing an alkyl halide and water:

$$R{-}OH + HX \longrightarrow R{-}X + H_2O$$

The order of reactivity of the hydrogen halides is HI > HBr > HCl (HF is generally unreactive), and the order of reactivity of alcohols is 3° > 2° > 1° < methyl.

The reaction is *acid catalyzed.* Alcohols react with the strongly acidic hydrogen halides, HCl, HBr, and HI, but they do not react with nonacidic NaCl, NaBr, or NaI. Primary and secondary alcohols can be converted to alkyl chlorides and bromides by allowing them to react with a mixture of a sodium halide and sulfuric acid.

$$ROH + NaX \xrightarrow{H_2SO_4} RX + NaHSO_4 + H_2O$$

10.14A MECHANISMS OF THE REACTIONS OF ALCOHOLS WITH HX

Secondary, tertiary, allylic, and benzylic alcohols appear to react by a mechanism that involves the formation of a carbocation — one that is recognizable *as an S_N1-type reaction with the protonated alcohol acting as the substrate.* We illustrate this mechanism with the reaction of *tert*-butyl alcohol and hydrochloric acid.

The first two steps are the same as in the mechanism for the dehydration of an alcohol (Section 8.13). The alcohol accepts a proton and then the protonated alcohol dissociates to form a carbocation and water.

Step 1

$$CH_3-\overset{\overset{\displaystyle CH_3}{|}}{\underset{\underset{\displaystyle CH_3}{|}}{C}}-\overset{..}{\overset{..}{O}}-H + H-\overset{..}{\overset{..}{\underset{\displaystyle H}{O}}}{}^{\pm}H \underset{}{\overset{\text{fast}}{\rightleftharpoons}} CH_3-\overset{\overset{\displaystyle CH_3}{|}}{\underset{\underset{\displaystyle CH_3}{|}}{C}}-\overset{\overset{\displaystyle H}{|}}{O}{}^{\pm}H + :\overset{..}{\underset{\displaystyle H}{O}}-H$$

Step 2

$$CH_3-\overset{\overset{\displaystyle CH_3}{|}}{\underset{\underset{\displaystyle CH_3}{|}}{C}}-\overset{\overset{\displaystyle H}{|}}{\overset{..}{O}}{}^{\pm}H \underset{}{\overset{\text{slow}}{\rightleftharpoons}} CH_3-\overset{\overset{\displaystyle CH_3}{|}}{\underset{\underset{\displaystyle CH_3}{|}}{C}}{}^{+} + :\overset{..}{O}-H$$

In step 3 the mechanisms for the dehydration of an alcohol and the formation of an alkyl halide differ. In dehydration reactions the carbocation loses a proton in an

E1-type reaction to form an alkene. In the formation of an alkyl halide, the carbocation reacts with a nucleophile (a halide ion) in an S_N1-type reaction.

Step 3

$$CH_3-\underset{\underset{CH_3}{|}}{\overset{\overset{CH_3}{|}}{C^+}} + :\ddot{C}l:^- \overset{fast}{\rightleftharpoons} CH_3-\underset{\underset{CH_3}{|}}{\overset{\overset{CH_3}{|}}{C}}-\ddot{C}l:$$

How can we account for the different course of these two reactions?

When we dehydrate alcohols we usually carry out the reaction in concentrated sulfuric acid. The only nucleophiles present in this reaction mixture are water and hydrogen sulfate (HSO_4^-) ions. Both are poor nucleophiles and both are usually present in low concentrations. Under these conditions, the highly reactive carbocation stabilizes itself by losing a proton and becoming an alkene. The net result is *an E1 reaction.*

In the reverse reaction, that is, the hydration of an alkene (Section 9.4), the carbocation *does* react with a nucleophile. It reacts with water. Alkene hydrations are carried out in dilute sulfuric acid where the water concentration is high. In some instances, too, carbocations may react with HSO_4^- ions or with sulfuric acid, itself. When they do they form alkyl hydrogen sulfates ($R-OSO_2OH$).

When we convert an alcohol to an alkyl halide, we carry out the reaction in the presence of acid and *in the presence of halide ions.* Halide ions are good nucleophiles (much stronger nucleophiles than water), and since they are present in high concentration, most of the carbocations stabilize themselves by accepting the electron pair of a halide ion. The overall result is an S_N1 reaction.

These two reactions, dehydration and the formation of an alkyl halide, also furnish us another example of the competition between nucleophilic substitution and elimination (cf. Section 6.20). Very often, in conversions of alcohols to alkyl halides, we find that the reaction is accompanied by the formation of some alkene (i.e., by elimination). The free energies of activation for these two reactions of carbocations are not very different from one another. Thus, not all of the carbocations react with nucleophiles; some stabilize themselves by losing protons.

Not all acid-catalyzed conversions of alcohols to alkyl halides proceed through the formation of carbocations. Primary alcohols and methanol apparently react through a mechanism that we recognize as *an S_N2 type.* In these reactions the function of the acid is to produce *a protonated alcohol.* The halide ion then displaces a molecule of water (a good leaving group) from carbon; this produces an alkyl halide.

$$:\ddot{X}:^- + -\overset{\overset{H}{|}}{\underset{|}{C}}-\overset{\overset{H}{|}}{\underset{\cdot\cdot}{O}}{}^+-H \longrightarrow :\ddot{X}-\overset{\overset{H}{|}}{\underset{|}{C}}- + :\overset{\overset{H}{|}}{O}-H$$

(protonated 1°   (a good
or methanol)   leaving
                              group)

Although halide ions (particularly iodide and bromide ions) are strong nucleophiles, they are not strong enough to carry out substitution reactions with alcohols themselves. That is, reactions of the following type do not occur to any appreciable extent.

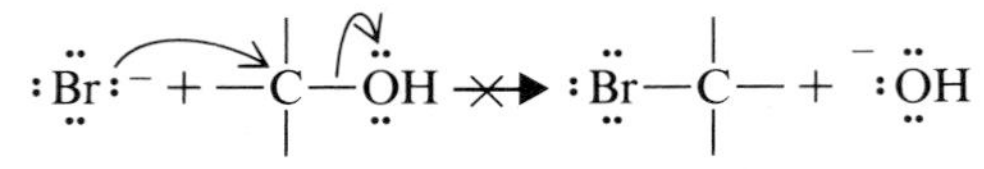

$$\ddot{B}r\!:^- + \!-\!\overset{|}{\underset{|}{C}}\!-\!\ddot{O}H \;\nrightarrow\; \ddot{B}r\!-\!\overset{|}{\underset{|}{C}}\!- + \;^-\!:\!\ddot{O}H$$

They do not occur because the leaving group would have to be a strongly basic hydroxide ion.

> The reverse reaction, that is, the reaction of an alkyl halide with hydroxide ion, does occur and is a method for the synthesis of alcohols. We saw this reaction in Chapter 6.

We can see now why the reactions of alcohols with hydrogen halides are acid catalyzed. With tertiary and secondary alcohols the function of the acid is to help produce a carbocation. With methanol and primary alcohols, the function of the acid is to produce a substrate in which the leaving group is a weakly basic water molecule rather than a strongly basic hydroxide ion.

As we might expect, many reactions of alcohols with hydrogen halides, particularly those in which carbocations are formed, *are accompanied by rearrangements.*

Because the chloride ion is a weaker nucleophile than bromide or iodide ions, hydrogen chloride does not react with primary or secondary alcohols unless zinc chloride or some similar Lewis acid is added to the reaction mixture as well. Zinc chloride, a good Lewis acid, forms a complex with the alcohol through association with an unshared pair of electrons on the oxygen atom. This provides a better leaving group for the reaction than H_2O.

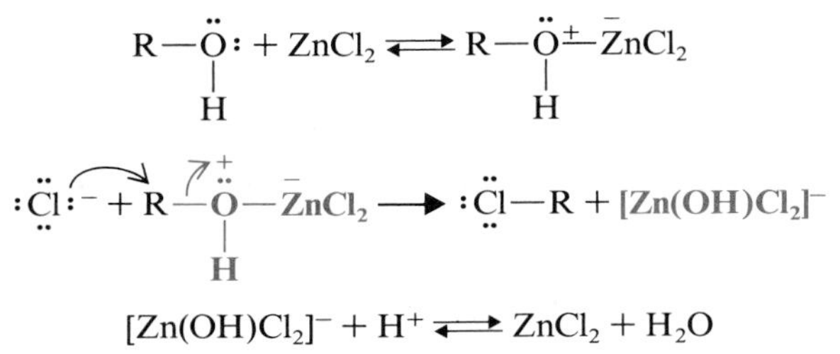

$$R\!-\!\overset{..}{\underset{|}{O}}\!:\, + ZnCl_2 \;\rightleftharpoons\; R\!-\!\overset{..}{\underset{|}{O}}\!\overset{\pm}{-}\!\overset{-}{Z}nCl_2$$
$$\qquad H \qquad\qquad\qquad H$$

$$:\!\overset{..}{\underset{..}{Cl}}\!:^- + R\!-\!\overset{\pm}{\underset{|}{O}}\!-\!\overset{-}{Z}nCl_2 \;\longrightarrow\; :\!\overset{..}{\underset{..}{Cl}}\!-\!R + [Zn(OH)Cl_2]^-$$
$$\qquad\qquad\quad H$$

$$[Zn(OH)Cl_2]^- + H^+ \;\rightleftharpoons\; ZnCl_2 + H_2O$$

Problem 10.15

(a) What factor explains the observation that tertiary alcohols react with HX faster than secondary alcohols? (b) What factor explains the observation that methanol reacts with HX faster than a primary alcohol?

Problem 10.16

Treating 3-methyl-2-butanol (see following reaction) with HBr yields 2-bromo-2-methylbutane as the sole product. Outline a mechanism for the reaction.

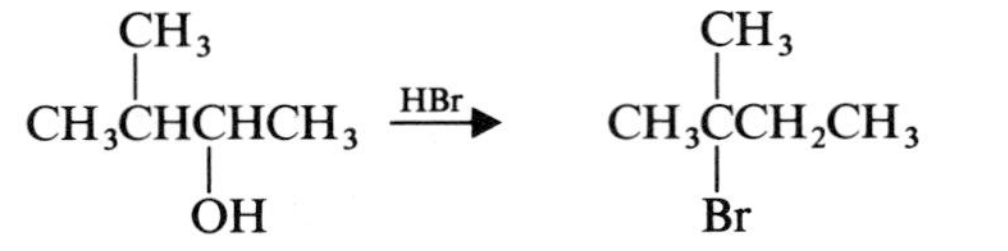

$$\underset{\textbf{3-Methyl-2-butanol}}{\overset{\displaystyle CH_3}{\underset{\displaystyle OH}{CH_3CHCHCH_3}}} \xrightarrow{\text{HBr}} \underset{\textbf{2-Bromo-2-methylbutane}}{\overset{\displaystyle CH_3}{\underset{\displaystyle Br}{CH_3CCH_2CH_3}}}$$

10.15 ALKYL HALIDES FROM THE REACTIONS OF ALCOHOLS WITH PBr₃ OR SOCl₂

Primary and secondary alcohols react with phosphorus tribromide to yield alkyl bromides.

$$3R\text{—}OH + PBr_3 \longrightarrow 3R\text{—}Br + H_3PO_3$$
(1° or 2°)

Unlike the reaction of an alcohol with HBr, the reaction of an alcohol with PBr₃ does not involve the formation of a carbocation and *usually occurs without rearrangement* of the carbon skeleton (especially if the temperature is kept below 0 °C). For this reason phosphorus tribromide is often preferred as a reagent for the transformation of an alcohol to the corresponding alkyl bromide.

The mechanism for the reaction involves the initial formation of a protonated alkyl dibromophosphite (see following reaction) by a nucleophilic displacement on phosphorus; the alcohol acts as the nucleophile:

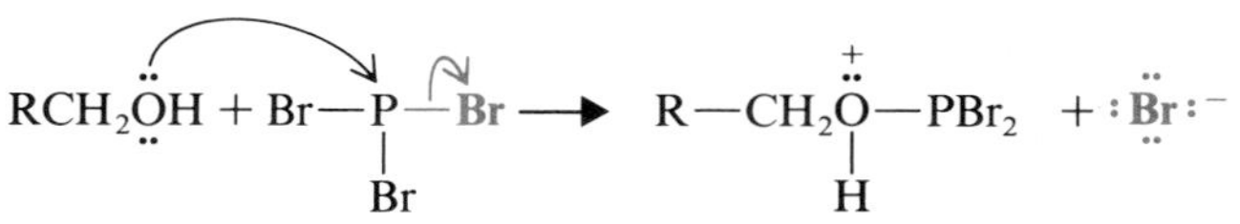

$$RCH_2\overset{..}{O}H + Br\text{—}P\text{—}Br \longrightarrow R\text{—}CH_2\overset{+}{O}\text{—}PBr_2 \ + \ :\overset{..}{Br}:^-$$

**Protonated
alkyl dibromophosphite**

Then a bromide ion acts as a nucleophile and displaces HOPBr₂.

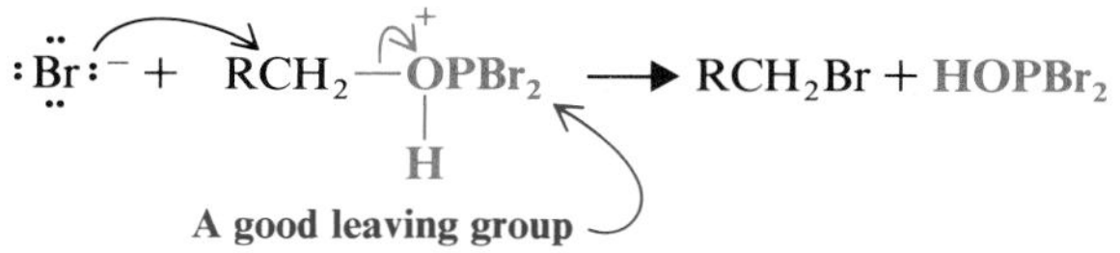

$$:\overset{..}{Br}:^- + \ RCH_2\overset{+}{—}OPBr_2 \longrightarrow RCH_2Br + HOPBr_2$$

A good leaving group

The HOPBr₂ can react with more alcohol so the net result is the conversion of 3 mol of alcohol to alkyl bromide by 1 mol of phosphorus tribromide.

Thionyl chloride (SOCl₂) converts primary and secondary alcohols to alkyl chlorides (usually without rearrangement).

$$R\text{—}OH + SOCl_2 \xrightarrow{\text{reflux}} R\text{—}Cl + SO_2 + HCl$$
(1° or 2°)

Often a tertiary amine is added to the mixture to promote the reaction by reacting with the HCl.

$$R_3N: + HCl \longrightarrow R_3NH^+ + Cl^-$$

The reaction mechanism involves initial formation of the alkyl chlorosulfite:

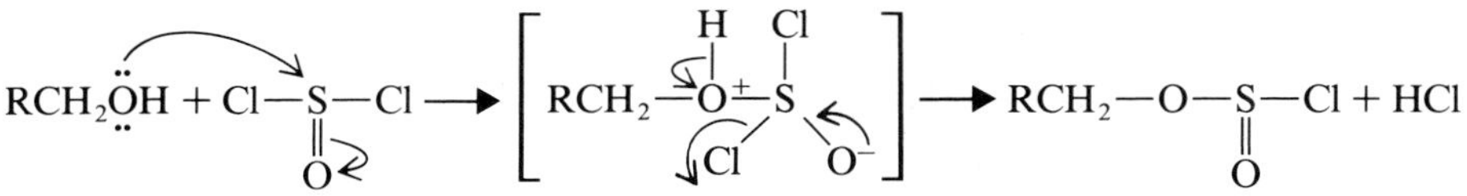

$$RCH_2\overset{..}{O}H + Cl\text{—}S\text{—}Cl \longrightarrow \left[RCH_2\text{—}\overset{\pm}{O}\text{—}S \right] \longrightarrow RCH_2\text{—}O\text{—}S\text{—}Cl + HCl$$

**Alkyl
chlorosulfite**

Then a chloride ion (from $R_3N + HCl \longrightarrow R_3NH^+ + Cl^-$) can bring about an S_N2 displacement of a very good leaving group, $ClSO_2^-$, which, by decomposing (to the gas SO_2 and Cl^- ion), helps drive the reaction to completion.

$$:\ddot{\underset{\cdot\cdot}{Cl}}:^- + RCH_2{-}O{-}\overset{O}{\underset{\|}{S}}{-}Cl \longrightarrow RCH_2Cl + {}^-O{-}\overset{O}{\underset{\|}{S}}{-}Cl \longrightarrow RCH_2Cl + SO_2{\uparrow} + Cl^-$$

Sample Problem

Starting with alcohols, outline a synthesis of each of the following. (a) Benzyl bromide, (b) cyclohexyl chloride, and (c) butyl bromide.

Possible Answers:

(a) $C_6H_5CH_2OH \xrightarrow{PBr_3} C_6H_5CH_2Br$

(b) ⬡—OH $\xrightarrow{SOCl_2}$ ⬡—Cl

(c) $CH_3CH_2CH_2CH_2OH \xrightarrow{PBr_3} CH_3CH_2CH_2CH_2Br$

10.16 SYNTHESIS OF ETHERS

10.16A ETHERS BY INTERMOLECULAR DEHYDRATION OF ALCOHOLS

Alcohols can dehydrate to form alkenes. We studied this in Sections 8.13–8.15. Primary alcohols can also dehydrate to form ethers.

$$R{-}OH + HO{-}R \xrightarrow[(-H_2O)]{H^+} R{-}O{-}R$$

Dehydration to an ether usually takes place at a lower temperature than dehydration to the alkene, and dehydration to the ether can be aided by distilling the ether as it is formed. Diethyl ether is made commercially by dehydration of ethanol. Diethyl ether is the predominant product at 140 °C; ethene is the major product at 180 °C:

$$CH_3CH_2OH \begin{cases} \xrightarrow[180\ °C]{H_2SO_4} CH_2{=}CH_2 \quad \textbf{Ethene} \\[2ex] \xrightarrow[140\ °C]{H_2SO_4} CH_3CH_2OCH_2CH_3 \quad \textbf{Diethyl ether} \end{cases}$$

The formation of the ether occurs by an S_N2 mechanism with one molecule of the alcohol acting as the nucleophile and with another protonated molecule of the alcohol acting as the substrate (see Section 10.9).

$$CH_3CH_2-\ddot{O}H + H-OSO_3H \rightleftharpoons CH_3CH_2-OH_2^+ + {}^-OSO_3H$$

$$CH_3CH_2\ddot{O}H + CH_3CH_2-\overset{+}{O}H_2 \rightleftharpoons CH_3CH_2-\underset{\underset{H}{|}}{O}-CH_2CH_3 + H_2O \rightleftharpoons$$

$$CH_3CH_2OCH_2CH_3 + H_3O^+$$

This method of preparing ethers is of limited usefulness, however. Attempts to synthesize ethers with secondary alkyl groups by intermolecular dehydration of secondary alcohols are usually unsuccessful because alkenes form too easily. Attempts to make ethers with tertiary alkyl groups lead exclusively to the alkenes. And, finally, this method is not useful for the preparation of unsymmetrical ethers from primary alcohols because the reaction leads to a mixture of products.

$$\underbrace{ROH + R'OH}_{1°\ alcohols} \underset{H_2SO_4}{\rightleftharpoons} \begin{matrix} ROR \\ + \\ ROR' + H_2O \\ + \\ R'OR' \end{matrix}$$

Problem 10.17

An exception to what we have just said has to do with syntheses of unsymmetrical ethers in which one alkyl group is a *tert*-butyl group and the other group is primary. This synthesis can be accomplished by adding *tert*-butyl alcohol to a mixture of the primary alcohol and H_2SO_4 at room temperature. Give a likely mechanism for this reaction and explain why it is successful.

10.16B THE WILLIAMSON SYNTHESIS OF ETHERS

An important route to unsymmetrical ethers is a nucleophilic substitution reaction known as the Williamson synthesis. This synthesis consists of an S_N2 reaction of a sodium alkoxide with alkyl halide, alkyl sulfonate, or alkyl sulfate:

$$R-O^-Na^+ + R'-L \longrightarrow R-O-R' + Na^+L^-$$
$$L = Br, I, OSO_2R'', \text{ or } OSO_2OR''$$

The following reaction is a specific example of the Williamson synthesis.

$$\underset{\text{Propyl alcohol}}{CH_3CH_2CH_2OH} + Na \longrightarrow \underset{\text{Sodium propoxide}}{CH_3CH_2CH_2\ddot{O}:^-Na^+} + \tfrac{1}{2}H_2$$

$$\downarrow {\scriptstyle CH_3CH_2I}$$

$$\underset{\substack{\text{Ethyl propyl ether} \\ \text{(70\%)}}}{CH_3CH_2OCH_2CH_2CH_3} + Na^+\ I^-$$

The usual limitations of S_N2 reactions apply here. Best results are obtained when the alkyl halide, sulfonate, or sulfate is primary (or methyl). If the substrate is tertiary, elimination is the exclusive result. Substitution is also favored over elimination at lower temperatures.

Problem 10.18

(a) Outline two methods for preparing isopropyl methyl ether by a Williamson synthesis. (b) One method gives a much better yield of the ether than the other. Explain which is the better method and why.

Problem 10.19

The two syntheses of 2-ethoxy-1-phenylpropane shown here give products with opposite optical rotations.

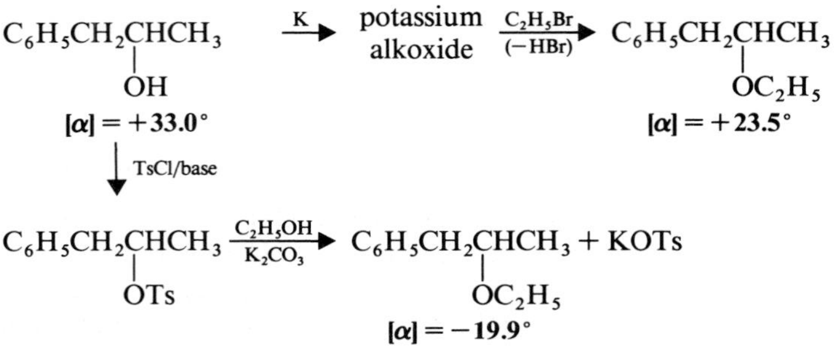

$$C_6H_5CH_2CHCH_3 \xrightarrow{K} \underset{\text{alkoxide}}{\text{potassium}} \xrightarrow[(-HBr)]{C_2H_5Br} C_6H_5CH_2CHCH_3$$

$$\underset{\substack{|\\ OH \\ [\alpha] = +33.0°}}{} \qquad\qquad \underset{\substack{|\\ OC_2H_5 \\ [\alpha] = +23.5°}}{}$$

$$\downarrow \text{TsCl/base}$$

$$C_6H_5CH_2CHCH_3 \xrightarrow[K_2CO_3]{C_2H_5OH} C_6H_5CH_2CHCH_3 + KOTs$$

$$\underset{\substack{|\\ OTs}}{} \qquad \underset{\substack{|\\ OC_2H_5 \\ [\alpha] = -19.9°}}{}$$

How can you explain this result?

Problem 10.20

Write a mechanism that explains the formation of tetrahydrofuran (THF) from the reaction of 4-chloro-1-butanol and aqueous sodium hydroxide.

Problem 10.21

Epoxides can be synthesized by treating halohydrins with aqueous base. For example, treating $ClCH_2CH_2OH$ with aqueous sodium hydroxide yields ethylene oxide. (a) Propose a mechanism for this reaction. (b) *trans*-2-Chlorocyclohexanol reacts readily with sodium hydroxide to yield cyclohexene oxide. *cis*-2-Chlorocyclohexanol does not undergo this reaction, however. How can you account for this difference?

10.16C *TERT*-BUTYL ETHERS BY ALKYLATION OF ALCOHOLS

Primary alcohols can be converted to *tert*-butyl ethers by dissolving them in a strong acid such as sulfuric acid and then adding isobutylene to the mixture. (This procedure minimizes dimerization and polymerization of the isobutylene.)

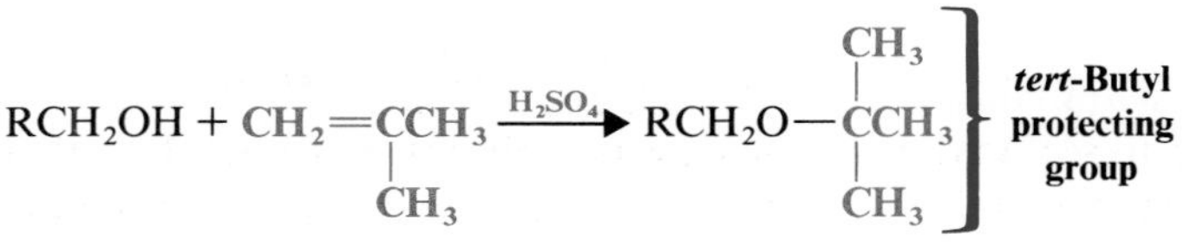

$$RCH_2OH + CH_2{=}CCH_3 \xrightarrow{H_2SO_4} RCH_2O{-}CCH_3 \quad \left.\begin{array}{l} \\ \\ \\ \end{array}\right\} \begin{array}{l} \textit{tert-}\textbf{Butyl} \\ \textbf{protecting} \\ \textbf{group} \end{array}$$

with CH_3 substituents as shown.

This method is often used to "protect" the hydroxyl group of a primary alcohol while another reaction is carried out on some other part of the molecule. The protecting *tert*-butyl group can be removed easily by treating the ether with dilute aqueous acid.

Suppose, for example, we wanted to prepare 4-pentyn-1-ol from 3-bromo-1-propanol and sodium acetylide. If we allow them to react directly, the strongly basic sodium acetylide will react first with the hydroxyl group.

$$HOCH_2CH_2CH_2Br + NaC\equiv CH \longrightarrow BrCH_2CH_2CH_2ONa + HC\equiv CH$$
3-Bromo-1-propanol

However, if we protect the —OH group first, the synthesis becomes feasible.

$$HOCH_2CH_2CH_2Br \xrightarrow[\text{(2) } CH_2=C(CH_3)_2]{\text{(1) } H_2SO_4} (CH_3)_3COCH_2CH_2CH_2Br \xrightarrow{NaC\equiv CH}$$

$$(CH_3)_3COCH_2CH_2CH_2C\equiv CH \xrightarrow{H_3O^+/H_2O} HOCH_2CH_2CH_2C\equiv CH + (CH_3)_3COH$$
4-Pentyn-1-ol

Problem 10.22

(a) The mechanism for the formation of the *tert*-butyl ether from a primary alcohol and isobutylene is similar to that discussed in Problem 10.17. Propose such a mechanism. (b) What factor makes it possible to remove the protecting *tert*-butyl group so easily? (Other ethers require much more forcing conditions for their cleavage, as we shall see in Section 10.17.) (c) Propose a mechanism for the removal of the protecting *tert*-butyl group.

10.16D TRIMETHYLSILYL ETHERS. SILYLATION

A hydroxyl group can also be protected in neutral or basic solutions by converting it to a trimethylsilyl ether group, $—OSi(CH_3)_3$. This reaction, called **silylation,** is done by allowing the alcohol to react with chlorotrimethylsilane in the presence of a tertiary amine:

$$R—OH + (CH_3)_3SiCl \xrightarrow{(CH_3CH_2)_3N} R—O—Si(CH_3)_3$$
Chlorotrimethylsilane

This protecting group can also be removed with aqueous acid.

$$R—O—Si(CH_3)_3 \xrightarrow{H_3O^+/H_2O} R—OH + (CH_3)_3SiOH$$

Converting an alcohol to a trimethylsilyl ether also makes it much more volatile. (Why?) This increased volatility makes the alcohol (as a trimethylsilyl ether) much more amenable to analysis by gas–liquid chromatography.

10.17 REACTIONS OF ETHERS

Dialkyl ethers react with very few reagents other than acids. The only reactive sites that molecules of a dialkyl ether present to another reactive substance are the C—H bonds of the alkyl groups and the $-\overset{..}{\underset{..}{O}}-$ group of the ether linkage. Ethers resist attack by nucleophiles (why?) and by bases. This lack of reactivity, coupled with the ability of ethers to solvate cations (by donating an electron pair from their oxygen atom) makes ethers especially useful as solvents for many reactions.

Ethers are like alkanes in that they undergo halogenation reactions (Chapter 7), but these are of little synthetic importance.

The oxygen of the ether linkage makes ethers basic. Ethers can react with proton donors to form **oxonium salts.**

$$CH_3CH_2\overset{..}{\underset{..}{O}}CH_2CH_3 + HBr \rightleftharpoons CH_3CH_2-\overset{+}{\underset{\underset{H}{|}}{\overset{..}{O}}}-CH_2CH_3 \; Br^-$$

An oxonium salt

Heating dialkyl ethers with very strong acids (HI, HBr, and H_2SO_4) causes them to undergo reactions in which the carbon–oxygen bond breaks. Diethyl ether, for example, reacts with hot concentrated hydrobromic acid to give two molar equivalents of ethyl bromide.

$$CH_3CH_2OCH_2CH_3 + 2 \; HBr \longrightarrow 2 \; CH_3CH_2Br + H_2O \qquad \text{Cleavage of an ether}$$

The mechanism for this reaction begins with formation of an oxonium ion. Then an S_N2 reaction with a bromide ion acting as the nucleophile produces ethanol and ethyl bromide.

$$CH_3CH_2\overset{..}{\underset{..}{O}}CH_2CH_3 + H\overset{..}{\underset{..}{Br}}: \rightleftharpoons CH_3CH_2\overset{+}{\underset{\underset{H}{|}}{O}}-CH_2CH_3 + :\overset{..}{\underset{..}{Br}}:^- \longrightarrow$$

$$CH_3CH_2\overset{..}{\underset{\underset{H}{|}}{O}}: + \; CH_3CH_2Br$$

Ethanol   **Ethyl bromide**

In the next step the ethanol (just formed) reacts with HBr to form a second molar equivalent of ethyl bromide.

$$CH_3CH_2\overset{..}{O}H + H\overset{..}{\underset{..}{Br}}: \rightleftharpoons :\overset{..}{\underset{..}{Br}}:^- + CH_3CH_2\overset{+}{\underset{\underset{H}{|}}{\overset{..}{O}}}-H \longrightarrow CH_3CH_2-\overset{..}{\underset{..}{Br}}: + :\overset{..}{\underset{\underset{H}{|}}{O}}-H$$

Problem 10.23 _____

When an ether is treated with *cold* concentrated HI, cleavage occurs as follows:

$$R-O-R + HI \longrightarrow ROH + RI$$

When mixed ethers are used, the alcohol and alkyl iodide that form depend on the nature of the alkyl groups. Explain the following observations. (a) When (R)-2-methoxybutane reacts, the products are methyl iodide and (R)-2-butanol. (b) When *tert*-butyl methyl ether reacts, the products are methanol and *tert*-butyl iodide.

10.18 EPOXIDES

Epoxides are cyclic ethers with three-membered rings. In IUPAC nomenclature epoxides are called **oxiranes.** The simplest epoxide has the common name ethylene oxide.

An epoxide	IUPAC: Oxirane
	Common: Ethylene oxide

The most widely used method for synthesizing epoxides is the reaction of an alkene with an organic **peroxy acid** (sometimes called simply a **peracid**), a process that is called **epoxidation.**

$$RCH=CHR + R'C\overset{O}{\overset{\|}{-}}O-OH \xrightarrow{\text{epoxidation}} RHC-CHR + R'C\overset{O}{\overset{\|}{-}}OH$$

An alkene	A peroxy acid	An epoxide
		(or oxirane)

In this reaction the peroxy acid transfers an oxygen atom to the alkene. The following mechanism has been proposed.

The addition of oxygen to the double bond in an epoxidation reaction is, of necessity, a **syn** addition. In order to form a three-membered ring, the oxygen atom must add to both carbon atoms of the double bond at the same face.

The peroxy acids most commonly used are peroxyacetic acid $\left(CH_3C\overset{O}{\overset{\|}{C}}OOH\right)$ and peroxybenzoic acid $\left(C_6H_5C\overset{O}{\overset{\|}{C}}OOH\right)$. Cyclohexene, for example, reacts with peroxybenzoic acid to give 1,2-epoxycyclohexane in a quantitative yield.

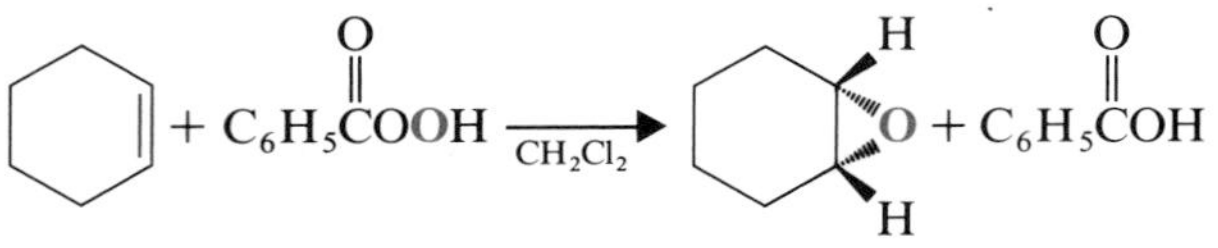

Peroxybenzoic
acid

1,2-Epoxy-
cyclohexane
(100%)

The reaction of alkenes with peroxy acids takes place in a stereospecific way: *cis*-2-Butene, for example, yields only *cis*-2,3-dimethyloxirane, and *trans*-2-butene yields only the *trans*-2,3-dimethyloxiranes.

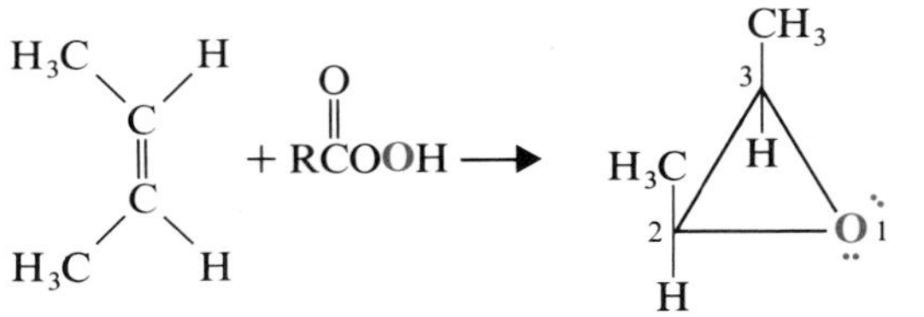

cis-2-Butene

cis-2,3-Dimethyloxirane
(a meso compound)

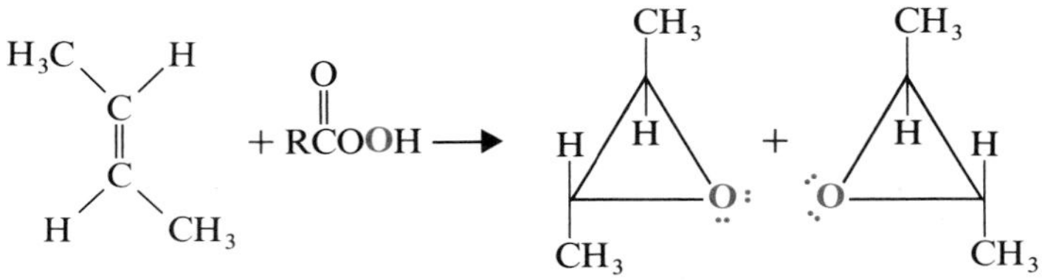

trans-2-Butene

Enantiomeric *trans*-2,3-dimethyloxiranes

10.19 REACTIONS OF EPOXIDES

The highly strained three-membered ring in molecules of epoxides makes them much more reactive toward nucleophilic substitution than other ethers.

Acid catalysis assists epoxide ring opening by providing a better leaving group (an alcohol) at the carbon atom undergoing nucleophilic attack. This catalysis is especially important if the nucleophile is a weak nucleophile such as water or an alcohol:

Acid-Catalyzed Ring Opening

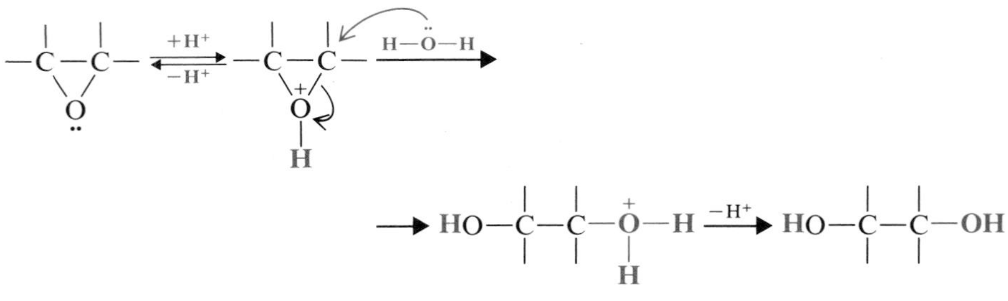

In the absence of an acid catalyst the leaving group must be a strongly basic alkoxide ion. Such reactions do not occur with other ethers, but they are possible with epoxides (because of ring strain), provided that the attacking nucleophile is also a strong base such as an alkoxide ion.

Base-Catalyzed Ring Opening

$$RO:^- + -\overset{|}{\underset{|}{C}} - \overset{|}{\underset{\diagdown O \diagup}{C}} - \longrightarrow RO - \overset{|}{\underset{|}{C}} - \overset{|}{\underset{|}{C}} - O^- \xrightarrow{ROH}$$

A strong   An alkoxide
nucleophile   ion

$$RO - \overset{|}{\underset{|}{C}} - \overset{|}{\underset{|}{C}} - OH + RO:^-$$

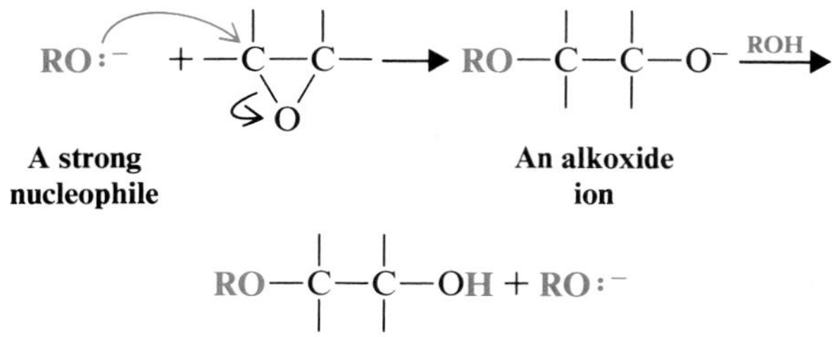

If the epoxide is unsymmetrical, in **base-catalyzed ring-opening** attack by the alkoxide ion occurs primarily *at the less substituted carbon atom.* For example, methyloxirane reacts with an alkoxide ion mainly at its primary carbon atom:

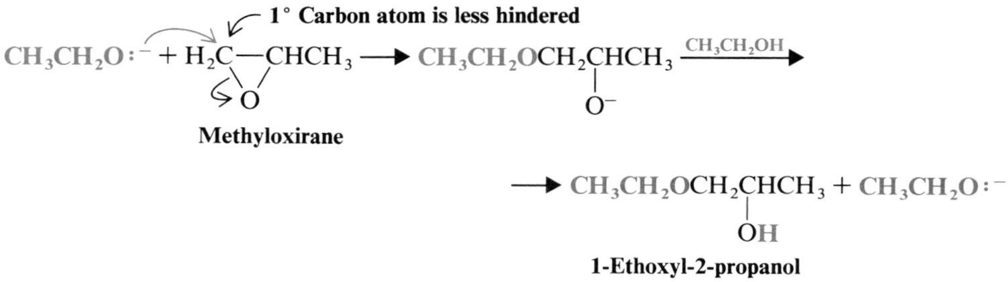

1° Carbon atom is less hindered

$$CH_3CH_2O:^- + H_2C - CHCH_3 \longrightarrow CH_3CH_2OCH_2CHCH_3 \xrightarrow{CH_3CH_2OH}$$
$$\underset{\diagdown O \diagup}{} \qquad\qquad\qquad \underset{O^-}{}$$

Methyloxirane

$$\longrightarrow CH_3CH_2OCH_2\underset{OH}{CHCH_3} + CH_3CH_2O:^-$$

1-Ethoxyl-2-propanol

This is just what we should expect: The reaction is, after all, an S_N2 reaction, and as we learned earlier (Section 6.15A), primary substrates react more rapidly in S_N2 reactions because they are less sterically hindered.

In the **acid-catalyzed ring opening** of an unsymmetrical epoxide the nucleophile attacks primarily *at the more substituted carbon atom.* For example,

$$CH_3OH + CH_3 - \overset{CH_3}{\underset{\diagdown O \diagup}{C}} - CH_2 \xrightarrow{H^+} CH_3 - \overset{CH_3}{\underset{OCH_3}{C}} - CH_2OH$$

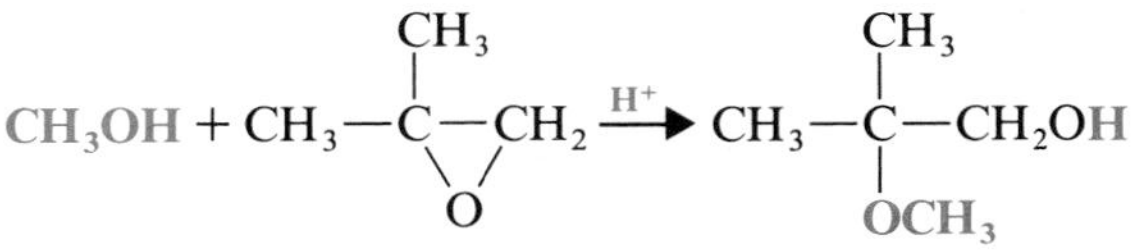

The reason: Bonding in the protonated epoxide (see following reaction) is unsymmetrical with the more highly substituted carbon atom bearing a considerable positive charge. The nucleophile, therefore, attacks this carbon atom even though it is more highly substituted.

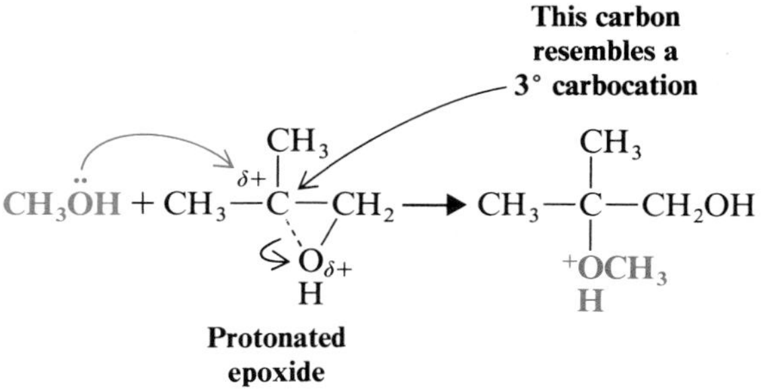

This carbon
resembles a
3° carbocation

$$CH_3\overset{..}{O}H + CH_3 - \overset{CH_3}{\underset{\underset{H}{\diagdown O_{\delta+} \diagup}}{\overset{\delta+}{C}}} - CH_2 \longrightarrow CH_3 - \overset{CH_3}{\underset{\underset{H}{^+OCH_3}}{C}} - CH_2OH$$

Protonated
epoxide

The more highly substituted carbon atom bears a greater positive charge because it resembles a more stable tertiary carbocation. [Notice how this reaction (and its explanation) resembles that given for halohydrin formation from unsymmetrical alkenes in Section 9.8.]

Problem 10.24

Propose structures for each of the following products:

(a) Oxirane $\xrightarrow[\text{CH}_3\text{OH}]{\text{H}^+}$ $C_3H_8O_2$ (an industrial solvent called Methyl Cellosolve)

(b) Oxirane $\xrightarrow[\text{CH}_3\text{CH}_2\text{OH}]{\text{H}^+}$ $C_4H_{10}O_2$ (Ethyl Cellosolve)

(c) Oxirane $\xrightarrow[\text{H}_2\text{O}]{\text{KI}}$ C_2H_4IO

(d) Oxirane $\xrightarrow{\text{NH}_3}$ C_2H_7NO

(e) Oxirane $\xrightarrow[\text{CH}_3\text{OH}]{\text{CH}_3\text{ONa}}$ $C_3H_8O_2$

Problem 10.25

Treating 2,2-dimethyloxirane, $H_2C\overset{\diagdown}{\underset{O}{}}C(CH_3)_2$, with sodium methoxide in methanol gives primarily 1-methoxy-2-methyl-2-propanol. What factor accounts for this result?

Problem 10.26

When sodium ethoxide reacts with 1-(chloromethyl)oxirane, labeled with ^{14}C as shown by the asterisk in **I**, the major product is an epoxide bearing the label as in **II**. Provide an explanation for this reaction.

$$Cl-CH_2-CH\underset{O}{\overset{\diagup}{\diagdown}}\overset{*}{C}H_2 \xrightarrow{\text{NaOC}_2\text{H}_5} CH_2-CH\underset{O}{\overset{\diagup}{\diagdown}}\overset{*}{C}H_2-OC_2H_5$$

I   **II**

1-(Chloromethyl)oxirane (epichlorohydrin)

10.20 ANTI HYDROXYLATION OF ALKENES VIA EPOXIDES

Epoxidation of cyclopentene produces 1,2-epoxycyclopentane:

(1)

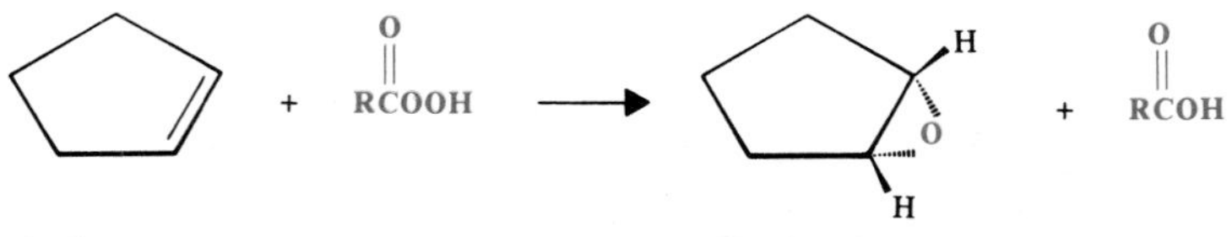

Cyclopentene   1.2–Epoxycyclopentane

Acid-catalyzed hydrolysis of 1,2-epoxycyclopentane yields a *trans*-diol, *trans*-1,2-cyclopentanediol. Water acting as a nucleophile attacks the protonated epoxide from the side opposite the epoxide group. The carbon atom being attacked undergoes an inversion of configuration. We show here only one carbon atom being attacked. Attack at the other carbon atom of this symmetrical system is equally likely and produces the enantiomeric form of *trans*-1,2-cyclopentanediol.

trans-1, 2-Cyclopentanediol

Epoxidation followed by acid-catalyzed hydrolysis gives us, therefore, a method for *anti hydroxylation* of a double bond (as opposed to syn hydroxylation, Section 9.11). The stereochemistry of this technique parallels closely the stereochemistry of the bromination of cyclopentene given earlier (Section 9.7).

Problem 10.27

Outline a mechanism similar to the one just given that shows how the enantiomeric form of *trans*-1,2-cyclopentanediol is produced.

Sample Problem

In Section 10.18 we showed the epoxidation of *cis*-2-butene to yield *cis*-2,3-dimethyloxirane and epoxidation of *trans*-2-butene to yield *trans*-2,3-dimethyloxirane. (a) Now consider acid-catalyzed hydrolysis of these two epoxides and show what product or products would result from each. (b) Are these reactions stereospecific?

Answer:
The meso compound, *cis*-2,3-dimethyloxirane (Fig. 10.3), yields on hydrolysis (2R,3R)-2,3-butanediol and (2S,3S)-2,3-butanediol. These products are enantiomers. Since the attack by water at either carbon [path (a) or path (b)] occurs at the same rate, the product is obtained in a racemic form.

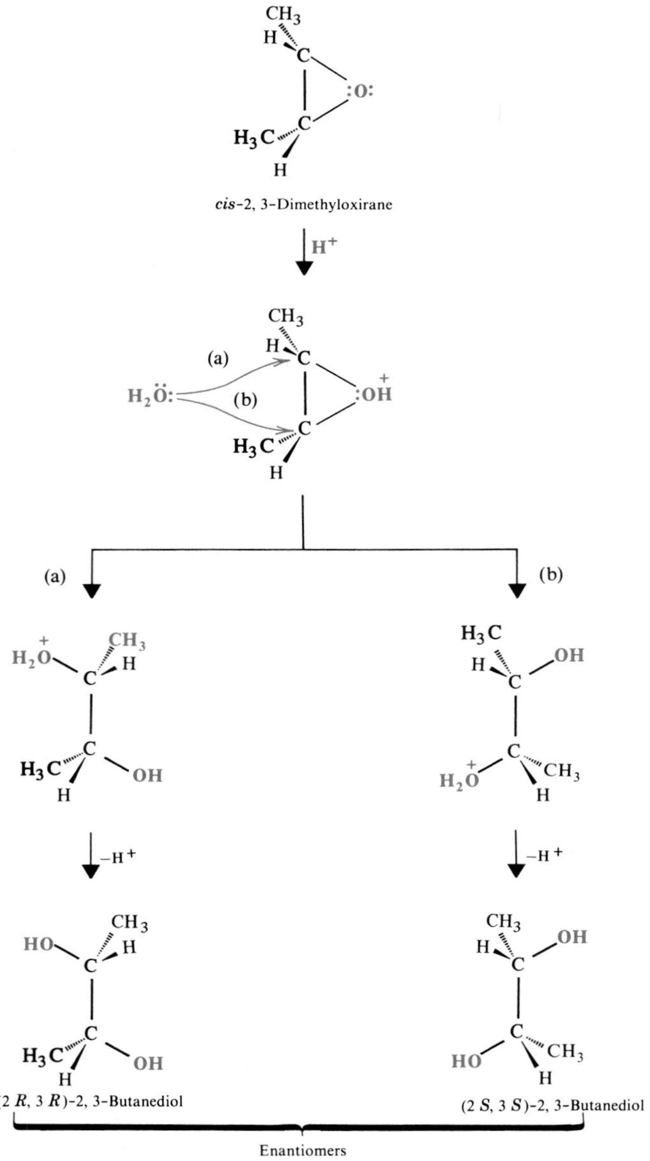

FIGURE 10.3 Acid-catalyzed hydrolysis of *cis*-2,3-dimethyloxirane yields (2R,3R)-2,3-butanediol by path (a) and (2S,3S)-2,3-butanediol by path (b). (Use models to convince yourself.)

When either of the *trans*-2,3-dimethyloxirane enantiomers undergoes acid-catalyzed hydrolysis, the only product that is obtained is the meso compound, (2R,3S)-2,3-butanediol. The hydrolysis of one enantiomer is shown in Fig. 10.4. (You might construct a similar diagram showing the hydrolysis of the other enantiomer to convince yourself that it, too, yields the same product.)

Since both steps in this method for the conversion of an alkene to a diol (glycol) are stereospecific (i.e., both the epoxidation step and the acid-catalyzed hydrolysis), the net result is a stereospecific anti hydroxylation of the double bond (Fig. 10.5).

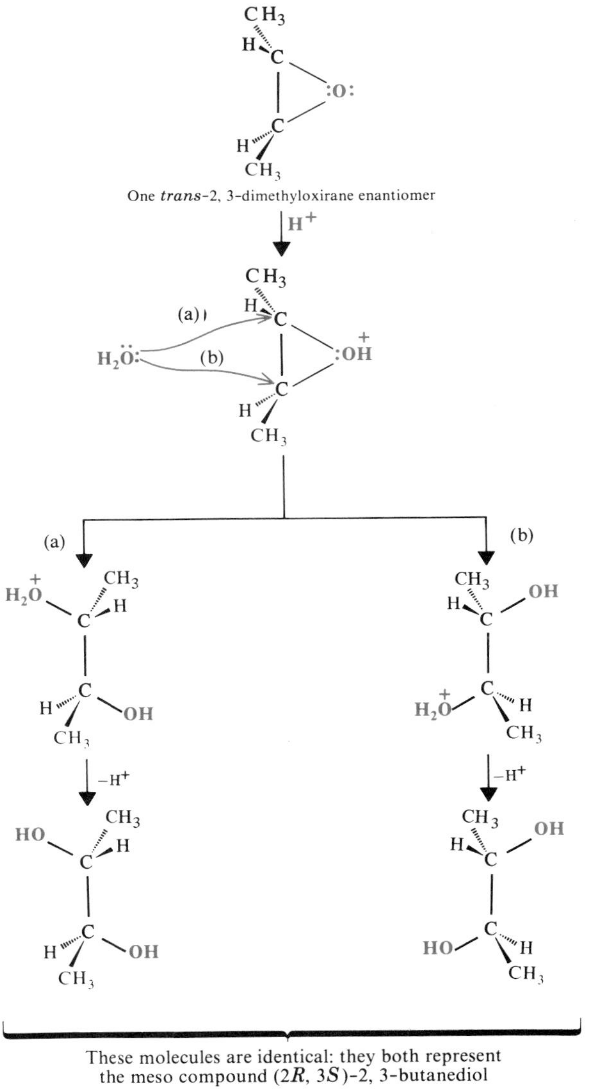

These molecules are identical: they both represent the meso compound (2R, 3S)-2, 3-butanediol

FIGURE 10.4 The acid-catalyzed hydrolysis of one *trans*-2,3-dimethyloxirane enantiomer produces the meso compound, (2R,3S)-2,3-butanediol, by path (a) or (b). Hydrolysis of the other enantiomer (or the racemic modification) would yield the same product. (You should use models to convince yourself that the two structures given for the products above do represent the same compound.)

10.21 SUMMARY OF REACTIONS OF ALCOHOLS AND ETHERS

Most of the important reactions of alcohols and ethers that we have studied thus far are summarized in Fig. 10.6.

10.21A ALKENES IN SYNTHESIS

We have studied reactions in this chapter and in Chapter 9 that can be extremely useful in designing syntheses. For example, if we want to **hydrate a double bond in a Markovnikov orientation,** we have three methods for doing so: (1) *oxymercuration–*

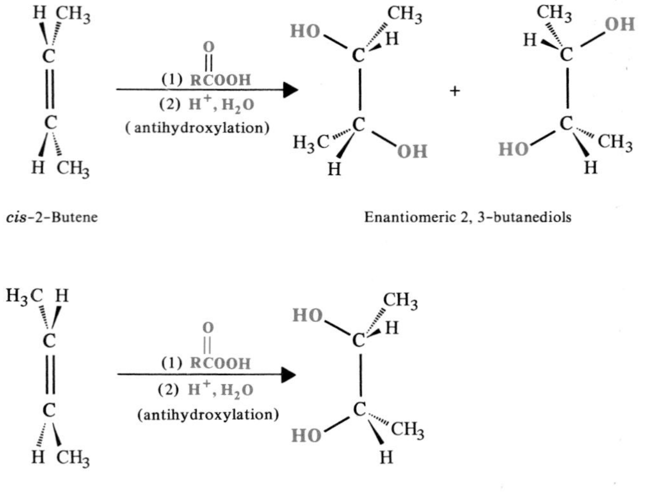

cis-2-Butene — Enantiomeric 2, 3-butanediols

trans-2-Butene — meso-2, 3-Butanediol

FIGURE 10.5 The overall result of epoxidation followed by acid-catalyzed hydrolysis is a stereospecific anti hydroxylation of the double bond. *cis*-2-Butene yields the enantiomeric 2,3-butanediols; *trans*-2-butene yields the meso compound.

demercuration (Section 10.5), (2) *acid-catalyzed hydration* (Section 9.5), and (3) *addition of sulfuric acid followed by hydrolysis* (Section 9.4). Of these methods oxymercuration–demercuration is the most useful in the laboratory because it is easy to carry out and because it *is not accompanied by rearrangements.*

If we want to **hydrate a double bond in an anti-Markovnikov orientation,** we can use *hydroboration–oxidation* (Section 10.7). With hydroboration–oxidation we can also achieve a *syn addition of the H— and —OH groups.* Remember, too, **the boron group of an organoborane can be replaced by hydrogen, deuterium, or tritium** (Section 10.7B), and that hydroboration, itself, involves a *syn addition of H— and —B.*

If we want to **add HX to a double bond in a Markovnikov sense** (Section 9.2), we treat the alkene with HF, HCl, HBr, or HI.

If we want to **add HBr in an anti-Markovnikov orientation** (Section 9.9), we treat the alkene with HBr *and a peroxide.* (The other hydrogen halides do not undergo anti-Markovnikov addition when peroxides are present.)

We can **add bromine or chlorine to a double bond** (Section 9.6), and the addition is an *anti addition* (Section 9.7). We can also **add X— and —OH** to a double bond (i.e., synthesize a halohydrin) by carrying out the bromination or chlorination in water (Section 9.8). This addition, too, is an *anti addition.*

If we want to carry out a **syn hydroxylation of a double bond,** we can use either $KMnO_4$ in a cold, dilute, and basic solution or use OsO_4 followed by $NaHSO_3$ (Section 9.11). Of these two methods, the latter is preferable because of the tendency of $KMnO_4$ to overoxidize the alkene and cause cleavage at the double bond.

Anti hydroxylation of a double bond can be achieved by converting the alkene to an *epoxide* and then carrying out an acid-catalyzed hydrolysis (Section 10.20).

Equations for most of these reactions are given in Figs. 9.8 and 10.7.

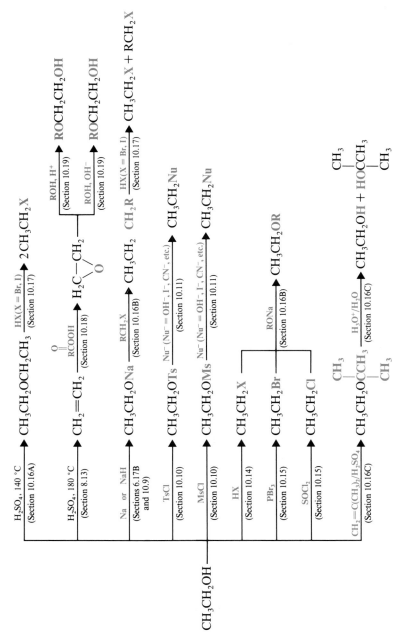

FIGURE 10.6 A summary of important reactions of alcohols and ethers starting with ethanol.

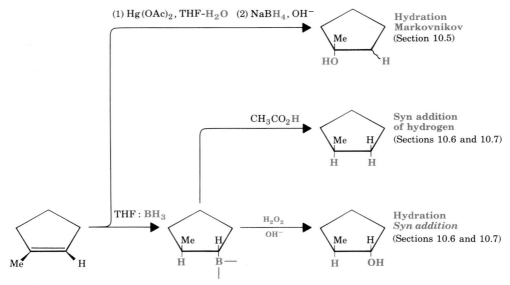

FIGURE 10.7 Oxymercuration–demercuration and hydroboration reactions of 1-methyl-cyclopentene. This figure supplements Fig. 9.5.

10.22 CROWN ETHERS: NUCLEOPHILIC SUBSTITUTION REACTIONS IN RELATIVELY NONPOLAR APROTIC SOLVENTS BY PHASE-TRANSFER CATALYSIS

When we studied the effect of the solvent on nucleophilic substitution reactions in Section 6.15A, we found that S_N2 reactions take place much more rapidly in polar aprotic solvents such as dimethyl sulfoxide and *N,N*-dimethylformamide. The reason: ***In these polar aprotic solvents the nucleophile is only very slightly solvated and is, consequently, highly reactive.***

This increased reactivity of nucleophiles is a distinct advantage. Reactions that might have taken many hours or days are often over in a matter of minutes. There are, unfortunately, certain disadvantages that accompany the use of solvents such as DMSO and DMF. These solvents have very high boiling points, and as a result, they are often difficult to remove after the reaction is over. Purification of these solvents is also time consuming, and they are expensive. At high temperatures certain of these polar aprotic solvents decompose.

In some ways the ideal solvent for an S_N2 reaction would be a *nonpolar* aprotic solvent such as a hydrocarbon or relatively nonpolar chlorinated hydrocarbon. They have low boiling points, they are cheap, and they are relatively stable.

Until recently, aprotic solvents such as a hydrocarbon or chlorinated hydrocarbon were seldom used for nucleophilic substitution reactions because of their inability to dissolve ionic compounds. This situation has changed with the development of a procedure called **phase-transfer catalysis.**

With phase-transfer catalysis, we usually use two immiscible phases that are in contact — often an aqueous phase containing an ionic reactant and an organic phase (benzene, $CHCl_3$, etc.) containing the organic substrate. Normally the reaction of two substances in separate phases like this is inhibited because of the inability of the reagents to come together. Adding a phase-transfer catalyst solves this problem by transferring the ionic reactant into the organic phase. And again, because the reaction medium is aprotic, an S_N2 reaction occurs rapidly.

An example of phase-transfer catalysis is outlined in Fig. 10.8. The phase-transfer catalyst (Q^+X^-) is usually a quaternary ammonium halide ($R_4N^+X^-$) such as tetrabutylammonium halide, $(CH_3CH_2CH_2CH_2)_4N^+X^-$. The phase-transfer catalyst causes the transfer of the nucleophile (e. g., CN^-) as an ion pair $[Q^+CN^-]$ into the organic phase. This transfer apparently takes place because the cation (Q^+) of the ion pair, with its four alkyl groups, resembles a hydrocarbon in spite of its positive charge. It is said to be **lipophilic**—it prefers a nonpolar environment to an aqueous one. In the organic phase the nucleophile of the ion pair (CN^-) reacts with the organic substrate RX. The cation (Q^+) [and anion (X^-)] then migrate back into the aqueous phase to complete the cycle. This process continues until all of the nucleophile or the organic substrate has reacted.

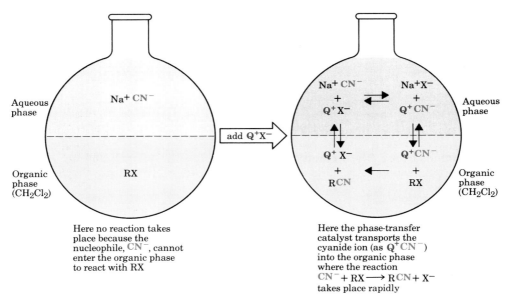

FIGURE 10.8 Phase-transfer catalysis of the S_N2 reaction between sodium cyanide and an alkyl halide.

An example of a nucleophilic substitution reaction carried out with phase-transfer catalysis is the reaction of 1-chlorooctane (in decane) and sodium cyanide (in water). The reaction (at 105 °C) is complete in less than 2 h and gives a 95% yield of the substitution product.

$$CH_3(CH_2)_6CH_2Cl \text{ (in decane)} \xrightarrow[\text{aqueous NaCN, 105 °C}]{R_4N^+Br^-} CH_3(CH_2)_6CH_2CN$$
(95%)

Many other nucleophilic substitution reactions have been carried out in a similar way.

Phase-transfer catalysis, however, is not limited to nucleophilic substitutions. Many other types of reactions are also amenable to phase-transfer catalysis. Oxidations of alkenes dissolved in benzene can be accomplished in excellent yield using potassium permanganate (in water) when a quaternary ammonium salt is present:

$$CH_3(CH_2)_5CH{=}CH_2 \text{ (benzene)} \xrightarrow[\text{aqueous KMnO}_4, \text{ 35 °C}]{R_4N^+X^-} CH_3(CH_2)_5CO_2H$$
$$(99\%)$$

Potassium permanganate can also be transferred to benzene by quaternary ammonium salts for the purpose of chemical tests. The resulting "purple benzene" can be used as a test reagent for unsaturated compounds. As an unsaturated compound is added to the benzene solution of $KMnO_4$, the purple color disappears and the solution becomes brown (because of the presence of MnO_2), indicating a positive test (see Section 9.19D).

Problem 10.28

Outline a scheme such as the one shown in Fig. 10.8 showing how the reaction of $CH_3(CH_2)_6CH_2Cl$ with cyanide ion (just shown) takes place by phase-transfer catalysis. Be sure to indicate which ions are present in the organic phase, which are in the aqueous phase, and which pass from one phase to the other.

10.22A CROWN ETHERS

Compounds called **crown ethers** are also phase-transfer catalysts and are able to transport ionic compounds into an organic phase. Crown ethers are cyclic polymers of ethylene glycol such as the 18-crown-6 that follows:

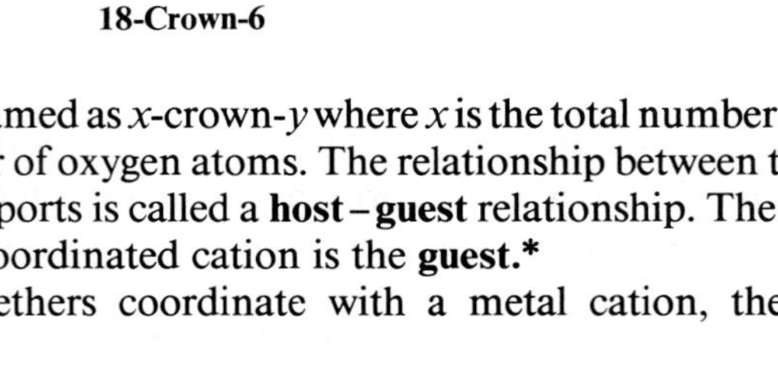

18-Crown-6

Crown ethers are named as *x*-crown-*y* where *x* is the total number of atoms in the ring and *y* is the number of oxygen atoms. The relationship between the crown ether and the ion that it transports is called a **host–guest** relationship. The crown ether acts as the **host,** and the coordinated cation is the **guest.***

When crown ethers coordinate with a metal cation, they thereby convert

---

* The Nobel Prize for Chemistry in 1987 was awarded to Charles J. Pedersen (retired from the Du Pont company), Donald J. Cram (University of California, Los Angeles), and to Jean-Marie Lehn (Louis Pasteur University, Strasbourg, France) for their development of crown ethers and other molecules "with structure specific interactions of high selectivity." Their contributions to our understanding of what is now called "molecular recognition" has implications for how enzymes recognize their substrates, how hormones cause their effects, how antibodies recognize antigens, how neurotransmitters propagate their signals, and many other aspects of biochemistry. Molecular recognition is one of the most exciting areas in chemical research today.

the metal ion into a species with a hydrocarbonlike exterior. The crown ether 18-crown-6, for example, coordinates very effectively with potassium ions because the cavity size is correct and because the six oxygen atoms are ideally situated to donate their electron pairs to the central ion.

Crown ethers render many salts soluble in nonpolar solvents. Salts such as KF, KCN, and CH_3CO_2K, for example, can be transferred into aprotic solvents by using catalytic amounts of 18-crown-6. In the organic phase the relatively unsolvated anions of these salts can carry out a nucleophilic substitution reaction on an organic substrate.

$$K^+CN^- + RCH_2X \xrightarrow[\text{benzene}]{\text{18-crown-6}} RCH_2CN + K^+X^-$$

$$C_6H_5CH_2Cl + K^+F^- \xrightarrow[\text{acetonitrile}]{\text{18-crown-6}} C_6H_5CH_2F + K^+Cl^-$$
$$(100\%)$$

Crown ethers can also be used as phase-transfer catalysts for many other types of reactions. The following reaction is one example of the use of a crown ether in an oxidation.

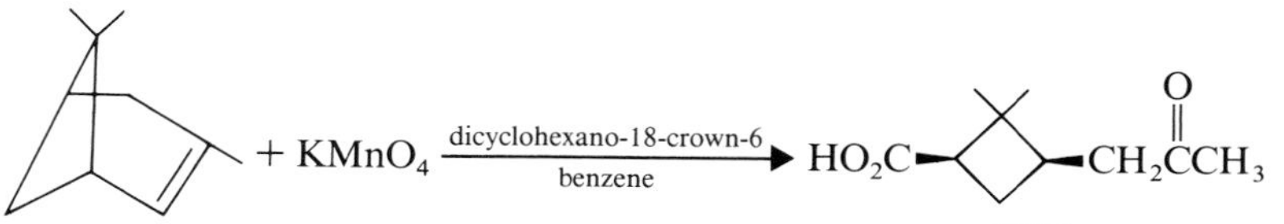

$$+ KMnO_4 \xrightarrow[\text{benzene}]{\text{dicyclohexano-18-crown-6}}$$

(90%)

Dicyclohexano-18-crown-6 has the following structure:

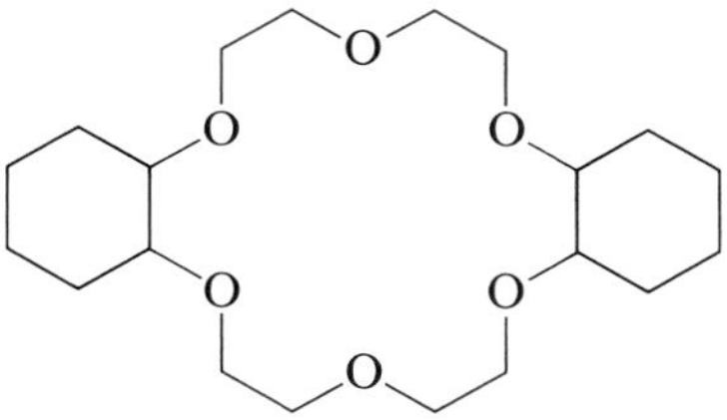

Dicyclohexano-18-crown-6

Problem 10.29

Write structures for (a) 15-crown-5 and (b) 12-crown-4.

10.22B TRANSPORT ANTIBIOTICS AND CROWN ETHERS

There are several antibiotics, called ionophores most notably *nonactin* and *valinomycin,* that coordinate with metal cations in a manner similar to that of crown ethers. Normally, cells must maintain a gradient between the concentrations of sodium and potassium ions inside and outside the cell wall. Potassium ions are "pumped" in; sodium ions are pumped out. The cell membrane, in its interior, is like a hydrocarbon, because it consists in this region primarily of the hydrocarbon portions of lipids (Chapter 23). The transport of hydrated sodium and potassium ions through the cell membrane is slow, and this transport requires an expenditure of energy by the cell. Nonactin, for example, upsets the concentration gradient of these ions by coordinating more strongly with potassium ions than with sodium ions. Because the potassium ions are bound in the interior of the nonactin, this host–guest complex becomes hydrocarbon-like on its surface and passes readily through the interior of the membrane. The cell membrane thereby becomes permeable to potassium ions, and the essential concentration gradient is destroyed.

Nonactin

Additional Problems

10.30   Give an IUPAC substitutive name for each of the following alcohols:

(a) $(CH_3)_3CCH_2CH_2OH$

(b) $CH_2{=}CHCH_2\overset{\underset{\displaystyle CH_3}{|}}{C}HOH$

(c) $HOCH_2\overset{\underset{\displaystyle CH_3}{|}}{C}HCH_2CH_2OH$

(d) $C_6H_5CH_2CH_2OH$

(e)

(f)

10.31   Write structural formulas for each of the following:

(a) (Z)-2-Buten-1-ol
(b) (R)-1,2,4-Butanetriol
(c) (1R,2R)-1,2-Cyclopentanediol
(d) 1-Ethylcyclobutanol
(e) 2-Chloro-3-hexyn-1-ol
(f) Tetrahydrofuran
(g) 2-Ethoxypentane
(h) Ethyl phenyl ether
(i) Diisopropyl ether
(j) 2-Ethoxyethanol

10.32   Starting with each of the following, outline a practical synthesis of 1-butanol.
(a) 1-Butene   (b) 1-Chlorobutane   (c) 2-Chlorobutane   (d) 1-Butyne

10.33   Show how you might prepare 2-bromobutane from
(a) 2-Butanol, $CH_3CH_2CHOHCH_3$ (c) 1-Butene
(b) 1-Butanol, $CH_3CH_2CH_2CH_2OH$ (d) 1-Butyne

10.34   Show how you might carry out the following transformations:
(a) Cyclohexanol $\longrightarrow$ chlorocyclohexane
(b) Cyclohexene $\longrightarrow$ chlorocyclohexane
(c) 1-Methylcyclohexene $\longrightarrow$ 1-bromo-1-methylcyclohexane
(d) 1-Methylcyclohexene $\longrightarrow$ *trans*-2-methylcyclohexanol
(e) 1-Bromo-1-methylcyclohexane $\longrightarrow$ cyclohexylmethanol

ADDITIONAL PROBLEMS

10.35 Give structures and names for the compounds that would be formed when 1-propanol is treated with each of the following reagents:

(a) Sodium metal

(b) Sodium metal, then 1-bromobutane

(c) Methanesulfonyl chloride

(d) *p*-Toluenesulfonyl chloride

(e) Product of (c), then CH$_3$ONa

(f) Product of (d), then KI

(g) Phosphorus trichloride

(h) Thionyl chloride

(i) Sulfuric acid at 140 °C

(j) Refluxing concentrated hydrobromic acid

10.36 Give structures and names for the compounds that would be formed when 2-propanol is treated with each of the reagents given in Problem 10.35.

10.37 What compounds would you expect to be formed when each of the following ethers is refluxed with excess concentrated hydrobromic acid?

(a) Ethyl methyl ether (b) *tert*-Butyl ethyl ether (c) Tetrahydrofuran (d) 1,4-Dioxane

10.38 Write a mechanism that accounts for the following reaction:

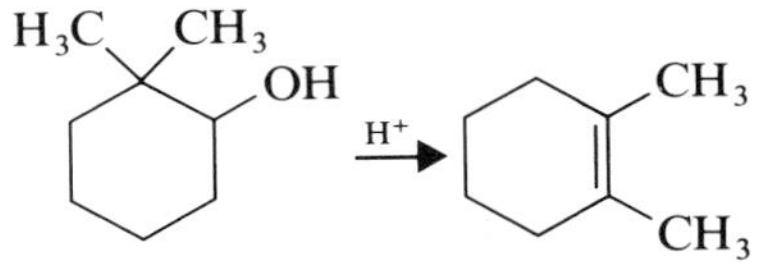

10.39 Show how you would utilize the hydroboration–oxidation procedure to prepare each of the following alcohols:

(a) 3,3-Dimethyl-1-butanol

(b) 1-Hexanol

(c) 2-Phenylethanol

(d) *trans*-2-Methylcyclopentanol

10.40 Write a three-dimensional formula for the product formed when 1-methylcyclohexene is treated with each of the following reagents. In each case, designate the location of deuterium or tritium atoms.

(a) (1) THF:BH$_3$ (2) CH$_3$CO$_2$T

(b) (1) THF:BD$_3$ (2) CH$_3$CO$_2$D

(c) (1) THF:BD$_3$ (2) NaOH, H$_2$O$_2$, H$_2$O

10.41 Starting with isobutane show how each of the following could be synthesized. (You need not repeat the synthesis of a compound prepared in an earlier part of this problem.)

(a) *tert*-Butyl bromide

(b) 2-Methylpropene

(c) Isobutyl bromide

(d) Isobutyl iodide

(e) Isobutyl alcohol (two ways)

(f) *tert*-Butyl alcohol

(g) Isobutyl methyl ether

(h) CH$_3$CHCH$_2$OCCH$_3$ with CH$_3$ and O substituents

(i) CH$_3$CHCH$_2$CN with CH$_3$ substituent

(j) CH$_3$CHCH$_2$SCH$_3$ with CH$_3$ substituent (two ways)

(k) CH$_3$CCH$_2$CBr$_3$ with CH$_3$ and Br substituents

10.42 Vicinal halo alcohols (halohydrins) can be synthesized by treating epoxides with HX. (a) Show how you would use this method to synthesize 2-chlorocyclopentanol from cyclopentene. (b) Would you expect the product to be *cis*-2-chlorocyclopentanol or *trans*-2-chlorocyclopentanol, that is, would you expect a net syn addition or a net anti addition of —Cl and —OH? Explain.

10.43 Pheromones are substances secreted by animals (especially insects) that produce a specific behavioral reaction in other members of the same species. Pheromones are effective at very low concentrations and include sex attractants, warning substances, and "aggregation" compounds. After many years of research, the sex attractant of the gypsy moth has been identified and synthesized in the laboratory. This sex pheromone is unusual in that it appears to be equally attractive to male and female gypsy moths. (It has been useful in their control even though this may seem somewhat unfair.) The final step in the synthesis of the pheromone involves treatment of *cis*-2-methyl-7-octadecene with a peroxy acid. What is the structure of the gypsy moth sex pheromone?

10.44 Starting with 2-methylpropene (isobutylene) and using any other needed reagents, outline a synthesis of each of the following:

(a) $(CH_3)_2CHCH_2OH$

(b) $(CH_3)_2CHCH_2T$

(c) $(CH_3)_2CDCH_2T$

(d) $(CH_3)_2CHCH_2OCH_2CH_3$

10.45 Show how you would use oxymercuration–demercuration to prepare each of the following alcohols from the appropriate alkene:

(a) 2-Pentanol

(b) 1-Cyclopentylethanol

(c) 3-Methyl-3-pentanol

(d) 1-Ethylcyclopentanol

10.46 Give stereochemical formulas for each product **A** – **L** and answer the questions given in parts (b) and (g).

(a) 1-Methylcyclobutene $\xrightarrow[\text{(2) H}_2\text{O}_2,\text{ OH}^-]{\text{(1) THF:BH}_3}$ **A** $(C_5H_{10}O)$ $\xrightarrow[\text{OH}^-]{\text{TsCl}}$

B $(C_{12}H_{16}SO_3)$ $\xrightarrow{\text{OH}^-}$ **C** $(C_5H_{10}O)$

(b) What is the stereoisomeric relationship between **A** and **C**?

(c) **B** $(C_{12}H_{16}SO_3)$ $\xrightarrow{\text{I}^-}$ **D** (C_5H_9I)

(d) *trans*-4-Methylcyclohexanol $\xrightarrow[\text{OH}^-]{\text{MsCl}}$ **E** $(C_8H_{16}SO_3)$ $\xrightarrow{\text{HC}\equiv\text{CNa}}$

F (C_9H_{14})

(e) (*R*)-2-Butanol $\xrightarrow{\text{NaH}}$ [**H** (C_4H_9ONa)] $\xrightarrow{\text{CH}_3\text{I}}$ **J** $(C_5H_{12}O)$

(f) (*R*)-2-Butanol $\xrightarrow{\text{MsCl}}$ **K** $(C_5H_{12}SO_3)$ $\xrightarrow{\text{CH}_3\text{ONa}}$ **L** $(C_5H_{12}O)$

(g) What is the stereoisomeric relationship between **J** and **L**?

10.47 When the 3-bromo-2-butanol with the stereochemical structure **A** is treated with concentrated HBr it yields *meso*-2,3-dibromobutane; a similar reaction of the 3-bromo-2-butanol **B** yields (±)-2,3-dibromobutane. This classic experiment performed in 1939 by S. Winstein and H. J. Lucas was the starting point for a series of investigations of what are called *neighboring group effects* (cf. Special Topic N). Propose mechanisms that will account for the stereochemistry of these reactions.

A   B

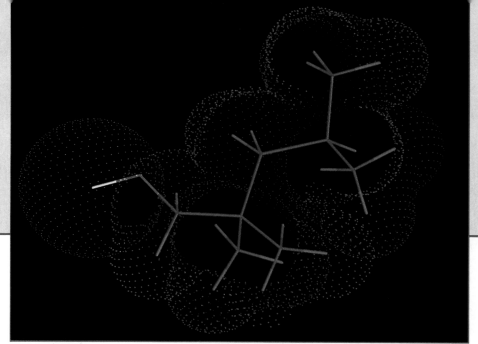

A Grignard reagent (see Section 11.6B).

11

ALCOHOLS FROM CARBONYL COMPOUNDS. OXIDATION- REDUCTION AND ORGANOMETALLIC COMPOUNDS

11.1 INTRODUCTION

Carbonyl compounds are a broad group of compounds that includes aldehydes, ketones, carboxylic acids, and esters.

| The carbonyl group | An aldehyde | A ketone | A carboxylic acid | A carboxylate ester |

Although we shall not study the chemistry of these compounds in detail until we reach Chapters 16–18, it will be useful now to consider reactions by which these compounds are converted to alcohols. Before we do this, however, let us consider the structure of the carbonyl group and its relationship to the reactivity of carbonyl compounds.

11.1A STRUCTURE OF THE CARBONYL GROUP

The carbonyl carbon atom is sp^2 hybridized; thus it and the three groups attached to it lie in the same plane. The bond angles between the three attached atoms are what we would expect of a trigonal planar structure; they are approximately 120°.

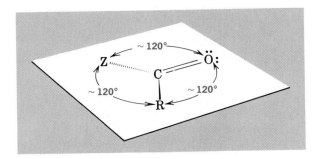

The carbon–oxygen double bond consists of a σ bond and a π bond.

The π bond is formed by overlap of the carbon p orbital with a p orbital from the oxygen atom.

The more electronegative oxygen atom strongly attracts the electrons of both the σ bond and the π bond causing the carbonyl group to be highly polarized; the carbon atom bears a substantial positive charge and the oxygen atom bears a substantial negative charge. Polarization of the π bond can be represented by the following resonance structures for the carbonyl group (see also Section 3.5B).

Resonance structures for the carbonyl group   **Hybrid**

Evidence for the polarity of the carbon–oxygen bond can be found in the rather large dipole moments associated with carbonyl compounds.

Formaldehyde   **Acetone**
$\mu = 2.27$ D $\mu = 2.88$ D

11.1B REACTION OF CARBONYL COMPOUNDS WITH NUCLEOPHILES

From a synthetic point of view, one of the most important reactions of carbonyl compounds is one in which the carbonyl compound undergoes **nucleophilic addition.** The carbonyl group is susceptible to nucleophilic attack because, as we have just seen, the carbonyl carbon bears a partial positive charge. When the nucleophile adds to the carbonyl group it uses its electron pair to form a bond to the carbonyl carbon atom. The carbonyl carbon can accept this electron pair because one pair of electrons of the carbon–oxygen double bond can shift out to the oxygen.

$$\text{Nu:}^{-} \quad + \quad \overset{\delta+}{\underset{}{C}}\!\!=\!\!\overset{\delta-}{\ddot{O}}\text{:} \longrightarrow \text{Nu}-\overset{|}{\underset{|}{C}}-\ddot{O}\text{:}^{-}$$

As the reaction takes place, the carbon atom undergoes a change in its geometry and its hybridization state. It goes from a trigonal planar geometry and sp^2 hybridization to a tetrahedral geometry and sp^3 hybridization.

Two important nucleophiles that add to carbonyl compounds are **hydride ions** from compounds such as $NaBH_4$ or $LiAlH_4$ (Section 11.3), and **carbanions** from compounds such as RLi or RMgX (11.7C).

Another related set of reactions are reactions in which alcohols and carbonyl compounds are **oxidized** and **reduced** (Sections 11.2–11.4). For example, primary alcohols can be oxidized to aldehydes and aldehydes can be reduced to alcohols.

$$\underset{\substack{\textbf{A primary} \\ \textbf{alcohol}}}{R-\overset{\overset{\displaystyle H}{|}}{\underset{\underset{\displaystyle H}{|}}{C}}-\ddot{O}-H} \underset{\underset{[H]}{\text{reduction}}}{\overset{\overset{[O]}{\text{oxidation}}}{\rightleftharpoons}} \underset{\textbf{An aldehyde}}{\overset{R}{\underset{H}{>}}C\!\!=\!\!\ddot{O}\text{:}}$$

Let us begin by examining some general principles that apply to the oxidation and reduction of organic compounds.

11.2 OXIDATION-REDUCTION REACTIONS IN ORGANIC CHEMISTRY

Reduction of an organic molecule usually corresponds to increasing its hydrogen content or to decreasing its oxygen content. For example, converting a carboxylic acid to an aldehyde is a reduction because the oxygen content is decreased.

$$\underset{\substack{\textbf{Carboxylic} \\ \textbf{acid}}}{R-\overset{\overset{\displaystyle O}{\|}}{C}-OH} \overset{[H]}{\underset{\text{reduction}}{\longrightarrow}} \underset{\textbf{Aldehyde}}{R-\overset{\overset{\displaystyle O}{\|}}{C}-H}$$

oxygen content decreases

Converting an aldehyde to an alcohol is also a reduction.

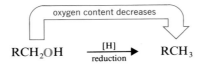

$$R-\overset{\overset{\displaystyle O}{\|}}{C}-H \xrightarrow[\text{reduction}]{[H]} RCH_2OH$$

Converting an alcohol to an alkane is also a reduction.

$$RCH_2OH \xrightarrow[\text{reduction}]{[H]} RCH_3$$

In these examples we have used the symbol [H] to indicate that a reduction of the organic compound has taken place. We do this when we want to write a general equation without specifying what the reducing agent is.

The opposite of reduction is **oxidation**. *Thus, increasing the oxygen content of an organic molecule or decreasing its hydrogen content is an oxidation* of the organic molecule. The reverse of each reaction that we have given is an oxidation of the organic molecule, and we can summarize these oxidation–reduction reactions as follows below. We use the symbol [O] to indicate in a general way that the organic molecule has been oxidized.

$$RCH_3 \underset{[H]}{\overset{[O]}{\rightleftarrows}} RCH_2OH \underset{[H]}{\overset{[O]}{\rightleftarrows}} R\overset{\overset{\displaystyle O}{\|}}{C}H \underset{[H]}{\overset{[O]}{\rightleftarrows}} R\overset{\overset{\displaystyle O}{\|}}{C}OH$$

Lowest oxidation state   **Highest oxidation state**

Oxidation of an organic compound may be more broadly defined as a reaction that increases its content of any element more electronegative than carbon. For example, replacing hydrogen atoms by chlorine atoms is an oxidation:

$$Ar-CH_3 \underset{[H]}{\overset{[O]}{\rightleftarrows}} Ar-CH_2Cl \underset{[H]}{\overset{[O]}{\rightleftarrows}} Ar-CHCl_2 \underset{[H]}{\overset{[O]}{\rightleftarrows}} Ar-CCl_3$$

Of course, when an organic compound is reduced, something else — **the reducing agent** — must be oxidized. And when an organic compound is oxidized, something else — **the oxidizing agent** — is reduced. These oxidizing and reducing agents are often inorganic compounds, and in the next two sections we shall see what some of them are.

Problem 11.1

One method for assigning an oxidation state to a carbon atom of an organic compound is to base that assignment on the groups attached to the carbon; a bond to hydrogen (or anything less electronegative than carbon) makes it -1, a bond to oxygen, nitrogen, or halogen (or to anything more electronegative than carbon) makes it $+1$, and a bond to another carbon 0. Thus the carbon of methane is assigned an oxidation state of -4, and that of carbon dioxide, $+4$.

(a) Use this method to assign oxidation states to the carbon atoms of methanol (CH_3OH), formic acid $\left(H\overset{\displaystyle O}{\overset{\|}{C}}OH \right)$, and formaldehyde $\left(H\overset{\displaystyle O}{\overset{\|}{C}}H \right)$. (b) Arrange the compounds methane, carbon dioxide, methanol, formic acid, and formaldehyde in order of increasing oxidation state. (c) What change in oxidation state accompanies the reaction, methanol $\longrightarrow$ formaldehyde? (d) Is this an oxidation or a reduction? (e) When H_2CrO_4 acts as an oxidizing agent in this reaction, the chromium of H_2CrO_4 becomes Cr^{3+}. What change in oxidation state does chromium undergo?

Problem 11.2

(a) Use the method described in the preceding problem to assign oxidation states to each carbon of ethanol and to each carbon of acetaldehyde. (b) What do these numbers reveal about the site of oxidation when ethanol is oxidized to acetaldehyde? (c) Repeat this procedure for the oxidation of acetaldehyde to acetic acid.

Problem 11.3

(a) Although we have described the hydrogenation of an alkene as an addition reaction, organic chemists often refer to it as a "reduction." Refer to the method described in Problem 11.1 and explain. (b) Make similar comments about the reaction:

$$CH_3-\overset{\displaystyle O}{\overset{\|}{C}}-H + H_2 \xrightarrow{\text{Ni}} CH_3CH_2OH$$

11.2A BALANCING OXIDATION–REDUCTION EQUATIONS

A method for balancing organic oxidation–reduction reactions is described in the Study Guide that accompanies this text.

11.3 ALCOHOLS BY REDUCTION OF CARBONYL COMPOUNDS

Primary and secondary alcohols can be synthesized by the reduction of a variety of compounds that contain the carbonyl $\left(\overset{\diagdown}{\underset{\diagup}{C}}{=}O \right)$ group. Several general examples are shown here.

$$R-\overset{\displaystyle O}{\overset{\|}{C}}-OH \xrightarrow{\text{[H]}} R-CH_2OH$$
Carboxylic acid   **1° Alcohol**

$$R-\overset{\displaystyle O}{\overset{\|}{C}}-OR' \xrightarrow{\text{[H]}} R-CH_2OH \; (+ \; R'OH)$$
Ester   **1° Alcohol**

$$\underset{\text{Aldehyde}}{R-\overset{\overset{\displaystyle O}{\|}}{C}-H} \xrightarrow{[H]} \underset{\text{1° Alcohol}}{R-CH_2OH}$$

$$\underset{\text{Ketone}}{R-\overset{\overset{\displaystyle O}{\|}}{C}-R'} \xrightarrow{[H]} \underset{\text{2° Alcohol}}{R-\underset{\overset{\displaystyle |}{OH}}{CH}-R'}$$

Reductions of carboxylic acids are the most difficult, and prior to 1946 direct reduction of acids was not possible. However, the discovery in 1946 of the powerful reducing agent **lithium aluminum hydride** (LiAlH$_4$, abb. LAH) gave organic chemists a method for reducing acids to primary alcohols in excellent yields.

$$4 \; RCO_2H + 3 \; \underset{\substack{\text{Lithium} \\ \text{aluminum} \\ \text{hydride}}}{LiAlH_4} \xrightarrow{Et_2O} [(RCH_2O)_4Al]Li + 4 \; H_2 + 2 \; LiAlO_2$$
$$\xrightarrow[H_2O]{} 4 \; RCH_2OH + Al(OH)_3 + LiOH$$

Two examples are the lithium aluminum hydride reductions of acetic acid and 2,2-dimethylpropanoic acid.

$$\underset{\text{Acetic acid}}{CH_3\overset{\overset{\displaystyle O}{\|}}{C}-OH} \xrightarrow[\text{(2) } H_2O]{\text{(1) } LiAlH_4/Et_2O} \underset{\substack{\text{Ethanol} \\ \text{(100\%)}}}{CH_3CH_2OH}$$

$$\underset{\substack{\text{2,2-Dimethylpropanoic} \\ \text{acid}}}{CH_3-\overset{\overset{\displaystyle CH_3}{|}}{\underset{\underset{\displaystyle CH_3}{|}}{C}}-CO_2H} \xrightarrow[\text{(2) } H_2O]{\text{(1) } LiAlH_4/Et_2O} \underset{\substack{\text{Neopentyl alcohol} \\ \text{(92\%)}}}{CH_3-\overset{\overset{\displaystyle CH_3}{|}}{\underset{\underset{\displaystyle CH_3}{|}}{C}}-CH_2OH}$$

Esters can be reduced by high-pressure hydrogenation (a reaction preferred for industrial processes and often referred to as "hydrogenolysis" because a carbon–oxygen bond is cleaved in the process), or through the use of lithium aluminum hydride.

$$R-\overset{\overset{\displaystyle O}{\|}}{C}OR' + H_2 \xrightarrow[\substack{175 \text{ °C} \\ 5000 \text{ psi}}]{CuO \cdot CuCr_2O_4} RCH_2OH + R'OH$$

$$R-\overset{\overset{\displaystyle O}{\|}}{C}OR' \xrightarrow[\text{(2) } H_2O]{\text{(1) } LiAlH_4/Et_2O} RCH_2OH + R'OH$$

The latter method is the one most commonly used now in small-scale laboratory synthesis.

Aldehydes and ketones can also be reduced to alcohols by hydrogen and a metal catalyst, by sodium in alcohol, and by lithium aluminum hydride. The reducing agent most often used, however, is sodium borohydride (NaBH$_4$).

11.3 ALCOHOLS BY REDUCTION OF CARBONYL COMPOUNDS

$$4 \; R\overset{\overset{\displaystyle O}{\|}}{C}H + NaBH_4 + 3 \; H_2O \longrightarrow 4 \; RCH_2OH + NaH_2BO_3$$

$$CH_3CH_2CH_2\overset{\overset{\displaystyle O}{\|}}{C}H \xrightarrow[\text{H}_2\text{O}]{\text{NaBH}_4} CH_3CH_2CH_2CH_2OH$$

Butanal   **1-Butanol**
(85%)

$$CH_3CH_2\underset{\underset{\displaystyle O}{\|}}{C}CH_3 \xrightarrow[\text{H}_2\text{O}]{\text{NaBH}_4} CH_3CH_2\underset{\underset{\displaystyle OH}{|}}{C}HCH_3$$

2-Butanone   **2-Butanol**
(87%)

The key step in the reduction of a carbonyl compound by either lithium aluminum hydride or sodium borohydride is the transfer of a **hydride ion** from the metal to the carbonyl carbon. In this transfer the hydride ion acts as a *nucleophile*. The mechanism for the reduction of a ketone by sodium borohydride is illustrated here.

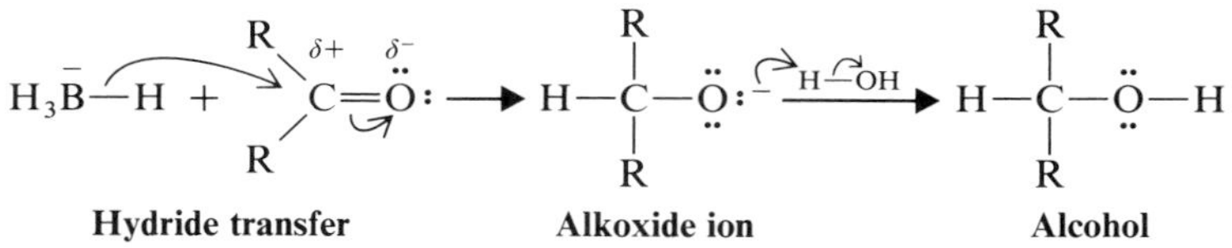

Hydride transfer   **Alkoxide ion**   **Alcohol**

These steps are repeated until all hydrogen atoms attached to boron have been transferred.

Sodium borohydride is a milder reducing agent than lithium aluminum hydride. Lithium aluminum hydride will reduce acids, esters, aldehydes, and ketones; but sodium borohydride will reduce only aldehydes and ketones.

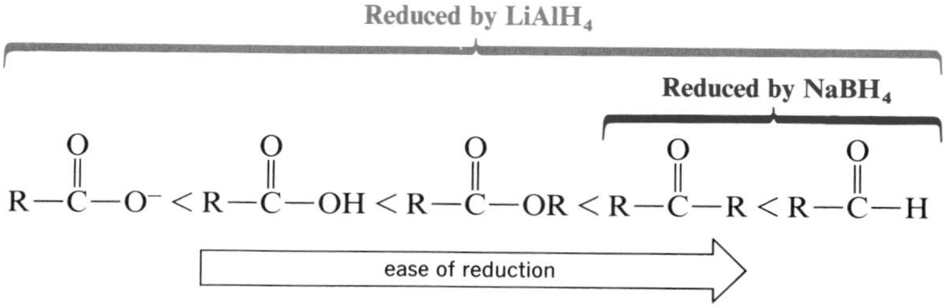

Lithium aluminum hydride reacts violently with water and therefore reductions with lithium aluminum hydride must be carried out in anhydrous solutions, usually in anhydrous ether. (Ethyl acetate is added cautiously after the reaction is over to decompose excess $LiAlH_4$, then water is added to decompose the aluminum complex.)* Sodium borohydride reductions, by contrast, can be carried out in water or alcohol solutions.

---

*Unless special precautions are taken, lithium aluminum hydride reductions can be very dangerous. You should consult an appropriate laboratory manual before attempting such a reduction, and the reaction should be carried out on a small scale.

Problem 11.4

Which reducing agent ($NaBH_4$ or $LiAlH_4$) would you use to carry out each of the following transformations?

(a)

(b)

(c)

11.4 OXIDATION OF ALCOHOLS

11.4A OXIDATION OF 1° ALCOHOLS TO ALDEHYDES: $RCH_2OH \longrightarrow RCHO$

Primary alcohols can be oxidized to aldehydes and carboxylic acids.

$$R-CH_2OH \xrightarrow{[O]} R-\overset{O}{\underset{\|}{C}}-H \xrightarrow{[O]} R-\overset{O}{\underset{\|}{C}}-OH$$

1° Alcohol   Aldehyde   Carboxylic acid

The oxidation of aldehydes to carboxylic acids in aqueous solutions usually takes place with milder oxidizing agents than those required to oxidize primary alcohols to aldehydes; thus it is difficult to stop the oxidation at the aldehyde stage. One way of avoiding this problem is to remove the aldehyde as soon as it is formed. This can often be done because aldehydes have lower boiling points than alcohols (why?), and therefore aldehydes can be distilled from the reaction mixture as they are formed. An example is the synthesis of butanal from 1-butanol using a mixture of $K_2Cr_2O_7$ and sulfuric acid:

$$CH_3CH_2CH_2CH_2OH \xrightarrow[H_2SO_4]{K_2Cr_2O_7} CH_3CH_2CH_2\overset{O}{\underset{\|}{C}}H$$

1-Butanol   Butanal
bp, 117.7 °C   bp, 75.7 °C
                        (50%)

This procedure does not give good yields with aldehydes that boil above 100 °C, however.

An industrial process for preparing low molecular weight aldehydes is **dehydrogenation** of a primary alcohol:

$$CH_3CH_2OH \xrightarrow[300 \text{ °C}]{Cu} CH_3\overset{O}{\underset{\|}{C}}H + H_2$$

[Notice that dehydrogenation of an organic compound corresponds to oxidation, whereas hydrogenation (cf. Problem 11.3) corresponds to reduction.]

11.4 OXIDATION OF ALCOHOLS

In most laboratory preparations we must rely on special oxidizing agents to prepare aldehydes from primary alcohols. A variety of reagents are available and to discuss them all here is beyond our scope. An excellent reagent for this purpose is the compound formed when CrO_3 is dissolved in hydrochloric acid and then treated with pyridine.

$$CrO_3 + HCl + \langle \bigcirc \rangle N: \longrightarrow \langle \bigcirc \rangle N\overset{+}{\underset{-}{}}H \quad Cr\,O_3Cl^-$$

Pyridine **Pyridinium chlorochromate**
(C_5H_5N) (PCC)

This compound, called **pyridinium chlorochromate** [abbreviated (PCC)], when dissolved in CH_2Cl_2, will oxidize a primary alcohol to an aldehyde and stop at that stage.

$$\underset{\substack{\text{2-Ethyl-2-methyl-1-} \\ \text{butanol}}}{\overset{\overset{\displaystyle CH_3}{|}}{(C_2H_5)_2C-CH_2OH}} + PCC \xrightarrow[\substack{25\ °C}]{CH_2Cl_2} \underset{\text{2-Ethyl-2-methylbutanal}}{\overset{\overset{\displaystyle CH_3}{|}\ \overset{\displaystyle O}{\|}}{(C_2H_5)_2C-CH}}$$

Pyridinium chlorochromate also does not attack double bonds.

One reason for the success of oxidation with pyridinium chlorochromate is that the oxidation can be carried out in a solvent such as CH_2Cl_2, in which PCC is soluble. Aldehydes themselves are not nearly as easily oxidized as are the *aldehyde hydrates*, *RCH(OH)$_2$*, that form (Section 16.7A) when aldehydes are dissolved in water, the usual medium for oxidation by chromium compounds.

$$RCHO + H_2O \rightleftharpoons RCH(OH)_2$$

We explain this further in Section 11.4D.

11.4B OXIDATION OF 1° ALCOHOLS TO CARBOXYLIC ACIDS: $RCH_2OH \longrightarrow RCO_2H$

Primary alcohols can be oxidized to **carboxylic acids** by potassium permanganate. The reaction is usually carried out in basic aqueous solution from which MnO_2 precipitates as the oxidation takes place. After the oxidation is complete, filtration allows removal of the MnO_2 and acidification of the filtrate gives the carboxylic acid.

$$R-CH_2OH + KMnO_4 \xrightarrow[\substack{H_2O \\ \text{heat}}]{OH^-} RCO_2^-K^+ + MnO_2$$
$$\downarrow H^+$$
$$RCO_2H$$

11.4C OXIDATION OF 2° ALCOHOLS TO KETONES:

$$\underset{RCHR'}{\overset{\overset{\displaystyle OH}{|}}{}} \longrightarrow \underset{R-C-R'}{\overset{\overset{\displaystyle O}{\|}}{}}$$

Secondary alcohols can be oxidized to ketones. The reaction usually stops at the ketone stage because further oxidation requires the breaking of a carbon–carbon bond.

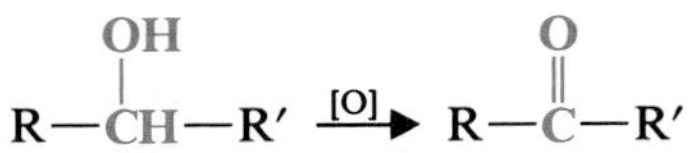

$$\underset{\substack{| \\ \text{2° Alcohol}}}{R-\overset{\text{OH}}{\underset{}{C}}H-R'} \xrightarrow{[O]} \underset{\text{Ketone}}{R-\overset{\text{O}}{\underset{}{C}}-R'}$$

Various oxidizing agents based on chromium(VI) have been used to oxidize secondary alcohols to ketones. The most commonly used reagent is chromic acid (H_2CrO_4). Chromic acid is usually prepared by adding chromium(VI) oxide (CrO_3) or sodium dichromate ($Na_2Cr_2O_7$) to aqueous sulfuric acid. Oxidations of secondary alcohols are generally carried out in acetone or acetic acid solutions. The balanced equation is shown here.

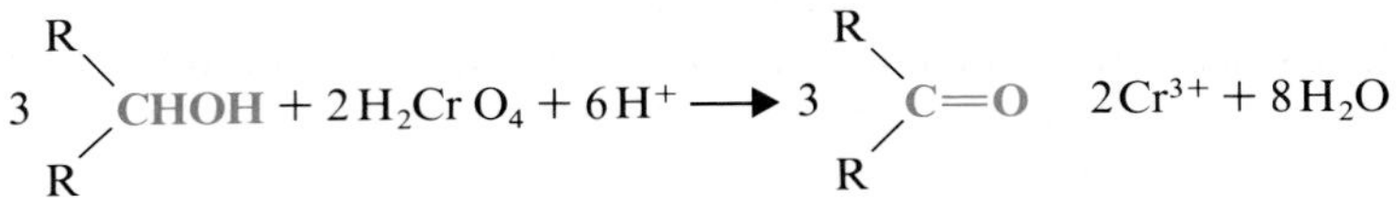

$$3 \underset{R}{\overset{R}{\diagdown}} CHOH + 2 H_2Cr O_4 + 6 H^+ \longrightarrow 3 \underset{R}{\overset{R}{\diagdown}} C{=}O \quad 2 Cr^{3+} + 8 H_2O$$

As chromic acid oxidizes the alcohol to the ketone, chromium is reduced from the +6 oxidation state (H_2CrO_4) to the +3 oxidation state (Cr^{3+}).* Chromic acid oxidations of secondary alcohols generally give ketones in excellent yields if the temperature is controlled. A specific example is the oxidation of cyclooctanol to cyclooctanone.

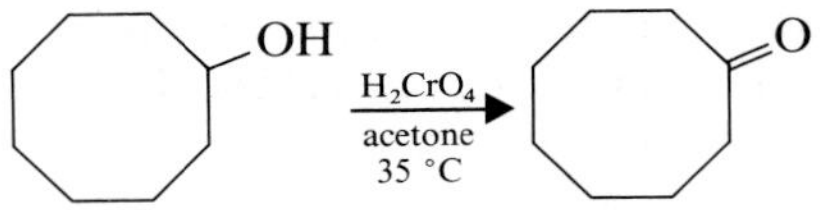

Cyclooctanol   Cyclooctanone
(92–96%)

The use of CrO_3 in aqueous acetone is usually called the **Jones oxidation** (or oxidation by the Jones reagent). This procedure rarely affects double bonds present in the molecule.

11.4D MECHANISM OF CHROMATE OXIDATIONS

The mechanism of chromic acid oxidations of alcohols has been investigated thoroughly. It is interesting because it shows how changes in oxidation states occur in a reaction between an organic and an inorganic compound. The first step is the formation of a chromate ester of the alcohol. Here we show this step using a 2° alcohol.

Step 1

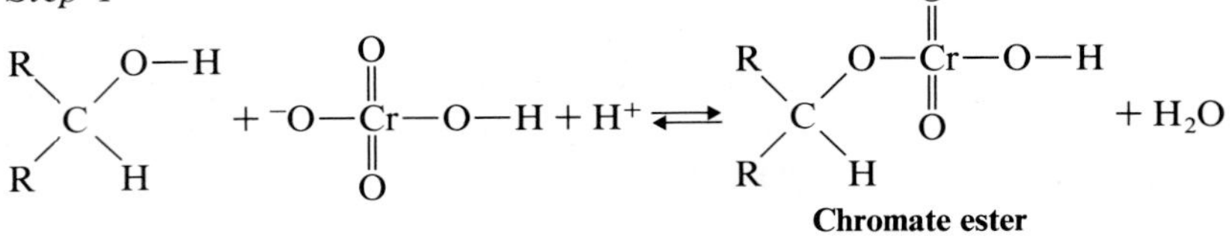

The chromate ester is unstable and is not isolated. It transfers a proton to a base (usually water) and simultaneously eliminates an $HCrO_3^-$ ion.

---

*It is the color change that accompanies this change in oxidation state that allows chromic acid to be used as a test for primary and secondary alcohols (Section 11.4E).

Step 2

The overall result of these two steps is the reduction of $HCrO_4^-$ to $HCrO_3^-$, a two-electron ($2e^-$) change in the oxidation state of chromium, from Cr(VI) to Cr(IV). At the same time the alcohol undergoes a $2e^-$ oxidation to the ketone.

The remaining steps of the mechanism are complicated and we need not give them in detail. Suffice it to say, that further oxidations (and disproportionations) take place, ultimately converting Cr(IV) compounds to Cr^{3+} ions.

The requirement for the formation of a chromate ester in step 1 of the mechanism helps us understand why 1° alcohols are easily oxidized beyond the aldehyde stage in aqueous solutions (and, therefore, why oxidation with PCC in CH_2Cl_2 stops at the aldehyde stage). The aldehyde initially formed from the 1° alcohol (produced by a mechanism similar to the one we have just given) reacts with water to form an aldehyde hydrate. The aldehyde hydrate can then react with $HCrO_4^-$ (and H^+) to form a chromate ester, and this can then be oxidized to the carboxylic acid. In the absence of water (i.e., using PCC in CH_2Cl_2), the aldehyde hydrate does not form; therefore, further oxidation does not take place.

The elimination that takes place in step 2 of the mechanism helps us to understand why 3° alcohols do not generally react in chromate oxidations. While 3° alcohols have no difficulty in forming chromate esters, the ester that is formed does not bear a hydrogen that can be eliminated and, therefore, no oxidation takes place.

11.4E A CHEMICAL TEST FOR PRIMARY AND SECONDARY ALCOHOLS

The relative ease of oxidation of primary and secondary alcohols compared with the difficulty of oxidizing tertiary alcohols forms the basis for a convenient chemical test. Primary and secondary alcohols are rapidly oxidized by a solution of CrO_3 in aqueous sulfuric acid. Chromic oxide (CrO_3) dissolves in aqueous sulfuric acid to give a clear orange solution containing $Cr_2O_7{}^{2-}$ ions. A positive test is indicated when this clear orange solution becomes opaque and takes on a greenish cast within 2 s.

$$
\begin{array}{l}
\text{RCH}_2\text{OH} \\
\quad \text{or} \quad + \text{CrO}_3/\text{aqueous H}_2\text{SO}_4 \longrightarrow
\end{array}
\quad
\begin{array}{l}
\text{greenish opaque solution} \\
\text{containing Cr}^{3+} \text{ and oxidation} \\
\text{products}
\end{array}
$$

RCHOH
|
R

Clear orange solution   Greenish-opaque solution

Not only will this test distinguish primary and secondary alcohols from tertiary alcohols, it will distinguish primary and secondary alcohols from most other compounds except aldehydes.

Problem 11.5

Show how each of the following transformations could be accomplished.

(a)

(b)

(c)

(d)

11.5 ORGANOMETALLIC COMPOUNDS

Compounds that contain carbon–metal bonds are called **organometallic compounds.** The natures of the carbon–metal bonds vary widely, ranging from bonds that are essentially ionic to those that are primarily covalent. While the structure of the organic portion of the organometallic compound has some effect on the nature of the carbon–metal bond, the identity of the metal itself is of far greater importance. Carbon–sodium and carbon–potassium bonds are largely ionic in character;

carbon–lead, carbon–tin, carbon–thallium, and carbon–mercury bonds are essentially covalent. Carbon–lithium and carbon–magnesium bonds lie between these extremes.

$$-\overset{|}{\underset{|}{C}}:^- \overset{+}{M} \qquad \overset{|}{\underset{|}{C}}\overset{\delta-\ \ \delta+}{:M} \qquad -\overset{|}{\underset{|}{C}}-M$$

Primarily ionic   **Primarily covalent**
(M = Na⁺ or K⁺)   **(M = Mg or Li)**   **(M = Pb, Sn, Hg, or Tl)**

The reactivity of organometallic compounds increases with the percent ionic character of the carbon–metal bond. Alkylsodium and alkylpotassium compounds are highly reactive and are among the most powerful of bases. They react explosively with water and burst into flame when exposed to air. Organomercury and organolead compounds are much less reactive; they are often volatile and are stable in air. They are all poisonous. They are generally soluble in nonpolar solvents. Tetraethyllead, for example, has been used as an "antiknock" compound in gasoline.

Organometallic compounds of lithium and magnesium are of great importance in organic synthesis. They are relatively stable in ether solutions, but their carbon–metal bonds have considerable ionic character. Because of this ionic nature, the carbon atom that is bonded to the metal atom of an organolithium or organomagnesium compound is a strong base and powerful nucleophile. We shall soon see reactions that illustrate both of these properties.

11.6 PREPARATION OF ORGANOLITHIUM AND ORGANOMAGNESIUM COMPOUNDS

11.6A ORGANOLITHIUM COMPOUNDS

Organolithium compounds are often prepared by the reduction of organic halides with lithium metal (see Section 3.8). These reductions are usually carried out in ether solvents, and since organolithium compounds are strong bases, care must be taken to exclude moisture. (Why?) The ethers most commonly used as solvents are diethyl ether and tetrahydrofuran. (Tetrahydrofuran is a cyclic ether.)

$$CH_3CH_2\ddot{O}CH_2CH_3$$

Diethyl ether   **Tetrahydrofuran**
(Et₂O)   **(THF)**

For example, butyl bromide reacts with lithium metal in diethyl ether to give a solution of butyllithium.

$$CH_3CH_2CH_2CH_2Br + 2\ Li \xrightarrow[Et_2O]{-10\ °C} CH_3CH_2CH_2CH_2Li + LiBr$$
Butyl bromide   **Butyllithium**
                              (80–90%)

Other organolithium compounds, such as methyllithium, ethyllithium, and phenyllithium, can be prepared in the same general way.

$$R-X \quad + 2 \text{ Li} \xrightarrow{\text{Et}_2\text{O}} \quad RLi \quad + LiX$$

(or Ar—X)   (or ArLi)

The order of reactivity of halides is RI > RBr > RCl. (Alkyl and aryl fluorides are seldom used in the preparation of organolithium compounds.)

Most organolithium compounds slowly attack ethers by bringing about an elimination reaction.

$$R\overset{\delta-}{:}Li + H-CH_2-CH_2-OCH_2CH_3 \longrightarrow RH + CH_2{=}CH_2 + \overset{+}{Li}\overset{-}{O}CH_2CH_3$$

For this reason, ether solutions of organolithium reagents are not usually stored but are used immediately after preparation. Organolithium compounds are much more stable in hydrocarbon solvents. Several alkyl- and aryllithium reagents are commercially available in hexane, paraffin wax, or mineral oil.

11.6B GRIGNARD REAGENTS

Organomagnesium halides were discovered by the French chemist Victor Grignard in 1900. Grignard received the Nobel Prize for his discovery in 1912, and organomagnesium halides are now called **Grignard reagents** in his honor. Grignard reagents have great use in organic synthesis.

Grignard reagents are usually prepared by the reaction of an organic halide and magnesium metal (turnings) in an ether solvent.

$$\left. \begin{array}{l} RX + Mg \xrightarrow{\text{Et}_2\text{O}} RMgX \\ ArX + Mg \xrightarrow{\text{Et}_2\text{O}} ArMgX \end{array} \right\} \begin{array}{l} \textbf{Grignard} \\ \textbf{reagents} \end{array}$$

The order of reactivity of halides with magnesium is also RI > RBr > RCl. Very few organomagnesium fluorides have been prepared. Aryl Grignard reagents are more easily prepared from aryl bromides and aryl iodides than from aryl chlorides, which react very sluggishly.

Grignard reagents are seldom isolated but are used for further reactions in ether solution. The ether solutions can be analyzed for the content of the Grignard reagent, however, and the yields of Grignard reagents are almost always very high (85–95%). Two examples are shown here.

$$CH_3I + Mg \xrightarrow[35\,°C]{\text{Et}_2\text{O}} CH_3MgI$$

**Methylmagnesium
iodide
(95%)**

$$C_6H_5Br + Mg \xrightarrow[35\,°C]{\text{Et}_2\text{O}} C_6H_5MgBr$$

**Phenylmagnesium
bromide
(95%)**

The actual structures of Grignard reagents are more complex than the general formula RMgX indicates. Experiments done with radioactive magnesium have established that, for most Grignard reagents, there is an equilibrium between an alkylmagnesium halide and a dialkylmagnesium.

$$2 \text{ RMgX} \;\rightleftharpoons\; \text{R}_2\text{Mg} \;+ \text{MgX}_2$$

Alkylmagnesium   **Dialkylmagnesium**
halide

For convenience in this text, however, we shall write the formula for the Grignard reagent as though it were simply RMgX.

A Grignard reagent forms a complex with its ether solvent; the structure of the complex can be represented as follows:

$$
\begin{array}{c}
\text{R} \quad\quad \text{R} \\
\diagdown \ddot{\text{O}} \diagup \\
\ddot{} \\
\text{R} - \text{Mg} - \text{X} \\
\ddot{} \\
\diagup \ddot{\text{O}} \diagdown \\
\text{R} \quad\quad \text{R}
\end{array}
$$

Complex formation with molecules of ether is an important factor in the formation and stability of Grignard reagents. Organomagnesium compounds can be prepared in nonethereal solvents, but the preparations are more difficult.

The mechanism by which Grignard reagents form is complicated and is still a matter of debate.* There seems to be general agreement that radicals are involved and that a mechanism similar to the following is likely.

$$\text{R}-\text{X} + \text{:Mg} \longrightarrow \text{R}\cdot + \cdot\text{MgX}$$
$$\text{R}\cdot + \cdot\text{MgX} \longrightarrow \text{RMgX}$$

11.7 REACTIONS OF ORGANOLITHIUM AND ORGANOMAGNESIUM COMPOUNDS

11.7A REACTIONS WITH COMPOUNDS CONTAINING ACIDIC HYDROGEN ATOMS

Grignard reagents and organolithium compounds are very strong bases. They react with any compound that has a hydrogen more acidic than the hydrogen atoms of the hydrocarbon from which the Grignard reagent or organolithium is derived. We can understand how these reactions occur if we represent the Grignard reagent and organolithium compounds in the following ways:

$$
\overset{\delta-}{\text{R}} \overset{\delta+}{\text{:MgX}} \quad \text{and} \quad \overset{\delta-}{\text{R}} \overset{\delta+}{\text{:Li}}
$$

When we do this, we can see that the reactions of Grignard reagents with water and alcohols are nothing more than acid–base reactions; they lead to the formation of the weaker conjugate acid and weaker conjugate base. The Grignard reagent behaves as if it contained the anion of an alkane, *as if it contained a carbanion.*

---

*Those interested may want to read the recent articles: John L. Garst and Brian L. Swift, *J. Am. Chem. Soc.,* **1989,** *111,* 241–250; H. M. Walborsky, *Acc. Chem Res.,* **1990,** *23,* 286–293; and John L. Garst, *Acc. Chem. Res.,* **1991,** *24,* 95–97.

$$\overset{\delta-\quad\delta+}{R:MgX} + \overset{}{H:\ddot{O}H} \longrightarrow R:H + H\ddot{O}:^- + Mg^{2+} + X^-$$

Grignard reagent (stronger base)	Water (stronger acid)	Alkane (weaker acid)	Hydroxide ion (weaker base)

$$\overset{\delta-\quad\delta+}{R:MgX} + \overset{}{H:\ddot{O}R} \longrightarrow R:H + R\ddot{O}:^- + Mg^{2+} + X^-$$

Grignard reagent (stronger base)	Alcohol (stronger acid)	Alkane (weaker acid)	Alkoxide ion (weaker base)

Problem 11.6

Write similar equations for the reactions that take place when butyllithium is treated with (a) water and (b) ethanol. Designate the stronger and weaker acids and the stronger and weaker bases.

Problem 11.7

Assuming you have *tert*-butyl bromide, magnesium, dry ether, and deuterium oxide (D$_2$O) available, show how you might synthesize the following deuterium-labeled alkane.

$$\begin{array}{c} CH_3 \\ | \\ CH_3-C-CH_3 \\ | \\ D \end{array}$$

Grignard reagents and organolithium compounds abstract protons that are much less acidic than those of water and alcohols. They react with the terminal hydrogen atoms of 1-alkynes, for example, and this is a useful method for the preparation of alkynylmagnesium halides and alkynyllithiums. These reactions are also acid–base reactions.

$$RC\equiv CH + \overset{\delta-\quad\delta+}{R':MgX} \longrightarrow RC\equiv \overset{\delta-\quad\delta+}{C:MgX} + R':H$$

Terminal alkyne (stronger acid)	Grignard reagent (stronger base)	Alkynylmagnesium halide (weaker base)	Alkane (weaker acid)

$$R-C\equiv CH + \overset{\delta-\quad\delta+}{R':Li} \longrightarrow R-C\equiv \overset{\delta-\quad\delta+}{C:Li} + R':H$$

Terminal alkyne (stronger acid)	Alkyl-lithium (stronger base)	Alkynyllithium (weaker base)	Alkane (weaker acid)

The fact that these reactions go to completion is not surprising when we recall that alkanes have pK_a values ≈ 50, while those of terminal alkynes are ≈ 25 (Table 3.1).

Grignard reagents are not only strong bases, they are also *powerful nucleophiles.* Reactions in which Grignard reagents act as nucleophiles are by far the most important. At this point, let us consider general examples that illustrate the ability of a Grignard reagent to act as a nucleophile by attacking saturated and unsaturated carbon atoms.

11.7B REACTION OF GRIGNARD REAGENTS WITH OXIRANES (EPOXIDES)

Grignard reagents carry out nucleophilic attack at a saturated carbon when they react with oxiranes. These reactions take the general form shown below and give us a convenient synthesis of primary alcohols.

The nucleophilic alkyl group of the Grignard reagent attacks the partially positive carbon of the oxirane ring. Because it is highly strained, the ring opens, and the reaction leads to the salt of a primary alcohol. Subsequent acidification produces the alcohol.

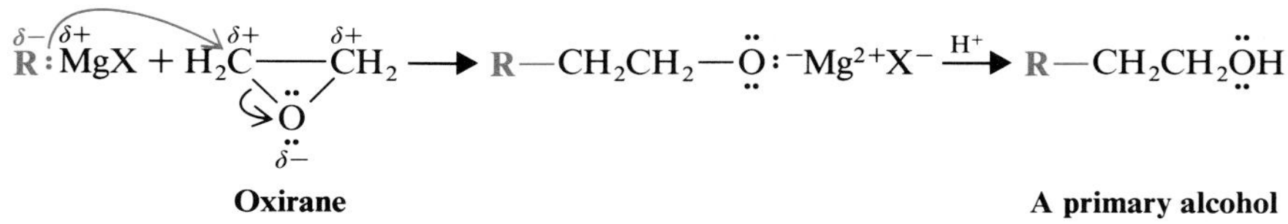

$$R\colon MgX + H_2C \underset{O}{\overset{}{\text{———}}} CH_2 \longrightarrow R\text{—}CH_2CH_2\text{—}\ddot{O}\colon {}^-Mg^{2+}X^- \overset{H^+}{\longrightarrow} R\text{—}CH_2CH_2\ddot{O}H$$

Oxirane   **A primary alcohol**

Specific Example

$$C_6H_5MgBr + H_2C\underset{O}{\overset{}{\text{———}}}CH_2 \xrightarrow{Et_2O} C_6H_5CH_2CH_2OMgBr \xrightarrow{H_3O^+} C_6H_5CH_2CH_2OH$$

Grignard reagents react primarily at the less-substituted ring carbon atom of substituted oxiranes.

Specific Example

$$C_6H_5MgBr + H_2C\underset{O}{\overset{}{\text{———}}}CH\text{—}CH_3 \xrightarrow{Et_2O} C_6H_5CH_2\underset{CH_3}{CHOMgBr} \xrightarrow{H_3O^+} C_6H_5CH_2\underset{CH_3}{CHOH}$$

11.7C REACTIONS OF GRIGNARD REAGENTS WITH CARBONYL COMPOUNDS

From a synthetic point of view, the most important reactions of Grignard reagents and organolithium compounds are those in which these reagents act as nucleophiles and attack an unsaturated carbon — *especially the carbon of a carbonyl group.*

We saw in Section 11.1B that carbonyl compounds are highly susceptible to nucleophilic attack. Grignard reagents react with carbonyl compounds (aldehydes and ketones) in the following way:

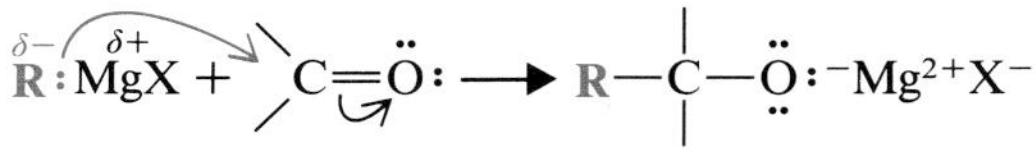

$$R\colon MgX + {\overset{}{\underset{}{}}}C{=}\ddot{O}\colon \longrightarrow R\text{—}\overset{|}{\underset{|}{C}}\text{—}\ddot{O}\colon {}^-Mg^{2+}X^-$$

This reaction is a nucleophilic addition to the carbon–oxygen double bond. The nucleophilic carbon of the Grignard reagent uses its electron pair to form a bond to the carbonyl carbon. The carbonyl carbon can accept this electron pair because one pair of electrons of the carbon–oxygen double bond can shift out to the oxygen.

The product formed when a Grignard reagent adds to a carbonyl group is an alkoxide ion $R-\overset{|}{\underset{|}{C}}-\overset{..}{\underset{..}{O}}:^-$ that is associated with $Mg^{2+}X^-$. When water or dilute acid is added to the reaction mixture after the Grignard addition is over, an acid–base reaction takes place to produce an alcohol.

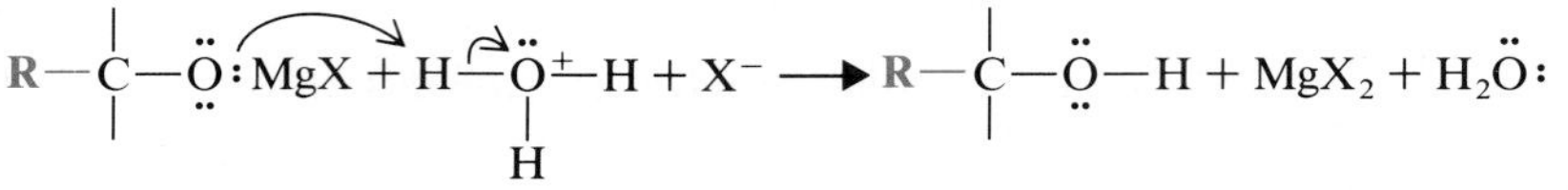

$$R-\overset{|}{\underset{|}{C}}-\overset{..}{\underset{..}{O}}:MgX + H-\overset{+}{\underset{\underset{H}{|}}{\overset{..}{O}}}-H + X^- \longrightarrow R-\overset{|}{\underset{|}{C}}-\overset{..}{O}-H + MgX_2 + H_2\overset{..}{O}:$$

Halomagnesium   **Alcohol**
alkoxide

11.8 ALCOHOLS FROM GRIGNARD REAGENTS

Grignard additions to carbonyl compounds are especially useful because they can be used to prepare primary, secondary, or tertiary alcohols.

1. A Grignard reagent reacts with formaldehyde, for example, to give a **primary alcohol.**

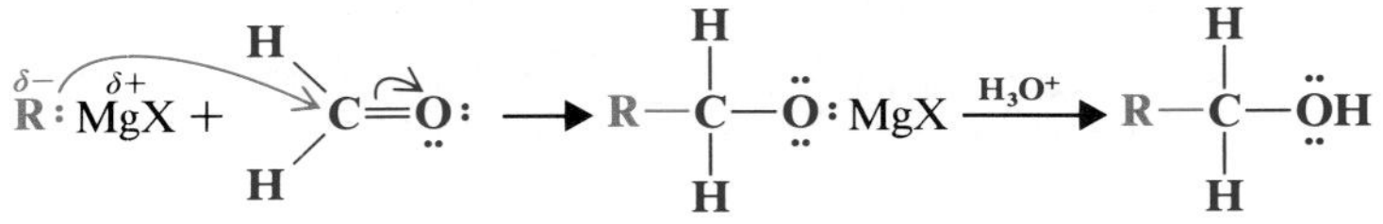

Formaldehyde   **1° Alcohol**

2. Grignard reagents react with higher aldehydes to give **secondary alcohols.**

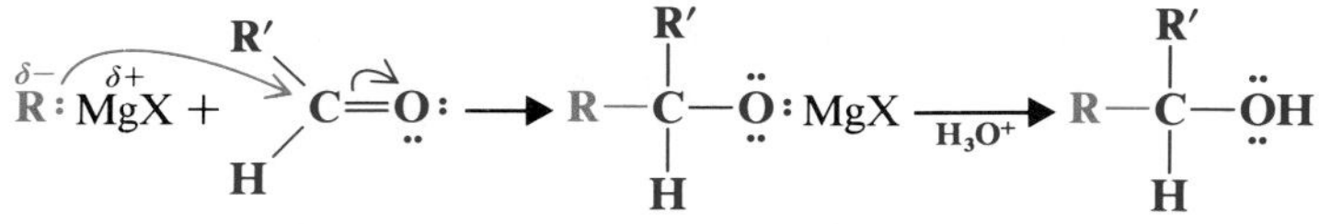

Higher   **2° Alcohol**
aldehyde

3. And Grignard reagents react with ketones to give **tertiary alcohols.**

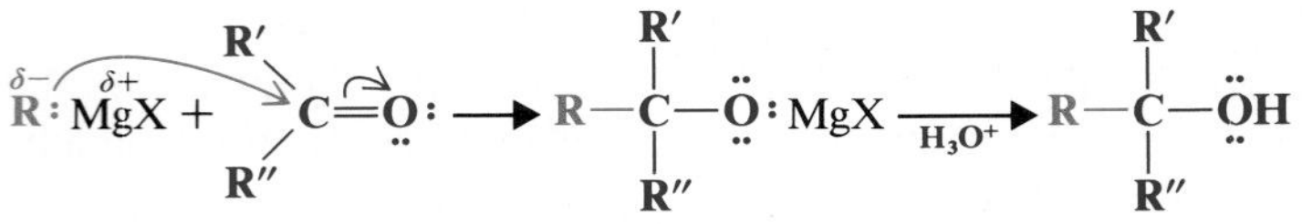

Ketone   **3° Alcohol**

Specific examples of these reactions are shown here.

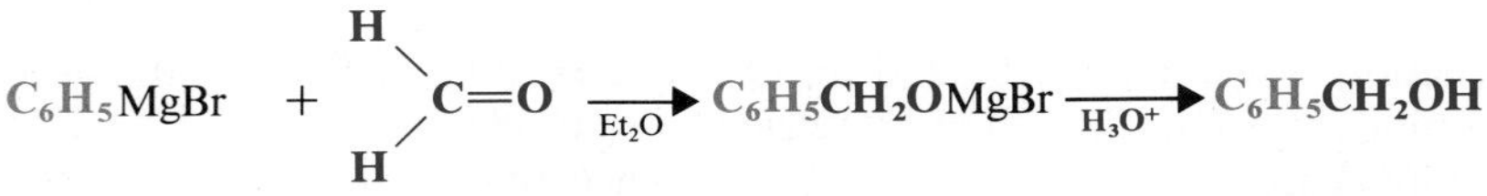

Phenylmagnesium   **Formaldehyde**   **Benzyl alcohol**
bromide   **(90%)**

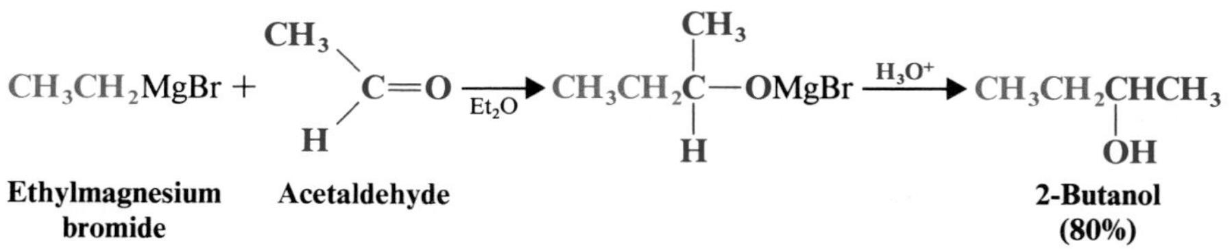

11.8 ALCOHOLS FROM GRIGNARD REAGENTS

$$CH_3CH_2MgBr + \underset{\substack{H}}{\overset{\substack{CH_3}}{C}}=O \xrightarrow{Et_2O} CH_3CH_2\underset{\substack{H}}{\overset{\substack{CH_3}}{C}}-OMgBr \xrightarrow{H_3O^+} CH_3CH_2\underset{\substack{OH}}{CH}CH_3$$

Ethylmagnesium bromide **Acetaldehyde** **2-Butanol (80%)**

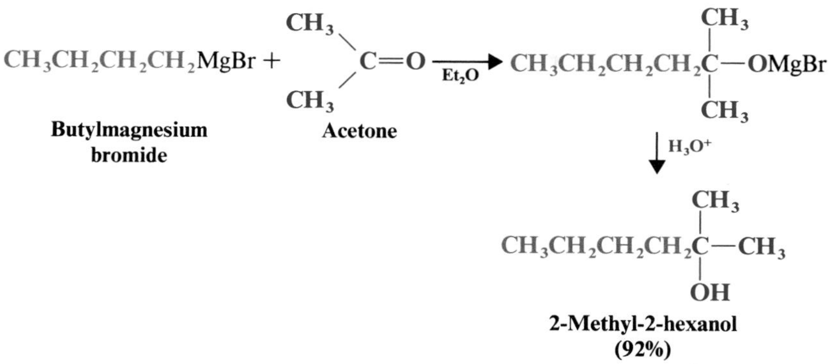

$$CH_3CH_2CH_2CH_2MgBr + \underset{\substack{CH_3}}{\overset{\substack{CH_3}}{C}}=O \xrightarrow{Et_2O} CH_3CH_2CH_2CH_2\underset{\substack{CH_3}}{\overset{\substack{CH_3}}{C}}-OMgBr$$

Butylmagnesium bromide **Acetone**

$$\Big\downarrow H_3O^+$$

$$CH_3CH_2CH_2CH_2\underset{\substack{OH}}{\overset{\substack{CH_3}}{C}}-CH_3$$

2-Methyl-2-hexanol (92%)

4. A Grignard reagent also adds to the carbonyl group of an ester. The initial product is unstable and it loses a magnesium alkoxide to form a ketone. Ketones are more reactive toward Grignard reagents than esters. Therefore as soon as a molecule of the ketone is formed in the mixture, it reacts with a second molecule of the Grignard reagent. After hydrolysis, **the product is a tertiary alcohol with two identical alkyl groups,** groups that correspond to the alkyl portion of the Grignard reagent.

$$R:MgX + \underset{\substack{R''\ddot{O}}}{\overset{\substack{R'}}{C}}=\ddot{O}: \longrightarrow \Bigg[R-\underset{\substack{\ddot{O}-R''}}{\overset{\substack{R'}}{C}}-\ddot{\overset{..}{O}}-MgX \Bigg] \xrightarrow[\text{spontaneously}]{-R''OMgX}$$

Ester **Initial product (unstable)**

$$\Bigg[\underset{\substack{R}}{\overset{\substack{R'}}{C}}=\ddot{O}: \Bigg] \xrightarrow{RMgX} R-\underset{\substack{R}}{\overset{\substack{R'}}{C}}-\ddot{O}MgX \xrightarrow{H_3O^+} R-\underset{\substack{R}}{\overset{\substack{R'}}{C}}-OH$$

Ketone **Salt of an alcohol (not isolated)** **3° Alcohol**

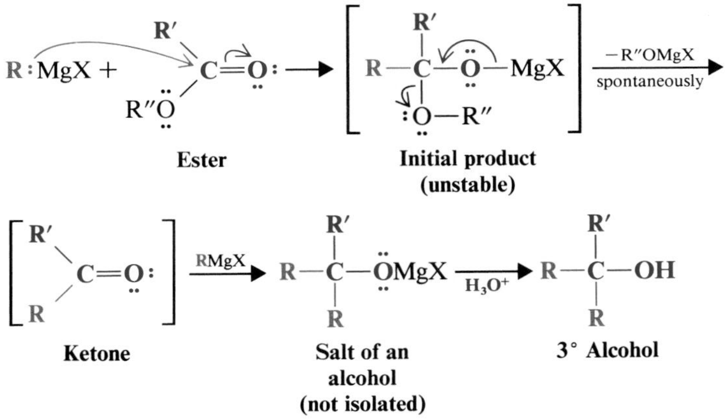

A specific example of this reaction is shown here.

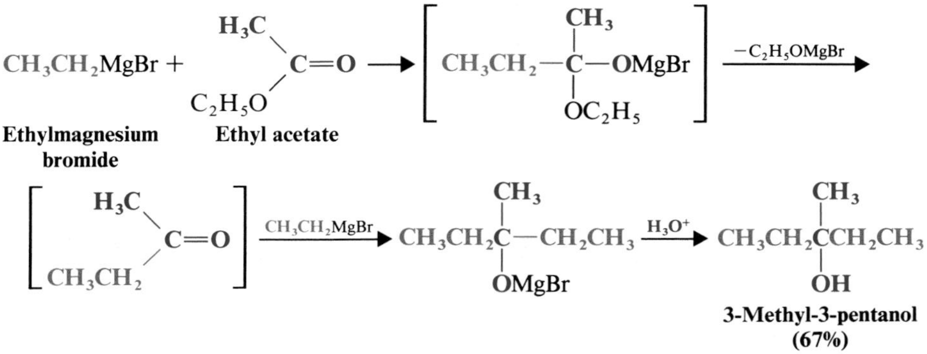

$$CH_3CH_2MgBr + \underset{\substack{C_2H_5O}}{\overset{\substack{H_3C}}{C}}=O \longrightarrow \Bigg[CH_3CH_2-\underset{\substack{OC_2H_5}}{\overset{\substack{CH_3}}{C}}-OMgBr \Bigg] \xrightarrow{-C_2H_5OMgBr}$$

Ethylmagnesium bromide **Ethyl acetate**

$$\Bigg[\underset{\substack{CH_3CH_2}}{\overset{\substack{H_3C}}{C}}=O \Bigg] \xrightarrow{CH_3CH_2MgBr} CH_3CH_2\underset{\substack{OMgBr}}{\overset{\substack{CH_3}}{C}}-CH_2CH_3 \xrightarrow{H_3O^+} CH_3CH_2\underset{\substack{OH}}{\overset{\substack{CH_3}}{C}}CH_2CH_3$$

3-Methyl-3-pentanol (67%)

Problem 11.8

Phenylmagnesium bromide reacts with benzoyl chloride, $C_6H_5\overset{\displaystyle O}{\overset{\|}{C}}Cl$, to form triphenylmethanol, $(C_6H_5)_3COH$. This reaction is typical of the reaction of Grignard reagents with acyl chlorides, and the mechanism is similar to that for the reaction of a Grignard reagent with an ester just shown. Show the steps that lead to the formation of triphenylmethanol.

11.8A PLANNING A GRIGNARD SYNTHESIS

By using Grignard synthesis skillfully we can synthesize almost any alcohol we wish. In planning a Grignard synthesis we must simply choose the correct Grignard reagent and the correct aldehyde, ketone, ester, or epoxide. We do this by examining the alcohol we wish to prepare and by paying special attention to the groups attached to the carbon atom bearing the $-OH$ group. Many times there may be more than one way of carrying out the synthesis. In these cases our final choice will probably be dictated by the availability of starting compounds. Let us consider an example.

Example

Suppose we want to prepare 3-phenyl-3-pentanol. We examine its structure and we see that the groups attached to the carbon atom bearing the $-OH$ are a *phenyl group*

$$CH_3CH_2-\overset{\overset{\displaystyle C_6H_5}{|}}{\underset{\underset{\displaystyle OH}{|}}{C}}-CH_2CH_3$$

3-Phenyl-3-pentanol

and *two ethyl groups.* This means that we can synthesize this compound in different ways.

1. We can use a ketone with two ethyl groups (3-pentanone) and allow it to react with phenylmagnesium bromide:

Analysis

$$CH_3CH_2-\overset{\overset{\displaystyle C_6H_5}{\wedge}}{\underset{\underset{\displaystyle OH}{|}}{C}}-CH_2CH_3 \Longrightarrow CH_3CH_2-\overset{\overset{\displaystyle }{}}{\underset{\underset{\displaystyle O}{\|}}{C}}-CH_2CH_3 + C_6H_5MgBr$$

Synthesis

$$C_6H_5MgBr \;+\; CH_3CH_2\overset{\overset{\displaystyle }{}}{\underset{\underset{\displaystyle O}{\|}}{C}}CH_2CH_3 \xrightarrow[\text{(2) H}_3\text{O}^{+*}]{\text{(1) Et}_2\text{O}} CH_3CH_2-\overset{\overset{\displaystyle C_6H_5}{|}}{\underset{\underset{\displaystyle OH}{|}}{C}}-CH_2CH_3$$

Phenylmagnesium   **3-Pentanone**   **3-Phenyl-3-pentanol**
bromide

*By writing (2) H_3O^+ under the arrow in equations like these, we mean that in a second step, after the Grignard reagent has reacted with the ketone, we add an acidic solution to convert the salt of the alcohol (ROMgX) to the alcohol itself. If the alcohol is tertiary, it will be susceptible to acid-catalyzed dehydration. In this case a solution of NH_4Cl in water is often used because it is acidic enough to convert ROMgX to ROH without causing dehydration.

2. We can use a ketone containing an ethyl group and a phenyl group (ethyl phenyl ketone) and allow it to react with ethylmagnesium bromide:

Analysis

$$\underset{\underset{\text{Synthesis}}{}}{\overset{\overset{C_6H_5}{|}}{CH_3CH_2-\underset{\underset{OH}{|}}{C}{\not{-}}CH_2CH_3}} \Longrightarrow \overset{\overset{C_6H_5}{|}}{CH_3CH_2-\underset{\underset{O}{||}}{C}} + CH_3CH_2MgBr$$

$$CH_3CH_2MgBr + \underset{CH_3CH_2}{\overset{C_6H_5}{\diagdown}}C{=}O \xrightarrow[\text{(2) } H_3O^+]{\text{(1)Et}_2\text{O}} CH_3CH_2-\underset{\underset{OH}{|}}{\overset{\overset{C_6H_5}{|}}{C}}-CH_2CH_3$$

Ethylmagnesium   Ethyl phenyl   3-Phenyl-3-pentanol
bromide   ketone

3. Or we can use an ester of benzoic acid and allow it to react with two molar equivalents of ethylmagnesium bromide:

Analysis

$$\underset{\underset{\text{Synthesis}}{}}{\overset{\overset{C_6H_5}{|}}{CH_3CH_2{\not{-}}\underset{\underset{OH}{|}}{C}{\not{-}}CH_2CH_3}} \Longrightarrow \underset{O}{\overset{C_6H_5}{\diagup}}\underset{\diagdown OCH_3}{\overset{\overset{|}{C}}{}} + 2\,CH_3CH_2MgBr$$

$$2\,CH_3CH_2MgBr + C_6H_5\overset{\overset{O}{||}}{C}OCH_3 \xrightarrow[\text{(2) } H_3O^+]{\text{(1) Et}_2\text{O}} CH_3CH_2-\underset{\underset{OH}{|}}{\overset{\overset{C_6H_5}{|}}{C}}-CH_2CH_3$$

Ethylmagnesium   Methyl   3-Phenyl-3-pentanol
bromide   benzoate

All of these methods will be likely to give us our desired compound in yields greater than 80%.

Sample Problem ————————————————————

Illustrating a Multistep Synthesis

Using an alcohol of no more than four carbon atoms as your only organic starting material, outline a synthesis of **A**.

$$\underset{\underset{CH_3}{|}}{CH_3CHCH_2}\overset{\overset{O}{||}}{C}\underset{\underset{CH_3}{|}}{CHCH_3}$$

A

Answer:

We can construct the carbon skeleton from two four-carbon atom compounds using a Grignard reaction. Then oxidation of the alcohol produced will yield the desired ketone.

Analysis

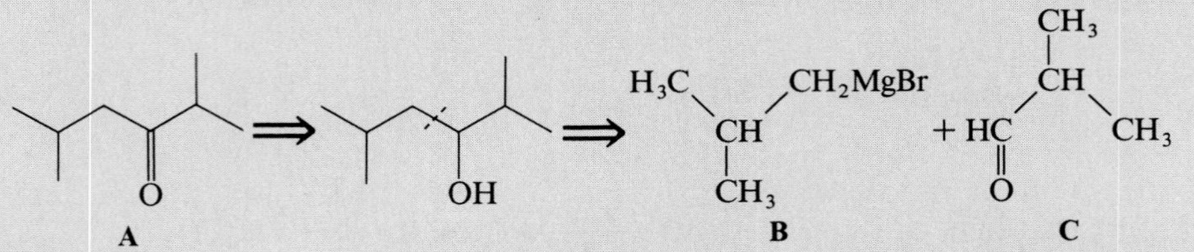

Synthesis

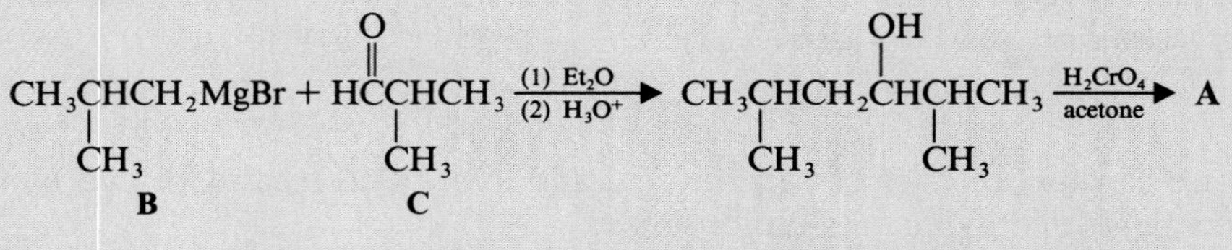

We can synthesize the Grignard reagent (**B**) and the aldehyde (**C**) from isobutyl alcohol.

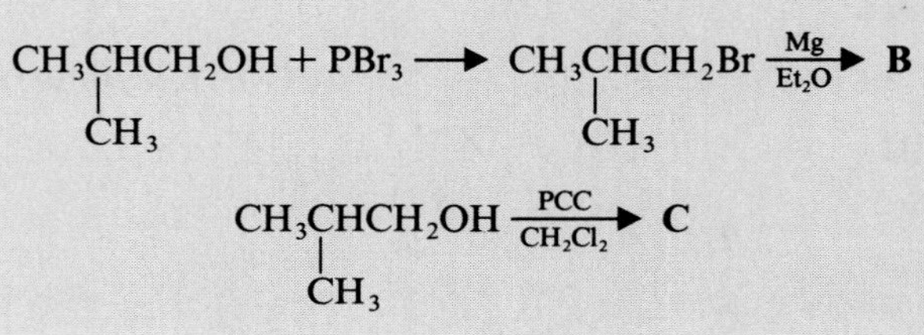

$$CH_3CHCH_2OH + PBr_3 \longrightarrow CH_3CHCH_2Br \xrightarrow[Et_2O]{Mg} B$$
$$\quad\quad |\quad\quad\quad\quad\quad\quad\quad\quad |$$
$$\quad CH_3 \quad\quad\quad\quad\quad\quad CH_3$$

$$CH_3CHCH_2OH \xrightarrow[CH_2Cl_2]{PCC} C$$
$$\quad\quad |$$
$$\quad CH_3$$

Sample Problem

Illustrating a Multistep Synthesis

Starting with bromobenzene and any other needed reagents, outline a synthesis of the following aldehyde.

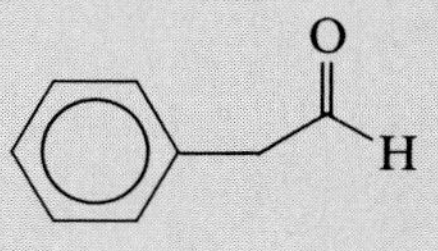

Answer:

Working backwards, we remember that we can synthesize the aldehyde from the corresponding alcohol by oxidation with PCC (Section 11.4A). The alcohol can be made by treating phenylmagnesium bromide with oxirane. [Adding oxirane to a Grignard reagent is a very useful method for adding a —CH_2CH_2OH unit to an organic group (Section 11.7B).] Phenylmagnesium bromide can be made in the usual way, by treating bromobenzene with magnesium in an ether solvent.

Analysis

Synthesis

$$C_6H_5Br \xrightarrow[\text{Et}_2\text{O}]{\text{Mg}} C_6H_5MgBr \xrightarrow[\text{(2) H}_3\text{O}^+]{\text{(1)} \triangle \text{O}} C_6H_5CH_2CH_2OH \xrightarrow[\text{CH}_2\text{Cl}_2]{\text{PCC}} C_6H_5CH_2CHO$$

Problem 11.9

Show how Grignard reactions could be used to synthesize each of the following compounds. (You must start with a Grignard reagent and you may use any other compounds needed.)

(a) *tert*-Butyl alcohol   (two ways)

(b) $CH_3CH_2CH_2CHOHCH_3$ (two ways)

(c) $C_6H_5\overset{\overset{\displaystyle CH_3}{|}}{\underset{\underset{\displaystyle OH}{|}}{C}}CH_2CH_3$ (three ways)

(d) $CH_3CH_2CH_2CH_2CH_2CH_2OH$ (two ways)

Problem 11.10

Outline a synthesis of each of the following. Permitted starting materials are benzene, oxirane, formaldehyde, and alcohols or esters of four carbon atoms or fewer. You may use any inorganic reagents and oxidizing agents such as pyridinium chlorochromate (PCC).

(a) $C_6H_5\overset{\underset{\underset{\displaystyle OH}{|}}{}}{C}HCH_2CH_3$

(b) $C_6H_5\overset{\overset{\displaystyle O}{\|}}{C}H$

(c) $C_6H_5\overset{\overset{\displaystyle OH}{|}}{\underset{\underset{\displaystyle C_6H_5}{|}}{C}}CH_2CH_3$

(d) $C_6H_5\overset{\underset{\underset{\displaystyle CH_3}{|}}{}}{C}H\overset{\overset{\displaystyle OH}{|}}{C}HCH_3$

11.8B RESTRICTIONS ON THE USE OF GRIGNARD REAGENTS

While the Grignard synthesis is one of the most versatile of all general synthetic procedures, it is not without its limitations. Most of these limitations arise from the very feature of the Grignard reagent that makes it so useful, its *extraordinary reactivity as a nucleophile and a base.*

The Grignard reagent is a very powerful base; in effect it contains a carbanion. Thus, it is not possible to prepare a Grignard reagent from an organic group that contains an *acidic hydrogen;* and by an acidic hydrogen we mean any hydrogen more acidic than the hydrogen atoms of an alkane or alkene. We cannot, for example, prepare a Grignard reagent from a compound containing an —OH group, an —NH— group, an —SH group, a —CO$_2$H group, or an —SO$_3$H group. If we were to attempt to prepare a Grignard reagent from an organic halide containing any of these groups, the formation of the Grignard reagent would simply fail to take place. (Even if a Grignard reagent were to form, it would immediately react with the acidic group.)

Since Grignard reagents are powerful nucleophiles we cannot prepare a Grignard reagent from any organic halide that contains a carbonyl, epoxy, nitro, or cyano (—CN) group. If we were to attempt to carry out this kind of reaction, any Grignard reagent that formed would only react with the unreacted starting material.

$$\left.\begin{array}{l} \text{—OH, —NH}_2\text{, —NHR, —CO}_2\text{H, —SO}_3\text{H, —SH, —C}{\equiv}\text{C—H} \\[10pt] \overset{\displaystyle O}{\overset{\|}{\text{—CH}}}, \;\; \overset{\displaystyle O}{\overset{\|}{\text{—CR}}}, \;\; \overset{\displaystyle O}{\overset{\|}{\text{—COR}}}, \;\; \overset{\displaystyle O}{\overset{\|}{\text{—CNH}_2}}, \;\; \text{—NO}_2\text{, —C}{\equiv}\text{N, } \underset{\displaystyle O}{\overset{}{\text{—C—C—}}} \end{array}\right\}$$

Grignard reagents containing these groups cannot be prepared

This means that when we prepare Grignard reagents, we are effectively limited to alkyl halides or to analogous organic halides containing carbon–carbon double bonds, internal triple bonds, ether linkages, and —NR$_2$ groups.

Grignard reactions are so sensitive to acidic compounds that when we prepare a Grignard reagent we must take special care to exclude moisture from our apparatus, and we must use an anhydrous ether as our solvent.

As we saw earlier, acetylenic hydrogens are acidic enough to react with Grignard reagents. This is a limitation that we can use, however. We can make acetylenic Grignard reagents by allowing terminal alkynes to react with alkyl Grignard reagents (cf. Section 11.7A). We can then use these acetylenic Grignard reagents to carry out other syntheses. For example,

$$\text{C}_6\text{H}_5\text{C}{\equiv}\text{CH} + \text{C}_2\text{H}_5\text{MgBr} \longrightarrow \text{C}_6\text{H}_5\text{C}{\equiv}\text{CMgBr} + \text{C}_2\text{H}_6{\uparrow}$$

$$\text{C}_6\text{H}_5\text{C}{\equiv}\text{CMgBr} + \text{C}_2\text{H}_5\overset{\displaystyle O}{\overset{\|}{\text{CH}}} \xrightarrow[\text{(2) H}_3\text{O}^+]{} \text{C}_6\text{H}_5\text{C}{\equiv}\text{C}-\underset{\displaystyle \text{OH}}{\text{CHC}_2\text{H}_5}$$

(52%)

When we plan Grignard syntheses we must also take care not to plan a reaction in which a Grignard reagent is treated with an aldehyde, ketone, epoxide, or ester that contains an acidic group (other than when we deliberately let it react with a terminal alkyne). If we were to do this, the Grignard reagent would simply react as a base with the acidic hydrogen rather than reacting at the carbonyl or epoxide carbon as a nucleophile. If we were to treat 4-hydroxy-2-butanone with methylmagnesium bromide, for example, the following reaction would take place first,

$$\text{CH}_3\text{MgBr} + \underset{\displaystyle O}{\text{HOCH}_2\text{CH}_2\overset{\|}{\text{CCH}}_3} \longrightarrow \text{CH}_4{\uparrow} + \underset{\displaystyle O}{\text{BrMgOCH}_2\text{CH}_2\overset{\|}{\text{CCH}}_3}$$

4-Hydroxy-2-butanone

rather than

$$\text{CH}_3\text{MgBr} + \underset{\displaystyle O}{\text{HOCH}_2\text{CH}_2\overset{\|}{\text{CCH}}_3} \xrightarrow{\;\;\times\;\;} \text{HOCH}_2\text{CH}_2\overset{\displaystyle \text{CH}_3}{\underset{\displaystyle \text{OMgBr}}{\overset{|}{\underset{|}{\text{C}}}}\text{—CH}_3}$$

If we are prepared to waste one molar equivalent of the Grignard reagent, we can treat 4-hydroxy-2-butanone with two molar equivalents of the Grignard reagent and thereby get addition to the carbonyl group.

$$HOCH_2CH_2CCH_3 \xrightarrow[-CH_4]{2\ CH_3MgBr} BrMgOCH_2CH_2\overset{\overset{\displaystyle CH_3}{|}}{C}CH_3 \xrightarrow{2\ H_3O^+} HOCH_2CH_2\overset{\overset{\displaystyle CH_3}{|}}{C}CH_3$$

This technique is sometimes employed in small-scale reactions when the Grignard reagent is inexpensive and the other reagent is expensive.

11.8C THE USE OF LITHIUM REAGENTS

Organolithium reagents (RLi) react with carbonyl compounds in the same way as Grignard reagents and thus provide an alternative method for preparing alcohols.

$$\overset{\delta-}{R}:\overset{\delta+}{Li} + {\textstyle\diagdown}C{=}\ddot{O}: \longrightarrow R-\overset{|}{\underset{|}{C}}-\ddot{O}:Li \xrightarrow{H_3O^+} R-\overset{|}{\underset{|}{C}}-OH$$

Organo-	Aldehyde	Lithium	Alcohol
lithium	or	alkoxide	
reagent	ketone		

Organolithium reagents have the advantage of being somewhat more reactive than Grignard reagents.

11.8D THE USE OF SODIUM ALKYNIDES

Sodium alkynides also react with aldehydes and ketones to yield alcohols. An example is the following:

$$CH_3C{\equiv}CH \xrightarrow[-NH_3]{NaNH_2} CH_3C{\equiv}CNa$$

Then,

$$CH_3C{\equiv}\overset{\delta-}{C}:\overset{\delta+}{Na} + \underset{CH_3}{\overset{CH_3}{\diagdown}}C{=}O \longrightarrow CH_3C{\equiv}C-\overset{\overset{\displaystyle CH_3}{|}}{\underset{\underset{\displaystyle CH_3}{|}}{C}}-ONa \xrightarrow{H_3O^+} CH_3C{\equiv}C-\overset{\overset{\displaystyle CH_3}{|}}{\underset{\underset{\displaystyle CH_3}{|}}{C}}-OH$$

Sample Problem

Illustrating Multistep Syntheses

Starting with hydrocarbons, organic halides, alcohols, aldehydes, ketones, or esters containing six carbon atoms or fewer and using any other needed reagents, outline a synthesis of each of the following:

(a) cyclohexane ring with OH and CH$_2$CH$_3$ substituents

(b) $CH_3-\overset{\overset{\displaystyle OH}{|}}{\underset{\underset{\displaystyle C_6H_5}{|}}{C}}-C_6H_5$

(c) cyclopentane ring with OH and C≡CH substituents

Answers:

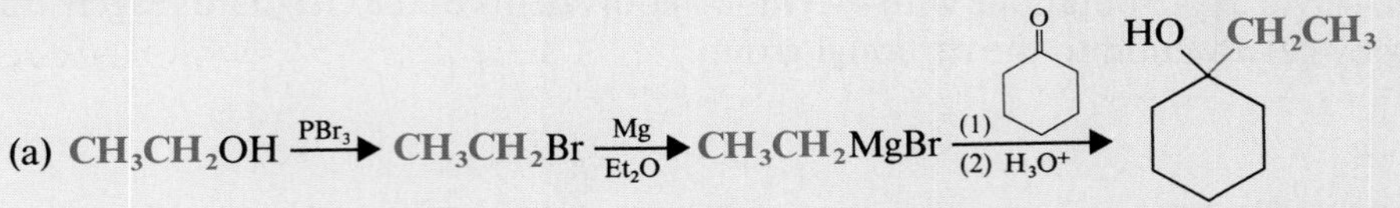

(a) $CH_3CH_2OH \xrightarrow{PBr_3} CH_3CH_2Br \xrightarrow[Et_2O]{Mg} CH_3CH_2MgBr \xrightarrow[(2)\ H_3O^+]{(1)}$

(b) $C_6H_5Br \xrightarrow[Et_2O]{Mg} C_6H_5MgBr \xrightarrow[(2)\ H_3O^+]{(1)\ CH_3COCH_3}$

$$CH_3-\underset{\underset{C_6H_5}{|}}{\overset{\overset{OH}{|}}{C}}-C_6H_5$$

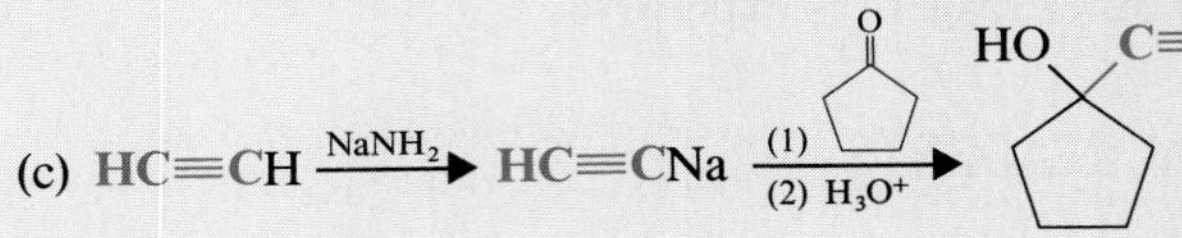

(c) $HC\equiv CH \xrightarrow{NaNH_2} HC\equiv CNa \xrightarrow[(2)\ H_3O^+]{(1)}$

11.9 ORGANOMETALLIC COMPOUNDS OF LESS ELECTROPOSITIVE ELEMENTS

Grignard reagents and alkyllithium reagents react with a number of halides of less electropositive elements to produce new organometallic compounds. Since Grignard reagents and alkyllithiums are easily prepared, these reactions furnish us with useful syntheses of alkyl derivatives of mercury, zinc, cadmium, copper, silicon, and phosphorus, for example. In general terms the reactions using Grignard reagents take the form shown here.

$$n\ RMgX + MX_n \longrightarrow R_nM + n\ MgX_2$$
(M is less electropositive than Mg)

Several specific examples are shown here.

$$2\ CH_3MgCl + HgCl_2 \longrightarrow (CH_3)_2Hg + 2\ MgCl_2$$
Dimethylmercury

$$2\ CH_3CH_2MgBr + ZnCl_2 \longrightarrow (CH_3CH_2)_2Zn + 2\ MgClBr$$
Diethylzinc
(100%)

$$2\ C_6H_5MgBr + CdCl_2 \longrightarrow (C_6H_5)_2Cd + 2\ MgClBr$$
Diphenylcadmium)
(>83%)

$$3\ CH_3CH_2CH_2CH_2MgBr + PCl_3 \longrightarrow (CH_3CH_2CH_2CH_2)_3P + 3\ MgClBr$$
Tributylphosphine
(57%)

$$4\ CH_3CH_2MgCl + SiCl_4 \longrightarrow (CH_3CH_2)_4Si + 4\ MgCl_2$$
Tetraethylsilane
(80%)

Additional Problems

11.11   What product would be formed from the reaction of isobutyl bromide, $(CH_3)_2CHCH_2Br$, with each of the following reagents?

(a) OH^-, H_2O

(b) CN^-, ethanol

(c) $(CH_3)_3CO^-$, $(CH_3)_3COH$

(d) CH_3O^-, CH_3OH

(e) Li, Et_2O, then $CH_3\overset{\displaystyle O}{\overset{\|}{C}}CH_3$, then H_3O^+

(f) Mg, Et_2O, then $CH_3\overset{\displaystyle O}{\overset{\|}{C}}H$, then H_3O^+

(g) Mg, Et_2O, then $CH_3\overset{\displaystyle O}{\overset{\|}{C}}OCH_3$, then H_3O^+

(h) Mg, Et_2O, then $H_2C\overset{\displaystyle O}{\overset{\diagup\ \diagdown}{-}}CH_2$, then H_3O^+

(i) Mg, Et_2O, then $H\overset{\displaystyle O}{\overset{\|}{-C-}}H$, then H_3O^+

(j) Li, Et_2O, then CH_3OH

(k) Li, Et_2O, then $CH_3C\equiv CH$

11.12   What products would you expect from the reaction of ethylmagnesium bromide (CH_3CH_2MgBr) with each of the following reagents?

(a) H_2O

(b) D_2O

(c) $C_6H_5\overset{\displaystyle O}{\overset{\|}{C}}H$, then H_3O^+

(d) $C_6H_5\overset{\displaystyle O}{\overset{\|}{C}}C_6H_5$, then H_3O^+

(e) $C_6H_5\overset{\displaystyle O}{\overset{\|}{C}}OCH_3$, then H_3O^+

(f) $C_6H_5\overset{\displaystyle O}{\overset{\|}{C}}CH_3$, then H_3O^+

(g) $CH_3CH_2C\equiv CH$, then $CH_3\overset{\displaystyle O}{\overset{\|}{C}}H$, then H_3O^+

(h) Cyclopentadiene

(i) $HgCl_2$

(j) $CdCl_2$

(k) PCl_3

11.13   What products would you expect from the reaction of propyllithium $(CH_3CH_2CH_2Li)$ with each of the following reagents?

(a) $(CH_3)_2CH\overset{\displaystyle O}{\overset{\|}{C}}H$, then H_3O^+

(b) $(CH_3)_2CH\overset{\displaystyle O}{\overset{\|}{C}}CH_3$, then H_3O^+

(c) 1-Pentyne, then $CH_3\overset{\displaystyle O}{\overset{\|}{C}}CH_3$, then H_3O^+

(d) Ethanol

(e) CuI, then $CH_2{=}CHCH_2Br$

(f) CuI, then cyclopentyl bromide

(g) CuI, then (Z)-1-iodopropene

(h) CuI, then CH_3I

(i) CH_3CO_2D

(j) $SiCl_4$

(k) $ZnCl_2$

11.14   Show how you might prepare each of the following alcohols through a Grignard synthesis. (Assume that you have available any necessary organic halides, aldehydes, ketones, esters, and epoxides as well as any necessary inorganic reagents.)

(a) $CH_3CH_2\overset{\displaystyle CH_3}{\underset{\displaystyle CH_3}{\overset{\displaystyle |}{\underset{\displaystyle |}{C}}}}OH$ (three ways)

(b) $\bigcirc\!\!-\!\!\overset{\displaystyle OH}{\underset{\displaystyle CH_2CH_3}{\overset{\displaystyle |}{\underset{\displaystyle |}{C}}}}CH_2CH_3$ (three ways)

(c)  [structure: cyclohexane ring with OH and C_6H_5 substituents]

(d) 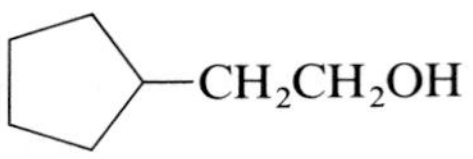 [structure: cyclopentane ring]—CH_2CH_2OH

(e) 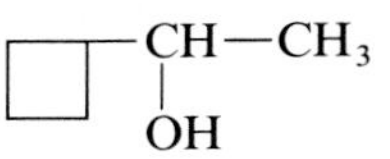 [structure: cyclobutane ring]—CH—CH_3 with OH below   (two ways)

11.15   Outline all steps in a synthesis that would transform isopropyl alcohol, $CH_3CH(OH)CH_3$, into each of the following:

(a) $(CH_3)_2CHCH(OH)CH_3$ (e) CH_3CHDCH_3

(b) $(CH_3)_2CHCH_2OH$

(c) $(CH_3)_2CHCH_2CH_2Cl$ (f) [cyclohexane ring]—CH with CH_3 and CH_3

(d) $(CH_3)_2CHCH(OH)CH(CH_3)_2$

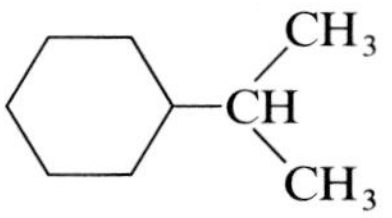

11.16   How might you carry out the following transformations?
(a) Bromocyclopentane $\longrightarrow$ methylcyclopentane
(b) 3-Bromocyclopentene $\longrightarrow$ 3-methylcyclopentene
(c) Allyl bromide (CH_2=$CHCH_2Br$) $\longrightarrow$ 1-pentene
(d) (*E*)-2-Iodo-2-butene $\longrightarrow$ (*E*)-3-methyl-2-heptene

11.17   What products would you expect from the following reactions?
(a) Phenyllithium + acetic acid $\longrightarrow$
(b) Phenyllithium + methanol $\longrightarrow$
(c) Methylmagnesium bromide + ammonia $\longrightarrow$
(d) (Four molar equivalents) methylmagnesium bromide + $SiCl_4$ $\longrightarrow$
(e) (Three molar equivalents) phenylmagnesium bromide + PCl_3 $\longrightarrow$
(f) (Two molar equivalents) ethylmagnesium bromide + $CdCl_2$ $\longrightarrow$

(g) Phenylmagnesium bromide + H—$\overset{\overset{\textstyle O}{\|}}{C}$—H $\xrightarrow{\text{(2) H}_3\text{O}^+}$

11.18   Show how each of the following transformations could be carried out.
(a) C_6H_5CH=CH_2 $\longrightarrow$ 1-phenylethanol   (two ways)
(b) C_6H_5CH=CH_2 $\longrightarrow$ 2-phenylethanol
(c) C_6H_5CH=CH_2 $\longrightarrow$ 1-methoxy-2-phenylethane
(d) 1-Phenylethanol $\longrightarrow$ ethyl 1-phenylethyl ether
(e) Phenylacetic acid ($C_6H_5CH_2CO_2H$) $\longrightarrow$ 2-phenylethanol
(f) Methyl phenyl ketone ($C_6H_5COCH_3$) $\longrightarrow$ 1-phenylethanol
(g) Methyl phenylacetate ($C_6H_5CH_2CO_2CH_3$) $\longrightarrow$ 2-phenylethanol

11.19   Show how 1-butanol could be transformed into each of the following compounds. (You may use any necessary inorganic reagents and you need not show the synthesis of a particular compound more than once.)
(a) 1-Butene   (d) 1-Bromobutane
(b) 2-Butanol   (e) 2-Bromobutane
(c) 2-Butanone ($CH_3COCH_2CH_3$)   (f) 1-Pentanol

ADDITIONAL PROBLEMS

(g) 1-Hexene

(h) 3-Methyl-3-heptanol

(i) Butanal ($CH_3CH_2CH_2CHO$)

(j) 4-Octanol

(k) 3-Methyl-4-heptanol

(l) Pentanoic acid ($CH_3CH_2CH_2CH_2CO_2H$)

(m) Butyl *sec*-butyl ether

(n) Dibutyl ether   (two ways)

(o) Butyllithium

(p) Octane

11.20 The alcohol shown below is used in making perfumes. Outline a synthesis of this alcohol from bromobenzene and 1-butene.

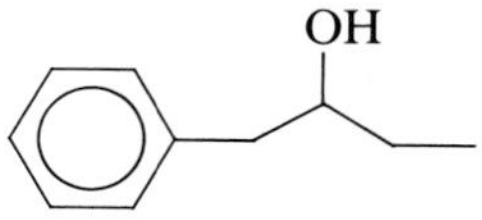

11.21 Show how a Grignard reagent might be used in the following synthesis.

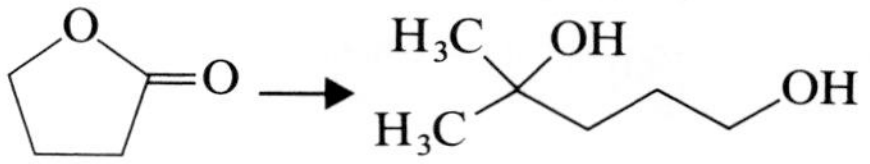

11.22 Starting with compounds of four carbon atoms or fewer, outline a synthesis of racemic Meparfynol, a mild hypnotic (sleep-inducing compound).

Meparfynol

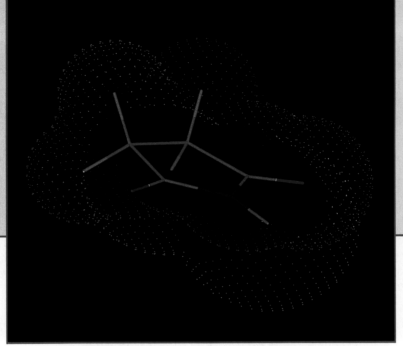

N-bromosuccinimide (see Section 12.B).

CHAPTER

12

CONJUGATED UNSATURATED SYSTEMS

12.1 INTRODUCTION

In our study of the reactions of alkenes in Chapter 9 we saw how important the π bond is in understanding the chemistry of unsaturated compounds. In this chapter we shall study a special group of unsaturated compounds and again we shall find that the π bond is the important part of the molecule. Here we shall examine *species that have a p orbital on an atom adjacent to a double bond.* The p orbital may be one that contains a single electron as in the allyl radical (CH_2=$CHCH_2\cdot$) (Section 12.2); it may be a vacant p orbital as in the allyl cation (CH_2=$CHCH_2^+$) (Section 12.4); or it may be the p orbital of another double bond as in 1,3-butadiene (CH_2=CH—CH=CH_2) (Section 12.7). We shall see that having a p orbital on an atom adjacent to a double bond allows the formation of an extended π bond — one that encompasses more than two nuclei.

Systems that have a p orbital on an atom adjacent to a double bond — molecules with delocalized π bonds — are called **conjugated unsaturated systems.** This general phenomenon is called **conjugation.** As we shall see, conjugation gives these systems special properties. We shall find, for example, that conjugated radicals, ions, or molecules are more stable than nonconjugated ones. We shall demonstrate this with the allyl radical, the allyl cation, and 1,3-butadiene. Conjugation also allows molecules to undergo unusual reactions, and we shall study these, too, including an important reaction for forming rings called the Diels – Alder reaction (Section 12.10).

12.2 ALLYLIC SUBSTITUTION AND THE ALLYL RADICAL

When propene reacts with bromine or chlorine at low temperatures, the reaction that takes place is the usual addition of halogen to the double bond.

$$CH_2{=}CH{-}CH_3 + X_2 \xrightarrow[\substack{CCl_4 \\ \text{(addition reaction)}}]{\text{low temperature}} \underset{\underset{X}{|}\quad\underset{X}{|}}{CH_2{-}CH{-}CH_3}$$

However, when propene reacts with chlorine or bromine at very high temperatures or under conditions in which the concentration of the halogen is very small, the reaction that occurs is a **substitution.** These two examples illustrate how we can often change the course of an organic reaction simply by changing the conditions. (They also illustrate the need for specifying the conditions of a reaction carefully when we report experimental results.)

$$\underset{\textbf{Propene}}{CH_2{=}CH{-}CH_3} + X_2 \xrightarrow[\substack{\text{or} \\ \text{low conc of } X_2 \\ \text{(substitution reaction)}}]{\text{high temperature}} CH_2{=}CH{-}CH_2X + HX$$

In this substitution a halogen atom replaces one of the hydrogen atoms of the methyl group of propene. These hydrogen atoms are called the **allylic hydrogen atoms** and the substitution reaction is known as an **allylic substitution.**

Allylic hydrogen atoms

These are general terms as well. The hydrogen atoms of any saturated carbon atom adjacent to a double bond, that is,

are called *allylic* hydrogen atoms and any reaction in which an allylic hydrogen atom is replaced is called an *allylic substitution.*

12.2A ALLYLIC CHLORINATION (HIGH TEMPERATURE)

Propene undergoes allylic chlorination when propene and chlorine react in the gas phase at 400 °C.

$$CH_2{=}CH{-}CH_3 + Cl_2 \xrightarrow[\text{gas phase}]{400\ °C} \underset{\substack{\textbf{3-Chloropropene} \\ \textbf{(allyl chloride)}}}{CH_2{=}CH{-}CH_2Cl} + HCl$$

The mechanism for allylic substitution is the same as the chain mechanism for alkane halogenations that we saw in Chapter 7. In the chain-initiating step, the chlorine molecule dissociates into chlorine atoms.

Chain-Initiating Step

$$:\ddot{\text{Cl}}:\ddot{\text{Cl}}: \xrightarrow{h\nu} 2 :\ddot{\text{Cl}}\cdot$$

In the first chain-propagating step the chlorine atom abstracts one of the allylic hydrogen atoms.

First Chain-Propagating Step

Allyl radical

The radical that is produced in this step is called an *allyl radical.**
In the second chain-propagating step the allyl radical reacts with a molecule of chlorine.

Second Chain-Propagating Step

Allyl chloride

This step results in the formation of a molecule of allyl chloride and a chlorine atom. The chlorine atom then brings about a repetition of the first chain-propagating step. The chain reaction continues until the usual chain-terminating steps consume the radicals.

The reason for substitution at the allylic hydrogen atoms of propene will be more understandable if we examine the bond dissociation energy of an allylic carbon–hydrogen bond and compare it with the bond dissociation energies of other carbon–hydrogen bonds (cf. Table 7.1).

$$CH_2{=}CHCH_2{-}H \longrightarrow CH_2{=}CHCH_2\cdot + H\cdot \qquad DH° = 85 \text{ kcal mol}^{-1}$$

Propene   Allyl radical

$$(CH_3)_3C{-}H \longrightarrow (CH_3)_3C\cdot + H\cdot \qquad DH° = 91 \text{ kcal mol}^{-1}$$

Isobutane   3° Radical

$$(CH_3)_2CH{-}H \longrightarrow (CH_3)_2CH\cdot + H\cdot \qquad DH° = 94.5 \text{ kcal mol}^{-1}$$

Propane   2° Radical

$$CH_3CH_2CH_2{-}H \longrightarrow CH_3CH_2CH_2\cdot + H\cdot \qquad DH° = 98 \text{ kcal mol}^{-1}$$

Propane   1° Radical

$$CH_2{=}CH{-}H \longrightarrow CH_2{=}CH\cdot + H\cdot \qquad DH° = 108 \text{ kcal mol}^{-1}$$

Ethene   Vinyl radical

---

*A radical of the general type $-\overset{|}{C}{=}\overset{|}{C}{-}\overset{|}{\underset{\cdot}{C}}{-}$ is called an *allylic* radical.

We see that an allylic carbon–hydrogen bond of propene is broken with greater ease than even the tertiary carbon–hydrogen bond of isobutane and with far greater ease than a vinylic carbon–hydrogen bond.

$$CH_2{=}CH{-}CH_2{-}H + \cdot X \longrightarrow CH_2{=}CH{-}CH_2\cdot + HX \qquad E_{act}\text{ is low}$$

Allyl radical

$$X\cdot + H{-}CH{=}CH{-}CH_3 \longrightarrow \cdot CH{=}CH{-}CH_3 + HX \qquad E_{act}\text{ is high}$$

Vinylic radical

The ease with which an allylic carbon–hydrogen bond is broken means that relative to primary, secondary, tertiary, and vinylic free radicals the allyl radical is the *most stable* (Fig. 12.1).

Relative stability   allylic or allyl > 3° > 2° > 1° > vinyl

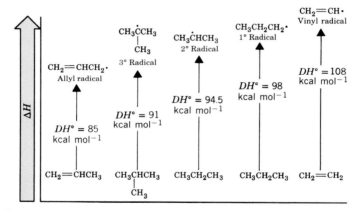

FIGURE 12.1 The relative stability of the allyl radical compared to 1°, 2°, 3°, and vinyl radicals. (The stabilities of the radicals are relative to the hydrocarbon from which each was formed, and the overall order of stability is allyl > 3° > 2° > 1° > vinyl.)

12.2B ALLYLIC BROMINATION WITH *N*-BROMOSUCCINIMIDE (LOW CONCENTRATION OF Br$_2$)

Propene undergoes allylic bromination when it is treated with *N*-bromosuccinimide (NBS) in CCl$_4$ in the presence of peroxides or light.

$$CH_2{=}CH{-}CH_3 + \underset{\substack{\text{\textit{N}-Bromosuccinimide}\\\text{(NBS)}}}{\text{[structure]} :N{-}Br} \xrightarrow[\text{CCl}_4]{\text{light or ROOR}} \underset{\substack{\text{3-Bromopropene}\\\text{(allyl bromide)}}}{CH_2{=}CH{-}CH_2Br} + \underset{\text{Succinimide}}{\text{[structure]} :N{-}H}$$

The reaction is initiated by the formation of a small amount of Br· (possibly formed by dissociation of the N—Br bond of the NBS). The main propagation steps for this reaction are the same as for allylic chlorination (Section 12.2A).

$$CH_2=CH-CH_2-H + \cdot Br \longrightarrow CH_2=CH-CH_2\cdot + HBr$$

$$CH_2=CH-CH_2\cdot + Br-Br \longrightarrow CH_2=CH-CH_2Br + \cdot Br$$

N-Bromosuccinimide is nearly insoluble in CCl_4 and provides a constant but very low concentration of bromine in the reaction mixture. It does this by reacting very rapidly with the HBr formed in the substitution reaction. Each molecule of HBr is replaced by one molecule of Br_2.

Under these conditions, that is, *in a nonpolar solvent and with a very low concentration of bromine,* very little bromine adds to the double bond; it reacts by substitution and replaces an allylic hydrogen atom instead.

OPTIONAL MATERIAL

Why, we might ask, does a low concentration of bromine favor allylic substitution over addition? To understand this we must recall the mechanism for addition and notice that in the first step only one atom of the bromine molecule becomes attached to the alkene *in a reversible step.*

The other atom (now the bromide ion) becomes attached in the second step. Now, if the concentration of bromine is low, the equilibrium for the first step will lie far to the left. Moreover, even when the bromonium ion forms, the probability of its finding a bromide ion in its vicinity will also be low. These two factors slow the addition so that allylic substitution competes successfully.

The use of a nonpolar solvent also slows addition. Since there are no polar molecules to solvate (and thus stabilize) the bromide ion formed in the first step, the bromide ion uses a bromine molecule as a substitute:

This means that in a nonpolar solvent the rate equation is second order with respect to bromine,

$$\text{rate} = k \left[\underset{/}{\overset{\backslash}{\text{C}}} = \underset{\backslash}{\overset{/}{\text{C}}} \right] [Br_2]^2$$

and that the low bromine concentration has an even more pronounced effect in slowing the rate of addition.

To understand why a high temperature favors allylic substitution over addition requires a consideration of the effect of entropy changes on equilibria (Section 3.6). The addition reaction, because it combines two molecules into one, has a substantial negative entropy change. At low temperatures, the $T\Delta S°$ term in $\Delta G° = \Delta H° - T\Delta S°$, is not large enough to offset the favorable $\Delta H°$ term. But as the temperature is increased, the $T\Delta S°$ term becomes more significant, $\Delta G°$ becomes more positive, and the equilibrium becomes more unfavorable.

12.3 THE STABILITY OF THE ALLYL RADICAL

An explanation of the stability of the allyl radical can be approached in two ways: in terms of molecular orbital theory and in terms of resonance theory (Section 1.8). As we shall see soon, both approaches give us equivalent descriptions of the allyl radical. The molecular orbital approach is easier to visualize, so we shall begin with it. (As preparation for this section, it would be a good idea to review the molecular orbital theory given in Sections 1.12 and 2.4.)

12.3A MOLECULAR ORBITAL DESCRIPTION OF THE ALLYL RADICAL

As an allylic hydrogen atom is abstracted from propene, the sp^3-hybridized carbon atom of the methyl group changes its hybridization state to sp^2 (cf. Section 7.8). The p orbital of this new sp^2-hybridized carbon atom overlaps with the p orbital of the central carbon atom. Thus, in the allyl radical three p orbitals overlap to form a set of π molecular orbitals that encompass all three carbon atoms. The new p orbital of the allyl radical is said to be *conjugated* with those of the double bond and the allyl radical is said to be a *conjugated unsaturated system.*

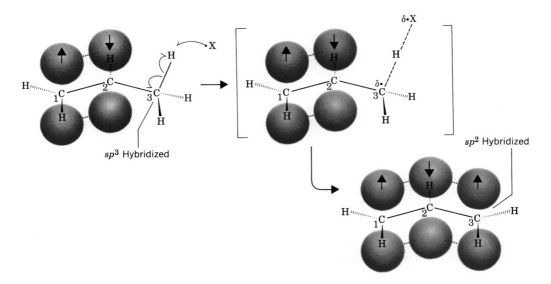

The unpaired electron of the allyl radical and the two electrons of the π bond are **delocalized** over all three carbon atoms. This delocalization of the unpaired electron accounts for the greater stability of the allyl radical when compared to primary, secondary, and tertiary radicals. Although some delocalization occurs in primary, secondary, and tertiary radicals, delocalization is not as effective because it occurs through σ bonds.

The diagram in Figure 12.2 illustrates how the three p orbitals of the allyl radical combine to form three π molecular orbitals. (*Remember:* The number of molecular orbitals that results always equals the number of atomic orbitals that combine, cf. Section 1.12.) The bonding π molecular orbital is of lowest energy; it encompasses all three carbon atoms and is occupied by two spin-paired electrons. This bonding π orbital is the result of having p orbitals with lobes of the same sign overlap between adjacent carbon atoms. This type of overlap, as we recall, increases the π electron density in the regions between the atoms where it is needed for bonding. The non-bonding π orbital is occupied by one unpaired electron and it has a node at the central carbon atom. This node means that the unpaired electron is located in the vicinity of carbon atoms **1** and **3** only. The antibonding π molecular orbital results when orbital lobes of opposite sign overlap between adjacent carbon atoms: Such overlap means

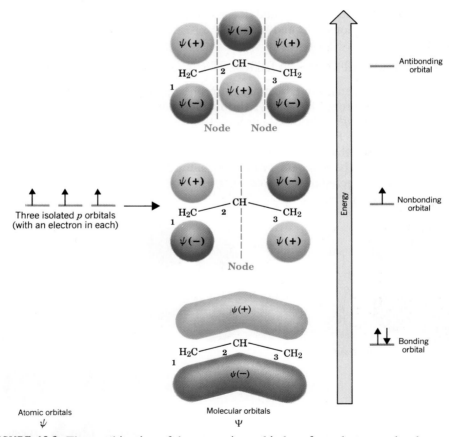

FIGURE 12.2 The combination of three atomic p orbitals to form three π molecular orbitals in the allyl radical. The bonding π molecular orbital is formed by the combination of the three p orbitals with lobes of the same sign overlapping above and below the plane of the atoms. The nonbonding π molecular orbital has a node at C-2. The antibonding π molecular orbital has two nodes: between C-1 and C-2, and between C-2 and C-3.

that in the antibonding π orbital there is a node between each pair of carbon atoms. This antibonding orbital of the allyl radical is of highest energy and is empty in the ground state of the radical.

We can illustrate the picture of the allyl radical given by molecular orbital theory in simpler terms with the following structure.

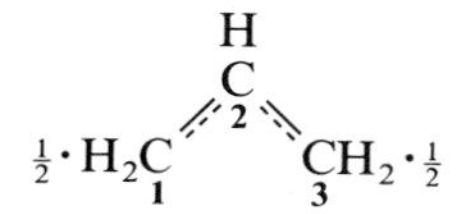

$$\tfrac{1}{2}\cdot H_2C \underset{1}{} \overset{\overset{\displaystyle H}{\displaystyle C}}{} \underset{3}{CH_2} \cdot \tfrac{1}{2}$$

We indicate with dotted lines that both carbon–carbon bonds are partial double bonds. This accommodates one of the things that molecular orbital theory tells us: *that there is a π bond encompassing all three atoms.* We also place the symbol $\tfrac{1}{2}\cdot$ beside C-1/C-3 atoms. This denotes a second thing molecular orbital theory tells us: *that the unpaired electron spends its time in the vicinity of C-1 and C-3.* Finally, implicit in the molecular orbital picture of the allyl radical is this: The two ends of the allyl radical are *equivalent.* This aspect of the molecular orbital description is also implicit in the formula just given.

12.3B RESONANCE DESCRIPTION OF THE ALLYL RADICAL

Earlier in this section we wrote the structure of the allyl radical as **A.**

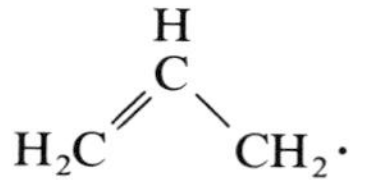

$$H_2C \overset{\overset{\displaystyle H}{\displaystyle C}}{=\!=} CH_2\cdot$$
A

However, we might just as well have written the equivalent structure, **B.**

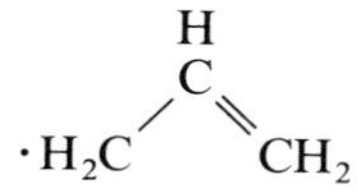

$$\cdot H_2C \overset{\overset{\displaystyle H}{\displaystyle C}}{=\!=} CH_2$$
B

In writing structure **B** we do not mean to imply that we have simply taken structure **A** and turned it over. What we have done is moved the electrons in the following way:

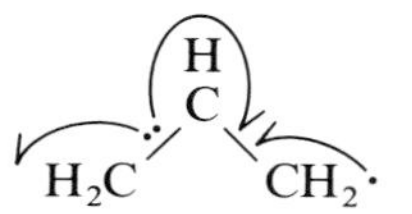

$$H_2C \overset{\overset{\displaystyle H}{\displaystyle C}}{} CH_2\cdot$$

We have not moved the atomic nuclei themselves.

Resonance theory (Section 1.8) tells us that whenever we can write two structures for a chemical entity *that differ only in the positions of the electrons,* the entity cannot be represented by either structure alone but is a *hybrid* of both. We can represent the hybrid in two ways: We can write both structures **A** and **B**, and connect them with a double-headed arrow, a special sign in resonance theory, that indicates they are resonance structures.

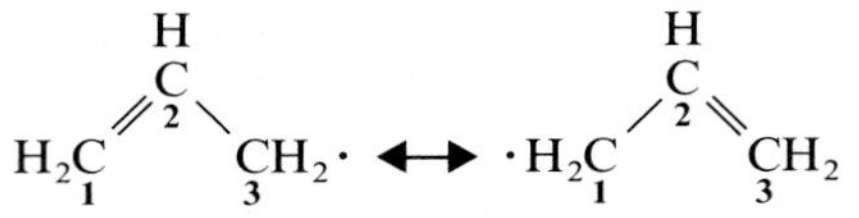

$$H_2C \overset{\overset{\displaystyle H}{\underset{2}{C}}}{\underset{1}{}} \diagdown \underset{3}{CH_2} \cdot \quad \longleftrightarrow \quad \cdot H_2C \overset{\overset{\displaystyle H}{\underset{2}{C}}}{\underset{1}{}} \diagdown \underset{3}{CH_2}$$

$$\text{A} \qquad\qquad\qquad \text{B}$$

Or we can write a single structure, **C**, that blends the features of both resonance structures.

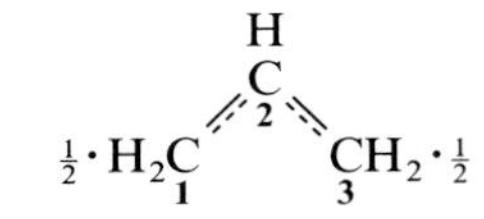

$$\tfrac{1}{2} \cdot H_2C \overset{\overset{\displaystyle H}{\underset{2}{C}}}{\underset{1}{}} \diagdown \underset{3}{CH_2} \cdot \tfrac{1}{2}$$

$$\text{C}$$

We see, then, that resonance theory gives us exactly the same picture of the allyl radical as we got from molecular orbital theory. Structure **C** describes the carbon–carbon bonds of the allyl radical as partial double bonds. The resonance structures **A** and **B** also tell us that the unpaired electron is associated only with C-1 and C-3 atoms. We indicate this in structure **C** by placing a $\tfrac{1}{2}\cdot$ beside C-1 and C-3.* Because resonance structures **A** and **B** are equivalent, *C-1 and C-3 are also equivalent.*

Another rule in resonance theory is that *whenever equivalent resonance structures can be written for a chemical species, the chemical species is much more stable than either resonance structure (when taken alone) would indicate.* If we were to examine either **A** or **B** alone, we might decide that it resembles a primary radical. Thus, we might estimate the stability of the allyl radical as approximately that of a primary radical. In doing so, we would greatly underestimate the stability of the allyl radical. Resonance theory tells us, however, that since **A** and **B** are *equivalent resonance structures,* the allyl radical should be much more stable than either, that is, much more stable than a primary radical. This correlates with what experiments have shown to be true; the allyl radical is even more stable than a tertiary radical.

Problem 12.1

(a) What product(s) would you expect to obtain if propene labeled with ^{14}C at C-1 were subjected to allylic chlorination or bromination? (b) Explain your answer.

$$^{14}CH_2{=}CHCH_3 + X_2 \xrightarrow[\substack{\text{or} \\ \text{low conc of } X_2}]{\text{high temperature}} \text{?}$$

(c) If more than one product would be obtained, what relative proportions would you expect?

---

* A resonance structure such as the one shown below would indicate that an unpaired electron is associated with C-2. This structure is not a proper resonance structure because resonance theory dictates that *all resonance structures must have the same number of unpaired electrons* (cf. Section 12.5).

$$\cdot CH_2{-}\overset{\displaystyle \cdot}{CH}{-}CH_2\cdot$$

(an incorrect resonance structure)

12.4 THE ALLYL CATION

Although we cannot go into the experimental evidence here, the allyl cation (CH_2=$CHCH_2^+$) is an unusually stable carbocation. It is even more stable than a secondary carbocation and is almost as stable as a tertiary carbocation. In general terms, the relative order of stabilities of carbocations is that given here.

Relative Order of Carbocation Stability

$$-\underset{|}{\overset{|}{C}}=\underset{|}{\overset{|}{C}}-\overset{+}{\underset{|}{C}}-\underset{|}{\overset{|}{C}}-\; >\; \overset{\overset{\displaystyle C}{|}}{\underset{\underset{\displaystyle C}{|}}{C-\overset{+}{C}}}\; >\; CH_2{=}CHCH_2^+\; >\; C-\overset{\overset{\displaystyle C}{|}}{\underset{\underset{\displaystyle H}{|}}{C^+}}\; >\; C-\overset{\overset{\displaystyle H}{|}}{\underset{\underset{\displaystyle H}{|}}{C^+}}\; >\; CH_2{=}CH^+$$

Allylic > **3°** > **Allyl** > **2°** > **1°** > **Vinyl**

As we might expect, the unusual stability of the allyl cation and other allylic cations can also be accounted for in terms of molecular orbital or resonance theory. The molecular orbital description of the allyl cation is shown in Fig. 12.3.

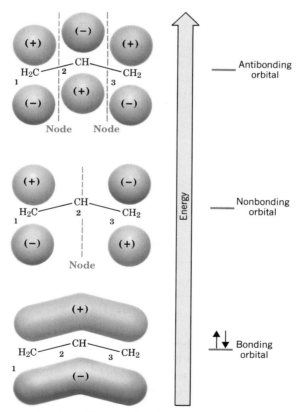

FIGURE 12.3 The π molecular orbitals of the allyl cation. The allyl cation, like the allyl radical (Fig. 12.2), is a conjugated unsaturated system.

The bonding π molecular orbital of the allyl cation, like that of the allyl radical (Fig. 12.2), contains two spin-paired electrons. The nonbonding π molecular orbital of the allyl cation, however, is empty. Since an allyl cation is what we would get if we removed an electron from an allyl radical, we can say, in effect, that we remove the electron from the nonbonding molecular orbital.

$$CH_2\!=\!CHCH_2\cdot \xrightarrow{\;-e^-\;} CH_2\!=\!CHCH_2^+$$

Removal of an electron from a nonbonding orbital (cf. Fig. 12.2) is known to require less energy than removal of an electron from a bonding orbital. In addition, the positive charge that forms on the allyl cation is *effectively delocalized* between C-1 and C-3. Thus, in molecular orbital theory these two factors, the ease of removal of a nonbonding electron and the delocalization of charge, account for the unusual stability of the allyl cation.

Resonance theory depicts the allyl cation as a hybrid of structures **D** and **E** represented here.

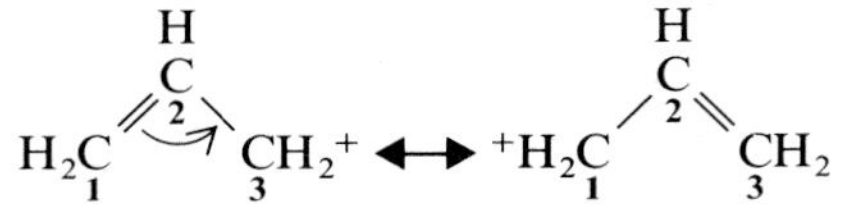

Because **D** and **E** are *equivalent* resonance structures, resonance theory predicts that the allyl cation should be unusually stable. Since the positive charge is located on C-3 in **D** and on C-1 in **E**, resonance theory also tells us that the positive charge should be delocalized over both carbon atoms. Carbon atom **2** carries none of the positive charge. The hybrid structure **F** (see following structure) includes charge and bond features of both **D** and **E**.

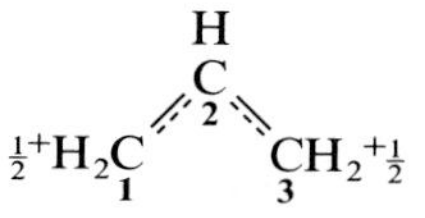

Problem 12.2

(a) Write structures corresponding to **D**, **E**, and **F** for the carbocation shown.

$$CH_3\!-\!\overset{+}{C}H\!-\!CH\!=\!CH_2$$

(b) This carbocation appears to be even more stable than a tertiary carbocation; how can you explain this?   (c) What product(s) would you expect to be formed if this carbocation reacted with a chloride ion?

12.5 SUMMARY OF RULES FOR RESONANCE

We have used resonance theory extensively in earlier sections of this chapter because we have been describing radicals and ions with delocalized electrons (and charges) in π bonds. Resonance theory is especially useful with systems like this, and we shall use it again and again in the chapters that follow. We had an introduction to resonance theory in Section 1.8 and it should be helpful now to summarize the rules for writing resonance structures and for estimating the relative contribution a given structure will make to the overall hybrid.

12.5A RULES FOR WRITING RESONANCE STRUCTURES

1. **Resonance structures exist only on paper.** They have no real existence of their own. Resonance structures are useful because they allow us to describe molecules, radicals, and ions for which a single Lewis structure is inadequate. We write two or more Lewis structures, calling them resonance structures or resonance contributors. We connect these structures by double-headed arrows (⟷), and we say that the real molecule, radical, or ion is like a hybrid of all of them.

2. **In writing resonance structures we are only allowed to move electrons.** The positions of the nuclei of the atoms must remain the same in all of the structures. Structure **3** is not a resonance structure for the allylic cation, for example, because in order to form it we would have to move a hydrogen atom and this is not permitted.

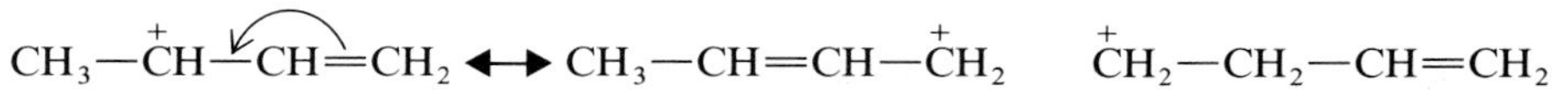

$$CH_3{-}\overset{+}{C}H{-}CH{=}CH_2 \longleftrightarrow CH_3{-}CH{=}CH{-}\overset{+}{C}H_2 \qquad \overset{+}{C}H_2{-}CH_2{-}CH{=}CH_2$$

| **1** | **2** | **3** |

These are resonance structures for the allylic cation formed when 1,3-butadiene accepts a proton

This is not a proper resonance structure for the allylic cation because a hydrogen atom has been moved

3. **All of the structures must be proper Lewis structures.** We should not write structures in which carbon has five bonds, for example.

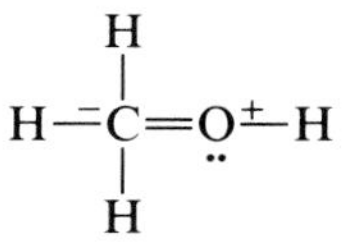

$$H{=}\overset{\underset{|}{H}}{\underset{\underset{H}{|}}{C}}{=}\overset{\pm}{\underset{\cdot\cdot}{O}}{-}H$$

This is not a proper resonance structure for methanol because carbon has five bonds. Elements of the first major row of the periodic table cannot have more than eight electrons in their valence shell.

4. **All resonance structures must have the same number of unpaired electrons.** The following structure is not a resonance structure for the allyl radical because it contains three unpaired electrons and the allyl radical contains only one.

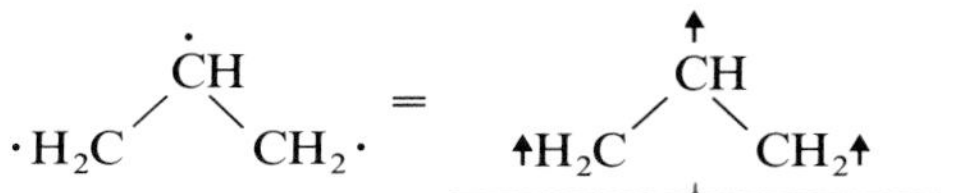

$$\cdot H_2 C \overset{\overset{\displaystyle \cdot}{CH}}{\diagup\diagdown} CH_2 \cdot \qquad = \qquad {\uparrow}H_2 C \overset{\overset{\displaystyle \uparrow}{CH}}{\diagup\diagdown} CH_2{\uparrow}$$

This is not a proper resonance structure for the allyl radical because it does not contain the same number of unpaired electrons as $CH_2{=}CHCH_2\cdot$

5. **All atoms that are a part of the delocalized system must lie in a plane or be nearly planar.** For example, 2,3-di-*tert*-butyl-1,3-butadiene behaves like a *nonconjugated* diene because the large *tert*-butyl groups twist the structure and prevent the double bonds from lying in the same plane. Because they are not in the same plane, the *p* orbitals at C-2 and C-3 do not overlap and delocalization (and therefore resonance) is prevented.

$$(CH_3)_3C \diagdown \qquad \diagup CH_2$$
$$C{-}C$$
$$H_2C \diagup \qquad \diagdown C(CH_3)_3$$

2,3-Di-*tert*-butyl-1,3-butadiene

6. **The energy of the actual molecule is lower than the energy that might be estimated for any contributing structure.** The actual allyl cation, for example, is more stable than either resonance structure **4** or **5** taken separately would indicate. Structures **4** and **5** resemble primary carbocations and yet the allyl cation is more stable (has lower energy) than a secondary carbocation. Chemists often call this kind of stabilization *resonance stabilization.*

$$CH_2{=}CH{-}\overset{+}{C}H_2 \longleftrightarrow \overset{+}{C}H_2{-}CH{=}CH_2$$
$$\mathbf{4} \qquad\qquad \mathbf{5}$$

In Chapter 13 we shall find that benzene is highly resonance-stabilized because it is a hybrid of the two equivalent forms that follow:

| Resonance structures for benzene | Representation of hybrid |

7. **Equivalent resonance structures make equal contributions to the hybrid, and a system described by them has a large resonance stabilization.** Structures **4** and **5** make equal contributions to the allylic cation because they are equivalent. They also make a large stabilizing contribution and account for allylic cations being unusually stable. The same can be said about the contributions made by the equivalent structures **A** and **B** (Section 12.3B) for the allyl radical and by the equivalent structures for benzene.

8. Structures that are not equivalent do not make equal contributions. Generally speaking, **the more stable a structure is (when taken by itself), the greater is its contribution to the hybrid.** For example, the following cation is a hybrid of structures **6** and **7**. Structure **6** makes a greater contribution than **7** because structure **6** is a more stable tertiary carbocation while structure **7** is a primary cation.

$$\underset{a}{CH_3}{-}\underset{\delta+}{\overset{\overset{\displaystyle CH_3}{|}}{\underset{b}{C}}}{=\!=\!=}\underset{c}{CH}{=\!=\!=}\underset{\delta+}{\underset{d}{CH_2}} = \left[\; CH_3{-}\overset{\overset{\displaystyle CH_3}{|}}{\underset{+}{C}}{\overset{\frown}{{-}CH}}{=}CH_2 \longleftrightarrow CH_3{-}\overset{\overset{\displaystyle CH_3}{|}}{C}{=}CH{-}\underset{+}{CH_2} \; \right]$$

$$\mathbf{6} \qquad\qquad\qquad\qquad \mathbf{7}$$

That **6** makes a larger contribution means that the partial positive charge on carbon *b* of the hybrid will be larger than the partial positive charge on carbon *d*. It also means that the bond between carbon atoms *c* and *d* will be more like a double bond than the bond between carbon atoms *b* and *c*.

12.5B ESTIMATING THE RELATIVE STABILITY OF RESONANCE STRUCTURES

The following rules will help us in making decisions about the relative stabilities of resonance structures.

   a. The more covalent bonds a structure has, the more stable it is. This is exactly what we would expect because we know that forming a covalent bond lowers the energy of atoms. This means that of the following structures for 1,3-butadiene, **8**, is by far the most stable and makes by far the largest contribution because it contains one more bond. (It is also most stable for the reason given under rule **c**.)

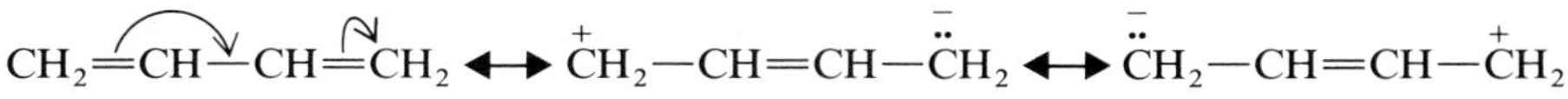

$$CH_2=CH-CH=CH_2 \longleftrightarrow \overset{+}{C}H_2-CH=CH-\overset{..}{\overset{-}{C}}H_2 \longleftrightarrow \overset{..}{\overset{-}{C}}H_2-CH=CH-\overset{+}{C}H_2$$

$$\quad\quad\quad\text{8}\quad\quad\quad\quad\quad\quad\quad\quad\quad\text{9}\quad\quad\quad\quad\quad\quad\quad\quad\quad\text{10}$$

This structure is the most stable because it contains more covalent bonds

   b. Structures in which all of the atoms have a complete valence shell of electrons (i.e., the noble gas structure) **are especially stable and make large contributions to the hybrid.** Again, this is what we would expect from what we know about bonding. This means, for example, that **12** makes a larger stabilizing contribution to the cation below than **11** because all of the atoms of **12** have a complete valence shell. (Notice too that **12** has more covalent bonds than **11**, cf. rule **a**.)

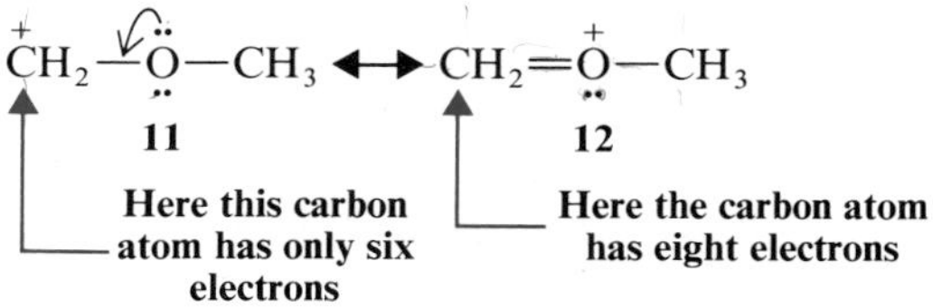

$$\overset{+}{C}H_2-\overset{..}{\overset{..}{O}}-CH_3 \longleftrightarrow CH_2=\overset{+}{\overset{..}{O}}-CH_3$$

$$\quad\quad\quad\text{11}\quad\quad\quad\quad\quad\quad\quad\text{12}$$

Here this carbon atom has only six electrons   Here the carbon atom has eight electrons

   c. Charge separation decreases stability. Separating opposite charges requires energy. Therefore, structures in which opposite charges are separated have greater energy (lower stability) than those that have no charge separation. This means that of the following two structures for vinyl chloride, structure **13** makes a larger contribution because it does not have separated charges. (This does not mean that structure **14** does not contribute to the hybrid, it just means that the contribution made by **14** is smaller.)

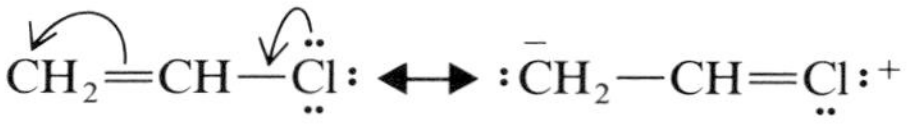

$$CH_2=CH-\overset{..}{\underset{..}{Cl}}: \longleftrightarrow :\overset{-}{C}H_2-CH=\overset{..}{\underset{..}{Cl}}:^+$$

$$\quad\quad\quad\text{13}\quad\quad\quad\quad\quad\quad\quad\text{14}$$

Problem 12.3

Give the important resonance structures for each of the following:

(a) $CH_2=\overset{\overset{\textstyle CH_3}{|}}{C}-CH_2\cdot$

(b) $CH_2=CH-\overset{+}{CH}-CH=CH_2$

(c)

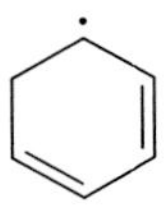

(d)

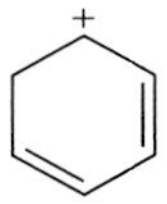

(e) $CH_3CH=CH-CH=\overset{+}{\underset{\cdot\cdot}{O}}H$

(f) $CH_2=CH-Br$

(g)

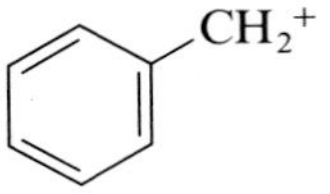

(h) $^-:CH_2-\overset{\overset{\textstyle O}{||}}{C}-CH_3$

(i) $CH_3-S-CH_2^+$

(j) CH_3-NO_2

Problem 12.4

From each set of resonance structures that follow, designate the one that would contribute most to the hybrid and explain your choice.

(a) $CH_3CH_2\overset{\overset{\textstyle CH_3}{|}}{C}=CH-CH_2^+ \longleftrightarrow CH_3CH_2\overset{\overset{\textstyle CH_3}{|}}{\underset{+}{C}}-CH=CH_2$

(b)

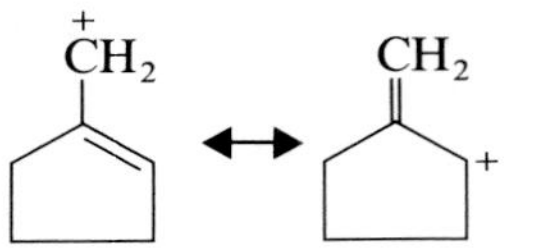

(c) $\overset{+}{C}H_2-\overset{\cdot\cdot}{N}(CH_3)_2 \longleftrightarrow CH_2=\overset{+}{N}(CH_3)_2$

(d) $CH_3-\overset{\overset{\textstyle O}{||}}{C}-O-H \longleftrightarrow CH_3-\overset{\overset{\textstyle O^-}{|}}{C}=\overset{+}{O}-H$

(e) $\underset{\cdot}{C}H_2CH=CHCH=CH_2 \longleftrightarrow CH_2=CH\underset{\cdot}{C}HCH=CH_2 \longleftrightarrow$

$CH_2=CHCH=CH\underset{\cdot}{C}H_2$

(f) $:NH_2-C\equiv N: \longleftrightarrow \overset{+}{N}H_2=C=\overset{\cdot\cdot}{N}:^-$

Problem 12.5

The following keto and enol forms differ in the positions for their electrons but they are not resonance structures. Explain why they are not.

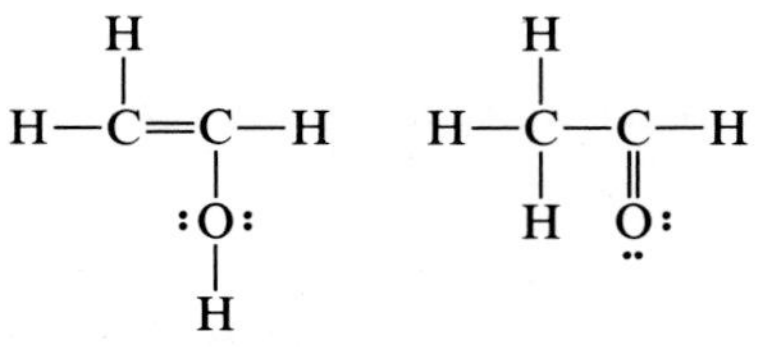

Enol form   **Keto form**

12.6 ALKADIENES AND POLYUNSATURATED HYDROCARBONS

Many hydrocarbons are known whose molecules contain more than one double or triple bond. A hydrocarbon whose molecules contain two double bonds is called an **alkadiene;** one whose molecules contain three double bonds is called an **alkatriene,** and so on. Colloquially, these compounds are often referred to simply as "dienes" or "trienes." A hydrocarbon with two triple bonds is called an **alkadiyne,** and a hydrocarbon with a double and triple bond is called an **alkenyne.**

The following examples of polyunsaturated hydrocarbons illustrate how specific compounds are named.

$$\overset{1}{C}H_2{=}\overset{2}{C}{=}\overset{3}{C}H_2 \qquad \overset{1}{C}H_2{=}\overset{2}{C}H{-}\overset{3}{C}H{=}\overset{4}{C}H_2$$

1,2-Propadiene　　　　**1,3-Butadiene**
(allene)

(3Z)-1,3-Pentadiene　　　　**(2E,4E)-2,4-Hexadiene**
(cis-1,3-pentadiene)　　　　**(trans,trans-2,4-hexadiene)**

(2Z,4E)-2,4-Hexadiene　　　**1-Penten-4-yne**
(cis,trans-2,4-hexadiene)

$$HC{\equiv}\overset{5}{C}{-}\overset{4}{C}H_2\overset{3}{C}H{=}\overset{2}{C}H_2$$

(2E,4E,6E)-2,4,6-Octatriene
(trans,trans,trans-2,4,6-octatriene)

1,3-Cyclohexadiene　　　**1,4-Cyclohexadiene**

The multiple bonds of polyunsaturated compounds are classified as being **cumu-lated, conjugated,** or **isolated.** The double bonds of allene (1,2-propadiene) are said to be cumulated because one carbon (the central carbon) participates in two double bonds. Hydrocarbons whose molecules have cumulated double bonds are called **cumulenes.** The name **allene** (Section 5.16) is also used as a class name for molecules with two cumulated double bonds.

$$CH_2{=}C{=}CH_2 \qquad \overset{\backslash}{\underset{/}{}}C{=}C{=}C\overset{/}{\underset{\backslash}{}}$$

Allene   A cumulated
                    diene

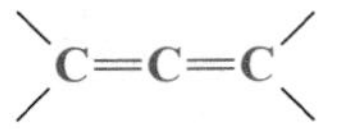

An example of a conjugated diene is 1,3-butadiene. In conjugated polyenes the double and single bonds *alternate* along the chain.

$$CH_2{=}CH{-}CH{=}CH_2 \qquad C{=}C \qquad C{=}C$$

1,3-Butadiene   A conjugated diene

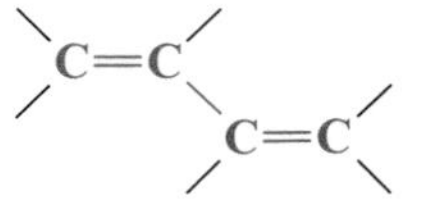

(2*E*,4*E*,6*E*)-2,4,6-Octatriene (p. 491) is an example of a conjugated alkatriene.

If one or more saturated carbon atoms intervene between the double bonds of an alkadiene, the double bonds are said to be *isolated.* An example of an isolated diene is 1,4-pentadiene.

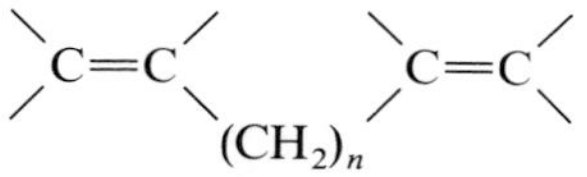

$$C{=}C \qquad C{=}C \qquad\qquad CH_2{=}CH{-}CH_2{-}CH{=}CH_2$$
$$(CH_2)_n$$

An isolated diene   1,4-Pentadiene
($n \neq 0$)

Problem 12.6

(a) Which other compounds in Section 12.6 are conjugated dienes? (b) Which other compound is an isolated diene? (c) Which compound is an isolated enyne?

In Chapter 5 we saw that appropriately substituted cumulated dienes (allenes) give rise to chiral molecules. Cumulated dienes have had some commercial importance and cumulated double bonds are occasionally found in naturally occurring molecules. In general, cumulated dienes are less stable than isolated dienes.

The double bonds of isolated dienes behave just as their name suggests—as isolated "enes." They undergo all of the reactions of alkenes, and except for the fact that they are capable of reacting twice, their behavior is not unusual. Conjugated dienes are far more interesting because we find that their double bonds interact with each other. This interaction leads to unexpected properties and reactions. We shall, therefore, consider the chemistry of conjugated dienes in detail.

12.7 1,3-BUTADIENE: ELECTRON DELOCALIZATION

12.7A BOND LENGTHS OF 1,3-BUTADIENE

The carbon–carbon bond lengths of 1,3-butadiene have been determined and are shown here.

$$\overset{1}{CH_2}=\!\!=\overset{2}{CH}\underset{1.47\ \text{Å}}{\underline{\quad\quad}}\overset{3}{CH}=\!\!=\overset{4}{CH_2}$$
$$\underset{1.34\ \text{Å}}{}\quad\quad\quad\underset{1.34\ \text{Å}}{}$$

The C-1—C-2 bond and the C-3—C-4 bond are (within experimental error) the same length as the carbon–carbon double bond of ethene. The central bond of 1,3-butadiene (1.47 Å), however, is considerably shorter than the single bond of ethane (1.54 Å).

This should not be surprising. All of the carbon atoms of 1,3-butadiene are sp^2 hybridized and, as a result, the central bond of butadiene results from overlapping sp^2 orbitals. And, as we know, a sigma bond that is sp^3-sp^3 is *longer*. There is, in fact, a steady decrease in bond length of carbon–carbon single bonds as the hybridization state of the bonded atoms changes from sp^3 to sp (Table 12.1).

TABLE 12.1 Carbon–carbon single bond lengths and hybridization state

COMPOUND	HYBRIDIZATION STATE	BOND LENGTH (Å)
H_3C—CH_3	sp^3-sp^3	1.54
CH_2=CH—CH_3	sp^2-sp^3	1.50
CH_2=CH—CH=CH_2	sp^2-sp^2	1.47
HC≡C—CH_3	sp-sp^3	1.46
HC≡C—CH=CH_2	sp-sp^2	1.43
HC≡C—C≡CH	sp-sp	1.37

12.7B CONFORMATIONS OF 1,3-BUTADIENE

There are two possible planar conformations of 1,3-butadiene: the s-cis and the s-trans conformations.

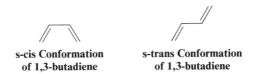

s-cis Conformation   **s-trans Conformation**
of 1,3-butadiene   **of 1,3-butadiene**

These are not true cis and trans forms since the s-cis and s-trans conformations of 1,3-butadiene can be interconverted through rotation about the single bond (hence the prefix s). The s-trans conformation is the predominant one at room temperature.

12.7C MOLECULAR ORBITALS OF 1,3-BUTADIENE

The central carbon atoms of 1,3-butadiene (Fig. 12.4) are close enough for overlap to occur between the *p* orbitals of C-2 and C-3. This overlap is not as great as that between the orbitals of C-1 and C-2 (or those of C-3 and C-4). The C-2–C-3 orbital overlap, however, gives the central bond partial double bond character and allows the four π electrons of 1,3-butadiene to be delocalized over all four atoms.

Figure 12.5 shows how the four *p* orbitals of 1,3-butadiene combine to form a set of four π molecular orbitals.

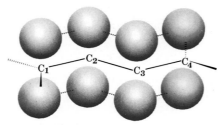

FIGURE 12.4 The *p* orbitals of 1,3-butadiene.

Two of the π molecular orbitals of 1,3-butadiene are bonding molecular orbitals. In the ground state these orbitals hold the four π electrons with two spin-paired electrons in each. The other two π molecular orbitals are antibonding molecular orbitals. In the ground state these orbitals are unoccupied. An electron can be excited from the highest occupied molecular orbital (HOMO) to the lowest unoccupied

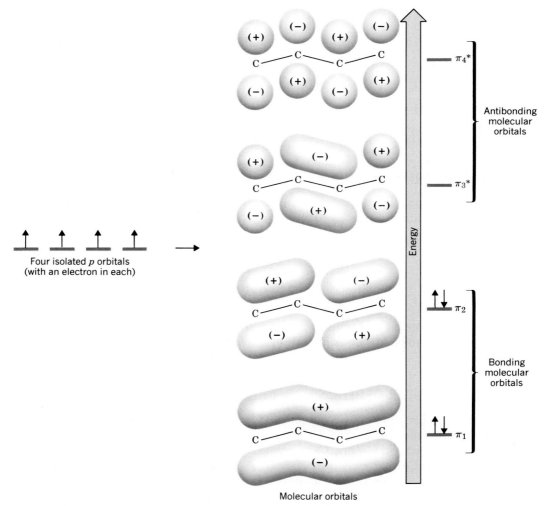

Molecular orbitals

FIGURE 12.5 Formation of the π molecular orbitals of 1,3-butadiene from four isolated *p* orbitals.

molecular orbital (LUMO) when 1,3-butadiene absorbs light with a wavelength of 217 nm. (We shall study the absorption of light by unsaturated molecules in Chapter 14.)

The delocalized bonding that we have just described for 1,3-butadiene is characteristic of all conjugated polyenes.

12.8 THE STABILITY OF CONJUGATED DIENES

Conjugated alkadienes are thermodynamically more stable than isomeric isolated alkadienes. Two examples of this extra stability of conjugated dienes can be seen in an analysis of the heats of hydrogenation given in Table 12.2.

In itself, 1,3-butadiene cannot be compared directly with an isolated diene of the same chain length. However, a comparison can be made between the heat of hydrogenation of 1,3-butadiene and that obtained when two molar equivalents of 1-butene is hydrogenated.

$$\Delta H° \text{ (kcal mol}^{-1})$$

$2\ CH_2{=}CHCH_2CH_3 + 2\ H_2 \longrightarrow 2\ CH_3CH_2CH_2CH_3\ (2 \times -30.3) = -60.6$
1-Butene

$CH_2{=}CHCH{=}CH_2 + 2\ H_2 \longrightarrow CH_3CH_2CH_2CH_3 \qquad = \underline{-57.1}$
1,3-Butadiene \hfill Difference \quad 3.5 kcal mol^{-1}

Because 1-butene has the same kind of monosubstituted double bond as either of those in 1,3-butadiene, we might expect that hydrogenation of 1,3-butadiene would liberate the same amount of heat (-60.6 kcal mol^{-1}) as two molar equivalents of 1-butene. We find, however, that 1,3-butadiene liberates only 57.1 kcal mol^{-1}, 3.5 kcal mol^{-1} *less* than expected. We conclude, therefore, that conjugation imparts some extra stability to the conjugated system (Fig. 12.6).

An assessment of the stabilization that conjugation provides *trans*-1,3-pentadiene can be made by comparing the heat of hydrogenation of *trans*-1,3-pentadiene to the sum of the heats of hydrogenation of 1-pentene and *trans*-2-pentene. This way we are comparing double bonds of comparable types.

TABLE 12.2   Heats of hydrogenation of alkenes and alkadienes

COMPOUND	H$_2$ (mol)	$\Delta H°$ (kcal mol^{-1})	(kJ mol^{-1})
1-Butene	1	-30.3	-126.8
1-Pentene	1	-30.1	-125.9
trans-2-Pentene	1	-27.6	-115.5
1,3-Butadiene	2	-57.1	-238.9
trans-1,3-Pentadiene	2	-54.1	-226.4
1,4-Pentadiene	2	-60.8	-254.4
1,5-Hexadiene	2	-60.5	-253.1

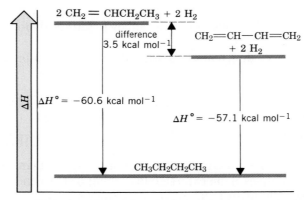

FIGURE 12.6 Heats of hydrogenation of 2 mol of 1-butene and 1 mol of 1,3-butadiene.

$$CH_2=CHCH_2CH_2CH_3 \qquad \Delta H° = -30.1 \text{ kcal mol}^{-1}$$

1-Pentene

$$\text{trans-2-Pentene} \qquad \begin{array}{l} \Delta H° = -27.6 \text{ kcal mol}^{-1} \\ \hline \text{Sum} = -57.7 \text{ kcal mol}^{-1} \end{array}$$

$$\text{trans-1,3-Pentadiene} \qquad \begin{array}{l} \Delta H° = -54.1 \text{ kcal mol}^{-1} \\ \hline \text{Difference} = \quad 3.6 \text{ kcal mol}^{-1} \end{array}$$

We see from these calculations that conjugation affords *trans*-1,3-pentadiene an extra stability of 3.6 kcal mol^{-1}, a value that is very close to the one we obtained for 1,3-butadiene (3.5 kcal mol^{-1}).

When calculations like these are carried out for other conjugated dienes, similar results are obtained; *conjugated dienes are found to be more stable than isolated dienes.* The question, then, is this: What is the source of the extra stability associated with conjugated dienes? There are two factors that contribute. The extra stability of conjugated dienes arises in part from the stronger central bond that they contain, and in part from the additional delocalization of the π electrons that occurs in conjugated dienes.

12.9 ELECTROPHILIC ATTACK ON CONJUGATED DIENES: 1,4 ADDITION

Not only are conjugated dienes somewhat more stable than nonconjugated dienes, they also display special behavior when they react with electrophilic reagents. For example, 1,3-butadiene reacts with one molar equivalent of hydrogen chloride to produce two products: 3-chloro-1-butene and 1-chloro-2-butene.

12.9 ELECTROPHILIC ATTACK ON CONJUGATED DIENES: 1,4 ADDITION

$$CH_2=CH-CH=CH_2 \xrightarrow[25\ ^{\circ}C]{HCl} CH_3-\underset{\underset{Cl}{|}}{CH}-CH=CH_2 + CH_3-CH=CH-CH_2Cl$$

1,3-Butadiene   **3-Chloro-1-butene**   **1-Chloro-2-butene**
                                        (78%)   **(22%)**

If only the first product (3-chloro-1-butene) were formed, we would not be particularly surprised. We would conclude that hydrogen chloride had added to one double bond of 1,3-butadiene in the usual way.

$$\overset{1}{C}H_2=\overset{2}{C}H-\overset{3}{C}H=\overset{4}{C}H_2 \xrightarrow{1,2\ addition} CH_2-CH-CH=CH_2$$
$$+ \qquad\qquad\qquad\qquad\qquad\quad |\quad\ |$$
$$H-Cl \qquad\qquad\qquad\qquad\qquad H\ \ Cl$$

3-Chloro-1-butene

It is the second product, 1-chloro-2-butene, that is unusual. Its double bond is between the central atoms, and the elements of hydrogen chloride have added to the C-1 and C-4 atoms.

$$\overset{1}{C}H_2=\overset{2}{C}H-\overset{3}{C}H=\overset{4}{C}H_2 \xrightarrow{1,4\ addition} CH_2-CH=CH-CH_2$$
$$+ \qquad\qquad\qquad\qquad\qquad\quad |\qquad\qquad\quad |$$
$$H-Cl \qquad\qquad\qquad\qquad\qquad H\qquad\qquad\ Cl$$

1-Chloro-2-butene

This unusual behavior of 1,3-butadiene can be attributed directly to the stability and the delocalized nature of an allylic cation (Section 12.4). In order to see this, consider a mechanism for the addition of hydrogen chloride.

Step 1

$$H^+ + CH_2=CH-CH=CH_2 \longrightarrow CH_3-\underset{+}{CH}-CH=CH_2 \longleftrightarrow CH_3-CH=CH-\underset{+}{CH_2}$$

An allylic cation
equivalent to

$$CH_3-\underset{\delta+}{CH}=\!=\!CH=\!=\underset{\delta+}{CH_2}$$

Step 2

$$CH_3\underset{\delta+}{CH}=\!=\!CH=\!=\underset{\delta+}{CH_2} + \overset{..}{\underset{..}{Cl}}:^-$$

(a) $\longrightarrow$ CH_3CH—CH=CH_2   **1,2 Addition**
                |
                Cl

(b) $\longrightarrow$ CH_3CH=CHCH_2Cl   **1,4 Addition**

In step 1 a proton adds to one of the terminal carbon atoms of 1,3-butadiene to form, as usual, the more stable carbocation, in this case a resonance-stabilized allylic cation. Addition to one of the inner carbon atoms would have produced a much less stable primary cation, one that could not be stabilized by resonance.

$$CH_2=CH-CH=CH_2 \xrightarrow{\quad\times\quad} {}^+CH_2-CH_2-CH=CH_2$$
$$\searrow H^+ \qquad\qquad\qquad \textbf{A 1}° \textbf{ carbocation}$$

In step 2 a chloride ion forms a bond to one of the carbon atoms of the allylic cation that bears a partial positive charge. Reaction at one carbon atom results in the 1,2-addition product; reaction at the other gives the 1,4-addition product.

Problem 12.7

(a) What products would you expect to obtain if hydrogen chloride were allowed to react with a 2,4-hexadiene, $CH_3CH=CHCH=CHCH_3$? (b) With 1,3-pentadiene, $CH_2=CHCH=CHCH_3$? (Neglect cis-trans isomerism.)

1,3-Butadiene shows 1,4-addition reactions with electrophilic reagents other than hydrogen chloride. Two examples are shown here, the addition of hydrogen bromide (in the absence of peroxides) and the addition of bromine.

$$CH_2=CHCH=CH_2 \xrightarrow[40\ °C]{HBr} CH_3CHBrCH=CH_2 + CH_3CH=CHCH_2Br$$
$$\text{(20\%)} \qquad\qquad \text{(80\%)}$$

$$CH_2=CHCH=CH_2 \xrightarrow[-15\ °C]{Br_2} CH_2BrCHBrCH=CH_2 + CH_2BrCH=CHCH_2Br$$
$$\text{(54\%)} \qquad\qquad \text{(46\%)}$$

Reactions of this type are quite general with other conjugated dienes. Conjugated trienes often show 1,6 addition. An example is the 1,6 addition of bromine to 1,3,5-cyclooctatriene:

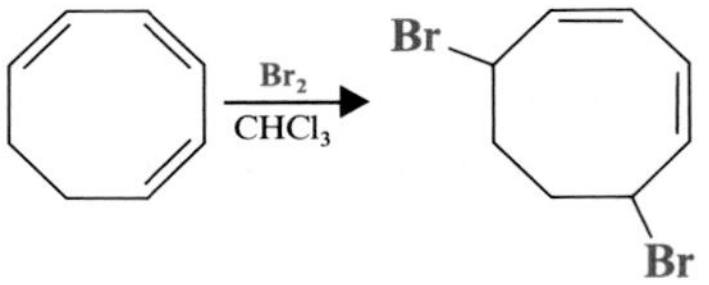

$$\text{(}>68\%\text{)}$$

12.9A RATE CONTROL VERSUS EQUILIBRIUM CONTROL OF A CHEMICAL REACTION

The addition of hydrogen bromide to 1,3-butadiene is interesting in another respect. The relative amounts of 1,2- and 1,4-addition products that we obtain are dependent on the temperature at which we carry out the reaction.

When 1,3-butadiene and hydrogen bromide react at a low temperature ($-80\ °C$) in the absence of peroxides, the major reaction is 1,2 addition; we obtain about 80% of the 1,2 product and only about 20% of the 1,4 product. At a higher temperature ($40\ °C$) the result is reversed. The major reaction is 1,4 addition; we obtain about 80% of the 1,4 product and only about 20% of the 1,2 product.

When the mixture formed at the lower temperature is brought to the higher temperature, moreover, the relative amounts of the two products change. This new reaction mixture eventually contains the same proportion of products given by the reaction carried out at the higher temperature.

12.9 ELECTROPHILIC ATTACK ON CONJUGATED DIENES: 1,4 ADDITION

$$CH_2\!=\!CHCH\!=\!CH_2 + HBr$$

$\xrightarrow{-80\ °C}$ $CH_3\overset{\underset{\displaystyle |}{Br}}{C}HCH\!=\!CH_2 + CH_3CH\!=\!CHCH_2Br$

(80%) $\quad\downarrow$ 40 °C $\quad$ (20%)

$\xrightarrow{40\ °C}$ $CH_3\overset{\underset{\displaystyle |}{Br}}{C}HCH\!=\!CH_2 + CH_3CH\!=\!CHCH_2Br$

(20%) $\qquad\qquad$ (80%)

It can also be shown that at the higher temperature and in the presence of hydrogen bromide, the 1,2-addition product rearranges to the 1,4 product and that an equilibrium exists between them.

$$CH_3\overset{\underset{\displaystyle |}{Br}}{C}HCH\!=\!CH_2 \underset{}{\overset{40\ °C,\ HBr}{\rightleftharpoons}} CH_3CH\!=\!CHCH_2Br$$

1,2-Addition $\qquad\qquad\qquad$ **1,4-Addition**
product $\qquad\qquad\qquad\qquad$ **product**

Because this equilibrium favors the 1,4-addition product, *it must be more stable.*

The reactions of hydrogen bromide with 1,3-butadiene serve as a striking illustration of the way that the outcome of a chemical reaction can be determined, in one instance, by relative rates of competing reactions and, in another, by the relative stabilities of the final products. At the lower temperature, the relative amounts of the products of the addition are determined by the relative rates at which the two additions occur; 1,2 addition occurs faster so the 1,2-addition product is the major product. At the higher temperature, the relative amounts of the products are determined by the position of an equilibrium. The 1,4-addition product is the more stable, so it is the major product.

This behavior of 1,3-butadiene and hydrogen bromide can be more fully understood if we examine the diagram shown in Fig. 12.7.

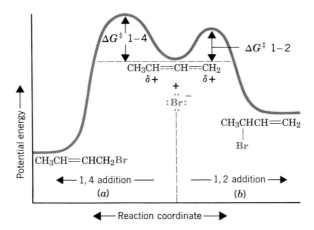

FIGURE 12.7 Potential energy versus reaction coordinate diagram for the reactions of an allylic cation with a bromide ion. One reaction pathway (a) leads to the 1,4-addition product and the other (b) leads to the 1,2-addition product.

The step that determines the overall outcome of the reaction is the step in which the hybrid allylic cation combines with a bromide ion, that is,

$$CH_2=CH-CH=CH_2 \xrightarrow{H^+}$$

$$CH_3-\overset{\delta+}{CH}\text{---}CH\text{---}\overset{\delta+}{CH_2} \longrightarrow$$

$$\xrightarrow{Br^-} CH_3-\underset{\underset{\text{1,2 Product}}{Br}}{CH}-CH=CH_2$$

$$\xrightarrow{Br^-} CH_3-CH=CH-CH_2Br$$
1,4 Product

{ This step determines the regioselectivity of the reaction

We see in Fig. 12.7 that, for this step, the free energy of activation leading to the 1,2-addition product is less than the free energy of activation leading to the 1,4-addition product, even though the 1,4 product is more stable. At low temperatures, a larger fraction of collisions between the intermediate ions will have enough energy to cross the lower barrier (leading to the 1,2 product), and only a very small fraction of collisions will have enough energy to cross the higher barrier (leading to the 1,4 product). In either case (and this is the *key point*), whichever barrier is crossed, product formation is *irreversible* because there is not enough energy available to lift either product out of its deep potential energy valley. Since 1,2 addition occurs faster, the 1,2 product predominates and the reaction is said to be under **rate control** or **kinetic control.**

At higher temperatures, the intermediate ions have sufficient energy to cross both barriers with relative ease. More importantly, however, *both reactions are reversible.* Sufficient energy is also available to take the products back over their energy barriers to the intermediate level of allylic cations and bromide ions. The 1,2 product is still formed faster, but being less stable than the 1,4 product, it also reverts to the allylic cation faster. Under these conditions, that is, at higher temperatures, the relative proportions of the products *do not reflect* the relative heights of the energy barriers leading from allylic cation to products. Instead, *they reflect the relative stabilities of the products themselves.* Since the 1,4 product is more stable, it is formed at the expense of the 1,2 product because the overall change from 1,2 product to 1,4 product is energetically favored. Such a reaction is said to be under **equilibrium control** or **thermodynamic control.**

Before we leave this subject one final point should be made. This example clearly demonstrates that predictions of relative reaction rates made on the basis of product stabilities alone can be wrong. This is not always the case, however. For many reactions in which a common intermediate leads to two or more products, the most stable product is formed fastest.

Problem 12.8

(a) Can you suggest a possible explanation for the fact that the 1,2-addition reaction of 1,3-butadiene and hydrogen bromide occurs faster than 1,4 addition? (*Hint:* Consider the relative contributions that the two forms $CH_3\overset{+}{C}HCH=CH_2$ and $CH_3CH=CH\overset{+}{C}H_2$ make to the resonance hybrid of the allylic cation.) (b) How can you account for the fact that the 1,4-addition product is more stable?

12.10 THE DIELS-ALDER REACTION: A 1,4-CYCLOADDITION REACTION OF DIENES

In 1928 two German chemists, Otto Diels and Kurt Alder, developed a 1,4-cycloaddition reaction of dienes that has since come to bear their names. The reaction proved to be one of such great versatility and synthetic utility that Diels and Alder were awarded the Nobel Prize for Chemistry in 1950.

An example of the Diels–Alder reaction is the reaction that takes place when 1,3-butadiene and maleic anhydride are heated together at 100 °C. The product is obtained in quantitative yield.

| 1,3-Butadiene (diene) | Maleic anhydride (dienophile) | (Adduct) (100%) |

or

In general terms, the reaction is one between a conjugated **diene** (a 4π-electron system) and a compound containing a double bond (a 2π-electron system) called a **dienophile** (diene + Greek: *philein,* to love). The product of a Diels–Alder reaction is often called an **adduct.** In the Diels–Alder reaction, two new σ bonds are formed at the expense of two π bonds of the diene and dienophile. Since σ bonds are usu lly stronger than π bonds, formation of the adduct is usually favored energetically *but most Diels–Alder reactions are reversible.*

We can account for all of the bond changes in a Diels–Alder reaction by using curved arrows in the following way:

Diene Dieno- Adduct
phile

We do not intend to imply a mechanism by the use of these curved arrows; they are used only to keep account of the electrons. (The mechanism of the Diels–Alder reaction is discussed in Special Topic O.)

The simplest example of a Diels–Alder reaction is the one that takes place between 1,3-butadiene and ethene. This reaction, however, takes place much more slowly than the reaction of butadiene with maleic anhydride and must also be carried out under pressure.

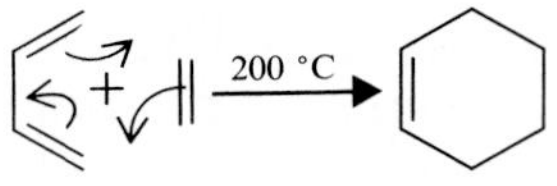

(20%)

Alder originally stated that the Diels–Alder reaction is favored by the presence of electron-withdrawing groups in the dienophile and by electron-releasing groups in the diene. Maleic anhydride, a very potent dienophile, has two carbonyl groups on carbon atoms adjacent to the double bond. Carbonyl groups are electron withdrawing because of the electronegativity of their oxygen atoms and because resonance structures such as the following contribute to the hybrid. The comparative yields of the two examples that we have given (1,3-butadiene + maleic anhydride and 1,3-butadiene + ethene) illustrate the help that electron-withdrawing groups in the dienophile give the Diels–Alder reaction.

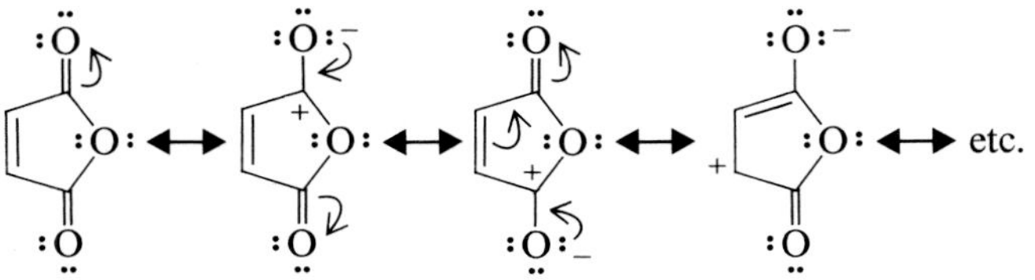

The helpful effect of electron-releasing groups in the diene can also be demonstrated; 2,3-dimethyl-1,3-butadiene, for example, is nearly five times as reactive in Diels–Alder reactions as is 1,3-butadiene. When 2,3-dimethyl-1,3-butadiene reacts with propenal (acrolein) at only 30 °C, the adduct is obtained in quantitative yield.

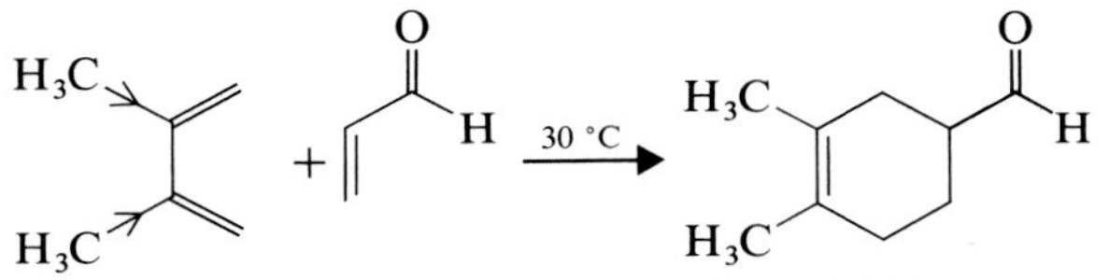

2,3-Dimethyl-1,3-   Propenal   **(100%)**
butadiene

Research (by C. K. Bradsher of Duke University) has shown that the locations of electron-withdrawing and electron-releasing groups in the dienophile and diene can be reversed without reducing the yields of the adducts. Dienes with electron-withdrawing groups have been found to react readily with dienophiles containing electron-releasing groups. Additional facts about the reaction are these.

The Diels–Alder reaction is highly stereospecific:

1. **The reaction is a *syn* addition and the configuration of the dienophile is *retained* in the product.** Two examples that illustrate this aspect of the reaction are shown here.

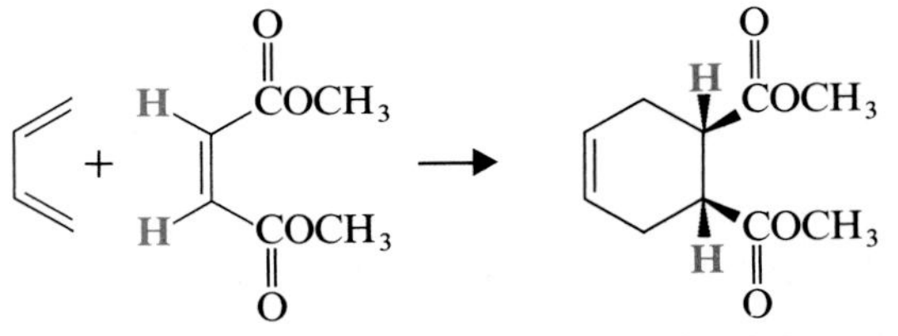

Dimethyl maleate   Dimethyl 4-cyclohexene-*cis*-
(a *cis*-dienophile)   1,2-dicarboxylate

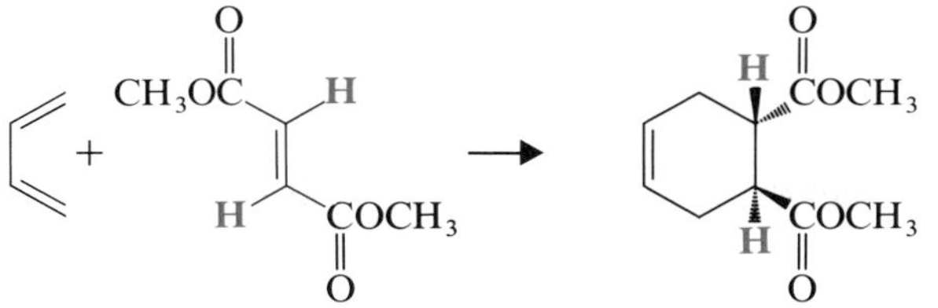

12.10 THE DIELS–ALDER REACTION

Dimethyl fumarate
(a *trans*-dienophile)

**Dimethyl 4-cyclohexene-*trans*-
1,2-dicarboxylate**

In the first example, a dienophile with cis ester groups reacts with 1,3-butadiene to give an adduct with cis ester groups. In the second example just the reverse is true. A *trans* dienophile gives a trans adduct.

2. **The diene, of necessity, must react in the s-cis conformation rather than the s-trans.**

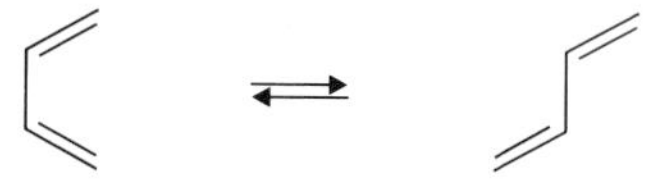

s-cis Conformation   **s-trans Conformation**

Reaction in the s-trans conformation would, if it occurred, produce a six-membered ring with a highly strained trans double bond. This course of the Diels–Alder reaction has never been observed.

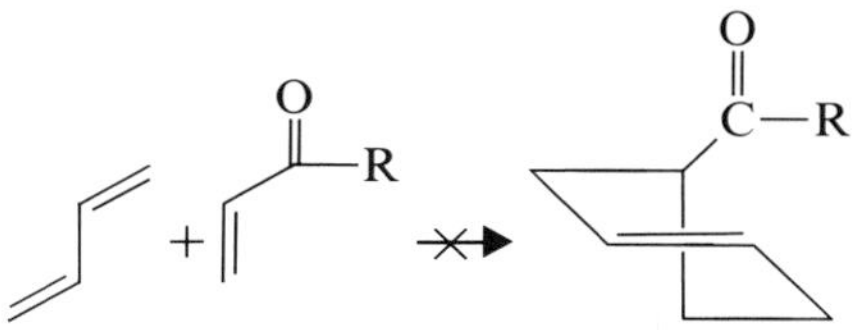

Highly strained

Cyclic dienes in which the double bonds are held in the s-cis configuration are usually highly reactive in the Diels–Alder reaction. Cyclopentadiene, for example, reacts with maleic anhydride at room temperature to give the following adduct in quantitative yield.

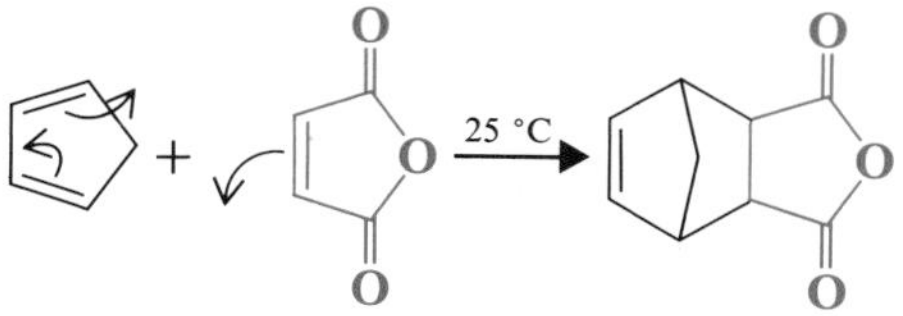

Cyclopentadiene is so reactive that on standing at room temperature it slowly undergoes a Diels–Alder reaction with itself.

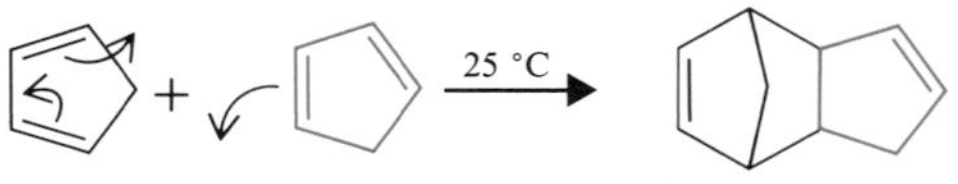

"Dicyclopentadiene"

The reaction is reversible, however. When "dicyclopentadiene" is distilled, it dissociates into two molar equivalents of cyclopentadiene.

The reactions of cyclopentadiene illustrate a third stereochemical characteristic of the Diels–Alder reaction.

3. **The Diels–Alder reaction occurs primarily in an *endo* rather than an *exo* fashion when the reaction is kinetically controlled** (cf. Problem 12.25). Endo and exo are terms used to designate the stereochemistry of bridged rings such as bicyclo[2.2.1]heptane. The point of reference is the longest bridge. A group that is anti to the longest bridge (the two-carbon bridge) is said to be exo; if it is on the same side, it is endo.*

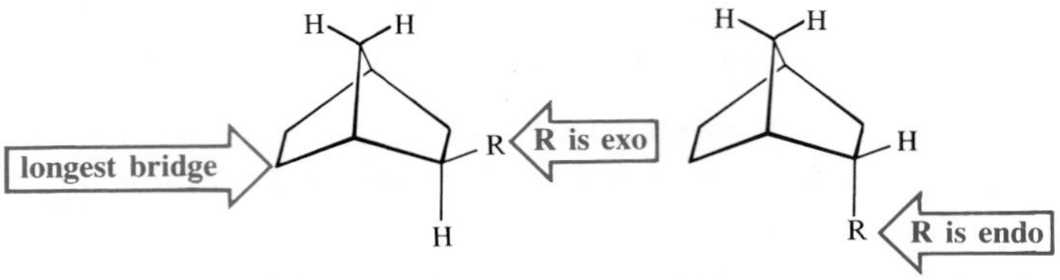

In the Diels–Alder reaction of cyclopentadiene with maleic anhydride the major product is the one in which the anhydride linkage, $-\overset{\|}{\underset{O}{C}}-O-\overset{\|}{\underset{O}{C}}-$, has assumed the endo configuration. See the following illustration. This favored endo stereochemistry seems to arise from favorable interactions between the π electrons of the developing double bond in the diene and the π electrons of unsaturated groups of the dienophile. In this example, the π electrons of the $-\overset{\|}{\underset{O}{C}}-O-\overset{\|}{\underset{O}{C}}-$ linkage of the anhydride interact with the π electrons of the developing double bond in cyclopentadiene.

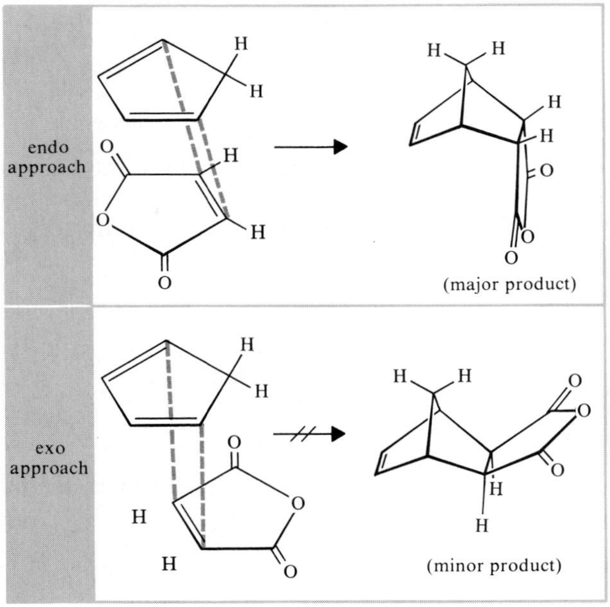

endo approach

(major product)

exo approach

(minor product)

* In general, the exo substituent is always on the side anti to the *longer* bridge of a bicyclic structure (exo, outside; endo, inside). For example,

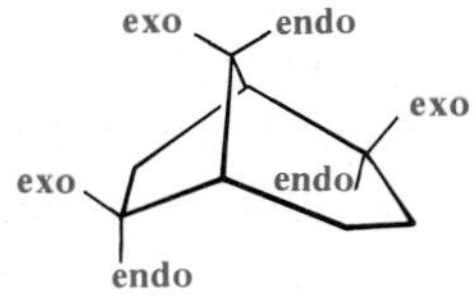

Problem 12.9

The dimerization of cyclopentadiene also occurs in an endo way. (a) Show how this happens. (b) Which π electrons interact? (c) What is the three-dimensional structure of the product?

Problem 12.10

What products would you expect from the following reactions?

(a)

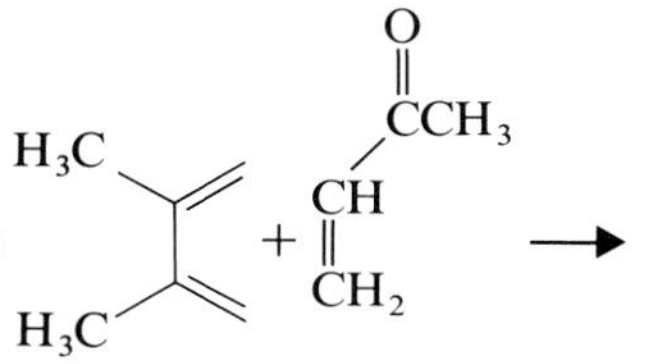

(c)

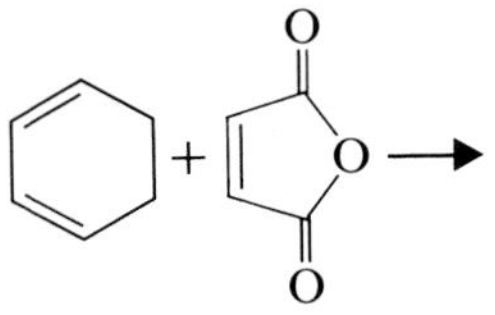

(b)

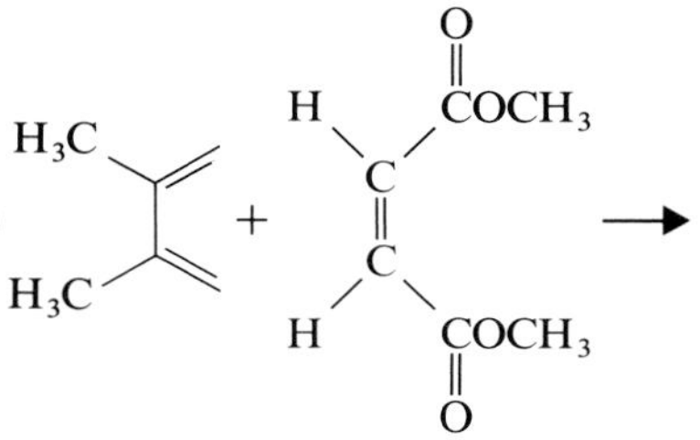

Problem 12.11

Which diene and dienophile would you employ to synthesize the following compound?

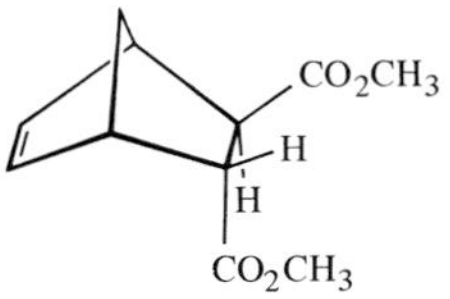

Problem 12.12

Diels–Alder reactions also take place with triple-bonded (acetylenic) dieno-philes. Which diene and which dienophile would you use to prepare:

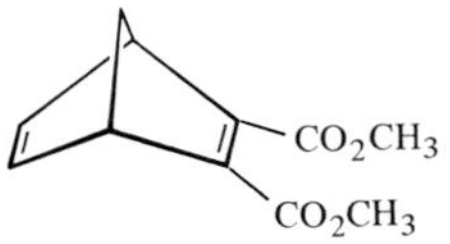

Additional Problems

12.13   Outline a synthesis of 1,3-butadiene starting from

(a) 1,4-Dibromobutane

(b) $HOCH_2(CH_2)_2CH_2OH$

(c) $CH_2{=}CHCH_2CH_2OH$

(d) $CH_2{=}CHCH_2CH_2Cl$

(e) $CH_2{=}CHCHClCH_3$

(f) $CH_2{=}CHCH(OH)CH_3$

(g) $HC{\equiv}CCH{=}CH_2$

12.14   What product would you expect from the following reaction?

$$(CH_3)_2C-C(CH_3)_2 + 2\ KOH \xrightarrow[\text{heat}]{\text{ethanol}}$$
$$\underset{Cl}{\vert}\quad\underset{Cl}{\vert}$$

12.15   What products would you expect from the reaction of 1 mol of 1,3-butadiene and each of the following reagents? (If no reaction would occur, you should indicate that as well.)

(a) One mole of Cl_2 (d) Two moles of H_2, Ni   (g) Hot $KMnO_4$

(b) Two moles of Cl_2 (e) $Ag(NH_3)_2{}^+OH^-$ (h) H^+, H_2O

(c) Two moles of Br_2 (f) One mole of Cl_2 in H_2O

12.16   Show how you might carry out each of the following transformations. (In some transformations several steps may be necessary.)

(a) 1-Butene $\longrightarrow$ 1,3-butadiene

(b) 1-Pentene $\longrightarrow$ 1,3-pentadiene

(c) $CH_3CH_2CH_2CH_2OH \longrightarrow CH_2BrCH\!\!=\!\!CHCH_2Br$

(d) $CH_3CH\!\!=\!\!CHCH_3 \longrightarrow CH_3CH\!\!=\!\!CHCH_2Br$

(f)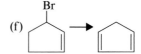

(e)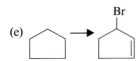

12.17   Conjugated dienes react with free radicals by both 1,2 and 1,4 addition. Account for this fact by using the peroxide-promoted addition of one molar equivalent of HBr to 1,3-buta-diene as an illustration.

12.18   Outline a simple chemical test that would distinguish between the members of each of the following pairs of compounds.

(a) 1,3-Butadiene and 1-butyne

(b) 1,3-Butadiene and butane

(c) Butane and $CH_2\!\!=\!\!CHCH_2CH_2OH$

(d) 1,3-Butadiene and $CH_2\!\!=\!\!CHCH_2CH_2Br$

(e) $CH_2BrCH\!\!=\!\!CHCH_2Br$ and $CH_3CBr\!\!=\!\!CBrCH_3$

12.19   (a) The hydrogen atoms attached to C-3 of 1,4-pentadiene are unusually susceptible to abstraction by radicals. How can you account for this?   (b) Can you also provide an explanation for the fact that the protons attached to C-3 of 1,4-pentadiene are more acidic than the methyl hydrogen atoms of propene?

12.20   When 2-methyl-1,3-butadiene (isoprene) undergoes a 1,4 addition of hydrogen chloride, the major product that is formed is 1-chloro-3-methyl-2-butene. Little or no 1-chloro-2-methyl-2-butene is formed. How can you explain this?

12.21   Which diene and dienophile would you employ in a synthesis of each of the following?

(a)

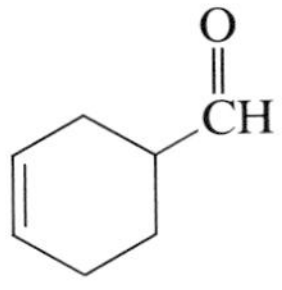

(b)

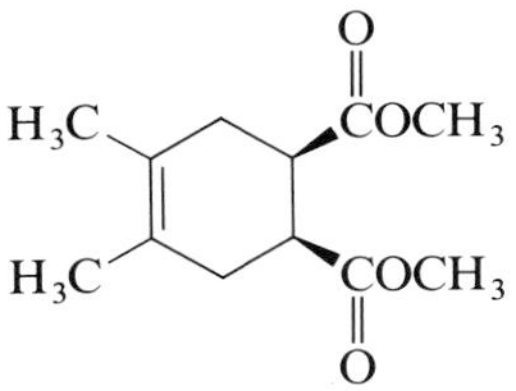

(c)

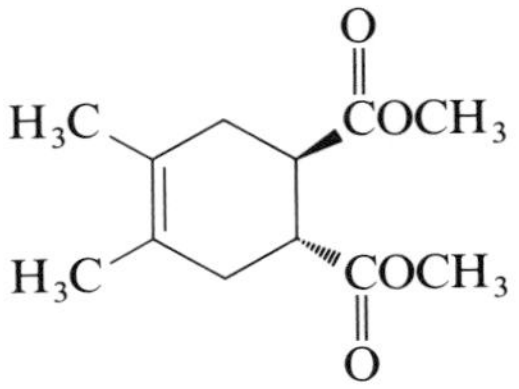

(d)

(e)

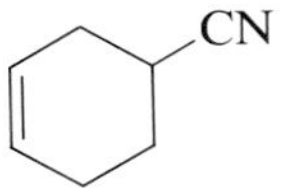

(f)

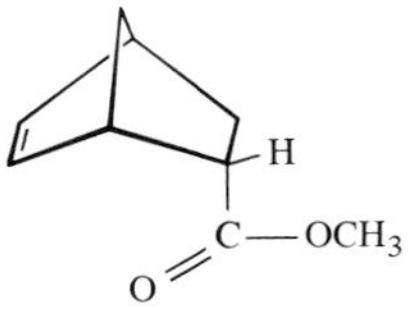

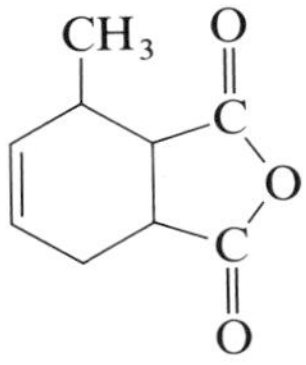

12.22   Account for the fact that neither of the following compounds undergoes a Diels–Alder reaction with maleic anhydride.

$$HC\equiv C-C\equiv CH \quad \text{or} \quad \text{(cyclohexadiene)}=CH_2$$

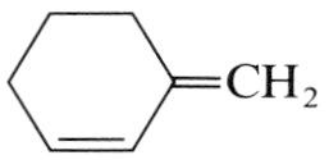

12.23   Acetylenic compounds may be used as dienophiles in the Diels–Alder reaction (cf. Problem 12.12). Write structures for the adducts that you expect from the reaction of 1,3-butadiene with:

(a) $CH_3OCC\equiv CCOCH_3$ (dimethyl acetylenedicarboxylate)

(b) $CF_3C\equiv CCF_3$ (hexafluoro-2-butyne)

12.24   Cyclopentadiene undergoes a Diels–Alder reaction with ethene at 160–180 °C. Write the structure of the product of this reaction.

12.25   When furan and maleimide undergo a Diels–Alder reaction at 25 °C, the major product is the endo adduct **G**. When the reaction is carried out at 90 °C, however, the major product is the exo isomer **H**. The endo adduct isomerizes to the exo adduct when it is heated to 90 °C. Propose an explanation that will account for these results.

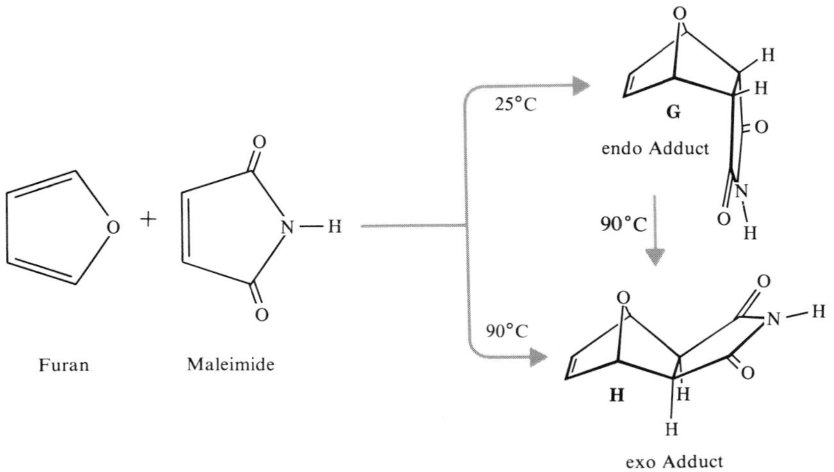

25°C

G

endo Adduct

90°C

Furan   Maleimide

90°C

H

exo Adduct

12.26   Two controversial "hard" insecticides are aldrin and dieldrin (see following diagram). [The Environmental Protection Agency (EPA) halted the use of these insecticides because of possible harmful side effects and because they are not biodegradable.] The commercial synthesis of aldrin begins with hexachlorocyclopentadiene and norbornadiene. Dieldrin is synthesized from aldrin. Show how these syntheses might be carried out.

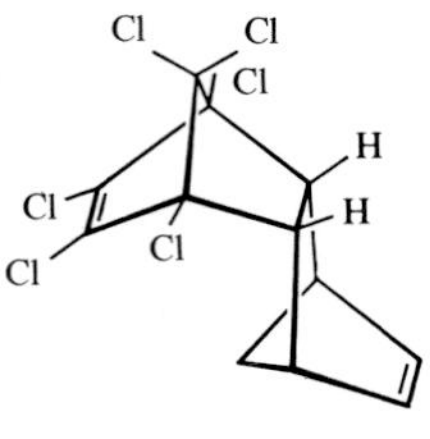

Aldrin 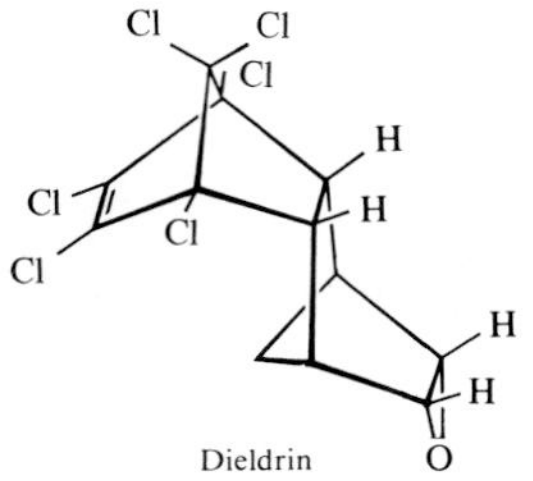   Dieldrin

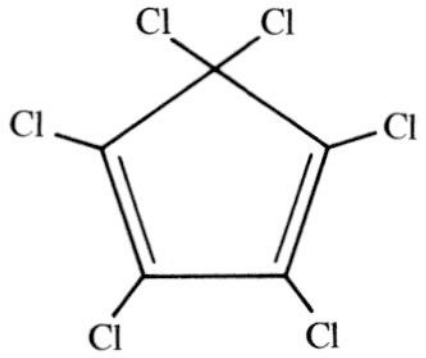

Hexachlorocyclopentadiene 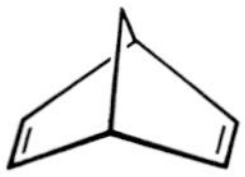   Norbornadiene

12.27   (a) Norbornadiene for the aldrin synthesis (Problem 12.26) can be prepared from cyclopentadiene and acetylene. Show the reaction involved. (b) It can also be prepared by allowing cyclopentadiene to react with vinyl chloride and treating the product with base. Outline this synthesis.

12.28   Two other hard insecticides (cf. Problem 12.26) are chlordan and heptachlor. Their commercial syntheses begin with cyclopentadiene and hexachlorocyclopentadiene. Show how these syntheses might be carried out.

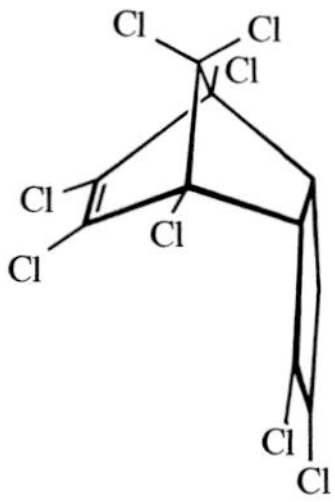

Chlordan 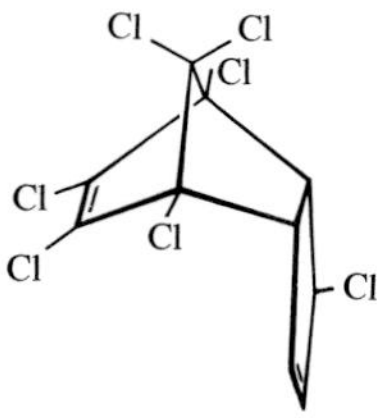   Heptachlor

12.29   Isodrin, an isomer of aldrin, is obtained when cyclopentadiene reacts with the hexachloronorbornadiene, shown here. Propose a structure for isodrin.

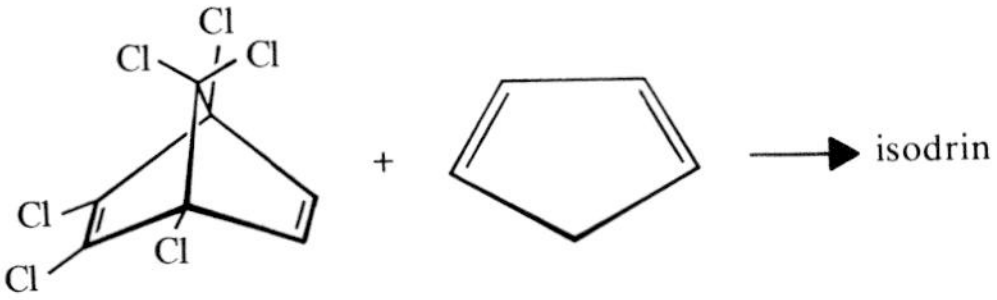

isodrin

12.30   When $CH_3CH{=}CHCH_2OH$ is treated with concentrated HCl, two products are produced, $CH_3CH{=}CHCH_2Cl$ and $CH_3CHClCH{=}CH_2$. Outline a mechanism that will explain this.

ADDITIONAL PROBLEMS

12.31   When a solution of 1,3-butadiene in CH_3OH is treated with chlorine, the products are $ClCH_2CH=CHCH_2OCH_3$ (30%) and $ClCH_2\overset{\underset{\mid}{OCH_3}}{CH}CH=CH_2$ (70%). Write a mechanism that accounts for their formation.

12.32   Dehydrohalogenation of *vic*-dihalides (with the elimination of two molar equivalents of HX) normally leads to an alkyne rather than to a conjugated diene. However, when 1,2-dibromocyclohexane is dehydrohalogenated, 1,3-cyclohexadiene is produced in good yield. What factor accounts for this?

12.33   When 1-pentene reacts with *N*-bromosuccinimide, two products with the formula C_5H_9Br are obtained. What are these products and how are they formed?

12.34   Treating either 1-chloro-3-methyl-2-butene or 3-chloro-3-methyl-1-butene with Ag_2O in water gives (in addition to AgCl) the same mixture of alcohols: $(CH_3)_2C=CHCH_2OH$ (15%) and $(CH_3)_2\overset{\underset{\mid}{OH}}{C}CH=CH_2$ (85%).   (a) Write a mechanism that accounts for the formation of these products.   (b) What might explain the relative proportions of the two alkenes that are formed?

12.35   The heat of hydrogenation of allene is 71.3 kcal mol^{-1} while that of propyne is 69.3 kcal mol^{-1}.   (a) Which compound is more stable?   (b) Treating allene with a strong base causes it to isomerize to propyne. Explain.

12.36   Mixing furan (Problem 12.25) with maleic anhydride in diethyl ether yields a crystalline solid with a melting point of 125 °C. When melting of this compound takes place, however, one can notice that the melt evolves a gas. If the melt is allowed to resolidify, one finds that it no longer melts at 125 °C but instead it melts at 56 °C. Consult an appropriate chemistry handbook and provide an explanation for what is taking place.

First Review Problem Set

1. Provide a reasonable mechanism for the following reactions:

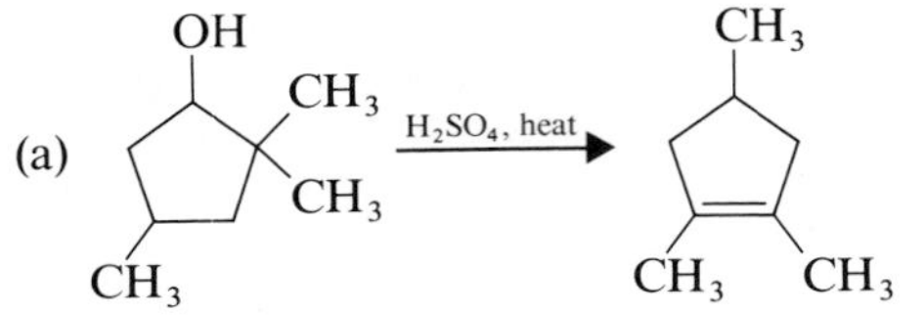

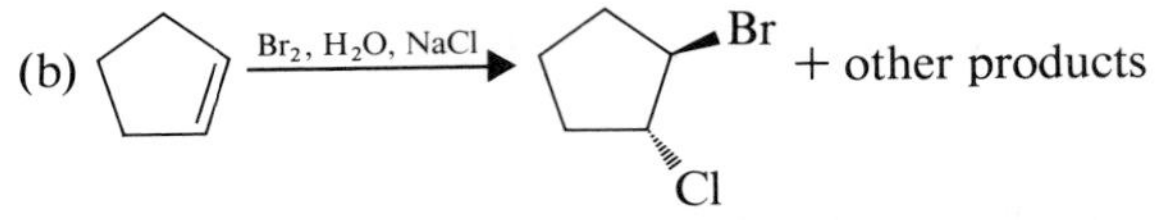

(a)

(b)

Br + other products

(c) What other products would you expect from the reaction given in part (b)?

2. What are compounds **A–C**?

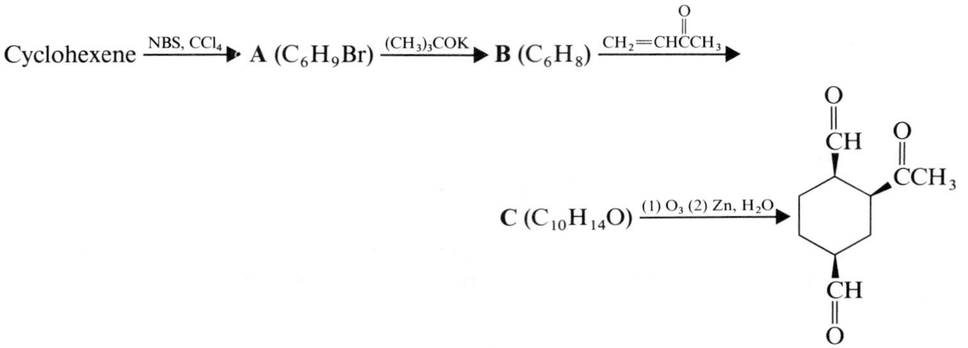

Cyclohexene $\xrightarrow{\text{NBS, CCl}_4}$ **A** (C_6H_9Br) $\xrightarrow{(CH_3)_3COK}$ **B** (C_6H_8) $\xrightarrow{CH_2=CHCCH_3}$

C $(C_{10}H_{14}O)$ $\xrightarrow{(1)\ O_3\ (2)\ Zn,\ H_2O}$

3. Given the following data:

	$CH_2=CH_2$	CH_3CH_2Cl	$CH_2=CHCl$
C—Cl bond length		1.76 Å	1.69 Å
C=C bond length	1.34 Å		1.38 Å
C—C bond length		1.54 Å	
Dipole moment	0	2.05 D	1.44 D

Use resonance theory to explain each of the following: (a) The shorter C—Cl bond length in $CH_2=CHCl$ when compared to that in CH_3CH_2Cl. (b) The longer C=C bond in $CH_2=CHCl$ when compared to that in $CH_2=CH_2$. (c) The greater dipole moment of CH_3CH_2Cl when compared to $CH_2=CHCl$.

4. The following is a synthesis of "muscalure," the sex-attractant pheromone of the common house fly. Give the structure of each intermediate and of muscalure itself.

$CH_3(CH_2)_{11}CH_2Br \xrightarrow{HC\equiv CNa}$ **A** $(C_{15}H_{28})$ $\xrightarrow{NaNH_2}$ **B** $(C_{15}H_{27}Na)$ $\xrightarrow{\text{1-bromooctane}}$

C $(C_{23}H_{44})$ $\xrightarrow{H_2,\ Ni_2B\ (P-2)}$ muscalure $(C_{23}H_{46})$

510

FIRST REVIEW PROBLEM SET

5. Write structures for the diastereomers of 2,3-diphenyl-2-butene and assign each diastereomer its (E) or (Z) designation. Hydrogenation of one of these diastereomers using a palladium catalyst produces a racemic form; similar treatment of the other produces a meso compound. On the basis of these experiments, tell which diastereomer is (E) and which is (Z).

6. A hydrocarbon (A) has the formula C_7H_{10}. On catalytic hydrogenation, A is converted to B (C_7H_{12}). On treatment with cold, dilute, and basic $KMnO_4$, A is converted to C $(C_7H_{12}O_2)$. When heated with $KMnO_4$ in basic solution, followed by acidification, either A or C produces the meso form of 1,3-cyclopentanedicarboxylic acid (see the following structure). Give structural formulas for A–C.

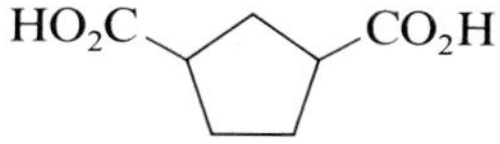

$$HO_2C \diagdown\diagup\diagdown CO_2H$$

1,3-Cyclopentanedicarboxylic acid

7. Starting with propyne, and using any other required reagents, show how you would synthesize each of the following compounds. You need not repeat steps carried out in earlier parts of this problem.

(a) 2-Butyne
(b) cis-2-Butene
(c) trans-2-Butene
(d) 1-Butene
(e) 1,3-Butadiene
(f) 1-Bromobutane

(g) 2-Bromobutane (as a racemic form)
(h) $(2R,3S)$-2,3-Dibromobutane
(i) $(2R,3R)$- and $(2S,3S)$-2,3-Dibromobutane (as a racemic form)
(j) meso-2,3-Butanediol
(k) (Z)-2-Bromo-2-butene

8. Bromination of 2-methylbutane yields predominantly one product with the formula $C_5H_{11}Br$. What is this product? Show how you could use this compound to synthesize each of the following. (You need not repeat steps carried out in earlier parts.)

(a) 2-Methyl-2-butene
(b) 2-Methyl-2-butanol
(c) 3-Methyl-2-butanol
(d) 3-Methyl-1-butanol
(e) 3-Methyl-1-butene
(f) 3-Methyl-1-butyne
(g) 1-Bromo-3-methylbutane
(h) 2-Chloro-3-methylbutane
(i) 2-Chloro-2-methylbutane
(j) 1-Iodo-3-methylbutane

(k) $CH_3\overset{O}{\overset{\|}{C}}CH_3$ and $CH_3\overset{O}{\overset{\|}{C}}H$

(l) $(CH_3)_2CH\overset{O}{\overset{\|}{C}}H$

9. An alkane (A) with the formula C_6H_{14} reacts with chlorine to yield three compounds with the formula $C_6H_{13}Cl$, B, C, and D. Of these only C and D undergo dehydrohalogenation with sodium ethoxide in ethanol to produce an alkene. Moreover, C and D yield the same alkene E (C_6H_{12}). Hydrogenation of E produces A. Treating E with HCl produces a compound (F) that is an isomer of B, C, and D. Treating F with Zn and acetic acid gives a compound (G) that is isomeric with A. Propose structures for A–G.

10. Compound A (C_4H_6) reacts with hydrogen and a platinum catalyst to yield butane. Compound A decolorizes Br_2 in CCl_4 and aqueous $KMnO_4$, but it does not react with

$Ag(NH_3)_2^+$. On treatment with hydrogen and Ni_2B (P-2 catalyst), **A** is converted to **B** (C_4H_8). When **B** is treated with OsO_4 and then with $NaHSO_3$, **B** is converted to C ($C_4H_{10}O_2$). Compound **C** cannot be resolved. Provide structures for **A–C**.

11. Dehalogenation of *meso*-2,3-dibromobutane occurs when it is treated with potassium iodide in ethanol. The product is *trans*-2-butene. Similar dehalogenation of either of the enantiomeric forms of 2,3-dibromobutane produces *cis*-2-butene. Give a mechanistic explanation of these results.

12. Dehydrohalogenation of *meso*-1,2-dibromo-1,2-diphenylethane by the action of sodium ethoxide in ethanol yields (E)-1-bromo-1,2-diphenylethene. Similar dehydrohalogenation of either of the enantiomeric forms of 1,2-dibromo-1,2-diphenylethane yields (Z)-1-bromo-1,2-diphenylethene. Provide an explanation for the results.

13. Give conformational structures for the major product formed when 1-*tert*-butylcyclohexene reacts with each of the following reagents. If the product would be obtained as a racemic form you should so indicate.

(a) Br_2, CCl_4

(b) OsO_4, then aqueous $NaHSO_3$

(c) $C_6H_5CO_3H$, then H_3O^+, H_2O

(d) $THF:BH_3$, then H_2O_2, OH^-

(e) $Hg(OAc)_2$ in $THF–H_2O$, then $NaBH_4$, OH^-

(f) Br_2, H_2O

(g) ICl

(h) O_3, then Zn, H_2O (conformational structure not required)

(i) D_2, Pt

(j) $THF:BD_3$, then CH_3CO_2T

14. Give structures for **A–C**.

$$\underset{\underset{Br}{|}}{\overset{\overset{CH_3}{|}}{CH_3CCH_2CH_2CH_3}} \xrightarrow{EtO^-/EtOH} \textbf{A } (C_6H_{12}) \text{ major product} \xrightarrow{THF:BH_3}$$

$$\textbf{B } (C_6H_{13})_2BH \xrightarrow{H_2O_2,\ OH^-} \textbf{C } (C_6H_{14}O)$$

15. (*R*)-3-Methyl-1-pentene is treated separately with the following reagents, and the products in each case are separated by fractional distillation. Write appropriate formulas for all of the components of each fraction, and tell whether each fraction would be optically active.

(a) Br_2, CCl_4 (d) $THF:BH_3$, then H_2O_2, OH^-

(b) H_2, Pt (e) $Hg(OAc)_2$, $THF–H_2O$, then $NaBH_4$, OH^-

(c) OsO_4, then $NaHSO_3$ (f) Peroxybenzoic acid, then H_3O^+, H_2O

16. Compound **A** ($C_8H_{15}Cl$) exists as a racemic form. Compound **A** does not decolorize either Br_2/CCl_4 or dilute aqueous $KMnO_4$. When **A** is treated with zinc and acetic acid, and the mixture is separated by gas-liquid chromatography, two fractions **B** and **C** are obtained. The components of both fractions have the formula C_8H_{16}. Fraction **B** consists of a racemic form and can be resolved. Fraction **C** cannot be resolved. Treating **A** with sodium ethoxide in ethanol converts **A** into **D** (C_8H_{14}). Hydrogenation of **D** using a platinum catalyst yields **C**. Ozonolysis of **D** followed by treatment with zinc and water yields.

FIRST REVIEW PROBLEM SET

$$CH_3\overset{\overset{\displaystyle O}{\|}}{C}CH_2CH_2CH_2CH_2\overset{\overset{\displaystyle O}{\|}}{C}CH_3$$

Propose structures for **A, B, C,** and **D** including, where appropriate, their stereochemistry.

17. There are nine stereoisomers of 1,2,3,4,5,6-hexachlorocyclohexane. Seven of these isomers are meso compounds, and two are a pair of enantiomers. (a) Write structures for all of these stereoisomers, labeling meso forms and the pair of enantiomers. (b) One of these stereoisomers undergoes E2 reactions much more slowly than any of the others. Which isomer is this and why does it react so slowly in an E2 reaction?

18. In addition to more highly fluorinated products, fluorination of 2-methylbutane yields a mixture of compounds with the formula $C_5H_{11}F$. (a) How many different isomers with the formula $C_5H_{11}F$ would you expect to be produced, taking stereochemistry into account? (b) If the mixture of $C_5H_{11}F$ isomers were subjected to fractional distillation, how many fractions would you expect to obtain? (c) Which fractions would be optically inactive? (d) Which would you be able to resolve into enantiomers?

19. Fluorination of (R)-2-fluorobutane yields a mixture of isomers with the formula $C_4H_8F_2$. (a) How many different isomers would you expect to be produced? Write their structures. (b) If the mixture of $C_4H_8F_2$ isomers were subjected to fractional distillation, how many fractions would you expect to obtain? (c) Which of these fractions would be optically active?

20. There are two optically inactive (and nonresolvable) forms of 1,3-di-*sec*-butylcyclohexane. Write their structures.

21. When the following deuterium-labeled isomer undergoes elimination, the reaction yields *trans*-2-butene and *cis*-2-butene-2-*d* (as well as some 1-butene-*3*-*d*). The reaction does not yield *cis*-2-butene or *trans*-2-butene-2-*d*.

trans-2-Butene   *cis*-2-Butene-2-*d*

(+ $CH_3CHDCH = CH_2$)

but no

cis-2-Butene   *trans*-2-Butene-2-*d*

How can you explain these results?

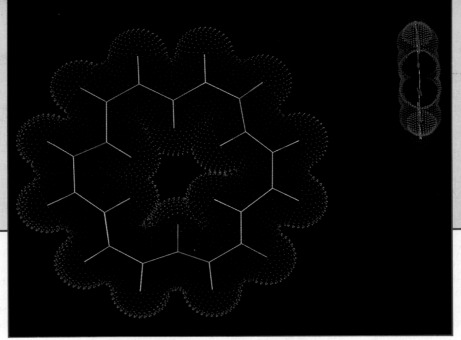

[18]Annulene (see Section 13.7A).

CHAPTER

13

AROMATIC COMPOUNDS

13.1 INTRODUCTION

The study of the class of compounds that organic chemists call aromatic compounds (Section 2.7) began with the discovery in 1825 of a new hydrocarbon by the English chemist Michael Faraday (Royal Institution). Faraday called this new hydrocarbon "bicarburet of hydrogen;" we now call it benzene. Faraday isolated benzene from a compressed illuminating gas that had been made by pyrolyzing whale oil.

In 1834 the German chemist Eilhardt Mitscherlich (University of Berlin) synthesized benzene by heating benzoic acid with calcium oxide. Using vapor density measurements Mitscherlich further showed that benzene has the molecular formula C_6H_6.

$$C_6H_5CO_2H + CaO \xrightarrow{\text{heat}} C_6H_6 + CaCO_3$$
Benzoic acid **Benzene**

The molecular formula itself was surprising. Benzene has *only as many hydrogen atoms as it has carbon atoms.* Most compounds that were known then had a far greater proportion of hydrogen atoms, usually twice as many. Benzene with the formula of C_6H_6 (or C_nH_{2n-6}) should be a highly unsaturated compound, because it has an index of hydrogen deficiency equal to four. Within a very short time chemists

514

began to find that benzene had unusual properties, and eventually they began to recognize that benzene was a member of a new class of organic compounds with unusual and interesting properties. As we shall see in Section 13.3 benzene does not show at all the behavior expected of a highly unsaturated compound.

During the latter part of the nineteenth century the Kekulé–Couper–Butlerov theory of valence was systematically applied to all known organic compounds. One result of this effort was the placing of organic compounds in either of two broad categories; compounds were classified as being either **aliphatic** or **aromatic.** To be classified as aliphatic meant then that the chemical behavior of a compound was "fatlike." (Now it means that the compound reacts like an alkane, an alkene, an alkyne, or one of their derivatives.) To be classified as aromatic meant then that the compound had a low hydrogen/carbon ratio and that it was "fragrant." Most of the early aromatic compounds were obtained from balsams, resins, or essential oils. Included among these were benzaldehyde (from oil of bitter almonds), benzoic acid and benzyl alcohol (from gum benzoin), and toluene (from tolu balsam).

Kekulé was the first to recognize that these early aromatic compounds all contain a six-carbon unit and that they retain this six-carbon unit through most chemical transformations and degradations. Benzene was eventually recognized as being the parent compound of this new series.

Since this new group of compounds proved to be distinctive in ways that are far more important than their odors, the term *aromatic* began to take on a purely chemical connotation. We shall see in this chapter that the meaning of aromatic has evolved as chemists have learned more about the reactions and properties of aromatic compounds.

13.2 NOMENCLATURE OF BENZENE DERIVATIVES

Two systems are used in naming monosubstituted benzenes. In certain compounds, *benzene* is the parent name and the substituent is simply indicated by a prefix. We have, for example,

F	Cl	Br	NO$_2$
Fluorobenzene	Chlorobenzene	Bromobenzene	Nitrobenzene

For other compounds, the substituent and the benzene ring taken together may form a new parent name. Methylbenzene is usually called *toluene,* hydroxybenzene is almost always called *phenol,* and aminobenzene is almost always called *aniline.* These and other examples are indicated here.

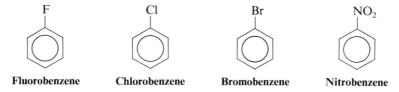

CH$_3$:Ö—H H / :N—H

Toluene   Phenol   Aniline

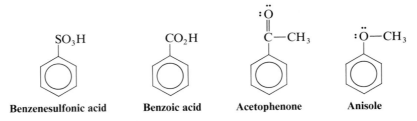

Benzenesulfonic acid   Benzoic acid   Acetophenone   Anisole

When two substituents are present, their relative positions are indicated by the prefixes **ortho, meta,** and **para** (abbreviated **o-, m-,** and **p-**) or by the use of numbers.*
For the dibromobenzenes we have

1,2-Dibromobenzene   **1,3-Dibromobenzene**   **1,4-Dibromobenzene**
(*o*-dibromobenzene)   (*m*-dibromobenzene)   (*p*-dibromobenzene)
ortho   *meta*   *para*

and for the nitrobenzoic acids:

2-Nitrobenzoic acid   **3-Nitrobenzoic acid**   **4-Nitrobenzoic acid**
(*o*-nitrobenzoic acid)   (*m*-nitrobenzoic acid)   (*p*-nitrobenzoic acid)

The dimethylbenzenes are called *xylenes.*

1,2-Dimethylbenzene   **1,3-Dimethylbenzene**   **1,4-Dimethylbenzene**
(*o*-xylene)   (*m*-xylene)   (*p*-xylene)

If more than two groups are present on the benzene ring, their positions must be indicated by the use of *numbers.* As examples, consider the following two compounds.

---

*Numbers can be used for two or more substituents, but ortho, meta, and para must never be used for more than two.

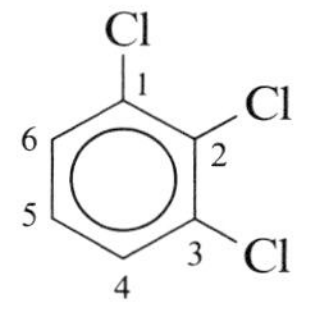

13.2 NOMENCLATURE OF BENZENE DERIVATIVES

1,2,3-Trichlorobenzene

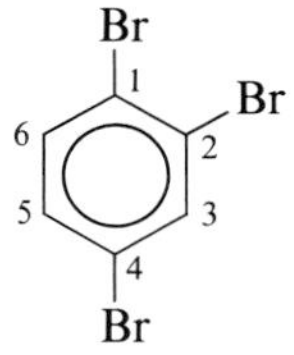

1,2,4-Tribromobenzene
(*not* 1,3,4-tribromobenzene)

We notice, too, that the benzene ring is numbered so as to give *the lowest possible numbers to the substituents.*

When more than two substituents are present and the substituents are different, they are listed in alphabetical order.

When a substituent is one that when taken together with the benzene ring gives a new base name, that substituent is assumed to be in position 1 and the new parent name is used:

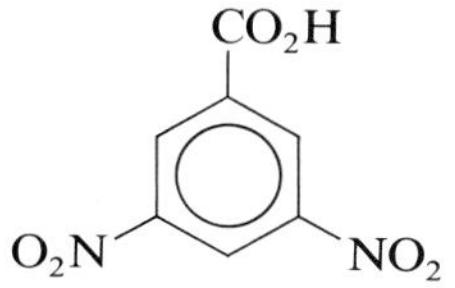

3,5-Dinitrobenzoic acid 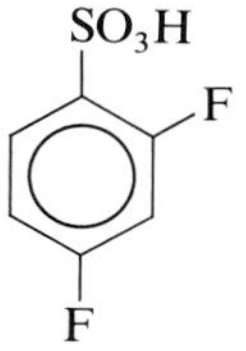   **2,4-Difluorobenzenesulfonic acid**

When the C_6H_5— group is named as a substituent, it is called a **phenyl** group. A hydrocarbon composed of one saturated chain and one benzene ring is usually named as a derivative of the larger structural unit. However, if the chain is unsaturated, the compound may be named as a derivative of that chain, regardless of ring size. The following are examples:

—$CH_2CH_2CH_2CH_3$ CH_3—$\overset{\displaystyle |}{C}$=$CH$—$CH_3$

Butylbenzene 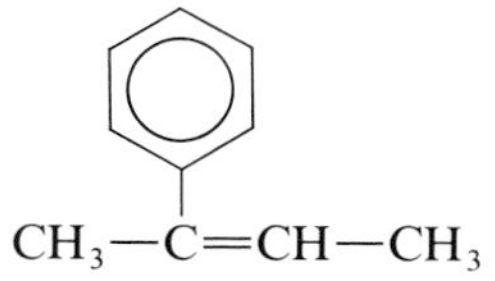   **2-Phenyl-2-butene**

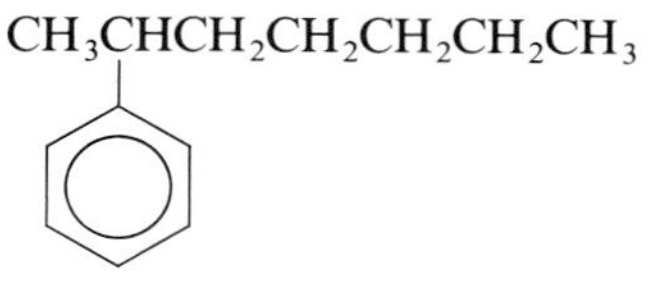

$CH_3CHCH_2CH_2CH_2CH_2CH_3$

2-Phenylheptane

The phenyl group is often abbreviated as C_6H_5—, Ph—, or ϕ—.
The name **benzyl** is an alternative name for the phenylmethyl group:

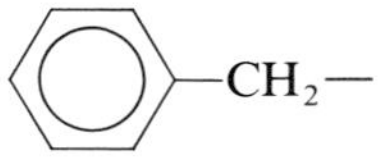

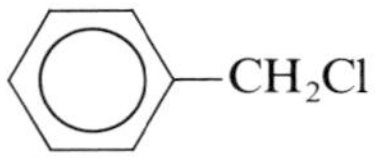

—CH_2—   —CH_2Cl

The benzyl group   **Benzyl chloride**
(the phenylmethyl   **(phenylmethyl chloride)**
group)

13.3 REACTIONS OF BENZENE

In the mid-nineteenth century, benzene presented chemists with a real puzzle. They knew from its formula (Section 13.1) that benzene was highly unsaturated, and they expected it to react accordingly. They expected it to react like an alkene by decolorizing bromine in carbon tetrachloride by *adding bromine.* They expected that it would decolorize aqueous potassium permanganate by being *oxidized,* that it would *add hydrogen* rapidly in the presence of a metal catalyst, and that it would *add water* in the presence of strong acids.

Benzene does none of these. When benzene is treated with bromine in carbon tetrachloride in the dark or with aqueous potassium permanganate or with dilute acids, none of the expected reactions occurs. Benzene does add hydrogen in the presence of finely divided nickel, but only at high temperatures and under high pressures.

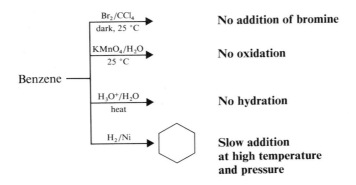

Benzene *does* react with bromine but only in the presence of a Lewis-acid catalyst such as ferric bromide. Most surprisingly, however, it reacts not by addition but by *substitution.*

Substitution

$$C_6H_6 + Br_2 \xrightarrow{FeBr_3} C_6H_5Br + HBr \qquad \text{Observed}$$

Addition

$$C_6H_6 + Br_2 \not\rightarrow C_6H_6Br_2 + C_6H_6Br_4 + C_6H_6Br_6 \qquad \text{Not observed}$$

When benzene reacts with bromine *only one monobromobenzene* is formed. That is, only one compound with the formula C_6H_5Br is found among the products. Similarly, when benzene is chlorinated *only one monochlorobenzene* results.

Two possible explanations can be given for these observations. The first is that only one of the six hydrogen atoms in benzene is reactive toward these reagents. The second is that all six hydrogen atoms in benzene are equivalent, and replacing any one of them with a substituent results in the same product. As we shall see, the second explanation is correct.

Problem 13.1 ─────────────────────────────────

The following are several compounds that have the formula C_6H_6. (a) For which of these compounds, if any, would a substitution of bromine for hydrogen yield only one *mono*bromo product? (b) Which of these compounds would you expect to react with bromine by substitution alone?

$$H—C{\equiv}C—CH_2CH_2—C{\equiv}C—H$$
(a)

$$H—C{\equiv}C—CH_2—C{\equiv}C—CH_3$$
(d)

$$CH_2{=}CH—CH{=}CH—C{\equiv}CH$$
(b)

$$CH_2{=}CH—C{\equiv}C—CH{=}CH_2$$
(e)

$$CH_3CH_2—C{\equiv}C—C{\equiv}C—H$$
(c)

13.4 THE KEKULÉ STRUCTURE FOR BENZENE

In 1865, August Kekulé, the originator of the structural theory (Section 1.3), proposed the first definite structure for benzene,* a structure that is still used today (although as we shall soon see, we give it a meaning different from the meaning Kekulé gave it). Kekulé suggested that the carbon atoms of benzene are in a ring, that they are bonded to each other by alternating single and double bonds, and that one hydrogen atom is attached to each carbon atom. This structure satisfied the requirements of the structural theory that carbon atoms form four bonds and that all the hydrogen atoms of benzene are equivalent.

The Kekulé formula for benzene

A problem soon arose with the Kekulé structure, however. The Kekulé structure predicts that there should be two different 1,2-dibromobenzenes. In one of these hypothetical compounds (below), the carbon atoms that bear the bromines are separated by a single bond, and in the other they are separated by a double bond. *Only one 1,2-dibromobenzene, however, has ever been found.*

In order to accommodate this objection, Kekulé proposed that the two forms of benzene (and of benzene derivatives) are in a state of equilibrium, and that this equilibrium is so rapidly established that it prevents isolation of the separate compounds.

---

* In 1861 the Austrian chemist Johann Josef Loschmidt represented the benzene ring with a circle, but made no attempt to indicate how the carbon atoms were actually arranged in the ring.

Thus, the two 1,2-dibromobenzenes would also be rapidly equilibrated, and this would explain why chemists had not been able to isolate the two forms.

We now know that this proposal was incorrect and that *no such equilibrium exists*. Nonetheless, the Kekulé formulation of benzene's structure was an important step forward and, for very practical reasons, it is still used today. We understand its meaning differently, however.

The tendency of benzene to react by substitution rather than addition gave rise to another concept of aromaticity. For a compound to be called aromatic meant, experimentally, that it gave substitution reactions rather than addition reactions even though it was highly unsaturated.

Before 1900, chemists assumed that the ring of alternating single and double bonds was the structural feature that gave rise to the aromatic properties. Since benzene and benzene derivatives (i.e., compounds with six-membered rings) were the only aromatic compounds known, chemists naturally sought other examples. The compound cyclooctatetraene seemed to be a likely candidate.

Cyclooctatetraene

In 1911, Richard Willstätter succeeded in synthesizing cyclooctatetraene. Willstätter found, however, that it is not at all like benzene. Cyclooctatetraene reacts with bromine by addition, it adds hydrogen readily, it decolorizes solutions of potassium permanganate, and thus it is clearly *not aromatic*. While these findings must have been a keen disappointment to Willstätter, they were very significant for what they did not prove. Chemists, as a result, had to look deeper to discover the origin of benzene's aromaticity.

13.5 THE STABILITY OF BENZENE

We have seen that benzene shows unusual behavior by undergoing substitution reactions when, on the basis of its Kekulé structure, we should expect it to undergo addition. Benzene is unusual in another sense: It is *more stable* than the Kekulé structure suggests. To see how, consider the following thermochemical results.

Cyclohexene, a six-membered ring containing one double bond, can be hydrogenated easily to cyclohexane. When the $\Delta H°$ for this reaction is measured it is found to be -28.6 kcal mol^{-1}, very much like that of any similarly substituted alkene.

13.5 THE STABILITY OF BENZENE

Cyclohexene $\quad + H_2 \xrightarrow{Pt}$ Cyclohexane $\qquad \Delta H° = -28.6 \text{ kcal mol}^{-1}$

We would expect that hydrogenation of 1,3-cyclohexadiene would liberate roughly twice as much heat and thus have a $\Delta H°$ equal to about $-57.2 \text{ kcal mol}^{-1}$. When this experiment is done, the result is a $\Delta H° = -55.4 \text{ kcal mol}^{-1}$. This result is quite close to what we calculated, and the difference can be explained by taking into account the fact that compounds containing conjugated double bonds are usually somewhat more stable than those that contain isolated double bonds (Section 12.8).

1,3-Cyclohexadiene $\quad + 2H_2 \xrightarrow{Pt}$ Cyclohexane

Calculated
$\Delta H° = (2 \times -28.6) = -57.2 \text{ kcal mol}^{-1}$
Observed
$\Delta H° = -55.4 \text{ kcal mol}^{-1}$

If we extend this kind of thinking, and if benzene is simply 1,3,5-cyclohexatriene, we would predict that benzene would liberate approximately 85.8 kcal mol^{-1} (3×-28.6) when it is hydrogenated. When the experiment is actually done the result is surprisingly different. The reaction is exothermic, but only by 49.8 kcal mol^{-1}.

Benzene $\quad + 3H_2 \xrightarrow{Pt}$ Cyclohexane

Calculated
$\Delta H° = (3 \times -28.6) = -85.8 \text{ kcal mol}^{-1}$
Observed $\qquad \Delta H° = -49.8 \text{ kcal mol}^{-1}$

Difference $\qquad = \quad 36.0 \text{ kcal mol}^{-1}$

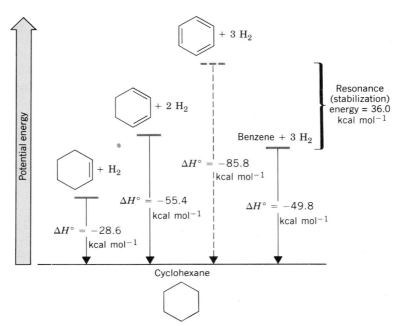

FIGURE 13.1 Relative stabilities of cyclohexene, 1,3-cyclohexadiene, 1,3,5-cyclohexatriene (hypothetically), and benzene.

When these results are represented as in Fig. 13.1, it becomes clear that benzene is much more stable than we calculated it to be. Indeed, it is more stable than the hypothetical 1,3,5-cyclohexatriene by 36 kcal mol^{-1}. This difference between the amount of heat actually released and that calculated on the basis of the Kekulé structure is now called the **resonance energy** of the compound.

13.6 MODERN THEORIES OF THE STRUCTURE OF BENZENE

It was not until the development of quantum mechanics in the 1920s that the unusual behavior and stability of benzene began to be understood. Quantum mechanics, as we have seen, produced two ways of viewing bonds in molecules: resonance theory and molecular orbital theory. We now look at both of these as they apply to benzene.

13.6A THE RESONANCE EXPLANATION OF THE STRUCTURE OF BENZENE

A basic postulate of resonance theory (Sections 1.8 and 12.5) is that whenever two or more Lewis structures can be written for a molecule *differing only in the positions of the electrons,* none of the structures will be in complete accord with the compound's chemical and physical properties. If we recognize this, we can now understand the true nature of the two Kekulé structures (**I** and **II**) for benzene. The two Kekulé structures differ only in the positions of the electrons. Structures **I** and **II**, then, do not represent two separate molecules in equilibrium as Kekulé had proposed. Instead, they are the closest we can get to a structure for benzene within the limitations of its molecular formula, the classical rules of valence, and the fact that the six hydrogen atoms are chemically equivalent. The problem with the Kekulé structures is that they are Lewis structures, and Lewis structures portray electrons in localized distributions. (With benzene, as we shall see, the electrons are delocalized.) Resonance theory, fortunately, does not stop with telling us when to expect this kind of trouble; it also gives us a way out. Resonance theory tells us to use structures **I** and **II** as resonance contributors to a picture of the real molecule of benzene. As such, **I** and **II** should be connected with a double-headed arrow and not with two separate ones (because we must reserve the symbol of two separate arrows for chemical equilibria). Resonance contributors, we emphasize again, are not in equilibrium. They are not structures of real molecules. They are the closest we can get if we are bound by simple rules of valence, but they are very useful in helping us visualize the actual molecule as a hybrid.

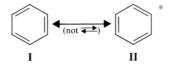

I   II

Look at the structures carefully. All of the single bonds in structure **I** are double bonds in structure **II**. If we blend **I** and **II**, that is, if we fashion a hybrid of them, then the carbon–carbon bonds in benzene are neither single bonds nor double bonds. Rather, they have a bond order between that of a single bond and that of a double bond. This is exactly what we find experimentally. Spectroscopic measurements show that molecules of benzene are planar and that all of its carbon–carbon bonds are of equal length. Moreover, the carbon–carbon bond lengths in benzene (Fig. 13.2) are 1.39 Å, a value in between that for a carbon–carbon single bond between

sp^2-hybridized atoms (1.47 Å) (cf. Table 12.1) and that for a carbon–carbon double bond (1.33 Å).

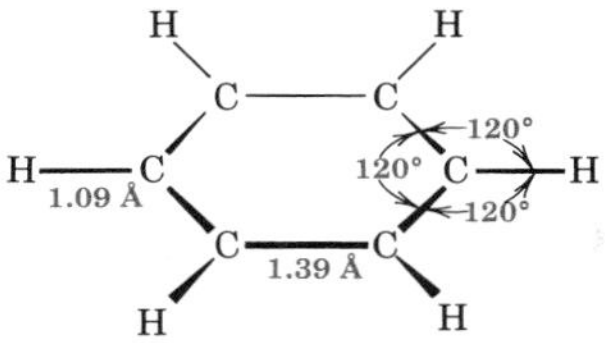

FIGURE 13.2 Bond lengths and angles in benzene. (Only the σ-bonds are shown.)

The hybrid structure is represented by inscribing a circle in the hexagon, and it is this new formula (**III**) that is most often used for benzene today. There are times, however, when an accounting of the electrons must be made, and for these purposes we may use one or the other of the Kekulé structures. We do this simply because the electron count in a Kekulé structure is obvious, while the number of electrons represented by a circle or portion of a circle is ambiguous. With benzene the circle represents the six electrons that are delocalized about the six carbon atoms of the benzene ring. With other systems, however, a circle in a ring may represent numbers of delocalized electrons other than six.

III

Problem 13.2 ———————————————————————————————

If benzene were 1,3,5-cyclohexatriene, the carbon–carbon bonds would be alternately long and short as indicated in the following structures. However, to consider the structures here as resonance contributors (or to connect them by a double-headed arrow) violates a basic principle of resonance theory. Explain.

Resonance theory (Section 12.5) also tells us that whenever equivalent resonance structures can be drawn for a molecule, the molecule (or hybrid) is much more stable than any of the resonance structures could be individually if they could exist. In this way resonance theory accounts for the much greater stability of benzene when compared to the hypothetical 1,3,5-cyclohexatriene. For this reason the extra stability associated with benzene is called its *resonance energy.*

13.6B THE MOLECULAR ORBITAL EXPLANATION OF THE STRUCTURE OF BENZENE

The fact that the bond angles of the carbon atoms in the benzene ring are 120° strongly suggests that the carbon atoms are sp^2 *hybridized.* If we accept this suggestion and construct a planar six-membered ring from sp^2 carbon atoms as shown in Fig. 13.3, another picture of benzene begins to emerge. Because the carbon–carbon bond lengths are all 1.39 Å, the p orbitals are close enough to overlap effectively. The p orbitals overlap equally all around the ring.

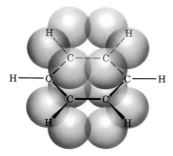

FIGURE 13.3 Overlapping p orbitals in benzene.

According to molecular orbital theory, the six overlapping p orbitals combine to form a set of six π molecular orbitals. Molecular orbital theory also allows us to calculate the relative energies of the π molecular orbitals. These calculations are beyond the scope of our discussion, but the energy levels are shown in Fig. 13.4.

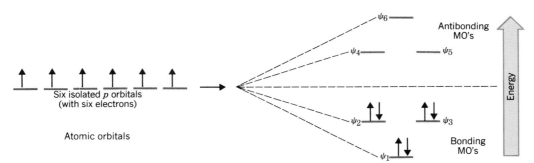

FIGURE 13.4 How six p atomic orbitals (one from each carbon of the benzene ring) combine to form six π molecular orbitals. Three of the molecular orbitals have energies lower than that of an isolated p orbital; these are the bonding molecular orbitals. Three of the molecular orbitals have energies higher than that of an isolated p orbital; these are the antibonding molecular orbitals. Orbitals ψ_2 and ψ_3 have the same energy and are said to be degenerate; the same is true of orbitals ψ_4 and ψ_5.

A molecular orbital, as we have seen, can accommodate two electrons if their spins are opposed. Thus, the electronic structure of the ground state of benzene is obtained by adding the six electrons to the π molecular orbitals starting with those of lowest energy, as shown in Fig. 13.4. Notice that in benzene, all of the bonding orbitals are filled, all of the electrons have their spins paired, and there are no electrons in antibonding orbitals. Benzene is, thus, said to have a *closed bonding shell* of delocalized π electrons. This closed bonding shell accounts, in part, for the stability of benzene. (The shapes of the molecular orbitals are given in Fig. 13.5.)

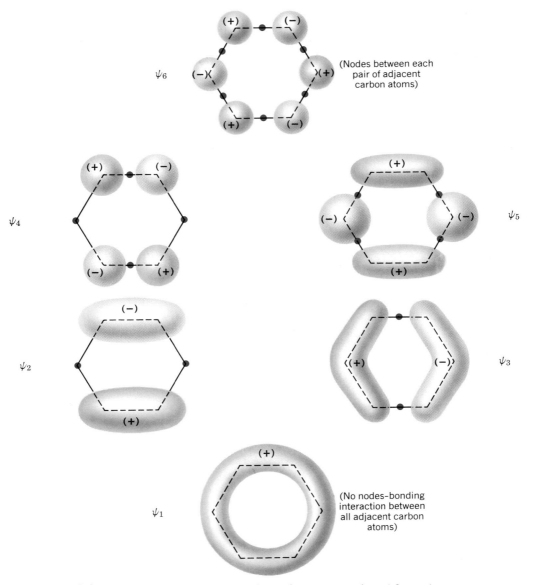

FIGURE 13.5 Shapes of the π molecular orbitals of benzene as viewed from above.

13.7 HÜCKEL'S RULE: THE $(4n + 2)$ π ELECTRON RULE

In 1931 the German physicist Erich Hückel carried out a series of mathematical calculations based on the kind of theory that we have just described. Hückel concerned himself with compounds containing **planar monocyclic rings in which each atom has a p orbital** as in benzene. His calculations show that planar monocyclic rings containing $(4n + 2)$ π electrons where $n = 1, 2, 3, \ldots$, and so on (i. e., rings containing 2, 6, 10, 14, . . . , etc. π electrons), have closed shells of delocalized electrons like benzene, and should have substantial resonance energies. In other words **planar monocyclic rings with 2, 6, 10, 14, . . . , delocalized electrons should be aromatic.**

Although Hückel's calculations are beyond our scope, we can get a picture of the relative energies of the π molecular orbitals of conjugated monocyclic systems in a relatively easy way. *We simply inscribe in a circle a regular polygon corresponding to the ring of the compound being considered so that one corner of the polygon is at the bottom.* **The points where the corners of the polygon touch the circle correspond to the energy levels of the π molecular orbitals of the system.** With benzene, for example, this method (Fig. 13.6) furnishes the same energy levels that we saw earlier in Fig. 13.4, energy levels that were based on quantum mechanical calculations.

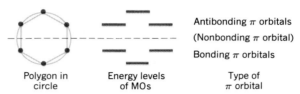

Antibonding π orbitals

(Nonbonding π orbital)

Bonding π orbitals

Polygon in circle   Energy levels of MOs   Type of π orbital

FIGURE 13.6 The polygon-and-circle method for deriving the relative energies of the π molecular orbitals of benzene. A horizontal line halfway up the circle divides the bonding orbitals from the antibonding orbitals. If an orbital falls on this line, it is a nonbonding orbital.

We can now understand why cyclooctatetraene is not aromatic. Cyclooctatetraene has a total of 8 π electrons. Eight is not a Hückel number; it is a *4n number*, not a *4n + 2 number*. Using the polygon-and-circle method (Fig. 13.7) we find that cyclooctatetraene, if it were planar, *would not* have a closed shell of π electrons like benzene; it would have an unpaired electron in each of two nonbonding orbitals. Molecules with unpaired electrons (radicals) are *not* unusually stable; they are typically highly reactive and unstable. A planar form of cyclooctatetraene, therefore, should not be at all like benzene and should not be aromatic.

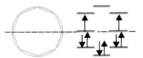

FIGURE 13.7 The π molecular orbitals that cyclooctatetraene would have if it were planar. Notice that, unlike benzene, this molecule is predicted to have two nonbonding orbitals and since it has eight π electrons it would have an unpaired electron in each of the two nonbonding orbital. Such a system would not be expected to be aromatic.

Because cyclooctatetraene does not gain stability by becoming planar, it occurs as the tub-shaped molecule shown below. (In Section 13.7C we shall see that cyclooctatetraene would actually lose stability by becoming planar.)

The bonds of cyclooctatetraene are known to be alternately long and short; X-ray studies indicate that they are 1.48 and 1.34 Å, respectively.

13.7A THE ANNULENES

The name annulene has been proposed as a general name for monocyclic compounds that can be represented by structures having alternating single and double bonds. The ring size of an annulene is indicated by a number in brackets. Thus, benzene is [6]annulene and cyclooctatetraene is [8]annulene.* Hückel's rule predicts that annulenes will be aromatic, provided their molecules have $(4n + 2)$ π electrons and have a planar carbon skeleton.

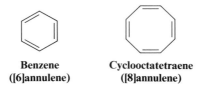

Benzene
([6]annulene)

Cyclooctatetraene
([8]annulene)

Before 1960 the only annulenes that were available to test Hückel's predictions were benzene and cyclooctatetraene. During the 1960s, and largely as a result of research by Franz Sondheimer, a number of large-ring annulenes were synthesized, and the predictions of Hückel's rule were verified.

Consider the [14], [16], [20], [22], and [24]annulenes as examples. Of these, *as Hückel's rule predicts,* the [14], [18], and [22]annulenes ($4n + 2$ when $n = 3, 4, 5,$ respectively) have been found to be aromatic. The [16]annulene and the [24]annulene are not aromatic. They are $4n$ compounds, not $4n + 2$ compounds.

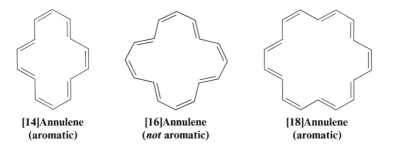

[14]Annulene
(aromatic)

[16]Annulene
(*not* aromatic)

[18]Annulene
(aromatic)

Examples of [10] and [12]annulenes have also been synthesized and none is aromatic. We would not expect [12]annulenes to be aromatic since they have 12 π electrons and, thus, do not obey Hückel's rule. The following [10]annulenes would be expected to be aromatic on the basis of electron count, but their rings are not planar.

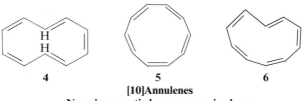

H
H

4

5

6

[10]Annulenes
None is aromatic because none is planar

*These names are seldom used for benzene and cyclooctatetraene. They are often used, however, for conjugated rings of 10 or more carbon atoms.

The [10]annulene (**4**) has two trans double bonds. Its bond angles are approximately 120°; therefore, it has no appreciable angle strain. The carbon atoms of its ring, however, are prevented from becoming coplanar because the two hydrogen atoms in the center of the ring interfere with each other. Because the ring is not planar, the *p* orbitals of the carbon atoms are not parallel and, therefore, cannot overlap effectively around the ring to form the π molecular orbitals of an aromatic system.

The [10]annulene with all cis double bonds (**5**) would, if it were planar, have considerable angle strain because the internal bond angles would be 144°. Consequently, any stability this isomer gained by becoming planar in order to become aromatic, would be more than offset by the destabilizing effect of the increased angle strain. A similar problem of a large angle strain associated with a planar form, prevents molecules of the [10]annulene isomer with one trans double bond (**6**) from being aromatic.

After many unsuccessful attempts over many years, in 1965 [4]annulene (or cyclobutadiene) was synthesized by R. Pettit and his co-workers at the University of Texas, Austin. Cyclobutadiene is a $4n$ molecule not a $4n + 2$ molecule, and, as we would expect, it is a highly unstable compound and *it is not aromatic.*

▯▯

**Cyclobutadiene
or [4]annulene
(*not* aromatic)**

Problem 13.3 ———————————————————————

Use the polygon-and-circle method to outline the π molecular orbitals of cyclobutadiene and explain why, on this basis, you would not expect it to be aromatic.

13.7B AROMATIC IONS

In addition to the neutral molecules that we have discussed so far, there are a number of monocyclic species that bear either a positive or a negative charge. Some of these ions show unexpected stabilities that suggest that they, too, are aromatic. Hückel's rule is helpful in accounting for the properties of these ions as well. We shall consider two examples: the cyclopentadienyl anion and the cycloheptatrienyl cation.

Cyclopentadiene is not aromatic; however, it is unusually acidic for a hydrocarbon. (The pK_a for cyclopentadiene is 15 and, by contrast, the pK_a for cycloheptatriene is 36.) Because of its acidity, cyclopentadiene can be converted to its anion by treatment with moderately strong bases. The cyclopentadienyl anion, moreover, is unusually stable and nuclear magnetic resonance (NMR) spectroscopy (Chapter 14) shows that all five hydrogen atoms in the cyclopentadienyl anion are equivalent.

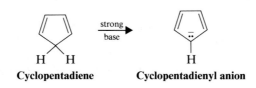

H H   H
Cyclopentadiene   **Cyclopentadienyl anion**

The orbital structure of cyclopentadiene (Fig. 13.8) shows why cyclopentadiene, itself, is not aromatic. Not only does it not have the proper number of π electrons, but the π electrons cannot be delocalized about the entire ring because of the intervening sp^3-hybridized —CH_2— group with no available p orbital.

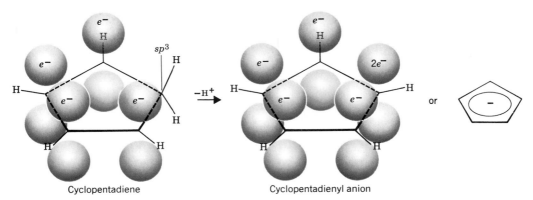

FIGURE 13.8 The p orbitals of cyclopentadiene and of the cyclopentadienyl anion.

On the other hand, if the —CH_2— carbon atom becomes sp^2 hybridized after it loses a proton (Fig. 13.8), the two electrons left behind can occupy the new p orbital that is produced. Moreover, this new p orbital can overlap with the p orbitals on either side of it and give rise to a ring with *six* delocalized π electrons. Because the electrons are delocalized, all of the hydrogen atoms are equivalent and this agrees with what NMR spectroscopy tells us.

Six is, of course, a Hückel number $(4n + 2$, where $n = 1)$, and the cyclopentadienyl anion is, in fact, an **aromatic anion.** The unusual acidity of cyclopentadiene is a result of the unusual stability of its anion.

Problem 13.4

(a) Outline the π molecular orbitals of the cyclopentadienyl system by inscribing a regular pentagon in a circle and explain on this basis why the cyclopentadienyl anion is aromatic. (b) What electron distribution would you expect for the cyclopentadienyl cation? (c) Would you expect it to be aromatic? Explain your answer. (d) Would you expect the cyclopentadienyl cation to be aromatic on the basis of Hückel's rule?

Cycloheptatriene (Fig. 13.9) (a compound with the common name, tropylidene) has six π electrons. However, the six π electrons of cycloheptatriene cannot be fully delocalized because of the presence of the —CH_2—group, a group that does not have an available p orbital (Fig. 13.9).

When cycloheptatriene is treated with a reagent that can abstract a hydride ion, it is converted to the cycloheptatrienyl (or tropylium) cation. The loss of a hydride ion from cycloheptatriene occurs with unexpected ease, and the cycloheptatrienyl cation is found to be unusually stable. The NMR spectrum of the cycloheptatrienyl cation

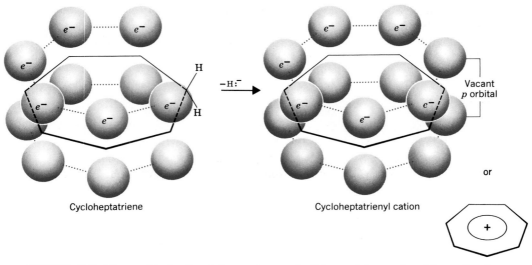

FIGURE 13.9 The *p* orbitals of cycloheptatriene and of the cycloheptatrienyl (tropylium) cation.

indicates that all seven hydrogen atoms are equivalent. If we look closely at Fig. 13.9, we see how we can account for these observations.

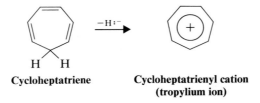

Cycloheptatriene   **Cycloheptatrienyl cation (tropylium ion)**

As a hydride ion is removed from the —CH$_2$— group of cycloheptatriene, a vacant *p* orbital is created, and the carbon atom becomes *sp^2* hybridized. The cation that results has seven overlapping *p* orbitals containing *six* delocalized π electrons. The cycloheptatrienyl cation is, therefore, an aromatic cation, and all of its hydrogen atoms should be equivalent; again this is exactly what we find experimentally.

Problem 13.5

(a) Use the polygon-and-circle method to sketch the relative energies of the π molecular orbitals of the cycloheptatrienyl cation and explain why it is aromatic. (b) Would you expect the cycloheptatrienyl anion to be aromatic on the basis of the electron distribution in its π molecular orbitals? Explain. (c) Would you expect the cycloheptatrienyl anion to be aromatic on the basis of Hückel's rule?

Problem 13.6

The conversion of cycloheptatriene to the cycloheptatrienyl cation can be accomplished by treating cycloheptatriene with triphenylcarbenium perchlorate $[(C_6H_5)_3C^+ClO_4^-]$. (a) Write the structure of triphenylcarbenium perchlorate and show how it abstracts a hydride ion from cycloheptatriene. (b) What other product is formed in this reaction? (c) What anion is associated with the cycloheptatrienyl cation that is produced?

Problem 13.7

Tropylium bromide (7-bromo-1,3,5-cycloheptatriene) is insoluble in nonpolar solvents but dissolves readily in water. When an aqueous solution of tropylium bromide is treated with silver nitrate, a precipitate of AgBr forms immediately. The melting point of tropylium bromide is above 200 °C, quite high for an organic compound. How can you account for these experimental observations?

13.7C AROMATIC, ANTIAROMATIC, AND NONAROMATIC COMPOUNDS

What do we mean when we say that a compound is aromatic? We mean that its π electrons are *delocalized* over the entire ring and that it is *stabilized* by the π-electron delocalization.

One of the best ways to determine whether or not the π electrons of a cyclic system are delocalized is through the use of NMR spectroscopy. It provides direct physical evidence of whether or not the π electrons are delocalized. We shall have more to say about how this is done in Chapter 14.

But what do we mean by saying that a compound is stabilized by π-electron delocalization? We have an idea of what this means from our comparison of the heat of hydrogenation of benzene and that calculated for the hypothetical 1,3,5-cyclohexatriene. We saw that benzene—in which the π electrons are delocalized—is much more stable than 1,3,5-cyclohexatriene (a model in which the π electrons are not delocalized). We call the energy difference between them the resonance energy (delocalization energy) or stabilization energy.

In order to make similar comparisons for other aromatic compounds we need to choose proper models. But what should these models be?

One proposal is that we should compare the π-electron energy of the cyclic system with that of the corresponding open-chain compound. This approach is particularly useful because it furnishes us with models not only for annulenes but for aromatic cations and anions as well. (Corrections need to be made, of course, when the cyclic system is strained.)

When we use this approach we take as our model a linear chain of sp^2-hybridized atoms that carries the same number of π electrons as our cyclic compound. Then we imagine ourselves removing two hydrogen atoms from the end of this chain and joining the ends to form a ring. If the ring has *lower* π-electron energy than the open chain, then the ring is *aromatic*. If the ring and chain have *the same* π-electron energy, then the ring is *nonaromatic*. If the ring has *greater* π-electron energy than the open chain, then the ring is *antiaromatic*.

The actual calculations and experiments used in determining π-electron energies are beyond our scope, but we can study four examples that illustrate how this approach has been used.

Cyclobutadiene. For cyclobutadiene we consider the change in π-electron energy for the following *hypothetical* transformation.

1,3-Butadiene
4 π electrons

Cyclobutadiene
4 π electrons (antiaromatic)

Calculations indicate and experiments appear to confirm that the π-electron energy of cyclobutadiene is higher than that of its open-chain counterpart. Thus cyclobutadiene is classified as being antiaromatic.

Benzene. Here our comparison is based on the following hypothetical transformation.

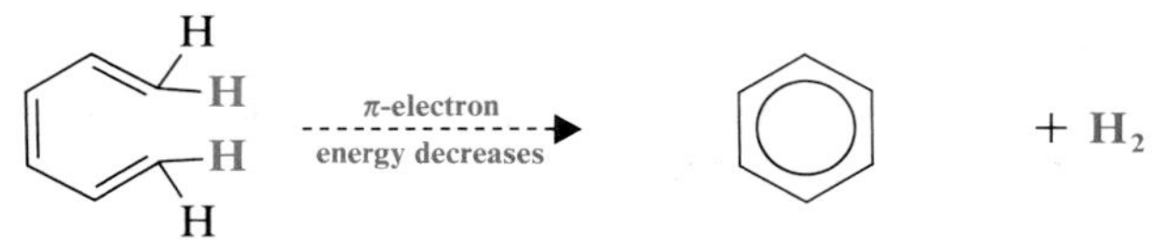

1,3,5-Hexatriene
6 π electrons

Benzene
6 π electrons (aromatic)

Calculations indicate and experiments confirm that benzene has a much lower π-electron energy than 1,3,5-hexatriene. Benzene is classified as being aromatic on the basis of this comparison as well.

Cyclopentadienyl Anion. Here we use a linear anion for our hypothetical transformation:

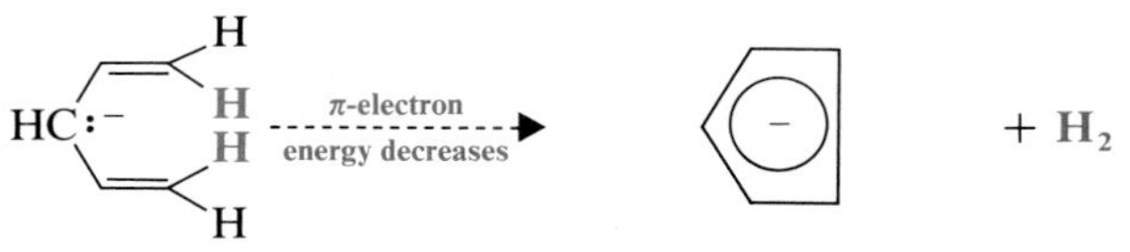

6 π electrons

Cyclopentadienyl anion
6 π electrons (aromatic)

Both calculations and experiments confirm that the cyclic anion has a lower π-electron energy than its open-chain counterpart. Therefore the cyclopentadienyl anion is classified as being aromatic.

Cyclooctatetraene. For cyclooctatetraene we consider the following hypothetical transformation.

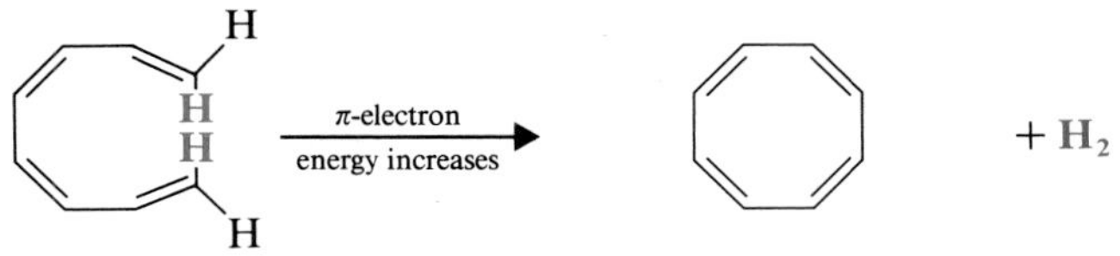

8 π electrons

Cyclooctatetraene
8 π electrons (antiaromatic)

Here calculations and experiments indicate that a planar cyclooctatetraene would have higher π-electron energy than the open-chain octatetraene. Therefore, a planar form of cyclooctatetraene would, if it existed, be *antiaromatic.* As we saw earlier, cyclooctatetraene is not planar and behaves like a simple cyclic polyene.

Problem 13.8

(a) What open-chain compound would you use for comparison in assessing the π-electron energy of the cycloheptatrienyl cation? (b) Both theory and experiments indicate that the cycloheptatrienyl cation has a lower π-electron energy than its open-chain counterpart. What conclusion does this justify?

Problem 13.9

The cyclopentadienyl cation is apparently *antiaromatic*. Explain what this means in terms of the π-electron energies of a cyclic and an open-chain compound.

Problem 13.10

The cyclopropenyl cation is known from experiments to be aromatic. Give an explanation that accounts for the aromaticity of this cation in terms of Hückel's rule, and in terms of the distribution of electrons in its π molecular orbitals.

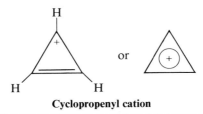

Cyclopropenyl cation

13.8 OTHER AROMATIC COMPOUNDS

13.8A BENZENOID AROMATIC COMPOUNDS

In addition to those that we have seen so far, there are many other examples of aromatic compounds. Representatives of one broad class of aromatic compounds, called **polycyclic benzenoid aromatic hydrocarbons,** are illustrated in Fig. 13.10.

Naphthalene
$C_{10}H_8$

Anthracene
$C_{14}H_{10}$

Phenanthrene
$C_{14}H_{10}$

Pyrene
$C_{16}H_{10}$

Benzo[a]pyrene
$C_{20}H_{12}$

FIGURE 13.10 Benzenoid aromatic hydrocarbons.

All of these consist of molecules having two or more benzene rings *fused* together. A close look at one, naphthalene, will illustrate what we mean by this.

According to resonance theory, a molecule of naphthalene can be considered to be a hybrid of three Kekulé structures. One of these Kekulé structures is shown in Fig. 13.11. There are two carbon atoms in naphthalene (C-9 and C-10) that are common to both rings. These two atoms are said to be at the points of *ring fusion*. They direct all of their bonds toward other carbon atoms and do not bear hydrogen atoms.

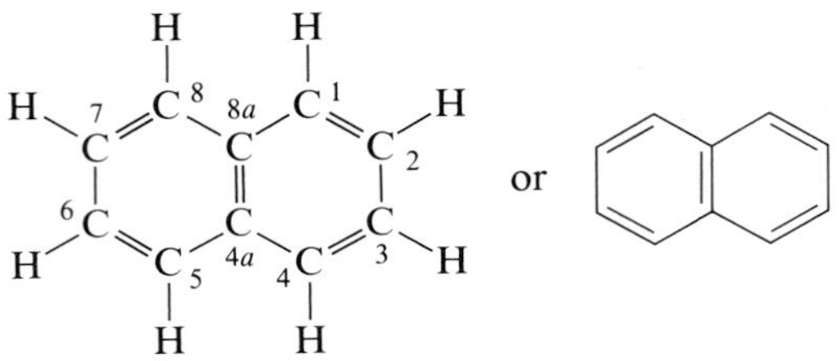

FIGURE 13.11 One Kekulé structure for naphthalene.

Problem 13.11

(a) Write the three resonance structures for naphthalene. (b) The C-1—C-2 bond of naphthalene is shorter than the C-2—C-3 bond. Do the resonance structures you have written account for this? Explain.

Molecular orbital calculations for naphthalene begin with the model shown in Fig. 13.12. The *p* orbitals overlap around the periphery of both rings and across the points of ring fusion.

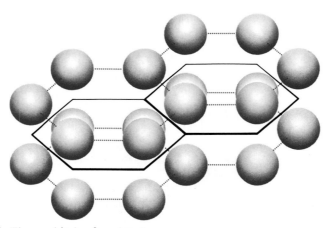

FIGURE 13.12 The *p* orbitals of naphthalene.

When molecular orbital calculations are carried out for naphthalene using the model shown in Fig. 13.12, the results of the calculations correlate well with our experimental knowledge of naphthalene. The calculations indicate that delocalization of the 10 π electrons over the two rings produces a structure with considerably lower energy than that calculated for any individual Kekulé structure. Naphthalene, consequently, has a substantial resonance energy. Based on what we know about benzene, moreover, naphthalene's tendency to react by substitution rather than addition and to show other properties associated with aromatic compounds is understandable.

Anthracene and phenanthrene are isomers. In anthracene the three rings are fused in a linear way, and in phenanthrene they are fused so as to produce an angular molecule. Both of these molecules also show large resonance energies and chemical properties typical of aromatic compounds.

Pyrene is also aromatic. Pyrene itself has been known for a long time; a pyrene derivative, however, has been the object of research that shows another interesting application of Hückel's rule.

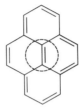

FIGURE 13.13 One Kekulé structure for pyrene. The internal double bond is enclosed in a dotted circle for emphasis.

In order to understand this particular research we need to pay special attention to the Kekulé structure for pyrene (Fig. 13.13). The total number of π electrons in pyrene is 16 (8 double bonds = 16 π electrons). Sixteen is a non-Hückel number, but Hückel's rule is intended to be applied only to monocyclic compounds and pyrene is clearly tetracyclic. If we disregard the internal double bond of pyrene, however, and look only at the periphery, we see that the periphery is a planar monocyclic ring with 14 π electrons. The periphery is, in fact, very much like that of the following [14]annulene. Fourteen *is* a Hückel number ($4n + 2$, where $n = 3$) and one might then predict that the periphery of pyrene would be aromatic by itself, in the absence of the internal double bond.

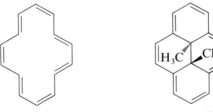

[14]Annulene   *trans*-15,16-Dimethyldihydropyrene

This prediction was confirmed when V. Boekelheide (University of Oregon) synthesized the very unusual *trans*-15,16-dimethyldihydropyrene and showed that it is aromatic.

13.8B NONBENZENOID AROMATIC COMPOUNDS

Naphthalene, phenanthrene, and anthracene are examples of *benzenoid* aromatic compounds. On the other hand, the cyclopentadienyl anion, the cycloheptatrienyl cation, *trans*-15,16-dimethyldihydropyrene, and the aromatic annulenes (except for [6]annulene) are classified as **nonbenzenoid aromatic compounds.**

Another example of a *nonbenzenoid* aromatic hydrocarbon is the compound azulene. Azulene has a resonance energy of 49 kcal mol^{-1}.

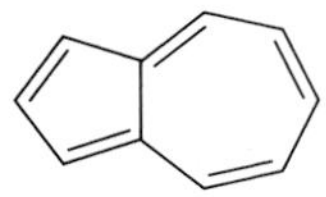

Azulene

This deep-blue hydrocarbon (its name is derived from the word *azure*) is an isomer of naphthalene. It has the same number of π electrons as naphthalene and, for this reason, azulene is also said to be *isoelectronic* with naphthalene. In addition to its deep-blue color (naphthalene by contrast is colorless), azulene differs from naphthalene in another respect that seems, at first, to be peculiar. Azulene is found to have a substantial dipole moment. The dipole moment of azulene is 1.0 D, whereas the dipole moment of naphthalene is zero.

That azulene has a dipole moment at all indicates that charge separation exists in the molecule. If we recognize this and begin writing resonance structures for azulene that involve charge separation, we find that we can write a number of structures like the one shown in Fig. 13.14.

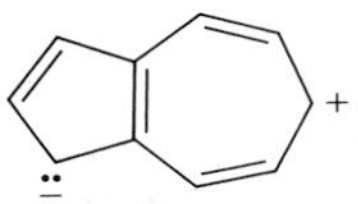

FIGURE 13.14 One resonance structure for azulene that has separated charges.

Charge-separated resonance structures are not normally important. However, when we inspect this resonance structure, we see that the five-membered ring is very much like the *aromatic* cyclopentadienyl anion and that the seven-membered ring resembles the *aromatic* cycloheptatrienyl cation. Both structures would be especially stable. If resonance structures of this type contribute to the overall hybrid for azulene, then we not only understand why azulene has a dipole moment, but we also have some insight into why it is aromatic. Such speculation is strengthened by the results of studies done with substituted azulenes that show quite conclusively that the five-membered ring is negatively charged and the seven-membered ring is positive.

Problem 13.12

Diphenylcyclopropenone (**I**) has a much larger dipole moment than benzophenone (**II**). Can you think of an explanation that would account for this?

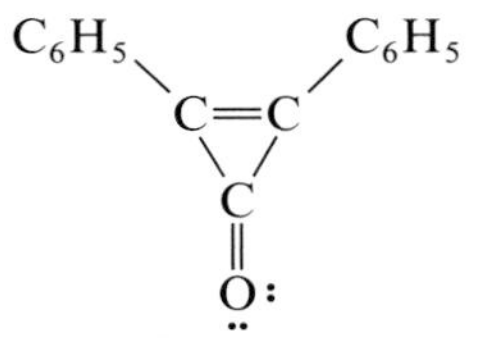

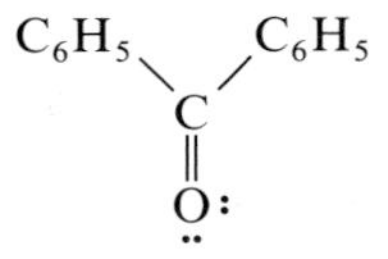

13.9 REDUCTION OF AROMATIC COMPOUNDS: THE BIRCH REDUCTION

Hydrogenation of benzene under pressure using a metal catalyst such as nickel results in the addition of three molar equivalents of hydrogen and the formation of cyclohexane (Section 13.3). The intermediate cyclohexadienes and cyclohexene cannot be isolated because these undergo catalytic hydrogenation faster than benzene does.

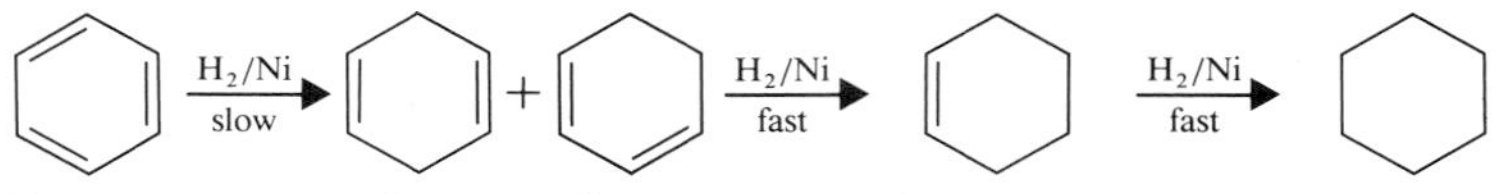

Benzene **Cyclohexadienes** **Cyclohexene** **Cyclohexane**

13.9A THE BIRCH REDUCTION

Benzene can be reduced to 1,4-cyclohexadiene by treating it with an alkali metal (sodium, lithium, or potassium) in a mixture of liquid ammonia and an alcohol.

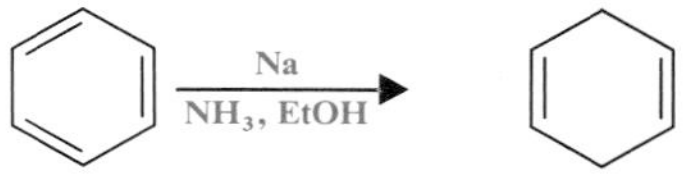

Benzene **1,4-Cyclohexadiene**

This is another dissolving metal reduction and the mechanism for it resembles the mechanism for the reduction of alkynes that we studied in Section 8.7B. A sequence of electron transfers from the alkali metal and proton transfers from the alcohol takes place. (See the following reaction sequence.) The first electron transfer produces a delocalized benzene radical anion. Protonation produces a cyclohexadienyl radical (also a delocalized species). Transfer of another electron leads to the formation of a delocalized cyclohexadienyl anion and protonation of this produces the 1,4-cyclohexadiene.

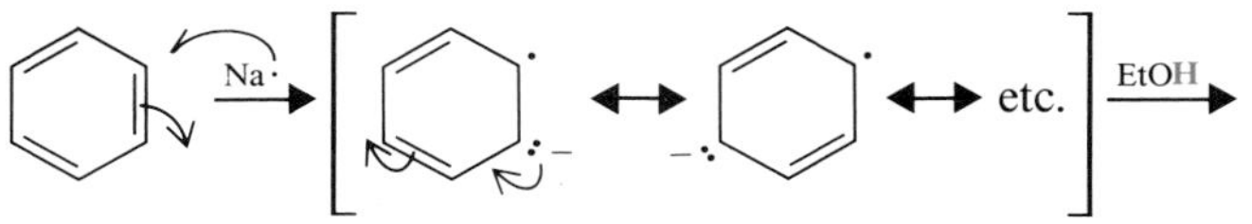

Benzene **Benzene anion radical**

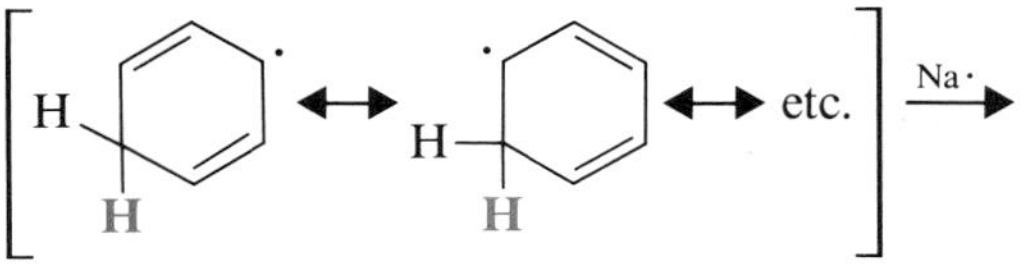

Cyclohexadienyl radical

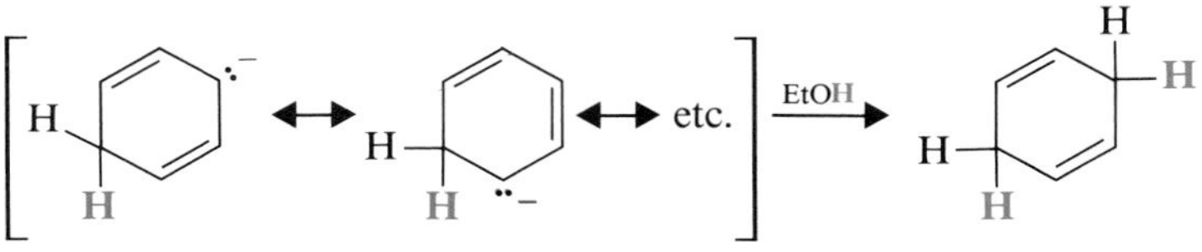

Cyclohexadienyl anion **1,4-Cyclohexadiene**

Formation of a 1,4-cyclohexadiene in a reaction of this type is quite general, but the reason for its formation in preference to the more stable conjugated 1,3-cyclohexadiene is not understood.

Dissolving metal reductions of this type were developed by the Australian chemist A. J. Birch and have come to be known as **Birch reductions.**

Substituent groups on the benzene ring influence the course of the reaction. Birch reduction of methoxybenzene (anisole) produces the following result:

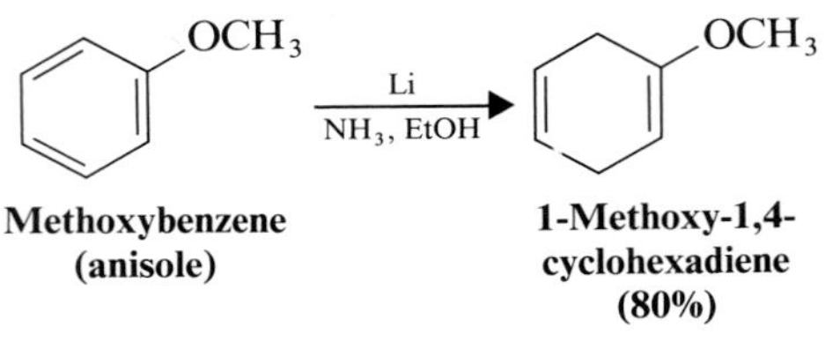

Methoxybenzene
(anisole)

1-Methoxy-1,4-
cyclohexadiene
(80%)

Reduction of 1,2-dimethylbenzene (o-xylene) gives 1,2-dimethyl-1,4-cyclohexadiene:

1,2-Dimethylbenzene

1,2-Dimethyl-1,4-
cyclohexadiene
(77–92%)

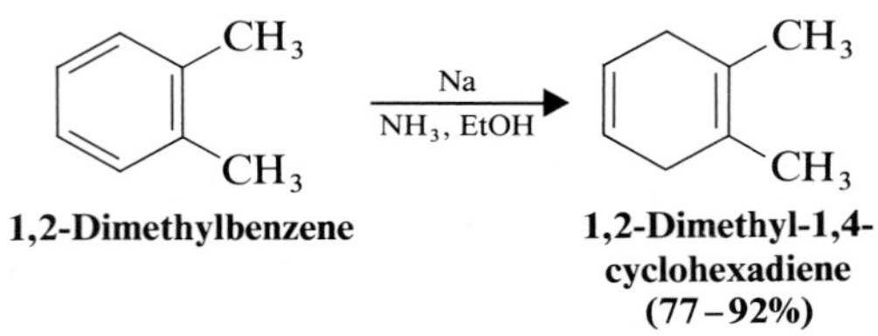

Birch reduction of sodium benzoate, however, yields a product with the substituent on the saturated carbon atom.

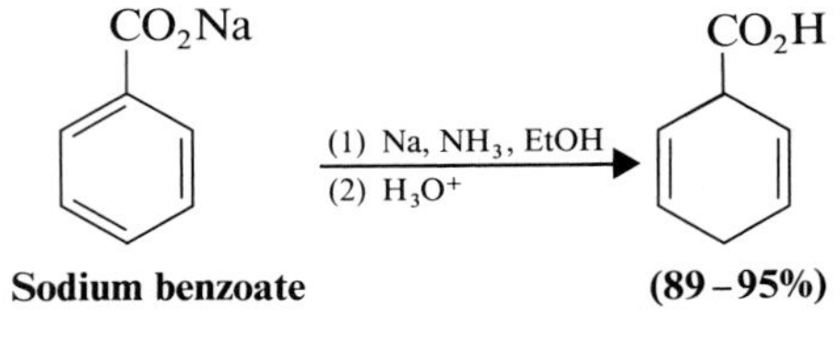

Sodium benzoate

(89–95%)

Problem 13.13

That the product of the Birch reduction of benzene is 1,4-cyclohexadiene and not 1,3-cyclohexadiene can be demonstrated by ozonolysis. (a) Explain how this can be done by showing the products that would be obtained in each instance. (b) What would ozonolysis of the product obtained from the Birch reduction of 1,2-dimethylbenzene yield?

Problem 13.14

Birch reduction of toluene yields a product **X** with the molecular formula C_7H_{10}. On ozonolysis **X** is transformed into CH_3COCH_2CHO and $OHCCH_2CHO$. What is the structure of **X**?

Problem 13.15

Acidic hydrolysis of the Birch reduction product obtained from methoxyben-zene (i.e., 1-methoxy-1,4-cyclohexadiene) yields 2-cyclohexenone. Propose a mechanism for this reaction. (*Hint:* Recall that molecules with conjugated double bonds are more stable than those with isolated double bonds.)

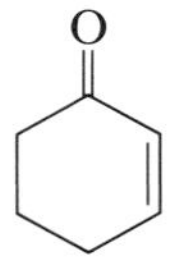

2-Cyclohexenone

Problem 13.16

Syn hydroxylation of 1,4-cyclohexadiene with OsO_4 yields two products. (a) Write the structures of these products and (b) tell whether either product could be resolved into separate enantiomers.

13.10 BENZYLIC RADICALS AND CATIONS

Removal of a hydrogen atom from the methyl group of methylbenzene (toluene) produces a radical called the **benzyl radical:**

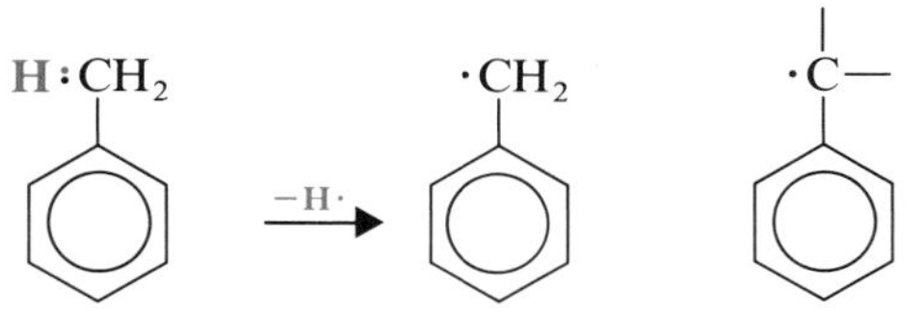

$H:CH_2$ $\cdot CH_2$

Methylbenzene   The benzyl   A benzylic
(toluene)   radical   radical

Benzylic carbon

A benzylic hydrogen

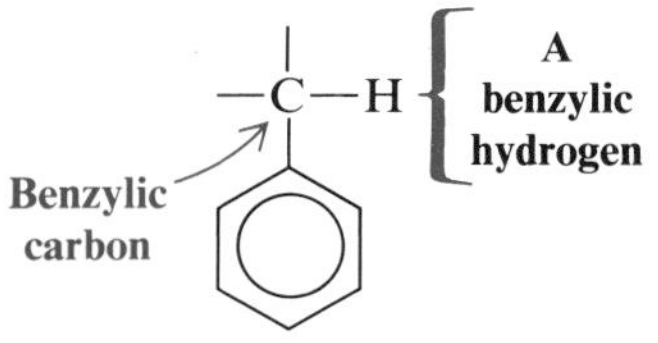

The name benzyl radical is used as a specific name for the radical produced in this reaction. The general name **benzylic radical** applies to all radicals that have an unpaired electron on the side chain carbon atom that is directly attached to the benzene ring. The hydrogen atoms of the carbon atom directly attached to the benzene ring are called **benzylic hydrogen atoms.**

Removal of an electron from a benzylic radical produces a **benzylic cation:**

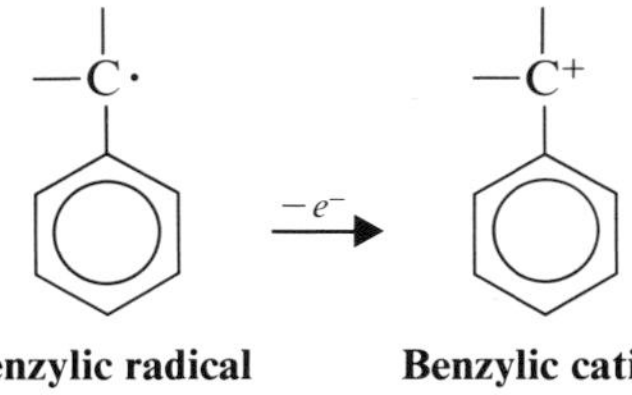

Benzylic radical   Benzylic cation

Benzylic radicals and benzylic cations are *conjugated unsaturated systems* and *both are unusually stable.* They have approximately the same stabilities as allylic radicals and allylic cations. This exceptional stability of benzylic radicals and cations is easily explained by resonance theory. (It can also be explained by molecular orbital theory, but we shall not go into this here.) In the case of each of the following entities several resonance structures can be written. Each entity, therefore, is highly stabilized by resonance.

**Benzylic radicals are
stabilized by resonance**

**Benzylic cations are
stabilized by resonance**

13.11 ALLYLIC AND BENZYLIC HALIDES IN NUCLEOPHILIC SUBSTITUTION REACTIONS

Allylic and benzylic halides can be classified in the same way that we have classified other organic halides:

$$-\overset{|}{C}=\overset{|}{C}-CH_2X \qquad -\overset{|}{C}=\overset{|}{C}-\overset{\overset{R}{|}}{C}HX \qquad -\overset{|}{C}=\overset{|}{C}-\overset{\overset{R}{|}}{\underset{\underset{R'}{|}}{C}}X$$

1° Allylic   2° Allylic   3° Allylic

$$ArCH_2X \qquad Ar\overset{\overset{R}{|}}{C}HX \qquad Ar\overset{\overset{R}{|}}{\underset{\underset{R'}{|}}{C}}X$$

1° Benzylic   2° Benzylic   3° Benzylic

All of these compounds undergo nucleophilic substitution reactions. As with other tertiary halides (Section 6.15A), the steric hindrance associated with having three bulky groups on the carbon bearing the halogen prevents tertiary allylic and tertiary benzylic halides from reacting by an S_N2 mechanism. They react with nucleophiles only by an S_N1 mechanism.

Primary and secondary allylic and benzylic halides can react either by an S_N2 mechanism or by an S_N1 mechanism in ordinary nonacidic solvents. We would expect these halides to react by an S_N2 mechanism because they are structurally similar to primary and secondary alkyl halides. (Having only one or two groups attached to the carbon bearing the halogen does not prevent S_N2 attack.) But primary and secondary allylic and benzylic halides can also react by an S_N1 mechanism

TABLE 13.1 A summary of alkyl, allylic, and benzylic halides in S_N reactions

These halides give mainly S_N2 reactions	These halides give mainly S_N1 reactions
CH_3—X; R—CH_2—X; R—CH(R′)—X	R′—C(R)(R″)—X
These halides may give either S_N1 or S_N2 reactions	Ar—C(R)(R′)—X
Ar—CH_2—X; Ar—CH(R)—X	—C=C—C(R)(R′)—X
—C=CCH_2—X; —C=CCH(R)—X	

because they can form relatively stable carbocations and in this regard they differ from primary and secondary alkyl halides.*

Overall we can summarize the effect of structure on the reactivity of alkyl, allylic, and benzylic halides in the ways shown in Table 13.1.

Sample Problem

When either enantiomer of 3-chloro-1-butene [(*R*) or (*S*)] is subjected to hydrolysis, the products of the reaction are optically inactive. Explain these results.

Answer:
The solvolysis reaction is S_N1. The intermediate allylic cation is achiral and therefore reacts with water to give the enantiomeric 3-buten-2-ols in equal amounts and to give some of the achiral 2-buten-1-ol.

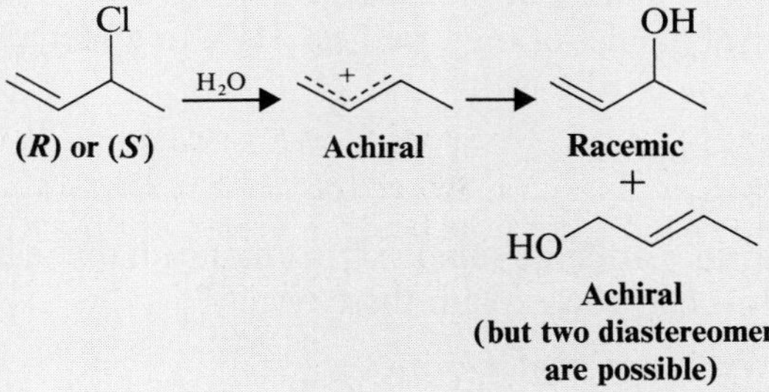

*There is some dispute as to whether 2° alkyl halides react by an S_N1 mechanism to any appreciable extent in ordinary nonacidic solvents such as mixtures of water and alcohol or acetone, but it is clear that reaction by an S_N2 mechanism is, for all practical purposes, the more important pathway.

Problem 13.17

Account for the following observations: (a) When 1-chloro-2-butene is allowed to react with a relatively concentrated solution of sodium ethoxide in ethanol, the reaction rate depends on the concentration of the allylic halide and on the concentration of ethoxide ion. The product of the reaction is almost exclusively $CH_3CH=CHCH_2OCH_2CH_3$. (b) When 1-chloro-2-butene is allowed to react with very dilute solutions of sodium ethoxide in ethanol (or with ethanol alone), the reaction rate is independent of the concentration of ethoxide ion; it depends only on the concentration of the allylic halide. Under these conditions the reaction produces a mixture of $CH_3CH=CHCH_2OCH_2CH_3$ and $CH_3\underset{\underset{\displaystyle OCH_2CH_3}{|}}{C}HCH=CH_2$. (c) In the presence of traces of water 1-chloro-2-butene is slowly converted to a mixture of 1-chloro-2-butene and 3-chloro-1-butene.

Problem 13.18

1-Chloro-3-methyl-2-butene undergoes hydrolysis in a mixture of water and dioxane at a rate that is more than a thousand times that of 1-chloro-2-butene. (a) What factor accounts for the difference in reactivity? (b) What products would you expect to obtain? [Dioxane is a cyclic ether (below) that is miscible with water in all proportions and is a useful cosolvent for conducting reactions like these. Dioxane is carcinogenic (i.e., cancer-causing), however, and like most ethers, it tends to form peroxides.]

Dioxane

Problem 13.19

Primary halides of the type $ROCH_2X$ apparently undergo S_N1 type reactions, whereas most primary halides do not. Can you propose a resonance explanation for the ability of halides of the type $ROCH_2X$ to undergo S_N1 reactions?

Problem 13.20

The following chlorides undergo solvolysis in ethanol at the relative rates given in parentheses. How can you explain these results?

$C_6H_5CH_2Cl$	$C_6H_5\underset{\underset{\displaystyle Cl}{|}}{C}HCH_3$	$(C_6H_5)_2CHCl$	$(C_6H_5)_3CCl$
(0.08)	**(1)**	**(300)**	**(3×10^6)**

13.12 HETEROCYCLIC AROMATIC COMPOUNDS

Almost all of the cyclic molecules that we have discussed so far have had rings composed solely of carbon atoms. However, in molecules of many cyclic compounds an element other than carbon is present in the ring. These compounds are called **heterocyclic compounds.** Heterocyclic molecules are quite commonly encountered in nature. For this reason, and because the structures of some of these molecules are closely related to the compounds that we discussed earlier, we shall now describe a few examples.

Heterocyclic compounds containing nitrogen, oxygen, or sulfur are by far the most common. Four important examples are given here in their Kekulé forms. *These four compounds are all aromatic.*

| Pyridine | Pyrrole | Furan | Thiophene |

If we examine these structures, we shall see that pyridine is electronically related to benzene, and that pyrrole, furan, and thiophene are related to the cyclopentadienyl anion.

The nitrogen atoms in molecules of both pyridine and pyrrole are sp^2 hybridized. In pyridine (Fig. 13.15) the sp^2-hybridized nitrogen donates one electron to the π system. This electron, together with one from each of the five carbon atoms, gives pyridine a sextet of electrons like benzene. The two unshared electrons of the nitrogen of pyridine are in an sp^2 orbital that lies in the same plane as the atoms of the ring. This sp^2 orbital does not overlap with the p orbitals of the ring (it is, therefore, said to be *orthogonal* to the p orbitals). The unshared pair on nitrogen is not a part of the π system, and these electrons confer on pyridine the properties of a weak base.

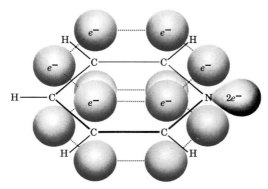

FIGURE 13.15 The orbital structure of pyridine.

Sample Problem

Write resonance structures for pyridine.

Answer:
We can write the following structures, which are analogous to the Kekulé structures for benzene.

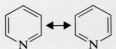

In pyrrole (Fig. 13.16) the electrons are arranged differently. Because only four π electrons are contributed by the carbon atoms of the pyrrole ring, the sp^2-hybridized nitrogen must contribute two electrons to give an aromatic sextet. Because these electrons are a part of the aromatic sextet, they are not available for donation to a proton. Thus, in aqueous solution, pyrrole is not appreciably basic.

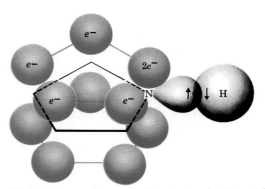

FIGURE 13.16 The orbital structure of pyrrole. (Compare with the orbital structure of the cyclopentadienyl anion in Fig. 13.8.)

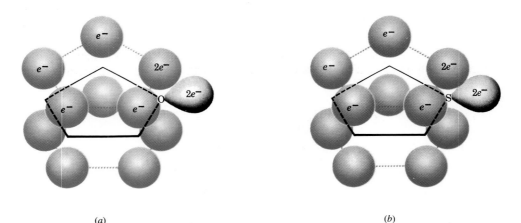

(a)   (b)

FIGURE 13.17 The orbital structures of furan (a) and thiophene (b).

Furan and thiophene are structurally quite similar to pyrrole. The oxygen atom in furan and the sulfur atom in thiophene are sp^2 hybridized. In both compounds the p orbital of the heteroatom donates two electrons to the π system. The oxygen and sulfur atoms of furan and thiophene carry an unshared pair of electrons in an sp^2 orbital (Fig. 13.17) that is orthogonal to the π system.

13.13 AROMATIC COMPOUNDS IN BIOCHEMISTRY

Compounds with aromatic rings occupy numerous and important positions in reactions that occur in living systems. It would be impossible to describe them all in this chapter. We shall, however, point out a few examples now and we shall see others later.

Two amino acids necessary for protein synthesis contain the benzene ring:

Phenylalanine   Tyrosine

A third aromatic amino acid, tryptophan, contains a benzene ring fused to a pyrrole ring. (This aromatic ring system is called an indole system, cf. Section 19.1B.)

Tryptophan   Indole

It appears that humans, because of the course of evolution, do not have the biochemical ability to synthesize the benzene ring. As a result, phenylalanine and tryptophan derivatives are essential in the human diet. Because tyrosine can be synthesized from phenylalanine in a reaction catalyzed by an enzyme known as *phenylalanine hydroxylase,* it is not essential in the diet as long as phenylalanine is present.

Heterocyclic aromatic compounds are also present in many biochemical systems. Derivatives of purine and pyrimidine are essential parts of DNA and RNA.

Purine   Pyrimidine

DNA is the molecule responsible for the storage of genetic information and RNA is prominently involved in the synthesis of enzymes and other proteins (Chapter 25).

Problem 13.21

Classify each nitrogen atom in the purine molecule as to whether it is of the pyridine type or of the pyrrole type.

Both a pyridine derivative (nicotinamide) and a purine derivative (adenine) are present in one of the most important coenzymes (Section 24.8) in biological oxidations. This molecule, **nicotinamide adenine dinucleotide** (NAD$^+$, the oxidized form), is shown in Fig. 13.18. NADH is the reduced form.

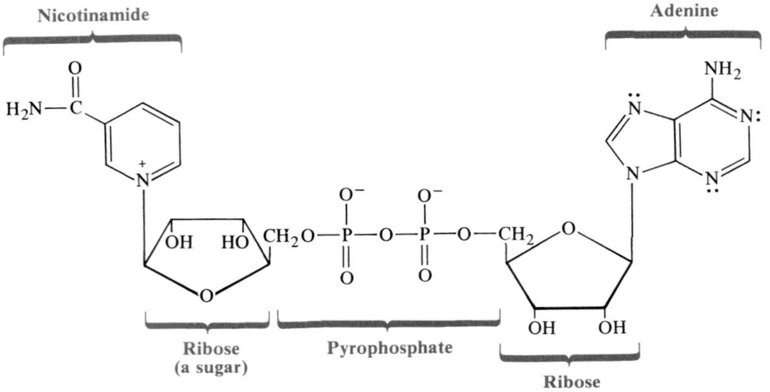

FIGURE 13.18 Nicotinamide adenine dinucleotide (NAD$^+$).

NAD$^+$, together with another compound in the liver (an apoenzyme), is capable of oxidizing alcohols to aldehydes. While the overall change is quite complex, a look at one aspect of it will illustrate a *biological use* of the extra stability (resonance or delocalization energy) associated with an aromatic ring.

A simplified version of the oxidation of an alcohol to an aldehyde is illustrated here:

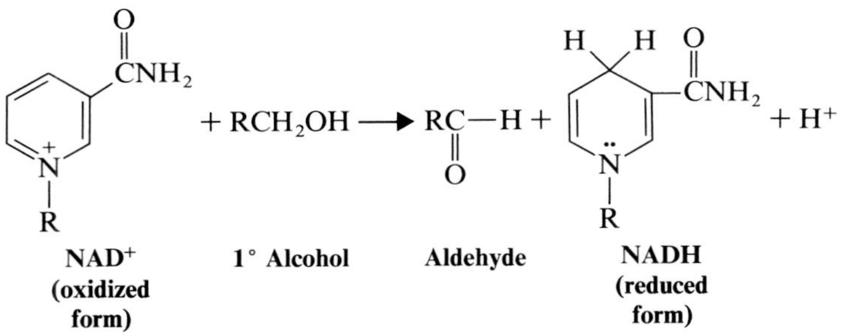

The *aromatic* pyridine ring (actually a *pyridinium* ring, because it is positively charged) in NAD$^+$ is converted to a *nonaromatic* ring in NADH. The extra stability of the pyridine ring is lost in this change; and, as a result, the potential energy of NADH is greater than that of NAD$^+$. The conversion of the alcohol to the aldehyde, however, occurs with a decrease in potential energy. Because these reactions are coupled in biological systems (Fig. 13.19), a portion of the potential energy contained in the alcohol becomes chemically contained in NADH. This stored energy in NADH is used to bring about other biochemical reactions that require energy and that are necessary to life.

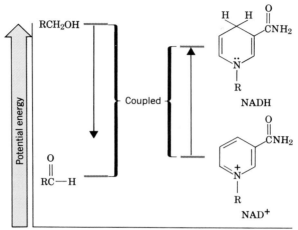

FIGURE 13.19 Potential energy diagram for the biologically coupled oxidation of an alcohol and reduction of nicotinamide adenine dinucleotide.

Although many aromatic compounds are essential to life, others are hazardous. Many are quite toxic and several benzenoid compounds, including benzene itself, are **carcinogenic.** Two other examples are benzo[*a*]pyrene and 7-methylbenz[*a*]anthracene.

Benzo[*a*]pyrene   **7-Methylbenz[*a*]anthracene**

The hydrocarbon benzo[*a*]pyrene has been found in cigarette smoke and in the exhaust from automobiles. It is also formed in the incomplete combustion of any fossil fuel. It is found on charcoal-broiled steaks and exudes from asphalt streets on a hot summer day. Benzo[*a*]pyrene is so carcinogenic that one can induce skin cancers in mice with almost total certainty simply by shaving an area of the body of the mouse and applying a coating of benzo[*a*]pyrene.

13.14 A SUMMARY OF IMPORTANT TERMS AND CONCEPTS

An *aliphatic compound* is a compound such as an alkane, alkene, alkyne, cyclo-alkane, cycloalkene, or any of their derivatives.

An *aromatic compound* traditionally means one "having the chemistry typified by benzene." The molecules of aromatic compounds are cyclic, planar, and conjugated. They have a stability significantly greater than that of a hypothetical resonance structure (e.g., a Kekulé structure). Many aromatic compounds react with electrophilic reagents (Br_2, HNO_3, H_2SO_4) by substitution rather than addition even though they are unsaturated (Chapter 15). A modern definition of any aromatic compound compares the energy of the π electrons of the cyclic conjugated molecule or ion with that of its open-chain counterpart. If on ring closure the π-electron energy *decreases,* the molecule is classified as being **aromatic,** if it *increases* the molecule is classified as being **antiaromatic,** and if it remains the same the molecule is classified as being **nonaromatic.**

The *resonance energy* of an aromatic compound is the difference in energy between the actual aromatic compound and that calculated for one of the hypothetical resonance structures (e.g., a Kekulé structure). The resonance energy is also referred to as *stabilization energy* or *delocalization energy.*

Hückel's rule states that planar monocyclic conjugated rings with $(4n + 2)$ π electrons (i.e., with 2, 6, 10, 14, 18, or 22 π electrons) should be aromatic.

An *annulene* is a monocyclic compound that can be represented by a structure having alternating single and double bonds. For example, cyclobutadiene is [4]annulene and benzene is [6]annulene.

A *benzenoid* aromatic compound is one whose molecules contain benzene rings or fused benzene rings. Examples are benzene, naphthalene, anthracene, and phenanthrene.

A *nonbenzenoid* aromatic compound is one whose molecules contain a ring that is not six membered. Examples are [14]annulene, azulene, the cyclopentadienyl anion, and the cycloheptatrienyl cation.

A *heterocyclic* compound is one whose molecules have a ring containing an element other than carbon. Some heterocyclic compounds (e.g., pyridine, pyrrole, and thiophene) are aromatic.

Additional Problems

13.22 Draw structural formulas for the following:

(a) 4-Nitrobenzenesulfonic acid

(b) *o*-Chlorotoluene

(c) *m*-Dichlorobenzene

(d) *p*-Dinitrobenzene

(e) 4-Bromo-1-methoxybenzene

(f) *m*-Nitrobenzoic acid

(g) *p*-Iodophenol

(h) 2-Chlorobenzoic acid

(i) 2-Bromonaphthalene

(j) 9-Chloroanthracene

(k) 3-Nitrophenanthrene

(l) 4-Nitropyridine

(m) 2-Methylpyrrole

(n) 2,4-Dichloro-1-nitrobenzene

(o) *p*-Nitrobenzyl bromide

(p) *o*-Chloroaniline

(q) 2,5-Dibromo-3-nitrobenzoic acid

(r) 1,3,5-Trimethylbenzene (mesitylene)

(s) *p*-Hydroxybenzoic acid

(t) Vinylbenzene (styrene)

(u) Benzo[*a*]pyrene

(v) 2-Phenylcyclohexanol

(w) 2,4,6-Trinitrotoluene (TNT)

(x) A [12]annulene

(y) A [14]annulene

(z) An [18]annulene

ADDITIONAL PROBLEMS

13.23 Write structural formulas and give names for all representatives of the following:

(a) Trichlorobenzenes

(b) Dibromonitrobenzenes

(c) Dichlorotoluenes

(d) Monochloronaphthalenes

(e) Nitropyridines

(f) Methylfurans

(g) Chlorodinitrobenzenes

(h) Chlorodimethylbenzenes

(i) Cresols (methylphenols)

13.24 (a) Write the five principal resonance structures for phenanthrene. (b) On the basis of these can you speculate about the length of the C-9–C-10 bond? (c) About its double-bond character? (d) Phenanthrene, in contrast to most aromatic molecules, tends to *add* 1 mol of bromine to form a molecule with the formula $C_{14}H_{10}Br_2$. How can you account for this behavior?

13.25 3-Methoxy-1,2,3-trimethylcyclopropene (**III**) has been found to react with fluoroboric acid to yield methanol and a compound with the formula $C_6H_9^+ BF_4^-$ (**IV**).

$$H_3C \quad \overset{CH_3}{\underset{OCH_3}{\diagup}} \quad H_3C \qquad + HBF_4 \longrightarrow C_6H_9^+ BF_4^- + CH_3OH$$

III   **IV**

(a) What is the structure of $C_6H_9^+ BF_4^-$? (b) How can you account for its formation?

13.26 Diphenylcyclopropenone (cf. Problem 13.12) reacts with hydrogen bromide to form a stable crystalline hydrobromide. What is its structure?

13.27 Cyclooctatetraene has been shown by Thomas Katz of Columbia University to react with two molar equivalents of potassium to yield an unusually stable compound with the formula $2 K^+ C_8H_8^{2-}$ (**V**). The NMR spectrum of **V** indicates that all of its hydrogen atoms are equivalent. (a) What is the structure of **V**? (b) How can you account for the formation of **V**?

$$2 K + \quad \bigcirc \longrightarrow K_2C_8H_8$$

Cyclooctatetraene   **V**

13.28 Indicate whether each of the following molecules or ions would or would not be aromatic. Explain your answer in each instance.

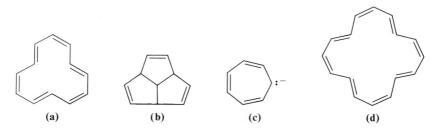

(a)   (b)   (c)   (d)

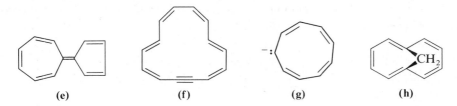

(e)   (f)   (g)   (h)

*13.29   Cycloheptatrienone (**I**) is very stable. Cyclopentadienone (**II**) by contrast is quite unstable and rapidly undergoes a Diels–Alder reaction with itself.   (a) Propose an explanation for the different stabilities of these two compounds.   (b) Write the structure of the Diels–Alder adduct of cyclopentadienone.

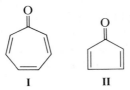

I   II

*13.30   5-Chloro-1,3-cyclopentadiene (below) undergoes S_N1 solvolysis in the presence of silver ion extremely slowly even though the chlorine is doubly allylic. Provide an explanation for this behavior.

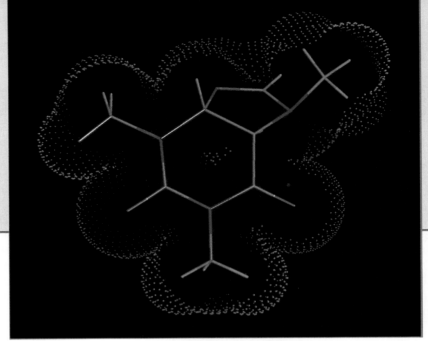

Caffeine (see Problem 14.40).

SPECTROSCOPIC METHODS OF STRUCTURE DETERMINATION

14.1 INTRODUCTION. THE ELECTROMAGNETIC SPECTRUM

The names of most forms of electromagnetic energy have become familiar terms. The *X-rays* used in medicine, the *light* that we see, the *ultraviolet* (UV) rays that produce sunburns, and the *radio* and *radar* waves used in communication are all different forms of the same phenomenon: electromagnetic radiation.

According to quantum mechanics, electromagnetic radiation has a dual and seemingly contradictory nature. Electromagnetic radiation has the properties of both a wave and a particle. Electromagnetic radiation can be described as a wave occurring simultaneously in electrical and magnetic fields. It can also be described as if it consisted of particles called quanta or photons. Different experiments disclose these two different aspects of electromagnetic radiation. They are not seen together in the same experiment.

A wave is usually described in terms of its **wavelength** (λ) or its **frequency** (ν). A simple wave is shown in Fig. 14.1. The distance between consecutive crests (or troughs) is the wavelength. The number of full cycles of the wave that pass a given point each second, as the wave moves through space, is called the *frequency.*

551

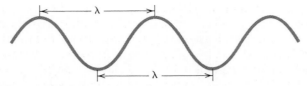

FIGURE 14.1 A simple wave and the wavelength, λ.

All electromagnetic radiation travels through a vacuum at the same velocity. This velocity (c), called the velocity of light, is 2.99792458×10^8 m s^{-1}. The frequencies of electromagnetic waves are usually reported in cycles per second or **hertz.*** The wavelengths of electromagnetic radiation are expressed in either meters (m), millimeters (1 mm = 10^{-3} m), micrometers (1 μm = 10^{-6} m), or nanometers (1 nm = 10^{-9} m). [An older term for micrometer is *micron* (abbreviated μ) and an older term for nanometer is *millimicron*.]

The energy of a quantum of electromagnetic energy is directly related to its frequency.

$$E = h\nu$$

where h = Planck's constant, 6.63×10^{-34} J s,

and $\qquad\qquad\qquad\qquad \nu$ = the frequency (Hz)

This means that the higher the frequency of radiation the greater is its energy. X-rays, for example, are much more energetic than rays of visible light. The frequencies of X-rays are of the order of 10^{19} Hz, while those of visible light are of the order of 10^{15} Hz.

Since $\nu = c/\lambda$, the energy of electromagnetic radiation is inversely proportional to its wavelength.

$$E = \frac{hc}{\lambda} \qquad (c = \text{the velocity of light})$$

Thus, per quantum, electromagnetic radiation of long wavelength has low energy, while that of short wavelength has high energy. X-rays have wavelengths of the order of 0.1 nm, while visible light has wavelengths between 400 and 750 nm.†

It may be helpful to point out, too, that for visible light, wavelengths (and, thus, frequencies) are related to what we perceive as colors. The light that we call red light has a wavelength of approximately 750 nm. The light we call violet light has a wavelength of approximately 400 nm. All of the other colors of the visible spectrum (the rainbow) lie in between these wavelengths.

---

* The term hertz (after the German physicist H. R. Hertz), abbreviated Hz, is now often used in place of *cycles per second* (cps). Frequency of electromagnetic radiation is also sometimes expressed in *wavenumbers,* that is, the number of waves per centimeter.

† A convenient formula that relates wavelength (in nm) to the energy of electromagnetic radiation is the following:

$$E \text{ (in kcal mol}^{-1}) = \frac{2.86 \times 10^4 \text{ kcal} \cdot \text{nm mol}^{-1}}{\text{wavelength in nanometers}}$$

The different regions of the electromagnetic spectrum are shown in Fig. 14.2. Nearly every portion of the electromagnetic spectrum from the region of X-rays to those of microwaves and radio waves has been used in elucidating structures of atoms and molecules. Later in this chaper we discuss the use that can be made of the infrared (IR) and radio regions when we take up IR spectroscopy and nuclear magnetic resonance (NMR) spectroscopy. At this point we direct our attention to electromagnetic radiation in the near UV and visible regions and see how it interacts with conjugated polyenes.

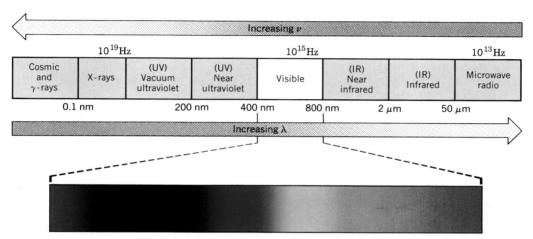

FIGURE 14.2 The electromagnetic spectrum.

14.2 VISIBLE AND ULTRAVIOLET SPECTROSCOPY

When electromagnetic radiation in the UV and visible regions passes through a compound containing multiple bonds, a portion of the radiation is usually absorbed by the compound. Just how much of the radiation is absorbed depends on the wavelength of the radiation and the structure of the compound. The absorption of radiation is caused by the subtraction of energy from the radiation beam when electrons in orbitals of lower energy are excited into orbitals of higher energy.

Instruments called visible–UV spectrometers are used to measure the amount of light absorbed at each wavelength of the visible and UV regions. In these instruments a beam of light is split; one half of the beam (the sample beam) is directed through a transparent cell containing a solution of the compound being analyzed, and one half (the reference beam) is directed through an identical cell that does not contain the compound but contains the solvent. Solvents are chosen to be transparent in the region being analyzed. The instrument is designed so that it can make a comparison of the intensities of the two beams at each wavelength of the region. If the compound absorbs light at a particular wavelength, the intensity of the sample beam (I_S) will be less than that of the reference beam (I_R). The instrument indicates this by producing a graph — a plot of the wavelength of the entire region *versus* the absorbance (A) of light at each wavelength. [The absorbance at a particular wavelength is defined by the equation: $A_\lambda = \log(I_R/I_S)$.] Such a graph is called an **absorption spectrum.**

A typical UV absorption spectrum, that of 2,5-dimethyl-2,4-hexadiene, is shown in Fig. 14.3. It shows a broad absorption band in the region between 210 and 260 nm.

The absorption is at a maximum at 242.5 nm. It is this wavelength that is usually reported in the chemical literature.

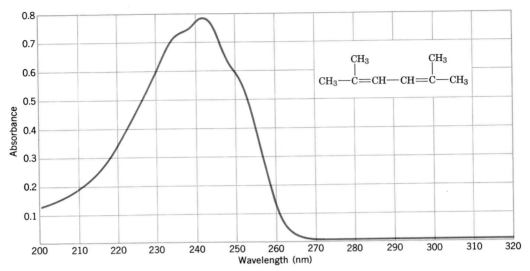

FIGURE 14.3 The UV absorption spectrum of 2,5-dimethyl-2,4-hexadiene in methanol. (Spectrum courtesy of Sadtler Research Laboratories, Philadelphia.)

In addition to reporting the wavelength of maximum absorption (λ_{max}), chemists often report another quantity that indicates the strength of the absorption, called the **molar absorptivity, ε.†**

The molar absorptivity is simply the proportionality constant that relates the observed absorbance (A) at a particular wavelength (λ) to the molar concentration (C) of the sample and the length (l) (in centimeters), of the path of the light beam through the sample cell.

$$A = \varepsilon \times C \times l \quad \text{or} \quad \varepsilon = \frac{A}{C \times l}$$

For 2,5-dimethyl-2,4-hexadiene dissolved in methanol the molar absorptivity at the wavelength of maximum absorbance (242.5 nm) is 13,100 M^{-1} cm^{-1}. In the chemical literature this would be reported as

2,5-Dimethyl-2,4-hexadiene, $\lambda_{max}^{methanol}$ 242.5 nm $\quad$ ($\varepsilon = 13,100$)

As we noted earlier, when compounds absorb light in the UV and visible regions, electrons are excited from lower electronic energy levels to higher ones. For this reason, visible and UV spectra are often called **electronic spectra.** The absorption spectrum of 2,5-dimethyl-2,4-hexadiene is a typical electronic spectrum because the absorption band (or peak) is very broad. Most absorption bands in the visible and UV region are broad because each electronic energy level has associated with it vibrational and rotational levels. Thus, electron transitions may occur from any of several

† In older literature, the molar absorptivity (ε) is often referred to as the molar extinction coefficient.

vibrational and rotational states of one electronic level to any of several vibrational and rotational states of a higher level.

Alkenes and nonconjugated dienes usually have absorption maxima below 200 nm. Ethene, for example, gives an absorption maximum at 171 nm; 1,4-pentadiene gives an absorption maximum at 178 nm. These absorptions occur at wavelengths that are out of the range of operation of most visible–ultraviolet spectrometers because they occur where the oxygen in air also absorbs. Special air-free techniques must be employed in measuring them.

Compounds whose molecules contain *conjugated* multiple bonds have maxima at wavelengths longer than 200 nm. For example, 1,3-butadiene absorbs at 217 nm. This longer-wavelength absorption by conjugated dienes is a direct consequence of conjugation.

We can understand how conjugation of multiple bonds brings about absorption of light at longer wavelengths if we examine Fig. 14.4.

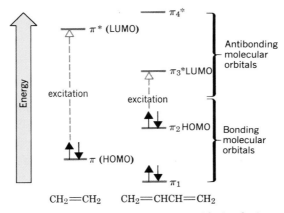

FIGURE 14.4 The relative energies of the π molecular orbitals of ethene and 1,3-butadiene (Section 12.7).

When a molecule absorbs light at its longest wavelength, an electron is excited from its highest occupied molecular orbital (HOMO) to the lowest unoccupied molecular orbital (LUMO). For most alkenes and alkadienes the HOMO is a bonding π orbital and the LUMO is an antibonding π^* orbital. The wavelength of the absorption maximum is determined by the difference in energy between these two levels. The energy gap between the HOMO and LUMO of ethene is greater than that between the corresponding orbitals of 1,3-butadiene. Thus, the $\pi \longrightarrow \pi^*$ electron excitation of ethene requires absorption of light of greater energy (shorter wavelength) than the corresponding $\pi_2 \longrightarrow \pi_3^*$ excitation in 1,3-butadiene. The energy difference between the HOMOs and the LUMOs of the two compounds is reflected in their absorption spectra. Ethene has its λ_{max} at 171 nm; 1,3-butadiene has a λ_{max} at 217 nm.

The narrower gap between the HOMO and the LUMO in 1,3-butadiene results from the conjugation of the double bonds. Molecular orbital calculations indicate that a much larger gap should occur in isolated alkadienes. This is borne out experimentally. Isolated alkadienes give absorption spectra similar to those of alkenes. Their λ_{max} are at shorter wavelengths, usually below 200 nm. As we mentioned, 1,4-pentadiene has its λ_{max} at 178 nm.

Conjugated alkatrienes absorb at longer wavelengths than conjugated alka-dienes, and this too can be accounted for in molecular orbital calculations. The energy gap between the HOMO and the LUMO of an alkatriene is even smaller than that of an alkadiene. In fact, there is a general rule that states that *the greater the number of conjugated multiple bonds a compound contains, the longer will be the wavelength at which the compound absorbs light.*

Polyenes with eight or more conjugated double bonds absorb light in the visible region of the spectrum. For example, β-carotene, a precursor of Vitamin A and a compound that imparts its orange color to carrots, has 11 conjugated double bonds; β-carotene has an absorption maximum at 497 nm, well into the visible region. Light of 497 nm has a blue-green color; this is the light that is absorbed by β-carotene. We perceive the complementary color of blue green, which is red orange.

β-Carotene

Lycopene, a compound partly responsible for the red color of tomatoes, also has 11 conjugated double bonds. Lycopene has an absorption maximum at 505 nm, and it absorbs there intensely. (Approximately 0.02 g of lycopene can be isolated from 1 kg of fresh, ripe tomatoes.)

Lycopene

Table 14.1 gives the values of λ_{max} for a number of unsaturated compounds.

Compounds with carbon–oxygen double bonds also absorb light in the UV region. Acetone, for example, has a broad absorption peak at 280 nm that corresponds to the excitation of an electron from one of the unshared pairs (a nonbonding or "*n*" electron) to the π^* orbital of the carbon–oxygen double bond:

Acetone
$\lambda_{max} = 280nm$
$\varepsilon_{max} = 15$

Compounds in which the carbon–oxygen double bond is conjugated with a carbon–carbon double bond have absorption maxima corresponding to $n \longrightarrow \pi^*$ excitations and $\pi \longrightarrow \pi^*$ excitations. The $n \longrightarrow \pi^*$ absorption maximum occurs at longer wave-lengths but is much weaker.

14.2 VISIBLE AND ULTRAVIOLET SPECTROSCOPY

$$CH_2=CH-C=O$$
$$\mid$$
$$CH_3$$

$n \longrightarrow \pi^* \; \lambda_{max} = 324 \text{ nm}, \; \varepsilon_{max} = 24$

$\pi \longrightarrow \pi^* \; \lambda_{max} = 219 \text{ nm}, \; \varepsilon_{max} = 3600$

TABLE 14.1 Long-wavelength absorption maxima of unsaturated hydrocarbons

COMPOUND	STRUCTURE	λ_{max} (nm)	ε_{max}
Ethene	$CH_2=CH_2$	171	15,530
trans-3-Hexene	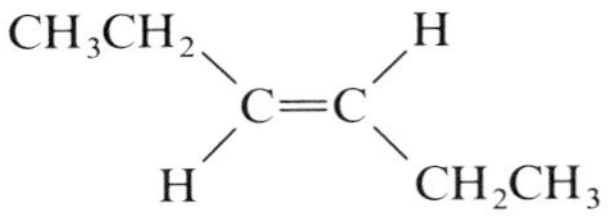 CH_3CH_2 and H on $C=C$ with H and CH_2CH_3	184	10,000
Cyclohexene	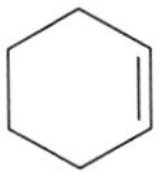	182	7,600
1-Octene	$CH_3(CH_2)_5CH=CH_2$	177	12,600
1-Octyne	$CH_3(CH_2)_5C\equiv CH$	185	2,000
1,3-Butadiene	$CH_2=CHCH=CH_2$	217	21,000
cis-1,3-Pentadiene	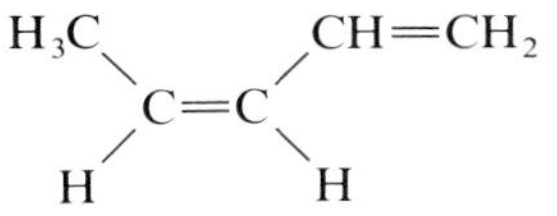 H_3C, $CH=CH_2$ on $C=C$ with H, H	223	22,600
trans-1,3-Pentadiene	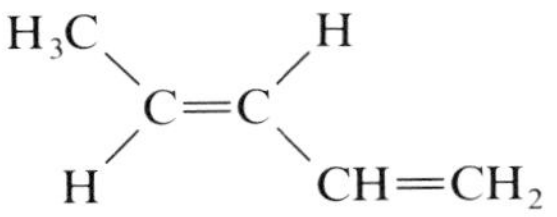 H_3C, H on $C=C$ with H, $CH=CH_2$	223.5	23,000
1-Buten-3-yne	$CH_2=CHC\equiv CH$	228	7,800
1,4-Pentadiene	$CH_2=CHCH_2CH=CH_2$	178	17,000
1,3-Cyclopentadiene		239	3,400
1,3-Cyclohexadiene		256	8,000
trans-1,3,5-Hexatriene	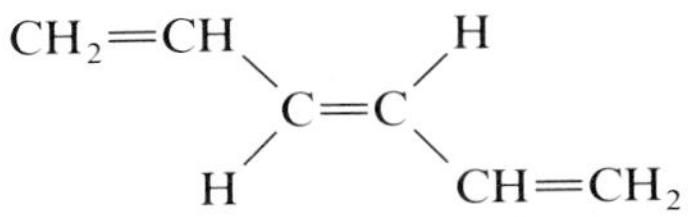 $CH_2=CH$, H on $C=C$ with H, $CH=CH_2$	274	50,000

Problem 14.1

Two compounds, **A** and **B**, have the same molecular formula C_6H_8. Both **A** and **B** decolorize bromine in carbon tetrachloride and both give positive tests with cold dilute potassium permanganate. Both **A** and **B** react with two molar equivalents of hydrogen in the presence of platinum to yield cyclohexane. Compound **A** shows an absorption maximum at 256 nm, while **B** shows no absorption maximum beyond 200 nm. What are the structures of **A** and **B**?

Problem 14.2 ─────────────────────────────────

Three compounds, **D**, **E**, and **F**, have the same molecular formula C_5H_6. In the presence of a platinum catalyst, all three compounds absorb 3 molar equivalents of hydrogen and yield pentane. Compounds **E** and **F** give a precipitate when treated with ammoniacal silver nitrate; compound **D** gives no reaction. Compounds **D** and **E** show an absorption maximum near 230 nm. Compound **F** shows no absorption maximum beyond 200 nm. Propose structures for **D**, **E**, and **F**.

14.3 INFRARED SPECTROSCOPY

We saw in Section 14.2 that many organic compounds absorb radiation in the visible and UV regions of the electromagnetic spectrum. We also saw that when compounds absorb radiation of the visible and UV regions, electrons are excited from lower energy molecular orbitals to higher ones.

Organic compounds also absorb electromagnetic energy in the infrared (IR) region of the spectrum. Infrared radiation does not have sufficient energy to cause the excitation of electrons, but it does cause atoms and groups of atoms of organic compounds to vibrate faster about the covalent bonds that connect them. These vibrations are *quantized,* and as they occur, the compounds absorb IR energy in particular regions of the spectrum.

Infrared spectrometers operate in a manner similar to that of visible–UV spectrometers. A beam of IR radiation is passed through the sample and is constantly compared with a reference beam as the frequency of the incident radiation is varied. The spectrometer plots the results as a graph showing absorption versus frequency or wavelength.

The location of an IR absorption band (or peak) can be specified in **frequency units** by its **wavenumber** ($\bar{\nu}$) measured in reciprocal centimeters (cm^{-1}), or by its **wavelength** (λ) measured in micrometers (μm; old name micron, μ). The wavenumber is the number of cycles of the wave in each centimeter along the light beam, and the wavelength is the length of the wave, crest to crest.

$$\bar{\nu} = \frac{1}{\lambda} \text{ (with } \lambda \text{ in cm)} \quad \text{or} \quad \bar{\nu} = \frac{10,000}{\lambda} \text{ (with } \lambda \text{ in } \mu m)$$

In their vibrations covalent bonds behave as if they were tiny springs connecting the atoms. When the atoms vibrate they can do so only at certain frequencies, as if the bonds were "tuned." Because of this, covalently bonded atoms have only particular vibrational energy levels. The excitation of a molecule from one vibrational energy level to another occurs only when the compound absorbs IR radiation of a particular energy, meaning a particular wavelength or frequency (since $\Delta E = h\nu$).

Molecules can vibrate in a variety of ways. Two atoms joined by a covalent bond can undergo a stretching vibration where the atoms move back and forth as if joined by a spring.

A stretching vibration

Three atoms can also undergo a variety of stretching and bending vibrations:

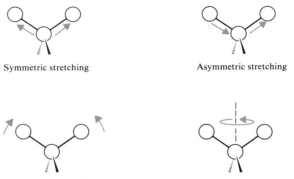

Symmetric stretching   Asymmetric stretching

An in-plane bending   An out-of-plane bending
vibration   vibration

The *frequency* of a given stretching vibration and thus *its location in an IR spectrum* can be related to two factors. These are *the masses of the bonded atoms* — light atoms vibrate at higher frequencies than heavier ones — *and the relative stiffness of the bond*. Triple bonds are stiffer (and vibrate at higher frequencies) than double bonds and double bonds are stiffer (and vibrate at higher frequencies) than single bonds. We can see some of these effects in Table 14.2. Notice that stretching frequencies of groups involving hydrogen (a light atom) such as C—H, N—H, and O—H all occur at relatively high frequencies:

Group	Bond	Frequency Range (cm^{-1})
Alkyl	C—H	2853–2962
Alcohol	O—H	3590–3650
Amine	N—H	3300–3500

Notice too, that triple bonds vibrate at higher frequencies than double bonds:

Bond	Frequency Range (cm^{-1})
C≡C	2100–2260
C≡N	2220–2260
C=C	1620–1680
C=O	1630–1780

The IR spectra of even relatively simple compounds contain many absorption peaks. It can be shown that a nonlinear molecule of n atoms has $3n - 6$ possible *fundamental* vibrational modes that can be responsible for the absorption of IR radiation. This means that, theoretically, methane has 9 possible fundamental absorption peaks and benzene has 30.

Not all molecular vibrations result in the absorption of IR energy. ***In order for a vibration to occur with the absorption of IR energy, the dipole moment of the molecule must change as the vibration occurs.*** Thus when the four hydrogen atoms of methane

TABLE 14.2 Characteristic infrared absorptions of groups

GROUP		FREQUENCY RANGE (cm^{-1})	INTENSITY^a
A. Alkyl			
C—H (stretching)		2853–2962	(m–s)
Isopropyl, —CH(CH$_3$)$_2$		1380–1385	(s)
	and	1365–1370	(s)
tert-Butyl, —C(CH$_3$)$_3$		1385–1395	(m)
	and	~1365	(s)
B. Alkenyl			
C—H (stretching)		3010–3095	(m)
C=C (stretching)		1620–1680	(v)
R—CH=CH$_2$		985–1000	(s)
	and	905–920	(s)
R$_2$C=CH$_2$ (out-of-plane		880–900	(s)
cis-RCH=CHR C—H bendings)		675–730	(s)
trans-RCH=CHR		960–975	(s)
C. Alkynyl			
≡C—H (stretching)		~3300	(s)
C≡C (stretching)		2100–2260	(v)
D. Aromatic			
Ar—H (stretching)		~3030	(v)
Aromatic substitution type (C—H out-of-plane bendings)			
Monosubstituted		690–710	(very s)
	and	730–770	(very s)
o-Disubstituted		735–770	(s)
m-Disubstituted		680–725	(s)
	and	750–810	(very s)
p-Disubstituted		800–840	(very s)
E. Alcohols, Phenols, and Carboxylic Acids			
O—H (stretching)			
Alcohols, phenols (dilute solutions)		3590–3650	(sharp, v)
Alcohols, phenols (hydrogen bonded)		3200–3550	(broad, s)
Carboxylic acids (hydrogen bonded)		2500–3000	(broad, v)
F. Aldehydes, Ketones, Esters, and Carboxylic Acids			
C=O (stretching)		1630–1780	(s)
Aldehydes		1690–1740	(s)

TABLE 14.2   (continued)

GROUP	FREQUENCY RANGE (cm^{-1})	INTENSITY[a]
Ketones	1680–1750	(s)
Esters	1735–1750	(s)
Carboxylic acids	1710–1780	(s)
Amides	1630–1690	(s)
G. Amines		
N—H	3300–3500	(m)
H. Nitriles		
C≡N	2220–2260	(m)

[a] Abbreviations: s = strong, m = medium, w = weak, v = variable, ~ = approximately.

vibrate symmetrically, methane does not absorb IR energy. Symmetrical vibrations of the carbon–carbon double and triple bonds of ethene and ethyne do not result in the absorption of IR radiation, either.

Vibrational absorption may occur outside the region measured by a particular IR spectrophotometer and vibrational absorptions may occur so closely together that peaks fall on top of peaks. These factors, together with the absence of absorptions because of vibrations that have no dipole moment change, cause most IR spectra to contain fewer peaks than the formula $3n - 6$ would predict.

However, other factors bring about even more absorption peaks. Overtones (harmonics) of fundamental absorption bands may be seen in IR spectra even though these overtones occur with greatly reduced intensity. Bands called combination bands and difference bands also appear in IR spectra.

Because IR spectra contain so many peaks, the possibility that two compounds will have the same IR spectrum is exceedingly small. It is because of this that an IR

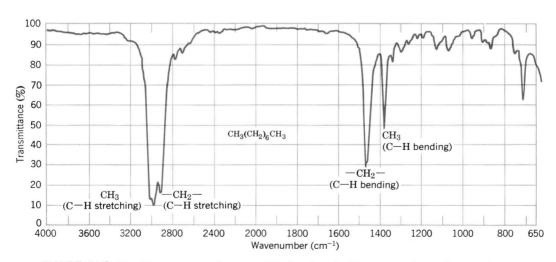

FIGURE 14.5   The IR spectrum of octane. (Notice that, in IR spectra, the peaks are "upside down." This is simply a result of the way IR spectrophotometers operate.)

spectrum has been called the "fingerprint" of a molecule. Thus, with organic compounds, if two pure samples give different IR spectra, one can be certain that they are different compounds. If they give the same IR spectrum then they are the same compound.

In the hands of one skilled in their interpretation, IR spectra contain a wealth of information about the structures of compounds. We show some of the information that can be gathered from the spectra of octane and toluene in Figs. 14.5 and 14.6. We have neither the time nor the space here to develop the skill that would lead to complete interpretations of IR spectra, but we can learn how to recognize the presence of absorption peaks in the IR spectrum that result from vibrations of characteristic functional groups in the compound. By doing only this, however, we shall be able to use the information we gather from IR spectra in a powerful way, particularly when we couple it with the information we gather from NMR spectra.

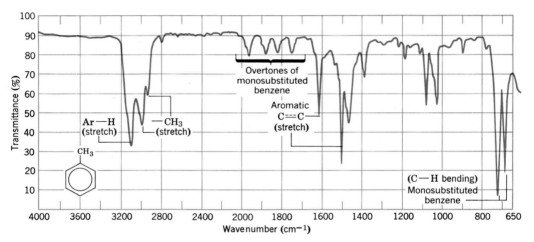

FIGURE 14.6 The IR spectrum of toluene.

Let us now see how we can apply the data given in Table 14.2 to the interpretation of IR spectra.

14.3A HYDROCARBONS

All hydrocarbons give absorption peaks in the $2800-3300$-cm^{-1} region that are associated with carbon–hydrogen stretching vibrations. We can use these peaks in interpreting IR spectra because the exact location of the peak depends on the strength (and stiffness) of the C—H bond, which in turn depend on the hybridization state of the carbon that bears the hydrogen. We have already seen that C—H bonds involving sp-hybridized carbon are strongest and those involving sp^3-hybridized carbon are weakest. The order of bond strength is

$$sp > sp^2 > sp^3$$

This too is the order of the bond stiffness.

The carbon–hydrogen stretching peaks of hydrogen atoms attached to sp-hybridized carbon atoms occur at highest frequencies, about 3300 cm^{-1}. Thus, $\equiv$C—H groups of terminal alkynes give peaks in this region. We can see the absorption of the acetylenic hydrogen of 1-hexyne at 3320 cm^{-1} in Fig. 14.7.

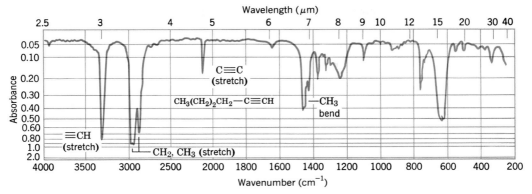

FIGURE 14.7 The IR spectrum of 1-hexyne. (Spectrum courtesy of Sadtler Research Laboratories, Inc., Philadelphia.)

The carbon–hydrogen stretching peaks of hydrogen atoms attached to sp^2-hybridized carbon atoms occur in the 3000–3100-cm^{-1} region. Thus, alkenyl hydrogen atoms and the C—H groups of aromatic rings give absorption peaks in this region. We can see the alkenyl C—H absorption peak of 3080 cm^{-1} in the spectrum of 1-hexene (Fig. 14.8) and we can see the C—H absorption of the aromatic hydrogen atoms at 3090 cm^{-1} in the spectrum of toluene (Fig. 14.6).

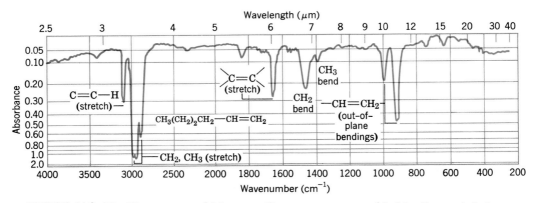

FIGURE 14.8 The IR spectrum of 1-hexene. (Spectrum courtesy of Sadtler Research Laboratories, Inc., Philadelphia.)

The carbon–hydrogen stretching bands of hydrogen atoms attached to sp^3-hybridized carbon atoms occur at lowest frequencies, in the 2800–3000-cm^{-1} region. We can see methyl and methylene absorption peaks in the spectra of octane (Fig. 14.5), toluene (Fig. 14.6), 1-hexyne (Fig. 14.7), and 1-hexene (Fig. 14.8).

Hydrocarbons also give absorption peaks in their IR spectra that result from carbon–carbon bond stretchings. Carbon–carbon single bonds normally give rise to very weak peaks that are usually of little use in assigning structures. More useful peaks arise from multiple carbon–carbon bonds, however. Carbon–carbon double bonds give absorption peaks in the 1620–1680-cm^{-1} region and carbon–carbon triple bonds give absorption peaks between 2100 and 2260 cm^{-1}. These absorptions are not usually strong ones and they will not be present at all if the double or triple bond is symmetrically substituted. (No dipole moment change will be associated with the vibration.) The stretchings of the carbon–carbon bonds of benzene rings usually give a set of characteristic sharp peaks in the 1450–1600-cm^{-1} region.

Absorptions arising from carbon–hydrogen bending vibrations of alkenes occur in the 600–1000-cm^{-1} region. The exact location of these peaks can often be used to determine the *nature of the double bond and its configuration.*

Monosubstituted alkenes give two strong peaks in the 905–920- and the 985–1000-cm^{-1} regions. Disubstituted alkenes of the type $R_2C{=}CH_2$ give a strong peak in the 880–900-cm^{-1} range. *cis*-Alkenes give an absorption peak in the 675–730-cm^{-1} region and *trans*-alkenes give a peak between 960 and 975 cm^{-1}. These ranges for the carbon–hydrogen bending vibrations can be used with fair reliability for alkenes that do not have an electron-releasing or electron-withdrawing substituent (other than an alkyl group) on one of the carbon atoms of the double bond. When electron-releasing or electron-withdrawing substituents are present on a double-bond carbon, the bending absorption peaks may be shifted out of the regions we have given.

14.3B SUBSTITUTED BENZENES

Ortho-, meta-, and para-disubstituted benzenes give absorption peaks in the 680–840-cm^{-1} region that characterize their substitution patterns. **Ortho-disubstituted benzenes** show a strong absorption peak arising from bending motions of the aromatic hydrogen atoms between 735 and 770 cm^{-1}. **Meta-disubstituted benzenes** show two peaks: one strong peak between 680 and 725 cm^{-1} and one very strong peak between 750 and 810 cm^{-1}. **Para-disubstituted benzenes** give a single very strong absorption between 800 and 840 cm^{-1}

Monosubstituted benzenes give two very strong peaks, between 690 and 710 cm^{-1} and between 730 and 770 cm^{-1} (see Fig. 14.6).

Problem 14.3 ———————————————————————————————————

Four benzenoid compounds, all with the formula C_7H_7Br, gave only the following IR peaks in the 680–840-cm^{-1} region.

A, 740 cm^{-1} (s)   **C**, 680 cm^{-1} (s) and 760 cm^{-1} (very s)
B, 800 cm^{-1} (very s)   **D**, 693 cm^{-1} (very s) and 765 cm^{-1} (very s)

Propose structures for **A**, **B**, **C**, and **D**.

14.3C OTHER FUNCTIONAL GROUPS

Infrared spectroscopy gives us an invaluable method for recognizing quickly and simply the presence of certain functional groups in a molecule. One important functional group that gives a prominent absorption peak in IR spectra is the **carbonyl group** $\diagdown \!\! C{=}O$. This group is present in aldehydes, ketones, esters, carboxylic acids, amides, and so forth. The carbon–oxygen double bond stretching frequency of all these groups gives a strong peak between 1630 and 1780 cm^{-1}. The exact location of the peak depends on whether it arises from an aldehyde, ketone, ester, and so forth. These locations are the following and we shall have more to say about carbonyl absorption peaks when we discuss these compounds in later chapters.

$$
\begin{array}{ccc}
\overset{\textstyle O}{\underset{\textstyle \|}{}} & \overset{\textstyle O}{\underset{\textstyle \|}{}} & \overset{\textstyle O}{\underset{\textstyle \|}{}} \\
R-C-H & R-C-R & R-C-OR \\
\text{Aldehyde} & \text{Ketone} & \text{Ester} \\
1690-1740\ cm^{-1} & 1680-1750\ cm^{-1} & 1735-1750\ cm^{-1}
\end{array}
$$

$$
\begin{array}{cc}
\overset{\textstyle O}{\underset{\textstyle \|}{}} & \overset{\textstyle O}{\underset{\textstyle \|}{}} \\
R-C-OH & R-C-NH_2 \\
\text{Carboxylic acid} & \text{Amide} \\
1710-1780\ cm^{-1} & 1630-1690\ cm^{-1}
\end{array}
$$

The **hydroxyl groups** of alcohols and phenols are also easy to recognize in IR spectra by their O—H stretching absorptions. These bonds also give us direct evidence for hydrogen bonding. If an alcohol or phenol is present as a very dilute solution in CCl_4, O—H absorption occurs as a very sharp peak in the 3590–3650-cm^{-1} region. In very dilute solution or in the gas phase, formation of intermolecular hydrogen bonds does not take place because the molecules are too widely separated. The sharp peak in the 3590–3650-cm^{-1} region, therefore, is attributed to "free" (unassociated) hydroxyl groups. Increasing the concentration of the alcohol or phenol causes the sharp peak to be replaced by a broad band in the 3200–3550-cm^{-1} region. This absorption is attributed to OH groups that are associated through intermolecular hydrogen bonding.

Very dilute solutions of 1° and 2° **amines** also give sharp peaks in the 3300–3500-cm^{-1} region arising from free N—H stretching vibrations. Primary amines give two sharp peaks; secondary amines give only one. Tertiary amines, because they have no N—H bond do not absorb in this region.

$$
\begin{array}{cc}
RNH_2 & R_2NH \\
\text{1° Amine} & \text{2° Amine} \\
\text{Two peaks in} & \text{One peak in} \\
3300-3500\text{-}cm^{-1} & 3300-3500\text{-}cm^{-1} \\
\text{region} & \text{region}
\end{array}
$$

Hydrogen bonding causes these peaks to broaden. The NH groups of **amides** also give similar absorption peaks.

14.4 NUCLEAR MAGNETIC RESONANCE SPECTROSCOPY

The nuclei of certain elements and isotopes behave as though they were spinning about an axis. The nuclei of ordinary hydrogen (^1H) and those of carbon-13 (^{13}C) have this property. When one places a compound containing ^1H or ^{13}C in a very strong magnetic field and simultaneously irradiates it with electromagnetic energy, the nuclei of the compound may absorb energy through a process called magnetic resonance.* This absorption of energy is *quantized*. Absorption of energy does not

---

* Magnetic resonance is an entirely different phenomenon from the resonance theory that we have discussed in earlier chapters.

CHAPTER 14. SPECTROSCOPIC METHODS OF STRUCTURE DETERMINATION

occur unless the strength of the magnetic field and the frequency of electromagnetic radiation are at specific values.

Instruments known as nuclear magnetic resonance (NMR) spectrometers allow chemists to measure the absorption of energy by ^1H or ^{13}C nuclei and by the nuclei of other elements that we shall learn in Section 14.5. These instruments use very powerful magnets and irradiate the sample with electromagnetic radiation in the radio frequency (rf) region. Two types of NMR spectrometers based on different designs are now used by organic chemists.

Nuclear magnetic resonance spectrometers can be designed so that they irradiate the compound with electromagnetic energy of a constant frequency while the magnetic field strength is varied (Fig. 14.9) or swept. (This amounts to the same thing as holding the magnetic field constant while the electromagnetic frequency is swept and is easier to do.) When the magnetic field reaches the correct strength, the nuclei absorb energy and resonance occurs. This absorption causes a tiny electrical current to flow in an antenna coil surrounding the sample. The instrument then amplifies this current and displays it as a signal (a peak or series of peaks) in frequency units (Hz) on a strip of calibrated chart paper.

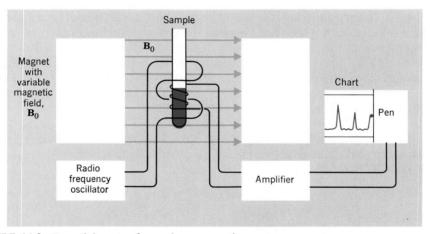

FIGURE 14.9 Essential parts of a nuclear magnetic resonance spectrometer.

Currently, the *state of the art* NMR instruments use superconducting magnets that have a much higher magnetic field strength than their predecessors; this gives these instruments much increased resolution and greater sensitivity. Instead of sweeping the magnetic field while irradiating the sample with electromagnetic energy in the rf region, the instrument irradiates the sample with a short pulse of rf radiation (for $\sim 10^{-5}$ s). This rf pulse excites all the nuclei at once, as opposed to each nucleus being individually excited as with the sweep method. The data obtained from the pulse method of excitement, however, are very different from that obtained by the sweep method. One difference is that the sweep method takes 2–5 min to give a complete spectrum, while the pulse method can produce a spectrum in as little as 5 s. Another difference is that the sweep method gives us directly a spectrum as a function of frequency (in Hz). With the pulse method, however, the data are collected as a function of time. After the pulse, a signal is produced in the probe, and this signal contains information about all the peaks simultaneously. Thus, the signal must be transformed into a function of frequency before the individual peaks can be identified.

To transform the signal from the time domain to the frequency domain, a computer must carry out what is called a Fourier transformation (or FT). The mathematics of this process need not be of concern to us; the only important point is that in it data are sampled and stored as discreet points, that is, they are *digitized.* The signal from a pulsed NMR experiment is treated in this way: After excitation by an rf pulse, the signal is detected as a voltage in the NMR probe. Then, after amplification, the signal is converted to a number and stored in the memory of the computer. Once enough data points are acquired to give sufficient digital resolution, the acquired data can be transformed by the Fourier method to the frequency spectrum.

We begin our study of NMR spectroscopy in this section with a brief examination of the main features of spectra arising from hydrogen nuclei. These spectra are often called proton magnetic resonance (PMR) spectra or ^{1}H NMR spectra. After this brief overview we shall examine in more detail other aspects of NMR spectroscopy.

If hydrogen nuclei were stripped of their electrons and isolated from other nuclei, all hydrogen nuclei (protons) would absorb energy at the same magnetic field strength for a given frequency of electromagnetic radiation. If this were the case, NMR spectrometers would only be very expensive instruments for analysis for hydrogen.

Fortunately, the nuclei of hydrogen atoms of compounds of interest to the organic chemist are not stripped of their electrons, and they are not isolated from each other. Some hydrogen nuclei are in regions of greater electron density than others. Because of this, the protons of these compounds absorb energy at *slightly different* magnetic field strengths. The actual field strength at which absorption occurs is highly dependent on the magnetic environment of each proton. This magnetic environment depends on two factors: magnetic fields generated by circulating electrons and magnetic fields that result from other nearby protons (or other magnetic nuclei).

Figure 14.10 shows the ^{1}H NMR spectrum of *p*-xylene. The spectrum is the blue line. The black line is called the "integral curve" and we shall explain this later.

Magnetic field strength is measured along the bottom of the spectrum on a delta (δ) scale in units of parts per million (ppm) and along the top in hertz (cycles per second, cps). We shall have more to say about these units later; for the moment, we need only point out that the externally applied magnetic field strength increases from left to right. A signal that occurs at $\delta = 7$ ppm occurs at a lower external magnetic field strength than one that occurs at $\delta = 2$ ppm. Signals on the left of the spectrum are also said to occur **downfield** and those on the right are said to be **upfield.**

The spectrum in Fig. 14.10 shows a small signal at $\delta = 0$ ppm. This is caused by a compound that has been added to the sample to allow calibration of the instrument.

The first feature we want to notice is the relation between the number of signals in the spectrum and the number of different types of hydrogen atoms in the compound.

p-Xylene has only *two* different types of hydrogen atoms, and it gives only *two* signals in its NMR spectrum.

The two different types of hydrogen atoms of *p*-xylene are the hydrogen atoms of the methyl groups and the hydrogen atoms of the benzene ring. The six methyl hydrogen atoms of *p*-xylene are all *equivalent* and they are in a different environment from the four hydrogen atoms of the ring. The six methyl hydrogen atoms give rise to the signal that occurs at $\delta = 2.30$ ppm. The four hydrogen atoms of the benzene ring are also equivalent; they give rise to the signal at $\delta = 7.05$ ppm.

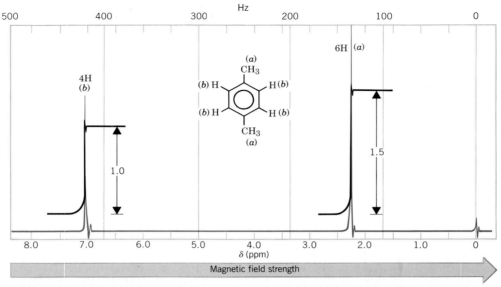

FIGURE 14.10 The ^{1}H NMR spectrum of p-xylene. (Spectrum courtesy of Varian Associates, Palo Alto, CA.)

Next, we want to examine the relative magnitude of the peaks (or signals), for these are often helpful in assigning peaks to particular groups of hydrogen atoms. What is important here is not necessarily the height of each peak, but *the area underneath it.* These areas, when accurately measured (the spectrometers do this automatically), are in the same ratio as the number of hydrogen atoms causing each signal. We can see, however, without measuring, that the area under the signal for the methyl hydrogen atoms of p-xylene (6H) is larger than that for the phenyl hydrogen atoms (4H). When these areas are measured accurately they are found to be in a ratio of 1.5:1 or 3:2 or 6:4.

The black line superimposed on each peak in the spectrum of p-xylene shows one way that nuclear magnetic spectrometers display the relative area under each peak. This line, called **the integral curve,** rises by an amount that is proportional to the area under each peak. Figure 14.10 shows how these heights are measured. In this case the ratio of heights on the integral curve is 1.5:1 or 3:2 or 6:4.

A third feature of ^{1}H NMR spectra that provides us with information about the structure of a compound can be illustrated if we examine the spectrum for 1,1,2-trichloroethane (Fig. 14.11).

In Fig. 14.11 we have an example of signal splitting. Signal splitting is a phenomenon that arises from magnetic influences of hydrogens on atoms adjacent to those bearing the hydrogen atoms causing the general signal. The signal (b) from the two equivalent hydrogen atoms of the $-CH_2Cl$ group is split into two peaks (a doublet) by the magnetic influence of the hydrogen of the $-CHCl_2$ group. Conversely, the signal (a) from the hydrogen of the $-CHCl_2$ group is split into three peaks (a triplet) by the magnetic influences of the two equivalent hydrogens of the $-CH_2Cl$ group.

At this point signal splitting may seem like an unnecessary complication. As we gain experience in interpreting ^{1}H NMR spectra we shall find that because signal splitting occurs in a predictable way, it often provides us with important information about the structure of the compound.

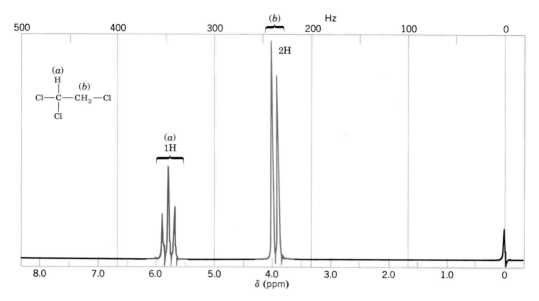

FIGURE 14.11 The ^{1}H NMR spectrum of 1,1,2-trichloroethane. (Spectrum courtesy of Varian Associates, Palo Alto, CA.)

Now that we have had an introduction to the important features of ^{1}H NMR spectra, we are in a position to consider them in greater detail.

14.5 NUCLEAR SPIN: THE ORIGIN OF THE SIGNAL

We are already familiar with the concept of electron spin and with the fact that the spins of electrons confer on them the spin quantum states of $+\frac{1}{2}$ or $-\frac{1}{2}$. Electron spin is the basis for the Pauli exclusion principle (Section 1.11); it allows us to understand how two electrons with paired spins may occupy the same atomic or molecular orbital.

The nuclei of certain isotopes also spin and therefore these nuclei possess spin quantum numbers, I. The nucleus of ordinary hydrogen, ^{1}H (i.e., a proton), is like the electron; its spin quantum number I is $\frac{1}{2}$ and it can assume either of two spin states: $+\frac{1}{2}$ or $-\frac{1}{2}$. These correspond to the magnetic moments allowed for $I = \frac{1}{2}$, $m = +\frac{1}{2}$ or $-\frac{1}{2}$. Other nuclei with spin quantum numbers $I = \frac{1}{2}$ are ^{13}C, ^{19}F, and ^{31}P. Some nuclei, such as ^{12}C, ^{16}O, and ^{32}S, have no spin ($I = 0$) and these nuclei do not give an NMR spectrum. Other nuclei have spin quantum numbers greater than $\frac{1}{2}$. In our treatment here, however, we shall be primarily concerned with the spectra that arise from protons and from ^{13}C, both of which have $I = \frac{1}{2}$. We shall begin with proton spectra.

Since the proton is electrically charged, the spinning proton generates a tiny magnetic moment — one that coincides with the axis of spin (Fig. 14.12). This tiny magnetic moment confers on the spinning proton the properties of a tiny bar magnet.

In the absence of a magnetic field (Fig. 14.13a), the magnetic moments of the protons of a given sample are randomly oriented. When a compound containing hydrogen (and thus protons) is placed in an applied external magnetic field, however, the protons may assume one of two possible orientations with respect to the external

CHAPTER 14. SPECTROSCOPIC METHODS OF STRUCTURE DETERMINATION

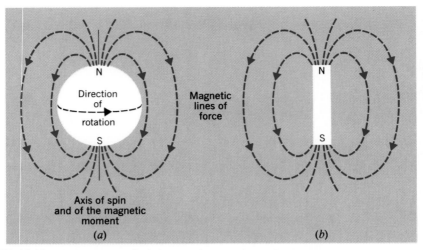

FIGURE 14.12 (a) The magnetic field associated with a spinning proton. (b) The spinning proton resembles a tiny bar magnet.

magnetic field. The magnetic moment of the proton may be aligned "with" the external field or "against" it (Fig. 14.13b). These alignments correspond to the two spin states mentioned earlier.

As we might expect, the two alignments of the proton in an external field are not of equal energy. When the proton is aligned with the magnetic field, its energy is lower than when it is aligned against the magnetic field.

Energy is required to "flip" the proton from its lower energy state (with the field) to its higher energy state (against the field). In an NMR spectrometer this energy is supplied by electromagnetic radiation in the rf region. When this energy absorption occurs, the nuclei are said to be *in resonance* with the electromagnetic radiation. The energy required is proportional to the strength of the magnetic field (Fig. 14.14). One can show by relatively simple calculations that, in a magnetic field of approximately 14,100 G, electromagnetic radiation of 60×10^6 cycles per second (cps) (60 MHz)

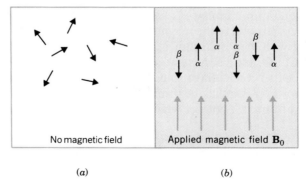

FIGURE 14.13 (a) In the absence of a magnetic field the magnetic moments of protons (represented by arrows) are randomly oriented. (b) When an external magnetic field ($\mathbf{B_0}$) is applied the protons orient themselves. Some are aligned with the applied field (α spin state) and some against it (β spin state).

supplies the correct amount of energy for protons.* The spectra given in this chapter are 60-MHz spectra.

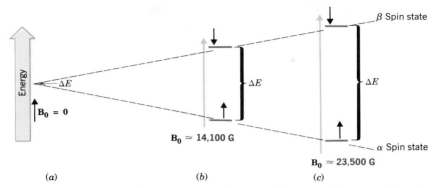

FIGURE 14.14 The energy difference between the two spin states of a proton depends on the strength of the applied external magnetic field, $\mathbf{B}_0$. (a) If there is no applied field ($\mathbf{B}_0 = 0$), there is no energy difference between the two states. (b) If $\mathbf{B}_0 \simeq 14,100$ G, the energy difference corresponds to that of electromagnetic radiation of 60×10^6 Hz (60 MHz). (c) In a magnetic field of approximately 23,500 G, the energy difference corresponds to electromagnetic radiation of 100×10^6 Hz (100 MHz). Instruments are available that operate at these and even higher frequencies (as high as 500 MHz).

14.6 SHIELDING AND DESHIELDING OF PROTONS

All protons do not absorb energy at the same external magnetic field strength. The two spectra that we examined earlier demonstrate this for us. The aromatic protons of p-xylene absorb at lower field strength (δ 7.05 ppm); the various alkyl protons of p-xylene and 1,1,2-trichloroethane all absorb at higher magnetic fields strengths.

The general position of a signal in an NMR spectrum — that is, the strength of the magnetic field required to bring about absorption of energy — can be related to electron densities and electron circulations in the compounds. Under the influence of an external magnetic field the electrons move in certain preferred paths. Because they do, and because electrons are charged particles, they generate tiny magnetic fields.

We can see how this happens if we consider the electrons around the proton in a σ bond of a C—H group. In doing so, we shall oversimplify the situation by assuming that σ electrons move in generally circular paths. The magnetic field generated by these σ electrons is shown in Fig. 14.15.

The small magnetic field generated by the electrons is called **an induced field.** *At the proton, the induced magnetic field opposes the external magnetic field.* This means that the actual magnetic field sensed by the proton is slightly less than the external field. The electrons are said *to shield* the proton.

A proton shielded by electrons will not, of course, absorb at the same external field strength as a proton that has no electrons. A shielded proton will absorb *at higher*

---

* The relationship between the frequency of the radiation (v) and the strength of the magnetic field ($\mathbf{B}_0$) is,

$$v = \frac{\mu \mathbf{B}_0}{2\pi}$$

where μ is the magnetogyric (or gyromagnetic) ratio. For a proton, $\mu = 26,753$ rad s^{-1} G^{-1}.

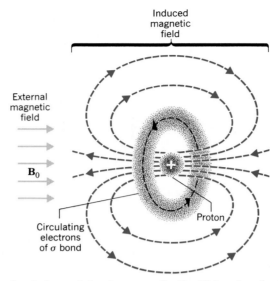

FIGURE 14.15 The circulations of the electrons of a C—H bond under the influence of an external magnetic field. The electron circulations generate a small magnetic field (an induced field) that shields the proton from the external field.

external field strengths; the external field must be made larger by the spectrometer in order to compensate for the small induced field (Fig. 14.16).

The extent to which a proton is shielded by the circulation of σ electrons depends on the relative electron density around the proton. This electron density depends largely on the presence or absence of electronegative groups. Electronegative groups withdraw electron density from the C—H bond, particularly if they are attached to the same carbon. We can see an example of this effect in the spectrum of 1,1,2-trichloroethane (Fig. 14.11). The proton of C-1 absorbs at a lower magnetic field strength (δ 5.77 ppm) than the protons of C-2 (δ 3.95 ppm). Carbon-1 bears two highly electronegative chloro groups, whereas C-2 bears only one. The protons of C-2, consequently, are more effectively shielded because the σ electron density around them is greater.

The circulations of delocalized π electrons generate magnetic fields that can either **shield or deshield** nearby protons. Whether shielding or deshielding occurs depends on the location of the proton in the *induced* field. The aromatic protons of benzene derivatives (Fig. 14.17) are *deshielded* because their locations are such that the induced magnetic field reinforces the applied magnetic field.

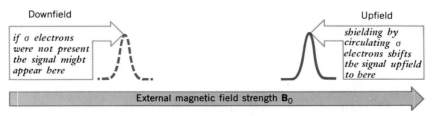

FIGURE 14.16 Shielding by σ electrons causes ^{1}H NMR absorption to be shifted to higher external magnetic field strengths.

14.6 SHIELDING AND DESHIELDING OF PROTONS

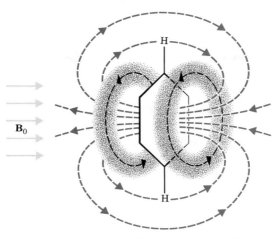

FIGURE 14.17 The induced magnetic field of the π electrons of benzene deshields the benzene protons. Deshielding occurs because at the location of the protons the induced field is in the same direction as the applied field.

Because of this deshielding effect the absorption of energy by phenyl protons occurs downfield at relatively low magnetic field strength. The protons of benzene itself absorb at δ 7.27 ppm. The aromatic protons of *p*-xylene (Fig. 14.10) absorb at δ 7.05 ppm.

The deshielding of external aromatic protons that results from the circulating π electrons is one of the best pieces of physical evidence that we have for π electron delocalization in aromatic rings. In fact, low field strength proton absorption is often used as a criterion for aromaticity in newly synthesized conjugated cyclic compounds.

Not all aromatic protons absorb at low magnetic field strengths, however. Large-ring aromatic compounds have been synthesized that have hydrogens *in the center of the ring* (in the π electron cavity). The protons of these internal hydrogen atoms absorb at unusually high magnetic field strengths because they are highly shielded by the opposing induced field in the center of the ring (cf. Fig. 14.17). These internal protons often absorb at field strengths greater than that used for the reference point, δ 0. The internal protons of [18]annulene (Fig. 14.18) absorb at δ −3.0 ppm.

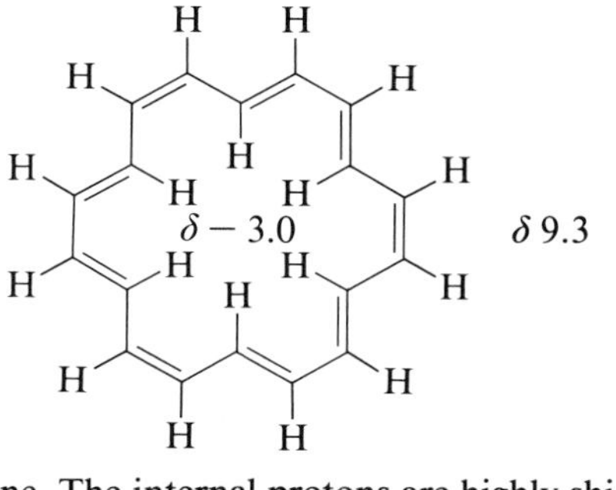

FIGURE 14.18 [18]Annulene. The internal protons are highly shielded and absorb at δ −3.0 ppm. The external protons are highly deshielded and absorb at δ 9.3 ppm.

Problem 14.4

The methyl protons of *trans*-15,16-dimethyldihydropyrene (Section 13.8A) absorb at very high magnetic field strengths, $\delta - 4.2$. Can you account for this?

Pi-electron circulations also *shield* the protons of ethyne causing them to absorb at higher magnetic field strengths than we might otherwise expect. If we were to consider *only* the relative electronegativities of carbon in its three hybridization states, we might expect the following order of protons attached to each type of carbon:

$$\text{(low field strength)} \quad sp < sp^2 < sp^3 \quad \text{(high field strength)}$$

In fact, acetylenic protons absorb between $\delta .2.0$ ppm and $\delta 3.0$ ppm and the order is

$$\text{(low field strength)} \quad sp^2 < sp < sp^3 \quad \text{(high field strength)}$$

This upfield shift of the absorption of acetylenic protons is a result of shielding produced by the circulating π electrons of the triple bond. The origin of this shielding is illustrated in Fig. 14.19.

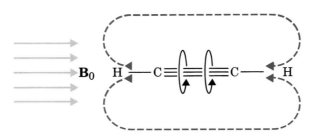

FIGURE 14.19 The shielding of acetylenic protons by π electron circulations. Shielding causes acetylenic protons to absorb further upfield than vinylic protons.

14.7 THE CHEMICAL SHIFT

We see now that shielding and deshielding effects cause the absorptions of protons to be shifted from the position at which a bare proton would absorb (i.e., a proton stripped of its electrons). Since these shifts result from the circulation of electrons in *chemical* bonds, they are called **chemical shifts.**

Chemical shifts are measured with reference to the absorption of protons of reference compounds. A reference is used because it is impractical to measure the actual value of the magnetic field at which absorptions occur. The reference compound most often used is tetramethylsilane (TMS). A small amount of tetramethylsilane is usually added to the sample whose spectrum is being measured, and the signal from the 12 equivalent protons of TMS is used to establish the zero point on the delta scale.

$$Si(CH_3)_4$$

Tetramethylsilane
(TMS)

14.7 THE CHEMICAL SHIFT

Tetramethylsilane was chosen as a reference compound for several reasons. It has 12 hydrogen atoms and, therefore, a very small amount of TMS gives a relatively large signal. Because the hydrogen atoms are all equivalent, they give a *single signal.* Since silicon is less electronegative than carbon, the protons of TMS are in regions of high electron density. They are, as a result, highly shielded, and the signal from TMS occurs in a region of the spectrum where few other hydrogen atoms absorb. Thus, their signal seldom interferes with the signals from other hydrogen atoms. Tetramethylsilane, like an alkane, is relatively inert. Finally, it is volatile; its boiling point is 27 °C. After the spectrum has been determined, the TMS can be removed easily by evaporation.

TABLE 14.3   Approximate proton chemical shifts

TYPE OF PROTON	CHEMICAL SHIFT (δ, ppm)
1° Alkyl, RCH_3	0.8–1.0
2° Alkyl, RCH_2R	1.2–1.4
3° Alkyl, R_3CH	1.4–1.7
Allylic, $R_2C=C-CH_3$ $\quad\quad\quad\quad$ $\vert$ $\quad\quad\quad\quad$ R	1.6–1.9
Benzylic, $ArCH_3$	2.2–2.5
Alkyl chloride, RCH_2Cl	3.6–3.8
Alkyl bromide, RCH_2Br	3.4–3.6
Alkyl iodide, RCH_2I	3.1–3.3
Ether, $ROCH_2R$	3.3–3.9
Alcohol, $HOCH_2R$	3.3–4.0
Ketone, $RCCH_3$ $\quad\quad$ $\Vert$ $\quad\quad$ O	2.1–2.6
Aldehyde, RCH $\quad\quad$ $\Vert$ $\quad\quad$ O	9.5–9.6
Vinylic, $R_2C=CH_2$	4.6–5.0
Vinylic, $R_2C=CH$ $\quad\quad\quad\quad$ $\vert$ $\quad\quad\quad\quad$ R	5.2–5.7
Aromatic, ArH	6.0–9.5
Acetylenic, $RC{\equiv}CH$	2.5–3.1
Alcohol hydroxyl, ROH	0.5–6.0[a]
Carboxylic, $RCOH$ $\quad\quad\quad$ $\Vert$ $\quad\quad\quad$ O	10–13[a]
Phenolic, $ArOH$	4.5–7.7[a]
Amino, $R-NH_2$	1.0–5.0[a]

[a] The chemical shifts of these protons vary in different solvents and with temperature and concentration.

Chemical shifts are measured in hertz (cps), as if the frequency of the electromagnetic radiation were being varied. In actuality it is the magnetic field that is changed. But since the values of frequency and the strength of the magnetic field are mathematically proportional, frequency units (Hz) are appropriate ones.

The chemical shift of a proton, when expressed in hertz, is proportional to the strength of the external magnetic field. Since spectrometers with different magnetic field strengths are commonly used, it is desirable to express chemical shifts in a form that is independent of the strength of the external field. This can be done easily by dividing the chemical shift by the frequency of the spectrometer, with both numerator and denominator of the fraction expressed in frequency units (Hz). Since chemical shifts are always very small (typically < 500 Hz) compared with the total field strength (commonly the equivalent of 30, 60, or 100 *million* Hz), it is convenient to express these fractions in units of *parts per million* (ppm). This is the origin of the delta scale for the expression of chemical shifts relative to TMS.

$$\delta = \frac{(\text{observed shift from TMS in hertz}) \times 10^6}{(\text{operating frequency of the instrument in hertz})}$$

Table 14.3 gives the *approximate* values of proton chemical shifts for some common hydrogen-containing groups.

14.8 CHEMICAL SHIFT EQUIVALENT AND NONEQUIVALENT PROTONS

Two or more protons that are in identical environments have the same chemical shift and, therefore, give only one ^{1}H NMR signal. How do we know when protons are in the same environment? For most compounds, protons that are in the same environment are also equivalent in chemical reactions. That is, **chemically equivalent** protons are **chemical shift equivalent** in ^{1}H NMR spectra.

We saw, for example, that the six methyl protons of *p*-xylene give a single ^{1}H NMR signal. We probably recognize, intuitively, that these six hydrogen atoms are chemically equivalent. We can demonstrate their equivalence, however, by replacing each hydrogen in turn with some other group. If in making these substitutions we get the same compound from each replacement, then the protons are chemically equivalent and are chemical shift equivalent. The replacements can be replacements that occur in an actual chemical reaction or they can be purely imaginary. For the methyl hydrogen atoms of *p*-xylene we can think of an actual chemical reaction that demonstrates their equivalence, *benzylic bromination*. Benzylic bromination produces the same monobromo product regardless of which of the six hydrogen atoms is replaced.

We can also think of a chemical reaction that demonstrates the equivalence of the four aromatic hydrogen atoms of *p*-xylene, *ring bromination*. Once again, we get the same compound regardless of which of the four hydrogen atoms is replaced.

Problem 14.5

How many different sets of equivalent protons do each of the following compounds have? How many signals would each compound give in its ^{1}H NMR spectrum?

(a) CH_3CH_3

(b) $CH_3CH_2CH_3$

(c) CH_3OCH_3

(d) CH_3CH_2—⟨⟩—CH_2CH_3

(e) $CH_3\overset{\overset{\displaystyle O}{\|}}{C}-OCH_3$

(f) $CH_3\overset{\overset{\displaystyle O}{\|}}{C}-OCH(CH_3)_2$

14.8A ENANTIOTOPIC AND DIASTEREOTOPIC HYDROGEN ATOMS

If replacement of each of two hydrogen atoms by the same group yields compounds that are enantiomers, the two hydrogen atoms are said to be **enantiotopic**. *Enantiotopic hydrogen atoms have the same chemical shift and give only one ^{1}H NMR signal.**

The two hydrogen atoms of the —CH_2Br group of ethyl bromide are enantiotopic. Ethyl bromide, then, gives two signals in its ^{1}H NMR spectrum. The three equivalent protons of the CH_3— group give one signal; the two enantiotopic protons of the —CH_2Br group give the other signal. (The ^{1}H NMR spectrum of ethyl bromide as we shall see, actually consists of seven peaks. This is a result of signal splitting, which will be explained in Section 14.9.)

If replacement of each of two hydrogen atoms by a group, **Z**, gives compounds that are diastereomers, the two hydrogens are said to be **diastereotopic**. Except for

---

*Enantiotopic hydrogen atoms may not have the same chemical shift if the compound is dissolved in a chiral solvent. However, most ^{1}H NMR spectra are determined using achiral solvents and in this situation enantiotopic protons have the same chemical shift.

accidental coincidence, *diasterotopic protons do not have the same chemical shift and give rise to different ^1H NMR signals.*

The two protons of the $=CH_2$ group of chloroethene are diastereotopic.

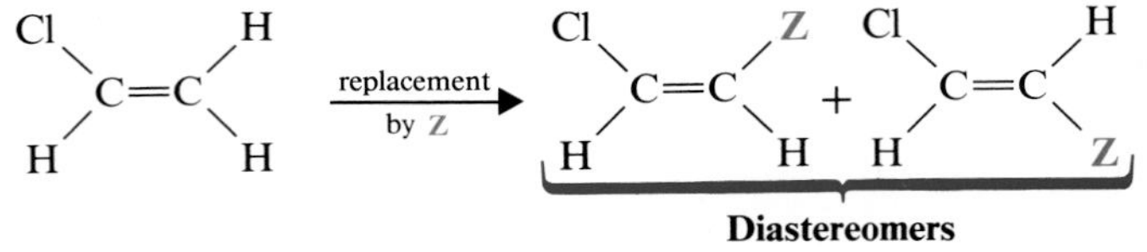

Diastereomers

Chloroethene, then, should give signals from three nonequivalent protons; one for the proton of the ClCH$=$ group, and one for each of the diastereotopic protons of the $=CH_2$ group.

The two methylene ($-CH_2-$) protons of *sec*-butyl alcohol are also diastereotopic. We can illustrate this with one enantiomer of *sec*-butyl alcohol in the following way:

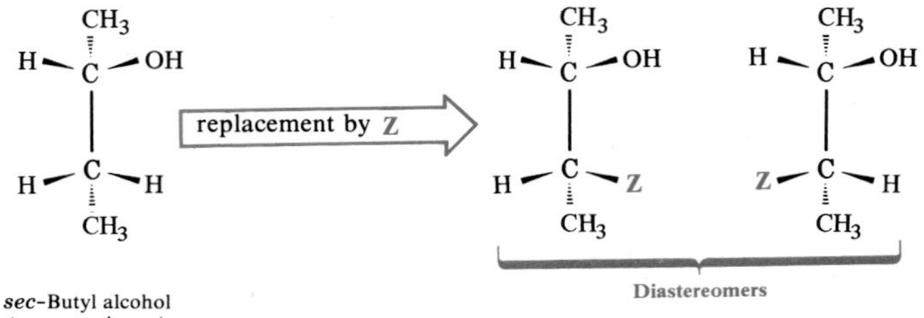

sec-Butyl alcohol
(one enantiomer)

Diastereomers

These two protons will have different chemical shifts and will give two signals in the ^1H NMR spectrum. The two signals may be close enough to overlap, however.

Problem 14.6 ———————————————————————————

(a) Show that replacing each of the two methylene protons of the other *sec*-butyl alcohol enantiomer by Z also leads to a pair of diastereomers. (b) How many chemically different kinds of protons are there in *sec*-butyl alcohol? (c) How many ^1H NMR signals would you expect to find in the spectrum of *sec*-butyl alcohol?

Problem 14.7 ———————————————————————————

How many ^1H NMR signals would you expect from each of the following compounds? (Neglect signal splitting.)

(a) $CH_3CH_2CH_2CH_3$
(b) CH_3CH_2OH
(c) $CH_3CH=CH_2$
(d) *trans*-2-Butene
(e) 1,2-Dibromopropane

(f) 1,1-Dimethylcyclopropane
(g) *trans*-1,2-Dimethylcyclopropane
(h) *cis*-1,2-Dimethylcyclopropane
(i) 1-Pentene

14.9 SIGNAL SPLITTING: SPIN-SPIN COUPLING

Signal splitting is caused by magnetic fields of protons on nearby atoms. We have seen an example of signal splitting in the spectrum of 1,1,2-trichloroethane (Fig. 14.11). The signal from the two equivalent protons of the —CH_2Cl group of 1,1,2-trichloroethane is split into two peaks by the single proton of the $CHCl_2$—group. The signal from the proton of the $CHCl_2$— group is split into three peaks by the two protons of the —CH_2Cl group. This is further illustrated in Fig. 14.20.

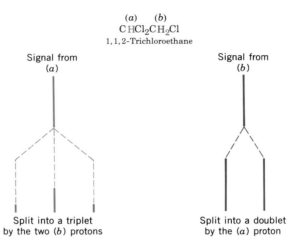

FIGURE 14.20 Signal splitting in 1,1,2-trichloroethane.

Signal splitting arises from a phenomenon known as **spin–spin coupling,** which we shall soon examine. Spin–spin coupling effects are transferred primarily through the bonding electrons and *are not usually observed if the coupled protons are separated by more than three σ bonds.* Thus, we observe signal splitting from the protons of *adjacent σ-bonded* atoms as in 1,1,2-trichloroethane (Fig. 14.11). However, we would not observe splitting of either signal of *tert*-butyl methyl ether (see following structure) because the protons labeled (*b*) are separated from those labeled (*a*) by more than three σ bonds. Both signals from *tert*-butyl methyl ether are singlets.

$$\overset{(a)}{CH_3}$$

$$\overset{(a)}{CH_3}-\overset{|}{\underset{|}{C}}-O-\overset{(b)}{CH_3}$$

$$\underset{(a)}{CH_3}$$

tert-Butyl methyl ether
(no signal splitting)

Signal splitting is not observed for protons that are chemically equivalent or enantiotopic. That is, signal splittings do not occur between protons that have *exactly the same chemical shift.* Thus, we would not expect, and do not find, signal splitting in the signal from the six equivalent hydrogen atoms of ethane.

$$CH_3CH_3 \quad \text{(no signal splitting)}$$

Nor do we find signal splitting occurring from enantiotopic protons of methoxy-acetonitrile (Fig. 14.21).

There is a subtle distinction between *spin–spin coupling* and *signal splitting*. Spin–spin coupling often occurs between sets of protons that have the same chemical shift (and this coupling can be detected by methods that we shall not go into here). However, spin–spin coupling *leads to signal splitting only when the sets of protons have different chemical shifts*.

Let us now explain how signal splitting arises from coupled sets of protons that are not chemical shift equivalent.

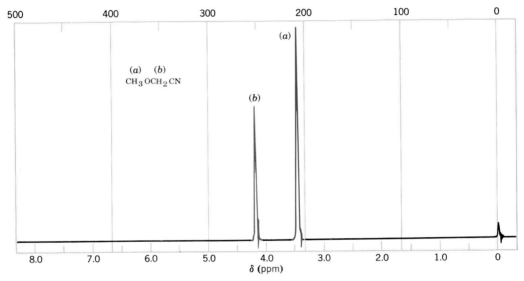

FIGURE 14.21 The ^{1}H NMR spectrum of methoxyacetonitrile. The signal of the enantio-topic protons (*b*) is not split. (Spectrum courtesy of Varian Associates, Palo Alto, CA.)

We have seen that protons can be aligned in only two ways in an external magnetic field: with the field or against it. Therefore, the magnetic moment of a proton on an adjacent atom may affect the magnetic field at the proton whose signal we are observing in only one of two ways. The occurrence of these two slightly different effects causes the appearance of a smaller peak somewhat upfield (from where the signal might have occurred) and another peak somewhat downfield.

Figure 14.22 shows how two possible orientations of a neighboring proton, H_b, split the signal of the proton H_a. (H_b and H_a are not equivalent.)

The separation of these peaks in frequency units is called the **coupling constant** and is abbreviated J_{ab}. Coupling constants are generally reported in hertz (cps). Because coupling is caused entirely by internal forces, the magnitudes of coupling constants *are not* dependent on the magnitude of the applied field. Coupling constants measured (in Hz) on an instrument operating at 60 MHz will be the same as those measured on an instrument operating at 100 MHz.

When we determine ^{1}H NMR spectra we are, of course, observing effects produced by billions of molecules. Since the difference in energy between the two possible orientations of the proton of H_b is very small, the two orientations will be present in roughly (but not exactly) equal numbers. The signal that we observe from H_a is, therefore, split into two peaks of roughly equal intensity, *a 1:1 doublet*.

14.9 SIGNAL SPLITTING: SPIN–SPIN COUPLING

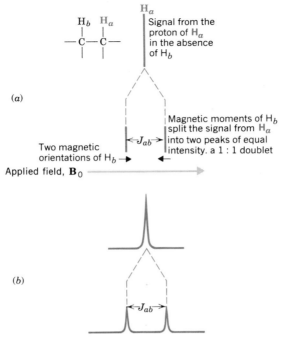

FIGURE 14.22 Signal splitting arising from spin–spin coupling with one nonequivalent proton of a neighboring hydrogen atom. A theoretical analysis is shown in (*a*) and the actual appearance of the spectrum in (*b*). The distance between the centers of the peaks of the doublet is called the coupling constant, J_{ab}. The term J_{ab} is measured in hertz (cps). The magnitudes of coupling constants are *not* dependent on the magnitude of the applied field and their values (in Hz) are the same, regardless of the operating frequency of the spectrometer.

Problem 14.8

Sketch the ^1H NMR spectrum of $CHBr_2CHCl_2$. Which signal would you expect to occur at lower magnetic field strength; that of the proton of the $CHBr_2$— group or of the —$CHCl_2$ group? Why?

Two equivalent protons on an adjacent carbon (or carbon atoms) split the signal from an absorbing proton into a 1:2:1 *triplet*. Figure 14.23 illustrates how this pattern occurs.

In compounds of either type (Fig. 14.23), both protons may be aligned with the applied field. This orientation causes a peak to appear at a lower applied field strength than would occur in the absence of the two hydrogen atoms H_b. Conversely, both protons may be aligned against the applied field. This orientation of the protons of H_b causes a peak to appear at higher applied field strengths than would occur in their absence. Finally, there are two ways in which the two protons may be aligned in which one opposes the applied field and one reinforces it. These arrangements do not displace the signal. Since the probability of this last arrangement is twice that of either of the other two, the center peak of the triplet is twice as intense.

The proton of the —$CHCl_2$ group of 1,1,2-trichloroethane is an example of a proton of the type having two equivalent protons on an adjacent carbon. The signal from the —$CHCl_2$ group (Fig. 14.11) appears as a 1:2:1 triplet and, as we would

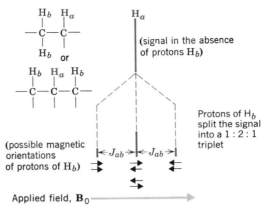

FIGURE 14.23 Two equivalent protons (H_b) on an adjacent carbon atom split the signal from H_a into a 1:2:1 triplet.

expect, the signal of the $-CH_2Cl$ group of 1,1,2-trichloroethane is split into a 1:1 doublet by the proton of the $-CHCl_2$ group.

The spectrum of 1,1,2,3,3-pentachloropropane (Fig. 14.24) is similar to that of 1,1,2-trichloroethane in that it also consists of a 1:2:1 triplet and a 1:1 doublet. The two hydrogen atoms H_b of 1,1,2,3,3-pentachloropropane are equivalent even though they are on separate carbon atoms.

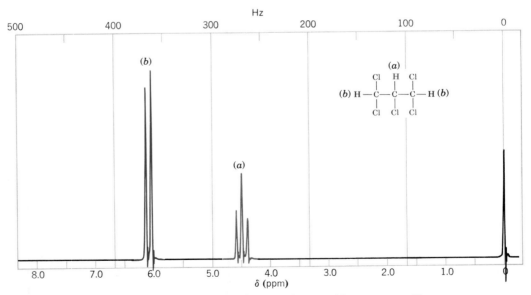

FIGURE 14.24 The ^1H NMR spectrum of 1,1,2,3,3-pentachloropropane. (Spectrum courtesy of Varian Associates, Palo Alto, CA.)

Problem 14.9

The relative positions of the doublet and triplet of 1,1,2-trichloroethane (Fig. 14.11) and 1,1,2,3,3-pentachloropropane (Fig. 14.24) are reversed. Explain this.

14.9 SIGNAL SPLITTING: SPIN–SPIN COUPLING

Three equivalent protons (H_b) on a neighboring carbon split the signal from the H_a into a 1:3:3:1 quartet. This pattern is shown in Fig. 14.25.

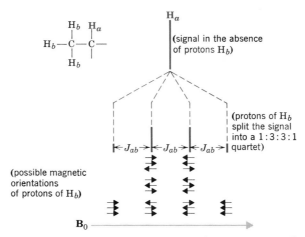

FIGURE 14.25 Three equivalent protons (H_b) on an adjacent carbon split the signal from H_a into a 1:3:3:1 quartet.

The signal from two equivalent protons of the $-CH_2Br$ group of ethyl bromide (Fig. 14.26) appears as a 1:3:3:1 quartet because of this type of signal splitting. The three equivalent protons of the CH_3- group are split into a 1:2:1 triplet by the two protons of the $-CH_2Br$ group.

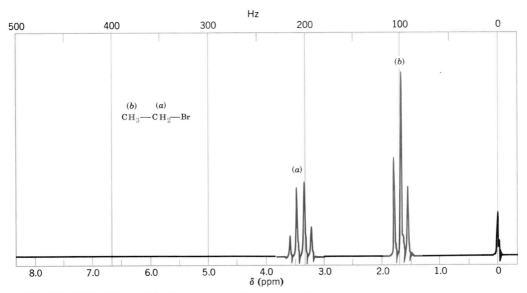

FIGURE 14.26 The ¹H NMR spectrum of ethyl bromide.

The kind of analysis that we have just given can be extended to compounds with even larger numbers of equivalent protons on adjacent atoms. These analyses show that *if there are n equivalent protons on adjacent atoms these will split a signal into*

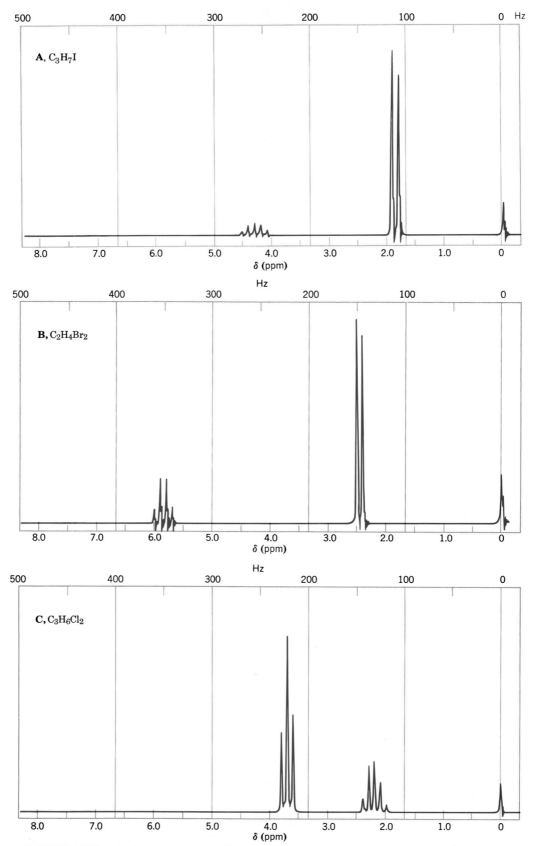

FIGURE 14.27 The ^{1}H NMR spectra for Problem 14.11. (Spectra courtesy of Varian Associates, Palo Alto, CA.)

n + 1 peaks. (We may not always see all of these peaks in actual spectra, however, because some of them may be very small.)

Problem 14.10

What kind of ^{1}H NMR spectrum would you expect the following compound to give?

$$(Cl_2CH)_3CH$$

Sketch the spectrum showing the splitting patterns and relative position of each signal.

Problem 14.11

Propose structures for each of the compounds whose spectra are shown in Fig. 14.27, and account for the splitting pattern of each signal.

The splitting patterns shown in Fig. 14.27 are fairly easy to recognize because in each compound there are only two sets of nonequivalent hydrogen atoms. One feature present in all spectra, however, will help us recognize splitting patterns in more complicated spectra: the **reciprocity of coupling constants.**

The separation of the peaks in hertz gives us the value of the coupling constants. Therefore, if we look for doublets, triplets, quartets, and so on, that have *the same coupling constants,* the chances are good that these multiplets are related to each other because they arise from reciprocal spin-spin couplings.

The two sets of protons of an ethyl group, for example, appear as a triplet and a quartet as long as the ethyl group is attached to an atom that does not bear any hydrogen atoms. The spacings of the peaks of the triplet and the quartet of an ethyl group will be the same because the coupling constants (J_{ab}) are the same (Fig. 14.28).

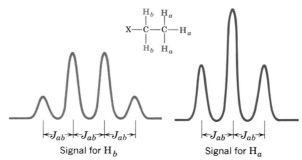

FIGURE 14.28 A theoretical splitting pattern for an ethyl group. For an example, see the spectrum of ethyl bromide (Fig. 14.26).

Proton NMR spectra have other features, however, that are not at all helpful when we try to determine the structure of a compound.

1. Signals may overlap. This happens when the chemical shifts of the signals are very nearly the same. In the spectrum of ethyl chloroacetate (Fig. 14.29) we see

that the singlet of the —CH$_2$Cl group falls directly on top of one of the outermost peaks of the ethyl quartet.

2. Spin–spin couplings between the protons of nonadjacent atoms may occur. This long-range coupling happens frequently when π bonded atoms intervene between the atoms bearing the coupled protons.

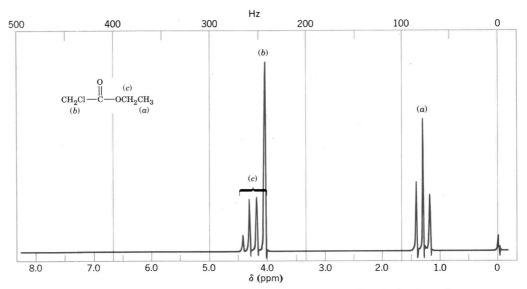

FIGURE 14.29 The ^{1}H NMR spectrum of ethyl chloroacetate. The singlet from the protons of (b) falls on one of the outermost peaks of the quartet from (c). (Spectrum courtesy of Varian Associates, Palo Alto, CA.)

3. The splitting patterns of aromatic groups are difficult to analyze. A monosubstituted benzene ring (a phenyl group) has three different kinds of protons.

The chemical shifts of these protons may be so similar that the phenyl group gives a signal that resembles a singlet. Or the chemical shifts may be different and because of long-range couplings, the phenyl group appears as a very complicated multiplet.

Disubstituted benzenes show a range of complicated splitting patterns. In many instances these patterns can be analyzed by using techniques that are beyond the scope of our discussion here. We saw earlier in this chapter that IR spectroscopy gives us a relatively easy method for deciding whether the substituents of disubstituted benzenes are ortho, meta, or para to each other.

14.9 SIGNAL SPLITTING: SPIN–SPIN COUPLING

In all of the ^{1}H NMR spectra that we have considered so far, we have restricted our attention to signal splittings arising from interactions of only two sets of equivalent protons on adjacent atoms. What kind of patterns should we expect from compounds in which more than two sets of equivalent protons are interacting? We cannot answer this question completely because of limitations of space, but we can give an example that illustrates the kind of analysis that is involved. Let us consider a 1-substituted propane.

$$\overset{(a)}{CH_3}-\overset{(b)}{CH_2}-\overset{(c)}{CH_2}-Z$$

Here, there are three sets of equivalent protons. We have no problem in deciding what kind of signal splitting to expect from the protons of the $CH_3—$ group or the $—CH_2Z$ group. The methyl group is spin–spin coupled only to the two protons of the central $—CH_2—$ group. Therefore, the methyl group should appear as a triplet. The protons of the $—CH_2Z$ group are similarly coupled only to the two protons of the central $—CH_2—$ group. Thus, the protons of the $—CH_2Z$ group should also appear as a triplet.

But what about the protons of the central $—CH_2—$ group (b)? They are spin–spin coupled with the three protons at (a) and with two protons at (c). The protons at (a) and (c), moreover, are not equivalent. If the coupling constants J_{ab} and J_{bc} have quite different values, then the protons at (b) could be split into a quartet by the three protons (a) and each line of the quartet could be split into a triplet by the two protons (c) (Fig. 14.30).

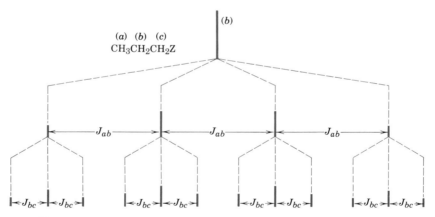

FIGURE 14.30 The splitting pattern that would occur for the (b) protons of $CH_3CH_2CH_2Z$ if J_{ab} is much larger than J_{bc}. Here $J_{ab} = 3J_{bc}$.

It is unlikely, however, that we would observe as many as 12 peaks in an actual spectrum because the coupling constants are such that peaks usually fall on top of peaks. The ^{1}H NMR spectrum of 1-nitropropane (Fig. 14.31) is typical of 1-substituted propane compounds. We see that the (b) protons are split into six major peaks, each of which shows a slight sign of further splitting.

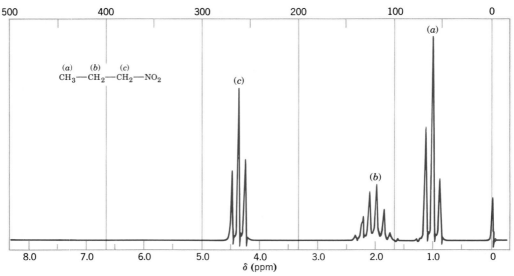

FIGURE 14.31 The ¹H NMR spectrum of 1-nitropropane. (Spectrum courtesy of Varian Associates, Palo Alto, CA.)

Problem 14.12 ———————————————

Carry out an analysis like that shown in Fig. 14.30 and show how many peaks the signal from (b) would be split into if $J_{ab} = 2J_{bc}$ and if $J_{ab} = J_{bc}$. (*Hint:* In both cases peaks will fall on top of peaks so that the total number of peaks in the signal is fewer than 12.)

The presentation we have given here applies only to what are called *first-order spectra*. In first-order spectra, the distance in hertz (Δv) that separates the coupled signals is very much larger than the coupling constant, J. That is, $\Delta v \gg J$. In *second-order spectra* (which we have not discussed) Δv approaches J in magnitude and the situation becomes much more complex. The number of peaks increases and the intensities are not those that might be expected from first-order considerations.

14.10 PROTON NMR SPECTRA OF COMPOUNDS CONTAINING FLUORINE AND DEUTERIUM

The fluorine (¹⁹F) nucleus has spin quantum numbers of $+\frac{1}{2}$ and $-\frac{1}{2}$. In this respect ¹⁹F nuclei resemble protons and fluorine magnetic spectra can be observed. When measured at the same rf, the signals from ¹⁹F absorptions occur at considerably different magnetic field strengths than those of protons, so we do not see peaks due to ¹⁹F absorption in ¹H NMR spectra. We do, however, see splitting of proton signals caused by spin–spin couplings between protons and ¹⁹F nuclei. The signal from the two protons of 1,2-dichloro-1,1-difluoroethane, for example, is split into a triplet by the fluorine atoms on the adjacent carbon (Fig. 14.32).

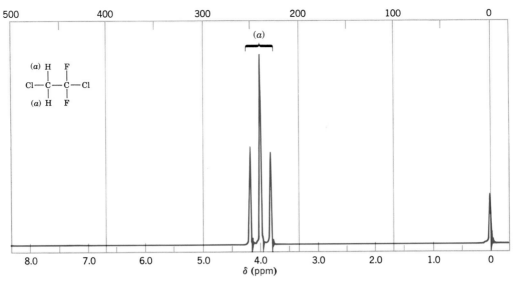

FIGURE 14.32 The ^{1}H NMR spectrum of 1,2-dichloro-1,1-difluoroethane. The J_{HF} coupling constant is about 12 Hz. (Spectrum courtesy of Varian Associates, Palo Alto, CA.)

The nucleus of a deuterium atom (a deuteron) has a much smaller magnetic moment than a proton, and signals from deuteron absorption do not occur in ^{1}H NMR spectra. [Deuterium (^{2}H) has a spin quantum number, $I = 1$, unlike ^{1}H, where $I = \frac{1}{2}$.]

Spin–spin couplings between deuterons and protons are small but the presence of deuterium on an adjacent atom can cause splitting of the proton signal.

Problem 14.13 ————————————————————————

Sketch the ^{1}H NMR spectrum that you would expect from each of the following compounds: (a) $CH_3CF_2CH_3$, (b) CH_3CF_2Cl, (c) CH_3CFCl_2, and (d) CH_3CF_3.

14.11 PROTON NMR SPECTRA AND RATE PROCESSES

J. D. Roberts (of the California Institute of Technology), a pioneer in the application of NMR spectroscopy to problems of organic chemistry, has compared the NMR spectrometer to a camera with a relatively slow shutter speed. Just as a camera with a slow shutter speed blurs photographs of objects that are moving rapidly, the NMR spectrometer blurs its picture of molecular processes that are occurring rapidly.

What are some of the rapid processes that occur in organic molecules?

At temperatures near room temperature, groups connected by carbon–carbon single bonds rotate very rapidly. Because of this, when we determine spectra of compounds with single bonds, the spectra that we obtain often reflect the individual hydrogen atoms in their average environment—that is, in an environment that is an average of all the environments that the protons have as a result of the group rotations.

To see an example of this effect, let us consider the spectrum of ethyl bromide again. The most stable conformation of ethyl bromide is the one in which the groups are perfectly staggered. In this staggered conformation one hydrogen of the methyl group (in red in following figure) is in a different environment from that of the other two methyl hydrogen atoms. If the NMR spectrometer were to detect this particular conformation of ethyl bromide, it would show the proton of this hydrogen of the methyl group at *a different chemical shift.* We know, however, that in the spectrum of ethyl bromide (Fig. 14.26), the three protons of the methyl group give *a single signal* (a signal that is split into a triplet by spin–spin coupling with the two protons of the adjacent carbon).

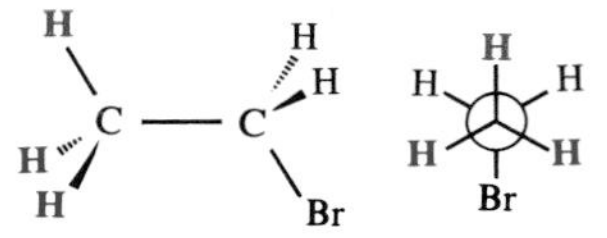

The methyl protons of ethyl bromide give a single signal because at room temperature the groups connected by the carbon–carbon single bond rotate approximately 1 million times each second. The "shutter speed" of the NMR spectrometer is too slow to "photograph" this rapid rotation; instead, it photographs the methyl hydrogen atoms in their average environments, and in this sense, it gives us a blurred picture of the methyl group.

Rotations about single bonds slow down as the temperature of the compound is lowered. Sometimes, this slowing of rotations allows us to "see" the different conformations of a molecule when we determine the spectrum at a sufficiently low temperature.

An example of this phenomenon, and one that also shows the usefulness of deuterium labeling, can be seen in the low temperature ^{1}H NMR spectra of cyclohexane and of undecadeuteriocyclohexane. (These experiments originated with F. A. L. Anet of the University of California, Los Angeles, another pioneer in the applications of NMR spectroscopy to organic chemistry, especially to conformational analysis.)

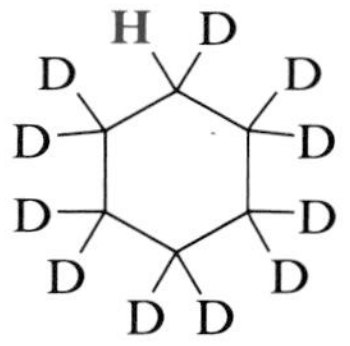

Undecadeuteriocyclohexane

At room temperature, ordinary cyclohexane gives one signal because interconversions between the various chair forms occur very rapidly. At low temperatures, however, ordinary cyclohexane gives a very complex ^{1}H NMR spectrum. At low temperatures interconversions are slow; the axial and equatorial protons have different chemical shifts; and complex spin–spin couplings occur.

At -100 °C, however, undecadeuteriocyclohexane gives only two signals of equal intensity. These signals correspond to the axial and equatorial hydrogen atoms of the following two chair conformations. Interconversions between these conformations occur at this low temperature, but they happen slowly enough for the NMR spectrometer to detect the individual conformations.

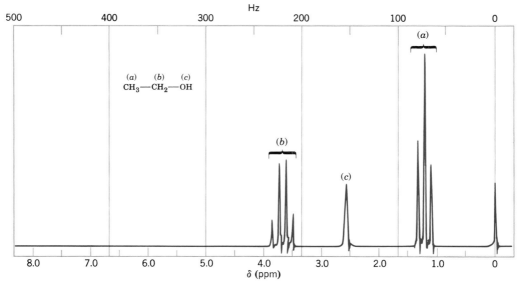

Problem 14.14

What kind of ^{1}H NMR spectrum would you expect to obtain from undecadeuteriocyclohexane at room temperature?

Another example of a rapidly occurring process can be seen in ^{1}H NMR spectra of ethanol. The ^{1}H NMR spectrum of ordinary ethanol shows the hydroxyl proton as a singlet and the protons of the $-CH_2-$ group as a quartet (Fig. 14.33). In ordinary ethanol we observe *no signal splitting arising from coupling between the hydroxyl proton and the protons of the $-CH_2-$ group even though they are on adjacent atoms.*

FIGURE 14.33 The ^{1}H NMR spectrum of ordinary ethanol. (Spectrum courtesy of Varian Associates, Palo Alto, CA.)

If we were to examine a ^{1}H NMR spectrum of *very pure* ethanol, however, we would find that the signal from the hydroxyl proton was split into a triplet, and that the signal from the protons of the $-CH_2-$ group was split into a multiplet of eight peaks. Clearly, in very pure ethanol the spin of the proton of the hydroxyl group is coupled with the spins of the protons of the $-CH_2-$ groups.

Whether or not coupling occurs between the hydroxyl protons and the methylene protons depends on the length of time the proton spends on a particular ethanol molecule. Protons attached to electronegative atoms with lone pairs such as oxygen can undergo rapid **chemical exchange**. That is, they can be transferred rapidly from one molecule to another. The chemical exchange in very pure ethanol is slow and, as a consequence, we see the signal splitting of and by the hydroxyl proton in the spectrum. In ordinary ethanol, acidic and basic impurities catalyze the chemical exchange; the exchange occurs so rapidly that the hydroxyl proton gives an unsplit signal and those of the methylene protons are split only by coupling with the protons of the methyl group. We say, then, that rapid exchange causes **spin decoupling.**

Spin decoupling is often found in the ^{1}H NMR spectra of alcohols, amines, and carboxylic acids.

Problem 14.15

Apply principles that you have learned in this and in earlier sections, and assign structures to each of the compounds in Fig. 14.34.

14.12 PROTON NMR SPECTRA OF CARBOCATIONS

Olah (Section 6.13) has developed methods for preparing carbocations under conditions where they are stable enough to be studied by NMR spectroscopy. Olah has found, for example, that in liquid sulfur dioxide, alkyl fluorides react with antimony pentafluoride to yield solutions of carbocations.

$$R-F + SbF_5 \xrightarrow[\text{liq. SO}_2]{} R^+ + SbF_6^-$$

Antimony pentafluoride is a powerful Lewis acid.

When the ^{1}H NMR spectrum of *tert*-butyl fluoride is measured in liquid sulfur dioxide, the nine protons appear as a doublet centered at δ 1.3. (Why do the protons of *tert*-butyl fluoride appear as a doublet?) When antimony pentafluoride is added to the solution, the doublet at δ 1.35 is replaced by a singlet at δ 4.35. Both the change in the splitting pattern of the methyl protons and the downfield shift are consistent with the formation of a *tert*-butyl cation. (Why?)

$$(CH_3)_3C-F + SbF_5 \xrightarrow[\text{SO}_2]{\text{liq.}} (CH_3)_3C^+ + SbF_6^-$$
$$\delta\ 1.35 \qquad\qquad \delta\ 4.35$$
$$\text{(doublet)} \qquad\qquad \text{(singlet)}$$

When a solution of isopropyl fluoride in liquid sulfur dioxide is treated with antimony pentafluoride, an even more remarkable downfield shift occurs.

$$(CH_3)_2CHF + SbF_5 \longrightarrow (CH_3)_2CH^+ + SbF_6^-$$
$$\delta\ 1.23 \quad \delta\ 4.64 \qquad\qquad \delta\ 5.03 \quad \delta\ 13.50$$
$$\text{(doublet of} \quad \text{(multiplet)} \qquad \text{(doublet) (septet)}$$
$$\text{doublets)}$$

Problem 14.16

When 2-methyl-1,1-diphenyl-2-propanol in liquid sulfur dioxide was treated with the "superacid" FSO_3H-SbF_5, the spectrum of the solution showed the ^{1}H NMR absorptions given on page 594.

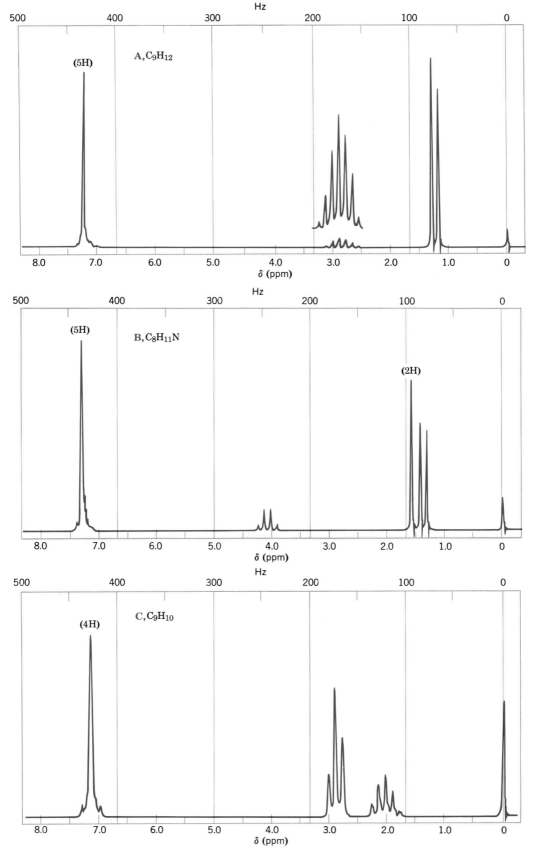

FIGURE 14.34 The ^{1}H NMR spectra for Problem 14.15. (Spectra courtesy of Varian Associates, Palo Alto, CA.)

$$C_6H_5-\overset{\overset{\displaystyle H}{|}}{\underset{\underset{\displaystyle C_6H_5}{|}}{C}}-\overset{\overset{\displaystyle OH}{|}}{\underset{\underset{\displaystyle CH_3}{|}}{C}}-CH_3 \xrightarrow[\text{liq. } SO_2]{FSO_3H-SbF_5} \quad ?$$

2-Methyl-1,1-diphenyl-   Doublet, δ 1.48 (6H)
2-propanol   Multiplet, δ 4.45 (1H)
                                        Multiplet, δ 8.0 (10H)

What carbocation is formed in this reaction?

14.13 CARBON-13 NMR SPECTROSCOPY

The most abundant isotope of the element carbon is carbon-12 (^{12}C) (natural abundance $\sim$ 99%). Nuclei of carbon-12 have no net magnetic spin and therefore they cannot give NMR signals. This is not true, however, of nuclei of the much less abundant isotope of carbon, ^{13}C (natural abundance $\sim$ 1%). Carbon-13 nuclei have a net magnetic spin and can give NMR signals. The nuclei of ^{13}C are like the nuclei of ^1H in that they can assume spin states of $+\frac{1}{2}$ or $-\frac{1}{2}$.

The low natural abundance of ^{13}C means that highly sensitive spectrometers employing pulse FT techniques must be used to measure ^{13}C spectra. These spectrometers have now become widely available, and ^{13}C spectroscopy has become another powerful method for determining the structures of organic molecules.

With ^1H spectroscopy (^1H NMR) we obtain indirect information about the carbon skeleton of an organic molecule because *most* (but not all) of the carbon atoms have at least one attached hydrogen. In ^{13}C spectroscopy, we observe the carbon skeleton directly and, therefore, we see peaks arising from all of the carbon atoms, whether they bear hydrogen atoms or not.

One great advantage of ^{13}C spectroscopy is the wide range of chemical shifts over which ^{13}C nuclei absorb. In ^{13}C spectroscopy signals from organic compounds are spread over a chemical shift range of 200 ppm, compared with a range less than 20 ppm in proton spectra. Carbon-13 spectra are generally simpler because signals are less likely to overlap.

The very low natural abundance of ^{13}C has an important effect that further simplifies ^{13}C spectra. Because of its low natural abundance, there is a very low probability that two adjacent carbon atoms will both have ^{13}C nuclei. Therefore, in ^{13}C spectra we do not observe spin–spin couplings between the carbon nuclei.

Electronic techniques are also available to allow *decoupling* of spin–spin interactions between ^{13}C nuclei and ^1H nuclei. Thus, it is possible to obtain ^{13}C spectra in which all carbon resonances appear as singlets. Spectra obtained in this mode of operation of the spectrometer are called **proton-decoupled** spectra.

Carbon-13 spectrometers can also be operated in another mode, one that allows one-bond couplings between ^{13}C and ^1H nuclei to occur. This mode of operation is called **proton off-resonance decoupling.** It produces spectra in which $-CH_3$ groups appear as quartets, $-CH_2-$ groups appear as triplets, $\overset{\diagdown}{\underset{\diagup}{-}}CH$ groups as doublets, and carbon atoms with no attached hydrogen atoms as singlets.

An excellent illustration of the application of ^{13}C spectroscopy is shown in spectra of 4-(N,N-diethylamino)benzaldehyde (Fig. 14.35). Bear in mind as you examine Fig. 14.35 that *in most* ^{13}C *spectra the areas under signals are not proportional to the number of atoms causing the signal.*[*]

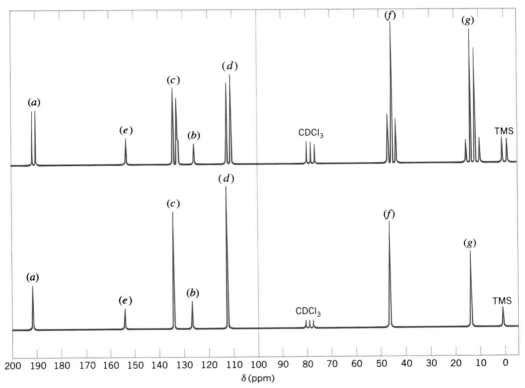

4-(*N,N*-Diethylamino)benzaldehyde

FIGURE 14.35 The ^{13}C NMR spectra of 4-(*N,N*-diethylamino)benzaldehyde,

HC——$N(CH_2CH_3)_2$. (Spectra courtesy of Philip L. Fuchs, Purdue University.)

The top spectrum is the proton off-resonance decoupled spectrum. In it, the multiplicity (i.e., the number of peaks in an individual signal) of each signal helps to match the signal with the carbon atom responsible for it. The multiplicity of the signal is one greater than the number of hydrogen atoms bonded to the carbon atom giving the signal. The bottom spectrum is the proton-decoupled spectrum. In it, all the signals from the compound being analyzed are singlets.

---

[*] Integrated ^{13}C spectra can be obtained, but in the integration mode the instrument is less sensitive, and more sample and time are required. Consequently, most ^{13}C spectra are not integrated.

The bottom spectrum in Fig. 14.35 is the *proton-decoupled* spectrum in which all the signals from 4-(N,N-diethylamino)benzaldehyde appear as singlets. The triplet centered at δ 79 (ppm) is caused by the solvent, $CDCl_3$. (The ^{13}C signal of $CDCl_3$ is split into a triplet by coupling with the deuterium atom, spin quantum number = 1, spin states +1, 0, −1.) The signal at δ 0 arises from $(CH_3)_4Si$.

The top spectrum in Fig. 14.35 is the *proton off-resonance decoupled* spectrum. It shows us immediately which signals belong to the ^{13}C nuclei of the ethyl groups. The triplet at δ 47 is caused by the equivalent —CH_2— groups and the quartet at δ 13 arises from the equivalent —CH_3 groups.

The two singlets in the top spectrum at δ 126 and δ 154 correspond to the carbon atoms of the benzene ring that do not bear hydrogen atoms, (*b*) and (*e*). The greater electronegativity of nitrogen (when compared to carbon) causes the signal from (*e*) to be further downfield (at δ 154). The doublet at δ 193 arises from the carbon of the aldehyde group. Its chemical shift is the most downfield of all the peaks because of the great electronegativity of its attached oxygen and because of resonance contribution of the second structure that follows. Both factors cause the electron density at this carbon to be very low and, therefore, the carbon is not well shielded.

Resonance contributors for an aldehyde group

This leaves the signals at δ 112 and δ 135 and the two sets of carbon atoms of the benzene ring labeled (*c*) and (*d*) to be accounted for. Both signals appear as doublets in the proton off-resonance decoupled spectrum because both types of carbon have one attached hydrogen. But which signal belongs to which set of carbon atoms? Here we find another interesting application of resonance theory.

If we write resonance structures **A** – **D** involving the unshared electron pair of the amino group, we see that contributions made by **B** and **D** increase the electron

density at the set of carbon atoms labeled (*d*). On the other hand, writing structures **E** to **H** involving the aldehyde group shows us that contributions made by **F** and **H** decrease the electron density at the set of carbon atoms labeled (c). (Other resonance structures are possible but are not pertinent to the argument here.)

Increasing the electron density at a carbon should increase its shielding and should shift its signal upfield. Therefore, we assign the signal at δ 112 to the set of carbon atoms labeled (d). Conversely, decreasing the electron density at a carbon should shift its signal downfield, so we assign the signal at δ 135 to the set labeled (c).

Table 14.4 gives *approximate* carbon-13 chemical shifts for a variety of carbon-containing groups.

Carbon-13 spectroscopy can be especially useful in recognizing a compound with a high degree of symmetry. The following sample problem illustrates one such application.

TABLE 14.4   Approximate carbon-13 chemical shifts

TYPE OF CARBON ATOM	CHEMICAL SHIFT (δ, ppm)
1° Alkyl, RCH_3	0–40
2° Alkyl, RCH_2R	10–50
3° Alkyl, $RCHR_2$	15–50
Alkyl halide or amine, $-\overset{\mid}{\underset{\mid}{C}}-X \left(X = Cl, Br, \text{ or } \overset{\mid}{N}- \right)$	10–65
Alcohol or ether, $-\overset{\mid}{\underset{\mid}{C}}-O$	50–90
Alkyne, $-C\equiv$	60–90
Alkene, $\diagdown C=$	100–170
Aryl, ⬡$C-$	100–170
Nitriles, $-C\equiv N$	120–130
Amides, $-\overset{O}{\overset{\|}{C}}-\overset{\mid}{N}-$	150–180
Carboxylic acids, esters, $-\overset{O}{\overset{\|}{C}}-O$	160–185
Aldehydes, ketones, $-\overset{O}{\overset{\|}{C}}-$	182–215

Sample Problem

The proton-decoupled ^{13}C spectrum given in Fig. 14.36 is of a tribromobenzene ($C_6H_3Br_3$). Which tribromobenzene is it?

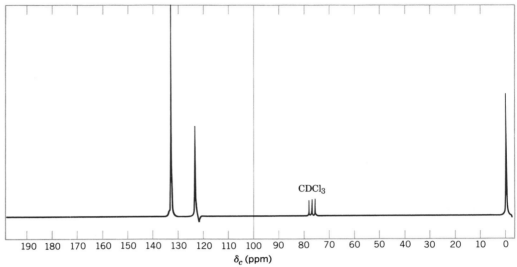

FIGURE 14.36 The ^{13}C NMR spectrum of a tribromobenzene. (Spectrum adapted with permission from L. F. Johnson and W. C. Jankowski, *Carbon-13 NMR Spectra: A Collection of Assigned, Coded, and Indexed Spectra,* Wiley–Interscience, New York, 1972.)

Answer:
There are three possible tribromobenzenes:

| 1,2,3-Tribromobenzene | 1,2,4-Tribromobenzene | 1,3,5-Tribromobenzene |

Our spectrum (Fig. 14.36) consists of only two signals, indicating that only two different types of carbon atoms are present in the compound. Only 1,3,5-tribromobenzene has a degree of symmetry such that it would give only two signals, and, therefore, it is the correct answer. 1,2,3-Tribromobenzene would give four ^{13}C signals and 1,2,4-tribromobenzene would give six.

Problem 14.17 ——————————————————————————

Explain how ^{13}C spectroscopy could be used to distinguish the *ortho-*, *meta-*, and *para-*dibromobenzene isomers one from another.

Problem 14.18 ——————————————————————————

Compounds **A**, **B**, and **C** are isomers with the formula $C_5H_{11}Cl$. Their proton-decoupled ^{13}C spectra are given in Fig. 14.37. The letters s, d, t, and q give the multiplicities of each peak in the proton off-resonance decoupled ^{13}C spectrum. Give structures for **A**, **B**, and **C**.

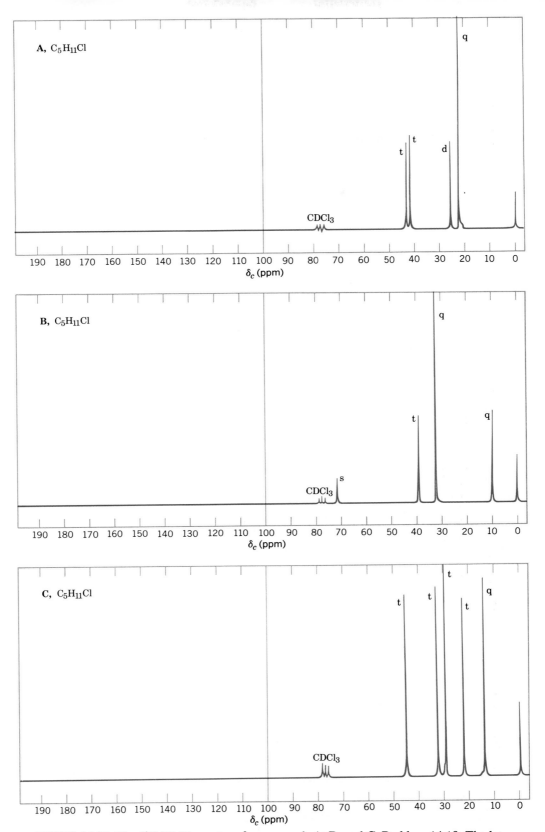

FIGURE 14.37 The ^{13}C NMR spectra of compounds **A**, **B**, and **C**, Problem 14.18. The letters indicate the multiplicities of the signals in the proton off-resonance decoupled spectra (s = singlet, d = doublet, t = triplet, q = quartet). (Adapted with permission from L. F. Johnson and W. C. Jankowski, *Carbon-13 NMR Spectra: A Collection of Assigned, Coded, and Indexed Spectra*, Wiley–Interscience, New York, 1972.)

14.14 MAGNETIC RESONANCE IMAGING IN MEDICINE

An important application of ^{1}H NMR spectroscopy in medicine today is a technique called **magnetic resonance imaging** or **MRI.** One great advantage of MRI is that, unlike X-rays, it does not use dangerous ionizing radiation, and it does not require the injection of potentially harmful chemicals in order to produce contrasts in the image. In MRI, a portion of the patient's body is placed in a powerful magnetic field and irradiated with rf energy.

A typical MRI image is given in Fig. 14.38. The instruments used in producing images like this one use the pulse method (Section 14.4) to excite the protons in the tissue under observation and use a Fourier transformation to translate the information into an image. The brightness of various regions of the image are related to two things. The first factor is the number of protons in the tissue at that particular place. The second factor arises from what are called the **relaxation times** of the protons. When protons are excited to a higher energy state by the pulse of rf energy, they absorb energy. They must lose this energy to return to the lower energy spin state before they can be excited again by a second pulse. The process by which the nuclei lose this energy is called **relaxation,** and the time it takes to occur is the relaxation time. There are two basic modes of relaxation available to protons. In one, called *spin-lattice relaxation,* the extra energy is transferred to neighboring molecules in the surroundings (or lattice). The time required for this to happen is called T_1 and is characteristic of the time required for the spin system to return to thermal equilibrium with its surroundings. In solids, T_1 can be hours long. For protons in pure liquid water, T_1 is only a few seconds. In the other type of relaxation, called *spin–spin*

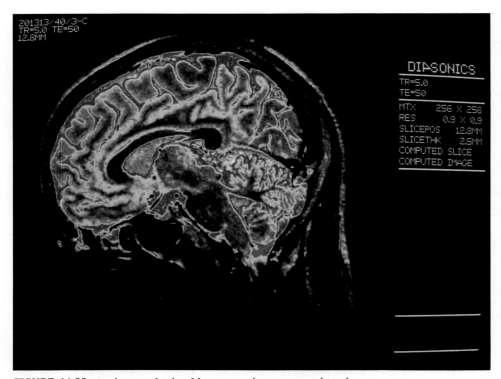

FIGURE 14.38 An image obtained by magnetic resonance imaging.

relaxation, the extra energy is dissipated by being transferred to nuclei of nearby atoms. The time required for this is called T_2. In liquids the magnitude of T_2 is approximately equal to T_1. In solids, however, the T_1 is very much larger.

Various techniques based on the time between pulses of rf radiation have been developed to utilize the differences in relaxation times in order to produce contrasts between different regions in soft tissues. The soft tissue contrast is inherently higher than that produced with X-ray techniques. Magnetic resonance imaging is being used to great effect in locating tumors, lesions, and edemas. Improvements in this technique are occurring rapidly, and the method is not restricted to observation of proton signals.

One important area of medical research is based on the observation of signals from ^{31}P. Compounds that contain phosphorus as phosphate esters (Section 10.12) such as adenosine triphosphate (ATP) and adenosine diphosphate (ADP) are involved in most metabolic processes. By using techniques based on NMR, researchers now have a noninvasive way to follow cellular metabolism.

Additional Problems

14.19   Listed here are ^1H NMR absorption peaks for several compounds. Propose a structure that is consistent with each set of data. (In some cases characteristic IR absorptions are given as well.)

(a) $C_4H_{10}O$ ^1H NMR spectrum
             singlet, δ 1.28 (9H)
             singlet, δ 1.35 (1H)

(b) C_3H_7Br ^1H NMR spectrum
             doublet, δ 1.71 (6H)
             septet, δ 4.32 (1H)

(c) C_4H_8O ^1H NMR spectrum   IR spectrum
             triplet, δ 1.05 (3H)   strong peak
             singlet, δ 2.13 (3H)   near 1720 cm^{-1}
             quartet, δ 2.47 (2H)

(d) C_7H_8O ^1H NMR spectrum   IR spectrum
             singlet, δ 2.43 (1H)   broad peak in
             singlet, δ 4.58 (2H)   3200–3550-cm^{-1}
             multiplet, δ 7.28 (5H)   region

(e) C_4H_9Cl ^1H NMR spectrum
             doublet, δ 1.04 (6H)
             multiplet, δ 1.95 (1H)
             doublet, δ 3.35 (2H)

(f) $C_{15}H_{14}O$ ^1H NMR spectrum   IR spectrum
             singlet, δ 2.20 (3H)   strong peak
             singlet, δ 5.08 (1H)   near 1720 cm^{-1}
             multiplet, δ 7.25 (10H)

(g) $C_4H_7BrO_2$ ^1H NMR spectrum   IR spectrum
             triplet, δ 1.08 (3H)   broad peak in
             multiplet, δ 2.07 (2H)   2500–3000-cm^{-1}
             triplet, δ 4.23 (1H)   region and a peak
             singlet, δ 10.97 (1H)   at 1715 cm^{-1}

(h) C_8H_{10} ^1H NMR spectrum
             triplet, δ 1.25 (3H)
             quartet, δ 2.68 (2H)
             multiplet, δ 7.23 (5H)

(i) $C_4H_8O_3$ ¹H NMR spectrum   IR spectrum
triplet, δ 1.27 (3H)   broad peak in
quartet, δ 3.66 (2H)   2500–3000-cm⁻¹
singlet, δ 4.13 (2H)   region and a peak
singlet, δ 10.95 (1H)   at 1715 cm⁻¹

(j) $C_3H_7NO_2$ ¹H NMR spectrum
doublet, δ 1.55 (6H)
septet, δ 4.67 (1H)

(k) $C_4H_{10}O_2$ ¹H NMR spectrum
singlet, δ 3.25 (6H)
singlet, δ 3.45 (4H)

(l) $C_5H_{10}O$ ¹H NMR spectrum   IR spectrum
doublet, δ 1.10 (6H)   strong peak
singlet, δ 2.10 (3H)   near 1720 cm⁻¹
septet, δ 2.50 (1H)

(m) C_8H_9Br ¹H NMR spectrum
doublet, δ 2.0 (3H)
quartet, δ 5.15 (1H)
multiplet, δ 7.35 (5H)

14.20   The IR spectrum of compound **E** (C_8H_6) is shown in Fig. 14.39. Compound **E** decolorizes bromine in carbon tetrachloride and gives a precipitate when treated with ammoniacal silver nitrate. What is the structure of **E**?

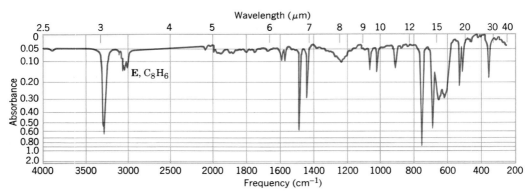

FIGURE 14.39 The IR spectrum of compound E, Problem 14.20. (Spectrum courtesy of Sadtler Research Laboratories, Inc., Philadelphia.)

14.21   The ¹H NMR spectrum of cyclooctatetraene consists of a single line located at δ 5.78. What does the location of this signal suggest about electron delocalization in cyclooctatetraene?

14.22   Give a structure for compound **F** that is consistent with the ¹H NMR and IR spectra in Fig. 14.40.

14.23   Propose structures for the compounds **G** and **H** whose ¹H NMR spectra are shown in Figs. 14.41 and 14.42.

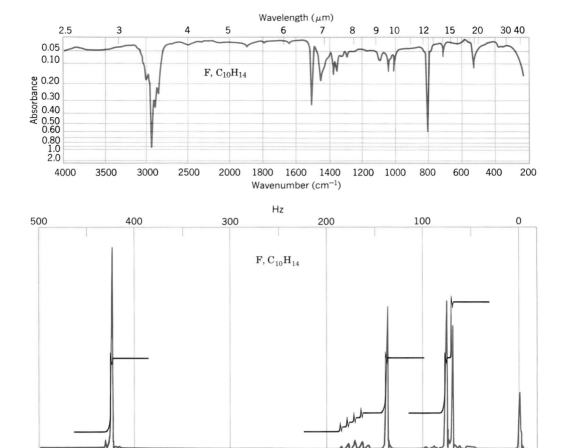

FIGURE 14.40 The ^{1}H NMR and IR spectra of compound **F**, Problem 14.22. (Proton NMR spectrum adapted from Varian Associates, Palo Alto, CA. Infrared spectrum adapted from Sadtler Research Laboratories, Inc., Philadelphia.)

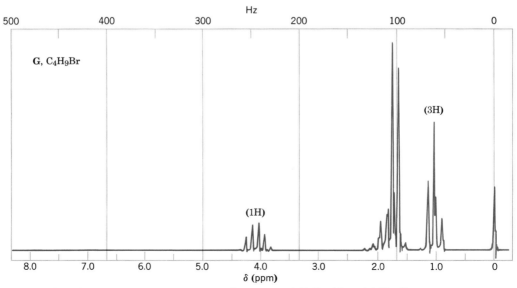

FIGURE 14.41 The ^{1}H NMR spectrum of compound **G**, Problem 14.23. (Spectrum courtesy of Varian Associates, Palo Alto, CA.)

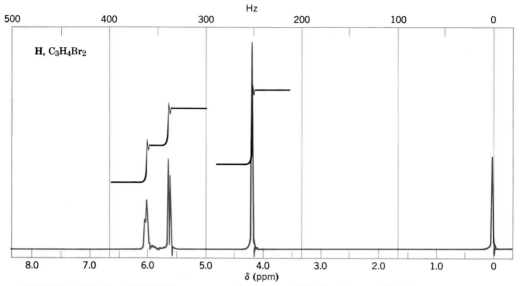

FIGURE 14.42 The ^{1}H NMR spectrum of compound **H**, Problem 14.23. (Spectrum courtesy of Varian Associates, Palo Alto, CA.)

14.24 Propose a structure for compound **I** whose ^{1}H NMR and IR spectra are given in Figs. 14.43 and 14.44.

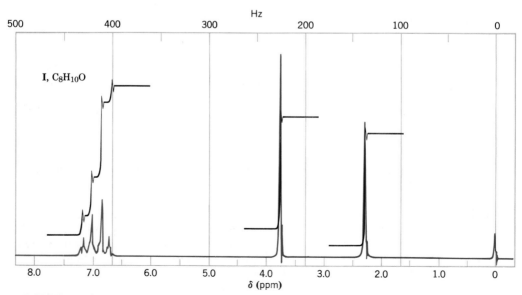

FIGURE 14.43 The ^{1}H NMR spectrum of compound **I**, Problem 14.24. (Spectrum courtesy of Varian Associates, Palo Alto, CA.)

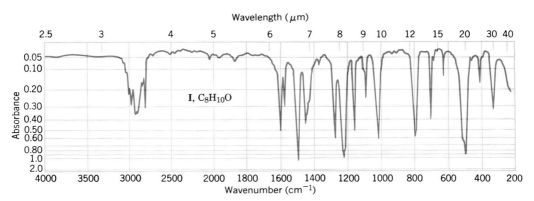

Wavelength (μm)

FIGURE 14.44 The IR spectrum of compound **I**, Problem 14.24. (Spectrum courtesy of Sadtler Research Laboratories, Inc., Philadelphia.)

14.25 A two-carbon compound (**J**) contains only carbon, hydrogen, and chlorine. Its IR spectrum is relatively simple and shows the following absorbance peaks: 3125 cm^{-1}(m), 1625 cm^{-1}(m), 1280 cm^{-1}(m), 820 cm^{-1}(s), 695 cm^{-1}(s). The ^{1}H NMR spectrum of **J** consists of a singlet at δ 6.3. Using Table 14.2, make as many IR assignments as you can and propose a structure for compound **J**.

14.26 When dissolved in CDCl$_3$, a compound (**K**) with the molecular formula C$_4$H$_8$O$_2$ gives a ^{1}H NMR spectrum that consists of a doublet at δ 1.35, a singlet at δ 2.15, a broad singlet at δ 3.75 (1H), and a quartet at δ 4.25 (1H). When dissolved in D$_2$O, the compound gives a similar ^{1}H NMR spectrum with the exception that the signal at δ 3.75 has disappeared. The IR spectrum of the compound shows a strong absorption peak near 1720 cm^{-1}. (a) Propose a structure for compound **K** and   (b) explain why the NMR signal at δ 3.75 disappears when D$_2$O is used as the solvent.

14.27 A compound (**L**) with the molecular formula C$_9$H$_{10}$ decolorizes bromine in carbon tetrachloride and gives an IR absorption spectrum that includes the following absorption peaks: 3035 cm^{-1}(m), 3020 cm^{-1}(m), 2925 cm^{-1}(m), 2853 cm^{-1}(w), 1640 cm^{-1}(m), 990 cm^{-1}(s), 915 cm^{-1}(s), 740 cm^{-1}(s), 695 cm^{-1}(s). The ^{1}H NMR spectrum of **L** consists of:

Doublet δ 3.1 (2H)   Multiplet δ 5.1   Multiplet δ 7.1 (5H)
Multiplet δ 4.8   Multiplet δ 5.8

The UV spectrum shows a maximum at 255 nm. Propose a structure for compound **L** and make assignments for each of the IR peaks.

14.28 Assume that in a certain ^{1}H NMR spectrum you find two peaks of roughly equal intensity. You are not certain whether these two peaks are *singlets* arising from uncoupled protons at different chemical shifts, or whether they are two peaks of a *doublet* that arises from protons coupling with a single adjacent proton. What simple experiment would you perform to distinguish between these two possibilities?

14.29 Compound **M** has the molecular formula C$_9$H$_{12}$. The ^{1}H NMR spectrum of **M** is given in Fig. 14.45 and the IR spectrum in Fig. 14.46. Propose a structure for **M**.

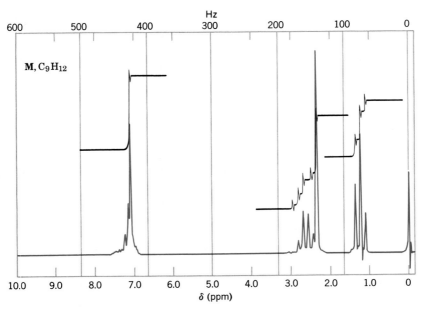

FIGURE 14.45 The ^{1}H NMR spectrum of compound **M**, Problem 14.29. (Spectrum courtesy of Aldrich Chemical Co., Milwaukee, WI.)

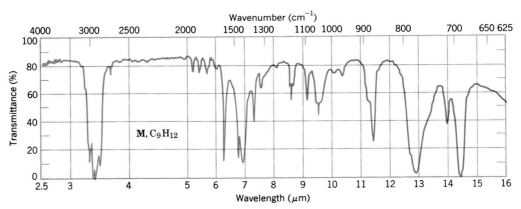

FIGURE 14.46 The IR spectrum of compound **M**, Problem 14.29. (Spectrum courtesy of Aldrich Chemical Co., Milwaukee, WI.)

14.30 A compound (**N**) with the molecular formula $C_9H_{10}O$ gives a positive test with cold dilute aqueous potassium permanganate. The ^{1}H NMR spectrum of **N** is shown in Fig. 14.47 and the IR spectrum of **N** is shown in Fig. 14.48. Propose a structure for **N**.

14.31 When 2,3-dibromo-2,3-dimethylbutane is treated with SbF$_5$ in liquid SO$_2$ at -60 °C, the ^{1}H NMR spectrum does not show the two signals that would be expected of a carbocation like $CH_3CBr{-}\overset{+}{C}CH_3$. Instead only one signal (at δ 2.9) is observed. What carbo-
$\quad\quad\quad\quad\quad\quad\;\; |\quad\;\; |$
$\quad\quad\quad\quad\quad\; CH_3\;\; CH_3$
cation is formed in this reaction and of what special significance is this experiment?

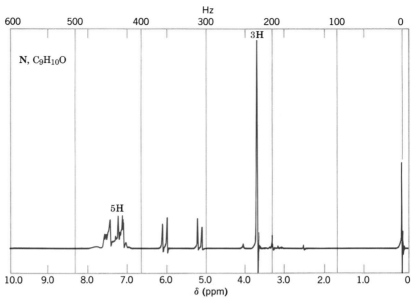

FIGURE 14.47 The ^{1}H NMR spectrum of compound N, Problem 14.34. (Spectrum courtesy of Aldrich Chemical Co., Milwaukee, WI.)

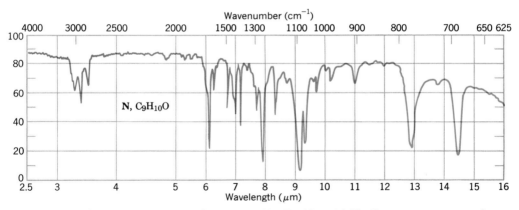

FIGURE 14.48 The IR spectrum of compound N, Problem 14.30. (Spectrum courtesy of Aldrich Chemical Co., Milwaukee, WI.)

14.32 Compound **O** (C_6H_8) reacts with two molar equivalents of hydrogen in the presence of a catalyst to produce **P** (C_6H_{12}). The proton-decoupled ^{13}C spectrum of **O** consists of two singlets, one at δ 26.0 and one at δ 124.5. In the proton off-resonance ^{13}C spectrum of **O** the signal at δ 26.0 appears as a triplet and the one at δ 124.5 appears as a doublet. Propose structures for **O** and **P**.

14.33 Compound **Q**, has the molecular formula C_7H_8. On catalytic hydrogenation **Q** is converted to **R** (C_7H_{12}). The proton-decoupled ^{13}C spectrum of **Q** is given in Fig. 14.49. Propose structures for **Q** and **R**.

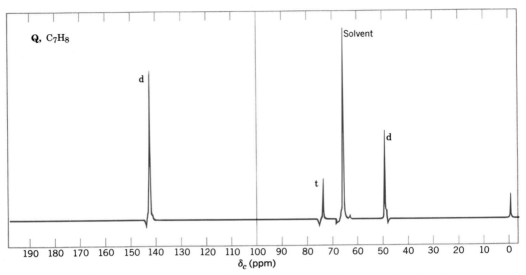

FIGURE 14.49 The proton-decoupled ^{13}C NMR spectrum of compound **Q**, Problem 14.33. The letters d and t refer to the signal splitting (doublet and triplet) in the proton off-resonance decoupled spectrum. (Adapted from L. F. Johnson and W. C. Jankowski, *Carbon-13 NMR Spectra: A Collection of Assigned, Coded, and Indexed Spectra*, Wiley–Interscience, New York, 1972.)

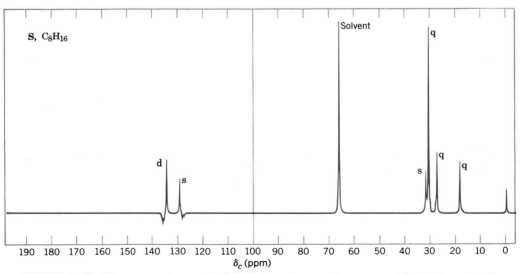

FIGURE 14.50 The proton-decoupled ^{13}C NMR spectrum of compound **S**, Problem 14.34. The letters s, d, and q refer to signal splitting (singlet, doublet, and quartet) in the proton off-resonance decoupled spectrum. (Adapted from L. F. Johnson and W. C. Jankowski, *Carbon-13 NMR Spectra: A Collection of Assigned, Coded, and Indexed Spectra*, Wiley–Interscience, New York, 1972.)

14.34 Compound S (C_8H_{16}) decolorizes a solution of bromine in carbon tetrachloride. The proton-decoupled ^{13}C spectrum of S is given in Fig. 14.50. Propose a structure for S.

14.35 Compound T (C_5H_8O) has a strong IR absorption band at 1745 cm^{-1}. The proton-decoupled ^{13}C spectrum of T is given in Fig. 14.51. Propose a structure for T.

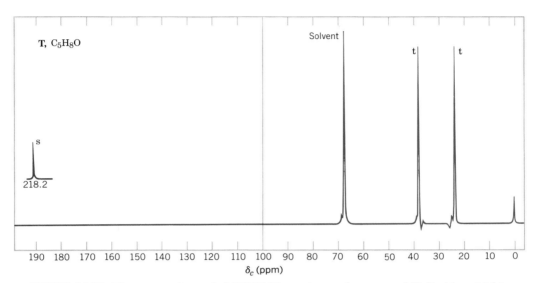

FIGURE 14.51 The proton-decoupled ^{13}C NMR spectrum of compound T, Problem 14.35. The letters s and t refer to the signal splitting (singlet and triplet) in the proton off-resonance decoupled spectrum. (Adapted from L. F. Johnson and W. C. Jankowski, *Carbon-13 NMR Spectra: A Collection of Assigned, Coded, and Indexed Spectra*, Wiley–Interscience, New York, 1972.)

14.36 The IR and ^1H NMR spectra for compound X (C_8H_{10}) are given in Fig. 14.52. Propose a structure for compound X.

14.37 The IR and ^1H NMR spectra of compound Y ($C_9H_{12}O$) are given in Fig. 14.53. Propose a structure for Y.

14.38 The following [14]annulene obeys Hückel's rule. Its ^1H NMR spectrum shows signals at δ 7.78 (10H) and δ − 0.61 (4H). Dehydro[14]annulene gives ^1H NMR signals at δ 8.0 (10H) and δ 0.0 (2H). How can you account for the relative intensities of the signals given by the two compounds?

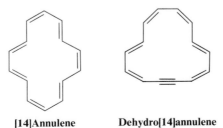

[14]Annulene   Dehydro[14]annulene

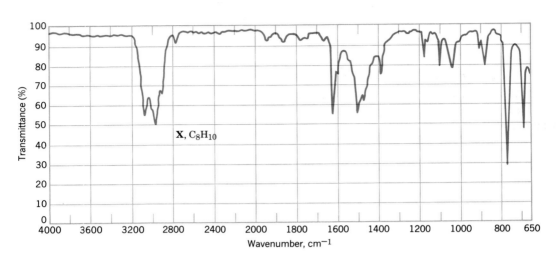

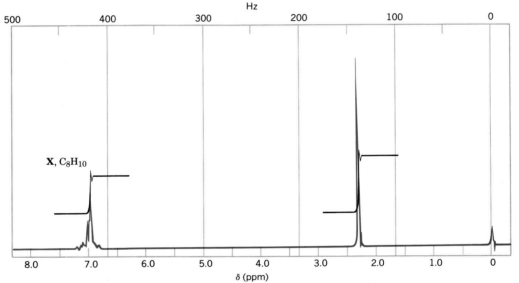

FIGURE 14.52 The IR and ^{1}H NMR spectra of compound **X**, Problem 14.36. (Spectra courtesy of Varian Associates, Palo Alto, CA.)

14.39 (a) When butyl fluoride and *sec*-butyl fluoride are treated separately with excess SbF_5, their solutions give identical ^{1}H NMR spectra. These spectra, moreover, are the same as that obtained when *tert*-butyl fluoride is treated with SbF_5. Explain these results. (b) Treating the eight isomeric fluoropentanes with excess SbF_5 furnishes solutions that give identical ^{1}H NMR spectra. What species is formed in these reactions? Sketch the spectrum that you would expect to obtain.

14.40 (a) How many peaks would you expect to find in the ^{1}H NMR spectrum of caffeine?

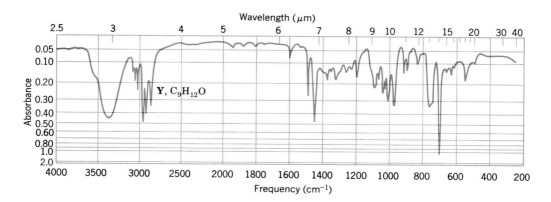

Caffeine

(b) What characteristic peaks would you expect to find in the IR spectrum of caffeine?

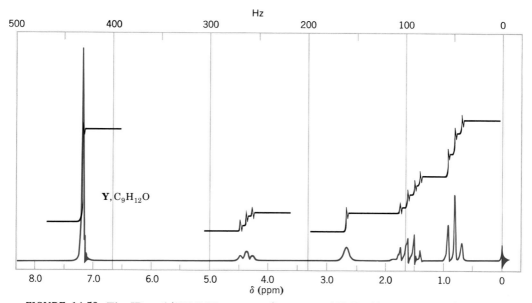

FIGURE 14.53 The IR and ^{1}H NMR spectra of compound **Y**, Problem 14.37. (Infrared spectrum courtesy of Sadtler Research Laboratories, Philadelphia. The ^{1}H NMR spectrum courtesy of Varian Associates, Palo Alto, CA.)

14.41   3,4-Dichloro-1,2,3,4-tetramethylcyclobutene, **I** (see following structure), gives a ^{1}H NMR signal at δ 1.15 corresponding to the protons labeled **A** and a signal at δ 1.26 corresponding to the protons labeled **B**. When **I** is added to SbF$_5$—SO$_2$ at -78 °C, a pale-yellow solution is formed whose ^{1}H NMR spectrum shows the following singlets: δ 2.05 (3H), δ 2.20 (3H), δ 2.65 (6H). After several minutes, these peaks begin to be replaced by a sharp singlet at δ 3.68. Recall that SbF_5 is a powerful Lewis acid and explain what is taking place.

I

*14.42 Given the following information predict the appearance of the ^{1}H NMR spectrum given by the vinyl hydrogen atoms of p-chlorostyrene.

Deshielding by the induced magnetic field of the ring is greatest at proton (c) (δ 6.7) and is least at proton (b) (δ 5.3). The chemical shift of (a) is about δ 5.7. The coupling constants have the following approximate magnitudes: $J_{ac} \simeq 18$ Hz, $J_{bc} \simeq 11$ Hz, and $J_{ab} \simeq 2$ Hz. (These coupling constants are typical of those given by vinylic systems: coupling constants for trans hydrogen atoms are larger than those for cis hydrogen atoms and coupling constants for geminal hydrogen atoms are very small.)

SPECIAL TOPIC

D

MASS SPECTROMETRY

D.1 THE MASS SPECTROMETER

In a mass spectrometer (Fig. D.1) molecules in the gaseous state under low pressure are bombarded with a beam of high-energy electrons. The energy of the beam of electrons is usually 70 eV (electron volts) and one of the things this bombardment can do is dislodge one of the electrons of the molecule and produce a positively charged ion called *the molecular ion.*

$$M \quad + \quad e^- \quad \longrightarrow \quad M^{\ddagger} \quad + 2e^-$$

Molecule   **High-energy**   **Molecular**
electron   **ion**

The molecular ion is not only a cation, but because it contains an odd number of electrons, it also is a free radical. Thus it belongs to a general group of ions called *radical cations.* If, for example, the molecule under bombardment is a molecule of ammonia, the following reaction will take place.

$$H\!:\!\overset{\cdot\cdot}{\underset{\overset{\textstyle|}{H}}{N}}\!:\!H + e^- \longrightarrow \left[H\!:\!\overset{\cdot}{\underset{\overset{\textstyle|}{H}}{N}}\!:\!H \right]^+ + 2e^-$$

Molecular ion, M⁺
(a radical cation)

An electron beam with an energy of 70 eV (~ 1600 kcal mol^{-1}) not only dislodges electrons from molecules, producing molecular ions, it also imparts to the molecular ions considerable surplus energy. Not all molecular ions will have the same amount of surplus energy, but for most, the surplus will be far in excess of that required to break covalent bonds (50–100 kcal mol^{-1}). Thus, soon after they are formed, most molecular ions literally fly apart—they undergo *fragmentation.* Fragmentation can take place in a variety of ways depending on the nature of the particular molecular ion, and as we shall see later, the way a molecular ion fragments can give us highly useful information about the structure of a complex molecule. Even with a relatively simple molecule like ammonia, however, fragmentation can produce several new cations. The molecular ion can eject a hydrogen atom, for example, and produce the cation NH_2^+.

$$H\!:\!\overset{\cdot +}{\underset{\overset{\textstyle|}{H}}{N}}\!:\!H \longrightarrow H\!:\!\overset{+}{\underset{\overset{\textstyle|}{H}}{N}}\!:\! + H\cdot$$

This $\overset{+}{N}H_2$ cation can then lose a hydrogen atom to produce $\overset{+}{N}H\cdot$, which can lead, in turn, to $\overset{+}{N}$.

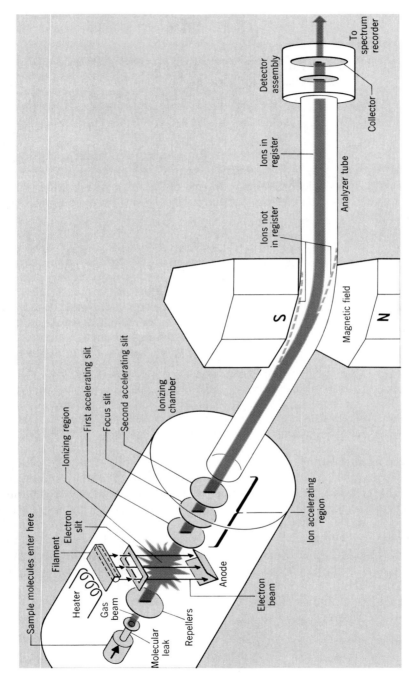

FIGURE D.1 Mass spectrometer. Schematic diagram of CEG model 21-103. The magnetic field that brings ions of varying mass/charge (m/z) ratios into register is perpendicular to the page. (From John R. Holum, *Organic Chemistry: A Brief Course*, Wiley, New York, 1975. Used with permission.)

SPECIAL TOPIC D

$$H\!:\!\overset{+}{\underset{H}{N}}\!: \longrightarrow H\!:\!\overset{+}{N}\!: + H\cdot$$

$$H\!:\!\overset{+}{N}\!: \longrightarrow :\overset{+}{N}\!: + H\cdot$$

The mass spectrometer then *sorts* these cations on the basis of their mass/charge or m/z ratio. Since for all practical purposes the charge on all of the ions is $+1$, this amounts to sorting them on the basis of their mass. The conventional mass spectrometer does this by accelerating the ions through a series of slits and then it sends the ion beam into a curved tube (see Fig. D.1 again). This curved tube passes through a variable magnetic field and the magnetic field exerts an influence on the moving ions. Depending on its strength at a given moment, the magnetic field will cause ions with a particular m/z ratio to follow a curved path that exactly matches the curvature of the tube. These ions are said to be "in register." Because they are in register, these ions pass through another slit and impinge on an ion collector where the intensity of the ion beam is measured electronically. The intensity of the beam is simply a measure of the relative abundance of the ions with a particular m/z ratio. Some mass spectrometers are so sensitive that they can detect the arrival of a *single ion.*

The actual sorting of ions takes place in the magnetic field, and this sorting takes place because laws of physics govern the paths followed by charged particles when they move through magnetic fields. Generally speaking, a magnetic field such as this will cause ions moving through it to move in a path that represents part of a circle. The radius of curvature of this circular path is related to the m/z ratio of the ions, to the strength of the magnetic field (H, in gauss) and to the accelerating voltage. If we keep the accelerating voltage constant and progressively increase the magnetic field, ions whose m/z ratios are progressively larger will travel in a circular path that exactly matches that of the curved tube. Hence, by steadily increasing H, ions with progressively increasing m/z ratios will be brought into register and thus will be detected at the ion collector. Since, as we said earlier, the charge on nearly all of the ions is unity, this means that *ions of progressively increasing mass arrive at the collector and are detected.*

What we have described is called "magnetic focusing" (or "magnetic scanning"), and all of this is done automatically by the mass spectrometer. The spectrometer displays the results by plotting a series of peaks of varying intensity in which each peak corresponds to ions of a particular m/z ratio. This display (Fig. D.2) is one form of a *mass spectrum.*

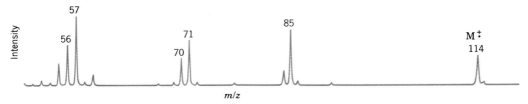

FIGURE D.2 A portion of the mass spectrum of octane.

Ion sorting can also be done with "electrical focusing." In this technique, the magnetic field is held constant and the accelerating voltage is varied. Both methods, of course, accomplish the same thing, and some high-resolution mass spectrometers employ both techniques.

To summarize: A mass spectrometer bombards organic molecules with a beam of high-energy electrons causing them to ionize and fragment. It then separates the resulting mixture of ions on the basis of their m/z ratios and records the relative abundance of each ionic fragment. It displays this result as a plot of ion abundance versus m/z.

D.2 THE MASS SPECTRUM

Mass spectra are usually published as bar graphs or in tabular form, as illustrated in Fig. D.3 for the mass spectrum of ammonia. In either presentation, the most intense peak — called the *base peak* — is arbitrarily assigned an intensity of 100%. The intensities of all other peaks are given proportionate values, as percentages of the base peak.

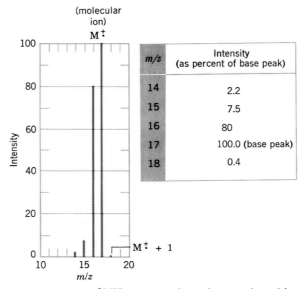

m/z	Intensity (as percent of base peak)
14	2.2
15	7.5
16	80
17	100.0 (base peak)
18	0.4

FIGURE D.3 The mass spectrum of NH_3 presented as a bar graph and in tabular form.

The masses of the ions given in a mass spectrum are those that we would calculate for the ion by assigning to the constituent atoms *masses rounded off to the nearest whole number.* For the commonly encountered atoms the nearest whole-number masses are

$$H = 1 \quad O = 16$$
$$C = 12 \quad F = 19$$
$$N = 14$$

In the mass spectrum of ammonia we see peaks at $m/z = 14, 15, 16,$ and 17. These correspond to the molecular ion and to the fragments we saw earlier.

$$NH_3 \xrightarrow{-e^-} [NH_3]^{\ddagger} \xrightarrow{-H \cdot} [NH_2]^+ \xrightarrow{-H \cdot} [NH]^{\ddagger} \xrightarrow{-H \cdot} [N]^+$$
$$m/z = \underset{\substack{\text{(molecular} \\ \text{ion)}}}{17} \qquad 16 \qquad 15 \qquad 14$$

SPECIAL TOPIC D

By convention we express,

$$H:\overset{..+}{\underset{\underset{H}{..}}{N}}:H \quad \text{as} \quad [NH_3]^{\ddagger}$$

$$H:\overset{+}{\underset{\underset{H}{..}}{N}}: \quad \text{as} \quad [NH_2]^{+}$$

$$H:\overset{+}{\underset{.}{N}}: \quad \text{as} \quad [NH]^{\ddagger}$$

and

$$:\overset{+}{N}: \quad \text{as} \quad [N]^{+}$$

In the case of ammonia, the base peak is the peak arising from the molecular ion. This is not always the case, however; in many of the spectra that we shall see later the base peak (the most intense peak) will be at an m/z value different from that of the molecular ion. This happens because in many instances the molecular ion fragments so rapidly that some other ion at a smaller m/z value produces the most intense peak. In a few cases the molecular ion peak is extremely small, and sometimes it is absent altogether.

One other feature in the spectrum of ammonia requires explanation: the small peak that occurs at m/z 18. In the bar graph we have labeled this peak $M^{\ddagger} + 1$ to indicate that it is one mass unit greater than the molecular ion. The $M^{\ddagger} + 1$ peak appears in the spectrum because most elements (e.g., nitrogen and hydrogen) have more than one naturally occurring isotope (Table D.1). Although most of the NH_3 molecules in a sample of ammonia are composed of $^{14}N^1H_3$, a small but detectable fraction of molecules are composed of $^{15}N^1H_3$. (A very tiny fraction of molecules is

TABLE D.1 Principal stable isotopes of common elements[a]

ELEMENT	MOST COMMON ISOTOPE		NATURAL ABUNDANCE OF OTHER ISOTOPES (BASED ON 100 ATOMS OF MOST COMMON ISOTOPE)			
Carbon	^{12}C	100	^{13}C	1.11		
Hydrogen	^1H	100	^2H	0.016		
Nitrogen	^{14}N	100	^{15}N	0.38		
Oxygen	^{16}O	100	^{17}O	0.04	^{18}O	0.20
Fluorine	^{19}F	100				
Silicon	^{28}Si	100	^{29}Si	5.10	^{30}Si	3.35
Phosphorus	^{31}P	100				
Sulfur	^{32}S	100	^{33}S	0.78	^{34}S	4.40
Chlorine	^{35}Cl	100	^{37}Cl	32.5		
Bromine	^{79}Br	100	^{81}Br	98.0		
Iodine	^{127}I	100				

[a]Data obtained from R. M. Silverstein, G. C. Bassler, and T. C. Morrill, *Spectrometric Identification of Organic Compounds,* 5th ed., Wiley, New York, 1991, p. 9.

also composed of $^{14}N^{1}H_{2}^{2}H$.) These molecules ($^{15}N^{1}H_{3}$ or $^{14}N^{1}H_{2}^{2}H$) produce molecular ions at m/z 18, that is at M‡ + 1.

The spectrum of ammonia begins to show us with a simple example how the masses (or m/z values) of individual ions can give us information about the composition of the ions and how this information can allow us to arrive at possible structures for a compound. Problems D.1 to D.3 will allow us further practice with this technique.

Problem D.1

Propose a structure for the compound whose mass spectrum is given in Fig. D.4 and make reasonable assignments for each peak.

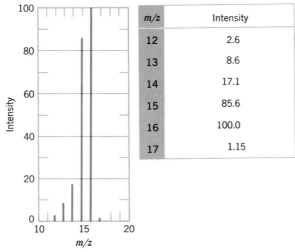

m/z	Intensity
12	2.6
13	8.6
14	17.1
15	85.6
16	100.0
17	1.15

FIGURE D.4 Mass spectrum for Problem D.1.

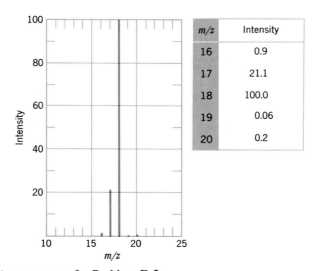

m/z	Intensity
16	0.9
17	21.1
18	100.0
19	0.06
20	0.2

FIGURE D.5 Mass spectrum for Problem D.2.

Problem D.2

Propose a structure for the compound whose mass spectrum is given in Fig. D.5 and make reasonable assignments for each peak.

Problem D.3

The compound whose mass spectrum is given in Fig. D.6 contains three elements, one of which is fluorine. Propose a structure for the compound and make reasonable assignments for each peak.

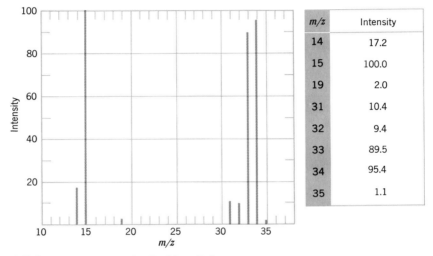

m/z	Intensity
14	17.2
15	100.0
19	2.0
31	10.4
32	9.4
33	89.5
34	95.4
35	1.1

FIGURE D.6 Mass spectrum for Problem D.3.

D.3 DETERMINATION OF MOLECULAR FORMULAS AND MOLECULAR WEIGHTS

D.3A The Molecular Ion and Isotopic Peaks

Look at Table D.1 for a moment. Notice that most of the common elements found in organic compounds have naturally occurring *heavier* isotopes. For three of the elements — carbon, hydrogen, and nitrogen — the principal heavier isotope is one mass unit greater than the most common isotope. The presence of these elements in a compound will give rise to a small isotopic peak one unit greater than the molecular ion — at $M^{\ddagger} + 1$. For four of the elements — oxygen, sulfur, chlorine, and bromine — the principal heavier isotope is two mass units greater than the most common isotope. The presence of these elements in a compound gives rise to an isotopic peak at $M^{\ddagger} + 2$.

$$M^{\ddagger} + 1 \text{ Elements:} \quad \text{C, H, N}$$

$$M^{\ddagger} + 2 \text{ Elements:} \quad \text{O, S, Br, Cl}$$

Isotopic peaks give us one method for determining molecular formulas. To understand how this can be done, let us begin by noticing that the isotope abundances in Table D.1 are based on 100 atoms of the normal isotope. Now let us suppose, as an example, that we have 100 molecules of methane (CH_4). On the average there will be 1.11 molecules that contain ^{13}C and 4×0.016 molecules that contain ^2H. Altogether then, these heavier isotopes should contribute an $M^{+} + 1$ peak whose intensity is about 1.17% of the intensity of the peak for the molecular ion.

$$1.11 + 4(0.016) \simeq 1.17\%$$

This correlates well with the observed intensity of the $M^{+} + 1$ peak in the actual spectrum of methane given in Fig. D.4.

For molecules with a modest number of atoms we can determine molecular formulas in the following way. If the M^{+} peak is not the base peak the first thing we do with the mass spectrum of an unknown compound is to recalculate the intensities of the $M^{+} + 1$ and $M^{+} + 2$ peaks to express them as percentages of the intensity of the M^{+} peak. Consider, for example, the mass spectrum given in Fig. D.7. The M^{+} peak at $m/z = 72$ is not the base peak. Therefore, we need to recalculate the intensities of the peaks in our spectrum at m/z 72, 73, and 74 as percents of the peak at m/z 72. We do this by dividing each intensity by the intensity of the M^{+} peak, which is 73%, and multiply by 100. These results are shown here and in the second column of Fig. D.7.

m/z	INTENSITY (% OF M^{+})
72	$73.0/73 \times 100 = 100$
73	$3.3/73 \times 100 = 4.5$
74	$0.2/73 \times 100 = 0.3$

Then we use the following guides to determine the molecular formula.

1. **Is M^{+} odd or even? According to the nitrogen rule, if it is even, then the compound must contain an even number of nitrogen atoms (zero is an even number).**

    For our unknown, M^{+} is even. The compound must have an even number of nitrogen atoms.

2. **The relative abundance of the $M^{+} + 1$ peak indicates the number of carbon atoms. Number of C atoms = relative abundance of $(M^{+} + 1)/1.1$**

    For our unknown (Fig. D.7), number of C atoms $= \dfrac{4.5}{1.1} = 4$

    (This formula works because ^{13}C is the most important contributor to the $M^{+} + 1$ peak and the approximate natural abundance of ^{13}C is 1.1%.)

3. **The relative abundance of the $M^{+} + 2$ peak indicates the presence (or absence) of S, (4.4%); Cl, (33%); or Br (98%) (see Table D.1).**

    For our unknown, $M^{+} + 2 = 0.2\%$; thus we can assume that S, Cl, and Br are absent.

4. **The molecular formula can now be established by determining the number of hydrogen atoms and adding the appropriate number of oxygen atoms, if necessary.**

m/z	Intensity (as percent of base peak)	m/z		Intensity (as percent of $M^{\ddot{+}}$)
27	59.0	72	$M^{\ddot{+}}$	100.0
28	15.0	73	$M^{\ddot{+}} + 1$	4.5
29	54.0	74	$M^{\ddot{+}} + 2$	0.3
39	23.0		Recalculated to base on $M^{\ddot{+}}$	
41	60.0			
42	12.0			
43	79.0			
44	100.0 (base)			
72	73.0 $M^{\ddot{+}}$			
73	3.3			
74	0.2			

FIGURE D.7 Mass spectrum of an unknown compound.

For our unknown the $M^{\ddot{+}}$ peak at m/z 72 gives us the molecular weight. It also tells us (since it is even) that nitrogen is absent because C_4N_2 has a molecular weight (76) greater than that of our compound.

For a molecule composed of C and H only:

$$H = 72 - (4 \times 12) = 24, \text{ but } C_4H_{24} \text{ is impossible.}$$

For a molecule composed of C, H, and one O:

$$H = 72 - (4 \times 12) - 16 = 8 \text{ and thus our unknown has the molecular formula } C_4H_8O.$$

Problem D.4

(a) Write structural formulas for at least 14 stable compounds that have the formula C_4H_8O. (b) The IR spectrum of the unknown compound shows a strong peak near 1730 cm^{-1}. Which structures now remain as possible formulas for the compound? (We continue with this compound in Problem D.14.)

Problem D.5

Determine the molecular formula of the following compound. (The complete mass spectrum of this compound is given in Fig. D.18; cf. Problem D.19.)

m/z	INTENSITY (as % of base peak)
86 $M^{\ddot{+}}$	10.00
87	0.56
88	0.04

Problem D.6

(a) What approximate intensities would you expect for the M^+ and $M^+ + 2$ peaks of CH_3Cl? (b) For the M^+ and $M^+ + 2$ peaks of CH_3Br? (c) An organic compound gives an M^+ peak at m/z 122 and a peak of nearly equal intensity at m/z 124. What is a likely molecular formula for the compound?

Problem D.7

Use the mass spectral data given in Fig. D.8 to determine the molecular formula for the compound.

FIGURE D.8 Mass spectrum for Problem D.7.

m/z	INTENSITY (as % of base peak)
14	8.0
15	38.6
18	16.3
28	39.7
29	23.4
42	46.6
43	10.7
44	100.0 (base)
73	86.1 M^+
74	3.2
75	0.2

Problem D.8

(a) Determine the molecular formula of the compound whose mass spectrum is given here. (b) The ^1H NMR spectrum of this compound consists only of a large doublet and a small septet. What is the structure of the compound?

m/z	INTENSITY (as % of base peak)
27	34
39	11
41	22
43	100 (base)
63	26
65	8
78	24 M^+
79	0.8
80	8

SPECIAL TOPIC D

TABLE D.2 Relative intensities of $M^{\ddagger} + 1$ and $M^{\ddagger} + 2$ peaks for various combinations of C, H, N, and O for masses 72 and 73

$M^{\ddagger}$	FORMULAS	PERCENTAGE OF $M^{\ddagger}$ INTENSITY		$M^{\ddagger}$	FORMULAS	PERCENTAGE OF $M^{\ddagger}$ INTENSITY	
		$M^{\ddagger} + 1$	$M^{\ddagger} + 2$			$M^{\ddagger} + 1$	$M^{\ddagger} + 2$
72	CH_2N_3O	2.30	0.22	73	CHN_2O_2	1.94	0.41
	CH_4N_4	2.67	0.03		CH_3N_3O	2.31	0.22
	$C_2H_2NO_2$	2.65	0.42		CH_5N_4	2.69	0.03
	$C_2H_4N_2O$	3.03	0.23		C_2HO_3	2.30	0.62
	$C_2H_6N_3$	3.40	0.04		$C_2H_3NO_2$	2.67	0.42
	$C_3H_4O_2$	3.38	0.44		$C_2H_5N_2O$	3.04	0.23
	C_3H_6NO	3.76	0.25		$C_2H_7N_3$	3.42	0.04
	$C_3H_8N_2$	4.13	0.07		$C_3H_5O_2$	3.40	0.44
	C_4H_8O	4.49	0.28		C_3H_7NO	3.77	0.25
	$C_4H_{10}N$	4.86	0.09		$C_3H_9N_2$	4.15	0.07
	C_5H_{12}	5.60	0.13		C_4H_9O	4.51	0.28
					$C_4H_{11}N$	4.88	0.10
					C_6H	6.50	0.18

Data from J. H. Beynon, *Mass Spectrometry and Its Application to Organic Chemistry,* Elsevier, Amsterdam, 1960.

As the number of atoms in a molecule increases, calculations like this become more and more complex and time consuming. Fortunately, however, these calculations can be done readily with computers, and tables are now available that give relative values for the $M^{\ddagger} + 1$ and $M^{\ddagger} + 2$ peaks for all combinations of common elements with molecular formulas up to mass 500. Part of the data obtained from one of these tables is given in Table D.2. Use Table D.2 to check the results of our example (Fig. D.7) and your answer to Problem D.7.

D.3B High-Resolution Mass Spectrometry

All of the spectra that we have described so far were determined on what are called "low-resolution" mass spectrometers. These spectrometers, as we noted earlier, measure m/z values to the nearest whole-number mass unit. Some laboratories are equipped with this type of mass spectrometer.

Many laboratories, however, are equipped with the more expensive "high-resolution" mass spectrometers. These spectrometers can measure m/z values to three or four decimal places and thus they provide an extremely accurate method for determining molecular weights. And because molecular weights can be measured so accurately, these spectrometers also allow us to determine molecular formulas.

The determination of a molecular formula by an accurate measurement of a molecular weight is possible because the actual masses of atomic particles (nuclides) are not integers (see Table D.3). Consider, as examples, the three molecules, O_2, N_2H_4, and CH_3OH. The actual atomic masses of the molecules are all different.

$$O_2 = 2(15.9949) = 31.9898$$

$$N_2H_4 = 2(14.0031) + 4(1.00783) = 32.0375$$

$$CH_4O = 12.0000 + 4(1.00783) + 15.9949 = 32.0262$$

High-resolution mass spectrometers are available that are capable of measuring mass with an accuracy of 1 part in 40,000 or better. Thus, such a spectrometer can easily distinguish among these three molecules and, in effect, tell us the molecular formula.

TABLE D.3   Exact masses of nuclides

ISOTOPE	MASS	ISOTOPE	MASS
^1H	1.00783	^{19}F	18.9984
^2H	2.01410	^{32}S	31.9721
^{12}C	12.00000 (std)	^{33}S	32.9715
^{13}C	13.00336	^{34}S	33.9679
^{14}N	14.0031	^{35}Cl	34.9689
^{15}N	15.0001	^{37}Cl	36.9659
^{16}O	15.9949	^{79}Br	78.9183
^{17}O	16.9991	^{81}Br	80.9163
^{18}O	17.9992	^{127}I	126.9045

D.4 FRAGMENTATION

In most instances the molecular ion is a highly energetic species, and in the case of a complex molecule a great many things can happen to it. The molecular ion can break apart in a variety of ways and the fragments that are produced can then undergo further fragmentation, and so on. In a certain sense mass spectroscopy is a "brute force" technique. Striking an organic molecule with 70-eV electrons is a little like firing a howitzer at a house made of matchsticks. That fragmentation takes place in any sort of predictable way is truly remarkable—and yet it does. Many of the same factors that govern ordinary chemical reactions seem to apply to fragmentation processes, and many of the principles that we have learned about the relative stabilities of carbocations, radicals, and molecules will help us to make some sense out of what takes place. And as we learn something about what kind of fragmentations to expect, we shall be much better able to use mass spectra as aids in determining the structures of organic molecules.

We cannot, of course, in the limited space that we have here, look at these processes in great detail, but we can examine some of the more important ones.

As we begin, keep two important principles in mind. (1) The reactions that take place in a mass spectrometer are usually *unimolecular*—that is, they involve only a *single* molecular fragment. This is true because the pressure in a mass spectrometer is kept so low ($\sim 10^{-6}$ torr) that reactions requiring bimolecular collisions usually do not occur. (2) The relative ion abundances, as measured by peak intensities, are extremely important. We shall see that the appearance of certain prominent peaks in the spectrum gives us important information about the structures of the fragments produced and about their original locations in the molecule.

SPECIAL TOPIC D

D.4A Fragmentation by Cleavage at a Single Bond

One important type of fragmentation is the simple cleavage at a single bond. With a radical cation this cleavage can take place in at least two ways; each way produces a *cation* and a *radical*. Only the cations are detected in a mass spectrometer. (The radicals, because they are not charged, are not deflected by the magnetic field and, therefore, are not detected.) With the molecular ion obtained from propane, for example, two possible modes of cleavage are

$$CH_3CH_2\!\overset{+}{\cdot}\!CH_3 \longrightarrow CH_3CH_2^+ + \cdot CH_3$$
$$m/z\ 29$$

$$CH_3CH_2\!\overset{+}{\cdot}\!CH_3 \longrightarrow CH_3CH_2\cdot + {}^+CH_3$$
$$m/z\ 15$$

These two modes of cleavage do not take place at equal rates, however. While the relative abundance of cations produced by such a cleavage is influenced both by the stability of the carbocation and by the stability of the free radical, *the carbocation's stability is more important.** In the spectrum of propane the peak at m/z 29 ($CH_3CH_2^+$) is the most intense peak; the peak at m/z 15 (CH_3^+) has an intensity of only 5.6%. This reflects the greater stability of $CH_3CH_2^+$ when compared to CH_3^+.

D.4B Fragmentation Equations

Before we go further, we need to examine some of the conventions that are used in writing equations for fragmentation reactions. In the two equations for cleavage at the single bond of propane that we have just written, we have localized the odd electron and the charge on one of the carbon – carbon sigma bonds of the molecular ion. When we write structures this way, the choice of just where to localize the odd electron and the charge is sometimes arbitrary. When possible, however, we write the structure showing the molecular ion that would result from the removal of one of the most loosely held electrons of the original molecule. Just which electrons these are can usually be estimated from ionization potentials (Table D.4). [The ionization potential of a molecule is the amount of energy (in eV) required to remove an electron from the molecule.] As we might expect, ionization potentials indicate that the nonbonding electrons of nitrogen and oxygen and the π electrons of alkenes and

TABLE D.4   Ionization potentials
of selected molecules

COMPOUND	IONIZATION POTENTIAL (eV)
$CH_3(CH_2)_3NH_2$	8.7
C_6H_6	9.2
C_2H_4	10.5
CH_3OH	10.8
C_2H_6	11.5
CH_4	12.7

*This can be demonstrated through thermochemical calculations that we cannot go into here. The interested student is referred to F. W. McLafferty, *Interpretation of Mass Spectra,* 2nd ed., Benjamin, Reading, MA, 1973, p. 41 and pp. 210–211.

aromatic molecules are held more loosely than the electrons of carbon–carbon and carbon–hydrogen sigma bonds. Thus the convention of localizing the odd electron and charge is especially applicable when the molecule contains an oxygen, nitrogen, double bond, or aromatic ring. If the molecule contains only carbon–carbon and carbon–hydrogen sigma bonds, and if it contains a great many of these, then the choice of where to localize the odd electron and the charge is so arbitrary as to be impractical. In these instances we usually resort to another convention. We write the formula for the radical cation in brackets and place the odd electron and charge outside. Using this convention we would write the two fragmentation reactions of propane in the following way:

$$[CH_3CH_2CH_3]^{\ddagger} \longrightarrow CH_3CH_2^+ + \cdot CH_3$$

$$[CH_3CH_2CH_3]^{\ddagger} \longrightarrow CH_3CH_2\cdot + CH_3^+$$

Problem D.9

The most intense peak in the mass spectrum of 2,2-dimethylbutane occurs at m/z 57. (a) What carbocation does this peak represent? (b) Using the convention that we have just described, write an equation that shows how this carbocation arises from the molecular ion.

Figure D.9 shows us the kind of fragmentation a longer chain alkane can undergo. The example here is hexane and we see a reasonably abundant molecular ion at m/z 86 accompanied by a small $M^{\ddagger} + 1$ peak. There is also a smaller peak at m/z 71 ($M^{\ddagger} - 15$) corresponding to the loss of $\cdot CH_3$, and the base peak is at m/z 57 ($M^{\ddagger} - 29$) corresponding to the loss of $\cdot CH_2CH_3$. The other prominent peaks are at m/z 43 ($M^{\ddagger} - 43$) and m/z 29 ($M^{\ddagger} - 57$) corresponding to the loss of $\cdot CH_2CH_2CH_3$ and $\cdot CH_2CH_2CH_2CH_3$, respectively. The important fragmentations are just the ones we would expect:

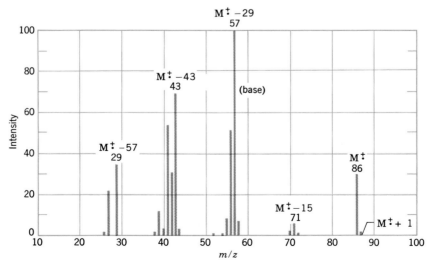

FIGURE D.9 Mass spectrum of hexane.

$$\text{[CH}_3\text{CH}_2\text{CH}_2\text{CH}_2\text{CH}_2\text{CH}_3\text{]}^{\dot{+}} \longrightarrow$$

$$\longrightarrow \text{CH}_3\text{CH}_2\text{CH}_2\text{CH}_2\text{CH}_2{}^+ + \cdot\text{CH}_3$$
$$m/z\ 71$$

$$\longrightarrow \text{CH}_3\text{CH}_2\text{CH}_2\text{CH}_2{}^+ + \cdot\text{CH}_2\text{CH}_3$$
$$m/z\ 57$$

$$\longrightarrow \text{CH}_3\text{CH}_2\text{CH}_2{}^+ + \cdot\text{CH}_2\text{CH}_2\text{CH}_3$$
$$m/z\ 43$$

$$\longrightarrow \text{CH}_3\text{CH}_2{}^+ + \cdot\text{CH}_2\text{CH}_2\text{CH}_2\text{CH}_3$$
$$m/z\ 29$$

Chain branching increases the likelihood of cleavage at a branch point because a more stable carbocation can result. When we compare the mass spectrum of 2-methylbutane (Fig. D.10) with the spectrum of hexane, we see a much more intense peak at $M^{\dot{+}} - 15$. Loss of a methyl radical from the molecular ion of 2-methylbutane can give a secondary carbocation:

$$\left[\begin{array}{c}\text{CH}_3 \\ | \\ \text{CH}_3\text{CHCH}_2\text{CH}_3\end{array}\right]^{\dot{+}} \longrightarrow \text{CH}_3\overset{+}{\text{C}}\text{HCH}_2\text{CH}_3 + \cdot\text{CH}_3$$

$$\begin{array}{cc} m/z\ 72 & m/z\ 57 \\ M^{\dot{+}} & M^{\dot{+}} - 15 \end{array}$$

whereas with hexane, loss of a methyl radical can yield only a primary carbocation.

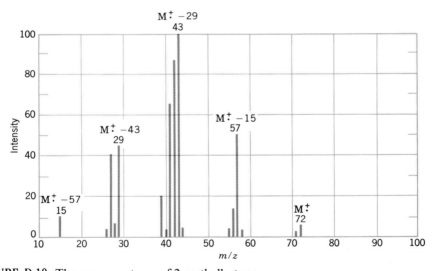

FIGURE D.10 The mass spectrum of 2-methylbutane.

With neopentane (Fig. D.11), this effect is even more dramatic. Loss of a methyl radical by the molecular ion produces a *tertiary* carbocation, and this reaction takes place so readily that virtually none of the molecular ions survives long enough to be detected.

$$\left[\begin{array}{c}\text{CH}_3 \\ | \\ \text{CH}_3-\text{C}-\text{CH}_3 \\ | \\ \text{CH}_3\end{array}\right]^{\dot{+}} \longrightarrow \begin{array}{c}\text{CH}_3 \\ | \\ \text{CH}_3-\overset{+}{\text{C}} \\ | \\ \text{CH}_3\end{array} + \cdot\text{CH}_3$$

$$\begin{array}{cc} m/z\ 72 & m/z\ 57 \\ M^{\dot{+}} & M^{\dot{+}} - 15 \end{array}$$

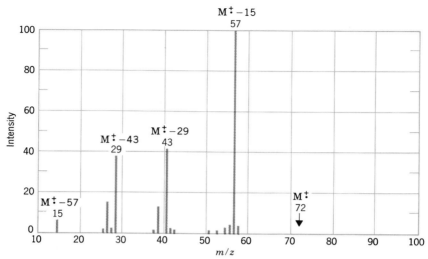

FIGURE D.11 Mass spectrum of neopentane.

Problem D.10

In contrast to 2-methylbutane and neopentane, the mass spectrum of 3-methylpentane (not given) has a peak of very low intensity at $M^{+} - 15$. It has a peak of very high intensity at $M^{+} - 29$, however. Explain.

Carbocations stabilized by resonance are usually also prominent in mass spectra. Several ways that resonance-stabilized carbocations can be produced are outlined in the following list.

1. Alkenes frequently undergo fragmentations that yield allylic cations.

$$CH_2 \overset{+ \cdot}{=\!=} CH \overset{}{=\!=} CH_2 \vdots R \longrightarrow \overset{+}{CH_2} - CH = CH_2 + \cdot R$$
$$\textbf{\textit{m/z 41}}$$

2. Carbon–carbon bonds next to an atom with an unshared electron pair usually break readily because the resulting carbocation is resonance stabilized.

$$R \overset{+ \cdot}{=\!=} Z \overset{}{=\!=} CH_2 \vdots CH_3 \longrightarrow R \overset{+}{=} Z = CH_2 + \cdot CH_3$$
$$\updownarrow$$
$$R - \overset{..}{Z} - \overset{+}{CH_2}$$

    $Z = N$, O, or S; R may also be H

3. Carbon–carbon bonds next to the carbonyl group of an aldehyde or ketone break readily because resonance-stabilized ions called acylium ions are produced.

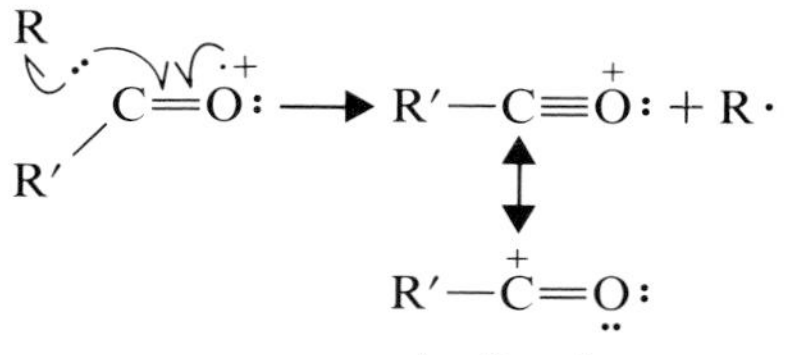

SPECIAL TOPIC D

$$R'-C\equiv\overset{+}{O}: + R\cdot$$

$$R'-\overset{+}{C}=\overset{..}{O}:$$

Acylium ion

or

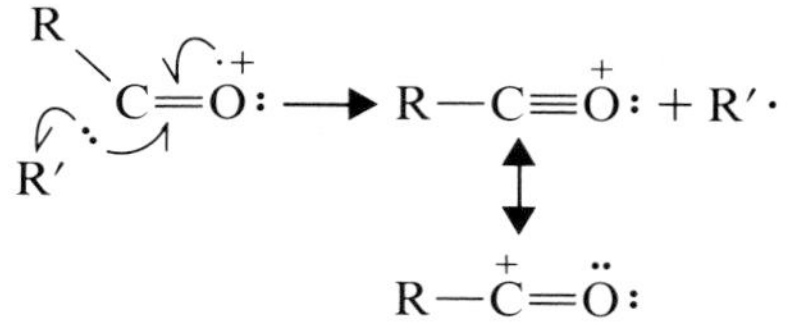

$$R-C\equiv\overset{+}{O}: + R'\cdot$$

$$R-\overset{+}{C}=\overset{..}{O}:$$

Acylium ion

4. Alkyl-substituted benzenes undergo loss of a hydrogen atom or methyl group to yield the relatively stable tropylium ion (cf. Section 13.7). This fragmentation gives a prominent peak (sometimes the base peak) at m/z 91.

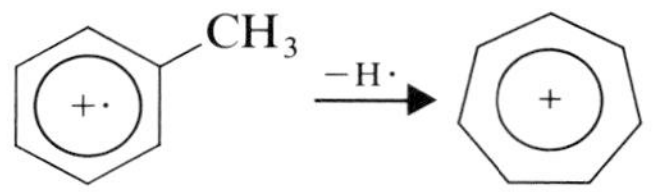

m/z **91**

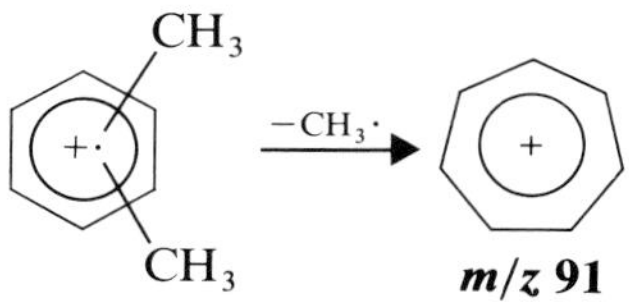

m/z **91**

5. Substituted benzenes also lose their substituent and yield a phenyl cation at m/z 77.

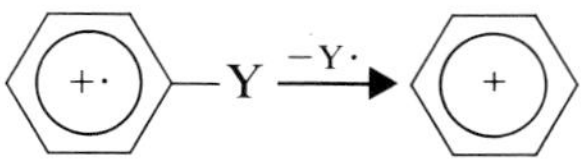

m/z **77**

$$\text{Y} = \text{halogen}, -\text{NO}_2, -\overset{\overset{\displaystyle O}{\|}}{\text{C}}\text{R}, -\text{R}, \text{ and so on}$$

Problem D.11

The mass spectrum of 4-methyl-1-hexene (not given) shows intense peaks at m/z 57 and m/z 41. What fragmentation reactions account for these peaks?

Problem D.12

Explain the following observations that can be made about the mass spectra of alcohols: (a) The molecular ion peak of a primary or secondary alcohol is very small; with a tertiary alcohol it is usually undetectable. (b) Primary alcohols show a prominent peak at m/z 31. (c) Secondary alcohols usually give prominent peaks at m/z 45, 59, 73, and so on. (d) Tertiary alcohols have prominent peaks at m/z 59, 73, 87, and so on.

Problem D.13

The mass spectra of butyl isopropyl ether and butyl propyl ether are given in Figs. D.12 and D.13. (a) Which spectrum represents which ether? (b) Explain your choice.

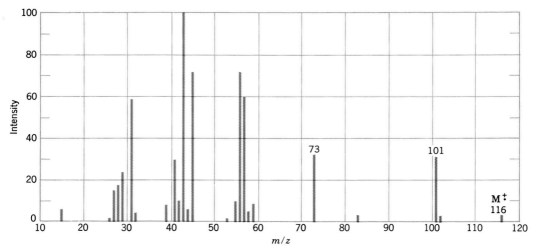

FIGURE D.12 Mass spectrum for Problem D.13.

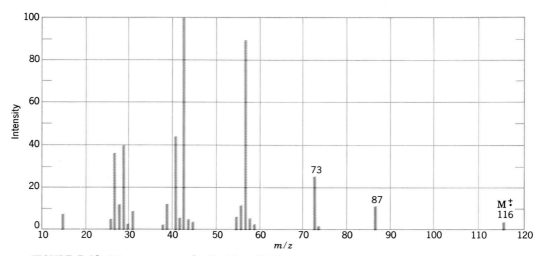

FIGURE D.13 Mass spectrum for Problem D.13.

D.4C Fragmentation by Cleavage of Two Bonds

Many peaks in mass spectra can be explained by fragmentation reactions that involve the breaking of two covalent bonds. When a radical–cation undergoes this type of fragmentation the products are *a new radical–cation* and *a neutral molecule.* Some important examples are the following:

1. Alcohols frequently show a prominent peak at $M^{\ddagger} - 18$. This corresponds to the loss of a molecule of water.

$$R-\overset{\overset{\displaystyle H}{\frown}}{C}H\overset{\overset{\displaystyle +\ddot{O}H}{|}}{\underset{\displaystyle M^{\ddagger}}{C}}H_2 \longrightarrow \underset{\displaystyle M^{\ddagger}-18}{R-CH^{\cdot+}CH_2} + H-\ddot{O}-H$$

or
$$\underset{\displaystyle M^{\ddagger}}{[R-CH_2-CH_2-OH]^{\ddagger}} \longrightarrow \underset{\displaystyle M^{\ddagger}-18}{[R-CH=CH_2]^{\ddagger}} + H_2O$$

2. Cycloalkenes can undergo a retro-Diels–Alder reaction that produces an alkene and an alkadienyl radical cation.

$$\left[\bighexagon\right]^{\ddagger} \longrightarrow \left[\bigpentagon\right]^{\ddagger} + \overset{\displaystyle CH_2}{\underset{\displaystyle CH_2}{\|}}$$

3. Carbonyl compounds with a hydrogen on their γ carbon undergo a fragmentation called the *McLafferty rearrangement.*
   Y may be R, H, OR, OH, and so on

$$\left[\begin{array}{c} O \quad H \\ \| \diagup \diagdown \\ Y-C \quad CHR \\ \diagdown \diagup | \\ H_2C-CH_2 \end{array}\right]^{\ddagger} \longrightarrow \left[\begin{array}{c} H \\ O \diagup \\ \| \\ Y-C \\ \diagdown CH_2 \end{array}\right]^{\ddagger} + RCH=CH_2$$

Y may be R, H, OR, OH, and so on

In addition to these reactions, we frequently find peaks in mass spectra that result from the elimination of other small stable neutral molecules, for example, H_2, NH_3, CO, HCN, H_2S, alcohols and alkenes.

Additional Problems

D.14 Reconsider Problem D.4 and the spectrum given in Fig. D.7. Important clues to the structure of this compound are the peaks at m/z 44 (the base peak) and m/z 29. Propose a structure for the compound and write fragmentation equations showing how these peaks arise.

D.15 The homologous series of primary amines, $CH_3(CH_2)_nNH_2$, from CH_3NH_2 to $CH_3(CH_2)_{13}NH_2$ all have their base (largest) peak at m/z 30. What ion does this peak represent and how is it formed?

D.16 The mass spectrum of compound **A** is given in Fig. D.14. The ^1H NMR spectrum of **A** consists of two singlets with area ratios of 9:2. The larger singlet is at $\delta 1.2$, the smaller one at δ 1.3. Propose a structure for compound **A**.

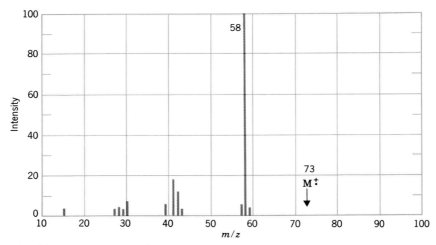

FIGURE D.14 Mass spectrum of compound **A** (Problem D.16).

D.17   The mass spectrum of compound **B** is given in Fig. D.15. The IR spectrum of **B** shows a broad peak between 3200 and 3550 cm⁻¹. The ¹H NMR spectrum of **B** shows the following peaks: a triplet at δ 0.9, a singlet at δ 1.1, and a quartet at δ 1.6. The area ratio of these peaks is 3:7:2, respectively. Propose a structure for **B**.

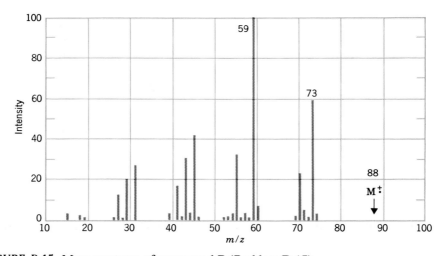

FIGURE D.15 Mass spectrum of compound **B** (Problem D.17).

D.18   The mass spectrum of compound **C** is given in Fig. D.16. Compound **C** is an isomer of **B** and the IR spectrum of **C** also shows a broad peak in the 3200–3550-cm⁻¹ region. The ¹H NMR spectrum of **C** is given in Fig. D.17. Propose a structure for **C**.

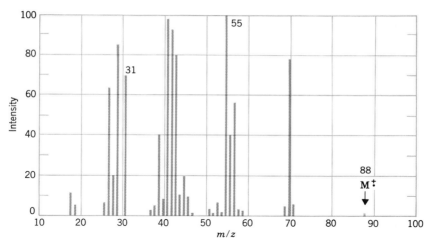

FIGURE D.16 Mass spectrum of compound **C** (Problem D.18).

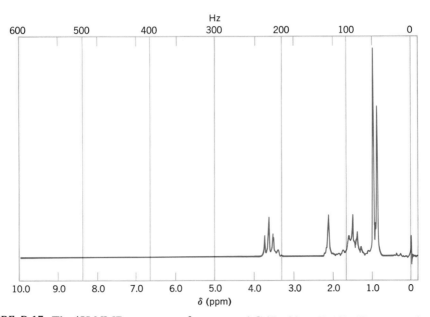

FIGURE D.17 The ¹H NMR spectrum of compound **C** (Problem D.18). (Courtesy of Aldrich Chemical Co., Milwaukee, WI.)

D.19 The mass spectrum of compound **D** is given in Fig. D.18. (**D** is also the subject of Problem D.5.) **D** shows a strong IR peak at 1710 cm⁻¹. The ¹H NMR spectrum of **D** is given in Fig. D.19. Propose a structure for **D**.

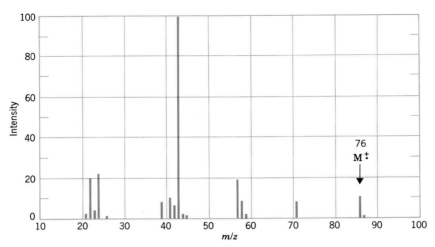

FIGURE D.18 Mass spectrum of compound **D** (Problem D.19).

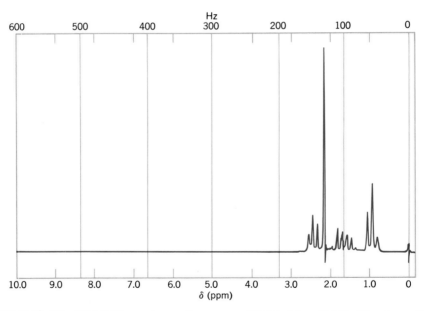

FIGURE D.19 The ^{1}H NMR spectrum of compound **D** (Problem D.19). (Courtesy of Aldrich Chemical Co., Milwaukee, WI.)

D.20 Propose a structure for compound **E** whose mass spectrum is given in Fig. D.20.

SPECIAL TOPIC D

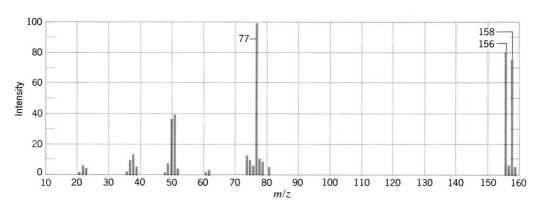

FIGURE D.20 The mass spectrum of compound **E** (Problem D.20).

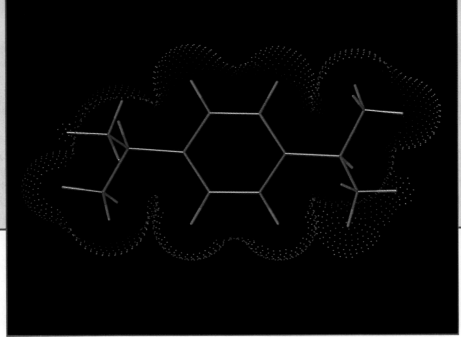

p-Diisopropylbenzene (see Section 15.8).

CHAPTER

15

ELECTROPHILIC AROMATIC SUBSTITUTION

15.1 ELECTROPHILIC AROMATIC SUBSTITUTION REACTIONS

Aromatic hydrocarbons are known generally as **arenes.** An **aryl group** is one derived from an arene by removal of a hydrogen atom and its symbol is Ar— . Thus, arenes are designated ArH just as alkanes are designated RH.

The most characteristic reactions of benzenoid arenes are the substitution reactions that occur when they react with electrophilic reagents. These reactions are of the general type shown below.

$$ArH + E^+ \longrightarrow Ar{-}E + H^+$$

or ⬡ $+ E^+ \longrightarrow$ ⬡^{E} $+ H^+$

The electrophiles are either a positive ion (E^+) or some other electron-deficient species with a large partial positive charge. As we shall learn in Section 15.3, for example, benzene can be brominated when it reacts with bromine in the presence of

636

FeBr$_3$. Bromine and FeBr$_3$ reacts to produce positive bromine ions, Br$^+$. These positive bromine ions act as electrophiles and attack the benzene ring replacing one of the hydrogen atoms in a reaction that is called an electrophilic aromatic substitution (EAS).

Electrophilic aromatic substitutions allow the direct introduction of a wide variety of groups onto an aromatic ring and because of this they provide synthetic routes to many important compounds. The five electrophilic aromatic substitutions that we shall study in this chapter are outlined in Fig. 15.1. All of these reactions involve the attack on the benzene ring by an electron-deficient species — by an electrophile. In Sections 15.3–15.7 we shall learn what the electrophile is in each instance.

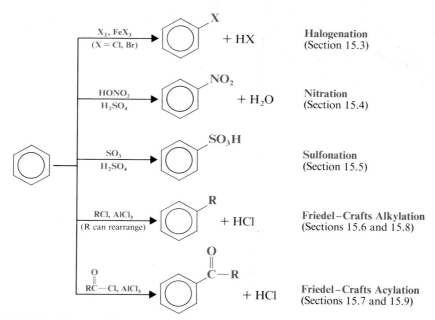

FIGURE 15.1 Electrophilic aromatic substitution reactions.

15.2 A GENERAL MECHANISM FOR ELECTROPHILIC AROMATIC SUBSTITUTION: ARENIUM IONS

Benzene is susceptible to electrophilic attack primarily because of its exposed π electrons. In this respect benzene resembles an alkene, for in the reaction of an alkene with an electrophile the site of attack is the exposed π bond.

We saw in Chapter 13, however, that benzene differs from an alkene in a very significant way. Benzene's closed shell of six π electrons gives it a special stability. So while benzene is susceptible to electrophilic attack, it undergoes *substitution reactions* rather than *addition reactions*. Substitution reactions allow the aromatic sextet of π electrons to be regenerated after attack by the electrophile has occurred. We can see how this happens if we examine a general mechanism for electrophilic aromatic substitution.

A considerable body of experimental evidence indicates that electrophiles attack the π system of benzene to form a ***delocalized nonaromatic carbocation*** known as an arenium ion (or sometimes as a σ *complex*). In this step it is convenient to use Kekulé structures, because these make it much easier to keep track of the π electrons.

Step 1

Arenium ion
(σ complex)

In step 1 the electrophile takes two electrons of the six-electron π system to form a σ bond to one carbon atom of the benzene ring. Formation of this bond interrupts the cyclic system of π electrons, because in the formation of the arenium ion the carbon that forms a bond to the electrophile becomes sp^3 hybridized and, thus, no longer has an available *p* orbital. Now only five carbon atoms of the ring are still sp^2 hybridized and still have *p* orbitals. The four π electrons of the arenium ion are delocalized through these five *p* orbitals.

In step 2 the arenium ion loses a proton from the carbon atom that bears the electrophile. The two electrons that bonded this proton to carbon become a part of the π system. The carbon atom that bears the electrophile becomes sp^2 hybridized again, and a benzene derivative with six fully delocalized π electrons is formed. We can represent step 2 with any one of the resonance structures for the arenium ion.

Step 2

(The proton displaced is transferred to any of the bases present, for example, to the anion derived from the electrophile.)

Problem 15.1

Show the second step of this mechanism using each of the other two resonance structures for the arenium ion.

Kekulé structures are more appropriate for writing mechanisms such as electrophilic aromatic substitution because they permit the use of resonance theory, which as we shall soon see, will be invaluable as an aid to our understanding. If, for brevity, however, we wish to show the mechanism using the modern formula for benzene we can do it in the following way:

Step 1

Arenium ion

Step 2

There is firm experimental evidence that the arenium ion is a true *intermediate* in electrophilic substitution reactions. It is not a transition state. This means that in a potential energy diagram (Fig. 15.2) the arenium ion lies in an energy valley between two transition states.

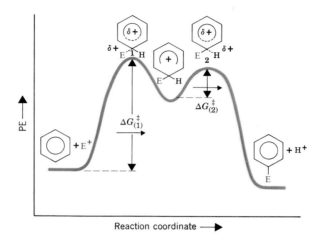

FIGURE 15.2 The potential energy diagram for an electrophilic aromatic substitution reaction. The arenium ion is a true intermediate lying between transition states **1** and **2**. In transition state **1** the bond between the electrophile and one carbon atom of the benzene ring is only partially formed. In transition state **2** the bond between the same benzene carbon atom and its hydrogen atom is partially broken.

The free energy of activation, $\Delta G^{\ddagger}$, for the reaction leading from benzene and the electrophile, E^{+}, to the arenium ion has been shown to be much greater than the free energy of activation, $\Delta G^{\ddagger}$, leading from the arenium ion to the final product. This is consistent with what we would expect. The reaction leading from benzene and an electrophile to the arenium ion is highly endothermic, because the benzene ring loses its resonance energy. The reaction leading from the arenium ion to the substituted benzene, by contrast, is highly exothermic because in it the benzene ring regains its resonance energy.

Of the following two steps, step 1—the formation of the arenium ion—is the rate-determining step in electrophilic aromatic substitution.

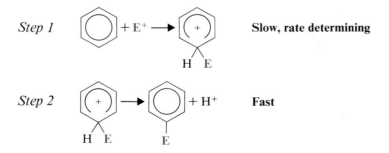

Step 2, the loss of a proton, occurs rapidly relative to step 1 and has no effect on the overall rate of reaction.

15.3 HALOGENATION OF BENZENE

Benzene does not react with bromine or chlorine unless a Lewis acid is present in the mixture. (As a consequence, benzene does not decolorize a solution of bromine in carbon tetrachloride.) When Lewis acids are present, however, benzene reacts readily with bromine or chlorine, and the reactions give bromobenzene and chlorobenzene in good yields.

$$\text{benzene} + Cl_2 \xrightarrow[25\ °C]{FeCl_3} \text{chlorobenzene} + HCl$$

Chlorobenzene (90%)

$$\text{benzene} + Br_2 \xrightarrow[\text{heat}]{FeBr_3} \text{bromobenzene} + HBr$$

Bromobenzene (75%)

The Lewis acids most commonly used to effect chlorination and bromination reactions are $FeCl_3$, $FeBr_3$, and $AlCl_3$ all in the anhydrous form. Ferric chloride and ferric bromide are usually generated in the reaction mixture by adding iron to it. The iron then reacts with halogen to produce the ferric halide:

$$2\ Fe + 3\ X_2 \longrightarrow 2\ FeX_3$$

The mechanism for aromatic bromination is as follows:

Step 1 $:\!\ddot{B}r\!-\!\ddot{B}r\!: + FeBr_3 \longrightarrow :\ddot{B}r^+ + FeBr_4^-$

Step 2

Arenium ion

Step 3

The function of the Lewis acid can be seen in step 1. The ferric bromide reacts with bromine to produce a positive bromine ion, Br^+ (and $FeBr_4^-$). In step 2 this Br^+ ion attacks the benzene ring to produce an arenium ion. Then finally in step 3 the arenium ion transfers a proton to $FeBr_4^-$. This results in the formation of bromobenzene and hydrogen bromide — the products of the reaction. At the same time this step regenerates the catalyst — $FeBr_3$.

The mechanism of the chlorination of benzene in the presence of ferric chloride is analogous to the one for bromination. Ferric chloride serves the same purpose in aromatic chlorinations as ferric bromide does in aromatic brominations. It assists in the generation and transfer of a positive halogen ion.

Fluorine reacts so rapidly with benzene that aromatic fluorination requires special conditions and special types of apparatus. Even then, it is difficult to limit the reaction to monofluorination. Fluorobenzene can be made, however, by an indirect method that we shall see in Section 19.8D.

Iodine, on the other hand, is so unreactive that a special technique has to be used to effect direct iodination; the reaction has to be carried out in the presence of an oxidizing agent such as nitric acid:

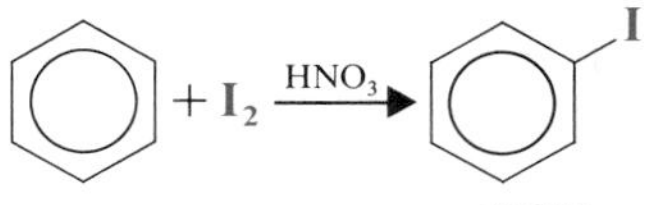

(86%)

15.4 NITRATION OF BENZENE

Benzene reacts slowly with hot concentrated nitric acid to yield nitrobenzene. The reaction is much faster if it is carried out by heating benzene with a mixture of concentrated nitric acid and concentrated sulfuric acid.

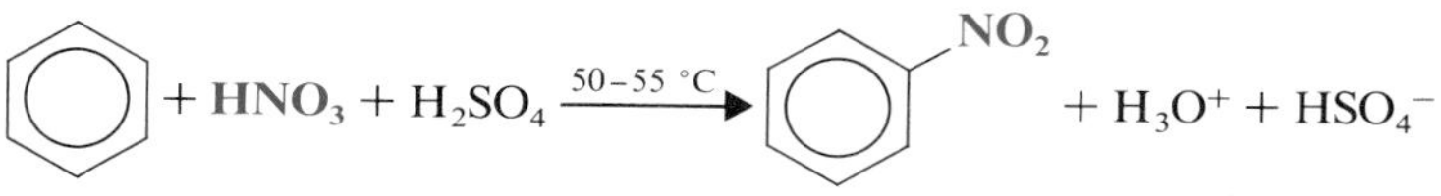

(85%)

Concentrated sulfuric acid increases the rate of the reaction by increasing the concentration of the electrophile—the nitronium ion (NO_2^+).

Step 1 $$H{-}\ddot{O}{-}NO_2 + HOSO_3H \;(H_2SO_4) \rightleftharpoons H{-}\overset{+}{\ddot{O}}(H){-}NO_2 + HSO_4^-$$

Step 2 $$H{-}\overset{+}{\ddot{O}}(H){-}NO_2 + H_2SO_4 \rightleftharpoons \overset{+}{N}O_2 + H_3O^+ + HSO_4^-$$

Nitronium ion

In step 1 nitric acid acts as a base and accepts a proton from the stronger acid, sulfuric acid. In step 2 the protonated nitric acid dissociates and produces a nitronium ion.

The nitronium ion reacts with benzene by attacking the π cloud and forming an arenium ion.

Step 3

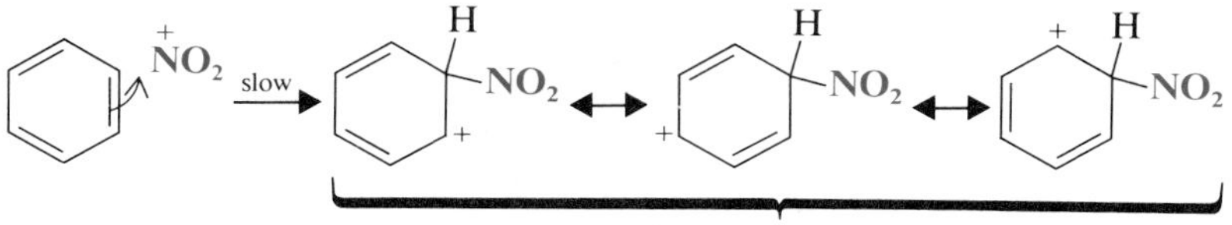

Arenium ion

The arenium ion then transfers a proton to some base in the mixture such as HSO_4^- and becomes nitrobenzene.

Step 4

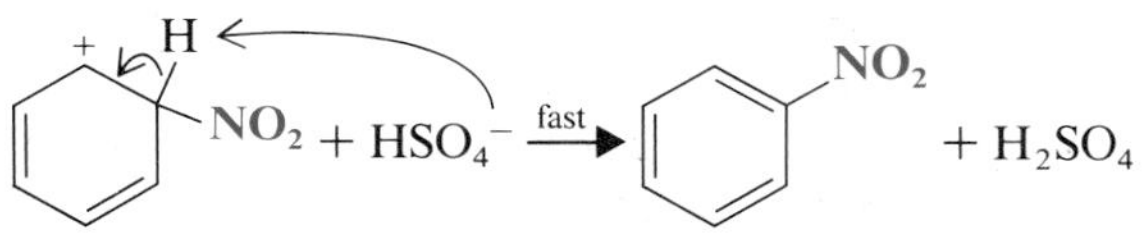

Problem 15.2

Write equations that show how nitronium ions might be formed in nitration reactions in which concentrated nitric acid is used by itself.

15.5 SULFONATION OF BENZENE

Benzene reacts with fuming sulfuric acid at room temperature to produce benzenesulfonic acid. Fuming sulfuric acid is sulfuric acid that contains added sulfur trioxide (SO_3). Sulfonation also takes place in concentrated sulfuric acid alone, but more slowly.

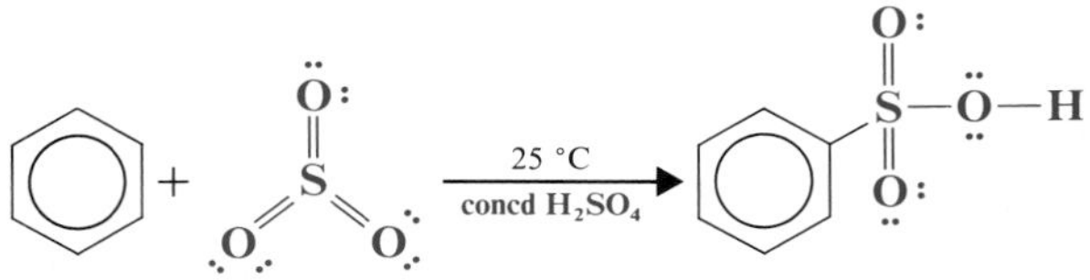

Sulfur trioxide

Benzenesulfonic acid (56%)

In either reaction the electrophile appears to be sulfur trioxide. In concentrated sulfuric acid, sulfur trioxide is produced in the following equilibrium in which H_2SO_4 acts as both an acid and a base.

Step 1 $2\ H_2SO_4 \rightleftharpoons SO_3 + H_3O^+ + HSO_4^-$

When sulfur trioxide reacts with benzene the following steps occur.

Step 2

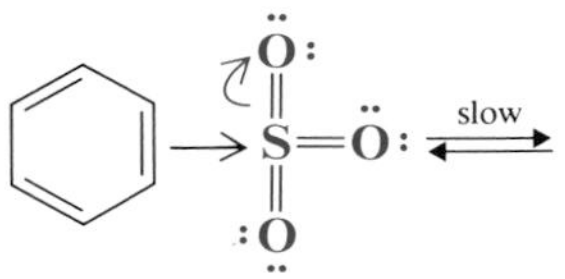

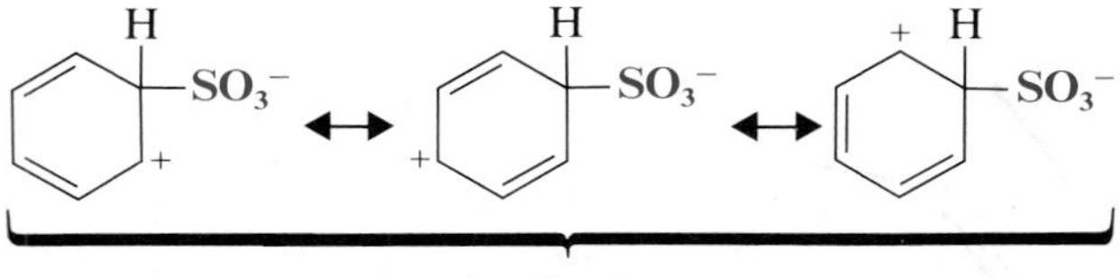

Arenium ion

Step 3

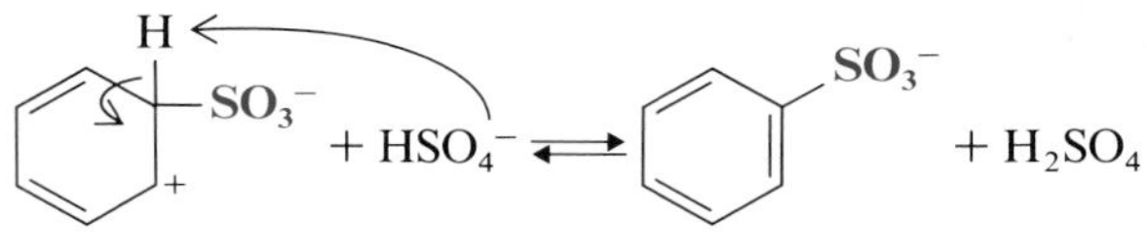

$+ HSO_4^- \rightleftharpoons$ $+ H_2SO_4$ **Fast**

Step 4

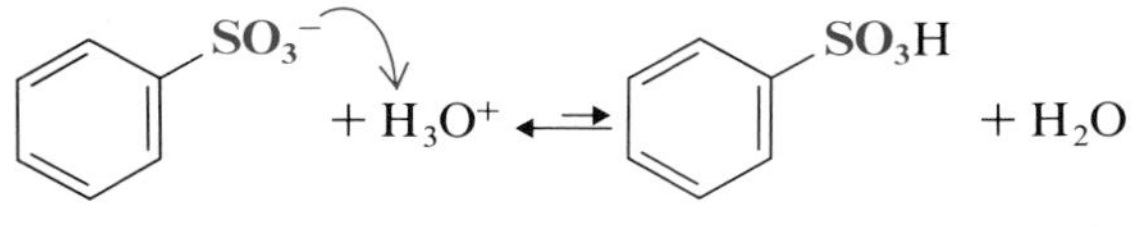

$+ H_3O^+ \rightleftharpoons$ $+ H_2O$ **Fast**

All of the steps are equilibria, including step 1 in which sulfur trioxide is formed from sulfuric acid. This means that the overall reaction is an equilibrium as well. In concentrated sulfuric acid, the overall equilibrium is the sum of steps 1–4.

$$\text{benzene} + H_2SO_4 \rightleftharpoons \text{benzenesulfonic acid (}SO_3H\text{)} + H_2O$$

In fuming sulfuric acid, step 1 is unimportant because the dissolved sulfur trioxide reacts directly.

Because all of the steps are equilibria, the position of equilibrium can be influenced by the conditions we employ. If we want to sulfonate benzene we use concentrated sulfuric acid or—better yet—fuming sulfuric acid. Under these conditions the position of equilibrium lies appreciably to the right and we obtain benzenesulfonic acid in good yield.

On the other hand, we may want to remove a sulfonic acid group from a benzene ring. To do this we employ dilute sulfuric acid and usually pass steam through the mixture. Under these conditions—with a high concentration of water—the equilibrium lies appreciably to the left and desulfonation occurs. The equilibrium is shifted even further to the left with volatile aromatic compounds because the aromatic compound distills with the steam.

We shall see later that sulfonation and desulfonation reactions are often used in synthetic work. We may, for example, introduce a sulfonic acid group into a benzene ring to influence the course of some further reaction. Later, we may remove the sulfonic acid group by desulfonation.

15.6 FRIEDEL–CRAFTS ALKYLATION

In 1877 a French chemist, Charles Friedel, and his American collaborator, James M. Crafts, discovered new methods for the preparation of alkylbenzenes (ArR) and acylbenzenes (ArCOR). These reactions are now called the Friedel–Crafts alkylation and acylation reactions. We shall study the Friedel–Crafts alkylation reaction here and take up the Friedel–Crafts acylation reaction in Section 15.7.

A general equation for a Friedel–Crafts alkylation reaction is the following:

$$\text{benzene} + R-X \xrightarrow{AlCl_3} \text{benzene-}R + HX$$

The mechanism for the reaction (shown in the following steps—with isopropyl chloride as R—X) starts with the formation of a carbocation (step 1). The carbocation then acts as an electrophile (step 2) and attacks the benzene ring to form an arenium ion. The arenium ion (step 3) then loses a proton to generate isopropylbenzene.

Step 1

$$\underset{\substack{\text{Isopropyl}\\\text{chloride}}}{(H_3C)(H_3C)CH-Cl} + AlCl_3 \rightleftharpoons \underset{\text{Carbocation}}{(H_3C)(H_3C)CH^+} + AlCl_4^-$$

Step 2

$$\text{benzene} + {}^+CH(CH_3)(CH_3) \rightleftharpoons \underset{\text{Arenium ion}}{\text{arenium ion with } H, CH(CH_3)(CH_3)}$$

Step 3

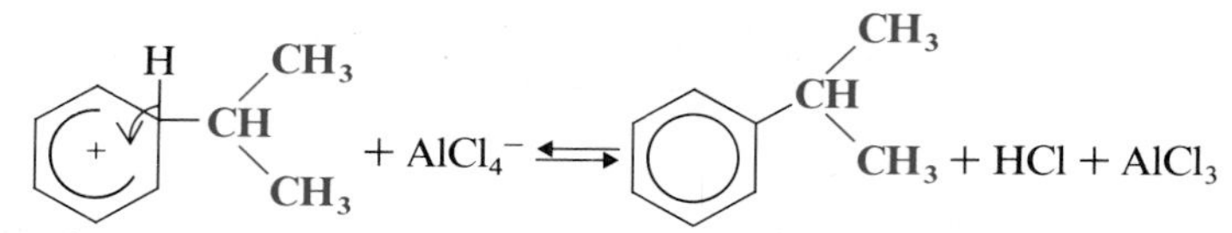

Isopropylbenzene

When R—X is a primary halide, a simple carbocation probably does not form. Rather, the aluminum chloride forms a complex with the alkyl halide and this complex acts as the electrophile. The complex is one in which the carbon–halogen bond is nearly broken — and one in which the carbon atom has a considerable positive charge:

$$\overset{\delta+}{R CH_2} \text{---} \overset{\delta-}{Cl} : AlCl_3$$

Even though this complex is not a simple carbocation, it acts as if it were and it transfers a positive alkyl group to the aromatic ring. As we shall see in Section 15.8, these complexes are so carbocationlike that they also undergo typical carbocation rearrangements.

Friedel–Crafts alkylations are not restricted to the use of alkyl halides and aluminum chloride. Many other pairs of reagents that form carbocations (or carbocationlike species) may be used as well. These possibilities include the use of a mixture of an alkene and an acid.

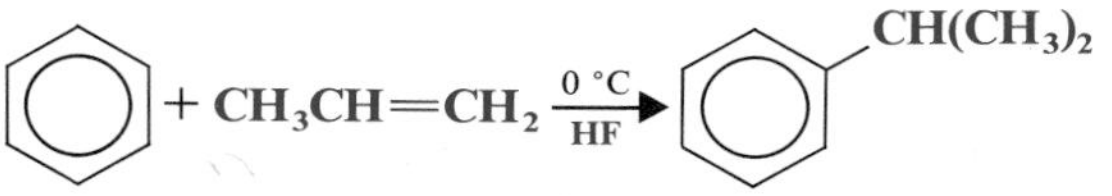

Propene   Isopropylbenzene
(84%)

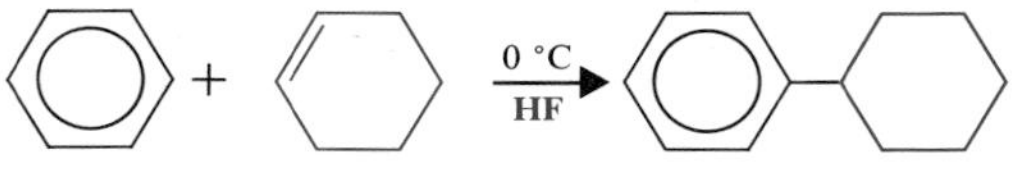

Cyclohexene   Cyclohexylbenzene
(62%)

A mixture of an alcohol and an acid may also be used

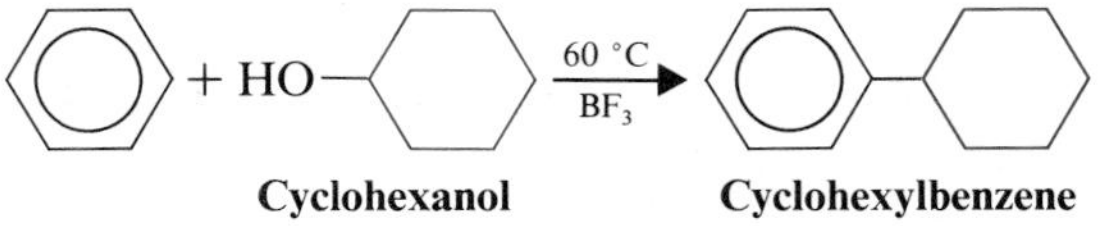

Cyclohexanol   Cyclohexylbenzene
(56%)

There are several important limitations of the Friedel–Crafts reaction. These are discussed in Section 15.8.

Problem 15.3

Assume that carbocations are involved and propose step-by-step mechanisms for both of the syntheses of cyclohexylbenzene given previously.

15.7 FRIEDEL–CRAFTS ACYLATION

The $R\overset{\overset{O}{\|}}{C}$— group is called an **acyl group,** and a reaction whereby an acyl group is introduced into a compound is called an **acylation** reaction. Two common acyl groups are the acetyl group and the benzoyl group.

$CH_3\overset{\overset{O}{\|}}{C}$—

**Acetyl
group
(ethanoyl group)**

$\text{Ph}\overset{\overset{O}{\|}}{C}$—

**Benzoyl
group**

The Friedel–Crafts acylation reaction is an effective means of introducing an acyl group into an aromatic ring. The reaction is often carried out by treating the aromatic compound with an acyl halide. Unless the aromatic compound is one that is highly reactive, the reaction requires the addition of at least one equivalent of a Lewis acid (such as $AlCl_3$) as well. The product of the reaction is an aryl ketone.

C_6H_6 + $CH_3\overset{\overset{O}{\|}}{C}$—Cl $\xrightarrow[\substack{\text{excess}\\ \text{benzene}\\ 80\ °C}]{AlCl_3}$ $\text{Ph}\overset{\overset{O}{\|}}{C}CH_3$ + HCl

**Acetyl
chloride**

**Acetophenone
(methyl phenyl ketone)
(97%)**

Acyl chlorides, also called **acid chlorides,** are easily prepared by treating carboxylic acids with thionyl chloride ($SOCl_2$) or phosphorus pentachloride (PCl_5).

$CH_3\overset{\overset{O}{\|}}{C}OH$ + $SOCl_2$ $\xrightarrow{80\ °C}$ $CH_3\overset{\overset{O}{\|}}{C}Cl$ + SO_2 + HCl

**Acetic
acid** **Thionyl
chloride** **Acetyl
chloride
(80–90%)**

$\text{Ph}\overset{\overset{O}{\|}}{C}OH$ + PCl_5 $\longrightarrow$ $\text{Ph}\overset{\overset{O}{\|}}{C}Cl$ + $POCl_3$ + HCl

**Benzoic
acid** **Phosphorus
pentachloride** **Benzoyl
chloride
(90%)**

Friedel–Crafts acylations can also be carried out using carboxylic acid anhydrides. For example:

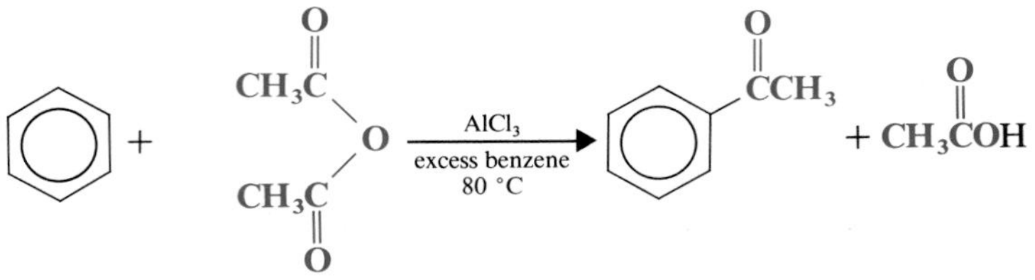

Acetic anhydride
(a carboxylic acid
anhydride)

Acetophenone
(82–85%)

In most Friedel–Crafts acylations the electrophile appears to be an **acylium ion** formed from an acyl halide in the following way:

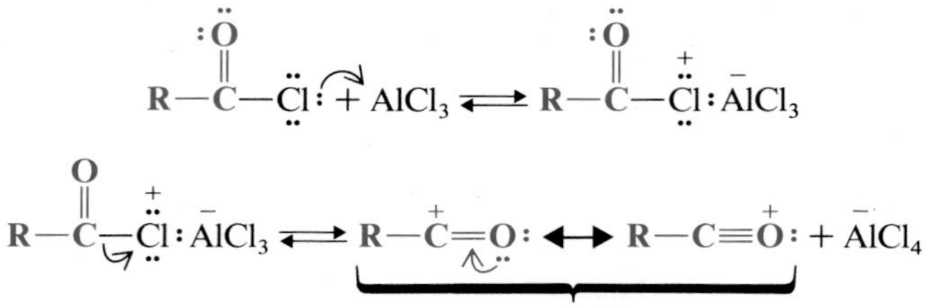

An acylium ion
(a resonance hybrid)

Problem 15.4

Show how an acylium ion could be formed from an acid anhydride.

The remaining steps in the Friedel–Crafts acylation of benzene are the following:

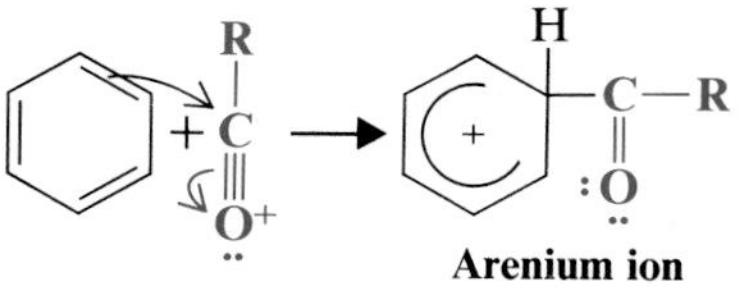

Arenium ion

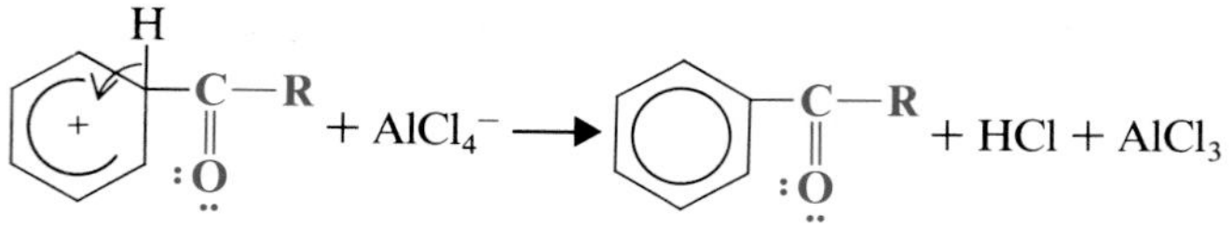

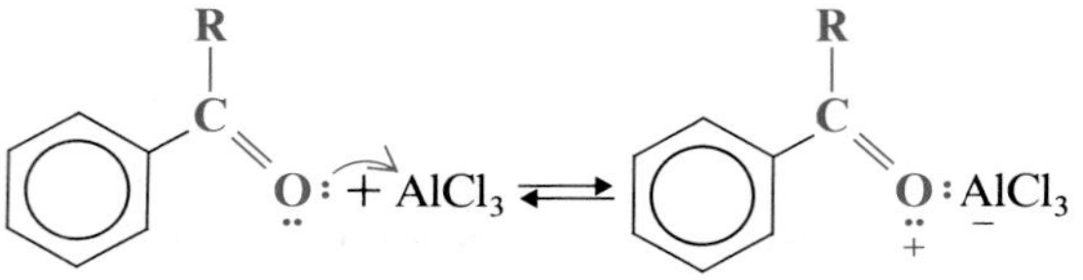

In the last step aluminum chloride (a Lewis acid) forms a complex with the ketone (a Lewis base). After the reaction is over, treating the complex with water liberates the ketone.

$$\underset{C_6H_5}{\overset{R}{\diagdown}}C=\overset{..}{\underset{+}{O}}:\overset{-}{AlCl_3} + 3\ H_2O \longrightarrow \underset{C_6H_5}{\overset{R}{\diagdown}}C=\overset{..}{O}: + Al(OH)_3 + 3\ HCl$$

Several important synthetic applications of the Friedel–Crafts reaction are given in Section 15.9C.

15.8 LIMITATIONS OF FRIEDEL-CRAFTS REACTIONS

Several restrictions limit the usefulness of Friedel–Crafts reactions.

1. **When the carbocation formed from an alkyl halide, alkene, or alcohol can rearrange to a more stable carbocation, it usually does so and the major product obtained from the reaction is usually the one from the more stable carbocation.**

When benzene is alkylated with butyl bromide, for example, some of the developing butyl cations rearrange by a hydride shift—some developing 1° carbocations (see following reactions) become more stable 2° carbocations. Then benzene reacts with both kinds of carbocations to form both butylbenzene and *sec*-butylbenzene:

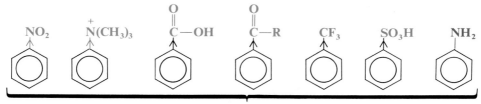

Butylbenzene	*sec*-Butylbenzene
(32–36% of mixture)	(64–68% of mixture)

2. **Friedel–Crafts reactions do not occur when powerful electron-withdrawing groups (Section 15.11) are present on the aromatic ring or when the ring bears an —NH₂, —NHR, or —NR₂ group.** This applies to alkylations and acylations.

These do not undergo
Friedel–Crafts reactions

We shall learn in Section 15.10 that groups present on an aromatic ring can have a large effect on the reactivity of the ring towards electrophilic aromatic substitution.

Electron-withdrawing groups make the ring less reactive by making it electron deficient. Any substituent more electron withdrawing (or deactivating) than a halogen, that is, **any meta-directing group** (Section 15.11C), **makes an aromatic ring too electron deficient to undergo a Friedel–Crafts reaction.** The amino groups, $-NH_2$, $-NHR$, and $-NR_2$, are changed into powerful electron-withdrawing groups by the Lewis acids used to catalyze Friedel–Crafts reactions. For example:

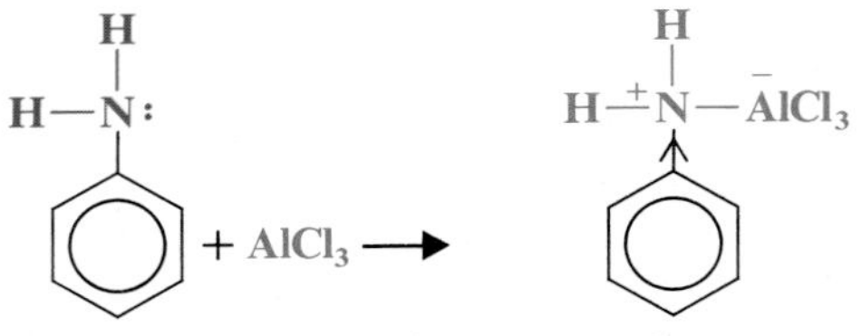

**Does not undergo
a Friedel–Crafts reaction**

3. **Aryl and vinylic halides cannot be used as the halide component because they do not form carbocations readily** (cf. Section 6.16).

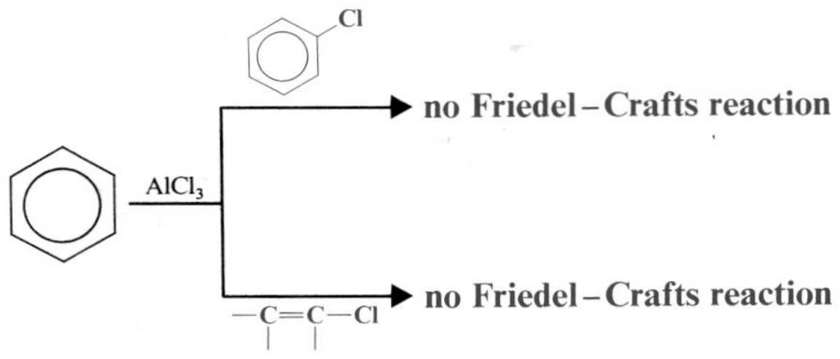

no Friedel–Crafts reaction

no Friedel–Crafts reaction

4. **Polyalkylations often occur.** Alkyl groups are electron-releasing groups, and once one is introduced into the benzene ring it activates the ring toward further substitution (cf. Section 15.10).

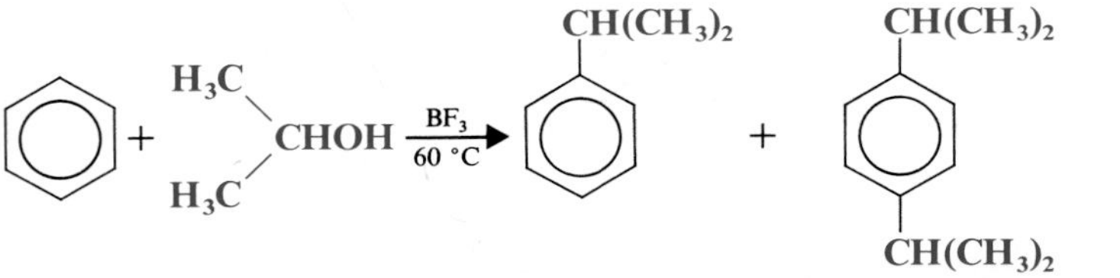

**Isopropyl-
benzene
(24%)**

**p-Diisopropylbenzene
(14%)**

Polyacylations are not a problem in Friedel–Crafts acylations, however. The acyl group $(RCO-)$ by itself is an electron-withdrawing group, and when it forms a complex with $AlCl_3$ in the last step of the reaction (Section 15.7), it is made even more electron withdrawing. This strongly inhibits further substitution and makes monoacylation easy.

Problem 15.5

When benzene reacts with neopentyl chloride, $(CH_3)_3CCH_2Cl$, in the presence of aluminum chloride, the major product is 2-methyl-2-phenylbutane, not neopentylbenzene. Explain this result.

Problem 15.6 ——————————————————————————

When benzene reacts with propyl alcohol in the presence of boron trifluoride, both propylbenzene and isopropylbenzene are obtained as products. Write a mechanism that accounts for this.

15.9 SYNTHETIC APPLICATIONS OF FRIEDEL-CRAFTS ACYLATIONS: THE CLEMMENSEN REDUCTION

Rearrangements of the carbon chain do not occur in Friedel–Crafts acylations. The acylium ion, because it is stabilized by resonance, is more stable than most other carbocations. Thus, there is no driving force for a rearrangement. Because rearrangements do not occur, Friedel–Crafts acylations often give us much better routes to unbranched alkylbenzenes than do Friedel–Crafts alkylations.

As an example, let us consider the problem of synthesizing propylbenzene. If we attempt this synthesis through a Friedel–Crafts alkylation, a rearrangement occurs and the major product is isopropylbenzene (see also Problem 15.6).

By contrast, the Friedel–Crafts acylation of benzene with propanoyl chloride produces a ketone with an unrearranged carbon chain in excellent yield.

This ketone can then be reduced to propylbenzene by several methods. One general method—called **the Clemmensen reduction**—consists of refluxing the ketone with hydrochloric acid containing amalgamated zinc. [*Caution:* As we shall discuss later (Section 19.5), zinc and hydrochloric acid will also reduce nitro groups to amino groups.]

or $\quad$ $$ArCR \xrightarrow[\text{HCl, reflux}]{\text{Zn(Hg)}} ArCH_2R$$

When cyclic anhydrides are used as one component, the Friedel–Crafts acylation provides a means of adding a new ring to an aromatic compound. One illustration is shown here.

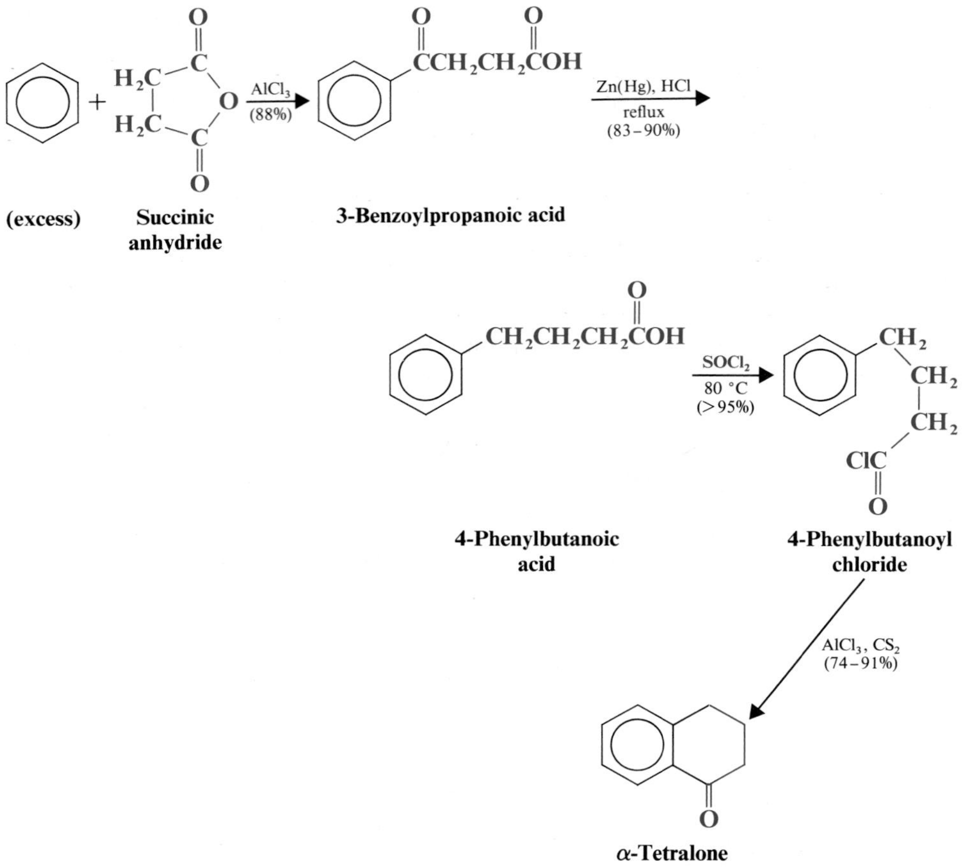
AlCl$_3$
(88%)
Zn(Hg), HCl
reflux
(83–90%)
SOCl$_2$
80 °C
(>95%)
AlCl$_3$, CS$_2$
(74–91%)
(excess)
Succinic anhydride
3-Benzoylpropanoic acid
4-Phenylbutanoic acid
4-Phenylbutanoyl chloride
α-Tetralone

Problem 15.7

Starting with benzene and the appropriate acid chloride or anhydride, outline a synthesis of each of the following:

(a) Hexylbenzene
(b) Isobutylbenzene
(c) Diphenylmethane
(d) Anthrone

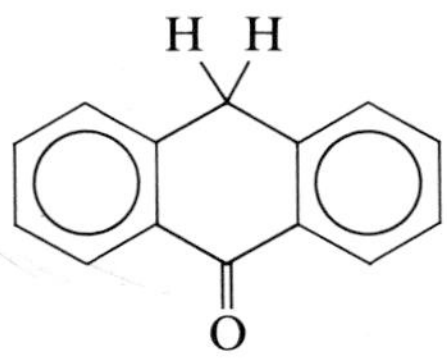

Anthrone

15.10 EFFECT OF SUBSTITUENTS ON REACTIVITY AND ORIENTATION

When substituted benzenes undergo electrophilic attack, groups already on the ring affect both the rate of the reaction and the site of attack. We say, therefore, that substituent groups affect both **reactivity** and **orientation** in electrophilic aromatic substitutions.

We can divide substituent groups into two classes according to their influence on the reactivity of the ring. Those that cause the ring to be more reactive than benzene itself we call **activating groups.** Those that cause the ring to be less reactive than benzene we call **deactivating groups.**

We also find that we can divide substituent groups into two classes according to the way they influence the orientation of attack by the incoming electrophile. Substituents in one class tend to bring about electrophilic substitution primarily at the positions *ortho* and *para* to themselves. We call these groups *ortho – para directors* because they tend to *direct* the incoming group into the ortho and para positions. Substituents in the second category tend to direct the incoming electrophile to the *meta* position. We call these groups *meta directors.*

Several examples will illustrate more clearly what we mean by these terms.

15.10A ACTIVATING GROUPS: ORTHO – PARA DIRECTORS

The methyl group is an **activating** group and **an ortho – para director.** Toluene reacts considerably faster than benzene in all electrophilic substitutions.

An activating group

**More reactive than benzene
toward electrophilic substitution**

We observe the greater reactivity of toluene in several ways. We find, for example, that with toluene, milder conditions — lower temperatures and lower concentrations of the electrophile — can be used in electrophilic substitutions than with benzene. We also find that under the same conditions, toluene reacts faster than benzene. In nitration, for example, toluene reacts 25 times as fast as benzene.

We find, moreover, that when toluene undergoes electrophilic substitution, most of the substitution takes place at its ortho and para positions. When we nitrate toluene with nitric and sulfuric acids, we get mononitrotoluenes in the following relative proportions.

o-Nitrotoluene
(59%)

p-Nitrotoluene
(37%)

m-Nitrotoluene
(4%)

Of the mononitrotoluenes obtained from the reaction, 96% (59% + 37%) has the nitro group in an ortho or para position. Only 4% has the nitro group in a meta position.

Problem 15.8 ───────────────────────────────

What percentage of each nitrotoluene would you expect if substitution were to take place on a purely *statistical* basis?

───

Predominant substitution at the ortho and para positions of toluene is not restricted to nitration reactions. The same behavior is observed in halogenation, sulfonation, and so forth.

All alkyl groups are activating groups, and they are all also ortho–para directors. The methoxyl group, CH_3O—, and the acetamido group, CH_3CONH—, are strong activating groups and both are ortho–para directors.

The hydroxyl group and the amino group are very powerful activating groups and are also powerful ortho–para directors. Phenol and aniline react with bromine in water (no catalyst is required) to produce products in which both of the ortho positions and the para position are substituted. These tribromo products are obtained in nearly quantitative yield.

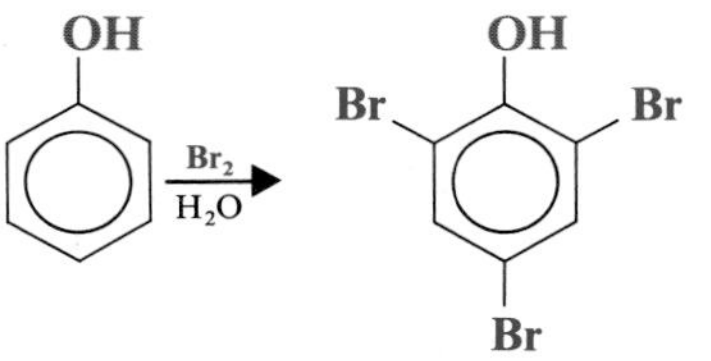

2,4,6-Tribromophenol
(~100%)

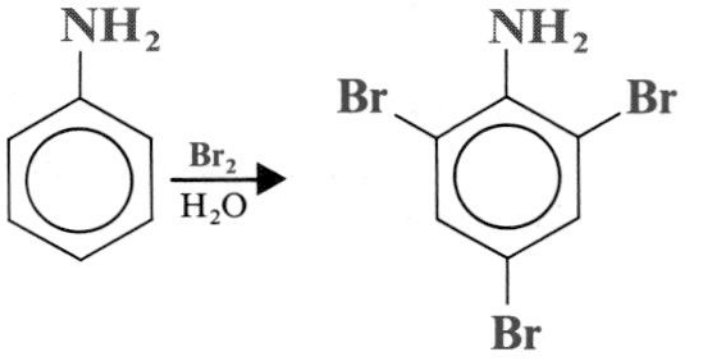

2,4,6-Tribromoaniline
(~100%)

15.10B DEACTIVATING GROUPS: META DIRECTORS

The nitro group is a very strong **deactivating group.** Nitrobenzene undergoes nitration at a rate only 10^{-4} times that of benzene. The nitro group is a meta director. When nitrobenzene is nitrated with nitric and sulfuric acids, 93% of the substitution occurs at the meta position.

(6%)   (1%)   (93%)

The carboxyl group ($-CO_2H$), the sulfo group ($-SO_3H$), and the trifluoromethyl group ($-CF_3$) are also deactivating groups; they are also meta directors.

15.10C HALO SUBSTITUENTS: DEACTIVATING ORTHO-PARA DIRECTORS

The chloro and bromo groups are weak deactivating groups. Chlorobenzene and bromobenzene undergo nitration at rates that are, respectively, 33 and 30 times slower than for benzene. The chloro and bromo groups are ortho–para directors, however. The relative percentages of monosubstituted products that are obtained when chlorobenzene is chlorinated, brominated, nitrated, and sulfonated are shown in Table 15.1.

TABLE 15.1   Electrophilic substitutions of chlorobenzene

REACTION	ORTHO PRODUCT (%)	PARA PRODUCT (%)	TOTAL ORTHO AND PARA (%)	META PRODUCT (%)
Chlorination	39	55	94	6
Bromination	11	87	98	2
Nitration	30	70	100	
Sulfonation		100	100	

Similar results are obtained from electrophilic substitutions of bromobenzene.

15.10D CLASSIFICATION OF SUBSTITUENTS

Studies like the ones that we have presented in this section have been done for a number of other substituted benzenes. The effects of these substituents on reactivity and orientation are included in Table 15.2.

Problem 15.9

What would be the major monochloro product (or products) formed when each of the following compounds reacts with chlorine in the presence of ferric chloride?

(a) Ethylbenzene, $C_6H_5CH_2CH_3$

(b) (Trifluoromethyl)benzene, $C_6H_5CF_3$

(c) Trimethylphenylammonium chloride, $C_6H_5\overset{+}{N}(CH_3)_3Cl^-$

(d) Methyl benzoate, $C_6H_5CO_2CH_3$.

TABLE 15.2 Effect of substituents on electrophilic aromatic substitution

ORTHO–PARA DIRECTORS	META DIRECTORS
Strongly Activating	**Moderately Deactivating**
$-\ddot{N}H_2, -\ddot{N}HR, -\ddot{N}R_2$	$-C\equiv N$
$-\ddot{O}H, -\ddot{O}:^-$	$-SO_3H$
	$-CO_2H, -CO_2R$
Moderately Activating	$-CHO, -COR$
$-\ddot{N}HCOCH_3, -\ddot{N}HCOR$	**Strongly Deactivating**
$-\ddot{O}CH_3, -\ddot{O}R$	$-NO_2$
	$-NR_3{}^+$
Weakly Activating	$-CF_3, -CCl_3$
$-CH_3, -C_2H_5, -R$	
$-C_6H_5$	
Weakly Deactivating	
$-\ddot{\underset{..}{F}}:, -\ddot{\underset{..}{C}l}:, -\ddot{\underset{..}{B}r}:, -\ddot{\underset{..}{I}}:$	

15.11 THEORY OF SUBSTITUENT EFFECTS ON ELECTROPHILIC AROMATIC SUBSTITUTION

15.11A REACTIVITY: THE EFFECT OF ELECTRON-RELEASING AND ELECTRON-WITHDRAWING GROUPS

We have now seen that certain groups *activate* the benzene ring toward electrophilic substitution, while other groups *deactivate* the ring. When we say that a group activates the ring, what we mean, of course, is that the group increases the relative rate of the reaction. We mean that an aromatic compound with an activating group reacts faster in electrophilic substitutions than benzene. When we say that a group deactivates the ring, we mean that an aromatic compound with a deactivating group reacts slower than benzene.

We have also seen that we can account for relative reaction rates by examining the transition state for the rate-determining steps. We know that any factor that increases the energy of the transition state relative to that of the reactants decreases the relative rate of the reaction. It does this because it increases the free energy of activation of the reaction. In the same way, any factor that decreases the energy of the transition state relative to that of the reactants lowers the free energy of activation and increases the relative rate of the reaction.

The rate-determining step in electrophilic substitutions of substituted benzenes is the step that results in the formation of the arenium ion. We can write the formula for a substituted benzene in a generalized way if we use the letter **S** to represent any ring substituent including hydrogen. (If **S** is hydrogen the compound is benzene itself.) We can also write the structure for the arenium ion in the way shown here. By this formula we mean that **S** can be in any position — ortho, meta, or para — relative

15.11 THEORY OF SUBSTITUENT EFFECTS ON ELECTROPHILIC AROMATIC SUBSTITUTION

to the electrophile, **E**. Using these conventions, then, we are able to write the rate-determining step for electrophilic aromatic substitution in the following general way.

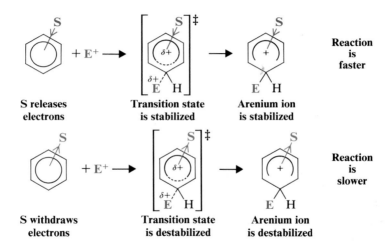

When we examine this step for a large number of reactions, we find that the relative rates of the reactions depend on whether **S withdraws** or **releases** electrons. If **S** is an electron-releasing group (relative to hydrogen), the reaction occurs faster than the corresponding reaction of benzene. If **S** is an electron-withdrawing group, the reaction is slower than that of benzene.

It appears, then, that the substituent **(S)** must affect the stability of the transition state relative to that of the reactants. Electron-releasing groups apparently make the transition state more stable, while electron-withdrawing groups make it less stable. That this is so is entirely reasonable, because the transition state resembles the arenium ion, and the arenium ion is a delocalized *carbocation.*

This effect illustrates another application of the Hammond-Leffler postulate (Section 6.15A). The arenium ion is a high-energy intermediate, and the step that leads to it is a *highly endothermic step.* Thus, according to the Hammond-Leffler postulate there should be a strong resemblance between the arenium ion itself and the transition state leading to it.

Since the arenium ion is positively charged, we would expect an electron-releasing group to stabilize it *and the transition state leading to the arenium ion,* for the transition state is a developing delocalized carbocation. We can make the same kind of arguments about the effect of electron-withdrawing groups. An electron-withdrawing group should make the arenium ion *less stable* and in a corresponding way it should make the transition state leading to the arenium ion *less stable.*

Figure 15.3 shows how the electron-withdrawing and electron-releasing abilities of substituents affect the relative free energies of activation of electrophilic aromatic substitution reactions.

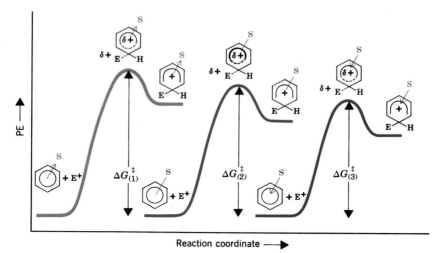

FIGURE 15.3 Energy profiles for the formation of the arenium ion in three electrophilic aromatic substitution reactions. In (1), S is an electron-withdrawing group. In (2) S = H. In (3) S is an electron-releasing group. $\Delta G^{\ddagger}_{(1)} > \Delta G^{\ddagger}_{(2)} > \Delta G^{\ddagger}_{(3)}$.

15.11B INDUCTIVE AND RESONANCE EFFECTS: THEORY OF ORIENTATION

We can account for the electron-withdrawing and electron-releasing properties of groups on the basis of two factors: *inductive effects and resonance effects.* We shall also see that these two factors determine orientation in aromatic substitution reactions.

The **inductive effect** of a substituent S arises from the electrostatic interaction of the polarized S to ring bond with the developing positive charge in the ring as it is attacked by an electrophile. If, for example, S is a more electronegative atom (or group) than carbon, then the ring will be at the positive end of the dipole:

$$\overset{\delta-}{S} \overset{\delta+}{\longleftarrow} \bigcirc \qquad \text{(e.g., S = F, Cl, or Br)}$$

Attack by an electrophile will be retarded because this will lead to an additional full positive charge on the ring. The halogens are all more electronegative than carbon and exert an electron-withdrawing inductive effect. Other groups have an electron-withdrawing inductive effect because the atom directly attached to the ring bears a full or partial positive charge. Examples are the following:

$$\rightarrow \overset{+}{N}R_3 \qquad (R = \text{alkyl or H}) \qquad \overset{X^{\delta-}}{\underset{X^{\delta-}}{\rightarrow C^{\delta+} \rightarrow X^{\delta-}}} \qquad \rightarrow N^+ \overset{O}{\underset{O^-}{\Vert}} \qquad \rightarrow \overset{O^-}{\underset{O}{\overset{\Vert}{S^{\pm}}}} - OH$$

$$\overset{\cdot\cdot}{\underset{\Vert}{O}}: \qquad \qquad :\overset{\cdot\cdot}{O}:^- \\ \rightarrow C - G \longleftrightarrow \rightarrow C^+ - G \qquad (G = \text{H, R, OH, or OR})$$

Electron-withdrawing groups with a full or partial charge on the atom attached to the ring

The **resonance effect** of a substituent S refers to the possibility that the presence of S may increase or decrease the resonance stabilization of the intermediate arenium ion. The S substituent may, for example, cause one of the three contributors to the resonance hybrid for the arenium ion to be better or worse than the case when S is hydrogen. Moreover, when S is an atom bearing one or more nonbonding electron pairs, it may lend extra stability to the arenium ion by providing a *fourth* resonance contributor in which the positive charge resides on S.

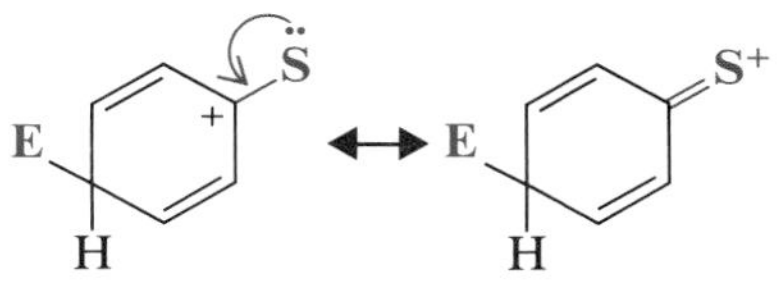

This electron-donating resonance effect applies with decreasing strength in the following order:

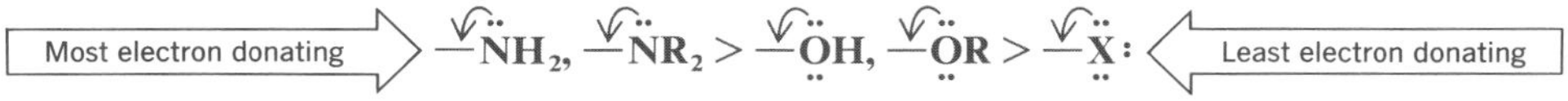

This is also the order of the activating ability of these groups. Amino groups are highly activating, hydroxyl and alkoxyl groups are somewhat less activating, and halogen substituents are weakly deactivating. When X = F, this order can be related to the electronegativity of the atoms with the nonbonding pair. The more electronegative the atom is the less able it is to accept the positive charge (fluorine is the most electronegative, nitrogen the least). When X = Cl, Br, or I, the relatively poor electron-donating ability of the halogens by resonance is understandable on a different basis. These atoms (Cl, Br, and I) are all larger than carbon and, therefore, the orbitals that contain the nonbonding pairs are further from the nucleus and do not overlap well with the $2p$ orbital of carbon. (This is a general phenomenon: Resonance effects are not transmitted well between atoms of different rows in the periodic table.)

15.11C META-DIRECTING GROUPS

All meta-directing groups have either a partial positive charge or a full positive charge on the atom directly attached to the ring. As a typical example let us consider the trifluoromethyl group.

The trifluoromethyl group, because of the three highly electronegative fluorine atoms, is strongly electron withdrawing. It is a strong deactivating group and a powerful meta director in electrophilic aromatic substitution reactions. We can account for both of these characteristics of the trifluoromethyl group in the following way.

The trifluoromethyl group affects reactivity by causing the transition state leading to the arenium ion to be highly unstable. It does this by withdrawing electrons from the developing carbocation thus increasing the positive charge in the ring.

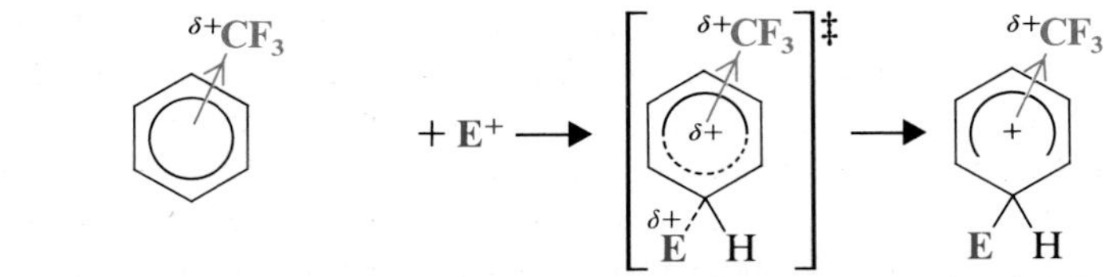

(Trifluoromethyl)benzene   Transition state   Arenium ion

We can understand how the trifluoromethyl group affects *orientation* in electrophilic aromatic substitution if we examine the resonance structures for the arenium ion that would be formed when an electrophile attacks the ortho, meta, and para positions of (trifluoromethyl)benzene.

Ortho attack

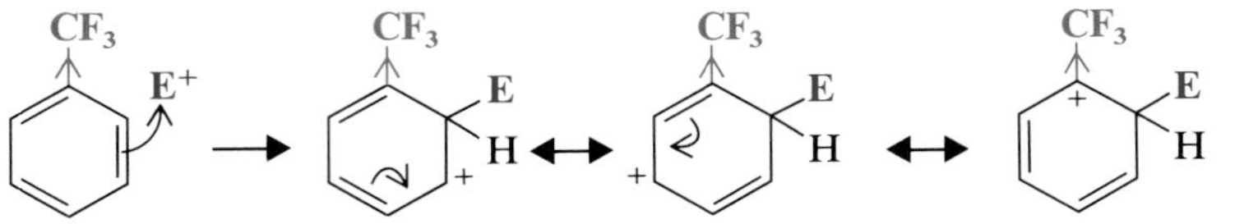

Highly unstable
contributor

Meta attack

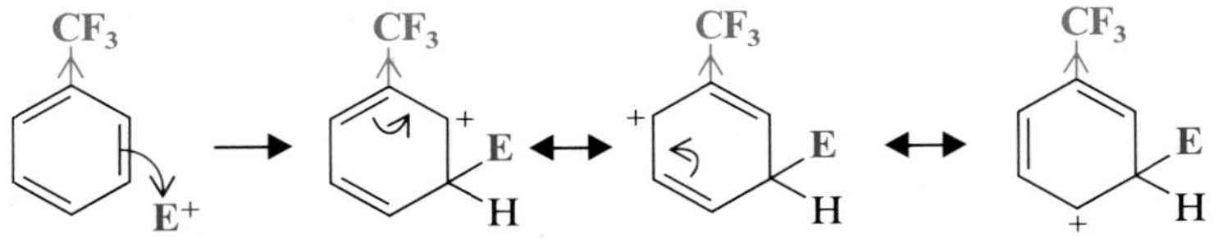

Para attack

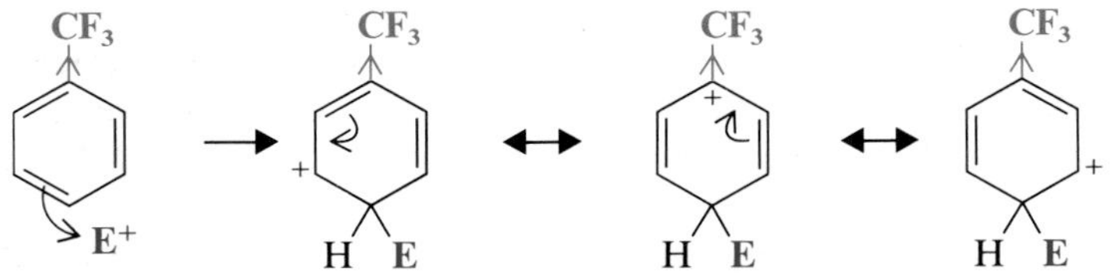

Highly unstable
contributor

We see in the resonance structures for the arenium ion arising from ortho and para attack that *one contributing structure is highly unstable relative to all the others because the positive charge is located on the ring carbon that bears the electron-withdrawing group.* We see *no* such highly unstable resonance structure in the arenium ion arising from meta attack. This means that the arenium ion formed by meta attack should be the most stable of the three. By the usual reasoning we would also expect the transition state leading to the meta-substituted arenium ion to be the most stable and, therefore, that meta attack would be favored. This is exactly what we find experimentally. The trifluoromethyl group is a powerful meta director.

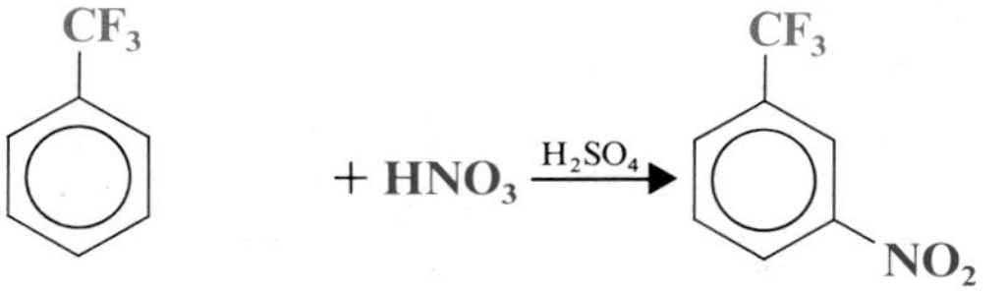

(Trifluoromethyl)benzene   (~100%)

Bear in mind, however, that meta substitution is favored only in the sense that *it is the least unfavorable of three unfavorable pathways.* The free energy of activation for substitution at the meta position of (trifluoromethyl)benzene is less than that for attack at an ortho or para position, but it is still far greater than that for an attack on benzene. Substitution occurs at the meta position of (trifluoromethyl)benzene faster than substitution takes place at the ortho and para positions, but it occurs much more slowly than it does with benzene.

The nitro group, the carboxyl group, and other meta-directing groups are all powerful electron-withdrawing groups and all act in a similar way.

15.11D ORTHO–PARA-DIRECTING GROUPS

Except for the alkyl and phenyl substituents, all of the ortho–para-directing groups in Table 15.2 are of the following general type:

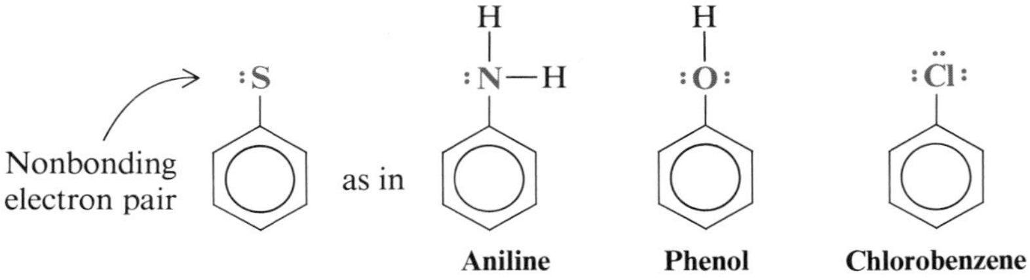

Aniline   **Phenol**   **Chlorobenzene**

All of these ortho–para directors have at least one pair of nonbonding electrons on the atom adjacent to the benzene ring.

This structural feature—an unshared electron pair on the atom adjacent to the ring—determines the orientation and influences reactivity in electrophilic substitution reactions.

The *directive effect* of these groups with an unshared pair is predominantly caused by an electron-releasing resonance effect. The resonance effect, moreover, operates primarily in the arenium ion and, consequently, in the transition state leading to it.

Except for the halogens, the primary effect on reactivity of these groups is also caused by an electron-releasing resonance effect. And, again, this effect operates primarily in the transition state leading to the arenium ion.

In order to understand these resonance effects let us begin by recalling the effect of the amino group on electrophilic aromatic substitution reactions. The amino group is not only a powerful activating group, it is also a powerful ortho–para director. We saw earlier (Section 15.10A) that aniline reacts with bromine in aqueous solution at room temperature and in the absence of a catalyst to yield a product in which both ortho positions and the para position are substituted.

The inductive effect of the amino group makes it slightly electron withdrawing. Nitrogen, as we know, is more electronegative than carbon. The difference between the electronegativities of nitrogen and carbon in aniline is not large, however, because the carbon of the benzene ring is sp^2 hybridized and thus is somewhat more electronegative than it would be if it were sp^3 hybridized.

The resonance effect of the amino group is far more important than its inductive effect in electrophilic aromatic substitution, and this resonance effect makes the amino group electron releasing. We can understand this effect if we write the resonance structures for the arenium ions that would arise from ortho, meta, and para attack on aniline.

Ortho attack

Relatively stable
contributor

Meta attack

Para attack

Relatively stable
contributor

We see that four reasonable resonance structures can be written for the arenium ions resulting from ortho and para attack, whereas only three can be written for the arenium ion that results from meta attack. This, in itself, suggests that the ortho- and para-substituted arenium ions should be more stable. Of greater importance, however, are the relatively stable structures that contribute to the hybrid for the ortho- and para-substituted arenium ions. In these structures, nonbonding pairs of electrons from nitrogen form an extra bond to the carbon of the ring. This extra bond — and the fact that every atom in each of these structures has a complete outer octet of electrons — makes these structures the most stable of all of the contributors. Because these structures are unusually stable, they make a large — *and stabilizing* — contribution to the hybrid. This means, of course, that the ortho- and para-substituted arenium ions themselves are considerably more stable than the arenium ion that results from the meta attack. The transition states leading to the ortho- and para-substituted arenium ions occur at unusually low potential energies. As a result, electrophiles react at the ortho and para positions very rapidly.

Problem 15.10

(a) Write resonance structures for the arenium ions that would result from electrophilic attack on the ortho, meta, and para positions of phenol. (b) Can you account for the fact that phenol is highly susceptible to electrophilic attack? (c) Can you account for the fact that the hydroxyl group is an ortho and para director? (d) Would you expect the phenoxide ion, $C_6H_5O^-$, to be more or less reactive than phenol in electrophilic substitution? (e) Explain.

Problem 15.11

(a) Ignore resonance structures involving electrons of the ring and write *one* other resonance structure for acetanilide. (Your structure will contain + and −

Acetanilide   Phenyl acetate

charges.) (b) Acetanilide is less reactive toward electrophilic substitution than aniline. How can you explain this on the basis of the resonance structure you have just written? (c) Acetanilide, however, is much more reactive than benzene and the acetamido group, $CH_3CONH—$, is an ortho–para director. Can you account for these facts in terms of resonance structures that involve the ring? (d) Would you expect phenyl acetate to be *more* or *less* reactive than phenol? Explain. (e) What kind of directional influence would you expect the

acetoxy group, $CH_3C—\overset{..}{\underset{..}{O}}—$, to show? (f) Would you expect phenyl acetate

to be *more* or *less* reactive in electrophilic substitution than benzene? Explain.

The directive and reactivity effects of halo substituents may, at first, seem to be contradictory. *The halo groups are the only ortho–para directors* (in Table 15.2) *that are deactivating groups.* All other deactivating groups are meta directors. We can readily account for the behavior of halo substituents, however, if we assume that their electron-withdrawing inductive effect influences reactivity and their electron-donating resonance effect governs orientation.

Let us apply these assumptions specifically to chlorobenzene. The chloro atom is highly electronegative. Thus, we would expect a chloro atom to withdraw electrons from the benzene ring and thereby deactivate it.

Inductive effect of chloro group deactivates ring

On the other hand, when electrophilic attack does take place, the chloro group stabilizes the arenium ions resulting from ortho and para attack relative to that from meta attack. The chloro group does this in the same way as amino groups and hydroxyl groups do — *by donating an unshared pair of electrons.* These electrons give rise to relatively stable resonance structures contributing to the hybrids for the ortho- and para-substituted arenium ions (Section 15.11D).

Ortho attack

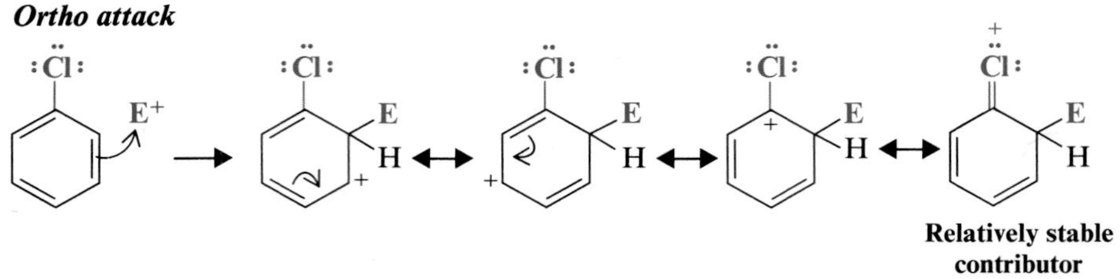

Relatively stable
contributor

Meta attack

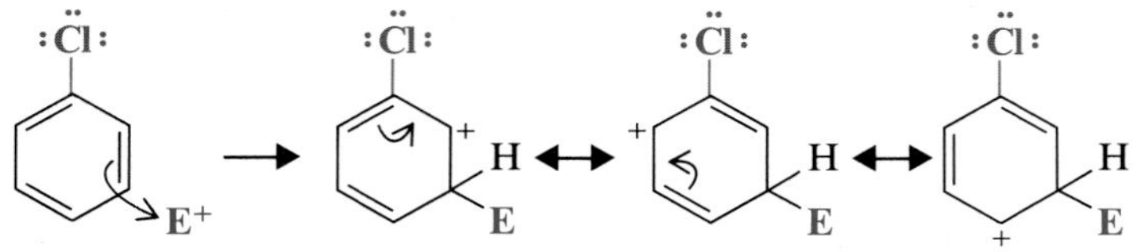

Para attack

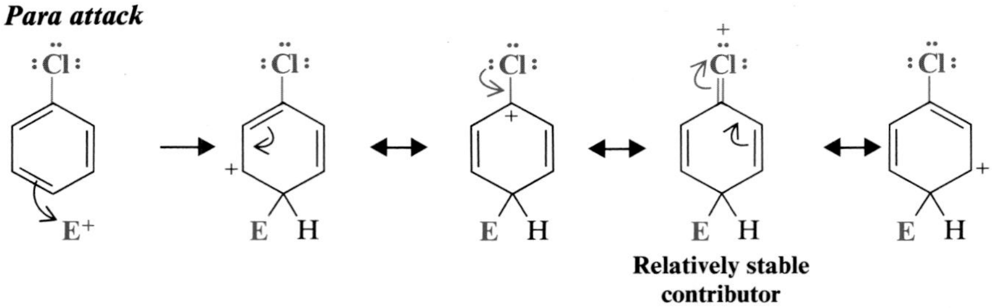

Relatively stable
contributor

What we have said about chlorobenzene is, of course, true of bromobenzene.

We can summarize the inductive and resonance effects of halo substituents in the following way. Through their electron-withdrawing inductive effect halo groups make the ring more positive than that of benzene. This causes the free energy of activation for any electrophilic aromatic substitution reaction to be greater than that for benzene, and, therefore, halo groups are deactivating. Through their electron-donating resonance effect, however, halo substituents cause the free energies of activation leading to ortho and para substitution to be lower than the free energy of activation leading to meta substitution. This makes halo substituents ortho–para directors.

Problem 15.12

Chloroethene adds hydrogen chloride more slowly than ethene and the product is 1,1-dichloroethane. How can you explain this using resonance and inductive effects?

$$Cl-CH=CH_2 \xrightarrow{HCl} Cl-CH-CH_2$$
$$\begin{matrix} | & | \\ Cl & H \end{matrix}$$

15.11E ORTHO–PARA DIRECTION AND REACTIVITY OF ALKYLBENZENES

Alkyl groups are better electron-releasing groups than hydrogen. Because of this they can activate a benzene ring toward electrophilic substitution by stabilizing the transition state leading to the arenium ion:

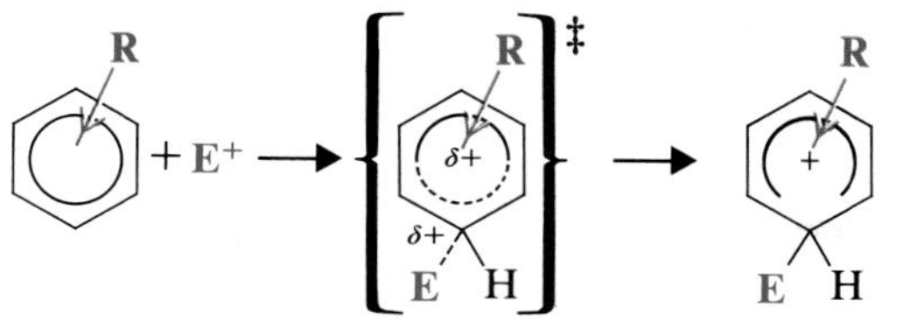

Transition state
is stabilized

Arenium ion
is stabilized

For an alkylbenzene the free energy of activation of the step leading to the arenium ion (just shown) is lower than that for benzene, and alkylbenzenes react faster.

Alkyl groups are ortho–para directors. We can also account for this property of alkyl groups on the basis of their ability to release electrons—an effect that is particularly important when the alkyl group is attached directly to a carbon that bears a positive charge. (Recall the ability of alkyl groups to stabilize carbocations that we discussed in Section 6.13B and in Fig. 6.10.)

If, for example, we write resonance structures for the arenium ions formed when toluene undergoes electrophilic substitution, we get the following results:

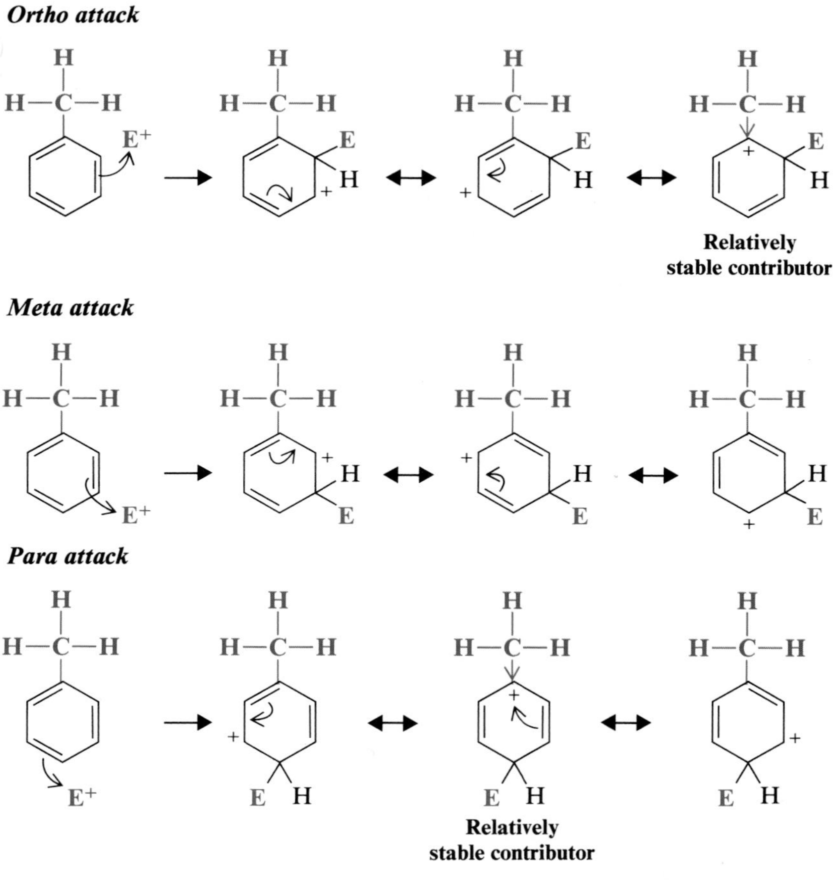

Ortho attack

Relatively
stable contributor

Meta attack

Para attack

Relatively
stable contributor

In ortho attack and para attack we find that we can write resonance structures in which the methyl group is directly attached to a positively charged carbon of the ring. These structures are more *stable* relative to any of the others because in them the stabilizing influence of the methyl group (by electron release) is most effective. These structures, therefore, make a large (stabilizing) contribution to the overall hybrid for ortho- and para-substituted arenium ions. No such relatively stable structure contributes to the hybrid for the meta-substituted arenium ion, and as a result it is less stable than the ortho- or para-substituted arenium ion. Since the ortho- and para-substituted arenium ions are more stable, the transition states leading to them occur at lower energy and ortho and para substitution take place most rapidly.

Problem 15.13

Write resonance structures for the arenium ions formed when ethylbenzene undergoes electrophilic attack.

Problem 15.14

Resonance structures can also be used to account for the fact that a phenyl group is an ortho–para director and that it is an activating group. Show how this is possible.

15.11F SUMMARY OF SUBSTITUENT EFFECTS ON ORIENTATION AND REACTIVITY

We can summarize the effects that groups have on orientation and reactivity in the following way.

Full or partial (+) charge on directly attached atoms	At least one nonbonding pair on directly attached atom		Alkyl or aryl
	Halogen	$-\ddot{N}H_2, -\ddot{O}H$, etc.	

←—meta directing—→ ←————ortho–para directing————→
←————deactivating————→ ←————activating————→

15.12 REACTIONS OF THE SIDE CHAIN OF ALKYLBENZENES

Hydrocarbons that consist of both aliphatic and aromatic groups are also known as **arenes.** Toluene, ethylbenzene, and isopropylbenzene are **alkylbenzenes.**

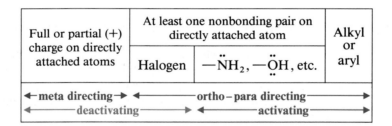

CH_3	CH_2CH_3	$CH(CH_3)_2$	$CH=CH_2$
Methylbenzene (toluene)	Ethylbenzene	Isopropyl-benzene (cumene)	Phenylethene (styrene or vinylbenzene)

Phenylethene, usually called styrene, is an example of an **alkenylbenzene.** The aliphatic portion of these compounds is commonly called the **side chain.**

Styrene is one of the most important industrial chemicals—more than 6 billion lb is produced each year. The starting material for the commercial synthesis of styrene is ethylbenzene, produced by Friedel–Crafts alkylation of benzene:

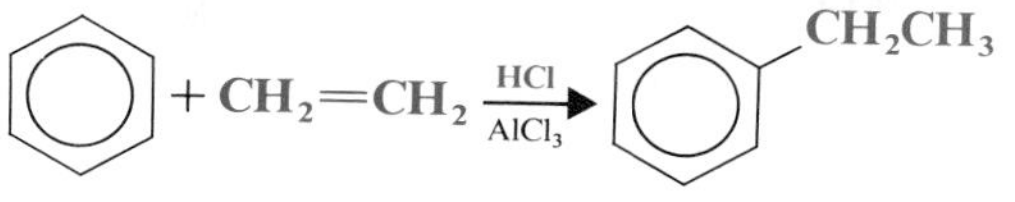

Ethylbenzene

Ethylbenzene is then dehydrogenated in the presence of a catalyst (zinc oxide or chromium oxide) to produce styrene.

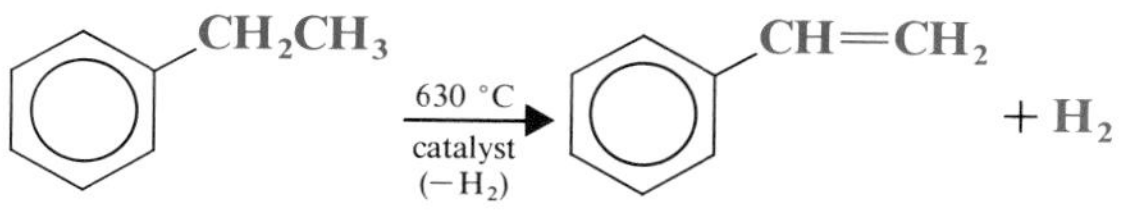

Styrene
(90–92% yield)

Most styrene is polymerized (Special Topic B) to the familiar plastic, polystyrene.

$$C_6H_5CH{=}CH_2 \xrightarrow{\text{catalyst}} -CH_2\underset{\substack{|\\ C_6H_5}}{CH}-(CH_2\underset{\substack{|\\ C_6H_5}}{CH})_n-CH_2\underset{\substack{|\\ C_6H_5}}{CH}-$$

Polystyrene

15.12A HALOGENATION OF THE SIDE CHAIN. BENZYLIC RADICALS

We have seen that bromine and chlorine replace hydrogen atoms on the ring of toluene when the reaction takes place in the presence of a Lewis acid. In ring halogenations the electrophiles are *positive* chlorine or bromine ions or they are Lewis-acid complexes that have positive halogens. These positive electrophiles attack the π electrons of the benzene ring and aromatic substitution takes place.

Chlorine and bromine can also be made to replace hydrogens of the methyl group of toluene. Side-chain halogenation takes place when the reaction is carried out *in the absence of Lewis acids* and under conditions that favor the formation of radicals. When toluene reacts with *N*-bromosuccinimide (NBS) in the presence of light, for example, the major product is benzyl bromide. *N*-Bromosuccinimide furnishes a low concentration of Br_2 and the reaction is analogous to that for allylic bromination that we studied in Section 12.2.

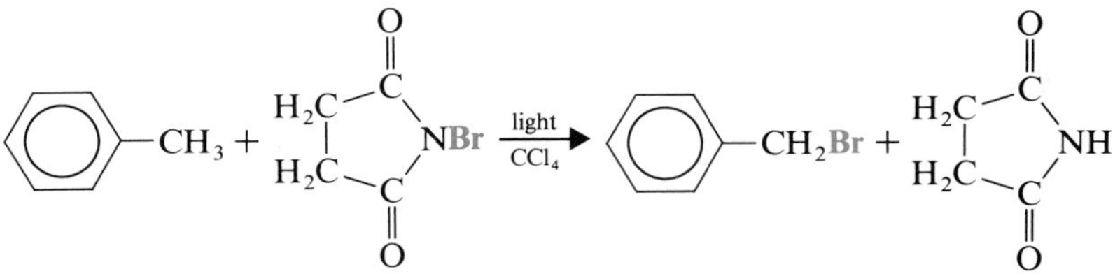

NBS **Benzyl bromide**
(α-bromotoluene)
(64%)

Side-chain chlorination of toluene also takes place in the gas phase at 400–600 °C or in the presence of UV light. When an excess of chlorine is used, multiple chlorinations of the side chain occur.

| | Benzyl chloride | (Dichloromethyl)-benzene | (Trichloromethyl)-benzene |

These halogenations take place through the same radical mechanisms we saw for alkanes in Section 7.4. The halogens dissociate to produce halogen atoms and then the halogen atoms initiate chains by abstracting hydrogens of the methyl group.

Chain Initiation

Step 1 $X_2 \xrightarrow[\text{or light}]{\substack{\text{peroxides,} \\ \text{heat,}}} 2X \cdot$

Chain Propagation

Step 2 $C_6H_5CH_3 + X\cdot \longrightarrow C_6H_5CH_2\cdot + HX$

                                Benzyl radical

Step 3 $C_6H_5CH_2\cdot + X_2 \longrightarrow C_6H_5CH_2X + X\cdot$

        Benzyl radical   Benzyl halide

Abstraction of a hydrogen from the methyl group of toluene produces *a benzyl radical.* The benzyl radical then reacts with a halogen molecule to produce a benzyl halide and a halogen atom. The halogen atom then brings about a repetition of step 2, then step 3 occurs again, and so on.

Benzylic halogenations are similar to allylic halogenations (Section 12.2) in that they involve the formation of *unusually stable radicals* (Section 13.10). Benzylic and allylic radicals are even more stable than tertiary radicals.

The greater stability of benzylic radicals accounts for the fact that when ethylbenzene is halogenated the major product is the 1-halo-1-phenylethane. The benzylic radical is formed faster than the 1° radical:

Benzylic radical (more stable)   1-Halo-1-phenylethane (major product)

1° Radical (less stable)   1-Halo-2-phenylethane (minor product)

Problem 15.15

When propylbenzene reacts with chlorine in the presence of UV radiation, the major product is 1-chloro-1-phenylpropane. Both 2-chloro-1-phenylpropane and 3-chloro-1-phenylpropane are minor products. Write the structure of the radical leading to each product and account for the fact that 1-chloro-1-phenylpropane is the major product.

Sample Problem

Illustrating a Multistep Synthesis

Starting with ethylbenzene, outline a synthesis of phenylacetylene ($C_6H_5C\equiv CH$).

Answer:

Working backward, that is, using *retrosynthetic analysis,* we realize that we could make phenylacetylene by dehydrohalogenating either of the following compounds using sodium amide in mineral oil (Section 8.18).

$$C_6H_5CBr_2CH_3 \xrightarrow[\text{(2) } H^+]{\text{(1) NaNH}_2\text{, mineral oil, heat}} C_6H_5C\equiv CH$$

$$C_6H_5CHBrCH_2Br \xrightarrow[\text{(2) } H^+]{\text{(1) NaNH}_2\text{, mineral oil, heat}} C_6H_5C\equiv CH$$

We could make the first compound from ethylbenzene by allowing it to react with 2 mol of NBS.

$$C_6H_5CH_2CH_3 \xrightarrow{\text{NBS, light}} C_6H_5CBr_2CH_3$$

We could make the second compound by adding bromine to styrene, and we could make styrene from ethylbenzene as follows:

$$C_6H_5CH_2CH_3 \xrightarrow{\text{NBS, light}} C_6H_5CHBrCH_3 \xrightarrow{\text{KOH, heat}}$$

$$C_6H_5CH=CH_2 \xrightarrow{Br_2, CCl_4} C_6H_5CHBrCH_2Br$$

Problem 15.16

Starting with phenylacetylene ($C_6H_5C\equiv CH$), outline a synthesis of (a) 1-phenylpropyne, (b) 1-phenyl-1-butyne, (c) (*Z*)-1-phenylpropene, and (d) (*E*)-1-phenylpropene.

15.12B BENZYL AND BENZYLIC CATIONS

Recall that benzyl and benzylic cations are unusually stable carbocations; they are approximately as stable as tertiary cations (Section 13.10).

Problem 15.17

Write resonance structures for the *benzyl cation* $(C_6H_5\overset{+}{C}H_2)$ that account for its unusual stability.

15.13 ALKENYLBENZENES

15.13A STABILITY OF CONJUGATED ALKENYLBENZENES

Alkenylbenzenes that have their side-chain double bond conjugated with the benzene ring are more stable than those that do not.

Conjugated system   **more stable than**   **Nonconjugated system**

Part of the evidence for this comes from acid-catalyzed alcohol dehydrations, which are known to yield the most stable alkene (Section 8.15). For example, dehydration of the following alcohol yields exclusively the conjugated system.

Because conjugation always lowers the energy of an unsaturated system by allowing the π electrons to be delocalized, this behavior is just what we would expect.

15.13B ADDITIONS TO THE DOUBLE BOND OF ALKENYLBENZENES

In the presence of peroxides, hydrogen bromide adds to the double bond of 1-phenylpropene to give 2-bromo-1-phenylpropane as the major product.

1-Phenylpropene   **2-Bromo-1-phenylpropane**

In the absence of peroxides, HBr adds in just the opposite way.

1-Phenylpropene   **1-Bromo-1-phenylpropane**

The addition of hydrogen bromide to 1-phenylpropene proceeds through a benzylic radical in the presence of peroxides, and through a benzylic cation in their absence (cf. Problem 15.18 and Section 9.9).

Problem 15.18

Write mechanisms for the reactions whereby HBr adds to 1-phenylpropene (a) in the presence of peroxides and (b) in the absence of peroxides. In each case account for the regiochemistry of the addition (i. e., explain why the major product is 2-bromo-1-phenylpropane when peroxides are present, and why it is 1-bromo-1-phenylpropane when peroxides are absent.

Problem 15.19

(a) What would you expect to be the major product when 1-phenylpropene reacts with HCl? (b) When it is subjected to oxymercuration–demercuration?

15.13C OXIDATION OF THE SIDE CHAIN

Strong oxidizing agents oxidize toluene to benzoic acid. The oxidation can be carried out by the action of hot alkaline potassium permanganate. This method gives benzoic acid in almost quantitative yield.

Benzoic acid
(~100%)

An important characteristic of side-chain oxidations is that oxidation takes place initially at the benzylic carbon; **alkylbenzenes with alkyl groups longer than methyl are ultimately degraded to benzoic acids.**

An alkylbenzene   Benzoic acid

Side-chain oxidations are similar to benzylic halogenations, because in the first step the oxidizing agent abstracts a benzylic hydrogen. Once oxidation is begun at the benzylic carbon, it continues at that site. Ultimately, the oxidizing agent oxidizes the benzylic carbon to a carboxyl group and, in the process, it cleaves off the remaining carbon atoms of the side chain. (*tert*-Butylbenzene is resistant to side-chain oxidation. Why?)

Side-chain oxidation is not restricted to alkyl groups. **Alkenyl, alkynyl, and acyl groups are oxidized by hot alkaline potassium permanganate in the same way.**

15.13D OXIDATION OF THE BENZENE RING

The benzene ring of an alkylbenzene can be converted to a carboxyl group by ozonolysis, followed by treatment with hydrogen peroxide:

$$R-C_6H_5 \xrightarrow[\text{(2) } H_2O_2]{\text{(1) } O_3,\ CH_3CO_2H} R-\overset{\overset{\displaystyle O}{\parallel}}{C}OH$$

15.14 SYNTHETIC APPLICATIONS

The substitution reactions of aromatic rings and the reactions of the side chains of alkyl- and alkenylbenzenes, when taken together, offer us a powerful set of reactions for organic synthesis. By using these reactions skillfully, we shall be able to synthesize a large number of benzene derivatives.

Part of the skill in planning a synthesis is in deciding the order in which reactions should be carried out. Let us suppose, for example, that we want to synthesize o-bromonitrobenzene. We can see very quickly that we should introduce the bromine into the ring first because it is an ortho–para director.

o-Bromonitro-   p-Bromonitro-
benzene   benzene

The ortho and para compounds that we get as products can be separated by various methods. However, had we introduced the nitro group first, we would have obtained m-bromonitrobenzene as the major product.

Other examples in which choosing the proper order for the reactions are important are the syntheses of the ortho-, meta-, and para-nitrobenzoic acids. We can synthesize the ortho- and para-nitrobenzoic acids from toluene by nitrating it, separating the ortho- and para-nitrotoluenes, and then oxidizing the methyl groups to carboxyl groups.

p-Nitrotoluene   p-Nitrobenzoic
(separate)   acid

o-Nitrotoluene   o-Nitrobenzoic acid

We can synthesize *m*-nitrobenzoic acid by reversing the order of the reactions.

Benzoic acid   **m-Nitrobenzoic acid**

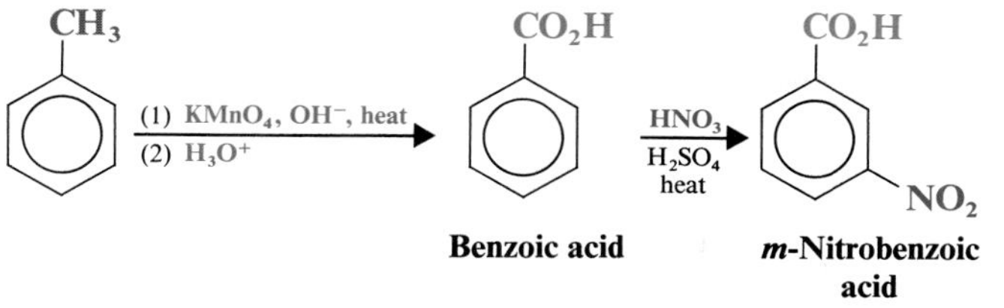

Sample Problem

Starting with toluene, outline a synthesis of (a) 1-bromo-2-(trichloromethyl)-benzene, (b) 1-bromo-3-(trichloromethyl)benzene, and (c) 1-bromo-4-(trichloromethyl)benzene.

Answer:

Compounds (a) and (c) can be obtained by ring bromination of toluene followed by chlorination of the side chain using three molar equivalents of chlorine:

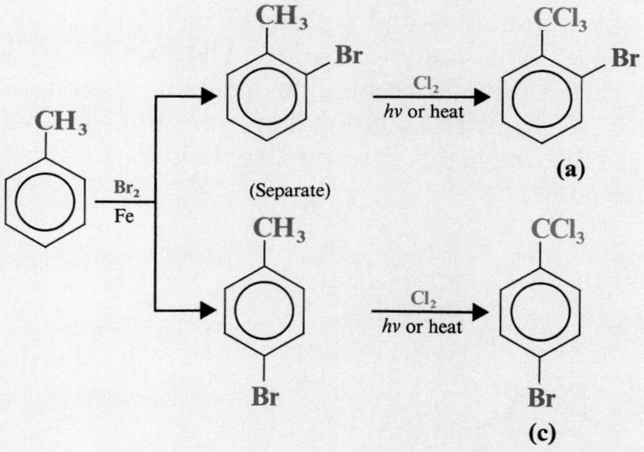

To make compound (b) we reverse the order of the reactions. By converting the side chain to a —CCl₃ group first, we create a meta director, which causes the bromine to enter the desired position.

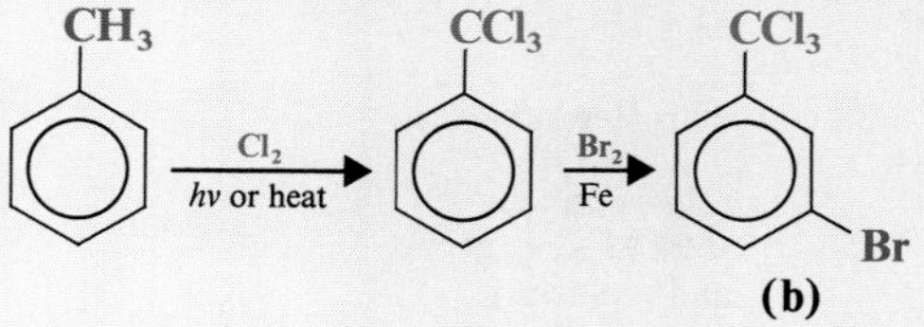

Problem 15.20

Suppose you needed to synthesize 1-(*p*-chlorophenyl)propene from propyl-benzene.

You could introduce the double bond into the side chain through a benzylic halogenation and subsequent dehydrohalogenation. You could introduce the chlorine into the benzene ring through a Lewis-acid catalyzed chlorination. Which reaction would you carry out first? Why?

Very powerful activating groups such as amino groups and hydroxyl groups cause the benzene ring to be so reactive that undesirable reactions may take place. Some reagents used for electrophilic substitution reactions, such as nitric acid, are also strong *oxidizing agents.* (Both electrophiles and oxidizing agents seek electrons.) Thus, amino groups and hydroxyl groups not only activate the ring toward electrophilic substitution, they also activate it toward oxidation. Nitration of aniline, for example, results in considerable destruction of the benzene ring because it is oxidized by the nitric acid. Direct nitration of aniline, consequently, is not a satisfactory method for the preparation of *o*- and *p*-nitroaniline.

Treating aniline with acetyl chloride, CH_3COCl, or acetic anhydride, $(CH_3CO)_2O$, converts aniline to acetanilide. The amino group is converted to an acetamido group ($-NHCOCH_3$), a group that is only moderately activating and one that does not make the ring highly susceptible to oxidation. With acetanilide, direct nitration becomes possible.

Nitration of acetanilide gives *p*-nitroacetanilide in excellent yield with only a trace of the ortho isomer. Acidic hydrolysis of p-nitroacetanilide (Section 18.8F) removes the acetyl group and gives p-nitroaniline, also in good yield.

Suppose, however, that we need o-nitroaniline. The synthesis that we just outlined would obviously not be a satisfactory method, for only a trace of o-nitroacetanilide is obtained in the nitration reaction. (The acetamido group is purely a para director in many reactions. Bromination of acetanilide, for example, gives p-bromoacetanilide almost exclusively.)

We can synthesize o-nitroacetanilide, however, through the reactions that follow:

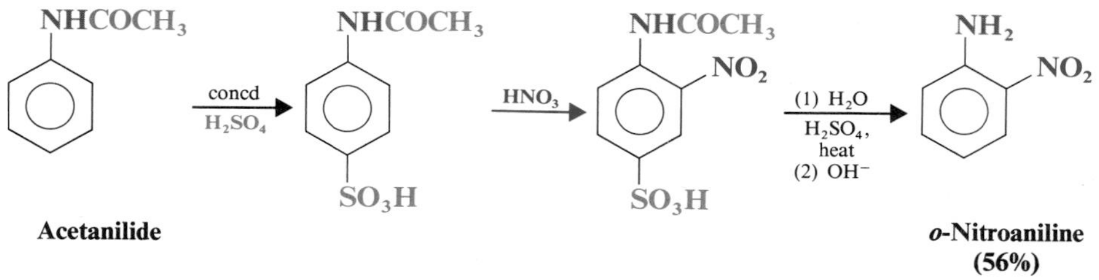

Here we see how a sulfonic acid group can be used as a "blocking group." We can remove the sulfonic acid group by desulfonation at a later stage. In this example, the reagent used for desulfonation (dilute H_2SO_4) also conveniently removes the acetyl group that we employed to "protect" the benzene ring from oxidation by nitric acid.

15.14A ORIENTATION IN DISUBSTITUTED BENZENES

The problem of orientation is somewhat more complicated when two substituents are present on a benzene ring. We find, however, that in many instances we can make very good estimates of the outcomes of the reaction by relatively simple analyses.

If two groups are located so that their directive effects reinforce each other, then predicting the outcome is easy. Consider the examples shown here. In each case the entering substituent is directed by both groups into the position indicated by the arrows.

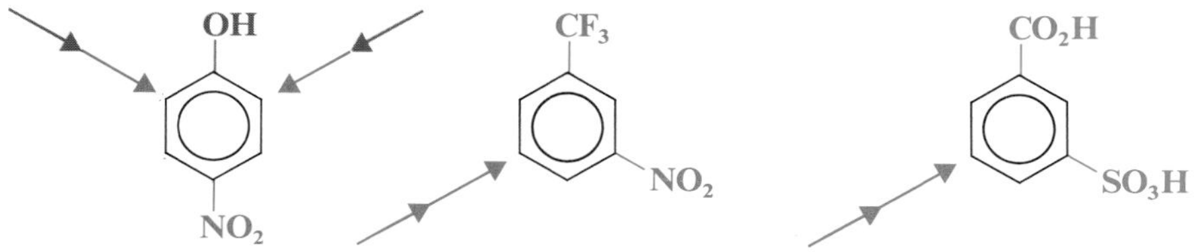

When the directive effects of two groups oppose each other, **the more powerful activating group** (Table 15.2) **generally determines the outcome of the reaction.** Let us consider, as an example, the orientation of electrophilic substitution of p-methylacetanilide. The acetamido group is a much stronger activating group than the methyl group. The following example shows that the acetamido group determines the outcome of the reaction. Substitution occurs primarily at the position ortho to the acetamido group.

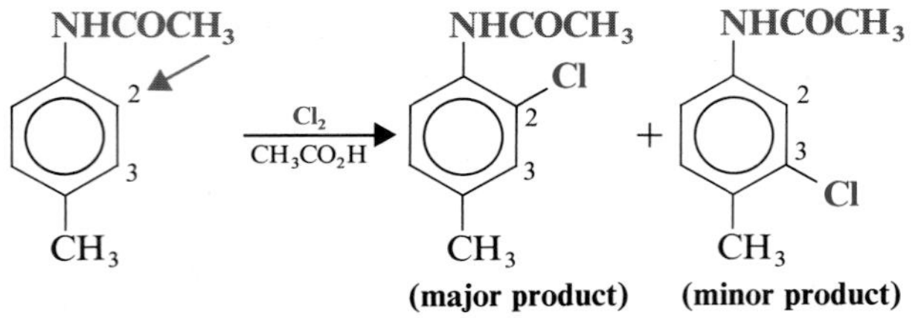

*Because all ortho–para- directing groups are more activating than meta direc-tors, **the ortho–para director determines the orientation of the incoming group.*** For example,

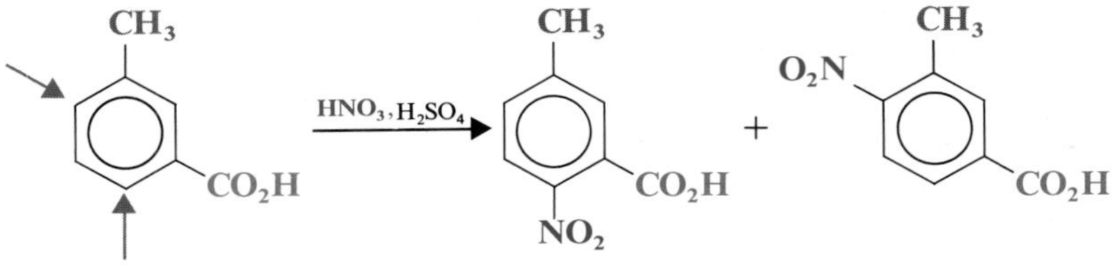

When two opposing groups have approximately the same directive effect, the results are not nearly so clear-cut. The following reaction is a typical example:

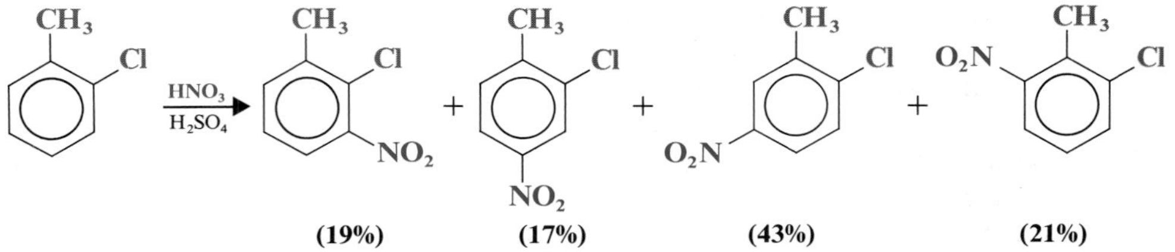

(19%)   (17%)   (43%)   (21%)

Steric effects are also important in aromatic substitutions. ***Substitution does not occur to an appreciable extent between meta substituents if another position is open.*** A good example of this effect can be seen in the nitration of *m*-bromochlorobenzene.

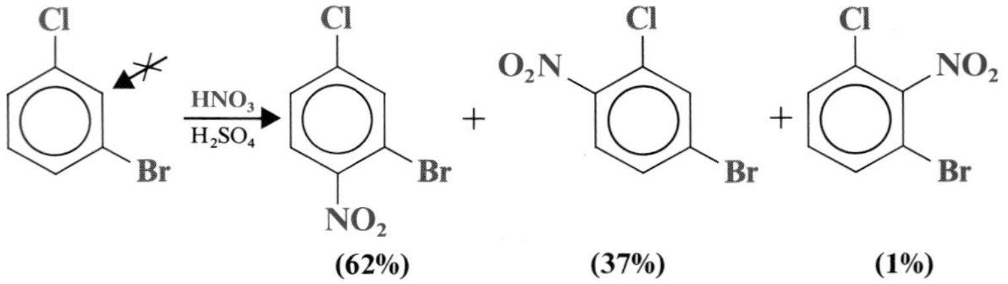

(62%)   (37%)   (1%)

Only 1% of the mononitro product has the nitro group between the bromine and chlorine.

Problem 15.21

Predict the major product (or products) that would be obtained when each of the following compounds is nitrated.

(a) 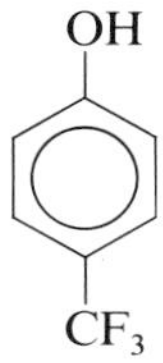 *p*-Hydroxy-trifluoromethylbenzene with OH at top, CF$_3$ at bottom

(b) 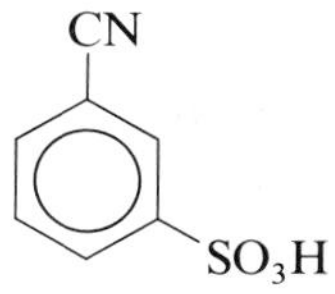 benzene ring with CN at top and SO$_3$H at meta position

(c) 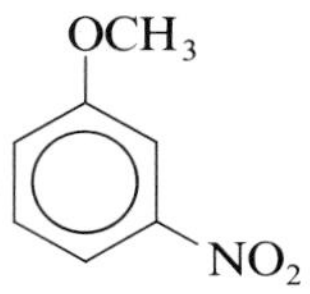 benzene ring with OCH$_3$ at top and NO$_2$ at meta position

---

Additional Problems

15.22 Outline ring bromination, nitration, and sulfonation reactions of the following compounds. In each case give the structure of the major reaction product or products. Also indicate whether the reaction would occur faster or slower than the corresponding reaction of benzene.

(a) Anisole, $C_6H_5OCH_3$

(b) (Difluoromethyl)benzene, $C_6H_5CHF_2$

(c) Ethylbenzene

(d) Nitrobenzene

(e) Chlorobenzene

(f) Benzenesulfonic acid

15.23 Predict the major products of the following reactions:

(a) Sulfonation of p-$CH_3C_6H_4COCH_3$

(b) Nitration of m-dichlorobenzene

(c) Nitration of 1,3-dimethoxybenzene

(d) Monobromination of p-$CH_3CONHC_6H_4NH_2$

(e) Nitration of p-$HO_3SC_6H_4OH$

(f) Nitration of [benzene ring]—CH_2—[benzene ring]—CO_2H

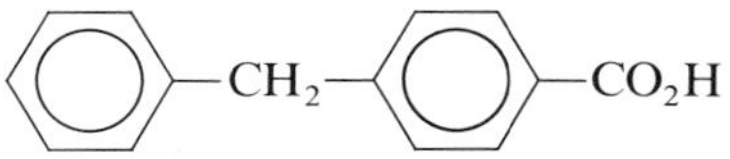

(g) Chlorination of $C_6H_5CCl_3$

15.24 Give the structures of the major products of the following reactions:

(a) Styrene + HCl $\longrightarrow$

(b) 2-Bromo-1-phenylpropane + C_2H_5ONa $\longrightarrow$

(c) $C_6H_5CH_2CHOHCH_2CH_3$ $\xrightarrow{H^+,\ heat}$

(d) Product of (c) + HBr $\xrightarrow{peroxides}$

(e) Product of (c) + H_2O $\xrightarrow[heat]{H^+}$

(f) Product of (c) + H_2 (1 molar equivalent) $\xrightarrow[25\ °C]{Pt}$

(g) Product of (f) $\xrightarrow[(2)\ H_3O^+]{(1)\ KMnO_4,\ OH^-,\ heat}$

15.25 Starting with benzene, outline a synthesis of each of the following:

(a) Isopropylbenzene

(b) *tert*-Butylbenzene

(c) Propylbenzene

(d) Butylbenzene

(e) 1-*tert*-Butyl-4-chlorobenzene

(f) 1-Phenylcyclopentene

(g) *trans*-2-Phenylcyclopentanol

(h) *m*-Dinitrobenzene

(i) m-Bromonitrobenzene　　　(l) o-Chloronitrobenzene

(j) p-Bromonitrobenzene　　　(m) m-Nitrobenzenesulfonic acid

(k) p-Chlorobenzenesulfonic acid

15.26　Starting with styrene, outline a synthesis of each of the following:

(a) $C_6H_5CHClCH_2Cl$　　　(f) $C_6H_5CHBrCH_3$　　　(k) $C_6H_5CH_2CH_2CN$

(b) $C_6H_5CH_2CH_3$　　　(g) $C_6H_5CH_2CH_2OH$　　　(l) $C_6H_5CHDCH_2D$

(c) $C_6H_5CHOHCH_2OH$　　　(h) $C_6H_5CH_2CH_2D$　　　(m) Cyclohexylbenzene

(d) $C_6H_5CO_2H$　　　(i) $C_6H_5CH_2CH_2Br$　　　(n) $C_6H_5CH_2CH_2OCH_3$

(e) $C_6H_5CHOHCH_3$　　　(j) $C_6H_5CH_2CH_2I$

15.27　Starting with toluene, outline a synthesis of each of the following:

(a) m-Chlorobenzoic acid　　　(f) p-Isopropyltoluene

(b) p-Acetyltoluene　　　(g) 1-Cyclohexyl-4-methylbenzene

(c) 2-Bromo-4-nitrotoluene　　　(h) 2,4,6-Trinitrotoluene (TNT)

(d) p-Bromobenzoic acid　　　(i) 4-Chloro-2-nitrobenzoic acid

(e) 1-Chloro-3-(trichloromethyl)benzene　　　(j) 1-Butyl-4-methylbenzene

15.28　Starting with aniline, outline a synthesis of each of the following:

(a) p-Bromoaniline　　　(c) 2-Bromo-4-nitroaniline　　　(e) 2,4,6-Tribromoaniline

(b) o-Bromoaniline　　　(d) 4-Bromo-2-nitroaniline

15.29　(a) Which ring of benzanilide would you expect to undergo electrophilic substitution more readily?　(b) Write resonance structures that explain your choice.

Benzanilide

15.30　What products would you expect from the nitration of phenyl benzoate?

Phenyl benzoate

15.31　Naphthalene can be synthesized from benzene through the following sequence of reactions. Write the structure of each intermediate.

Benzene + succinic anhydride $\xrightarrow{\text{AlCl}_3}$ **A** $\xrightarrow[\text{HCl}]{\text{Zn(Hg)}}$ **B** $\xrightarrow{\text{SOCl}_2}$

$(C_{10}H_{10}O_3)$　　　$(C_{10}H_{12}O_2)$

C $\xrightarrow{\text{AlCl}_3}$ **D** $\xrightarrow[\text{HCl}]{\text{Zn(Hg)}}$ **E** $\xrightarrow[\text{peroxides}]{\text{NBS}}$

$(C_{10}H_{11}ClO)$　　　$(C_{10}H_{10}O)$　　　$(C_{10}H_{12})$

F $\xrightarrow[\text{heat}]{\text{KOH, ethanol}}$ **G** $\xrightarrow[\text{heat}]{\text{Pt}}$ naphthalene + H_2

$(C_{10}H_{11}Br)$　　　$(C_{10}H_{10})$

ADDITIONAL PROBLEMS

15.32 Anthracene and many other polycyclic aromatic compounds have been synthesized by a cyclization reaction known as the *Bradsher reaction* or *aromatic cyclodehydration*. This method, developed by C. K. Bradsher of Duke University, can be illustrated by the conversion of an *o*-benzylphenyl ketone to a substituted anthracene.

An *o*-benzylphenyl
ketone

Substituted anthracene

An arenium ion is an intermediate in this reaction and the last step involves the dehydration of an alcohol. Propose a mechanism for the Bradsher reaction.

15.33 Propose structures for compounds **G–I**.

$$(C_6H_6S_2O_8) \qquad (C_6H_5NS_2O_{10}) \qquad (C_6H_5NO_4)$$

15.34 2,6-Dichlorophenol has been isolated from the females of two species of ticks (*Amblyomma americanum* and *A. maculatum*), where it apparently serves as a sex attractant. Each female tick yields about 5 ng of 2,6-dichlorophenol. Assume that you need larger quantities than this, and outline a synthesis of 2,6-dichlorophenol from phenol. (*Hint:* When phenol is sulfonated at 100 °C, the product is chiefly *p*-hydroxybenzenesulfonic acid.)

15.35 The addition of a hydrogen halide (hydrogen bromide or hydrogen chloride) to 1-phenyl-1,3-butadiene produces (only) 1-phenyl-3-halo-1-butene. (a) Write a mechanism that accounts for the formation of this product. (b) Is this 1,4 addition or 1,2 addition to the butadiene system? (c) Is the product of the reaction consistent with the formation of the most stable intermediate carbocation? (d) Does the reaction appear to be under kinetic control or equilibrium control? Explain.

15.36 We have seen that benzene undergoes ring substitution when it reacts with chlorine in the presence of a Lewis acid. However, benzene can be made to undergo *addition* of chlorine by irradiating a mixture of benzene and chlorine with UV light. The addition reaction produces a mixture of 1,2,3,4,5,6-hexachlorocyclohexanes. One of these hexachlorocyclohexanes is *lindane,* a very effective (but potentially hazardous) insecticide. The chloro groups of lindane at carbon atoms 1, 2, and 3 are equatorial; those at 4, 5, and 6 are axial. (a) Write the structure of lindane. (b) Would you expect lindane to exist in enantiomeric forms? (c) If not, why not? (d) One isomeric form of 1,2,3,4,5,6-hexachlorocyclohexane isomer does exist in enantiomeric forms. Write its structure.

15.37 Naphthalene undergoes electrophilic attack at the 1 position much more rapidly than it does at the 2 position.

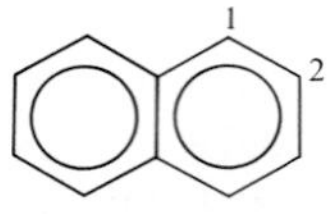

Naphthalene

The greater reactivity at the 1 position can be accounted for by writing resonance structures for the ring that undergoes electrophilic attack. Show how this is possible.

*15.38   Write mechanisms that account for the products of the following reactions:

(a)

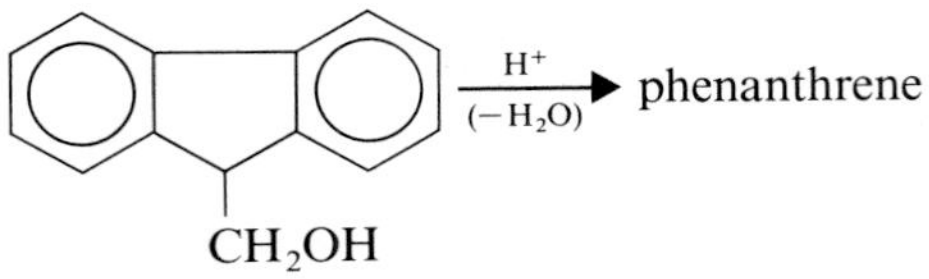

$\xrightarrow[(-H_2O)]{H^+}$ phenanthrene

(b) $2\ CH_3{-}\underset{\underset{C_6H_5}{|}}{C}{=}CH_2 \xrightarrow{H^+}$

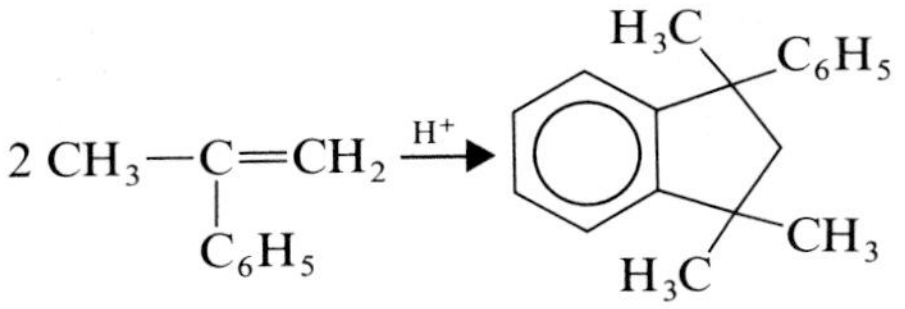

15.39   In most desulfonation reactions the electrophile is a proton. Other electrophiles may be used, however. (a) Show all steps of the desulfonation reaction that would occur when benzenesulfonic acid is desulfonated with deuterium sulfate (D_2SO_4) dissolved in D_2O. (b) When benzenesulfonic acid reacts with bromine in the presence of ferric bromide, bromo-benzene is obtained from the reaction mixture. What is the electrophile in this reaction? Show all steps in the mechanism for this desulfonation.

*15.40   The compound phenylbenzene ($C_6H_5{-}C_6H_5$) is called *biphenyl* and the rings are numbered in the following manner.

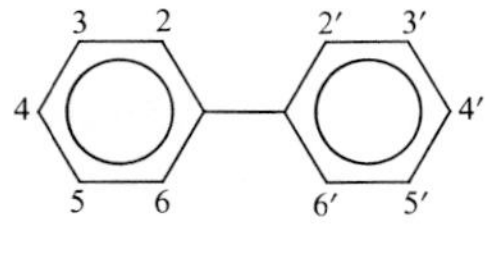

Use models to answer the following questions about substituted biphenyls. (a) When certain large groups occupy three or four of the *ortho* positions (e.g., 2,6,2', and 6'), the substituted biphenyl may exist in enantiomeric forms. An example of a biphenyl that exists in enantio-meric forms is the compound in which the following substituents are present. 2-NO_2, 6-CO_2H, 2'-NO_2, 6'-CO_2H. What factors account for this? (b) Would you expect a biphenyl with 2-Br, 6-CO_2H, 2'-CO_2H, 6'-H to exist in enantiomeric forms? (c) The biphenyl with 2-NO_2, 6-NO_2, 2'-CO_2H, 6'-Br cannot be resolved into enantiomeric forms. Explain.

*15.41   Give structures (including stereochemistry where appropriate) for compounds A – G.

(a) Benzene + $CH_3CH_2\overset{\overset{\textstyle O}{\|}}{C}Cl \xrightarrow{AlCl_3}$ A $\xrightarrow[0\ °C]{PCl_5}$

$B\ (C_9H_{10}Cl_2) \xrightarrow[\substack{\text{mineral oil,}\\\text{heat}}]{2\ NaNH_2}$ C $(C_9H_8) \xrightarrow{H_2,\ Ni_2B\ (P\text{-}2)}$ D (C_9H_{10})

(b) **C** $\xrightarrow[\text{(2) H}_2\text{O}]{\text{(1) Li, liq. NH}_3}$ **E** (C_9H_{10})

(c) **D** $\xrightarrow[\text{2–5 °C}]{\text{Br}_2,\ \text{CCl}_4}$ **F** + enantiomer (major products)

(d) **E** $\xrightarrow[\text{2–5 °C}]{\text{Br}_2,\ \text{CCl}_4}$ **G** + enantiomer (major products)

15.42 Friedel–Crafts acylation of azulene gives mainly one isomer:

Azulene   (mainly one isomer)

One ring of azulene is attacked by $CH_3C{\equiv}O^+$ preferentially because an especially stable arenium ion forms. (a) What is the structure of this arenium ion and (b) why is it especially stable? (c) What is the structure of the acetylazulene that forms as the major product?

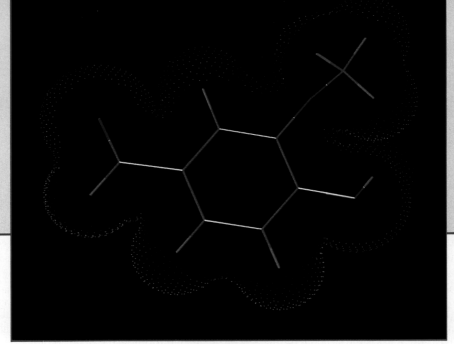

Vanillin (see Section 16.3).

16

ALDEHYDES AND KETONES I. NUCLEOPHILIC ADDITIONS TO THE CARBONYL GROUP

16.1 INTRODUCTION

Except for formaldehyde, the simplest aldehyde, all aldehydes have a carbonyl group,

$$\overset{O}{\underset{\|}{-C}}-$$

, bonded on one side to a carbon, and on the other side to a hydrogen. In ketones, the carbonyl group is situated between two carbon atoms.

$$H-\overset{O}{\underset{\|}{C}}-H$$	$$R-\overset{O}{\underset{\|}{C}}-H$$	$$R-\overset{O}{\underset{\|}{C}}-R'$$
Formaldehyde	**General formula for an aldehyde**	**General formula for a ketone**

Although earlier chapters have given us some insight into the chemistry of carbonyl compounds, we shall now consider their chemistry in detail. The reason: The chemistry of the carbonyl group is central to the chemistry of most of the chapters that follow.

In this chapter our attention will be focused on the preparation of aldehydes and ketones, on their physical properties, and especially on *the nucleophilic addition reactions that take place at their carbonyl groups.* In Chapter 17 we shall study the chemistry of aldehydes and ketones *that results from the acidity of the hydrogen atoms on the carbon atoms adjacent to their carbonyl groups.*

16.2 NOMENCLATURE OF ALDEHYDES AND KETONES

In the IUPAC system aliphatic aldehydes are named *substitutively* by replacing the final **e** of the name of the corresponding alkane with **al**. Since the aldehyde group must be at the end of the chain of carbon atoms, there is no need to indicate its position. When other substituents are present, however, the carbonyl group carbon is assigned position 1. Many aldehydes also have common names; these are given here in parentheses. These common names are derived from the common names for the corresponding carboxylic acids (Section 18.2A) and some of them are retained by the IUPAC as acceptable names.

$$
\begin{array}{ccc}
\overset{O}{\underset{\|}{}} & \overset{O}{\underset{\|}{}} & \overset{O}{\underset{\|}{}} \\
H-C-H & CH_3C-H & CH_3CH_2C-H \\
\textbf{Methanal} & \textbf{Ethanal} & \textbf{Propanal} \\
\textbf{(formaldehyde)} & \textbf{(acetaldehyde)} & \textbf{(propionaldehyde)}
\end{array}
$$

$$
\begin{array}{cc}
\overset{O}{\underset{\|}{}} & \overset{O}{\underset{\|}{}} \\
ClCH_2CH_2CH_2CH_2C-H & C_6H_5CH_2C-H \\
\textbf{5-Chloropentanal} & \textbf{Phenylethanal} \\
& \textbf{(phenylacetaldehyde)}
\end{array}
$$

Aldehydes in which the —CHO group is attached to a ring system are named substitutively by adding the suffix *carbaldehyde.* Several examples follow:

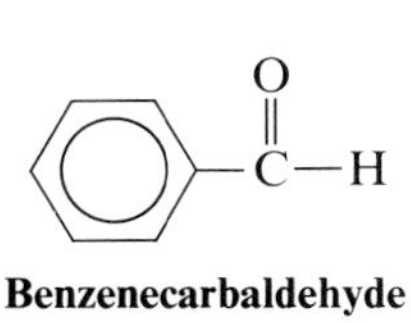

Benzenecarbaldehyde   **Cyclohexanecarbaldehyde** 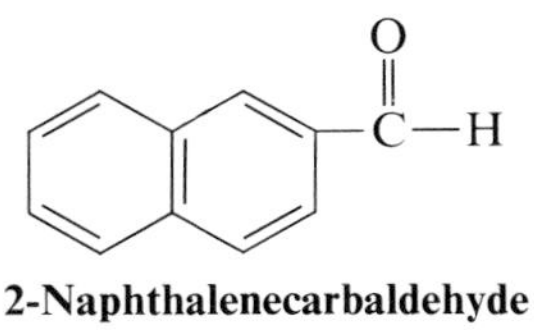   **2-Naphthalenecarbaldehyde**
(benzaldehyde)

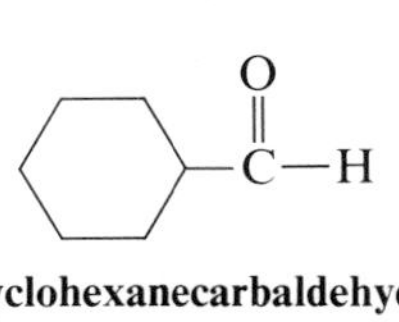

The common name *benzaldehyde* is far more frequently used than benzenecarbaldehyde for C_6H_5CHO, and it is the name we shall use in this text.

Aliphatic ketones are named substitutively by replacing the final **e** of the name of the corresponding alkane with **one**. The chain is then numbered in the way that gives the carbonyl carbon atom the lower possible number, and this number is used to designate its position.

$$
\begin{array}{ccc}
& \overset{O}{\underset{\|}{}} & \overset{O}{\underset{\|}{}} \\
CH_3CH_2CCH_3 & CH_3CCH_2CH_2CH_3 & CH_3CCH_2CH=CH_2 \\
\underset{\|}{} & & \\
O & & \\
\textbf{2-Butanone} & \textbf{2-Pentanone} & \textbf{4-Penten-2-one} \\
\textbf{(ethyl methyl ketone)} & \textbf{(methyl propyl ketone)} & \textbf{(\textit{not} 1-penten-4-one)}
\end{array}
$$

Common radicofunctional names for ketones (in parentheses above) are obtained simply by separately naming the two groups attached to the carbonyl group and adding the word **ketone** as a separate word.

Some ketones have common names that are retained in the IUPAC system.

$$CH_3\overset{O}{\overset{\|}{C}}CH_3$$

Acetone
(2-propanone or
dimethyl ketone)

$$\overset{O}{\overset{\|}{C}}CH_3$$

Acetophenone
(1-phenylethanone or
methyl phenyl ketone)

$$\overset{O}{\overset{\|}{C}}$$

Benzophenone
(diphenylmethanone or
diphenyl ketone)

When it is necessary to name the $-\overset{O}{\overset{\|}{C}}H$ group as a prefix, it is the **methanoyl** or **formyl group.** When $R\overset{O}{\overset{\|}{C}}-$ groups are named as substituents, they are called **alkanoyl** or **acyl groups.**

$$\overset{O}{\overset{\|}{C}}-H$$

$$-CO_2H$$

2-Methanoylbenzoic acid
(o-formylbenzoic acid)

$$CH_3\overset{O}{\overset{\|}{C}}--SO_3H$$

4-Ethanoylbenzenesulfonic acid
(p-acetylbenzenesulfonic acid)

Problem 16.1

(a) Give IUPAC substitutive names for the seven isomeric aldehydes and ketones with the formula $C_5H_{10}O$. (b) Give structures and names (common or IUPAC substitutive names) for all the aldehydes and ketones that contain a benzene ring and have the formula C_8H_8O.

16.3 PHYSICAL PROPERTIES

The carbonyl group is a polar group; therefore aldehydes and ketones have higher boiling points than hydrocarbons of the same molecular weight. However, since aldehydes and ketones cannot have strong hydrogen bonds between their molecules, they have lower boiling points than corresponding alcohols.

$$CH_3CH_2CH_2CH_3$$

Butane
bp, −0.5 °C

$$CH_3CH_2\overset{O}{\overset{\|}{C}}H$$

Propanal
bp, 49 °C

$$CH_3\overset{O}{\overset{\|}{C}}CH_3$$

Acetone
bp, 56.1 °C

$$CH_3CH_2CH_2OH$$

1-Propanol
bp, 97.2 °C

Problem 16.2

Which compound in each of the following pairs listed has the higher boiling point? (Answer this problem without consulting tables.)

(a) Pentanal or 1-pentanol   (d) Acetophenone or 2-phenylethanol

(b) 2-Pentanone or 2-pentanol   (e) Benzaldehyde or benzyl alcohol

(c) Pentane or pentanal

The carbonyl oxygen atom allows molecules of aldehydes and ketones to form strong hydrogen bonds to molecules of water. As a result, low molecular weight aldehydes and ketones show appreciable solubilities in water. Acetone and acetaldehyde are soluble in water in all proportions.

Table 16.1 lists the physical properties of a number of common aldehydes and ketones.

TABLE 16.1 Physical properties of aldehydes and ketones

FORMULA	NAME	mp (°C)	bp (°C)	SOLUBILITY IN WATER
HCHO	Formaldehyde	−92	−21	Very soluble
CH_3CHO	Acetaldehyde	−125	21	∞
CH_3CH_2CHO	Propanal	−81	49	Very soluble
$CH_3(CH_2)_2CHO$	Butanal	−99	76	Soluble
$CH_3(CH_2)_3CHO$	Pentanal	−91.5	102	Sl. soluble
$CH_3(CH_2)_4CHO$	Hexanal	−51	131	Sl. soluble
C_6H_5CHO	Benzaldehyde	−26	178	Sl. soluble
$C_6H_5CH_2CHO$	Phenylacetaldehyde	33	193	Sl. soluble
CH_3COCH_3	Acetone	−95	56.1	∞
$CH_3COCH_2CH_3$	2-Butanone	−86	79.6	Very soluble
$CH_3COCH_2CH_2CH_3$	2-Pentanone	−78	102	Soluble
$CH_3CH_2COCH_2CH_3$	3-Pentanone	−39	102	Soluble
$C_6H_5COCH_3$	Acetophenone	21	202	Insoluble
$C_6H_5COC_6H_5$	Benzophenone	48	306	Insoluble

Some aromatic aldehydes obtained from natural sources have very pleasant fragrances. Some of these are the following:

Benzaldehyde
(from bitter almonds)

Vanillin
(from vanilla beans)

Salicylaldehyde
(from meadowsweet)

Cinnamaldehyde
(from cinnamon)

Piperonal
(made from safrole;
odor of heliotrope)

16.4 SYNTHESIS OF ALDEHYDES

We learned in Section 11.4A that the oxidation state of aldehydes lies between that of 1° alcohols and carboxylic acids and that aldehydes can be prepared from 1° alcohols by oxidation with pyridinium chlorochromate:

$$R-CH_2OH \underset{[H]}{\overset{[O]}{\rightleftharpoons}} R-\overset{O}{\overset{\|}{C}}-H \underset{[H]}{\overset{[O]}{\rightleftharpoons}} R-\overset{O}{\overset{\|}{C}}-OH$$

1° Alcohol   **Aldehyde**   **Carboxylic acid**

$$R-CH_2OH \xrightarrow[CH_2Cl_2]{C_5H_5NH^+CrO_3Cl^- \text{ (PCC)}} R-\overset{O}{\overset{\|}{C}}-H$$

1° Alcohol   **Aldehyde**

An example of this synthesis of aldehydes is the oxidation of 1-heptanol to heptanal:

$$CH_3(CH_2)_5CH_2OH \xrightarrow[CH_2Cl_2]{C_5H_5NH^+CrO_3Cl^- \text{ (PCC)}} CH_3(CH_2)_5CHO$$

1-Heptanol   **Heptanal**
                                                       (93%)

Theoretically, it ought to be possible to prepare aldehydes by reduction of carboxylic acids. In practice, this is not possible, because the only reagent that will reduce a carboxylic acid directly is lithium aluminum hydride ($LiAlH_4$ or LAH) and when any carboxylic acid is treated with LAH, it is reduced all the way to the 1° alcohol. This happens because LAH is a very powerful reducing agent and aldehydes are very easily reduced. Any aldehyde that might be formed in the reaction mixture is immediately reduced by the LAH to the 1° alcohol. (It does not help to use a stoichiometric amount of LAH, because as soon as the first few molecules of aldehyde are formed in the mixture, there will still be much unreacted LAH present and it will reduce the aldehyde.)

$$R-\overset{O}{\overset{\|}{C}}-OH \xrightarrow{LiAlH_4} \left[R-\overset{O}{\overset{\|}{C}}-H \right] \xrightarrow{LiAlH_4} R-CH_2OH$$

Carboxylic acid   **Aldehyde**   **1° Alcohol**

The secret to success here is not to use a carboxylic acid itself, but to use a derivative of a carboxylic acid that is more easily reduced, and to use an aluminum hydride derivative that is less reactive than LAH. We shall study derivatives of carboxylic acids in detail in Chapter 18, but suffice it to say here, that acyl chlorides (RCOCl), esters (RCO$_2$R′), and nitriles (RCN) are all easily prepared from carboxylic acids, and they all are more easily reduced. (Acyl chlorides, esters, and nitriles all also have the same oxidation state as carboxylic acids. Convince yourself of this by applying the principles that you learned in Problem 11.1.) Two derivatives of aluminum hydride that are less reactive than LAH (in part because they are much more sterically hindered and, therefore, have difficulty in transferring hydride ions) are lithium tri-*tert*-butoxyaluminum hydride and diisobutylaluminum hydride.

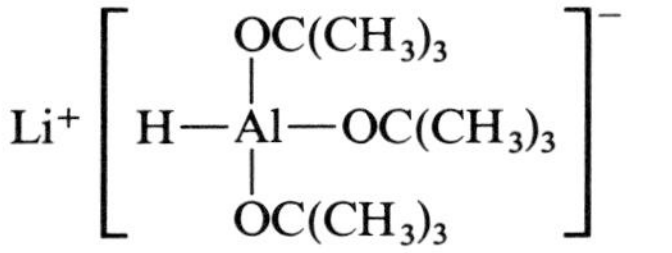

Lithium tri-*tert*-butoxy-aluminum hydride

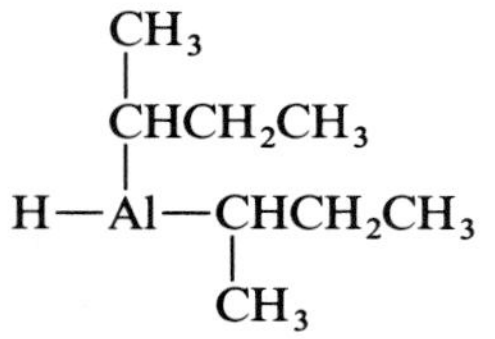

Diisobutylaluminum hydride (abbreviated *i*-Bu$_2$AlH or DIBAL-H)

The following scheme summarizes how these reagents are used to synthesize aldehydes from acid derivatives.

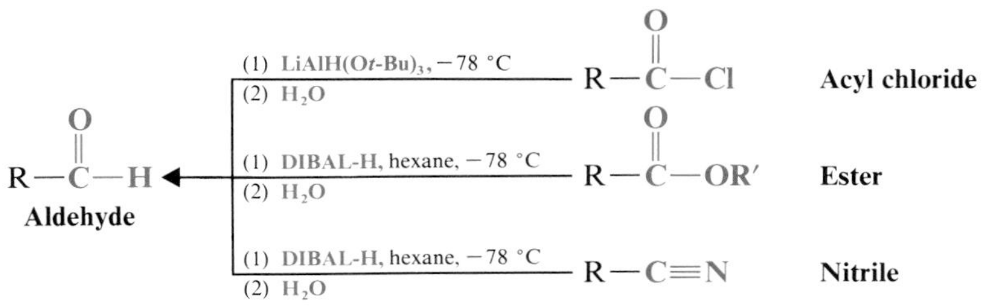

Notice that all of these reactions are carried out at a very low temperature (-78 °C, the temperature of a dry ice–acetone bath). Use of a low temperature decreases the reactivity of these reducing agents and helps prevent reduction of the aldehyde that is initially produced (and is the desired product) to a 1° alcohol.

We now examine each of these aldehyde syntheses in more detail.

Aldehydes from Acyl Chlorides: RCOCl ⟶ RCHO. Acyl chlorides can be reduced to aldehydes by treating them with lithium tri-*tert*-butoxyaluminum hydride, LiAlH[OC(CH$_3$)$_3$]$_3$, at -78 °C. (Carboxylic acids can be converted to acyl chlorides by using SOCl$_2$, Section 15.7.)

The following is a specific example:

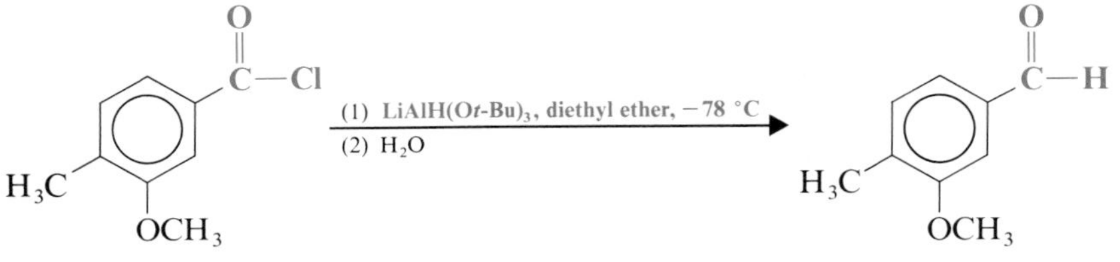

Mechanistically, the reduction is brought about by the transfer of a hydride ion from the aluminum atom to the carbonyl carbon of the acyl chloride (cf. Section 11.3). Subsequent hydrolysis frees the aldehyde.

Aldehydes from Esters and Nitriles: $RCO_2R' \longrightarrow RCHO$ *and* $RC\equiv N \longrightarrow RCHO$.
Both esters and nitriles can be reduced to aldehydes by use of diisobutylaluminum hydride. Carefully controlled amounts of the reagent must be used to avoid overreduction and the reactions must be carried out at low temperatures. Both reductions result in the formation of a relatively stable intermediate by the addition of a hydride ion to the carbonyl carbon of the ester or to the carbon of the $-C\equiv N$ group of the nitrile. Hydrolysis of the intermediate liberates the aldehyde. Schematically, the reactions can be viewed this way:

Reduction of Esters to Aldehydes

Reduction of Nitriles to Aldehydes

The following specific examples illustrate these syntheses.

$$CH_3(CH_2)_{10}\overset{\displaystyle O}{\overset{\|}{C}}OEt \xrightarrow[\text{hexane, } -78\ °C]{(i\text{-Bu})_2\text{AlH}} CH_3(CH_2)_{10}\underset{\underset{\displaystyle OEt}{|}}{\overset{\overset{\displaystyle OAl(i\text{-Bu})_2}{|}}{C}}H \xrightarrow{H_2O} CH_3(CH_2)_{10}\overset{\displaystyle O}{\overset{\|}{C}}H$$

$$\textbf{(88\%)}$$

$$CH_3CH{=}CHCH_2CH_2CH_2C{\equiv}N \xrightarrow[\text{hexane, } -78\ °C]{(i\text{-Bu})_2\text{AlH}} CH_3CH{=}CHCH_2CH_2CH_2\overset{\overset{\displaystyle NAl(i\text{-Bu})_2}{\|}}{C}H$$

$$\xrightarrow{H_2O} CH_3CH{=}CHCH_2CH_2CH_2\overset{\displaystyle O}{\overset{\|}{C}}H$$

Problem 16.3

Show how you would synthesize propanal from each of the following:
(a) 1-propanol and (b) propanoic acid ($CH_3CH_2CO_2H$).

16.5 SYNTHESIS OF KETONES

We have seen three laboratory methods for the preparation of ketones in earlier chapters.

1. **Ketones (and Aldehydes) by Ozonolysis of Alkenes** (discussed in Section 9.16).

$$\underset{R'}{\overset{R}{>}}C{=}C\underset{H}{\overset{R''}{<}} \xrightarrow[\text{(2) Zn, H}_2\text{O}]{\text{(1) O}_3} \underset{R'}{\overset{R}{>}}C{=}O + O{=}C\underset{H}{\overset{R''}{<}}$$

$$\text{Ketone} \qquad \text{Aldehyde}$$

2. **Ketones from Friedel–Crafts Acylations** (discussed in Section 15.7).

$$ArH + R\overset{\displaystyle O}{\overset{\|}{C}}{-}Cl \xrightarrow{\text{AlCl}_3} Ar{-}\overset{\displaystyle O}{\overset{\|}{C}}{-}R + HCl$$

$$\textbf{An alkyl aryl}$$
$$\textbf{ketone}$$

or

$$ArH + Ar\overset{\displaystyle O}{\overset{\|}{C}}{-}Cl \xrightarrow{\text{AlCl}_3} Ar{-}\overset{\displaystyle O}{\overset{\|}{C}}{-}Ar + HCl$$

$$\textbf{A diaryl ketone}$$

3. **Ketones from Oxidations of Secondary Alcohols** (discussed in Section 11.4).

$$R{-}\underset{\underset{\displaystyle}{}}{\overset{\overset{\displaystyle OH}{|}}{C}}H{-}R' \xrightarrow{\text{H}_2\text{CrO}_4} R{-}\overset{\displaystyle O}{\overset{\|}{C}}{-}R'$$

A new method for preparing ketones is based on hydration of alkynes.

4. **Ketones from Alkynes.** Alkynes add water readily when the reaction is catalyzed by strong acids and mercuric (Hg^{2+}) ions. Aqueous solutions of sulfuric acid and mercuric sulfate are often used for this purpose. The vinylic alcohol that is initially produced is usually unstable, and it rearranges rapidly to a ketone [or in the case of ethyne to ethanal]. The rearrangement involves the loss of a proton from the hydroxyl group, the addition of a proton to the vicinal carbon atom, and the relocation of the double bond.

$$-C\equiv C- + H-OH \xrightarrow[\text{H}_2\text{SO}_4]{\text{HgSO}_4} \left[\begin{array}{c} H \\ | \\ -C=C- \\ | \\ OH \end{array} \right] \longrightarrow \begin{array}{c} H \\ | \\ -C-C- \\ | \parallel \\ H \ O \end{array}$$

A vinylic
alcohol
(unstable)

Ketone

This kind of rearrangement, known as a **tautomerization,** is acid catalyzed and occurs in the following way:

$$H-\overset{+}{\underset{..}{O}}-H + -C=C- \longrightarrow -C-C- \xrightarrow{\text{H}_2\ddot{O}:} -C-C- + H_3O^+$$

Vinylic
alcohol

Ketone

The vinylic alcohol accepts a proton at one carbon atom of the double bond to yield a cationic intermediate that then loses a proton from the oxygen atom to produce a ketone.

Vinylic alcohols are often called **enols** (-*en,* the ending for alkenes, plus -*ol,* the ending for alcohols). The product of the rearrangement is usually a ketone, and these rearrangements are known as **keto–enol tautomerizations.**

$$-\overset{|}{C}=\overset{|}{C}- \underset{}{\overset{\text{H}^+}{\rightleftharpoons}} -\overset{|}{C}-\overset{|}{C}-$$

Enol form   Keto form

We examine this phenomenon in greater detail in Section 17.2.

Only when ethyne itself undergoes addition of water is the product an alde-hyde.

$$H-C\equiv C-H + H_2O \xrightarrow[\text{H}_2\text{SO}_4]{\text{HgSO}_4} \left[\begin{array}{c} H \qquad H \\ C=C \\ H \qquad OH \end{array} \right] \longrightarrow \begin{array}{c} H \\ | \\ H-C-C-H \\ | \parallel \\ H \ O \end{array}$$

Ethyne

Ethanal
(acetaldehyde)

This method has been important in the commercial production of ethanal.

The addition of water to alkynes also follows Markovnikov's rule—the hydrogen atom becomes attached to the carbon atom with the greater number of hydrogen atoms. Therefore, when higher terminal alkynes are hydrated, ketones, rather than aldehydes, are the products.

$$R-C\equiv C-H \xrightarrow[\text{H}_2\text{O, H}^+]{\text{Hg}^{2+}} \left[\begin{array}{c} H \\ | \\ RC=C-H \\ | \\ OH \end{array} \right] \longrightarrow \begin{array}{c} H \\ | \\ R-C-C-H \\ \parallel \ | \\ O \ H \end{array}$$

A ketone

Two examples of this ketone synthesis are listed here.

16.5 SYNTHESIS OF KETONES

$$CH_3C\equiv CH \xrightarrow[H_2O,\ H^+]{Hg^{2+}} \left[CH_3-\underset{\underset{OH}{|}}{C}=CH_2 \right] \longrightarrow CH_3-\underset{\underset{O}{\|}}{C}-CH_3$$

Acetone

$$CH_3CH_2CH_2CH_2C\equiv CH \xrightarrow[\substack{H_2SO_4 \\ H_2O}]{HgSO_4} CH_3CH_2CH_2CH_2\underset{\underset{O}{\|}}{C}CH_3$$

(80%)

Two other laboratory methods for the preparation of ketones are based on the use of organometallic compounds.

5. **Ketones from Lithium Dialkylcuprates.** When an ether solution of a lithium dialkylcuprate is treated with an acyl chloride at $-78\ °C$, the product is a ketone. This ketone synthesis is a variation of the Corey–Posner, Whitesides–House alkane synthesis (Section 4.15C).

General Reaction

$$R_2CuLi \ + R'-\underset{\underset{O}{\|}}{C}-Cl \longrightarrow R'-\underset{\underset{O}{\|}}{C}-R$$

| **Lithium dialkylcuprate** | **Acyl chloride** | **Ketone** |

Specific Example

(81%)

6. **Ketones from the Reaction of Nitriles with RMgX or RLi.** Treating a nitrile $(R-C\equiv N)$ with either a Grignard reagent or an organolithium reagent followed by hydrolysis yields a ketone.

General Reactions

$$R-C\equiv N + R'-MgX \longrightarrow R-\underset{\underset{N^-MgX^+}{\|}}{C}-R' \xrightarrow{H_3O^+} R-\underset{\underset{O}{\|}}{C}-R' + NH_4^+ + Mg^{2+} + X^-$$

$$R-C\equiv N + R'-Li \longrightarrow R-\underset{\underset{N^-Li^+}{\|}}{C}-R' \xrightarrow{H_3O^+} R-\underset{\underset{O}{\|}}{C}-R' + NH_4^+ + Li^+$$

Specific Examples

$$C_6H_5-C\equiv N + CH_3CH_2CH_2CH_2Li \xrightarrow[\text{(2) } H_3O^+]{\text{(1) diethyl ether}} C_6H_5-\underset{\underset{O}{\|}}{C}-CH_2CH_2CH_2CH_3$$

$$CH_3\underset{\underset{CH_3}{|}}{CH}-C\equiv N + C_6H_5MgBr \xrightarrow[\text{(2) } H_3O^+]{\text{(1) diethyl ether}} CH_3\underset{\underset{CH_3}{|}}{CH}-\underset{\underset{O}{\|}}{C}-C_6H_5$$

Even though a nitrile has a triple bond, addition of the Grignard or lithium reagent takes place only once. The reason: If addition took place twice, this would place a double negative charge on the nitrogen:

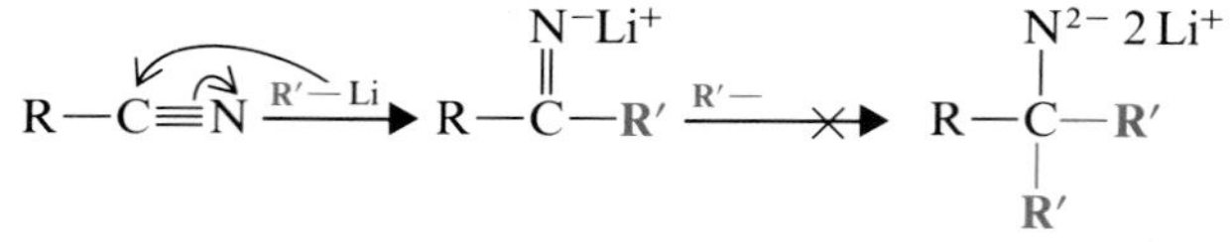

$$R-C\equiv N \xrightarrow{R'-Li} \underset{\substack{\| \\ N^-Li^+}}{R-C-R'} \xrightarrow{R'^-} \underset{\substack{| \\ R'}}{\overset{N^{2-}\,2\,Li^+}{R-C-R'}}$$

(does not form)

Sample Problem

Illustrating a Multistep Synthesis

With 1-butanol as your only organic starting compound, outline a synthesis of 5-nonanone.

Answer:

5-Nonanone can be synthesized by adding butylmagnesium bromide to the following nitrile.

Analysis:

$$CH_3CH_2CH_2CH_2-\overset{\overset{O}{\|}}{C}\!\!+\!\!CH_2CH_2CH_2CH_3 \Longrightarrow CH_3CH_2CH_2CH_2-\overset{\delta+\,\,\delta-}{C\equiv N:}$$
$$+ \overset{\delta+\,\,\,\,\delta-}{BrMg-CH_2CH_2CH_2CH_3}$$

Synthesis

$$CH_3CH_2CH_2CH_2C\equiv N + CH_3CH_2CH_2CH_2\,MgBr \xrightarrow[(2)\ H_3O^+]{}$$

$$\underset{\textbf{5-Nonanone}}{CH_3(CH_2)_3\overset{\overset{O}{\|}}{C}(CH_2)_3CH_3}$$

The nitrile can be synthesized from butyl bromide and sodium cyanide in an S_N2 reaction.

$$CH_3CH_2CH_2CH_2\,Br + NaCN \longrightarrow CH_3CH_2CH_2CH_2C\equiv N + NaBr$$

Butyl bromide also can be used to prepare the Grignard reagent.

$$CH_3CH_2CH_2CH_2\,Br + Mg \xrightarrow[\text{diethyl ether}]{} CH_3CH_2CH_2CH_2\,MgBr$$

And, finally, butyl bromide can be prepared from 1-butanol.

$$CH_3CH_2CH_2CH_2OH \xrightarrow{PBr_3} CH_3CH_2CH_2CH_2\,Br$$

Problem 16.4

Which reagents would you use to carry out each of the following reactions?

(a) Benzene $\longrightarrow$ bromobenzene $\longrightarrow$ phenylmagnesium bromide $\longrightarrow$
   benzyl alcohol $\longrightarrow$ benzaldehyde

(b) Toluene $\longrightarrow$ benzoic acid $\longrightarrow$ benzoyl chloride $\longrightarrow$ benzaldehyde

(c) Ethyl bromide $\longrightarrow$ 1-butyne $\longrightarrow$ 2-butanone

(d) 2-Butyne $\longrightarrow$ 2-butanone

(e) 1-Phenylethanol $\longrightarrow$ acetophenone

(f) Benzene $\longrightarrow$ acetophenone

(g) Benzoyl chloride $\longrightarrow$ acetophenone

(h) Benzoic acid $\longrightarrow$ acetophenone

(i) Benzyl bromide $\longrightarrow$ $C_6H_5CH_2CN$ $\longrightarrow$ 1-phenyl-2-butanone

(j) $C_6H_5CH_2CN$ $\longrightarrow$ 2-phenylethanal

(k) $CH_3(CH_2)_4CO_2CH_3$ $\longrightarrow$ hexanal

16.6 NUCLEOPHILIC ADDITION TO THE CARBON-OXYGEN DOUBLE BOND

One highly characteristic reaction of aldehydes and ketones is *nucleophilic addition* to the carbon-oxygen double bond.

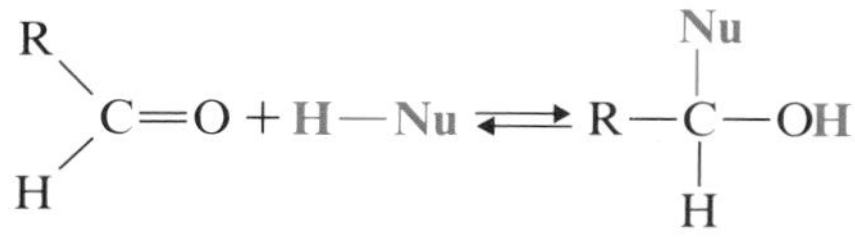

$$\underset{H}{\overset{R}{>}}C=O + H-Nu \rightleftharpoons R-\underset{H}{\overset{Nu}{\underset{|}{\overset{|}{C}}}}-OH$$

Specific Examples

$$\underset{H}{\overset{H_3C}{>}}C=O + H-OCH_2CH_3 \rightleftharpoons CH_3-\underset{H}{\overset{OCH_2CH_3}{\underset{|}{\overset{|}{C}}}}-OH$$

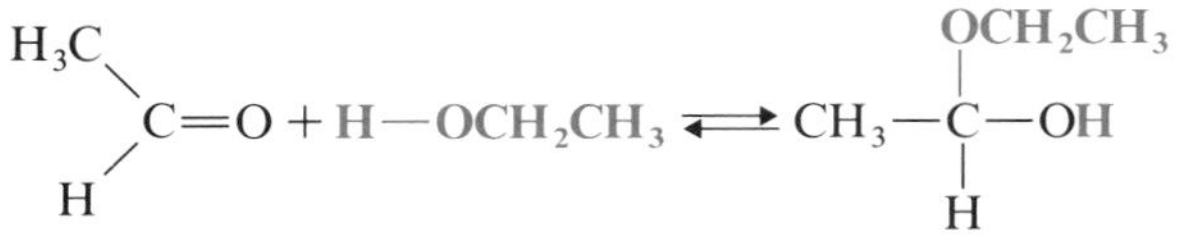

(a hemiacetal, see
Section 16.7)

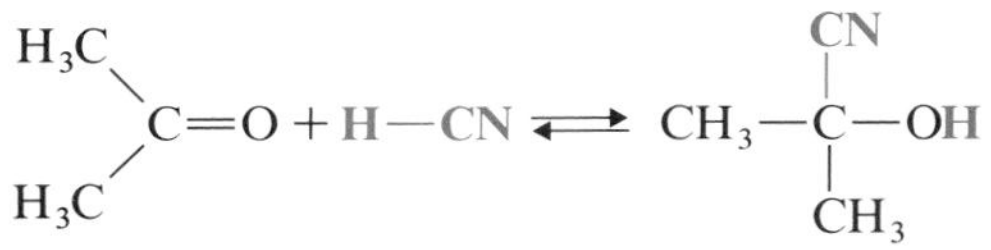

$$\underset{H_3C}{\overset{H_3C}{>}}C=O + H-CN \rightleftharpoons CH_3-\underset{CH_3}{\overset{CN}{\underset{|}{\overset{|}{C}}}}-OH$$

(a cyanohydrin, see
Section 16.9)

Aldehydes and ketones are especially susceptible to nucleophilic addition because of the structural features that we discussed in Section 11.1 and which are shown below.

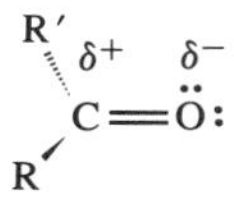

$$\underset{R}{\overset{R'}{>}}C \overset{\delta+}{=} \overset{\delta-}{\ddot{O}}:$$

Aldehyde or ketone
(R or R′ may be H)

The trigonal planar arrangement of groups around the carbonyl carbon atom means that the carbonyl carbon atom is relatively open to attack from above or below. The positive charge on the carbonyl carbon atom means that it is especially susceptible to attack by a nucleophile. The negative charge on the carbonyl oxygen atom means that nucleophilic addition is susceptible to acid catalysis. We can visualize nucleophilic addition to the carbon–oxygen double bond occurring in either of two general ways:

1. When the reagent is a particularly strong nucleophile, addition will usually take place in the following way:

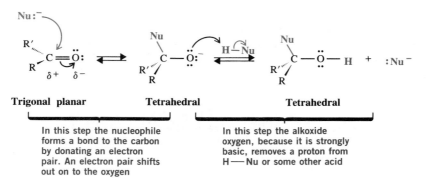

| Trigonal planar | Tetrahedral | Tetrahedral |

In this step the nucleophile forms a bond to the carbon by donating an electron pair. An electron pair shifts out on to the oxygen

In this step the alkoxide oxygen, because it is strongly basic, removes a proton from H——Nu or some other acid

In this type of addition the nucleophile uses its electron pair to form a bond to the carbonyl carbon atom. As this happens an electron pair of the carbon–oxygen π bond shifts out to the carbonyl oxygen atom and the hybridization state of the carbon changes from sp^2 to sp^3. ***The important aspect of this step is the ability of the carbonyl oxygen atom to accommodate the electron pair of the carbon–oxygen double bond.***

In the second step the oxygen atom accepts a proton. This happens because the oxygen atom is now much more basic; it carries a full negative charge, and it is an alkoxide ion.

2. A second general mechanism that operates in nucleophilic additions to carbon–oxygen double bonds is an acid-catalyzed mechanism:

In this step an electron pair of the carbonyl oxygen accepts a proton from the acid (or associates with a Lewis acid), producing an oxonium ion. Because one resonance structure of the oxonium ion has a full positive charge on the carbon, the carbon is more susceptible to nucleophilic attack

In the first of these two steps, the oxonium ion accepts the electron pair of the nucleophile. In the second step, a base removes a proton from the positively charged atom, regenerating the acid

This mechanism operates when carbonyl compounds are treated with *strong acids* in the presence of *weak nucleophiles.* In the first step the acid donates a proton to an electron pair of the carbonyl oxygen atom. The resulting protonated carbonyl compound, an **oxonium ion,** * is highly reactive toward nucleophilic attack at the carbonyl carbon atom because the carbonyl carbon atom carries more positive charge than it does in the unprotonated compound.

16.6A REVERSIBILITY OF NUCLEOPHILIC ADDITIONS TO THE CARBON–OXYGEN DOUBLE BOND

Many nucleophilic additions to carbon–oxygen double bonds are reversible; the overall results of these reactions will depend, therefore, on the position of an equilibrium. This behavior contrasts markedly with most electrophilic additions to carbon–carbon double bonds and with nucleophilic substitutions at saturated carbon atoms. The latter reactions are essentially irreversible, and overall results are a function of relative reaction rates.

16.6B SUBSEQUENT REACTIONS OF ADDITION PRODUCTS

Nucleophilic addition to a carbon–oxygen double bond may lead to a product that is stable under the reaction conditions that we employ. If this is the case we are then able to isolate products with the following general structure:

$$\begin{array}{c} R \quad\; Nu \\ \diagdown\;\diagup \\ C \\ \diagup\;\diagdown \\ R \quad\; OH \end{array}$$

In other reactions the product formed initially may be unstable and may spontaneously undergo subsequent reactions. Even if the initial addition product is stable, however, we may deliberately bring about a subsequent reaction by changing the reaction conditions. When we begin our study of specific reactions, we shall see that one common subsequent reaction is an *elimination reaction,* especially *dehydration.*

Problem 16.5

The reaction of an aldehyde or ketone with a Grignard reagent (Section 11.8) is a nucleophilic addition to the carbon–oxygen double bond. (a) What is the nucleophile? (b) The magnesium portion of the Grignard reagent plays an important part in this reaction. What is its function? (c) What product is formed initially? (d) What product forms when water is added?

Problem 16.6

The reactions of aldehydes and ketones with $LiAlH_4$ and $NaBH_4$ (Section 11.3) are nucleophilic additions to the carbonyl group. What is the nucleophile in these reactions?

---

* Any compound containing a positively charged oxygen atom that forms three covalent bonds is an *oxonium ion.*

16.7 THE ADDITION OF WATER AND ALCOHOLS: HYDRATES, ACETALS, AND KETALS

16.7A ALDEHYDE HYDRATES: *GEM*-DIOLS

Dissolving an aldehyde such as acetaldehyde in water causes the establishment of an equilibrium between the aldehyde and its **hydrate.** This hydrate is in actuality a 1,1-diol, called a *gem*-diol.

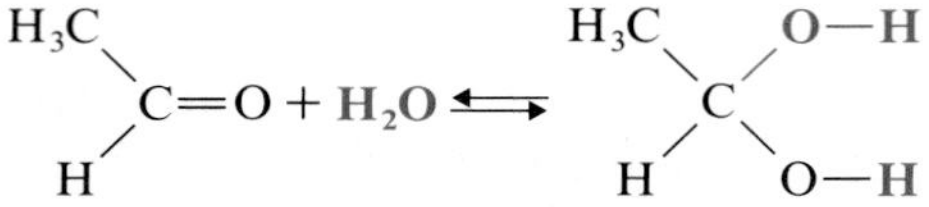

Acetaldehyde — Hydrate (a *gem*-diol)

The *gem*-diol results from a nucleophilic addition of water to the carbonyl group of the aldehyde:

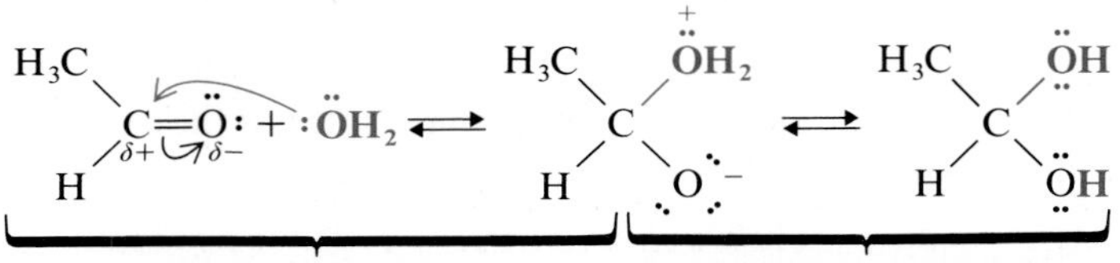

In this step water attacks the carbonyl carbon atom

In two steps a proton is lost from the positive oxygen atom and a proton is gained at the negative oxygen atom

Problem 16.7

Dissolving formaldehyde in water leads to a solution containing primarily the *gem*-diol, $CH_2(OH)_2$. Show the steps in its formation from formaldehyde.

The addition of water is subject to catalysis by both acids and bases. That is, addition takes place much more rapidly in the presence of small amounts of acids or bases than it does in pure water.

The mechanism for the **base-catalyzed reaction** is as follows:

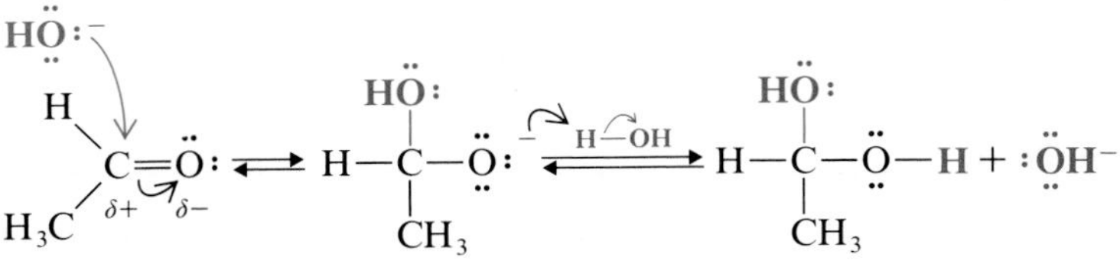

The important factor here in increasing the rate is the greater nucleophilicity of the hydroxide ion when compared to water.

The **acid-catalyzed mechanism** involves an initial rapid protonation of the carbonyl oxygen atom:

Protonation makes the carbonyl carbon atom more susceptible to attack by water, and here this factor is the key to the rate acceleration.

Problem 16.8

When acetone is dissolved in water containing ^{18}O instead of ordinary ^{16}O (i.e., $H_2{}^{18}O$ instead of $H_2{}^{16}O$), the acetone soon begins to acquire ^{18}O and becomes

$$CH_3\overset{\overset{\displaystyle ^{18}O}{\|}}{C}CH_3.$$

The formation of this oxygen-labeled acetone is catalyzed by traces of strong acids and by strong bases (e.g., OH^-). Show the steps that explain both the acid-catalyzed reaction and the base-catalyzed reaction.

The equilibrium for the addition of water to most ketones is unfavorable, whereas some aldehydes (e. g., formaldehyde) exist primarily as the *gem*-diol in aqueous solution.

It is not possible to isolate most *gem*-diols from the aqueous solutions in which they are formed. Evaporation of the water, for example, simply displaces the overall equilibrium to the left and the *gem*-diol (or hydrate) reverts to the carbonyl compound.

Compounds with strong electron-withdrawing groups attached to the carbonyl group can form stable *gem*-diols. An example is the compound called chloral hydrate.

Chloral hydrate

16.7B HEMIACETALS AND HEMIKETALS

Dissolving an aldehyde in an alcohol causes the establishment of an equilibrium between these two compounds and a new compound called a **hemiacetal:**

Aldehyde   Alcohol   Hemiacetal
                                              (usually too unstable to isolate)

In this step the alcohol   In two steps a proton is lost
attacks the carbonyl carbon   from the positive oxygen and a
                                    proton is gained at the negative
                                    oxygen

The essential structural features of a hemiacetal are an —OH and an —OR group attached to the same carbon atom (and since this carbon atom came from an aldehyde, the carbon also has one hydrogen atom attached to it).

Most open-chain hemiacetals are not sufficiently stable to allow their isolation. Cyclic hemiacetals with five- or six-membered rings, however, are usually much more stable:

Most simple sugars (Chapter 22) exist primarily in a cyclic hemiacetal form. Glucose is an example:

(+)-Glucose
(a cyclic hemiacetal)

Ketones undergo similar reactions when they are dissolved in an alcohol. The products (also unstable in open-chain compounds) are called **hemiketals.**

Ketone   Hemiketal

The formation of hemiacetals and hemiketals is also catalyzed by acids and bases:

Acid-Catalyzed Hemiacetal Formation

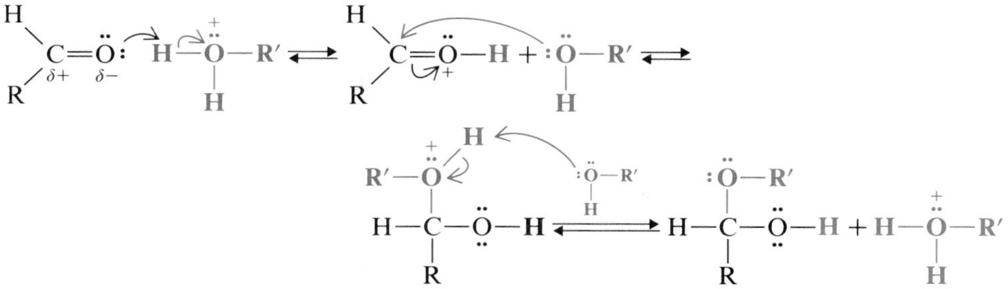

Base-Catalyzed Hemiacetal Formation

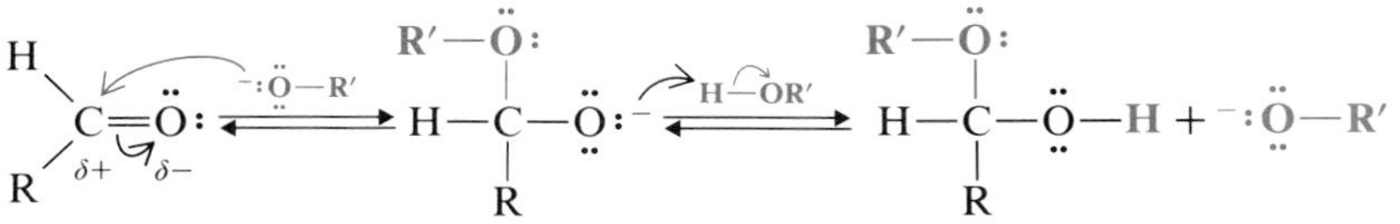

16.7C ACETALS AND CYCLIC KETALS

If we take an alcohol solution of an aldehyde (or ketone) and pass into it a small amount of gaseous HCl the hemiacetal (or hemiketal) forms, and then a second reaction takes place. The hemiacetal (or hemiketal) reacts with a second molar equivalent of the alcohol to produce an **acetal** (or **ketal**). An acetal or ketal has two —OR groups attached to the same carbon atom.

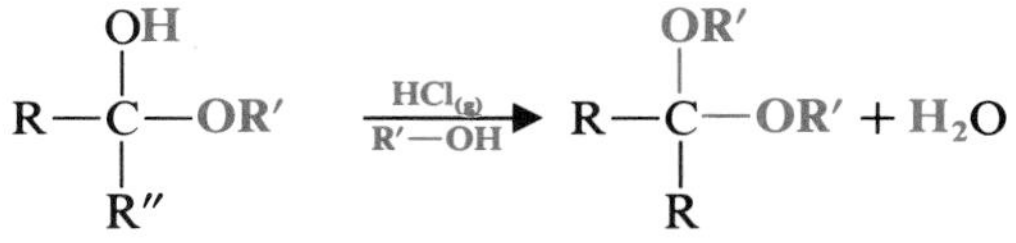

Hemiacetal (R″=H)
or Hemiketal

An acetal (R″=H)
or Ketal

Problem 16.9

Shown below is the structural formula for sucrose (table sugar). Sucrose has an acetal grouping and a ketal grouping. Identify these.

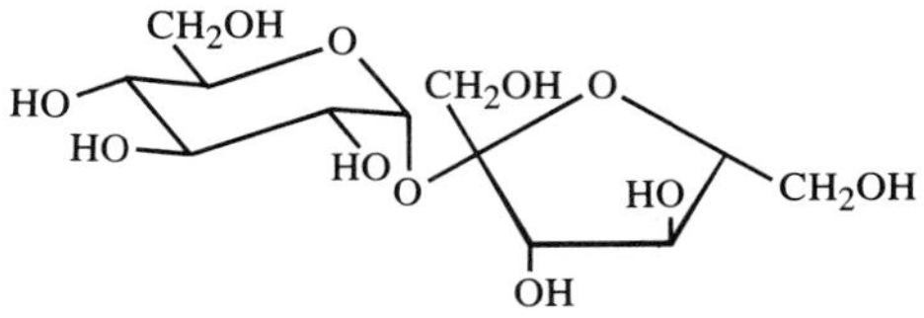

Sucrose

The mechanism for acetal (or ketal) formation involves acid-catalyzed formation of the hemiacetal (or hemiketal), then an acid-catalyzed elimination of water, followed by a second *addition* of the alcohol and loss of a proton.

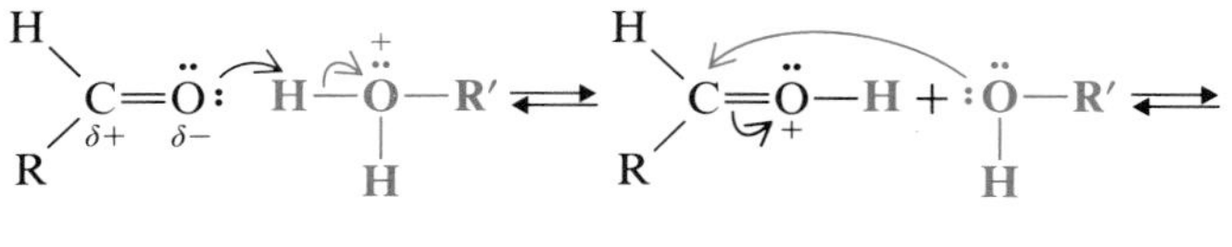

Acid-catalyzed formation of a hemiacetal

Acid-catalyzed elimination of water

Reaction with a second molecule of the alcohol

Problem 16.10

Write out all the steps (as just shown) for the formation of an acetal from benzaldehyde and methanol in the presence of an acid catalyst.

All steps in the formation of an acetal from an aldehyde are reversible. If we dissolve an aldehyde in a large excess of an anhydrous alcohol and add a small amount of an anhydrous acid (e.g., gaseous HCl or concd. H_2SO_4), the equilibrium will strongly favor the formation of an acetal. After the equilibrium is established, we can isolate the acetal by neutralizing the acid and evaporating the excess alcohol.

If we then place the acetal in water and add a small amount of acid, all of the steps reverse. Under these conditions (an excess of water), the equilibrium favors the formation of the aldehyde. The acetal undergoes *hydrolysis.*

Acetal   **Aldehyde**

Ketal formation is not favored when ketones are treated with simple alcohols and gaseous HCl. Cyclic ketal formation *is* favored, however, when a ketone is treated with an excess of a 1,2-diol and a trace of acid.

(excess)   **Cyclic ketal**

16.7 THE ADDITION OF WATER AND ALCOHOLS: HYDRATES, ACETALS, AND KETALS

This reaction, too, can be reversed by treating the ketal with aqueous acid.

$$\underset{R}{\overset{R}{>}}C\underset{O-CH_2}{\overset{O-CH_2}{<}} + H_2O \underset{}{\overset{H^+}{\rightleftharpoons}} \underset{R}{\overset{R}{>}}C=O + \underset{CH_2OH}{\overset{CH_2OH}{|}}$$

Problem 16.11

Outline all steps in the mechanism for the formation of a cyclic ketal from acetone and ethylene glycol in the presence of gaseous HCl.

16.7D ACETALS AND CYCLIC KETALS AS PROTECTING GROUPS

Although acetals and cyclic ketals are hydrolyzed to aldehydes and ketones in aqueous acid, *they are stable in basic solutions.*

$$\underset{H}{\overset{R}{>}}C\underset{OR'}{\overset{OR'}{<}} + H_2O \xrightarrow{OH^-} \text{no reaction}$$

$$\underset{R}{\overset{R}{>}}C\underset{O-CH_2}{\overset{O-CH_2}{<}} + H_2O \xrightarrow{OH^-} \text{no reaction}$$

Because of this property, acetals and ketals give us a convenient method for protecting aldehyde and ketone groups from undesired reactions in basic solutions. (Acetals and ketals are really *gem*-diethers and, like ethers, they are relatively unreactive toward bases.) We can convert an aldehyde or ketone to an acetal or cyclic ketal, carry out a reaction on some other part of the molecule, and then hydrolyze the acetal or ketal with aqueous acid.

As an example, let us consider the problem of converting

$$\underset{\textbf{A}}{\text{O} \diagdown \text{COC}_2\text{H}_5} \quad \text{to} \quad \underset{\textbf{B}}{\text{O} \diagdown \text{CH}_2\text{OH}}$$

Keto groups are more easily reduced than ester groups. Any reducing agent (e.g., LiAlH$_4$ or H$_2$/Ni) that will reduce the ester group of **A** will reduce the keto group as well. But if we "protect" the keto group by converting it to a cyclic ketal (the ester group does not react), we can reduce the ester group in basic solution without affecting the cyclic ketal. After we finish the ester reduction, we can hydrolyze the cyclic ketal and obtain our desired product, **B**.

$$\text{O} \diagdown \text{COC}_2\text{H}_5 \xrightarrow[\text{CH}_2\text{OHCH}_2\text{OH}]{\text{H}^+} \text{[cyclic ketal]COC}_2\text{H}_5 \xrightarrow[\substack{(C_2H_5)_2O \\ (2)\ H_2O}]{(1)\ \text{LiAlH}_4}$$

$$\text{[cyclic ketal]CH}_2\text{OH} \xrightarrow[\text{H}_2\text{O}]{\text{H}^+} \text{O} \diagdown \text{CH}_2\text{OH}$$

Problem 16.12

What product would be obtained if **A** were treated with lithium aluminum hydride without first converting it to a cyclic ketal?

Problem 16.13

(a) Show how you might use a cyclic ketal in carrying out the following transformation:

(b) Why would a direct addition of methylmagnesium bromide to **A** fail to give **C**?

Problem 16.14

Dihydropyran reacts readily with an alcohol in the presence of a trace of anhydrous HCl or H_2SO_4 to form a tetrahydropyranyl ether.

Dihydropyran **Tetrahydropyranyl ether**

(a) Write a plausible mechanism for this reaction. (b) Tetrahydropyranyl ethers are stable in aqueous base but hydrolyze rapidly in aqueous acid to yield the original alcohol and another compound. Explain. (What is the other compound?) (c) The tetrahydropyranyl group can be used as a protecting group for alcohols and phenols. Show how you might use it in a synthesis of 5-methyl-1,5-hexanediol starting with 4-chloro-1-butanol.

16.7E THIOACETALS AND THIOKETALS:

$$\overset{O}{\overset{\|}{R C R'}} \longrightarrow RCH_2R'$$

Aldehydes and ketones react with thiols to form *thioacetals* and *thioketals*.

Thioacetal

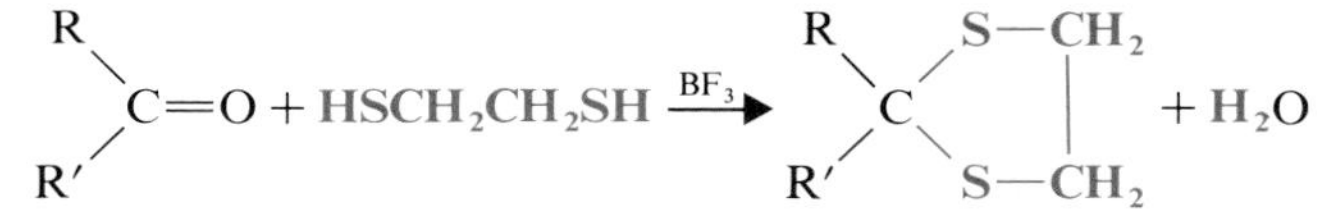

$$\underset{R'}{\overset{R}{\diagdown}}C=O + HSCH_2CH_2SH \xrightarrow{BF_3} \underset{R'}{\overset{R}{\diagdown}}C\underset{S-CH_2}{\overset{S-CH_2}{\diagup}} + H_2O$$

Cyclic thioketal

Thioacetals and thioketals are important in organic synthesis because they react with Raney nickel to yield hydrocarbons.* These reactions (i.e., thioacetal or thioketal formation and subsequent "desulfurization") give us an additional method for

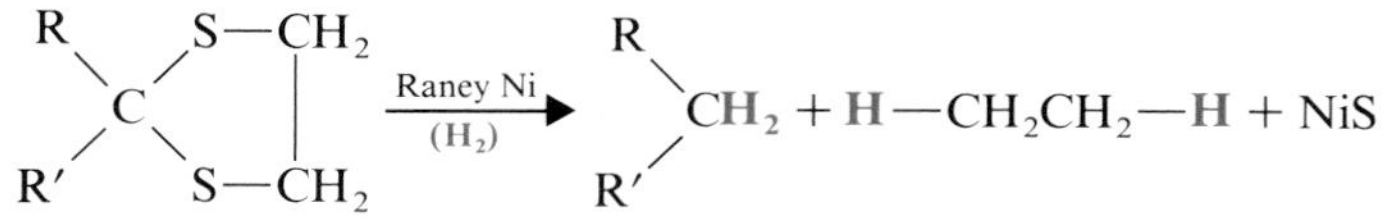

$$\underset{R'}{\overset{R}{\diagdown}}C\underset{S-CH_2}{\overset{S-CH_2}{\diagup}} \xrightarrow[(H_2)]{Raney\ Ni} \underset{R'}{\overset{R}{\diagdown}}CH_2 + H-CH_2CH_2-H + NiS$$

converting carbonyl groups of aldehydes and ketones to $-CH_2-$ groups. The other method we have studied is the **Clemmensen reduction** (Section 15.9). In the next section (16.8C), we shall see how this can also be accomplished with the **Wolff–Kishner reduction.**

Problem 16.15

Show how you might use thioacetal and thioketal formation and Raney nickel desulfurization to convert: (a) cyclohexanone to cyclohexane and (b) benzaldehyde to toluene.

16.8 THE ADDITION OF DERIVATIVES OF AMMONIA

Aldehydes and ketones react with a number of derivatives of ammonia in the general way shown in the following sequence:

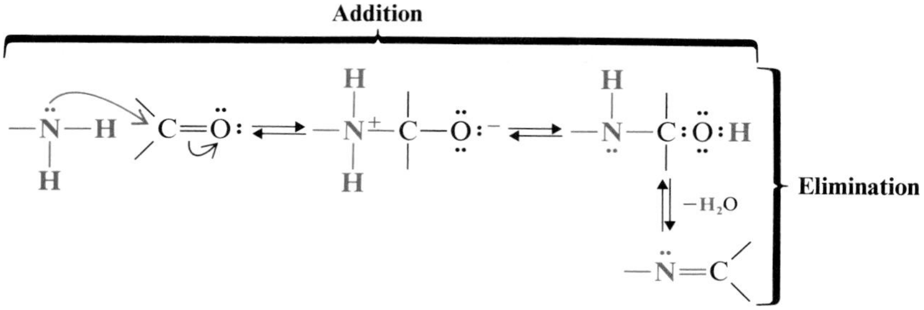

Addition

$$-\overset{\overset{H}{|}}{\underset{H}{N}}-H \quad C=\overset{..}{\overset{..}{O}}: \rightleftarrows -\overset{\overset{H}{|}}{\underset{H}{N}}{}^{+}-\overset{|}{C}-\overset{..}{\overset{..}{O}}:^{-} \rightleftarrows -\overset{\overset{H}{|}}{N}-\overset{|}{C}:\overset{..}{O}:H$$

Elimination

$$\Big\updownarrow -H_2O$$

$$-\overset{..}{N}=C\diagup$$

Table 16.2 lists several important examples of this general reaction.

16.8A 2,4-DINITROPHENYLHYDRAZONES, SEMICARBAZONES, AND OXIMES

The products of the reactions of aldehydes and ketones with 2,4-dinitrophenylhydrazine, semicarbazide, and hydroxylamine are often used to identify unknown alde-

---

*Raney nickel is a special nickel catalyst that contains adsorbed hydrogen.

TABLE 16.2 Reactions of aldehydes and ketones with derivatives of ammonia

1. Reaction with Hydroxylamine

General Reaction

$$\text{\Large$\diagdown$}C=O \; + \; H_2N-OH \longrightarrow \text{\Large$\diagdown$}C=N-OH + H_2O$$

Aldehyde or   Hydroxylamine   An oxime
ketone

Specific Example

$$\begin{array}{c} H_3C \\ \diagdown \\ \diagup \\ H \end{array} C=O + H_2NOH \longrightarrow \begin{array}{c} H_3C \\ \diagdown \\ \diagup \\ H \end{array} C=NOH + H_2O$$

Acetaldehyde   Acetaldoxime

2. Reactions with Hydrazine, Phenylhydrazine, and 2,4-Dinitrophenylhydrazine

General Reactions

Aldehyde or ketone

$$\text{\Large$\diagdown$}C=O + H_2NNH_2 \longrightarrow \text{\Large$\diagdown$}C=NNH_2 + H_2O$$

Hydrazine   A hydrazone

$$\text{\Large$\diagdown$}C=O + H_2NNHC_6H_5 \longrightarrow \text{\Large$\diagdown$}C=NNHC_6H_5 + H_2O$$

Phenylhydrazine   A phenylhydrazone

$$\text{\Large$\diagdown$}C=O + H_2NNH-\!\!\bigcirc\!\!-NO_2 \longrightarrow \text{\Large$\diagdown$}C=NNH-\!\!\bigcirc\!\!-NO_2 + H_2O$$

$$\overset{\displaystyle NO_2}{} \qquad\qquad \overset{\displaystyle NO_2}{}$$

2,4-Dinitrophenylhydrazine   A 2,4-dinitrophenylhydrazone

Specific Examples

$$\begin{array}{c} C_6H_5 \\ \diagdown \\ \diagup \\ CH_3CH_2 \end{array} C=O + H_2NNH_2 \xrightarrow{heat} \begin{array}{c} C_6H_5 \\ \diagdown \\ \diagup \\ CH_3CH_2 \end{array} C=NNH_2 + H_2O$$

Propiophenone   Propiophenone hydrazone

$$\begin{array}{c} C_6H_5 \\ \diagdown \\ \diagup \\ H_3C \end{array} C=O + H_2NNHC_6H_5 \xrightarrow[CH_3CO_2H]{H_3O^+} \begin{array}{c} C_6H_5 \\ \diagdown \\ \diagup \\ H_3C \end{array} C=NNHC_6H_5 + H_2O$$

Acetophenone   Acetophenone phenylhydrazone

TABLE 16.2   (continued)

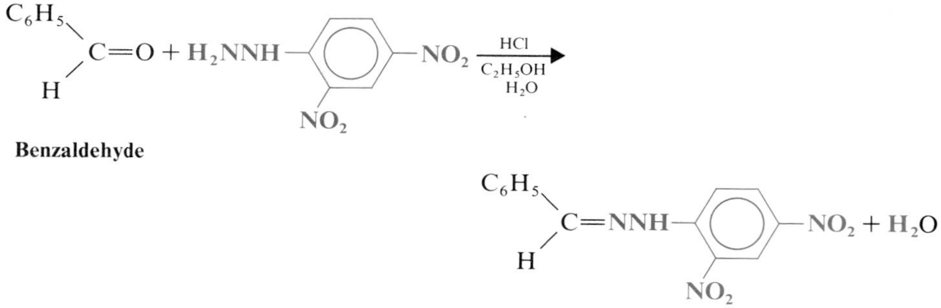

Benzaldehyde

Benzaldehyde
2,4-dinitrophenylhydrazone

3. Reaction with Semicarbazide

General Reaction

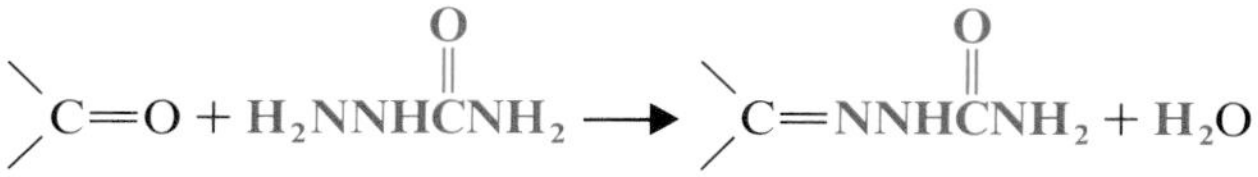

Aldehyde   **Semicarbazide**   **A semicarbazone**
or ketone

Specific Example

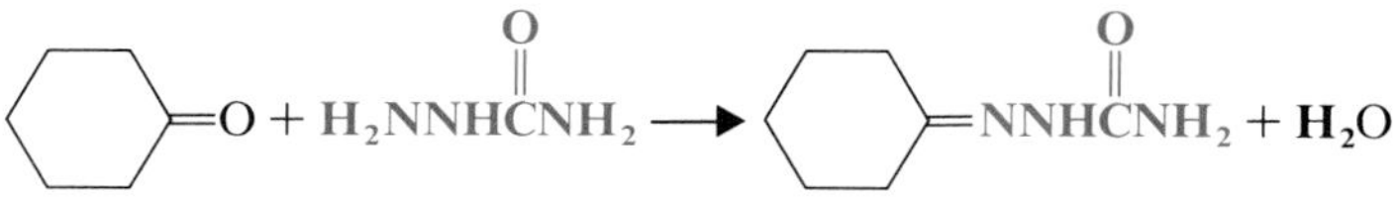

Cyclohexanone
semicarbazone

hydes and ketones. These compounds, that is, 2,4-dinitrophenylhydrazones, semi-carbazones, and oximes, are usually relatively insoluble solids that have sharp characteristic melting points. Table 16.3 gives representative examples from the very extensive tables of these derivatives.

TABLE 16.3   Derivatives of aldehydes and ketone

ALDEHYDE OR KETONE	mp (°C) OF 2,4-DINITRO-PHENYLHYDRAZONE	mp (°C) OF SEMICARBAZONE	mp (°C) OF OXIME
Acetaldehyde	168.5	162	46.5
Acetone	128	187 dec	61
Benzaldehyde	237	222	35
o-Tolualdehyde	195	208	49
m-Tolualdehyde	211	204	60
p-Tolualdehyde	233	234	79
Phenylacetaldehyde	121	156	103

16.8B IMINES AND ENAMINES

Aldehydes and ketones react with primary amines to form **imines**. (Such N-substituted imines are also called Schiff bases.)

$$CH_3\overset{\overset{\displaystyle H}{|}}{C}{=}O + H_2\ddot{N}{-}CH_3 \xrightarrow[\substack{Na_2SO_4 \\ (-H_2O)}]{\text{diethyl ether}} CH_3\overset{\overset{\displaystyle H}{|}}{C}{=}\ddot{N}CH_3$$

Acetaldehyde	Methylamine	Acetaldimine
		(an imine)
		(40%)

     Imines are important in many biochemical reactions because many enzymes use an $-NH_2$ group of an amino acid to react with an aldehyde or ketone to form an imine linkage.

     Imines are also formed as intermediates in a useful synthesis of amines (Section 19.5).

16.8C HYDRAZONES: THE WOLFF–KISHNER REDUCTION

Hydrazones are occasionally used to identify aldehydes and ketones. But unlike 2,4-dinitrophenylhydrazones, simple hydrazones often have low melting points. Hydrazones, however, are the basis for a useful method to reduce carbonyl groups of aldehydes and ketones to $-CH_2-$ groups, called the **Wolff–Kishner reduction:**

$$\overset{\diagdown}{\underset{\diagup}{C}}{=}\ddot{O}: + H_2N{-}NH_2 \xrightarrow[\text{heat}]{\text{base}} \left[\overset{\diagdown}{\underset{\diagup}{C}}{=}N{-}NH_2 \right] + H_2O$$

Aldehyde	Hydrazone
or ketone	(not isolated)

$$\downarrow$$

$$\overset{\diagdown}{\underset{\diagup}{C}}H_2 + N_2$$

Specific Example

$$\text{C}_6\text{H}_5{-}\overset{\overset{\displaystyle O}{\|}}{C}CH_2CH_3 + H_2NNH_2 \xrightarrow[\substack{\text{triethylene glycol} \\ 200\ °C}]{\text{NaOH}} \text{C}_6\text{H}_5{-}CH_2CH_2CH_3$$

(82%)

     The Wolff–Kishner reduction can be accomplished at much lower temperatures if dimethyl sulfoxide is used as the solvent.

     The Wolff–Kishner reduction complements the Clemmensen reduction (Section 15.9) and the reduction of thioacetals (Section 16.7E), because all three reactions convert $\overset{\diagdown}{\underset{\diagup}{C}}{=}O$ groups into $-CH_2-$ groups. The Clemmensen reduction takes place in strongly acidic media and can be used for those compounds that are sensitive to base. The Wolff–Kishner reduction takes place in strongly basic solutions and can be used for those compounds that are sensitive to acid. The reduction of thioacetals takes place in neutral solution and can be used for compounds that are sensitive to both acids and bases.

The mechanism of the Wolff–Kishner reduction is as follows. The first step is the formation of the hydrazone. Then the strong base brings about an isomerization of the hydrazone to a derivative with the structure $\overset{\diagdown}{\underset{\diagup}{}}\text{CH}-\text{N}{=}\text{NH}$. This derivative then undergoes the base-catalyzed elimination of a molecule of nitrogen. The loss of the especially stable molecule of nitrogen provides the driving force for the reaction.

1. $-\underset{|}{\overset{|}{\text{C}}}{=}\text{O} + \text{H}_2\text{N}-\text{NH}_2 \rightleftharpoons -\underset{|}{\overset{|}{\text{C}}}{=}\text{N}-\text{NH}_2 + \text{H}_2\text{O}$

2. $-\underset{|}{\overset{|}{\text{C}}}{=}\text{N}-\text{NH}_2 \underset{\text{H}_2\text{O}}{\overset{\text{OH}^-}{\rightleftharpoons}} \left[-\underset{|}{\overset{|}{\text{C}}}{=}\text{N}-\ddot{\text{N}}\text{H} \longleftrightarrow -\underset{|}{\overset{|}{\ddot{\text{C}}}}-\text{N}{=}\text{NH} \right] \underset{\text{OH}^-}{\overset{\text{H}_2\text{O}}{\rightleftharpoons}}$

$-\underset{|}{\overset{\overset{\textstyle H}{|}}{\text{C}}}-\text{N}{=}\text{N}-\text{H} \underset{\text{H}_2\text{O}}{\overset{\text{OH}^-}{\rightleftharpoons}} -\underset{|}{\overset{\overset{\textstyle H}{|}}{\text{C}}}-\text{N}{\overset{\curvearrowleft}{=}}\text{N}\colon^- \overset{-\text{N}_2}{\longrightarrow} -\underset{|}{\overset{\overset{\textstyle H}{|}}{\text{C}}}\colon^- \overset{\text{H}_2\text{O}}{\longrightarrow} -\underset{|}{\overset{\overset{\textstyle H}{|}}{\text{C}}}-\text{H}$

16.9 THE ADDITION OF HYDROGEN CYANIDE AND OF SODIUM BISULFITE

16.9A HYDROGEN CYANIDE ADDITION

Hydrogen cyanide adds to the carbonyl groups of aldehydes and most ketones to form compounds called **cyanohydrins.** Ketones in which the carbonyl group is highly hindered do not undergo this reaction.

$$\text{R}\overset{\overset{\textstyle O}{\|}}{\text{C}}\text{H} + \text{HCN} \rightleftharpoons \underset{\text{H}}{\overset{\text{R}}{\diagdown}}\text{C}\underset{\text{CN}}{\overset{\text{OH}}{\diagup}}$$

$$\text{R}-\overset{\overset{\textstyle O}{\|}}{\text{C}}-\text{R}' + \text{HCN} \rightleftharpoons \underset{\text{R}'}{\overset{\text{R}}{\diagdown}}\text{C}\underset{\text{CN}}{\overset{\text{OH}}{\diagup}}$$

Cyanohydrins

The addition of hydrogen cyanide itself takes place very slowly because HCN is a poor nucleophile. The addition of potassium cyanide, or any base that can generate cyanide ions from the weak acid HCN, causes a dramatic increase in the rate of reaction. This effect was discovered in 1903 by the British chemist Arthur Lapworth, and in his studies of the addition of HCN, Lapworth became one of the originators of the mechanistic view of organic chemistry. Lapworth assumed that the addition was ionic in nature (a remarkable insight considering that Lewis and Kössel's theories of bonding were some 13 years in the future).

He proposed "that the formation of cyanohydrins is to be represented as a comparatively slow union of the negative cyanide ion with carbonyl, followed by almost instantaneous combination of the complex with hydrogen."*

*A. Lapworth, *J. Chem. Soc.,* **1903,** *83,* 995. For a fine review of Lapworth's work see M. Saltzman, *J. Chem. Educ.,* **1972,** *49,* 750.

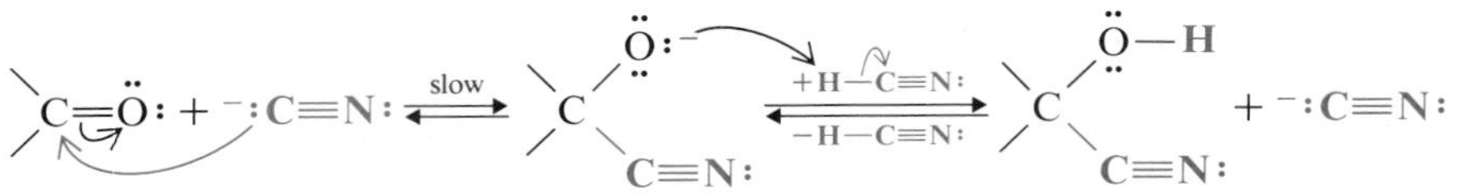

The cyanide ion, being a stronger nucleophile, is able to attack the carbonyl carbon atom much more rapidly than HCN itself and this is the source of its catalytic effect. Once the addition of cyanide ion has taken place, the strongly basic alkoxide oxygen atom of the intermediate removes a proton from any available acid. If this acid is HCN, this step regenerates the cyanide ion.

Bases stronger than cyanide ion catalyze the reaction by converting HCN ($pK_a \approx 9$) to cyanide ion in an acid–base reaction. The cyanide ions, thus formed, can go on to attack the carbonyl group.

Liquid hydrogen cyanide can be used for this reaction (HCN is a gas at room temperature), but since HCN is very toxic and volatile, it is safer to generate it in the reaction mixture. This can be done by mixing the aldehyde or ketone with aqueous sodium cyanide and then slowly adding sulfuric acid to the mixture. *Even with this procedure, however, great care must be taken and the reaction must be carried out in a very efficient fume hood.*

Cyanohydrins are useful intermediates in organic synthesis. Depending on the conditions used, acidic hydrolysis converts cyanohydrins to α-hydroxy acids or to α,β-unsaturated acids. (The mechanism for this hydrolysis is discussed in Section 18.8H.)

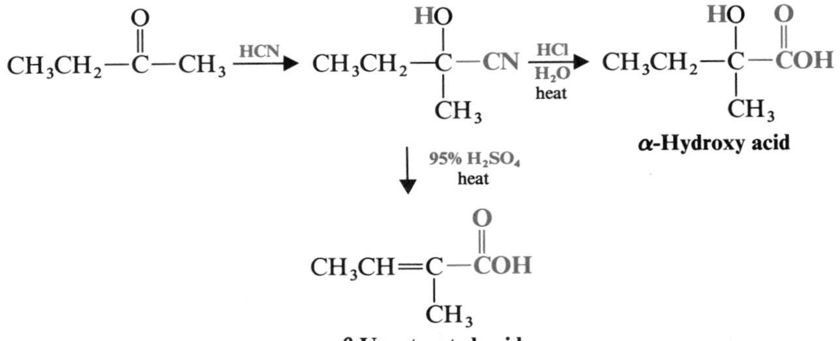

Reducing a cyanohydrin with lithium aluminum hydride gives a β-amino alcohol:

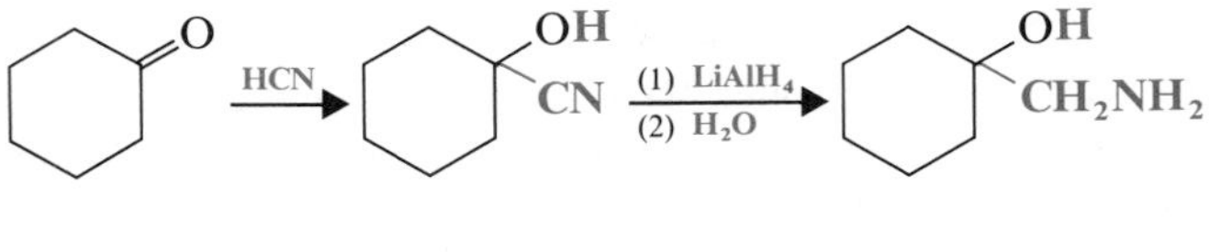

Problem 16.16

(a) Show how you might prepare lactic acid ($CH_3CHOHCO_2H$) from acetaldehyde through a cyanohydrin intermediate. (b) What stereoisomeric form of lactic acid would you expect to obtain?

16.9B SODIUM BISULFITE ADDITION

Sodium bisulfite ($NaHSO_3$) adds to a carbonyl group in a way that is very similar to the addition of HCN.

$$\underset{}{\overset{O}{\underset{}{\|}}}\diagdown C \diagup + \ ^-:SO_3H \underset{Na^+}{} \rightleftharpoons -\overset{:\ddot{O}:^- \ Na^+}{\underset{}{\overset{|}{\underset{|}{C}}}}-SO_3H \rightleftharpoons -\overset{:\ddot{O}-H}{\underset{}{\overset{|}{\underset{|}{C}}}}-SO_3^- \ Na^+$$

Bisulfite addition product

This reaction takes place with aldehydes and some ketones. Most aldehydes react with one molar equivalent of sodium bisulfite to give the addition product in 70–90% yield. Under the same conditions, methyl ketones give yields varying from 12 to 56%. Most higher ketones do not give bisulfite addition products in appreciable amounts because the addition is very sensitive to steric hindrance. However, since the reaction involves an equilibrium, yields from aldehydes and methyl ketones can be improved by using an excess of sodium bisulfite.

Because bisulfite addition compounds are crystalline salts, a bisulfite addition reaction is often used in separating aldehydes and methyl ketones from other substances. Since bisulfite addition is reversible, the aldehyde or methyl ketone can be regenerated   fter a separation has been made, by adding either an acid or a base. These additions displace the equilibrium to the left by converting the HSO_3^- ion to SO_2 (in acid) or to SO_3^{2-} (in base).

16.10 THE ADDITION OF YLIDES: THE WITTIG REACTION

Aldehydes and ketones react with phosphorus ylides to yield *alkenes* and triphenylphosphine oxide. (An ylide is a neutral molecule having a negative carbon adjacent to a positive heteroatom.) Phosphorus ylides are also called phosphoranes.

$$\underset{R'}{\overset{R}{\diagdown}} C=O + (C_6H_5)_3\overset{+}{P}-\overset{..}{\underset{R'''}{\overset{R''}{\underset{\diagup}{C\diagdown}}}} \longrightarrow \underset{R'}{\overset{R}{\diagdown}}C=C\underset{R'''}{\overset{R''}{\diagup}} + O=P(C_6H_5)_3$$

| **Aldehyde or ketone** | **Phosphorus ylide (or phosphorane)** | **Alkene** | **Triphenylphosphine oxide** |

This reaction, known as the **Wittig reaction,*** has proved to be a valuable method for synthesizing alkenes. The Wittig reaction is applicable to a wide variety of compounds, and although a mixture of (E) and (Z) isomers may result, the Wittig reaction gives a great advantage over most other alkene syntheses in that *no ambiguity exists as to the location of the double bond in the product.*

Phosphorus ylides are easily prepared from triphenylphosphine and alkyl halides. Their preparation involves two reactions:

---

*Discovered in 1954 by Georg Wittig, then at the University of Tübingen. Wittig was a co-winner of the Nobel prize for chemistry in 1979.

General Reaction

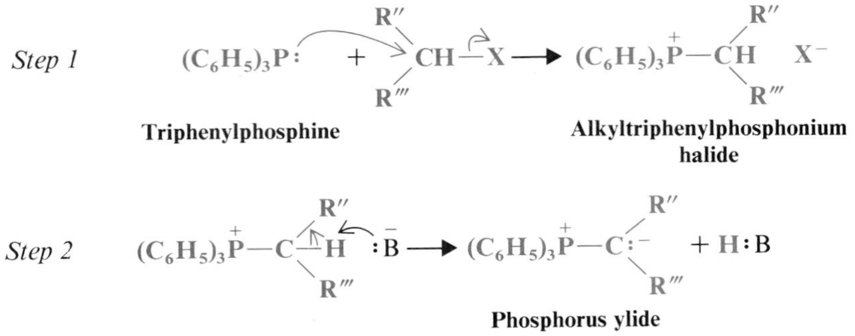

Step 1 $(C_6H_5)_3P\colon$ + $\overset{R''}{\underset{R'''}{>}}CH\overset{\frown}{-}X$ → $(C_6H_5)_3\overset{+}{P}-\overset{R''}{\underset{R'''}{CH}}$ X^-

Triphenylphosphine

Alkyltriphenylphosphonium
halide

Step 2 $(C_6H_5)_3\overset{+}{P}-\overset{R''}{\underset{R'''}{C}}\overset{\frown}{H}\ \colon\!\bar{B}$ → $(C_6H_5)_3\overset{+}{P}-\overset{R''}{\underset{R'''}{C}}\colon^-$ + $H\colon B$

Phosphorus ylide

Specific Example

Step 1 $(C_6H_5)_3P\colon + CH_3Br \xrightarrow{C_6H_6}$ $(C_6H_5)_3\overset{+}{P}-CH_3\ Br^-$

Methyltriphenylphosphonium
bromide
(89%)

Step 2 $(C_6H_5)_3\overset{+}{P}-CH_3 + C_6H_5Li \longrightarrow (C_6H_5)_3\overset{+}{P}-CH_2\colon^- + C_6H_6$
Br^- $+ LiBr$

The first reaction is a nucleophilic substitution reaction. Triphenylphosphine is an excellent nucleophile and a weak base. It reacts readily with 1° and 2° alkyl halides by an S_N2 mechanism to displace a halide ion from the alkyl halide to give an alkyltriphenylphosphonium salt. The second reaction is an acid–base reaction. A strong base (usually an alkyllithium or phenyllithium) removes a proton from the carbon that is attached to phosphorus to give the ylide.

Phosphorus ylides can be represented as a hybrid of the two resonance structures shown here. Quantum mechanical calculations indicate that the contribution made by the first structure is relatively unimportant.

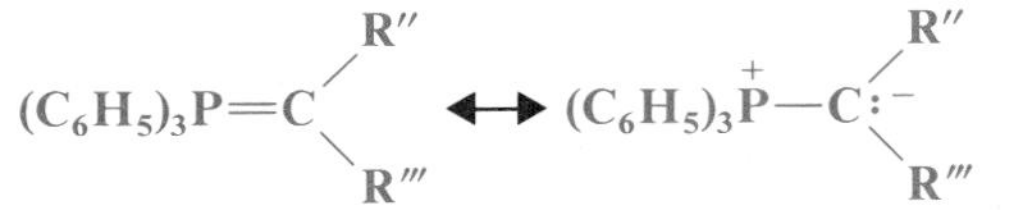

$$(C_6H_5)_3P{=}C\overset{R''}{\underset{R'''}{\big<}} \longleftrightarrow (C_6H_5)_3\overset{+}{P}-C\colon^-\overset{R''}{\underset{R'''}{\big<}}$$

The mechanism of the Wittig reaction has been the subject of considerable study. An early mechanistic proposal suggested that the ylide, acting as a carbanion, attacks the carbonyl carbon of the aldehyde or ketone to form an unstable intermediate with separated charges called a **betaine.** In the next step, the betaine is envisioned as becoming an unstable four-membered cyclic system called an **oxaphosphatane,** which then spontaneously loses triphenylphosphine oxide to become an alkene. More recently, studies by E. Vedejs (of the University of Wisconsin) and others suggest that the betaine is not an intermediate and that the oxaphosphatane is formed directly by a cycloaddition reaction. The driving force for the Wittig reaction is the formation of the very strong ($DH° = 130$ kcal mol^{-1}) phosphorus–oxygen bond in triphenylphosphine oxide.

16.10 THE ADDITION OF YLIDES: THE WITTIG REACTION

General Mechanism

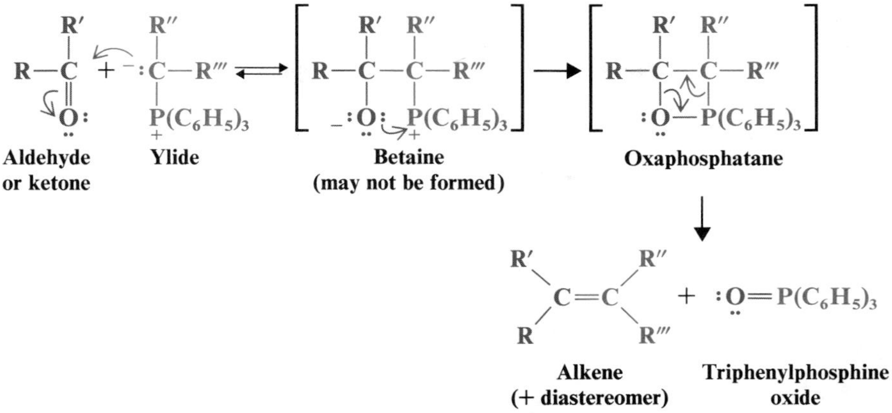

| Aldehyde | Ylide | Betaine | Oxaphosphatane |
| or ketone | | (may not be formed) | |

C=C + :O=P(C$_6$H$_5$)$_3$

Alkene   **Triphenylphosphine**
(+ diastereomer)   **oxide**

Specific Example

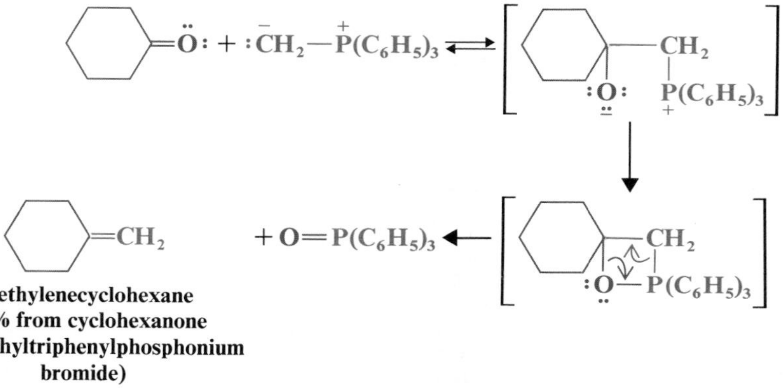

=CH$_2$ +O=P(C$_6$H$_5$)$_3$ ←

Methylenecyclohexane
(86% from cyclohexanone
and methyltriphenylphosphonium
bromide)

The elimination of triphenylphosphine oxide from the betaine if, indeed, it forms, may occur in two separate steps as we have just shown, or both steps may occur simultaneously.

While Wittig syntheses may appear to be complicated, in actual practice they are easy to carry out. Most of the steps can be carried out in the same reaction vessel, and the entire synthesis can be accomplished in a matter of hours.

The overall result of a Wittig synthesis is

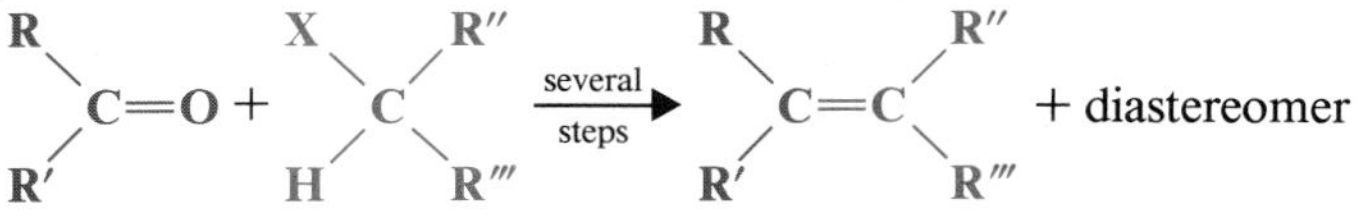

Planning a Wittig synthesis begins with recognizing in the desired alkene what can be the aldehyde or ketone component and what can be the halide component. Any or all of the R groups may be hydrogen. The halide component must be a primary, secondary, or methyl halide.

Sample Problem

Outline a Wittig synthesis of 2-methyl-1-phenyl-1-propene.

Answer:
We examine the structure of the compound, paying attention to the groups on each side of the double bond.

$$\overset{\quad CH_3}{C_6H_5CH{=}CCH_3}$$

2-Methyl-1-phenyl-1-propene

Two general approaches to the synthesis are possible:

(a)
$$\underset{H}{\overset{C_6H_5}{>}}C{=}O + \underset{H}{\overset{X}{>}}C\underset{CH_3}{\overset{CH_3}{<}} \longrightarrow \underset{H}{\overset{C_6H_5}{>}}C{=}C\underset{CH_3}{\overset{CH_3}{<}}$$

or

(b)
$$\underset{H}{\overset{C_6H_5}{>}}C\underset{X}{\overset{H}{<}} + O{=}C\underset{CH_3}{\overset{CH_3}{<}} \longrightarrow \underset{H}{\overset{C_6H_5}{>}}C{=}C\underset{CH_3}{\overset{CH_3}{<}}$$

In (a) we first make the ylide from a 2-halopropane and then allow it to react with benzaldehyde.

(a) $(CH_3)_2CHBr + (C_6H_5)_3P \longrightarrow (CH_3)_2CH{-}\overset{+}{P}(C_6H_5)_3\ Br^- \xrightarrow{RLi}$

$(CH_3)_2\overset{..}{C}{-}\overset{+}{P}(C_6H_5)_3 \xrightarrow{C_6H_5CHO} (CH_3)_2C{=}CHC_6H_5 + (C_6H_5)_3P{=}O$

In (b) we would make the ylide from a benzyl halide and allow it to react with acetone.

(b) $C_6H_5CH_2Br + (C_6H_5)_3P \longrightarrow C_6H_5CH_2{-}\overset{+}{P}(C_6H_5)_3\ Br^- \xrightarrow{RLi}$

$C_6H_5\overset{..}{C}H{-}\overset{+}{P}(C_6H_5)_3 \xrightarrow{(CH_3)_2C=O} C_6H_5CH{=}C(CH_3)_2 + (C_6H_5)_3P{=}O$

Problem 16.17

In addition to triphenylphosphine assume that you have available as starting materials any necessary aldehydes, ketones, and organic halides. Show how you might synthesize each of the following alkenes using the Wittig reaction:

(a) $\underset{CH_3}{\overset{}{C_6H_5C}}{=}CH_2$

(b) $\underset{CH_3}{\overset{}{C_6H_5C}}{=}CHCH_3$

(c) $\underset{H_3C}{\overset{H_3C}{>}}C{=}CH_2$

(d) (cyclopentane ring with $=CH_2$)

(e) $CH_3CH_2CH{=}\overset{CH_3}{\overset{|}{C}}CH_2CH_3$

(f) $C_6H_5CH{=}CHCH{=}CH_2$

(g) $C_6H_5CH{=}CHC_6H_5$

Problem 16.18

Triphenylphosphine can be used to convert epoxides to alkenes, for example,

$$C_6H_5CH\underset{\diagdown O\diagup}{-}CHCH_3 + (C_6H_5)_3P: \longrightarrow C_6H_5CH\text{=}CHCH_3 + (C_6H_5)_3PO$$

Propose a likely mechanism for this reaction.

16.11 THE ADDITION OF ORGANOMETALLIC REAGENTS: THE REFORMATSKY REACTION

In Section 11.8 we studied the addition of Grignard reagents, organolithium compounds, and sodium alkynides to aldehydes and ketones. These reactions, as we saw then, can be used to produce a wide variety of alcohols:

$$R:MgX + \overset{\delta-}{\underset{}{}}\overset{\delta+}{\diagup}C\text{=}O \longrightarrow R-\overset{|}{\underset{|}{C}}-OMgX \xrightarrow{H_3O^+} R-\overset{|}{\underset{|}{C}}-OH$$

$$R:Li + \overset{\delta-}{\underset{}{}}\overset{\delta+}{\diagup}C\text{=}O \longrightarrow R-\overset{|}{\underset{|}{C}}-OLi \xrightarrow{H_3O^+} R-\overset{|}{\underset{|}{C}}-OH$$

$$RC\equiv C:Na + \overset{\delta-}{\underset{}{}}\overset{\delta+}{\diagup}C\text{=}O \longrightarrow RC\equiv C-\overset{|}{\underset{|}{C}}-ONa \xrightarrow{H_3O^+} RC\equiv C-\overset{|}{\underset{|}{C}}-OH$$

We shall now examine a similar reaction that involves the addition of an organozinc reagent to the carbonyl group of an aldehyde or ketone. This reaction, called the *Reformatsky reaction,* extends the carbon skeleton of an aldehyde or ketone and yields β-hydroxy esters. It involves treating an aldehyde or ketone with an α-bromo ester in the presence of zinc metal; the solvent most often used is benzene. The initial product is a zinc alkoxide, which must be hydrolyzed to yield the β-hydroxy ester.

$$\underset{\substack{\text{Aldehyde} \\ \text{or} \\ \text{ketone}}}{\diagdown C\text{=}O} + \underset{\alpha\text{-Bromoester}}{Br-\overset{|}{\underset{|}{C}}-CO_2R} \xrightarrow[\text{benzene}]{Zn} \overset{BrZnO}{\underset{}{}}-\overset{|}{\underset{|}{C}}-\overset{|}{\underset{|}{C}}-CO_2R \xrightarrow{H_3O^+} \underset{\substack{\beta\text{-Hydroxy} \\ \text{ester}}}{\overset{HO}{\underset{}{}}-\overset{|}{\underset{|}{C}}\overset{\beta}{}-\overset{|}{\underset{|}{C}}\overset{\alpha}{}-CO_2R}$$

The intermediate in the reaction appears to be an organozinc reagent that adds to the carbonyl group in a manner analogous to that of a Grignard reagent.

$$Br-\overset{|}{\underset{|}{C}}-CO_2R \xrightarrow[\text{benzene}]{Zn} BrZn:\overset{\delta+}{\underset{|}{\overset{|}{C}}}\overset{\delta-}{}-CO_2R \xrightarrow{\diagdown C\text{=}O}$$

$$\overset{BrZnO}{\underset{}{}}-\overset{|}{\underset{|}{C}}-\overset{|}{\underset{|}{C}}-CO_2R \xrightarrow{H_3O^+} \overset{HO}{\underset{}{}}-\overset{|}{\underset{|}{C}}-\overset{|}{\underset{|}{C}}-CO_2R$$

Because the organozinc reagent is less reactive than a Grignard reagent, it does not add to the ester group. The β-hydroxy esters produced in the Reformatsky reaction are easily dehydrated to α,β-unsaturated esters, because dehydration yields a system in which the carbon–carbon double bond is conjugated with the carbon–oxygen double bond of the ester.

$$
\begin{array}{c}
\underset{\substack{\text{HO} \\ | \\ -\text{C}-\text{C}-\text{COR} \\ | \quad | \\ \quad \text{H}}}{\quad} \xrightarrow[\substack{\text{heat} \\ (-\text{H}_2\text{O})}]{\text{H}_3\text{O}^+} \quad -\text{C}=\text{C}-\text{COR}
\end{array}
$$

β-Hydroxy α,β-Unsaturated
ester   ester

Examples of the Reformatsky reaction are the following:

$$
\text{CH}_3\text{CH}_2\text{CH}_2\overset{\text{O}}{\overset{||}{\text{CH}}} + \text{BrCH}_2\text{CO}_2\text{Et} \xrightarrow[\text{(2) H}_3\text{O}^+]{\text{(1) Zn}} \text{CH}_3\text{CH}_2\text{CH}_2\overset{\text{OH}}{\underset{|}{\text{CH}}}\text{CH}_2\text{CO}_2\text{Et}
$$

$\text{Et} = \text{CH}_3\text{CH}_2-$

$$
\text{CH}_3\overset{\text{O}}{\overset{||}{\text{CH}}} + \text{Br}-\overset{\text{CH}_3}{\underset{\text{CH}_3}{\overset{|}{\underset{|}{\text{C}}}}}-\text{CO}_2\text{Et} \xrightarrow[\text{(2) H}_3\text{O}^+]{\text{(1) Zn}} \text{CH}_3\overset{\text{OH}}{\underset{|}{\text{CH}}}-\overset{\text{CH}_3}{\underset{\text{CH}_3}{\overset{|}{\underset{|}{\text{C}}}}}-\text{CO}_2\text{Et}
$$

$$
\text{C}_6\text{H}_5\overset{\text{O}}{\overset{||}{\text{CH}}} + \text{Br}-\overset{\text{CH}_3}{\underset{}{\overset{|}{\text{CH}}}}-\text{CO}_2\text{Et} \xrightarrow[\text{(2) H}_3\text{O}^+]{\text{(1) Zn}} \text{C}_6\text{H}_5\overset{\text{OH}}{\underset{|}{\text{CH}}}-\overset{\text{CH}_3}{\underset{}{\overset{|}{\text{CH}}}}-\text{CO}_2\text{Et}
$$

Problem 16.19

Show how you would use a Reformatsky reaction in the synthesis of each of the following compounds. (Additional steps may be necessary in some instances.)

(a) $(\text{CH}_3)_2\overset{\text{OH}}{\underset{|}{\text{C}}}\text{CH}_2\text{CO}_2\text{CH}_2\text{CH}_3$

(c) $\text{CH}_3\text{CH}_2\text{CH}_2\text{CH}_2\text{CO}_2\text{CH}_2\text{CH}_3$

(b) ⬡ $-\overset{\text{OH}}{\underset{\text{CH}_3}{\overset{|}{\underset{|}{\text{CH}}}}}\text{CO}_2\text{CH}_2\text{CH}_3$

16.12 OXIDATION OF ALDEHYDES AND KETONES

Aldehydes are much more easily oxidized than ketones. Aldehydes are readily oxidized by strong oxidizing agents such as potassium permanganate, and they are also oxidized by such mild oxidizing agents as silver oxide.

$$
\overset{\text{O}}{\overset{||}{\text{RCH}}} \xrightarrow{\text{KMnO}_4,\ \text{OH}^-} \overset{\text{O}}{\overset{||}{\text{RCO}^-}} \xrightarrow{\text{H}_3\text{O}^+} \overset{\text{O}}{\overset{||}{\text{RCOH}}}
$$

16.12 OXIDATION OF ALDEHYDES AND KETONES

$$\underset{RCH}{\overset{O}{\|}} \xrightarrow{Ag_2O,\ OH^-} \underset{RCO^-}{\overset{O}{\|}} \xrightarrow{H_3O^+} \underset{RCOH}{\overset{O}{\|}}$$

Notice that in these oxidations aldehydes lose the hydrogen that is attached to the carbonyl carbon atom. Because ketones lack this hydrogen, they are more resistant to oxidation.

16.12A THE BAEYER–VILLIGER OXIDATION OF ALDEHYDES AND KETONES

Both aldehydes and ketones are oxidized by peroxy acids. This reaction, called the *Baeyer–Villiger oxidation,* is especially useful with ketones, because it converts them to carboxylic esters. For example, treating acetophenone with a peroxy acid converts it to the ester, phenyl acetate.

$$\underset{\textbf{Acetophenone}}{C_6H_5-\overset{O}{\overset{\|}{C}}-CH_3} \xrightarrow{RCOOH} \underset{\textbf{Phenyl acetate}}{C_6H_5-O-\overset{O}{\overset{\|}{C}}-CH_3}$$

The mechanism proposed for this reaction involves the following steps:

$$CH_3-\overset{O}{\overset{\|}{\underset{C_6H_5}{C}}} + \ :\overset{H}{\underset{}{O}}-O-\overset{O}{\overset{\|}{C}}-R \underset{}{\overset{(1)}{\rightleftharpoons}} CH_3-\overset{O-H}{\underset{C_6H_5}{\overset{|}{C}}}-O-O-\overset{O}{\overset{\|}{C}}-R \overset{(2)\ H^+}{\rightleftharpoons}$$

$$CH_3-\overset{O-H}{\underset{C_6H_5}{\overset{|}{C}}}-O-O-\overset{O-H^+}{\overset{\|}{C}}-R \underset{(3a)}{\overset{-RC-OH}{\longrightarrow}} CH_3-\overset{O-H}{\underset{C_6H_5}{\overset{|}{C}}}-\ddot{\overset{..}{O}}:^+ \underset{(3b)}{\overset{\text{phenyl}\ \text{migration}}{\longrightarrow}}$$

$$CH_3\overset{O}{\overset{\|}{C}}-O-C_6H_5 + H^+$$

In step 1 the peroxy acid adds to the carbonyl group of the ketone. At this point there are several equilibria involving the attachment of a proton to one of the oxygen atoms of this addition product. When a proton attaches itself to one of the oxygen atoms of the carboxylic acid portion, it makes this part a good leaving group, which in step 3a departs. Simultaneously with the departure of RCO_2H, the phenyl group migrates (as an anion) to the electron-deficient oxygen that is being created (step 3b). After that, the loss of a proton produces the ester.

Step 3b shows that a phenyl group has a greater tendency to migrate than a methyl group; otherwise the product would have been $C_6H_5COOCH_3$ and not $CH_3COOC_6H_5$. This tendency of a group to migrate is called its **migratory aptitude.** Studies of the Baeyer–Villiger oxidation and other reactions have shown that the migratory aptitude of groups is H > phenyl > 3 ° alkyl > 2 ° alkyl > 1 ° alkyl > methyl. In all cases, this order is for groups migrating with their electron pairs, that is, as anions.

Problem 16.20

When benzaldehyde reacts with a peroxy acid, the product is benzoic acid. The mechanism for this reaction is analogous to the one just given for the oxidation of acetophenone, and the outcome illustrates the greater migratory aptitude of a hydrogen atom compared to phenyl. Outline all the steps involved.

Problem 16.21

Give the structure of the product that would result from a Baeyer–Villiger oxidation of cyclopentanone.

Problem 16.22

What would be the major product formed in the Baeyer–Villiger oxidation of 3-methyl-2-butanone?

16.13 CHEMICAL AND SPECTROSCOPIC ANALYSIS FOR ALDEHYDES AND KETONES

Aldehydes and ketones can be differentiated from noncarbonyl compounds through their reactions with derivatives of ammonia (Section 16.8). Semicarbazide, 2,4-dinitrophenylhydrazine, and hydroxylamine react with aldehydes and ketones to form precipitates. Semicarbazones and oximes are usually colorless, while 2,4-dinitrophenylhydrazones are usually orange. The melting points of these derivatives can also be used in identifying specific aldehydes and ketones.

The ease with which aldehydes undergo oxidation provides a useful test that differentiates aldehydes from most ketones.

16.13A TOLLENS' TEST (SILVER MIRROR TEST)

Mixing aqueous silver nitrate with aqueous ammonia produces a solution known as Tollens' reagent. The reagent contains the diamminosilver(I) ion, $Ag(NH_3)_2^+$. Although this ion is a very weak oxidizing agent, it will oxidize aldehydes to carboxylate ions. As it does this, silver is reduced from the $+1$ oxidation state [of $Ag(NH_3)_2^+$] to metallic silver. If the rate of reaction is slow and the walls of the vessel are clean, metallic silver deposits on the walls of the test tube as a mirror; if not, it deposits as a gray to black precipitate. Tollens' reagent gives a negative result with all ketones except α-hydroxy ketones.

TABLE 16.4   Carbonyl stretching bands of aldehydes and ketones

C=O STRETCHING FREQUENCIES			
COMPOUND	RANGE (cm^{-1})	COMPOUND	RANGE (cm^{-1})
R—CHO	1720–1740	RCOR	1705–1720
Ar—CHO	1695–1715	ArCOR	1680–1700
$-\overset{\|}{C}=\overset{\|}{C}-CHO$	1680–1690	$-\overset{\|}{C}=\overset{\|}{C}-COR$	1665–1680
		Cyclohexanone	1715
		Cyclopentanone	1751

16.13B SPECTROSCOPIC PROPERTIES OF ALDEHYDES AND KETONES

Carbonyl groups of aldehydes and ketones give rise to very strong C=O stretching bands in the 1665–1780-cm^{-1} region of the **IR spectrum.** The exact location of the peak (Table 16.4) depends on the structure of the aldehyde or ketone. This peak is one of the most useful and characteristic absorptions in the IR spectrum.

Vibrations of the C—H bond of the CHO group of aldehydes also gives two weak bands in the 2700–2775 and 2820–2900-cm^{-1} regions of the IR spectrum that are easily identified.

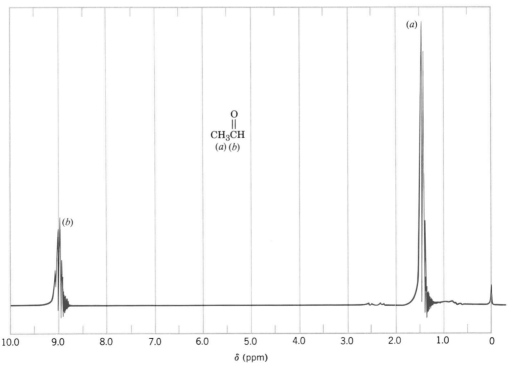

FIGURE 16.1 The ^{1}H NMR spectrum of acetaldehyde. Notice that spin–spin coupling between the aldehydic proton and the protons of the methyl group cause both signals to be split. The aldehydic proton signal occurs as a quartet and that for the methyl protons occurs as a doublet. The coupling constant is about 3 Hz.

The aldehydic proton gives a signal far downfield (δ 9–10) in **¹H NMR spectra.** An example is given in the ¹H NMR spectrum of acetaldehyde (Fig. 16.1).

The carbonyl groups of saturated aldehydes and ketones give a weak absorption band in the **UV region** between 270 and 300 nm. This band is shifted to longer wavelengths (300–350 nm) when the carbonyl group is conjugated with a double bond.

16.14 SUMMARY OF THE ADDITION REACTIONS OF ALDEHYDES AND KETONES

Table 16.5 summarizes the nucleophilic addition reactions of aldehydes and ketones occurring at the carbonyl carbon atom that we have studied so far. In Chapter 17 we shall see other examples.

TABLE 16.5 Nucleophilic addition reactions of aldehydes and ketones

1. Addition of Organometallic Compounds

General Reaction

$$\overset{\delta-}{R}:\overset{\delta+}{M} + \;\; \underset{}{C}{=}\ddot{O}: \longrightarrow R-\overset{|}{\underset{|}{C}}-O^-M^+ \xrightarrow[H^+]{} R-\overset{|}{\underset{|}{C}}-O-H$$

Specific Example Using a Grignard Reagent (Section 11.7)

$$CH_3CH_2MgBr + CH_3\overset{O}{\overset{\|}{C}}-H \xrightarrow[(2)\ H^+]{(1)\ \text{diethyl ether}} CH_3CH_2\overset{OH}{\underset{|}{CH}}CH_3$$
$$\textbf{(67\%)}$$

Specific Example Using the Reformatsky Reaction (Section 16.11)

$$CH_3\underset{\underset{CH_3}{|}}{CH}CH_2\overset{O}{\overset{\|}{C}}H + Br-\underset{\underset{CH_3}{|}}{\overset{CH_3}{\overset{|}{C}}}-CO_2CH_2CH_3 \xrightarrow[(2)\ H_3O^+]{(1)\ Zn} CH_3\underset{\underset{CH_3}{|}}{CH}CH_2\overset{HO}{\underset{\underset{CH_3}{|}}{CH}}\overset{CH_3}{\overset{|}{C}}-CO_2CH_2CH_3$$
$$\textbf{(65\%)}$$

2. Addition of Hydride Ion

General Reaction

$$\overset{-}{H}: + \;\; \underset{}{C}{=}O \longrightarrow H-\overset{|}{\underset{|}{C}}-O^- \xrightarrow[H^+]{} H-\overset{|}{\underset{|}{C}}-OH$$

Specific Examples Using Metal Hydrides (Section 11.3)

$$\square{=}O + LiAlH_4 \xrightarrow[(2)\ H^+]{(1)\ \text{diethyl ether}} \square\overset{H}{\underset{OH}{\diagdown}}$$
$$\textbf{(90\%)}$$

$$CH_3\overset{O}{\overset{\|}{C}}CH_2CH_2CH_3 + NaBH_4 \xrightarrow[OH^-]{CH_3OH} CH_3\overset{OH}{\underset{|}{CH}}CH_2CH_2CH_3$$
$$\textbf{(100\%)} \qquad\qquad (continued)$$

16.14 SUMMARY OF THE ADDITION REACTIONS OF ALDEHYDES AND KETONES

TABLE 16.5 (continued)

---

3. Addition of Hydrogen Cyanide and Sodium Bisulfite (Section 16.9)

General Reaction

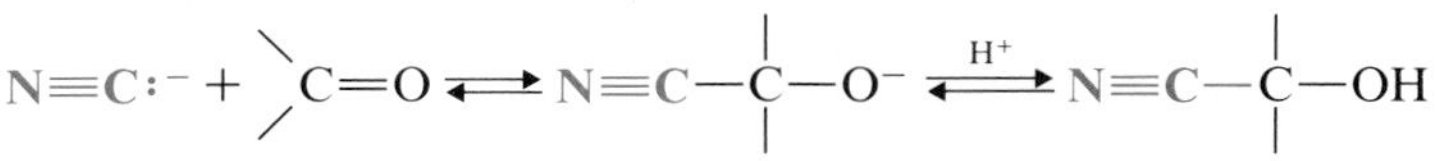

$$N\equiv C:^- + \;{\Large\diagdown}\!C{=}O \;\rightleftharpoons\; N\equiv C-\overset{|}{\underset{|}{C}}-O^- \;\overset{H^+}{\rightleftharpoons}\; N\equiv C-\overset{|}{\underset{|}{C}}-OH$$

Specific Example

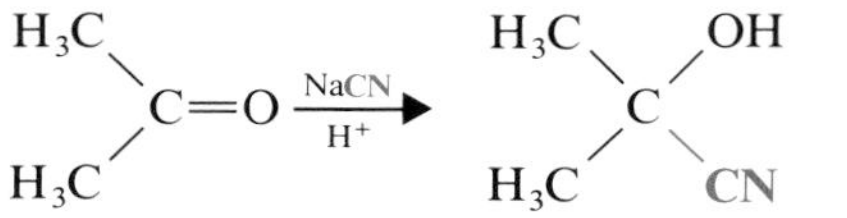

Acetone cyanohydrin
(78%)

General Reaction

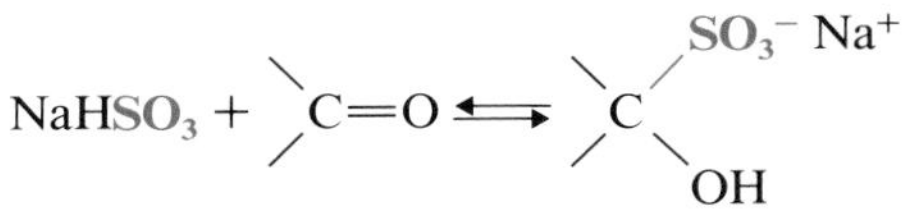

$$NaHSO_3 + \;{\Large\diagdown}\!C{=}O \;\rightleftharpoons\; {\Large\diagdown}\!C{\diagdown}^{SO_3^- \; Na^+}_{OH}$$

Specific Example

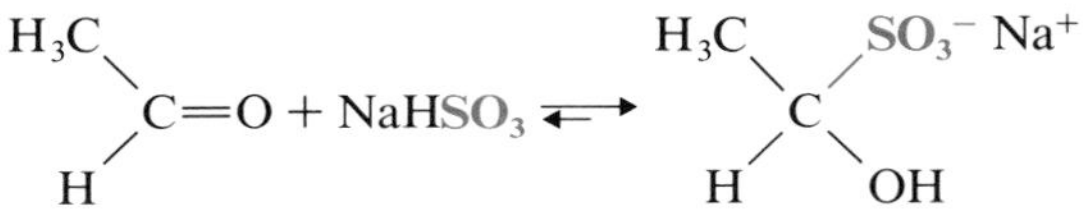

(88%)

4. Addition of Ylides (Section 16.10)

The Wittig Reaction

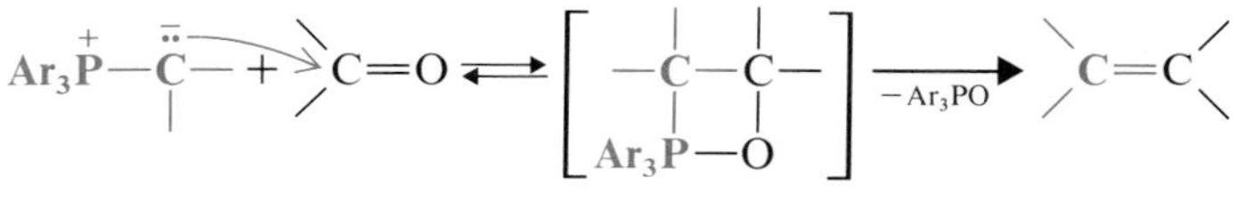

$$Ar_3\overset{+}{P}-\overset{..}{\underset{|}{C}}- \;+\; {\Large\diagdown}\!C{=}O \;\rightleftharpoons\; \left[-\overset{|}{\underset{|}{C}}-\overset{|}{\underset{Ar_3P-O}{C}}- \right] \;\xrightarrow{-Ar_3PO}\; {\Large\diagdown}\!C{=}C{\Large\diagup}$$

5. Addition of Alcohols (Section 16.7)

General Reaction

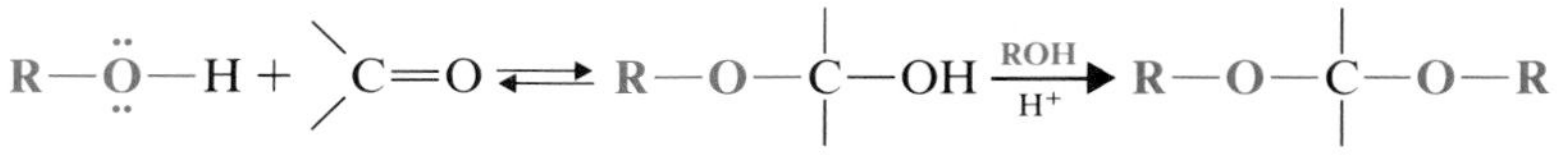

$$R-\overset{..}{\underset{..}{O}}-H + \;{\Large\diagdown}\!C{=}O \;\rightleftharpoons\; R-O-\overset{|}{\underset{|}{C}}-OH \;\xrightarrow[H^+]{ROH}\; R-O-\overset{|}{\underset{|}{C}}-O-R$$

Hemiacetal   **Acetal or**
or hemiketal   **ketal**

Specific Example

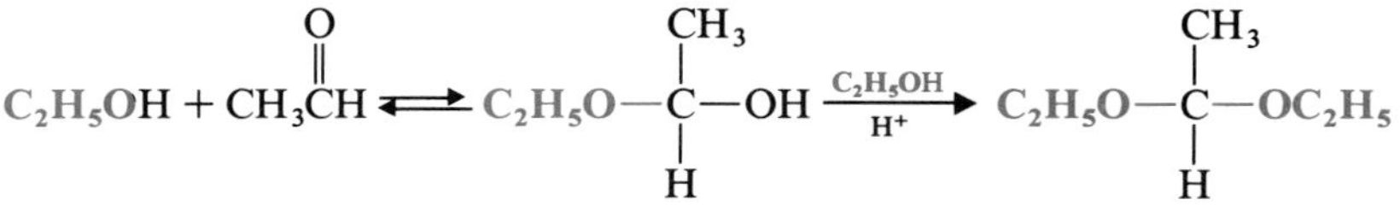

$$C_2H_5OH + CH_3\overset{O}{\overset{||}{C}}H \;\rightleftharpoons\; C_2H_5O-\overset{CH_3}{\underset{H}{\overset{|}{C}{|}}}-OH \;\xrightarrow[H^+]{C_2H_5OH}\; C_2H_5O-\overset{CH_3}{\underset{H}{\overset{|}{C}{|}}}-OC_2H_5$$

(continued)

TABLE 16.5 (continued)

6. Addition of Derivatives of Ammonia (Section 16.8)

General Reaction

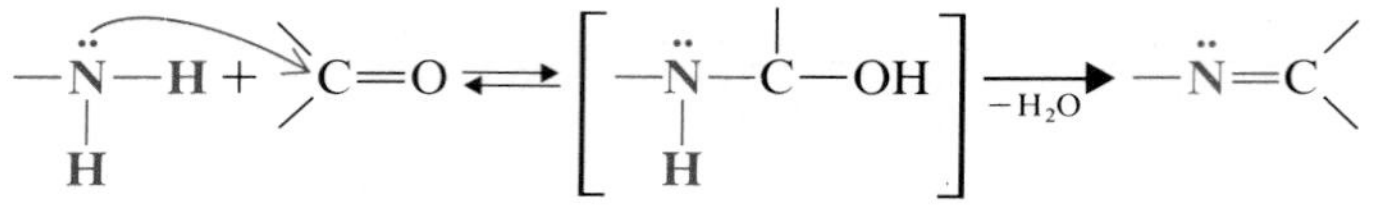

$$-\overset{\overset{\displaystyle\cdot\cdot}{\vert}}{\underset{\displaystyle H}{N}}-H + \overset{\diagdown}{\diagup}C{=}O \rightleftharpoons \left[-\overset{\overset{\displaystyle\cdot\cdot}{\vert}}{\underset{\displaystyle H}{N}}-\overset{\vert}{\underset{\vert}{C}}-OH \right] \xrightarrow[-H_2O]{} -\ddot{N}{=}C\overset{\diagup}{\diagdown}$$

Specific Examples

$$CH_3\overset{\overset{\displaystyle O}{\|}}{C}H + NH_2OH \longrightarrow CH_3CH{=}NOH$$
Acetaldoxime

$$C_6H_5\overset{\overset{\displaystyle O}{\|}}{C}H + H_2NNHC_6H_5 \longrightarrow C_6H_5CH{=}NNHC_6H_5$$
Benzaldehyde phenylhydrazone

Additional Problems

16.23 Give a structural formula and another acceptable name for each of the following compounds:

(a) Formaldehyde

(b) Acetaldehyde

(c) Phenylacetaldehyde

(d) Acetone

(e) Ethyl methyl ketone

(f) Acetophenone

(g) Benzophenone

(h) Salicylaldehyde

(i) Vanillin

(j) Diethyl ketone

(k) Ethyl isopropyl ketone

(l) Diisopropyl ketone

(m) Dibutyl ketone

(n) Dipropyl ketone

(o) Cinnamaldehyde

16.24 Write structural formulas for the products formed when propanal reacts with each of the following reagents:

(a) $NaBH_4$ in aqueous NaOH

(b) C_6H_5MgBr, then H_2O

(c) $LiAlH_4$, then H_2O

(d) Ag_2O, OH^-

(e) $(C_6H_5)_3P{=}CH_2$

(f) H_2 and Pt

(g) $HOCH_2CH_2OH$ and H^+

(h) $CH_3\ddot{C}H{-}\overset{+}{P}(C_6H_5)_3$

(i) (1) $BrCH_2CO_2C_2H_5$, Zn; (2) H_3O^+

(j) $Ag(NH_3)_2^+$

(k) Hydroxylamine

(l) Semicarbazide

(m) Phenylhydrazine

(n) Cold dilute $KMnO_4$

(o) $HSCH_2CH_2SH$, H^+

(p) $HSCH_2CH_2SH$, H^+, then Raney nickel

16.25 Give structural formulas for the products formed (if any) from the reaction of acetone with each reagent in Problem 16.24.

16.26 What products would be obtained from each of the following reactions of acetophenone?

(a) Acetophenone + $HNO_3 \xrightarrow[H_2SO_4]{}$

(b) Acetophenone + $C_6H_5NHNH_2 \longrightarrow$

(c) Acetophenone + $\overset{-}{:}CH_2{-}\overset{+}{P}(C_6H_5)_3 \longrightarrow$

(d) Acetophenone + $NaBH_4 \xrightarrow[OH^-]{H_2O}$

(e) Acetophenone + $C_6H_5MgBr \xrightarrow[(2)\ H_2O]{}$

16.27 (a) Give three methods for synthesizing phenyl propyl ketone from benzene and any other needed reagents. (b) Give three methods for transforming phenyl propyl ketone into butylbenzene.

16.28 Show how you would convert benzaldehyde into each of the following. You may use any other needed reagents, and more than one step may be required.

(a) Benzyl alcohol   (g) 3-Methyl-1-phenyl-1-butanol   (m) $C_6H_5CH(OH)CN$
(b) Benzoic acid   (h) Benzyl bromide   (n) $C_6H_5CH=NOH$
(c) Benzoyl chloride   (i) Toluene   (o) $C_6H_5CH=NNHC_6H_5$
(d) Benzophenone   (j) $C_6H_5CH(OCH_3)_2$ (p) $C_6H_5CH=NNHCONH_2$
(e) Acetophenone   (k) $C_6H_5CH^{18}O$ (q) $C_6H_5CH=CHCH=CH_2$
(f) 1-Phenylethanol   (l) C_6H_5CHDOH (r) $C_6H_5CH(OH)SO_3Na$

16.29 Show how ethyl phenyl ketone ($C_6H_5COCH_2CH_3$) could be synthesized from each of the following:

(a) Benzene   (c) Benzonitrile, C_6H_5CN
(b) Benzoyl chloride   (d) Benzaldehyde

16.30 Show how benzaldehyde could be synthesized from each of the following:

(a) Benzyl alcohol   (c) Phenylethyne   (e) $C_6H_5CO_2CH_3$
(b) Benzoic acid   (d) Phenylethene (styrene) (f) $C_6H_5C\equiv N$

16.31 Give structures for compounds **A–E**.

Cyclohexanol $\xrightarrow[\text{acetone}]{H_2CrO_4}$ **A** $(C_6H_{10}O)$ $\xrightarrow[\text{(2) H}_3O^+]{\text{(1) CH}_3\text{MgI}}$ **B** $(C_7H_{14}O)$ $\xrightarrow[\text{heat}]{H^+}$

C (C_7H_{12}) $\xrightarrow[\text{(2) Zn, H}_2\text{O}]{\text{(1) O}_3}$ **D** $(C_7H_{12}O_2)$ $\xrightarrow[\text{(2) H}_3O^+]{\text{(1) Ag}_2\text{O, OH}^-}$ **E** $(C_7H_{12}O_3)$

16.32 The following reaction sequence shows how the carbon chain of an aldehyde may be lengthened by two carbon atoms. What are the intermediates **K–M**?

Propanal $\xrightarrow[\text{(2) H}^+]{\text{(1) BrCH}_2\text{CO}_2\text{Et, Zn}}$ **K** $(C_7H_{14}O_3)$ $\xrightarrow{H^+,\ heat}$ **L** $(C_7H_{12}O_2)$ $\xrightarrow{H_2,\ Pt}$

M $(C_7H_{14}O_2)$ $\xrightarrow[\text{(2) H}_2\text{O}]{\text{(1) DIBAL-H}}$ pentanal

16.33 Warming piperonal (Section 16.3) with dilute aqueous HCl converts it to a compound with the formula $C_7H_6O_3$. What is this compound and what type of reaction is involved?

16.34 Starting with benzyl bromide, show how you would synthesize each of the following:

(a) $C_6H_5CH_2CHOHCH_3$ (c) $C_6H_5CH=CH-CH=CHC_6H_5$
(b) $C_6H_5CH_2CH_2CHO$ (d) $C_6H_5CH_2COCH_2CH_3$

16.35 Compounds **A** and **D** do not give positive Tollens' tests; however, compound **C** does. Give structures for **A–D**.

4-Bromobutanal $\xrightarrow{\text{HOCH}_2\text{CH}_2\text{OH, H}^+}$ **A** $(C_6H_{11}O_2Br)$ $\xrightarrow{\text{Mg, diethyl ether}}$

[**B** $(C_6H_{11}MgO_2Br)$] $\xrightarrow[\text{(2) H}_3O^+,\ \text{H}_2\text{O}]{\text{(1) CH}_3\text{CHO}}$ **C** $(C_6H_{12}O_2)$ $\xrightarrow[\text{H}^+]{\text{CH}_3\text{OH}}$ **D** $(C_7H_{14}O_2)$

16.36 Provide the missing reagents and intermediate in the following synthesis:

$$HO-\underset{}{\bigcirc}-CH_2OH \xrightarrow{(a)} CH_3O-\underset{}{\bigcirc}-CH_2OH \xrightarrow{(b)} ? \xrightarrow{(c)}$$

$$CH_3O-\underset{}{\bigcirc}-\underset{\underset{CH_3}{|}}{\underset{|}{\overset{OH}{\overset{|}{C}H}CHCO_2Et}} \xrightarrow{(d)} CH_3O-\underset{}{\bigcirc}-\underset{\underset{CH_3}{|}}{\overset{OH}{\overset{|}{C}HCHCH_2OH}}$$

16.37 Outlined here is a synthesis of glyceraldehyde (Section 5.13A). What are the intermediates **A–C**, and what stereoisomeric form of glyceraldehyde would you expect to obtain?

$$CH_2=CHCH_2OH \xrightarrow[CH_2Cl_2]{PCC} A\ (C_3H_4O) \xrightarrow{CH_3OH,\ H^+}$$

$$B\ (C_5H_{10}O_2) \xrightarrow[\text{cold, dilute}]{KMnO_4,\ OH^-} C\ (C_5H_{12}O_4) \xrightarrow[H_2O]{H_3O^+} \text{glyceraldehyde}$$

16.38 Consider the reduction of (R)-3-phenyl-2-pentanone by sodium borohydride. After the reduction is complete, the mixture is separated by gas–liquid chromatography into two fractions. These fractions contain isomeric compounds, and each isomer is optically active. What are these two isomers, and what is the stereoisomeric relationship between them?

16.39 The structure of the sex pheromone (attractant) of the female tsetse fly has been confirmed by the following synthesis. Compound **C** appears to be identical to the natural pheromone in all respects (including the response of the male tsetse fly). Provide structures for **A, B,** and **C**.

$$BrCH_2(CH_2)_7CH_2Br \xrightarrow[(2)\ 2\ RLi]{(1)\ 2\ (C_6H_5)_3P} A\ (C_{45}H_{46}P_2) \xrightarrow{2\ CH_3(CH_2)_{11}\overset{\overset{O}{\|}}{C}CH_3}$$

$$B\ (C_{37}H_{72}) \xrightarrow{H_2,\ Pt} C\ (C_{37}H_{76})$$

16.40 Outline simple chemical tests that would distinguish between each of the following:
(a) Benzaldehyde and benzyl alcohol
(b) Hexanal and 2-hexanone
(c) 2-Hexanone and hexane
(d) 2-Hexanol and 2-hexanone
(e) $C_6H_5CH=CHCOC_6H_5$ and $C_6H_5COC_6H_5$
(f) Pentanal and diethyl ether

(g) $CH_3\overset{\overset{O}{\|}}{C}CH_2\overset{\overset{O}{\|}}{C}CH_3$ and $CH_3\overset{\overset{OH}{|}}{C}=CH\overset{\overset{O}{\|}}{C}CH_3$

(h) [structure with OCH₃] and [structure with OH]

16.41 Compounds **W** and **X** are isomers; they have the molecular formula C_9H_8O. The IR spectrum of each compound shows a strong absorption band near 1715 cm^{-1}. Oxidation of either compound with hot, basic potassium permanganate followed by acidification yields phthalic acid. The ^{1}H NMR spectrum of **W** shows a multiplet at δ 7.3 and a singlet at δ 3.4. The ^{1}H NMR spectrum of **X** shows a multiplet at δ 7.5, a triplet at δ 3.1, and a triplet at δ 2.5. Propose structures for **W** and **X**.

Phthalic acid

16.42 Compounds **Y** and **Z** are isomers with the molecular formula $C_{10}H_{12}O$. The IR spectrum of each compound shows a strong absorption band near 1710 cm^{-1}. The ^{1}H NMR spectra of **Y** and **Z** are given in Figs. 16.2 and 16.3. Propose structures for **Y** and **Z**.

16.43 Compound **A** ($C_9H_{18}O$) forms a phenylhydrazone, but gives a negative Tollens' test. The IR spectrum of **A** has a strong band near 1710 cm^{-1}. The proton-decoupled ^{13}C NMR spectrum of **A** is given in Fig. 16.4. Propose a structure for **A**.

16.44 Compound **B** ($C_8H_{12}O_2$) shows a strong carbonyl absorption in its IR spectrum. The proton-decoupled ^{13}C NMR spectrum of **B** is given in Fig. 16.5. Propose a structure for **B**.

16.45 When semicarbazide ($H_2NNHCONH_2$) reacts with a ketone (or an aldehyde) to form a semicarbazone (Section 16.8) only one nitrogen atom of semicarbazide acts as a nucleophile and attacks the carbonyl carbon atom of the ketone. The product of the reaction, consequently, is $R_2C{=}NNHCONH_2$ rather than $R_2C{=}NCONHNH_2$. What factor accounts for the fact that two nitrogen atoms of semicarbazide are relatively nonnucleophilic?

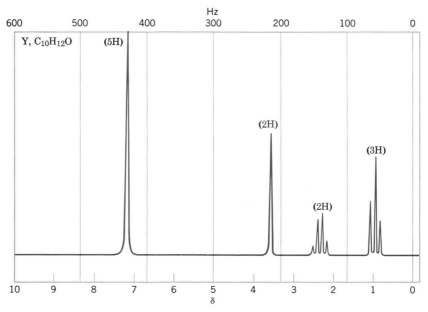

FIGURE 16.2 The ^{1}H NMR spectrum of compound **Y**, Problem 16.42. (Courtesy Aldrich Chemical Co., Milwaukee, WI.)

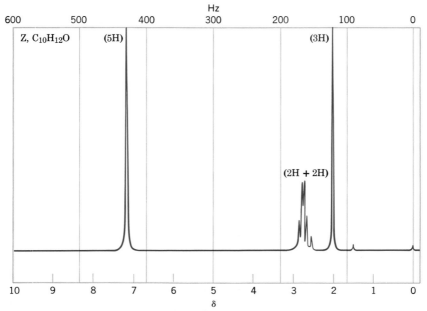

FIGURE 16.3 The ^{1}H NMR spectrum of compound **Z**, Problem 16.42. (Courtesy Aldrich Chemical Co., Milwaukee, WI.)

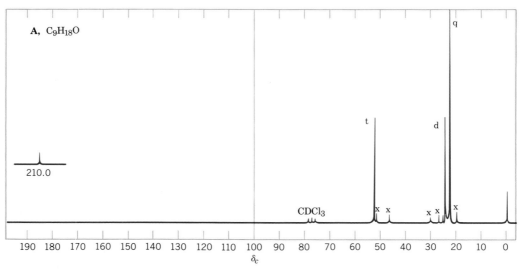

FIGURE 16.4 The proton-decoupled ^{13}C NMR spectrum of compound **A**, Problem 16.43. The letters d, t, and q refer to the splitting of the signal (doublet, triplet, and quartet) in the proton off-resonance decoupled spectrum. A signal marked with an x arises from an impurity and should be ignored. (Adapted from L. F. Johnson and W. C. Jankowski, *Carbon-13 NMR Spectra: A Collection of Assigned, Coded, and Indexed Spectra,* Wiley–Interscience, New York, 1972.)

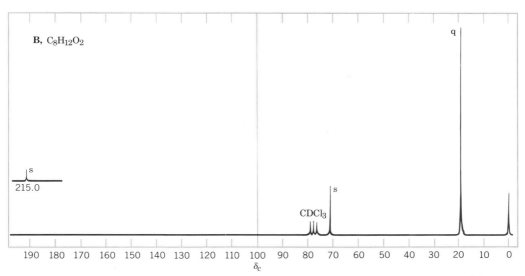

FIGURE 16.5 The proton-decoupled ^{13}C NMR spectrum of compound **B**, Problem 16.44. The letters s and q refer to the splitting of the signal (singlet and quartet) in the proton off-resonance decoupled spectrum. (Adapted from L. F. Johnson and W. C. Jankowski, *Carbon-13 NMR Spectra: Assigned, A Collection of Coded, and Indexed Spectra,* Wiley – Interscience, New York, 1972.)

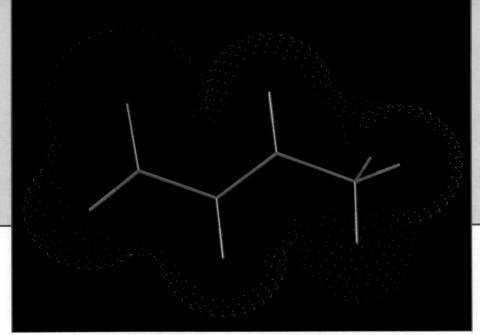

Crotonaldehyde (see Problem 17.29).

ALDEHYDES AND KETONES II. ALDOL REACTIONS

17.1 THE ACIDITY OF THE α HYDROGENS OF CARBONYL COMPOUNDS: ENOLATE IONS

In Chapter 16, we found that one important characteristic of aldehydes and ketones is their ability to undergo nucleophilic addition at their carbonyl groups.

$$\diagup\!\!\!\!\diagdown C=O + H-Nu \longrightarrow \diagup\!\!\!\!\diagdown C\diagup\overset{OH}{\underset{Nu}{\diagdown}}$$
Nucleophilic addition

A second important characteristic of carbonyl compounds is an unusual acidity of hydrogen atoms on carbon atoms adjacent to the carbonyl group. (These hydrogen atoms are usually called the **α hydrogens,** and the carbon to which they are attached is called the **α carbon.**)

$$R-\overset{\overset{\displaystyle :\ddot{O}}{\|}}{C}-\overset{\overset{\alpha}{|}}{\underset{\underset{H}{|}}{C}}\overset{\overset{\beta}{|}}{\underset{\underset{H}{|}}{C}}-$$

α Hydrogens	β Hydrogens
are unusually acidic	are not acidic
($pK_a = 19-20$)	($pK_a = 40-50$)

When we say that the α hydrogens are acidic, *we mean that they are unusually acidic for hydrogen atoms attached to carbon.* The pK_a values for the α hydrogens of most simple aldehydes or ketones are of the order of $19-20$ ($K_a = 10^{-19}-10^{-20}$). This means that they are more acidic than hydrogen atoms of ethyne, $pK_a = 25$ ($K_a = 10^{-25}$) and are far more acidic than the hydrogens of ethene ($pK_a = 44$) or of ethane ($pK_a = 50$).

The reason for the unusual acidity of the α hydrogens of carbonyl compounds is straightforward: When a carbonyl compound loses an α proton, the anion that is produced is *stabilized by resonance. The negative charge of the anion is delocalized.*

Resonance-stabilized anion

We see from this reaction that two resonance structures, **A** and **B**, can be written for the anion. In structure **A** the negative charge is on carbon and in structure **B** the negative charge is on oxygen. Both structures contribute to the hybrid. Although structure **A** is favored by the strength of its carbon–oxygen π bond relative to the weaker carbon–carbon π bond of **B**, structure **B** makes a greater contribution to the hybrid because oxygen, being highly electronegative, is better able to accommodate the negative charge. We can depict the hybrid in the following way:

$$\overset{O^{\delta-}}{\underset{}{\diagdown}}\overset{}{\underset{}{C}}\overset{\delta-}{=\!=\!=}\overset{}{\underset{}{C}}\overset{}{\diagup}$$

When this resonance-stabilized anion accepts a proton, it can do so in either of two ways: it can accept the proton at carbon to form the original carbonyl compound in what is called the **keto form,** or it may accept the proton at oxygen to form an **enol.**

Enol form   Keto form

Both of these reactions are reversible. Because of its relation to the enol, the resonance-stabilized anion is called an **enolate ion.**

17.2 KETO AND ENOL TAUTOMERS

The keto and enol forms of carbonyl compounds are constitutional isomers, but of a special type. Because they are easily interconverted in the presence of traces of acids and bases, chemists use a special term to describe this type of constitutional isomerism. Interconvertible keto and enol forms are said to be **tautomers,** and their interconversion is called **tautomerization.**

Under most circumstances, we encounter keto–enol tautomers in a state of equilibrium. (The surfaces of ordinary laboratory glassware are able to catalyze the interconversion and establish the equilibrium.) For simple monocarbonyl compounds such as acetone and acetaldehyde, the amount of the enol form present at equilibrium is *very small.* In acetone it is much less than 1%; in acetaldehyde the enol concentration is too small to be detected. The greater stability of the following keto forms of monocarbonyl compounds can be related to the greater strength of the carbon–oxygen π bond compared to the carbon–carbon π bond (~ 87 kcal mol^{-1} vs ~ 60 kcal mol^{-1}).

	Keto Form	*Enol Form*
Acetaldehyde	$\overset{O}{\overset{\|}{CH_3CH}}$ ($\sim 100\%$)	$\overset{OH}{\overset{\|}{CH_2{=}CH}}$ (extremely small)
Acetone	$\overset{O}{\overset{\|}{CH_3CCH_3}}$ ($>99\%$)	$\overset{OH}{\overset{\|}{CH_2{=}CCH_3}}$ ($1.5 \times 10^{-4}\%$)
Cyclohexanone	(98.8%)	(1.2%)

In compounds whose molecules have two carbonyl groups separated by one —CH$_2$— group (called β-dicarbonyl compounds), the amount of enol present at equilibrium is far higher. For example, 2,4-pentanedione exists in the enol form to an extent of 76%.

$$\overset{O\quad\ O}{\overset{\|\quad\ \|}{CH_3CCH_2CCH_3}} \rightleftharpoons \overset{OH\quad O}{\overset{\|\quad\ \|}{CH_3C{=}CHCCH_3}}$$

2,4-Pentanedione   **Enol form**
   (24%)   (76%)

The greater stability of the enol form of β-dicarbonyl compounds can be attributed to stability gained through resonance stabilization of the conjugated double bonds and (in a cyclic form) through hydrogen bonding.

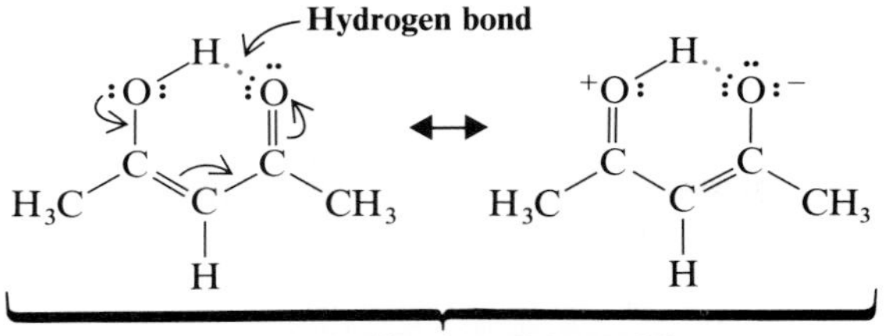

Resonance stabilization of the enol form

Problem 17.1

For all practical purposes, the compound 2,4-cyclohexadien-1-one exists totally in its enol form. Write the structure of 2,4-cyclohexadien-1-one and of its enol form. What special factor accounts for the stability of the enol form?

17.3 REACTIONS VIA ENOLS AND ENOLATE IONS

17.3A RACEMIZATION

When a solution of (+)-*sec*-butyl phenyl ketone (see following reaction) in aqueous ethanol is treated with either acids or bases, the solution gradually loses its optical activity. After a time, isolation of the ketone shows that it has been racemized.

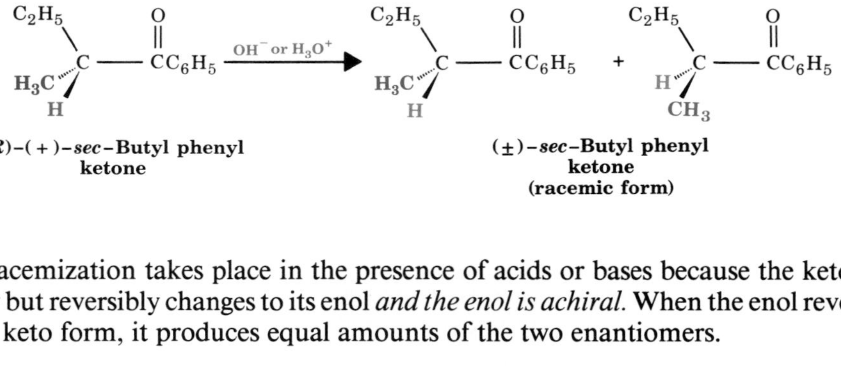

(*R*)-(+)-*sec*-Butyl phenyl ketone

(±)-*sec*-Butyl phenyl ketone (racemic form)

Racemization takes place in the presence of acids or bases because the ketone slowly but reversibly changes to its enol *and the enol is achiral.* When the enol reverts to the keto form, it produces equal amounts of the two enantiomers.

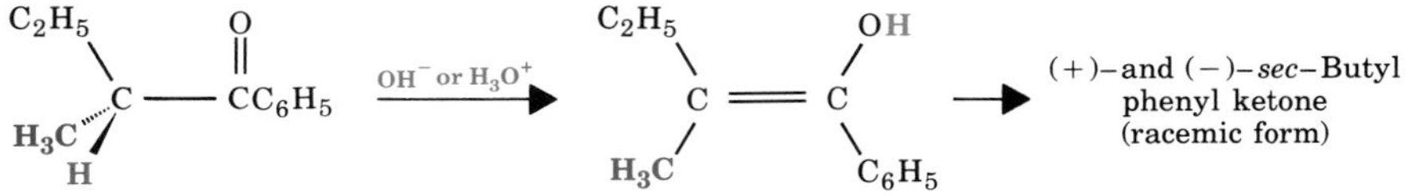

(*R*)-(+)-*sec*-Butyl phenyl ketone (chiral)

Enol (achiral)

Base catalyzes the formation of an enol through the intermediate formation of an enolate ion:

Base-Catalyzed Enolization

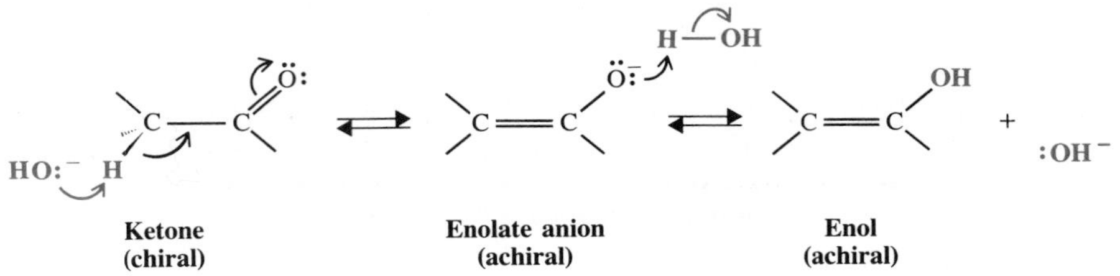
H—OH
Ö:
Ö:
OH
C
C
C=C
C=C
+
:OH⁻
HO:⁻ H
Ketone
(chiral)
Enolate anion
(achiral)
Enol
(achiral)

Acid can catalyze enolization in the following way:

Acid-Catalyzed Enolization

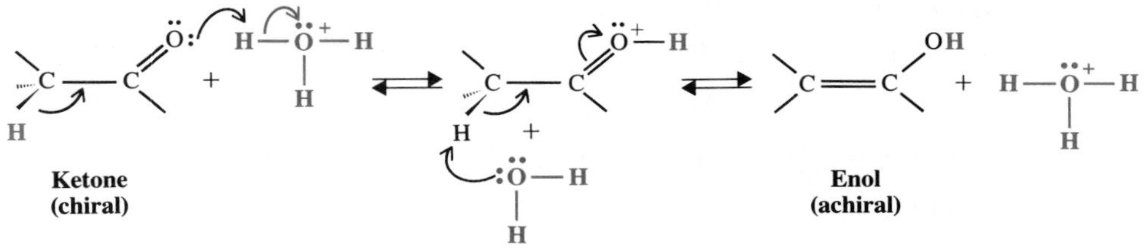
Ö:
H—Ö⁺—H
H
+
H
C
C
Ö⁺—H
H +
:Ö—H
H
OH
C=C
+ H—Ö⁺—H
H
Ketone
(chiral)
Enol
(achiral)

Problem 17.2

Would you expect optically active ketones such as the following to undergo acid- or base-catalyzed racemization? Explain your answer.

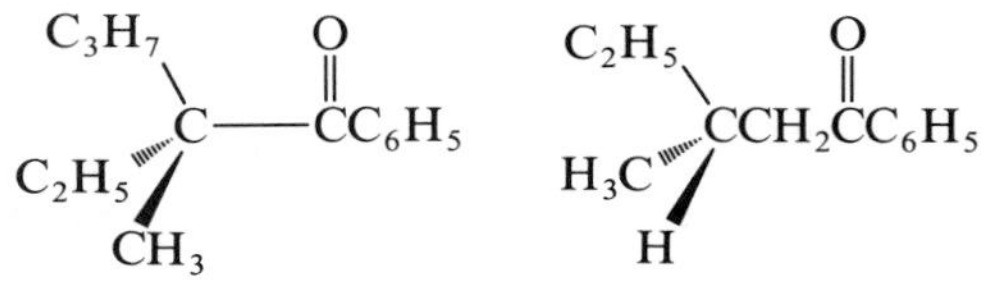
C₃H₇
O
C—CC₆H₅
C₂H₅
CH₃
C₂H₅
O
CCH₂CC₆H₅
H₃C
H

Problem 17.3

When *sec*-butyl phenyl ketone is treated with either OD^- or D_3O^+ in the presence of D_2O, the ketone undergoes hydrogen–deuterium exchange and produces:

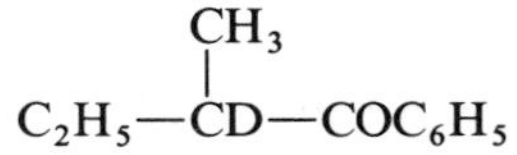
CH₃
C₂H₅—CD—COC₆H₅

Write mechanisms that account for this behavior.

17.3B HALOGENATION OF KETONES

Ketones that have an α hydrogen react readily with halogens by substitution. The rates of these halogenation reactions *increase when acids or bases are added and substitution takes place almost exclusively at the α carbon:*

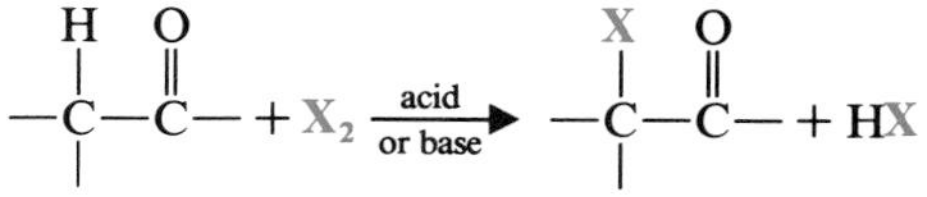

$$-\overset{H}{\underset{|}{\underset{|}{C}}}-\overset{O}{\underset{\|}{C}}-+X_2 \xrightarrow[\text{or base}]{\text{acid}} -\overset{X}{\underset{|}{\underset{|}{C}}}-\overset{O}{\underset{\|}{C}}-+HX$$

This behavior of ketones can be accounted for in terms of two related properties that we have already encountered: the acidity of the α hydrogens of ketones and the tendency of ketones to form enols.

Base-Promoted Halogenation

In the presence of bases, halogenation takes place through the slow formation of an enolate ion or an enol, followed by a rapid reaction of the enolate ion or enol with halogen.

1.

   Enolate ion   Enol

2a.

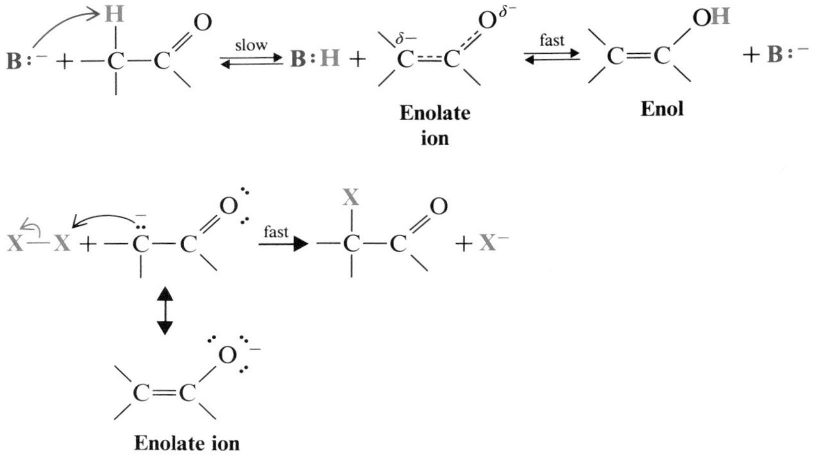

    Enolate ion

or

2b.

    Enol

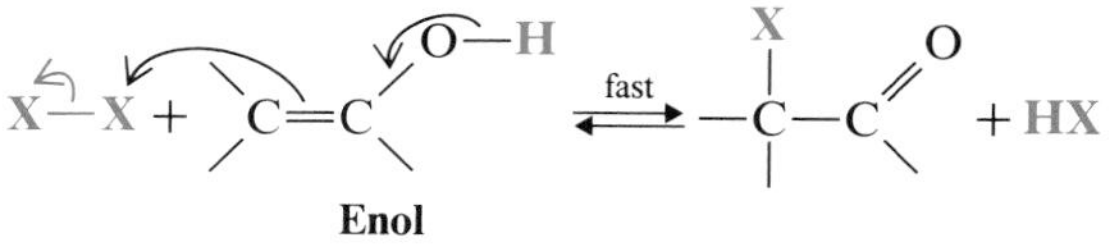

As we shall see in Section 17.4 multiple halogenations can occur.

Acid-Catalyzed Halogenation

In the presence of acids, halogenation takes place through slow formation of an enol followed by rapid reaction of the enol with the halogen.

1.

   Enol

2.

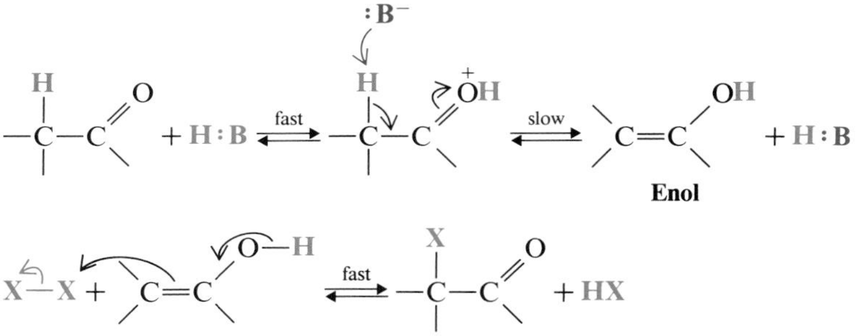

Part of the evidence that supports these mechanisms comes from studies of reaction kinetics. Both base-promoted and acid-catalyzed halogenations of ketones *show initial rates that are independent of the halogen concentration.* The mechanisms that we have written are in accord with this observation: In both instances the slow step of the mechanism occurs prior to the intervention of the halogen. (The initial rates are also independent of the nature of the halogen, see Problem 17.5.)

Problem 17.4 ——————————————————————————————————

Why do we say that the first reaction is "base promoted" rather than "base catalyzed?"

Problem 17.5 ——————————————————————————————————

Additional evidence for the halogenation mechanisms that we just presented comes from the following facts: (a) Optically active *sec*-butyl phenyl ketone undergoes acid-catalyzed racemization at a rate exactly equivalent to the rate at which it undergoes acid-catalyzed halogenation. (b) *sec*-Butyl phenyl ketone undergoes acid-catalyzed iodination at the same rate that it undergoes acid-catalyzed bromination. (c) *sec*-Butyl phenyl ketone undergoes base-catalyzed hydrogen–deuterium exchange at the same rate that it undergoes base-promoted halogenation. Explain how each of these observations supports the mechanisms that we have presented.

17.4 THE HALOFORM REACTION

When methyl ketones react with halogens in the presence of base (cf. Section 17.3), multiple halogenations always occur at the carbon of the methyl group. Multiple

$$\underset{\substack{|\\ H}}{\overset{\substack{O\ \ H\\ \|\ \ |}}{C_6H_5-C-C-H}} + 3\ X_2 + 3\ OH^- \xrightarrow{\text{base}} \underset{\substack{|\\ X}}{\overset{\substack{O\ \ X\\ \|\ \ |}}{C_6H_5-C-C-X}} + 3\ X^- + 3\ H_2O$$

halogenations occur because introduction of the first halogen (owing to its electronegativity) makes the remaining α hydrogens on the methyl carbon more acidic.

Enolate ion

Acidity is
increased by
electron-withdrawing
halogen

17.4 THE HALOFORM REACTION

When methyl ketones react with halogens in aqueous sodium hydroxide (i.e., in *hypohalite solutions**), an additional reaction takes place. Hydroxide ion attacks the carbonyl carbon atom of the trihalo ketone and causes a cleavage at the carbon–carbon bond between the carbonyl group and the trihalomethyl group, a moderately good leaving group. This cleavage ultimately produces a carboxylate ion and a *haloform* (i.e., either $CHCl_3$, $CHBr_3$, or CHI_3). The initial step is a nucleophilic attack by hydroxide ion on the carbonyl carbon atom. In the next step carbon–carbon bond cleavage occurs and the trihalomethyl anion ($:CX_3^-$) departs. This is one of the rare instances in which a carbanion acts as a leaving group. This step can occur because the trihalomethyl anion is unusually stable; its negative charge is dispersed by the three electronegative halogen atoms. In the last step, a proton transfer takes place between the carboxylic acid and the trihalomethyl anion.

The haloform reaction is of synthetic utility as a means of converting methyl ketones to carboxylic acids. When the haloform reaction is used in synthesis, chlorine and bromine are most commonly used as the halogen component. Chloroform ($CHCl_3$) and bromoform ($CHBr_3$) are both liquids and are easily separated from the acid.

When water is chlorinated in order to purify it for public consumption, chloroform is produced from organic impurities in the water via the haloform reaction. (Many of these organic impurities are naturally occurring, such as humic substances.) The presence of chloroform in public water is of concern for water treatment plants and environmental officers, because chloroform is carcinogenic. Thus, the technology that solves one problem creates another. It is worthwhile recalling, however, that before chlorination of water was introduced, thousands of people died in epidemics of diseases, such as cholera and dysentery.

---

*Dissolving a halogen in aqueous sodium hydroxide produces a solution containing sodium hypohalite (NaOX) because of the following equilibrium:

$$X_2 + 2\,NaOH \rightleftharpoons NaOX + NaX + H_2O$$

17.4A THE IODOFORM TEST

The haloform reaction using iodine and aqueous sodium hydroxide is called the *iodoform test*. The iodoform test was once frequently used in structure determinations (before the advent of NMR spectral analysis) because it allows identification of the following two groups:

$$-\overset{\|}{\underset{O}{C}}-CH_3 \quad \text{and} \quad -\overset{\|}{\underset{OH}{CH}}-CH_3$$

Compounds containing either of these groups react with iodine in sodium hydroxide to give a bright yellow precipitate of *iodoform* (CHI_3, mp 119 °C). Compounds containing the $-CHOHCH_3$ group give a positive iodoform test because they are first oxidized to methyl ketones:

$$-\underset{OH}{\overset{|}{CH}}CH_3 + I_2 + 2\,OH^- \longrightarrow -\underset{O}{\overset{\|}{C}}CH_3 + 2\,I^- + 2\,H_2O$$

Methyl ketones then react with iodine and hydroxide ion to produce iodoform:

$$-\underset{O}{\overset{\|}{C}}-CH_3 + 3\,I_2 + 3\,OH^- \longrightarrow -\underset{O}{\overset{\|}{C}}-CI_3 + 3\,I^- + 3\,H_2O$$

$$-\underset{O}{\overset{\|}{C}}-CI_3 + OH^- \longrightarrow -\underset{O}{\overset{\|}{C}}-O^- + \quad CHI_3\downarrow$$

Yellow
precipitate

The group to which the $-COCH_3$ or $-CHOHCH_3$ function is attached can be aryl, alkyl, or hydrogen. Thus, even ethanol and acetaldehyde give positive iodoform tests.

Problem 17.6

Which of the following compounds would give a positive iodoform test?

(a) Acetone   (e) 3-Pentanone   (i) Methyl 2-naphthyl ketone
(b) Acetophenone   (f) 1-Phenylethanol   (j) 3-Pentanol
(c) Pentanal   (g) 2-Phenylethanol
(d) 2-Pentanone   (h) 2-Butanol

17.5 THE ALDOL REACTION: THE ADDITION OF ENOLATE IONS TO ALDEHYDES AND KETONES

When acetaldehyde reacts with dilute sodium hydroxide at room temperature (or below), a dimerization takes place producing 3-hydroxybutanal. Since 3-hydroxy-

17.5 THE ALDOL REACTION: THE ADDITION OF ENOLATE IONS TO ALDEHYDES AND KETONES

$$2 \ CH_3CH \xrightarrow[5\ °C]{10\%\ NaOH,\ H_2O} CH_3CHCH_2CH$$

3-Hydroxybutanal
"aldol"
(50%)

butanal is both an **aldeh**yde and an alcoho**l**, it has been given the common name "**aldol**," and reactions of this general type have come to be known as **aldol additions** (or **aldol reactions**).

The mechanism for the aldol addition illustrates two important characteristics of carbonyl compounds: the acidity of their α hydrogens and the tendency of their carbonyl groups to undergo nucleophilic addition.

In the first step, the base (hydroxide ion) abstracts a proton from the α carbon of one molecule of acetaldehyde to give a resonance-stabilized enolate ion.

Step 1

$$HO:^- + H-CH_2CH \rightleftharpoons HOH + \left[:CH_2-CH \leftrightarrow CH_2=CH \right]$$

Enolate ion

In the second step the enolate ion acts as a nucleophile — *as a carbanion* — and attacks the carbonyl carbon atom of a second molecule of acetaldehyde. This step gives an alkoxide ion.

Step 2

$$CH_3CH + :CH_2-CH \rightleftharpoons CH_3CHCH_2CH$$

An alkoxide ion

$$CH_2=CH$$

In the third step, the alkoxide ion abstracts a proton from water to form aldol. This step takes place because the alkoxide ion is a stronger base than a hydroxide ion.

Step 3

$$CH_3CHCH_2CH + HOH \rightleftharpoons CH_3CHCH_2CH + :OH$$

Stronger base   Aldol   Weaker base

17.5A DEHYDRATION OF ADDITION PRODUCT

If the basic mixture containing the aldol (in the previous example) is heated, dehydration takes place and crotonaldehyde (2-butenal) is formed. Dehydration occurs readily because of the acidity of the remaining α hydrogens (even though the leaving group is a hydroxide ion) *and because the product is stabilized by having conjugated double bonds.*

$$\overset{..}{HO}{:}^- + CH_3CH-\overset{OH}{\underset{\underset{H}{Cl}}{CH}}-\overset{O}{\overset{\|}{CH}} \xrightarrow{-H_2O} CH_3CH-\overset{OH}{\underset{..^-}{CH}}-\overset{O}{\overset{\|}{CH}} \xrightarrow{-OH^-} CH_3CH=CH-\overset{O}{\overset{\|}{CH}}$$

Crotonaldehyde
(2-butenal)

In some aldol reactions, dehydration occurs so readily that we cannot isolate the product in the aldol form; we obtain the derived *enal* instead. An **aldol condensation** occurs rather than an aldol *addition*. A condensation reaction is one in which molecules are joined through the intermolecular elimination of a small molecule such as water or an alcohol.

Addition product   **Condensation product**

$$2\,RCH_2\overset{O}{\overset{\|}{CH}} \xrightarrow{base} \left[RCH_2\overset{OH}{\underset{\underset{R}{|}}{CH}}CH\overset{O}{\overset{\|}{CH}} \right] \xrightarrow{-H_2O} RCH_2CH=\overset{O}{\underset{\underset{R}{|}}{C}}-\overset{\|}{CH}$$

Not isolated   **An enal**

17.5B SYNTHETIC APPLICATIONS

The aldol reaction is a general reaction of aldehydes that possess an α hydrogen. Propanal, for example, reacts with aqueous sodium hydroxide to give 3-hydroxy-2-methylpentanal.

$$2\,CH_3CH_2\overset{O}{\overset{\|}{CH}} \xrightarrow[0-10\,°C]{OH^-} CH_3CH_2\overset{OH}{\underset{\underset{CH_3}{|}}{CH}}CH\overset{O}{\overset{\|}{CH}}$$

Propanal   **3-Hydroxy-2-methylpentanal**

(55–60%)

Problem 17.7

(a) Show all steps in the aldol addition that occur when propanal

$$\left(CH_3CH_2\overset{O}{\overset{\|}{CH}} \right)$$ is treated with base.   (b) How can you account for the fact that

the product of the aldol addition is $CH_3CH_2\overset{OH}{\underset{\underset{CH_3}{|}}{CH}}CH\overset{O}{\overset{\|}{CH}}$ and not

$CH_3CH_2\overset{OH}{\underset{|}{CH}}CH_2CH_2\overset{O}{\overset{\|}{CH}}$?   (c) What product would be formed if the reaction mixture were heated?

The aldol reaction is important in organic synthesis because it gives us a method for linking two smaller molecules by introducing a carbon–carbon bond between them. Because aldol products contain two functional groups, —OH and —CHO, we can use them to carry out a number of subsequent reactions. Examples are the following:

$$
2\ RCH_2CH\overset{O}{\overset{\|}{}}\ \xrightarrow[H_2O]{OH^-}\ RCH_2\overset{OH}{\overset{|}{C}}H\overset{O}{\overset{\|}{C}}HCH\ \xrightarrow{NaBH_4}\ RCH_2\overset{OH}{\overset{|}{C}}HCHCH_2OH
$$

Aldehyde   An aldol   A 1,3-diol

$$H^+ \downarrow -H_2O$$

$$
RCH_2CH_2\overset{}{\underset{R}{C}}HCH_2OH\ \xleftarrow[\substack{high \\ pressure}]{H_2/Ni}\ RCH_2CH{=}\overset{O}{\overset{\|}{C}}CH\ \xrightarrow{LiAlH_4*}\ RCH_2CH{=}\underset{R}{C}CH_2OH
$$

A saturated alcohol   An α,β-unsaturated   An allylic alcohol
                              aldehyde

$$\downarrow H_2,\ Pd-C$$

$$
RCH_2CH_2\underset{R}{C}H\overset{O}{\overset{\|}{C}}H
$$

An aldehyde

Problem 17.8

One industrial process for the synthesis of 1-butanol begins with acetaldehyde. Show how this synthesis might be carried out.

Problem 17.9

Show how each of the following products could be synthesized from butanal:
(a) 2-Ethyl-3-hydroxyhexanal
(b) 2-Ethyl-2-hexen-1-ol
(c) 2-Ethyl-1-hexanol
(d) 2-Ethyl-1,3-hexanediol (the insect repellent "6–12")

Ketones also undergo base-catalyzed aldol additions, but for them the equilibrium is unfavorable. This complication can be overcome, however, by carrying out the reaction in a special apparatus that allows the product to be removed from contact with the base as it is formed. This removal of product displaces the equilibrium to the right and permits successful aldol additions with many ketones. Acetone, for example, reacts as follows:

$$
2\ CH_3\overset{O}{\overset{\|}{C}}CH_3\ \underset{}{\overset{OH^-}{\rightleftharpoons}}\ CH_3\overset{OH}{\underset{CH_3}{\overset{|}{C}}}CH_2\overset{O}{\overset{\|}{C}}CH_3
$$

(80%)

*LiAlH$_4$ reduces the carbonyl group of α, β-unsaturated aldehydes and ketones cleanly. NaBH$_4$ often reduces the carbon–carbon double bond as well.

Problem 17.10

(a) Write a mechanism for an aldol-type (ketol) addition of acetone in base.

(b) What compound would you obtain when the product is dehydrated?

17.5C THE REVERSIBILITY OF ALDOL ADDITIONS

The aldol addition is reversible. If, for example, the aldol addition product obtained from acetone (see Problem 17.10) is heated with a strong base, it reverts to an equilibrium mixture that consists largely ($\sim 95\%$) of acetone. This type of reaction is called a *retro-aldol* reaction.

$$\underset{\substack{| \\ CH_3 \\ \textbf{(5\%)}}}{\overset{\substack{OH \quad\;\; O \\ | \qquad\; \parallel}}{CH_3C-CH_2CCH_3}} \underset{H_2O}{\overset{OH^-}{\rightleftharpoons}} \underset{\substack{| \\ CH_3}}{\overset{\substack{O^- \quad\; O \\ | \qquad \parallel}}{CH_3C-CH_2CCH_3}} \rightleftharpoons \underset{\substack{| \\ CH_3}}{\overset{\substack{O \\ \parallel}}{CH_3C}} + {}^-{:}CH_2CCH_3 \underset{OH^-}{\overset{H_2O}{\rightleftharpoons}} \underset{\textbf{(95\%)}}{\overset{\substack{O \\ \parallel}}{2\,CH_3CCH_3}}$$

17.6 CROSSED ALDOL REACTIONS

An aldol reaction that starts with two different carbonyl compounds is called a **crossed aldol reaction**. Crossed aldol reactions using aqueous sodium hydroxide solutions are of little synthetic importance if both reactants have α hydrogens, because these reactions give a complex mixture of products. If, for example, we were to carry out a crossed aldol addition using acetaldehyde and propanal, we would obtain at least four products.

$$\overset{\substack{O \\ \parallel}}{CH_3CH} + \overset{\substack{O \\ \parallel}}{CH_3CH_2CH} \underset{H_2O}{\overset{OH^-}{\longrightarrow}} \overset{\substack{OH \quad\; O \\ | \qquad \parallel}}{CH_3CHCH_2CH} + \underset{\substack{| \\ CH_3}}{\overset{\substack{OH \quad\; O \\ | \qquad \parallel}}{CH_3CH_2CHCHCH}}$$

3-Hydroxybutanal	3-Hydroxy-2-
(from 2 molecules	methylpentanal
of acetaldehyde)	(from 2 molecules
	of propanal)

$$+ \quad \underset{\substack{| \\ CH_3}}{\overset{\substack{OH \quad\; O \\ | \qquad \parallel}}{CH_3CHCHCH}} \quad \text{and} \quad \overset{\substack{OH \qquad O \\ | \qquad\quad \parallel}}{CH_3CH_2CHCH_2CH}$$

3-Hydroxy-2-methylbutanal   **3-Hydroxypentanal**
(from 1 molecule of acetaldehyde and 1 molecule of propanal)

Sample Problem

Show how each of the four products just given is formed in the crossed aldol addition between acetaldehyde and propanal.

Answer:

In the basic aqueous solution, four organic entities will be present: molecules of acetaldehyde, molecules of propanal, enolate ions derived from acetaldehyde, and enolate ions derived from propanal.

We have already seen (Section 17.5) how a molecule of acetaldehyde can react with its enolate ion to form 3-hydroxybutanal (aldol).

Reaction 1

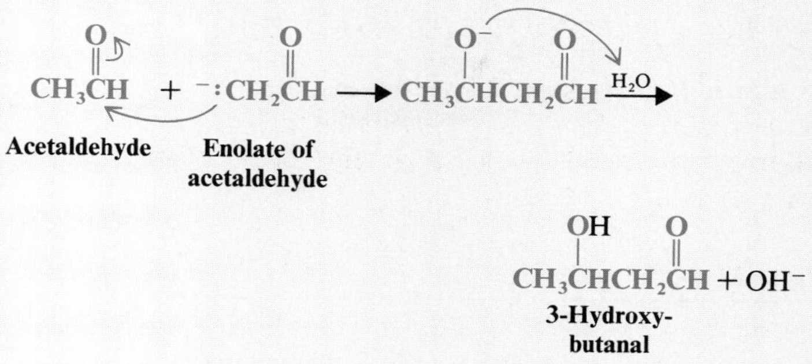

$$CH_3CH + \ ^-:CH_2CH \longrightarrow CH_3CHCH_2CH \xrightarrow{H_2O}$$

Acetaldehyde   Enolate of acetaldehyde

$$CH_3CHCH_2CH + OH^-$$
          OH   O

3-Hydroxy-butanal

We have also seen (Problem 17.7) how propanal can react with its enolate ion to form 3-hydroxy-2-methylpentanal.

Reaction 2

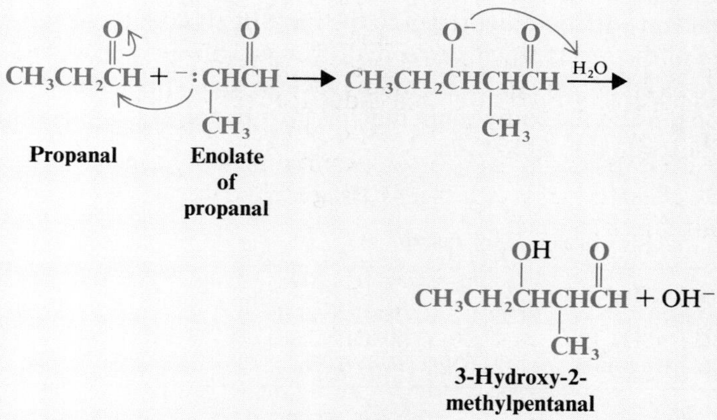

$$CH_3CH_2CH + \ ^-:CHCH \longrightarrow CH_3CH_2CHCHCH \xrightarrow{H_2O}$$
                        | |
                       CH_3   CH_3

Propanal   Enolate of propanal

$$CH_3CH_2CHCHCH + OH^-$$
          OH   O
                |
               CH_3

3-Hydroxy-2-methylpentanal

Acetaldehyde can also react with the enolate of propanal. This reaction leads to the third product, 3-hydroxy-2-methylbutanal.

Reaction 3

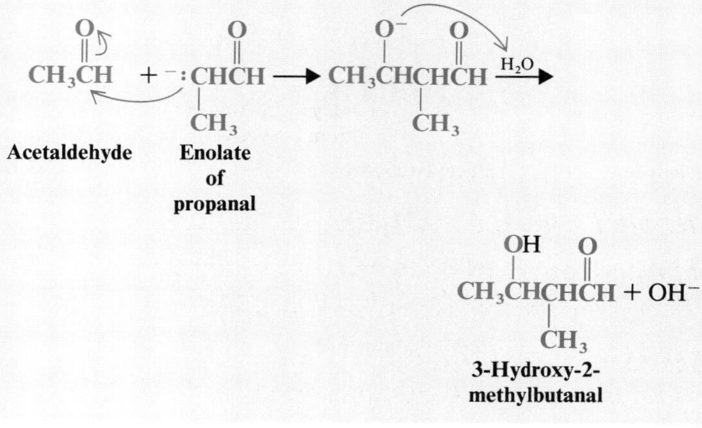

$$CH_3CH + \ ^-:CHCH \longrightarrow CH_3CHCHCH \xrightarrow{H_2O}$$
                    | |
                   CH_3   CH_3

Acetaldehyde   Enolate of propanal

$$CH_3CHCHCH + OH^-$$
          OH   O
                |
               CH_3

3-Hydroxy-2-methylbutanal

And finally, propanal can react with the enolate of acetaldehyde. This reaction accounts for the fourth product.

Reaction 4 $CH_3CH_2CH + ^-:CH_2CH \longrightarrow CH_3CH_2CHCH_2CH \xrightarrow{H_2O}$

Propanal   **Enolate of acetaldehyde**

$$CH_3CH_2CHCH_2CH + OH^-$$
3-Hydroxypentanal

17.6A PRACTICAL CROSSED ALDOL REACTIONS

Crossed aldol reactions are practical, with bases such as NaOH, when one reactant does not have an α hydrogen and, thus, cannot undergo self-condensation. We can avoid other side reactions by placing this component in base and then slowly adding the reactant with an α hydrogen to the mixture. Under these conditions the concentration of the reactant with an α hydrogen will always be low and much of it will be present as an enolate ion. The main reaction that will take place is one between this enolate ion and the component that has no α hydrogen. The examples listed in Table 17.1 illustrate this technique.

TABLE 17.1   Crossed aldol reactions

THIS REACTANT WITH NO α HYDROGEN IS PLACED IN BASE	THIS REACTANT WITH AN α HYDROGEN IS ADDED SLOWLY		PRODUCT
C_6H_5CH (O) Benzaldehyde	+	CH_3CH_2CH (O) Propanal $\xrightarrow[10\,°C]{OH^-}$	$C_6H_5CH{=}C{-}CH$ (CH$_3$, O) 2-Methyl-3-phenyl-2-propenal (α-methylcinnamaldehyde) (68%)
C_6H_5CH (O) Benzaldehyde	+	$C_6H_5CH_2CH$ (O) Phenylacetaldehyde $\xrightarrow[20\,°C]{OH^-}$	$C_6H_5CH{=}CCH$ (O, C_6H_5) 2,3-Diphenyl-2-propenal
HCH (O) Formaldehyde	+	$CH_3CH{-}CH$ (CH$_3$, O) 2-Methylpropanal $\xrightarrow[40\,°C]{dil.\ Na_2CO_3}$	$CH_3{-}C{-}CH$ (CH$_3$, O, CH$_2$OH) 3-Hydroxy-2,2-dimethylpropanal (>64%)

As the examples in Table 17.1 also show, the crossed aldol reaction is often accompanied by dehydration. Whether or not dehydration occurs can, at times, be determined by our choice of reaction conditions, but *dehydration is especially easy when it leads to an extended conjugated system.*

Problem 17.11

Show how you could use a crossed aldol reaction to synthesize cinnamaldehyde ($C_6H_5CH{=}CHCHO$).

Problem 17.12

When excess formaldehyde in basic solution is treated with acetaldehyde, the following reaction takes place:

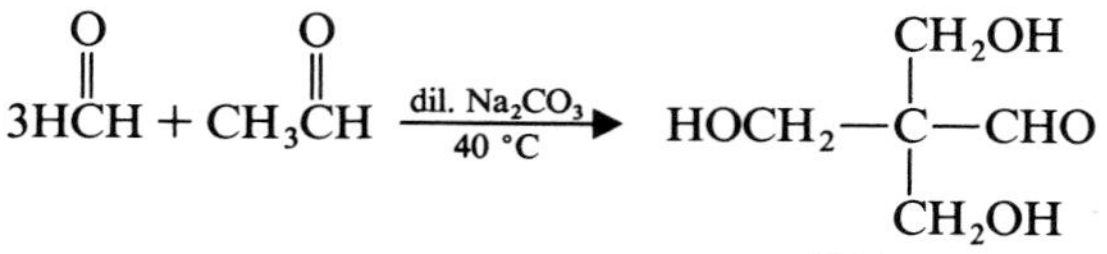

$$3HCH + CH_3CH \xrightarrow[40\ °C]{dil.\ Na_2CO_3} HOCH_2{-}\overset{\displaystyle CH_2OH}{\underset{\displaystyle CH_2OH}{\overset{\displaystyle |}{\underset{\displaystyle |}{C}}}}{-}CHO$$

(82%)

Write a mechanism that accounts for the formation of the product.

17.6B CLAISEN–SCHMIDT REACTIONS

When ketones are used as one component, the crossed aldol reactions are called **Claisen–Schmidt reactions,** after the German chemists, J. G. Schmidt (who discovered the reaction in 1880) and Ludwig Claisen (who developed it between 1881 and 1889). These reactions are practical when bases such as sodium hydroxide are used because, under these conditions ketones do not self-condense appreciably. (The equilibrium is unfavorable; cf. Section 17.5C.)

Two examples of Claisen–Schmidt reactions are the following:

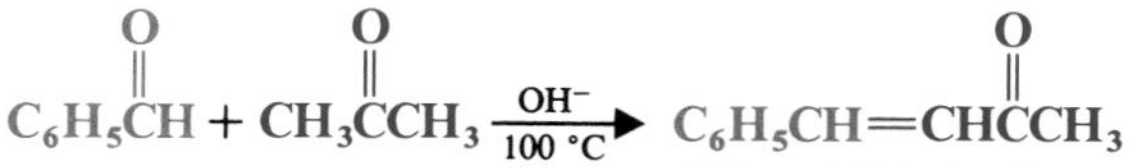

$$C_6H_5CH + CH_3CCH_3 \xrightarrow[100\ °C]{OH^-} C_6H_5CH{=}CHCCH_3$$

4-Phenyl-3-buten-2-one
(benzalacetone)
(70%)

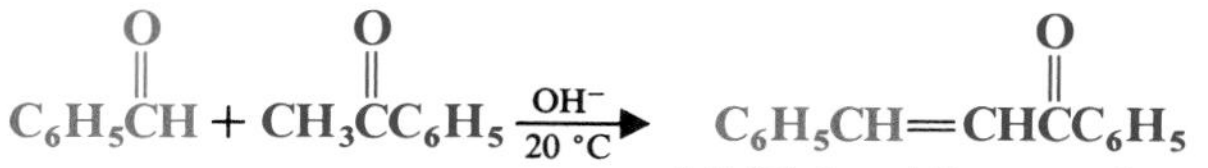

$$C_6H_5CH + CH_3CC_6H_5 \xrightarrow[20\ °C]{OH^-} C_6H_5CH{=}CHCC_6H_5$$

1,3-Diphenyl-2-propen-1-one
(benzalacetophenone)
(85%)

In both of these reactions dehydration occurs readily because the double bond that forms is conjugated both with the carbonyl group and with the benzene ring. The conjugated system is thereby extended.

An important step in a commercial synthesis of vitamin A makes use of a Claisen–Schmidt reaction between geranial and acetone:

Geranial + CH_3CCH_3 $\xrightarrow[\substack{C_2H_5OH \\ -5\,°C}]{C_2H_5ONa}$ **Pseudoionone (49%)**

Geranial is a naturally occurring aldehyde that can be obtained from lemongrass oil. Its α-hydrogen is *vinylic* and, therefore, not appreciably acidic. Notice, in this reaction, too, dehydration occurs readily because dehydration extends the conjugated system.

In Special Topic E we shall study another method of carrying out crossed aldol reactions based on the use of lithium enolates.

Problem 17.13

When pseudoionone is treated with BF_3 in acetic acid, ring closure takes place and α- and β-ionone are produced. This is the next step in the vitamin A synthesis.

Pseudoionone $\xrightarrow[\text{HOAc}]{BF_3}$ **α-Ionone** + **β-Ionone**

(a) Write mechanisms that explain the formation of α- and β-ionone. (b) β-Ionone is the major product. How can you explain this? (c) Which ionone would you expect to absorb at longer wavelengths in the visible–UV region? Why?

17.6C CONDENSATIONS WITH NITROALKANES

The α hydrogens of nitroalkanes are appreciably acidic ($pK_a = 10$), much more acidic than those of aldehydes and ketones. The acidity of these hydrogen atoms, like the α hydrogens of aldehydes and ketones, can be explained by resonance stabilization of the anion that is produced.

Resonance-stabilized anion

Nitroalkanes that have α hydrogens undergo base-catalyzed condensations with aldehydes and ketones that resemble aldol condensations. An example is the condensation of benzaldehyde with nitromethane.

$$C_6H_5\overset{\overset{\displaystyle O}{\|}}{C}H + CH_3NO_2 \xrightarrow{OH^-} C_6H_5CH{=}CHNO_2$$

This condensation is especially useful because the nitro group of the product can be easily reduced to an amino group. One technique that will bring about this transformation uses hydrogen and a nickel catalyst. This combination not only reduces the nitro group but also reduces the double bond:

$$C_6H_5CH{=}CHNO_2 \xrightarrow{\text{H}_2,\,\text{Ni}} C_6H_5CH_2CH_2NH_2$$

Problem 17.14

Assuming that you have available the required aldehydes, ketones, and nitro-alkanes, show how you would synthesize each of the following:

(a) $C_6H_5CH{=}\underset{\underset{CH_3}{|}}{C}NO_2$ (b) $HOCH_2CH_2NO_2$ (c)

17.6D CONDENSATIONS WITH NITRILES

The α hydrogens of nitriles are also appreciably acidic, but less so than aldehydes and ketones. The acidity constant for acetonitrile (CH_3CN) is about 10^{-25} ($pK_a \sim 25$). Other nitriles with α hydrogens show comparable acidities, and consequently these nitriles undergo condensations of the aldol type. An example is the condensation of benzaldehyde with phenylacetonitrile.

$$C_6H_5\overset{O}{\overset{\|}{C}}H + C_6H_5CH_2CN \xrightarrow{\text{EtO}^-/\text{EtOH}} C_6H_5CH{=}\underset{\underset{C_6H_5}{|}}{C}{-}CN$$

Problem 17.15

(a) Write resonance structures for the anion of acetonitrile that account for its being much more acidic than ethane.   (b) Give a step-by-step mechanism for the condensation of benzaldehyde with acetonitrile.

17.7 CYCLIZATIONS VIA ALDOL CONDENSATIONS

The aldol condensation also offers a convenient way to synthesize molecules with five- and six-membered rings (and sometimes even larger rings). This can be done by an intramolecular aldol condensation using a dialdehyde, a keto aldehyde, or a diketone as the substrate. For example, the following keto aldehyde cyclizes to yield 1-cyclopentenyl methyl ketone.

$$CH_3\overset{O}{\overset{\|}{C}}CH_2CH_2CH_2CH_2\overset{O}{\overset{\|}{C}}H \xrightarrow{\text{OH}^-}$$

(73%)

This reaction almost certainly involves the formation of at least three different enolates. However, it is the following enolate from the ketone side of the molecule that adds to the aldehyde group that leads to the product.

This enolate leads to the product

$$CH_3\overset{O}{\overset{\|}{C}}CH_2CH_2CH_2CH_2\overset{O}{\overset{\|}{C}}H \xrightarrow{OH^-} CH_3\overset{O}{\overset{\|}{C}}\overset{..}{\overset{..}{C}}HCH_2CH_2CH_2\overset{O}{\overset{\|}{C}}H \longrightarrow$$

The reason the aldehyde group undergoes addition preferentially may arise from the greater activity of aldehydes toward nucleophilic addition generally. The carbonyl carbon atom of a ketone is less positive (and therefore less reactive toward a nucleophile) because it bears two electron-releasing alkyl groups; it is also more sterically hindered.

$$\underset{\substack{\textbf{Ketones are less}\\ \textbf{reactive toward}\\ \textbf{nucleophiles}}}{R\!\!\succ\!\!\overset{O}{\overset{\|}{C}}\!\!\prec\!\!R} \qquad \underset{\substack{\textbf{Aldehydes are more}\\ \textbf{reactive toward}\\ \textbf{nucleophiles}}}{R\!\!\succ\!\!\overset{O}{\overset{\|}{C}}\!\!-\!\!H}$$

In reactions of this type, five-membered rings form far more readily than seven-membered rings.

Problem 17.16

Assuming that dehydration occurs in all instances, write the structures of the two other products that might have resulted from the aldol cyclization just given. (One of these products will have a five-membered ring and the other will have a seven-membered ring.)

Problem 17.17

What starting compound would you use in an aldol cyclization to prepare each of the following?

17.8 ACID-CATALYZED ALDOL CONDENSATIONS

Aldol condensations can also be brought about with acid catalysis. Treating acetone with hydrogen chloride, for example, leads to the formation of 4-methyl-3-penten-2-one, the aldol condensation product. In general, acid-catalyzed aldol reactions lead to dehydration of the initially formed aldol addition product.

The mechanism begins with acid-catalyzed formation of the enol:

$$CH_3CCH_3 + H-Cl \rightleftharpoons CH_3C-CH_2-H + Cl^- \rightleftharpoons CH_3C=CH_2 + HCl$$

Then the enol adds to the protonated carbonyl group of another molecule of acetone:

$$CH_3C=CH_2 + C=OH^+ \rightleftharpoons CH_3C-CH_2-C-OH$$

Then dehydration occurs leading to the product.

$$CH_3C-CH_2-C-OH \rightleftharpoons CH_3C-CH-C-OH_2 \xrightarrow{-H_2O, -H^+} CH_3CCH=CCH_3$$

4-Methyl-3-penten-2-one

Problem 17.18

The acid-catalyzed aldol condensation of acetone (just shown) also produces some 2,6-dimethyl-2,5-heptadien-4-one. Give a mechanism that explains the formation of this product.

Problem 17.19

Heating acetone with sulfuric acid leads to the formation of mesitylene (1,3,5-trimethylbenzene). Propose a mechanism for this reaction.

17.9 ADDITIONS TO α,β-UNSATURATED ALDEHYDES AND KETONES

When α,β-unsaturated aldehydes and ketones react with nucleophilic reagents, they may do so in two ways. They may react by a *simple addition,* that is, one in which the nucleophile adds across the double bond of the carbonyl group; or they may react by a *conjugate addition.* These two processes resemble the 1,2- and the 1,4-addition reactions of conjugated dienes (Section 12.9).

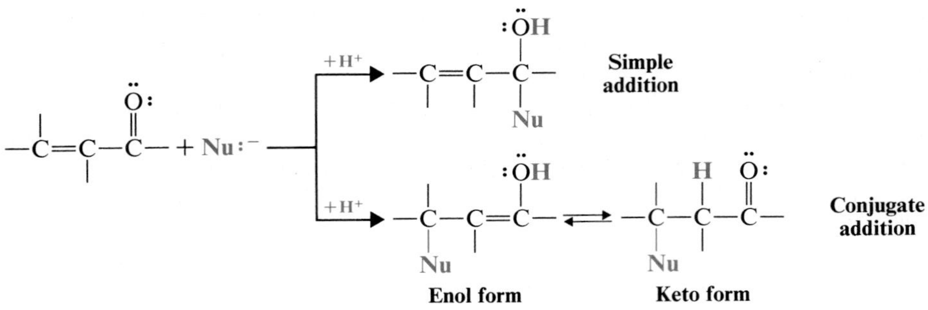

In many instances both modes of addition occur in the same mixture. As an example, let us consider the Grignard reaction shown here.

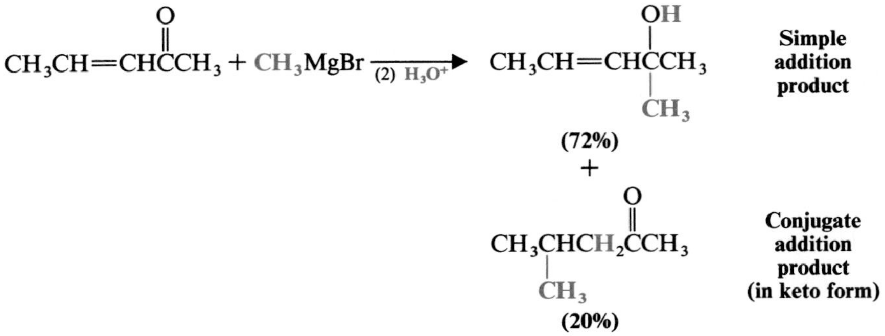

In this example we see that simple addition is favored, but that conjugate addition accounts for a substantial amount of the product.

If we examine the resonance structures that contribute to the overall hybrid for an α,β-unsaturated aldehyde or ketone (see structures **A–C**), we shall be in a better position to understand these reactions.

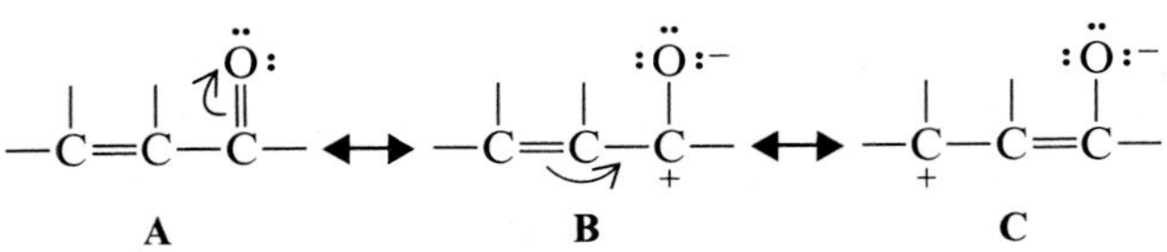

Although structures **B** and **C** involve separated charges, they make a significant contribution to the hybrid because, in each, the negative charge is carried by electronegative oxygen. Structures **B** and **C** not only indicate that the oxygen of the hybrid should bear a partial negative charge, but they also indicate that *both the carbonyl carbon and the β carbon should bear a partial positive charge.* They indicate that we should represent the hybrid in the following way:

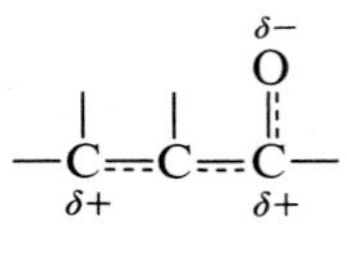

This structure tells us that we should expect an electrophilic reagent to attack the carbonyl oxygen and a nucleophilic reagent to attack either the carbonyl carbon or the β carbon.

This is exactly what happens in the Grignard reactions that we saw earlier. The electrophilic magnesium attacks the carbonyl oxygen; the nucleophilic carbon of the Grignard reagent attacks either the carbonyl carbon or the β carbon.

Simple Addition

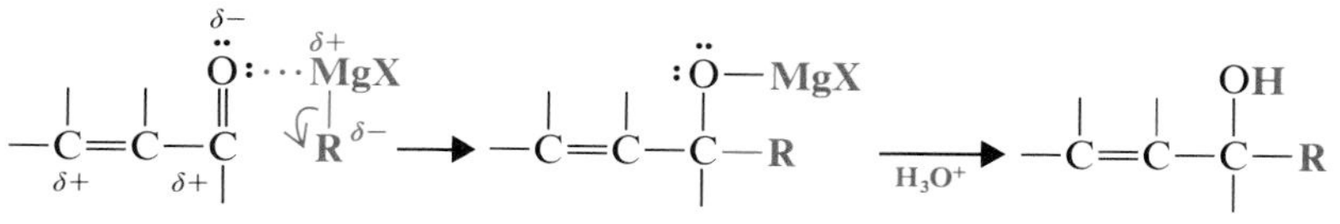

Conjugate Addition

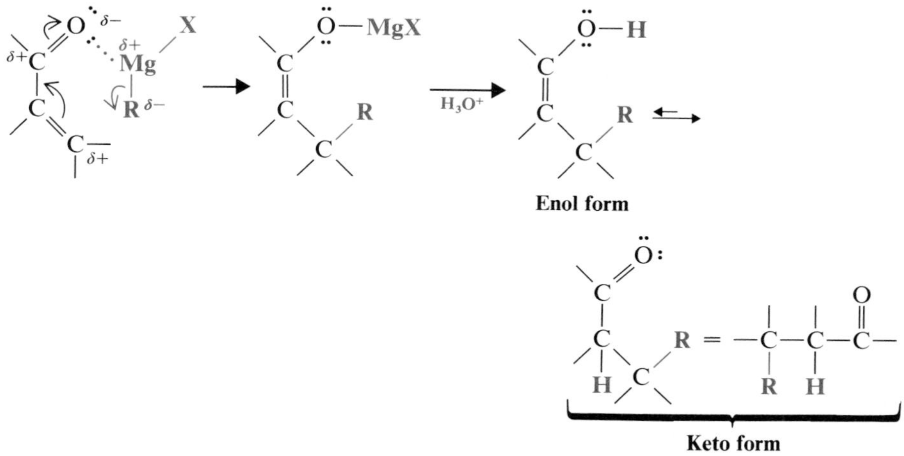

Enol form

Keto form

17.9A ADDITION OF OTHER NUCLEOPHILES

Grignard reagents are not the only nucleophilic reagents that add in a conjugate manner to α,β-unsaturated aldehydes and ketones. Almost every nucleophilic reagent that adds at the carbonyl carbon of a simple aldehyde or ketone is capable of adding at the β carbon of an α,β-unsaturated carbonyl compound. In many instances conjugate addition is the major reaction path:

$$C_6H_5CH{=}CHCC_6H_5 + CN^- \xrightarrow[CH_3CO_2H]{C_2H_5OH} C_6H_5CH{-}CH_2CC_6H_5$$

(95%)

Mechanism

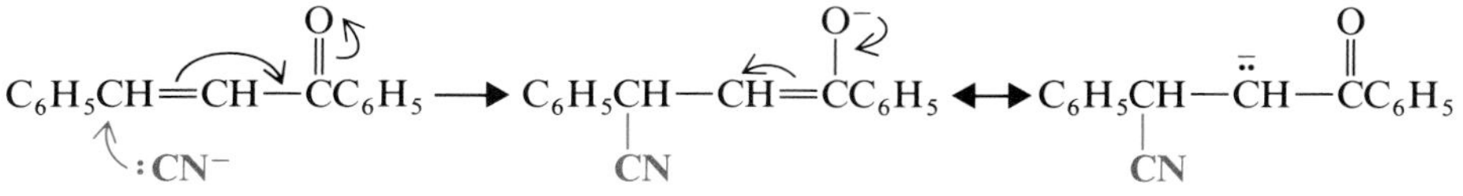

then,

$$C_6H_5CH-\overset{\delta-}{CH}=\!\!=\!\!\overset{O^{\delta-}}{\underset{\underset{CN}{|}}{CC_6H_5}} \xrightarrow{H^+}$$

$$\longrightarrow C_6H_5CH-CH=\overset{\overset{OH}{|}}{\underset{\underset{CN}{|}}{CC_6H_5}} \quad \textbf{Enol form}$$

$$\updownarrow$$

$$\longrightarrow C_6H_5\underset{\underset{CN}{|}}{CH}-CH_2-\overset{\overset{O}{\|}}{C}C_6H_5 \quad \textbf{Keto form}$$

Another example is the following:

$$\overset{\overset{CH_3}{|}}{CH_3C}=\overset{\overset{O}{\|}}{CHCCH_3} + CH_3NH_2 \xrightarrow{H_2O} \overset{\overset{CH_3}{|}}{CH_3C}-\overset{\overset{O}{\|}}{CH_2CCH_3}$$
$$\underset{CH_3NH}{|}$$
$$\textbf{(75\%)}$$

17.9B CONJUGATE ADDITION OF ORGANOCOPPER REAGENTS

Organocopper reagents, either RCu or R_2CuLi, add to α,β-unsaturated carbonyl compounds and, unlike Grignard reagents, **organocopper reagents add almost exclusively in the conjugate manner.**

$$CH_3CH=CH-\overset{\overset{O}{\|}}{C}-CH_3 \xrightarrow[\text{(2) H}_2\text{O}]{\text{(1) CH}_3\text{Cu}} CH_3\underset{\underset{CH_3}{|}}{CH}CH_2\overset{\overset{O}{\|}}{C}CH_3$$
$$\textbf{(85\%)}$$

With an alkyl-substituted cyclic α,β-unsaturated ketone, as the example just cited shows, lithium dialkylcuprates add predominantly in the less-hindered way to give the product with the alkyl groups trans to each other.

17.9C MICHAEL ADDITIONS

Conjugate additions of enolate ions to α,β-unsaturated carbonyl compounds are known generally as Michael additions (after their discoverer, in 1887, Arthur Michael, of Tufts University and later of Harvard University). An example is the addition of cyclohexanone to $C_6H_5CH=CHCOC_6H_5$:

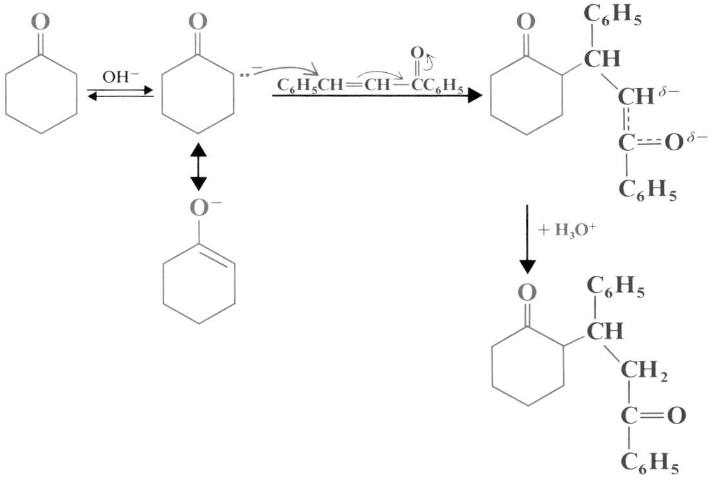

17.9 ADDITIONS TO α,β-UNSATURATED ALDEHYDES AND KETONES

The sequence that follows illustrates how a conjugate aldol addition (Michael addition) followed by a simple aldol condensation may be used to build one ring on to another. This procedure is known as the *Robinson annulation* (ring forming) reaction (after the English chemist, Sir Robert Robinson, who won the Nobel Prize for chemistry in 1947 for his research on naturally occurring compounds).

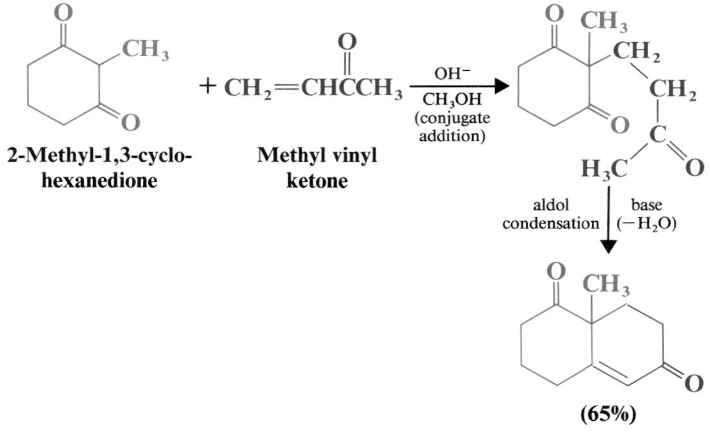

2-Methyl-1,3-cyclo-
hexanedione

Methyl vinyl
ketone

(65%)

Problem 17.20

(a) Propose step-by-step mechanisms for both transformations of the Robinson annulation sequence just shown. (b) Would you expect 2-methyl-1,3-cyclo-hexanedione to be more or less acidic than cyclohexanone? Explain your answer.

Problem 17.21

What product would you expect to obtain from the base-catalyzed Michael reaction (a) of 1,3-diphenyl-2-propen-1-one (Section 17.6B) and acetophenone? (b) of 1,3-diphenyl-2-propen-1-one and cyclopentadiene? Show all steps in each mechanism.

Problem 17.22

When acrolein reacts with hydrazine, the product is a dihydropyrazole:

$$CH_2=CHCHO + H_2N-NH_2 \longrightarrow$$

| Acrolein | Hydrazine | A dihydropyrazole |

Suggest a mechanism that explains this reaction.

We shall study further examples of the Michael addition in Chapter 20.

Additional Problems

17.23   Give structural formulas for the products of the reaction (if one occurs) when propanal is treated with each of the following reagents:

(a) OH^-, H_2O

(b) C_6H_5CHO, OH^-

(c) HCN

(d) $NaBH_4$

(e) $HOCH_2CH_2OH$, H^+

(f) Ag_2O, OH^-, then H^+

(g) CH_3MgI, then H^+

(h) $Ag(NH_3)_2{}^+OH^-$, then H^+

(i) NH_2OH

(j) $C_6H_5\overset{-}{C}H-\overset{+}{P}(C_6H_5)_3$

(k) C_6H_5Li, then H^+

(l) $HC\equiv CNa$, then H^+

(m) $HSCH_2CH_2SH$, H^+, then Raney Ni, H_2

(n) $CH_3CH_2CHBrCO_2Et$ and Zn, then H^+

17.24   Give structural formulas for the products of the reaction (if one occurs) when acetone is treated with each reagent of the preceding problem.

17.25   What products would form when 4-methylbenzaldehyde reacts with each of the following?

(a) CH_3CHO, OH^-

(b) $CH_3C\equiv CNa$, then H^+

(c) CH_3CH_2MgBr, then H^+

(d) Cold dilute $KMnO_4$, OH^-, then H^+

(e) Hot $KMnO_4$, OH^-, then H^+

(f) $^-\!:\!CH_2-\overset{+}{P}(C_6H_5)_3$

(g) $CH_3COC_6H_5$, OH^-

(h) $BrCH_2CO_2Et$ and Zn, then H^+

17.26   Show how each of the following transformations could be accomplished. You may use any other required reagents.

(a) $CH_3COC(CH_3)_3 \longrightarrow C_6H_5CH=CHCOC(CH_3)_3$

(b) $C_6H_5CHO \longrightarrow C_6H_5CH=$

(c) $C_6H_5CHO \longrightarrow C_6H_5CH_2\underset{\underset{\displaystyle CH_3}{|}}{CHNH_2}$

ADDITIONAL PROBLEMS

(d) 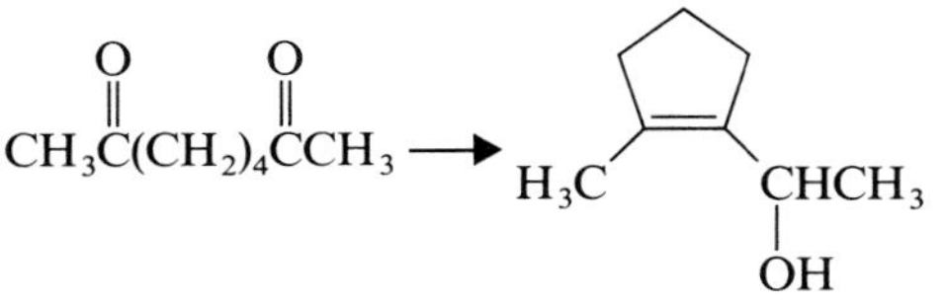 $CH_3\overset{O}{\underset{||}{C}}(CH_2)_4\overset{O}{\underset{||}{C}}CH_3 \longrightarrow$

(e) 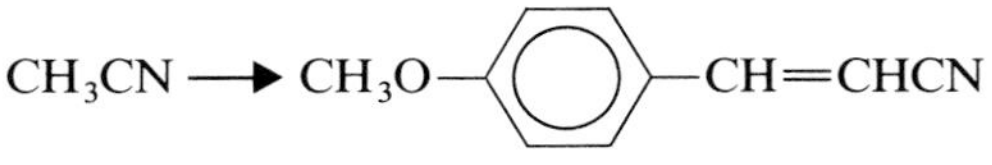 $CH_3CN \longrightarrow CH_3O-\!\!\!\!\bigcirc\!\!\!\!-CH\!\!=\!\!CHCN$

(f) $CH_3CH_2CH_2CH_2\overset{O}{\underset{||}{C}}H \longrightarrow CH_3(CH_2)_3CH\!\!=\!\!\overset{CH_2OH}{\underset{|}{C}}(CH_2)_2CH_3$

(g)

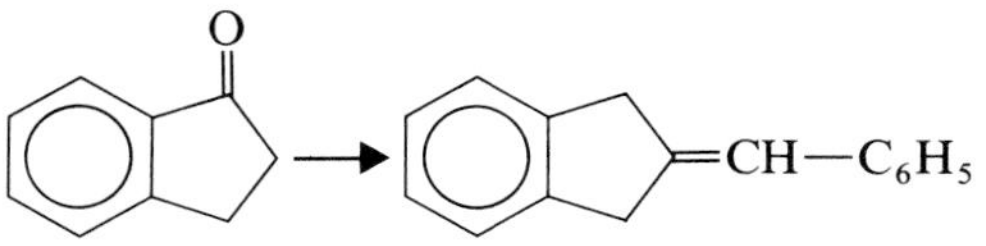

17.27 The following reaction illustrates the Robinson annulation reaction (Section 17.9C). Give mechanisms for the steps that occur.

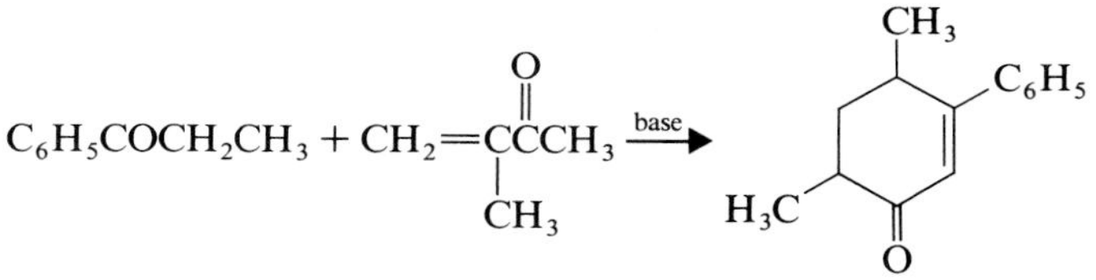

$$C_6H_5COCH_2CH_3 + CH_2\!\!=\!\!\overset{O}{\underset{||}{C}}\overset{|}{\underset{CH_3}{C}}CH_3 \xrightarrow{\text{base}}$$

17.28 Write structural formulas for **A**, **B**, and **C**.

$$HC\!\!\equiv\!\!CH \xrightarrow[\substack{(2)\ CH_3COCH_3 \\ (3)\ NH_4Cl/H_2O}]{(1)\ NaNH_2} \textbf{A}\ (C_5H_8O) \xrightarrow[H_2O]{Hg^{2+},\ H_3O^+} \textbf{B}\ (C_5H_{10}O_2) \xrightarrow{C_6H_5CHO,\ OH^-} \textbf{C}\ (C_{12}H_{14}O_2)$$

17.29 The hydrogen atoms of the γ carbon of crotonaldehyde are appreciably acidic ($pK_a \sim 20$).

(a) Write resonance structures that will explain this fact.

$$\overset{\gamma}{C}H_3\overset{\beta}{C}H\!\!=\!\!\overset{\alpha}{C}HCHO$$
Crotonaldehyde

(b) Write a mechanism that accounts for the following reaction:

$$C_6H_5CH\!\!=\!\!CHCHO + CH_3CH\!\!=\!\!CHCHO \xrightarrow[C_2H_5OH]{\text{base}} C_6H_5(CH\!\!=\!\!CH)_3CHO$$
$$\textbf{(87\%)}$$

17.30 What reagents would you use to bring about each step of the following syntheses?

(a)

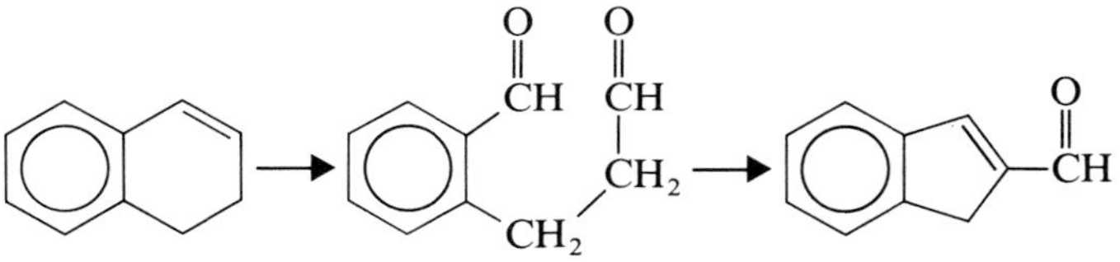

(b)

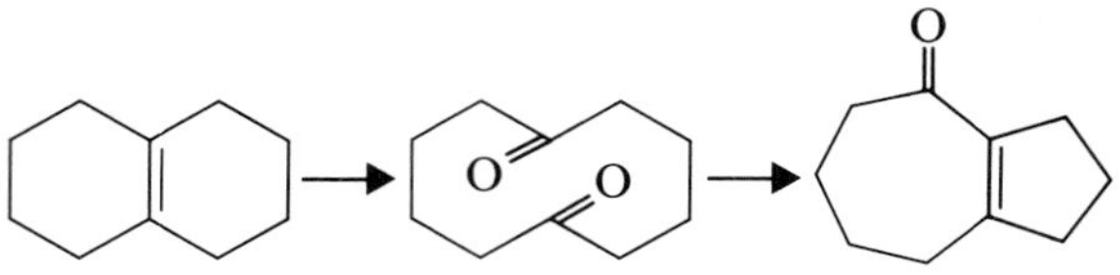

(c)

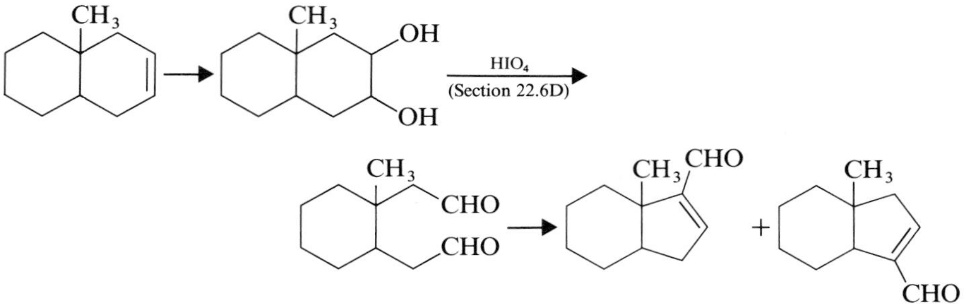

(d)

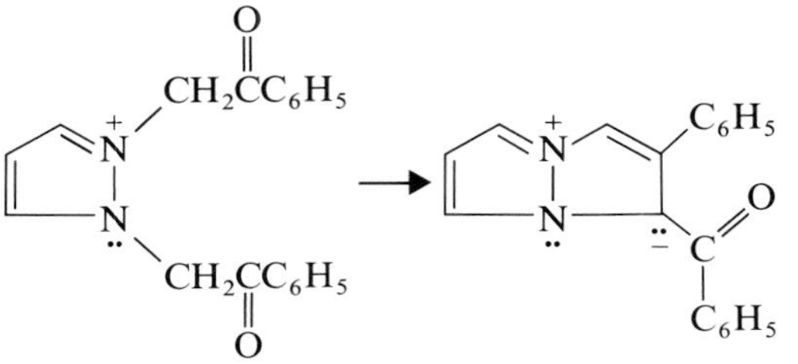

17.31 (a) Infrared spectroscopy gives an easy method for deciding whether the product obtained from the addition of a Grignard reagent to an α,β-unsaturated ketone is the simple addition product or the conjugate addition product. Explain. (What peak or peaks would you look for?) (b) How might you follow the rate of the following reaction using UV spectroscopy?

$$(CH_3)_2C{=}CHCCH_3 + CH_3NH_2 \xrightarrow[H_2O]{} (CH_3)_2CCH_2CCH_3$$

17.32 (a) A compound **U** ($C_9H_{10}O$) gives a negative iodoform test. The IR spectrum of **U** shows a strong absorption peak at 1690 cm^{-1}. The ^{1}H NMR spectrum of **U** gives the following:

Triplet	$\delta 1.2$ (3H)
Quartet	$\delta 3.0$ (2H)
Multiplet	$\delta 7.7$ (5H)

What is the structure of **U**?

(b) A compound **V** is an isomer of **U**. Compound **V** gives a positive iodoform test; its IR spectrum shows a strong peak at 1705 cm^{-1}. The ^{1}H NMR spectrum of **V** gives the following:

Singlet	$\delta 2.0$ (3H)
Singlet	$\delta 3.5$ (2H)
Multiplet	$\delta 7.1$ (5H)

What is the structure of **V**?

17.33 Compound **A** has the molecular formula $C_6H_{12}O_3$ and shows a strong IR absorption peak at 1710 cm^{-1}. When treated with iodine in aqueous sodium hydroxide, **A** gives a yellow precipitate. When **A** is treated with Tollens' reagent, no reaction occurs; however, if **A** is treated first with water containing a drop of sulfuric acid and then treated with Tollens' reagent, a silver mirror forms in the test tube. Compound **A** shows the following ^{1}H NMR spectrum.

Singlet	$\delta 2.1$
Doublet	$\delta 2.6$
Singlet	$\delta 3.2$ (6H)
Triplet	$\delta 4.7$

Write a structure for **A**.

*17.34 Treating a solution of *cis*-1-decalone with base causes an isomerization to take place. When the system reaches equilibrium, the solution is found to contain about 95% *trans*-1-decalone and about 5% *cis*-1-decalone. Explain this isomerization.

cis-1-Decalone

17.35 The Wittig reaction (Section 16.10) can be used in the synthesis of aldehydes, for example,

(a) How would you prepare $CH_3OCH{=}P(C_6H_5)_3$? (b) Show with a mechanism how the second reaction produces an aldehyde. (c) How would you use this method to prepare

CHO from cyclohexanone?

SPECIAL TOPIC

E

LITHIUM ENOLATES IN ORGANIC SYNTHESIS

E.1 ENOLATE IONS

Enolate ions are formed when a carbonyl compound with an α hydrogen is treated with a base (Section 17.1). The extent to which the enolate ion forms will depend on the strength of the base used. If the base employed is a weaker base than the enolate ion, then the equilibrium will lie to the left. This will be the case, for example, when a ketone is treated with an aqueous solution containing sodium hydroxide.

$$CH_3-\overset{O}{\overset{\|}{C}}-CH_3 + Na^+OH^- \rightleftharpoons CH_3-\overset{O^{\delta-}Na^+}{\overset{\|}{C}}=CH_2^{\delta-} + H_2O$$

| Weaker acid | Weaker base | Stronger base | Stronger acid |
| $(pK_a = 20)$ | | | $(pK_a = 16)$ |

On the other hand, if a very strong base is employed, the equilibrium will lie far to the right. One very useful strong base, for converting ketones to enolates is lithium diisopropylamide, $(i\text{-}C_3H_7)_2N^-Li^+$.

$$CH_3-\overset{O}{\overset{\|}{C}}-CH_3 + (i\text{-}C_3H_7)_2N^-Li^+ \longrightarrow CH_3-\overset{O^{\delta-}Li^+}{\overset{\|}{C}}=CH_2^{\delta-} + (i\text{-}C_3H_7)_2NH$$

| Stronger acid | Stronger base | Weaker base | Weaker acid |
| $(pK_a = 20)$ | | | $(pK_a = 38)$ |

Lithium diisopropylamide (abbreviated **LDA**) can be prepared by dissolving diisopropylamine in a solvent such as diethyl ether or THF, and treating it with an alkyllithium.

$$(i\text{-}C_3H_7)_2NH + CH_3^-Li^+ \xrightarrow{\text{diethyl ether}} (i\text{-}C_3H_7)_2N^-Li^+ + CH_4\uparrow$$

| Stronger acid | Stronger base | Weaker base | Weaker acid |
| $(pK_a = 38)$ | | | $(pK_a = 50)$ |

E.1A Enolate Ions As Ambident Nucleophiles

Because enolate ions have a partial negative charge on an oxygen atom they can react in nucleophilic substitution reactions as if they were **alkoxide ions.** Because they have a partial negative charge on a carbon atom they can also react as **carbanions.** Nucleophiles like this, *those that are capable of reacting at two sites,* are called **ambident nucleophiles.**

This site reacts as an alkoxide ion

$$CH_3-\overset{O^{\delta-}}{\overset{\|}{C}}=\overset{\delta-}{CH_2}$$

This site reacts as a carbanion

Just how an enolate ion reacts depends, in part, on the substrate with which it reacts. *One substrate that tends to react almost exclusively at the oxygen atom of an enolate is chlorotrimethylsilane, $(CH_3)_3SiCl$.*

$$CH_3\overset{O^{\delta-}}{\underset{}{C}}{=}\overset{\delta-}{C}H_2 + (CH_3)_3Si{-}Cl \xrightarrow{THF} CH_3\overset{OSi(CH_3)_3}{\underset{}{C}}{=}CH_2 + Cl^-$$

Enol trimethylsilyl ether
(85%)

This reaction, called **silylation** (cf. Section 10.16D), is a nucleophilic substitution at the silicon atom by the oxygen atom of the enolate, and it takes place as it does because the oxygen–silicon bond that forms in the enol trimethylsilyl ether is very strong (much stronger than a carbon–silicon bond). This factor makes formation of the enol trimethylsilyl ether highly exothermic, and, consequently, the free energy of activation for reaction at the oxygen atom is lower than that for reaction at the α carbon.

Enolate ions display their carbanionic character when they react with alkyl halides. In these reactions the major product is usually the one in which alkylation occurs at the carbon atom, called *C*-alkylation. (Alkylation at the oxygen atom is called *O*-alkylation.)

$$R{-}\overset{O^{\delta-}}{\underset{}{C}}{=}\overset{\delta-}{C}HR' + R''CH_2{-}X \longrightarrow R{-}\overset{O}{\underset{}{C}}{-}\overset{CH_2R''}{\underset{}{C}}HR'$$

C-alkylated
product
(major product)

Alkylation reactions like these have an important limitation. Because the reactions are S_N2 reactions and because enolate ions are strong bases, *successful alkylations occur only when primary alkyl, primary benzylic, and primary allylic halides are used.* With secondary and tertiary halides, elimination becomes the main course of the reaction.

Problem E.1

Write structures for the *C*-alkylated and *O*-alkylated products that form when the enolate derived from cyclohexanone reacts with benzyl bromide.

E.1B Regioselective Formation of Enolate Ions

An unsymmetrical ketone such as 2-methylcyclohexanone can form two possible enolates. Just which enolate will be formed predominantly depends on the base used and on the conditions employed. The enolate *with the more highly substituted double bond is the **thermodynamically more stable enolate*** in the same way that an alkene with the more highly substituted double bond is the more stable alkene (Section 8.9). This enolate, called the **thermodynamic enolate,** will be formed predominantly under conditions that permit the establishment of an equilibrium. This will generally be the case if the enolate is produced using a relatively weak base in a protic solvent.

2-Methylcyclohexanone

Thermodynamic enolate

This enolate is more stable because the double bond is more highly substituted. It is the predominant enolate present at equilibrium

On the other hand, *the enolate with the less substituted double bond is usually formed faster,* because removal of the hydrogen necessary to produce this enolate is less sterically hindered. This enolate, called the **kinetic enolate,** is formed predominantly when the reaction is kinetically controlled (or rate controlled).

The kinetically favored enolate can be formed cleanly through the use of lithium diisopropylamide (LDA). This strong, sterically hindered base rapidly removes the proton from the less-substituted α carbon of the ketone. The following sample, using 2-methylcyclohexanone, is an illustration. The solvent for the reaction is 1,2-dimethoxyethane ($CH_3OCH_2CH_2OCH_3$) abbreviated **DME**. The LDA removes the hydrogen from the $-CH_2-$ α carbon more rapidly because it is less hindered (and because there are twice as many hydrogens there to react).

Kinetic enolate

This enolate is formed faster because the hindered strong base removes the less-hindered proton faster

(99%)

The example just given also shows how the enolate ion can be "trapped" by converting it to the enol trimethylsilyl ether. This procedure is especially useful because the enol trimethylsilyl ether can be purified, if necessary, and then converted back to an enolate. One way of achieving this conversion is by treating the enol trimethylsilyl ether with a solution containing fluoride ions.

Kinetic enolate

This reaction is a nucleophilic substitution at the silicon atom brought about by a fluoride ion. Fluoride ions have an extremely high affinity for silicon atoms because Si—F bonds are very strong.

SPECIAL TOPIC E

Another way to convert an enol trimethylsilyl ether back to an enolate is to treat it with methyllithium.

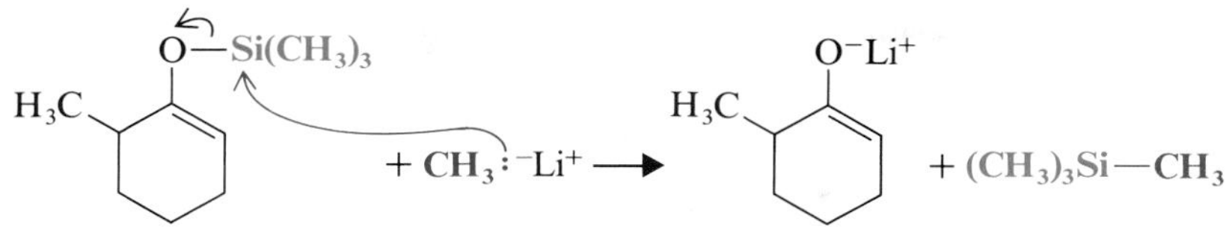

E.2 DIRECT ALKYLATION OF KETONES VIA LITHIUM ENOLATES

The formation of lithium enolates using lithium diisopropylamide furnishes a useful way of alkylating ketones in a regioselective way. For example, the lithium enolate formed from 2-methylcyclohexanone (Section E.1B) can be methylated and benzylated by allowing it to react with methyliodide and benzyl bromide, respectively.

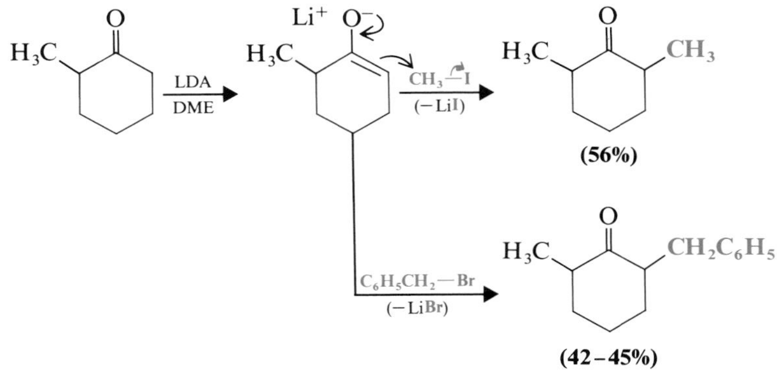

(56%)

(42–45%)

E.3 LITHIUM ENOLATES IN DIRECTED ALDOL REACTIONS

One of the most effective and versatile ways to bring about a crossed aldol reaction is to use a lithium enolate obtained from a ketone as one component and an aldehyde or ketone as the other. An example of what is called a **directed aldol reaction** is shown in Fig. E.1.

Regioselectivity can be achieved when unsymmetrical ketones are used in directed aldol reactions by generating the kinetic enolate using lithium diisopropylamide. This will ensure production of the enolate in which the proton has been removed from the less-substituted α carbon. The following is an example:

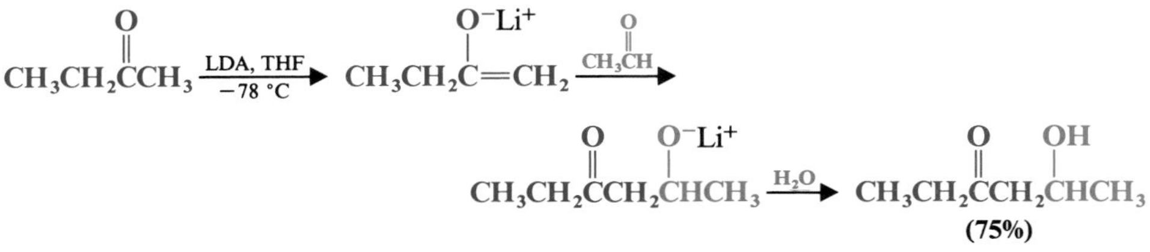

(75%)

If the aldol (Claisen–Schmidt) reaction had been carried out in the classical way (Section 17.6B) using hydroxide ion as the base then at least two products would have been formed in significant amounts. Both the kinetic and thermodynamic enolates

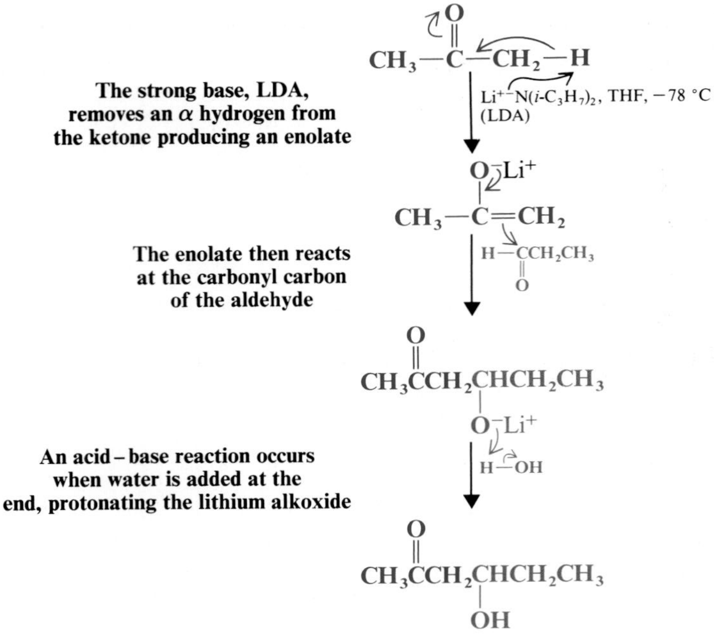

SPECIAL TOPIC E

The strong base, LDA, removes an α hydrogen from the ketone producing an enolate

$$CH_3-\overset{\overset{\displaystyle O}{\|}}{C}-CH_2-H \xrightarrow[\text{(LDA)}]{Li^+{}^-N(i\text{-}C_3H_7)_2,\ THF,\ -78\ ^\circ C}$$

$$CH_3-\overset{\overset{\displaystyle O^-Li^+}{|}}{C}=CH_2$$

$$H-\overset{\overset{\displaystyle}{}}{\underset{\overset{\displaystyle O}{\|}}{C}}CH_2CH_3$$

The enolate then reacts at the carbonyl carbon of the aldehyde

$$CH_3\overset{\overset{\displaystyle O}{\|}}{C}CH_2\overset{\overset{\displaystyle}{}}{\underset{\overset{\displaystyle O^-Li^+}{|}}{C}}HCH_2CH_3$$

$$H-OH$$

An acid–base reaction occurs when water is added at the end, protonating the lithium alkoxide

$$CH_3\overset{\overset{\displaystyle O}{\|}}{C}CH_2\overset{\overset{\displaystyle}{}}{\underset{\overset{\displaystyle OH}{|}}{C}}HCH_2CH_3$$

FIGURE E.1 A directed aldol synthesis.

would have been formed from the ketone and each of these would have added to the carbonyl carbon of the aldehyde:

$$CH_3CH_2-\overset{\overset{\displaystyle O}{\|}}{C}-CH_3 \xrightarrow{^-OH} CH_3CH_2-\overset{\overset{\displaystyle O^-}{|}}{C}=CH_2 + CH_3CH=\overset{\overset{\displaystyle O^-}{|}}{C}-CH_3$$

Kinetic enolate   Thermodynamic enolate

$$\Big\downarrow \overset{\overset{\displaystyle O}{\|}}{CH_3CH} \qquad\qquad \Big\downarrow \overset{\overset{\displaystyle O}{\|}}{CH_3CH}$$

$$CH_3CH_2\overset{\overset{\displaystyle O}{\|}}{C}CH_2\overset{\overset{\displaystyle O^-}{|}}{C}HCH_3 \qquad CH_3\overset{\overset{\displaystyle O}{}}{C}H\overset{\overset{\displaystyle O}{\|}}{C}CH_3$$

$$\overset{\overset{\displaystyle}{}}{\underset{\overset{\displaystyle O^-}{}}{C}}HCH_3$$

$$\Big\downarrow H_2O \qquad\qquad\qquad \Big\downarrow H_2O$$

$$CH_3CH_2\overset{\overset{\displaystyle O}{\|}}{C}CH_2\overset{\overset{\displaystyle OH}{|}}{C}HCH_3 \qquad CH_3\overset{\overset{\displaystyle O}{}}{C}H\overset{\overset{\displaystyle O}{\|}}{C}CH_3$$

$$\overset{\overset{\displaystyle}{}}{\underset{\overset{\displaystyle OH}{}}{C}}HCH_3$$

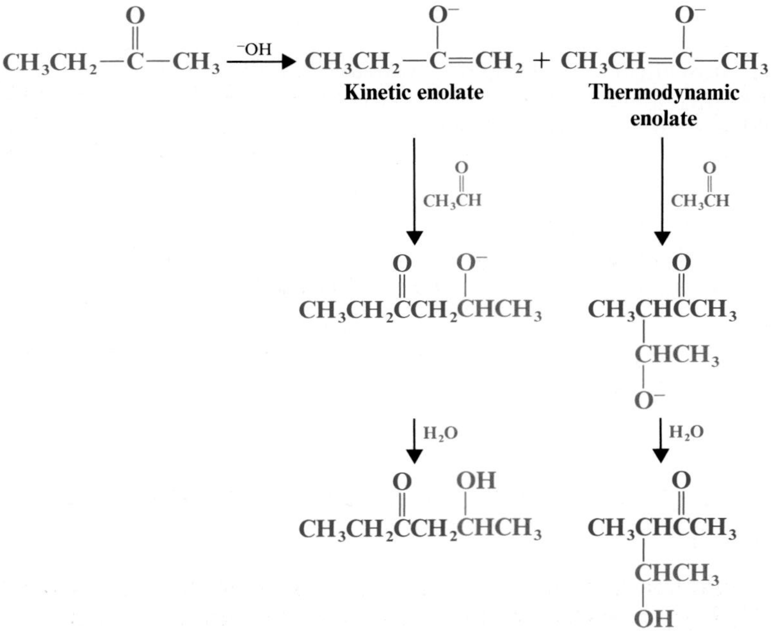

Problem E.2

Starting with ketones and aldehydes of your choice outline a directed aldol synthesis of each of the following:

(a)

(b) $CH_3CH_2\overset{O}{\overset{\|}{C}}CH_2\overset{OH}{\overset{|}{C}}HC_6H_5$

(c) $CH_3\overset{O}{\overset{\|}{C}}H\overset{O}{\overset{\|}{C}}CH_2\overset{OH}{\overset{|}{C}}HCH_2CH_3$
$\quad\quad\overset{|}{C}H_3$

(d) $CH_3CH=CH\overset{O}{\overset{\|}{C}}CH_2\overset{OH}{\overset{|}{C}}HCH_3$

Problem E.3

The compounds called α-bisabolanone and ocimenone have both been synthesized by directed aldol syntheses. In both syntheses one starting compound was $(CH_3)_2C=CHCOCH_3$. Choose other appropriate starting compounds and outline syntheses of (a) α-bisabolanone and (b) ocimenone.

α-Bisabolanone   Ocimenone

Problem E.4

Treating the enol trimethylsilyl ether derived from cyclohexanone with benzaldehyde and tetrabutylammonium fluoride, $(C_4H_9)_4N^+F^-$ (abbreviated TBAF), gave the following product. Outline the steps that occur in this reaction.

E.4 α-SELENATION: A SYNTHESIS OF α,β-UNSATURATED CARBONYL COMPOUNDS

Lithium enolates react with benzeneselenenyl bromide (C_6H_5SeBr) (or with C_6H_5SeCl) to yield products containing a C_6H_5Se- group at the α position.

Treating the α-benzeneselenyl ketone with hydrogen peroxide at room temperature converts it to an α,β-unsaturated ketone.

These are very mild conditions for the introduction of a double bond (room temperature and a neutral solution), and this is one reason why this method is a valuable one.

Mechanistically, two steps are involved in the conversion of the α-benzeneselenyl ketone to the α,β-unsaturated ketone. The first step is an oxidation brought about by the H_2O_2. The second step is a spontaneous intramolecular elimination in which the negatively charged oxygen atom attached to the selenium atom acts as a base.

When we study the Cope elimination in Section 19.13B, we shall find another example of this kind of intramolecular elimination.

SPECIAL TOPIC E

Problem E.5

Starting with 2-methylcyclohexanone, show how you would use α-selenation in a synthesis of the following compound:

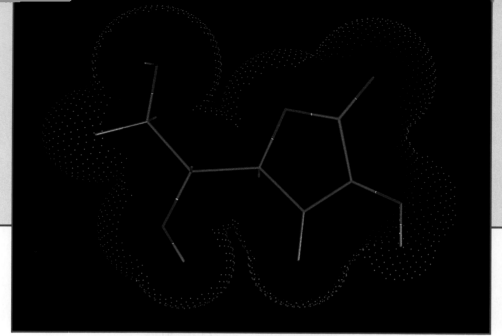

Vitamin C (see Section 18.7C).

18

CARBOXYLIC ACIDS AND THEIR DERIVATIVES. NUCLEOPHILIC SUBSTITUTION AT THE ACYL CARBON

18.1 INTRODUCTION

The carboxyl group, $-\overset{\overset{\displaystyle O}{\|}}{C}OH$ (abbreviated $-CO_2H$ or $-COOH$), is one of the most widely occurring functional groups in chemistry and biochemistry. Not only are carboxylic acids themselves important, but the carboxyl group is the parent group of a large family of related compounds (Table 18.1).

All of these carboxylic acid derivatives contain the acyl group, $R\overset{\overset{\displaystyle O}{\|}}{C}-$. As a result, they are often called *acyl compounds*. They are called *carboxylic acid derivatives*

because they are derived from a carboxylic acid by replacing the $-OH$ of $R\overset{\overset{\displaystyle O}{\|}}{C}OH$ by some other group.

TABLE 18.1 Carboxylic acid derivatives

STRUCTURE	NAME	STRUCTURE	NAME
$R-\overset{\overset{O}{\|}}{C}-Cl$	Acyl (or acid) chloride	$R-\overset{\overset{O}{\|}}{C}-NH_2$	
$R-\overset{\overset{O}{\|}}{C}-O-\overset{\overset{O}{\|}}{C}-R$	Acid anhydride	$R-\overset{\overset{O}{\|}}{C}-NHR'$	Amide
$R-\overset{\overset{O}{\|}}{C}-O-R'$	Ester	$R-\overset{\overset{O}{\|}}{C}-NR'R''$	
$R-C\equiv N$	Nitrile		

18.2 NOMENCLATURE AND PHYSICAL PROPERTIES

18.2A CARBOXYLIC ACIDS

IUPAC systematic or substitutive names for carboxylic acids are obtained by dropping the final *e* of the name of the alkane corresponding to the longest chain in the acid and by adding *-oic acid.* The carboxyl carbon atom is assigned number 1. The examples listed here illustrate how this is done.

$$\underset{6}{C}H_3\underset{5}{C}H_2\underset{4}{C}H\underset{3}{C}H_2\underset{2}{C}H_2\overset{\overset{O}{\|}}{C}OH \qquad \underset{6}{C}H_3\underset{5}{C}H=\underset{4}{C}H\underset{3}{C}H_2\underset{2}{C}H_2\overset{\overset{O}{\|}}{C}OH$$
$$\qquad\quad |$$
$$\qquad\quad CH_3$$

4-Methylhexanoic acid **4-Hexenoic acid**

Many carboxylic acids have common names that are derived from Latin or Greek words that indicate one of their natural sources (Table 18.2). Methanoic acid is called formic acid (from the Latin, *formica,* or ant). Ethanoic acid is called acetic acid (from the Latin, *acetum,* or vinegar). Butanoic acid is one compound responsible for the odor of rancid butter, thus its common name is butyric acid (from the Latin, *butyrum,* or butter). Pentanoic acid, as a result of its occurrence in valerian, a perennial herb, is named valeric acid. Hexanoic acid is one compound associated with the odor of goats, hence its common name, caproic acid (from the Latin *caper,* or goat). Octadecanoic acid takes its common name, stearic acid, from the Greek word *stear,* for tallow.

Most of these common names have been with us for a long time and some are likely to remain in common usage for even longer, so it is helpful to be familiar with them. In this text we shall always refer to methanoic acid and ethanoic acid as formic acid and acetic acid. However, in almost all other instances we shall use IUPAC systematic or substitutive names.

Carboxylic acids are polar substances. Their molecules can form strong hydrogen bonds with each other and with water. As a result, carboxylic acids generally have high boiling points, and low molecular weight carboxylic acids show appreciable solubility in water. The first four carboxylic acids (Table 18.2) are miscible with water in all proportions. As the length of the carbon chain increases, water solubility declines.

18.2B CARBOXYLIC SALTS

Salts of carboxylic acids are named as -*ates;* in both common and systematic names, -*ate* replaces -*ic acid.* Thus, CH_3CO_2Na is sodium acetate or sodium ethanoate.

Sodium and potassium salts of most carboxylic acids are readily soluble in water. This is true even of the long-chain carboxylic acids. Sodium or potassium salts of long-chain carboxylic acids are the major ingredients of soap (cf. Section 23.2C).

Problem 18.1

Give an IUPAC systematic name for each of the following:

(a) $CH_3CH_2CHCO_2H$
         |
         CH_3

(b) $CH_3CH=CHCH_2CO_2H$

(c) $BrCH_2CH_2CH_2CO_2Na$

(d) $C_6H_5CH_2CH_2CH_2CH_2CO_2H$

(e) $CH_3CH=CCH_2CO_2H$
              |
              CH_3

18.2C ACIDITY OF CARBOXYLIC ACIDS

Most unsubstituted carboxylic acids have K_a values in the range of $10^{-4}-10^{-5}$ ($pK_a = 4-5$) as seen in Table 18.2. The pK_a of water is about 16 and the apparent pK_a of H_2CO_3 is about 7. These relative acidities mean that carboxylic acids react readily with aqueous solutions of sodium hydroxide and sodium bicarbonate to form soluble sodium salts. We can use solubility tests, therefore, to distinguish water-insoluble carboxylic acids from water-insoluble phenols (Chapter 20) and alcohols. Water-insoluble carboxylic acids will dissolve in either aqueous sodium hydroxide or aqueous sodium bicarbonate:

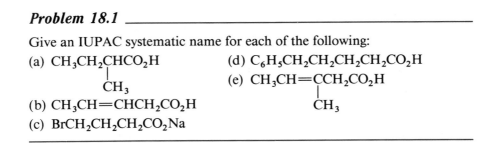

Water-insoluble phenols (Section 21.5) dissolve in aqueous sodium hydroxide but (except for some nitrophenols) do not dissolve in aqueous sodium bicarbonate. Water-insoluble alcohols do not dissolve in either aqueous sodium hydroxide or sodium bicarbonate.

We see in Table 18.2 that carboxylic acids having electron-withdrawing groups are stronger than unsubstituted acids. The chloroacetic acids, for example, show the following order of acidities:

TABLE 18.2 Carboxylic acids

STRUCTURE	SYSTEMATIC NAME	COMMON NAME	mp (°C)	bp (°C)	WATER SOLUBILITY (g 100 mL^{-1} H$_2$O) 25 °C	pK_a
HCO$_2$H	Methanoic acid	Formic acid	8	100.5	∞	3.75
CH$_3$CO$_2$H	Ethanoic acid	Acetic acid	16.6	118	∞	4.75
CH$_3$CH$_2$CO$_2$H	Propanoic acid	Propionic acid	−21	141	∞	4.87
CH$_3$(CH$_2$)$_2$CO$_2$H	Butanoic acid	Butyric acid	−6	164	∞	4.81
CH$_3$(CH$_2$)$_3$CO$_2$H	Pentanoic acid	Valeric acid	−34	187	4.97	4.82
CH$_3$(CH$_2$)$_4$CO$_2$H	Hexanoic acid	Caproic acid	−3	205	1.08	4.84
CH$_3$(CH$_2$)$_6$CO$_2$H	Octanoic acid	Caprylic acid	16	239	0.07	4.89
CH$_3$(CH$_2$)$_8$CO$_2$H	Decanoic acid	Capric acid	31	269	0.015	4.84
CH$_3$(CH$_2$)$_{10}$CO$_2$H	Dodecanoic acid	Lauric acid	44	179^{18}	0.006	5.30
CH$_3$(CH$_2$)$_{12}$CO$_2$H	Tetradecanoic acid	Myristic acid	59	200^{20}	0.002	
CH$_3$(CH$_2$)$_{14}$CO$_2$H	Hexadecanoic acid	Palmitic acid	63	219^{17}	0.0007	6.46
CH$_3$(CH$_2$)$_{16}$CO$_2$H	Octadecanoic acid	Stearic acid	70	383	0.0003	
CH$_2$ClCO$_2$H	Chloroethanoic acid	Chloroacetic acid	63	189	Very soluble	2.85
CHCl$_2$CO$_2$H	Dichloroethanoic acid	Dichloroacetic acid	10.8	192	Very soluble	1.48
CCl$_3$CO$_2$H	Trichloroethanoic acid	Trichloroacetic acid	56.3	198	Very soluble	0.70
CH$_3$CHClCO$_2$H	2-Chloropropanoic acid	α-Chloropropionic acid		186	Soluble	2.83
CH$_2$ClCH$_2$CO$_2$H	3-Chloropropanoic acid	β-Chloropropionic acid	61	204	Soluble	3.98
C$_6$H$_5$CO$_2$H	Benzoic acid	Benzoic acid	122	250	0.34	4.19
p-CH$_3$C$_6$H$_4$CO$_2$H	4-Methylbenzoic acid	p-Toluic acid	180	275	0.03	4.36
p-ClC$_6$H$_4$CO$_2$H	4-Chlorobenzoic acid	p-Chlorobenzoic acid	242		0.009	3.98
p-NO$_2$C$_6$H$_4$CO$_2$H	4-Nitrobenzoic acid	p-Nitrobenzoic acid	242		0.03	3.41
	1-Naphthoic acid	α-Naphthoic acid	160	300	Insoluble	3.70
	2-Naphthoic acid	β-Naphthoic acid	185	>300	Insoluble	4.17

$$\underset{0.7}{Cl{\leftarrow}\overset{Cl}{\underset{Cl}{C}}{-}CO_2H} > \underset{1.48}{Cl{\leftarrow}\overset{Cl}{\underset{H}{C}}{-}CO_2H} > \underset{2.85}{Cl{\leftarrow}\overset{H}{\underset{H}{C}}{-}CO_2H} > \underset{4.75}{H{-}\overset{H}{\underset{H}{C}}{-}CO_2H}$$

pK$_a$ = 0.7, 1.48, 2.85, 4.75

As we saw in Sections 3.5B and 3.7 this acid-strengthening effect of electron-withdrawing groups arises from a combination of inductive effects and entropy effects. Since inductive effects are not transmitted very effectively through covalent bonds, the acid-strengthening effect decreases as distance between the electron-withdrawing group and the carboxyl group increases. Of the chlorobutanoic acids that follow the strongest acid is 2-chlorobutanoic acid:

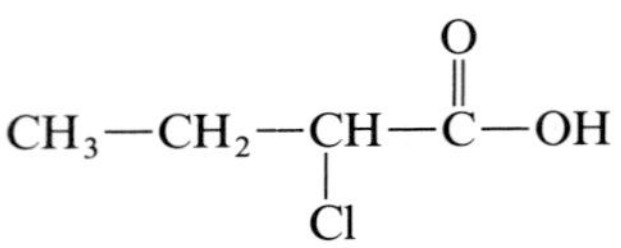

$$CH_3-CH_2-\underset{\underset{Cl}{|}}{CH}-\overset{\overset{O}{||}}{C}-OH \qquad CH_3-\underset{\underset{Cl}{|}}{CH}-CH_2-\overset{\overset{O}{||}}{C}-OH \qquad \underset{\underset{Cl}{|}}{CH_2}-CH_2-CH_2-\overset{\overset{O}{||}}{C}-OH$$

2-Chlorobutanoic acid   **3-Chlorobutanoic acid**   **4-Chlorobutanoic acid**
($pK_a = 2.85$)   ($pK_a = 4.05$)   ($pK_a = 4.50$)

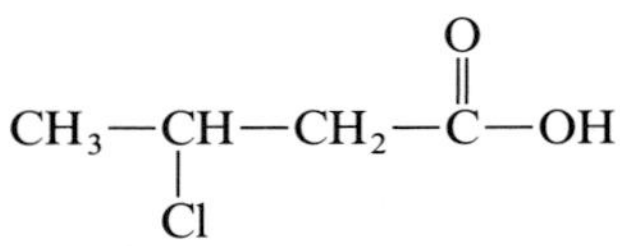

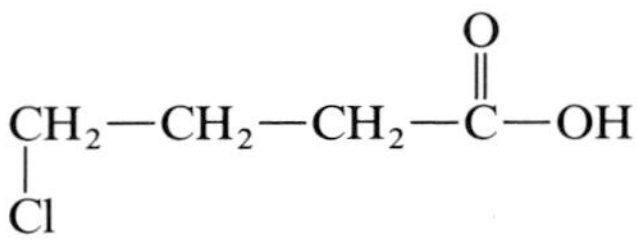

Problem 18.2

Which acid of each pair shown here would you expect to be stronger?

(a) CH_3CO_2H or CH_2FCO_2H

(b) CH_2FCO_2H or CH_2ClCO_2H

(c) CH_2ClCO_2H or CH_2BrCO_2H

(d) $CH_2FCH_2CH_2CO_2H$ or $CH_3CHFCH_2CO_2H$

(e) $CH_3CH_2CHFCO_2H$ or $CH_3CHFCH_2CO_2H$

(f)  $(CH_3)_3\overset{+}{N}$—⬡—CO_2H or   ⬡—CO_2H

(g) 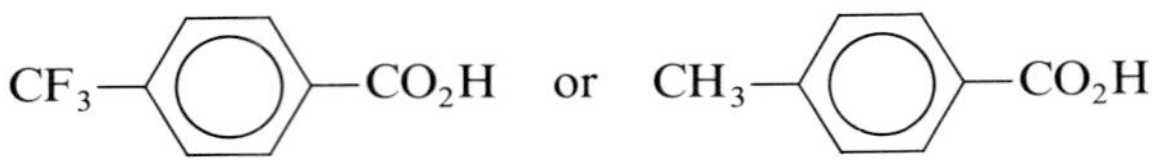 CF_3—⬡—CO_2H or CH_3—⬡—CO_2H

18.2D DICARBOXYLIC ACIDS

Dicarboxylic acids are named as **alkanedioic acids** in the IUPAC systematic or substitutive system. Most simple dicarboxylic acids have common names (Table 18.3), and these are the names that we shall use.

Problem 18.3

Suggest explanations for the following facts: (a) pK_1 for all of the dicarboxylic acids in Table 18.3 are smaller than the pK_a for monocarboxylic acids with the same number of carbon atoms.   (b) The difference between pK_1 and pK_2 for dicarboxylic acids of type $HO_2C(CH_2)_nCO_2H$ decreases as n increases.

18.2E ESTERS

The names of esters are derived from the names of the alcohol (with the ending **-yl**) and the acid (with the ending **-ate** or **-oate**). The portion of the name derived from the alcohol comes first.

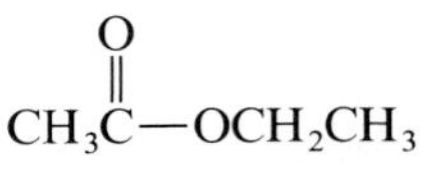

$$\underset{\text{Ethyl acetate or}}{CH_3\overset{\overset{O}{||}}{C}-OCH_2CH_3} \qquad \underset{\text{\textit{tert}-Butyl propanoate}}{CH_3CH_2\overset{\overset{O}{||}}{C}-\underset{\underset{CH_3}{|}}{\overset{\overset{CH_3}{|}}{O}C}-CH_3} \qquad \underset{\text{Vinyl acetate or}}{CH_3\overset{\overset{O}{||}}{C}OCH=CH_2}$$

Ethyl acetate or   **tert-Butyl propanoate** 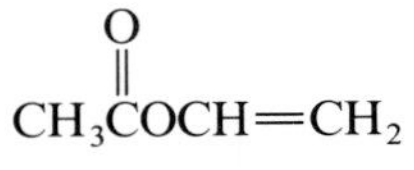   **Vinyl acetate or**
ethyl ethanoate   **ethenyl ethanoate**

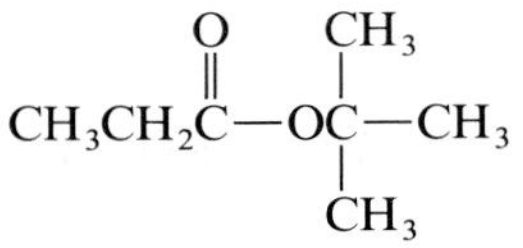

$$Cl-\bigotimes-\overset{\overset{\displaystyle O}{\|}}{C}OCH_3 \qquad CH_3CH_2O\overset{\overset{\displaystyle O}{\|}}{C}CH_2\overset{\overset{\displaystyle O}{\|}}{C}OCH_2CH_3$$

Methyl _p_-chlorobenzoate   **Diethyl malonate**

Esters are polar compounds but lacking a hydrogen attached to oxygen, their molecules cannot form strong hydrogen bonds to each other. As a result, esters have boiling points that are lower than those of acids and alcohols of comparable molecular weight. The boiling points (Table 18.4) of esters are about the same as those of comparable aldehydes and ketones.

Unlike the low molecular weight acids, esters usually have pleasant odors, some resembling those of fruits, and these are used in the manufacture of synthetic flavors:

$$CH_3\overset{\overset{\displaystyle O}{\|}}{C}OCH_2CH_2\underset{\underset{\displaystyle CH_3}{|}}{C}HCH_3 \qquad CH_3CH_2CH_2CH_2\overset{\overset{\displaystyle O}{\|}}{C}-OCH_2CH_2\underset{\underset{\displaystyle CH_3}{|}}{C}HCH_3$$

Isopentyl acetate   **Isopentyl pentanoate**
(used in synthetic banana flavor)   **(used in synthetic apple flavor)**

TABLE 18.3   Dicarboxylic acids

STRUCTURE	COMMON NAME	mp (°C)	pK$_a$ (at 25 °C) pK$_1$	pK$_2$
HO_2C-CO_2H	Oxalic acid	189 dec	1.2	4.2
$HO_2CCH_2CO_2H$	Malonic acid	136	2.9	5.7
$HO_2C(CH_2)_2CO_2H$	Succinic acid	187	4.2	5.6
$HO_2C(CH_2)_3CO_2H$	Glutaric acid	98	4.3	5.4
$HO_2C(CH_2)_4CO_2H$	Adipic acid	153	4.4	5.6
cis-$HO_2C-CH=CH-CO_2H$	Maleic acid	131	1.9	6.1
trans-$HO_2C-CH=CH-CO_2H$	Fumaric acid	287	3.0	4.4
(benzene ring with two CO_2H ortho)	Phthalic acid	206–208 dec	2.9	5.4
(benzene ring with two CO_2H meta)	Isophthalic acid	345–348	3.5	4.6
(benzene ring with two CO_2H para)	Terephthalic acid	Sublimes	3.5	4.8

TABLE 18.4   Carboxylic esters

NAME	STRUCTURE	mp (°C)	bp (°C)	SOLUBILITY IN WATER (g 100 mL^{-1} at 20 °C)
Methyl formate	HCO$_2$CH$_3$	−99	31.5	Very soluble
Ethyl formate	HCO$_2$CH$_2$CH$_3$	−79	54	Soluble
Methyl acetate	CH$_3$CO$_2$CH$_3$	−99	57	24.4
Ethyl acetate	CH$_3$CO$_2$CH$_2$CH$_3$	−82	77	7.39 (25 °C)
Propyl acetate	CH$_3$CO$_2$CH$_2$CH$_2$CH$_3$	−93	102	1.89
Butyl acetate	CH$_3$CO$_2$CH$_2$(CH$_2$)$_2$CH$_3$	−74	125	1.0 (22 °C)
Ethyl propanoate	CH$_3$CH$_2$CO$_2$CH$_2$CH$_3$	−73	99	1.75
Ethyl butanoate	CH$_3$(CH$_2$)$_2$CO$_2$CH$_2$CH$_3$	−93	120	0.51
Ethyl pentanoate	CH$_3$(CH$_2$)$_3$CO$_2$CH$_2$CH$_3$	−91	145	0.22
Ethyl hexanoate	CH$_3$(CH$_2$)$_4$CO$_2$CH$_2$CH$_3$	−68	168	0.063
Methyl benzoate	C$_6$H$_5$CO$_2$CH$_3$	−12	199	0.15
Ethyl benzoate	C$_6$H$_5$CO$_2$CH$_2$CH$_3$	−35	213	0.08
Phenyl acetate	CH$_3$CO$_2$C$_6$H$_5$		196	V. sl. soluble
Methyl salicylate	o-HOC$_6$H$_4$CO$_2$CH$_3$	−9	223	0.74 (30°C)

18.2F CARBOXYLIC ANHYDRIDES

Most anhydrides are named by dropping the word **acid** from the name of the carboxylic acid and then adding the word **anhydride.**

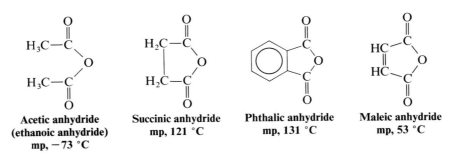

| Acetic anhydride (ethanoic anhydride) mp, −73 °C | Succinic anhydride mp, 121 °C | Phthalic anhydride mp, 131 °C | Maleic anhydride mp, 53 °C |

18.2G ACYL CHLORIDES

Acyl chlorides are also called **acid chlorides.** They are named by dropping **-ic acid** from the name of the acid and then adding **-yl chloride.** Examples are

CH$_3$C—Cl
Acetyl chloride
(ethanoyl chloride)
mp, −112 °C; bp, 51 °C

CH$_3$CH$_2$C—Cl
Propanoyl chloride
mp, −94 °C; bp, 80 °C

C$_6$H$_5$C—Cl
Benzoyl chloride
mp, −1 °C; bp, 197 °C

Acyl chlorides and carboxylic anhydrides have boiling points in the same range as esters of comparable molecular weight.

18.2H AMIDES

Amides that have no substituent on nitrogen are named by dropping **-ic acid** from the common name of the acid (or *-oic acid* from the substitutive name) and then adding **-amide**. Alkyl groups on the nitrogen atom of amides are named as substituents and the named substituent is prefaced by *N-*, or *N,N-*. Examples are

$$
\begin{array}{ccc}
\underset{\substack{\text{Acetamide}\\ \text{(ethanamide)}\\ \text{mp, 82 °C; bp, 221 °C}}}{CH_3\overset{\overset{\displaystyle O}{\|}}{C}-NH_2}
&
\underset{\substack{\textit{N,N-}\text{Dimethylacetamide}\\ \text{mp, }-20\text{ °C; bp, 166 °C}}}{CH_3\overset{\overset{\displaystyle O}{\|}}{C}-N\begin{smallmatrix}CH_3\\ \\CH_3\end{smallmatrix}}
&
\underset{\substack{\textit{N-}\text{Ethylacetamide}\\ \text{bp, 205 °C}}}{CH_3\overset{\overset{\displaystyle O}{\|}}{C}-NHC_2H_5}
\end{array}
$$

$$
\underset{\substack{\textit{N-}\text{Phenyl-}\textit{N-}\text{propylacetamide}\\ \text{mp, 49 °C; bp, 266 °C at 712 torr}}}{CH_3\overset{\overset{\displaystyle O}{\|}}{C}-N\begin{smallmatrix}C_6H_5\\ \\CH_2CH_2CH_3\end{smallmatrix}}
\qquad
\underset{\substack{\text{Benzamide}\\ \text{mp, 130 °C; bp, 290 °C}}}{C_6H_5-\overset{\overset{\displaystyle O}{\|}}{C}-NH_2}
$$

Molecules of amides with one (or no) substituent on nitrogen are able to form strong hydrogen bonds to each other and, consequently, such amides have high melting points and boiling points. Molecules of *N,N-*disubstituted amides cannot form strong hydrogen bonds to each other; they have lower melting points and boiling points.

**Hydrogen bonding
between molecules of an amide**

18.2 I NITRILES

In IUPAC substitutive nomenclature, acyclic nitriles are named by adding the suffix *nitrile* to the name of the corresponding hydrocarbon. The carbon atom of the $-C{\equiv}N$ group is assigned number 1. The name acetonitrile is an acceptable common name for CH_3CN and acrylonitrile is an acceptable common name for $CH_2{=}CHCN$.

$$
\underset{\substack{\text{Ethanenitrile}\\ \text{(acetonitrile)}}}{\overset{2}{C}H_3-\overset{1}{C}{\equiv}N\colon}
\qquad
\underset{\text{Butanenitrile}}{\overset{4}{C}H_3\overset{3}{C}H_2\overset{2}{C}H_2-\overset{1}{C}{\equiv}N\colon}
$$

$$\overset{3}{C}H_2=\overset{2}{C}H-\overset{1}{C}\equiv N\colon \qquad \overset{5}{C}H_2=\overset{4}{C}H-\overset{3}{C}H_2\overset{2}{C}H_2-\overset{1}{C}\equiv N\colon$$

Propenenitrile   **4-Pentenenitrile**
(acrylonitrile)

Cyclic nitriles are named by adding the suffix *carbonitrile* to the name of the ring system to which the —CN group is attached. Benzonitrile is an acceptable common name for C_6H_5CN.

Benzenecarbonitrile   **Cyclohexanecarbonitrile**
(benzonitrile)

Problem 18.4

Give IUPAC names for the following:

(a) $HO_2C(CH_2)_5CO_2H$ (e) $CH_3CH_2CH_2COCl$

(b) $CH_3CH_2CH_2CO_2CH_3$ (f) $CH_3CH_2CONH_2$

(c) $CH_3CH_2CHClCO_2H$ (g) $CH_3CH_2CH_2CONHCH_3$

(d) $(CH_3CH_2CO)_2O$ (h) $C_6H_5CH_2CH_2CH_2COCl$

Problem 18.5

Write structural formulas for the following:

(a) Methyl propanoate   (f) Dimethyl phthalate

(b) Ethyl *p*-nitrobenzoate   (g) Dipropyl maleate

(c) Dimethyl malonate   (h) *N,N*-Dimethylformamide

(d) *N,N*-Dimethylbenzamide   (i) 2-Bromopropanoyl bromide

(e) Pentanenitrile   (j) Diethyl succinate

18.2J SPECTROSCOPIC PROPERTIES OF ACYL COMPOUNDS

Infrared spectroscopy is of considerable importance in identifying carboxylic acids and their derivatives. The C=O stretching band is one of the most prominent in their IR spectra since it is always a strong band. The C=O stretching band occurs at different frequencies for acids, esters, and amides, and its precise location is often helpful in structure determination. Table 18.5 gives the location of this band for most acyl compounds.

The hydroxyl groups of carboxylic acids also give rise to a broad peak in the $2500-2700\text{-cm}^{-1}$ region arising from O—H stretching vibrations. The N—H stretching vibrations of amides absorb between 3140 and 3500 cm^{-1}.

The acidic protons of carboxylic acids usually absorb very far downfield (δ 10–12) in their ^{1}H NMR spectra. The carbon of the —CO_2H group absorbs in the range δ 165–185 in ^{13}C spectra.

TABLE 18.5 Carbonyl stretching absorptions of acyl compounds

TYPE OF COMPOUND	FREQUENCY RANGE (cm^{-1})
Carboxylic Acids	
$R-CO_2H$	1700–1725
$-\underset{|}{C}=\underset{|}{C}-CO_2H$	1690–1715
$ArCO_2H$	1680–1700
Acid Anhydrides	
$R-\overset{O}{\overset{\|}{C}}-O-\overset{O}{\overset{\|}{C}}-R$	1800–1850 and 1740–1790
$Ar-\overset{O}{\overset{\|}{C}}-O-\overset{O}{\overset{\|}{C}}-Ar$	1780–1860 and 1730–1780
Acyl Chlorides	
$R-\overset{O}{\overset{\|}{C}}Cl$ and $Ar-\overset{O}{\overset{\|}{C}}Cl$	1780–1850
Esters	
$R-\overset{O}{\overset{\|}{C}}-OR'$	1735–1750
$Ar-\overset{O}{\overset{\|}{C}}-OR'$	1715–1730
Amides	
$R\overset{O}{\overset{\|}{C}}NH_2$, $R\overset{O}{\overset{\|}{C}}NHR$, and $R\overset{O}{\overset{\|}{C}}NR_2$	1630–1690
Carboxylate Ions	
RCO_2^-	1550–1630

18.3 PREPARATION OF CARBOXYLIC ACIDS

Most of the methods for the preparation of carboxylic acids are familiar ones.

1. **By oxidation of alkenes.** We learned in Section 9.12 that alkenes can be oxidized to carboxylic acid with hot alkaline $KMnO_4$.

$$RCH=CHR' \xrightarrow[\substack{\text{heat} \\ (2)\ H_3O^+}]{(1)\ KMnO_4,\ OH^-} RCO_2H + R'CO_2H$$

Alternatively, ozonides (Section 9.12A) can be subjected to an oxidative workup that yields carboxylic acids.

$$RCH=CHR' \xrightarrow[\text{(2) } H_2O_2]{\text{(1) } O_3} RCO_2H + R'CO_2H$$

2. **By oxidation of aldehydes and primary alcohols.** Aldehydes can be oxidized to carboxylic acids with mild oxidizing agents such as $Ag(NH_3)_2^+OH^-$ (Section 16.12). Primary alcohols can be oxidized with $KMnO_4$.

$$R-CHO \xrightarrow[\text{(2) } H_3O^+]{\text{(1) } Ag_2O \text{ or } Ag(NH_3)_2^+OH^-} RCO_2H$$

$$RCH_2OH \xrightarrow[\text{(2) } H_3O^+]{\substack{\text{(1) } KMnO_4, \text{ OH}^- \\ \text{heat}}} RCO_2H$$

3. **By oxidation of alkylbenzenes.** Primary and secondary alkyl groups (but not 3° groups) directly attached to a benzene ring are oxidized by $KMnO_4$ to a $-CO_2H$ group (Section 15.12).

$$\bigcirc -CH_3 \xrightarrow[\text{(2) } H_3O^+]{\substack{\text{(1) } KMnO_4, \text{ OH}^- \\ \text{heat}}} \bigcirc -CO_2H$$

4. **By oxidation of methyl ketones.** Methyl ketones can be converted to carboxylic acids via the haloform reaction (Section 17.4).

$$\underset{\substack{\| \\ O}}{Ar-C-CH_3} \xrightarrow[\text{(2) } H_3O^+]{\text{(1) } X_2/NaOH} \underset{\substack{\| \\ O}}{Ar-COH} + CHX_3$$

5. **By hydrolysis of cyanohydrins and other nitriles.** We saw, in Section 16.9A, that aldehydes and ketones can be converted to cyanohydrins, and that these can be hydrolyzed to α-hydroxy acids. In the hydrolysis the $-CN$ group is converted to a $-CO_2H$ group. The mechanism of hydrolysis is discussed in Section 18.8H.

$$\underset{R'}{\overset{R}{>}}C=O + HCN \rightleftharpoons \underset{R'}{\overset{R}{>}}\underset{CN}{\overset{OH}{C}} \xrightarrow[H_2O]{H^+} R-\underset{\underset{R'}{|}}{\overset{\overset{OH}{|}}{C}}-CO_2H$$

Nitriles can also be prepared by nucleophilic substitution reactions of alkyl halides with sodium cyanide. Hydrolysis of the nitrile yields a carboxylic acid *with a chain one carbon atom longer* than the original alkyl halide.

General Reaction

$$R-CH_2X + CN^- \longrightarrow RCH_2CN \xrightarrow[\substack{H_2O \\ \text{heat}}]{H^+} RCH_2CO_2H + NH_4^+$$

$$\xrightarrow[\substack{H_2O \\ \text{heat}}]{OH^-} RCH_2CO_2^- + NH_3$$

Specific Examples

$$HOCH_2CH_2Cl \xrightarrow[(80\%)]{NaCN} \underset{\substack{\textbf{3-Hydroxy-} \\ \textbf{propanenitrile}}}{HOCH_2CH_2CN} \xrightarrow[\text{(2) } H_3O^+]{\text{(1) } OH^-, H_2O} \underset{\substack{(75-80\%) \quad \textbf{3-Hydroxypropanoic} \\ \textbf{acid}}}{HOCH_2CH_2CO_2H}$$

$$BrCH_2CH_2CH_2Br \xrightarrow[(77-86\%)]{NaCN} \underset{\textbf{Pentanedinitrile}}{NCCH_2CH_2CH_2CN} \xrightarrow[(83-85\%)]{H_3O^+} \underset{\textbf{Glutaric acid}}{HO_2CCH_2CH_2CH_2CO_2H}$$

This synthetic method is generally limited to the use of *primary alkyl* halides. The cyanide ion is a relatively strong base, and the use of a secondary or tertiary alkyl halide leads primarily to an alkene (through elimination) rather than to a nitrile (through substitution). Aryl halides (except for those with ortho and para nitro groups) do not react with sodium cyanide.

6. **By carbonation of Grignard reagents.** Grignard reagents react with carbon dioxide to yield magnesium carboxylates. Acidification produces carboxylic acids.

$$R{-}X + Mg \xrightarrow[\text{diethyl ether}]{} RMgX \xrightarrow{CO_2} RCO_2MgX \xrightarrow{H_3O^+} RCO_2H$$

or

$$Ar{-}Br + Mg \xrightarrow[\text{diethyl ether}]{} ArMgBr \xrightarrow{CO_2} ArCO_2MgBr \xrightarrow{H_3O^+} ArCO_2H$$

This synthesis of carboxylic acids is applicable to primary, secondary, tertiary, allyl, benzyl, and aryl halides, provided they have no groups incompatible with a Grignard reaction (cf. Section 11.8B).

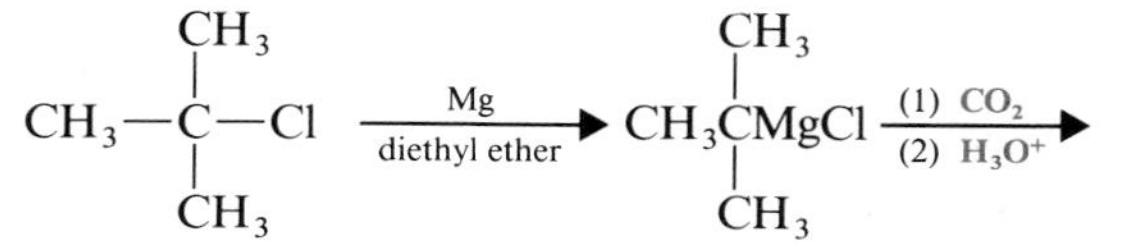

***tert*-Butyl chloride** → **2,2-Dimethylpropanoic acid (79–80% overall)**

$$CH_3CH_2CH_2CH_2Cl \xrightarrow[\text{diethyl ether}]{Mg} CH_3CH_2CH_2CH_2MgCl \xrightarrow[(2)\ H_3O^+]{(1)\ CO_2} CH_3CH_2CH_2CH_2CO_2H$$

Butyl chloride → **Pentanoic acid (80% overall)**

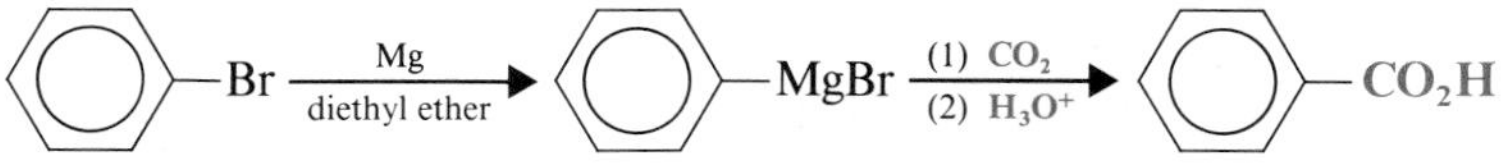

Benzoic acid (85%)

Problem 18.6

Show how each of the following compounds could be converted to benzoic acid.

(a) Ethylbenzene (c) Acetophenone (e) Benzyl alcohol
(b) Bromobenzene (d) Phenylethene (styrene) (f) Benzaldehyde

Problem 18.7

Show how you would prepare each of the following carboxylic acids through a Grignard synthesis.

(a) Phenylacetic acid (c) 3-Butenoic acid (e) Hexanoic acid
(b) 2,2-Dimethylpentanoic acid (d) 4-Methylbenzoic acid

Problem 18.8

(a) Which of the carboxylic acids in Problem 18.7 could be prepared by a nitrile synthesis as well? (b) Which synthesis, Grignard or nitrile, would you choose to prepare $HOCH_2CH_2CH_2CH_2CO_2H$ from $HOCH_2CH_2CH_2CH_2Br$? Why?

18.4 NUCLEOPHILIC SUBSTITUTIONS AT THE ACYL CARBON

In our study of carbonyl compounds in Chapter 17, we saw that a characteristic reaction of aldehydes and ketones is one of *nucleophilic addition* to the carbon–oxygen double bond.

Nucleophilic addition

As we study carboxylic acids and their derivatives in this chapter we shall find that their reactions are characterized by **nucleophilic substitutions** that take place at their acyl (carbonyl) carbon atoms. We shall encounter many reactions of the following general type.

Nucleophilic substitution

Although the final results obtained from the reactions of acyl compounds with nucleophiles (substitutions) differ from those obtained from aldehydes and ketones (additions), the two reactions have one characteristic in common. *The initial step in both reactions involves nucleophilic addition at the carbonyl carbon atom.* With both groups of compounds this initial attack is facilitated by the same factors: the relative steric openness of the carbonyl carbon atom and the ability of the carbonyl oxygen atom to accommodate an electron pair of the carbon–oxygen double bond.

It is after the initial nucleophilic attack has taken place that the two reactions differ. The tetrahedral intermediate formed from an aldehyde or ketone usually accepts a proton to form a stable addition product. By contrast, the intermediate formed from an acyl compound usually *eliminates* a leaving group; this **elimination** leads to regeneration of the carbon–oxygen double bond and to a *substitution product.* The overall process in the case of **acyl substitution** occurs, therefore, by a **nucleophilic addition–elimination** mechanism.

18.4 NUCLEOPHILIC SUBSTITUTIONS AT THE ACYL CARBON

Acyl compounds react as they do because they all have good leaving groups attached to the carbonyl carbon atom. An acyl chloride, for example, generally reacts by losing *a chloride ion*—a very weak base, and thus, a very good leaving group.

Example

The reaction of an acyl chloride with water.

Loss of a chloride ion

An acid anhydride generally reacts by losing *a carboxylate ion* or a molecule of a *carboxylic acid*—both are weak bases and good leaving groups.

Example

The reaction of a carboxylic acid anhydride with an alcohol.

leaving group is a carboxylate ion

leaving group is a carboxylic acid

As we shall see later, esters generally undergo nucleophilic substitution by losing a molecule of an *alcohol,* acids react by losing a molecule of *water,* and amides react by losing a molecule of *ammonia* or of an *amine.* All of the molecules lost in these reactions are weak bases and are reasonably good leaving groups.

For an aldehyde or ketone to react by substitution, the tetrahedral intermediate would have to eject a hydride ion ($H:^-$) or an alkanide ion ($R:^-$). Both are *very powerful bases* and both are, therefore, *very poor leaving groups.*

[The haloform reaction (Section 17.4) is one of the rare instances in which an alkanide ion can act as a leaving group.]

18.4A RELATIVE REACTIVITY OF ACYL COMPOUNDS

Of the acid derivatives that we shall study in this chapter, acyl chlorides are the most reactive toward nucleophilic substitution and amides are the least reactive. In general, the overall order of reactivity is

The general order of reactivity of acid derivatives can be explained by taking into account the basicity of the leaving groups. When acyl chlorides react, the leaving group is a *chloride ion.* When acid anhydrides react, the leaving group is a carboxylic acid or a carboxylate ion. When esters react, the leaving group is an alcohol, and when amides react, the leaving group is an amine (or ammonia). Of all of these bases, chloride ions are the *weakest bases* and acyl chlorides are the *most reactive* acyl compounds. Amines (or ammonia) are the *strongest bases* and amides are the *least reactive* acyl compounds.

18.4B SYNTHESIS OF ACID DERIVATIVES

As we begin now to explore the syntheses of carboxylic acid derivatives we shall find that in many instances one acid derivative can be synthesized through a nucleophilic substitution reaction of another. The order of reactivities that we have presented gives us a clue as to which syntheses are practical and which are not. In general, *less reactive acyl compounds can be synthesized from more reactive ones, but the reverse is usually difficult and, when possible, requires special conditions.*

18.5 ACYL CHLORIDES

18.5A SYNTHESIS OF ACYL CHLORIDES

Since acyl chlorides are the most reactive of the acid derivatives, we must use special reagents to prepare them. We use other acid chlorides, *the acid chlorides of inorganic acids:* we use PCl_5 (an acid chloride of phosphoric acid), PCl_3 (an acid chloride of phosphorous acid), and $SOCl_2$ (an acid chloride of sulfurous acid).

All of these reagents react with carboxylic acids to give acyl chlorides in good yield.

General Reactions

$$RCOH + SOCl_2 \longrightarrow R-C-Cl + SO_2 + HCl$$
Thionyl chloride

$$3\ RCOH + PCl_3 \longrightarrow 3\ RCCl + H_3PO_3$$
Phosphorus trichloride

$$RCOH + PCl_5 \longrightarrow RCCl + POCl_3 + HCl$$
Phosphorus pentachloride

These reactions all involve nucleophilic substitutions by chloride ion on a highly reactive intermediate: a protonated acyl chlorosulfite, a protonated acyl chlorophosphite, or a protonated acyl chlorophosphate. Thionyl chloride, for example, reacts with a carboxylic acid in the following way:

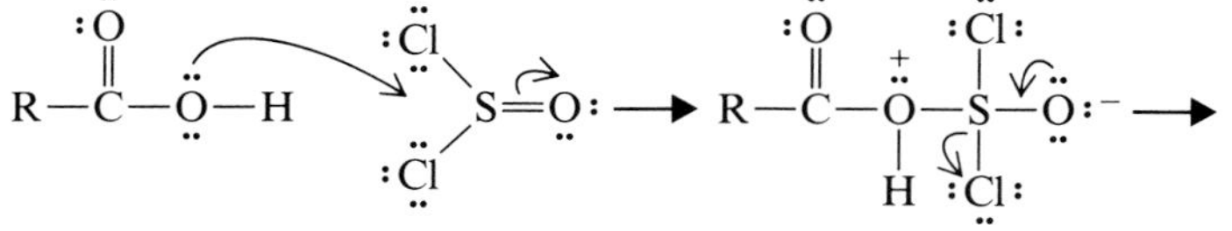

Protonated acyl chlorosulfite

$$HCl + SO_2$$

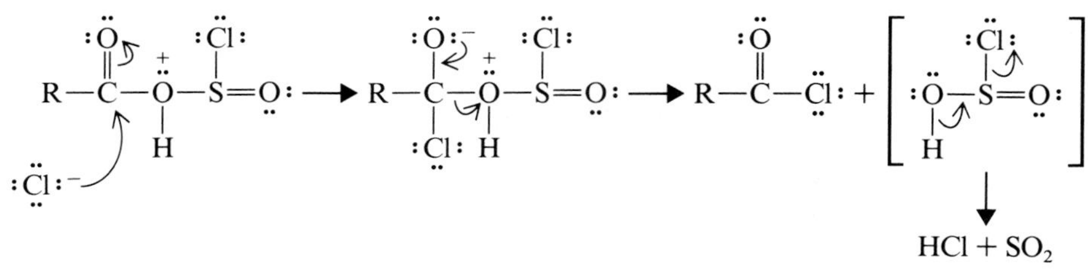

18.5B REACTIONS OF ACYL CHLORIDES

Because acyl chlorides are the most reactive of the acyl derivatives, they are easily converted to less reactive ones. Many times, therefore, the best synthetic route to an anhydride, an ester, or an amide will involve an initial synthesis of the acyl chloride from the acid, and then conversion of the acyl chloride to the desired acid derivative. The scheme given in Fig. 18.1 illustrates how this can be done. We will examine these reactions in detail in Sections 18.6–18.8.

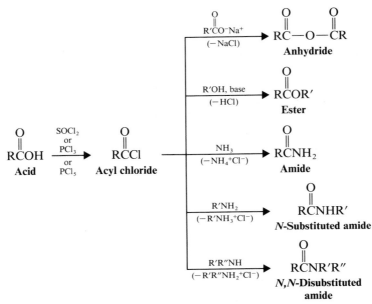

FIGURE 18.1 A scheme showing how acid anhydrides, esters, and amides may be synthesized from acids by first converting the acid to the acyl chloride. (These reactions are described in Sections 18.6–18.8.)

Acyl chlorides also react with water and (even more rapidly) with aqueous base:

18.6 CARBOXYLIC ACID ANHYDRIDES

18.6A SYNTHESIS OF CARBOXYLIC ACID ANHYDRIDES

Carboxylic acids react with acyl chlorides in the presence of pyridine to give carboxylic acid anhydrides.

$$R-\overset{O}{\underset{\|}{C}}-OH + R'-\overset{O}{\underset{\|}{C}}-Cl + \underset{N}{\bigcirc} \longrightarrow R-\overset{O}{\underset{\|}{C}}-O-\overset{O}{\underset{\|}{C}}-R' + \underset{\overset{|}{\underset{H}{N^+}}}{\bigcirc} Cl^-$$

This method is frequently used in the laboratory for the preparation of anhydrides. The method is quite general and can be used to prepare mixed anhydrides ($R \neq R'$) or simple anhydrides ($R = R'$).

Sodium salts of carboxylic acids also react with acyl chlorides to give anhydrides:

$$R-\overset{O}{\underset{\|}{C}}-O^-Na^+ + R'-\overset{O}{\underset{\|}{C}}-Cl \longrightarrow R-\overset{O}{\underset{\|}{C}}-O-\overset{O}{\underset{\|}{C}}-R' + Na^+Cl^-$$

In this reaction a carboxylate ion acts as a nucleophile and brings about a nucleophilic substitution reaction at the acyl carbon of the acyl chloride.

Cyclic anhydrides can sometimes be prepared by simply heating the appropriate dicarboxylic acid. This method succeeds, however, only when anhydride formation leads to a five- or six-membered ring.

Succinic acid → (300 °C) → Succinic anhydride + H_2O

Phthalic acid → (230 °C) → Phthalic anhydride (~100%) + H_2O

Problem 18.9

When maleic acid is heated to 200 °C, it loses water and becomes maleic anhydride. Fumaric acid, a diastereomer of maleic acid, requires a much higher temperature before it dehydrates; when it does, it also yields maleic anhydride. Provide an explanation for these observations.

18.6B REACTIONS OF CARBOXYLIC ACID ANHYDRIDES

Because carboxylic acid anhydrides are highly reactive they can be used to prepare esters and amides (Fig. 18.2). We shall study these reactions in detail in Sections 18.7 and 18.8.

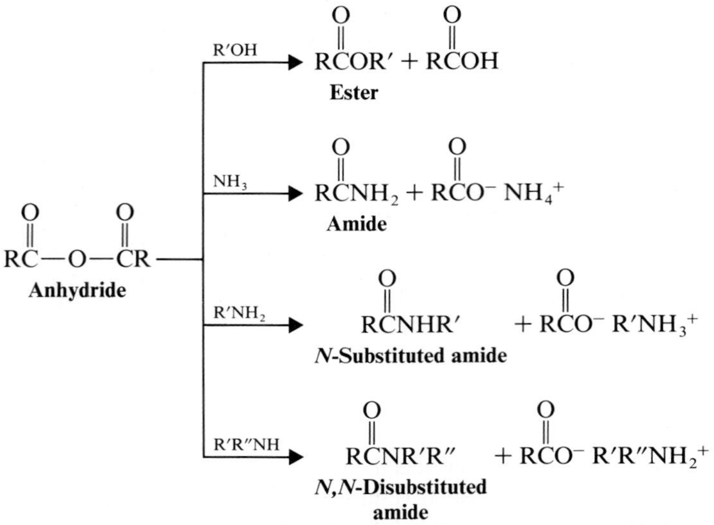

$$RC-O-CR \quad \text{(Anhydride)}$$

- $\xrightarrow{R'OH}$ $\overset{O}{\underset{}{RCOR'}} + \overset{O}{\underset{}{RCOH}}$ **Ester**
- $\xrightarrow{NH_3}$ $\overset{O}{\underset{}{RCNH_2}} + \overset{O}{\underset{}{RCO^-}} NH_4^+$ **Amide**
- $\xrightarrow{R'NH_2}$ $\overset{O}{\underset{}{RCNHR'}} + \overset{O}{\underset{}{RCO^-}} R'NH_3^+$ **N-Substituted amide**
- $\xrightarrow{R'R''NH}$ $\overset{O}{\underset{}{RCNR'R''}} + \overset{O}{\underset{}{RCO^-}} R'R''NH_2^+$ **N,N-Disubstituted amide**

FIGURE 18.2 A scheme showing how esters and amides can be prepared from carboxylic acid anhydrides. (These reactions are described in Sections 18.7 and 18.8.)

Carboxylic acid anhydrides also undergo hydrolysis:

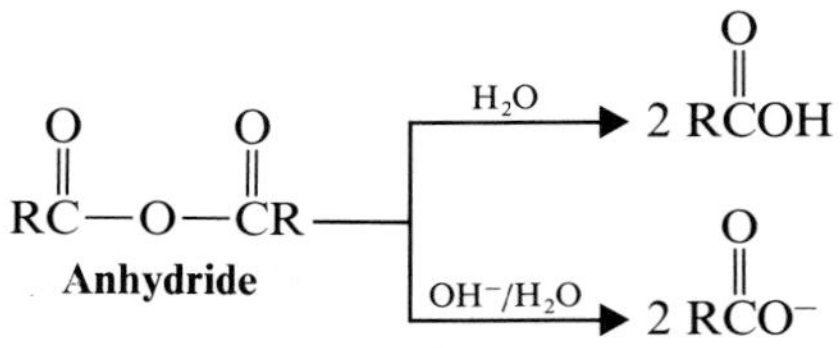

$$RC-O-CR \quad \text{(Anhydride)}$$

- $\xrightarrow{H_2O}$ $2 \overset{O}{\underset{}{RCOH}}$
- $\xrightarrow{OH^-/H_2O}$ $2 \overset{O}{\underset{}{RCO^-}}$

18.7 ESTERS

18.7A SYNTHESIS OF ESTERS: ESTERIFICATION

Carboxylic acids react with alcohols to form esters through a condensation reaction known as **esterification**:

General Reaction

$$R-\overset{O}{\underset{}{C}}-OH + R'-OH \underset{}{\overset{H^+}{\rightleftharpoons}} R-\overset{O}{\underset{}{C}}-OR' + H_2O$$

Specific Examples

$$\underset{\textbf{Acetic acid}}{CH_3\overset{O}{\underset{}{C}}OH} + \underset{\textbf{Ethanol}}{CH_3CH_2OH} \overset{H^+}{\rightleftharpoons} \underset{\textbf{Ethyl acetate}}{CH_3\overset{O}{\underset{}{C}}OCH_2CH_3} + H_2O$$

$$\underset{\textbf{Benzoic acid}}{C_6H_5\overset{O}{\underset{}{C}}OH} + \underset{\textbf{Methanol}}{CH_3OH} \overset{H^+}{\rightleftharpoons} \underset{\textbf{Methyl benzoate}}{C_6H_5\overset{O}{\underset{}{C}}OCH_3} + H_2O$$

Esterification reactions are acid catalyzed. They proceed very slowly in the absence of strong acids, but reach equilibrium within a matter of a few hours when an acid and an alcohol are refluxed with a small amount of concentrated sulfuric acid or hydrogen chloride. Since the position of equilibrium controls the amount of the ester formed, the use of an excess of either the carboxylic acid or the alcohol increases the yield based on the limiting reagent. Just which component we choose to use in excess will depend on its availability and cost. The yield of an esterification reaction can also be increased by removing water from the reaction mixture as it is formed.

When benzoic acid reacts with methanol that has been labeled with ^{18}O, the labeled oxygen appears in the ester: This result reveals just which bonds break in the esterification.

$$C_6H_5C \overset{O}{\overset{\|}{\,}}{+}OH + CH_3{-}^{18}O{+}H \underset{}{\overset{H^+}{\rightleftharpoons}} C_6H_5C \overset{O}{\overset{\|}{\,}}{-}^{18}OCH_3 + H_2O$$

The results of the labeling experiment and the fact that esterifications are acid catalyzed are both consistent with the mechanism that follows. This mechanism is typical of acid-catalyzed nucleophilic substitution reactions at acyl carbon atoms.

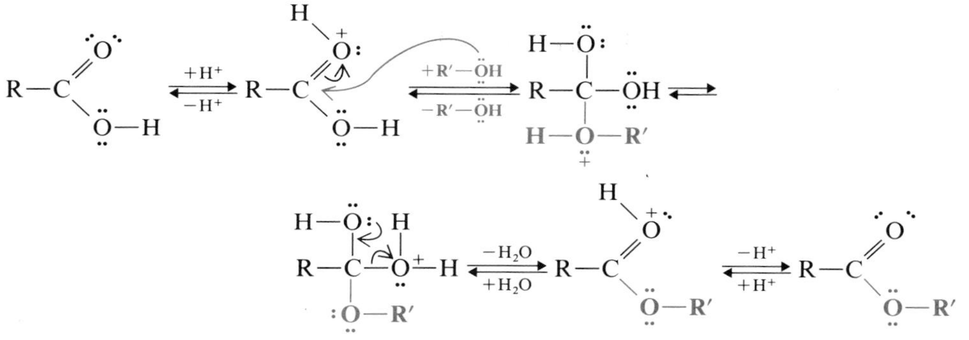

If we follow the forward reactions in this mechanism, we have the mechanism for the *acid-catalyzed esterification of an acid.* If, however, we follow the reverse reactions, we have the mechanism for the *acid-catalyzed hydrolysis of an ester:*

Acid-Catalyzed Ester Hydrolysis

$$R{-}\overset{O}{\overset{\|}{C}}{-}OR' \quad H_2O \underset{}{\overset{H_3O^+}{\rightleftharpoons}} R{-}\overset{O}{\overset{\|}{C}}{-}OH + R'{-}OH$$

Which result we obtain will depend on the conditions we choose. If we want to esterify an acid, we use an excess of the alcohol and, if possible, remove the water as it is formed. If we want to hydrolyze an ester, we use a large excess of water; that is, we reflux the ester with dilute aqueous HCl or dilute aqueous H_2SO_4.

Problem 18.10

Where would you expect to find the labeled oxygen if you carried out an acid-catalyzed hydrolysis of methyl benzoate in ^{18}O-labeled water?

Steric factors strongly affect the rates of acid-catalyzed hydrolyses of esters. Large groups near the reaction site, whether in the alcohol component or the acid component, slow both reactions markedly. Tertiary alcohols, for example, react so slowly in acid-catalyzed esterifications that they usually undergo elimination instead. However, they can be converted to esters safely through the use of acyl chlorides and anhydrides in the ways that follow.

Esters from Acyl Chlorides. Esters can also be synthesized by the reaction of acyl chlorides with alcohols. Since acyl chlorides are much more reactive toward nucleophilic substitution than carboxylic acids, the reaction of an acyl chloride and an alcohol occurs rapidly and does not require an acid catalyst. Pyridine is usually added to the reaction mixture to react with the HCl that forms.

General Reaction

$$R-C\overset{\ddot{O}}{\underset{\ddot{C}l:}{}} + R'-\ddot{O}-H \xrightarrow{-HCl} R-C\overset{\ddot{O}}{\underset{\ddot{O}-R'}{}}$$

Specific Example

$$\underset{\text{Benzoyl chloride}}{C_6H_5\overset{O}{\overset{\|}{C}}-Cl} + CH_3CH_2OH + \underset{N}{\bigcirc} \longrightarrow \underset{\substack{\text{Ethyl benzoate}\\(80\%)}}{C_6H_5\overset{O}{\overset{\|}{C}}OCH_2CH_3} + \underset{\overset{N^+}{\underset{H}{|}}}{\bigcirc} Cl^-$$

Esters from Carboxylic Acid Anhydrides. Carboxylic acid anhydrides also react with alcohols to form esters in the absence of an acid catalyst.

General Reaction

$$\underset{RC\underset{O}{\overset{\diagup}{\diagdown}}}{RC\overset{O}{\overset{\diagup}{\diagdown}}} O + R'-OH \longrightarrow RC\overset{O}{\underset{O-R'}{\overset{\diagup}{\diagdown}}} + R\overset{O}{\overset{\|}{C}}OH$$

Specific Example

$$\left(\underset{\substack{\text{Acetic}\\\text{anhydride}}}{CH_3\overset{O}{\overset{\|}{C}}-}\right)_2 O + \underset{\substack{\text{Benzyl}\\\text{alcohol}}}{C_6H_5CH_2OH} \longrightarrow \underset{\text{Benzyl acetate}}{CH_3\overset{O}{\overset{\|}{C}}OCH_2C_6H_5} + CH_3CO_2H$$

The reaction of an alcohol with an anhydride or an acyl chloride is often the best method for preparing an ester.

Cyclic anhydrides react with one molar equivalent of an alcohol to form compounds that are *both esters and acids.*

| Phthalic anhydride | *sec*-Butyl alcohol | | *sec*-Butyl hydrogen phthalate (97%) |

Problem 18.11

Esters can also be synthesized by *transesterification*:

$$\underset{\substack{\text{High-boiling} \\ \text{ester}}}{R-\overset{\displaystyle O}{\overset{\|}{C}}-OR'} + \underset{\substack{\text{High-boiling} \\ \text{alcohol}}}{R''-OH} \underset{}{\overset{H^+, \text{ heat}}{\rightleftharpoons}} \underset{\substack{\text{Higher boiling} \\ \text{ester}}}{R\overset{\displaystyle O}{\overset{\|}{C}}-OR''} + \underset{\substack{\text{Lower boiling} \\ \text{alcohol}}}{R'-OH}$$

In this procedure we shift the equilibrium to the right by allowing the low boiling alcohol to distill from the reaction mixture. The mechanism for transesterification is similar to that for an acid-catalyzed esterification (or an acid-catalyzed ester hydrolysis). Write a mechanism for the following transesterification.

$$\underset{\substack{\text{Methyl acrylate}}}{CH_2{=}CH\overset{\displaystyle O}{\overset{\|}{C}}OCH_3} + \underset{\substack{\text{Butyl alcohol}}}{CH_3CH_2CH_2CH_2OH} \overset{H^+}{\rightleftharpoons}$$

$$\underset{\substack{\text{Butyl acrylate} \\ \text{(94\%)}}}{CH_2{=}CH\overset{\displaystyle O}{\overset{\|}{C}}OCH_2CH_2CH_2CH_3} + \underset{\substack{\text{Methanol}}}{CH_3OH}$$

18.7B BASE-PROMOTED HYDROLYSIS OF ESTERS: SAPONIFICATION

Esters not only undergo acid hydrolysis, they also undergo *base-promoted hydrolysis.* Base-promoted hydrolysis is sometimes called *saponification* (from the Latin *sapo* for soap (see Section 23.2B). Refluxing an ester with aqueous sodium hydroxide, for example, produces an alcohol and the sodium salt of the acid:

$$\underset{\substack{\text{Ester}}}{R\overset{\displaystyle O}{\overset{\|}{C}}-OR'} + NaOH \overset{H_2O}{\longrightarrow} \underset{\substack{\text{Sodium carboxylate}}}{R-\overset{\displaystyle O}{\overset{\|}{C}}-O^-Na^+} + \underset{\substack{\text{Alcohol}}}{R'OH}$$

The carboxylate ion is very unreactive toward nucleophilic substitution because it is negatively charged. Base-promoted hydrolysis of an ester, as a result, is an essentially irreversible reaction.

The accepted mechanism for the base-promoted hydrolysis of an ester also involves a nucleophilic substitution at the acyl carbon:

Evidence for this mechanism comes from studies done with isotopically labeled esters. When ethyl propanoate labeled with ^{18}O in the ether-type oxygen of the ester (below) is subjected to hydrolysis with aqueous NaOH, all of the ^{18}O shows up in the ethanol that is produced. None of the ^{18}O appears in the propanoate ion.

$$CH_3CH_2-\overset{\overset{\displaystyle O}{\|}}{C}-\overset{18}{O}-CH_2CH_3 + NaOH \xrightarrow{H_2O} CH_3CH_2-\overset{\overset{\displaystyle O}{\|}}{C}-O^-Na^+ + H\overset{18}{O}-CH_2CH_3$$

This labeling result is completely consistent with the mechanism given above (outline the steps for yourself and follow the labeled oxygen through to the products). If the hydroxide ion had attacked the alkyl carbon instead of the acyl carbon, the alcohol obtained would not have been labeled. Attack at the alkyl carbon is almost never observed. (For one exception see Problem 18.13.)

$$CH_3CH_2-\overset{\overset{\displaystyle O}{\|}}{C}-\overset{18}{O}-CH_2CH_3 + {}^-OH \xrightarrow{H_2O}\!\!\!\times\!\!\!\longrightarrow CH_3CH_2-\overset{\overset{\displaystyle O}{\|}}{C}-\overset{18}{O}^- + HO-CH_2CH_3$$

$$CH_3CH_2-\overset{\overset{\displaystyle O^-}{|}}{C}\overset{18}{=}O$$

These products are not formed

Further evidence that nucleophilic attack occurs at the acyl carbon comes from studies in which esters of chiral alcohols were subjected to base-promoted hydrolysis. Reaction by path A (at the acyl carbon) should lead to retention of configuration in the alcohol. Reaction by path B (at the alkyl carbon) should lead to an inversion of configuration of the alcohol. *Inversion of configuration is almost never observed.* In almost every instance basic hydrolysis of a carboxylic ester of a chiral alcohol proceeds with *retention of configuration.*

Path A: Nucleophilic Substitution at the Acyl Carbon

Path B: Nucleophilic Substitution at the Alkyl Carbon

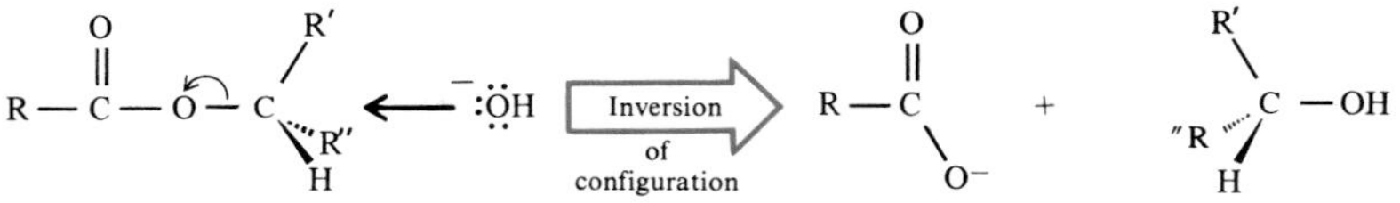

Although nucleophilic attack at the alkyl carbon seldom occurs with esters of carboxylic acids, it is the preferred mode of attack with esters of sulfonic acids (Section 10.11).

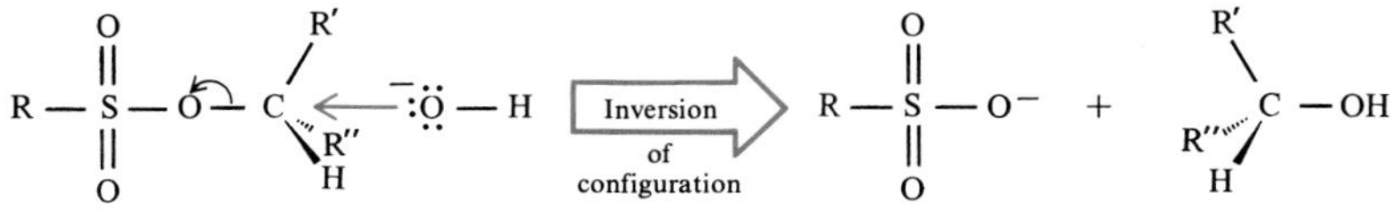

An alkyl sulfonate

Problem 18.12

(a) Write stereochemical formulas for compounds **A–F**.

1. *cis*-3-Methylcyclopentanol + $C_6H_5SO_2Cl \longrightarrow$

$$A \xrightarrow[\text{heat}]{OH^-} B + C_6H_5SO_3^-$$

2. *cis*-3-Methylcyclopentanol + $C_6H_5\overset{O}{\overset{\|}{C}}-Cl \longrightarrow$

$$C \xrightarrow[\text{reflux}]{OH^-} D + C_6H_5CO_2^-$$

3. (*R*)-2-Bromooctane + $CH_3CO_2^-Na^+ \longrightarrow E + NaBr$

$$\downarrow \begin{array}{c} OH^-, H_2O \\ (\text{reflux}) \end{array}$$

$$F$$

4. (*R*)-2-Bromooctane + $OH^- \xrightarrow{\text{acetone}} F + Br^-$

(b) Which of the last two methods, **(3)** or **(4)**, would you expect to give a higher yield of **F**? Why?

Problem 18.13

Base-promoted hydrolysis of methyl mesitoate occurs through an attack on the alcohol carbon instead of the acyl carbon.

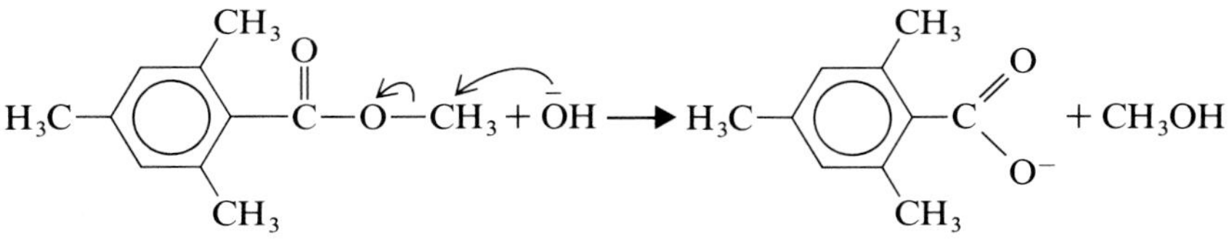

Methyl mesitoate

(a) Can you suggest a reason that will account for this unusual behavior?
(b) Suggest an experiment with labeled compounds that would confirm this mode of attack.

18.7C LACTONES

Carboxylic acids whose molecules have a hydroxyl group on a γ- or δ-carbon undergo an intramolecular esterification to give cyclic esters known as γ- or *δ-lactones*. The reaction is acid catalyzed:

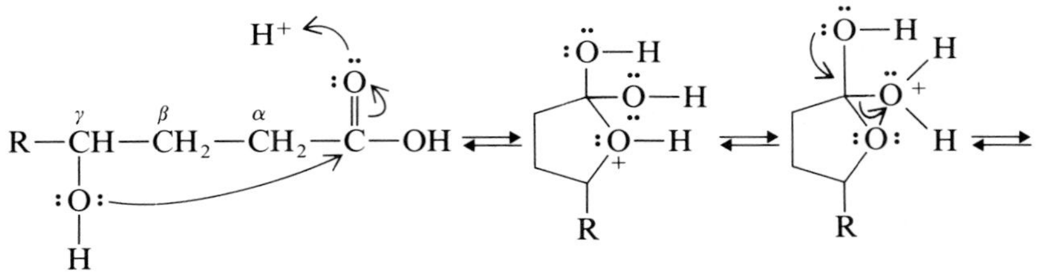

A γ-hydroxy acid

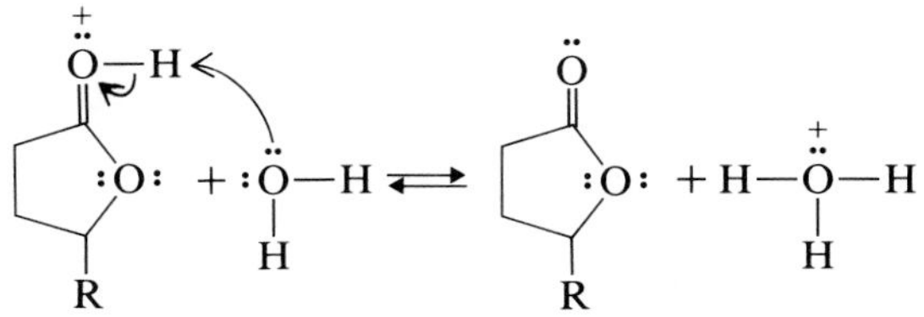

A γ-lactone

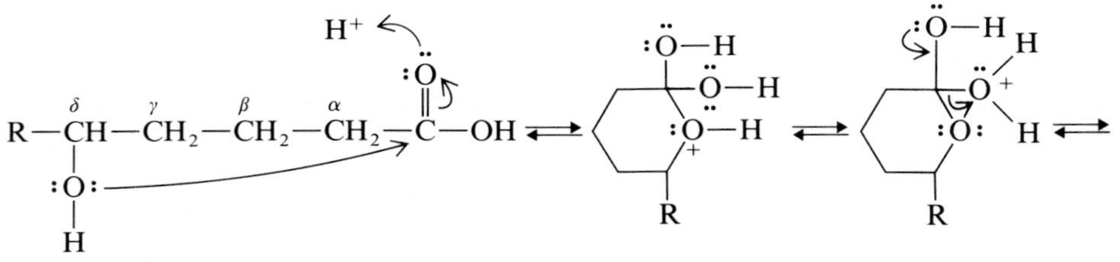

A δ-hydroxy acid

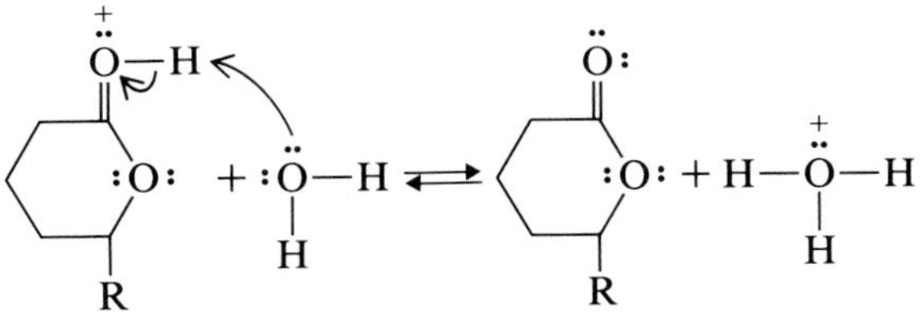

A δ-lactone

Lactones are hydrolyzed by aqueous base just as other esters are. Acidification of the sodium salt, however, may lead spontaneously back to the γ- or δ-lactone, particularly if excess acid is used.

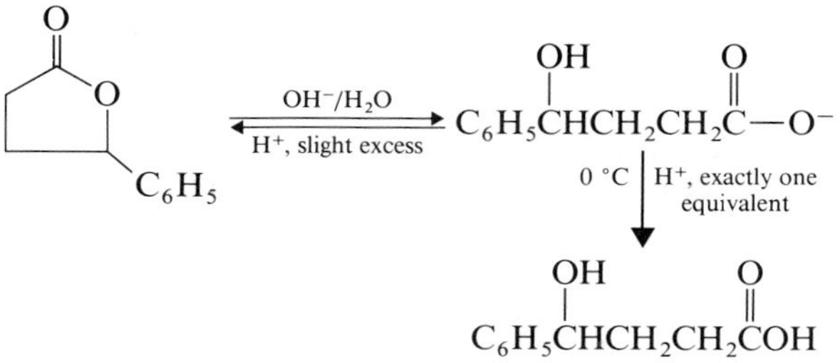

Many lactones occur in nature. Vitamin C (below), for example, is a γ-lactone. Some antibiotics, such as erythromycin, are lactones with very large rings, but most naturally occurring lactones are γ- or δ-lactones; that is, most contain five- or six-membered rings.

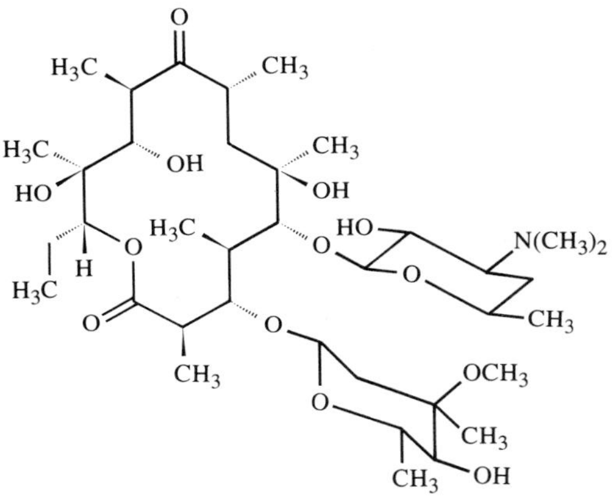

Erythromycin A

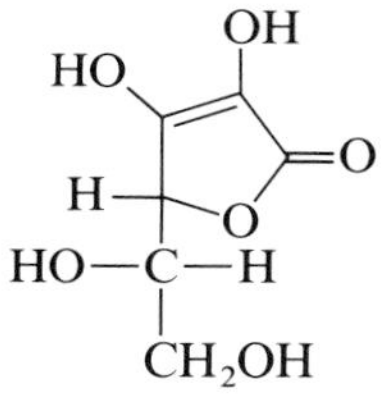

Vitamin C

β-Lactones (lactones with four-membered rings) have been detected as intermediates in some reactions and several have been isolated. They are highly reactive, however. If one attempts to prepare a β-lactone from a β-hydroxy acid, β elimination usually occurs instead:

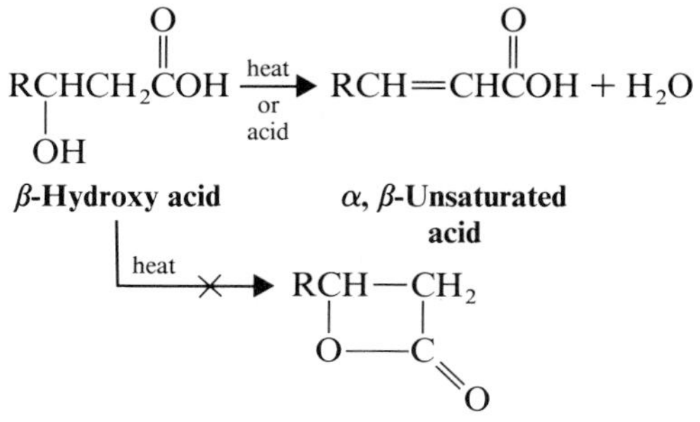

β-Hydroxy acid   **α, β-Unsaturated acid**

β-Lactone
(does not form)

When α-hydroxy acids are heated, they form cyclic diesters called *lactides*.

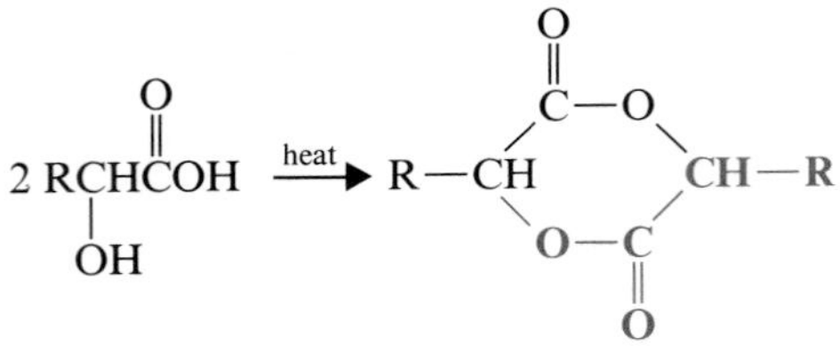

$$2 \; RCHCOH \xrightarrow{heat}$$

α-Hydroxy acid   **A lactide**

α-Lactones occur as intermediates in some reactions (cf. Special Topic H).

18.8 AMIDES

18.8A SYNTHESIS OF AMIDES

Amides can be prepared in a variety of ways starting with acyl chlorides, acid anhydrides, esters, carboxylic acids, and carboxylic salts. All of these methods involve nucleophilic substitution reactions by ammonia or an amine at an acyl carbon. As we might expect, acid chlorides are the most reactive and carboxylate ions are the least.

18.8B AMIDES FROM ACYL CHLORIDES

Primary amines, secondary amines, and ammonia all react rapidly with acid chlorides to form amides. An excess of ammonia or amine is used to neutralize the HCl that would be formed otherwise.

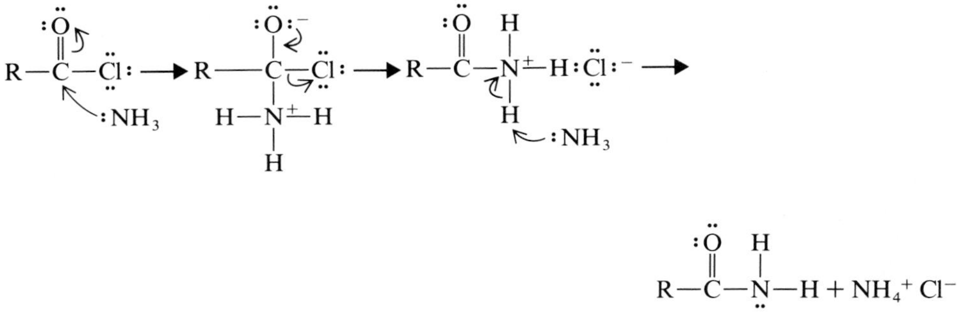

An amide

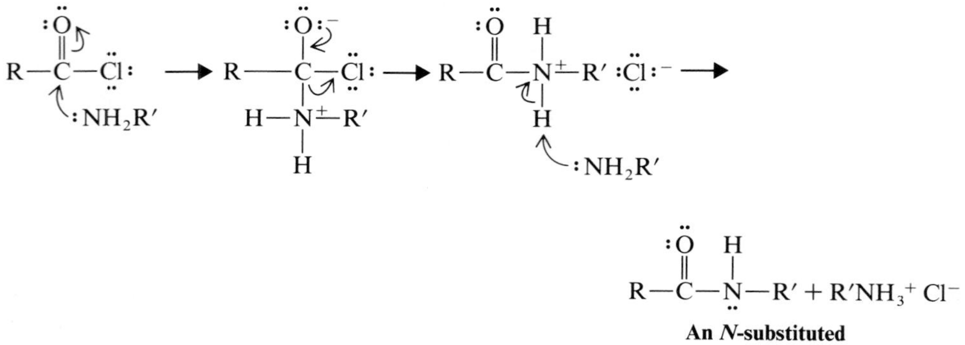

An N-substituted amide

$$R-\overset{:\overset{..}{O}}{\underset{\underset{:NHR'R''}{\uparrow}}{\overset{||}{C}}}-\overset{..}{\underset{..}{Cl}}: \longrightarrow R-\overset{:\overset{..}{O}:^-}{\underset{\underset{R'}{\overset{|}{N^{\pm}}-R''}}{\overset{|}{C}}}-\overset{..}{\underset{..}{Cl}}: \longrightarrow R-\overset{:\overset{..}{O} \quad R''}{\underset{\underset{:NHR'R''}{\uparrow}}{\overset{||}{C}-\overset{|}{\underset{H}{N^{\pm}}}-R'}} \quad :\overset{..}{\underset{..}{Cl}}:^- \longrightarrow$$

$$R-\overset{:\overset{..}{O} \quad R''}{\underset{}{\overset{||}{C}-\overset{|}{\underset{..}{N}}-R'}} + R'R''NH_2{}^+ \; Cl^-$$

An *N,N*-disubstituted amide

Since acyl chlorides are easily prepared from carboxylic acids this is one of the most widely used laboratory methods for the synthesis of amides. The reaction between the acyl chloride and the amine (or ammonia) usually takes place at room temperature (or below) and produces the amide in high yield.

Acyl chlorides also react with tertiary amines by a nucleophilic substitution reaction. The acylammonium ion that forms, however, is not stable in the presence of water or any hydroxylic solvent.

$$R-\overset{O}{\overset{\diagup}{\underset{\diagdown}{C}}}_{Cl} + R_3N: \longrightarrow R-\overset{O}{\overset{||}{C}}-\overset{+}{N}R_3 \; Cl^- \xrightarrow{H_2O} R-\overset{O}{\overset{||}{C}}OH + H\overset{+}{N}R_3 \; Cl^-$$

Acyl chloride   3° Amine   Acylammonium chloride

Acylpyridinium ions are probably involved as intermediates in those reactions of acyl chlorides that are carried out in the presence of pyridine.

18.8C AMIDES FROM CARBOXYLIC ANHYDRIDES

Acid anhydrides react with ammonia and with primary and secondary amines and form amides through reactions that are analogous to those of acyl chlorides.

$$\left(R\overset{O}{\overset{||}{C}}- \right)_2 O + 2 \; \overset{..}{N}H_3 \longrightarrow R\overset{O}{\overset{||}{C}}-\overset{..}{N}H_2 + RCO_2{}^-NH_4{}^+$$

$$\left(R\overset{O}{\overset{||}{C}}- \right)_2 O + 2 \; R'-\overset{..}{N}H_2 \longrightarrow R\overset{O}{\overset{||}{C}}-\overset{..}{N}H-R' + RCO_2{}^-R'\overset{+}{N}H_3$$

$$\left(R\overset{O}{\overset{||}{C}}- \right)_2 O + 2 \; R'-\underset{\underset{R''}{|}}{\overset{..}{N}}H \longrightarrow R\overset{O}{\overset{||}{C}}-\underset{\underset{R''}{|}}{\overset{..}{N}}-R' + RCO_2{}^-R'R''\overset{+}{N}H_2$$

Cyclic anhydrides react with ammonia or an amine in the same general way as acyclic anhydrides; however, the reaction produces a product that is both an amide and an ammonium salt. Acidifying the ammonium salt gives a compound that is both an amide and an acid:

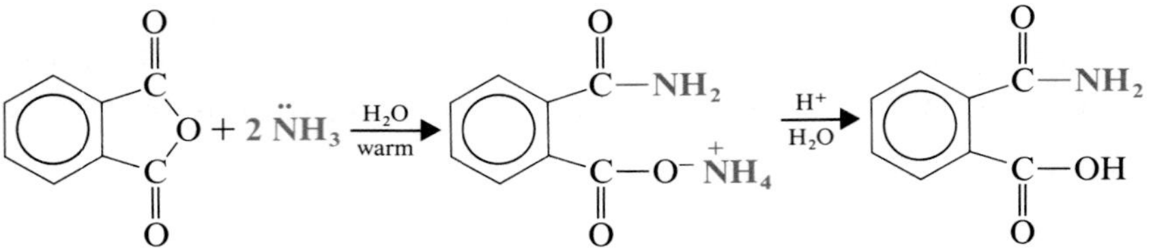

Phthalic	Ammonium	Phthalamic
anhydride	phthalamate	acid
	(94%)	(81%)

Heating the amide acid causes dehydration to occur and gives an *imide.* Imides

contain the linkage $-\overset{\overset{O}{\|}}{C}-NH-\overset{\overset{O}{\|}}{C}-$.

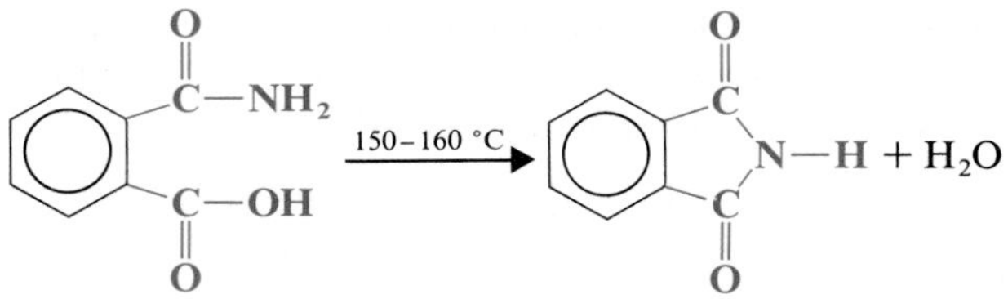

Phthalamic acid   Phthalimide
                                 ($\sim$ 100%)

18.8D AMIDES FROM ESTERS

Esters undergo nucleophilic substitution at their acyl carbon atoms when they are treated with ammonia (called *ammonolysis*) or with primary and secondary amines. These reactions take place more slowly than those of acyl chlorides and anhydrides, but they are synthetically useful.

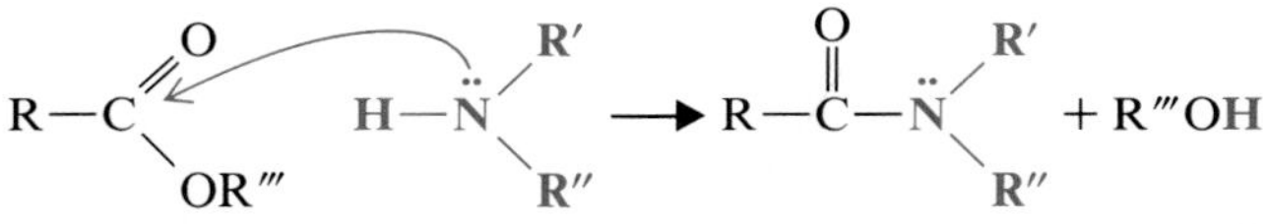

R' and/or R''
may be H

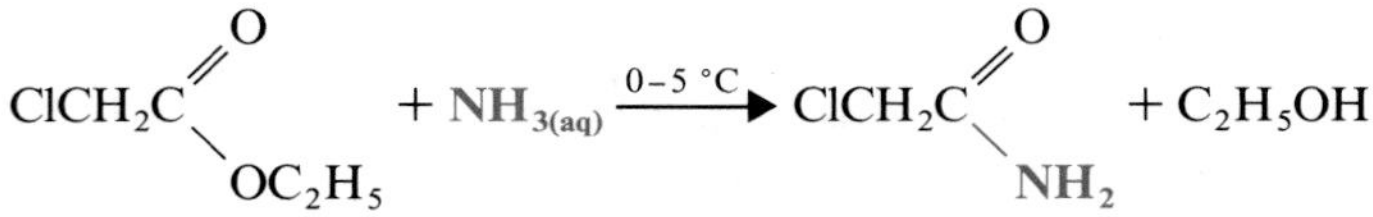

Ethyl chloroacetate   Chloroacetamide
                                      (62–87%)

18.8E AMIDES FROM CARBOXYLIC ACIDS AND AMMONIUM CARBOXYLATES

Carboxylic acids react with aqueous ammonia to form ammonium salts.

An ammonium
carboxylate

Because of the low reactivity of the carboxylate ion toward nucleophilic substitution, further reaction does not usually take place in aqueous solution. However, if we evaporate the water and subsequently heat the dry salt, dehydration produces an amide.

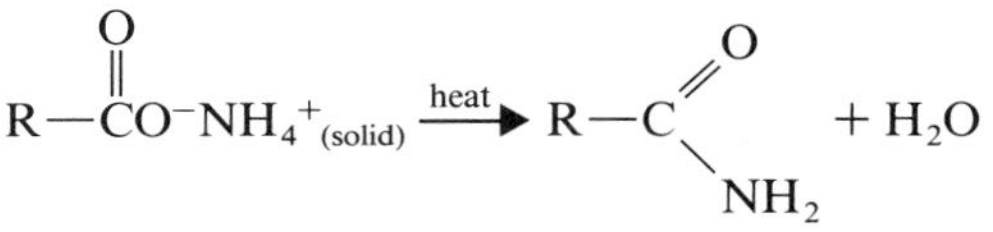

$$R-\underset{\underset{\displaystyle \|}{\displaystyle O}}{C}O^-NH_4{}^+{}_{(solid)} \xrightarrow{\text{heat}} R-C\underset{NH_2}{\overset{O}{\diagup\hspace{-0.3em}\diagdown}} + H_2O$$

This is generally a poor method for preparing amides. A much better method is to convert the acid to an acyl chloride and then treat the acyl chloride with ammonia or an amine (Section 18.8B).

Amides are of great importance in biochemistry. The linkages that join individual amino acids together to form proteins are primarily amide linkages. As a consequence, much research has been done to find new and mild ways for amide synthesis. One especially useful reagent is the compound dicyclohexylcarbodiimide, $C_6H_{11}-N=C=N-C_6H_{11}$. Dicyclohexylcarbodiimide promotes amide formation by reacting with the carboxyl group of an acid and activating it toward nucleophilic substitution.

Dicyclohexyl-
carbodiimide
(DCC)

Reactive
intermediate

(H⁺ shift)

An amide   N,N'-Dicyclohexylurea

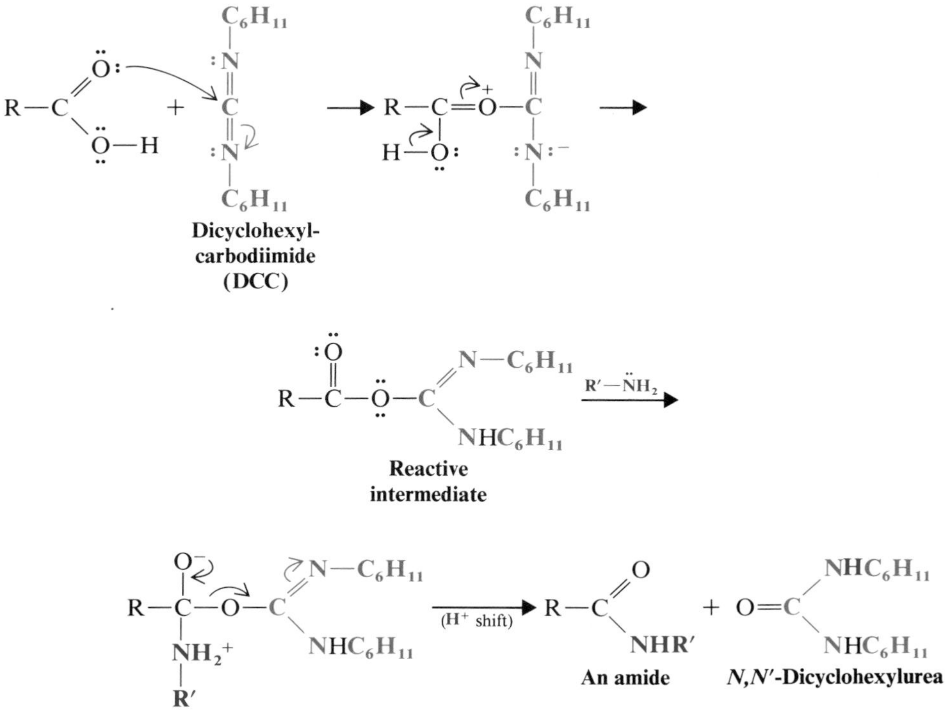

The intermediate in this synthesis does not need to be isolated, and both steps take place at room temperature. Amides are produced in very high yield. In Chapter 24 we shall see how dicyclohexylcarbodiimide can be used in an automated synthesis of proteins.

18.8F HYDROLYSIS OF AMIDES

Amides undergo hydrolysis when they are heated with aqueous acid or aqueous base.

Acidic Hydrolysis

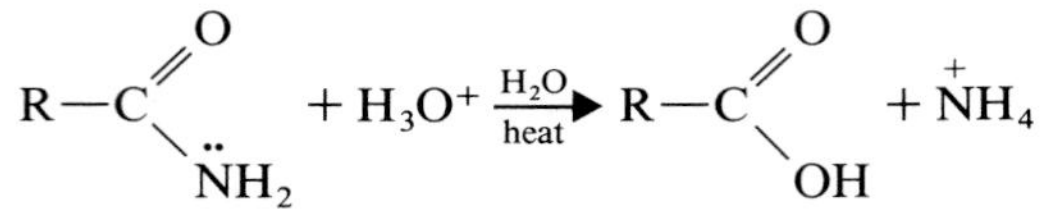

$$R-C\!\!\!\!\diagdown^{\!\!O}_{\!\!NH_2} + H_3O^+ \xrightarrow[\text{heat}]{H_2O} R-C\!\!\!\!\diagdown^{\!\!O}_{\!\!OH} + \overset{+}{N}H_4$$

Basic Hydrolysis

$$R-C\!\!\!\!\diagdown^{\!\!O}_{\!\!NH_2} + Na^+OH^- \xrightarrow[\text{heat}]{H_2O} R-C\!\!\!\!\diagdown^{\!\!O}_{\!\!O^-Na^+} + \overset{..}{N}H_3$$

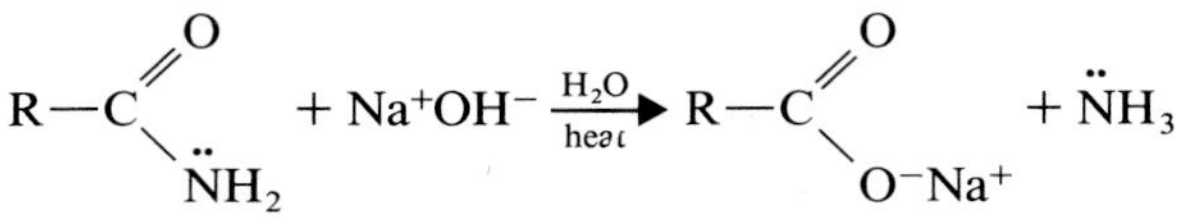

N-Substituted amides and *N,N*-disubstituted amides also undergo hydrolysis in aqueous acid or base. Amide hydrolysis by either method takes place more slowly than the corresponding hydrolysis of an ester. Thus, amide hydrolyses generally require more forcing conditions.

The mechanism for acid hydrolysis of an amide is similar to that given in Section 18.7A for the acid hydrolysis of an ester. Water acts as a nucleophile and attacks the protonated amide. The leaving group in the acidic hydrolysis of an amide is ammonia (or an amine).

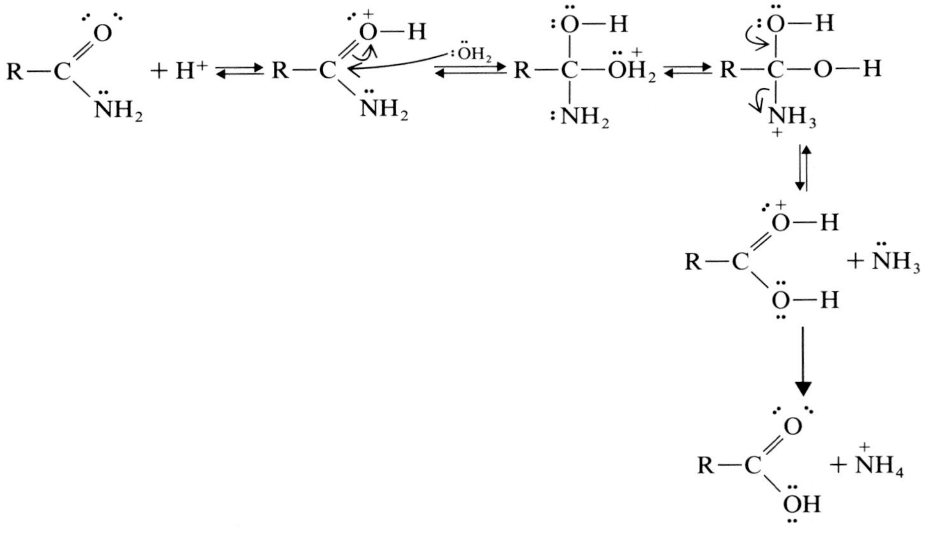

There is evidence that in basic hydrolyses of amides, hydroxide ions act both as nucleophiles and as bases. In the first step (in the following reaction) a hydroxide ion attacks the acyl carbon of the amide. In the second step, a hydroxide ion removes a proton to give a dianion. In the final step, the dianion loses a molecule of ammonia (or an amine); this step is synchronized with a proton transfer from water.

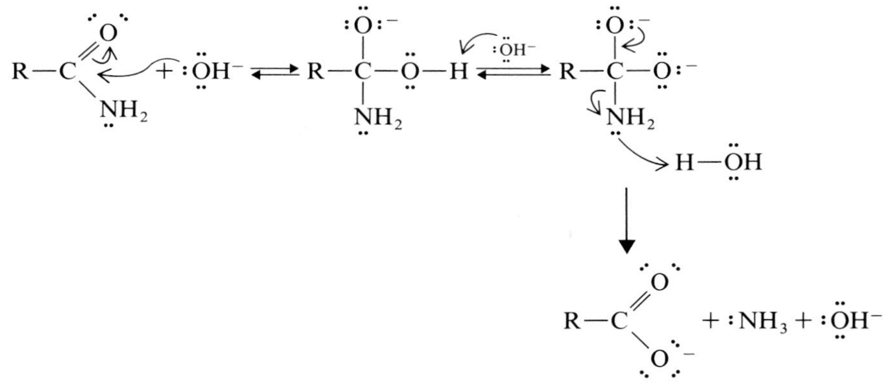

Problem 18.14

What products would you obtain from acidic and basic hydrolysis of each of the following amides?

(a) *N*,*N*-Diethylbenzamide

(b)

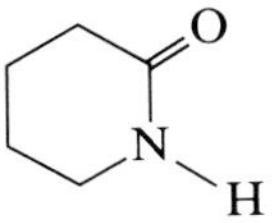

(c) 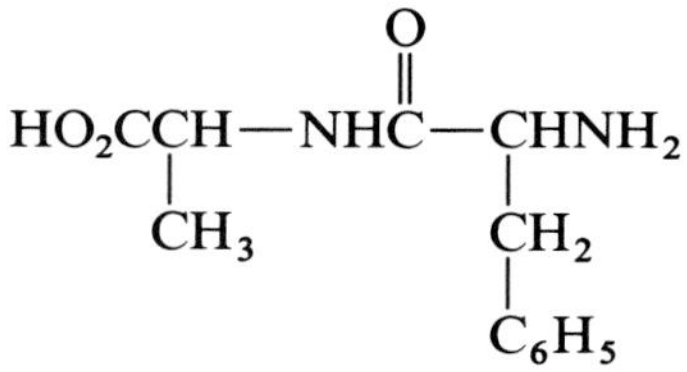 $HO_2CCH-NHC-CHNH_2$ (a dipeptide)
with CH_3 and CH_2/C_6H_5 substituents and a C=O

18.8G NITRILES FROM THE DEHYDRATION OF AMIDES

Amides react with P_4O_{10} (a compound that is often called phosphorus pentoxide and written P_2O_5) or with boiling acetic anhydride to form nitriles.

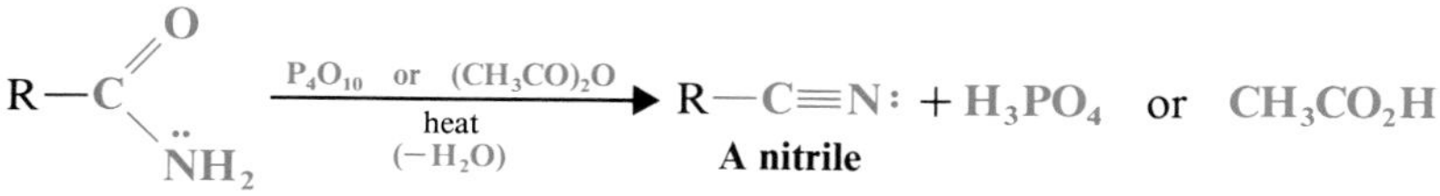

$$R-C\underset{NH_2}{\overset{O}{\big\backslash}} \xrightarrow[\text{heat} \atop (-H_2O)]{P_4O_{10} \text{ or } (CH_3CO)_2O} R-C\equiv N: + H_3PO_4 \text{ or } CH_3CO_2H$$

A nitrile

This is a useful synthetic method for preparing nitriles that are not available by nucleophilic substitution reactions between alkyl halides and cyanide ion.

Problem 18.15

(a) Show all steps in the synthesis of $(CH_3)_3CCN$ from $(CH_3)_3CCO_2H$.
(b) What product would you expect to obtain if you attempted to synthesize $(CH_3)_3CCN$ using the following method?

$$(CH_3)_3C-Br + CN^- \longrightarrow$$

18.8H HYDROLYSIS OF NITRILES

Although nitriles do not contain a carbonyl group, they are usually considered to be derivatives of carboxylic acids because complete hydrolysis of a nitrile produces a carboxylic acid or a carboxylate ion (Sections 16.9A and 18.3).

The mechanisms for these hydrolyses are related to those for the acidic and basic hydrolyses of amides. In **acidic hydrolysis** of a nitrile the first step is protonation of the nitrogen atom. This protonation (in the following sequence) polarizes the nitrile group and makes the carbon atom more susceptible to nucleophilic attack by the weak nucleophile, water. The loss of a proton from the oxygen atom then produces a tautomeric form of an amide. Gain of a proton at the nitrogen atom gives a **protonated amide** and from this point on the steps are the same as those given for the acidic hydrolysis of an amide in Section 18.8F. (In concentrated H_2SO_4 the reaction stops at the protonated amide and this is a useful way of making amides from nitriles.)

In **basic hydrolysis,** a hydroxide ion attacks the nitrile carbon atom and subsequent protonation leads to the amide tautomer. Further attack by hydroxide ion leads to hydrolysis in a manner analogous to that for the basic hydrolysis of an amide (Section 18.8F). (Under the appropriate conditions, amides can be isolated when nitriles are hydrolyzed.)

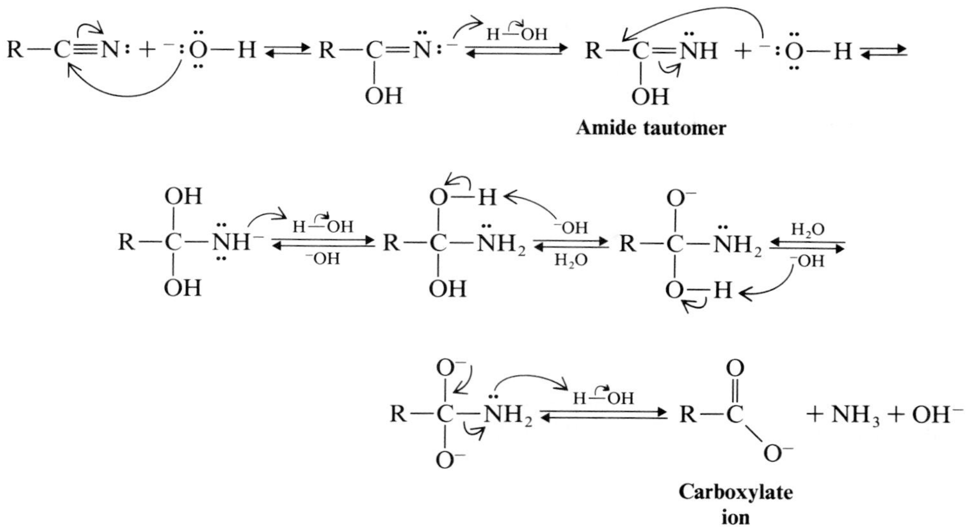

$$R-C\equiv N: + \ ^-:\ddot{O}-H \rightleftharpoons R-C=\ddot{N}: ^- \xrightarrow{H-OH} R-C=\ddot{N}H + \ ^-:\ddot{O}-H \rightleftharpoons$$

$$\underset{OH}{|}$$

$$\underset{OH}{|}$$

Amide tautomer

$$\underset{OH}{\overset{OH}{|}} R-C-\ddot{N}H^- \xrightarrow[^-OH]{H-OH} \underset{OH}{\overset{O-H}{|}} R-C-\ddot{N}H_2 \xrightleftharpoons[H_2O]{^-OH} \underset{O-H}{\overset{O^-}{|}} R-C-\ddot{N}H_2 \xrightleftharpoons[^-OH]{H_2O}$$

$$\underset{O^-}{\overset{O^-}{|}} R-C-\ddot{N}H_2 \xrightleftharpoons{H-OH} R-\overset{O}{\overset{\|}{C}} \diagdown O^- + NH_3 + OH^-$$

Carboxylate ion

18.8 I LACTAMS

Cyclic amides are called lactams. The size of the lactam ring is designated by Greek letters in a way that is analogous to lactone nomenclature.

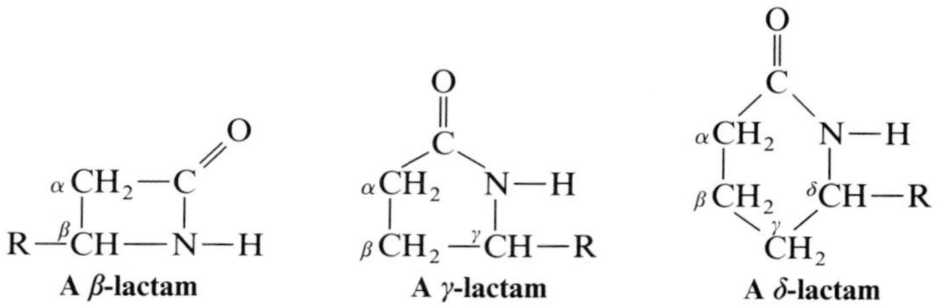

$$\underset{R-\overset{\beta}{C}H-N-H}{\alpha CH_2-C\diagup^O} \qquad \underset{\beta CH_2-\overset{\gamma}{C}H-R}{\overset{O}{\underset{\alpha CH_2\quad N-H}{\overset{\|}{C}}}} \qquad \underset{\overset{}{CH_2}}{\overset{O}{\underset{\beta CH_2\quad \overset{\delta}{C}H-R}{\overset{\|}{\underset{\alpha CH_2\quad N-H}{C}}}}}$$

A β-lactam   A γ-lactam   A δ-lactam

γ-Lactams and δ-lactams often form spontaneously from γ- and δ-amino acids. β-Lactams, however, are highly reactive; their strained four-membered rings open easily in the presence of nucleophilic reagents. The penicillin antibiotics (see following structures) contain a β-lactam ring.

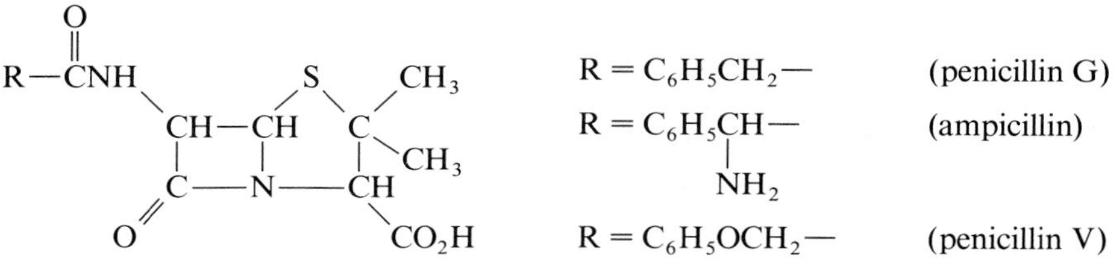

$$\underset{O}{\overset{O}{\underset{\diagdown}{R-\overset{\|}{C}NH}}} \quad \underset{}{\overset{S\quad CH_3}{\underset{C-N-CH}{CH-CH\quad C}}}\diagdown^{CH_3}_{CO_2H}$$

R = C₆H₅CH₂—	(penicillin G)
R = C₆H₅CH— | NH₂	(ampicillin)
R = C₆H₅OCH₂—	(penicillin V)

The penicillins apparently act by interfering with the synthesis of the bacterial cell walls. It is thought that they do this by reacting with an amino group of an essential enzyme of the cell wall biosynthetic pathway. This reaction, which involves ring opening of the β-lactam and acylation of the amino group, inactivates the enzyme.

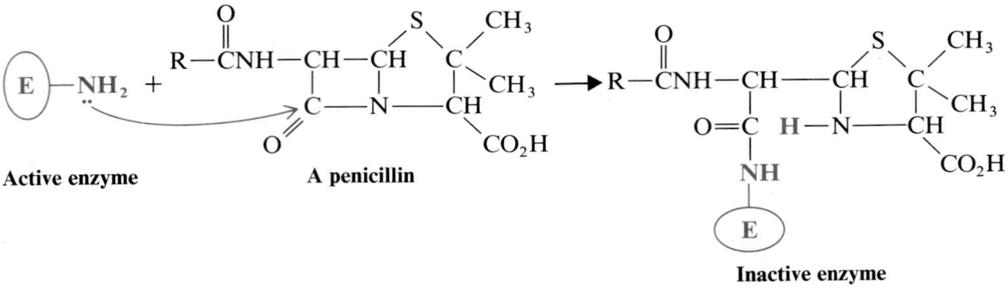

Active enzyme   A penicillin   Inactive enzyme

18.9 α-HALO ACIDS: THE HELL–VOLHARD–ZELINSKI REACTION

Aliphatic carboxylic acids react with bromine or chlorine in the presence of phosphorus (or a phosphorus halide) to give α-halo acids through a reaction known as the Hell–Volhard–Zelinski reaction.

General Reaction

$$RCH_2CO_2H \xrightarrow[\text{(2) } H_2O]{\text{(1) } X_2, P} RCHCO_2H$$
$$\qquad\qquad\qquad\qquad\ \ |$$
$$\qquad\qquad\qquad\qquad\ X$$

α-Halo acid

Specific Example

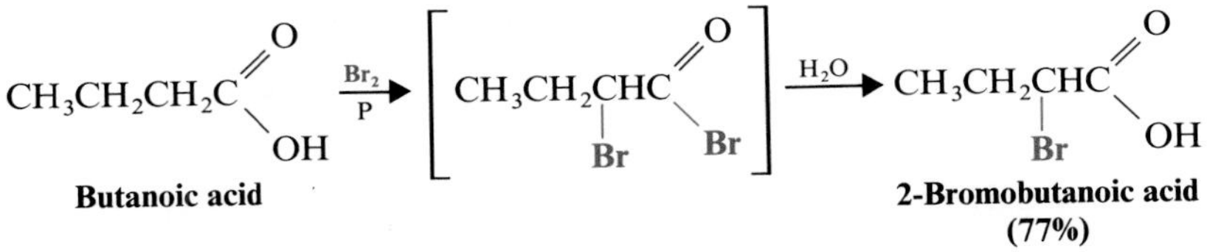

Butanoic acid   2-Bromobutanoic acid
                       (77%)

Halogenation occurs specifically at the α carbon. If more than one molar equivalent of bromine or chlorine is used in the reaction, the products obtained are α,α-dihalo acids or α,α,α-trihalo acids.

The mechanism for the Hell–Volhard–Zelinski reaction is outlined here. The key step involves the formation of an enol from an acyl halide. (Carboxylic acids do not form enols readily.) Enol formation accounts for specific halogenation at the α position.

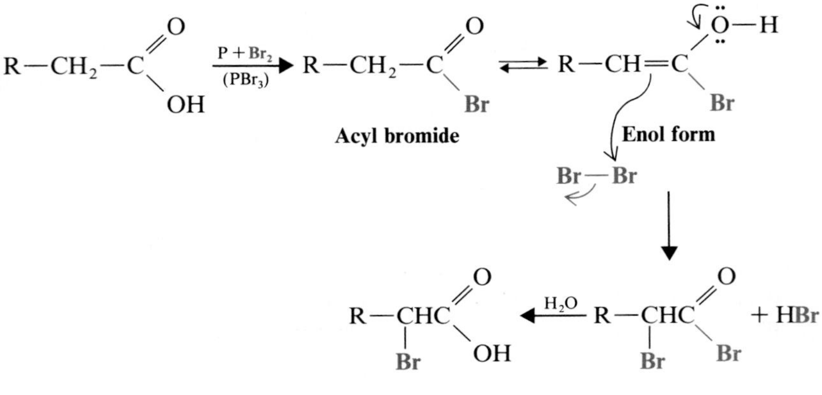

Acyl bromide   Enol form

18.10 α-HALO ACIDS: THE HELL–VOLHARD–ZELINSKI REACTION

A more versatile method for α-halogenation has been developed by David N. Harpp (of McGill University). Acyl chlorides, formed *in situ* by the reaction of the carboxylic acid with $SOCl_2$, are treated with the appropriate N-halosuccinimide and a trace of HX to produce α-chloro and α-bromo acyl chlorides.

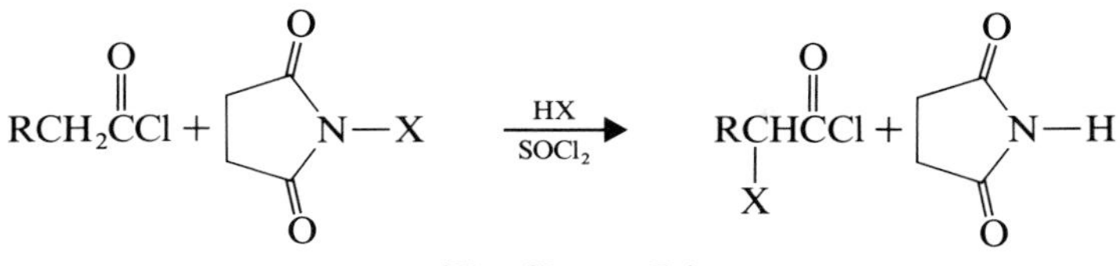

$$RCH_2CCl + \overset{O}{\underset{O}{\overset{\|}{\bigcirc}}}\!\!N\!-\!X \quad \xrightarrow[SOCl_2]{HX} \quad RCHCCl + \overset{O}{\underset{O}{\overset{\|}{\bigcirc}}}\!\!N\!-\!H$$

$$(X = Cl \quad or \quad Br)$$

α-Iodo acyl chlorides can be obtained by using molecular iodine in a similar reaction.

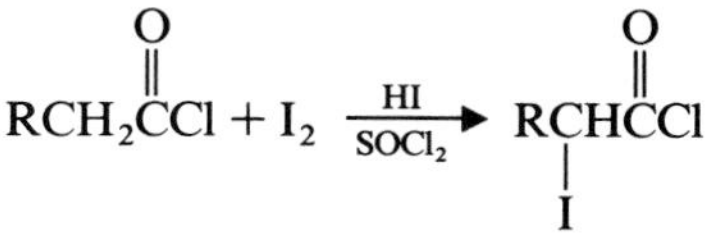

$$RCH_2CCl + I_2 \xrightarrow[SOCl_2]{HI} RCHCCl$$

α-Halo acids are important synthetic intermediates because they are capable of reacting with a variety of nucleophiles:

Conversion to α-Hydroxy Acids

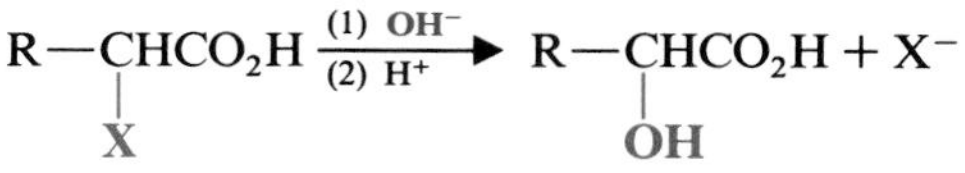

$$\underset{X}{R-CHCO_2H} \xrightarrow[(2)\ H^+]{(1)\ OH^-} \underset{OH}{R-CHCO_2H} + X^-$$

α-Halo acid   **α-Hydroxy acid**

Specific Example

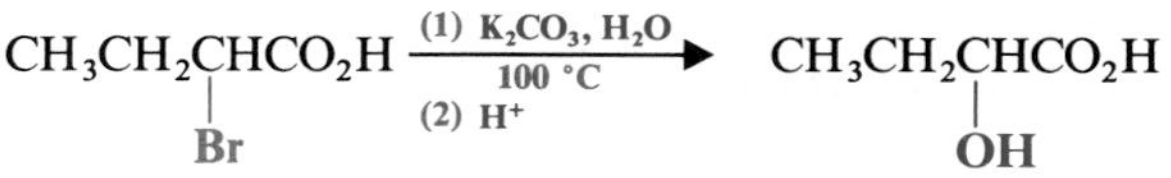

$$\underset{Br}{CH_3CH_2CHCO_2H} \xrightarrow[(2)\ H^+]{\overset{(1)\ K_2CO_3,\ H_2O}{100\ °C}} \underset{OH}{CH_3CH_2CHCO_2H}$$

2-Hydroxybutanoic acid
(69%)

Conversion to α-Amino Acids

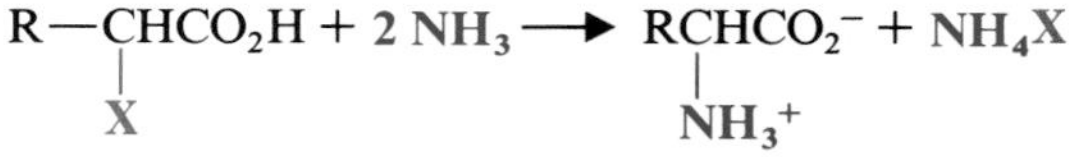

$$\underset{X}{R-CHCO_2H} + 2\ NH_3 \longrightarrow \underset{NH_3^+}{RCHCO_2^-} + NH_4X$$

α-Halo   **α-Amino**
acid   **acid**

Specific Example

$$\underset{Br}{CH_2CO_2H} + 2\ NH_3 \longrightarrow \underset{NH_3^+}{CH_2CO_2^-} + NH_4Br$$

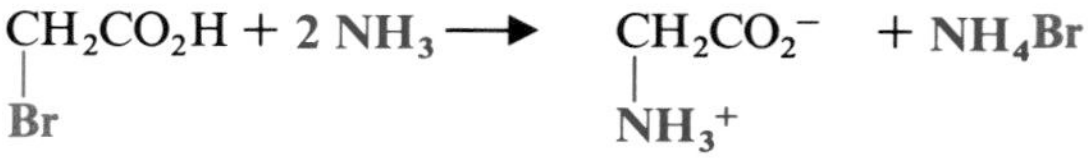

Aminoacetic acid
(glycine)
(60–64%)

18.10 DERIVATIVES OF CARBONIC ACID

Carbonic acid $\left(\begin{matrix} O \\ \| \\ HOCOH \end{matrix}\right)$ is an unstable compound that decomposes spontaneously (to produce carbon dioxide and water) and, therefore, cannot be isolated. However, many acyl chlorides, esters, and amides that are derived from carbonic acid (on paper, not in the laboratory) are stable compounds that have important applications.

Carbonyl dichloride (ClCOCl), a highly toxic compound that is also called *phosgene,* can be thought of as the diacyl chloride of carbonic acid. Carbonyl dichloride reacts with two molar equivalents of an alcohol to yield a **dialkyl carbonate.**

$$\underset{\substack{\textbf{Carbonyl} \\ \textbf{dichloride}}}{Cl-\overset{\overset{\textstyle O}{\|}}{C}-Cl} + 2\ CH_3CH_2OH \longrightarrow \underset{\textbf{Diethyl carbonate}}{CH_3CH_2O\overset{\overset{\textstyle O}{\|}}{C}OCH_2CH_3} + 2\ HCl$$

A tertiary amine is usually added to the reaction to neutralize the hydrogen chloride that is produced.

Carbonyl dichloride reacts with ammonia to yield **urea** (Section 1.2A).

$$Cl-\overset{\overset{\textstyle O}{\|}}{C}-Cl + 4\ NH_3 \longrightarrow \underset{\textbf{Urea}}{H_2N\overset{\overset{\textstyle O}{\|}}{C}NH_2} + 2\ NH_4Cl$$

Urea is the end product of the metabolism of nitrogen-containing compounds in most mammals and is excreted in the urine.

18.10A ALKYL CHLOROFORMATES AND CARBAMATES (URETHANES)

Treating carbonyl dichloride with one molar equivalent of an alcohol leads to the formation of an alkyl chloroformate:

$$ROH + Cl-\overset{\overset{\textstyle O}{\|}}{C}-Cl \longrightarrow \underset{\substack{\textbf{Alkyl} \\ \textbf{chloroformate}}}{RO-\overset{\overset{\textstyle O}{\|}}{C}-Cl} + HCl$$

Specific Example

$$C_6H_5CH_2OH + Cl-\overset{\overset{\textstyle O}{\|}}{C}-Cl \longrightarrow \underset{\substack{\textbf{Benzyl} \\ \textbf{chloroformate}}}{C_6H_5CH_2O-\overset{\overset{\textstyle O}{\|}}{C}-Cl} + HCl$$

Alkyl chloroformates react with ammonia or amines to yield compounds called *carbamates* or *urethanes:*

$$RO-\overset{\overset{\textstyle O}{\|}}{C}-Cl + R'NH_2 \xrightarrow{OH^-} \underset{\substack{\textbf{A carbamate} \\ \textbf{(or urethane)}}}{RO-\overset{\overset{\textstyle O}{\|}}{C}-NHR'}$$

18.10 DERIVATIVES OF CARBONIC ACID

Benzyl chloroformate is used to install on an amino group a protecting group called the benzyloxycarbonyl group. We shall see in Section 24.7 how use is made of this protecting group in the synthesis of peptides and proteins. One advantage of the benzyloxycarbonyl group is that it can be removed under mild conditions. Treating the benzyloxycarbonyl derivative with hydrogen and a catalyst or with cold HBr in acetic acid removes the protecting group.

$$R-NH_2 + C_6H_5CH_2O\overset{\overset{\displaystyle O}{\|}}{C}Cl \xrightarrow{OH^-} \left. R-NH-\overset{\overset{\displaystyle O}{\|}}{C}OCH_2C_6H_5 \right\} \begin{array}{l}\text{Protected}\\\text{amine}\end{array}$$

$$R-NH-\overset{\overset{\displaystyle O}{\|}}{C}OCH_2C_6H_5 \left\langle \begin{array}{l} \xrightarrow{H_2,\ Pd} R-NH_2 + CO_2 + C_6H_5CH_3 \\[2em] \xrightarrow{HBr,\ CH_3CO_2H} R-\overset{+}{N}H_3 + CO_2 + C_6H_5CH_2Br \end{array} \right.$$

Carbamates can also be synthesized by allowing an alcohol to react with an isocyanate, $R-N=C=O$. (Carbamates tend to be nicely crystalline solids and are useful derivatives for identifying alcohols.) The reaction is an example of nucleophilic addition to the acyl carbon.

$$ROH + C_6H_5-N=C=O \longrightarrow RO\overset{\overset{\displaystyle O}{\|}}{C}-NH-C_6H_5$$

Phenyl isocyanate

The insecticide called *Sevin* is a carbamate made by allowing 1-naphthol to react with methyl isocyanate.

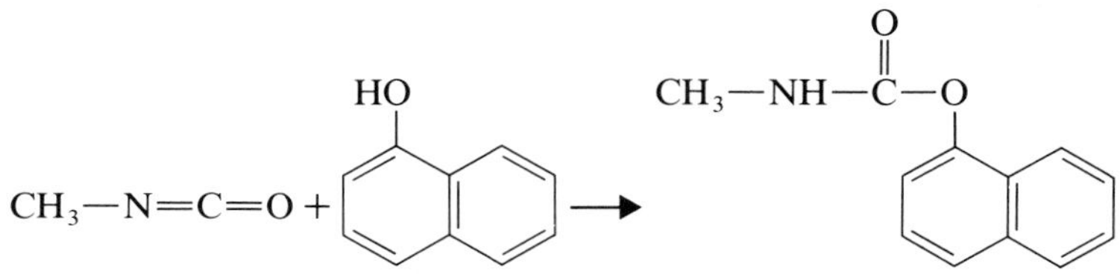

| Methyl isocyanate | 1-Naphthol | | Sevin |

A tragic accident that occurred at Bhopal, India, in 1984, was caused by leakage of methyl isocyanate from a manufacturing plant. Methyl isocyanate is a highly toxic gas and more than 1800 people living near the plant lost their lives.

Problem 18.16

Write structures for the products of the following reactions:
(a) $C_6H_5CH_2OH + C_6H_5N=C=O \longrightarrow$
(b) $ClCOCl + \text{excess } CH_3NH_2 \longrightarrow$
(c) Glycine $(H_3\overset{+}{N}CH_2CO_2^-) + C_6H_5CH_2OCOCl \xrightarrow{OH^-}$
(d) Product of (c) + H_2, Pd $\longrightarrow$

(e) Product of (c) + cold HBr, $CH_3CO_2H \longrightarrow$

(f) Urea + OH^-, H_2O, heat

Although alkyl chloroformates $\left(\overset{\overset{\displaystyle O}{\|}}{ROCCl} \right)$, dialkyl carbonates $\left(\overset{\overset{\displaystyle O}{\|}}{ROCOR} \right)$, and carbamates $\left(\overset{\overset{\displaystyle O}{\|}}{ROCNH_2}, \overset{\overset{\displaystyle O}{\|}}{ROCNHR}, \text{etc.} \right)$ are stable, chloroformic acid $\left(\overset{\overset{\displaystyle O}{\|}}{HOCCl} \right)$, alkyl hydrogen carbonates $\left(\overset{\overset{\displaystyle O}{\|}}{ROCOH} \right)$, and carbamic acid $\left(\overset{\overset{\displaystyle O}{\|}}{HOCNH_2} \right)$ are not. These latter compounds decompose spontaneously to liberate carbon dioxide.

$$HO-\overset{\overset{\displaystyle O}{\|}}{C}-Cl \longrightarrow HCl + CO_2$$
Unstable

$$RO-\overset{\overset{\displaystyle O}{\|}}{C}-OH \longrightarrow ROH + CO_2$$
Unstable

$$HO-\overset{\overset{\displaystyle O}{\|}}{C}-NH_2 \longrightarrow NH_3 + CO_2$$
Unstable

This instability is a characteristic that these compounds share with their functional parent, carbonic acid.

$$HO-\overset{\overset{\displaystyle O}{\|}}{C}-OH \longrightarrow H_2O + CO_2$$
Unstable

18.11 DECARBOXYLATION OF CARBOXYLIC ACIDS

The reaction whereby a carboxylic acid loses CO_2 is called a *decarboxylation*.

$$R-\overset{\overset{\displaystyle O}{\|}}{C}-OH \xrightarrow{\text{decarboxylation}} R-H + CO_2$$

Although the unusual stability of carbon dioxide means that decarboxylation of most acids is exothermic, in practice the reaction is not always easy to carry out because the reaction is very slow. Special groups usually have to be present in the molecule for decarboxylation to be rapid enough to be synthetically useful.

Acids whose molecules have a carbonyl group one carbon removed from the carboxylic acid group, **called β-keto acids,** decarboxylate readily when they are heated to 100–150 °C. (Some β-keto acids even decarboxylate slowly at room temperature.)

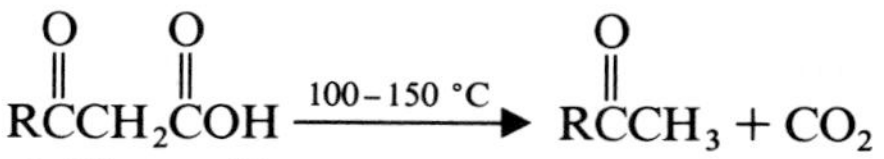

$$RCCH_2COH \xrightarrow{\text{100–150 °C}} RCCH_3 + CO_2$$

A β-keto acid

There are two reasons for this ease of decarboxylation:

1. When the carboxylate ion decarboxylates, it forms a resonance-stabilized enolate anion:

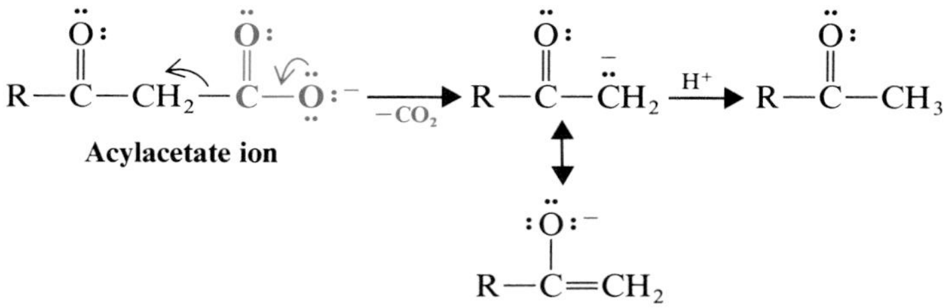

Acylacetate ion

Resonance-stabilized anion

This anion is much more stable than the anion $RCH_2:^-$ that would be produced by decarboxylation of an ordinary carboxylic acid anion.

2. When the acid itself decarboxylates, it can do so through a six-membered cyclic transition state:

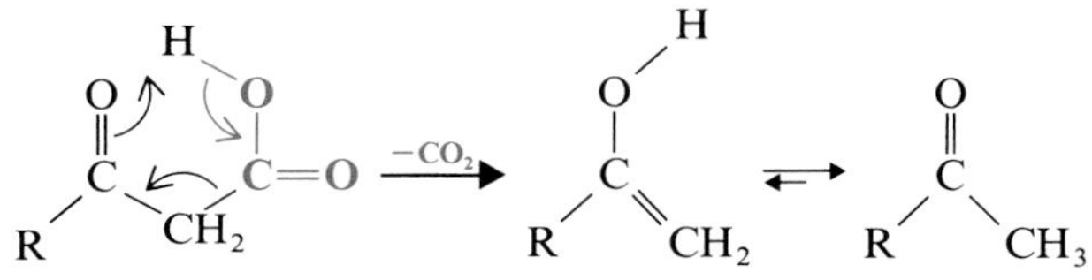

β-Keto acid   **Enol**   **Ketone**

This reaction produces an enol directly and avoids an anionic intermediate. The enol then tautomerizes to a methyl ketone.

Malonic acids also decarboxylate readily and for similar reasons.

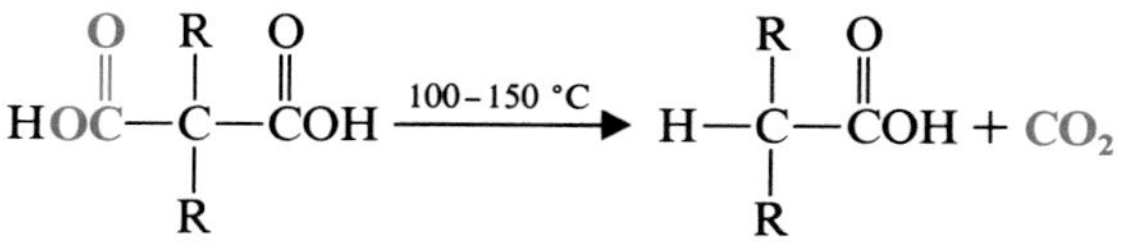

A malonic acid

Notice that malonic acids undergo decarboxylation so readily that they do not form cyclic anhydrides (Section 18.6).

We shall see in Chapter 20 how decarboxylations of β-keto acids and malonic acids are synthetically useful.

Aromatic carboxylic acids decarboxylate when their salts are heated with copper and quinoline (the structure of quinoline is given in Section 19.1B):

$$ArCO_2^- + OH^- \xrightarrow[\text{heat}]{\text{Cu-quinoline}} ArH + CO_3^{2-}$$

These are extremely forcing conditions. The mechanism of the reaction is not known.

18.11A DECARBOXYLATION OF CARBOXYL RADICALS

Although the carboxylate ions (RCO_2^-) of simple aliphatic acids do not decarboxylate readily, carboxyl radicals ($RCO_2\cdot$) do. They decarboxylate by losing CO_2 and producing alkyl radicals:

$$RCO_2\cdot \longrightarrow R\cdot + CO_2$$

Carboxyl radicals can be generated by electrolysis, in a reaction known as the *Kolbe electrolysis,* or they can be generated chemically in a reaction known as the *Hunsdiecker reaction.*

In the **Kolbe electrolysis** an aqueous solution of the sodium or potassium salt of a carboxylic acid is subjected to electrolysis. At the anode the carboxylate ion loses an electron to become a carboxyl radical.

Step 1

$$R-\overset{\overset{\displaystyle :\ddot{O}}{\|}}{C}-\ddot{\underset{\cdot\cdot}{O}}:^- \xrightarrow[(-e^-)]{\text{anode}} R-\overset{\overset{\displaystyle :\ddot{O}}{\|}}{C}-\ddot{\underset{\cdot\cdot}{O}}\cdot$$

Then the carboxyl radical decarboxylates and the alkyl radicals that are produced combine to form an alkane.

Step 2

$$R-\overset{\overset{\displaystyle :\ddot{O}}{\|}}{C}-\ddot{\underset{\cdot\cdot}{O}}\cdot \longrightarrow R\cdot + CO_2$$

Step 3 $2\,R\cdot \longrightarrow R-R$

In the **Hunsdiecker reaction** the silver salt of a carboxylic acid is heated with bromine in CCl_4. A carboxyl radical is produced in a two-step process as follows:

Step 1

$$R-\overset{\overset{\displaystyle O}{\|}}{C}-OAg + Br_2 \xrightarrow{CCl_4} R\overset{\overset{\displaystyle O}{\|}}{C}-OBr + AgBr$$

Step 2

$$R-\overset{\overset{\displaystyle O}{\|}}{C}-OBr \longrightarrow R-\overset{\overset{\displaystyle O}{\|}}{C}-O\cdot + Br\cdot$$

Then the carboxyl radical decarboxylates. The resulting alkyl radical abstracts a bromine atom from $R\overset{\overset{\displaystyle O}{\|}}{C}OBr$ to produce an alkyl bromide and regenerate a carboxyl radical.

Step 3 $R-\overset{O}{\overset{||}{C}}-O\cdot \longrightarrow R\cdot + CO_2$

Step 4 $R\cdot + R-\overset{O}{\overset{||}{C}}-OBr \longrightarrow R-Br + R-\overset{O}{\overset{||}{C}}-O\cdot$

Then steps 3 and 4 are repeated, and so on.

Overall the Hunsdiecker reaction amounts to the following:

$$R-CO_2Ag + Br_2 \xrightarrow[\text{heat}]{CCl_4} RBr + CO_2 + AgBr$$

A more convenient way to carry out the Hunsdiecker reaction (called the Cristol–Firth modification) is to heat the acid with mercuric oxide and bromine.

$$RCO_2H \xrightarrow[\text{heat}]{Br_2,\ HgO} RBr + CO_2$$

Problem 18.17

Using decarboxylation reactions, outline a synthesis of each of the following from appropriate starting materials.

(a) Decane   (d) Benzyl bromide   (g) Cyclohexanone

(b) 2-Hexanone   (e) 2-Butanone   (h) Pentanoic acid

(c) 2-Methylbutanoic acid (f) Cyclohexane

Problem 18.18

Diacyl peroxides $\left(R\overset{O}{\overset{||}{C}}-O-O-\overset{O}{\overset{||}{C}}R \right)$ decompose readily when heated. (a) What factor accounts for this instability? (b) The decomposition of a diacyl peroxide produces CO_2. How is it formed? (c) Diacyl peroxides are often used to initiate free radical reactions, for example, the polymerization of an alkene:

$$n\ CH_2=CH_2 \xrightarrow[(-CO_2)]{R\overset{O}{\overset{||}{C}}-O-O-\overset{O}{\overset{||}{C}}R} R\text{-}(CH_2CH_2)_n\text{-}H$$

Show the steps involved.

18.12 CHEMICAL TESTS FOR ACYL COMPOUNDS

Carboxylic acids are weak acids and their acidity helps us to detect them. Aqueous solutions of water-soluble carboxylic acids give an acid test with blue litmus paper. Water-insoluble carboxylic acids dissolve in aqueous sodium hydroxide and aqueous sodium bicarbonate (cf. Section 18.2C). The latter reagent helps us distinguish carboxylic acids from most phenols. Except for the di- and trinitrophenols, phenols do not dissolve in aqueous sodium bicarbonate. Carboxylic acids not only dissolve in aqueous sodium bicarbonate, they also cause the evolution of carbon dioxide.

In identifying a carboxylic acid, it is often helpful to determine its equivalent weight by titrating a measured quantity of the acid with a standard solution of sodium hydroxide. For a monocarboxylic acid, the equivalent weight equals the molecular weight; for a dicarboxylic acid, the equivalent weight is one half the molecular weight, and so on.

All acid derivatives can be hydrolyzed to carboxylic acids. The conditions required to bring about hydrolysis vary greatly, with acyl chlorides being the easiest to hydrolyze and amides being the most difficult.

Acyl chlorides hydrolyze in water and thus give a precipitate when treated with aqueous silver nitrate. Acid anhydrides dissolve when heated briefly with aqueous sodium hydroxide.

Esters and amides hydrolyze slowly when they are refluxed with sodium hydroxide. An ester produces a carboxylate ion and an alcohol; an amide produces a carboxylate ion and an amine or ammonia. The hydrolysis products, the acid and the alcohol or amine, can be isolated and identified. Since base-promoted hydrolysis of an unsubstituted amide produces ammonia, this ammonia can often be detected by holding moist red litmus paper in the vapors above the reaction mixture.

Base-promoted hydrolysis of an ester (saponification) consumes one molar equivalent of hydroxide ion for each molar equivalent of the ester. It is often convenient, therefore, to carry out the hydrolysis quantitatively.

$$RCO_2R' + OH^- \longrightarrow RCO_2^- + R'OH$$

$$\text{1 molar} \quad \text{1 molar}$$
$$\text{equivalent} \quad \text{equivalent}$$

This reaction allows us to determine the *equivalent weight* of the ester. We can make this determination by hydrolyzing a known weight of the ester with an excess of a standard solution of sodium hydroxide. After the hydrolysis is complete, we can titrate the excess sodium hydroxide with a standard acid. For an ester containing one —CO_2R group the equivalent weight will equal the molecular weight.

Amides can be distinguished from amines with dilute HCl. Most amines dissolve in dilute HCl, whereas most amides do not (cf. Problem 18.37).

18.13 SUMMARY OF THE REACTIONS OF CARBOXYLIC ACIDS AND THEIR DERIVATIVES

The reactions of carboxylic acids and their derivatives are summarized here.

18.13A REACTIONS OF CARBOXYLIC ACIDS

1. As acids (discussed in Sections 3.5B, 3.7, and 18.2A).

$$RCO_2H + NaOH \longrightarrow RCO_2^-Na^+ + H_2O$$

$$RCO_2H + NaHCO_3 \longrightarrow RCO_2^-Na^+ + H_2O + CO_2$$

2. Reduction (discussed in Section 11.3).

$$RCO_2H + LiAlH_4 \xrightarrow[\text{(2) } H_2O]{\text{(1) diethyl ether}} RCH_2OH$$

3. Conversion to acyl chlorides (discussed in Section 18.5).

$$RCO_2H + SOCl_2 \longrightarrow RCOCl + SO_2 + HCl$$

$$3\ RCO_2H + PCl_3 \longrightarrow 3\ RCOCl + H_3PO_3$$

$$RCO_2H + PCl_5 \longrightarrow RCOCl + POCl_3 + HCl$$

4. Conversion to acid anhydrides (discussed in Section 18.6).

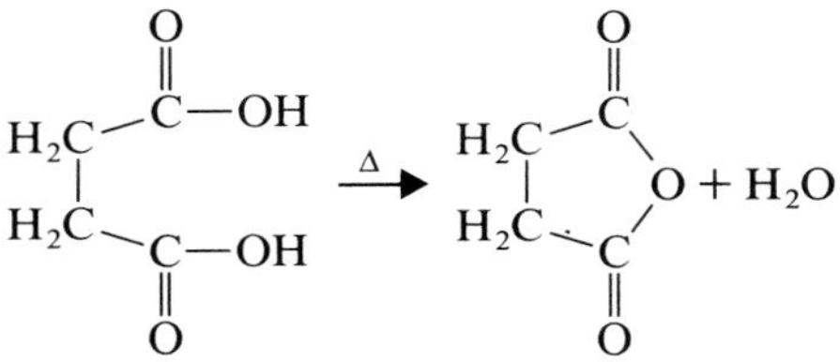

5. Conversion to esters (discussed in Section 18.7).

$$R{-}\overset{\overset{\large O}{\|}}{C}OH + R'{-}OH \overset{H^+}{\rightleftharpoons} R{-}\overset{\overset{\large O}{\|}}{C}{-}OR' + H_2O$$

6. Conversion to lactones (discussed in Section 18.7).

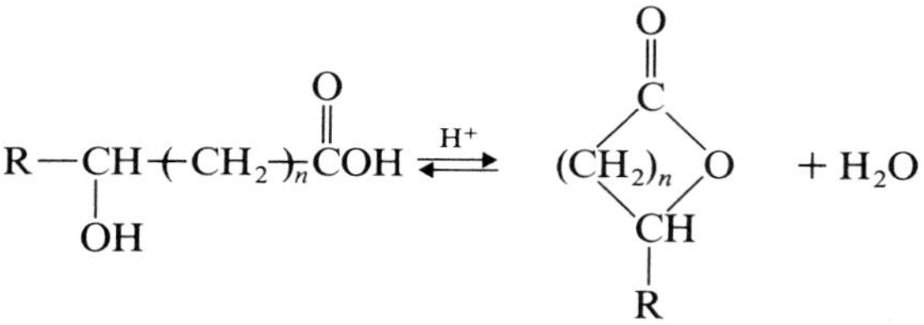

$n = 2$, a γ-lactone
$n = 3$, a δ-lactone

7. Conversion to amides and imides (discussed in Section 18.8).

$$R{-}\overset{\overset{\large O}{\|}}{C}{-}OH + NH_3 \rightleftharpoons R{-}\overset{\overset{\large O}{\|}}{C}{-}O^-NH_4^+ \xrightarrow{\text{heat}} R{-}\overset{\overset{\large O}{\|}}{C}{-}NH_2 + H_2O$$

An amide

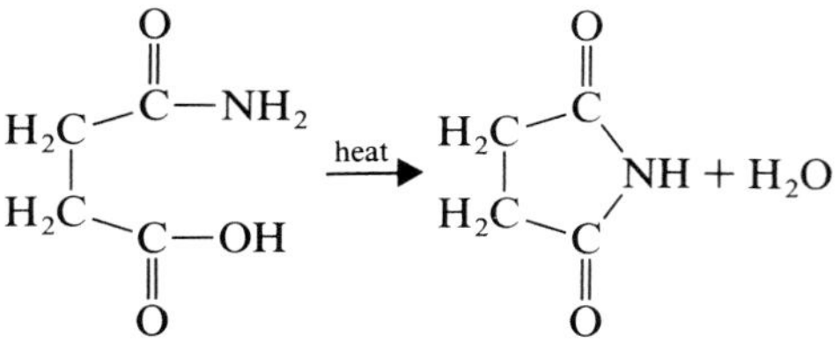

A cyclic imide

8. Conversion to lactams (discussed in Section 18.8).

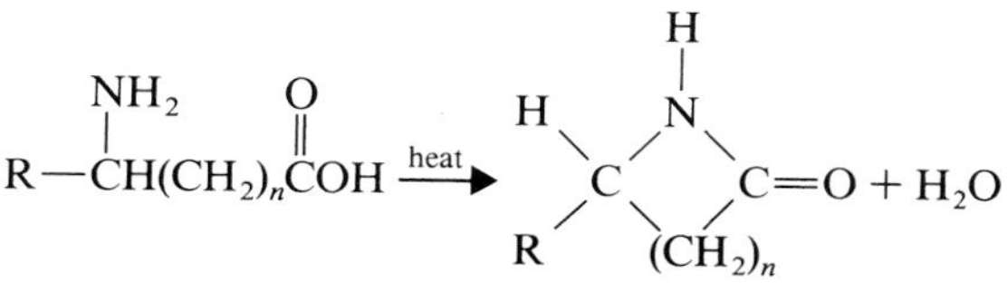

$n = 2$, a γ-lactam
$n = 3$, a δ-lactam

9. α-Halogenation (discussed in Section 18.9).

$$R-CH_2CO_2H + X_2 \xrightarrow{\text{P}} R-\underset{\underset{X}{|}}{C}HCO_2H$$

$$X_2 = Cl_2 \quad \text{or} \quad Br_2$$

10. Decarboxylation (discussed in Section 18.11).

$$\underset{\text{R}\overset{O}{\overset{||}{C}}CH_2\overset{O}{\overset{||}{C}}OH}{} \xrightarrow{\text{heat}} R\overset{O}{\overset{||}{C}}CH_3 + CO_2$$

$$HO\overset{O}{\overset{||}{C}}CH_2\overset{O}{\overset{||}{C}}OH \xrightarrow{\text{heat}} CH_3\overset{O}{\overset{||}{C}}OH + CO_2$$

18.13B REACTIONS OF ACYL CHLORIDES

1. Conversion to acids (discussed in Section 18.4).

$$R-\overset{O}{\overset{||}{C}}-Cl + H_2O \longrightarrow R-\overset{O}{\overset{||}{C}}-OH + HCl$$

2. Conversion to anhydrides (discussed in Section 18.6).

$$R-\overset{O}{\overset{||}{C}}-Cl + R-\overset{O}{\overset{||}{C}}-O^- \longrightarrow R-\overset{O}{\overset{||}{C}}-O-\overset{O}{\overset{||}{C}}-R + Cl^-$$

3. Conversion to esters (discussed in Section 18.7).

$$R-\overset{O}{\overset{||}{C}}-Cl + R'-OH \xrightarrow{\text{pyridine}} R-\overset{O}{\overset{||}{C}}-OR'$$

4. Conversion to amides (discussed in Section 18.8).

$$R-\overset{O}{\overset{||}{C}}-Cl + NH_3(\text{excess}) \longrightarrow R-\overset{O}{\overset{||}{C}}-NH_2 + NH_4Cl$$

$$R-\overset{O}{\overset{||}{C}}-Cl + R'NH_2(\text{excess}) \longrightarrow R-\overset{O}{\overset{||}{C}}-NHR' + R'NH_3Cl$$

$$R-\overset{O}{\overset{||}{C}}-Cl + R_2'NH(\text{excess}) \longrightarrow R-\overset{O}{\overset{||}{C}}-NR_2' + R_2'NH_2Cl$$

5. Conversion to ketones

$$R-\overset{O}{\overset{||}{C}}-Cl + \bigcirc \xrightarrow{\text{AlCl}_3} \bigcirc\overset{\overset{O}{\overset{||}{C}}-R}{} \quad \text{(discussed in Sections 15.7–15.9)}$$

$$R-\overset{O}{\overset{||}{C}}-Cl + R_2'CuLi \longrightarrow R-\overset{O}{\overset{||}{C}}-R' \quad \text{(discussed in Section 16.5)}$$

6. Conversion to aldehydes (discussed in Section 16.4).

$$R-\overset{\overset{\displaystyle O}{\|}}{C}-Cl + LiAlH[OC(CH_3)_3]_3 \xrightarrow[\text{(2) } H_2O]{\text{(1) diethyl ether}} R-\overset{\overset{\displaystyle O}{\|}}{C}-H$$

18.13C REACTIONS OF ACID ANHYDRIDES

1. Conversion to acids (cf. Section 18.12).

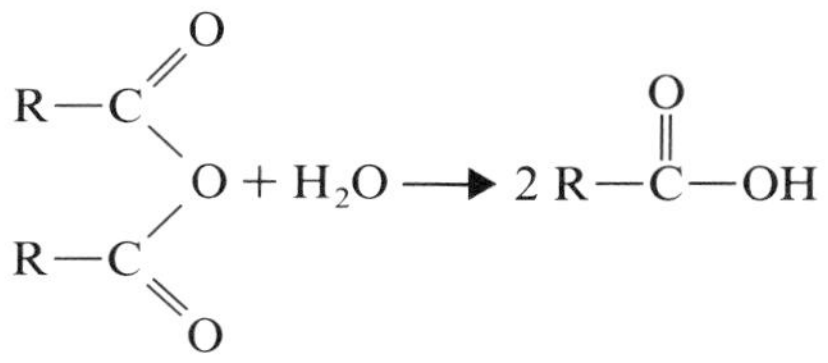

$$
\begin{array}{c}
R-C\overset{\displaystyle O}{\diagup}\\[-2pt]
\diagdown O + H_2O \longrightarrow 2\,R-\overset{\overset{\displaystyle O}{\|}}{C}-OH\\[-2pt]
R-C\diagup\\[-6pt]
\diagdown O
\end{array}
$$

2. Conversion to esters (discussed in Sections 18.4 and 18.7).

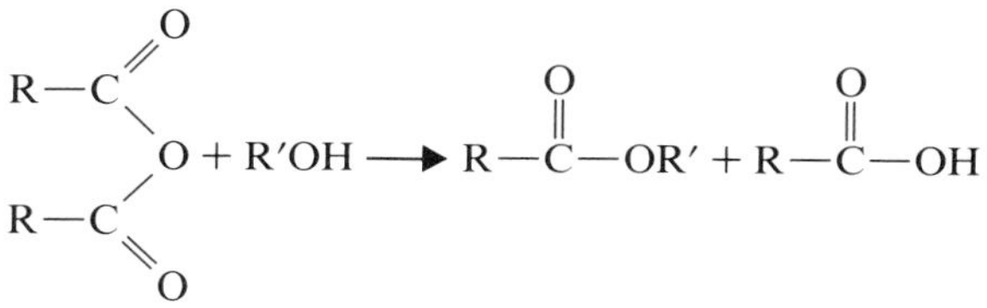

$$
\begin{array}{c}
R-C\overset{\displaystyle O}{\diagup}\\[-2pt]
\diagdown O + R'OH \longrightarrow R-\overset{\overset{\displaystyle O}{\|}}{C}-OR' + R-\overset{\overset{\displaystyle O}{\|}}{C}-OH\\[-2pt]
R-C\diagup\\[-6pt]
\diagdown O
\end{array}
$$

3. Conversion to amides and imides (discussed in Section 18.8).

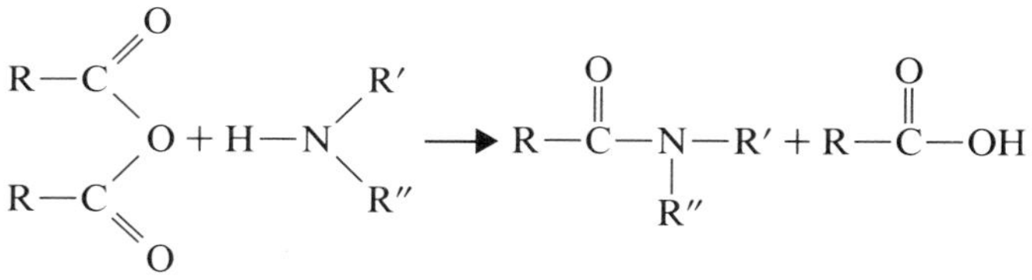

$$
\begin{array}{c}
R-C\overset{\displaystyle O}{\diagup}\\[-2pt]
\diagdown O + H-N\overset{\diagup R'}{\diagdown R''} \longrightarrow R-\overset{\overset{\displaystyle O}{\|}}{C}-\underset{\underset{\displaystyle R''}{|}}{N}-R' + R-\overset{\overset{\displaystyle O}{\|}}{C}-OH\\[-2pt]
R-C\diagup\\[-6pt]
\diagdown O
\end{array}
$$

R' and/or R'' may be H

or

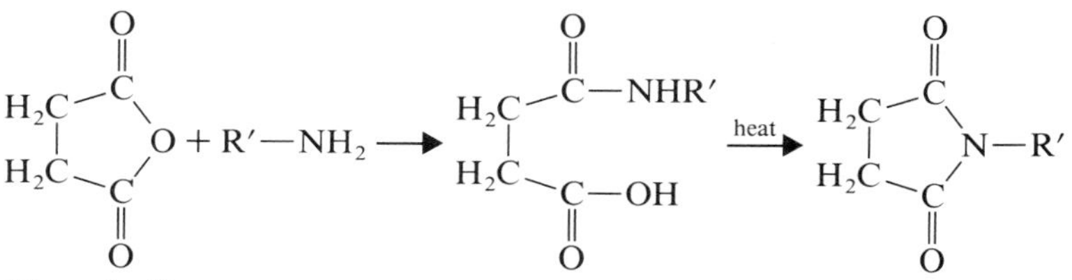

R' may be H

4. Conversion to ketones (discussed in Sections 15.17–15.19).

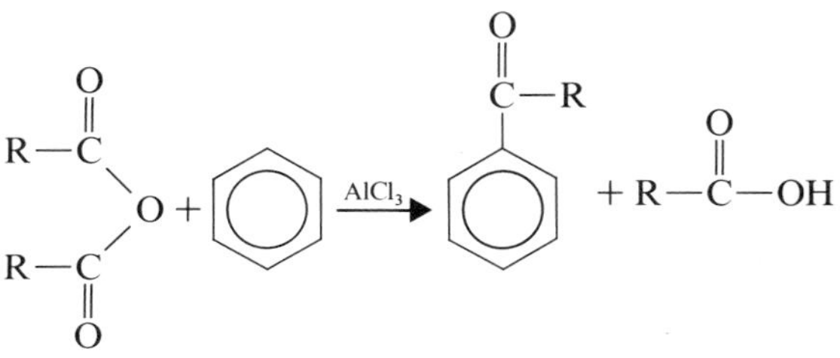

18.13D REACTIONS OF ESTERS

1. Hydrolysis (discussed in Section 18.7).

$$R-\overset{\overset{\displaystyle O}{\|}}{C}-O-R' + H_2O \underset{}{\overset{H^+}{\rightleftarrows}} R-\overset{\overset{\displaystyle O}{\|}}{C}-OH + R'-OH$$

$$R-\overset{\overset{\displaystyle O}{\|}}{C}-O-R' + OH^- \xrightarrow[H_2O]{} R-\overset{\overset{\displaystyle O}{\|}}{C}-O^- + R'-OH$$

2. Conversion to other esters: transesterification (discussed in Problem 18.11).

$$R-\overset{\overset{\displaystyle O}{\|}}{C}-O-R' + R''-OH \overset{H^+}{\rightleftarrows} R-\overset{\overset{\displaystyle O}{\|}}{C}-O-R'' + R'-OH$$

3. Conversion to amides (discussed in Section 18.8).

$$R-\overset{\overset{\displaystyle O}{\|}}{C}-OR' + HN\overset{R''}{\underset{R'''}{\diagdown}} \longrightarrow R-\overset{\overset{\displaystyle O}{\|}}{C}-N\overset{R''}{\underset{R'''}{\diagdown}} + R'-OH$$

R″ and/or R‴ may be H

4. Reaction with Grignard reagents (discussed in Section 11.8).

$$R-\overset{\overset{\displaystyle O}{\|}}{C}-OR' + 2\,R''MgX \xrightarrow{\text{diethyl ether}} R-\overset{\overset{\displaystyle OMgX}{|}}{\underset{\underset{\displaystyle R''}{|}}{C}}-R'' + R'OMgX$$

$$\Big\downarrow H^+$$

$$R-\overset{\overset{\displaystyle OH}{|}}{\underset{\underset{\displaystyle R''}{|}}{C}}-R''$$

5. Reduction (discussed in Section 11.3).

$$R-\overset{\overset{\displaystyle O}{\|}}{C}-O-R' + H_2 \xrightarrow{Ni} R-CH_2OH + R'-OH$$

$$R-\overset{\overset{\displaystyle O}{\|}}{C}-O-R' + LiAlH_4 \xrightarrow[(2)\ H_2O]{(1)\ \text{diethyl ether}} R-CH_2OH + R'-OH$$

$$R-\overset{\overset{\displaystyle O}{\|}}{C}-O-R' + Na \xrightarrow[(2)\ H^+]{(1)\ C_2H_5OH} R-CH_2OH + R'-OH$$

18.13E REACTIONS OF AMIDES

1. Hydrolysis (discussed in Section 18.8).

$$R-\overset{\overset{\displaystyle O}{\|}}{\underset{\underset{\displaystyle R''}{|}}{C}}-NR' + H_3O^+ \xrightarrow{H_2O} R-\overset{\overset{\displaystyle O}{\|}}{C}-OH + R'-\overset{\overset{\displaystyle +}{}}{\underset{\underset{\displaystyle R''}{|}}{N}}H_2$$

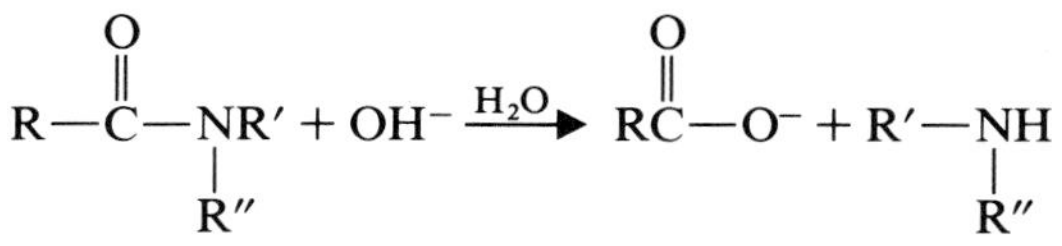

$$R-\overset{\overset{\displaystyle O}{\|}}{C}-NR' + OH^- \xrightarrow{H_2O} R\overset{\overset{\displaystyle O}{\|}}{C}-O^- + R'-NH$$

with R″ below the first carbon and R″ below the nitrogen

R, R′, and/or R″ may be H

2. Conversion to nitriles: dehydration (discussed in Section 18.8).

$$R-\overset{\overset{\displaystyle O}{\|}}{C}NH_2 \xrightarrow[\substack{heat \\ (-H_2O)}]{P_4O_{10}} R-C\equiv N$$

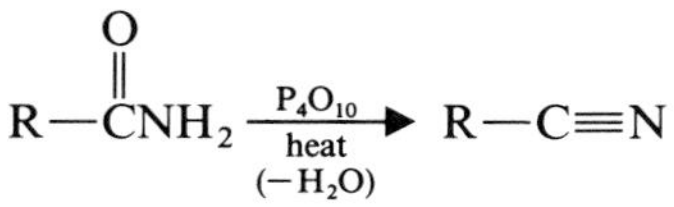

3. Conversion to imides (discussed in Section 18.8).

$$\xrightarrow[(-H_2O)]{heat}$$

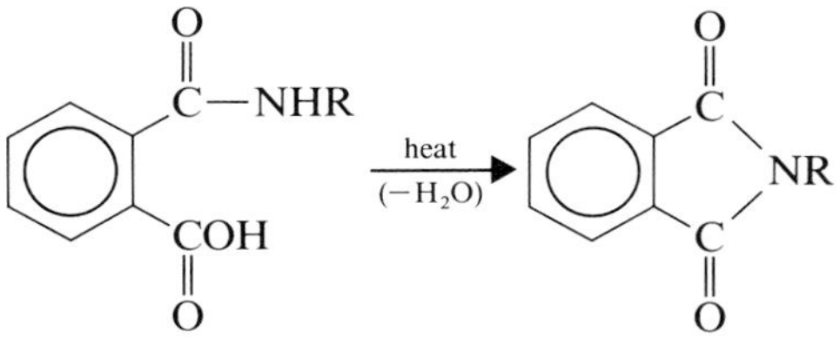

Additional Problems

18.19 Write a structural formula for each of the following compounds:

(a) Hexanoic acid
(b) Hexanamide
(c) *N*-Ethylhexanamide
(d) *N,N*-Diethylhexanamide
(e) 3-Hexenoic acid
(f) 2-Methyl-4-hexenoic acid
(g) Hexanedioic acid
(h) Phthalic acid
(i) Isophthalic acid
(j) Terephthalic acid
(k) Diethyl oxalate

(l) Diethyl adipate
(m) Isobutyl propanoate
(n) 2-Naphthoic acid
(o) Maleic acid
(p) 2-Hydroxybutanedioic acid (malic acid)
(q) Fumaric acid
(r) Succinic acid
(s) Succinimide
(t) Malonic acid
(u) Diethyl malonate

18.20 Give an IUPAC systematic or common name for each of the following compounds:

(a) $C_6H_5CO_2H$
(b) C_6H_5COCl
(c) $C_6H_5CONH_2$
(d) $(C_6H_5CO)_2O$
(e) $C_6H_5CO_2CH_2C_6H_5$
(f) $C_6H_5CO_2C_6H_5$
(g) $CH_3CO_2CH(CH_3)_2$
(h) $CH_3CON(CH_3)_2$
(i) CH_3CN

(j)

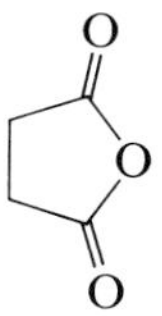

(k)

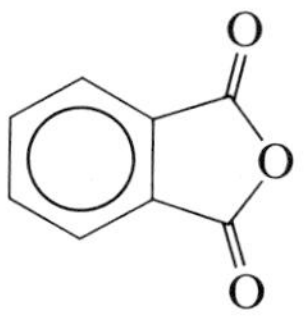

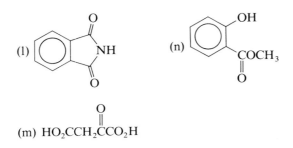

(m) $HO_2CCH_2\overset{O}{\overset{\|}{C}}CO_2H$

18.21   Show how benzoic acid can be synthesized from each of the following:

(a) Bromobenzene   (d) Acetophenone   (g) Benzyl alcohol

(b) Toluene   (e) Benzaldehyde

(c) Benzonitrile, C_6H_5CN (f) Styrene

18.22   Show how phenylacetic acid can be prepared from each of the following:

(a) Phenylacetaldehyde   (b) Benzyl bromide (two ways)

18.23   Show how pentanoic acid can be prepared from each of the following:

(a) 1-Pentanol   (c) 5-Decene

(b) 1-Bromobutane (two ways)   (d) Pentanal

18.24   What major organic product would you expect to obtain when acetyl chloride reacts with each of the following?

(a) H_2O (i) CH_3NH_2 (excess)

(b) $AgNO_3/H_2O$ (j) $C_6H_5NH_2$ (excess)

(c) $CH_3(CH_2)_2CH_2OH$ and pyridine   (k) $(CH_3)_2NH$ (excess)

(d) NH_3 (excess)   (l) CH_3CH_2OH and pyridine

(e) $C_6H_5CH_3$ and $AlCl_3$ (m) $CH_3CO_2^-Na^+$

(f) $LiAlH[OC(CH_3)_3]_3$ (n) CH_3CO_2H and pyridine

(g) $(CH_3)_2CuLi$ (o)   Phenol and pyridine

(h) $NaOH/H_2O$

18.25   What major organic product would you expect to obtain when acetic anhydride reacts with each of the following?

(a) NH_3 (excess)   (c) $CH_3CH_2CH_2OH$ (e) $CH_3CH_2NH_2$ (excess)

(b) H_2O (d) $C_6H_6 + AlCl_3$ (f) $(CH_3CH_2)_2NH$ (excess)

18.26   What major organic product would you expect to obtain when succinic anhydride reacts with each of the reagents given in Problem 18.25?

18.27   Show how you might carry out the following transformations:

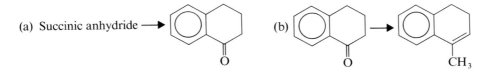

(c) 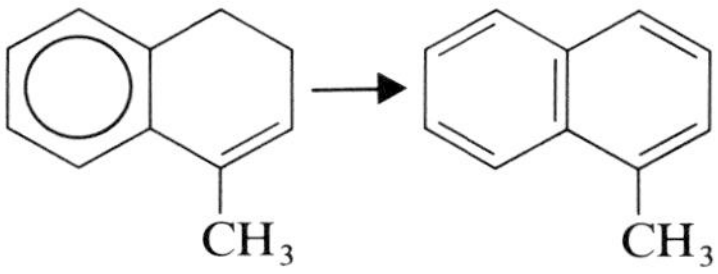
CH₃   CH₃

(d) Phthalic anhydride ⟶

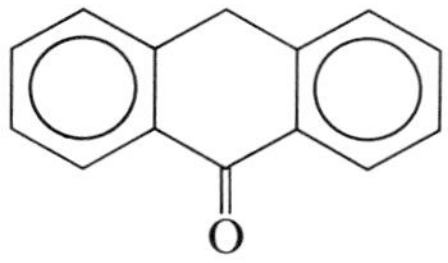

(e) Phthalic anhydride ⟶ N-methylphthalimide

(f) Maleic anhydride ⟶

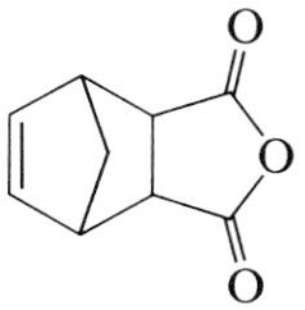

(g) Maleic anhydride ⟶

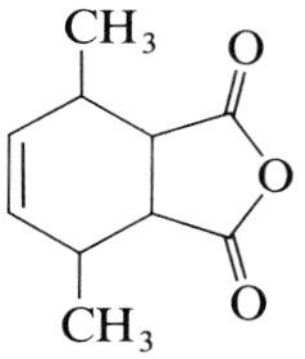

18.28 What products would you expect to obtain when ethyl propanoate reacts with each of the following?

(a) H_3O^+, H_2O (c) 1-Octanol, HCl   (e) $LiAlH_4$, then H_2O

(b) OH^-, H_2O (d) CH_3NH_2 (f) C_6H_5MgBr, then H_2O

18.29 What products would you expect to obtain when propanamide reacts with each of the following?

(a) H_3O^+, H_2O (b) OH^-, H_2O (c) P_4O_{10} and heat

18.30 Outline a simple chemical test that would serve to distinguish between

(a) Benzoic acid and methyl benzoate   (e) Ethyl benzoate and benzamide

(b) Benzoic acid and benzoyl chloride   (f) Benzoic acid and cinnamic acid

(c) Benzoic acid and benzamide   (g) Ethyl benzoate and benzoyl chloride

(d) Benzoic acid and 4-methylphenol   (h) 2-Chlorobutanoic acid and butanoic acid

18.31 What products would you expect to obtain when each of the following compounds is heated?

(a) 4-Hydroxybutanoic acid

(b) 3-Hydroxybutanoic acid

(c) 2-Hydroxybutanoic acid

(d) Glutaric acid

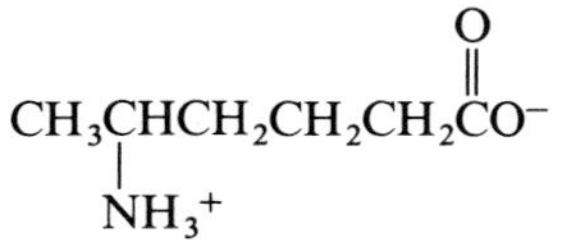

(f)

(e) $CH_3CHCH_2CH_2CH_2CO^-$ with NH_3^+ substituent

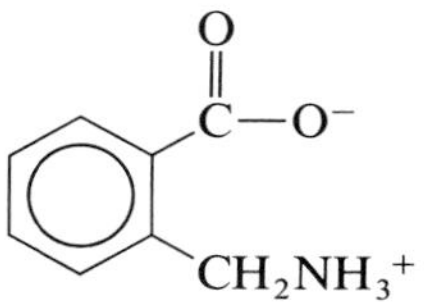

18.32   Give stereochemical formulas for compounds **A**–**Q**.

(a) (R)-$(-)$-2-Butanol $\xrightarrow[\text{pyridine}]{\text{TsCl}}$ **A** $\xrightarrow{\text{CN}^-}$ **B**(C_5H_9N) $\xrightarrow[H_2O]{H_2SO_4}$

(+)-**C**$(C_5H_{10}O_2)$ $\xrightarrow[\text{(2) }H_2O]{\text{(1) LiAlH}_4}$ $(-)$-**D**$(C_5H_{12}O)$

(b) (R)-$(-)$-2-Butanol $\xrightarrow[\text{pyridine}]{\text{PBr}_3}$ **E**(C_4H_9Br) $\xrightarrow{\text{CN}^-}$ **F**(C_5H_9N) $\xrightarrow[H_2O]{H_2SO_4}$

$(-)$-**C**$(C_5H_{10}O_2)$ $\xrightarrow[\text{(2) }H_2O]{\text{(1) LiAlH}_4}$ (+)-**D**$(C_5H_{12}O)$

(c) **A** $\xrightarrow{\text{CH}_3\text{CO}_2^-}$ **G**$(C_6H_{12}O_2)$ $\xrightarrow{\text{OH}^-}$ (+)-**H**$(C_4H_{10}O)$ + $CH_3CO_2^-$

(d) $(-)$-**D** $\xrightarrow{\text{PBr}_3}$ **J**$(C_5H_{11}Br)$ $\xrightarrow[\text{diethyl ether}]{\text{Mg}}$ **K**$(C_5H_{11}MgBr)$ $\xrightarrow[\text{(2) }H^+]{\text{(1) CO}_2}$ **L**$(C_6H_{12}O_2)$

(e) (R)-(+)-Glyceraldehyde $\xrightarrow{\text{HCN}}$ $\underbrace{\text{**M**}(C_4H_7NO_3) + \text{**N**}(C_4H_7NO_3)}$

Diastereomers, separated
by fractional crystallization

(f) **M** $\xrightarrow[H_2O]{H_2SO_4}$ **P**$(C_4H_8O_5)$ $\xrightarrow[\text{HNO}_3]{[O]}$ *meso*-tartaric acid

(g) **N** $\xrightarrow[H_2O]{H_2SO_4}$ **Q**$(C_4H_8O_5)$ $\xrightarrow[\text{HNO}_3]{[O]}$ $(-)$-tartaric acid

18.33   (a) (±)-Pantetheine and (±)-pantothenic acid, important intermediates in the synthesis of coenzyme A, were prepared by the following route. Give structures for compounds **A**–**D**.

(b) The γ-lactone, (±) **D**, can be resolved. If the $(-)$-γ-lactone is used in the last step, the pantetheine that is obtained is identical with that obtained naturally. The $(-)$-γ-lactone has the (R) configuration. What is the stereochemistry of naturally occurring pantetheine? (c) What products would you expect to obtain when (±)-pantetheine is heated with aqueous sodium hydroxide?

ADDITIONAL PROBLEMS

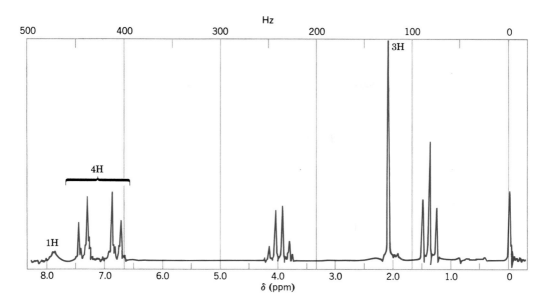

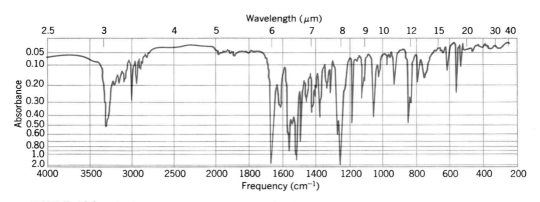

FIGURE 18.3 The ^{1}H NMR and IR spectra of phenacetin. (The ^{1}H NMR spectrum, courtesy Varian Associates, Palo Alto, CA. Infrared spectrum, courtesy Sadtler Research Laboratories, Philadelphia.)

18.34 The IR and ^{1}H NMR spectra of phenacetin ($C_{10}H_{13}NO_2$) are given in Fig. 18.3. Phenacetin is an analgesic and antipyretic compound, and was the P of A-P-C tablets (Aspirin–Phenacetin–Caffeine). (Because of its toxicity phenacetin is no longer used medically.) When phenacetin is heated with aqueous sodium hydroxide, it yields phenetidine ($C_8H_{11}NO$) and sodium acetate. Propose structures for phenacetin and phenetidine.

18.35 Given here are the ^{1}H NMR spectra and carbonyl absorption peaks of five acyl compounds. Propose structures for each.

(a) $C_8H_{14}O_4$ ^{1}H NMR spectrum   IR spectrum

                Triplet δ 1.2 (6H)   1740 cm^{-1}

                Singlet δ 2.5 (4H)

                Quartet δ 4.1 (4H)

(b) $C_{11}H_{14}O_2$ ^1H NMR spectrum   IR spectrum

Doublet	δ 1.0 (6H)	1720 cm^{-1}
Multiplet	δ 2.1 (1H)	
Doublet	δ 4.1 (2H)	
Multiplet	δ 7.8 (5H)	

(c) $C_{10}H_{12}O_2$ ^1H NMR spectrum   IR spectrum

Triplet	δ 1.2 (3H)	1740 cm^{-1}
Singlet	δ 3.5 (2H)	
Quartet	δ 4.1 (2H)	
Multiplet	δ 7.3 (5H)	

(d) $C_2H_2Cl_2O_2$ ^1H NMR spectrum   IR spectrum

Singlet	δ 6.0	Broad peak 2500–2700 cm^{-1}
Singlet	δ 11.70	1705 cm^{-1}

(e) $C_4H_7ClO_2$ ^1H NMR spectrum   IR spectrum

Triplet	δ 1.3	1745 cm^{-1}
Singlet	δ 4.0	
Quartet	δ 4.2	

18.36   The active ingredient of the insect repellent "Off" is *N,N*-diethyl-*m*-toluamide, *m*-CH$_3$C$_6$H$_4$CON(CH$_2$CH$_3$)$_2$. Outline a synthesis of this compound starting with *m*-toluic acid.

18.37   Amides are weaker bases than corresponding amines. For example, most water-insoluble amines (RNH$_2$) will dissolve in dilute aqueous acids (e.g., aqueous HCl, H$_2$SO$_4$, etc.) by forming water-soluble alkylaminium salts (RNH$_3{}^+$X$^-$). Corresponding amides (RCONH$_2$) *do not dissolve in dilute aqueous acids,* however. Propose an explanation for the much lower basicity of amides when compared to amines.

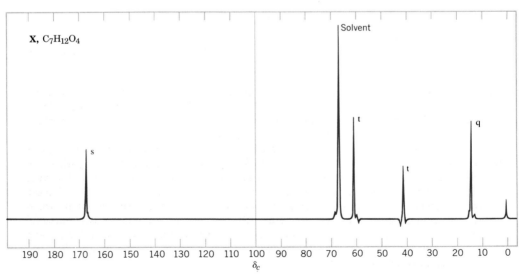

FIGURE 18.4 The proton-decoupled ^{13}C NMR spectrum of compound **X**, Problem 18.39. The letters s, t, and q refer to the signal splitting (singlet, triplet, and quartet) in the proton off-resonance decoupled spectrum. (Adapted from L. F. Johnson and W. C. Jankowski, *Carbon-13 NMR Spectra: A Collection of Assigned, Coded, and Indexed Spectra,* Wiley–Interscience, New York, 1972.)

ADDITIONAL PROBLEMS

18.38 While amides are much less basic than amines, they are much stronger acids. Amides have pK_a values in the range 14–16, while for amines, $pK_a = 33$–35. (a) What factor accounts for the much greater acidity of amides? (b) *Imides,* that is,

$$\overset{\text{O}}{\overset{\|}{}}$$

compounds with the structure $(RC)_2NH$, are even stronger acids than amides. For imides, $K_a = 10^{-9}$–10^{-10} and, as a consequence, water-insoluble imides dissolve in aqueous NaOH by forming soluble sodium salts. What extra factor accounts for the greater acidity of imides?

18.39 Compound $X(C_7H_{12}O_4)$ is insoluble in aqueous sodium bicarbonate. The IR spectrum of **X** has a strong absorption peak near 1740 cm^{-1}, and its proton-decoupled ^{13}C spectrum is given in Fig. 18.4. Propose a structure for **X**.

18.40 Alkylthiyl acetates $\left(\overset{\text{O}}{\overset{\|}{CH_3CSCH_2CH_2R}} \right)$ can be prepared by a peroxide-initiated reaction between thiolacetic acid $\left(\overset{\text{O}}{\overset{\|}{CH_3CSH}} \right)$ and an alkene ($CH_2{=}CHR$). (a) Outline a reasonable mechanism for this reaction. (b) Show how you might use this reaction in a synthesis of 3-methyl-2-butanethiol from 2-methyl-2-butene.

18.41 On heating, *cis*-4-hydroxycyclohexanecarboxylic acid forms a lactone but *trans*-4-hydroxycyclohexanecarboxylic acid does not. Explain.

18.42 (R)-(+)-Glyceraldehyde can be transformed into (+)-malic acid by the following synthetic route. Give stereochemical structures for the products of each step.

(R)-(+)-Glyceraldehyde $\xrightarrow[\text{oxidation}]{\text{Br}_2, \text{H}_2\text{O}}$ (−)-glyceric acid $\xrightarrow{\text{PBr}_3}$

(−)-3-bromo-2-hydroxypropanoic acid $\xrightarrow{\text{NaCN}}$ $C_4H_5NO_3$ $\xrightarrow[\text{heat}]{\text{H}_3\text{O}^+}$ (+)-malic acid

18.43 (R)-(+)-Glyceraldehyde can also be transformed into (−)-malic acid. This synthesis begins with the conversion of (R)-(+)-glyceraldehyde into (−)-tartaric acid as shown in Problem 18.32, parts (e) and (g). Then (−)-tartaric acid is allowed to react with phosphorus tribromide in order to replace one alcoholic —OH group with —Br. This step takes place with inversion of configuration at the carbon that undergoes attack. Treating the product of this reaction with zinc and acid produces (−)-malic acid. (a) Outline all steps in this synthesis by writing stereochemical structures for each intermediate. (b) The step in which (−)-tartaric acid is treated with phosphorus tribromide produces only one stereoisomer even though there are two replaceable —OH groups. How is this possible? (c) Suppose that the step in which (−)-tartaric acid is treated with phosphorus tribromide had taken place with "mixed" stereochemistry—with both inversion and retention at the carbon under attack. How many stereoisomers would have been produced? (d) What difference would this have made to the overall outcome of the synthesis?

18.44 Cantharidin is a powerful vesicant that can be isolated from dried beetles (*Cantharis vesicatoria* or "Spanish fly"). Outlined here is the stereospecific synthesis of cantharidin reported by Gilbert Stork of Columbia University in 1953. Supply the missing reagents (a)– (n).

Cantharidin

*18.45   Examine the structure of cantharidin (Problem 18.44) carefully and (a) suggest a possible two-step synthesis of cantharidin starting with furan (Section 13.12). (b) F. von Bruchhausen and H. W. Bersch at the University of Münster attempted this two-step synthesis in 1928 only a few months after Diels and Alder published their first paper describing their new diene addition and found that the expected addition failed to take place. von Bruchhausen and Bersch also found that although cantharidin is stable at relatively high temperatures, heating cantharidin with a palladium catalyst causes cantharidin to decompose. They identified furan and dimethylmaleic anhydride among the decomposition products. What has happened in the decomposition and what does this suggest about why the first step of their attempted synthesis failed?

18.46   Compound Y ($C_8H_4O_3$) dissolves slowly when warmed with aqueous sodium bicarbonate. The IR spectrum of Y has strong peaks at 1779 and at 1854 cm^{-1}. The proton-decoupled ^{13}C spectrum of Y is given in Fig. 18.5. Propose a structure for Y.

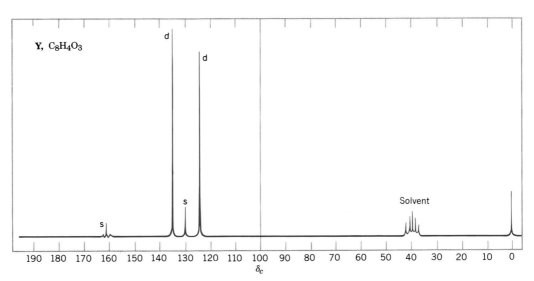

Y, C₈H₄O₃

FIGURE 18.5   The proton-decoupled ^{13}C NMR spectrum of compound Y, Problem 18.46. The letters s and d refer to the signal splitting (singlet and doublet) in the proton off-reso-nance decoupled spectrum. (Adapted from L. F. Johnson and W. C. Jankowski, *Carbon-13 NMR Spectra: A Collection of Assigned, Coded and Indexed Spectra,* Wiley–Interscience, New York, 1972.)

SPECIAL TOPIC

F

CONDENSATION POLYMERS

We saw, in Special Topic B, that large molecules with many repeating subunits—called *polymers*—can be prepared by addition reactions of alkenes. These polymers, we noted, are called *addition polymers*.

Another broad group of polymers has been called *condensation polymers*. These polymers, as their name suggests, are prepared by condensation reactions—reactions in which monomeric subunits are joined through intermolecular eliminations of small molecules such as water or alcohols. Among the most important condensation polymers are *polyamides, polyesters, polyurethanes,* and *formaldehyde resins*.

F.1 POLYAMIDES

Silk and wool are two naturally occurring polymers that humans have used for centuries to fabricate articles of clothing. They are examples of a family of compounds that are called *proteins*—a group of compounds that we shall discuss in detail in Chapter 24. At this point we need only to notice (below) that the repeating subunits of proteins are derived from α-amino acids and that these subunits are joined by amide linkages. Proteins, therefore, are polyamides.

$$\underset{\substack{|\\ \text{R}}}{\text{H}_2\text{N}-\text{CH}}-\overset{\overset{\text{O}}{\|}}{\text{C}}-\text{OH}$$

An α-amino acid

Amide linkages

$$-\text{NH}-\underset{\substack{|\\ \text{R}}}{\text{CH}}-\overset{\overset{\text{O}}{\|}}{\text{C}}-\text{NH}-\underset{\substack{|\\ \text{R}}}{\text{CH}}-\overset{\overset{\text{O}}{\|}}{\text{C}}-\text{NH}-\underset{\substack{|\\ \text{R}}}{\text{CH}}-\overset{\overset{\text{O}}{\|}}{\text{C}}-\text{NH}-\underset{\substack{|\\ \text{R}}}{\text{CH}}-$$

**A portion of a polyamide chain as
it might occur in a protein**

The search for a synthetic material with properties similar to those of silk led to the discovery of a family of synthetic polyamides called nylons.

One of the most important nylons, called *nylon 6,6,* can be prepared from the six-carbon dicarboxylic acid, adipic acid, and the six-carbon diamine, hexamethylenediamine. In the commercial process these two compounds are allowed to react in equimolar proportions in order to produce a 1 : 1 salt,

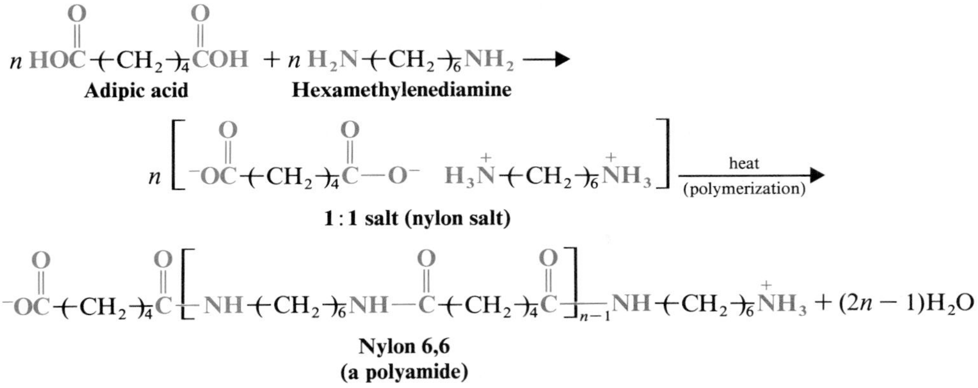

$$n \ HOC\!\!-\!\!(CH_2)_4\!\!-\!\!COH \ + \ n \ H_2N\!\!-\!\!(CH_2)_6\!\!-\!\!NH_2 \longrightarrow$$

Adipic acid　　　**Hexamethylenediamine**

$$n \left[{}^-OC\!\!-\!\!(CH_2)_4\!\!-\!\!C\!\!-\!\!O^- \quad H_3\overset{+}{N}\!\!-\!\!(CH_2)_6\!\!-\!\!\overset{+}{N}H_3 \right] \xrightarrow[\text{(polymerization)}]{\text{heat}}$$

1 : 1 salt (nylon salt)

$$^-OC\!\!-\!\!(CH_2)_4\!\!-\!\!C\!\!\left[NH\!\!-\!\!(CH_2)_6\!\!-\!\!NH\!\!-\!\!C\!\!-\!\!(CH_2)_4\!\!-\!\!C \right]_{n-1}\!\!\!NH\!\!-\!\!(CH_2)_6\!\!-\!\!\overset{+}{N}H_3 + (2n-1)H_2O$$

Nylon 6,6
(a polyamide)

Then, heating the 1 : 1 salt (nylon salt) to a temperature of 270 °C at a pressure of 250 psi (pounds per square inch) causes a polymerization to take place. Water molecules are lost as condensation reactions occur between $-\overset{O}{\underset{\|}{C}}-O^-$ and $-NH_3^+$ groups of the salt to give the polyamide.

The nylon 6,6 produced in this way has a molecular weight of about 10,000, has a melting point of about 250 °C, and when molten can be spun into fibers from a melt. The fibers are then stretched to about four times their original length. This orients the linear polyamide molecules so that they are parallel to the fiber axis and allows hydrogen bonds to form between $-NH-$ and $C=O$ groups on adjacent chains. Called "cold drawing," stretching greatly increases the fibers' strength.

Another type of nylon, nylon 6, can be prepared by a ring-opening polymerization of ε-caprolactam:

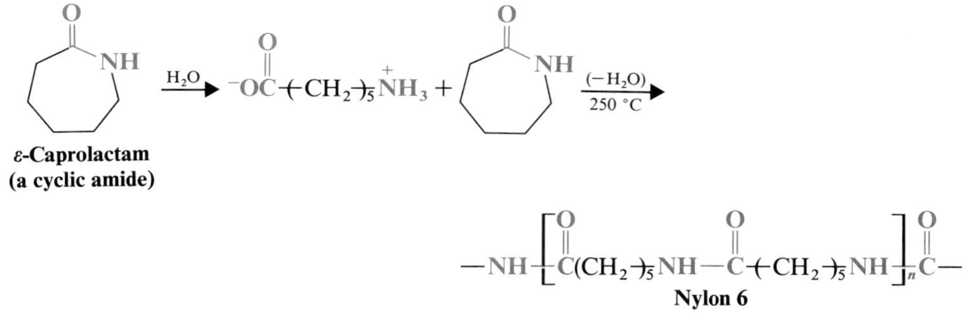

ε-Caprolactam
(a cyclic amide)

$$-NH\!\!\left[\overset{O}{\underset{\|}{C}}(CH_2)_5\!\!-\!\!NH\!\!-\!\!\overset{O}{\underset{\|}{C}}\!\!-\!\!(CH_2)_5\!\!-\!\!NH \right]_n\!\!\overset{O}{\underset{\|}{C}}-$$

Nylon 6

In this process ε-caprolactam is allowed to react with water, converting some of it to ε-aminocaproic acid. Then heating this mixture at 250 °C drives off water as ε-caprolactam and ε-aminocaproic acid react to produce the polyamide. Nylon 6 can also be converted into fibers by melt spinning.

Problem F.1

The raw materials for the production of nylon 6,6 can be obtained in several ways as indicated below. Give equations for each synthesis of adipic acid and of hexamethylenediamine.

(a) Cyclohexanone $\xrightarrow{[O]}$ adipic acid

(b) Adipic acid $\xrightarrow{2\ NH_3}$ a salt $\xrightarrow{heat}$ $C_6H_{12}N_2O_2$ $\xrightarrow[catalyst]{350\ °C}$

$$C_6H_8N_2 \xrightarrow[catalyst]{4\ H_2} \text{hexamethylenediamine}$$

(c) 1,3-Butadiene $\xrightarrow{Cl_2}$ $C_4H_6Cl_2$ $\xrightarrow{2\ NaCN}$ $C_6H_6N_2$ $\xrightarrow{H_2}{Ni}$

$$C_6H_8N_2 \xrightarrow[catalyst]{4\ H_2} \text{hexamethylenediamine}$$

(d) Tetrahydrofuran $\xrightarrow{2\ HCl}$ $C_4H_8Cl_2$ $\xrightarrow{2\ NaCN}$ $C_6H_8N_2$ $\xrightarrow[catalyst]{4\ H_2}$

hexamethylenediamine

F.2 POLYESTERS

One of the most important polyesters is poly(ethylene terephthalate), a polymer that is marketed under the names *Dacron, Terylene,* and *Mylar.*

$$-OCH_2CH_2-O\left[\overset{O}{\overset{\|}{C}}-\bigcirc-\overset{O}{\overset{\|}{C}}-OCH_2CH_2-O\right]_n\overset{O}{\overset{\|}{C}}-\bigcirc-\overset{O}{\overset{\|}{C}}-$$

Poly(ethylene terephthalate)
(Dacron, Terylene, or Mylar)

One can obtain poly(ethylene terephthalate) by a direct acid-catalyzed esterification of ethylene glycol and terephthalic acid.

$$HO-CH_2CH_2-OH + HO-\overset{O}{\overset{\|}{C}}-\bigcirc-\overset{O}{\overset{\|}{C}}-OH \xrightarrow[heat]{H^+}$$

Ethylene glycol   **Terephthalic acid**

Poly(ethylene terephthalate) + H_2O

Another method for synthesizing poly(ethylene terephthalate) is based on transesterification reactions—reactions in which one ester is converted into another. One commercial synthesis utilizes two transesterifications. In the first, dimethyl terephthalate and excess ethylene glycol are heated to 200 °C in the presence of a basic catalyst. Distillation of the mixture results in the loss of methanol (bp, 64.7 °C) and the formation of a new ester, one formed from 2 mol of ethylene glycol and 1 mol of terephthalic acid. When this new ester is heated to a higher temperature (~280 °C), ethylene glycol (bp, 198 °C) distills and polymerization (the second transesterification) takes place.

$$CH_3O-\overset{O}{\overset{\|}{C}}-\bigcirc-\overset{O}{\overset{\|}{C}}-OCH_3 + 2\ HO-CH_2CH_2-OH \xrightarrow[200\ °C]{base}$$

Dimethyl terephthalate   **Ethylene glycol**

$$HO-CH_2CH_2-O-\overset{\overset{\displaystyle O}{\|}}{C}-\langle\bigcirc\rangle-\overset{\overset{\displaystyle O}{\|}}{C}-O-CH_2CH_2-OH + 2\ CH_3OH$$

$$n\ HO-CH_2CH_2-O-\overset{\overset{\displaystyle O}{\|}}{C}-\langle\bigcirc\rangle-\overset{\overset{\displaystyle O}{\|}}{C}-O-CH_2CH_2-OH \xrightarrow[280\ °C]{}$$

$$\left[\overset{\overset{\displaystyle O}{\|}}{C}-\langle\bigcirc\rangle-\overset{\overset{\displaystyle O}{\|}}{C}-O-CH_2CH_2-O\right]_n + n\ HO-CH_2CH_2-OH$$

Poly(ethylene terephthalate)

The poly(ethylene terephthalate) thus produced melts at about 270 °C. It can be melt spun into fibers to produce Dacron or Terylene; it can also be made into a film, in which form it is marketed as Mylar.

Problem F.2

Transesterifications are catalyzed by either acids or bases. Using the transesterification reaction that takes place when dimethyl terephthalate is heated with ethylene glycol as an example, outline reasonable mechanisms for (a) the base-catalyzed reaction and (b) the acid-catalyzed reaction.

Problem F.3

Kodel is another polyester that enjoys wide commercial use.

$$\left(\overset{\overset{\displaystyle O}{\|}}{C}-\langle\bigcirc\rangle-\overset{\overset{\displaystyle O}{\|}}{C}-O-CH_2-\langle\bigcirc\rangle-CH_2-O\right)_n$$

Kodel

Kodel is also produced by a transesterification. (a) What methyl ester and what alcohol are required for the synthesis of Kodel? (b) The alcohol can be prepared from dimethyl terephthalate. How might this be done?

Problem F.4

Heating phthalic anhydride and glycerol together yields a polyester called a glyptal resin. A glyptal resin is especially rigid because the polymer chains are "cross-linked." Write a portion of the structure of a glyptal resin and show how cross-linking occurs.

Problem F.5

Lexan, a high molecular weight "polycarbonate," is manufactured by mixing bisphenol A with phosgene in the presence of pyridine. Suggest a structure for Lexan.

HO—⬡—C(CH₃)(CH₃)—⬡—OH   Cl—C(=O)—Cl

Bisphenol A   **Phosgene**

Problem F.6

The familiar "epoxy resins" or "epoxy glues" usually consist of two components that are sometimes labeled "resin" and "hardener." The resin is manufactured by allowing bisphenol A (Problem F.5) to react with an excess of epichlorohydrin, H_2C—$CHCH_2Cl$, in the presence of a base until a low molec

ular weight polymer is obtained. (a) What is a likely structure for this polymer and (b) what is the purpose of using an excess of epichlorohydrin? The hardener is usually an amine such as $H_2NCH_2CH_2NHCH_2CH_2NH_2$. (c) What reaction takes place when the resin and hardener are mixed?

F.3 POLYURETHANES

A *urethane* is the product formed when an alcohol reacts with an isocyanate:

$$R—OH + O=C=N—R' \longrightarrow R—O—\overset{\overset{\displaystyle O}{\|}}{C}—\overset{\overset{\displaystyle H}{|}}{N}—R'$$

Alcohol   **Isocyanate**   **A urethane**
(a carbamate)

The reaction probably takes place in the following way:

$$R—\ddot{O}H + \overset{\overset{\displaystyle O}{\|}}{\underset{\underset{\displaystyle R'}{|}}{C}}—\!—\!\longrightarrow R—\overset{+}{O}—C\overset{\overline{O}}{=}N—R' \longrightarrow R—O—\overset{\overset{\displaystyle O}{\|}}{C}—\overset{\overset{\displaystyle H}{|}}{N}—R'$$

A urethane is also called a *carbamate* because formally it is an ester of an alcohol (ROH) and a carbamic acid (R'NHCO₂H).

Polyurethanes are usually made by allowing a *diol* to react with a *diisocyanate*. The diol is typically a polyester with —CH₂OH end groups. The diisocyanate is usually toluene 2,4-diisocyanate.*

---

* Toluene 2,4-diisocyanate is a hazardous chemical that has caused acute respiratory problems among workers synthesizing polyurethanes.

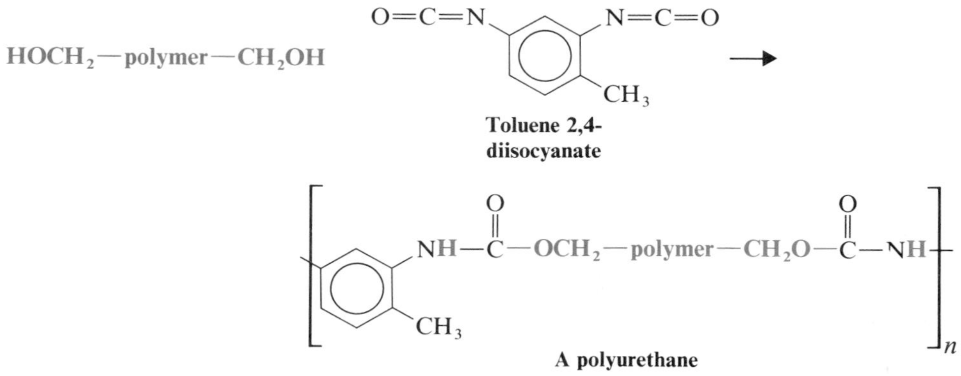

Toluene 2,4-
diisocyanate

A polyurethane

Problem F.7

A typical polyurethane can be made in the following way. Adipic acid is polymerized with an excess of ethylene glycol. The resulting polyester is then
treated with toluene 2,4-diisocyanate. (a) Write the structure of the polyurethane. (b) Why is an excess of ethylene glycol used in making the polyester?

Polyurethane foams, as used in pillows and paddings, are made by adding small
amounts of water to the reaction mixture during the polymerization with the diisocyanate. Some of the isocyanate groups react with water to produce carbon dioxide,
and this gas acts as the foaming agent.

$$R—N=C=O + H_2O \longrightarrow R—NH_2 + CO_2\uparrow$$

F.4 PHENOL–FORMALDEHYDE POLYMERS

One of the first synthetic polymers to be produced was a polymer (or resin) known as
Bakelite. Bakelite is made by a condensation reaction between phenol and formaldehyde; the reaction can be catalyzed by either acids or bases. The base-catalyzed
reaction probably takes place in the general way shown here. Reaction can take place
at the ortho and para positions of phenol.

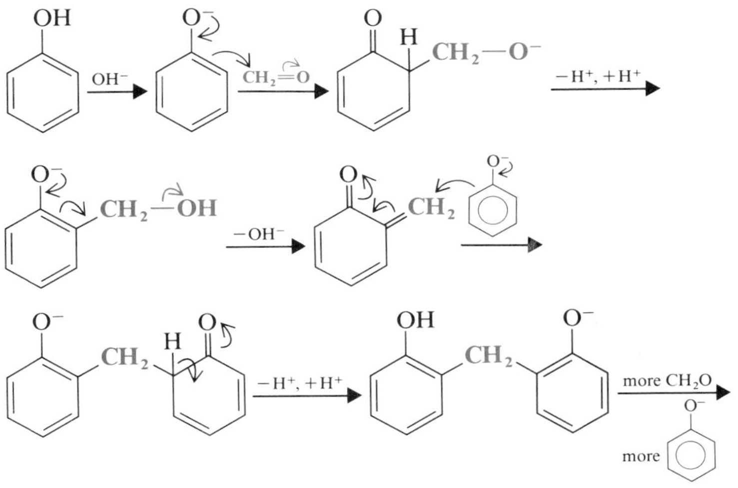

Bakelite

Generally, the polymerization is carried out in two stages. The first polymerization produces a low molecular weight fusible (meltable) polymer called a *resole*. The resole can be molded to the desired shape, and then further polymerization produces a very high molecular weight polymer, which, because it is highly cross-linked, is infusible.

Problem F.8

Using a para-substituted phenol such as *p*-cresol yields a phenol–formaldehyde polymer that is *thermoplastic* rather than *thermosetting.* That is, the polymer remains fusible; it does *not* become impossible to melt. What accounts for this?

Problem F.9

Outline a general mechanism for acid-catalyzed polymerization of phenol and formaldehyde.

F.5 CASCADE POLYMERS

One exciting development in polymer chemistry in the last 10 years has been the synthesis of high molecular weight, symmetrical, highly branched, polyfunctional molecules called **cascade polymers.** George R. Newkome (of the University of South Florida) and Donald A. Tomalia (of the Michigan Molecular Institute) have been pioneers in this area of research.

All of the polymers that we have considered so far are inevitably nonhomogeneous. While they consist of molecules with common repetitive monomeric units, the molecules of the material obtained from the polymerization reactions vary widely in molecular weight (and, therefore, in size). Cascade polymers, by contrast, can be synthesized in ways that yield polymers consisting of molecules of uniform molecular weight and size.

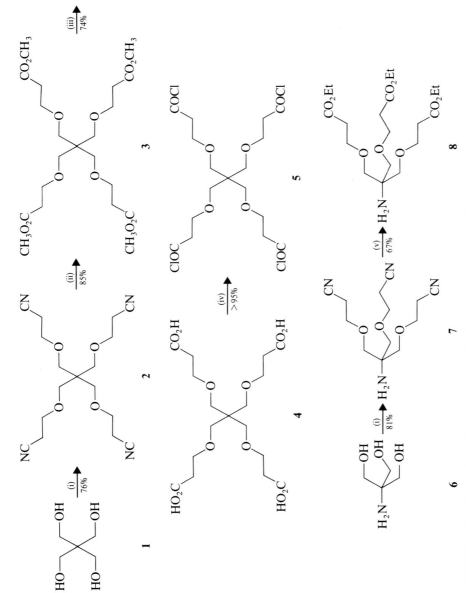

FIGURE F.1 Synthesis of the starting materials for a cascade polymer. Reagents and conditions: (i) CH₂=CHCN, KOH, *p*-dioxane, 25 °C, 24 h; (ii) MeOH, dry HCl, reflux, 2 h; (iii) 3 *N* NaOH, 70 °C, 24 h; (iv) SOCl₂, CH₂Cl₂, reflux, 1 h; (v) EtOH, dry HCl, reflux, 3 h (adapted from George R. Newkome and Xiaofeng Lin, *Macromolecules, 1991, 24*, 1443–1444).

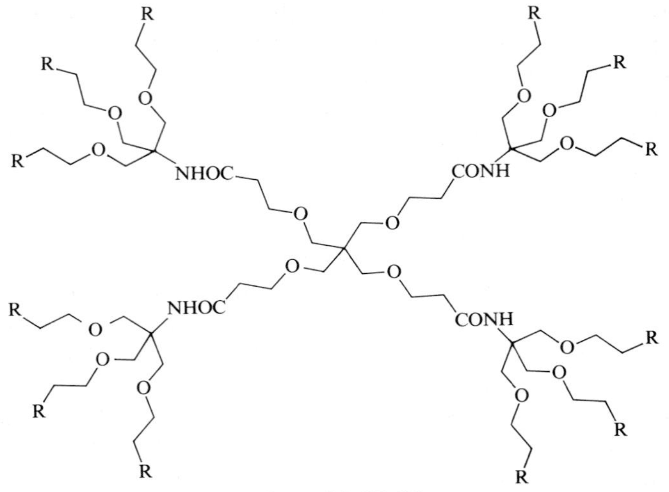

9 R = CO$_2$CH$_2$CH$_3$
10 R = COOH

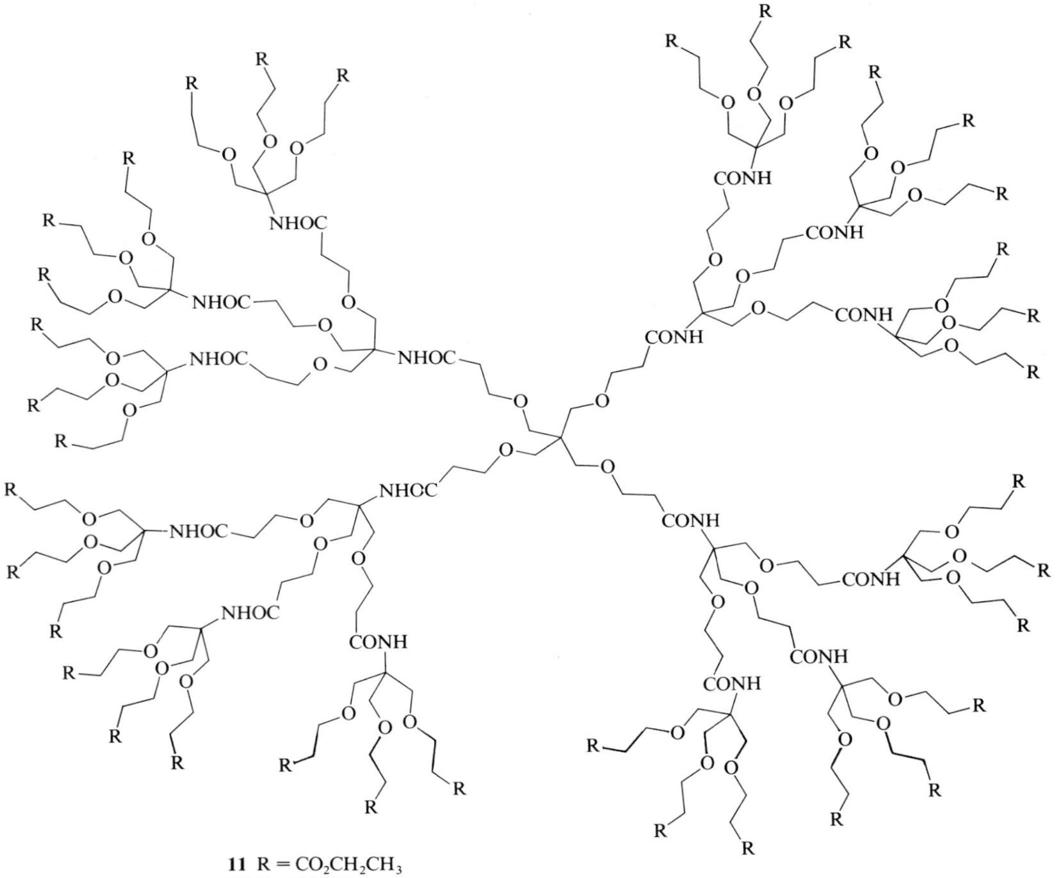

11 R = CO$_2$CH$_2$CH$_3$
12 R = COOH
13 R = CONHC(CH$_2$OCH$_2$CH$_2$CO$_2$CH$_2$CH$_3$)$_3$
14 R = CONHC(CH$_2$OCH$_2$CH$_2$CO$_2$H)$_3$
15 R = CONHC[CH$_2$OCH$_2$CH$_2$CONHC(CH$_2$OCH$_2$CH$_2$CO$_2$CH$_2$CH$_3$)$_3$]$_3$

FIGURE F.2 Cascade polymers (adapted from George R. Newkome and Xiaofeng Lin, *Macromolecules, 1991, 24,* 1443–1444).

SPECIAL TOPIC F

Syntheses of cascade polymers begin with a core building block that can lead to branching in one, two, three, or even four directions. Starting with this core molecule, through repetitive reactions, layers (called **cascade spheres**) are added. Each new sphere increases (usually by three times) the number of branch points from which the next sphere can be constructed. Because of this multiplying effect, very large molecules can be built up very quickly.

Figures F.1 and F.2 show how a four directional cascade molecule has been constructed. All of the reactions are closely related to ones that we have studied already. The starting material for construction of the core molecule is a branched tetraol, **1**. In the first step (i), **1** is allowed to react with propenenitrile ($CH_2=CHCN$) in a conjugate addition called *cyanoethylation to produce* **2**. Treating **2** with methanol and acid [step (ii)] converts the cyano groups to methyl carboxylate groups. (Instead of hydrolyzing the cyano groups to carboxylic acids and then esterifying them, this process accomplishes the same result in one step.) In step (iii), the ester groups are hydrolyzed, and in step (iv), the carboxyl groups are converted to acyl chlorides. Compound **5** is the core building block.

The synthesis of the compound used in constructing the next cascade sphere is shown in the sequence **6** → **7** → **8** (cyanoethylation followed by esterification). Treating the core compound, **5**, with an excess of the amine, **8**, produced compound **9** with 12 surface ester groups (called, for convenience, the [12]-ester). The key to this step is the formation of amide linkages between **5** and four molecules of **8**. The [12-ester], **9**, was hydrolyzed to the [12]-acid, **10**. Treating **10** with **8** using dicyclohexylcarbodiimide (Section 18.8E) to promote amide formation led to the [36]-ester, **11**. The [36]-ester, **11**, was then hydrolyzed to the [36]-acid **12** which, in turn, was allowed to react with **8** to produce the next cascade molecule, a [108]-ester, **13**.

Repeating these steps one more time produced the [324]-ester, **15**, a compound with a molecular weight of 60,604! At each step the cascade molecules were isolated, purified, and identified. Because the yields for each step are 40–60%, and because the starting materials are inexpensive, this method offers a reasonable route to large homogeneous spherical polymers.

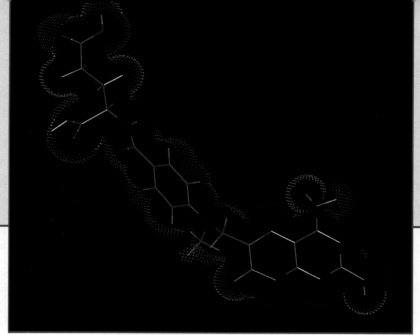

Methotrexate (see Section 19.11C).

CHAPTER

19

AMINES

19.1 NOMENCLATURE

In common nomenclature most primary amines are named as *alkylamines*. In systematic nomenclature (in parentheses below) they are named by adding the suffix -*amine* to the name of the chain or ring system to which the NH_2 group is attached with elision of the final *e*.

Primary Amines

$CH_3\ddot{N}H_2$
Methylamine
(methanamine)

$CH_3CH_2\ddot{N}H_2$
Ethylamine
(ethanamine)

$$CH_3CHCH_2\ddot{N}H_2$$
$$\overset{|}{C}H_3$$
Isobutylamine
(2-methyl-1-propanamine)

⬡—$\ddot{N}H_2$
Cyclohexylamine
(cyclohexanamine)

Most secondary and tertiary amines are named in the same general way. In common nomenclature we either designate the organic groups individually if they are different, or use the prefixes *di-* or *tri-* if they are the same. In systematic nomenclature we use the locant *N* to designate substituents attached to a nitrogen atom.

Secondary Amines

$$CH_3\overset{..}{N}HCH_2CH_3 \qquad (CH_3CH_2)_2\overset{..}{N}H$$

Ethylmethylamine   **Diethylamine**
(*N*-methylethanamine)   (*N*-ethylethanamine)

Tertiary Amines

$$CH_2CH_3$$
$$|$$
$$(CH_3CH_2)_3\overset{..}{N} \qquad CH_3\overset{..}{N}CH_2CH_2CH_3$$

Triethylamine   **Ethylmethylpropylamine**
(*N*,*N*-diethylethanamine)   (*N*-ethyl-*N*-methyl-1-propanamine)

In the IUPAC system, the substituent $-NH_2$ is called the *amino* group. We often use this system for naming amines containing an OH group or a CO_2H group.

$$H_2\overset{..}{N}CH_2CH_2OH \qquad H_2\overset{..}{N}CH_2CH_2\overset{O}{\overset{\|}{C}}OH$$

2-Aminoethanol   **3-Aminopropanoic acid**

19.1A ARYLAMINES

Three common arylamines have the following names:

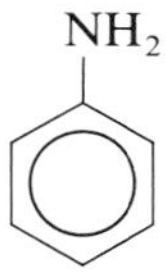

Aniline   *N*-**Methylaniline**   *p*-**Toluidine**
(benzenamine)   (*N*-methyl-   (4-methyl-
            benzenamine)   benzenamine)

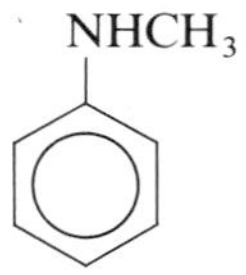

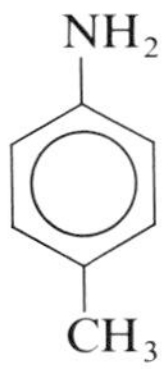

19.1B HETEROCYCLIC AMINES

The important *heterocyclic* amines all have common names. In systematic replacement nomenclature the prefixes *aza-*, *diaza-*, and *triaza-* are used to indicate that nitrogen atoms have replaced carbon atoms in the corresponding hydrocarbon.

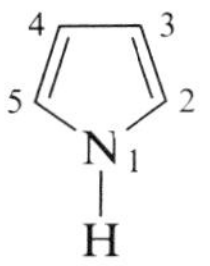

Pyrrole   **Pyrazole**   **Imidazole**   **Indole**
(1-azacyclopenta-   (1,2-diazacyclo-   (1,3-diazacyclo-   (1-azaindene)
2,4-diene)   penta-2,4-diene)   penta-2,4-diene)

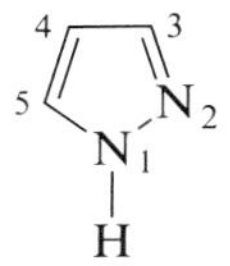

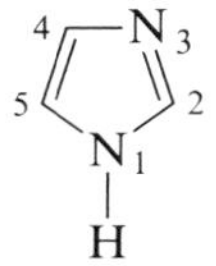

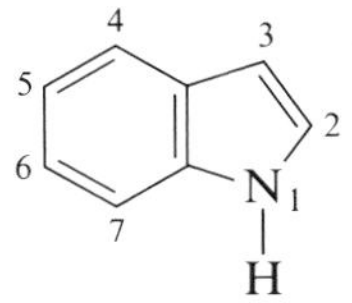

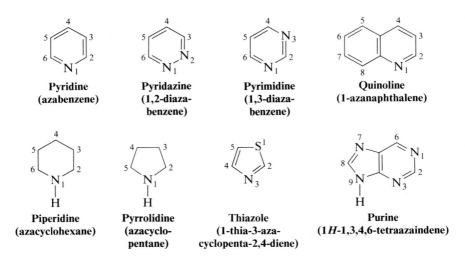

Pyridine
(azabenzene)

Pyridazine
(1,2-diaza-
benzene)

Pyrimidine
(1,3-diaza-
benzene)

Quinoline
(1-azanaphthalene)

Piperidine
(azacyclohexane)

Pyrrolidine
(azacyclo-
pentane)

Thiazole
(1-thia-3-aza-
cyclopenta-2,4-diene)

Purine
(1*H*-1,3,4,6-tetraazaindene)

19.2 PHYSICAL PROPERTIES AND STRUCTURE OF AMINES

19.2A PHYSICAL PROPERTIES

Amines are moderately polar substances; they have boiling points that are higher than those of alkanes but generally lower than those of alcohols of comparable molecular weight. Molecules of primary and secondary amines can form strong hydrogen bonds to each other and to water. Molecules of tertiary amines cannot form hydrogen bonds to each other, but they can form hydrogen bonds to molecules of water or other hydroxylic solvents. As a result, tertiary amines generally boil at lower temperatures than primary and secondary amines of comparable molecular weight, but all low molecular weight amines are very water soluble.

Table 19.1 lists the physical properties of some common amines.

19.2B STRUCTURE OF AMINES

The nitrogen atom of most amines is like that of ammonia; it is approximately sp^3 hybridized. The three alkyl groups (or hydrogen atoms) occupy corners of a tetrahedron; the sp^3 orbital containing the unshared electron pair is directed toward the other corner. We describe the geometry of the amine by the location of the atoms as being **trigonal pyramidal** (Section 1.17). However, if we were to consider the unshared electron pair as being a group we would describe the amine as being tetrahedral.

Structure of an amine

The bond angles are what one would expect of a tetrahedral structure; they are very close to 109.5°. The bond angles for trimethylamine, for example, are 108°.

If the alkyl groups of a tertiary amine are all different the amine will be chiral. There will be two enantiomeric forms of the tertiary amine and, theoretically, we

TABLE 19.1   Physical properties of amines

NAME	STRUCTURE	mp (°C)	bp (°C)	WATER SOLUBILITY (25 °C) (g 100 mL^{-1})	pK_b	pK_a (aminium ion)
Primary Amines						
Methylamine	CH_3NH_2	− 94	−6	Very soluble	3.36	10.64
Ethylamine	$CH_3CH_2NH_2$	− 81	17	Very soluble	3.25	10.75
Propylamine	$CH_3CH_2CH_2NH_2$	− 83	49	Very soluble	3.33	10.67
Isopropylamine	$(CH_3)_2CHNH_2$	−101	33	Very soluble	3.27	10.73
Butylamine	$CH_3(CH_2)_2CH_2NH_2$	− 51	78	Very soluble	3.39	10.61
Isobutylamine	$(CH_3)_2CHCH_2NH_2$	− 86	68	Very soluble	3.51	10.49
sec-Butylamine	$CH_3CH_2CH(CH_3)NH_2$	−104	63	Very soluble	3.44	10.56
tert-Butylamine	$(CH_3)_3CNH_2$	− 68	45	Very soluble	3.55	10.45
Cyclohexylamine	Cyclo-$C_6H_{11}NH_2$	− 18	134	Sl. soluble	3.36	10.64
Benzylamine	$C_6H_5CH_2NH_2$	− 10	185	Sl. soluble	4.70	9.30
Aniline	$C_6H_5NH_2$	− 6	184	3.7	9.42	4.58
p-Toluidine	p-$CH_3C_6H_4NH_2$	44	200	Sl. soluble	8.92	5.08
p-Anisidine	p-$CH_3OC_6H_4NH_2$	57	244	V. sl. soluble	8.70	5.30
p-Chloroaniline	p-$ClC_6H_4NH_2$	73	232	Insoluble	10.00	4.00
p-Nitroaniline	p-$NO_2C_6H_4NH_2$	148	332	Insoluble	13.00	1.00
Secondary Amines						
Dimethylamine	$(CH_3)_2NH$	− 92	7	Very soluble	3.28	10.72
Diethylamine	$(CH_3CH_2)_2NH$	− 48	56	Very soluble	3.02	10.98
Dipropylamine	$(CH_3CH_2CH_2)_2NH$	− 40	110	Very soluble	3.02	10.98
N-Methylaniline	$C_6H_5NHCH_3$	− 57	196	Sl. soluble	9.30	4.70
Diphenylamine	$(C_6H_5)_2NH$	53	302	Insoluble	13.20	0.80
Tertiary Amines						
Trimethylamine	$(CH_3)_3N$	−117	2.9	Very soluble	4.30	9.70
Triethylamine	$(CH_3CH_2)_3N$	−115	90	14	3.24	10.76
Tripropylamine	$(CH_3CH_2CH_2)_3N$	− 93	156	Sl. soluble	3.36	10.64
N,N-Dimethylaniline	$C_6H_5N(CH_3)_2$	3	194	Sl. soluble	8.94	5.06

ought to be able to resolve (separate) these enantiomers. In practice, however, resolution is usually impossible because the enantiomers interconvert rapidly.

Interconversion of amine enantiomers

This interconversion occurs through what is called a **pyramidal or nitrogen inversion.** The barrier to the interconversion is about 6 kcal mol^{-1} for most simple amines. In the transition state for the inversion, the nitrogen atom becomes sp^2 hybridized with the unshared electron pair occupying a p orbital.

Ammonium salts cannot undergo inversion because they do not have an unshared pair. Therefore, those quaternary ammonium salts with four different groups are chiral and can be resolved into separate (relatively stable) enantiomers.

Quaternary ammonium salts such as these
can be resolved

19.3 BASICITY OF AMINES: AMINE SALTS

Amines are relatively weak bases. They are stronger bases than water but are far weaker bases than hydroxide ions, alkoxide ions, and carbanions.

A convenient expression for relating basicities is a quantity called the *basicity constant, K_b,* or its negative logarithm, pK_b. When an amine dissolves in water, the following equilibrium is established:

$$\overset{..}{R}NH_2 + H_2O \rightleftharpoons R\overset{+}{N}H_3 + \overset{-}{O}H$$

K_b and pK_b are given by the expressions:

$$K_b = \frac{[RNH_3{}^+]\,[OH^-]}{[RNH_2]} \qquad pK_b = -\log K_b$$

The larger the value of K_b (or the *smaller* the value of pK_b), the greater is the tendency of the amine to accept a proton from water and, thus, the greater will be the concentrations of $RNH_3{}^+$ and OH^- in the solution. Larger values of K_b, therefore, are associated with those amines that are stronger bases, and smaller values of K_b are associated with those amines that are weaker bases. (Just the opposite is true for values of pK_b.)

The basicity constant of ammonia at 25 °C is 1.8×10^{-5}.

$$\ddot{N}H_3 + H_2O \rightleftharpoons \overset{+}{N}H_4 + OH^-$$

$$K_b = 1.8 \times 10^{-5} = \frac{[NH_4^+][OH^-]}{[NH_3]} \qquad pK_b = -\log(1.8 \times 10^{-5}) = 4.74$$

Another way to compare the base strength of amines is to compare the acidity constants (or pK_a values) of their conjugate acids, the alkylaminium ions (Section 3.3C). The expression for this acidity constant is as follows:

$$R\overset{+}{N}H_3 + H_2O \rightleftharpoons RNH_2 + H_3O^+$$

$$K_a = \frac{[RNH_2][H_3O^+]}{[RNH_3^+]} \qquad pK_a = -\log K_a$$

If the amine is *strongly basic,* the aminium ion will hold the proton tightly and, consequently, will not be very acidic (it will have a large pK_a). On the other hand if the amine is *weakly basic,* the aminium ion will not hold the proton tightly and will be much more acidic (it will have a small pK_a).

Multiplying the expression for the K_b of an amine by the expression for the K_a of its conjugate acid, the alkylaminium ion, yields the expression for the ion product constant of water, which is equal to $1.0 \times 10^{-14} M^2$.

$$K_a K_b = \frac{[RNH_2][H_3O^+]}{[RNH_3^+]} \times \frac{[RNH_3^+][OH^-]}{[RNH_2]} = [H_3O^+][OH^-] = 10^{-14} M^2$$

therefore, $\qquad\qquad K_a K_b = 1.0 \times 10^{-14} M^2$

and $\qquad\qquad\qquad pK_a + pK_b = 14$

When we examine the pK_b values of the amines given in Table 19.1, we see that most primary aliphatic amines (e.g., methylamine and ethylamine) are somewhat stronger bases than ammonia:

	$\ddot{N}H_3$	$CH_3\ddot{N}H_2$	$CH_3CH_2\ddot{N}H_2$	$CH_3CH_2CH_2\ddot{N}H_2$
pK_b	4.74	3.36	3.25	3.33

We can account for this on the basis of the electron-releasing ability of an alkyl group. An alkyl group releases electrons, and it *stabilizes* the alkylaminium ion that results from the acid–base reaction *by dispersing its positive charge.* It stabilizes the alkyl-aminium ion to a greater extent than it stabilizes the amine.

By releasing electrons, R⤳
stabilizes the alkylaminium ion
through dispersal of charge

This explanation is supported by measurements showing that in the *gas phase* the basicities of the following amines increase with increasing methyl substitution:

$$(CH_3)_3N > (CH_3)_2NH > CH_3NH_2 > NH_3$$

This is not the order of basicity of these amines in aqueous solution, however. In aqueous solution (Table 19.1) the order is

$$(CH_3)_2NH > CH_3NH_2 > (CH_3)_3N > NH_3$$

The reason for this apparent anomaly is now known. In aqueous solution the aminium ions formed from secondary and primary amines are stabilized by solvation through hydrogen bonding much more effectively than are the aminium ions formed from tertiary amines. The aminium ion formed from a tertiary amine, $(CH_3)_3NH^+$, has only one hydrogen to use in hydrogen bonding to water molecules, whereas the aminium ions from secondary and primary amines have two and three hydrogens, respectively. Poorer solvation of the aminium ion formed from a tertiary amine more than counteracts the electron-releasing effect of the three methyl groups and makes the tertiary amine less basic than primary and secondary amines in aqueous solution. However, the electron-releasing effect does make the tertiary amine more basic than ammonia.

19.3A BASICITY OF ARYLAMINES

When we examine the pK_b values of the aromatic amines (e.g., aniline and p-toluidine) in Table 19.1, we see that they are much weaker bases than the corresponding nonaromatic amine, cyclohexylamine.

	Cyclo-$C_6H_{11}NH_2$	$C_6H_5NH_2$	p-$CH_3C_6H_4NH_2$
pK_b	3.36	9.42	8.92

We can account for this effect on the basis of resonance contributions to the overall hybrid of an arylamine. For aniline, the following contributors are important.

Structures **1** and **2** are the Kekulé structures that contribute to any benzene derivative. Structures **3–5**, however, *delocalize* the unshared electron pair of the nitrogen over the ortho and para positions of the ring. This delocalization of the electron pair makes it less available to a proton but, more importantly, *delocalization of the electron pair stabilizes aniline.*

When aniline accepts a proton it becomes an anilinium ion.

$$C_6H_5\overset{..}{N}H_2 + H_2O \rightleftharpoons C_6H_5\overset{+}{N}H_3 + \overset{-}{O}H$$

Anilinium ion

Since the electron pair of the nitrogen atom accepts the proton, we are able to write only *two* resonance structures for the anilinium ion — the two Kekulé structures:

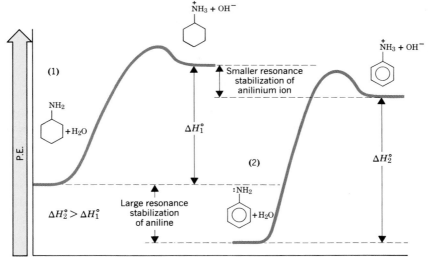

Structures corresponding to **3–5** are not possible for the anilinium ion and, consequently, resonance does not stabilize the anilinium ion to as great an extent as it does
aniline itself. This greater stabilization of the reactant (aniline) when compared to
that of the product (anilinium ion) means that $\Delta H°$ for the reaction,

$$\text{Aniline} + H_2O \longrightarrow \text{anilinium ion} + OH^- \qquad \text{(Fig. 19.1)}$$

will be a larger positive quantity than that for the reaction,

$$\text{Cyclohexylamine} + H_2O \longrightarrow \text{cyclohexylaminium ion} + OH^-$$

Aniline, as a result, is the weaker base.

FIGURE 19.1 Potential energy diagram for the reaction of cyclohexylamine with H_2O (1),
and for the reaction of aniline with H_2O (2). (The curves are aligned for comparison only.)

19.3B AMINES VERSUS AMIDES

Although amides are superficially similar to amines, they are far less basic (even less
basic than arylamines). The pK_b of a typical amide is about 14.

This lower basicity of amides when compared to amines can also be understood
in terms of resonance. An amide is stabilized by resonance involving the nonbonding
pair of electrons on the nitrogen atom. However, an amide protonated on its nitrogen
atom lacks this type of resonance stabilization. This is shown in the resonance
structures on the next page.

Amide

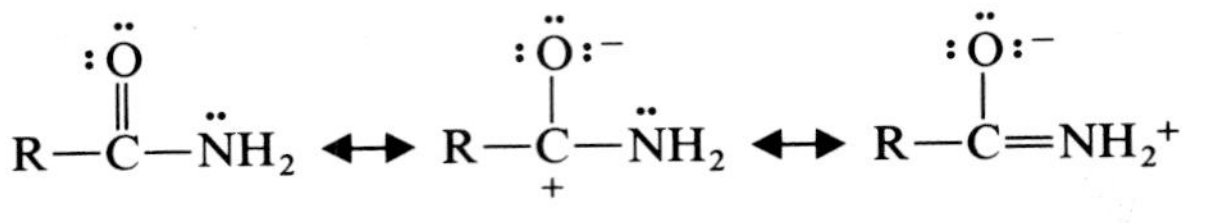

$$R-\overset{\overset{\displaystyle ..}{\overset{\displaystyle O}{\|}}}{C}-\ddot{N}H_2 \longleftrightarrow R-\overset{\overset{\displaystyle ..}{\overset{\displaystyle :\ddot{O}:^-}{|}}}{\underset{+}{C}}-\ddot{N}H_2 \longleftrightarrow R-\overset{\overset{\displaystyle ..}{\overset{\displaystyle :\ddot{O}:^-}{|}}}{C}=NH_2^+ \qquad \text{Larger resonance stabilization}$$

N-Protonated Amide

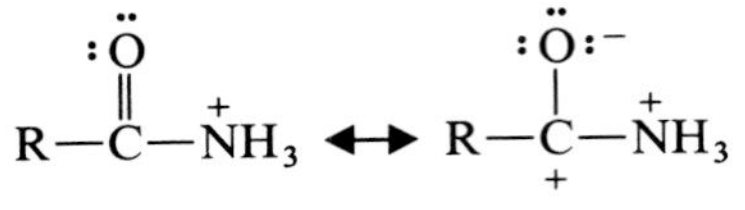

$$R-\overset{\overset{\displaystyle ..}{\overset{\displaystyle O}{\|}}}{C}-\overset{+}{N}H_3 \longleftrightarrow R-\overset{\overset{\displaystyle ..}{\overset{\displaystyle :\ddot{O}:^-}{|}}}{\underset{+}{C}}-\overset{+}{N}H_3 \qquad \text{Smaller resonance stabilization}$$

However, a more important factor accounting for amides being weaker bases than amines is the powerful electron-withdrawing effect of the carbonyl group of the amide. This means that the equilibrium for the following reaction,

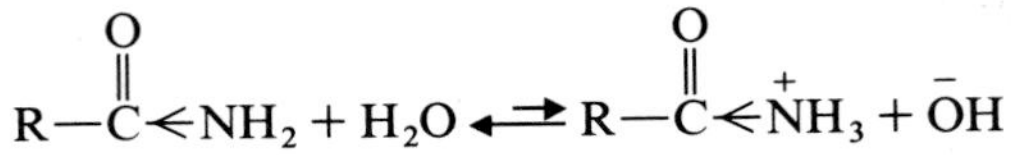

$$R-\overset{\overset{\displaystyle O}{\|}}{C}\!\!\prec\!NH_2 + H_2O \rightleftharpoons R-\overset{\overset{\displaystyle O}{\|}}{C}\!\!\prec\!\overset{+}{N}H_3 + \bar{O}H$$

lies more to the left than that for the reaction,

$$R\!\!\succ\!\ddot{N}H_2 + H_2O \rightleftharpoons R\!\!\succ\!\overset{+}{N}H_3 + \bar{O}H$$

and explains why the amide is the weaker base.

The nitrogen atoms of amides are so weakly basic that when an amide accepts a proton, it does so on its oxygen atom instead. Protonation on the oxygen atom occurs even though oxygen atoms (because of their greater electronegativity) are typically less basic than nitrogen atoms. Notice, however, that if an amide accepts a proton on its oxygen atom, resonance stabilization involving the nonbonding electron pair of the nitrogen atom is possible.

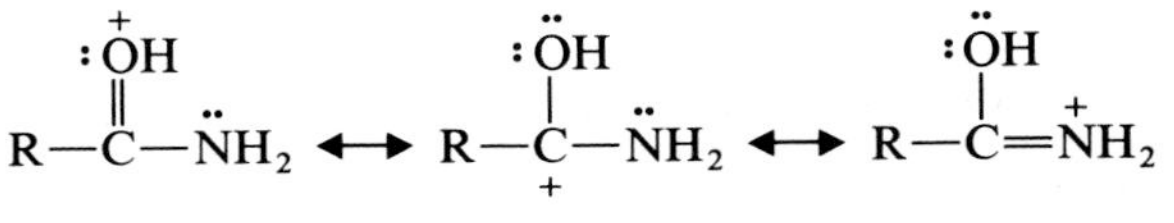

$$R-\overset{\overset{\displaystyle +}{\overset{\displaystyle :\ddot{O}H}{\|}}}{C}-\ddot{N}H_2 \longleftrightarrow R-\overset{\overset{\displaystyle ..}{\overset{\displaystyle :\ddot{O}H}{|}}}{\underset{+}{C}}-\ddot{N}H_2 \longleftrightarrow R-\overset{\overset{\displaystyle ..}{\overset{\displaystyle :\ddot{O}H}{|}}}{C}=\overset{+}{N}H_2$$

19.3C AMINIUM SALTS AND QUATERNARY AMMONIUM SALTS

When primary, secondary, and tertiary amines act as bases and react with acids, they form compounds called **aminium salts**. In an aminium salt the positively charged nitrogen atom is attached to at least one hydrogen atom.

$$CH_3CH_2\ddot{N}H_2 + HCl \xrightarrow{H_2O} CH_3CH_2\overset{+}{N}H_3 \quad Cl^-$$
Ethylaminium chloride
(an amine salt)

$$(CH_3CH_2)_2\ddot{N}H + HBr \xrightarrow{H_2O} (CH_3CH_2)_2\overset{+}{N}H_2 \quad Br^-$$
Diethylaminium bromide

$$(CH_3CH_2)_3\ddot{N} + HI \xrightarrow{H_2O} (CH_3CH_2)_3\overset{+}{N}H \quad I^-$$
Triethylaminium iodide

19.3 BASICITY OF AMINES: AMINE SALTS

When the central nitrogen atom of a compound is positively charged *but is not attached to a hydrogen atom* the compound is called a **quaternary ammonium salt.** For example,

$$CH_3CH_2 \overset{\overset{\displaystyle CH_2CH_3}{|}}{\underset{\underset{\displaystyle CH_2CH_3}{|}}{N^+}} CH_2CH_3 \quad Br^-$$

Tetraethylammonium bromide
(a quaternary ammonium salt)

Quaternary ammonium halides—because they do not have an unshared electron pair on the nitrogen atom—cannot act as bases.

$$(CH_3CH_2)_4\overset{+}{N} \quad Br^-$$

Tetraethylammonium bromide
(does not undergo reaction with acid)

Quaternary ammonium *hydroxides,* however, are strong bases. As solids, or in solution, they consist *entirely* of quaternary ammonium cations (R_4N^+) and hydroxide ions (OH^-); they are, therefore, strong bases—as strong as sodium or potassium hydroxide. Quaternary ammonium hydroxides react with acids to form quaternary ammonium salts:

$$(CH_3)_4\overset{+}{N} \quad OH^- + HCl \longrightarrow (CH_3)_4\overset{+}{N} \quad Cl^- + H_2O$$

Almost all alkylaminium chlorides, bromides, iodides, and sulfates are soluble in water. Thus, primary, secondary, or tertiary amines that are not soluble in water will dissolve in dilute aqueous HCl, HBr, HI, or H_2SO_4. Solubility in dilute acid provides a convenient chemical method for distinguishing amines from nonbasic compounds that are insoluble in water. Solubility in dilute acid also gives us a useful method for separating amines from nonbasic compounds that are insoluble in water.

$$\overset{\diagdown}{\underset{\diagup}{N}} : \quad + \quad \underset{\text{(or } H_2SO_4)}{HX} \quad \longrightarrow \quad \overset{\diagdown}{\underset{\diagup}{N}}\overset{+}{-}H \quad \underset{\text{(or } HSO_4^-)}{X^-}$$

Water-insoluble   **Water-soluble**
amine   **aminium salt**

Because amides are far less basic than amines, water-insoluble amides *do not dissolve* in dilute aqueous HCl, HBr, HI, or H_2SO_4.

$$R \overset{\overset{\displaystyle O}{\|}}{-}C - NH_2$$

Water-insoluble amide
(not soluble in aqueous acids)

Problem 19.1

Outline a procedure for separating hexylamine from cyclohexane using dilute HCl, aqueous NaOH, and diethyl ether.

Problem 19.2

Outline a procedure for separating a mixture of benzoic acid, *p*-cresol, aniline, and benzene using acids, bases, and organic solvents.

19.3D AMINES AS RESOLVING AGENTS

Enantiomerically pure amines are often used to resolve racemic forms of acidic compounds. We can illustrate the principles involved in this procedure by showing how a racemic form of an organic acid might be resolved (separated) into its enantiomers with the single enantiomer of an amine (Fig. 19.2) used as a resolving agent.

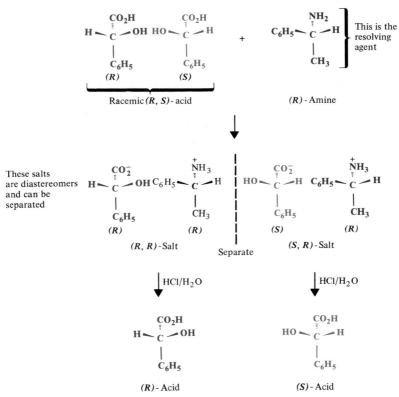

FIGURE 19.2 The resolution of the racemic form of an organic acid by the use of an optically active amine. Acidification of the separated diastereomeric salts causes the enantiomeric acids to precipitate (assuming they are insoluble in water) and leaves the resolving agent in solution as its conjugate acid.

In this procedure the single enantiomer of an amine (*R*)-1-phenylethylamine is added to a solution of the racemic form of an acid. The salts that form are not enantiomers. They are diastereomers. (The stereocenters of the acid portion of the salts are enantiomerically related to each other, but the stereocenters of the amine portion are not.) The diastereomers have different solubilities and can be separated by careful crystallization. The separated salts are then acidified with hydrochloric acid and the enantiomeric acids are obtained from the separate solutions. The amine remains in solution as its hydrochloride salt.

Single enantiomers that are employed as resolving agents are often readily available from natural sources. Because most of the chiral organic molecules that occur in living organisms are synthesized by enzymatically catalyzed reactions, most of them occur as single enantiomers. Naturally occurring optically active amines such as (−)-quinine (Section 19.4), (−)-strychnine, and (−)-brucine are often employed as resolving agents for racemic acids. Acids such as (+)- or (−)-tartaric acid (Section 5.13) are often used for resolving racemic bases.

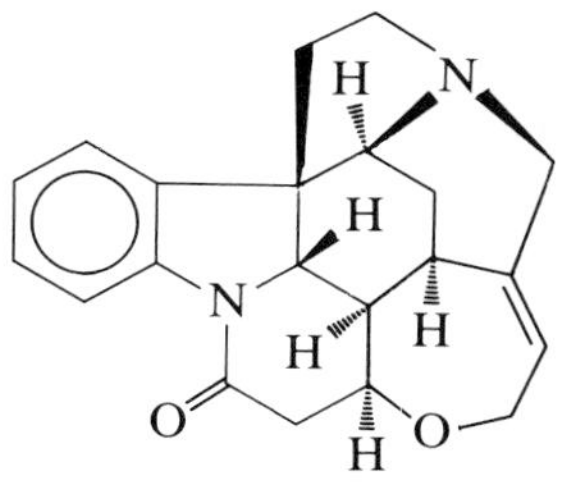

(−)-**Strychnine** 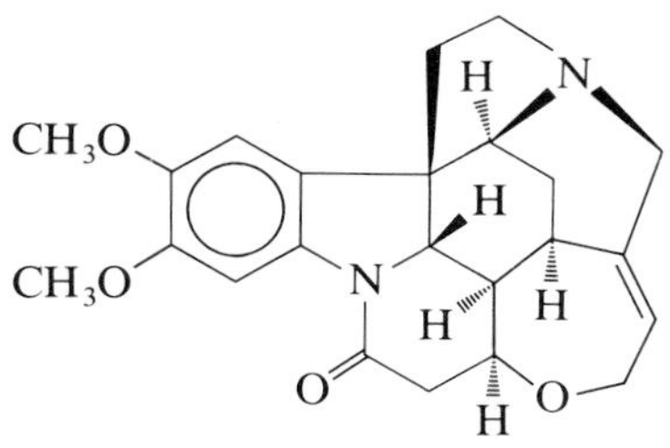   (−)-**Brucine**

One of the newest techniques for resolving racemates is based on high-performance liquid chromatography (HPLC) using a **chiral stationary phase** (CSP). This technique, developed by William H. Pirkle of the University of Illinois, has been used to separate many amines, alcohols, amino acids, and related compounds. We do not have the space here to discuss this technique in detail,* but suffice it to say that a solution of the racemate is passed through a column (called a **Pirkle column**) containing small silica microporous beads. Chemically attached to the surface of the beads is a chiral group such as the one that follows:

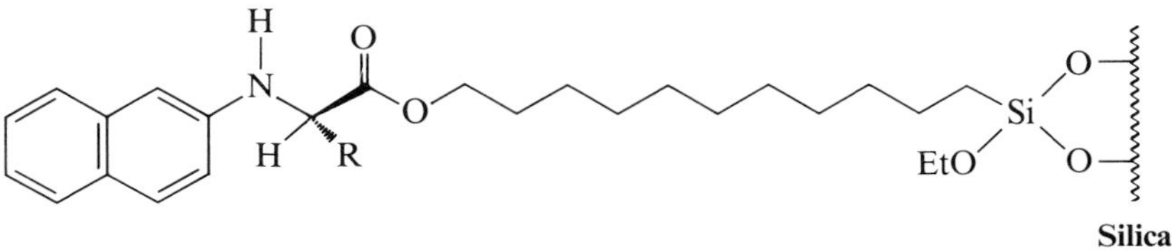

Silica

The compound to be resolved is first converted to a derivative containing a 3,5-dinitrophenyl group. An amine, for example, is converted to a 3,5-dinitrobenzamide:

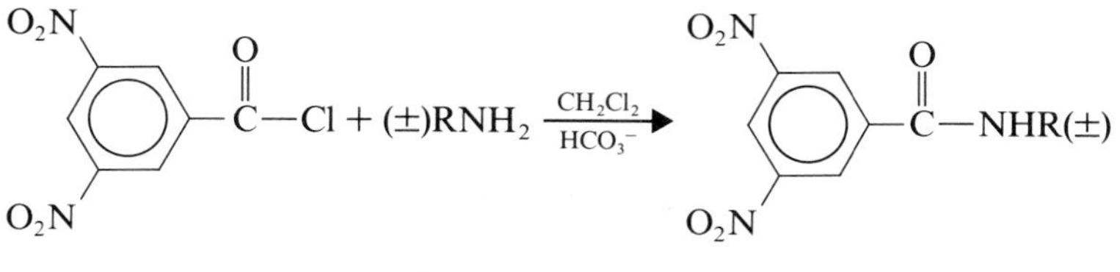

An alcohol is converted to a carbamate (Section 18.10A) through a variation of the Curtius rearrangement (Section 19.5E):

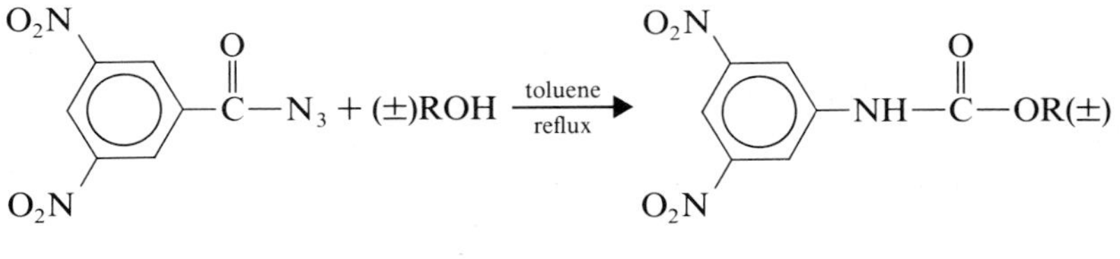

* You may want to consult a laboratory manual or read the following article: W. H. Pirkle, T. C. Pochapsky, G. S. Mahler, D. E. Corey, D. S. Reno, and D. M. Alessi, *J. Org. Chem.,* **1986,** *51,* 4991.

The stationary phase, because it is chiral, binds one enantiomer much more tightly than the other. This binding increases the retention time of that enantiomer and permits separation. The binding comes partially from hydrogen-bonding interactions between the derivative and the CSP, but highly important is a $\pi-\pi$ interaction between the electron-deficient 3,5-dinitrophenyl ring of the derivative and the electron-rich naphthalene ring of the CSP.

19.4 SOME BIOLOGICALLY IMPORTANT AMINES

A large number of medically and biologically important compounds are amines. Listed here are some important examples.

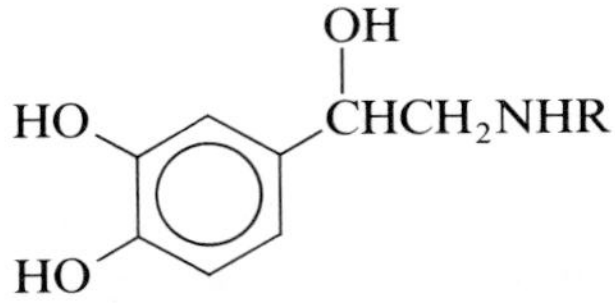

R = CH₃, Adrenaline (epinephrine)
R = H, Noradrenaline (norepinephrine)

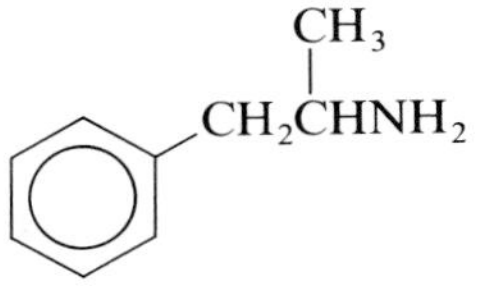

Amphetamine (benzedrine)

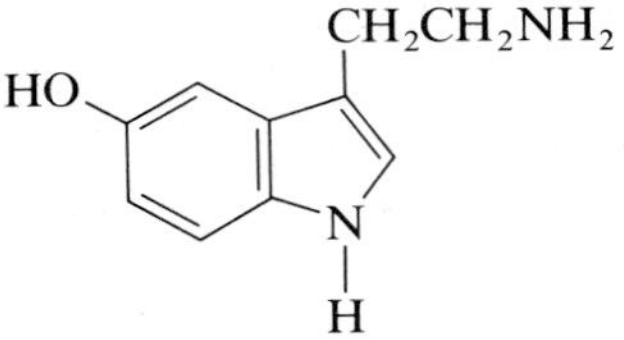

Serotonin

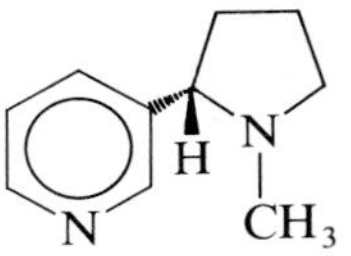

Nicotine

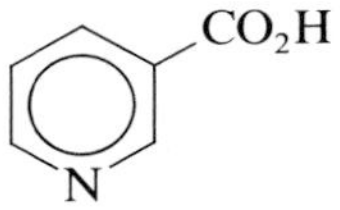

Nicotinic acid (niacin)

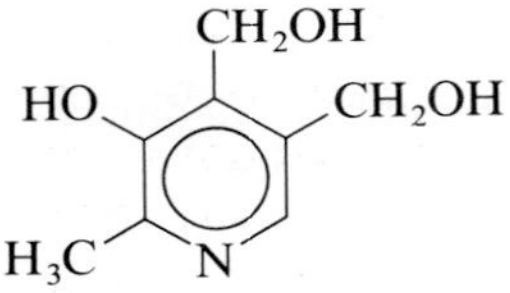

Pyridoxine (vitamin B₆)

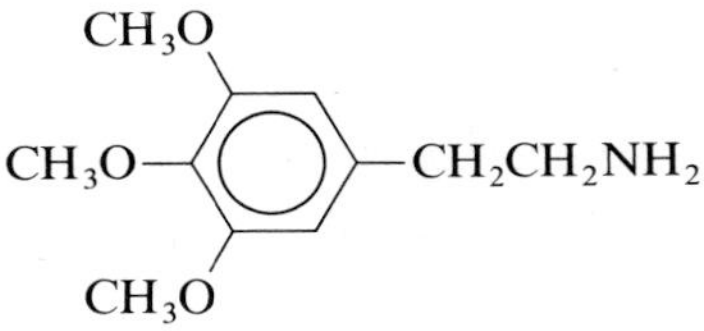

Mescaline

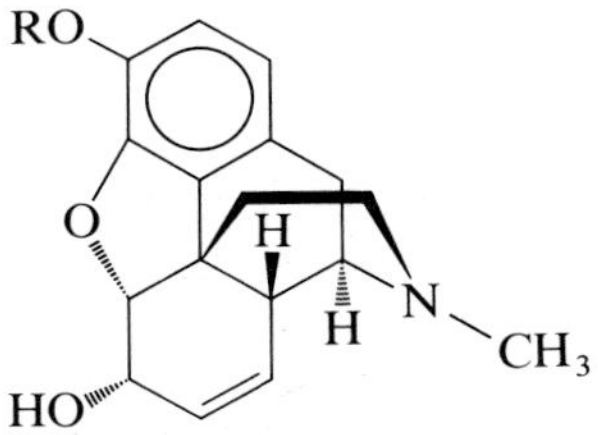

Morphine (R = H)
Codeine (R = CH₃)

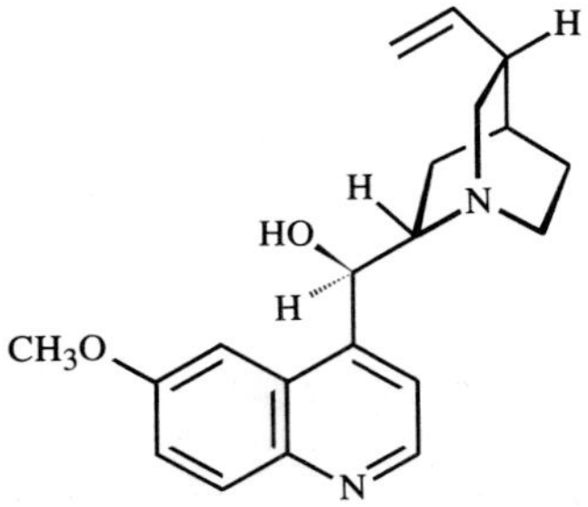

(−)-Quinine

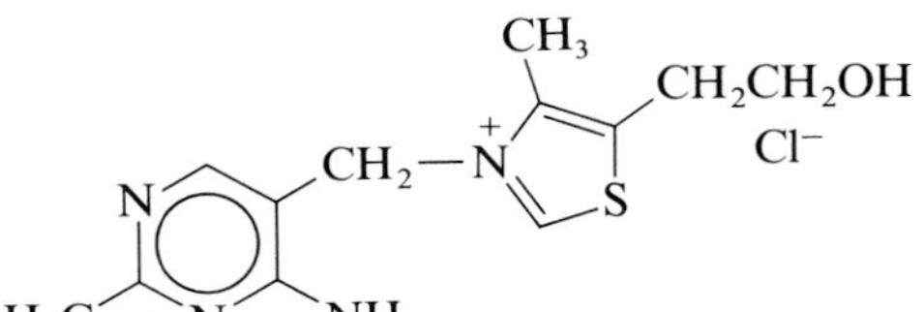

Thiamine chloride (vitamin B₁)

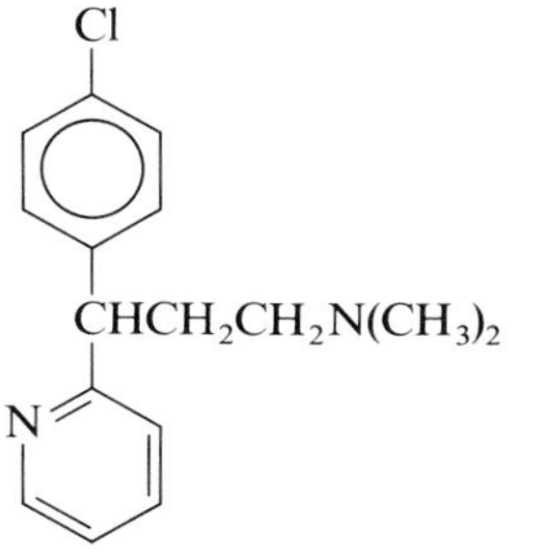

19.4 SOME BIOLOGICALLY IMPORTANT AMINES

Chlorpheniramine

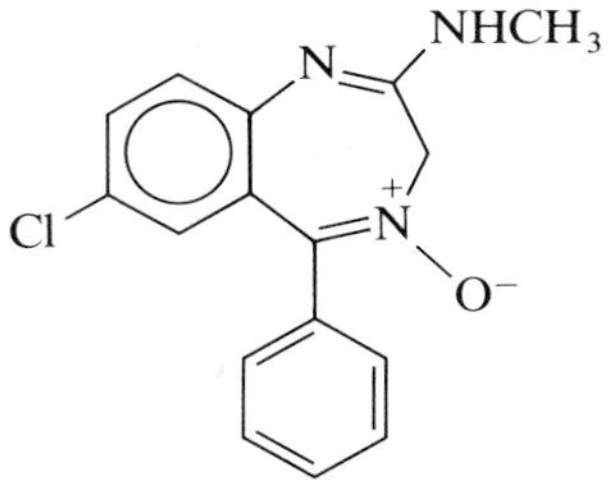

Chlorodiazepoxide (librium)

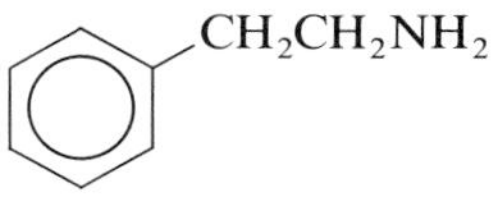

2-Phenylethylamine

Many of these compounds have powerful physiological and psychological effects. Adrenaline and noradrenaline are two hormones secreted in the medulla of the adrenal gland. Released into the bloodstream when an animal senses danger, adrenaline causes an increase in blood pressure, a strengthening of the heart rate, and a widening of the passages of the lungs. All of these effects prepare the animal to fight or flee. Noradrenaline also causes an increase in blood pressure, and it is involved in the transmission of impulses from the end of one nerve fiber to the next. Serotonin is a compound of particular interest because it appears to be important in maintaining stable mental processes. It has been suggested that the mental disorder schizophrenia may be connected with abnormalities in the metabolism of serotonin.

Amphetamine (a powerful stimulant) and mescaline (a hallucinogen) have structures similar to those of serotonin, adrenaline, and noradrenaline. They are all derivatives of 2-phenylethylamine (see following structure). (In serotonin the nitrogen is connected to the benzene ring to create a five-membered ring.) The structural similarities of these compounds must be related to their physiological and psychological effects because many other compounds with similar properties are also derivatives of 2-phenylethylamine. Examples (not shown) are N-methylamphetamine and LSD. Even morphine and codeine, two powerful analgesics, have a 2-phenylethylamine system as a part of their structures. (Morphine and codeine are examples of compounds called alkaloids, which are discussed in more detail in Special Topic H. Try to locate the 2-phenylethylamine system in their structures now, however.)

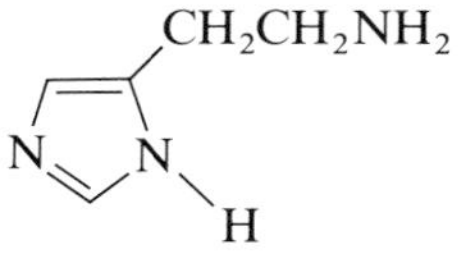

Histamine

A number of amines are vitamins. These include nicotinic acid and nicotinamide (the antipellagra factors), pyridoxine (vitamin B_6), and thiamine chloride (vitamin B_1). Nicotine is a toxic alkaloid found in tobacco that makes smoking habit forming. Histamine, another toxic amine, is found bound to proteins in nearly all tissues of the body. Release of free histamine causes the symptoms associated with allergic reactions and the common cold. Chlorpheniramine, an "antihistamine," is an ingredient of many over-the-counter cold remedies.

Chlorodiazepoxide, an interesting compound with a seven-membered ring, is one of the most widely prescribed tranquilizers. (Chlorodiazepoxide also contains a positively charged nitrogen, present as an N-oxide.)

Acetylcholine and choline (see following reaction) contain a quaternary ammonium group. Being small and ionic, both compounds are highly soluble in water. Acetylcholine is vital in the process by which impulses are transmitted across junctions between nerves in muscles. After acetylcholine is released by the nerve and moves to a receptor site, contraction of the muscle is stimulated. For the muscle to contract again, the acetylcholine must be removed. This is done by an enzyme, cholinesterase, which hydrolyzes acetylcholine to choline and acetic acid (or acetate ion).

$$\overset{+}{(CH_3)_3}NCH_2CH_2O\overset{O}{\overset{\|}{C}}CH_3 + H_2O \xrightarrow{\text{cholinesterase}} \overset{+}{(CH_3)_3}NCH_2CH_2OH + CH_3CO_2H$$

$$\text{Acetylcholine} \qquad\qquad\qquad\qquad\qquad \text{Choline}$$

The group that binds acetylcholine to the enzyme is the quaternary ammonium group $\overset{+}{(CH_3)_3}NCH_2-$. Other compounds that have this grouping can inhibit cholinesterase. Included among them are compounds used in surgery as muscle relaxants:

$$\overset{+}{(CH_3)_3}NCH_2CH_2CH_2CH_2CH_2CH_2CH_2CH_2CH_2CH_2\overset{+}{N}(CH_3)_3 \quad 2\ Br^-$$

$$\text{Decamethonium bromide*}$$

$$\overset{+}{(CH_3)_3}NCH_2CH_2O\overset{O}{\overset{\|}{C}}CH_2CH_2\overset{O}{\overset{\|}{C}}OCH_2CH_2\overset{+}{N}(CH_3)_3 \quad 2\ Br^-$$

$$\text{Succinylcholine bromide*}$$

Decamethonium bromide has a relatively long-lasting effect. Succinylcholine bromide, because it is an ester and can be hydrolyzed, has a muscle-relaxing effect of much shorter duration.

19.5 PREPARATION OF AMINES

19.5A THROUGH NUCLEOPHILIC SUBSTITUTION REACTIONS

Salts of primary amines can be prepared from ammonia and alkyl halides by nucleophilic substitution reactions. Subsequent treatment of the resulting aminium salts with base gives primary amines.

$$\overset{..}{N}H_3 + R-X \longrightarrow R-\overset{+}{N}H_3X^- \xrightarrow{OH^-} RNH_2$$

This method is of very limited synthetic application because multiple alkylations occur. When ethyl bromide reacts with ammonia, for example, the ethylammonium bromide that is produced initially can react with ammonia to liberate ethylamine. Ethylamine can then compete with ammonia and react with ethyl bromide to give diethylammonium bromide. Repetitions of acid–base and alkylation reactions ultimately produce some tertiary amines and even some quaternary ammonium salts if the alkyl halide is present in excess.

*These names are nonsystematic names.

$$\ddot{N}H_3 + CH_3CH_2\overset{\frown}{-}Br \longrightarrow CH_3CH_2 \overset{+}{-} NH_3 + Br^-$$

$$CH_3CH_2 \overset{H \leftarrow}{\underset{H}{-\overset{|}{N}\overset{+}{-}H}} + :NH_3 \longrightarrow CH_3CH_2\ddot{N}H_2 + \overset{+}{N}H_4$$

$$CH_3CH_2\ddot{N}H_2 + CH_3CH_2\overset{\frown}{-}Br \longrightarrow (CH_3CH_2)_2\overset{+}{N}H_2 + Br^- \text{ etc.}$$

Multiple alkylations can be minimized by using a large excess of ammonia. (Why?) An example of this technique can be seen in the synthesis of alanine from 2-bromopropanoic acid:

$$\underset{\substack{Br \\ \textbf{(1 mol)}}}{CH_3CHCO_2H} + \underset{\textbf{(70 mol)}}{NH_3} \longrightarrow \underset{\substack{NH_2 \\ \textbf{Alanine} \\ \textbf{(65–70\%)}}}{CH_3CHCO_2^-NH_4^+}$$

A much better method for preparing a primary amine from an alkyl halide is first to convert the alkyl halide to an alkyl azide ($R-N_3$) by a nucleophilic substitution reaction:

$$R-X + N_3^- \xrightarrow[(-X^-)]{S_N2} R-\overset{+}{N}=\overset{}{N}=\overset{-}{N} \xrightarrow[\substack{or \\ LiAlH_4}]{Na/alcohol} RNH_2$$

Azide   **Alkyl**

ion   **azide**

Then the alkyl azide can be reduced to a primary amine with sodium and alcohol or with lithium aluminum hydride. A word of *caution:* Alkyl azides are explosive and low molecular weight alkyl azides should not be isolated but should be kept in solution.

Potassium phthalimide (see following reaction) can also be used to prepare primary amines by a method known as the *Gabriel synthesis.* This synthesis also avoids the complications of multiple alkylations that occur when alkyl halides are treated with ammonia:

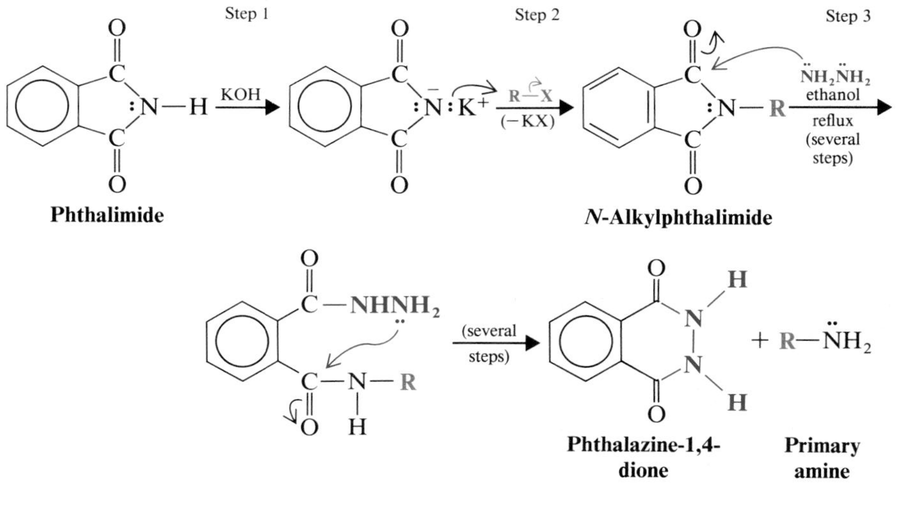

Phthalimide is quite acidic ($pK_a = 9$); it can be converted to potassium phthalimide by potassium hydroxide (step 1). The phthalimide anion is a strong nucleophile and (in step 2) it reacts with an alkyl halide to give an N-alkylphthalimide. At this point, the N-alkylphthalimide can be hydrolyzed with aqueous acid or base, but the hydrolysis is often difficult. It is often more convenient to treat the N-alkylphthalimide with hydrazine (NH_2NH_2) in refluxing ethanol (step 3) to give a primary amine and phthalazine-1,4-dione.

Syntheses of amines using the Gabriel synthesis are, as we might expect, restricted to the use of methyl, primary, and secondary alkyl halides. The use of tertiary halides leads almost exclusively to eliminations.

Problem 19.3

(a) Write resonance structures for the phthalimide anion that will account for the acidity of phthalimide. (b) Would you expect phthalimide to be more or less acidic than benzamide? Why?

Problem 19.4

Outline a preparation of benzylamine using the Gabriel synthesis.

Multiple alkylations are not a problem when tertiary amines are alkylated with methyl or primary halides. Reactions such as the following take place in good yield.

$$R_3\overset{\frown}{N:} + \overset{\frown}{RCH_2}\overset{\frown}{-Br} \longrightarrow R_3\overset{+}{N}-CH_2R \ Br^-$$

19.5B PREPARATION OF AMINES THROUGH REDUCTION OF NITRO COMPOUNDS

The most widely used method for preparing aromatic amines involves nitration of the ring and subsequent reduction of the nitro group to an amino group.

$$Ar-H \xrightarrow[H_2SO_4]{HNO_3} Ar-NO_2 \xrightarrow{[H]} Ar-NH_2$$

We studied ring nitration in Chapter 15 and saw there that it is applicable to a wide variety of aromatic compounds. Reduction of the nitro group can also be carried out in a number of ways. The most frequently used methods employ catalytic hydrogenation, or treatment of the nitro compound with acid and iron. (Zinc, or tin, or a metal salt such as $SnCl_2$ can also be used.)

$$Ar-NO_2 \xrightarrow[\text{or} \quad (1) \text{ Fe, HCl} \quad (2) \text{ OH}^-]{H_2, \text{ cat.}} Ar-NH_2$$

Specific Example

(97%)

19.5 PREPARATION OF AMINES

Selective reduction of one nitro group of a dinitro compound can often be achieved through the use of hydrogen sulfide in aqueous (or alcoholic) ammonia:

m-Dinitrobenzene   *m*-Nitroaniline
(70–80%)

When this method is used, the amount of the hydrogen sulfide must be carefully measured because the use of an excess may result in the reduction of more than one nitro group.

It is not always possible to predict just which nitro group will be reduced, however. Treating 2,4-dinitrotoluene with hydrogen sulfide and ammonia results in reduction of the 4-nitro group:

On the other hand, monoreduction of 2,4-dinitroaniline causes reduction of the 2-nitro group:

(52–58%)

19.5C PREPARATION OF AMINES THROUGH REDUCTIVE AMINATION

Aldehydes and ketones can be converted to amines through catalytic or chemical reduction in the presence of ammonia or an amine. Primary, secondary, and tertiary amines can be prepared this way:

This process, called *reductive amination* of the aldehyde or ketone (or *reductive alkylation* of the amine), appears to proceed through the following general mechanism (illustrated with a 1° amine):

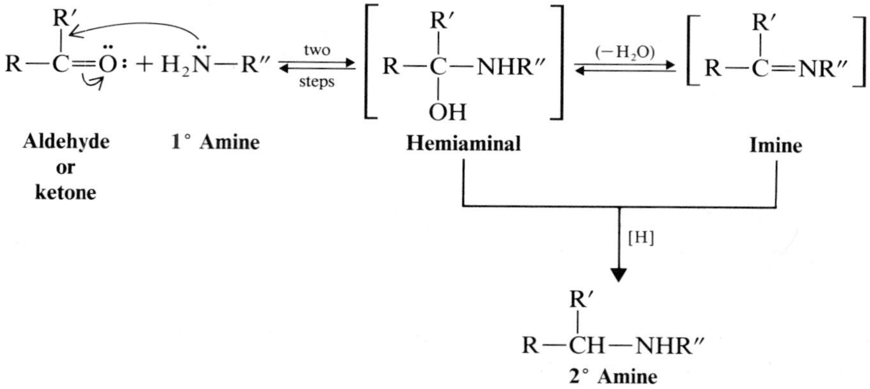

$$R-\overset{R'}{\underset{}{C}}{=}\overset{..}{O}{:} + H_2\overset{..}{N}-R'' \underset{\text{steps}}{\overset{\text{two}}{\rightleftharpoons}} \left[R-\overset{R'}{\underset{OH}{C}}-NHR'' \right] \overset{(-H_2O)}{\rightleftharpoons} \left[R-\overset{R'}{\underset{}{C}}{=}NR'' \right]$$

| Aldehyde or ketone | 1° Amine | Hemiaminal | Imine |

$$\downarrow [H]$$

$$R-\overset{R'}{\underset{}{CH}}-NHR''$$

2° Amine

When ammonia or a primary amine is used, there are two possible pathways to the product — via an amino alcohol that is similar to a hemiacetal and is called a *hemiaminal,* or via an imine. When secondary amines are used, an imine cannot form and, therefore, the pathway is through the hemiaminal or through an iminium ion.

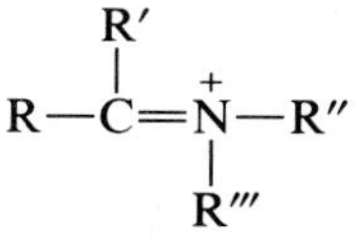

$$R-\overset{R'}{\underset{R'''}{C}}{=}\overset{+}{N}-R''$$

Iminium ion

The reducing agents employed include hydrogen and a catalyst (such as nickel), or $NaBH_3CN$ or $LiBH_3CN$. The latter two reducing agents are similar to $NaBH_4$ and are especially effective in reductive aminations. Three specific examples of reductive amination follow:

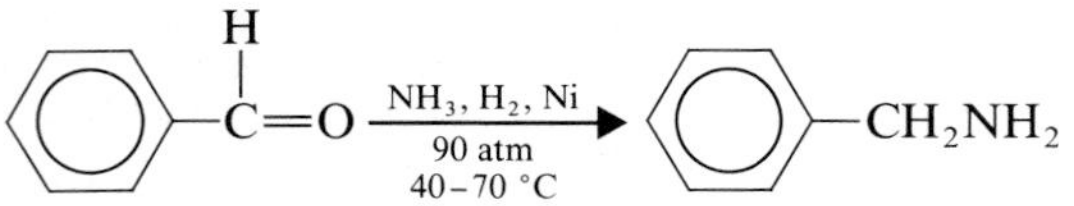

Benzaldehyde $\xrightarrow[\substack{90 \text{ atm} \\ 40-70 \text{ °C}}]{NH_3, H_2, Ni}$ **Benzylamine** $-CH_2NH_2$ **(89%)**

Benzaldehyde $\xrightarrow[LiBH_3CN]{CH_3CH_2NH_2}$ **N-Benzylethanamine** $-CH_2-NHCH_2CH_3$ **(89%)**

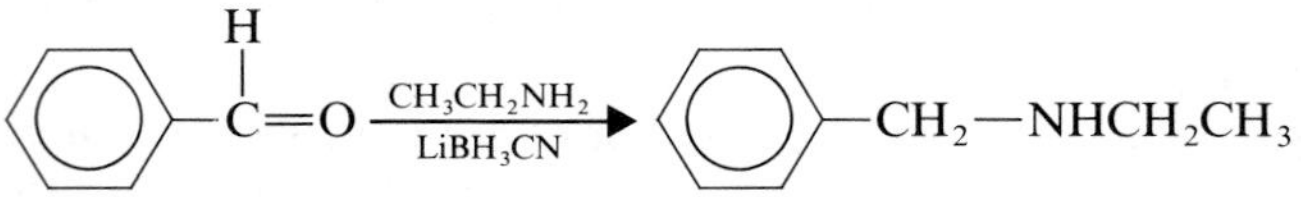

Cyclohexanone $\xrightarrow[NaBH_3CN]{(CH_3)_2NH}$ **N,N-Dimethylcyclohexanamine** $-N\underset{CH_3}{\overset{CH_3}{<}}$ **(52–54%)**

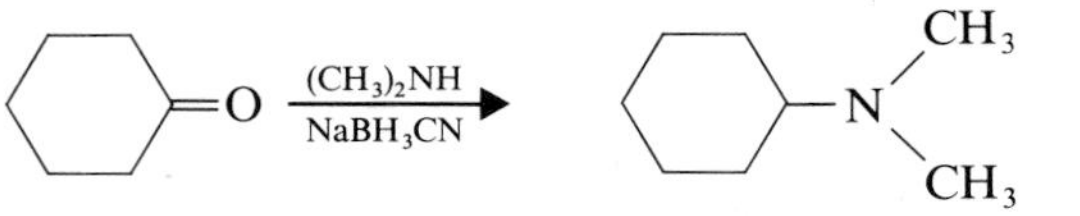

Problem 19.5

Show how you might prepare each of the following amines through reductive amination:

(a) $CH_3(CH_2)_3CH_2NH_2$ (c) $CH_3(CH_2)_4CH_2NHC_6H_5$

(b) $C_6H_5CH_2CHCH_3$ (d) $C_6H_5CH_2N(CH_3)_2$
         |
        NH_2

(amphetamine)

Problem 19.6

Reductive amination of a ketone is almost always a better method for the

               R'
                |

preparation of amines of the type $RCHNH_2$ than treatment of an alkyl halide with ammonia. Why would this be true?

19.5D PREPARATION OF AMINES THROUGH REDUCTION OF AMIDES, OXIMES, AND NITRILES

Amides, oximes, and nitriles can be reduced to amines. Reduction of a nitrile or an oxime yields a primary amine; reduction of an amide can yield a primary, secondary, or tertiary amine.

$$R-C\equiv N \xrightarrow{[H]} RCH_2NH_2$$

Nitrile   **1° Amine**

> Nitriles can be prepared from alkyl halides and CN^- (Section 18.3) or from aldehydes and ketones as cyanohydrins (Section 16.9A)

$$RCH=NOH \xrightarrow{[H]} RCH_2NH_2$$

Oxime   **1° Amine**

> Oximes can be prepared from aldehydes and ketones (Section 16.8A)

$$R-\overset{\overset{\displaystyle O}{\|}}{C}-\underset{\underset{\displaystyle R''}{|}}{N}-R' \xrightarrow{[H]} RCH_2\underset{\underset{\displaystyle R''}{|}}{N}-R'$$

Amide   **3° Amine**

> Amides can be prepared from acid chlorides, acid anhydrides, and esters (Section 18.8)

(In the last example, if R' and R'' = H, the product is a 1° amine; if R' = H, the product is a 2° amine.)

All of these reductions can be carried out with hydrogen and a catalyst or with $LiAlH_4$. Oximes are also conveniently reduced with sodium in alcohol—a safer method than the use of $LiAlH_4$.

Specific examples follow:

$$\text{\Large$\bigcirc$}=N-OH \xrightarrow{Na,\ C_2H_5OH} \text{\Large$\bigcirc$}-NH_2$$

(50–60%)

2-Phenylethanenitrile
(phenylacetonitrile)

2-Phenylethylamine
(71%)

N-Methylacetanilide

N-Ethyl-*N*-methylaniline

Reduction of an amide is the last step in a useful procedure for **monoalkylation of an amine.** The process begins with *acylation* of the amine using an acyl chloride or acid anhydride; then the amide is reduced with lithium aluminum hydride. For example,

$$C_6H_5CH_2NH_2 \xrightarrow[base]{CH_3COCl} C_6H_5CH_2NHCCH_3 \xrightarrow[(2)\ H_2O]{(1)\ LiAlH_4,\ diethyl\ ether} C_6H_5CH_2NHCH_2CH_3$$

Benzylamine

Benzylethylamine

Problem 19.7

Show how you might utilize the reduction of an amide, oxime, or nitrile to carry out each of the following transformations:

(a) Benzoic acid ⟶ benzylethylamine

(b) 1-Bromopentane ⟶ hexylamine

(c) Propanoic acid ⟶ tripropylamine

(d) 2-Butanone ⟶ *sec*-butylamine

19.5E PREPARATION OF AMINES THROUGH THE HOFMANN AND CURTIUS REARRANGEMENTS

Amides with no substituent on the nitrogen react with solutions of bromine or chlorine in sodium hydroxide to yield amines through a reaction known as the *Hofmann rearrangement* or *Hofmann degradation:*

$$R-\overset{O}{\overset{\|}{C}}-NH_2 + Br_2 + 4\ NaOH \xrightarrow{H_2O} RNH_2 + 2\ NaBr + Na_2CO_3 + 2\ H_2O$$

From this equation we can see that the carbonyl carbon atom of the amide is lost (as CO_3^{2-}) and that the R group of the amide becomes attached to the nitrogen of the amine. Primary amines made this way are not contaminated by 2° or 3° amines.

The mechanism for this interesting reaction is shown in Fig. 19.3. In the first two steps the amide undergoes a base-promoted bromination, in a manner analogous to the base-promoted halogenation of a ketone that we studied in Section 17.3B. (The electron-withdrawing acyl group of the amide makes the amido protons much more acidic than those of an amine.) The *N*-bromo amide then reacts with hydroxide ion to

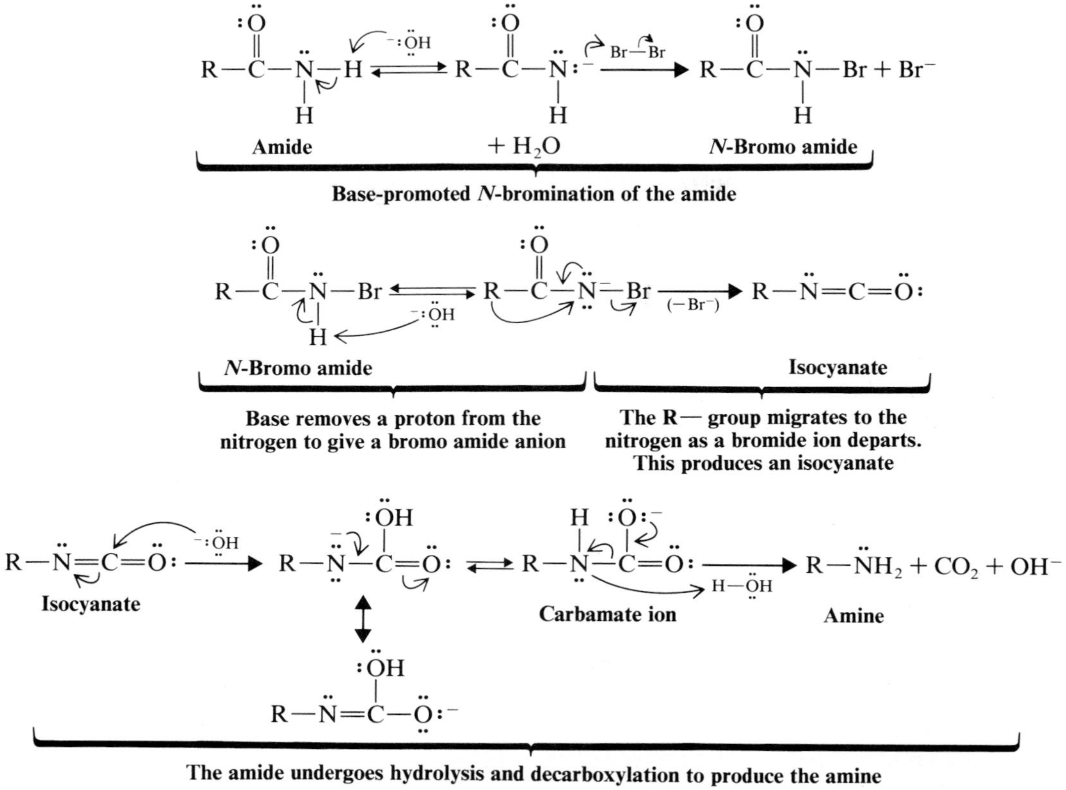

19.5 PREPARATION OF AMINES

Base-promoted N-bromination of the amide

N-Bromo amide   **Isocyanate**

Base removes a proton from the nitrogen to give a bromo amide anion   The R— group migrates to the nitrogen as a bromide ion departs. This produces an isocyanate

Isocyanate   **Carbamate ion**   **Amine**

The amide undergoes hydrolysis and decarboxylation to produce the amine

FIGURE 19.3 A mechanism for the Hofmann rearrangement.

produce an anion, which spontaneously rearranges with the loss of a bromide ion to produce an isocyanate (Section 18.10A). In the rearrangement the R— group migrates with its electrons from the acyl carbon to the nitrogen atom at the same time the bromide ion departs. The isocyanate that forms in the mixture is quickly hydrolyzed by the aqueous base to a carbamate ion, which undergoes spontaneous decarboxylation resulting in the formation of the amine.

An examination of the first two steps of this mechanism shows that, initially, two hydrogen atoms must be present on the nitrogen of the amide for the reaction to occur. Consequently, the Hofmann rearrangement is limited to amides of the type $RCONH_2$.

> Studies of Hofmann rearrangement of optically active amides in which the stereocenter is directly attached to the carbonyl group have shown that these reactions occur with *retention of configuration*. Thus, the R group migrates to nitrogen with its electrons, *but without inversion*.

The Curtius rearrangement is a rearrangement that occurs with acyl azides. It resembles the Hofmann rearrangement in that an R— group migrates from the acyl carbon to the nitrogen atom as the leaving group departs. In this instance the leaving group is N_2 (the best of all possible leaving groups since it is highly stable, virtually nonbasic, and being a gas removes itself from the medium). Acyl azides are easily prepared by allowing acyl chlorides to react with sodium azide. Heating the acyl azide brings about the rearrangement; afterwards, adding water causes hydrolysis and decarboxylation of the isocyanate.

$$R-\overset{\overset{\displaystyle ::O}{\|}}{C}-\ddot{\underset{..}{Cl}}: \xrightarrow[(-NaCl)]{NaN_3} R-\overset{\overset{\displaystyle ::O}{\|}}{C}-\ddot{N}-\overset{+}{N}\equiv N: \xrightarrow{heat} R-\ddot{N}=C=\ddot{O}: \xrightarrow{H_2O} R-\ddot{N}H_2 + CO_2$$

Acyl chloride   **Acyl azide**   **Isocyanate**   **Amine**

Problem 19.8

Using a different method for each part, but taking care in each case to select a *good* method, show how each of the following transformations might be accomplished:

(a) CH_3O-⬡$\longrightarrow CH_3O-$⬡$-NH_2$

(b) CH_3O-⬡$\longrightarrow CH_3O-$⬡$-\underset{\underset{\displaystyle NH_2}{|}}{C}HCH_3$

(c) ⬡$-CH_3 \longrightarrow$ ⬡$-CH_2\overset{+}{N}(CH_3)_3\ \overset{-}{Cl}$

(d) NO_2-⬡$-CH_3 \longrightarrow NO_2-$⬡$-NH_2$

(e) ⬡$-CH_3 \longrightarrow$ ⬡$-CH_2CH_2NH_2$

19.6 REACTIONS OF AMINES

We have encountered a number of important reactions of amines in earlier sections of this book. In Section 19.3 we saw reactions in which primary, secondary, and tertiary amines act *as bases*. In Section 19.5 we saw their reactions as *nucleophiles* in *alkylation reactions,* and in Chapter 18 as *nucleophiles* in *acylation reactions.* In Chapter 15 we saw that an amino group on an aromatic ring acts as a powerful *activating group* and as an *ortho–para director.*

The structural feature of amines that underlies all of these reactions and that forms a basis for our understanding of most of the chemistry of amines is the ability of nitrogen to share an electron pair:

$$\overset{\diagdown}{\underset{\diagup}{N}}: + H^+ \rightleftharpoons \overset{\diagdown}{\underset{\diagup}{N}}\overset{+}{-}H$$

An amine acting as a base

$$\overset{\diagdown}{\underset{\diagup}{N}}: + R-CH_2-Br \longrightarrow \overset{\diagdown}{\underset{\diagup}{N}}\overset{+}{-}CH_2R + Br^-$$

An amine acting as a nucleophile in an alkylation reaction

An amine acting as a nucleophile in an acylation reaction

In the preceding examples the amine acts as a nucleophile by donating its electron pair to an electrophilic reagent. In the following example, resonance contributions involving the nitrogen electron pair make *carbon* atoms nucleophilic.

The amino group acting as an activating group and as an ortho–para director in electrophilic aromatic substitution

Problem 19.9

Review the chemistry of amines given in earlier sections and provide a specific example for each of the previously illustrated reactions.

19.6A OXIDATION OF AMINES

Primary and secondary aliphatic amines are subject to oxidation, although in most instances useful products are not obtained. Complicated side reactions often occur, causing the formation of complex mixtures.

Tertiary amines can be oxidized cleanly to tertiary amine oxides. This transformation can be brought about by using hydrogen peroxide or a peroxy acid.

A tertiary amine
oxide

Tertiary amine oxides undergo a useful elimination reaction as discussed in Section 19.13B.

Arylamines are very easily oxidized by a variety of reagents including the oxygen in air. Oxidation is not confined to the amino group but also occurs in the ring. (The amino group through its electron-donating ability makes the ring electron rich and hence especially susceptible to oxidation.) The oxidation of other functional groups on an aromatic ring cannot usually be accomplished when an amino group is present on the ring, because oxidation of the ring takes place first.

19.7 REACTIONS OF AMINES WITH NITROUS ACID

Nitrous acid (HONO) is a weak, unstable acid. It is always prepared *in situ,* usually treating sodium nitrite ($NaNO_2$) with an aqueous solution of a strong acid:

$$HCl_{(aq)} + NaNO_{2(aq)} \longrightarrow HONO_{(aq)} + NaCl_{(aq)}$$
$$H_2SO_4 + 2\,NaNO_{2(aq)} \longrightarrow 2\,HONO_{(aq)} + Na_2SO_{4(aq)}$$

Nitrous acid reacts with all classes of amines. The products that we obtain from these reactions depend on whether the amine is primary, secondary, or tertiary and whether the amine is aliphatic or aromatic.

19.7A REACTIONS OF PRIMARY ALIPHATIC AMINES WITH NITROUS ACID

Primary aliphatic amines react with nitrous acid through a reaction called *diazotization* to yield highly unstable aliphatic *diazonium salts.* Even at low temperatures, *aliphatic* diazonium salts decompose spontaneously by losing nitrogen to form carbocations. The carbocations go on to produce mixtures of alkenes, alcohols, and alkyl halides by elimination of H^+, reaction with H_2O, and reaction with X^-.

General Reaction

$$R\!-\!NH_2 + NaNO_2 + 2\,HX \xrightarrow[H_2O]{(HONO)} \left[R\!-\!\overset{+}{N}\!\equiv\!N\!: \quad X^- \right] + NaX + 2\,H_2O$$

1° Aliphatic amine   **Aliphatic diazonium salt (highly unstable)**

$$\Big\downarrow \; -N_2 \;(\text{i.e., } :N\!\equiv\!N:)$$

$$R^+ + X^-$$

$$\Big\downarrow$$

alkenes, alcohols, alkyl halides

Diazotizations of primary aliphatic amines are of little synthetic importance because they yield such a complex mixture of products. Diazotizations of primary aliphatic amines are used in some analytical procedures, however, because the evolution of nitrogen is quantitative. They can also be used to generate and thus study the behavior of carbocations in water, acetic acid, and other solvents.

19.7B REACTIONS OF PRIMARY ARYLAMINES WITH NITROUS ACID

The most important reaction of amines with nitrous acid, by far, is the reaction of primary arylamines. We shall see why in Section 19.8. Primary arylamines react with nitrous acid to give arenediazonium salts. While arenediazonium salts are unstable, they are far more stable than aliphatic diazonium salts; they do not decompose at an appreciable rate when the temperature of the reaction mixture is kept below 5 °C.

$$Ar-NH_2 \;+\; NaNO_2 + 2\,HX \longrightarrow Ar-\overset{+}{N}\equiv N\!:\; \overset{-}{X} + NaX + 2\,H_2O$$

Primary arylamine   **Arenediazonium salt**
(stable if kept below 5° C)

Diazotization of a primary amine takes place through a series of steps. In the presence of strong acid, nitrous acid dissociates to produce $^+$NO ions. These ions then react with the nitrogen of the amine to form an unstable N-nitrosoammonium ion as an intermediate. This intermediate then loses a proton to form an N-nitrosoamine, which, in turn, tautomerizes by a proton shift to a diazohydroxide in a reaction that is similar to keto–enol tautomerization. Then, in the presence of acid, the diazohydroxide loses water to form the diazonium ion.

$$H\ddot{O}\ddot{N}O + H_3O^+ \rightleftharpoons H_2O\overset{+}{-}\ddot{N}O + H_2O \rightleftharpoons 2\,H_2O + \overset{+}{\ddot{N}}=O$$

$$Ar-\underset{H}{\overset{H}{N}}\!: + {}^+\ddot{N}=O \longrightarrow Ar-\underset{H}{\overset{H}{N}}\overset{+}{-}\ddot{N}=O \xrightarrow{-H^+} Ar-\underset{H}{\overset{\cdot\cdot}{N}}-\ddot{N}=O \xrightarrow[\text{shift}]{\text{proton}}$$

1° Aryl or alkyl amine   ***N*-Nitroso-ammonium ion**   ***N*-Nitrosoamine**

$$Ar-\ddot{N}=\ddot{N}-OH \underset{-H^+}{\overset{+H^+}{\rightleftharpoons}} Ar-\ddot{N}=\ddot{N}-\overset{+}{O}H_2 \rightleftharpoons$$

Diazohydroxide

$$\underbrace{Ar-\overset{+}{N}\equiv N\!: \longleftrightarrow Ar-\ddot{N}=\overset{+}{\ddot{N}} + H_2O}$$

Diazonium ion

Diazotization reactions of primary arylamines are of considerable synthetic importance because the diazonium group, $-\overset{+}{N}\equiv N\!:$, can be replaced by a variety of other functional groups. We shall examine these reactions in Section 19.8.

19.7C REACTIONS OF SECONDARY AMINES WITH NITROUS ACID

Secondary amines — both aryl and alkyl — react with nitrous acid to yield N-nitrosoamines. N-Nitrosoamines usually separate from the reaction mixture as oily yellow liquids.

Specific Examples

$$(CH_3)_2\ddot{N}H \;+\; HCl + NaNO_2 \xrightarrow[H_2O]{(HONO)} (CH_3)_2\ddot{N}-\ddot{N}=O$$

Dimethylamine   ***N*-Nitrosodimethylamine (a yellow oil)**

N-Methylaniline   ***N*-Nitroso-*N*-methylaniline (87–93%) (a yellow oil)**

N-Nitrosoamines are very powerful carcinogens which many scientists fear may be present in many foods, especially in cooked meats that have been cured with sodium nitrite. Sodium nitrite is added to many meats (e.g., bacon, ham, frankfurters, sausages, and corned beef) to inhibit the growth of *Clostridium botulinum* (the bacterium that produces botulinus toxin) and to keep red meats from turning brown. (Food poisoning by botulinus toxin is often fatal.) In the presence of acid or under the influence of heat, sodium nitrite reacts with amines always present in the meat to produce *N*-nitrosoamines. Cooked bacon, for example, has been shown to contain *N*-nitrosodimethylamine and *N*-nitrosopyrrolidine. There is also concern that nitrites from food may produce nitrosoamines when they react with amines in the presence of the acid found in the stomach. In 1976, the FDA reduced the permissible amount of nitrite allowed in cured meats from 200 parts per million (ppm) to 50–125 ppm. Nitrites (and nitrates that can be converted to nitrites by bacteria) also occur naturally in many foods. Cigarette smoke is known to contain *N*-nitrosodimethylamine. Someone smoking a pack of cigarettes a day inhales about 0.8 μg of *N*-nitrosodimethylamine and even more has been shown to be present in the side-stream smoke.

19.7D REACTIONS OF TERTIARY AMINES WITH NITROUS ACID

When a tertiary aliphatic amine is mixed with nitrous acid, an equilibrium is established between the tertiary amine, its salt, and an *N*-nitrosoammonium compound.

$$2 \text{ R}_3\text{N} \colon \quad + \text{ HX} + \text{NaNO}_2 \rightleftharpoons \overset{+}{\text{R}}_3\text{NH } \overset{-}{\text{X}} \; + \; \overset{+}{\text{R}}_3\text{N}\!-\!\text{N}\!=\!\text{O } \text{X}^-$$

Tertiary aliphatic   **Amine salt**   ***N*-Nitrosoammonium**
amine   **compound**

While *N*-nitrosoammonium compounds are stable at low temperatures, at higher temperatures and in aqueous acid they decompose to produce aldehydes or ketones. These reactions are of little synthetic importance, however.

Tertiary arylamines react with nitrous acid to form *C*-nitroso aromatic compounds. Nitrosation takes place almost exclusively at the para position if it is open and, if not, at the ortho position. The reaction (see Problem 19.10) is another example of electrophilic aromatic substitution.

Specific Example

p-Nitroso-*N*,*N*-dimethylaniline
(80–90%)

Problem 19.10

Para-nitrosation of *N*,*N*-dimethylaniline (*C*-nitrosation) is believed to take place through an electrophilic attack of $\overset{+}{\text{N}}\text{O}$ ions. (a) Show how $\overset{+}{\text{N}}\text{O}$ ions might be formed in an aqueous solution of NaNO_2 and HCl. (b) Write a mechanism for *p*-nitrosation of *N*,*N*-dimethylaniline. (c) Tertiary aromatic amines and phenols undergo *C*-nitrosation reactions, whereas most other benzene derivatives do not. How can you account for this difference?

19.8 REPLACEMENT REACTIONS OF ARENEDIAZONIUM SALTS

Diazonium salts are highly useful intermediates in the synthesis of aromatic compounds, because the diazonium group can be replaced by any one of a number of other atoms or groups, including —F, —Cl, —Br, —I, —CN, —OH, and —H.

Diazonium salts are almost always prepared by diazotizing primary aromatic amines. Primary arylamines can be synthesized through reduction of nitro compounds that are readily available through direct nitration reactions.

19.8A SYNTHESES USING DIAZONIUM SALTS

$$Ar-NH_2 \xrightarrow[0-5\ °C]{HONO} Ar-\overset{+}{N}_2$$

- $\xrightarrow{H_3O^+,\ heat} Ar-OH$
- $\xrightarrow{CuCl} Ar-Cl$
- $\xrightarrow{CuBr} Ar-Br$
- $\xrightarrow{CuCN} Ar-CN$
- $\xrightarrow{KI} Ar-I$
- $\xrightarrow[\text{(2) heat}]{\text{(1) }HBF_4} Ar-F$
- $\xrightarrow{H_3PO_2} Ar-H$

Most arenediazonium salts are unstable at temperatures above 5–10 °C, and many explode when dry. Fortunately, however, most of the replacement reactions of diazonium salts do not require their isolation. We simply add another reagent (CuCl, CuBr, KI, etc.) to the mixture, gently warm the solution, and the replacement (accompanied by the evolution of nitrogen) takes place.

Only in the replacement of the diazonium group by —F need we isolate a diazonium salt. We do this by adding HBF_4 to the mixture, causing the sparingly soluble and reasonably stable arenediazonium fluoborate, $ArN_2^+\ BF_4^-$, to precipitate.

19.8B THE SANDMEYER REACTION: REPLACEMENT OF THE DIAZONIUM GROUP BY —Cl, —Br, or —CN

Arenediazonium salts react with cuprous chloride, cuprous bromide, and cuprous cyanide to give products in which the diazonium group has been replaced by —Cl, —Br, and —CN, respectively. These reactions are known generally as *Sandmeyer reactions*. Several specific examples follow:

o-Toluidine $\xrightarrow[\substack{H_2O \\ (0-5\ °C)}]{HCl,\ NaNO_2}$ [$\overset{+}{N}_2\ Cl^-$] $\xrightarrow[15-60\ °C]{CuCl}$ *o*-Chlorotoluene (74–79% overall) $+ N_2$

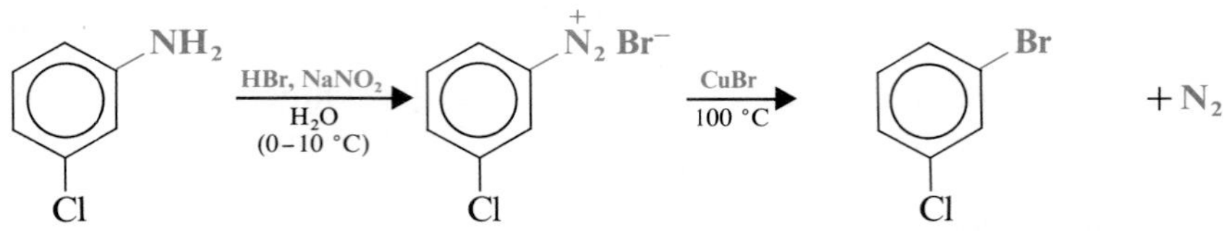

m-Chloroaniline

**m-Bromochlorobenzene
(70% overall)**

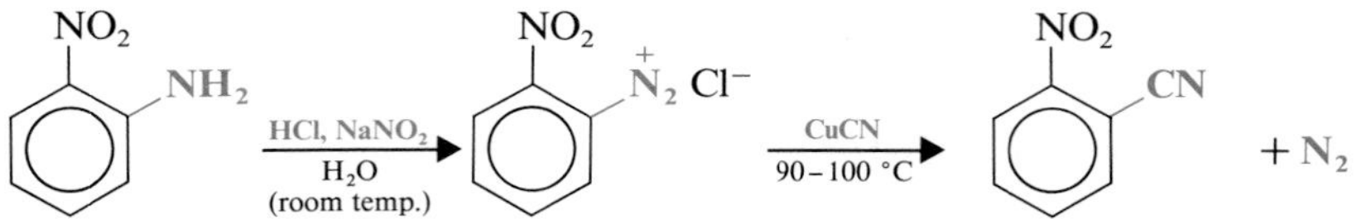

o-Nitroaniline

**o-Nitrobenzonitrile
(65% overall)**

19.8C REPLACEMENT BY —I

Arenediazonium salts react with potassium iodide to give products in which the diazonium group has been replaced by —I. An example is the synthesis of *p*-iodo-nitrobenzene:

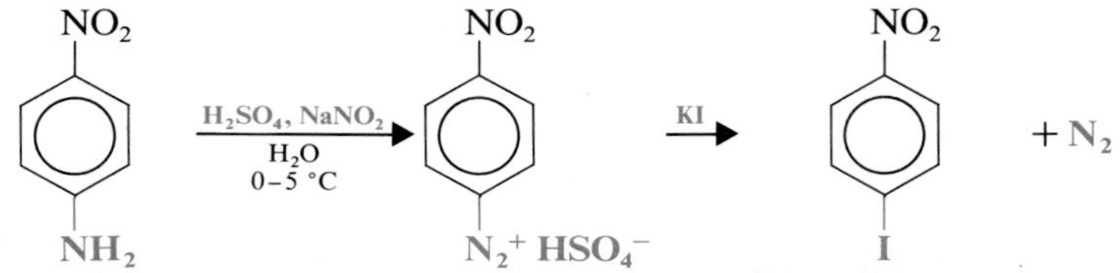

p-Nitroaniline

**p-Iodonitrobenzene
(81% overall)**

19.8D REPLACEMENT BY —F

The diazonium group can be replaced by fluorine by treating the diazonium salt with fluoboric acid (HBF_4). The diazonium fluoborate that precipitates is isolated, dried, and heated until decomposition occurs. An aryl fluoride is produced.

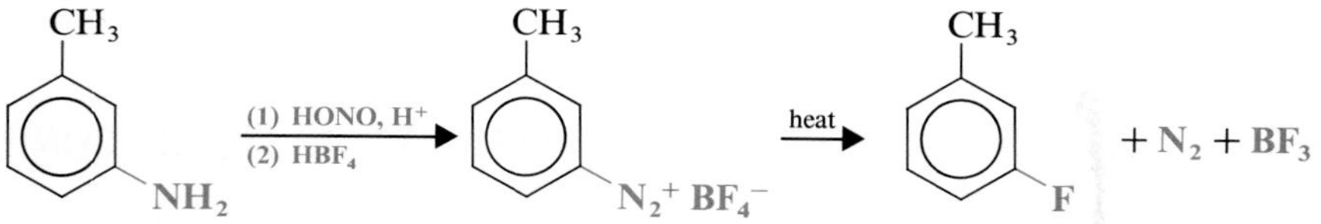

m-Toluidine

**m-Toluenediazonium
fluoborate
(79%)**

**m-Fluorotoluene
(69%)**

19.8E REPLACEMENT BY —OH

The diazonium group can be replaced by a hydroxyl group simply by acidifying the aqueous mixture strongly and heating it:

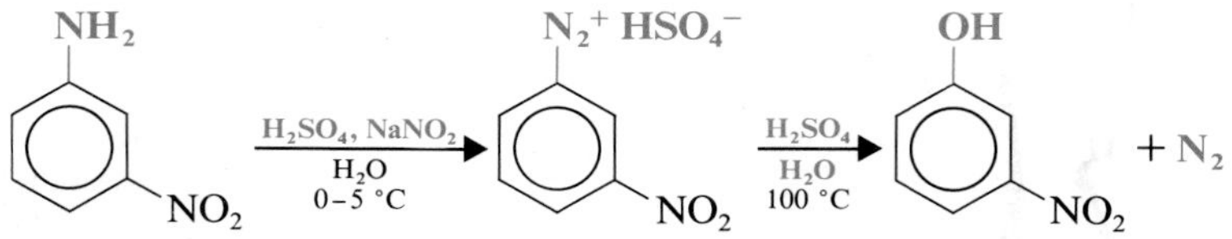

m-Nitroaniline

**m-Nitrophenol
(74–79%)**

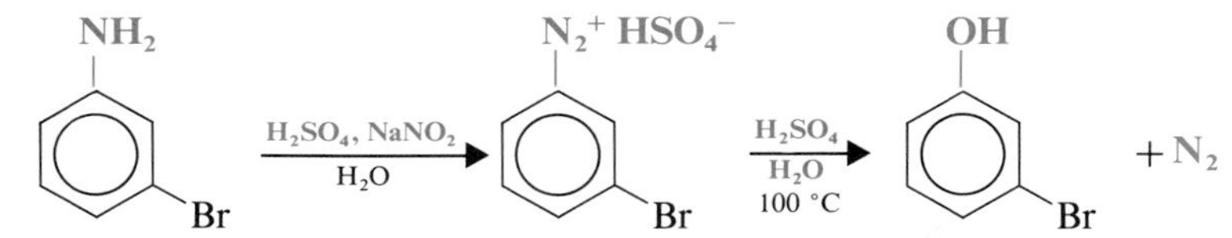

m-Bromoaniline → **m-Bromophenol** (78% overall)

Sulfuric acid is used for the diazotization, because HSO_4^- competes poorly with water in the second step of the sequence.

Problem 19.11

In the preceding examples of diazonium reactions, we have illustrated syntheses beginning with the compounds (a)–(e) here. Show how you might prepare each of the following compounds from benzene.

(a) *m*-Nitroaniline (c) *m*-Bromoaniline (e) *p*-Nitroaniline
(b) *m*-Chloroaniline (d) *o*-Nitroaniline

19.8F REPLACEMENT BY —H: DEAMINATION BY DIAZOTIZATION

Arenediazonium salts react with hypophosphorous acid (H_3PO_2) to yield products in which the diazonium group has been replaced by —H.

Since we usually begin a synthesis using diazonium salts by nitrating an aromatic compound, that is, replacing —H by —NO_2 and then by —NH_2, it may seem strange that we would ever want to replace a diazonium group by —H. However, replacement of the diazonium group by —H can be a useful reaction. We can introduce an amino group into an aromatic ring to influence the orientation of a subsequent reaction. Later we can remove the amino group (i.e., carry out a *deamination*) by diazotizing it and treating the diazonium salt with H_3PO_2.

We can see an example of the usefulness of a deamination reaction in the following synthesis of *m*-bromotoluene. We cannot prepare *m*-bromotoluene by

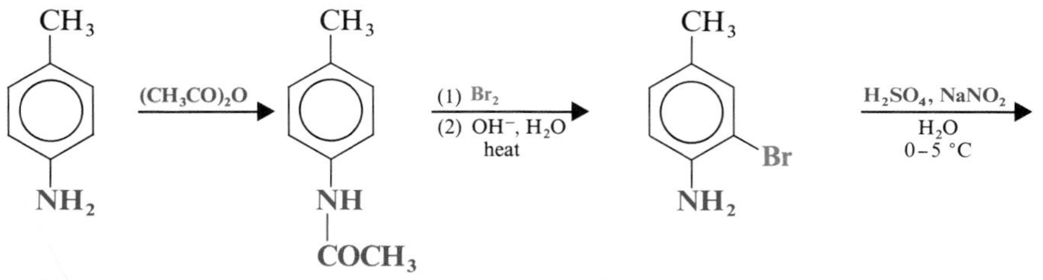

p-Toluidine   (65% from p-toluidine)

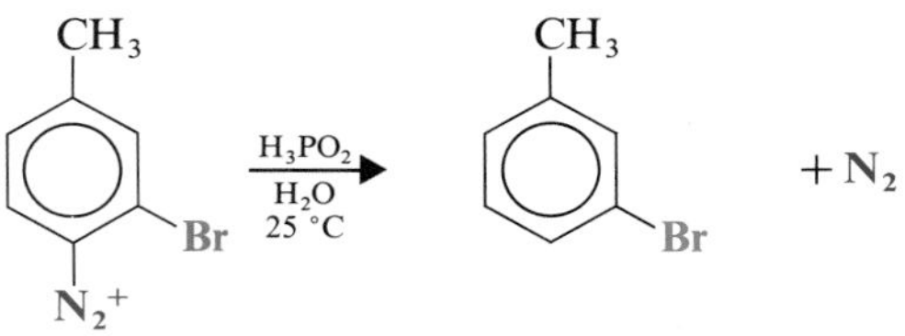

m-Bromotoluene
(85% from 2-bromo-4-
methylaniline)

direct bromination of toluene or by a Friedel–Crafts alkylation of bromobenzene because both reactions give *o*- and *p*-bromotoluene. (Both CH₃— and Br— are ortho–para directors.) However, if we begin with *p*-toluidine (prepared by nitrating toluene, separating the para isomer, and reducing the nitro group), we can carry out the sequence of reactions shown and obtain *m*-bromotoluene in good yield. The first step, synthesis of the *N*-acetyl derivative of *p*-toluidine, is done to reduce the activating effect of the amino group. (Otherwise both ortho positions would be brominated.) Later, the acetyl group is removed by hydrolysis.

Problem 19.12

Suggest how you might modify the preceding synthesis in order to prepare 3,5-dibromotoluene.

Problem 19.13

(a) In Section 19.8D we showed a synthesis of *m*-fluorotoluene starting with *m*-toluidine. How would you prepare *m*-toluidine from toluene? (b) How would you prepare *m*-chlorotoluene? (c) *m*-Bromotoluene? (d) *m*-Iodotoluene? (e) *m*-Tolunitrile (*m*-CH₃C₆H₄CN)? (f) *m*-Toluic acid?

Problem 19.14

Starting with *p*-nitroaniline [Problem 19.11(e)] show how you might synthesize 1,2,3-tribromobenzene.

19.9 COUPLING REACTIONS OF ARENEDIAZONIUM SALTS

Arenediazonium ions are weak electrophiles; they react with highly reactive aromatic compounds—with phenols and tertiary arylamines—to yield *azo* compounds. This electrophilic aromatic substitution is often called a *diazo coupling reaction.*

General Reaction

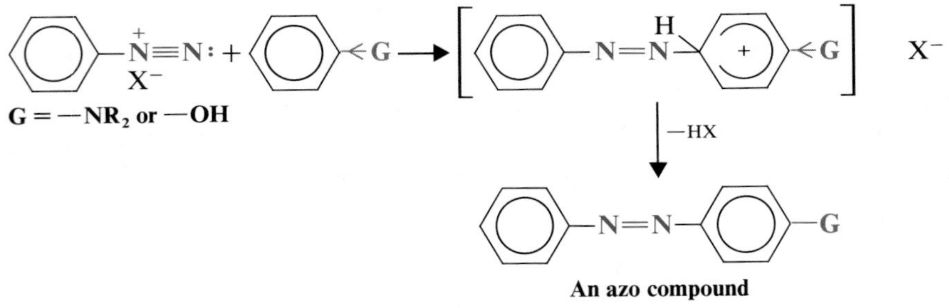

$G = -NR_2$ or $-OH$

An azo compound

Specific Examples

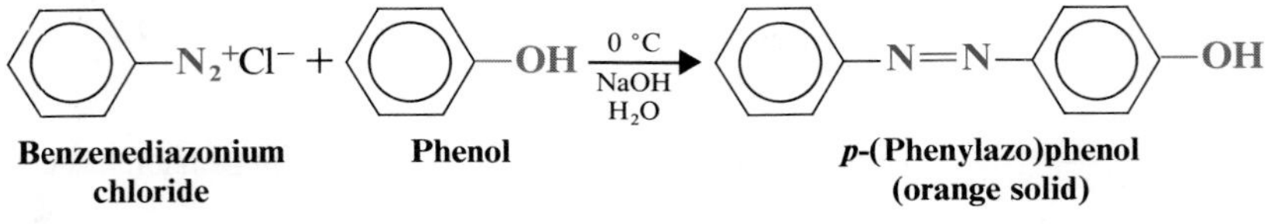

Benzenediazonium chloride   Phenol   *p*-(Phenylazo)phenol (orange solid)

Benzenediazonium chloride + **N,N-Dimethylaniline** $\xrightarrow[\substack{0\ °C \\ H_2O}]{CH_3CO^- Na^+}$ **N,N-Dimethyl-p-(phenylazo)aniline** (yellow solid)

Couplings between arenediazonium cations and phenols take place most rapidly in *slightly* alkaline solution. Under these conditions an appreciable amount of the phenol is present as a phenoxide ion, ArO^-, and phenoxide ions are even more reactive toward electrophilic substitution than are phenols themselves. (Why?) If the solution is too alkaline, however (pH > 10), the arenediazonium salt itself reacts with hydroxide ion to form a relatively unreactive diazohydroxide or diazotate ion:

Phenol (couples slowly)   **Phenoxide ion** (couples rapidly)

$$Ar-\overset{+}{N}\equiv N : \underset{H^+}{\overset{OH^-}{\rightleftarrows}} Ar-\ddot{N}=\ddot{N}-OH \underset{H^+}{\overset{OH^-}{\rightleftarrows}} Ar-\ddot{N}=\ddot{N}-\ddot{O}:^-$$

Arenediazonium ion (couples)   **Diazohydroxide** (does not couple)   **Diazoate ion** (does not couple)

Couplings between arenediazonium cations and amines take place most rapidly in slightly acidic solutions (pH 5–7). Under these conditions the concentration of the arenediazonium salt is at a maximum; at the same time an excessive amount of the amine has not been converted to an unreactive aminium salt:

Amine (couples)   **Aminium salt** (does not couple)

If the pH of the solution is lower than 5, the rate of amine coupling is low.

With phenols and aniline derivatives, coupling takes place almost exclusively at the para position if it is open. If it is not, coupling takes place at the ortho position.

4-Methylphenol (*p*-cresol)   **4-Methyl-2-(phenylazo)phenol**

Azo compounds are usually intensely colored because the azo (diazenediyl) linkage —N=N— brings the two aromatic rings into conjugation. This gives an extended system of delocalized π electrons and allows absorption of light in the visible region. Azo compounds, because of their intense colors, and because they can be synthesized from relatively inexpensive compounds, are used extensively as *dyes*.

Azo dyes almost always contain one or more —SO_3^- Na^+ groups to confer water solubility on the dye and assist in binding the dye to the surfaces of polar fibers (wool, cotton, or nylon). Many dyes are made by coupling reactions of naphthylamines and naphthols.

Orange II, a dye introduced in 1876, is made from 2-naphthol.

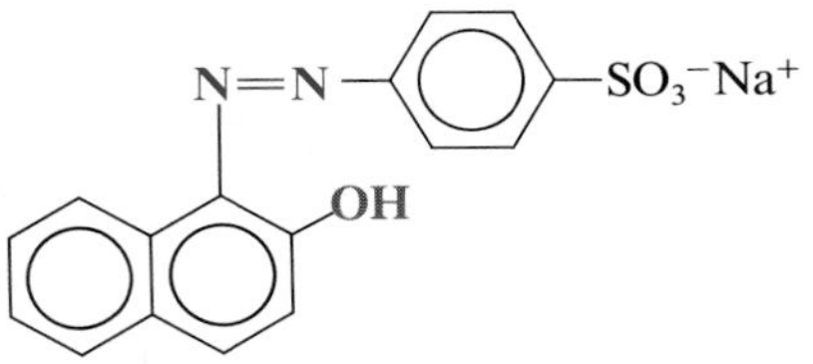

Orange II

Problem 19.15

Outline a synthesis of Orange II from 2-naphthol and *p*-aminobenzenesulfonic acid.

Problem 19.16

Butter Yellow is a dye once used to color margarine. It has since been shown to be carcinogenic and its use in food is no longer permitted. Outline a synthesis of Butter Yellow from benzene and *N,N*-dimethylaniline.

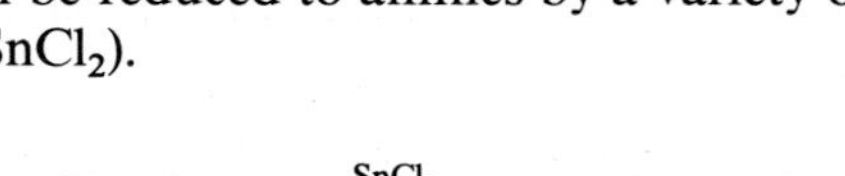

Butter Yellow

Problem 19.17

Azo compounds can be reduced to amines by a variety of reagents including stannous chloride ($SnCl_2$).

$$Ar-N=N-Ar' \xrightarrow{SnCl_2} ArNH_2 + Ar'NH_2$$

This reduction can be useful in synthesis as the following example shows:

4-Ethoxyaniline $\xrightarrow[\text{(2) phenol, OH}^-]{\text{(1) HONO, H}_3\text{O}^+}$ **A** ($C_{14}H_{14}N_2O_2$) $\xrightarrow{\text{NaOH, CH}_3\text{CH}_2\text{Br}}$

B ($C_{16}H_{18}N_2O_2$) $\xrightarrow{SnCl_2}$ two molar equivalents of

C ($C_8H_{11}NO$) $\xrightarrow{\text{acetic anhydride}}$ phenacetin ($C_{10}H_{13}NO_2$)

Give a structure for phenacetin and for the intermediates **A**, **B**, **C**. (Phenacetin, formerly used as an analgesic, is also the subject of Problem 18.34.)

19.10 REACTIONS OF AMINES WITH SULFONYL CHLORIDES

Primary and secondary amines react with sulfonyl chlorides to form *sulfonamides*.

When heated with aqueous acid, sulfonamides are hydrolyzed to amines:

This hydrolysis is much slower, however, than hydrolysis of carboxamides.

19.10A THE HINSBERG TEST

Sulfonamide formation is the basis for a chemical test, called the Hinsberg test, that can be used to demonstrate whether an amine is primary, secondary, or tertiary. A Hinsberg test involves two steps. First, a mixture containing a small amount of the amine and benzenesulfonyl chloride is shaken with *excess* potassium hydroxide. Next, after allowing time for a reaction to take place, the mixture is acidified. Each type of amine—primary, secondary, or tertiary—gives a different set of *visible* results after each of these two stages of the test.

Primary amines react with benzenesulfonyl chloride to form N-substituted benzenesulfonamides. These, in turn, undergo acid–base reactions with the excess potassium hydroxide to form water-soluble potassium salts. (These reactions take place because the hydrogen attached to nitrogen is made acidic by the strongly electron-withdrawing —SO₂— group.) At this stage our test tube will contain a clear solution. Acidification of this solution will, in the next stage, cause the water-insoluble N-substituted sulfonamide to precipitate.

Secondary amines react with benzenesulfonyl chloride in aqueous potassium hydroxide to form insoluble N,N-disubstituted sulfonamides that precipitate after the first stage. N,N-Disubstituted sulfonamides do not dissolve in aqueous potassium hydroxide because they do not have an acidic hydrogen. Acidification of the mixture obtained from a secondary amine produces no visible result—the nonbasic N,N-disubstituted sulfonamide remains as a precipitate and no new precipitate forms.

If the amine is a tertiary amine and if it is water insoluble, no apparent change will take place in the mixture as we shake it with benzenesulfonyl chloride and aqueous KOH. When we acidify the mixture, the tertiary amine will dissolve because it will form a water-soluble salt.

Problem 19.18

An amine **A** has the molecular formula C_7H_9N. Compound **A** reacts with benzenesulfonyl chloride in aqueous potassium hydroxide to give a clear solution; acidification of the solution gives a precipitate. When **A** is treated with $NaNO_2$ and HCl at 0–5 °C, and then with 2-naphthol, an intensely colored compound is formed. Compound **A** gives a single strong absorption peak in the 680–840-cm^{-1} region at 815 cm^{-1}. What is the structure of **A**?

Problem 19.19

Sulfonamides of primary amines are often used to synthesize *pure* secondary amines. Suggest how this synthesis is carried out.

19.11 THE SULFA DRUGS: SULFANILAMIDE

19.11A CHEMOTHERAPY

Chemotherapy is defined as the use of chemical agents selectively to destroy infectious organisms without simultaneously destroying the host. Although it may be difficult to believe in this age of "wonder drugs," chemotherapy is a relatively modern phenomenon. Prior to 1900 only three specific chemical remedies were known: mercury (for syphilis—but often with disastrous results), cinchona bark (for malaria), and ipecacuanha (for dysentery).

Modern chemotherapy began with the work of Paul Ehrlich early in this century—particularly with his discovery in 1907 of the curative properties of a dye called Trypan Red I when used against experimental trypanosomiasis and with his discovery in 1909 of Salvarsan as a remedy for syphilis (Special Topic K). Ehrlich invented the term "chemotherapy," and in his research sought what he called "magic bullets," that is, chemicals that would be toxic to infectious microorganisms but harmless to humans.*

As a medical student, Ehrlich had been impressed with the ability of certain dyes to stain tissues selectively. Working on the idea that "staining" was a result of a chemical reaction between the tissue and the dye, Ehrlich sought dyes with selective affinities for microorganisms. He hoped that in this way he might find a dye that could be modified so as to render it specifically lethal to microorganisms.

19.11B SULFA DRUGS

Between 1909 and 1935, tens of thousands of chemicals, including many dyes, were tested by Ehrlich and others in a search for such "magic bullets." Very few compounds, however, were found to have any promising effect. Then, in 1935, an amazing event happened. The daughter of Gerhard Domagk, a doctor employed by a German dye manufacturer, contracted a streptococcal infection from a pin prick. As his daughter neared death, Domagk decided to give her an oral dose of a dye called Prontosil. Prontosil had been developed at Domagk's firm (I. G. Farbenindustrie) and tests with mice had shown that Prontosil inhibited the growth of streptococci. Within a short time the little girl recovered. Domagk's gamble not only saved his daughter's life, but it also initiated a new and spectacularly productive phase in modern chemotherapy.†

A year later, in 1936, Ernest Fourneau of the Pasteur Institute in Paris demonstrated that Prontosil breaks down in the human body to produce sulfanilamide, and that sulfanilamide is the actual active agent against streptococci.

Prontosil   Sulfanilamide

Fourneau's announcement of this result set in motion a search for other chemicals (related to sulfanilamide) that might have even better chemotherapeutic effects.

---

*P. Ehrlich was awarded the Nobel Prize for medicine in 1908.
†G. Domagk was awarded the Nobel Prize for medicine in 1939 but was unable to accept it until 1947.

Literally thousands of chemical variations were played on the sulfanilamide theme; the structure of sulfanilamide was varied in almost every imaginable way. The best therapeutic results were obtained from compounds in which one hydrogen of the $-SO_2NH_2$ group was replaced by some other group, usually a heterocyclic amine. Among the most successful variations were the following compounds. Sulfanilamide itself is too toxic for general use.

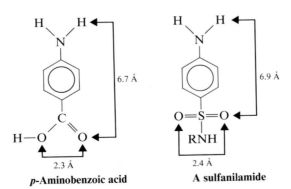

Sulfapyridine was shown to be effective against pneumonia in 1938. (Prior to that time pneumonia epidemics had brought death to tens of thousands.) Sulfacetamide was first used successfully in treating urinary tract infections in 1941. Succinoylsulfathiazole and the related compound phthalylsulfathiazole were used as chemotherapeutic agents against infections of the gastrointestinal tract beginning in 1942. (Both compounds are slowly hydrolyzed internally to sulfathiazole.) Sulfathiazole saved the lives of countless wounded soldiers during World War II.

FIGURE 19.4 The structural similarity of *p*-aminobenzoic acid and a sulfanilamide. (From A. Korolkovas, *Essentials of Molecular Pharmacology*, Wiley, New York, 1970, p. 105. Used with permission.)

In 1940 a discovery by D. D. Woods laid the groundwork for our understanding of how the sulfa drugs work. Woods observed that the inhibition of growth of certain microorganisms by sulfanilamide is competitively overcome by *p*-aminobenzoic acid. Woods noticed the structural similarity between the two compounds (Fig. 19.4) and reasoned that the two compounds compete with each other in some essential metabolic process.

19.11C ESSENTIAL NUTRIENTS AND ANTIMETABOLITES

All higher animals and many microorganisms lack the biochemical ability to synthesize certain essential organic compounds. These essential nutrients include vitamins, certain amino acids, unsaturated carboxylic acids, purines, and pyrimidines. The aromatic amine *p*-aminobenzoic acid is an essential nutrient for those bacteria that are sensitive to sulfanilamide therapy. Enzymes within these bacteria use *p*-aminobenzoic acid to synthesize another essential compound called *folic acid*.

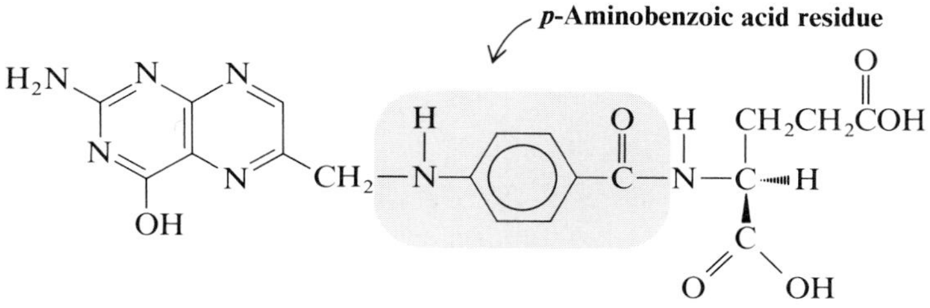

Folic acid

Chemicals that inhibit the growth of microbes are called *antimetabolites*. The sulfanilamides are antimetabolites for those bacteria that require *p*-aminobenzoic acid. The sulfanilamides apparently inhibit those enzymatic steps of the bacteria that are involved in the synthesis of folic acid. The bacterial enzymes are apparently unable to distinguish between a molecule of a sulfanilamide and a molecule of *p*-aminobenzoic acid; thus, sulfanilamide "inhibits" the bacterial enzyme. Because the microorganism is unable to synthesize enough folic acid when sulfanilamide is present, it dies. Humans are unaffected by sulfanilamide therapy because we derive our folic acid from dietary sources (folic acid is a vitamin) and do not synthesize it from *p*-aminobenzoic acid.

The discovery of the mode of action of the sulfanilamides has led to the discovery of many new and effective antimetabolites. One example is *methotrexate*, a derivative of folic acid that has been used successfully in treating certain carcinomas:

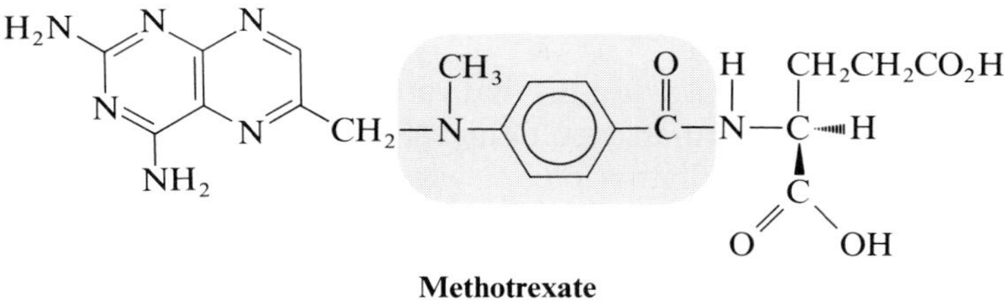

Methotrexate

Methotrexate, by virtue of its resemblance to folic acid, can enter into some of the same reactions as folic acid, but it cannot serve the same function, particularly in important reactions involved in cell division. Although methotrexate is toxic to all dividing cells, those cells that divide most rapidly — *cancer cells* — are most vulnerable to its effect.

19.11D SYNTHESIS OF SULFA DRUGS

Sulfanilamides can be synthesized from aniline through the following sequence of reactions.

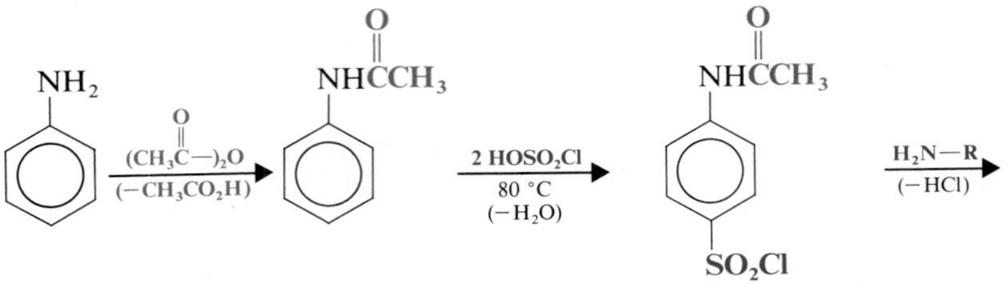

Aniline **Acetanilide** *p*-Acetamidobenzene-
1 **2** sulfonyl chloride
3

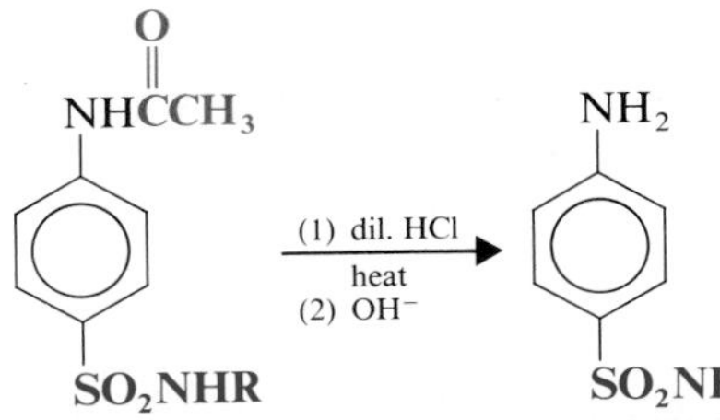

4

A sulfanilamide
5

Acetylation of aniline produces acetanilide, **2**, and protects the amino group from the reagent to be used next. Treatment of **2** with chlorosulfonic acid brings about an electrophilic aromatic substitution reaction and yields *p*-acetamidobenzenesulfonyl chloride, **3**. Addition of ammonia or a primary amine gives the diamide, **4** (an amide of both a carboxylic acid and a sulfonic acid). Finally, refluxing **4** with dilute hydrochloric acid selectively hydrolyzes the carboxamide linkage and produces sulfanilamide. (Hydrolysis of carboxamides is much more rapid than that of sulfonamides.)

Problem 19.20

(a) Starting with aniline and assuming that you have 2-aminothiazole available, show how you would synthesize sulfathiazole. (b) How would you convert sulfathiazole to succinylsulfathiazole?

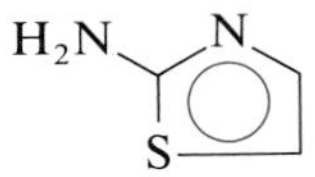

2-Aminothiazole

19.12 ANALYSIS OF AMINES

19.12A CHEMICAL ANALYSIS

Amines are characterized by their basicity and, thus, by their ability to dissolve in dilute aqueous acid (Section 19.3A). Primary, secondary, and tertiary amines can be distinguished from each other on the basis of the Hinsberg test (Section 19.10A). Primary aromatic amines are often detected through diazonium salt formation and subsequent coupling with 2-naphthol to form a brightly colored azo dye (Section 19.9).

19.12B SPECTROSCOPIC ANALYSIS

The *infrared spectra* of primary and secondary amines are characterized by absorption bands in the $3300-3555$-cm^{-1} region that arise from N—H stretching vibration. Primary amines give two bands in this region; secondary amines generally give only one. Absorption bands arising from C—N stretching vibrations of aliphatic amines occur in the $1020-1220$-cm^{-1} region but are usually weak and difficult to identify. Aromatic amines generally give a strong C—N stretching band in the $1250-1360$-cm^{-1} region.

The *^1H NMR spectra* of primary and secondary amines show N—H proton absorptions in the region δ $1-5$. These peaks are sometimes difficult to identify and are best detected by proton counting.

19.13 ELIMINATIONS INVOLVING AMMONIUM COMPOUNDS

19.13A THE HOFMANN ELIMINATION

All of the eliminations that we have described so far have involved electrically neutral substrates. However, eliminations are known in which the substrate bears a positive charge. One of the most important of these is the elimination that takes place when a quaternary ammonium hydroxide is heated. The products are an alkene, water, and tertiary amine.

$$\overset{..}{HO}:^- \overset{\frown}{} H$$
$$-\overset{|}{\underset{|}{C}}-\overset{|}{\underset{|}{C}}-\overset{+}{N}R_3 \longrightarrow C=C + HOH + :NR_3$$

$$\text{A quaternary} \longrightarrow \text{an alkene } + \text{ water } + \text{ a tertiary}$$
$$\text{ammonium hydroxide} \qquad \qquad \text{amine}$$

This reaction was discovered in 1851 by August W. von Hofmann and has since come to bear his name.

Quaternary ammonium hydroxides can be prepared from quaternary ammonium halides in aqueous solution through the use of silver oxide or an ion exchange resin.

$$2\ RCH_2CH_2\overset{+}{N}(CH_3)_3X^- + Ag_2O + H_2O \longrightarrow 2\ RCH_2CH_2\overset{+}{N}(CH_3)_3\ OH^- + 2\ AgX\downarrow$$
$$\text{A quaternary ammonium} \qquad\qquad\qquad \text{Quaternary ammonium}$$
$$\text{halide} \qquad\qquad\qquad\qquad \text{hydroxide}$$

Silver halide precipitates from the solution and can be removed by filtration. The quaternary ammonium hydroxide can then be obtained by evaporation of the water.

While most eliminations involving neutral substrates tend to follow the *Zaitsev rule* (Section 8.12A), eliminations with charged substrates tend to follow what is called the *Hofmann rule* and *yield mainly the least substituted alkene*. We can see an example of this behavior if we compare the following reactions.

$$C_2H_5O^-Na^+ + CH_3CH_2\overset{\underset{|}{Br}}{C}HCH_3 \xrightarrow[25\ °C]{C_2H_5OH}$$

$$CH_3CH=CHCH_3 + CH_3CH_2CH=CH_2 + NaBr + C_2H_5OH$$
$$(75\%) \qquad\qquad (25\%)$$

$$CH_3CH_2\overset{\underset{|}{\overset{+}{N}(CH_3)_3}}{C}HCH_3\ OH^- \xrightarrow[150\ °C]{}$$

$$CH_3CH=CHCH_3 + CH_3CH_2CH=CH_2 + (CH_3)_3N\colon + H_2O$$
$$(5\%) \qquad\qquad (95\%)$$

$$CH_3CH_2\overset{\underset{|}{\overset{+}{S}(CH_3)_2}}{C}HCH_3\ \overset{-}{O}C_2H_5 \longrightarrow$$

$$CH_3CH=CHCH_3 + CH_3CH_2CH=CH_2 + (CH_3)_2S + C_2H_5OH$$
$$(26\%) \qquad\qquad (74\%)$$

The precise mechanistic reasons for these differences are complex and are not yet fully understood. One possible explanation is that the transition states of elimination reactions with charged substrates have considerable carbanion character. Therefore, these transition states show little resemblance to the final alkene product and, thus, are not stabilized appreciably by a developing double bond.

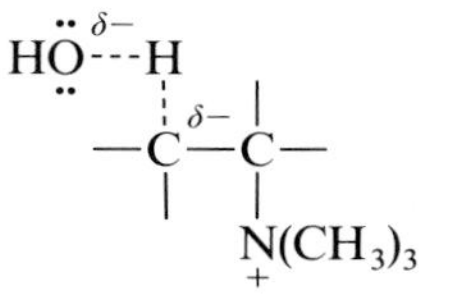

$$HO^{\delta-}\cdots H \qquad\qquad HO^{\delta-}\cdots H$$

Carbanion-like transition state   **Alkene-like transition state**
(gives Hofmann orientation)   **(gives Zaitsev orientation)**

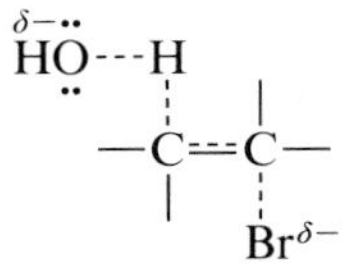

With a charged substrate, the base attacks the most acidic hydrogen instead. A primary hydrogen atom is more acidic because its carbon atom bears only one electron-releasing group.

19.13B THE COPE ELIMINATION

Tertiary amine oxides undergo the elimination of a dialkylhydroxylamine when they are heated. This reaction is called the Cope elimination.

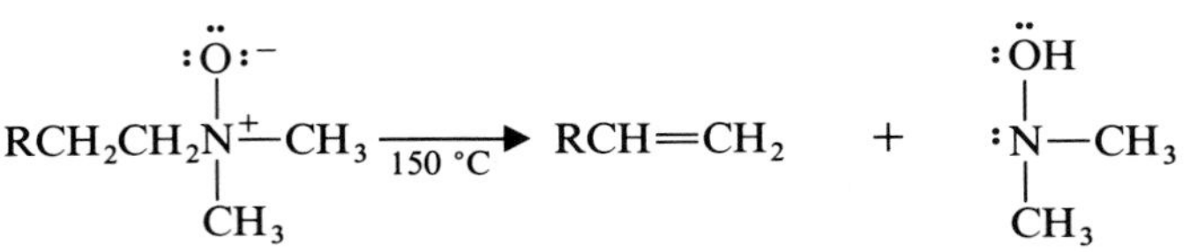

$$RCH_2CH_2\overset{\underset{|}{CH_3}}{\underset{}{\overset{\overset{\displaystyle :\!\overset{..}{O}\!:^-}{|}}{N^+}}}\!-CH_3 \xrightarrow[150\ °C]{} RCH=CH_2 \quad + \quad \overset{\underset{|}{CH_3}}{\underset{}{\overset{\overset{\displaystyle :\!\overset{..}{O}H}{|}}{\colon\!N}}}\!-CH_3$$

A tertiary amine   **An alkene**   *N,N*-**Dimethylhydroxylamine**
oxide

The Cope elimination is a syn elimination and proceeds through a cyclic transition state:

Tertiary amine oxides are easily prepared by treating tertiary amines with hydrogen peroxide (Section 19.6A).

19.14 SUMMARY OF PREPARATIONS AND REACTIONS OF AMINES

19.14A PREPARATION OF AMINES

1. Gabriel synthesis (discussed in Section 19.5A).

2. By reductions of alkyl azides (discussed in Section 19.5A).

$$R-Br \xrightarrow[\text{ethanol}]{NaN_3} R-\ddot{N}-\overset{+}{N}\equiv N: \xrightarrow[\substack{\text{or} \\ LiAlH_4}]{\text{Na/alcohol}} R-NH_2$$

3. By amination of alkyl halides (discussed in Section 19.5A).

$$R-Br + NH_3 \longrightarrow RNH_3^+Br^- + R_2NH_2^+Br^- + R_3N^+Br^- + R_4N^+Br^-$$
$$\downarrow OH^-$$
$$RNH_2 + R_2NH + R_3N + R_4N^+$$

(R is a 1° alkyl group)

4. By reduction of nitroarenes (discussed in Section 19.5B).

$$Ar-NO_2 \xrightarrow[\substack{\text{or} \\ \text{(1) Fe/HCl (2) NaOH}}]{H_2,\ cat} Ar-NH_2$$

5. By reductive amination (discussed in Section 19.5C).

$$R-C=O \quad \text{(Aldehyde or ketone)}$$

with R' substituent

- $\xrightarrow[\text{[H]}]{NH_3}$ $R-\overset{R'}{\underset{}{CH}}-NH_2$ **1° Amine**
- $\xrightarrow[\text{[H]}]{R''NH_2}$ $R-\overset{R'}{\underset{}{CH}}-NHR''$ **2° Amine**
- $\xrightarrow[\text{[H]}]{R''R'''NH}$ $R-\overset{R'}{\underset{}{CH}}-NR''R'''$ **3° Amine**

6. By reduction of amides, nitriles, and oximes (discussed in Section 19.5D).

$$R-\overset{O}{\overset{\|}{C}}-\overset{}{\underset{H}{N}}-H \xrightarrow[\text{(2) } H_2O]{\text{(1) LiAlH}_4\text{, diethyl ether}} R-CH_2-\overset{}{\underset{H}{N}}-H \quad \textbf{1° Amine}$$

$$R-\overset{O}{\overset{\|}{C}}-\overset{}{\underset{H}{N}}-R' \xrightarrow[\text{(2) } H_2O]{\text{(1) LiAlH}_4\text{, diethyl ether}} R-CH_2-\overset{}{\underset{H}{N}}-R' \quad \textbf{2° Amine}$$

$$R-\overset{O}{\overset{\|}{C}}-\overset{}{\underset{R''}{N}}-R' \xrightarrow[\text{(2) } H_2O]{\text{(1) LiAlH}_4\text{, diethyl ether}} R-CH_2-\overset{}{\underset{R''}{N}}-R' \quad \textbf{3° Amine}$$

$$R-C\equiv N \xrightarrow[\text{(2) } H_2O]{\text{(1) LiAlH}_4\text{, diethyl ether}} R-CH_2-\overset{}{\underset{H}{N}}-H \quad \textbf{1° Amine}$$

$$R-\overset{N-OH}{\overset{\|}{C}}-R' \xrightarrow{\text{Na/alcohol}} R-\overset{NH_2}{\underset{}{CH}}-R' \quad \textbf{1° Amine}$$

7. Through the Hofmann and Curtius rearrangements (discussed in Section 19.5E).

Hofmann Rearrangement

$$R-\overset{O}{\overset{\|}{C}}-\overset{}{\underset{H}{N}}-H \xrightarrow{Br_2,\ OH^-} R-NH_2 + CO_3^{2-}$$

Curtius Rearrangement

$$R-\overset{O}{\overset{\|}{C}}-Cl \xrightarrow[(-NaCl)]{NaN_3} R-\overset{O}{\overset{\|}{C}}-N_3 \xrightarrow[-N_2]{\text{heat}} R-N=C=O \xrightarrow{H_2O} R-NH_2 + CO_2$$

19.14B REACTIONS OF AMINES

1. As bases (discussed in Section 19.3).

19.14 SUMMARY OF PREPARATIONS AND REACTIONS OF AMINES

$$R-CH_2-\ddot{N}-R' + H-A \longrightarrow R-CH_2-\overset{H}{\underset{R''}{\overset{|}{N^{\pm}}}}-R' \ A^-$$

(R, R', or R" may be H or Ar)

2. Diazotization of 1° arylamines and replacement of the diazonium group (discussed in Sections 19.8 and 19.9).

$$Ar-NH_2 \xrightarrow{\text{HONO}} Ar-\overset{+}{N}_2$$

$\xrightarrow{H_3O^+,\ heat}$	$Ar-OH$
$\xrightarrow{CuCl}$	$Ar-Cl$
$\xrightarrow{CuBr}$	$Ar-Br$
$\xrightarrow{CuCN}$	$Ar-CN$
$\xrightarrow{KI}$	$Ar-I$
$\xrightarrow[(2)\ heat]{(1)\ HBF_4}$	$Ar-F$
$\xrightarrow{H_3PO_2}$	$Ar-H$

3. Conversion to sulfonamides (discussed in Section 19.10).

$$R-\overset{H}{\underset{}{\overset{|}{N}}}-H \xrightarrow[(2)\ HCl]{(1)\ ArSO_2Cl,\ OH^-} R-\overset{H}{\underset{}{\overset{|}{N}}}-\overset{O}{\underset{O}{\overset{\|}{S}}}-Ar$$

$$R-\overset{R'}{\underset{}{\overset{|}{N}}}-H \xrightarrow{ArSO_2Cl,\ OH^-} R-\overset{R'}{\underset{}{\overset{|}{N}}}-\overset{O}{\underset{O}{\overset{\|}{S}}}-Ar$$

4. Conversion to amides (discussed in Section 18.8).

$$R-\overset{H}{\underset{}{\overset{|}{N}}}-H \xrightarrow[base]{R''C-Cl} R-\overset{H}{\underset{}{\overset{|}{N}}}-\overset{O}{\overset{\|}{C}}-R''$$

$$R-\overset{H}{\underset{}{\overset{|}{N}}}-H \xrightarrow{(R''C)_2O} R-\overset{H}{\underset{}{\overset{|}{N}}}-\overset{O}{\overset{\|}{C}}-R'' + R''-\overset{O}{\overset{\|}{C}}-OH$$

$$R-\overset{R'}{\underset{}{\overset{|}{N}}}-H \xrightarrow[base]{R''C-Cl} R-\overset{R'}{\underset{}{\overset{|}{N}}}-\overset{O}{\overset{\|}{C}}-R''$$

5. Hofmann and Cope eliminations (discussed in Section 19.13).

Hofmann Elimination

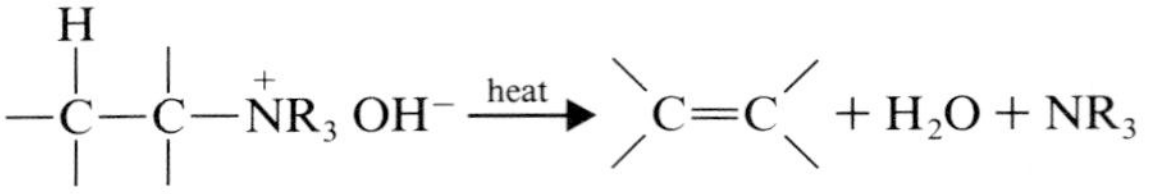

$$-\overset{|}{\underset{|}{C}}-\overset{|}{\underset{|}{C}}-\overset{+}{N}R_3\ OH^- \xrightarrow{\text{heat}} \ \ce{C=C} + H_2O + NR_3$$

Cope Elimination

$$-\overset{|}{\underset{|}{C}}-\overset{H\ \overset{+}{N}(CH_3)_2}{\underset{|}{\underset{|}{C}}}- \xrightarrow[\text{(syn elimination)}]{\text{heat}} \ \ce{C=C} + (CH_3)_2NOH$$

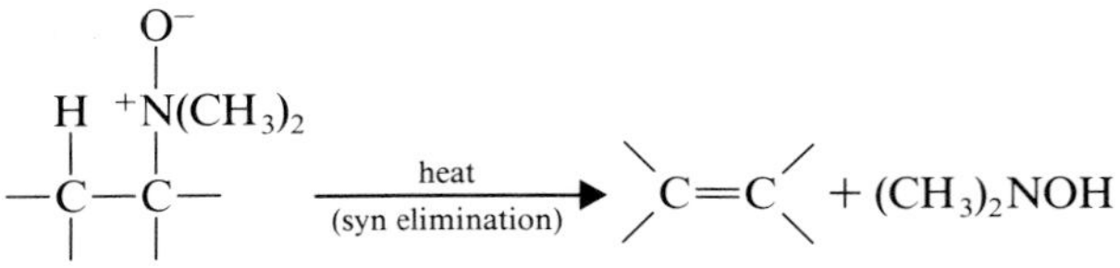

Additional Problems

19.21   Write structural formulas for each of the following compounds:

(a) Benzylmethylamine

(b) Triisopropylamine

(c) *N*-Ethyl-*N*-methylaniline

(d) *m*-Toluidine

(e) 2-Methylpyrrole

(f) *N*-Ethylpiperidine

(g) *N*-Ethylpyridinium bromide

(h) 3-Pyridinecarboxylic acid

(i) Indole

(j) Acetanilide

(k) Dimethylaminium chloride

(l) 2-Methylimidazole

(m) 3-Amino-1-propanol

(n) Tetrapropylammonium chloride

(o) Pyrrolidine

(p) *N,N*-Dimethyl-*p*-toluidine

(q) 4-Methoxyaniline

(r) Tetramethylammonium hydroxide

(s) *p*-Aminobenzoic acid

(t) *N*-Methylaniline

19.22   Give common or systematic names for each of the following compounds:

(a) $CH_3CH_2CH_2NH_2$

(b) $C_6H_5NHCH_3$

(c) $(CH_3)_2CH\overset{+}{N}(CH_3)_3\ I^-$

(d) $o\text{-}CH_3C_6H_4NH_2$

(e) $o\text{-}CH_3OC_6H_4NH_2$

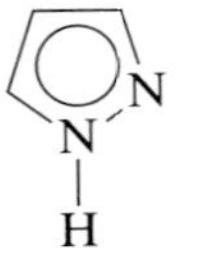

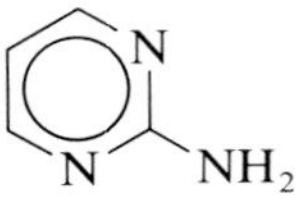

(i) $C_6H_5N(CH_2CH_2CH_3)_2$

(j) $C_6H_5SO_2NH_2$

(k) $CH_3NH_3{}^+CH_3CO_2{}^-$

(l) $HOCH_2CH_2CH_2NH_2$

(f)

(g)

(h) $C_6H_5CH_2NH_3{}^+\ Cl^-$

(m)

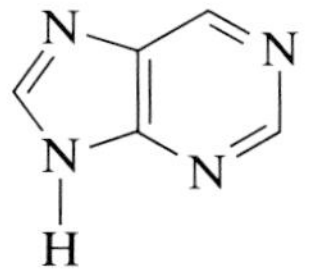

(n)

ADDITIONAL PROBLEMS

19.23 Show how you might prepare benzylamine from each of the following compounds:

(a) Benzonitrile

(b) Benzamide

(c) Benzyl bromide (two ways)

(d) Benzyl tosylate

(e) Benzaldehyde

(f) Phenylnitromethane

(g) Phenylacetamide

19.24 Show how you might prepare aniline from each of the following compounds:

(a) Benzene   (b) Bromobenzene   (c) Benzamide

19.25 Show how you might synthesize each of the following compounds from butyl alcohol:

(a) Butylamine (free of 2° and 3° amines)

(b) Pentylamine

(c) Propylamine

(d) Butylmethylamine

19.26 Show how you might convert aniline into each of the following compounds. (You need not repeat steps carried out in earlier parts of this problem.)

(a) Acetanilide

(b) *N*-Phenylphthalimide

(c) *p*-Nitroaniline

(d) Sulfanilamide

(e) *N,N*-Dimethylaniline

(f) Fluorobenzene

(g) Chlorobenzene

(h) Bromobenzene

(i) Iodobenzene

(j) Benzonitrile

(k) Benzoic acid

(l) Phenol

(m) Benzene

(n) *p*-(Phenylazo)phenol

(o) *N,N*-Dimethyl-*p*-(phenylazo)aniline

19.27 What products would you expect to be formed when each of the following amines reacts with aqueous sodium nitrite and hydrochloric acid?

(a) Propylamine

(b) Dipropylamine

(c) *N*-Propylaniline

(d) *N,N*-Dipropylaniline

(e) *p*-Propylaniline

19.28 (a) What products would you expect to be formed when each of the amines in the preceding problem reacts with benzenesulfonyl chloride and excess aqueous potassium hydroxide? (b) What would you observe in each reaction? (c) What would you observe when the resulting solution or mixture is acidified?

19.29 (a) What product would you expect to obtain from the reaction of piperidine with aqueous sodium nitrite and hydrochloric acid? (b) From the reaction of piperidine and benzenesulfonyl chloride in excess aqueous potassium hydroxide?

19.30 Give structures for the products of each of the following reactions:

(a) Ethylamine + benzoyl chloride $\longrightarrow$

(b) Methylamine + acetic anhydride $\longrightarrow$

(c) Methylamine + succinic anhydride $\longrightarrow$

(d) Product of (c) $\xrightarrow{\text{heat}}$

(e) Pyrrolidine + phthalic anhydride $\longrightarrow$

(f) Pyrrole + acetic anhydride $\longrightarrow$

(g) Aniline + propanoyl chloride $\longrightarrow$

(h) Tetraethylammonium hydroxide $\xrightarrow{\text{heat}}$

(i) m-Dinitrobenzene + H$_2$S $\xrightarrow[\text{C}_2\text{H}_5\text{OH}]{\text{NH}_3}$

(j) p-Toluidine + Br$_2$(excess) $\xrightarrow{\text{H}_2\text{O}}$

19.31 Starting with benzene or toluene, outline a synthesis of each of the following compounds using diazonium salts as intermediates. (You need not repeat syntheses carried out in earlier parts of this problem.)

(a) *o*-Cresol

(b) *m*-Cresol

(c) *p*-Cresol

(d) *m*-Dichlorobenzene

(e) *m*-C$_6$H$_4$(CN)$_2$

(f) *m*-Iodophenol

(g) *m*-Bromobenzonitrile

(h) 1,3-Dibromo-5-nitrobenzene

(i) 3,5-Dibromoaniline

(j) 3,4,5-Tribromophenol

(k) 3,4,5-Tribromobenzonitrile

(l) 2,6-Dibromobenzoic acid

(m) 1,3-Dibromo-2-iodobenzene

(n) 4-Bromo-2-nitrotoluene

(o) 4-Methyl-3-nitrophenol

(p) CH$_3$— (benzene ring with —Br and —CN substituents)

(q) CH$_3$— (benzene ring) —N=N— (benzene ring) —OH

(r) CH$_3$— (benzene ring) —N=N— (benzene ring with OH and CH$_3$ substituents)

19.32 Write equations for simple chemical tests that would distinguish between

(a) Benzylamine and benzamide

(b) Allylamine and propylamine

(c) *p*-Toluidine and *N*-methylaniline

(d) Cyclohexylamine and piperidine

(e) Pyridine and benzene

(f) Cyclohexylamine and aniline

(g) Triethylamine and diethylamine

(h) Tripropylaminium chloride and tetrapropylammonium chloride

(i) Tetrapropylammonium chloride and tetrapropylammonium hydroxide

19.33 Describe with equations how you might separate a mixture of aniline, *p*-cresol, benzoic acid, and toluene using ordinary laboratory reagents.

19.34 Show how you might synthesize β-aminopropionic acid ($\overset{+}{\text{H}_3}\text{NCH}_2\text{CH}_2\text{CO}_2^-$) from succinic anhydride. (β-Aminopropionic acid is used in the synthesis of pantothenic acid; cf. Problem 18.33.)

19.35 Show how you might synthesize each of the following from the compounds indicated and any other needed reagents.

(a) Decamethonium bromide (Section 19.4) from 1,10-decanediol

(b) Succinylcholine bromide from succinic acid, 2-bromoethanol, and trimethylamine

(c) Acetylcholine chloride from ethylene oxide

19.36 A commercial synthesis of folic acid consists of heating the following three compounds with aqueous sodium bicarbonate. Propose reasonable mechanisms for the reactions that lead to folic acid.

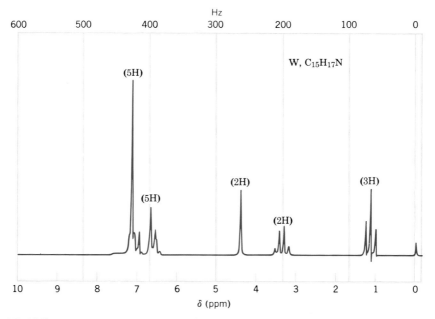

folic acid
(~10%)

19.37 When compound **W** ($C_{15}H_{17}N$) is treated with benzenesulfonyl chloride and aqueous potassium hydroxide, no apparent change occurs. Acidification of this mixture gives a clear solution. The ^1H NMR spectrum of **W** is shown in Fig. 19.5. Propose a structure for **W**.

FIGURE 19.5 The ^1H NMR spectrum of **W**, Problem 19.37. (Courtesy Aldrich Chemical Company, Inc., Milwaukee, WI.)

19.38 Propose structures for compounds **X**, **Y**, and **Z**.

$$\textbf{X}(C_7H_7Br) \xrightarrow{NaCN} \textbf{Y}(C_8H_7N) \xrightarrow{LiAlH_4} \textbf{Z}(C_8H_{11}N)$$

The ^1H NMR spectrum of **X** gives two signals, a multiplet at δ 7.3 (5H) and a singlet at δ 4.25 (2H); the 680–840-cm^{-1} region of the IR spectrum of **X** shows peaks at 690 and 770 cm^{-1}. The ^1H NMR spectrum of **Y** is similar to that of **X**: multiplet δ 7.3 (5H), singlet δ 3.7 (2H). The ^1H NMR and IR spectra of **Z** are shown in Fig. 19.6.

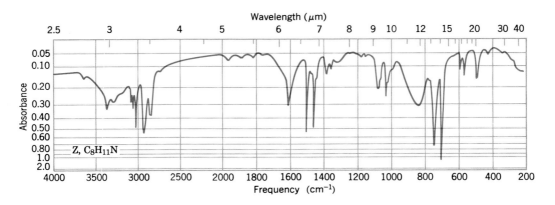

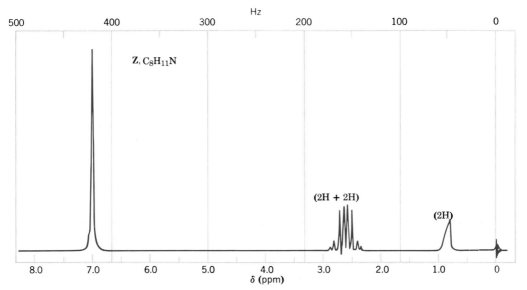

FIGURE 19.6 Infrared and ^{1}H NMR spectra for compound **Z**, Problem 19.38. (Courtesy Sadtler Research Laboratories, Inc., Philadelphia.)

19.39 Using reactions that we have studied in this chapter, propose a mechanism that accounts for the following reaction:

19.40 Give structures for compounds **R–W**:

N-Methylpiperidine + $CH_3I \longrightarrow$ **R** $(C_7H_{16}NI) \xrightarrow[H_2O]{Ag_2O}$

S $(C_7H_{17}NO) \xrightarrow[(-H_2O)]{heat}$ **T** $(C_7H_{15}N) \xrightarrow{CH_3I}$ **U** $(C_8H_{18}NI) \xrightarrow[H_2O]{Ag_2O}$

V $(C_8H_{19}NO) \xrightarrow{heat}$ **W** $(C_5H_8) + H_2O + (CH_3)_3N$

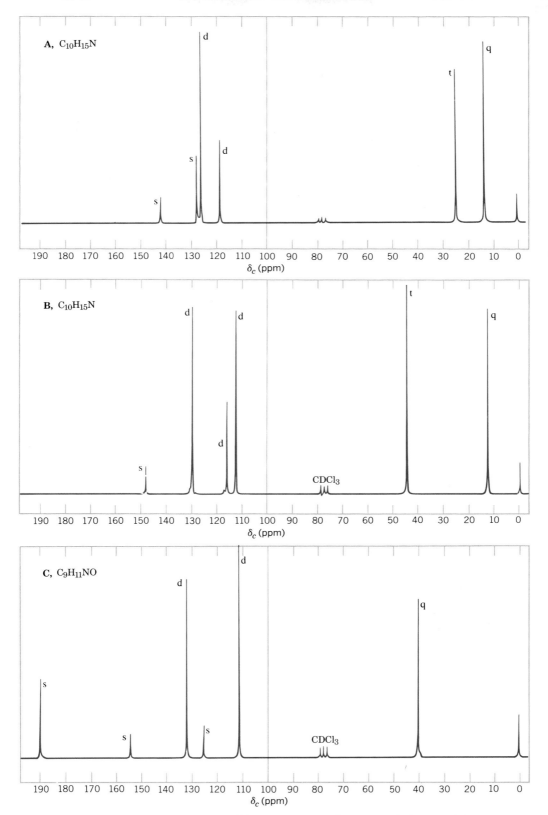

FIGURE 19.7 The proton-decoupled ^{13}C NMR spectra of compounds **A**, **B**, and **C**, Problems 19.41–19.43. The letters s, d, t, and q refer to the signal splitting in the proton off-resonance decoupled spectra (singlet, doublet, triplet, and quartet). (Adapted from L. F. Johnson and W. C. Jankowski, *Carbon-13 NMR Spectra: A Collection of Assigned, Coded, and Indexed Spectra,* Wiley–Interscience, New York, 1972.)

19.41   Compound **A** ($C_{10}H_{15}N$) is soluble in dilute HCl. The IR absorption spectrum shows two bands in the 3300–3500-cm^{-1} region. The proton-decoupled ^{13}C spectrum of **A** is given in Fig. 19.7. Propose a structure for **A**.

19.42   Compound **B**, an isomer of **A** (Problem 19.41), is also soluble in dilute HCl. The IR spectrum of **B** shows no bands in the 3300–3500-cm^{-1} region. The proton-decoupled ^{13}C spectrum of **B** is given in Fig. 19.7. Propose a structure for **B**.

19.43   Compound **C** ($C_9H_{11}NO$) gives a positive Tollens' test and is soluble in dilute HCl. The IR spectrum of **C** shows a strong band near 1695 cm^{-1} but shows no bands in the 3300–3500-cm^{-1} region. The proton-decoupled ^{13}C NMR spectrum of **C** is shown in Fig. 19.7. Propose a structure for **C**.

REACTIONS AND SYNTHESIS OF HETEROCYCLIC AMINES

Heterocyclic amines undergo many reactions that are similar to those of the amines that we have studied in earlier chapters.

G.1 HETEROCYCLIC AMINES AS BASES

Nonaromatic heterocyclic amines have basicity constants that are approximately the same as those of acyclic amines.

Piperidine
$pK_b = 2.80$

Pyrrolidine
$pK_b = 2.89$

Diethylamine
$pK_b = 3.02$

In aqueous solution, aromatic heterocyclic amines such as pyridine, pyrimidine, and pyrrole are much weaker bases than nonaromatic amines or ammonia ($pK_b = 4.74$). (In the gas phase, however, pyridine and pyrrole are more basic than ammonia, indicating that solvation has a very important effect on their relative basicities, cf. Section 19.3.)

Pyridine
$pK_b = 8.77$

Pyrimidine
$pK_b = 11.30$

Pyrrole
$pK_b = 13.60$

Quinoline
$pK_b = 9.5$

G.2 HETEROCYCLIC AMINES AS NUCLEOPHILES IN ALKYLATION AND ACYLATION REACTIONS

Most heterocyclic amines undergo alkylation and acylation reactions in much the same way as acyclic amines.

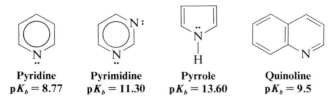

Piperidine

N-Alkylpiperidine

N,N-Dialkylpiper-
idinium bromide

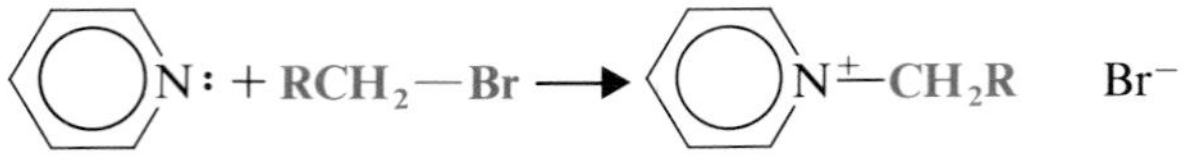

Pyridine + RCH_2—Br ⟶ N-Alkylpyridinium bromide + Br^-

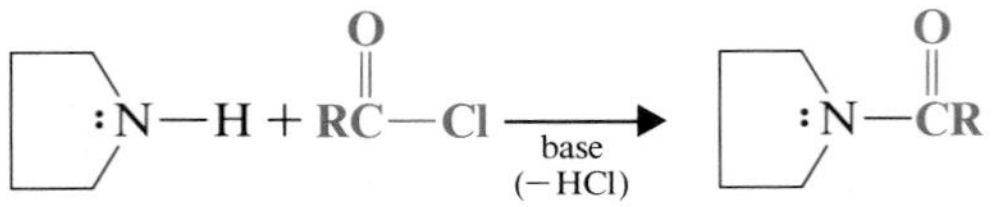

Pyrrolidine + RC—Cl $\xrightarrow[(-HCl)]{base}$ N-Acylpyrrolidine (an amide)

Problem G.1

What products would you expect to obtain from the following reactions?
(a) Piperidine + acetic anhydride ⟶
(b) Pyridine + methyl iodide ⟶
(c) Pyrrolidine + phthalic anhydride ⟶
(d) Pyrrolidine + (excess) methyl iodide $\xrightarrow{\text{(base)}}$
(e) Product of (d) + Ag_2O, H_2O, then heat ⟶

G.3 ELECTROPHILIC SUBSTITUTION REACTIONS OF AROMATIC HETEROCYCLIC AMINES

Pyrrole is highly reactive toward electrophilic substitution and substitution takes place primarily at position 2.

General Reaction

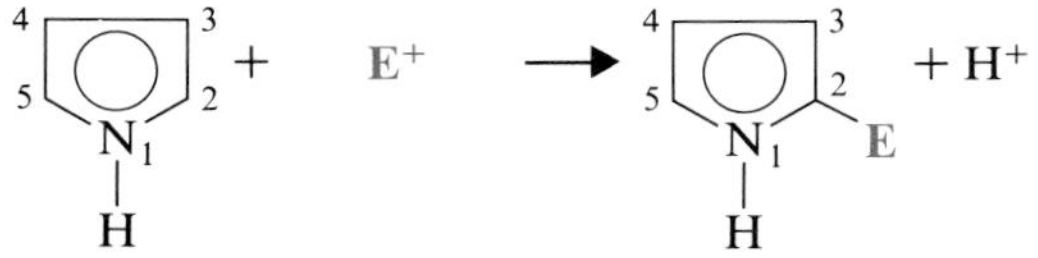

Pyrrole + Electrophile E^+ ⟶ 2-Substituted pyrrole + H^+

Specific Example

Pyrrole + C_6H_5—$\overset{+}{N}{\equiv}N$ $\bar{X}$ ⟶ product + HX

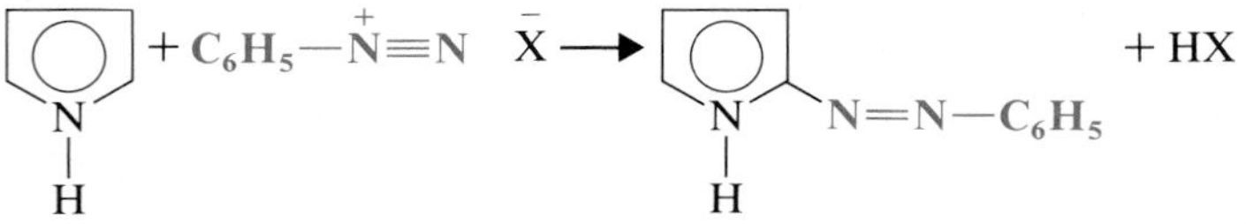

We can understand why electrophilic substitution at the 2 position is preferred if we examine the resonance structures that follow:

Substitution at the 2 Position of Pyrrole

Positive charge is delocalized over three atoms

Substitution at the 3 position of pyrrole

Positive charge is delocalized over
only two atoms

We see that while a relatively stable structure contributes to the hybrid for both intermediates, the intermediate arising from attack at the 2 position is stabilized by one additional resonance structure, and the positive charge is delocalized over three atoms rather than two. This means that this intermediate is more stable, and that attack at the 2 position has a lower free energy of activation.

Pyridine is much less reactive toward electrophilic substitution than benzene. Pyridine does not undergo Friedel–Crafts acylation or alkylation; it does not couple with diazonium compounds. Bromination of pyridine can be accomplished but only in the vapor phase at 200 °C where a free radical mechanism may operate. Nitration and sulfonation also require forcing conditions. Electrophilic substitution, when it occurs, nearly always takes place at the 3 position.

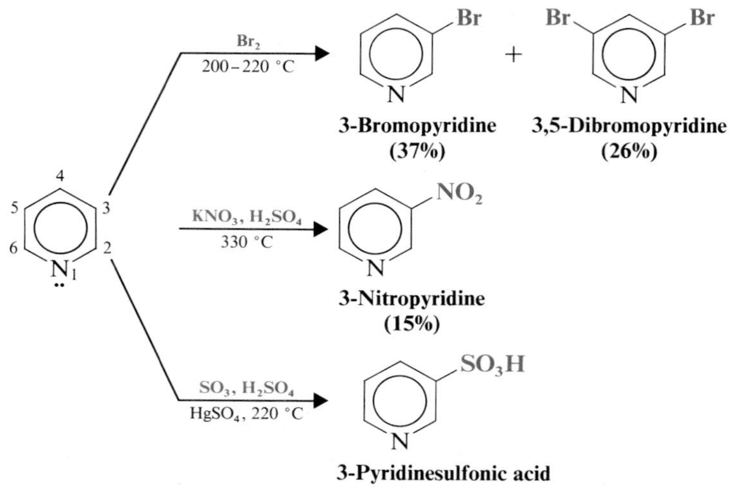

3-Bromopyridine
(37%)   **3,5-Dibromopyridine**
(26%)

3-Nitropyridine
(15%)

3-Pyridinesulfonic acid

We can, in part, attribute the lower reactivity of pyridine (when compared to benzene) to the greater electronegativity of nitrogen (when compared to carbon). Nitrogen, being more electronegative, is less able to accommodate the electron deficiency that characterizes the transition state leading to the positively charged ion (similar to an arenium ion) in electrophilic substitution.

Pyridine   **Transition state**   **Similar to**
is of higher energy   **an arenium**
because of greater   **ion**
electronegativity
of nitrogen

Benzene   **Transition state**   **Arenium ion**
is of lower energy
because of lower
electronegativity
of carbon

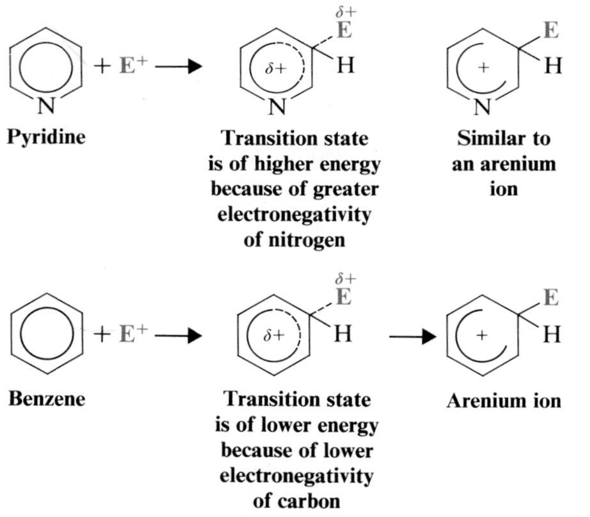

The low reactivity of pyridine toward electrophilic substitution may arise mainly from the fact that pyridine is converted initially to a pyridinium ion by a proton or other electrophile.

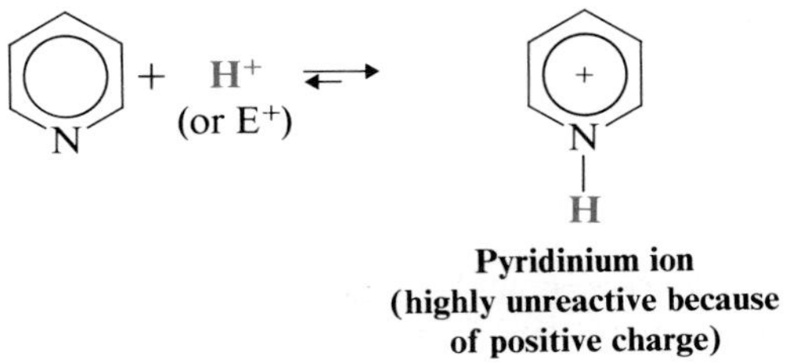

Pyridinium ion
(highly unreactive because
of positive charge)

Electrophilic attack at the 4 position (or the 2 position) is unfavorable because an especially unstable resonance structure contributes to the intermediate hybrid.

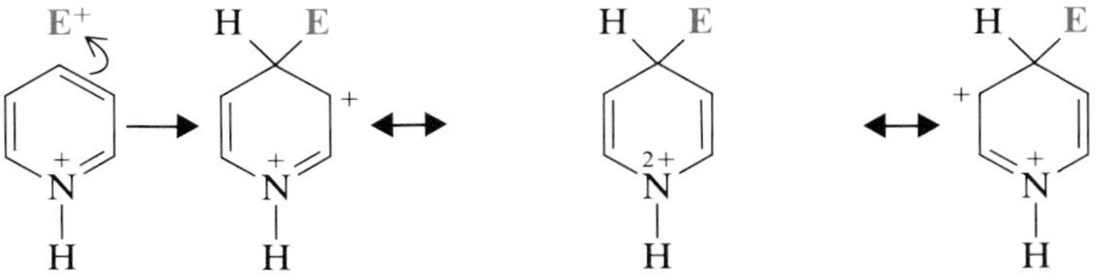

**Especially unstable because
nitrogen has a sextet
and two positive charges**

Similar resonance structures can be written for attack at the 2 position.

No especially unstable *or stable* structure contributes to the hybrid arising from attack at the 3 position; as a result, attack at the 3 position is preferred but occurs slowly.

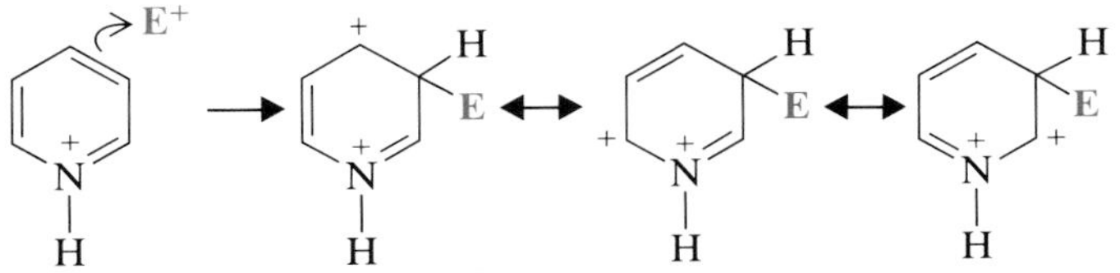

**No especially unstable or stable
structure contributes to the hybrid**

Pyrimidine is even less reactive toward electrophilic substitution than pyridine. (Why?) When electrophilic substitution takes place, it occurs at the 5 position.

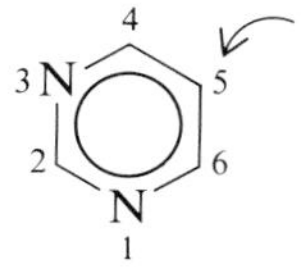

**Electrophilic substitution
takes place here**

Pyrimidine

Imidazole is much more susceptible to electrophilic substitution than pyridine or pyrimidine, but is less reactive than pyrrole. Imidazoles with 1 substituents undergo electrophilic substitution at the 4 position.

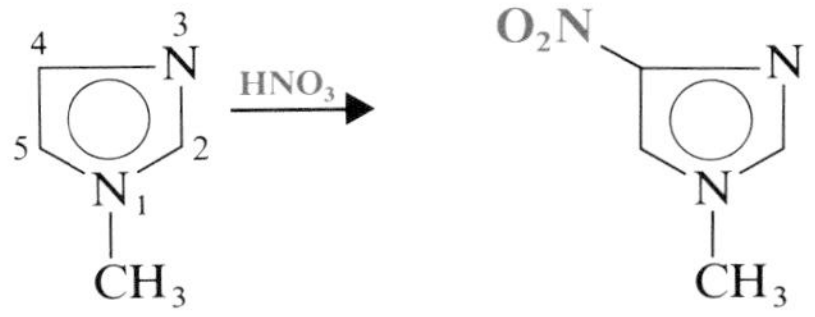

1-Methyl-4-nitroimidazole

Imidazole, itself, undergoes electrophilic substitution in a similar fashion. Tautomerism, however, makes the 4 and 5 positions equivalent.

4-(5)-Bromoimidazole

Problem G.2

Both pyrrole and imidazole are weak acids; they react with strong bases to form anions:

Pyrrole anion   **Imidazole anion**

(a) These anions resemble a carbocyclic anion that we have studied before. What is it? (b) Write resonance structures that account for the stabilities of pyrrole and imidazole anions.

G.4 NUCLEOPHILIC SUBSTITUTIONS OF PYRIDINE

In its reactions, the pyridine ring resembles a benzene ring with a strong electron-withdrawing group; pyridine is relatively unreactive toward electrophilic substitution but appreciably reactive toward nucleophilic substitution.

In the previous section we compared the reactivity of pyridine and benzene toward electrophilic substitution and there we attributed pyridine's lower reactivity to the greater electronegativity of its ring nitrogen. Because nitrogen is more electronegative than carbon, it is less able to accommodate the electron deficiency in the transition state of the rate-determining step in electrophilic aromatic substitution. On the other hand, nitrogen's greater electronegativity makes it *more* able to accommodate the excess *negative* charge that an aromatic ring must accept in *nucleophilic substitution.*

Pyridine reacts with sodium amide, for example, to form 2-aminopyridine. In this remarkable reaction (called the Chichibabin reaction), amide ion (NH_2^-) displaces a hydride ion (H^-).

2-Aminopyridine
(70–80%)

If we examine the resonance structures that contribute to the intermediate in this reaction, we shall be able to see how the ring nitrogen atom accommodates the negative charge:

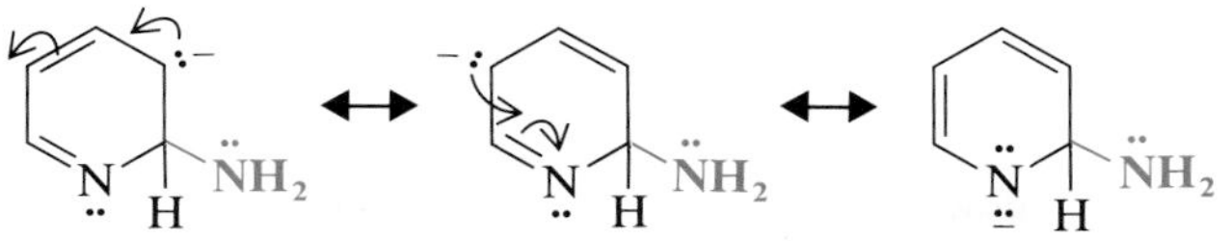

Relatively stable because negative charge is on electronegative nitrogen

In the next step the intermediate loses a hydride ion and becomes 2-aminopyridine.*

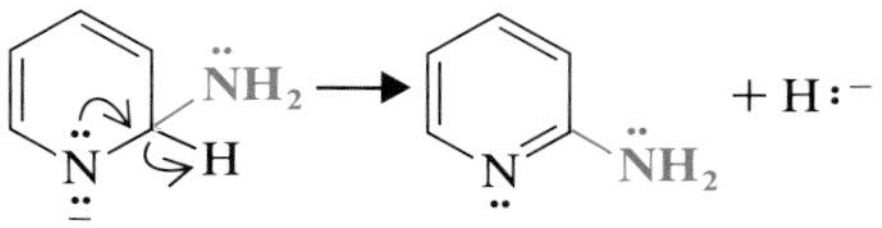

Pyridine undergoes similar nucleophilic substitution reactions with phenyllithium, butyllithium, and potassium hydroxide.

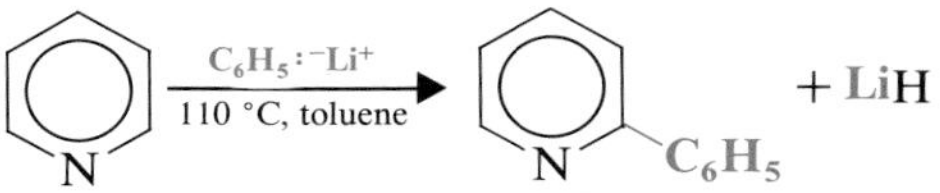

2-Phenylpyridine

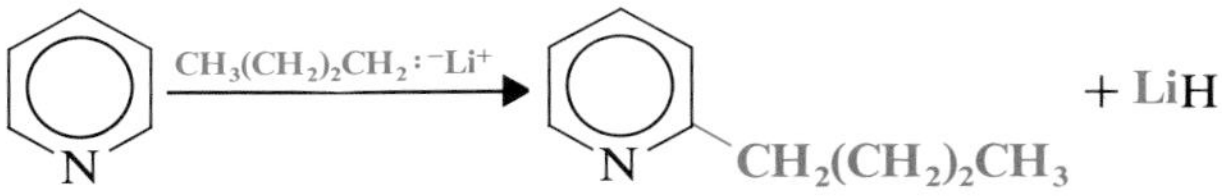

2-Butylpyridine

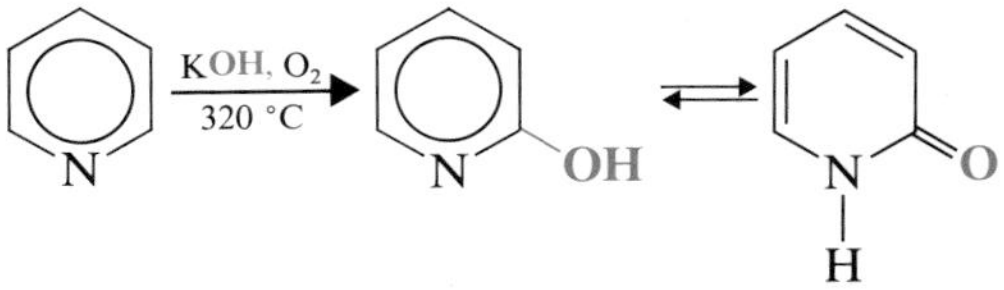

2-Pyridinol (50%)   **2-Pyridone**

2-Chloropyridine reacts with sodium methoxide to yield 2-methoxypyridine:

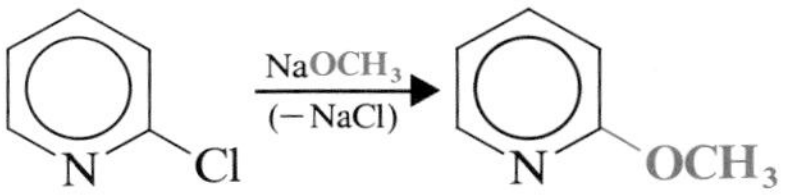

* In practice, a subsequent reaction occurs; 2-aminopyridine reacts with the sodium hydride to produce a sodio derivative:

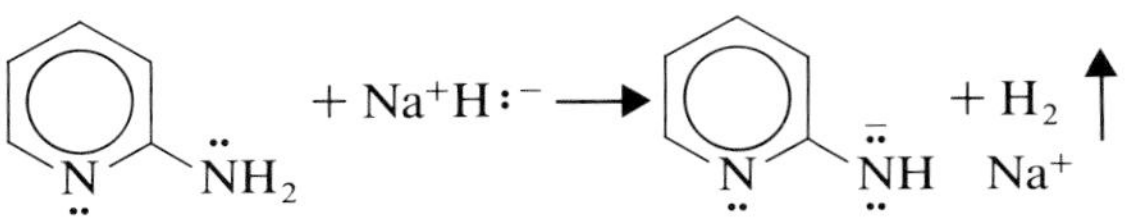

When the reaction is over, the addition of cold water to the reaction mixture converts the sodio derivative to 2-aminopyridine.

Problem G.3

An alternative mechanism to the one given for the amination of pyridine in Section G.4, involves a "pyridyne" intermediate, that is,

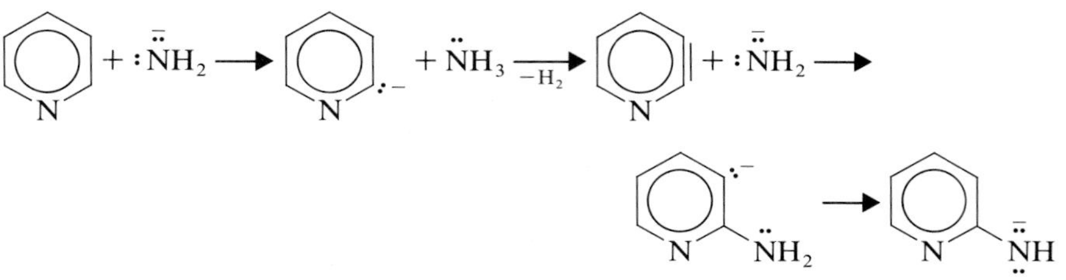

This mechanism was disallowed on the basis of an experiment in which 3-deuteriopyridine was allowed to react with sodium amide. Consider the fate of deuterium in both mechanisms and explain.

Problem G.4

2-Halopyridines undergo nucleophilic substitution much more readily than pyridine itself. What factor accounts for this?

G.5 NUCLEOPHILIC ADDITIONS TO PYRIDINIUM IONS

Pyridinium ions are especially susceptible to nucleophilic attack at the 2 or 4 position because of the contributions of the resonance forms shown here.

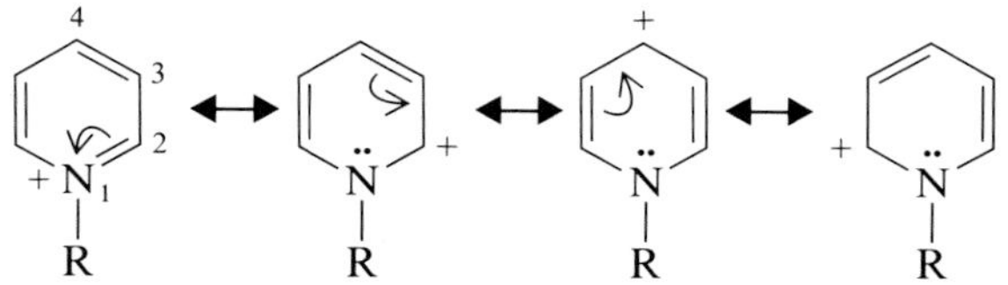

N-Alkylpyridinium halides, for example, react with hydroxide ions primarily at position 2; this causes the formation of an addition product called a *pseudo base*.

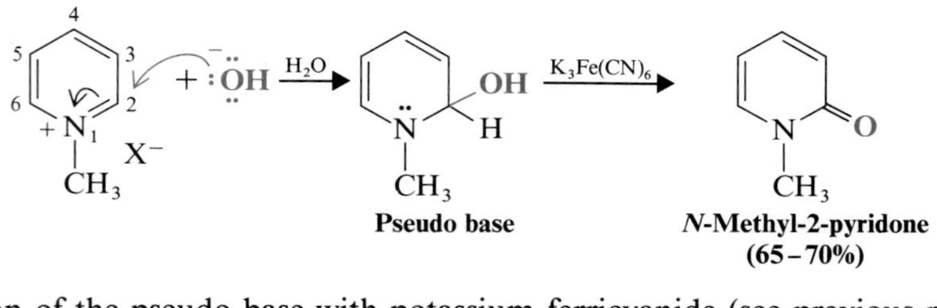

Pseudo base   **N-Methyl-2-pyridone**
(65–70%)

Oxidation of the pseudo base with potassium ferricyanide (see previous reaction) produces an N-alkylpyridone.

Nucleophilic additions to pyridinium ions, especially the addition of *hydride ions,* have been of considerable interest to chemists because these reactions resemble the biological reduction of the important coenzyme, nicotinamide adenine dinucleotide (NAD$^+$) (Section 13.13).

A number of model reactions have been carried out in connection with these studies. Treating an *N*-alkylpyridinium ion with sodium borohydride, for example, brings about hydride addition, but addition occurs at position 2 and is usually accompanied by over reduction:

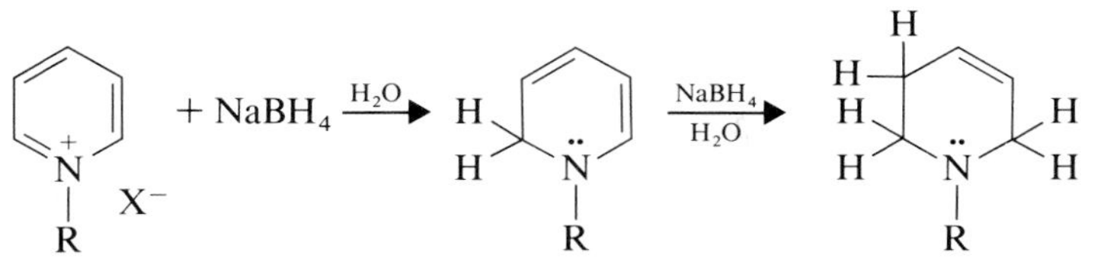

N-Alkyl-
pyridinium
halide

A 1,2-dihydro-
pyridine

A 1,2,3,6-tetrahydro-
pyridine

Treating a pyridinium ion with basic sodium dithionite ($Na_2S_2O_4$), however, brings about specific addition to position 4:

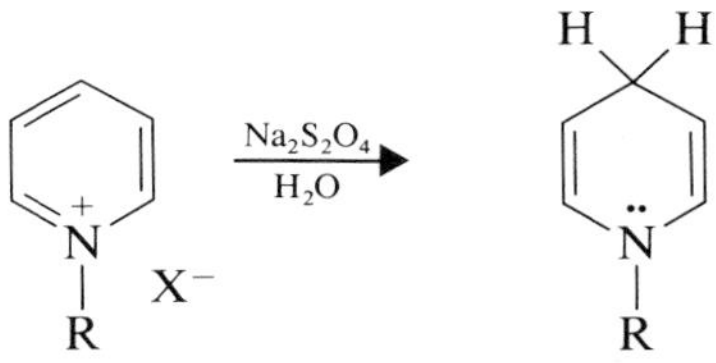

A 1,4-dihydropyridine

Sodium dithionite in aqueous base also reduces NAD^+ to NADH. The NADH formed by dithionite reduction has been shown to be biologically active and can be oxidized to NAD^+ with potassium ferricyanide.

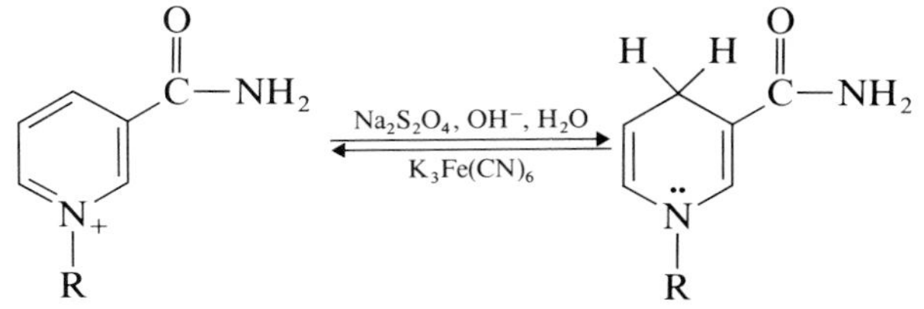

NAD$^+$
(see Section 13.12 for
the structure of R)

NADH

G.6 SYNTHESIS OF HETEROCYCLIC AMINES

The most general and widely used method for synthesizing pyrroles is to condense an α-amino ketone or α-amino-β-keto ester with a ketone or keto ester. This reaction, called the Knorr synthesis, is catalyzed by acids or bases. Two examples are shown here.

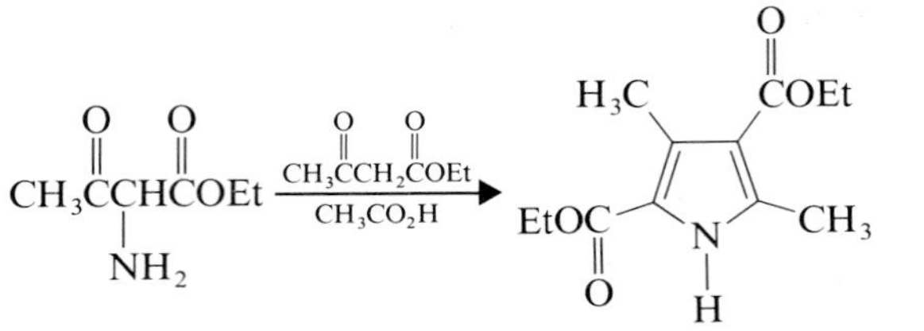

(57–64%)

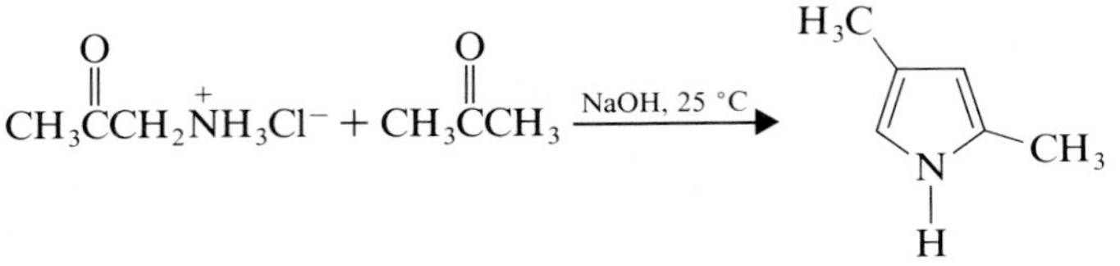

Problem G.5

Propose reasonable mechanisms for the two syntheses of substituted pyrroles just given.

Pyridine and many of its derivatives can be isolated from coal tar. Many pyridine derivatives are prepared from these coal-tar derivatives through substitution reactions. The most general overall pyridine synthesis is one called the Hantzsch synthesis. In this method a β-keto ester, an aldehyde, and ammonia are allowed to condense to produce a dihydropyridine; oxidation of the dihydropyridine yields the substituted pyridine. An example is the following:

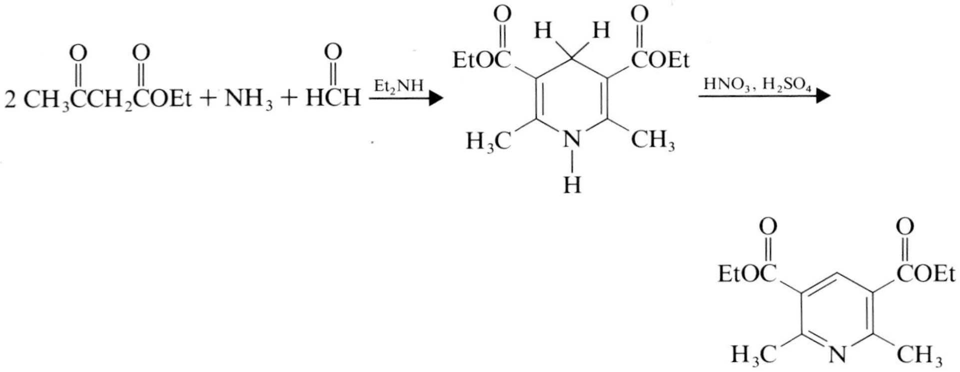

$$2\ CH_3CCH_2COEt + NH_3 + HCH \xrightarrow{Et_2NH}$$

(58–65%)

The most general quinoline synthesis is the Skraup synthesis. In this method, aniline is heated with glycerol in the presence of sulfuric acid and an oxidizing agent. Various oxidizing agents have been used including nitrobenzene and air.

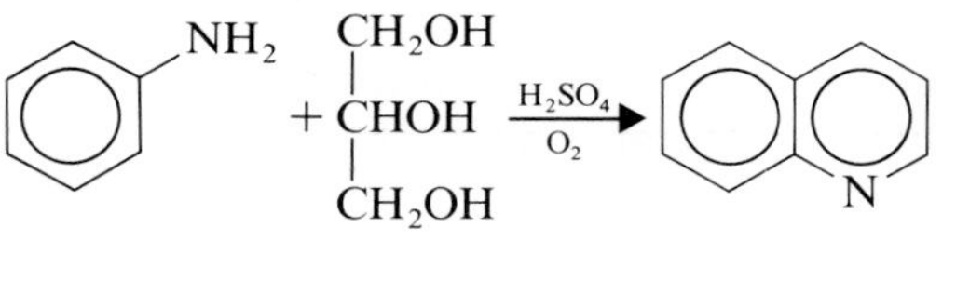

The mechanism for this reaction consists of the following steps:

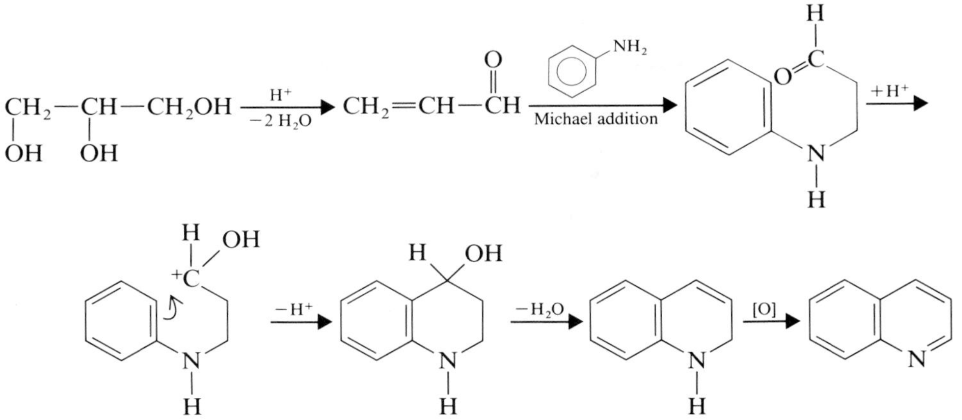

In the first step glycerol dehydrates in the presence of the acid to produce propenal (acrolein). Then a Michael addition of aniline to the propenal is followed by an acid-catalyzed cyclization to yield dihydroquinoline. Finally, oxidation of the dihydroquinoline produces quinoline.

Problem G.6

Give structures for compounds A–H.

(a) 2,5-Hexanedione + $(NH_4)_2CO_3$ $\xrightarrow{100\ °C}$ A (C_6H_9N)
A pyrrole

(b) $CH_3\overset{O}{\overset{\|}{C}}CH_2NH_2$ + acetone $\xrightarrow{base}$ B (C_6H_9N)
An isomer of A

(c) $CH_3NHNH_2 + (CH_3O)_2CHCH_2CH(OCH_3)_2$ $\xrightarrow[H_2O]{H^+}$ C $(C_4H_6N_2)$
A pyrazole

(d) 2,5-Hexanedione + hydrazine $\xrightarrow{heat}$ D $(C_6H_{10}N_2)$ $\xrightarrow{O_2}$ E $(C_6H_8N_2)$
A dihydropyridazine   **A pyridazine**

(e) Aniline + $CH_2{=}CH\overset{O}{\overset{\|}{C}}CH_3$ $\xrightarrow[FeCl_3]{ZnCl_2}$ F $(C_{10}H_9N)$
A quinoline

(f) 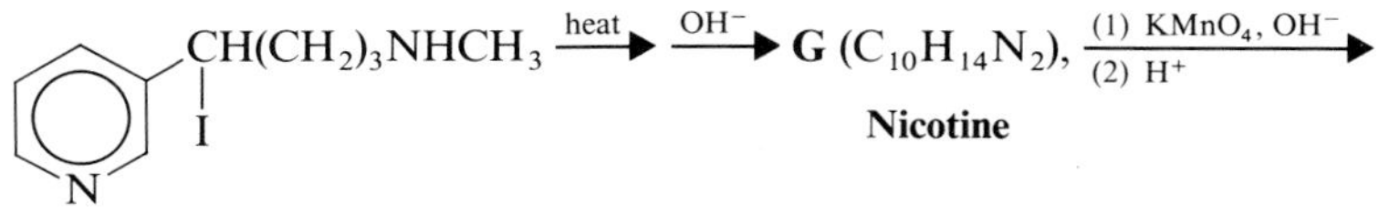 [pyridine ring]—$CH(CH_2)_3NHCH_3$ $\xrightarrow{heat}$ $\xrightarrow{OH^-}$ G $(C_{10}H_{14}N_2)$, $\xrightarrow[(2)\ H^+]{(1)\ KMnO_4,\ OH^-}$
Nicotine

H $(C_6H_5NO_2)$
Nicotinic acid

Phenobarbital (see Section 20.12).

CHAPTER

20

SYNTHESIS AND REACTIONS OF β-DICARBONYL COMPOUNDS: MORE CHEMISTRY OF ENOLATE IONS

20.1 INTRODUCTION

Compounds having two carbonyl groups separated by an intervening carbon are called β-dicarbonyl compounds, and these compounds are highly versatile reagents for organic synthesis. In this chapter we shall explore some of the methods for preparing β-dicarbonyl compounds and some of their important reactions.

$$
\begin{array}{ccc}
\underset{\beta\ \ \ \alpha}{-\overset{\overset{\displaystyle O}{\|}}{C}-\overset{\displaystyle |}{\underset{|}{C}}-\overset{\overset{\displaystyle O}{\|}}{C}-} &
\underset{\beta\ \ \alpha}{R\overset{\overset{\displaystyle O}{\|}}{C}CH_2\overset{\overset{\displaystyle O}{\|}}{C}OR'} &
\underset{\beta\ \ \ \alpha}{RO\overset{\overset{\displaystyle O}{\|}}{C}CH_2\overset{\overset{\displaystyle O}{\|}}{C}OR}
\end{array}
$$

The β-dicarbonyl system   A β-keto ester   A malonic ester
(Section 20.2)   (Section 20.4)

Central to the chemistry of β-dicarbonyl compounds is the acidity of protons located on the carbon between two carbonyl groups. The pK_a for such a proton is in the range 10–14.

$$-\overset{\overset{O}{\|}}{C}-\overset{|}{\underset{|}{C}}-\overset{\overset{O}{\|}}{C}- \qquad \overset{H}{} \quad -pK_a = 10-14$$

Early in this chapter we shall see how the acidity of these protons allows the synthesis of β-dicarbonyl compounds through reactions that are called *Claisen syntheses* (Section 20.2). Later in the chapter we shall study the *acetoacetic ester synthesis* (Section 20.3) and the *malonic ester synthesis* (Section 20.4), in which the acidity of these hydrogen atoms forms the basis for the synthesis of substituted acetones and substituted acetic acids. The acidity of the hydrogen atoms of a carbon located between two carbonyl groups allows easy conversion of the compound to an enolate ion, and these enolate ions can be alkylated and acylated. Similar chemistry underlies syntheses using a variety of other useful reactions (Section 20.5), including the Knoevenagel condensation (Section 20.8).

One other feature that will appear again and again in the syntheses that we study here is the decarboxylation of a β-keto acid:

$$-\overset{\overset{O}{\|}}{C}-\overset{|}{\underset{|}{C}}-\overset{\overset{O}{\|}}{C}OH \xrightarrow{\text{heat}} -\overset{\overset{O}{\|}}{C}-\overset{|}{\underset{|}{C}}-H + CO_2$$

We learned in Section 18.11 that these decarboxylations occur at relatively low temperatures, and it is this ease of decarboxylation that makes many of the syntheses in this chapter such useful ones.

20.2 THE CLAISEN CONDENSATION: THE SYNTHESIS OF β-KETO ESTERS

When ethyl acetate reacts with sodium ethoxide, it undergoes *a condensation reaction.* After acidification, the product is a β-keto ester, ethyl acetoacetate (commonly called *acetoacetic ester*).

$$2\ CH_3\overset{\overset{O}{\|}}{C}OC_2H_5 \xrightarrow{NaOC_2H_5} \left[CH_3\overset{\overset{O}{\|}}{C}\overset{..}{C}H\overset{\overset{O}{\|}}{C}OC_2H_5 \atop Na^+ \right] + C_2H_5OH$$

Sodioacetoacetic   **(removed by**
ester   **distillation)**

$$\downarrow HCl$$

$$CH_3\overset{\overset{O}{\|}}{C}CH_2\overset{\overset{O}{\|}}{C}OC_2H_5$$

Ethyl acetoacetate
(acetoacetic ester)
(75–76%)

Condensations of this type occur with many other esters and are known generally as *Claisen condensations.* Like the aldol condensation (Section 17.10), Claisen condensations involve the α carbon of one molecule and the carbonyl group of another.

Ethyl pentanoate, for example, reacts with sodium ethoxide to give the β-keto ester that follows:

$$2\ CH_3CH_2CH_2CH_2COC_2H_5 \xrightarrow{NaOCH_2CH_3} \left[CH_3CH_2CH_2CH_2\underset{\underset{\underset{CH_3}{|}}{\underset{\overset{|}{CH_2}}{\overset{|}{CH_2}}}}{C}-\overset{Na^+}{\underset{\cdot\cdot}{C}}-COC_2H_5 \right] + C_2H_5OH$$

$$\downarrow\ CH_3CO_2H$$

$$CH_3CH_2CH_2CH_2\overset{O}{\overset{||}{C}}-\underset{\underset{\underset{CH_3}{|}}{\underset{CH_2}{|}}}{\underset{CH_2}{\underset{|}{CH}}}-\overset{O}{\overset{||}{C}}OC_2H_5$$

(77%)

If we look closely at these examples, we can see that, overall, both reactions involve a condensation in which one ester loses an α hydrogen and the other loses an ethoxide ion; that is,

$$R-CH_2\overset{O}{\overset{||}{C}} \dashv OC_2H_5 + H \vdash \underset{R}{\underset{|}{CH}}\overset{O}{\overset{||}{C}}-OC_2H_5 \xrightarrow[(2)\ H^+]{(1)\ NaOC_2H_5}$$

(R may also be H)

$$R-CH_2\overset{O}{\overset{||}{C}}-\underset{R}{\underset{|}{CH}}\overset{O}{\overset{||}{C}}OC_2H_5 + C_2H_5OH$$

A β-keto ester

We can understand how this happens if we examine the reaction mechanism.

The first step of a Claisen condensation resembles that of an aldol addition. Ethoxide ion abstracts an α proton from the ester. Although the α protons of an ester are not as acidic as those of aldehydes and ketones, the enolate anion that forms is stabilized by resonance in a similar way.

Step 1 $$R\overset{\alpha}{\underset{\underset{H}{|}}{C}}H-\overset{O}{\overset{||}{C}}OC_2H_5 + \overset{\cdot\cdot}{\underset{\cdot\cdot}{O}}C_2H_5 \rightleftharpoons RCH\overset{\overset{\cdot\cdot}{O}:}{\overset{||}{-}}COC_2H_5 + C_2H_5OH$$

$$\updownarrow$$

$$\underset{RCH=COC_2H_5}{\overset{:\overset{\cdot\cdot}{O}:^-}{\overset{|}{}}}$$

In the second step the enolate anion attacks the carbonyl carbon atom of a second molecule of the ester. It is at this point that the Claisen condensation and the aldol addition *differ*, and they differ in an understandable way. In the aldol reaction nucleophilic attack leads to *addition;* in the Claisen condensation it leads to *substitution.*

Step 2

$$RCH_2C \overset{\overset{\ddot{O}}{\diagup\diagdown}}{\underset{OC_2H_5}{}} + ^-\!:\!CH\overset{\overset{\ddot{O}}{\|}}{\underset{R}{-}}COC_2H_5 \quad \rightleftharpoons \quad RCH_2\overset{:\ddot{O}:^-}{\underset{C_2H_5\ddot{O}:}{\overset{|}{C}}}\!-\!CH\overset{\overset{\ddot{O}:}{\|}}{\underset{R}{-}}COC_2H_5$$

$$\Updownarrow$$

$$RCH_2\overset{\overset{:\ddot{O}}{\|}}{C}\!-\!CH\overset{\overset{\ddot{O}:}{\|}}{\underset{R}{-}}COC_2H_5$$

$$+ \ ^-\!:\!\ddot{O}C_2H_5$$

Although the products of this second step are a β-keto ester and ethoxide ion, all of the equilibria up to this point have been unfavorable. Very little product would be formed if this were the last step in the reaction.

The final step of a Claisen condensation is an acid–base reaction that takes place between ethoxide ion and the β-keto ester. *The position of equilibrium for this step is favorable,* and we can make it even more favorable by distilling ethanol from the reaction mixture as it forms.

Step 3

$$RCH_2\overset{\overset{O}{\|}}{C}\!-\!\overset{\overset{H}{|}}{\underset{R}{\overset{|}{C}}}\!-\!\overset{\overset{O}{\|}}{C}OC_2H_5 + \ :\!\ddot{O}C_2H_5 \quad \rightleftharpoons$$

β-Keto ester　　　　　　**Ethoxide ion**
(**stronger acid**)　　　　　(**stronger base**)

$$RCH_2\overset{\overset{:\ddot{O}}{\|}}{C}\!-\!\overset{\overset{-}{\ddot{C}}}{\underset{R}{|}}\!-\!\overset{\overset{\ddot{O}:}{\|}}{C}OC_2H_5 + \ C_2H_5OH$$

β-Keto ester anion　　　　**Ethanol**
(**weaker base**)　　　　　（**weaker acid**)

β-Keto esters are stronger acids than ethanol. They react with ethoxide ion almost quantitatively to produce ethanol and anions of β-keto esters. (It is this reaction that pulls the equilibrium to the right.) β-Keto esters are much more acidic than ordinary esters, because their enolate anions are more stabilized by resonance: Their negative charge is delocalized into two carbonyl groups:

$$RCH_2\!-\!\overset{\overset{\ddot{O}:}{\|}}{C}\!-\!\overset{\overset{\ddot{:}}{C}}{\underset{R}{|}}\!-\!\overset{\overset{\ddot{O}:}{\|}}{C}OC_2H_5 \longleftrightarrow RCH_2\!-\!\overset{\overset{:\ddot{O}:^-}{}}{C}\!=\!\overset{}{\underset{R}{C}}\!-\!\overset{\overset{\ddot{O}:}{\|}}{C}OC_2H_5 \longleftrightarrow RCH_2\!-\!\overset{\overset{:\ddot{O}}{\|}}{C}\!-\!\overset{}{\underset{R}{C}}\!=\!\overset{\overset{:\ddot{O}:^-}{}}{C}OC_2H_5$$

$$RCH_2\!-\!\overset{\overset{\delta-}{\underset{}{O}}}{C}\!\cdots\!\overset{\delta-}{\underset{R}{\overset{|}{C}}}\!\cdots\!\overset{\overset{\delta-}{\underset{}{O}}}{C}OC_2H_5$$

Resonance hybrid

After steps 1 – 3 of a Claisen condensation have taken place, we add an acid to the reaction mixture. This addition brings about a rapid protonation of the anion and produces the β-keto ester as an equilibrium mixture of its keto and enol forms.

Step 4

$$\overset{\delta-}{\overset{\parallel}{O}}\quad \overset{\delta-}{\overset{\parallel}{O}}$$

RCH$_2$—C$\overset{\delta-}{=}$C$=$COC$_2$H$_5$ $\xrightarrow[\text{(rapid)}]{\text{H}^+}$ RCH$_2$—C—CH—COC$_2$H$_5$
              | |
              R   R

Keto form

OH   O
 | ‖
RCH$_2$—C=C—COC$_2$H$_5$
         |
         R

Enol form

Esters that have only one α hydrogen do not undergo the usual Claisen condensation. An example of an ester that does not react in a normal Claisen condensation is ethyl 2-methylpropanoate.

Only one α hydrogen ⟶

$$\overset{O}{\overset{\parallel}{}}$$
CH$_3$CHCOCH$_2$CH$_3$ **Does not undergo a**
     | **Claisen condensation**
     CH$_3$

Ethyl 2-methylpropanoate

Inspection of the mechanism just given will make clear why this is so. An ester with only one α hydrogen will not have an acidic hydrogen when step 3 is reached, and step 3 provides the favorable equilibrium that ensures the success of the reaction. (In Section 20.2A we shall see how esters with only one α hydrogen can be converted to a β-keto ester through the use of very strong bases.)

Problem 20.1 ⎯⎯⎯⎯⎯⎯⎯⎯⎯⎯⎯⎯⎯⎯⎯⎯⎯⎯

(a) Write a mechanism for all steps of the Claisen condensation that takes place when ethyl propanoate reacts with ethoxide ion. (b) What products form when the reaction mixture is acidified?

⎯⎯⎯⎯⎯⎯⎯⎯⎯⎯⎯⎯⎯⎯⎯⎯⎯⎯⎯⎯⎯⎯⎯⎯⎯⎯⎯⎯⎯⎯⎯⎯

When diethyl hexanedioate is heated with sodium ethoxide, subsequent acidification of the reaction mixture gives ethyl 2-oxocyclopentanecarboxylate.

O   O
‖   ‖
C$_2$H$_5$OC(CH$_2$)$_4$COC$_2$H$_5$ $\xrightarrow[\text{(2) H}^+]{\text{(1) NaOC}_2\text{H}_5}$

**Diethyl hexanedioate
(diethyl adipate)**

**Ethyl 2-oxocyclopentane-
carboxylate
(74–81%)**

This reaction, called the *Dieckmann condensation,* is an intramolecular Claisen condensation. The α carbon atom and the ester group for the condensation come from the same molecule. In general, the Dieckmann condensation is useful only for the preparation of five- and six-membered rings.

Problem 20.2

(a) Show all steps in the mechanism for the Dieckmann condensation. (b) What product would you expect from a Dieckmann condensation of diethyl heptanedioate (diethyl pimelate)? (c) Can you account for the fact that diethyl pentanedioate (diethyl glutarate) does not undergo a Dieckmann condensation?

20.2A CROSSED CLAISEN CONDENSATIONS

Crossed Claisen condensations (like crossed aldol condensations) are possible **when one ester component has no α hydrogens** and is, therefore, unable to undergo self-condensation. Ethyl benzoate, for example, condenses with ethyl acetate to give ethyl benzoylacetate.

Ethyl benzoate
(no α hydrogen)

Ethyl benzoylacetate
(60%)

Ethyl phenylacetate condenses with diethyl carbonate to give diethyl phenylmalonate.

Ethyl phenylacetate   **Diethyl carbonate**
(no α carbon)

Diethyl phenylmalonate
(65%)

Problem 20.3

Write mechanisms that account for the products that are formed in the two crossed Claisen condensations just illustrated.

Problem 20.4

What products would you expect to obtain from each of the following crossed Claisen condensations?

(a) Ethyl propanoate + diethyl oxalate $\xrightarrow[\text{(2) H}^+]{\text{(1) NaOCH}_2\text{CH}_3}$

(b) Ethyl acetate + ethyl formate $\xrightarrow[\text{(2) H}^+]{\text{(1) NaOCH}_2\text{CH}_3}$

As we learned earlier in this section, esters that have only one α hydrogen cannot be converted to β-keto esters by sodium ethoxide. However, they can be converted to β-keto esters by reactions that use very strong bases. The strong base converts the ester to its enolate anion in nearly quantitative yield. This allows us to *acylate* the enolate anion by treating it with an acyl chloride or an ester. An example of this technique that makes use of the very powerful base sodium triphenylmethanide is shown next.

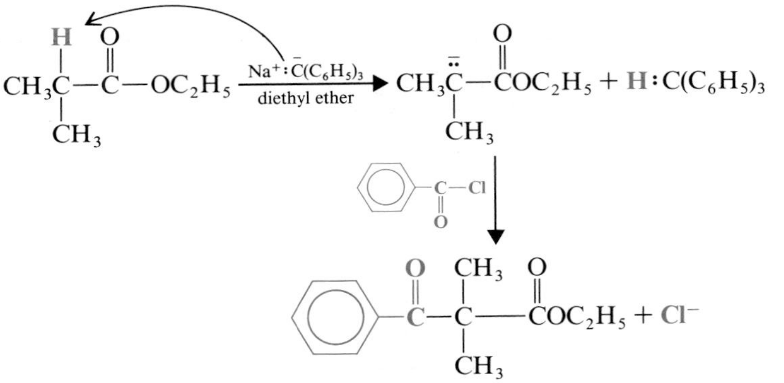

Ethyl 2,2-dimethyl-3-oxo-3-phenylpropanoate

20.2B ACYLATION OF OTHER CARBANIONS

Enolate anions derived from ketones also react with esters in nucleophilic substitution reactions that resemble Claisen condensations. In the following first example, although two anions are possible from the reaction of the ketone with sodium amide, the major product is derived from the primary carbanion. The primary α hydrogens are more acidic than the secondary α hydrogens.

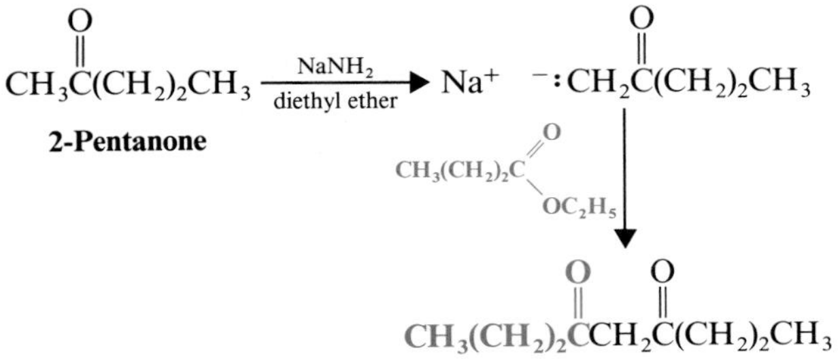

2-Pentanone

4,6-Nonanedione
(76%)

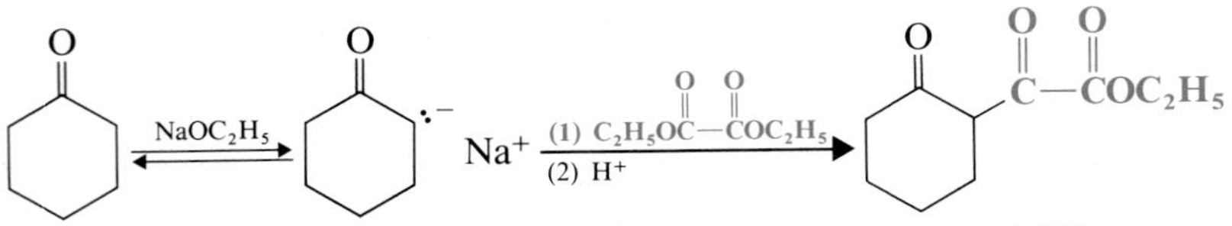

(67%)

Problem 20.5

Show how you might synthesize each of the following compounds using, as your starting materials, esters, ketones, acyl halides, and so on.

(a) 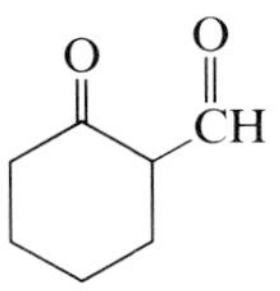   (b) 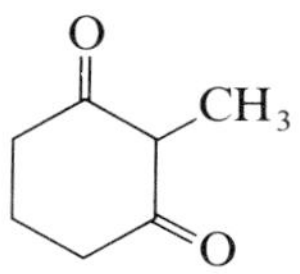   (c)

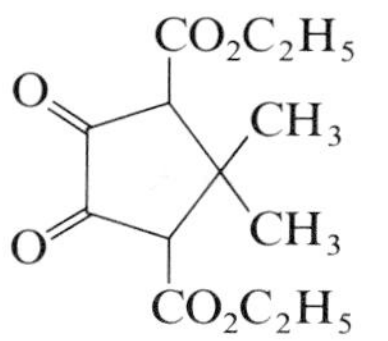

Problem 20.6

Keto esters are capable of undergoing cyclization reactions similar to the Dieckmann condensation. Write a mechanism that accounts for the product formed in the following reaction:

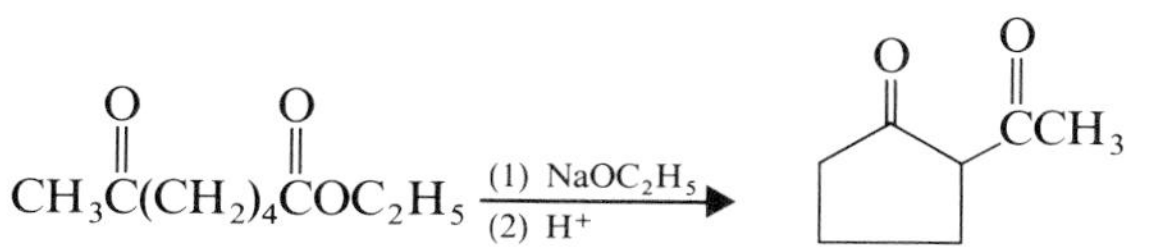

$$CH_3\overset{O}{\overset{\|}{C}}(CH_2)_4\overset{O}{\overset{\|}{C}}OC_2H_5 \xrightarrow[\text{(2) H}^+]{\text{(1) NaOC}_2H_5}$$

2-Acetylcyclopentanone

20.3 THE ACETOACETIC ESTER SYNTHESIS: SYNTHESIS OF SUBSTITUTED ACETONES

Acetoacetic esters are useful reagents for the preparation of methyl ketones of the types shown here:

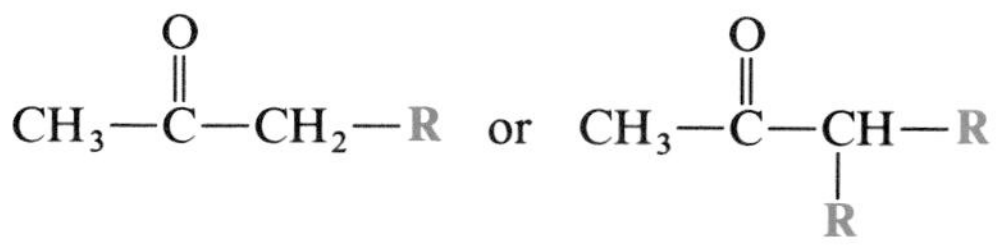

$$CH_3-\overset{O}{\overset{\|}{C}}-CH_2-R \quad \text{or} \quad CH_3-\overset{O}{\overset{\|}{C}}-\overset{\overset{\displaystyle |}{R}}{\underset{\displaystyle |}{C}H}-R$$

| Monosubstituted acetone | Disubstituted acetone |

Acetoacetic ester acts as the *synthetic equivalent* (Section 9.18) of the following three-carbon fragment:

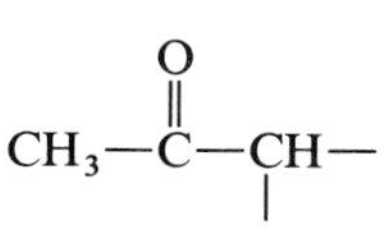

$$CH_3-\overset{O}{\overset{\|}{C}}-\overset{\overset{\displaystyle |}{}}{CH}-$$

Two factors make such syntheses practical: (1) The methylene protons of β-keto esters are appreciably acidic and (2) β-keto acids decarboxylate readily (cf. Section 18.11).

As we have seen (Section 20.2) the methylene protons of acetoacetic ester are more acidic than the —OH proton of ethanol because they are located between two carbonyl groups and yield a highly stabilized enolate anion. This acidity means that we can convert acetoacetic ester to an enolate anion using sodium ethoxide as a base. We can then carry out an alkylation reaction by treating the enolate anion with an alkyl halide.

Since the alkylation (see following reaction) is an S_N2 reaction, best yields are obtained from the use of primary alkyl halides (including primary allylic and benzylic halides) or methyl halides. Secondary halides give lower yields, and tertiary halides give only elimination.

$$CH_3\overset{\overset{\displaystyle \ddot{O}:}{\|}}{C}-CH_2-\overset{\overset{\displaystyle \ddot{O}:}{\|}}{C}OC_2H_5 + C_2H_5O^-Na^+ \;\rightleftharpoons\; CH_3\overset{\overset{\displaystyle \ddot{O}:}{\|}}{C}-\overset{\cdot\cdot}{\underset{}{C}}H-\overset{\overset{\displaystyle \ddot{O}:}{\|}}{C}-OC_2H_5 + C_2H_5OH$$

Acetoacetic ester   **Sodium ethoxide**   Na⁺   **Sodioacetoacetic ester**

$$\downarrow R-X$$

$$CH_3\overset{\overset{\displaystyle \ddot{O}:}{\|}}{C}-\underset{\underset{\displaystyle R}{|}}{C}H-\overset{\overset{\displaystyle \ddot{O}:}{\|}}{C}-OC_2H_5 + NaX$$

Monoalkylacetoacetic ester

The monoalkylacetoacetic ester still has one appreciably acidic hydrogen and, if we desire, we can carry out a second alkylation. Because the monoalkylacetoacetic ester is somewhat less acidic than acetoacetic ester itself (why?), it is usually helpful to use a base stronger than ethoxide ion.

$$CH_3\overset{\overset{\displaystyle O}{\|}}{C}-\underset{\underset{\displaystyle R}{|}}{C}H-\overset{\overset{\displaystyle O}{\|}}{C}-OC_2H_5 + (CH_3)_3CO^-K^+ \;\rightleftharpoons\; CH_3\overset{\overset{\displaystyle O}{\|}}{C}-\underset{\underset{\displaystyle R}{|}}{\overset{\cdot\cdot}{C}}-\overset{\overset{\displaystyle O}{\|}}{C}OC_2H_5 + (CH_3)_3COH$$

Monoalkylacetoacetic ester   **Potassium _tert_-butoxide**   K⁺

$$\downarrow R'-X$$

$$CH_3\overset{\overset{\displaystyle O}{\|}}{C}-\underset{\underset{\displaystyle R}{|}}{\overset{\overset{\displaystyle R'}{|}}{C}}-\overset{\overset{\displaystyle O}{\|}}{C}-OC_2H_5 + KX$$

Dialkylacetoacetic ester

If our goal is the preparation of a monosubstituted acetone, we carry out only one alkylation reaction. We then hydrolyze the monoalkylacetoacetic ester using dilute sodium or potassium hydroxide. Subsequent acidification of the mixture gives an alkylacetoacetic acid, and heating this β-keto acid to 100 °C brings about decarboxylation (Section 18.11).

$$CH_3\overset{\overset{\displaystyle O}{\|}}{C}-\underset{\underset{\displaystyle R}{|}}{C}H-\overset{\overset{\displaystyle O}{\|}}{C}OC_2H_5$$

Basic hydrolysis of the ester group }

$$\downarrow \text{dil. NaOH, heat}$$

$$CH_3\overset{\overset{\displaystyle O}{\|}}{C}-\underset{\underset{\displaystyle R}{|}}{C}H-\overset{\overset{\displaystyle O}{\|}}{C}-O^-Na^+$$

Acidification of the carboxylate salt }

$$\downarrow H_3O^+$$

20.3 THE ACETOACETIC ESTER SYNTHESIS: SYNTHESIS OF SUBSTITUTED ACETONES

$$CH_3\overset{\displaystyle O}{\overset{\|}{C}}-\overset{\displaystyle}{\underset{\underset{\displaystyle R}{|}}{CH}}-\overset{\displaystyle O}{\overset{\|}{C}}-OH$$

Alkylacetoacetic acid
(a β-keto acid)

$$\left.\begin{array}{l}\textbf{Decarboxylation of the}\\ \boldsymbol{\beta}\textbf{-keto acid}\end{array}\right\}\qquad\bigg\downarrow\ \text{heat, 100 °C}$$

$$CH_3-\overset{\displaystyle O}{\overset{\|}{C}}-CH_2-R+CO_2$$

A specific example is the following synthesis of 2-heptanone:

$$CH_3\overset{\displaystyle O}{\overset{\|}{C}}-CH_2-\overset{\displaystyle O}{\overset{\|}{C}}OC_2H_5 \xrightarrow[\text{(2) } CH_3CH_2CH_2CH_2Br]{\text{(1) } NaOC_2H_5/C_2H_5OH} CH_3\overset{\displaystyle O}{\overset{\|}{C}}-\underset{\underset{\displaystyle CH_2}{\underset{\underset{\displaystyle CH_2}{\underset{\underset{\displaystyle CH_2}{\underset{\displaystyle CH_3}{|}}{|}}{|}}{|}}}{CH}-\overset{\displaystyle O}{\overset{\|}{C}}OC_2H_5 \xrightarrow[\text{(2) } H_3O^+]{\text{(1) dil. NaOH}}$$

Ethyl acetoacetate
(acetoacetic ester)

Ethyl butylacetoacetate
(69–72%)

$$CH_3\overset{\displaystyle O}{\overset{\|}{C}}-\underset{\underset{\displaystyle CH_2}{\underset{\underset{\displaystyle CH_2}{\underset{\underset{\displaystyle CH_2}{\underset{\displaystyle CH_3}{|}}{|}}{|}}{|}}}{CH}-\overset{\displaystyle O}{\overset{\|}{C}}-OH \xrightarrow[-CO_2]{\text{heat}} CH_3\overset{\displaystyle O}{\overset{\|}{C}}-CH_2CH_2CH_2CH_2CH_3$$

2-Heptanone
(52–61% overall from
ethyl acetoacetate)

If our goal is the preparation of a disubstituted acetone, we carry out two successive alkylations, we hydrolyze the dialkylacetoacetic ester that is produced, and then we decarboxylate the dialkylacetoacetic acid. An example of this procedure is the synthesis of 3-butyl-2-heptanone.

$$CH_3\overset{\displaystyle O}{\overset{\|}{C}}CH_2\overset{\displaystyle O}{\overset{\|}{C}}OC_2H_5 \xrightarrow[\substack{\text{(2) } CH_3CH_2CH_2CH_2Br \\ \text{(first alkylation)}}]{\text{(1) } NaOC_2H_5,\ C_2H_5OH} CH_3\overset{\displaystyle O}{\overset{\|}{C}}\underset{\underset{\displaystyle (CH_2)_3}{\underset{\displaystyle CH_3}{|}}}{CH}\overset{\displaystyle O}{\overset{\|}{C}}OC_2H_5 \xrightarrow[\substack{\text{(2) } CH_3CH_2CH_2CH_2Br \\ \text{(second alkylation)}}]{\text{(1) } (CH_3)_3COK,\ (CH_3)_3COH}$$

Ethyl butylacetoacetate
(69–72%)

$$CH_3C-C-CO_2C_2H_5 \xrightarrow[\substack{(2)\ H_3O^+ \\ (hydrolysis)}]{(1)\ dil.\ NaOH} CH_3C-C-CO_2H \xrightarrow[\substack{-CO_2 \\ (decarboxylation)}]{heat}$$

Ethyl dibutylacetoacetate
(77%)

$$CH_3C-CH(CH_2)_3CH_3$$

3-Butyl-2-heptanone

Although both alkylations in the example just given were carried out with the same alkyl halide, we could have used different alkyl halides if our synthesis had required it.

Problem 20.7

Occasional side products of alkylations of sodioacetoacetic esters are compounds with the following general structure:

$$CH_3C=CHCOC_2H_5$$

Explain how these are formed.

Problem 20.8

Show how you would use the acetoacetic ester synthesis to prepare each of the following:
(a) 2-pentanone, (b) 3-propyl-2-hexanone, and (c) 4-phenyl-2-butanone.

Problem 20.9

The acetoacetic ester synthesis generally gives best yields when primary halides are used in the alkylation step. Secondary halides give low yields and tertiary halides give practically no alkylation product at all. (a) Explain. (b) What products would you expect from the reaction of sodioacetoacetic ester and *tert*-butyl bromide? (c) Bromobenzene cannot be used as an arylating agent in an acetoacetic ester synthesis in the manner we have just described. Why not?

Problem 20.10

Since the products obtained from Claisen condensations are β-keto esters, subsequent hydrolysis and decarboxylation of these products gives a general method for the synthesis of ketones. Show how you would employ this technique in a synthesis of 4-heptanone.

The acetoacetic ester synthesis can also be carried out using halo esters and halo ketones. The use of an α-halo ester provides a convenient synthesis of γ-keto acids:

$$CH_3\overset{O}{\overset{\|}{C}}-CH_2-\overset{O}{\overset{\|}{C}}-OC_2H_5 \xrightarrow{C_2H_5ONa} CH_3\overset{O}{\overset{\|}{C}}-\overset{Na^+}{\overset{\cdot\cdot}{C}H}-\overset{O}{\overset{\|}{C}}-OC_2H_5 \xrightarrow{BrCH_2\overset{O}{\overset{\|}{C}}-OC_2H_5}$$

$$CH_3\overset{O}{\overset{\|}{C}}-\underset{\underset{\underset{O}{\|}}{\underset{CH_2C-OC_2H_5}{|}}}{CH}-\overset{O}{\overset{\|}{C}}-OC_2H_5 \xrightarrow[\text{(2) H}_3O^+]{\text{(1) dil. NaOH}} CH_3\overset{O}{\overset{\|}{C}}-\underset{\underset{\underset{O}{\|}}{\underset{CH_2C-OH}{|}}}{CH}-\overset{O}{\overset{\|}{C}}-OH \xrightarrow[-CO_2]{\text{heat}}$$

$$CH_3\overset{O}{\overset{\|}{C}}-CH_2CH_2-\overset{O}{\overset{\|}{C}}-OH$$
4-Oxopentanoic acid

Problem 20.11

In the synthesis of the keto acid just given, the dicarboxylic acid decarboxylates in a specific way; it gives

$$CH_3\overset{O}{\overset{\|}{C}}CH_2CH_2\overset{O}{\overset{\|}{C}}OH \quad \text{rather than} \quad CH_3\overset{O}{\overset{\|}{C}}\underset{\underset{CH_3}{|}}{CH}\overset{O}{\overset{\|}{C}}OH$$

Explain.

The use of an α-halo ketone in an acetoacetic ester synthesis provides a general method for preparing γ-diketones:

$$CH_3\overset{O}{\overset{\|}{C}}-\overset{Na^+}{\overset{\cdot\cdot}{C}H}-\overset{O}{\overset{\|}{C}}-OC_2H_5 \xrightarrow{BrCH_2\overset{O}{\overset{\|}{C}}R} CH_3\overset{O}{\overset{\|}{C}}-\underset{\underset{\underset{R}{\underset{\|}{C=O}}}{\underset{\underset{CH_2}{|}}{|}}}{CH}-\overset{O}{\overset{\|}{C}}-OC_2H_5 \xrightarrow[\text{(2) H}_3O^+]{\text{(1) dil. NaOH}}$$

$$CH_3\overset{O}{\overset{\|}{C}}-\underset{\underset{\underset{R}{\underset{\|}{C=O}}}{\underset{\underset{CH_2}{|}}{|}}}{CH}-\overset{O}{\overset{\|}{C}}-OH \xrightarrow[-CO_2]{\text{heat}} CH_3\overset{O}{\overset{\|}{C}}-CH_2CH_2-\overset{O}{\overset{\|}{C}}-R$$
A γ-diketone

Problem 20.12

How would you use the acetoacetic ester synthesis to prepare the following?

$$\text{C}_6\text{H}_5-\overset{\displaystyle O}{\overset{\displaystyle \|}{\text{C}}}\text{CH}_2\text{CH}_2\overset{\displaystyle O}{\overset{\displaystyle \|}{\text{C}}}\text{CH}_3$$

Anions obtained from acetoacetic esters undergo acylation when they are treated with acyl chlorides or acid anhydrides. Because both of these acylating agents react with alcohols, acylation reactions cannot be carried out in ethanol and must be carried out in aprotic solvents such as DMF, DMSO, or HMPT (Section 6.15C). (If the reaction were to be carried out in ethanol, using sodium ethoxide, for example, then the acyl chloride would be rapidly converted to an ethyl ester and the ethoxide ion would be neutralized.) Sodium hydride can be used to generate the enolate anion in an aprotic solvent.

$$\text{CH}_3-\overset{O}{\overset{\|}{\text{C}}}-\text{CH}_2-\overset{O}{\overset{\|}{\text{C}}}-\text{OC}_2\text{H}_5 \xrightarrow[\substack{\text{aprotic solvent} \\ (-\text{H}_2)}]{\text{Na}^+ : \text{H}^-}$$

$$\overset{\text{Na}^+}{\underset{}{}}$$

$$\text{CH}_3-\overset{O}{\overset{\|}{\text{C}}}-\overset{\cdot\cdot}{\text{C}}\text{H}-\overset{O}{\overset{\|}{\text{C}}}-\text{OC}_2\text{H}_5 \xrightarrow[(-\text{NaCl})]{\text{RCCl}} \text{CH}_3-\overset{O}{\overset{\|}{\text{C}}}-\underset{\underset{\text{R}}{\underset{\|}{\text{C}=\text{O}}}}{\text{CH}}-\overset{O}{\overset{\|}{\text{C}}}-\text{OC}_2\text{H}_5 \xrightarrow[\text{(2) H}_3\text{O}^+]{\text{(1) dil. NaOH}}$$

$$\text{CH}_3-\overset{O}{\overset{\|}{\text{C}}}-\underset{\underset{\text{R}}{\underset{\|}{\text{C}=\text{O}}}}{\text{CH}}-\overset{O}{\overset{\|}{\text{C}}}-\text{OH} \xrightarrow[-\text{CO}_2]{\text{heat}} \text{CH}_3-\overset{O}{\overset{\|}{\text{C}}}-\text{CH}_2-\overset{O}{\overset{\|}{\text{C}}}-\text{R}$$
$$\textbf{A } \boldsymbol{\beta}\textbf{-diketone}$$

Acylations of acetoacetic esters followed by hydrolysis and decarboxylation give us a method for preparing β-diketones.

Problem 20.13

How would you use the acetoacetic ester synthesis to prepare the following?

$$\text{C}_6\text{H}_5-\overset{\displaystyle O}{\overset{\displaystyle \|}{\text{C}}}\text{CH}_2\overset{\displaystyle O}{\overset{\displaystyle \|}{\text{C}}}\text{CH}_3$$

Acetoacetic ester cannot be phenylated in a manner analogous to the alkylation reactions we have studied because bromobenzene is not susceptible to S_N2 reactions

20.3 THE ACETOACETIC ESTER SYNTHESIS: SYNTHESIS OF SUBSTITUTED ACETONES

[Section 6.16A and Problem 20.9(c)]. However, if acetoacetic ester is treated with bromobenzene and *two molar equivalents of sodium amide,* then phenylation does occur *by a benzyne mechanism* (Section 21.11). The overall reaction is as follows:

$$CH_3\overset{O}{\overset{||}{C}}CH_2\overset{O}{\overset{||}{C}}OC_2H_5 + C_6H_5Br + 2\ NaNH_2 \xrightarrow{\text{liq. NH}_3} CH_3\overset{O}{\overset{||}{C}}\overset{|}{CH}\overset{O}{\overset{||}{C}}OC_2H_5$$
$$\underset{C_6H_5}{}$$

Malonic esters $\left(RO\overset{O}{\overset{||}{C}}CH_2\overset{O}{\overset{||}{C}}OR\right)$ can be phenylated in an analogous way.

Problem 20.14

(a) Outline a step-by-step mechanism for the phenylation of acetoacetic ester by bromobenzene and two molar equivalents of sodium amide. (Why are two molar equivalents of $NaNH_2$ necessary?) (b) What product would be obtained by hydrolysis and decarboxylation of the phenylated acetoacetic ester? (c) How would you prepare phenylacetic acid from malonic ester?

One further variation of the acetoacetic ester synthesis involves the conversion of an acetoacetic ester to a resonance-stabilized *dianion* by using a very strong base such as potassium amide in liquid ammonia.

When this dianion is treated with 1 mol of a primary (or methyl) halide, it undergoes alkylation at its terminal carbon rather than at its interior one. This orientation of the alkylation reaction apparently results from the greater basicity (and thus nucleo-philicity) of the terminal carbanion. This carbanion is more basic because it is stabilized by only one adjacent carbonyl group. After monoalkylation has taken place, the anion that remains can be protonated by adding ammonium chloride.

Problem 20.15

Show how you could use ethyl acetoacetate in a synthesis of

$$C_6H_5CH_2CH_2\overset{\overset{\displaystyle O}{\|}}{C}CH_2\overset{\overset{\displaystyle O}{\|}}{C}OC_2H_5$$

20.4 THE MALONIC ESTER SYNTHESIS: SYNTHESIS OF SUBSTITUTED ACETIC ACIDS

A useful counterpart of the acetoacetic ester synthesis — one that allows the synthesis of *mono- and disubstituted acetic acids* — is called the *malonic ester synthesis.*

The malonic ester synthesis resembles the acetoacetic ester synthesis in several respects.

1. Diethyl malonate (malonic ester), the starting compound, forms a relatively stable enolate ion:

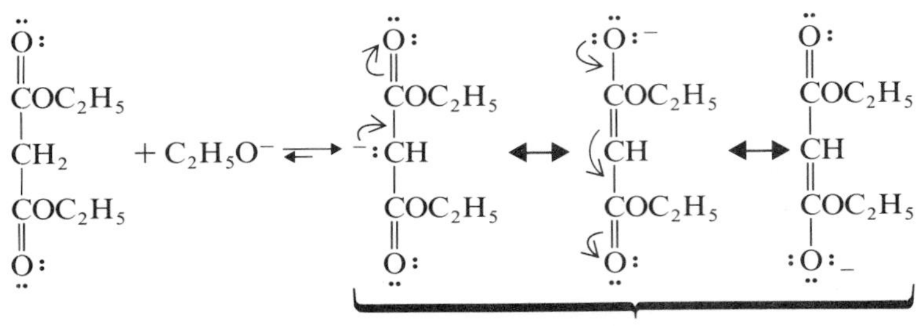

Resonance-stabilized anion

2. This enolate ion can be alkylated,

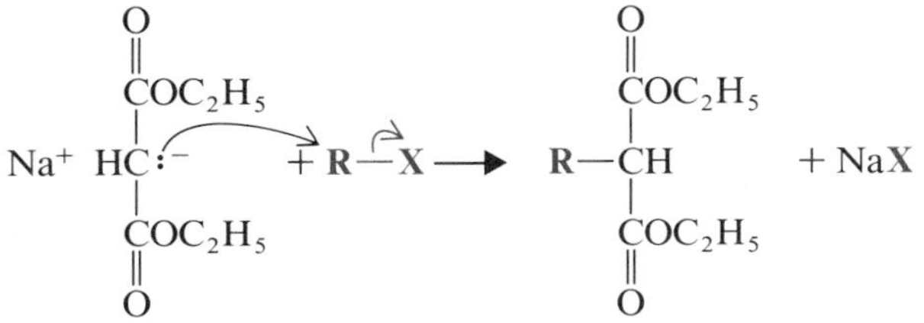

Sodiomalonic ester   Monoalkylmalonic ester

and the product can be alkylated again if our synthesis requires it:

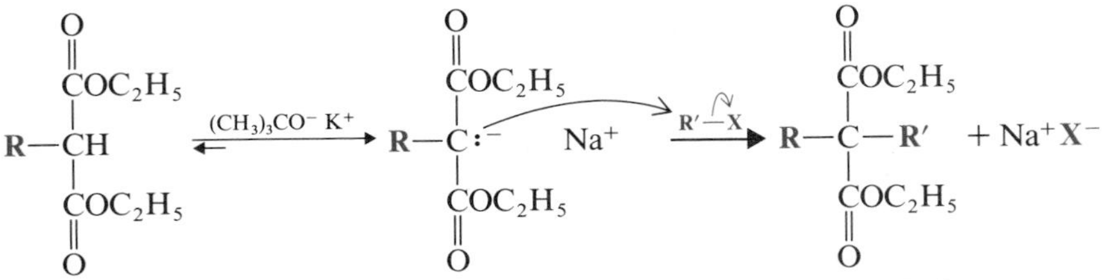

Dialkylmalonic ester

3. The mono- or dialkylmalonic ester can then be hydrolyzed to a mono- or dialkylmalonic acid, and substituted malonic acids decarboxylate readily. Decarboxylation gives a mono- or disubstituted acetic acid.

$$\underset{\substack{\text{Monoalkylmalonic}\\\text{ester}}}{\text{R—CH}\begin{smallmatrix}\text{C—OC}_2\text{H}_5\\\text{C—OC}_2\text{H}_5\end{smallmatrix}} \xrightarrow[\text{(2) H}_3\text{O}^+]{\text{(1) OH}^-,\text{H}_2\text{O}} \underset{\substack{\text{Monoalkyl-}\\\text{acetic acid}}}{\text{R—CH}\begin{smallmatrix}\text{C—OH}\\\text{C—OH}\end{smallmatrix}} \xrightarrow[-\text{CO}_2]{\text{heat}} \text{RCH}_2\text{CO}_2\text{H}$$

$$\underset{\substack{\text{Dialkylmalonic}\\\text{ester}}}{\text{R—C—R'}\begin{smallmatrix}\text{COC}_2\text{H}_5\\\text{COC}_2\text{H}_5\end{smallmatrix}} \xrightarrow[\text{(2) H}_3\text{O}^+]{\text{(1) OH}^-,\text{H}_2\text{O}} \underset{\substack{\text{Dialkylacetic}\\\text{acid}}}{\text{R—C—R'}\begin{smallmatrix}\text{C—OH}\\\text{C—OH}\end{smallmatrix}} \xrightarrow[-\text{CO}_2]{\text{heat}} \underset{\text{R'}}{\text{R—CHCO}_2\text{H}}$$

Two specific examples of the malonic ester synthesis are the syntheses of hexanoic acid and 2-ethylpentanoic acid that follow.

$$\begin{matrix}\text{COC}_2\text{H}_5\\\text{CH}_2\\\text{COC}_2\text{H}_5\end{matrix} \xrightarrow[\text{(2) CH}_3\text{CH}_2\text{CH}_2\text{CH}_2\text{Br}]{\text{(1) NaOC}_2\text{H}_5}$$

$$\underset{\substack{\text{Diethyl butylmalonate}\\\text{(80–90\%)}}}{\text{CH}_3\text{CH}_2\text{CH}_2\text{CH}_2\text{CH}\begin{matrix}\text{COC}_2\text{H}_5\\\text{COC}_2\text{H}_5\end{matrix}} \xrightarrow[\substack{\text{(2) dil. H}_2\text{SO}_4,\text{ reflux}\\(-\text{CO}_2)}]{\text{(1) 50\% KOH, reflux}} \underset{\substack{\text{Hexanoic acid}\\\text{(75\%)}}}{\text{CH}_3\text{CH}_2\text{CH}_2\text{CH}_2\text{CH}_2\text{CO}_2\text{H}}$$

$$\begin{matrix}\text{COC}_2\text{H}_5\\\text{CH}_2\\\text{COC}_2\text{H}_5\end{matrix} \xrightarrow[\text{(2) CH}_3\text{CH}_2\text{I}]{\text{(1) NaOC}_2\text{H}_5} \underset{\text{Diethyl ethylmalonate}}{\text{CH}_3\text{CH}_2\text{CH}\begin{matrix}\text{COC}_2\text{H}_5\\\text{COC}_2\text{H}_5\end{matrix}} \xrightarrow[\text{(2) CH}_3\text{CH}_2\text{CH}_2\text{Br}]{\text{(1) NaOC(CH}_3)_3}$$

$$CH_3CH_2\diagdown\atop{CH_3CH_2CH_2}\diagup C \diagup{\overset{O}{\overset{\|}{C}OC_2H_5}}\atop{\underset{O}{\underset{\|}{C}OC_2H_5}} \quad \xrightarrow[\text{(2) } H_3O^+]{\text{(1) } OH^-,\, H_2O} \quad CH_3CH_2\diagdown\atop{CH_3CH_2CH_2}\diagup C \diagup{\overset{O}{\overset{\|}{C}-OH}}\atop{\underset{O}{\underset{\|}{C}-OH}} \quad \xrightarrow[\text{180 °C}]{\text{heat}}$$

Diethyl ethylpropylmalonate   **Ethylpropylmalonic acid**

$$CH_3CH_2CH_2\underset{\underset{\displaystyle CH_3}{\overset{\displaystyle |}{\underset{\displaystyle |}{CH_2}}}}{\overset{\displaystyle |}{CH}}CO_2H$$

2-Ethylpentanoic acid

Problem 20.16

Outline all steps in a malonic ester synthesis of each of the following:
(a) pentanoic acid,   (b) 2-methylpentanoic acid, and   (c) 4-methylpentanoic acid.

Two variations of the malonic ester synthesis make use of dihaloalkanes. In the first of these, two molar equivalents of sodiomalonic ester are allowed to react with a dihaloalkane. Two consecutive alkylations occur giving a tetraester; hydrolysis and decarboxylation of the tetraester yield a dicarboxylic acid. An example is the synthesis of glutaric acid:

$$CH_2I_2 + 2\,Na^{+-}{:}\overset{\overset{O}{\overset{\|}{C}OC_2H_5}}{\underset{\underset{O}{\underset{\|}{C}OC_2H_5}}{CH}} \longrightarrow \overset{\overset{O}{\overset{\|}{C_2H_5OC}}}{\underset{\underset{O}{\underset{\|}{C_2H_5OC}}}{CH}}CH_2\overset{\overset{O}{\overset{\|}{C}OC_2H_5}}{\underset{\underset{O}{\underset{\|}{C}OC_2H_5}}{CH}} \quad \xrightarrow[\text{(2) evaporation, heat}]{\text{(1) HCl/}H_2O}$$

$$\overset{O}{\overset{\|}{HOCCH_2CH_2CH_2}}\overset{O}{\overset{\|}{C}OH} + 2\,CO_2 + 4\,C_2H_5OH$$

Glutaric acid
(80% from tetraester)

In a second variation, one molar equivalent of sodiomalonic ester is allowed to react with one molar equivalent of a dihaloalkane. This reaction gives a haloalkylmalonic ester, which when treated with sodium ethoxide, undergoes an internal alkylation reaction. This method has been used to prepare three-, four-, five-, and six-membered rings. An example is the synthesis of cyclobutanecarboxylic acid.

Cyclobutanecarboxylic acid

20.5 FURTHER REACTIONS OF ACTIVE HYDROGEN COMPOUNDS

Because of the acidity of their methylene hydrogens, malonic esters, acetoacetic esters, and similar compounds are often called *active hydrogen compounds* or *active methylene compounds*. Generally speaking, active hydrogen compounds have two electron-withdrawing groups attached to the same carbon atom:

$$Z—CH_2—Z'$$

Active hydrogen compound
(Z and Z' are electron-withdrawing groups)

The electron-withdrawing groups can be a variety of substituents including:

For example, ethyl cyanoacetate reacts with base to yield a resonance-stabilized anion:

$$:N\equiv C-CH_2-\overset{\overset{\displaystyle \ddot{O}:}{\|}}{C}OEt \xrightarrow[-H^+]{base} :N\equiv C-\overset{\overset{\displaystyle \ddot{O}:}{\|}}{\underset{}{C}H}-COEt$$

Ethyl cyanoacetate

$$^-:\ddot{N}=C=CH-\overset{\overset{\displaystyle \ddot{O}:}{\|}}{C}OEt$$

$$:N\equiv C-CH=\overset{\overset{\displaystyle :\ddot{O}:^-}{|}}{C}OEt$$

Ethyl cyanoacetate anions also undergo alkylations. They can be dialkylated with isopropyl iodide, for example.

$$\begin{array}{c} H_3C \\ \diagdown \\ CHI + \\ H_3C \diagup \end{array} \begin{array}{c} CO_2C_2H_5 \\ | \\ CH_2 \\ | \\ CN \end{array} \xrightarrow[(2)\ H_3O^+]{(1)\ C_2H_5ONa/C_2H_5OH} \begin{array}{c} H_3C \\ \diagdown \\ CHCH \\ H_3C \diagup \end{array} \begin{array}{c} CO_2C_2H_5 \\ | \\ \\ | \\ CN \end{array} \xrightarrow[\substack{(2)\ H_3C\diagdown CHI \\ H_3C\diagup}]{(1)\ C_2H_5ONa/C_2H_5OH}$$

(63%)

$$\begin{array}{c} H_3C \\ \diagdown \\ CH-C-CH \\ H_3C \diagup \end{array} \begin{array}{c} CO_2C_2H_5 \\ | \\ | \\ CN \end{array} \begin{array}{c} \\ CH_3 \\ \diagup \\ \diagdown CH_3 \end{array}$$

(95%)

Another way of preparing ketones is to use a β-keto sulfoxide as an active hydrogen compound:

$$\overset{\overset{\displaystyle O}{\|}}{R}C-CH_2-\overset{\overset{\displaystyle O}{\|}}{S}R' \xrightarrow[(2)\ R''X]{(1)\ base} \overset{\overset{\displaystyle O}{\|}}{R}C-\underset{\underset{\displaystyle R''}{|}}{C}H-\overset{\overset{\displaystyle O}{\|}}{S}R' \xrightarrow{Al-Hg} \overset{\overset{\displaystyle O}{\|}}{R}C-CH_2-R''$$

A β-keto sulfoxide

The β-keto sulfoxide is first converted to an anion and then the anion is alkylated. Treating the product of these steps with aluminum amalgam (Al-Hg) causes cleavage at the carbon–sulfur bond and gives the ketone in high yield.

20.6 DIRECT ALKYLATION OF ESTERS

We have seen in Sections 20.3–20.5 that it is easy to alkylate β-keto esters and other active hydrogen compounds. The hydrogens situated on the carbon atom between the two electron-withdrawing groups are unusually acidic and are easily removed by bases such as ethoxide ion. It is also possible, however, to alkylate esters that do not have a β-keto group. To do this we must use a stronger base, one that will convert the ester or nitrile into its enolate anion rapidly so that all of the ester is converted to its enolate before it can undergo Claisen condensation. We must also use a base that is sufficiently bulky not to react at the carbonyl carbon of the ester or at the carbon of the nitrile group. Such a base is lithium diisopropylamide (LDA).

Lithium diisopropylamide is a very strong base because it is the conjugate base of the very weak acid, diisopropylamine ($pK_a = 38$). Lithium diisopropylamide is prepared by treating LDA with methyllithium. Solvents commonly used for reactions in which LDA is the base are ethers such as tetrahydrofuran (THF) and 1,2-dimethoxyethane (DME). (The use of LDA in other syntheses is described in Special Topic E.)

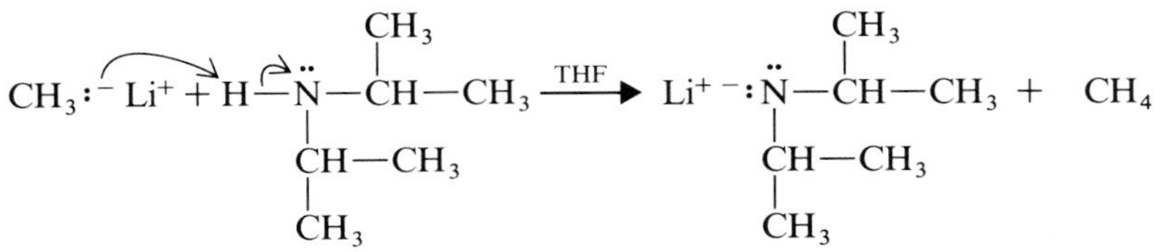

$pK_a = 38$

Lithium diisopropylamide [abbreviated LDA or $(i\text{-}C_3H_7)_2N^-Li^+$] **$pK_a = 50$**

Examples of the direct alkylation of esters are shown below. In the second example the ester is a lactone (Section 18.7C).

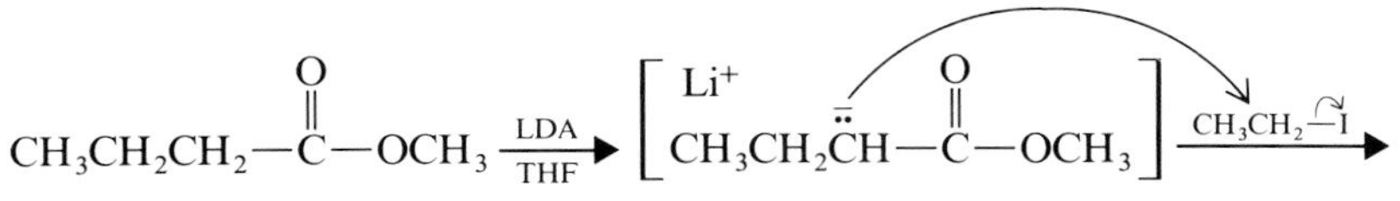

Methyl butanoate

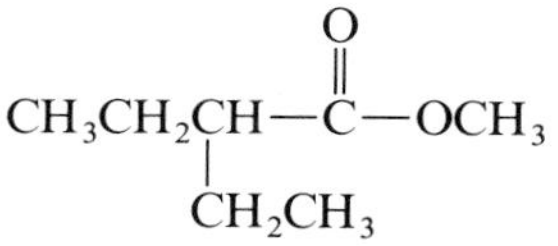

Methyl 2-ethylbutanoate (96%)

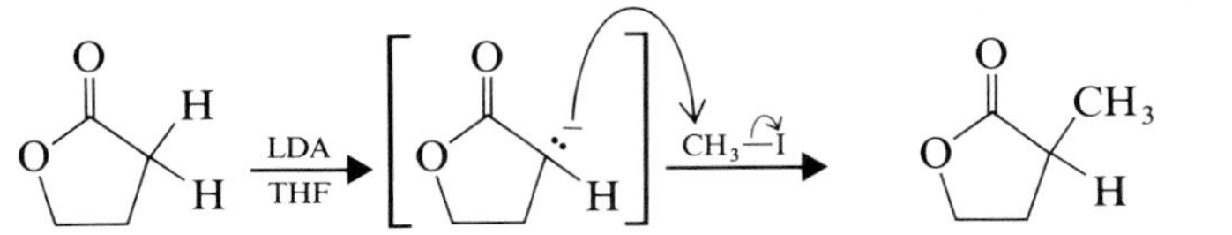

Butyrolactone **2-Methylbutyrolactone (88%)**

20.7 ALKYLATION OF 1,3-DITHIANES

Two sulfur atoms attached to the same carbon of 1,3-dithiane cause the hydrogen atoms of that carbon to be more acidic ($pK_a = 32$) than those of most alkyl carbon atoms.

1,3-Dithiane
$pK_a = 32$

Sulfur atoms, because they are easily polarized, can aid in stabilizing the negative charge of the anion (cf. Special Topic I). Strong bases such as butyllithium are usually used to convert a dithiane to its anion.

$$\text{S} \quad \text{S} + C_4H_9Li \longrightarrow \text{S} \quad \text{S} + C_4H_{10}$$

1,3-Dithianes are thioacetals (cf. Section 16.7E); they can be prepared by treating an aldehyde with 1,3-propanedithiol in the presence of a trace of acid.

$$\text{RCH} + HSCH_2CH_2CH_2SH \xrightarrow{H^+} \text{S} \quad \text{S}$$

A 1,3-dithiane

Alkylating the 1,3-dithiane with a primary halide and then hydrolyzing the product (a thioketal) is a method for converting an aldehyde to a ketone. Hydrolysis is usually carried out by using $HgCl_2$ either in methanol or in aqueous acetonitrile, CH_3CN.

$$\xrightarrow[\text{(2) } R'CH_2X(-LiX)]{\text{(1) } C_4H_9Li(-C_4H_{10})} \xrightarrow[\text{(} -HSCH_2CH_2CH_2SH\text{)}]{HgCl_2, CH_3OH, H_2O} R-\overset{O}{\overset{\|}{C}}-CH_2R'$$

Thioketal   **Ketone**

Notice that in these 1,3-dithiane syntheses the usual mode of reaction of an aldehyde is reversed. Normally the carbonyl carbon atom of an aldehyde is partially positive; it is electrophilic and, consequently, it reacts with nucleophiles. When the aldehyde is converted to a 1,3-dithiane and treated with butyllithium, this same carbon atom becomes negatively charged and reacts with electrophiles. This reversal of polarity of the carbonyl carbon atom is called **umpolung** (German for **polarity reversal**).

$$\overset{O^{\delta-}}{\underset{R \quad H}{\overset{\|}{\underset{}{C^{\delta+}}}}} \xrightarrow[\text{(2) } C_4H_9Li]{\text{(1) } HSCH_2CH_2CH_2SH, H^+} \text{S} \quad \text{S}$$

Aldehyde

Umpolung

The synthetic use of 1,3-dithianes was developed by E. J. Corey (Section 4.15) and D. Seebach and is often called the *Corey–Seebach* method.

Problem 20.17

(a) Which aldehyde would you use to prepare 1,3-dithiane itself? (b) How would you synthesize $C_6H_5CH_2CHO$ using a 1,3-dithiane as an intermediate? (c) How would you convert benzaldehyde to acetophenone?

Problem 20.18

The Corey–Seebach method can also be used to synthesize molecules with the structure RCH_2CH_2R'. How might this be done?

Problem 20.19

(a) The Corey–Seebach method has been used to prepare the following highly strained molecule called a metaparacyclophane. What are the structures of the intermediates $A-D$?

A metaparacyclophane

(b) What compound would be obtained by treating **B** with excess Raney Ni?

20.8 THE KNOEVENAGEL CONDENSATION

Active hydrogen compounds condense with aldehydes and ketones. Known as Knoevenagel condensations, these aldol-like condensations are catalyzed by weak bases. An example is the following:

$$Cl-\langle\bigcirc\rangle-CHO + CH_3\overset{O}{\underset{\parallel}{C}}CH_2\overset{O}{\underset{\parallel}{C}}OC_2H_5 \xrightarrow[C_2H_5OH]{(C_2H_5)_2NH}$$

$$\left[Cl-\langle\bigcirc\rangle-\underset{\underset{OH}{|}}{CH}-\underset{\underset{\overset{|}{C}CH_3}{\underset{\parallel}{O}}}{CH}\overset{\overset{O}{\parallel}}{\overset{|}{C}OC_2H_5} \right] \xrightarrow{-H_2O} Cl-\langle\bigcirc\rangle-CH=C\overset{\overset{\overset{O}{\parallel}}{C}OC_2H_5}{\underset{\underset{O}{\parallel}}{CCH_3}}$$

(86%)

20.9 MICHAEL ADDITIONS

Active hydrogen compounds also undergo conjugate additions to α,β-unsaturated carbonyl compounds. These reactions are known as Michael additions, a reaction that we studied in Section 17.9C. An example of the Michael addition of an active hydrogen compound is the following:

$$CH_3\underset{\underset{CH_3}{|}}{C}=CH\overset{O}{\underset{\parallel}{C}}OC_2H_5 + CH_2\overset{\overset{O}{\parallel}}{\underset{\underset{O}{\parallel}}{\overset{COC_2H_5}{COC_2H_5}}} \xrightarrow[\underset{25\ °C}{C_2H_5OH}]{C_2H_5O^-Na^+} CH_3\underset{\underset{CH(CO_2C_2H_5)_2}{|}}{\overset{\overset{CH_3}{|}}{C}}-CH_2\overset{O}{\underset{\parallel}{C}}OC_2H_5$$

(70%)

The mechanism for this reaction begins with formation of an anion from the active hydrogen compound,

Step 1
$$C_2H_5O^- + H-CH\overset{\overset{O}{\parallel}}{\underset{\underset{O}{\parallel}}{\overset{COC_2H_5}{COC_2H_5}}} \rightleftharpoons C_2H_5OH + {}^-{:}CH\overset{\overset{O}{\parallel}}{\underset{\underset{O}{\parallel}}{\overset{COC_2H_5}{COC_2H_5}}}$$

then conjugate addition of the anion to the α,β-unsaturated ester (step 2) is followed by the acceptance of a proton (step 3).

Step 2
$$CH_3-\underset{\underset{\underset{\underset{C_2H_5\ C_2H_5}{|\ \ |}}{O\ \ O}}{\underset{\parallel}{\overset{|}{CH^-}}}}{\overset{\overset{CH_3}{|}}{C}}=CH-\overset{\overset{\ddot{O}:}{\parallel}}{C}-OC_2H_5 \rightleftharpoons CH_3-\underset{\underset{\underset{\underset{C_2H_5\ C_2H_5}{|\ \ |}}{O\ \ O}}{\underset{\parallel}{\overset{|}{CH}}}}{\overset{\overset{CH_3}{|}}{C}}-CH=\overset{\overset{:\ddot{O}:^-}{|}}{C}-OC_2H_5 \longleftrightarrow$$

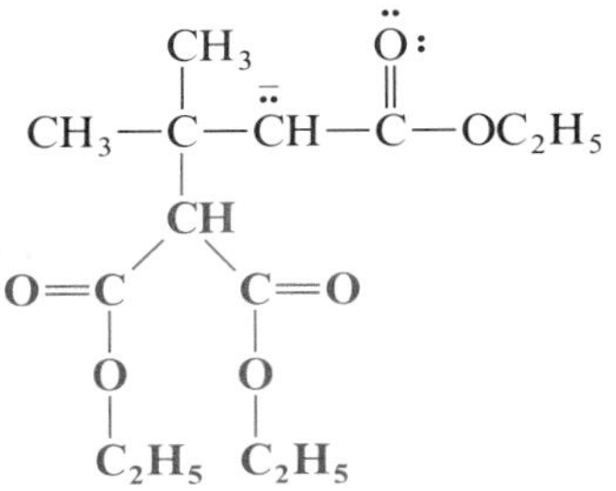

$$CH_3-\overset{\overset{\displaystyle CH_3}{|}}{C}-\overset{\overset{\displaystyle \ddot{O}:}{\|}}{CH}-\overset{\|}{C}-OC_2H_5$$

with CH group bearing

$$\underset{O=C \qquad C=O}{CH}$$

$$\underset{O \qquad O}{}$$

$$C_2H_5 \quad C_2H_5$$

Step 3

$$CH_3-\overset{\overset{\displaystyle CH_3}{|}}{\underset{\underset{O=C \quad C=O}{\underset{O \quad O}{CH}}}{C}}-\overset{\overset{\displaystyle \ddot{O}:}{\|}}{\overset{..}{CH}}-\overset{\|}{C}-OC_2H_5 \xrightarrow{+H^+} CH_3-\overset{\overset{\displaystyle CH_3}{|}}{\underset{\underset{O=C \quad C=O}{\underset{O \quad O}{CH}}}{C}}-CH_2-\overset{\overset{\displaystyle \ddot{O}:}{\|}}{C}-OC_2H_5$$

$$C_2H_5 \quad C_2H_5 \qquad\qquad C_2H_5 \quad C_2H_5$$

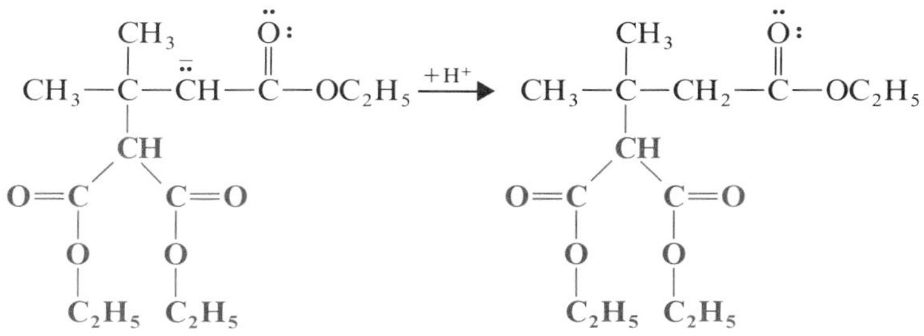

Problem 20.20

How would you prepare $\underset{\underset{CH_3}{|}}{HOCCH_2\overset{\overset{\displaystyle CH_3}{|}}{C}CH_2COH}$ (with O=C groups) from the product of the Michael addition given previously?

Michael additions take place with a variety of other reagents; these include acetylenic esters and α,β-unsaturated nitriles:

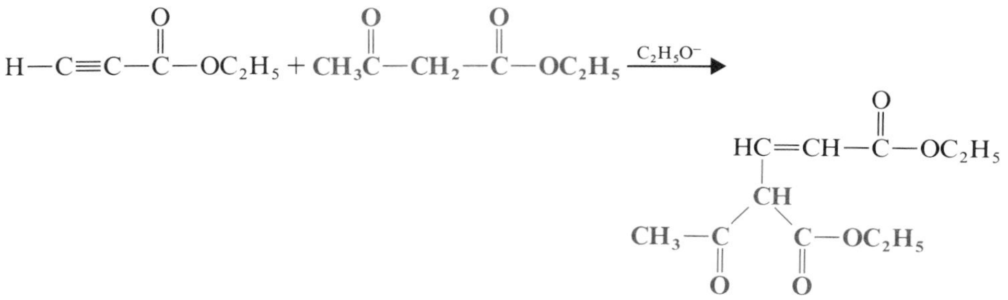

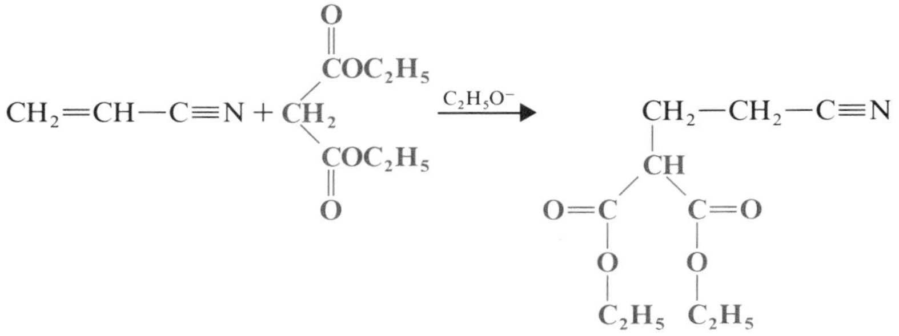

$$H-C\equiv C-\overset{\overset{\displaystyle O}{\|}}{C}-OC_2H_5 + CH_3\overset{\overset{\displaystyle O}{\|}}{C}-CH_2-\overset{\overset{\displaystyle O}{\|}}{C}-OC_2H_5 \xrightarrow{C_2H_5O^-}$$

$$HC=CH-\overset{\overset{\displaystyle O}{\|}}{C}-OC_2H_5$$

$$\underset{\underset{O \quad O}{CH_3-C \qquad C-OC_2H_5}}{CH}$$

$$CH_2=CH-C\equiv N + \overset{\overset{\displaystyle COC_2H_5}{|}}{\underset{\underset{\displaystyle COC_2H_5}{|}}{CH_2}} \xrightarrow{C_2H_5O^-} CH_2-CH_2-C\equiv N$$

$$\underset{\underset{O \quad O}{O=C \qquad C=O}}{CH}$$

$$C_2H_5 \quad C_2H_5$$

20.10 THE MANNICH REACTION

Active hydrogen compounds react with formaldehyde and a primary or secondary amine to yield compounds called Mannich bases. The following reaction of acetone, formaldehyde, and diethylamine is an example.

$$CH_3-\overset{O}{\overset{\|}{C}}-CH_3 + H-\overset{O}{\overset{\|}{C}}-H + (C_2H_5)_2NH \xrightarrow{HCl}$$

$$CH_3-\overset{O}{\overset{\|}{C}}-CH_2-CH_2-N(C_2H_5)_2 + H_2O$$

A Mannich base

The Mannich reaction apparently proceeds through a variety of mechanisms depending on the reactants and the conditions that are employed. One mechanism that appears to operate in neutral or acidic media involves (step 1) initial reaction of the secondary amine with formaldehyde to yield an iminium ion and (step 2) subsequent reaction of the iminium ion with the enol form of the active hydrogen compound.

Step 1

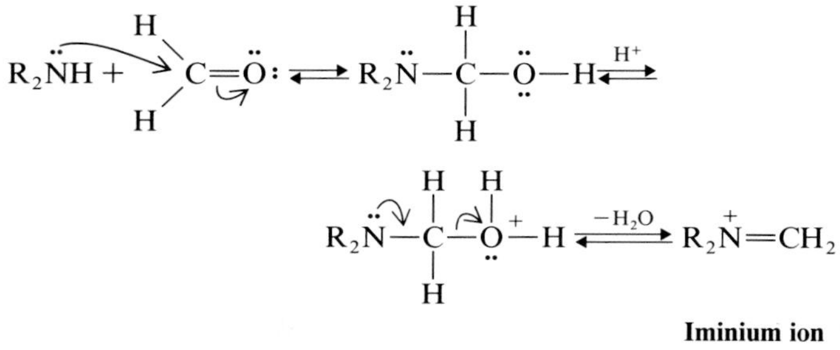

$$R_2\ddot{N}H + \overset{H}{\underset{H}{>}}C=\ddot{O}: \rightleftharpoons R_2\ddot{N}-\overset{H}{\underset{H}{\overset{|}{C}}}-\ddot{O}-H \xrightarrow{H^+}$$

$$R_2\ddot{N}-\overset{H}{\underset{H}{\overset{|}{C}}}\overset{H}{\overset{|}{\underset{\cdot\cdot}{O}}}-H \xrightarrow{-H_2O} R_2\overset{+}{N}=CH_2$$

Iminium ion

Step 2

$$CH_3-\overset{O}{\overset{\|}{C}}-CH_3 \underset{}{\overset{H^+}{\rightleftharpoons}} CH_3-\overset{O-H}{\overset{|}{C}}=CH_2 \quad \text{Enol}$$

$$\underset{CH_2=\overset{+}{N}R_2}{\Big\downarrow} \quad \text{Iminium ion}$$

$$CH_3-\overset{O}{\overset{\|}{C}}-CH_2-CH_2-\ddot{N}R_2 + H^+$$

Mannich base

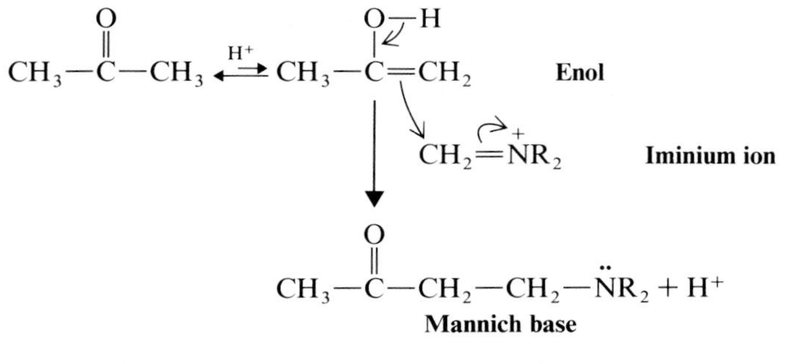

Problem 20.21 ───────────────────────────

Outline reasonable mechanisms that account for the products of the following Mannich reactions:

(a) (cyclohexanone) + CH_2O + (CH_3)_2NH ⟶ (2-(dimethylaminomethyl)cyclohexanone) with $CH_2N(CH_3)_2$

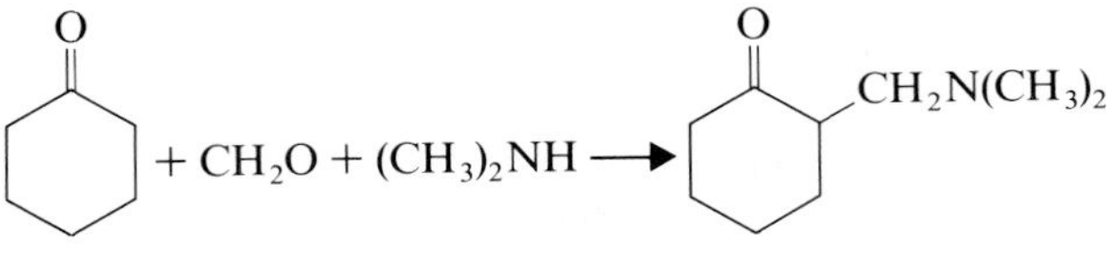

(b) (reaction scheme)

$$\text{(b)} \quad C_6H_5-\overset{O}{\overset{\|}{C}}CH_3 + CH_2O + \overset{\text{pyrrolidine}}{\underset{H}{N}} \longrightarrow C_6H_5-\overset{O}{\overset{\|}{C}}CH_2CH_2-N$$

(c) (reaction scheme)

$$\text{(c)} \quad p\text{-cresol} + 2\ CH_2O + 2\ (CH_3)_2NH \longrightarrow$$

20.11 SYNTHESIS OF ENAMINES: STORK ENAMINE REACTIONS

Aldehydes and ketones react with secondary amines to form compounds called *enamines*. The general reaction for enamine formation can be written as follows:

$$\underset{\substack{\text{Aldehyde} \\ \text{or ketone}}}{\overset{:\text{O}}{\overset{\|}{C}}} + \underset{2°\ \text{Amine}}{H\ddot{N}-R} \rightleftharpoons \underset{H}{-\overset{OH}{\underset{|}{C}}-\overset{|}{\underset{|}{C}}-\ddot{N}\overset{R}{\underset{R}{}}} \rightleftharpoons \underset{\text{Enamine}}{\overset{}{C}=C\overset{}{\underset{R}{\ddot{N}\overset{R}{}}}} + H_2O$$

(Enamines from ammonia and primary amines are unstable and cannot be isolated.)

Since enamine formation requires the loss of a molecule of water, enamine preparations are usually carried out in a way that allows water to be removed as an azeotrope or by a drying agent. This removal of water drives the reversible reaction to completion. Enamine formation is also catalyzed by the presence of a trace of an acid. The secondary amines most commonly used to prepare enamines are cyclic amines such as pyrrolidine, piperidine, and morpholine.

Pyrrolidine   Piperidine   Morpholine

Cyclohexanone, for example, reacts with pyrrolidine in the following way:

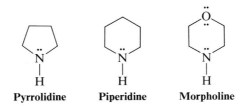

N-(1-Cyclohexenyl)pyrrolidine
(an enamine)

Enamines are good nucleophiles, and an examination of the resonance structures that follow will show us that we should expect enamines to have both a nucleophilic nitrogen and a *nucleophilic carbon.*

| Contribution to the hybrid made by this structure confers nucleophilicity on nitrogen | Contribution to the hybrid made by this structure confers nucleophilicity on carbon and decreases nucleophilicity of nitrogen |

The nucleophilicity of the carbon of enamines makes them particularly useful reagents in organic synthesis because they can be **acylated, alkylated,** and used in **Michael additions.** Development of these techniques originated with the work of Gilbert Stork of Columbia University and in his honor they have come to be known as **Stork enamine reactions.**

When an enamine reacts with an acyl halide or an acid anhydride, the product is the *C*-acylated compound. The iminium ion that forms hydrolyzes when water is added and the overall reaction provides a synthesis of β-diketones.

Iminium salt

**2-Acetylcyclohexanone
(a β-diketone)**

Although *N*-acylation may occur in this synthesis, the *N*-acyl product is unstable and can act as an acylating agent itself.

Enamine   ***N*-Acylated enamine**   ***C*-Acylated iminium salt**   **Enamine**

As a consequence, the yields of *C*-acylated products are generally high.

Enamines can be alkylated as well as acylated. While alkylation may lead to the formation of a considerable amount of *N*-alkylated product, heating the *N*-alkylated product often converts it to a *C*-alkyl compound. This rearrangement is particularly favored when the alkyl halide is an allylic halide, benzylic halide, or α-haloacetic ester.

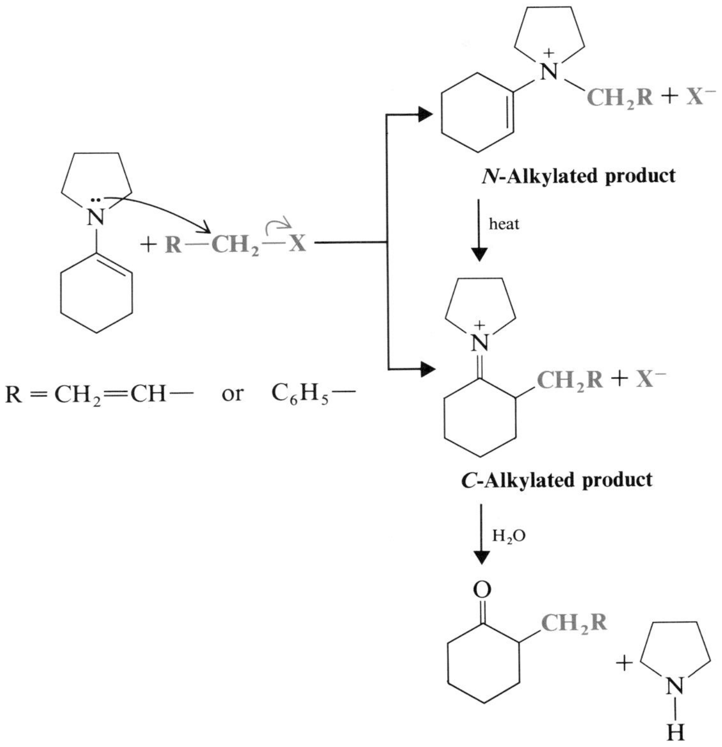

N-Alkylated product

heat

R = CH₂=CH—   or   C₆H₅—

C-Alkylated product

H₂O

Enamine alkylations are S$_N$2 reactions; thus, when we choose our alkylating agents, we are usually restricted to the use of methyl, primary, allylic, and benzylic halides. Alpha-halo esters can also be used as the alkylating agents, and this reaction provides a convenient synthesis of γ-keto esters:

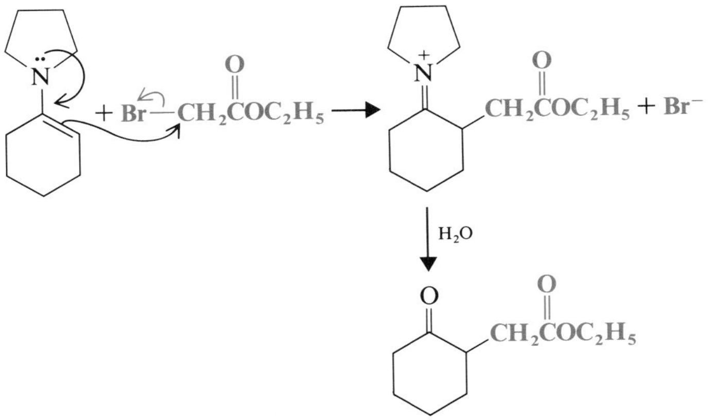

**A γ-keto ester
(75%)**

Problem 20.22

Show how you could employ enamines in syntheses of the following compounds:

(a)

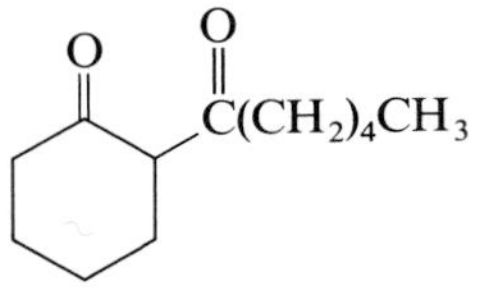

(c)

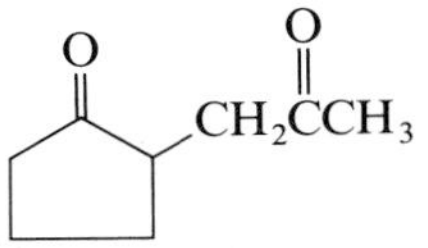

(b)

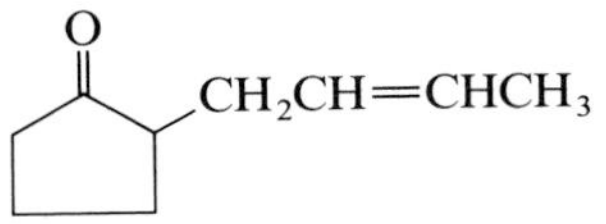

(d)

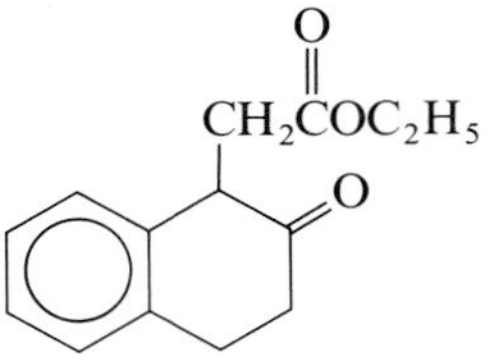

An especially interesting set of enamine alkylations is shown in the following reactions (developed by J. K. Whitesell of the University of Texas at Austin). The enamine (prepared from a single enantiomer of the secondary amine) is chiral. Alkylation from the bottom of the enamine is severely hindered by the methyl group. (Notice that this hindrance will exist even if rotation of the groups takes place about the bond connecting the two rings.) Consequently, alkylation takes place much more rapidly from the top side. This reaction yields (after hydrolysis) 2-substituted cyclohexanones consisting almost entirely of a single enantiomer.

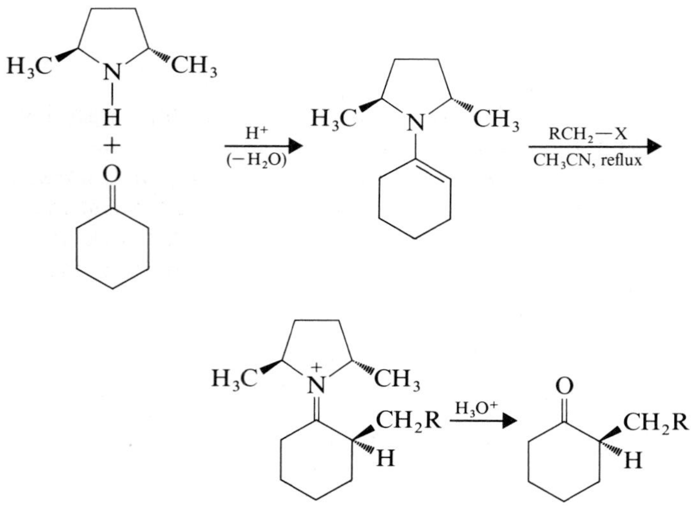

R Group	Chemical Yield (%)	Optical Purity (%)
H—	50	83
CH_3CH_2—	57	93
CH_2=CH—	80	82

Enamines can also be used in Michael additions. An example is the following:

20.12 BARBITURATES

In the presence of sodium ethoxide, diethyl malonate reacts with urea to yield a compound called barbituric acid.

Barbituric acid

Barbituric acid is a pyrimidine (cf. Section 19.1), and it exists in several tautomeric forms including one with an aromatic ring.

As its name suggests barbituric acid is a moderately strong acid, stronger even than acetic acid. Its anion is highly resonance stabilized.

Derivatives of barbituric acid are *barbiturates*. Barbiturates have been used in medicine as soporifics (sleep producers) since 1903. One of the earliest barbiturates introduced into medical use is the compound veronal (5,5-diethylbarbituric acid). Veronal is usually used as its sodium salt. Other barbiturates are seconal and phenobarbital.

Veronal	Seconal	Phenobarbital
(5,5-diethylbarbituric acid)	[5-allyl-5-(1-methylbutyl) barbituric acid]	(5-ethyl-5-phenylbarbituric acid)

Although barbiturates are very effective soporifics, their use is also hazardous. They are addictive, and overdosage, often with fatal results, is common.

Problem 20.23

Outlined here is a synthesis of phenobarbital.
(a) What are compounds **A – F**?   (b) Propose an alternative synthesis of **E** from diethyl malonate.

$$C_6H_5-CH_3 \xrightarrow[\text{CCl}_4]{\text{NBS}} \textbf{A } (C_7H_7Br) \xrightarrow[\text{(2) CO}_2, \text{ then H}^+]{\text{(1) Mg, Et}_2\text{O}} \textbf{B } (C_8H_8O_2) \xrightarrow{\text{SOCl}_2}$$

$$\textbf{C } (C_8H_7ClO) \xrightarrow{\text{EtOH}} \textbf{D } (C_{10}H_{12}O_2) \xrightarrow[\text{NaOEt}]{\text{EtOCOEt}} \textbf{E } (C_{13}H_{16}O_4) \xrightarrow[\text{CH}_3\text{CH}_2\text{Br}]{\text{KOC(CH}_3)_3}$$

$$\textbf{F } (C_{15}H_{20}O_4) \xrightarrow[]{\text{H}_2\text{NCNH}_2, \text{ NaOEt}} \text{ phenobarbital}$$

Problem 20.24

Starting with diethyl malonate, urea, and any other required reagents, outline a synthesis of veronal and seconal.

20.13 SUMMARY OF IMPORTANT REACTIONS

1. Claisen condensation (Section 20.2)

$$2\ R-CH_2-\overset{O}{\underset{\|}{C}}-OEt \xrightarrow[\text{(2) H}^+]{\text{(1) NaOEt}} R-CH_2-\overset{O}{\underset{\|}{C}}-\underset{\underset{R}{|}}{CH}-\overset{O}{\underset{\|}{C}}-OEt$$

2. Crossed Claisen condensation (Section 20.2A)

3. Acetoacetic ester synthesis (Section 20.3)

$$CH_3-\overset{O}{\overset{\|}{C}}-CH_2-\overset{O}{\overset{\|}{C}}-OEt \xrightarrow[\text{(2) RBr}]{\text{(1) NaOEt}} CH_3-\overset{O}{\overset{\|}{C}}-\underset{R}{\overset{\|}{C}}H-\overset{O}{\overset{\|}{C}}-OEt \xrightarrow[\substack{\text{(2) H}_3\text{O}^+ \\ \text{(3) heat, }(-CO_2)}]{\text{(1) OH}^-\text{, heat}}$$

$$CH_3-\overset{O}{\overset{\|}{C}}-CH_2-R$$

$$CH_3-\overset{O}{\overset{\|}{C}}-\underset{R}{\overset{\|}{C}}H-\overset{O}{\overset{\|}{C}}-OEt \xrightarrow[\text{(2) R'Br}]{\text{(1) NaOEt}} CH_3-\overset{O}{\overset{\|}{C}}-\overset{R'}{\underset{R}{\overset{\|}{C}}}-\overset{O}{\overset{\|}{C}}-OEt \xrightarrow[\substack{\text{(2) H}_3\text{O}^+ \\ \text{(3) heat, }(-CO_2)}]{\text{(1) OH}^-\text{, heat}}$$

$$CH_3-\overset{O}{\overset{\|}{C}}-\underset{R'}{\overset{\|}{C}}H-R$$

4. Malonic ester synthesis (Section 20.4)

$$EtO-\overset{O}{\overset{\|}{C}}-CH_2-\overset{O}{\overset{\|}{C}}-OEt \xrightarrow[\text{(2) RBr}]{\text{(1) NaOEt}} EtO-\overset{O}{\overset{\|}{C}}-\underset{R}{\overset{\|}{C}}H-\overset{O}{\overset{\|}{C}}-OEt \xrightarrow[\substack{\text{(2) H}_3\text{O}^+ \\ \text{(3) heat, }(-CO_2)}]{\text{(1) OH}^-\text{, heat}}$$

$$HO-\overset{O}{\overset{\|}{C}}-CH_2-R$$

$$EtO-\overset{O}{\overset{\|}{C}}-\underset{R}{\overset{\|}{C}}H-\overset{O}{\overset{\|}{C}}-OEt \xrightarrow[\text{(2) R'Br}]{\text{(1) NaOEt}} EtO-\overset{O}{\overset{\|}{C}}-\overset{R'}{\underset{R}{\overset{\|}{C}}}-\overset{O}{\overset{\|}{C}}-OEt \xrightarrow[\substack{\text{(2) H}_3\text{O}^+ \\ \text{(3) heat, }(-CO_2)}]{\text{(1) OH}^-\text{, heat}}$$

$$HO-\overset{O}{\overset{\|}{C}}-\underset{R'}{\overset{\|}{C}}H-R$$

5. Direct alkylation of esters (Section 20.6)

$$R-CH_2-\overset{O}{\overset{\|}{C}}-OEt \xrightarrow[\text{THF}]{\text{LDA}} R-\overset{..\,-}{C}H-\overset{O}{\overset{\|}{C}}-OEt \xrightarrow{R'CH_2-Br} R-\underset{\underset{R'}{\overset{|}{CH_2}}}{\overset{|}{C}}H-\overset{O}{\overset{\|}{C}}-OEt$$

Li$^+$

6. Alkylation of dithianes (Section 20.7)

$$R-\overset{O}{\overset{\|}{C}}-H \xrightarrow[\text{H}^+]{\text{HSCH}_2\text{CH}_2\text{CH}_2\text{SH}} \underset{R\quad H}{\overset{S\diagdown\diagup S}{\bigcirc}} \xrightarrow[\text{(2) R'CH}_2\text{X}]{\text{(1) BuLi}} \underset{R\quad CH_2R'}{\overset{S\diagdown\diagup S}{\bigcirc}} \xrightarrow[\text{H}_2\text{O}]{\text{HgCl}_2\text{, CH}_3\text{OH}} R-\overset{O}{\overset{\|}{C}}-CH_2R'$$

7. Knoevenagel condensation (Section 20.8)

8. Michael addition (Section 20.9)

α,β-Unsaturated
carbonyl compound

Or other active
methylene compound

9. Mannich reaction (Section 20.10)

10. Stork enamine reaction (Section 20.11)

Enamine

Additional Problems

20.25 Show all steps in the following syntheses. You may use any other needed reagents but should begin with the compound given. You need not repeat steps carried out in earlier parts of this exercise.

(a) $CH_3CH_2CH_2COC_2H_5 \longrightarrow CH_3CH_2CH_2CCHCOC_2H_5$
with substituent CH_2—CH_3

(b) $CH_3CH_2CH_2COC_2H_5 \longrightarrow CH_3CH_2CH_2CCH_2CH_2CH_3$

(c) $C_6H_5CH_2COC_2H_5 \longrightarrow C_6H_5CHCO_2H$ with CH_3

(d) $CH_3CH_2CH_2COC_2H_5 \longrightarrow CH_3CH_2CHCOC_2H_5$
with substituent C—COC_2H_5 (with two O)

(e) $CH_3CH_2CH_2COC_2H_5 \longrightarrow CH_3CH_2CH_2C$—$COC_2H_5$ (with two O)

ADDITIONAL PROBLEMS

(f) 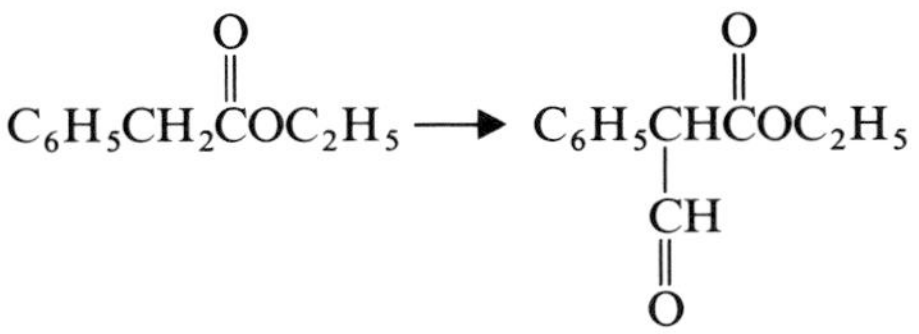 $C_6H_5CH_2\overset{\overset{O}{\|}}{C}OC_2H_5 \longrightarrow C_6H_5\overset{}{\underset{\underset{O}{\overset{\|}{CH}}}{CH}}\overset{\overset{O}{\|}}{C}OC_2H_5$

(g)

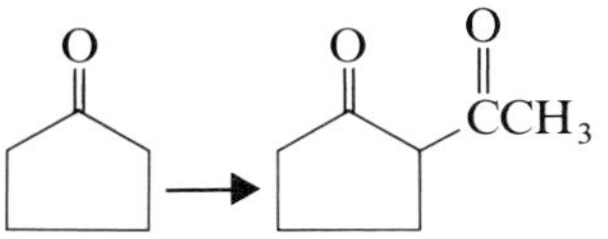

(h)

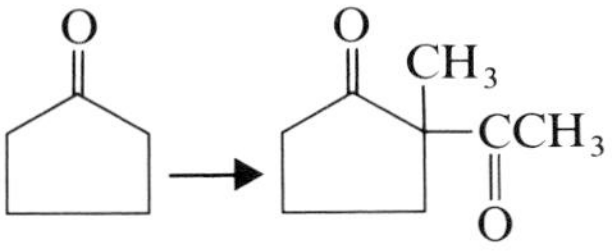

(i)

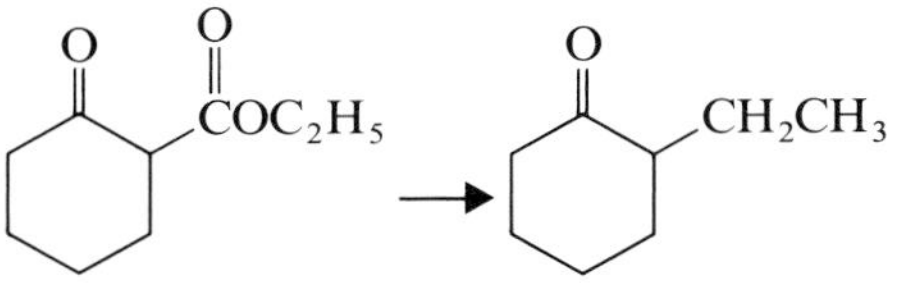

20.26 Outline syntheses of each of the following from acetoacetic ester and any other required reagents.

(a) *tert*-Butyl methyl ketone

(b) 2-Hexanone

(c) 2,5-Hexanedione

(d) 4-Hydroxypentanoic acid

(e) 2-Ethyl-1,3-butanediol

(f) 1-Phenyl-1,3-butanediol

20.27 Outline syntheses of each of the following from diethyl malonate and any other required reagents.

(a) 2-Methylbutanoic acid

(b) 4-Methyl-1-pentanol

(c) $CH_3CH_2\underset{\underset{CH_2OH}{|}}{C}HCH_2OH$

(d) $HOCH_2CH_2CH_2CH_2OH$

20.28 The synthesis of cyclobutanecarboxylic acid given on page 905 was first carried out by William Perkin, Jr., in 1883, and it represented one of the first syntheses of an organic compound with a ring smaller than six carbon atoms. (There was a general feeling at the time that such compounds would be too unstable to exist.) Earlier in 1883, Perkin reported what he mistakenly believed to be a cyclobutane derivative obtained from the reaction of acetoacetic ester and 1,3-dibromopropane. The reaction that Perkin had expected to take place was the following:

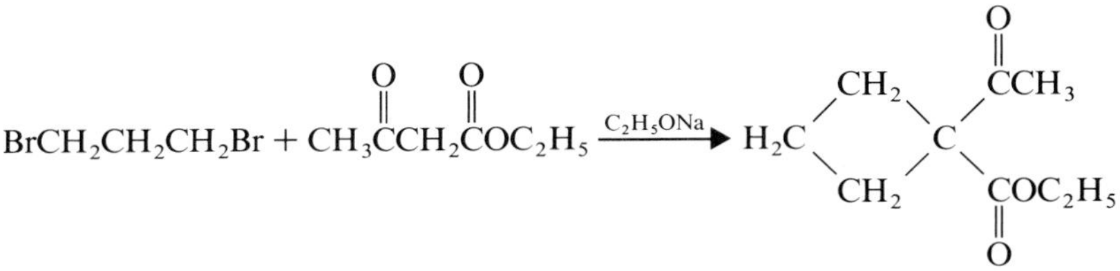

$$BrCH_2CH_2CH_2Br + CH_3\overset{\overset{O}{\|}}{C}CH_2\overset{\overset{O}{\|}}{C}OC_2H_5 \xrightarrow{C_2H_5ONa} \text{(cyclobutane product)}$$

The molecular formula for his product agreed with the formulation given in the preceding reaction, and alkaline hydrolysis and acidification gave a nicely crystalline acid (also having the expected molecular formula). The acid, however, was quite stable to heat and resisted decarboxylation. Perkin later found that both the ester and the acid contained six-membered rings (five carbon atoms and one oxygen atom). Recall the charge distribution in the enolate ion obtained from acetoacetic ester and propose structures for Perkin's ester and acid.

20.29 (a) In 1884 Perkin achieved a successful synthesis of cyclopropanecarboxylic acid from sodiomalonic ester and 1,2-dibromoethane. Outline the reactions involved in this synthesis. (b) In 1885 Perkin synthesized five-membered carbocyclic compounds **D** and **E** in the following way:

$$2 \text{ Na}^+ : \bar{\text{C}}\text{H}(\text{CO}_2\text{C}_2\text{H}_5)_2 + \text{BrCH}_2\text{CH}_2\text{CH}_2\text{Br} \longrightarrow \textbf{A} \ (\text{C}_{17}\text{H}_{28}\text{O}_8) \xrightarrow[]{2 \text{ C}_2\text{H}_5\text{O}^-\text{Na}^+} \xrightarrow[]{\text{Br}_2}$$

$$\textbf{B} \ (\text{C}_{17}\text{H}_{26}\text{O}_8) \xrightarrow[\text{(2) H}_3\text{O}^+]{\text{(1) OH}^-/\text{H}_2\text{O}} \textbf{C} \ (\text{C}_9\text{H}_{10}\text{O}_8) \xrightarrow[]{\text{heat}} \textbf{D} \ (\text{C}_7\text{H}_{10}\text{O}_4) + \textbf{E} \ (\text{C}_7\text{H}_{10}\text{O}_4)$$

D and **E** are diastereomers; **D** can be resolved into enantiomeric forms while **E** cannot. What are the structures of **A**–**E** ? (c) Ten years later Perkin was able to synthesize 1,4-dibromobutane; he later used this compound and diethyl malonate to prepare cyclopentanecarboxylic acid. Show the reactions involved.

20.30 Write mechanisms that account for the products of the following reactions:

(a)

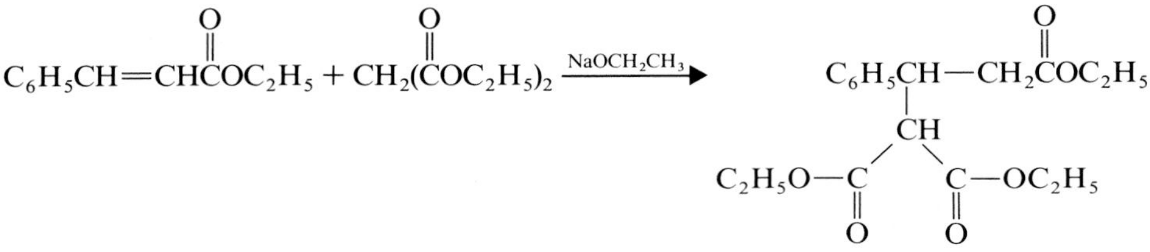

(b)

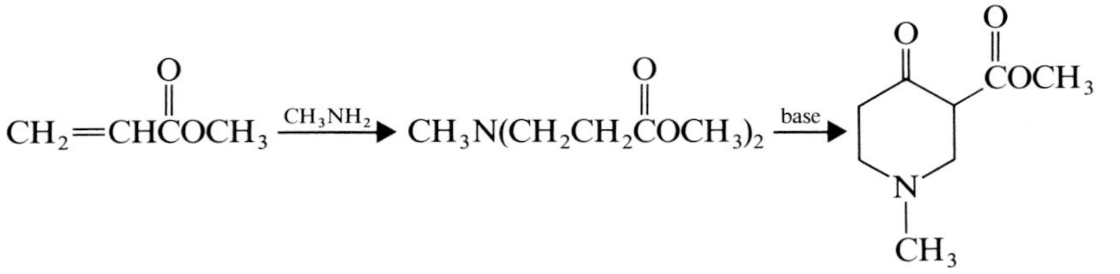

(c)

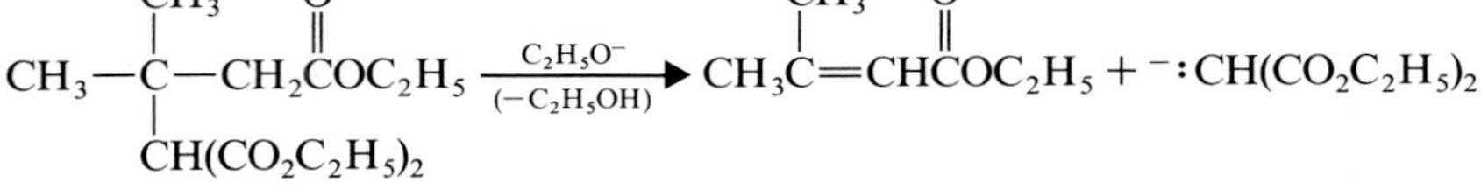

20.31 Knoevenagel condensations in which the active hydrogen compound is a β-keto ester or a β-diketone often yield products that result from one molecule of aldehyde or ketone and two molecules of the active methylene component. For example,

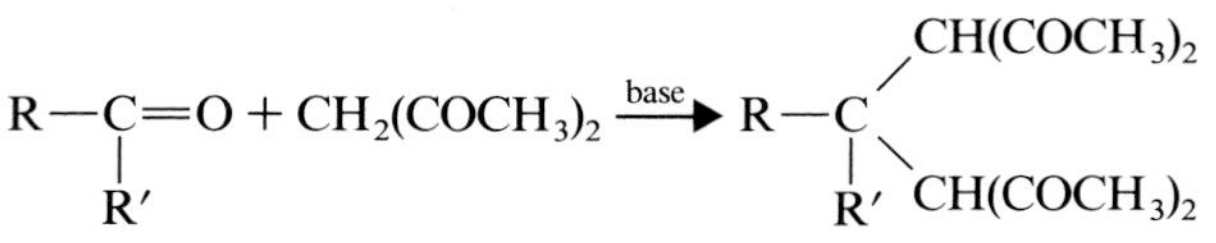

Suggest a reasonable mechanism that will account for the formation of these products.

20.32 Thymine is one of the heterocyclic bases found in DNA. Starting with ethyl propanoate and using any other needed reagents, show how you might synthesize thymine.

Thymine

20.33 The mandibular glands of queen bees secrete a fluid that contains a remarkable compound known as "queen substance." When even an exceedingly small amount of the queen substance is transferred to worker bees, it inhibits the development of their ovaries and prevents the workers from bearing new queens. Queen substance, a monocarboxylic acid with the molecular formula $C_{10}H_{16}O_3$, has been synthesized by the following route:

$$\text{Cycloheptanone} \xrightarrow[\text{(2) } H_3O^+]{\text{(1) } CH_3MgI} \textbf{A } (C_8H_{16}O) \xrightarrow{H^+,\ heat} \textbf{B } (C_8H_{14}) \xrightarrow[\text{(2) } Zn,\ H_2O]{\text{(1) } O_3}$$

$$\textbf{C } (C_8H_{14}O_2) \xrightarrow[\text{pyridine}]{CH_2(CO_2H)_2} \text{queen substance } (C_{10}H_{16}O_3)$$

On catalytic hydrogenation queen substance yields compound **D** which, on treatment with iodine in sodium hydroxide and subsequent acidification, yields a dicarboxylic acid **E**; that is,

$$\text{Queen substance} \xrightarrow[Pd]{H_2} \textbf{D } (C_{10}H_{18}O_3) \xrightarrow[\text{(2) } H_3O^+]{\text{(1) } I_2/NaOH} \textbf{E } (C_9H_{16}O_4)$$

Provide structures for the queen substance and compounds **A – E**.

20.34 Linalool, a fragrant compound that can be isolated from a variety of plants, is 3,7-dimethyl-1,6-octadien-3-ol. Linalool is used in making perfumes and it can be synthesized in the following way:

$$CH_2{=}\overset{\underset{\displaystyle CH_3}{|}}{C}{-}CH{=}CH_2 + HBr \longrightarrow \textbf{F } (C_5H_9Br) \xrightarrow[\text{ester}]{\text{sodioacetoacetic}}$$

$$\textbf{G } (C_{11}H_{18}O_3) \xrightarrow[\text{(2) } H_3O^+,\ \text{(3) heat}]{\text{(1) dil. NaOH}} \textbf{H } (C_8H_{14}O) \xrightarrow[\text{(2) } H_3O^+]{\text{(1) } LiC{\equiv}CH}$$

$$\textbf{I } (C_{10}H_{16}O) \xrightarrow[\substack{\text{Lindlar's} \\ \text{catalyst}}]{H_2} \text{linalool}$$

Outline the reactions involved. (*Hint:* Compound **F** is the more stable isomer capable of being produced in the first step.)

20.35 Compound **J**, a compound with two four-membered rings, has been synthesized by the following route. Outline the steps that are involved.

$$NaCH(CO_2C_2H_5)_2 + BrCH_2CH_2CH_2Br \longrightarrow (C_{10}H_{17}BrO_4) \xrightarrow{NaOC_2H_5}$$

$$C_{10}H_{16}O_4 \xrightarrow[\text{(2) } H_2O]{\text{(1) } LiAlH_4} C_6H_{12}O_2 \xrightarrow{HBr} C_6H_{10}Br_2 \xrightarrow[\text{2 } NaOC_2H_5]{CH_2(CO_2C_2H_5)_2}$$

$$C_{13}H_{20}O_4 \xrightarrow[\text{(2) } H_3O^+]{\text{(1) } OH^-,\ H_2O} C_9H_{12}O_4 \xrightarrow{heat} \textbf{J } (C_8H_{12}O_2) + CO_2$$

20.36 When an aldehyde or a ketone is condensed with ethyl α-chloroacetate in the presence of sodium ethoxide, the product is an α,β-epoxy ester called a *glycidic ester*. The synthesis is called the Darzens condensation.

$$R-\underset{\underset{R'}{|}}{C}=O + ClCH_2CO_2C_2H_5 \xrightarrow{C_2H_5ONa} R-\underset{\underset{R'}{|}}{C}\underset{O}{\overset{}{\diagup\diagdown}}CHCO_2C_2H_5 + NaCl + C_2H_5OH$$

A glycidic ester

(a) Outline a reasonable mechanism for the Darzens condensation. (b) Hydrolysis of the epoxy ester leads to an epoxy acid that, on heating with pyridine, furnishes an aldehyde.

$$R-\underset{\underset{R'}{|}}{C}\underset{O}{\overset{}{\diagup\diagdown}}CHCO_2H \xrightarrow[heat]{C_5H_5N} R-\underset{\underset{R'}{|}}{CH}-\overset{\overset{O}{||}}{CH} + CO_2$$

What is happening here? (c) Starting with β-ionone (Problem 17.13), show how you might synthesize the following aldehyde. (This aldehyde is an intermediate in an industrial synthesis of vitamin A.)

20.37 The *Perkin condensation* is an aldol-type condensation in which an aromatic aldehyde (ArCHO) reacts with a carboxylic acid anhydride $(RCH_2CO)_2O$, to give an α,β-unsaturated acid ($ArCH=CRCO_2H$). The catalyst that is usually employed is the potassium salt of the carboxylic acid (RCH_2CO_2K). (a) Outline the Perkin condensation that takes place when benzaldehyde reacts with propanoic anhydride in the presence of potassium propanoate. (b) How would you use a Perkin condensation to prepare p-chlorocinnamic acid, p-$ClC_6H_4CH=CHCO_2H$?

20.38 (+)-Fenchone is a terpenoid that can be isolated from fennel oil. (±)-Fenchone has been synthesized through the following route. Supply the missing intermediates and reagents.

SPECIAL TOPIC

H

ALKALOIDS

Extracting the bark, roots, leaves, berries, and fruits of plants often yields nitrogen-containing bases called *alkaloids.* The name alkaloid comes from the fact that these substances are "alkali-like"; that is, since alkaloids are amines they often react with acids to yield soluble salts. The nitrogen atoms of most alkaloids are present in heterocyclic rings. In a few instances, however, nitrogen may be present as a primary amine or as a quaternary ammonium group.

When administered to animals most alkaloids produce striking physiological effects, which effects *vary greatly* from alkaloid to alkaloid. Some alkaloids stimulate the central nervous system, others cause paralysis; some alkaloids elevate blood pressure, others lower it. Certain alkaloids act as pain relievers; others act as tranquilizers; still others act against infectious microorganisms. Most alkaloids are toxic when their dosage is large enough, and with some this dosage is very small. In spite of this, many alkaloids find use in medicine.

Systematic names are seldom used for alkaloids, and their common names have a variety of origins. In many instances the common name reflects the botanical source of the compound. The alkaloid strychnine, for example, comes from the seeds of the *Strychnos* plants. In other instances the names are more whimsical: The name of the opium alkaloid morphine comes from Morpheus, the ancient Greek god of dreams; the name of the tobacco alkaloid nicotine comes from Nicot, an early French ambassador who sent tobacco seeds to France. The one characteristic that alkaloid names have in common is the ending *-ine,* reflecting the fact that they are all amines.

Alkaloids have been of interest to chemists for nearly two centuries, and in that time thousands of alkaloids have been isolated. Most of these have had their structures determined through the application of chemical and physical methods, and in many instances these structures have been confirmed by independent synthesis. A complete account of the chemistry of the alkaloids would (and does) occupy volumes; here we have space to consider only a few representative examples.

H.1 ALKALOIDS CONTAINING A PYRIDINE OR REDUCED PYRIDINE RING

The predominant alkaloid of the tobacco plant is nicotine:

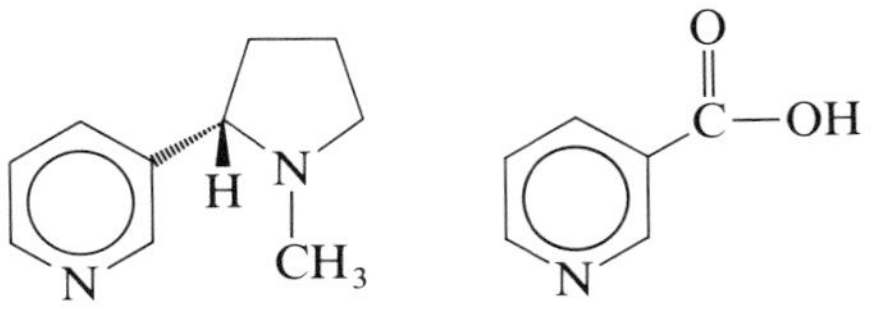

Nicotine   **Nicotinic acid**

In very small doses nicotine acts as a stimulant, but in larger doses it causes depression, nausea, and vomiting. In still larger doses it is a violent poison. Nicotine salts are used as insecticides.

Oxidation of nicotine by concentrated nitric acid produces pyridine-3-carboxylic acid—a compound that is called *nicotinic acid*. While the consumption of nicotine is of no benefit to humans, nicotinic acid is a vitamin; it is incorporated into the important coenzyme, nicotinamide adenine dinucleotide, commonly referred to as NAD^+ (oxidized form).

Problem H.1

Nicotine has been synthesized by the following route. All of the steps involve reactions that we have seen before. Suggest reagents that could be used for each.

A number of alkaloids contain a piperidine ring. These include coniine (from the poison hemlock, *Conium maculatum,* a member of the carrot family, Umbelliferae), atropine (from *Atropa belladonna* and other genera of the plant family Solanaceae), and cocaine (from *Erythroxylon coca*).

Coniine
[(+)-2-propylpiperidine]

Atropine

Cocaine

Coniine is toxic; its ingestion may cause weakness, drowsiness, nausea, labored respiration, paralysis, and death. Coniine was one toxic substance of the "hemlock" used in the execution of Socrates (other poisons may have been included as well).

In small doses cocaine decreases fatigue, increases mental activity, and gives a general feeling of well being. Prolonged use of cocaine, however, leads to physical addiction and to periods of deep depression. Cocaine is also a local anesthetic and, for a time, it was used medically in that capacity. When its tendency to cause addiction was recognized, efforts were made to develop other local anesthetics. This led, in 1905, to the synthesis of Novocain, a compound that is also called Procaine that has some of the same structural features as cocaine (i.e., its benzoic ester and tertiary amine groups).

Novocain
(procaine)

Atropine is an intense poison. In dilute solutions (0.5 – 1.0%) it is used to dilate the pupil of the eye in ophthalmic examinations. Compounds related to atropine are contained in the 12-h continuous-release capsules used to relieve symptoms of the common cold.

Problem H.2

The principal alkaloid of *Atropa belladonna* is the optically active alkaloid *hyoscyamine.* During its isolation hyoscyamine is often racemized by bases to optically inactive atropine. (a) What stereocenter is likely to be involved in the racemization? (b) In hyoscyamine this stereocenter has the (S) configuration. Write a three-dimensional structure for hyoscyamine.

Problem H.3

Hydrolysis of atropine gives tropine and (±)-tropic acid. (a) What are their structures? (b) Even though tropine has a stereocenter, it is optically inactive. Explain. (c) An isomeric form of tropine called ψ-tropine has also been prepared by heating tropine with base. ψ-Tropine is also optically inactive. What is its structure?

Problem H.4

In 1891 G. Merling transformed tropine (cf. Problem H.3) into 1,3,5-cyclohep-tatriene (tropylidene) through the following sequence of reactions.

$$Tropine\ (C_8H_{15}NO) \xrightarrow{-H_2O} C_8H_{13}N \xrightarrow{CH_3I} C_9H_{16}NI \xrightarrow[(2)\ heat]{(1)\ Ag_2O/H_2O}$$

$$C_9H_{15}N \xrightarrow{CH_3I} C_{10}H_{18}NI \xrightarrow[(2)\ heat]{(1)\ Ag_2O/H_2O}$$

$$1,3,5\text{-cycloheptatriene} + (CH_3)_3N + H_2O$$

Write out all of the reactions that take place.

Problem H.5

Many alkaloids appear to be synthesized in plants by reactions that resemble the Mannich reaction (Section 20.10). Recognition of this (by R. Robinson in 1917) led to a synthesis of tropinone that takes place under "physiological conditions," that is, at room temperature and at pH values near neutrality. This synthesis is shown here. Propose reasonable mechanisms that account for the overall course of the reaction.

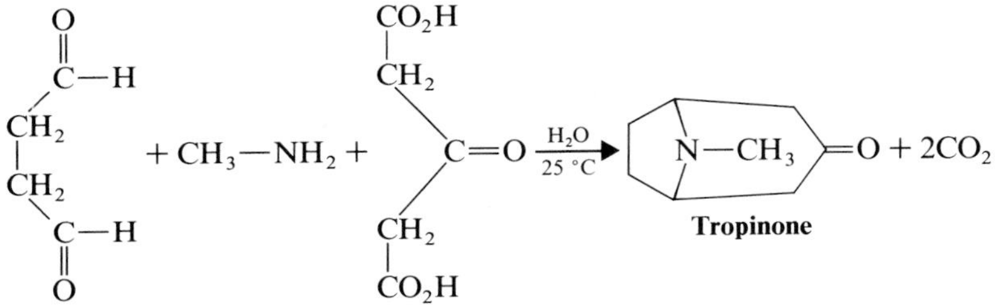

H.2 ALKALOIDS CONTAINING AN ISOQUINOLINE OR REDUCED ISOQUINOLINE RING

Papaverine, morphine, and codeine are all alkaloids obtained from the opium poppy, *Papaver somniferum.*

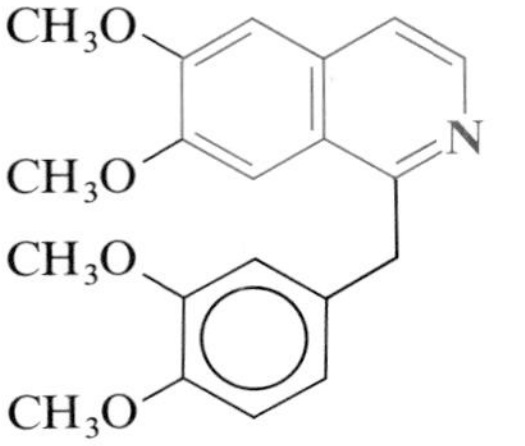

Papaverine

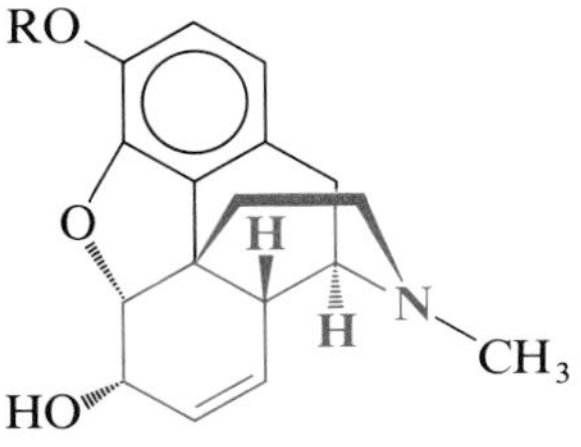

Morphine (R = H)
Codeine (R = CH₃)

Papaverine has an isoquinoline ring; in morphine and codeine the isoquinoline ring is partially hydrogenated (reduced).

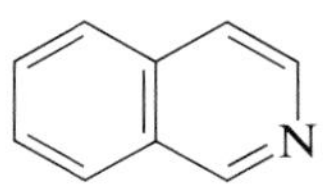

SPECIAL TOPIC H

Isoquinoline

Opium has been used since earliest recorded history. Morphine was first isolated from opium in 1803, and its isolation represented one of the first instances of the purification of the active principle of a drug. One hundred and twenty years were to pass, however, before the complicated structure of morphine was deduced, and its final confirmation through independent synthesis (by Marshall Gates of the University of Rochester) did not take place until 1952.

Morphine is one of the most potent analgesics known, and it is still used extensively in medicine to relieve pain, especially "deep" pain. Its greatest drawbacks, however, are its tendencies to lead to addiction and to depress respiration. These disadvantages have brought about a search for morphine-like compounds that do not have these disadvantages. One of the newest candidates is the compound pentazocine. Pentazocine is a highly effective analgesic and is nonaddictive; unfortunately however, like morphine, it depresses respiration.

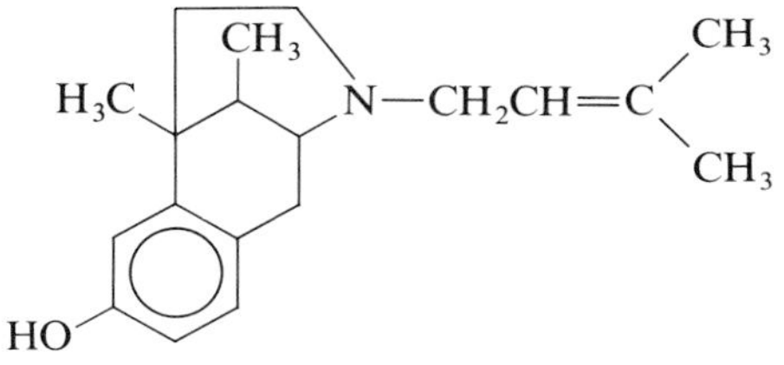

Pentazocine

Problem H.6

Papaverine has been synthesized by the following route:

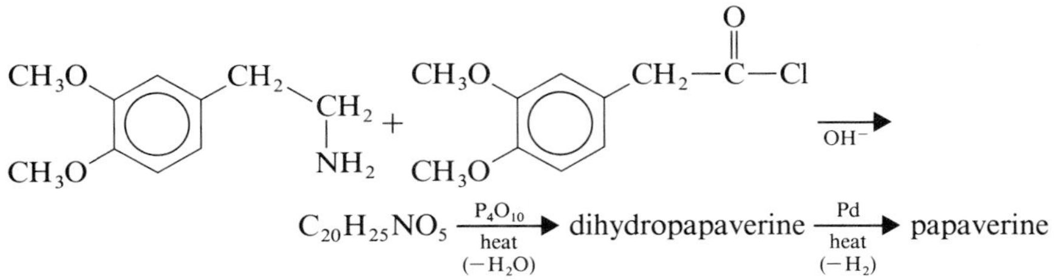

$$C_{20}H_{25}NO_5 \xrightarrow[\text{heat} \atop (-H_2O)]{P_4O_{10}} \text{dihydropapaverine} \xrightarrow[\text{heat} \atop (-H_2)]{Pd} \text{papaverine}$$

Outline the reactions involved.

Problem H.7

One of the important steps in the synthesis of morphine involved the following transformation:

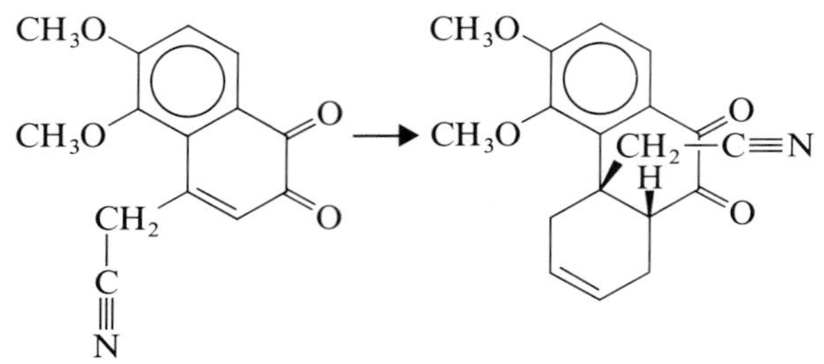

Suggest how this step was accomplished.

Problem H.8

When morphine reacts with 2 mol of acetic anhydride, it is transformed into the highly addictive narcotic, heroin. What is the structure of heroin?

H.3 ALKALOIDS CONTAINING INDOLE OR REDUCED INDOLE RINGS

A large number of alkaloids are derivatives of an indole ring system. These range from the relatively simple *gramine* to the highly complicated structures of *strychnine* and *reserpine*.

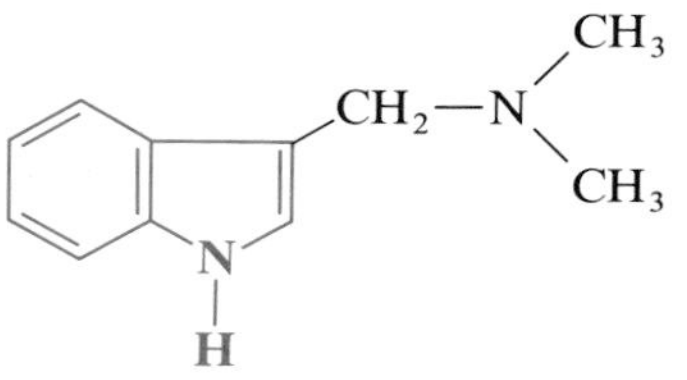

Gramine

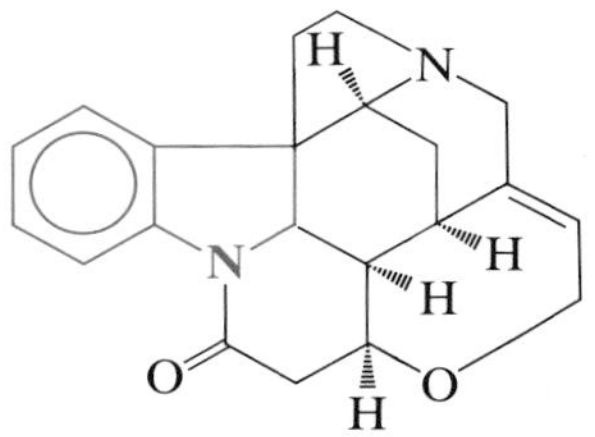

Strychnine

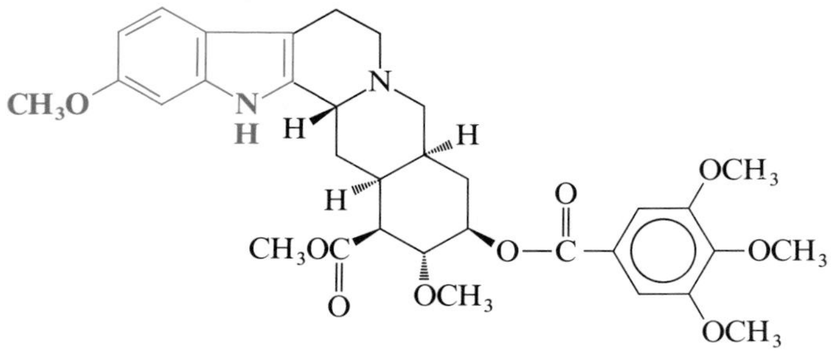

Reserpine

Gramine can be obtained from chlorophyll-deficient mutants of barley. Strychnine, a very bitter and highly poisonous compound, comes from the seeds of *Strychnos nux-vomica*. Strychnine is a central nervous system stimulant and has been used medically (in low dosage) to counteract poisoning by central nervous system depressants. Reserpine can be obtained from the Indian snakeroot *Rauwolfia serpentina*, a plant that has been used in native medicine for centuries. Reserpine is used in modern medicine as a tranquilizer and as an agent to lower blood pressure.

Problem H.9

Gramine has been synthesized by heating a mixture of indole, formaldehyde, and dimethylamine. (a) What general reaction is involved here? (b) Outline a reasonable mechanism for the gramine synthesis.

H.4 BIOSYNTHESIS OF ALKALOIDS

The primary starting materials for alkaloid synthesis in plants appear to be α-amino acids. More than 20 different α-amino acids occur naturally; they are the main building blocks for proteins (Chapter 24). Two amino acids, in particular, are important in alkaloid biosynthesis. These are tyrosine and tryptophan:

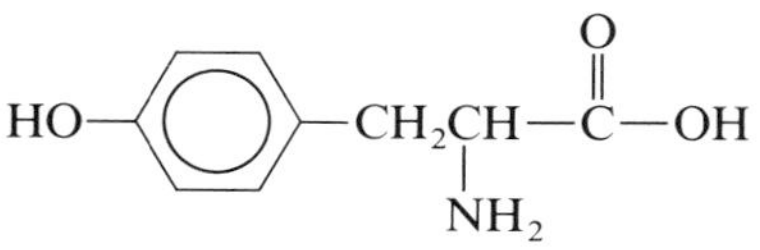

Tyrosine 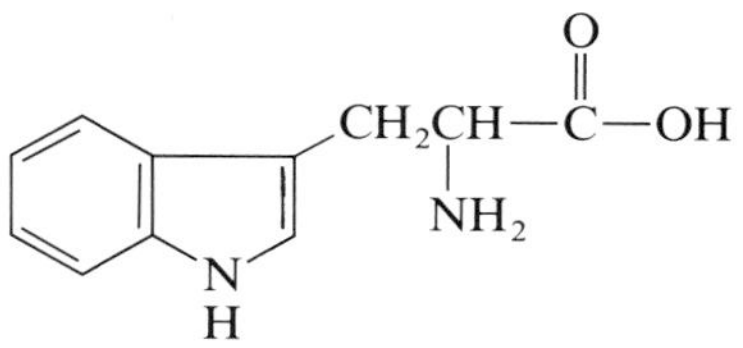   Tryptophan

Two general reactions appear to be of central importance in alkaloid biosynthesis—the Mannich reaction and the oxidative coupling of phenols. We studied the Mannich reaction in Section 20.10 (cf. also Problem H.5). The oxidative coupling of phenols is a free radical process that is catalyzed by enzymes in plants and that can also be carried out (usually less successfully) in the laboratory. A simple formulation of an oxidative phenol coupling is outlined using phenol itself as the starting compound. Loss of an electron and a proton from phenol leads to a resonance-stabilized free radical. Two free radicals can then undergo coupling in a variety of ways:

Oxidation

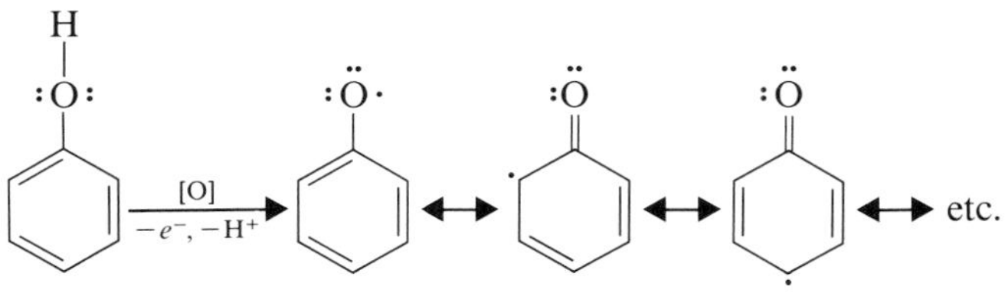

ortho–ortho Coupling

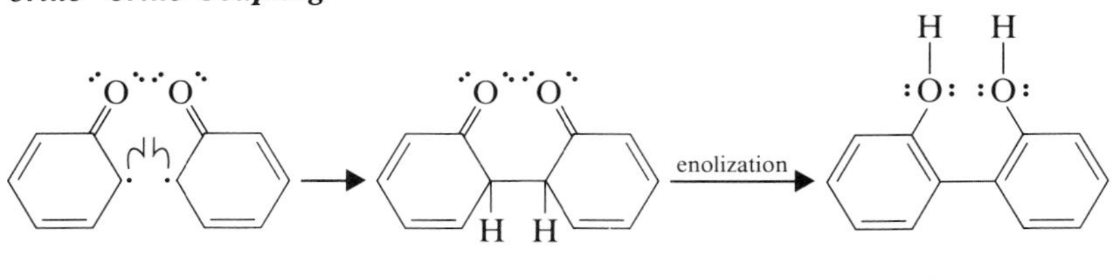

ortho–para Coupling

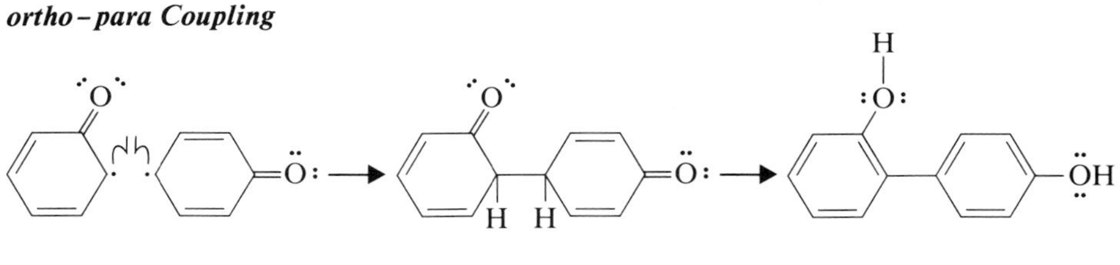

para – para Coupling

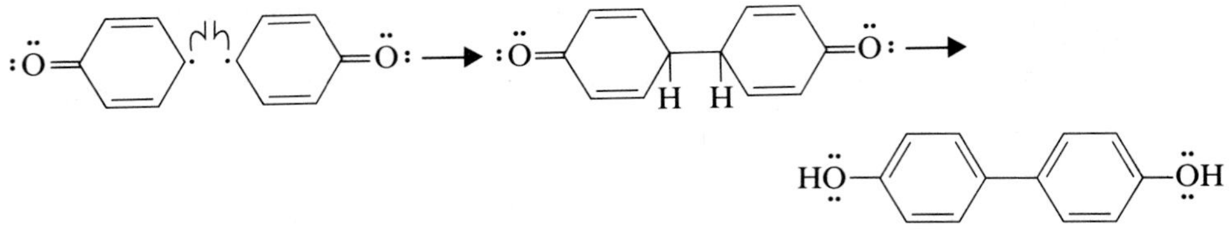

In most cases, oxidative coupling occurs intramolecularly.

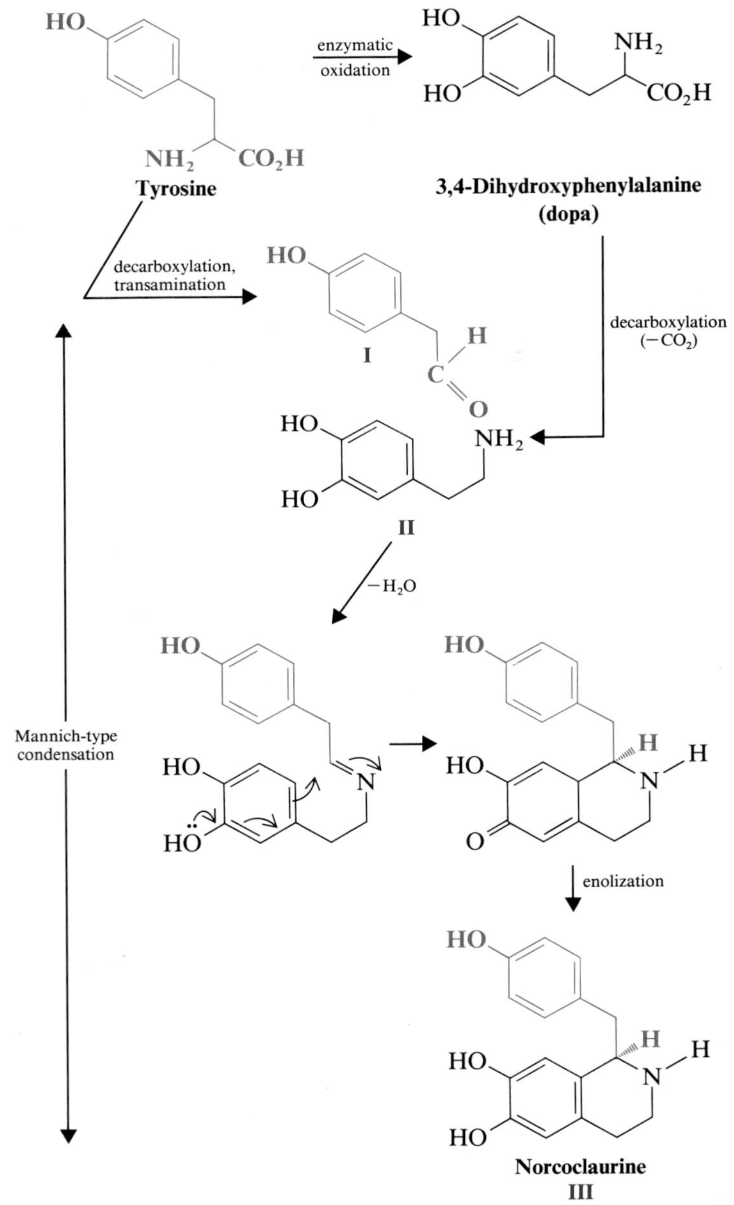

FIGURE H.1 The biosynthesis of norcoclaurine (III) from 2 mol of 3,4-dihydroxyphenyl-alanine.

The biosynthetic route that the opium poppy uses to synthesize morphine is now known. Most of the morphine molecule, it turns out, is constructed from two molecules of tyrosine.

The synthesis begins with the oxidation of tyrosine to 3,4-dihydroxyphenylalanine (dopa):

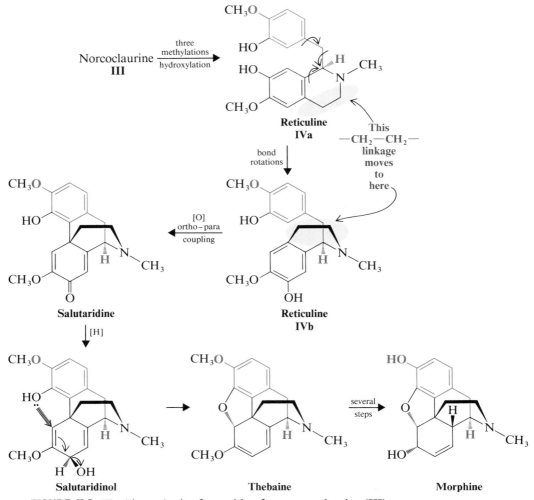

Further enzyme-catalyzed reactions transform 3,4-dihydroxyphenylalanine into 3,4-dihydroxyphenylethylamine [dopamine (**II**); see Fig. H.1]. The other part of the synthesis involves the conversion of tyrosine into *p*-hydroxyphenylacetaldehyde (**I**). These two molecules then react in a Mannich-type condensation to yield norcoclaurine (**III**).

FIGURE H.2 The biosynthesis of morphine from norcoclaurine (**III**).

Hydroxylation of the benzene ring derived from *p*-hydroxyphenylacetaldehyde and methylation of norcoclaurine at two of its —OH groups and at its —N—H group yields reticuline **(IVa)** (Fig. H.2). A reticuline molecule can be twisted into conformation **IVb,** one that allows an ortho–para oxidative phenolic coupling to take place yielding salutaridine. Reduction of salutaridine produces salutaridinol. Then salutaridinol is transformed into thebaine. (In this highly unusual step the oxygen bridge is installed through a reaction that is accompanied by *the displacement of a hydroxide ion.*) Finally, several additional enzymatic reactions transform thebaine into morphine.

Problem H.10

There is considerable evidence that oxidative phenol couplings are important in the biosynthesis of bulbocapnine and glaucine (see following structures). (These two alkaloids have what is called an *apomorphine* ring system.) Both compounds appear to arise from reticuline. Show the type of oxidative phenol coupling that is involved in each biosynthesis. (Assume that methylation of —OH groups in both alkaloids and synthesis of the —O—CH₂—O— bridge in bulbocapnine occur after the oxidative phenol couplings.)

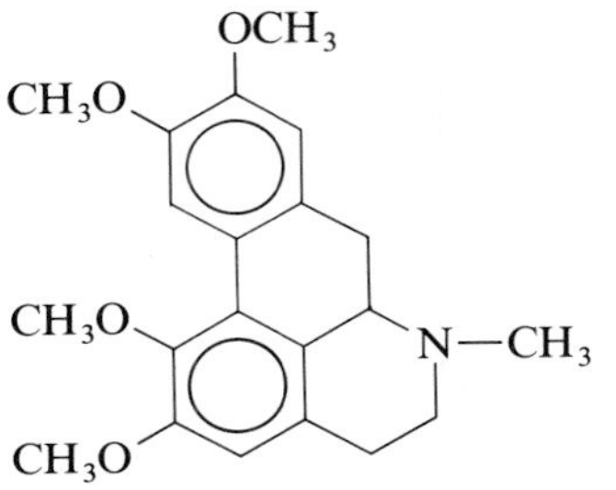

Glaucine 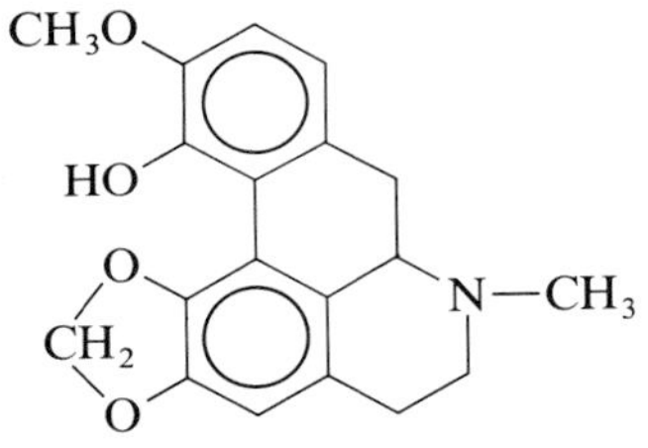   Bulbocapnine

Problem H.11

Harmine is an alkaloid isolated from *Peganum harmala* L. When tryptophan and pyruvic acid labeled in the positions shown were fed to the plant, the harmine produced had the labeling pattern indicated.

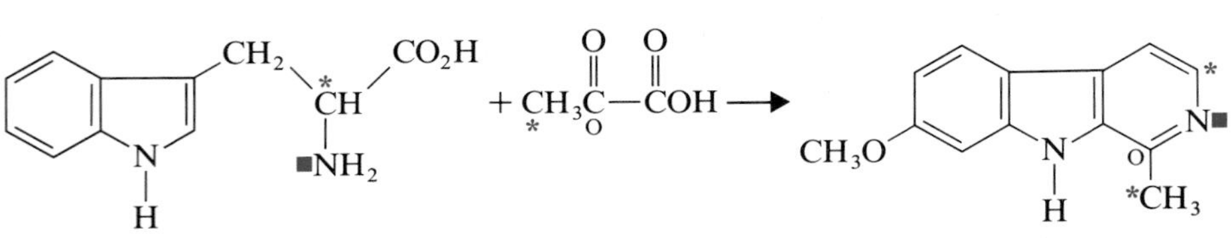

Tryptophan Pyruvic acid Harmine
* and O are ¹⁴C labels
■ is an ¹⁵N label

Show how these results are consistent with the following pathway: (1) decarboxylation of tryptophan (to tryptamine), (2) a Mannich-type condensation of tryptamine and pyruvic acid, then (3) dehydrogenation, (4) hydroxylation, and (5) methylation.

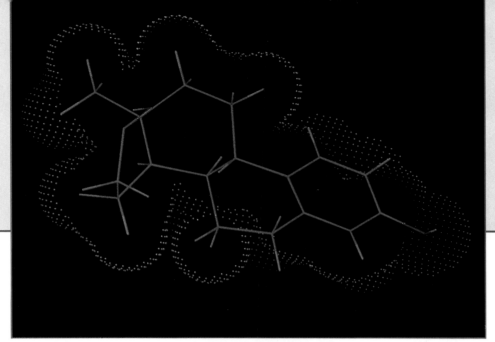

Estradiol (see Section 21.2).

PHENOLS AND ARYL HALIDES: NUCLEOPHILIC AROMATIC SUBSTITUTION

21.1 STRUCTURE AND NOMENCLATURE OF PHENOLS

Compounds that have a hydroxyl group directly attached to a benzene ring are called **phenols.** Thus, **phenol** is the specific name for hydroxybenzene and it is the general name for the family of compounds derived from hydroxybenzene:

Phenol

**4-Methylphenol
(a phenol)**

Compounds that have a hydroxyl group attached to a polycyclic benzenoid ring are chemically similar to phenols, but they are called **naphthols** and **phenanthrols,** for example.

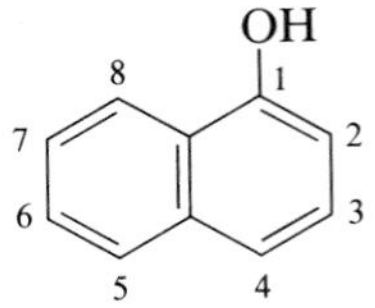

1-Naphthol
(α-naphthol)

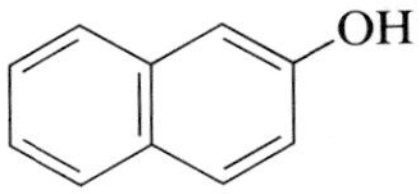

2-Naphthol
(β-naphthol)

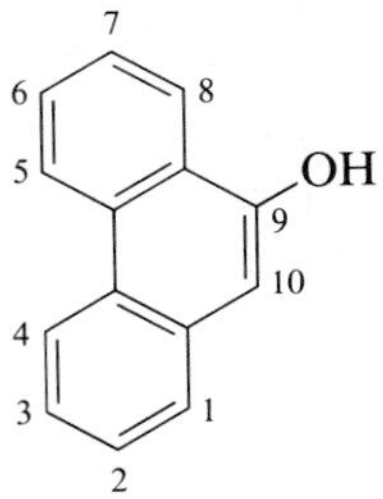

9-Phenanthrol

21.1A NOMENCLATURE OF PHENOLS

We studied the nomenclature of some of the phenols in Chapter 13. In many compounds *phenol* is the base name:

4-Chlorophenol
(*p*-chlorophenol)

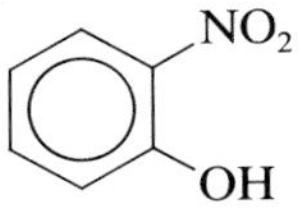

2-Nitrophenol
(*o*-nitrophenol)

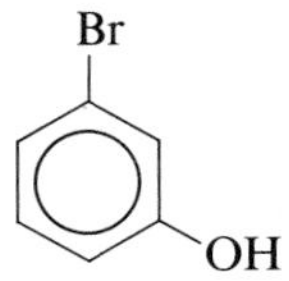

3-Bromophenol
(*m*-bromophenol)

The methylphenols are commonly called *cresols:*

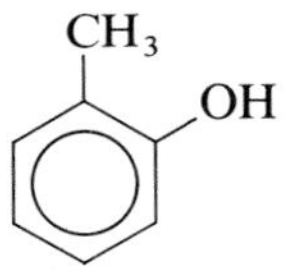

2-Methylphenol
(*o*-cresol)

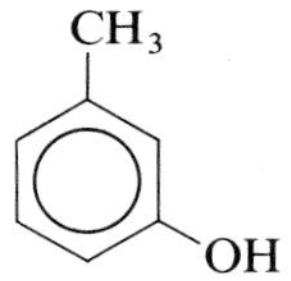

3-Methylphenol
(*m*-cresol)

4-Methylphenol
(*p*-cresol)

The benzenediols also have common names:

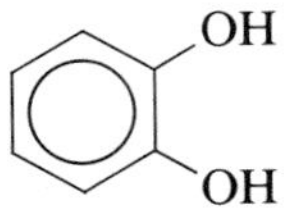

1,2-Benzenediol
(catechol)

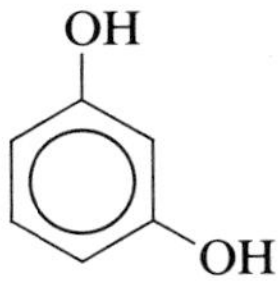

1,3-Benzenediol
(resorcinol)

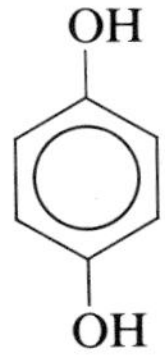

1,4-Benzenediol
(hydroquinone)

21.2 NATURALLY OCCURRING PHENOLS

Phenols and related compounds occur widely in nature. Tyrosine is an amino acid that occurs in proteins. Methyl salicylate is found in oil of wintergreen, eugenol is found in oil of cloves, and thymol is found in thyme.

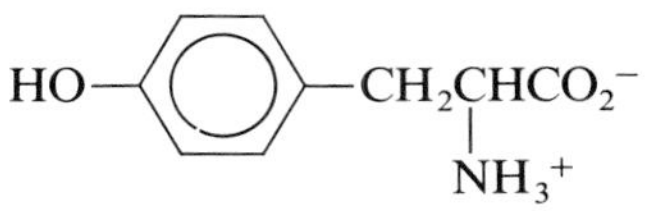

Tyrosine

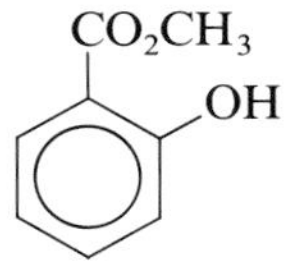

Methyl salicylate
(oil of wintergreen)

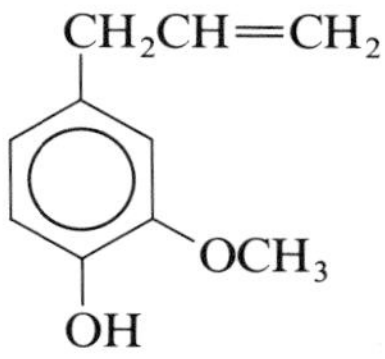

Eugenol
(oil of cloves)

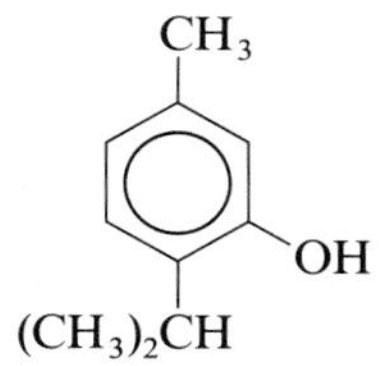

Thymol
(thyme)

The urushiols are blistering agents (vesicants) found in poison ivy.

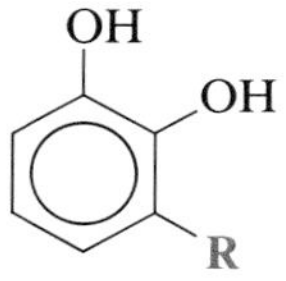

Urushiols

$R = -(CH_2)_{14}CH_3,$

$-(CH_2)_7CH=CH(CH_2)_5CH_3,$ or

$-(CH_2)_7CH=CHCH_2CH=CH(CH_2)_2CH_3$

Estradiol is a female sex hormone and the tetracyclines are important antibiotics.

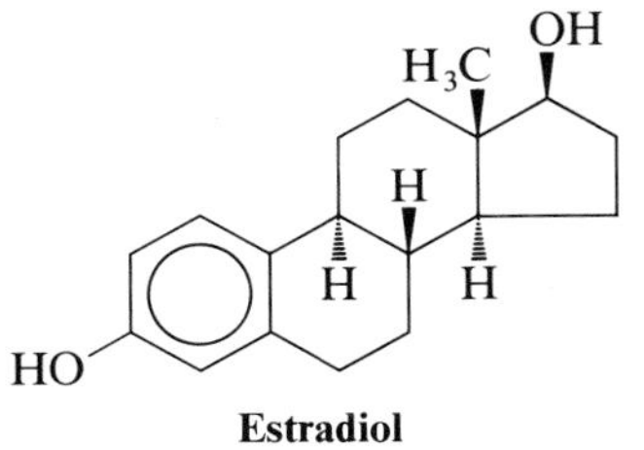

Estradiol

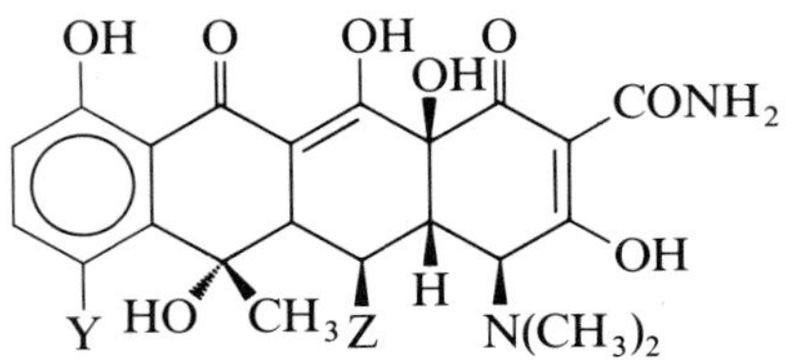

Tetracyclines
(Y = Cl, Z = H; Aureomycin)
(Y = H, Z = OH; Terramycin)

21.3 PHYSICAL PROPERTIES OF PHENOLS

The presence of hydroxyl groups in the molecules of phenols means that phenols are like alcohols (Section 10.2) in being able to form strong intermolecular hydrogen bonds. This hydrogen bonding causes phenols to be associated and, therefore, to have higher boiling points than hydrocarbons of the same molecular weight. For example, phenol (bp, 182 °C) has a boiling point more than 70 °C higher than toluene (bp, 110.6 °C), even though the two compounds have almost the same molecular weight.

TABLE 21.1   Physical properties of phenols

NAME	FORMULA	mp (°C)	bp (°C)	WATER SOLUBILITY (g $100 \ mL^{-1}$ of H_2O)
Phenol	C_6H_5OH	43	182	9.3
2-Methylphenol	o-$CH_3C_6H_4OH$	30	191	2.5
3-Methylphenol	m-$CH_3C_6H_4OH$	11	201	2.6
4-Methylphenol	p-$CH_3C_6H_4OH$	35.5	201	2.3
2-Chlorophenol	o-ClC_6H_4OH	8	176	2.8
3-Chlorophenol	m-ClC_6H_4OH	33	214	2.6
4-Chlorophenol	p-ClC_6H_4OH	43	220	2.7
2-Nitrophenol	o-$O_2NC_6H_4OH$	45	217	0.2
3-Nitrophenol	m-$O_2NC_6H_4OH$	96		1.4
4-Nitrophenol	p-$O_2NC_6H_4OH$	114		1.7
2,4-Dinitrophenol		113		0.6
2,4,6-Trinitrophenol (picric acid)		122		1.4

The ability to form strong hydrogen bonds to molecules of water confers on phenols a modest solubility in water. Table 21.1 lists the physical properties of a number of common phenols.

21.4 SYNTHESIS OF PHENOLS

21.4A LABORATORY SYNTHESIS

The most important laboratory synthesis of phenols is by hydrolysis of arenediazonium salts (Section 19.18E). This method is highly versatile, and the conditions required for the diazotization step and the hydrolysis step are mild. This means that other groups present on the ring are unlikely to be affected.

General Reaction

$$Ar{-}NH_2 \xrightarrow{\text{HONO}} Ar{-}\overset{+}{N}_2 \xrightarrow[\text{heat}]{H_3O^+} Ar{-}OH$$

Specific Examples

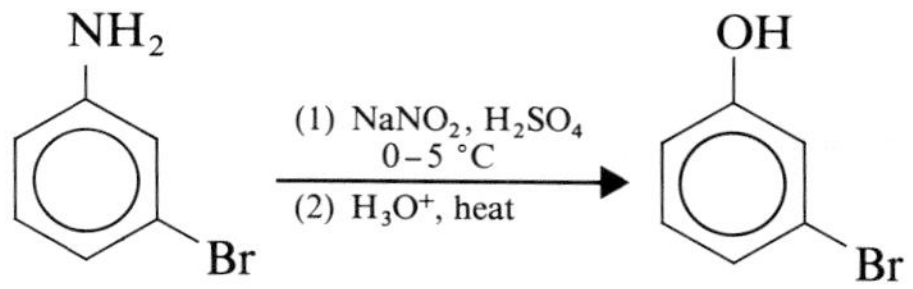

3-Bromophenol
(66%)

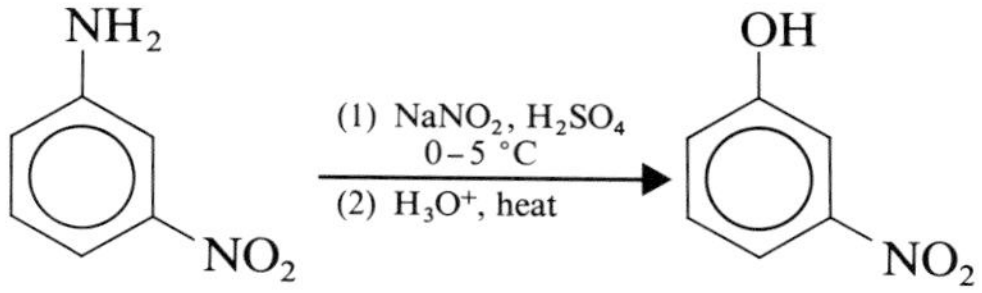

3-Nitrophenol
(80%)

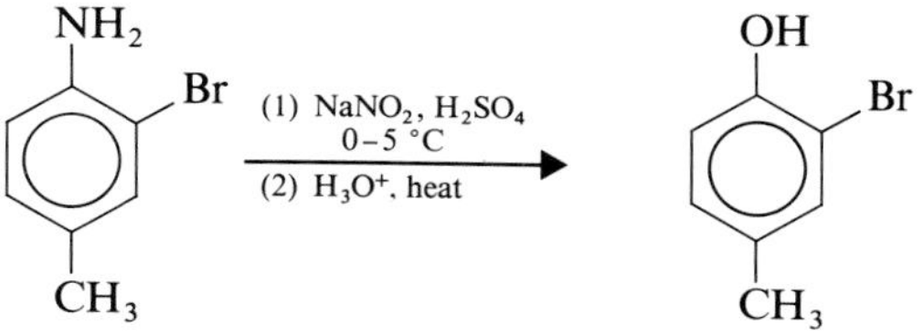

2-Bromo-4-methylphenol
(80–92%)

21.4B INDUSTRIAL SYNTHESES

Phenol is a highly important industrial chemical; it serves as the raw material for a large number of commercial products ranging from aspirin to a variety of plastics. Worldwide production of phenol is more than 3 million tons per year! Several methods have been used to synthesize phenol commercially.

1. **Hydrolysis of Chlorobenzene (Dow process).** In this process chlorobenzene is heated at 350 °C (under high pressure) with aqueous sodium hydroxide. The reaction produces sodium phenoxide which, on acidification, yields phenol. The mechanism for the reaction probably involves the formation of benzyne (Section 21.11B).

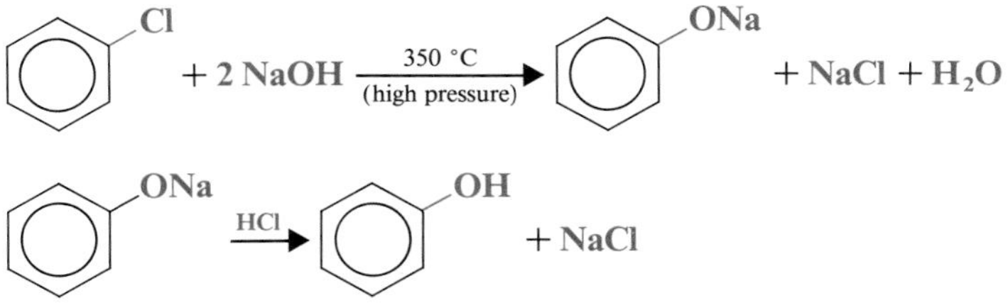

2. **Alkali Fusion of Sodium Benzenesulfonate.** This, the first commercial process for synthesizing phenol, was developed in Germany in 1890. Sodium benzenesulfonate is melted (fused) with sodium hydroxide (at 350 °C) to produce sodium phenoxide. Acidification then yields phenol.

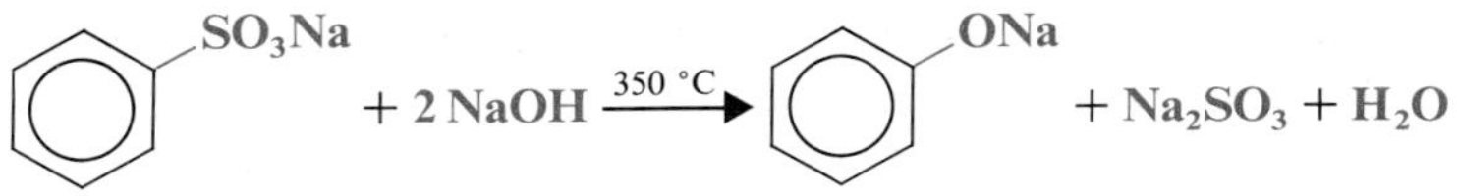

$$\underset{\substack{\text{Sodium}\\\text{benzenesulfonate}}}{C_6H_5SO_3Na} + 2\,NaOH \xrightarrow{350\ ^\circ C} C_6H_5ONa + Na_2SO_3 + H_2O$$

This procedure can also be used in the laboratory and works quite well for the preparation of *p*-cresol, as the following example shows. However, the conditions required to bring about the reaction are so vigorous that this method cannot be used for the preparation of many phenols.

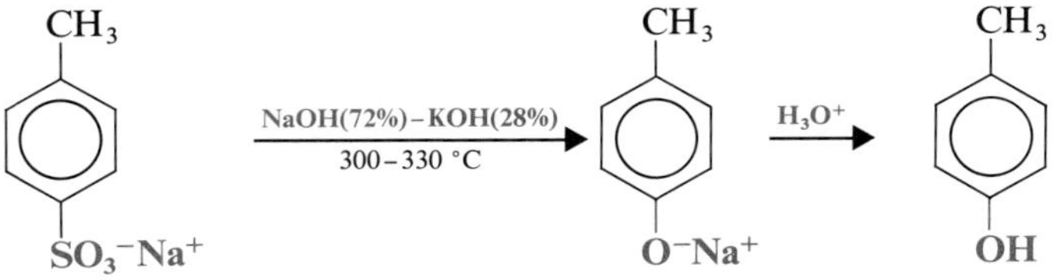

$$\underset{\substack{\text{Sodium}\\p\text{-toluenesulfonate}}}{CH_3C_6H_4SO_3^-Na^+} \xrightarrow[\substack{300-330\ ^\circ C}]{NaOH(72\%)-KOH(28\%)} CH_3C_6H_4O^-Na^+ \xrightarrow{H_3O^+} \underset{\substack{\text{4-Methylphenol}\\(63-70\%\ \text{overall})}}{CH_3C_6H_4OH}$$

3. **From Cumene Hydroperoxide.** This process illustrates industrial chemistry at its best. Overall, it is a method for converting two relatively inexpensive organic compounds — benzene and propene — into two more valuable ones — phenol and acetone. The only other substance consumed in the process is oxygen from air. Most of the worldwide production of phenol is now based on this method.

The synthesis begins with the Friedel–Crafts alkylation of benzene with propene to produce cumene (isopropylbenzene).

Reaction 1 $\quad C_6H_6 + CH_2{=}CHCH_3 \xrightarrow[\substack{H_3PO_4\\ \text{pressure}}]{250\ ^\circ C}$ Cumene

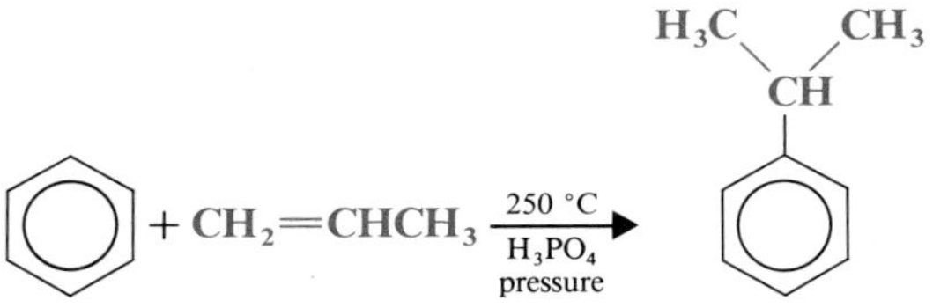

Then cumene is oxidized to cumene hydroperoxide:

Reaction 2 $\quad C_6H_5{-}\underset{\underset{CH_3}{|}}{\overset{\overset{CH_3}{|}}{CH}} + O_2 \xrightarrow{95-135^\circ C} C_6H_5{-}\underset{\underset{CH_3}{|}}{\overset{\overset{CH_3}{|}}{C}}{-}O{-}O{-}H$

Cumene hydroperoxide

Finally, when treated with 10% sulfuric acid, cumene hydroperoxide undergoes a hydrolytic rearrangement that yields phenol and acetone:

Reaction 3 $\quad C_6H_5{-}\underset{\underset{CH_3}{|}}{\overset{\overset{CH_3}{|}}{C}}{-}O{-}OH \xrightarrow[\substack{50-90\ ^\circ C}]{H^+,\ H_2O} \underset{\substack{\text{Phenol}}}{C_6H_5OH} + \underset{\substack{\text{Acetone}}}{\underset{\underset{CH_3}{|}}{\overset{\overset{CH_3}{|}}{C}}{=}O}$

The mechanism of each of these reactions requires some comment. The first is a familiar one. The isopropyl cation generated by the reaction of propene with the acid (H_3PO_4) alkylates benzene in a typical electrophilic aromatic substitution:

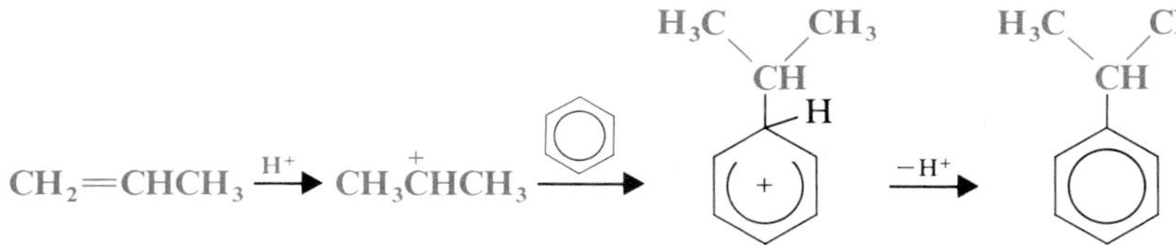

$$CH_2{=}CHCH_3 \xrightarrow{H^+} CH_3\overset{+}{C}HCH_3 \longrightarrow \cdots \xrightarrow{-H^+} \cdots$$

The second reaction is a radical chain reaction. A radical initiator abstracts the benzylic hydrogen atom of cumene producing a 3° benzylic radical. Then a chain reaction with oxygen produces cumene hydroperoxide:

Chain Initiation

Step 1

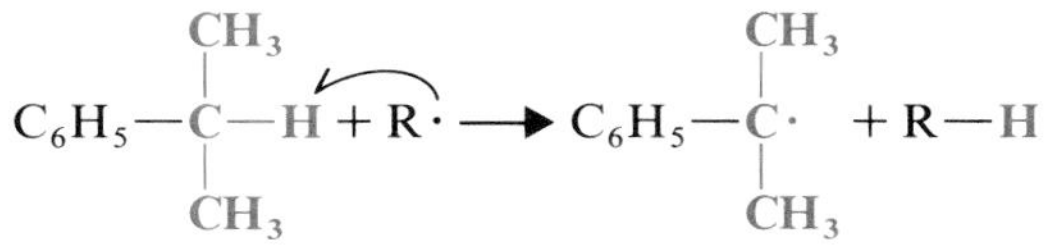

$$C_6H_5-\overset{\overset{\displaystyle CH_3}{|}}{\underset{\underset{\displaystyle CH_3}{|}}{C}}-H + R\cdot \longrightarrow C_6H_5-\overset{\overset{\displaystyle CH_3}{|}}{\underset{\underset{\displaystyle CH_3}{|}}{C}}\cdot \ + R-H$$

Chain Propagation

Step 2

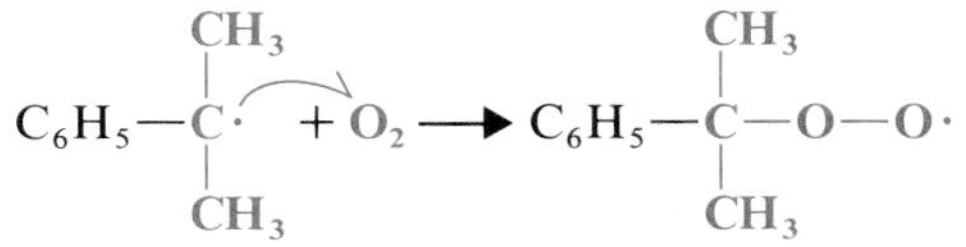

$$C_6H_5-\overset{\overset{\displaystyle CH_3}{|}}{\underset{\underset{\displaystyle CH_3}{|}}{C}}\cdot \ + O_2 \longrightarrow C_6H_5-\overset{\overset{\displaystyle CH_3}{|}}{\underset{\underset{\displaystyle CH_3}{|}}{C}}-O-O\cdot$$

Step 3

$$C_6H_5-\overset{\overset{\displaystyle CH_3}{|}}{\underset{\underset{\displaystyle CH_3}{|}}{C}}-O-O\cdot \ + H-\overset{\overset{\displaystyle CH_3}{|}}{\underset{\underset{\displaystyle CH_3}{|}}{C}}-C_6H_5 \longrightarrow$$

$$C_6H_5-\overset{\overset{\displaystyle CH_3}{|}}{\underset{\underset{\displaystyle CH_3}{|}}{C}}-O-O-H + C_6H_5-\overset{\overset{\displaystyle CH_3}{|}}{\underset{\underset{\displaystyle CH_3}{|}}{C}}\cdot$$

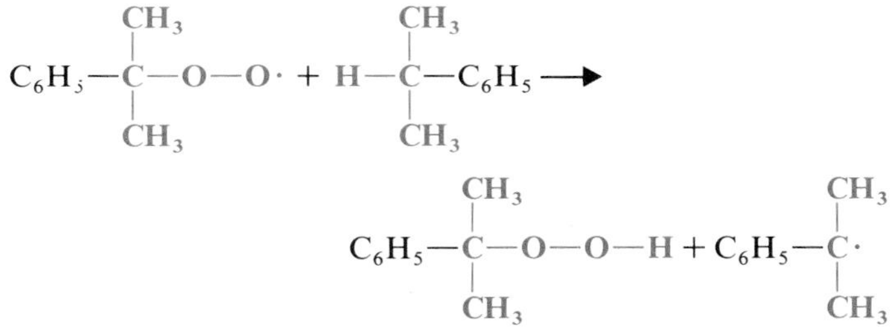

Then, step 2, step 3, step 2, step 3, etc.

The third reaction—the hydrolytic rearrangement—resembles the carbocation rearrangements that we have studied before. In this instance, however, the rearrangement involves the migration of a phenyl group to *a cationic oxygen atom*. Phenyl groups have a much greater tendency to migrate to a cationic center than do methyl groups (see Section 16.12A). The following equations show all the steps of the mechanism.

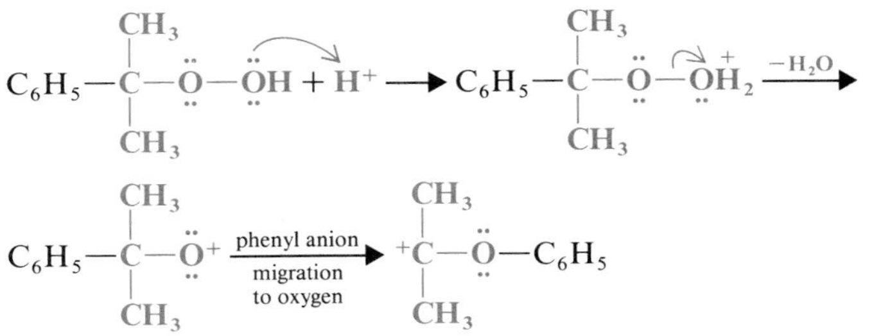

$$C_6H_5-\overset{\overset{\displaystyle CH_3}{|}}{\underset{\underset{\displaystyle CH_3}{|}}{C}}-\overset{..}{\underset{..}{O}}-\overset{..}{\underset{..}{O}}H + H^+ \longrightarrow C_6H_5-\overset{\overset{\displaystyle CH_3}{|}}{\underset{\underset{\displaystyle CH_3}{|}}{C}}-\overset{..}{\underset{..}{O}}-\overset{+}{\underset{..}{O}}H_2 \xrightarrow{-H_2O}$$

$$C_6H_5-\overset{\overset{\displaystyle CH_3}{|}}{\underset{\underset{\displaystyle CH_3}{|}}{C}}-\overset{..}{\underset{..}{O}}{}^+ \xrightarrow[\substack{\text{migration} \\ \text{to oxygen}}]{\text{phenyl anion}} {}^+\overset{\overset{\displaystyle CH_3}{|}}{\underset{\underset{\displaystyle CH_3}{|}}{C}}-\overset{..}{\underset{..}{O}}-C_6H_5$$

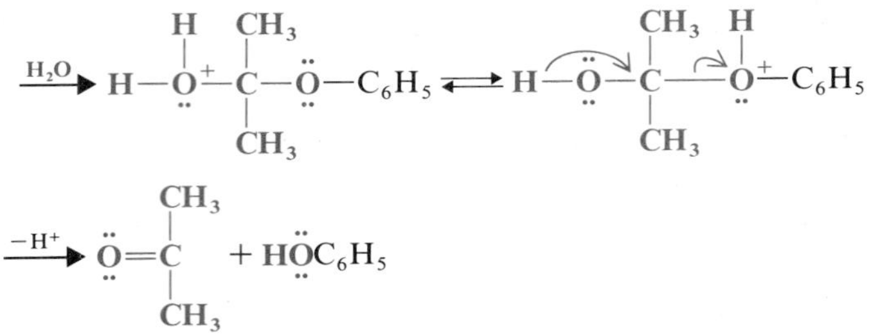

Acetone   Phenol

The second and third steps of the mechanism may actually take place at the same time, that is; the loss of H_2O and the migration of C_6H_5— may be concerted.

21.5 REACTIONS OF PHENOLS AS ACIDS

21.5A STRENGTH OF PHENOLS AS ACIDS

Although phenols are structurally similar to alcohols, they are much stronger acids. The pK_a values of most alcohols are of the order of 18. However, as we see in Table 21.2, the pK_a values of phenols are smaller than 11.

Let us compare two *superficially* similar compounds, cyclohexanol and phenol.

Cyclohexanol
$pK_a = 18$

Phenol
$pK_a = 9.89$

TABLE 21.2   The acidity constants of phenols

NAME	pK_a (in H_2O at 25 °C)
Phenol	9.89
2-Methylphenol	10.20
3-Methylphenol	10.01
4-Methylphenol	10.17
2-Chlorophenol	8.11
3-Chlorophenol	8.80
4-Chlorophenol	9.20
2-Nitrophenol	7.17
3-Nitrophenol	8.28
4-Nitrophenol	7.15
2,4-Dinitrophenol	3.96
2,4,6-Trinitrophenol (picric acid)	0.38
1-Naphthol	9.31
2-Naphthol	9.55

21.5 REACTIONS OF PHENOLS AS ACIDS

Although phenol is a weak acid when compared with a carboxylic acid such as acetic acid ($pK_a = 4.74$), phenol is a much stronger acid than cyclohexanol (by a factor of 8 pK_a units).

Recent experimental and theoretical results have shown that the greater acidity of phenol owes itself primarily to an electrical charge distribution in phenol that causes the —OH oxygen to be more positive; therefore, the proton is held less strongly. In effect, the benzene ring of phenol acts as if it were an electron-withdrawing group when compared with the cyclohexane ring of cyclohexanol.*

We can understand this effect by noting that the carbon atom that bears the hydroxyl group in phenol is sp^2 hybridized, whereas, in cyclohexane, it is sp^3 hybridized. Because of their greater s character, sp^2-hybridized carbon atoms are more electronegative than sp^3-hybridized carbon atoms (Section 6.18).

Another factor influencing the electron distribution may be the contributions to the overall resonance hybrid of phenol made by structures **2 – 4**. Notice that the effect of these structures is to withdraw electrons from the hydroxyl group and to make the oxygen positive.

Resonance structures for phenol

1a   1b   2   3   4

Problem 21.1

The carbon – oxygen bond of phenol is much stronger than that of an alcohol. Phenol, for example, is not converted to bromobenzene when it is refluxed with concentrated hydrobromic acid. Similar treatment of cyclohexanol, however, does give bromocyclohexane.

The resonance structures such as **2 – 4** for phenol help us understand why the carbon – oxygen bond of phenol is very strong. Explain.

---

* An older explanation, now known to be incorrect, explained the greater acidity of phenol primarily on the basis of resonance stabilization of phenoxide ion. For those who may be interested in pursuing this subject further, consult the following articles: M. R. F. Siggel and T. D. Thomas, *J. Am. Chem. Soc.* **1986,** *108,* 4360–4362, and M. R. F. Siggel, A. R. Streitwieser, Jr., and T. D. Thomas, *J. Am. Chem. Soc.* **1988** *110,* 8022–8028.

Problem 21.2

If we examine Table 21.2 we see that phenols having electron-withdrawing groups ($Cl—$ or $O_2N—$) attached to the benzene ring are more acidic than phenol itself. On the other hand, those phenols bearing electron-releasing groups (e.g., $CH_3—$) are less acidic than phenol. Account for this trend on the basis of resonance and inductive effects. [Notice that 2,4,6-trinitrophenol (called *picric acid*) is exceptionally acidic ($pK_a = 0.38$)—over 20,000 times as acidic as acetic acid ($pK_a = 4.74$).]

21.5B DISTINGUISHING AND SEPARATING PHENOLS FROM ALCOHOLS AND CARBOXYLIC ACIDS

Because phenols are more acidic than water, the following reaction goes essentially to completion and produces water-soluble sodium phenoxide.

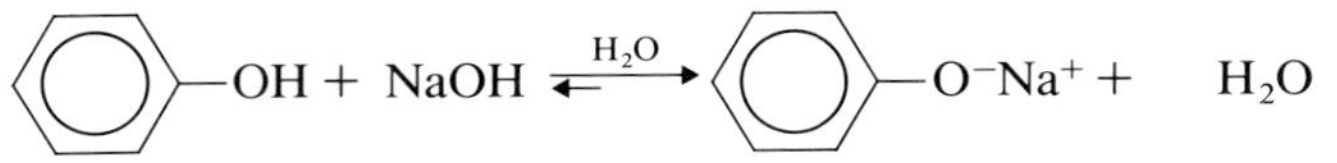

Stronger acid $pK_a \approx 10$ (slightly soluble)	**Stronger** base	**Weaker** base (soluble)	**Weaker acid** $pK_a \approx 16$

The corresponding reaction of 1-hexanol with aqueous sodium hydroxide does not occur to a significant extent because 1-hexanol is a weaker acid than water.

$$CH_3(CH_2)_4CH_2OH + NaOH \underset{H_2O}{\rightleftarrows} CH_3(CH_2)_4CH_2O^-Na^+ + H_2O$$

Weaker acid $pK_a \approx 18$ (very slightly soluble)	**Weaker** base	**Stronger** base (soluble)	**Stronger acid** $pK_a \approx 16$

The fact that phenols dissolve in aqueous sodium hydroxide, whereas most alcohols with six carbon atoms or more do not, gives us a convenient means for distinguishing and separating phenols from most alcohols. (Alcohols with five carbon atoms or fewer are quite soluble in water—some are infinitely so—and thus they dissolve in aqueous sodium hydroxide even though they are not converted to sodium alkoxides in appreciable amounts.)

Most phenols, however, are not soluble in aqueous sodium bicarbonate ($NaHCO_3$), but carboxylic acids are soluble. Thus, aqueous $NaHCO_3$ provides a method for distinguishing and separating most phenols from carboxylic acids.

Problem 21.3

The apparent pK_a for the first ionization of carbonic acid ($H_2CO_3 + H_2O \rightleftarrows HCO_3^- + H_3O^+$) is 6.37. Which of the following compounds would you expect to dissolve in aqueous sodium bicarbonate (aq. $NaHCO_3$)? Explain your answers.

(a) Phenol   (c) *o*-Chlorophenol   (e) 2,4,6-Trinitrophenol
(b) *p*-Cresol   (d) 2,4-Dinitrophenol   (f) Benzoic acid ($pK_a = 4.19$)

21.6 OTHER REACTIONS OF THE O—H GROUP OF PHENOLS

Phenols react with carboxylic acid anhydrides and acid chlorides to form esters. These reactions are quite similar to those of alcohols (Section 18.7).

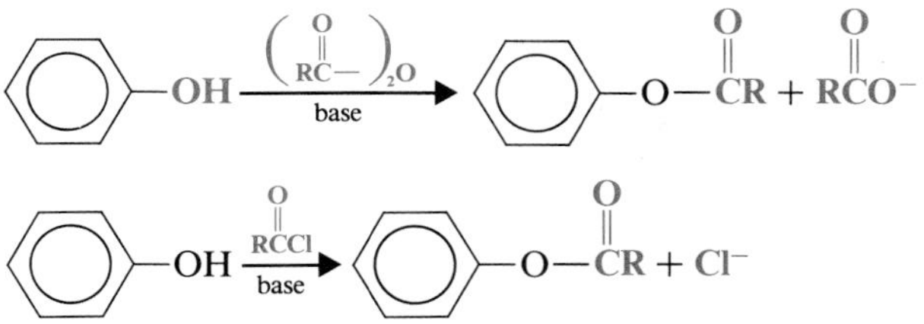

21.6A PHENOLS IN THE WILLIAMSON SYNTHESIS

Phenols can be converted to ethers through the Williamson synthesis (Section 10.16B). Because phenols are more acidic than alcohols, they can be converted to sodium phenoxides through the use of sodium hydroxide (rather than metallic sodium, the reagent used to convert alcohols to alkoxide ions).

General Reaction

$$ArOH \xrightarrow{NaOH} ArO^-Na^+ \xrightarrow[\substack{(X = Cl, Br, I, \\ OSO_2OR \text{ or} \\ OSO_2R')}]{R-X} ArOR + NaX$$

Specific Examples

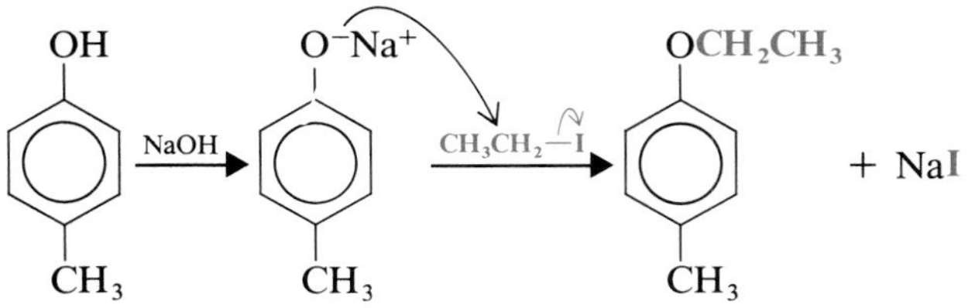

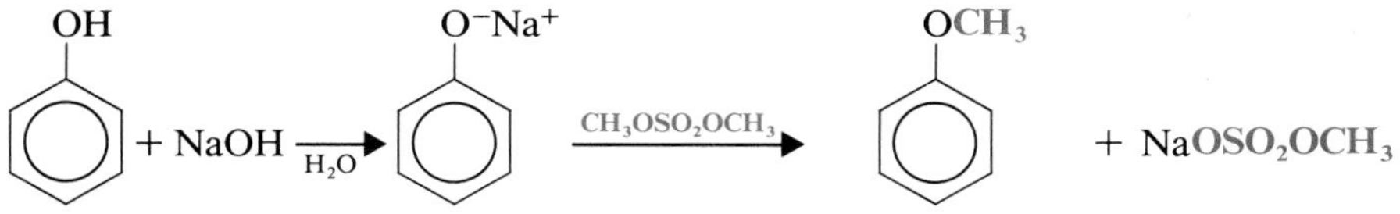

Anisole
(methoxybenzene)

21.7 CLEAVAGE OF ALKYL ARYL ETHERS

We learned in Section 10.17 that when dialkyl ethers are heated with excess concentrated HBr or HI, the ethers are cleaved and alkyl halides are produced from both alkyl groups.

$$R—O—R' \xrightarrow[heat]{concd\ HX} R—X + R'—X + H_2O$$

When alkyl aryl ethers react with strong acids such as HI and HBr, the reaction produces an alkyl halide and a phenol. The phenol does not react further to produce an aryl halide because the carbon–oxygen bond is very strong (cf. Problem 21.1) and because phenyl cations do not form readily.

General Reaction

$$Ar-O-R \xrightarrow[\text{heat}]{\text{concd HX}} Ar-OH + R-X$$

Specific Example

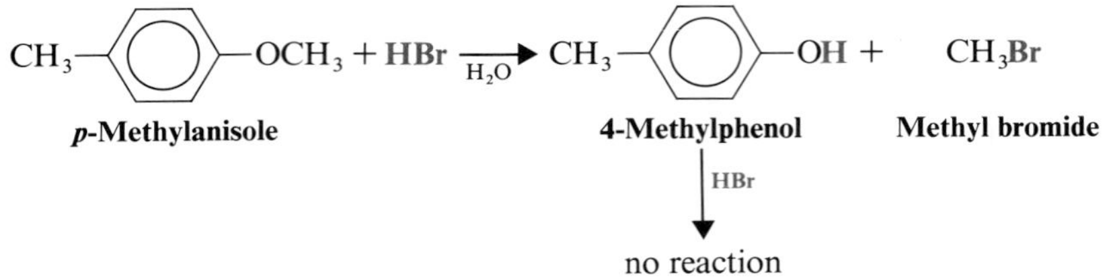

p-Methylanisole + HBr $\xrightarrow{H_2O}$ **4-Methylphenol** + **Methyl bromide**

no reaction

21.8 REACTIONS OF THE BENZENE RING OF PHENOLS

Bromination. The hydroxyl group is a powerful activating group—and an ortho–para director—in electrophilic substitutions. Phenol itself reacts with bromine in aqueous solution to yield 2,4,6-tribromophenol in nearly quantitative yield. Note that a Lewis acid is not required for the bromination of this highly activated ring.

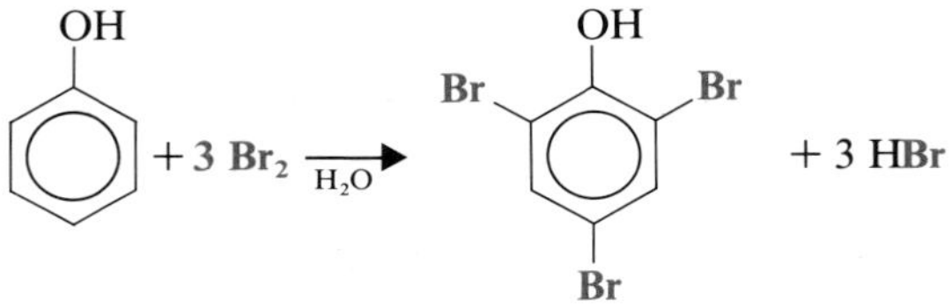

2,4,6-Tribromophenol
(~100%)

Monobromination of phenol can be achieved by carrying out the reaction in carbon disulfide at a low temperature, conditions that reduce the electrophilic reactivity of bromine. The major product is the para isomer.

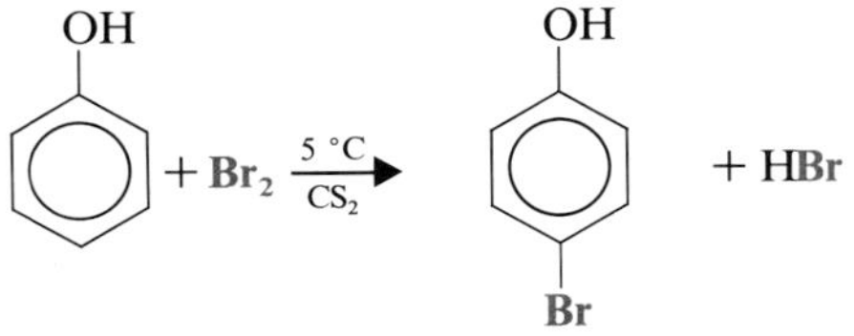

p-Bromophenol
(80–84%)

Nitration. Phenol reacts with dilute nitric acid to yield a mixture of *o*- and *p*-nitrophenol.

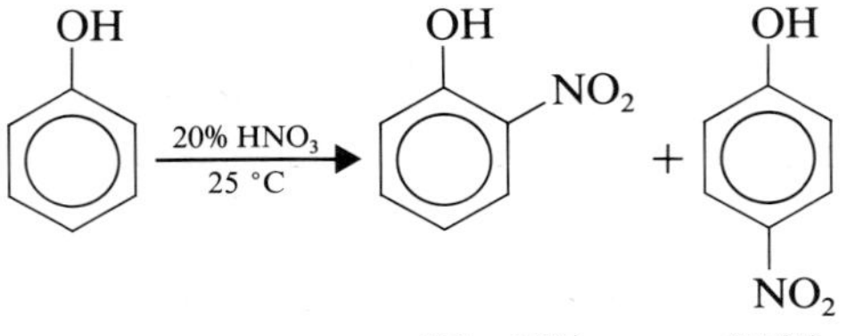

(30–40%)   **(15%)**

Although the yield is relatively low (because of oxidation of the ring), the ortho and para isomers can be separated by steam distillation. *o*-Nitrophenol is the more volatile isomer because its hydrogen bonding (see following structures) is *intramolecular.* *p*-Nitrophenol is less volatile because intermolecular hydrogen bonding causes association among its molecules. Thus, *o*-nitrophenol passes over with the steam, and *p*-nitrophenol remains in the distillation flask.

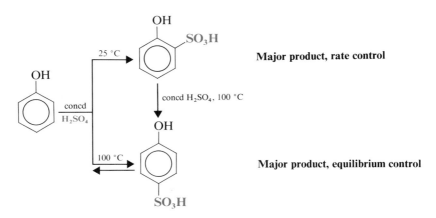

o-Nitrophenol
(more volatile because of
intramolecular hydrogen bonding)

p-Nitrophenol
(less volatile because of
intermolecular hydrogen bonding)

Sulfonation. Phenol reacts with concentrated sulfuric acid to yield mainly the ortho-sulfonated product if the reaction is carried out at 25 °C and mainly the para-sulfonated product at 100 °C. This is another example of equilibrium versus rate control of a reaction.

OH

SO₃H

25 °C

Major product, rate control

OH

concd
H₂SO₄

concd H₂SO₄, 100 °C

OH

100 °C

Major product, equilibrium control

SO₃H

Problem 21.4

(a) Which sulfonic acid (see previous reactions) is more stable? (b) For which sulfonation (ortho or para) is the free energy of activation lower?

Kolbe Reaction. The phenoxide ion is even more susceptible to electrophilic aromatic substitution than phenol itself. (Why?) Use is made of the high reactivity of the phenoxide ring in a reaction called the *Kolbe reaction.* In the Kolbe reaction carbon dioxide acts as the electrophile.

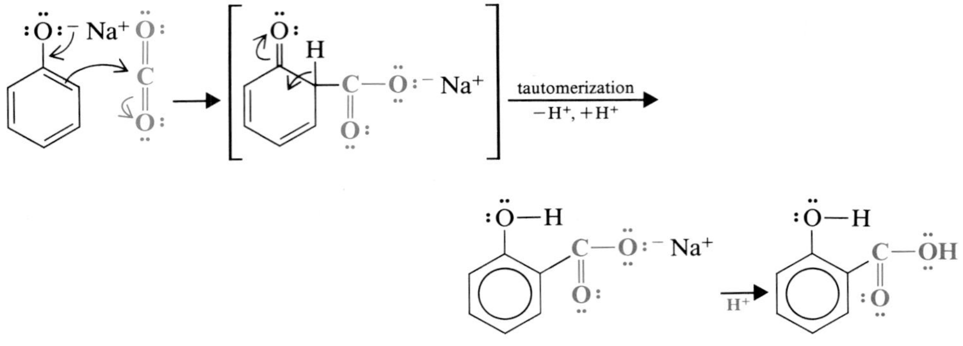

Sodium salicylate   **Salicylic acid**

The reaction is usually carried out by allowing sodium phenoxide to absorb carbon dioxide and then heating the product to 125 °C under a pressure of several atmospheres of carbon dioxide. The unstable intermediate undergoes a proton shift (a keto–enol tautomerization; see Section 17.2) that leads to sodium salicylate. Subsequent acidification of the mixture produces *salicylic acid.*

Reaction of salicylic acid with acetic anhydride yields the widely used pain reliever — *aspirin.*

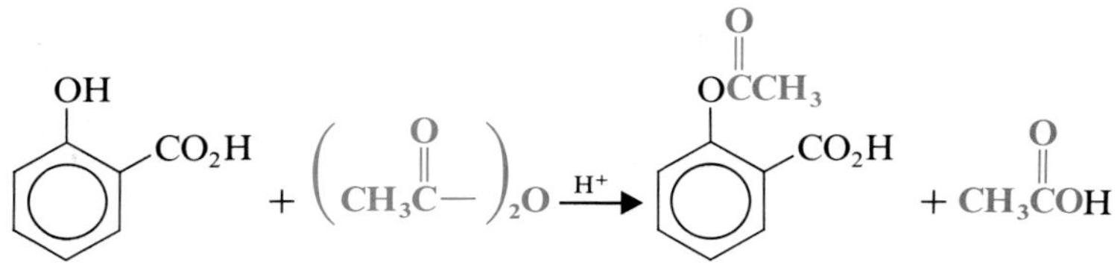

Salicylic acid	Acetic anhydride	Acetylsalicylic acid (aspirin)

21.9 THE CLAISEN REARRANGEMENT

Heating allyl phenyl ether to 200 °C effects an intramolecular reaction called a **Claisen rearrangement.** The product of the rearrangement is *o*-allylphenol:

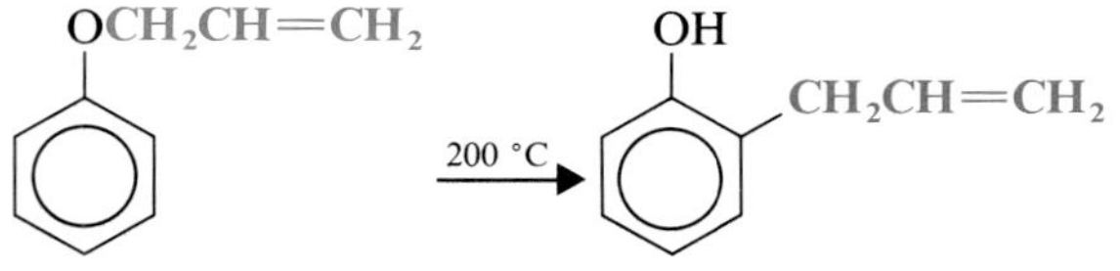

Allyl phenyl ether   ***o*-Allylphenol**

The reaction takes place through a **concerted rearrangement** in which the bond between C-3 of the allyl group and the ortho position of the benzene ring forms at the same time that the carbon–oxygen bond of the allyl phenyl ether breaks. The product of this rearrangement is an unstable intermediate that, like the unstable intermediate in the Kolbe reaction (Section 21.8) undergoes a proton shift (a keto–enol tautomerization, see Section 17.2) that leads to the *o*-allylphenol.

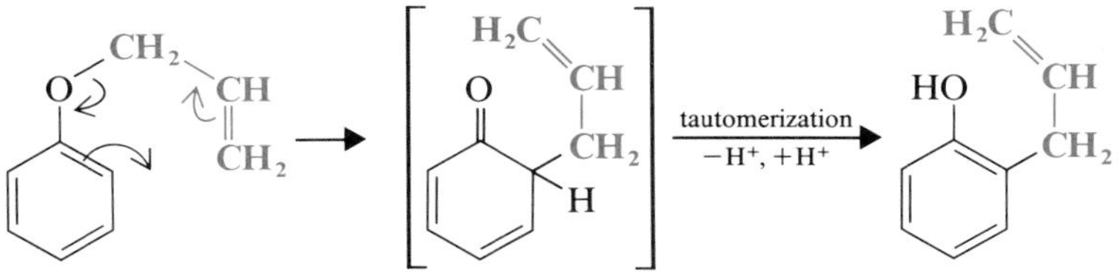

21.9 THE CLAISEN REARRANGEMENT

Unstable intermediate

That only C-3 of the allyl group becomes bonded to the benzene ring was demonstrated by carrying out the rearrangement with allyl phenyl ether containing ^{14}C at C-3. All of the product of this reaction had the labeled carbon atom bonded to the ring.

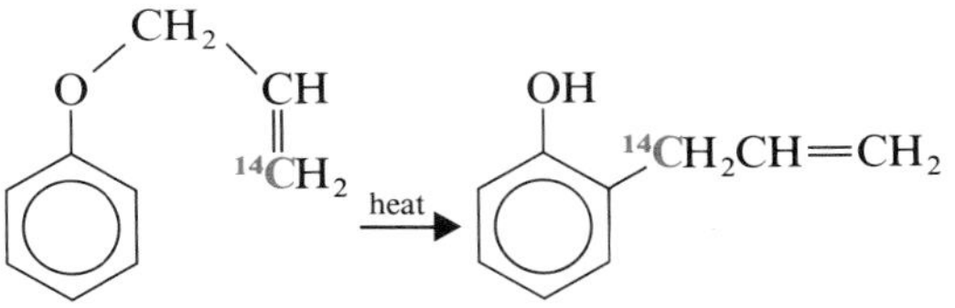

Only product

Problem 21.5

The labeling experiment just described eliminates from consideration a mechanism in which the allyl phenyl ether dissociates to produce an allyl cation (Section 12.4) and a phenoxide ion, which then subsequently undergo a Friedel–Crafts alkylation (Section 15.6) to produce the *o*-allylphenol. Explain how this alternative mechanism can be discounted by showing the product (or products) that would result from it.

Problem 21.6

Show how you would synthesize allyl phenyl ether through a Williamson synthesis (Section 21.6A) starting with phenol and allyl bromide.

A Claisen rearrangement also takes place when allyl vinyl ethers are heated. For example:

| Allyl vinyl ether | Aromatic transition state | 4-Pentenal |

The transition state for the Claisen rearrangement involves a cycle of six orbitals and six electrons. Having six electrons suggests that the transition state has aromatic character (Section 13.7). Other reactions of this general type are known and they are called **pericyclic reactions.**

Another similar pericyclic reaction is the **Cope rearrangement** shown here.

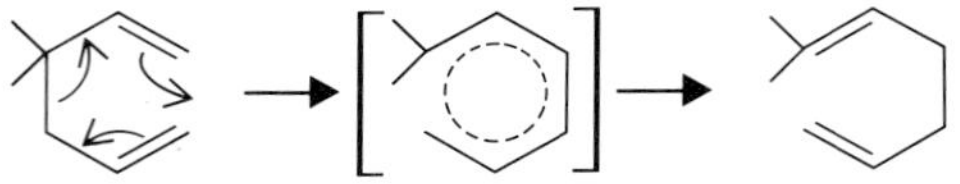

| 3,3-Dimethyl-1,5-hexadiene | Aromatic transition state | 2-Methyl-2,6-heptadiene |

The Diels–Alder reaction (Section 12.10) is also a pericyclic reaction. The transition state for the Diels–Alder reaction also involves six orbitals and six electrons.

Aromatic transition state

We shall discuss the mechanism of the Diels–Alder reaction further in Special Topic O.

21.10 QUINONES

Oxidation of hydroquinone (1,4-benzenediol) produces a compound known as *p*-benzoquinone. The oxidation can be brought about by mild oxidizing agents, and, overall, the oxidation amounts to the removal of a pair of electrons ($2e^-$) and two protons from hydroquinone. (Another way of visualizing the oxidation is as the loss of a hydrogen molecule, $H\!:\!H$, making it a dehydrogenation.)

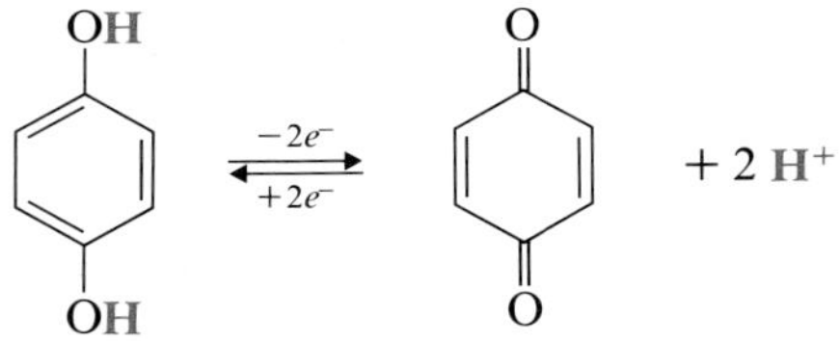

Hydroquinone   *p*-Benzoquinone

This reaction is reversible; *p*-benzoquinone is easily reduced by mild reducing agents to hydroquinone.

Nature makes much use of this type of reversible oxidation–reduction to transport a pair of electrons from one substance to another in enzyme-catalyzed reactions. Important compounds in this respect are the compounds called **ubiquinones** (from *ubiquitous* + quinone—these quinones are found everywhere in biological systems). Ubiquinones are also called coenzymes Q (CoQ).

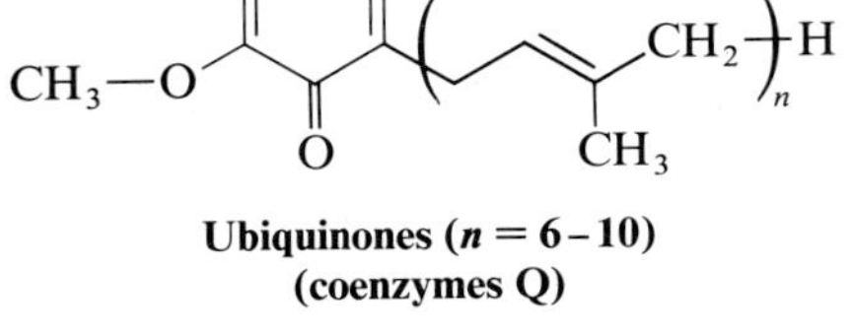

Ubiquinones ($n = 6–10$)
(coenzymes Q)

Vitamin K_1, the important dietary factor that is instrumental in maintaining the coagulant properties of blood, contains a 1,4-naphthoquinone structure.

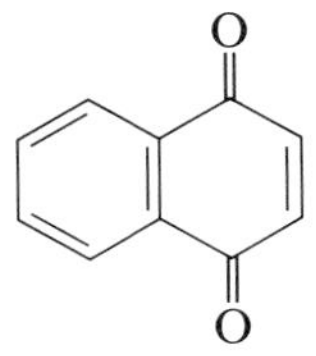

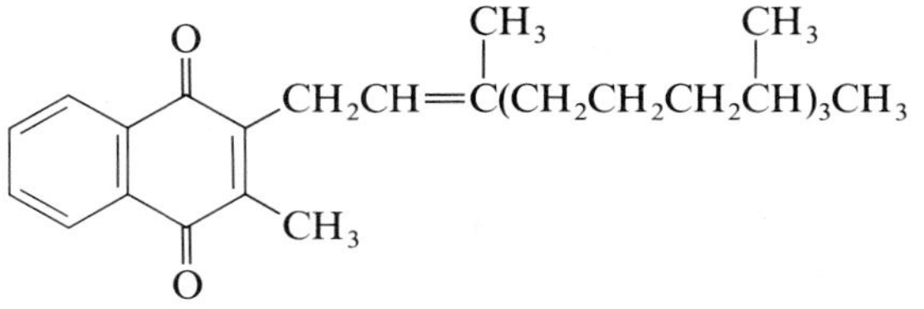

1,4-Naphthoquinone **Vitamin K_1**

Problem 21.7

p-Benzoquinone and 1,4-naphthoquinone act as dienophiles in Diels–Alder reactions. Give the structures of the products of the following reactions: (a) *p*-Benzoquinone + butadiene, (b) 1,4-Naphthoquinone + butadiene, and (c) *p*-Benzoquinone + 1,3-cyclopentadiene.

Problem 21.8

Outline a possible synthesis of the following compound.

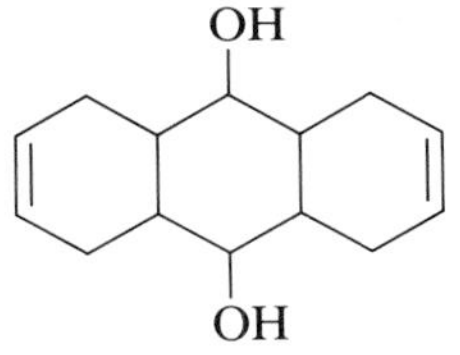

21.11 ARYL HALIDES AND NUCLEOPHILIC AROMATIC SUBSTITUTION

Simple aryl halides are like vinylic halides (Section 6.16A) in that they are relatively unreactive toward nucleophilic substitution under conditions that give facile nucleophilic substitution with alkyl halides. Chlorobenzene, for example, can be boiled with sodium hydroxide for days without producing a detectable amount of phenol (or sodium phenoxide). Similarly, when vinyl chloride is heated with sodium hydroxide, no substitution occurs:

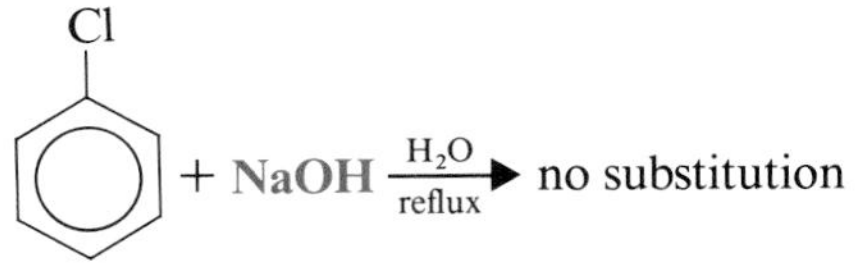

$$CH_2{=}CHCl + NaOH \xrightarrow[\text{reflux}]{H_2O} \text{no substitution}$$

Aryl halides and vinylic halides do not give a positive test (a silver halide precipitate) when treated with alcoholic silver nitrate (Section 9.19E).

We can understand this lack of reactivity on the basis of several factors. The benzene ring of an aryl halide prevents backside attack in an S_N2 reaction:

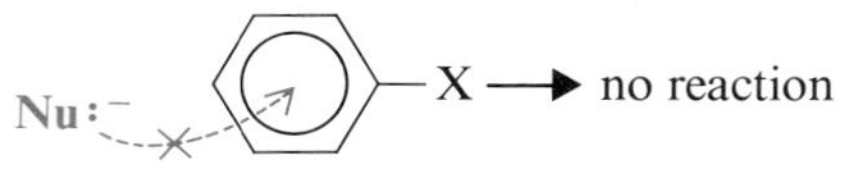

Phenyl cations are very unstable; thus S_N1 reactions do not occur. The carbon–halogen bonds of aryl (and vinylic) halides are shorter and stronger than those of alkyl, allylic, and benzylic halides. Stronger carbon–halogen bonds mean that bond breaking by either an S_N1 or S_N2 mechanism will require more energy.

Two effects make the carbon–halogen bonds of aryl and vinylic halides shorter and stronger. (1) The carbon of either type of halide is sp^2 hybridized and thus the electrons of the carbon orbital are closer to the nucleus than those of an sp^3-hybridized carbon. (2) Resonance of the type shown here strengthens the carbon–halogen bond by giving it *double-bond character.*

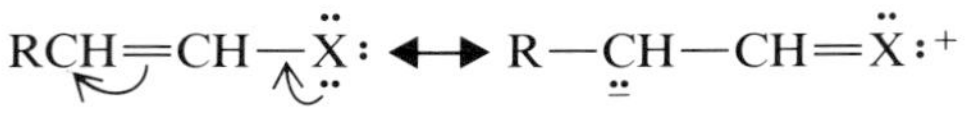

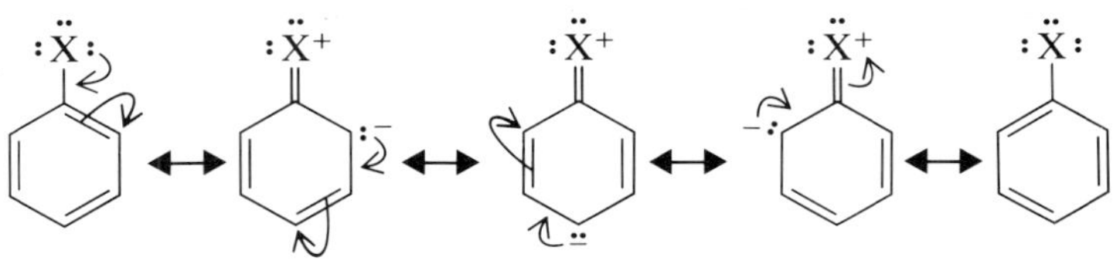

Having said all this, we shall find in the next two subsections that *aryl halides can be remarkably reactive toward nucleophiles* if they bear certain substituents or when we allow them to react under the proper conditions.

21.11A NUCLEOPHILIC AROMATIC SUBSTITUTION BY ADDITION–ELIMINATION: THE S_NAr MECHANISM

Nucleophilic substitution reactions of aryl halides *do* occur readily when an electronic factor makes the aryl carbon susceptible to nucleophilic attack. **Nucleophilic substitution can occur when strong electron-withdrawing groups are ortho or para to the halogen atom:**

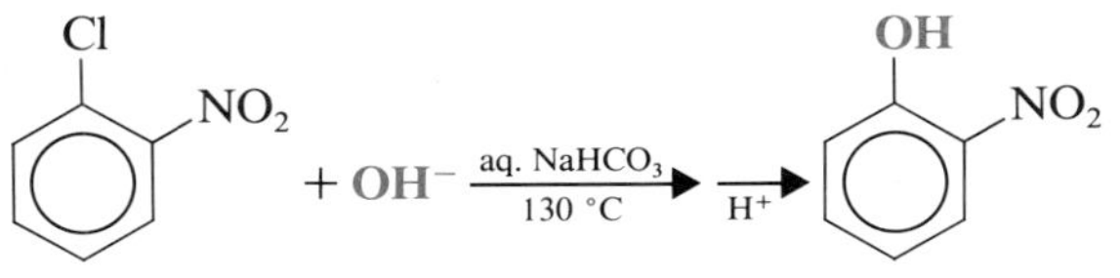

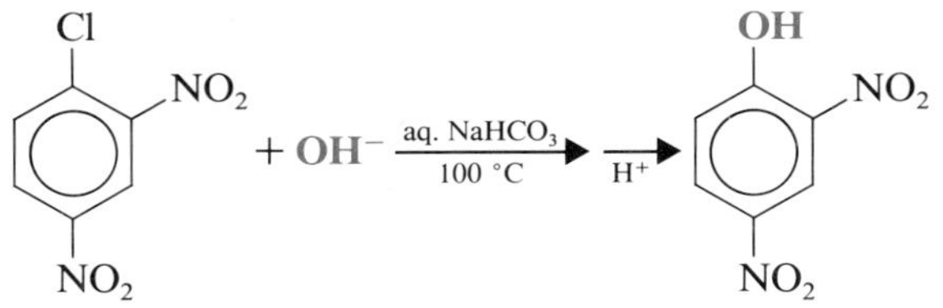

We also see in these examples that the temperature required to bring about the reaction is related to the number of ortho or para nitro groups. Of the three compounds, *o*-nitrochlorobenzene requires the highest temperature (*p*-nitrochlorobenzene reacts at 130 °C as well) and 2,4,6-trinitrochlorobenzene requires the lowest temperature.

A meta-nitro group does not produce a similar activating effect. For example, *m*-nitrochlorobenzene gives no corresponding reaction.

The mechanism that operates in these reactions is an *addition–elimination* mechanism involving the formation of a delocalized *carbanion* called a **Meisenheimer complex** after the German chemist, Jacob Meisenheimer, who proposed its correct structure. In the following first step addition of a hydroxide ion to *p*-nitrochlorobenzene, for example, produces the delocalized carbanion; then elimination of a chloride ion yields the substitution product as the aromaticity of the ring is recovered. This mechanism is called the $S_N Ar$ mechanism.

Delocalized carbanion (Meisenheimer complex)

The delocalized carbanion is stabilized by *electron-withdrawing groups* in the positions ortho and para to the halogen atom. If we examine the following resonance structures, we can see how.

Especially stable (negative charges are both on oxygen atoms)

Problem 21.9

What products would you expect from each of the following nucleophilic substitution reactions?

(a) *p*-Nitrochlorobenzene + CH_3ONa $\xrightarrow[100\ °C]{CH_3OH}$

(b) *o*-Nitrochlorobenzene + CH_3NH_2 $\xrightarrow[160\ °C]{C_2H_5OH}$

(c) 2,4-Dinitrochlorobenzene + $C_6H_5NH_2$ $\xrightarrow[95\ °C]{C_2H_5OH}$

21.11B NUCLEOPHILIC AROMATIC SUBSTITUTION THROUGH AN ELIMINATION–ADDITION MECHANISM: BENZYNE

Although aryl halides such as chlorobenzene and bromobenzene do not react with most nucleophiles under ordinary circumstances, they do react under highly forcing conditions. Chlorobenzene can be converted to phenol by heating it with aqueous sodium hydroxide in a pressurized reactor at 350 °C (Section 21.4).

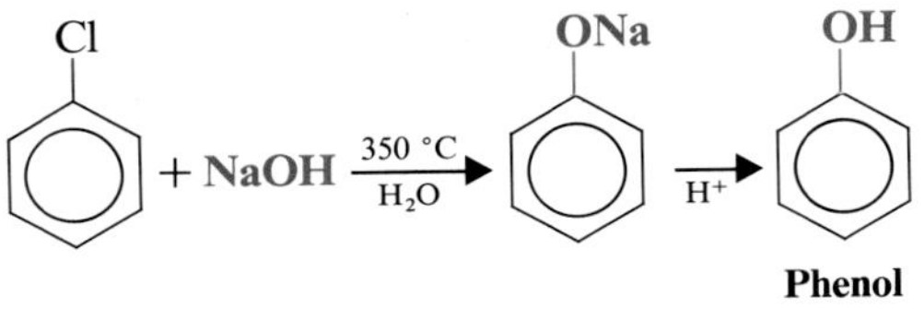

Bromobenzene reacts with the very powerful base, $\overline{N}H_2$, in liquid ammonia:

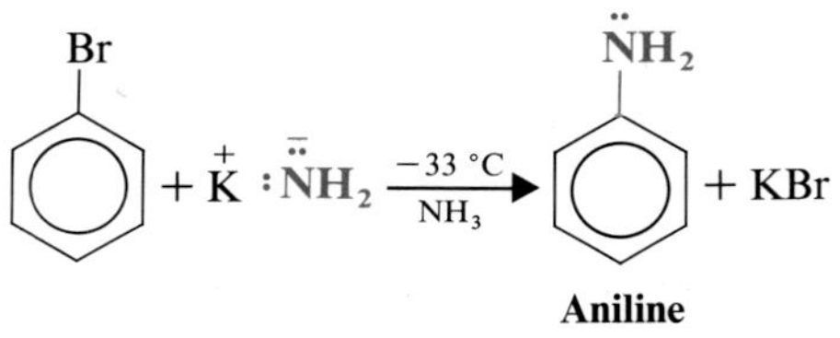

These reactions take place through an **elimination–addition mechanism** that involves the formation of an interesting intermediate called *benzyne* (or *dehydrobenzene*). We can illustrate this mechanism with the reaction of bromobenzene and amide ion.

In the first step (see following mechanism), the amide ion initiates an elimination by abstracting one of the ortho protons because they are the most acidic. The negative charge that develops on the ortho carbon is stabilized by the inductive effect of the bromine. The anion then loses a bromide ion. This elimination produces the highly unstable, and thus highly reactive, **benzyne.** Benzyne then reacts with any available nucleophile (in this case, an amide ion) by a two-step addition reaction to produce aniline.

21.11 ARYL HALIDES AND NUCLEOPHILIC AROMATIC SUBSTITUTION

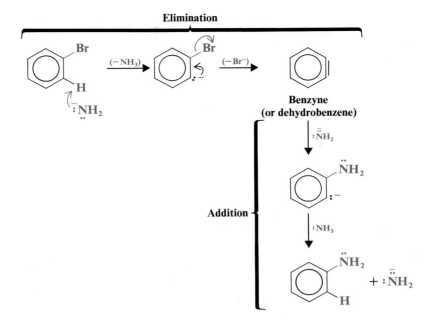

The nature of benzyne itself will become clearer if we examine the following orbital diagram.

Benzyne

The extra bond in benzyne results from the overlap of sp^2 orbitals on adjacent carbon atoms of the ring. The axes of these sp^2 orbitals lie in the same plane as that of the ring, and consequently they do not overlap with the π orbitals of the aromatic system. They do not appreciably disturb the aromatic system and they do not make an appreciable resonance contribution to it. The extra bond is weak. Even though the ring hexagon is probably somewhat distorted in order to bring the sp^2 orbitals closer together, overlap between them is not large. Benzyne, as a result, is highly unstable and highly reactive. It has never been isolated.

What, then, is some of the evidence for the existence of benzyne and for an elimination–addition mechanism in some nucleophilic aromatic substitutions?

The first piece of clear-cut evidence was an experiment done by J. D. Roberts (Section 14.11) in 1953—one that marked the beginning of benzyne chemistry. Roberts showed that when ^{14}C-labeled (C*) bromobenzene is treated with amide ion in liquid ammonia, the aniline that is produced has the label equally divided between the 1 and 2 positions. This result is consistent with the elimination–addition mechanism on the next page but is, of course, not at all consistent with a direct displacement or with an addition–elimination mechanism. (Why?)

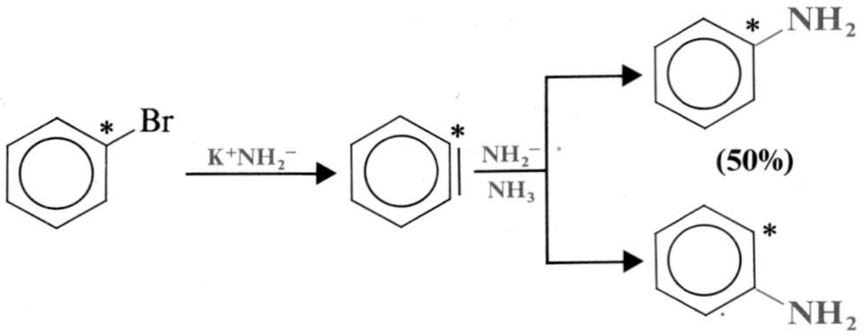

Elimination Addition

An even more striking illustration can be seen in the following reaction. When the ortho derivative **1** is treated with sodium amide, the only organic product obtained is *m*-(trifluoromethyl)aniline.

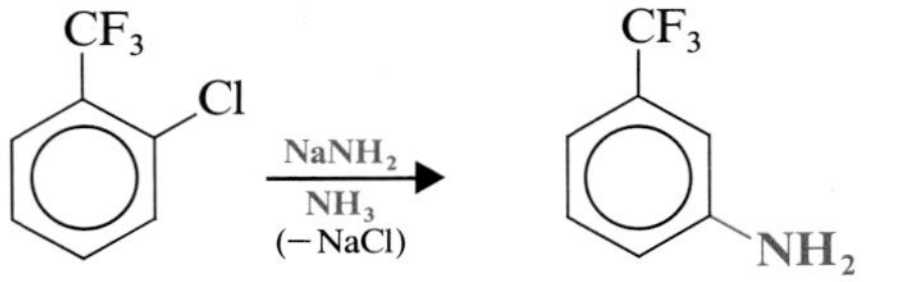

1 ***m*-(Trifluoromethyl)aniline**

This result can also be explained by an elimination–addition mechanism. The first step produces the benzyne **2**:

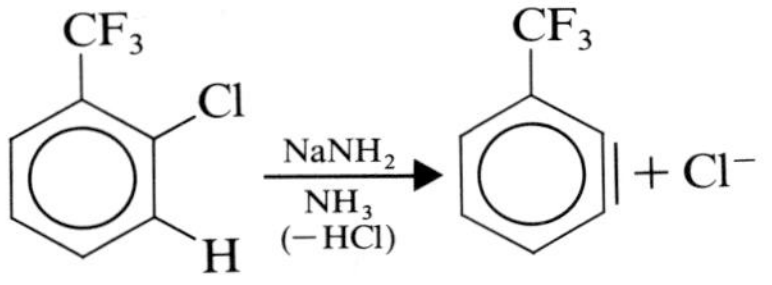

1 **2**

This benzyne then adds an amide ion in the way that produces the more stable carbanion **3** rather than the less stable carbanion **4**.

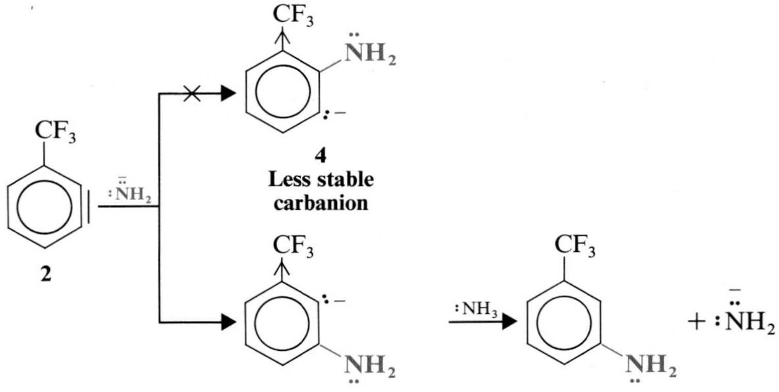

2

4
Less stable carbanion

3
More stable carbanion (negative charge is closer to the electronegative trifluoromethyl group)

Carbanion **3** then accepts a proton from ammonia to form *m*-(trifluoromethyl)aniline.

Carbanion **3** is more stable than **4** because the carbon atom bearing the negative charge is closer to the highly electronegative trifluoromethyl group. The trifluoromethyl group stabilizes the negative charge through its inductive effect. (Resonance effects are not important here because the sp^2 orbital that contains the electron pair does not overlap with the π orbitals of the aromatic system.)

Benzyne intermediates have been "trapped" through the use of Diels–Alder reactions. When benzyne is generated in the presence of the diene *furan*, the product is a Diels–Alder adduct.

Benzyne	**Furan**	**Diels–Alder adduct**
(generated by		
an elimination		
reaction)		

Problem 21.10

(a) When *p*-chlorotoluene is heated with aqueous sodium hydroxide at 340 °C, *p*-cresol and *m*-cresol are obtained in equal amounts. Write a mechanism that would account for this result. (b) What does this suggest about the mechanism of the Dow process (Section 21.4) for the synthesis of phenols?

Problem 21.11

When 2-bromo-3-methylanisole is treated with amide ion in liquid ammonia, no substitution takes place. This has been interpreted as providing evidence for the elimination–addition mechanism. Explain.

21.12 SUMMARY OF IMPORTANT REACTIONS

21.12A SYNTHESIS OF PHENOLS (SECTION 21.4)

1. Via arenediazonium salts

$$Ar\text{—}NH_2 \xrightarrow[0-5\,°C]{HONO} Ar\text{—}\overset{+}{N_2} \xrightarrow[heat]{H_2SO_4/H_2O} Ar\text{—}OH$$

2. Dow process

3. From sodium benzenesulfonates

SO_3Na $\xrightarrow{\text{NaOH, 350 °C}}$ O^-Na^+ $\xrightarrow{H^+}$ OH

4. Via cumene hydroperoxide

$\bigcirc$ $+ CH_2{=}CHCH_3$ $\xrightarrow[\text{high pressure}]{H_3PO_4,\ 350\ °C}$ $CH(CH_3)_2$ $\xrightarrow{O_2,\ 95-135\ °C}$

$HOO{-}C(CH_3)_2$ $\xrightarrow[\text{50-90 °C}]{H_3O^+,\ H_2O}$ OH $+ CH_3\overset{\overset{\displaystyle O}{\|}}{C}CH_3$

21.12B REACTIONS OF PHENOLS

1. As acids (Section 21.5A)

OH $\xrightarrow{\text{NaOH}}$ ONa

2. Williamson synthesis (Section 21.6A)

OH $\xrightarrow{\text{NaOH}}$ ONa $\xrightarrow{RCH_2{-}X}$ OCH_2R

3. Acylation (Section 18.7)

$\bigcirc{-}OH$ $\xrightarrow[\text{base}]{RCOCl\ \ \text{or}\ \ (RCO)_2O}$ $\bigcirc{-}O\overset{\overset{\displaystyle O}{\|}}{C}R$

4. Electrophilic aromatic substitution (Section 21.8)

$\bigcirc{-}OH$ $\xrightarrow{3\ Br_2,\ H_2O}$ Br — (benzene ring with Br, OH, Br) — OH

$\xrightarrow{Br_2,\ CS_2}$ Br — (benzene ring) — OH

$\left.\vphantom{\begin{array}{c}1\\1\\1\\1\end{array}}\right\}$ **Bromination**

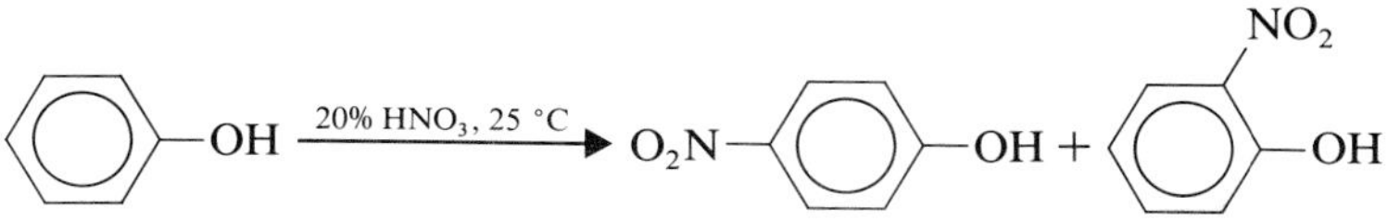

21.12 SUMMARY OF IMPORTANT REACTIONS

Nitration

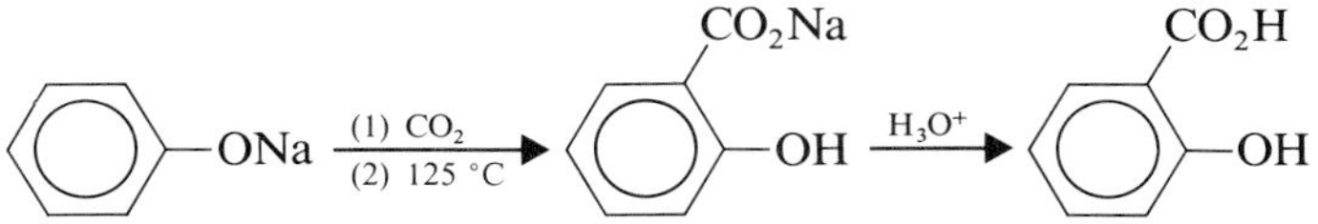

Kolbe reaction

21.12C CLAISSEN REARRANGEMENT (SECTION 21.9)

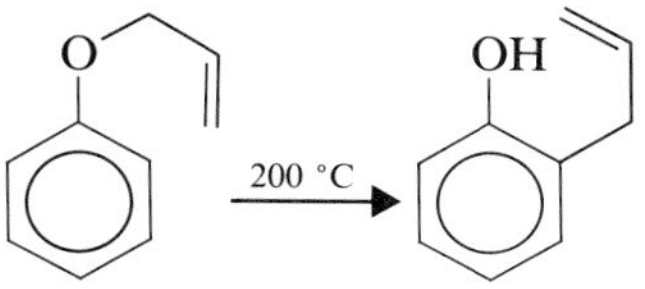

21.12D SYNTHESIS OF ARYL HALIDES

1. By electrophilic aromatic substitution (Section 15.3)

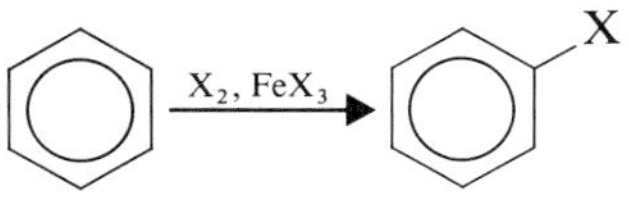

2. Via arenediazonium salts (Section 19.8)

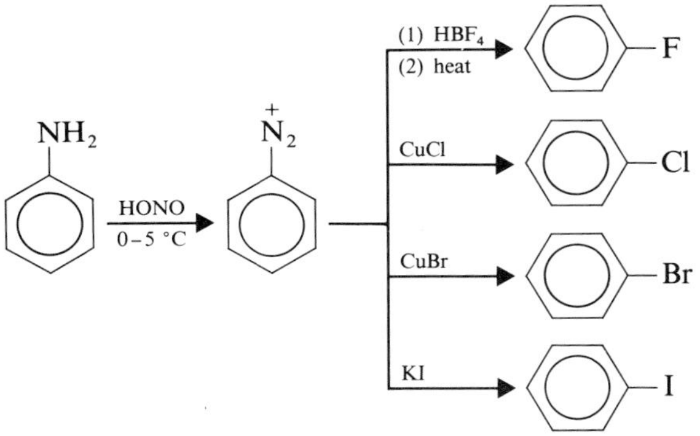

21.12E REACTIONS OF ARYL HALIDES

1. Electrophilic aromatic substitution (Sections 15.3 – 15.7)

2. Nucleophilic aromatic substitution (Section 21.11)

Additional Problems

21.12 What products would be obtained from each of the following acid–base reactions?

(a) Sodium ethoxide in ethanol + phenol ⟶

(b) Phenol + aqueous sodium hydroxide ⟶

(c) Sodium phenoxide + aqueous hydrochloric acid ⟶

(d) Sodium phenoxide + H_2O + CO_2 ⟶

21.13 Complete the following equations:

(a) Phenol + Br_2 $\xrightarrow{5\ °C,\ CS_2}$

(b) Phenol + concd H_2SO_4 $\xrightarrow{25\ °C}$

(c) Phenol + concd H_2SO_4 $\xrightarrow{100\ °C}$

(d)  CH_3-⬡$-OH$ + *p*-toluenesulfonyl chloride $\xrightarrow[OH^-]{}$

(e) Phenol + Br_2 $\xrightarrow{H_2O}$

(f) Phenol +

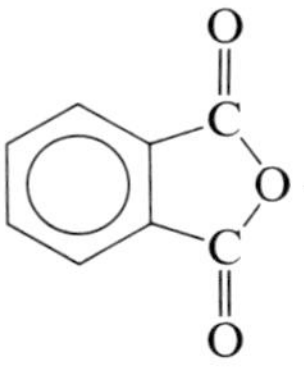

(g) *p*-Cresol + Br_2 $\xrightarrow{H_2O}$

(h) Phenol + $C_6H_5\overset{O}{\overset{\|}{C}}Cl$ $\xrightarrow{base}$

(i) Phenol + $\left(C_6H_5\overset{O}{\overset{\|}{C}}-\right)_2O$ $\xrightarrow{base}$

(j) Phenol + NaOH $\longrightarrow$

(k) Product of (j) + $CH_3OSO_2OCH_3$ $\longrightarrow$

(l) Product of (j) + CH_3I $\longrightarrow$

(m) Product of (j) + $C_6H_5CH_2Cl$ $\longrightarrow$

21.14 Describe a simple chemical test that could be used to distinguish between the members of each of the following pairs of compounds:

(a) *p*-Cresol and benzyl alcohol

(b) Phenol and cyclohexane

(c) Cyclohexanol and cyclohexene

(d) Allyl phenyl ether and phenyl propyl ether

(e) Methoxybenzene (anisole) and *p*-cresol

(f) 2,4,6-Trinitrophenol (picric acid) and 2,4,6-trimethylphenol

21.15 *Thymol* (see following structure) can be obtained from thyme oil. Thymol is an effective disinfectant and is used in many antiseptic preparations. (a) Suggest a synthesis of thymol from *m*-cresol and propylene. (b) Suggest a method for transforming thymol into menthol.

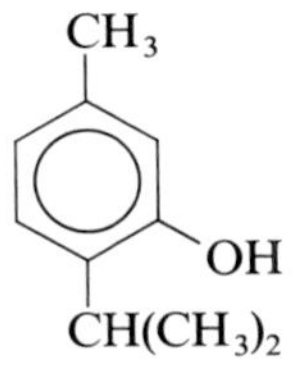

Thymol 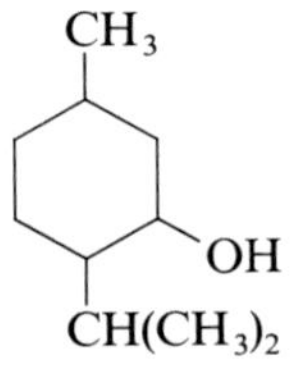   Menthol

21.16   *Carvacrol* is another naturally occurring phenol and it is an isomer of thymol (Problem 21.15). Carvacrol can be synthesized from *p*-cymene (*p*-isopropyltoluene) by ring sulfonation and treating the sulfonic acid with fused alkali. Explain why this synthesis yields mainly carvacrol and very little thymol.

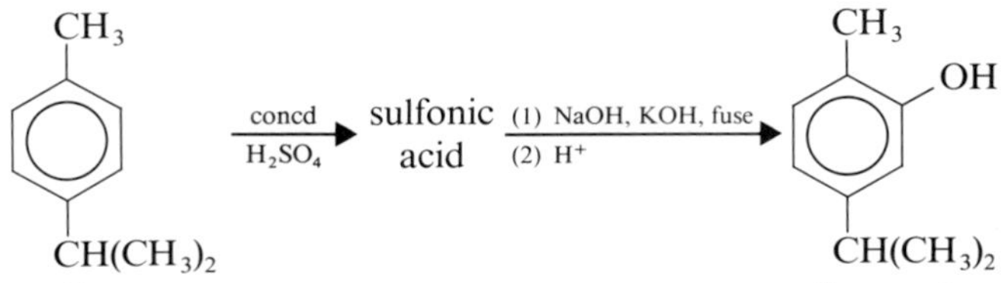

$$\text{p-Cymene} \xrightarrow[\text{H}_2\text{SO}_4]{\text{concd}} \text{sulfonic acid} \xrightarrow[\text{(2) H}^+]{\text{(1) NaOH, KOH, fuse}} \text{Carvacrol}$$

p-Cymene   Carvacrol

21.17   A widely used synthetic antiseptic is 4-*hexylresorcinol*. Suggest a synthesis of 4-hexylresorcinol from resorcinol and hexanoic acid.

21.18   *Anethole* (see following structure) is the chief component of anise oil. Suggest a synthesis of anethole from anisole and propanoic acid.

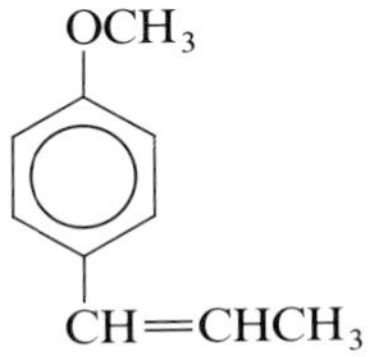

Anethole

21.19   A compound **X** ($C_{10}H_{14}O$) dissolves in aqueous sodium hydroxide but is insoluble in aqueous sodium bicarbonate. Compound **X** reacts with bromine in water to yield a dibromo derivative, $C_{10}H_{12}Br_2O$. The 3000–4000-cm^{-1} region of the IR spectrum of **X** shows a broad peak centered at 3250 cm^{-1}; the 680–840-cm^{-1} region shows a strong peak at 830 cm^{-1}. The ^{1}H NMR spectrum of **X** gives the following:

Singlet	δ 1.3 (9H)
Singlet	δ 4.9 (1H)
Multiplet	δ 7.0 (4H)

What is the structure of **X**?

21.20   The widely used antioxidant and food preservative called **BHA** (**B**utylated **H**ydroxy **A**nisole) is actually a mixture of 2-*tert*-butyl-4-methoxyphenol and 3-*tert*-butyl-4-methoxyphenol. **BHA** is synthesized from *p*-methoxyphenol and 2-methylpropene. (a) Suggest how this is done. (b) Another widely used antioxidant is **BHT** (**B**utylated **H**ydroxy **T**oluene). **BHT** is actually 2,6-di-*tert*-butyl-4-methylphenol, and the raw materials used in its production are *p*-cresol and 2-methylpropene. What reaction is used here?

21.21   The herbicide **2,4-D** (cf. Special Topic K) can be synthesized from phenol and chloroacetic acid. Outline the steps involved.

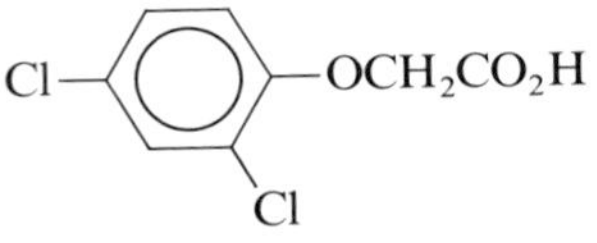

2,4-D
2,4-Dichlorophenoxyacetic acid

Chloroacetic
acid

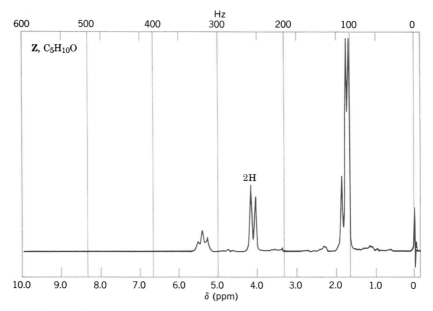

FIGURE 21.1 The ^{1}H NMR spectrum of compound Z, Problem 21.22. (Spectrum courtesy of Aldrich Chemical Co., Milwaukee, WI.)

*21.22   Compound Z ($C_5H_{10}O$) decolorizes bromine in carbon tetrachloride. The IR spectrum of Z shows a broad peak in the 3200–3600-cm^{-1} region. The ^{1}H NMR spectrum of Z is given in Fig. 21.1. Propose a structure for Z.

Second *Review* Problem Set

1. Arrange the compounds of each of the following series in order of increasing acidity.

(a) CH_3CH_2OH $CH_3\overset{\text{O}}{\overset{\|}{C}}OH$ $CH_3O\overset{\text{O}}{\overset{\|}{C}}CH_2\overset{\text{O}}{\overset{\|}{C}}OCH_3$ $CH_3\overset{\text{O}}{\overset{\|}{C}}CH_3$

(b) 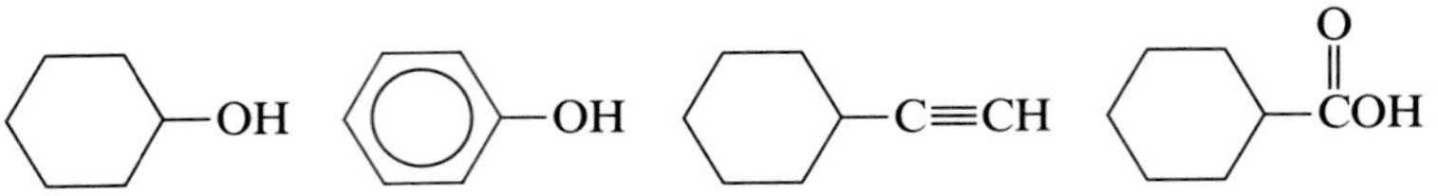 ⬡—OH   ⌬—OH   ⬡—C≡CH   ⬡—$\overset{\text{O}}{\overset{\|}{C}}OH$

(c) $(CH_3)_3\overset{+}{N}$—⌬—$\overset{\text{O}}{\overset{\|}{C}}OH$ $(CH_3)_3C$—⌬—$\overset{\text{O}}{\overset{\|}{C}}OH$ ⌬—$\overset{\text{O}}{\overset{\|}{C}}OH$

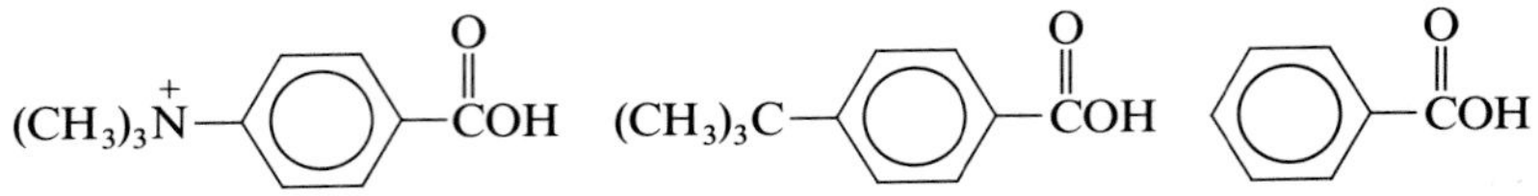

(d) $CH_3CCl_2\overset{\text{O}}{\overset{\|}{C}}OH$ $CH_3CH_2\overset{\text{O}}{\overset{\|}{C}}OH$ $CH_3CHCl\overset{\text{O}}{\overset{\|}{C}}OH$

(e) 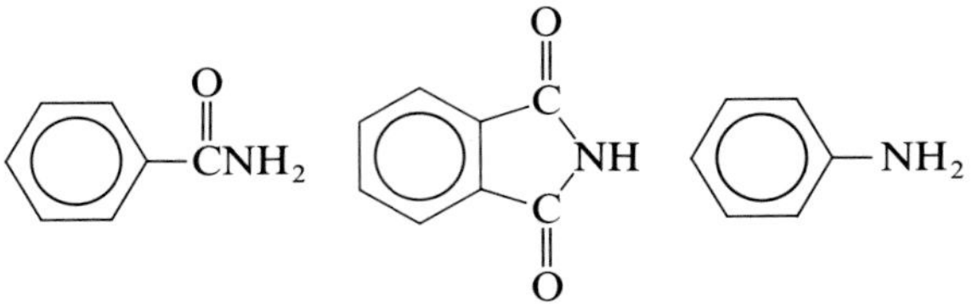 ⌬—$\overset{\text{O}}{\overset{\|}{C}}NH_2$ ⌬(phthalimide with NH)   ⌬—NH_2

2. Arrange the compounds of each of the following series in order of increasing basicity.

(a) $CH_3\overset{\text{O}}{\overset{\|}{C}}NH_2$ $CH_3CH_2NH_2$ NH_3

(b) 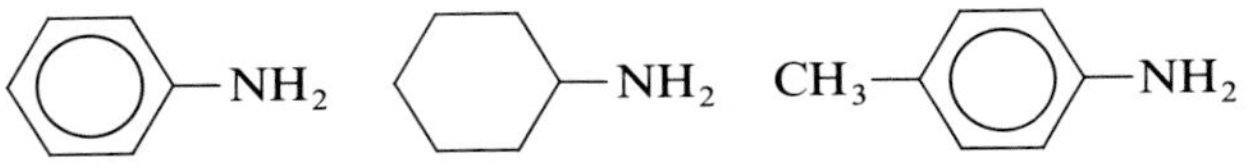 ⌬—NH_2 ⬡—NH_2 CH_3—⌬—NH_2

(c) 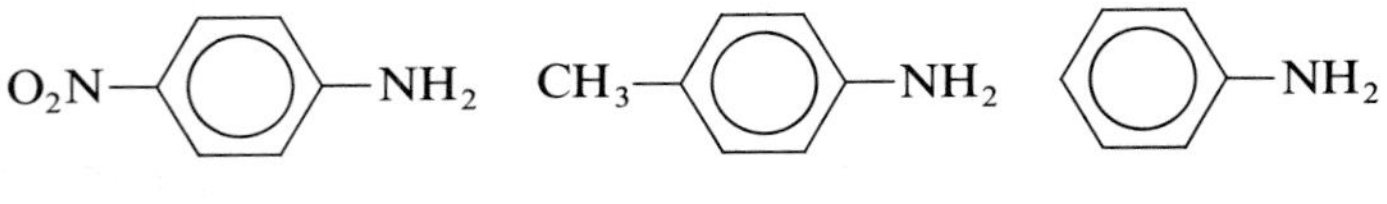 O_2N—⌬—NH_2 CH_3—⌬—NH_2 ⌬—NH_2

(d) $CH_3CH_2CH_3$ CH_3NHCH_3 CH_3OCH_3

3. Starting with 1-butanol and using any other required reagents, outline a synthesis of each of the following compounds. You need not repeat steps carried out in earlier parts of this problem.

(a) Butyl bromide
(b) Butylamine
(c) Pentylamine
(d) Butanoic acid
(e) Pentanoic acid
(f) Butanoyl chloride
(g) Butanamide
(h) Butyl butanoate
(i) Propylamine
(j) Butylbenzene
(k) Butanoic anhydride
(l) Hexanoic acid

4. Starting with benzene, toluene, or aniline and any other required reagents, outline a synthesis of each of the following.

964

SECOND REVIEW PROBLEM SET

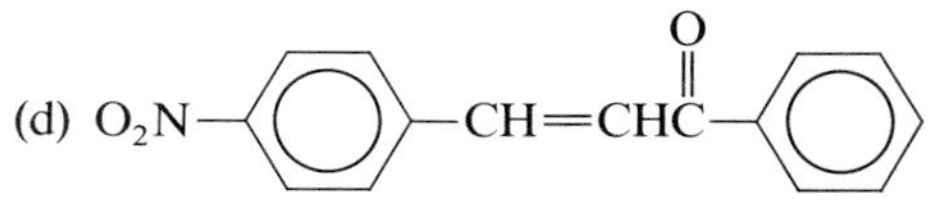

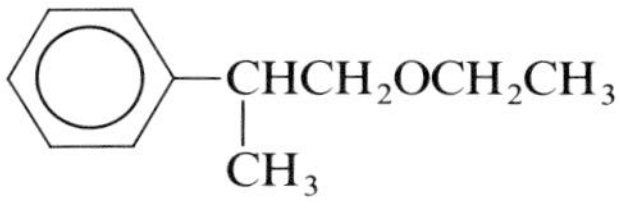

(a) 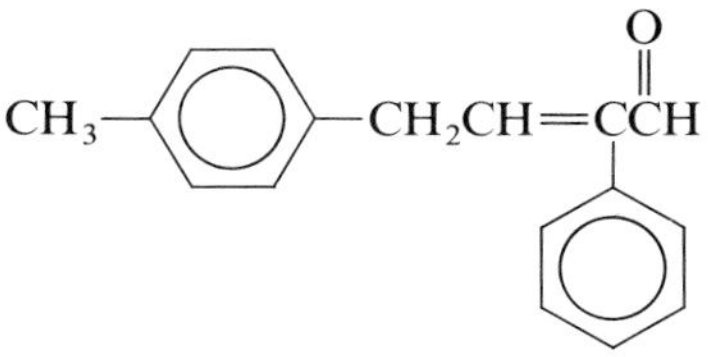 CH$_3$—⬡—CH$_2$CH=CCH with C=O and phenyl substituent

(d) O$_2$N—⬡—CH=CHC—⬡ with C=O

(b) ⬡—CHCH$_2$OCH$_2$CH$_3$ with CH$_3$

(e) C$_6$H$_5$CH=CCH$_3$ with CO$_2$H

(c) Cl—⬡ with Br and Br substituents

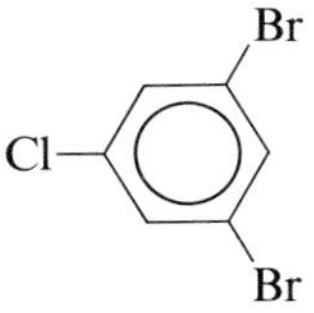

5. Give stereochemical structures for compounds **A – D.**

2-Methyl-1,3-butadiene + diethyl fumarate ⟶ **A** (C$_{13}$H$_{20}$O$_4$) $\xrightarrow{\text{(1) LiAlH}_4,\ \text{(2) H}_2\text{O}}$

B (C$_9$H$_{16}$O$_2$) $\xrightarrow{\text{PBr}_3}$ **C** (C$_9$H$_{14}$Br$_2$) $\xrightarrow{\text{Zn, H}^+}$ **D** (C$_9$H$_{16}$)

6. A Grignard reagent that is a key intermediate in an industrial synthesis of vitamin A (Section 17.6B) can be prepared in the following way:

HC≡CLi + CH$_2$=CHCCH$_3$ (with C=O) $\xrightarrow[\text{(2) NH}_4^+]{\text{(1) liq. NH}_3}$ **A** (C$_6$H$_8$O) $\xrightarrow{\text{H}^+}$

B HOCH$_2$CH=C—C≡CH (with CH$_3$) $\xrightarrow{\text{2 C}_2\text{H}_5\text{MgBr}}$ **C** (C$_6$H$_6$Mg$_2$Br$_2$O)

(a) What are the structures of compounds **A** and **C**?
(b) The acid-catalyzed rearrangement of **A – B** takes place very readily. What two factors account for this?

7. The remaining steps in the industrial synthesis of vitamin A (as an acetate) are as follows: The Grignard reagent **C** from Problem 6 is allowed to react with the aldehyde shown here.

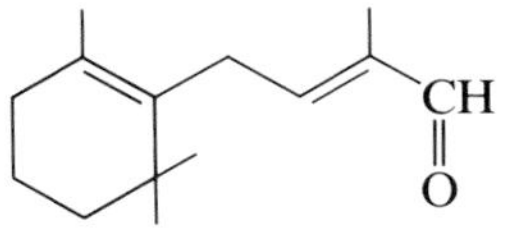

After acidification, the product obtained from this step is a diol **D.** Selective hydrogenation of the triple bond of **D** using Ni$_2$B (P-2) catalyst yields **E** (C$_{20}$H$_{32}$O$_2$). Treating **E** with one molar equivalent of acetic anhydride yields a monoacetate (**F**) and dehydration of **F** yields vitamin A acetate. What are the structures of **D – F?**

8. Heating acetone with an excess of phenol in the presence of hydrogen chloride is the basis for an industrial process used in the manufacture of a compound called "bisphenol A." (Bisphenol A is used in the manufacture of epoxy resins and a polymer called "Lexan," cf.

SECOND REVIEW PROBLEM SET

Problem F.5.) Bisphenol A has the molecular formula $C_{15}H_{16}O_2$ and the reactions involved in its formation are similar to those involved in the synthesis of DDT (Problem K.1). Write out these reactions and give the structure of bisphenol A.

9. Outlined here is a synthesis of the local anesthetic *procaine*. Provide structures for procaine and the intermediates **A–C**.

p-Nitrotoluene $\xrightarrow[\text{(2) } H_3O^+]{\text{(1) } KMnO_4, OH^-, \text{ heat}}$ **A** $(C_7H_5NO_4)$ $\xrightarrow{SOCl_2}$

B $(C_7H_4ClNO_3)$ $\xrightarrow{HOCH_2CH_2N(C_2H_5)_2}$ **C** $(C_{13}H_{18}N_2O_4)$ $\xrightarrow{H_2, \text{ cat.}}$ procaine $(C_{13}H_{20}N_2O_2)$

10. The sedative-hypnotic *ethinamate* can be synthesized by the following route. Provide structures for ethinamate and the intermediates **A** and **B**.

Cyclohexanone $\xrightarrow{\text{(1) } HC\equiv CNa. \text{ (2) } H^+}$ **A** $(C_8H_{12}O)$ $\xrightarrow{ClCOCl}$

B $(C_9H_{11}ClO_2)$ $\xrightarrow{NH_3}$ ethinamate $(C_9H_{13}NO_2)$

11. The prototype of the antihistamines, *diphenhydramine* (also called Benadryl), can be synthesized by the following sequence of reactions. (a) Give structures for diphenhydramine and for the intermediates **A** and **B**. (b) Comment on a possible mechanism for the last step of the synthesis.

Benzaldehyde $\xrightarrow{\text{(1) } C_6H_5MgBr, \text{ (2) } H_3O^+}$ **A** $(C_{13}H_{12}O)$ $\xrightarrow{PBr_3}$

B $(C_{13}H_{11}Br)$ $\xrightarrow{(CH_3)_2NCH_2CH_2OH}$ diphenhydramine $(C_{17}H_{21}NO)$

12. Show how you would modify the synthesis given in the previous problem to synthesize the following drugs.

(a) Br—⟨O⟩—CHOCH$_2$CH$_2$N(CH$_3$)$_2$ **Bromodiphenhydramine (an antihistamine)**
                      |
                      C$_6$H$_5$

(b) [structure with CH$_3$]—CHOCH$_2$CH$_2$N(CH$_3$)$_2$ **Orphenadrine (an antispasmodic, used in controlling Parkinson's disease)**
                      |
                      C$_6$H$_5$

13. Outlined here is a synthesis of 2-methyl-3-oxocyclopentanecarboxylic acid. Give the structure of each intermediate.

CH$_3$CHCO$_2$C$_2$H$_5$ $\xrightarrow{CH_2(CO_2C_2H_5)_2, \text{ EtO}^-}$ **A** $(C_{12}H_{20}O_6)$ $\xrightarrow{CH_2=CHCN, \text{ EtO}^-}$
   |
   Br

B $(C_{15}H_{23}NO_6)$ $\xrightarrow{EtOH, H^+}$ **C** $(C_{17}H_{28}O_8)$ $\xrightarrow{EtO^-}$ **D** $(C_{15}H_{22}O_7)$ $\xrightarrow[\text{(2) } H_3O^+, \text{ (3) heat}]{\text{(1) } OH^-, H_2O, \text{ heat}}$

SECOND REVIEW PROBLEM SET

14. Give structures for compounds **A–D**. Compound **D** decolorizes bromine in carbon tetrachloride and gives a strong IR absorption band near 1720 cm^{-1}.

$$CH_3\overset{\overset{\displaystyle O}{\|}}{C}CH_3 \xrightarrow{HCl} \textbf{A }(C_6H_{10}O) \xrightarrow[base]{CH_3\overset{\overset{\displaystyle O}{\|}}{C}CH_2\overset{\overset{\displaystyle O}{\|}}{C}OC_2H_5} [\textbf{B }(C_{12}H_{20}O_4)] \xrightarrow{base}$$

$$\textbf{C }(C_{12}H_{18}O_3) \xrightarrow{H^+,\ H_2O,\ heat} \textbf{D }(C_9H_{14}O)$$

15. A synthesis of the broad-spectrum antibiotic *chloramphenicol* is shown here. In the last step basic hydrolysis selectively hydrolyzes ester linkages in the presence of an amide group. What are the intermediates **A–E**?

Benzaldehyde $+ HOCH_2CH_2NO_2 \xrightarrow{EtO^-} \textbf{A }(C_9H_{11}NO_4) \xrightarrow{H_2,\ cat.}$

$\textbf{B }(C_9H_{13}NO_2) \xrightarrow{Cl_2CHCOCl} \textbf{C }(C_{11}H_{13}Cl_2NO_3) \xrightarrow{excess\ (CH_3CO)_2O}$

$\textbf{D }(C_{15}H_{17}Cl_2NO_5) \xrightarrow{HNO_3,\ H_2SO_4} \textbf{E }(C_{15}H_{16}Cl_2N_2O_7) \xrightarrow{OH^-,\ H_2O}$

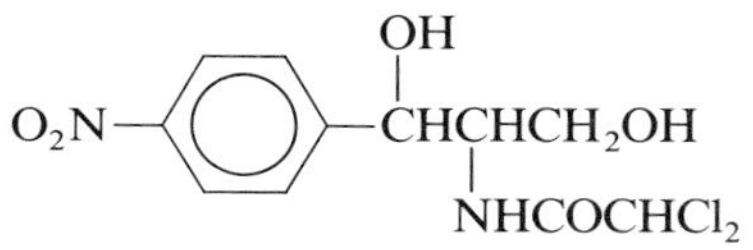

$$O_2N-\!\!\!\left\langle\bigcirc\right\rangle\!\!\!-\overset{\overset{\displaystyle OH}{|}}{C}H\overset{\overset{}{}}{C}H\underset{\underset{\displaystyle NHCOCHCl_2}{|}}{C}HCH_2OH$$

Chloramphenicol

16. The tranquilizing drug *meprobamate* (Equanil or Miltown) can be synthesized from 2-methylpentanal as follows. Give structures for meprobamate and for the intermediates **A–C**.

$$CH_3CH_2CH_2\underset{\underset{\displaystyle CH_3}{|}}{C}H\overset{\overset{\overset{\displaystyle O}{\|}}{}}{C}H \xrightarrow{HCHO,\ OH^-} [\textbf{A }(C_7H_{14}O_2)] \xrightarrow[OH^-]{HCHO} \textbf{B }(C_7H_{16}O_2) \xrightarrow{ClCOCl}$$

$$\textbf{C }(C_9H_{14}Cl_2O_4) \xrightarrow{NH_3} \text{meprobamate }(C_9H_{18}N_2O_4)$$

17. What are compounds **A–C**? Compound **C** is useful as an insect repellent.

Succinic anhydride $\xrightarrow{CH_3CH_2CH_2OH} \textbf{A }(C_7H_{12}O_4) \xrightarrow{SOCl_2}$

$$\textbf{B }(C_7H_{11}ClO_3) \xrightarrow{(CH_3CH_2)_2NH} \textbf{C }(C_{11}H_{21}NO_3)$$

18. Outlined here is the synthesis of a central nervous system stimulant called *fencamfamine*. Provide structural formulas for each intermediate and for fencamfamine itself.

1,3-Cyclopentadiene $+ (E)\text{-}C_6H_5CH{=}CHNO_2 \longrightarrow \textbf{A }(C_{13}H_{13}NO_2) \xrightarrow{H_2,\ Pt}$

$\textbf{B }(C_{13}H_{17}N) \xrightarrow{CH_3CHO} [\textbf{C }(C_{15}H_{19}N)] \xrightarrow{H_2,\ Ni} \text{fencamfamine }(C_{15}H_{21}N)$

19. What are compounds **A** and **B**? Compound **B** has a strong IR absorption band in the 1650–1730-cm^{-1} region and a broad strong band in the 3200–3550-cm^{-1} region.

1-Methylcyclohexene $\xrightarrow[\text{(2) NaHSO}_3]{\text{(1) OsO}_4} \textbf{A }(C_7H_{14}O_2) \xrightarrow[CH_3CO_2H]{CrO_3} \textbf{B }(C_7H_{12}O_2)$

SECOND REVIEW PROBLEM SET

20. Starting with phenol, outline a stereoselective synthesis of methyl *trans*-4-isopropyl-cyclohexanecarboxylate, that is,

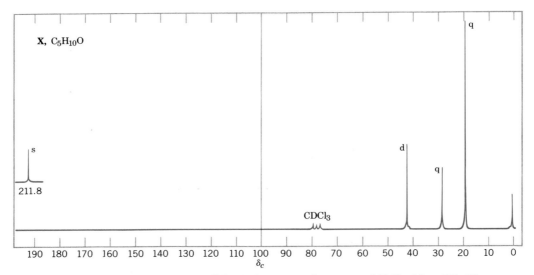

21. Compound X ($C_5H_{10}O$) gives a positive iodoform test and shows a strong IR absorption band near 1710 cm^{-1}. The proton-decoupled ^{13}C NMR spectrum of X is shown in Fig. 1. Propose a structure for X.

22. Compound Y ($C_6H_{14}O$) gives a green opaque solution when treated with CrO_3 in aqueous H_2SO_4. Compound Y gives a negative iodoform test. The proton-decoupled ^{13}C NMR spectrum of Y is given in Fig. 2. Propose a structure for Y.

23. Compound Z (C_8H_{16}) decolorizes bromine in carbon tetrachloride and is the more stable of a pair of stereoisomers. Ozonolysis of Z gives a single product. The proton-decoupled ^{13}C NMR spectrum of Z is given in Fig. 2. Propose a structure for Z.

X, $C_5H_{10}O$

q

s

d

q

211.8

CDCl$_3$

190 180 170 160 150 140 130 120 110 100 90 80 70 60 50 40 30 20 10 0

δ_c

FIGURE 1 The proton-decoupled ^{13}C NMR spectra of compound X (Problem 21). The letters s, d, and q, stand for the multiplicity of the peaks (singlet, doublet, and quartet) in the proton off-resonance decoupled spectrum. Spectra adapted from L. F. Johnson and W. C. Jankowski, *Carbon-13 NMR Spectra: A Collection of Assigned, Coded, and Indexed Spectra,* Wiley–Interscience, New York, 1972.

SECOND REVIEW PROBLEM SET

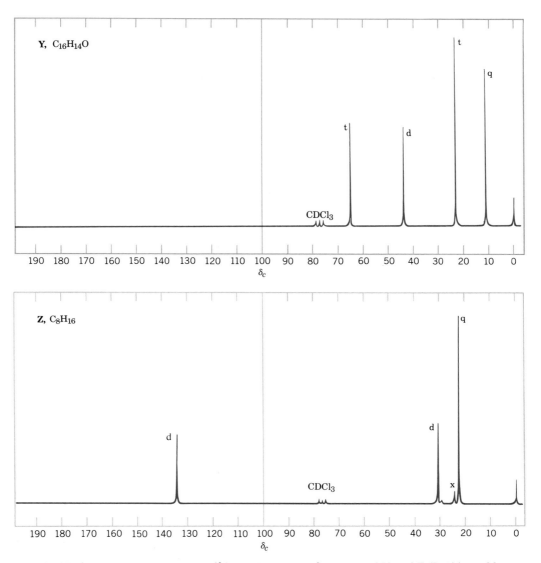

FIGURE 2 The proton-decoupled ^{13}C NMR spectra of compound **Y** and **Z** (Problems 22 and 23). The letters d, t, and q, stand for the multiplicity of the peaks (doublet, triplet, and quartet) in the proton off-resonance decoupled spectrum. The signal marked x arises from an impurity and should be ignored. Spectra adapted from L. F. Johnson and W. C. Jankowski, *Carbon-13 NMR Spectra: A Collection of Assigned, Coded, and Indexed Spectra*, Wiley–Interscience, New York, 1972.

SPECIAL TOPIC

I

THIOLS, THIOETHERS, AND THIOPHENOLS

Sulfur is directly below oxygen in Group **VI** of the periodic table and, as we might expect, there are sulfur counterparts of the oxygen compounds that we studied in Chapters 10 and 21 such as thiols, thioethers, and thiophenols.

These and other important examples of organosulfur compounds are the following:

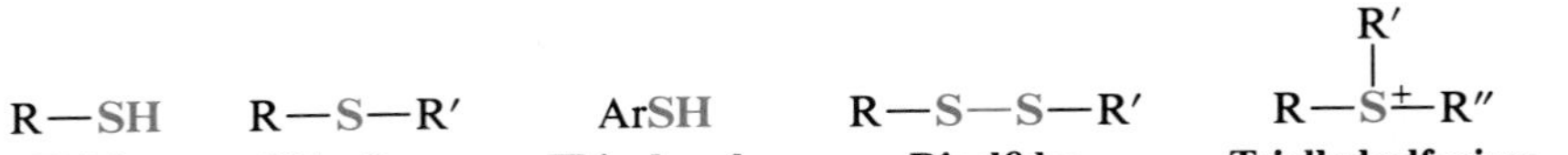

				$\overset{\displaystyle R'}{\underset{\displaystyle \vert}{}}$
R—SH	R—S—R'	ArSH	R—S—S—R'	R—$\overset{+}{\underset{-}{S}}$—R''
Thiols	**Thioethers**	**Thiophenols**	**Disulfides**	**Trialkylsulfonium ions**

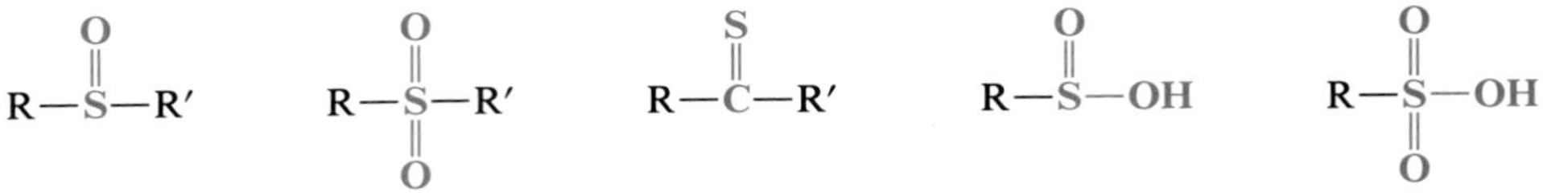

$\overset{\displaystyle O}{\underset{\displaystyle \Vert}{}}$ R—S—R'	$\overset{\displaystyle O}{\underset{\displaystyle \Vert}{}}$ R—S—R' $\underset{\displaystyle \overset{\Vert}{O}}{}$	$\overset{\displaystyle S}{\underset{\displaystyle \Vert}{}}$ R—C—R'	$\overset{\displaystyle O}{\underset{\displaystyle \Vert}{}}$ R—S—OH	$\overset{\displaystyle O}{\underset{\displaystyle \Vert}{}}$ R—S—OH $\underset{\displaystyle \overset{\Vert}{O}}{}$
Sulfoxides	**Sulfones**	**Thioketones**	**Sulfinic acids**	**Sulfonic acids**

The sulfur counterpart of an alcohol is called a *thiol* or a *mercaptan.* The name mercaptan comes from the Latin, *mercurium captans,* meaning "capturing mercury." Mercaptans react with mercuric ions and the ions of other heavy metals to form precipitates. The compound CH_2CHCH_2OH, known as British Anti-Lewisite
$\qquad\qquad\qquad\qquad\quad\ \ |\ \ |$
$\qquad\qquad\qquad\qquad\ \ SH\ SH$
(BAL), was developed as an antidote for poisonous arsenic compounds used as war gases. British Anti-Lewisite is also an effective antidote for mercury poisoning.

Several simple thiols are shown below.

		$\overset{\displaystyle CH_3}{\underset{\displaystyle \vert}{}}$	
CH_3CH_2SH	$CH_3CH_2CH_2SH$	$CH_3CHCH_2CH_2SH$	$CH_2{=}CHCH_2SH$
Ethanethiol	**1-Propanethiol**	**3-Methyl-1-butanethiol**	**2-Propene-1-thiol**
(ethyl mercaptan)	**(propyl mercaptan)**	**(isopentyl mercaptan)**	**(allyl mercaptan)**

Compounds of sulfur, in general, and the low molecular weight thiols, in particular, are noted for their disagreeable odors. Anyone who has passed anywhere near a general chemistry laboratory when hydrogen sulfide (H_2S) was being used has noticed the strong odor of that substance—the odor of rotten eggs. Another sulfur compound, 3-methyl-1-butanethiol, is one unpleasant constituent of the liquid that skunks use as a defensive weapon. 1-Propanethiol evolves from freshly chopped onions, and allyl mercaptan is one of the compounds responsible for the odor and flavor of garlic.

Aside from their odors, analogous sulfur and oxygen compounds show other chemical differences. These arise largely from the following features of sulfur compounds.

1. The sulfur atom is larger and more polarizable than the oxygen atom. As a result, sulfur compounds are more powerful nucleophiles and compounds containing —SH groups are stronger acids than their oxygen analogs. The ethanethiolate ion ($CH_3CH_2\ddot{\underset{..}{S}}:^-$), for example, is a much stronger nucleophile when it reacts at carbon atoms than is the ethoxide ion ($CH_3CH_2O^-$). On the other hand, since ethanol is a weaker acid than ethanethiol, the ethoxide ion is the stronger of the two conjugate bases.

2. The bond dissociation energy of the S—H bond of thiols (~ 80 kcal mol^{-1}) is much less than that of the O—H bond of alcohols (~ 100 kcal mol^{-1}). The weakness of the S—H bond allows thiols to undergo an oxidative coupling reaction when they react with mild oxidizing agents; the product is a disulfide:

$$2\ RS{-}H + H_2O_2 \longrightarrow RS{-}SR + 2\ H_2O$$

  A thiol   **A disulfide**

Alcohols do not undergo an analogous reaction. When alcohols are treated with oxidizing agents, oxidation takes place at the weaker C—H (~ 85 kcal mol^{-1}) bond rather than at the strong O—H bond.

3. Because sulfur atoms are easily polarized they can stabilize a negative charge on an adjacent atom. This means that hydrogen atoms on carbon atoms that are adjacent to an alkylthio group are more acidic than those adjacent to an alkoxy group. Thioanisole, for example, reacts with butyllithium in the following way:

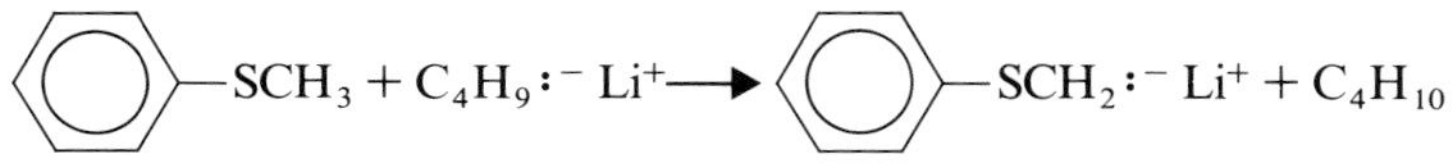

  Thioanisole

Anisole ($CH_3OC_6H_5$) does not undergo an analogous reaction.

The $\diagdown$S=O group of sulfoxides and the positive sulfur of sulfonium ions are even more effective in delocalizing negative charge on an adjacent atom:

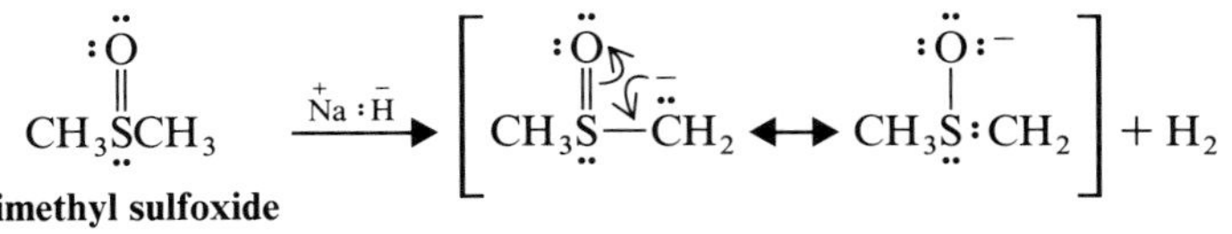

Dimethyl sulfoxide

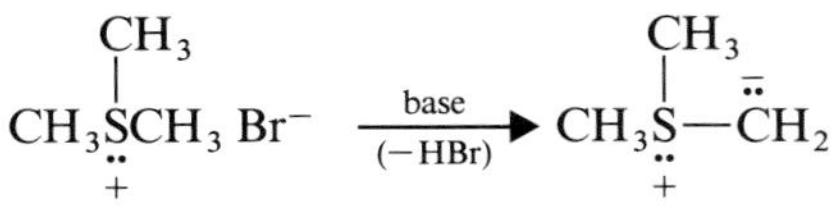

Trimethylsulfonium   **An ylide**
    bromide

The anions formed in the reactions just given are of synthetic use. They can be used to synthesize epoxides, for example (cf. Section I.3).

I.1 PREPARATION OF THIOLS

Alkyl bromides and iodides react with potassium hydrogen sulfide to form thiols. (Potassium hydrogen sulfide can be generated by passing gaseous H_2S into an alcoholic solution of potassium hydroxide.)

$$R{-}Br + KOH + \underset{\textbf{(excess)}}{H_2S} \xrightarrow[\text{heat}]{C_2H_5OH} R{-}SH + KBr + H_2O$$

The thiol that forms is sufficiently acidic to form a thiolate ion in the presence of potassium hydroxide. Thus, if excess H_2S is not employed in the reaction, the major product of the reaction will be a thioether. The thioether results from the following reactions:

$$R{-}SH + KOH \longrightarrow R{-}\ddot{\underset{..}{S}}{:}^- K^+ + H_2O$$

$$R{-}\ddot{\underset{..}{S}}{:}^- K^+ + R{-}\ddot{\underset{..}{Br}}{:} \longrightarrow R{-}\underset{..}{\overset{..}{S}}{-}R + KBr$$

Thioether

Alkyl halides also react with thiourea to form (stable) S-alkylisothiouronium salts. These can be used to prepare thiols.

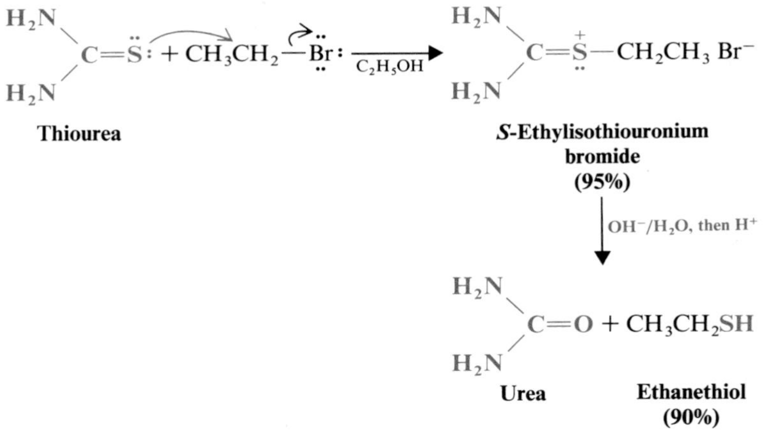

| Thiourea | S-Ethylisothiouronium bromide (95%) |

$$\downarrow \text{OH}^-/H_2O, \text{ then } H^+$$

| Urea | Ethanethiol (90%) |

I.2 PHYSICAL PROPERTIES OF THIOLS

Thiols form very weak hydrogen bonds; their hydrogen bonds are not nearly as strong as those of alcohols. Because of this, low molecular weight thiols have lower boiling points than corresponding alcohols. Ethanethiol, for example, boils more than 40 °C lower than ethanol (37 vs 78 °C). The relative weakness of hydrogen bonds between molecules of thiols is also evident when we compare the boiling points of ethanethiol and its isomer dimethyl sulfide:

$$\underset{\textbf{bp, 37 °C}}{CH_3CH_2SH} \qquad \underset{\textbf{bp, 38 °C}}{CH_3SCH_3}$$

Physical properties of several thiols are given in Table I.1.

TABLE I.1   Physical properties of thiols

COMPOUND	STRUCTURE	mp (°C)	bp (°C)
Methanethiol	CH_3SH	-123	6
Ethanethiol	CH_3CH_2SH	-144	37
1-Propanethiol	$CH_3CH_2CH_2SH$	-113	67
2-Propanethiol	$(CH_3)_2CHSH$	-131	58
1-Butanethiol	$CH_3(CH_2)_2CH_2SH$	-116	98

I.3 THE ADDITION OF SULFUR YLIDES TO ALDEHYDES AND KETONES

Sulfur ylides also react as nucleophiles at the carbonyl carbon of aldehydes and ketones. The betaine that forms usually decomposes to an *epoxide* rather than to an alkene.

Problem I.1

Show how you might use a sulfur ylide to prepare

I.4 THIOLS AND DISULFIDES IN BIOCHEMISTRY

Thiols and disulfides are important compounds in living cells and in many biochemical oxidation–reduction reactions they are interconverted.

$$2\ RSH \underset{[H]}{\overset{[O]}{\rightleftharpoons}} R-S-S-R$$

Lipoic acid, for example, an important cofactor in biological oxidations, undergoes this oxidation–reduction reaction.

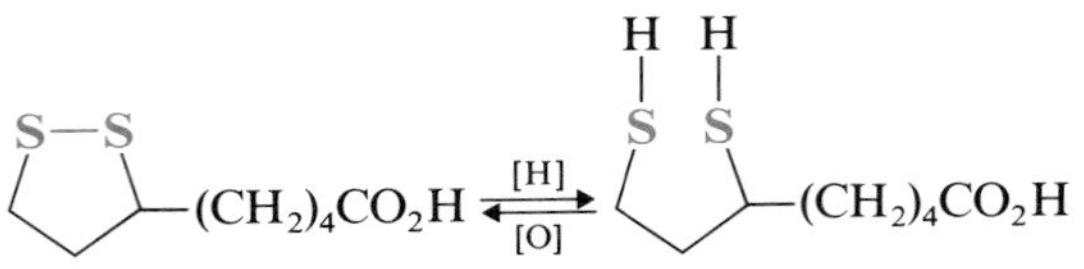

| Lipoic acid | Dihydrolipoic acid |

The amino acids *cysteine* and *cystine* are interconverted in a similar way:

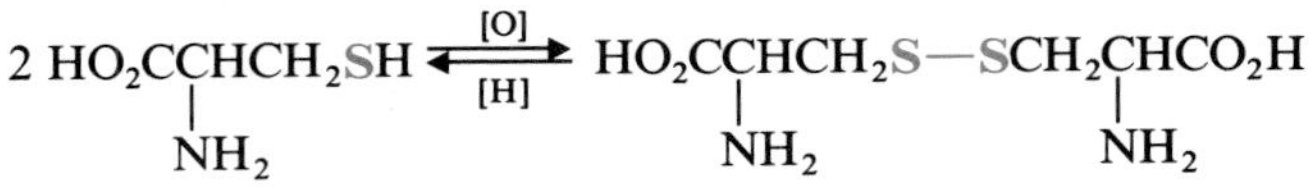

$$2\ HO_2CCHCH_2SH \underset{[H]}{\overset{[O]}{\rightleftharpoons}} HO_2CCHCH_2S-SCH_2CHCO_2H$$

| NH_2 | NH_2   NH_2 |
| Cysteine | Cystine |

As we shall see later, the disulfide linkages of cystine units are important in determining the overall shapes of protein molecules.

Problem I.2

Give structures for the products of the following reactions:
(a) Benzyl bromide + thiourea $\longrightarrow$
(b) Product of (a) + OH$^-$/H$_2$O, then H$^+$ $\longrightarrow$
(c) Product of (b) + H$_2$O$_2$ $\longrightarrow$
(d) Product of (b) + NaOH $\longrightarrow$
(e) Product of (d) + benzyl bromide $\longrightarrow$

Problem I.3

Allyl disulfide, $CH_2=CHCH_2S-SCH_2CH=CH_2$, is another important component of oil of garlic. Suggest a synthesis of allyl disulfide starting with allyl bromide.

Problem I.4

Starting with allyl alcohol, outline a synthesis of BAL, $CH_2SHCHSHCH_2OH$.

Problem I.5

A synthesis of lipoic acid (see structure just given) is outlined here. Supply the missing reagents and intermediates.

SPECIAL TOPIC I

$$Cl-\overset{\overset{\displaystyle O}{\|}}{C}(CH_2)_4CO_2C_2H_5 \xrightarrow[\text{AlCl}_3]{\text{CH}_2=\text{CH}_2} \text{ (a) } C_{10}H_{17}ClO_3 \xrightarrow{\text{NaBH}_4}$$

$$\underset{\overset{|}{\text{OH}}}{ClCH_2CH_2CH}(CH_2)_4CO_2C_2H_5 \xrightarrow{\text{(b)}} \underset{\overset{|}{\text{Cl}}}{ClCH_2CH_2CH}(CH_2)_4CO_2C_2H_5 \xrightarrow[\text{(d)}]{\text{(c)}}$$

$$\underset{\overset{|}{\text{SCH}_2C_6H_5}}{C_6H_5CH_2SCH_2CH_2CH}(CH_2)_4CO_2H \xrightarrow[\text{(2) H}^+]{\text{(1) Na, liq. NH}_3}$$

$$\text{(e) } C_8H_{16}S_2O_2 \xrightarrow{O_2} \text{ lipoic acid}$$

Problem I.6

One chemical-warfare agent used in World War I is a powerful vesicant called "mustard gas." (The name comes from its mustardlike odor; mustard gas, however, is not a gas but a high-boiling liquid that was dispersed as a mist of tiny droplets.) Mustard gas can be synthesized from oxirane in the following manner. Outline the reactions involved.

$$2\ \underset{\overset{\diagdown\ \diagup}{O}}{H_2C-CH_2} + H_2S \longrightarrow C_4H_{10}SO_2 \xrightarrow[\text{ZnCl}_2]{\text{HCl}} C_4H_8SCl_2$$
$$\textbf{``Mustard gas''}$$

J

TRANSITION METAL ORGANOMETALLIC COMPOUNDS

J.1 INTRODUCTION

One of the most active areas of chemical research in recent years has involved studying compounds in which a bond exists between the carbon atom of an organic group and a transition metal. This field, which combines aspects of organic chemistry and inorganic chemistry, has led to many important applications in organic synthesis. Many of these transition metal organic compounds act as catalysts of extraordinary selectivity.

The transition metals are defined as those elements that have partly filled d (or f) shells, either in the elemental state or in their important compounds. The transition metals that are of most concern to organic chemists are those shown in the green and yellow portion of the periodic table given in Fig. J.1. Transition metals react with a variety of molecules or groups, called *ligands,* to form *transition metal complexes.* In

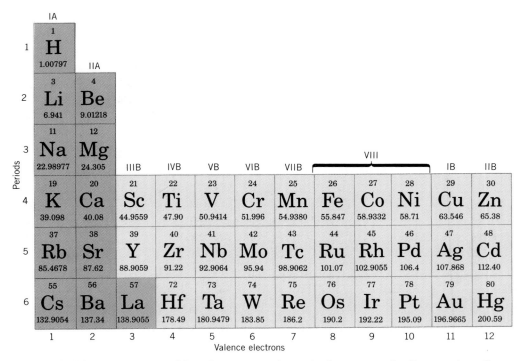

FIGURE J.1 Important transition elements are shown in the green and yellow portion of the periodic table. Given across the bottom are the total number of valence electrons (*s* and *d*) of each element.

forming a complex, the ligands donate electrons to vacant orbitals of the metal. The bonds between the ligand and the metal range from bonds that are very weak to those that are very strong. The bonds are covalent but often have considerable polar character.

Transition metal complexes can assume a variety of geometries depending on the metal and on the number of ligands around it. Rhodium can form complexes with four ligands, for example, that are *square planar.* On the other hand, rhodium can form complexes with five or six ligands that are trigonal bipyramidal or octahedral. These typical shapes are shown below with the letter L used to indicate a ligand.

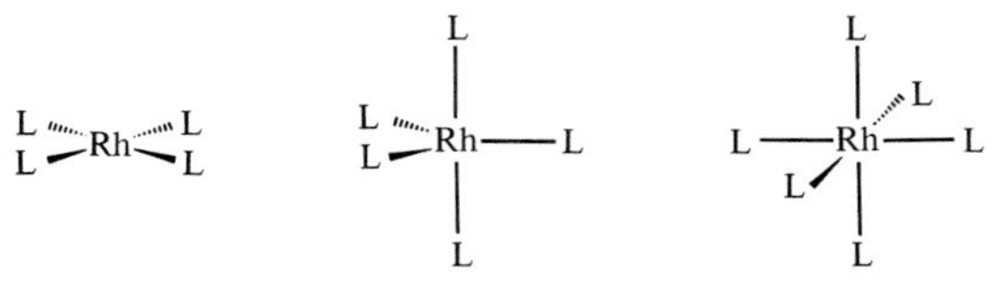

Square planar rhodium complex   Trigonal bipyramidal rhodium complex   Octahedral rhodium complex

J.2 ELECTRON COUNTING. THE 18-ELECTRON RULE

Transition metals are like the elements that we have studied earlier in that they are most stable when they have the electronic configuration of a noble gas. In addition to s and p orbitals, transition metals have five d orbitals (which can hold a total of 10 electrons). Therefore, the noble gas configuration for a transition metal is *18 electrons,* not 8 as with carbon, nitrogen, oxygen, and so on. When the metal of a transition metal complex has 18 valence electrons, it is said to be *coordinatively saturated.**

To determine the valence electron count of a transition metal in a complex, we take the total number of valence electrons of the metal in the elemental state (see Fig. J.1) and subtract from this number the oxidation state of the metal in the complex. This gives us what is called the d electron count, d^n. The oxidation state of the metal is the charge that would be left on the metal if all the ligands (Table J.1) were removed.

$$d^n = \frac{\text{total number of valence electrons}}{\text{of the elemental metal}} - \frac{\text{oxidation state of}}{\text{the metal in the complex}}$$

Then to get the total valence electron count of the metal *in the complex,* we add to d^n the number of electrons donated by all of the ligands. Table J.1 gives the number of electrons donated by several of the most common ligands.

$$\frac{\text{total number of valence electrons}}{\text{of the metal in the complex}} = d^n + \frac{\text{electrons donated}}{\text{by ligands}}$$

Let us now work out the valence electron count of two examples.

---

*We do not usually show the unshared electron pairs of a metal complex in our structures, because to do so would make the structure unnecessarily complicated.

TABLE J.1   Common ligands in transition metal complexes[a]

LIGAND	COUNT AS	NUMBER OF ELECTRONS DONATED
Negatively charged ligands		
H	H:⁻	2
R	R:⁻	2
X	X:⁻	2
Allyl		4
Cyclopentadienyl, Cp		6
Electrically neutral ligands		
Carbonyl (carbon monoxide)	CO	2
Phosphine	R_3P or Ph_3P	2
Alkene	$C=C$	2
Diene		4
Benzene		6

[a]Adapted from J. Schwartz and J. A. Labinger, *J. Chem. Educ.,* **1980,** *57,* 170.

Example A

Consider iron pentacarbonyl, $Fe(CO)_5$, a toxic liquid that forms when finely divided iron reacts with carbon monoxide.

$$Fe + 5\ CO \longrightarrow Fe(CO)_5 \quad \text{or}$$

Iron pentacarbonyl

From Fig. J.1 we find that an iron atom in the elemental state has 8 valence electrons. We arrive at the oxidation state of iron in iron pentacarbonyl by noting that the charge on the complex as a whole is zero (it is not an ion), and that the charge on each CO ligand is also zero. Therefore, the iron is in the zero oxidation state.

Using these numbers, we can now calculate d^n and, from it, the total number of valence electrons of the iron in the complex.

$$d^n = 8 - 0 = 8$$

$$\text{total number of valence electrons} = d^n + 5(CO) = 8 + 5(2) = 18$$

We find that the iron of $Fe(CO)_5$ has 18 valence electrons and is, therefore, coordinatively saturated.

Example B

Consider the rhodium complex $Rh[(C_6H_5)_3P]_3H_2Cl$, a complex that, as we shall see later, is an intermediate in certain alkene hydrogenations.

$$Cl\text{---}Rh\text{---}H \quad L = Ph_3P \;[i.\,e., (C_6H_5)_3P]$$

The oxidation state of rhodium in the complex is $+3$. (The two hydrogen atoms and the chlorine are each counted as -1, and the charge on each of the triphenylphosphine ligands is zero. Removing all the ligands would leave a Rh^{3+} ion.) From Fig. J.1 we find that in the elemental state, rhodium has 9 valence electrons. We can now calculate d^n for the rhodium of the complex.

$$d^n = 9 - 3 = 6$$

Each of the six ligands of the complex donates two electrons to the rhodium in the complex, and therefore, the total number of valence electrons of the rhodium is 18. The rhodium of $Rh[(C_6H_5)_3P]_3H_2Cl$ is coordinatively saturated.

$$\text{total number of valence electrons of rhodium} = d^n + 6(2) = 6 + 12 = 18$$

J.3 METALLOCENES: ORGANOMETALLIC SANDWICH COMPOUNDS

Cyclopentadiene reacts with phenylmagnesium bromide to give the Grignard reagent of cyclopentadiene. This reaction is not unusual for it is simply another acid–base reaction like those we saw earlier. The methylene hydrogen atoms of cyclopentadiene are much more acidic than the hydrogen atoms of benzene and, therefore, the reaction goes to completion. (The methylene hydrogen atoms of cyclopentadiene are acidic relative to ordinary methylene hydrogen atoms because the cyclopentadienyl anion is aromatic; cf. Section 13.7B.)

$$\text{Cyclopentadiene} + C_6H_5MgBr \xrightarrow{\text{diethyl ether}} \text{Cyclopentadienylmagnesium bromide} + C_6H_6$$

Cyclopentadiene   Phenylmagnesium bromide   Cyclopentadienylmagnesium bromide   Benzene

When the Grignard reagent of cyclopentadiene is treated with ferrous chloride, a reaction takes place that produces a product called *ferrocene*.

$$2 \left[\bigcirc \right] \overset{2+}{\text{Mg}} \overset{-}{\text{Br}} + \text{FeCl}_2 \longrightarrow \quad (\text{C}_5\text{H}_5)_2\text{Fe} \quad + 2\,\text{MgBrCl}$$

Ferrocene
(71% overall yield
from cyclopentadiene)

Ferrocene is an orange solid with a melting point of 174 °C. It is a highly stable compound; ferrocene can be sublimed at 100 °C and is not damaged when heated to 400 °C.

Many studies, including X-ray analysis, show that ferrocene is a compound in which the iron(II) ion is located between two cyclopentadienyl rings.

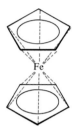

The carbon–carbon bond distances are all 1.40 Å and the carbon–iron bond distances are all 2.04 Å. Because of their structures, molecules such as ferrocene have been called "sandwich" compounds.

The carbon–iron bonding in ferrocene results from overlap between the inner lobes of the p orbitals of the cyclopentadienyl anions and $3d$ orbitals of the iron atom. Studies have shown, moreover, that this bonding is such that the rings of ferrocene are capable of essentially free rotation about an axis that passes through the iron atom and that is perpendicular to the rings.

The iron of ferrocene has 18 valence electrons and is, therefore, coordinatively saturated. We calculate this number as follows:

Iron has 8 valence electrons in the elemental state and its oxidation state in ferrocene is $+2$. Therefore, $d^n = 6$.

$$d^n = 8 - 2 = 6$$

Each cyclopentadienyl ligand of ferrocene donates 6 electrons to the iron. Therefore, for the iron, the valence electron count is 18.

$$\begin{matrix} \text{total number of} \\ \text{valence electrons} \end{matrix} = d^n + 2(\text{Cp}) = 6 + 2(6) = 18$$

Ferrocene is an *aromatic compound*. It undergoes a number of electrophilic aromatic substitutions, including sulfonation and Friedel–Crafts acylation.

The discovery of ferrocene (in 1951) was followed by the preparation of a number of similar aromatic compounds. These compounds, as a class, are called *metallocenes.** Metallocenes with five-, six-, seven-, and even eight-membered rings have

---

*Ernst O. Fischer (of the Technical University, Munich) and Geoffrey Wilkinson (of Imperial College, London) received the Nobel Prize in 1973 for their pioneering work (performed independently) on the chemistry of organometallic sandwich compounds—or metallocenes.

been synthesized from metals as diverse as zirconium, manganese, cobalt, nickel, chromium, and uranium.

"Half-sandwich" compounds have been prepared through the use of metal carbonyls. Several are shown here.

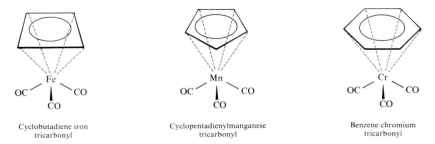

| Cyclobutadiene iron tricarbonyl | Cyclopentadienylmanganese tricarbonyl | Benzene chromium tricarbonyl |

Although cyclobutadiene itself is *not* stable, the cyclobutadiene iron tricarbonyl is.

Problem J.1

The metal of each of the previously given half-sandwich compounds is coordinatively saturated. Show that this is true by working out the valence electron count for the metal in each complex.

J.4 REACTIONS OF TRANSITION METAL COMPLEXES

Much of the chemistry of organic transition metal compounds will be more understandable if we are able to follow the mechanisms of the reactions that occur. These mechanisms will, in most cases, amount to nothing more than a sequence of reactions, each of which represents *a fundamental reaction type that is characteristic of a transition metal complex.* Let us examine three of the fundamental reaction types now. In each instance we shall use steps that occur when an alkene is hydrogenated using a catalyst called Wilkinson's catalyst. Later (in Section J.5) we shall examine the entire hydrogenation mechanism.

1. **Ligand Dissociation – Association (Ligand Exchange).** A transition metal complex can lose a ligand (by dissociation) and combine with another ligand (by association). In the process it undergoes *ligand exchange.* For example, the rhodium complex that we encountered in Example B can react with an alkene (in this example, with ethene) as follows:

$$L = Ph_3P \ [\text{i. e.,} \ (C_6H_5)_3P]$$

Two steps are actually involved. In the first step, one of the triphenylphosphine ligands dissociates. This leads to a complex in which the rhodium has only 16 electrons and is, therefore, coordinatively *unsaturated.*

$$\begin{array}{c} H \\ | \\ H - Rh - L \\ | \\ Cl \end{array} \text{(L above/below)} \quad \rightleftarrows \quad \begin{array}{c} H \\ | \\ H - Rh \begin{smallmatrix} L \\ L \end{smallmatrix} + L \\ | \\ Cl \end{array}$$

(18 electrons)   (16 electrons)

$$L = Ph_3P$$

In the second step, the rhodium associates with the alkene to become coordinatively saturated again.

$$\begin{array}{c} H \\ | \\ H - Rh \begin{smallmatrix} L \\ L \end{smallmatrix} + CH_2 = CH_2 \\ | \\ Cl \end{array} \quad \rightleftarrows \quad \begin{array}{c} H \\ | \\ H - Rh \leftarrow \begin{smallmatrix} CH_2 \\ || \\ CH_2 \end{smallmatrix} \\ | \\ Cl \end{array}$$

(16 electrons)   (18 electrons)

The complex between the rhodium and the alkene is called a *π complex*. In it, two electrons are donated by the alkene to the rhodium. Alkenes are often called π donors to distinguish them from σ donors such as $Ph_3P\!:$, Cl^-, and so on.

In a π complex such as the one just given, there is also a donation of electrons from a populated *d* orbital of the metal back to the vacant $π^*$ orbital of the alkene. This kind of donation is called "back-bonding."

2. **Insertion – Deinsertion.** An unsaturated ligand such as an alkene can undergo *insertion* into a bond between the metal of a complex and a hydrogen or a carbon. These reactions are reversible, and the reverse reaction is called *deinsertion*.

The following is an example of insertion – deinsertion.

$$\begin{array}{c} H \\ | \\ H - Rh \leftarrow \begin{smallmatrix} CH_2 \\ || \\ CH_2 \end{smallmatrix} \\ | \\ Cl \end{array} \quad \underset{\text{deinsertion}}{\overset{\text{insertion}}{\rightleftarrows}} \quad \begin{array}{c} CH_3 \\ | \\ CH_2 \\ | \\ H - Rh \begin{smallmatrix} L \\ L \end{smallmatrix} \\ | \\ Cl \end{array}$$

(18 electrons)   (16 electrons)

In this process, a π bond (between the rhodium and the alkene) and a σ bond (between the rhodium and the hydrogen) are exchanged for a new σ bond (between rhodium and carbon). The valence electron count of the rhodium decreases from 18 to 16.

This insertion – deinsertion occurs in a stereospecific way, as a *syn addition* of the M – H unit to the alkene.

$$\begin{array}{c} \overset{}{C} = \overset{}{C} \\ \downarrow \\ M - H \end{array} \quad \rightleftarrows \quad \begin{array}{c} \overset{}{C} - \overset{}{C} \\ / \qquad \backslash \\ M \qquad H \end{array}$$

3. **Oxidative Addition–Reductive Elimination.** Coordinatively unsaturated metal complexes can undergo oxidative addition of a variety of substrates in the following way.†

The substrates, A—B, can be H—H, H—X, R—X, RCO—H, RCO—X, and a number of other compounds.

In this type of oxidative addition, the metal of the complex undergoes an increase in the number of its valence electrons *and in its oxidation state.* Consider, as an example, the oxidative addition of hydrogen to the rhodium complex that follows ($L = Ph_3P$).

Reductive elimination is the reverse of oxidative addition. With this background, we are now in a position to examine a few interesting applications of transition metal complexes in organic synthesis.

J.5 HOMOGENEOUS HYDROGENATION

Until now, all of the hydrogenations that we have examined have been heterogeneous processes. Two phases have been involved in the reaction: the solid phase of the catalyst (Pt, Pd, Ni, etc.) containing the adsorbed hydrogen and the liquid phase of the solution containing the unsaturated compound. In homogeneous hydrogenation using a transition metal complex such as $Rh[(C_6H_5)_3P]_3Cl$ (called Wilkinson's catalyst), hydrogenation takes place *in a single phase*—in solution.

When Wilkinson's catalyst is used to carry out the hydrogenation of an alkene, the following steps take place ($L = Ph_3P$).

†Coordinatively saturated complexes also undergo oxidative addition. We shall see an example in Section J.8.

Step 2 (18 electrons) → (16 electrons) + L   Ligand dissociation

Step 3 (16 electrons) + CH_2=CH_2 → (18 electrons)   Ligand association

Step 4 (18 electrons) → (16 electrons)   Insertion

Step 5 (16 electrons) + L → (18 electrons)   Ligand association

Step 6 (18 electrons) → (16 electrons) + CH_3—CH_3 Reductive elimination

Then steps 1, 2, 3, 4, 5, 6, and so on.

Step 6 regenerates the catalyst, which can then cause hydrogenation of another molecule of the alkene.

Because the insertion step 4 and the reductive elimination step 6 are stereospecific, the net result of hydrogenation using Wilkinson's catalyst is a *syn addition* of hydrogen to the alkene. The following example (with D_2 in place of H_2) illustrates this aspect.

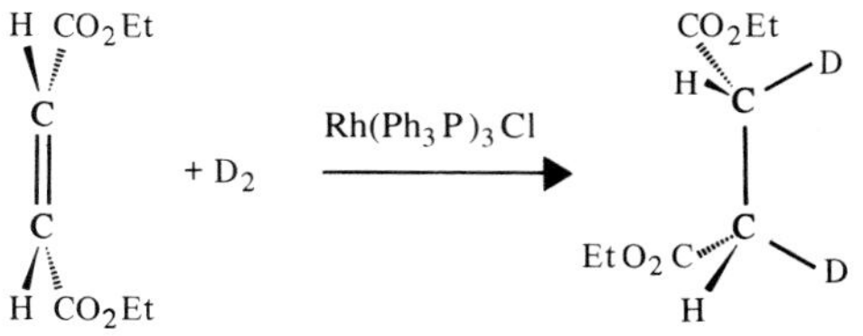

A *cis* alkene
(diethyl maleate)

A meso compound

Problem J.2

What product (or products) would be formed if the *trans* alkene corresponding to the *cis* alkene (see previous reaction) had been hydrogenated with D_2 and Wilkinson's catalyst?

J.6 CARBON – CARBON BOND FORMING REACTIONS USING RHODIUM COMPLEXES

Rhodium complexes have also been used to synthesize compounds in which the formation of a carbon–carbon bond is required. An example is the synthesis that follows:

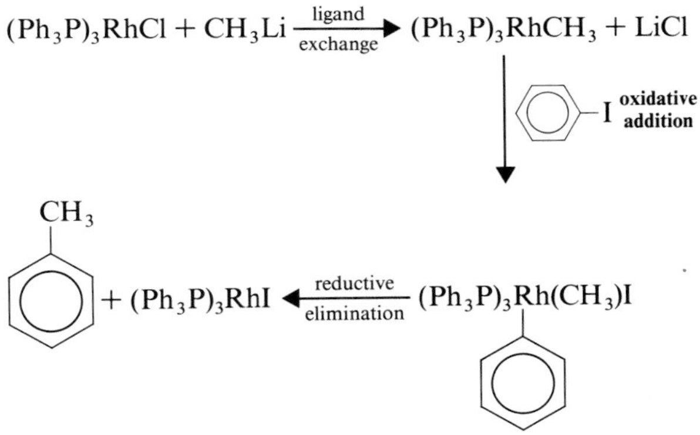

The first step, *a ligand exchange*, occurs by a combination of ligand association – dissociation steps and incorporates the methyl group into the coordination sphere of the rhodium. The next step, *an oxidative addition*, incorporates the phenyl group into the rhodium coordination sphere. Then, in the last step, *a reductive elimination* joins the methyl group and the benzene ring to form toluene.

Problem J.3

Give the total valence electron count for rhodium in each complex in the synthesis outlined previously.

Another example is the following ketone synthesis.

$$(Ph_3P)_2Rh(CO)Cl + CH_3Li \xrightarrow{(a)} (Ph_3P)_2Rh(CO)(CH_3) + LiCl$$

$$\mathbf{1} \qquad\qquad\qquad\qquad \mathbf{2}$$

$$(b) \downarrow \; C_6H_5\overset{\overset{\textstyle O}{\|}}{C}Cl$$

$$(Ph_3P)_2Rh(CO)Cl + C_6H_5\overset{\overset{\textstyle O}{\|}}{C}CH_3 \xleftarrow{(c)} (Ph_3P)_2Rh(CO)(COC_6H_5)(CH_3)Cl$$

$$\mathbf{3}$$

Problem J.4

Give the valence electron count and the oxidation state of rhodium in the complexes labeled **1**, **2**, **3**; then describe each step (a), (b), and (c) as to its fundamental type (oxidative addition, ligand exchange, etc.).

Still another carbon–carbon bond-forming reaction (below) illustrates the stereospecificity of these reactions.

$$(Ph_3P)_3Rh(CO)H + CH_3O\overset{\overset{\textstyle O}{\|}}{C}C\equiv C\overset{\overset{\textstyle O}{\|}}{C}OCH_3 \xrightarrow{-Ph_3P}$$

$$+ RhI(CO)(PPh_3)_2$$

Problem J.5

Give, in detail, a possible mechanism for the synthesis just outlined, describing each step according to its fundamental type.

Problem J.6

The actual mechanism of the Corey–Posner, Whitesides–House synthesis is not known with certainty. One possible mechanism involves the oxidative addition of R'—X or Ar—X to R$_2$CuLi followed by a reductive elimination to generate R—R' or R—Ar. Outline the steps in this mechanism using $(CH_3)_2CuLi$ and C_6H_5I.

J.7 HYDROFORMYLATION: THE OXO REACTION

An industrial process for the synthesis of aldehydes is called *hydroformylation* or the *oxo reaction*. In this reaction an alkene reacts with carbon monoxide and hydrogen in the presence of the cobalt catalyst, $HCo(CO)_4$, as follows:

$$RCH{=}CH_2 + CO + H_2 \xrightarrow[\text{2000 psi, } 110-150\ °C]{HCo(CO)_4} RCH_2CH_2CHO + \text{isomers}$$

The mechanism for hydroformylation has been studied extensively by Milton Orchin (University of Cincinnati) and is quite complex, if we take into account all of the reactions that occur. Essential to the mechanism, however, are the following fundamental steps.

Step 1 $HCo(CO)_4 \rightleftarrows HCo(CO)_3 + CO$ **Ligand dissociation**

Step 2 $RCH{=}CH_2 + HCo(CO)_3 \rightleftarrows \underset{\displaystyle HCo(CO)_3}{RCH{=}CH_2}$ **Ligand association**

Step 3 $\underset{\displaystyle HCo(CO)_3}{RCH{=}CH_2} \rightleftarrows RCH_2CH_2Co(CO)_3$ **Insertion**

Step 4 $RCH_2CH_2Co(CO)_3 + CO \rightleftarrows RCH_2CH_2Co(CO)_4$ **Ligand association**

Step 5 $RCH_2CH_2Co(CO)_4 \rightleftarrows RCH_2CH_2COCo(CO)_3$ **Insertion**

Step 6 $RCH_2CH_2COCo(CO)_3 + H_2 \rightleftarrows RCH_2CH_2CO\overset{\displaystyle H}{\underset{\displaystyle H}{Co}}(CO)_3$ **Oxidative addition**

Step 7 $RCH_2CH_2CO\overset{\displaystyle H}{\underset{\displaystyle H}{Co}}(CO)_3 \rightleftarrows RCH_2CH_2CHO + HCo(CO)_3$ **Reductive elimination**

Step 8 $HCo(CO)_3 + CO \rightleftarrows HCo(CO)_4$ **Ligand association**

An important step in the sequence just given is step 5. In this step a carbonyl group is inserted between the metal and the coordinated alkyl group. (One can also consider this step as a migration of the alkyl group from the metal to the carbon of a coordinated CO ligand.)

Carbonyl insertion reactions are reversible and can be exploited synthetically as "decarbonylation" reactions. In the following example, decarbonylation of benzaldehyde leads to the formation of benzene.

$$C_6H_5\overset{\displaystyle O}{\overset{\|}{C}}H + (Ph_3P)_3RhCl \xrightarrow[-Ph_3P]{}$$

$$C_6H_5RhH(CO)(Ph_3P)_2Cl \longrightarrow C_6H_6 + Rh(CO)(Ph_3P)_2Cl$$

Problem J.7

Outline a detailed mechanism for the decarbonylation of benzaldehyde and describe each step according to its fundamental type.

J.8 DISODIUM TETRACARBONYLFERRATE: COLLMAN'S REAGENT

Iron pentacarbonyl reacts with sodium to produce disodium tetracarbonylferrate, $Na_2Fe(CO)_4$, a highly versatile compound for organic synthesis.

$$Fe(CO)_5 + 2\ Na \xrightarrow{THF} Na_2Fe(CO)_4$$

1

Collman's reagent

This reagent, discovered by James P. Collman (Stanford University), reacts with alkyl halides in the following way:

$$R-X + Na_2Fe(CO)_4 \longrightarrow OC-Fe{\overset{CO}{\underset{CO}{\cdots}}}\ Na^+ + NaX$$

2

This reaction can be considered an oxidative addition to a *coordinatively saturated* metal complex. Equivalently, however, it can be viewed as an S_N2 attack on the carbon of the alkyl halide with an anion of $Na_2Fe(CO)_4$ acting as the nucleophile. Evidence supporting this view is the order of reactivities of alkyl halides:

$$CH_3X > RCH_2X > R_2CHX \quad \text{and} \quad RI > RBr > RCl$$

Furthermore, the reaction has been shown to take place with *inversion of configuration of the alkyl group.*

The alkyltetracarbonylferrate anion (**2**) undergoes insertion of carbon monoxide to yield **3**, and **3** can be converted to aldehydes, ketones, esters, and carboxylic acids.

3

(L = CO or R_3P)

$$\xrightarrow{H^+} R-\overset{\overset{\displaystyle O}{\|}}{C}H$$

$$\xrightarrow{R'X} R-\overset{\overset{\displaystyle O}{\|}}{C}-R'$$

$$\xrightarrow[R'OH]{X_2} R-\overset{\overset{\displaystyle O}{\|}}{C}OR'$$

$$\xrightarrow[H_2O]{O_2} R-\overset{\overset{\displaystyle O}{\|}}{C}OH$$

Compound **3** can also be synthesized from the reaction of **1** with an acid chloride.

$$RC\overset{\overset{\displaystyle O}{\|}}{-}Cl + Na_2Fe(CO)_4 \longrightarrow 3$$

The alkyltetracarbonylferrate anion **2** also undergoes useful reactions.

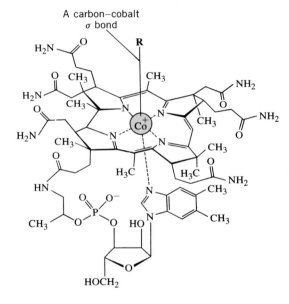

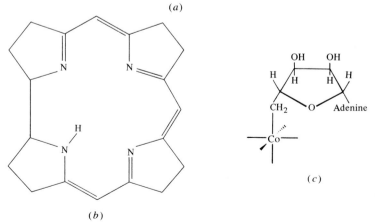

(a)

(b)

(c)

FIGURE J.2 (*a*) The structure of vitamin B_{12}. In the commercial form of the vitamin (cyanocobalamin) R = CN. (*b*) The corrin ring system. (*c*) In the biologically active form of the vitamin (5′-deoxyadenosylcobalamin) the 5′-carbon atom of 5′-deoxyadenosine is coordinated to the cobalt atom. For the structure of adenine see Section 24.2.

J.9 VITAMIN B$_{12}$: A TRANSITION METAL BIOMOLECULE

The discovery (in 1926) that pernicious anemia can be overcome by the ingestion of large amounts of liver led ultimately to the isolation (in 1948) of the curative factor, called vitamin B$_{12}$. The complete three-dimensional structure of vitamin B$_{12}$ (Fig. J.2) was elucidated in 1956 through the X-ray studies of Dorothy Hodgkin (Nobel Prize, 1964), and in 1972 the synthesis of this complicated molecule was announced by R. B. Woodward (Harvard University) and A. Eschenmoser (Swiss Federal Institute of Technology). The synthesis took 11 years and involved more than 90 separate reactions. One hundred co-workers took part in the project.

Vitamin B$_{12}$ is the only known biomolecule that possesses a carbon–metal bond. In the stable commercial form of the vitamin, a cyano group is bonded to the cobalt, and the cobalt is in the +3 oxidation state. The core of the vitamin B$_{12}$ molecule is a *corrin ring* with various attached side groups. The corrin ring consists of four pyrrole subunits, the nitrogen of each of which is coordinated to the central cobalt. The sixth ligand (below the corrin ring in Fig. J.2) is a nitrogen of a heterocyclic molecule called 5,6-dimethylbenzimidazole.

The cobalt of vitamin B$_{12}$ can be reduced to a +2 or a +1 oxidation state. When the cobalt is in the +1 oxidation state, vitamin B$_{12}$ (called B$_{12s}$) becomes one of the most powerful nucleophiles known, being more nucleophilic than methanol by a factor of 10^{14}.

Acting as a nucleophile, vitamin B$_{12s}$ reacts with adenosine triphosphate (Fig. 22.2) to yield the biologically active form of the vitamin (Fig. J.2c).

SPECIAL TOPIC

K

ORGANIC HALIDES AND ORGANOMETALLIC COMPOUNDS IN THE ENVIRONMENT

K.1 ORGANIC HALIDES AS INSECTICIDES

Since the discovery of the insecticidal properties of DDT in 1942, vast quantities of chlorinated hydrocarbons have been sprayed over the surface of the earth in an effort to destroy insects. These efforts initially met with incredible success in ridding large areas of the earth of disease-carrying insects, particularly those of typhus and malaria. As time has passed, however, we have begun to understand that this prodigious use of chlorinated hydrocarbons has not been without harmful — indeed tragic — side effects. Chlorinated hydrocarbons are usually highly stable compounds and are only slowly destroyed by natural processes in the environment. As a result, many chloroorganic insecticides will remain in the environment for years. These persistent pesticides are called "hard" pesticides.

Chlorohydrocarbons are also fat soluble and tend to accumulate in the fatty tissues of most animals. The food chain that runs from plankton to small fish to larger fish to birds and to larger animals, including man, tends to magnify the concentrations of chloroorganic compounds at each step.

The chlorohydrocarbon DDT is prepared from inexpensive starting materials, chlorobenzene and trichloroacetaldehyde. The reaction is catalyzed by acid.

DDT
[1,1,1-Trichloro-2,2-
bis(*p*-chlorophenyl)ethane]

In nature the principal decomposition product of DDT is DDE.

DDE
[1,1-Dichloro-2,2-
bis(*p*-chlorophenyl)ethene]

Estimates indicate that nearly 1 billion lb of DDE were spread throughout the world ecosystem. One pronounced environmental effect of DDE has been in its action on egg-shell formation of many birds. DDE inhibits the enzyme *carbonic anhydrase* that controls the calcium supply for shell formation. As a consequence, the shells are often very fragile and do not survive to the time of hatching. During the

991

late 1940s the populations of eagles, falcons, and hawks dropped dramatically. There can be little doubt that DDE was primarily responsible.

DDE also accumulates in the fatty tissues of humans. Although humans appear to have a short-range tolerance to moderate DDE levels, the long-range effects are far from certain.

Other hard insecticides are aldrin, dieldrin, and chlordan. Aldrin can be manufactured through the Diels–Alder reaction of hexachlorocyclopentadiene and norbornadiene.

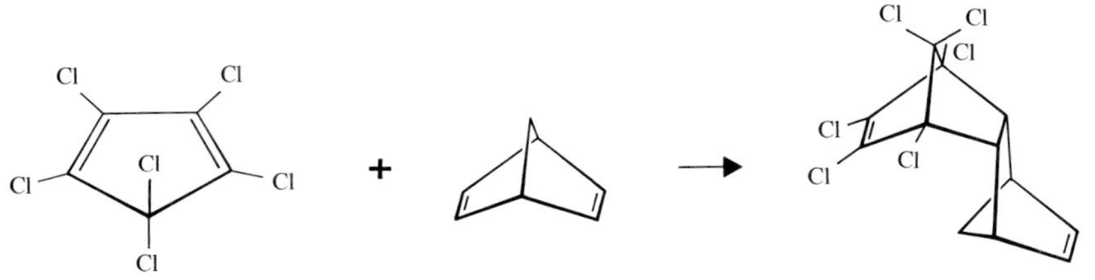

Hexachloro-cyclopentadiene   Norbornadiene   Aldrin

Chlordan can be made by adding chlorine to the unsubstituted double bond of the Diels–Alder adduct obtained from hexachlorocyclopentadiene and cyclopentadiene. Dieldrin can be made by converting an aldrin double bond to an epoxide. (This reaction also takes place in nature.)

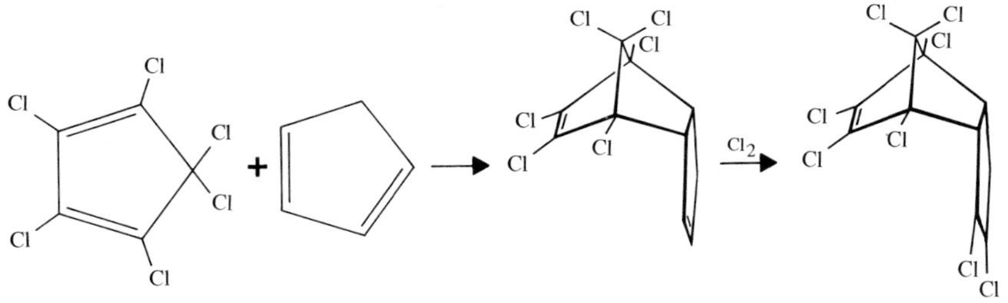

Chlordan

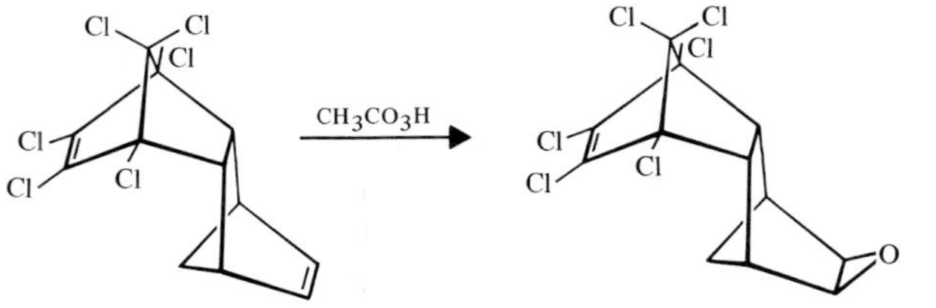

Aldrin   Dieldrin

During the 1970s the Environmental Protection Agency (EPA) banned the use of DDT, aldrin, dieldrin, and chlordan because of known or suspected hazards to human life. All of the compounds are suspected of causing cancers.

Problem K.1

The mechanism for the formation of DDT from chlorobenzene and trichloro-acetaldehyde in sulfuric acid involves two electrophilic aromatic substitution reactions. In the first electrophilic substitution reaction, the electrophile is protonated trichloroacetaldehyde. In the second, the electrophile is a carbocation. Propose a mechanism for the formation of DDT.

Problem K.2

What kind of reaction is involved in the conversion of DDT to DDE?

Mirex, kepone, and lindane are also hard insecticides whose use has been banned.

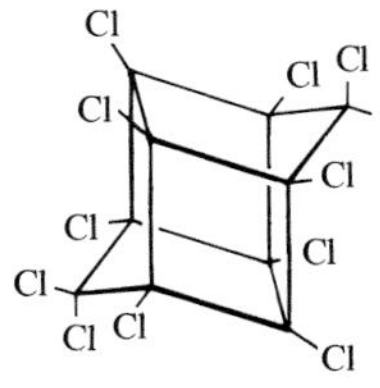

Mirex 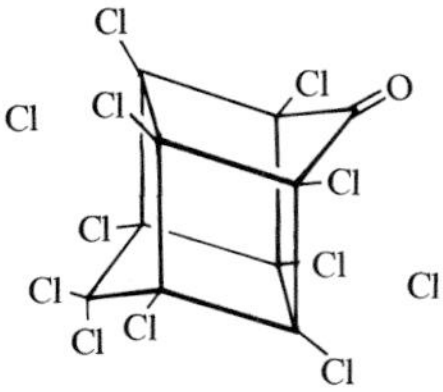   Kepone 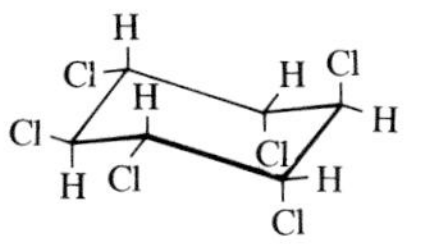   Lindane

K.2 ORGANIC HALIDES AS HERBICIDES

Other chlorinated organic compounds have been used extensively as herbicides. The following two examples are 2,4-D and 2,4,5-T.

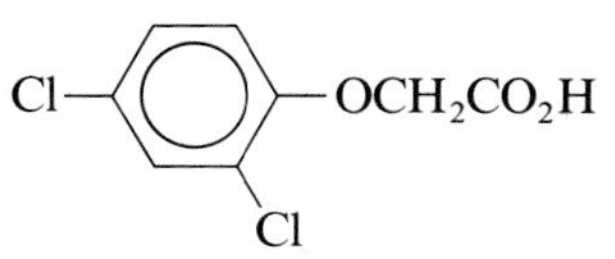

2,4-D
(2,4-Dichlorophenoxy-
acetic acid)

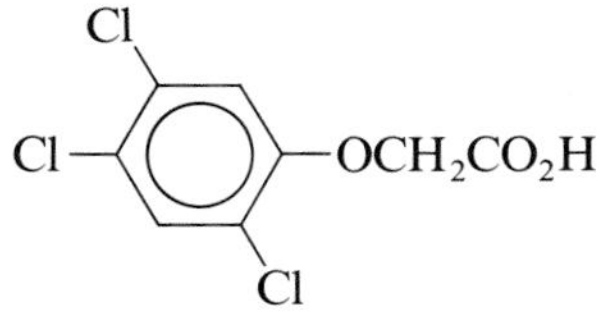

2,4,5-T
(2,4,5-Trichlorophenoxy-
acetic acid)

Enormous quantities of these two compounds were used as defoliants in the jungles of Indochina during the Vietnam war. Some samples of 2,4,5-T have been shown to be a teratogen (a fetus-deforming agent). This teratogenic effect was the result of an impurity present in commercial 2,4,5-T, the compound 2,3,7,8-tetrachlorodibenzodioxin. 2,3,7,8-Tetrachlorodibenzodioxin is also highly toxic; it is more toxic, for example, than cyanide ion, strychnine, and the nerve gases.

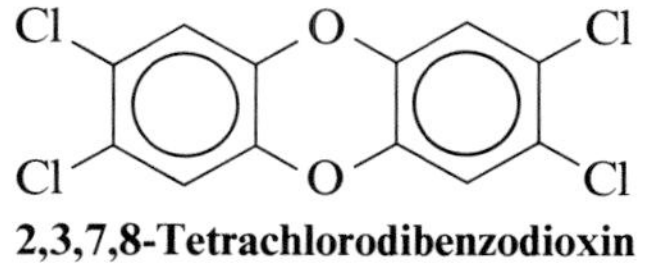

2,3,7,8-Tetrachlorodibenzodioxin
(also called TCDD)

This dioxin is also highly stable; it persists in the environment and because of its fat solubility can be passed up the food chain. In sublethal amounts it can cause a disfiguring skin disease called chloracne.

In July 1976 an explosion at a chemical plant in Seveso, Italy, caused the release of between 22 and 132 lb of this dioxin into the atmosphere. The plant was engaged in the manufacture of 2,4,5-trichlorophenol (used in making 2,4,5-T) using the following method:

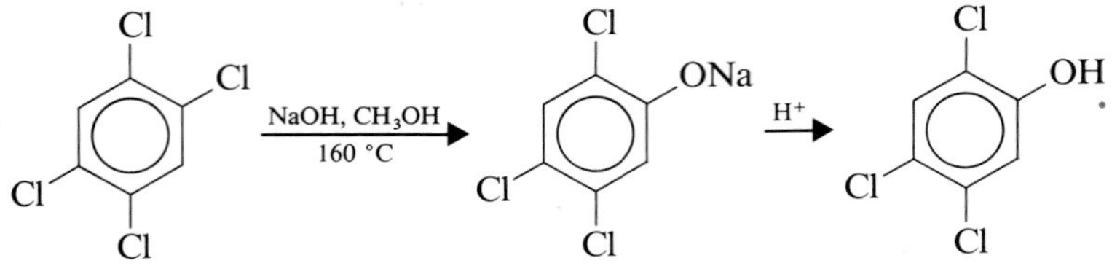

| 1,2,4,5-Tetra- | Sodium 2,4,5- | 2,4,5-Trichloro- |
| chlorobenzene | trichlorophenoxide | phenol |

The temperature of the first reaction must be very carefully controlled; if it is not, this dioxin forms in the reaction mixture:

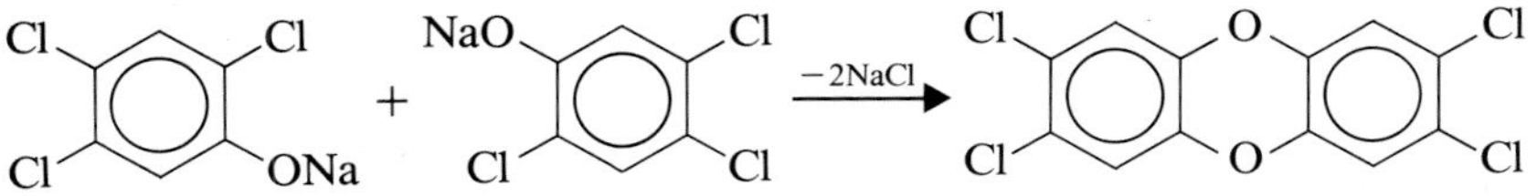

Apparently at the Italian factory, the temperature got out of control causing the pressure to build up. Eventually, a valve opened and released a cloud of trichlorophenol and the dioxin into the atmosphere. Many wild and domestic animals were killed and many people, especially children, were afflicted with severe skin rashes.

Problem K.3

(a) Assume that the ortho and para chlorine atoms provide enough activation by electron withdrawal for nucleophilic substitution to occur by an addition–elimination pathway and outline a possible mechanism for the conversion of 1,2,4,5-tetrachlorobenzene to sodium 2,4,5-trichlorophenoxide. (b) Do the same for the conversion of 2,4,5-trichlorophenoxide to the dioxin of Section K.2.

Problem K.4

2,4,5-T is made by allowing sodium 2,4,5-trichlorophenoxide to react with sodium chloroacetate ($ClCH_2COONa$). (This produces the sodium salt of 2,4,5-T which, on acidification, gives 2,4,5-T itself.) What kind of mechanism accounts for the reaction of sodium 2,4,5-trichlorophenoxide with $ClCH_2COONa$? Write the equation.

K.3 GERMICIDES

2,4,5-Trichlorophenol is also used in the manufacture of hexachlorophene, a germicide once widely used in soaps, shampoos, deodorants, mouthwashes, aftershave lotions, and other over-the-counter products.

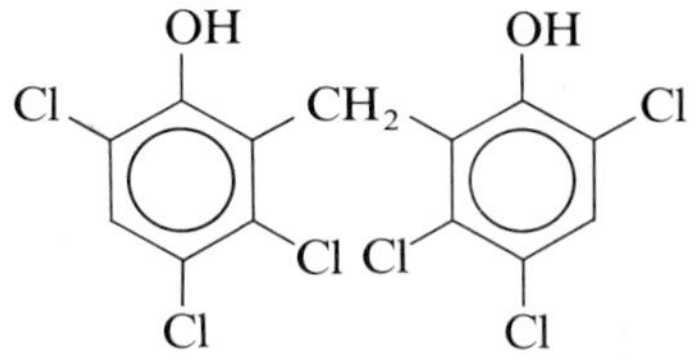

Hexachlorophene

Hexachlorophene is absorbed intact through the skin and tests with experimental animals have shown that it causes brain damage. Since 1972, the use of hexachlorophene in cleansers and cosmetics sold over the counter has been banned by the Food and Drug Administration.

K.4 POLYCHLORINATED BIPHENYLS (PCBs)

Mixtures of polychlorinated biphenyls have been produced and used commercially since 1929. In these mixtures, biphenyls with chlorine atoms at any of the numbered positions (see following structure) may be present. In all, there are 210 possible compounds. A typical commercial mixture may contain as many as 50 different PCBs. Mixtures are usually classified on the basis of their chlorine content, and most industrial mixtures contain from 40 to 60% chlorine.

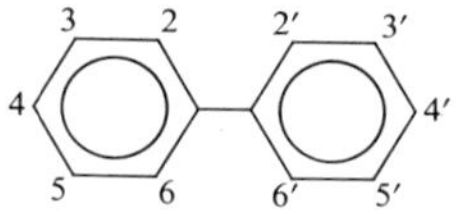

Biphenyl

Polychlorinated biphenyls have had a multitude of uses: as heat exchange agents in transformers; in capacitors, thermostats, and hydraulic systems; as plasticizers in polystyrene coffee cups, frozen food bags, bread wrappers, and plastic liners for baby bottles. They have been used in printing inks, in carbonless carbon paper, and as waxes for making molds for metal castings. Between 1929 and 1972, about 500,000 metric tons of PCBs were manufactured.

Although they were never intended for release into the environment, PCBs have become, perhaps more than any other chemical, the most widespread pollutant. They have been found in rain water, in many species of fish, birds, and other animals (including polar bears) all over the globe, and in human tissue.

Polychlorinated biphenyls are highly persistent and being fat soluble tend to accumulate in the food chain. Fish that feed in PCB-contaminated waters, for example, have PCB levels 1000 – 100,000 times the level of the surrounding water and this amount is further magnified in birds that feed on the fish. The toxicity of PCBs depends on the composition of the individual mixture. The largest incident of human poisoning by PCBs occurred in Japan in 1968 when about 1000 people ingested a cooking oil accidentally contaminated with PCBs.

As late as 1975, industrial concerns were legally discharging PCBs into the Hudson River. In 1977, the EPA banned the direct discharge into waterways and, since 1979, their manufacture, processing, and distribution have been prohibited.

K.5 POLYBROMOBIPHENYLS (PBBs)

Polybromobiphenyls are bromine analogs of PCBs that have been used as flame retardants. In 1973, in Michigan, a mistake at a chemical company led to PBBs being mixed into animal feeds that were sold to farmers. Before the mistake was recognized, PBBs had affected thousands of dairy cattle, hogs, chickens, and sheep, necessitating their destruction.

K.6 ORGANOMETALLIC COMPOUNDS

With few exceptions, organometallic compounds are toxic. This toxicity varies greatly depending on the nature of the organometallic compound and the identity of the metal. Organic compounds of arsenic, antimony, lead, thallium, and mercury are toxic because the metal ions, themselves, are toxic. Certain organic derivatives of silicon are toxic even though silicon and most of its inorganic compounds are non-toxic.

Early in this century the recognition of the biocidal effects of organoarsenic compounds led Paul Ehrlich to his pioneering work in chemotherapy. Ehrlich sought compounds (which he called "magic bullets") that would show greater toxicity toward disease-causing microorganisms than they would toward their hosts. Ehrlich's research led to the development of Salvarsan and Neosalvarsan, two organoarsenic compounds that were used successfully in the treatment of diseases caused by spirochetes (e.g., syphilis) and trypanosomes (e.g., sleeping sickness). Salvarsan and Neosalvarsan are no longer used in the treatment of these diseases; they have been displaced by safer and more effective antibiotics. Ehrlich's research, however, initiated the field of chemotherapy (cf. Section 19.11).

Many microorganisms actually synthesize organometallic compounds, and this discovery has an alarming ecological aspect. Mercury metal is toxic, but mercury metal is also unreactive. In the past, untold tons of mercury metal present in industrial wastes have been disposed of by simply dumping such wastes into lakes and streams. Since mercury is toxic, many bacteria protect themselves from its effect by converting mercury metal to methylmercury ions (CH_3Hg^+) and to gaseous dimethylmercury $(CH_3)_2Hg$. These organic mercury compounds are passed up the food chain (with modification) through fish to humans where methylmercury ions act as a deadly nerve poison. Between 1953 and 1964, 116 people in Minamata, Japan, were poisoned by eating fish containing methylmercury compounds. Arsenic is also methylated by organisms to the poisonous dimethylarsine, $(CH_3)_2AsH$.

Ironically, chlorinated hydrocarbons appear to inhibit the biological reactions that bring about mercury methylation. Lakes polluted with organochlorine pesticides show significantly lower mercury methylation. While this particular interaction of two pollutants may, in a certain sense, be beneficial, it is also instructive of the complexity of the environmental problems that we face.

Tetraethyllead and other alkyllead compounds have been used as antiknock agents in gasoline since 1923. Although this use has now been phased out, more than 1 trillion lb of lead have been introduced into the atmosphere. In the northern hemisphere, gasoline burning alone has spread about 10 mg of lead on each square meter of the earth's surface. In highly industrialized areas the amount of lead per square meter is probably several hundred times higher. Because of the well-known toxicity of lead, these facts are of great concern.

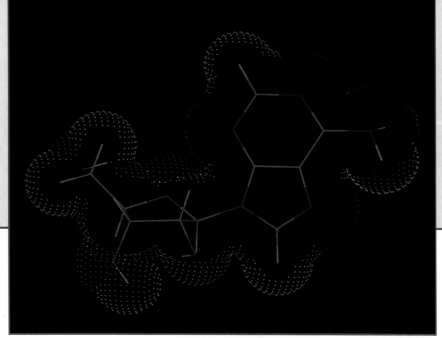

Adenosine (see Sections 22.1B and 25.2).

CHAPTER
22

CARBOHYDRATES

22.1 INTRODUCTION

22.1A CLASSIFICATION OF CARBOHYDRATES

The group of compounds known as carbohydrates received their general name because of early observations that they often have the formula $C_x(H_2O)_y$ —that is, they
appear to be "hydrates of carbon." Simple carbohydrates are also known as sugars or
saccharides (Latin *saccharum,* sugar) and the ending of the names of most sugars is
-ose. Thus, we have such names as *sucrose* for ordinary table sugar, *glucose* for the
principal sugar in blood, and *maltose* for malt sugar.

Carbohydrates are usually defined as *polyhydroxy aldehydes and ketones or
substances that hydrolyze to yield polyhydroxy aldehydes and ketones.* Although this
definition draws attention to the important functional groups of carbohydrates, it is
not entirely satisfactory. We shall later find that because carbohydrates contain

$\diagdown$
$\quad$C=O groups and —OH groups, they exist, primarily, as *hemiacetals* and *acetals*
$\diagup$

or as *hemiketals* and *ketals* (Section 16.7).

The simplest carbohydrates, those that cannot be hydrolyzed into smaller
simpler carbohydrates, are called *monosaccharides.* On a molecular basis, carbohydrates that undergo hydrolysis to produce only two molecules of monosaccharide are
called *disaccharides;* those that yield three molecules of monosaccharide are called

trisaccharides; and so on. (Carbohydrates that hydrolyze to yield 2 – 10 molecules of a monosaccharide are sometimes called *oligosaccharides.*) Carbohydrates that yield a large number of molecules of monosaccharide (> 10) are known as *polysaccharides.*

Maltose and sucrose are examples of disaccharides. On hydrolysis, 1 mol of maltose yields 2 mol of the monosaccharide glucose; sucrose undergoes hydrolysis to yield 1 mol of glucose and 1 mol of the monosaccharide fructose. Starch and cellulose are examples of polysaccharides; both are glucose polymers. Hydrolysis of either yields a large number of glucose units.

$$1 \text{ mol of maltose} \xrightarrow[\text{H}_3\text{O}^+]{\text{H}_2\text{O}} 2 \text{ mol of glucose}$$

A disaccharide   **A monosaccharide**

$$1 \text{ mol of sucrose} \xrightarrow[\text{H}_3\text{O}^+]{\text{H}_2\text{O}} \text{mol of glucose} + 1 \text{ mol of fructose}$$

A disaccharide   **Monosaccharides**

$$\left. \begin{array}{c} 1 \text{ mol of starch} \\ \text{or} \\ 1 \text{ mol of cellulose} \end{array} \right\} \xrightarrow[\text{H}_3\text{O}^+]{\text{H}_2\text{O}} \text{many moles of glucose}$$

Polysaccharides   **Monosaccharide**

Carbohydrates are the most abundant organic constituents of plants. They not only serve as an important source of chemical energy for living organisms (sugars and starches are important in this respect), but also in plants and in some animals they serve as important constituents of supporting tissues (this is the primary function of the cellulose found in wood, cotton, and flax, for example).

We encounter carbohydrates at almost every turn of our daily lives. The paper on which this book is printed is largely cellulose; so too, is the cotton of our clothes and the wood of our houses. The flour from which we make bread is mainly starch, and starch is also a major constituent of many other foodstuffs, such as potatoes, rice, beans, corn, and peas.

22.1B PHOTOSYNTHESIS AND CARBOHYDRATE METABOLISM

Carbohydrates are synthesized in green plants by *photosynthesis*—a process that uses solar energy to reduce, or "fix," carbon dioxide. The overall equation for photosynthesis can be written as follows:

$$x \text{ CO}_2 + y \text{ H}_2\text{O} + \text{solar energy} \longrightarrow \underset{\textbf{Carbohydrate}}{\text{C}_x(\text{H}_2\text{O})_y} + x \text{ O}_2$$

Many individual enzyme-catalyzed reactions take place in the general photosynthetic process and not all are fully understood. We know, however, that photosynthesis begins with the absorption of light by the important green pigment of plants, chlorophyll (Fig. 22.1). The green color of chlorophyll and, therefore, its ability to absorb sunlight in the visible region are due primarily to its extended conjugated system. As photons of sunlight are trapped by chlorophyll, energy becomes available to the plant in a chemical form that can be used to carry out the reactions that reduce carbon dioxide to carbohydrates and oxidize water to oxygen.

Carbohydrates act as a major chemical repository for solar energy. Their energy is released when animals or plants metabolize carbohydrates to carbon dioxide and water.

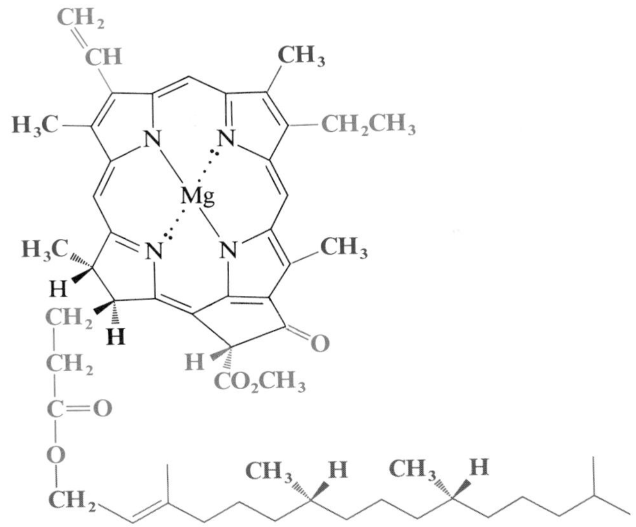

FIGURE 22.1 Chlorophyll-*a*. [The structure of chlorophyll-*a* was established largely through the work of H. Fischer (Munich), R. Willstätter (Munich), and J. B. Conant (Harvard). A synthesis of chlorophyll-*a* from simple organic compounds was achieved by R. B. Woodward (Harvard) in 1960, who won the Nobel Prize in 1965 for his outstanding contributions to synthetic organic chemistry.]

$$C_x(H_2O)_y + x\,O_2 \longrightarrow x\,CO_2 + y\,H_2O + \text{energy}$$

The metabolism of carbohydrates also takes place through a series of enzyme-catalyzed reactions in which each energy-yielding step is an oxidation (or the consequence of an oxidation).

Although some of the energy released in the oxidation of carbohydrates is inevitably converted to heat, much of it is conserved in a new chemical form through reactions that are coupled to the synthesis of adenosine triphosphate (ATP) from adenosine diphosphate (ADP) and inorganic phosphate (P_i) (Fig. 22.2). The phosphoric anhydride bond that forms between the terminal phosphate group of ADP and the phosphate ion becomes another repository of chemical energy. Plants and animals can use the conserved energy of ATP (or very similar substances) to carry out all of their energy-requiring processes: the contraction of a muscle, the synthesis of a macromolecule, and so on. When the energy in ATP is used, a coupled reaction takes place in which ATP is hydrolyzed:

$$\text{ATP} + H_2O \xrightarrow{(-\text{energy})} \text{ADP} + P_i$$

or a new anhydride linkage is created:

Acyl phosphate

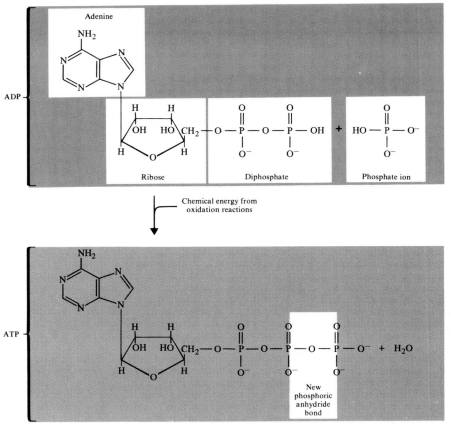

FIGURE 22.2 The synthesis of adenosine triphosphate (ATP) from adenosine diphosphate (ADP), and hydrogen phosphate ion. This reaction takes place in all living organisms, and adenosine triphosphate is the major compound into which the chemical energy released by biological oxidations is transformed.

22.2 MONOSACCHARIDES

22.2A CLASSIFICATION OF MONOSACCHARIDES

Monosaccharides are classified according to (1) the number of carbon atoms present in the molecule and (2) whether they contain an aldehyde or keto group. Thus, a monosaccharide containing three carbon atoms is called a *triose;* one containing four carbon atoms is called a *tetrose;* one containing five carbon atoms is a *pentose;* and one containing six carbon atoms is a *hexose.* A monosaccharide containing an aldehyde group is called an *aldose;* one containing a keto group is called a *ketose.* These two classifications are frequently combined. A C_4 aldose, for example, is called an *aldotetrose;* a C_5 ketose is called a *ketopentose.*

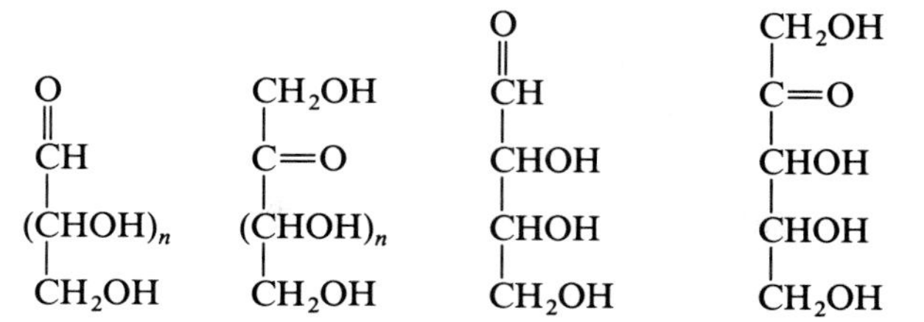

$$
\begin{array}{cccc}
\text{O} & \text{CH}_2\text{OH} & \text{O} & \text{CH}_2\text{OH} \\
\| & | & \| & | \\
\text{CH} & \text{C}=\text{O} & \text{CH} & \text{C}=\text{O} \\
| & | & | & | \\
(\text{CHOH})_n & (\text{CHOH})_n & \text{CHOH} & \text{CHOH} \\
| & | & | & | \\
\text{CH}_2\text{OH} & \text{CH}_2\text{OH} & \text{CHOH} & \text{CHOH} \\
& & | & | \\
& & \text{CH}_2\text{OH} & \text{CH}_2\text{OH}
\end{array}
$$

An aldose   A ketose   An aldotetrose   A ketopentose

Problem 22.1

How many stereocenters are contained in the (a) aldotetrose and (b) keto-pentose given previously? (c) How many stereoisomers would you expect from each general structure?

22.2B D AND L DESIGNATIONS OF MONOSACCHARIDES

The simplest monosaccharides are the compounds glyceraldehyde and dihydroxy-acetone (see following structures). Of these two compounds, only glyceraldehyde contains a stereocenter.

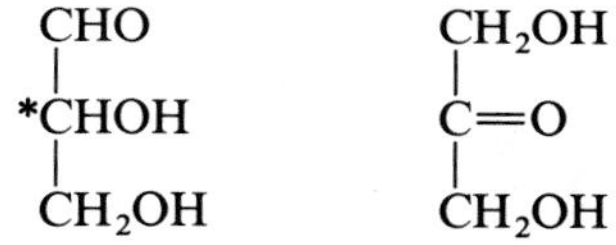

$$
\begin{array}{cc}
\text{CHO} & \text{CH}_2\text{OH} \\
| & | \\
{}^*\text{CHOH} & \text{C}=\text{O} \\
| & | \\
\text{CH}_2\text{OH} & \text{CH}_2\text{OH}
\end{array}
$$

Glyceraldehyde   Dihydroxyacetone
(an aldotriose)   (a ketotriose)

Glyceraldehyde exists, therefore, in two enantiomeric forms that are known to have the absolute configurations shown here.

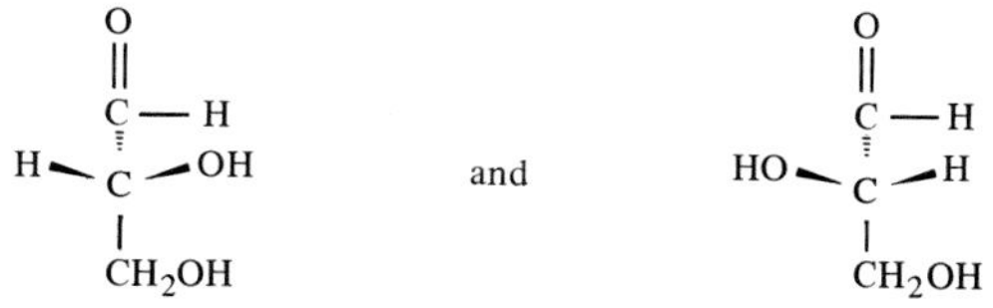

$$
\begin{array}{ccc}
\text{O} & & \text{O} \\
\| & & \| \\
\text{C}-\text{H} & & \text{C}-\text{H} \\
\text{H} \diagdown \text{C} \diagup \text{OH} & \text{and} & \text{HO} \diagdown \text{C} \diagup \text{H} \\
| & & | \\
\text{CH}_2\text{OH} & & \text{CH}_2\text{OH}
\end{array}
$$

(+)-Glyceraldehyde   (−)-Glyceraldehyde

We saw in Section 5.5 that, according to the Cahn–Ingold–Prelog convention, (+)-glyceraldehyde should be designated (R)-(+)-glyceraldehyde and (−)-glycer-aldehyde should be designated (S)-(−)-glyceraldehyde.

Early in this century, before the absolute configurations of any organic com-pounds were known, another system of stereochemical designations was introduced. According to this system (first suggested by M. A. Rosanoff of New York University in 1906), (+)-glyceraldehyde is designated D-(+)-glyceraldehyde and (−)-glyceralde-hyde is designated L-(−)-glyceraldehyde. These two compounds, moreover, serve as configurational standards for all monosaccharides. A monosaccharide *whose highest numbered stereocenter* (the penultimate carbon) has the same configuration as

D-(+)-glyceraldehyde is designated as a D sugar; one whose highest numbered stereo-center has the same configuration as L-glyceraldehyde is designated as an L sugar. By convention, acyclic forms of monosaccharides are drawn vertically with the aldehyde or keto group at or nearest the top. When drawn in this way, D-sugars have the —OH of their penultimate carbon on the right.

A D–aldopentose   An L–ketohexose

D and L designations are like (R) and (S) designations in that they are not necessarily related to the optical rotations of the sugars to which they are applied. Thus, one may encounter other sugars that are D-(+)- or D-(−)- and that are L-(+)- or L-(−)- .

The D–L system of stereochemical designations is thoroughly entrenched in the literature of carbohydrate chemistry, and even though it has the disadvantage of specifying the configuration of only one stereocenter — that of the highest numbered stereocenter — we shall employ the D–L system in our designations of carbohydrates.

Problem 22.2

Write three-dimensional formulas for each aldotetrose and ketopentose isomer in Problem 22.1 and designate each as a D or L sugar.

22.2C STRUCTURAL FORMULAS FOR MONOSACCHARIDES

Later in this chapter we shall see how the great carbohydrate chemist Emil Fischer* was able to establish the stereochemical configuration of the aldohexose D-(+)-glu-cose, the most abundant monosaccharide. In the meantime, however, we can use D-(+)-glucose as an example illustrating the various ways of representing the struc-tures of monosaccharides.

Fischer represented the structure of D-(+)-glucose with the cross formulation (1) in Fig. 22.3. This type of formulation is now called a Fischer projection formula (Section 5.11) and is still useful for carbohydrates. In Fischer projection formulas, by convention, *horizontal lines project out towards the reader and vertical lines project behind the plane of the page. When we use Fischer projection formulas, however, we must not* (in our mind's eye) *remove them from the plane of the page in order to test*

---

*Emil Fischer (1852–1919) was professor of organic chemistry at the University of Berlin. In addition to monumental work in the field of carbohydrate chemistry, where Fischer and his co-workers established the configuration of most of the monosaccharides, Fischer also made important contributions to studies of amino acids, proteins, purines, indoles, and stereochemistry generally. As a graduate student, Fischer discovered phenylhydrazine, a reagent that was highly important in his later work with carbohydrates. Fischer was the second recipient (in 1902) of the Nobel Prize for Chemistry.

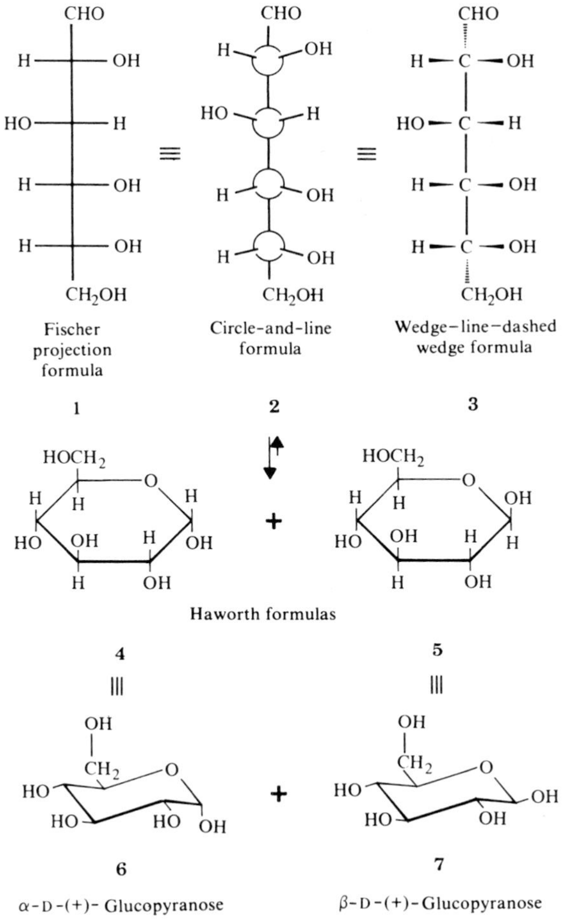

22.2 MONOSACCHARIDES

CHO   CHO   CHO

Fischer projection formula	Circle-and-line formula	Wedge–line–dashed wedge formula
1	**2**	**3**

$$\equiv$$

Haworth formulas

4   **5**

$$\| \|$$

6   **7**

α-D-(+)-Glucopyranose β-D-(+)-Glucopyranose

FIGURE 22.3 (*a*) **1–3** are formulas used for the open-chain structure of D-(+)-glucose. (*b*) **4–7** are formulas used for the two cyclic hemiacetal forms of D-(+)-glucose.

their superposability and we must not rotate them by 90°. In terms of more familiar formulations, the Fischer projection formula translates into formulas **2** and **3**.*

In IUPAC nomenclature and with the Cahn–Ingold–Prelog system of stereochemical designations, the open-chain form of D-(+)-glucose is (2*R*, 3*S*, 4*R*, 5*R*)-2,3,4,5,6-penta-hydroxyhexanal.

Although many of the properties of D-(+)-glucose can be explained in terms of an open-chain structure (**1, 2,** or **3**), a considerable body of evidence indicates that the open-chain structure exists, primarily, in equilibrium with two cyclic forms. These can be represented by structures **4** and **5** or **6** and **7**. The cyclic forms of D-(+)-glucose are *hemiacetals* formed by an intramolecular reaction of the —OH group at C-5 with

*The meaning of formulas **1**, **2**, and **3** can be seen best through the use of molecular models: We first construct a chain of six carbon atoms with the —CHO group at the top and a —CH$_2$OH group at the bottom. We then bring the —CH$_2$OH group up behind the chain until it almost touches the —CHO group. Holding this model so that the —CHO and —CH$_2$OH groups are directed generally away from us, we then begin placing —H and —OH groups on each of the four remaining carbon atoms. The —OH group of C-2 is placed on the right; that of C-3 on the left; and those of C-4 and C-5 on the right.

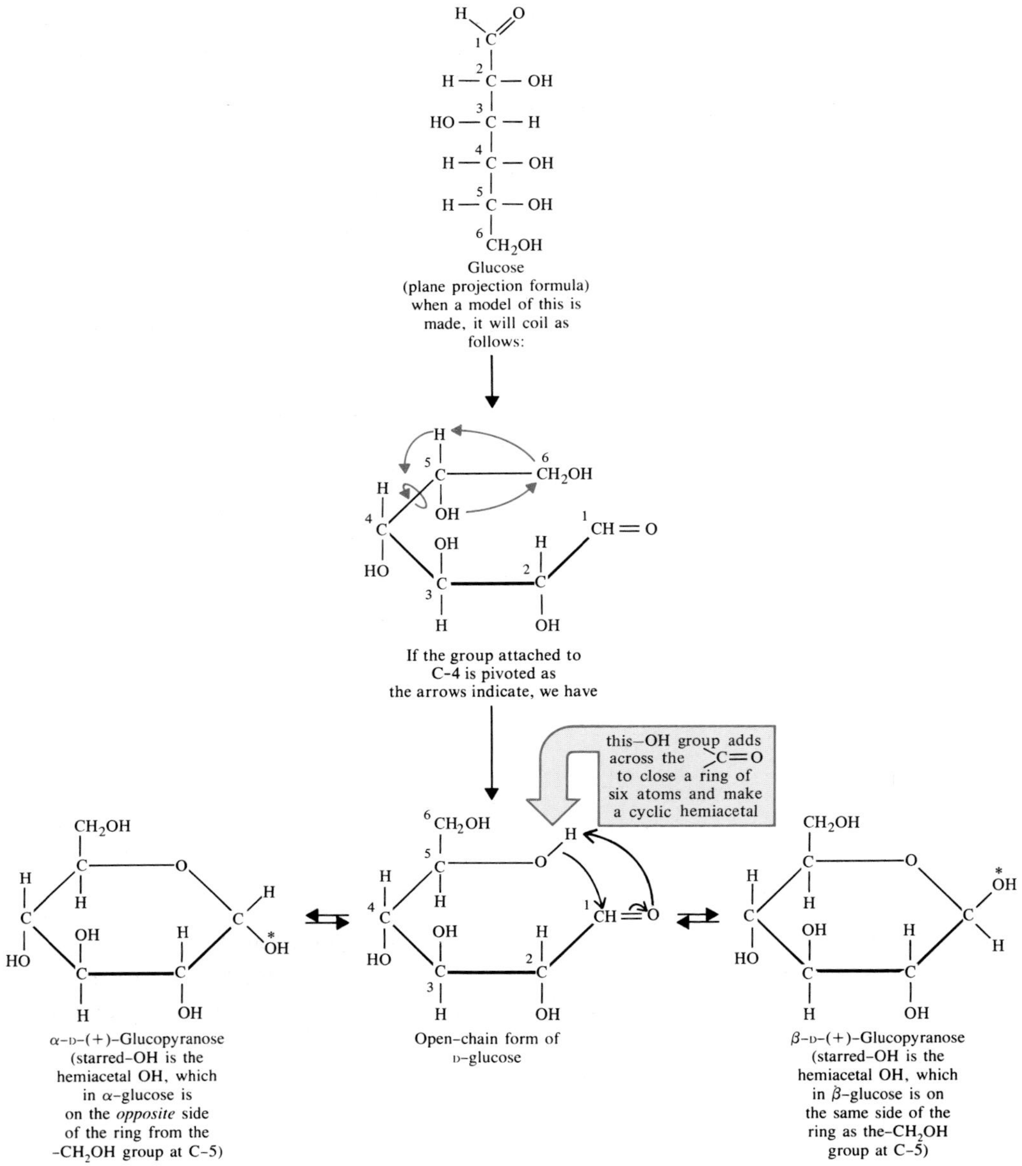

FIGURE 22.4 The Haworth formulas for the cyclic hemiacetal forms of D-(+)-glucose and their relation to the open-chain polyhydroxy aldehyde structure. [From John R. Holum, *Organic Chemistry: A Brief Course,* Wiley, New York, 1975, p. 332. Used by permission.]

the aldehyde group (Fig. 22.4). Cyclization creates a new stereocenter at C-1 and this stereocenter explains how two cyclic forms are possible. These two cyclic forms are *diastereomers* that differ only in the configuration of C-1. In carbohydrate chemistry diastereomers of this type are called *anomers,* and the hemiacetal carbon atom is called the *anomeric carbon atom.*

Structures **4** and **5** for the glucose anomers are called Haworth formulas* and, although they do not give an accurate picture of the shape of the six-membered ring, they have many practical uses. Figure 22.4 demonstrates how the representation of each stereocenter of the open-chain form can be correlated with its representation in the Haworth formula.

Each glucose anomer is designated as an *α anomer* or a *β anomer* depending on the location of the — OH group of C-1. When we draw the cyclic forms of a D sugar in the orientation shown in Figs. 22.3 or 22.4, the *α* anomer has the — OH *down* and the *β* anomer has the — OH *up*.

Studies of the structures of the cyclic hemiacetal forms of D-(+)-glucose using X-ray analysis have demonstrated that the actual conformations of the rings are the chair forms represented by conformational formulas **6** and **7** in Fig. 22.3. This shape is exactly what we would expect from our studies of the conformations of cyclohexane (Chapter 4) and, it is especially interesting to notice that in the *β* anomer of D-glucose, all of the large substituents, — OH or — CH$_2$OH, are equatorial. In the *α* anomer, the only bulky axial substituent is the — OH at C-1.

It is convenient at times to represent the cyclic structures of a monosaccharide without specifying whether the configuration of the anomeric carbon atom is *α* or *β*. When we do this, we shall use formulas such as the following:

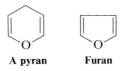

Not all carbohydrates exist in equilibrium with six-membered hemiacetal rings; in several instances the ring is five membered. (Even glucose exists, to a small extent, in equilibrium with five-membered hemiacetal rings.) Because of this variation, a system of nomenclature has been introduced to allow designation of the ring size. If the monosaccharide ring is six membered, the compound is called a *pyranose;* if the ring is five membered, the compound is designated as a *furanose.*† Thus, the full name of compound **4** (or **6**) is *α*-D-(+)-glucopyranose, while that of **5** (or **7**) is *β*-D-(+)-glucopyranose.

---

*After the English chemist W. N. Haworth (University of Birmingham) who, in 1926, along with E. L. Hirst, demonstrated that the cyclic form of glucose acetals consists of a six-membered ring. Haworth received the Nobel Prize for his work in carbohydrate chemistry in 1937. For an excellent discussion of Haworth formulas and their relation to open-chain forms see the following article: D. M. S. Wheeler, M. M. Wheeler, and T. S. Wheeler, "The Conversion of Open Chain Structures of Monosaccharides into the Corresponding Haworth Formulas," *J. Chem. Educ.,* **1982,** *59,* 969.

†These names come from the names of the oxygen heterocycles *pyran* and *furan + ose.*

A pyran   **Furan**

22.3 MUTAROTATION

Part of the evidence for the cyclic hemiacetal structure for D-(+)-glucose comes from experiments in which both α and β forms have been isolated. Ordinary D-(+)-glucose has a melting point of 146 °C. However, when D-(+)-glucose is crystallized by evaporating an aqueous solution kept above 98 °C, a second form of D-(+)-glucose with a melting point of 150 °C can be obtained. When the optical rotations of these two forms are measured, they are found to be significantly different, but when an aqueous solution of either form is allowed to stand, its rotation changes. The specific rotation of one form decreases and the rotation of the other increases, *until both solutions show the same value.* A solution of ordinary D-(+)-glucose (mp, 146 °C) has an initial specific rotation of +112° but, ultimately, the specific rotation of this solution falls to +52.7°. A solution of the second form of D-(+)-glucose (mp, 150 °C) has an initial specific rotation of +19°; but slowly, the specific rotation of this solution rises to +52.7°. This change in rotation towards an equilibrium value is called *mutarotation.*

The explanation for this mutarotation lies in the existence of an equilibrium between the open-chain form of D-(+)-glucose and the α and β forms of the cyclic hemiacetals.

α-D-(+)-Glucopyranose
(mp, 146°C $[\alpha]_D^{25} = +112°$)

Open-chain
form of
D-(+)-glucose

β-D-(+)-Glucopyranose
(mp, 150°C $[\alpha]_D^{25} = +18.7°$)

X-ray analysis has confirmed that ordinary D-(+)-glucose has the α configuration at the anomeric carbon atom and that the higher melting form has the β configuration.

The concentration of open-chain D-(+)-glucose in solution at equilibrium is very small. Solutions of D-(+)-glucose give no observable UV or IR absorption band for a carbonyl group, and solutions of D-(+)-glucose give a negative test with Schiff's reagent — a special reagent that requires a relatively high concentration of a free aldehyde group (rather than a hemiacetal) in order to give a positive test.

Assuming that the concentration of the open-chain form is negligible, one can, by use of the specific rotations in the preceding figures, calculate the percentages of the α and β anomers present at equilibrium. These percentages, 36% α anomer and 64% β anomer, are in accord with a greater stability for β-D-(+)-glucopyranose. This preference is what we might expect on the basis of its having only equatorial groups.

α-D-(+)-Glucopyranose
(36% at equilibrium)

β-D-(+)-Glucopyranose
(64% at equilibrium)

22.4 GLYCOSIDE FORMATION

The β anomer of a pyranose is not always the more stable, however. With D-mannose, the equilibrium favors the α anomer and this result is called an *anomeric effect*.

α-D-Mannopyranose
(69% at equilibrium)

β-D-Mannopyranose
(31% at equilibrium)

We shall not discuss anomeric effects further except to say that they arise from conformational aspects of the interactions of two electronegative oxygen atoms. An anomeric effect will frequently cause an electronegative substituent, such as a hydroxyl or alkoxy group, to prefer the axial orientation.

22.4 GLYCOSIDE FORMATION

When a small amount of gaseous hydrogen chloride is passed into a solution of D-(+)-glucose in methanol, a reaction takes place that results in the formation of anomeric methyl *acetals*.

D-(+)- Glucose

Methyl α-D-glucopyranoside
(mp, 165°C $[\alpha]_D^{25} = +158°$)

Methyl β-D-glucopyranoside
(mp, 107°C $[\alpha]_D^{25} = -33°$)

Carbohydrate acetals, generally, are called *glycosides* (see below) and an acetal of glucose is called a *glucoside*. (Acetals of mannose are *mannosides*, ketals of fructose are *fructosides*, and so on.) The methyl D-glucosides have been shown to have six-membered rings (Section 22.10) so they are properly named methyl α-D-glucopyranoside and methyl β-D-glucopyranoside.

The mechanism for the formation of the methyl glucosides (starting arbitrarily with β-D-glucopyranose) is as follows:

You should review the mechanism for acetal formation given in Section 16.7C and compare it with the steps given here. Notice, again, the important role played by the electron pair of the adjacent oxygen atom in stabilizing the carbocation that forms in the second step.

The mixed acetal of an aldose (or ketose) is called a **glycoside.** Because glycosides are acetals, they are stable in basic aqueous solutions. In acidic solutions, however, glycosides (again because they are acetals, Section 16.7C) undergo hydrolysis to produce a sugar and an alcohol. The alcohol obtained from a glycoside is known as an **aglycone.**

Glycoside
(stable in basic solutions)

Sugar **Aglycone**

For example, when an aqueous solution of methyl β-D-glucopyranoside is made acidic, the glycoside undergoes hydrolysis to produce D-glucose as a mixture of the two pyranose forms (in equilibrium with a small amount of the open-chain form).

Methyl β-D-glucopyranoside

Glycosides may be as simple as the methyl glucosides that we have just studied, or they may be considerably more complex. Many naturally occurring compounds are glycosides. An example is *salicin,* a compound found in the bark of willow trees.

Salicin

As early as the time of the ancient Greeks, preparations made from willow bark were used in relieving pain. Eventually, chemists isolated salicin from other plant materials and were able to show that it was responsible for the analgesic effect of the willow bark preparations. Salicin can be converted to salicylic acid which, in turn, can be converted into the most widely used modern analgesic, *aspirin* (Section 21.8).

Problem 22.3

(a) What products would be formed if salicin were treated with dilute aqueous HCl? (b) Outline a mechanism for the reactions involved in their formation.

Problem 22.4

How would you convert D-glucose to a mixture of ethyl α-D-glucopyranoside and ethyl β-D-glucopyranoside. Show all steps in the mechanism for their formation.

Problem 22.5

In neutral or basic aqueous solutions, glycosides do not show mutarotation. However, if the solutions are made acidic, glycosides do show mutarotation. Explain why this occurs.

22.5 REACTIONS OF MONOSACCHARIDES

Dissolving monosaccharides in aqueous base causes them to undergo a series of keto–enol tautomerizations that lead to isomerizations. For example, if a solution of D-glucose containing calcium hydroxide is allowed to stand for several days, several products can be isolated, including D-fructose and D-mannose (Fig. 22.5). This type of reaction is called the **Lobry de Bruyn–Alberda van Ekenstein transformation** after the two Dutch chemists who discovered it in 1895.

When carrying out reactions with monosaccharides it is usually important to prevent these isomerizations and thereby to preserve the stereochemistry at all of the stereocenters. One way to do this is to convert the monosaccharide to the methyl glycoside first. We can then safely carry out reactions in basic media because the aldehyde group has been converted to an acetal and acetals are stable in aqueous base.

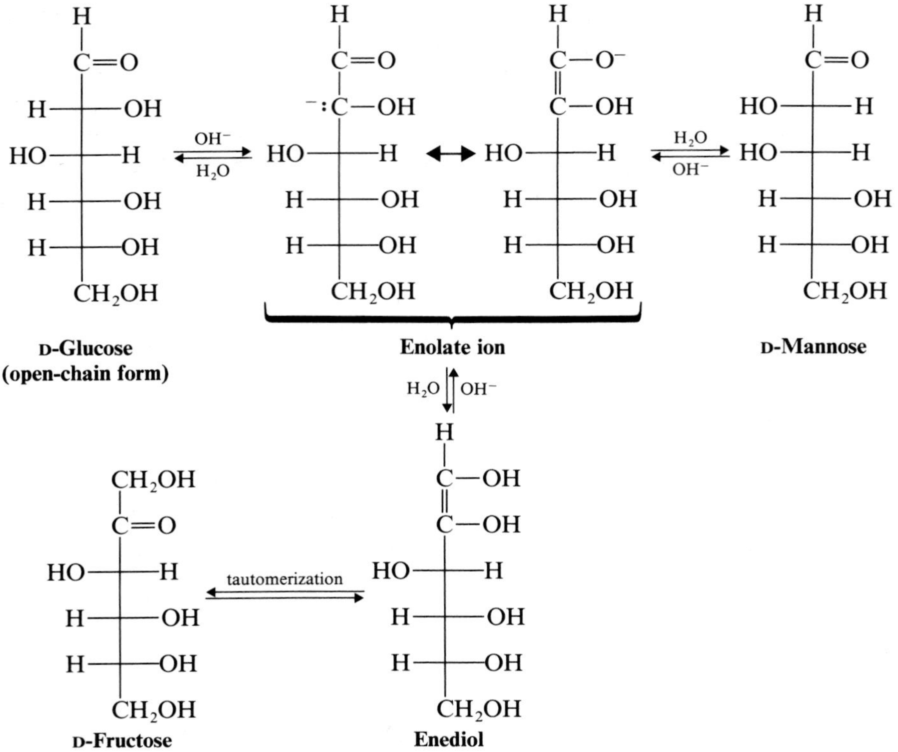

FIGURE 22.5 Monosaccharides undergo isomerizations via enolate ions and enediols when placed in aqueous base. Here we show how D-glucose isomerizes to D-mannose and to D-fructose.

22.5A FORMATION OF ETHERS

A methyl glucoside, for example, can be converted to the pentamethyl derivative by treating it with excess dimethyl sulfate in aqueous sodium hydroxide. This reaction is just a multiple Williamson synthesis (Section 10.16). The hydroxyl groups of monosaccharides are more acidic than those of ordinary alcohols because the monosaccharide contains so many electronegative oxygen atoms, all of which exert electron-withdrawing inductive effects on nearby hydroxyl groups. In aqueous NaOH, the hydroxyl groups are converted to alkoxide ions and each of these, in turn, reacts with dimethyl sulfate in an S_N2 reaction to yield a methyl ether. The process is called *exhaustive methylation*.

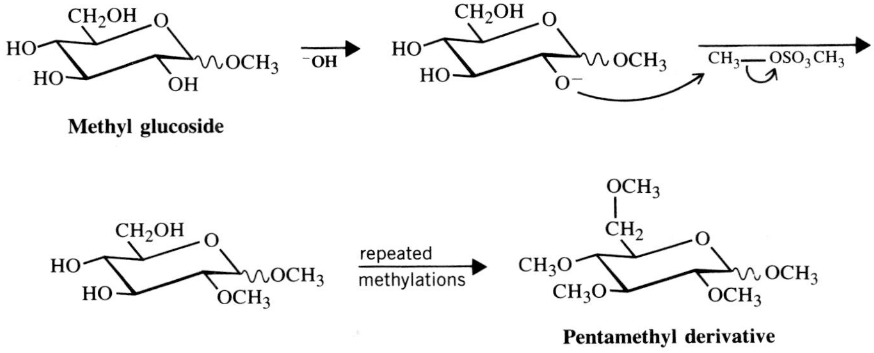

Pentamethyl derivative

The methoxy groups at C-2, C-3, C-4, and C-6 atoms of the pentamethyl derivative are ordinary ether groups. These groups, consequently, are stable in dilute aqueous acid. (To cleave ethers requires heating with concentrated HBr or HI, Section 10.17.) The methoxy group at C-1, however, is different from the others because it is part of an acetal linkage (it is glycosidic). Therefore, treating the pentamethyl derivative with dilute aqueous acid will cause hydrolysis of this glycosidic methoxy group and produce 2,3,4,6-tetra-O-methyl-D-glucose. (The O in this name means that the methyl groups are attached to oxygen atoms.)

Pentamethyl derivative

2, 3, 4, 6-Tetra-O-methyl-D-glucose

Notice in the open-chain form that the oxygen at C-5 does not bear a methyl group because it was originally a part of the cyclic hemiacetal linkage of D-glucose.

22.5B CONVERSION TO ESTERS

Treating a monosaccharide with excess acetic anhydride and a weak base (such as pyridine or sodium acetate) converts all of the hydroxyl groups, including the anomeric hydroxyl, to ester groups. If the reaction is carried out at a low temperature (e.g., 0 °C), the reaction occurs stereospecifically; the α anomer gives the α-acetate and the β-anomer gives the β-acetate.

22.5C CONVERSION TO CYCLIC ACETALS AND KETALS

In Section 16.7C we learned that aldehydes and ketones react with open-chain 1,2-diols to produce cyclic acetals and ketals.

1,2-Diol   **Cyclic ketal**

If the 1,2-diol is attached to a ring, as in a monosaccharide, **formation of the cyclic acetal or ketal occurs only when the vicinal hydroxyl groups are cis to each other.** For example, α-D-galactopyranose reacts with acetone in the following way:

The formation of cyclic acetals and ketals can be used to protect certain hydroxyl groups of a sugar while reactions are carried out on other parts of the molecule. We shall see examples of this in Problem 22.19 and in Chapter 25.

22.6 OXIDATION REACTIONS OF MONOSACCHARIDES

A number of oxidizing agents are used to identify functional groups of carbohydrates, in elucidating their structures, and for syntheses. The most important are (1) Benedict's or Tollens' reagents, (2) bromine water, (3) nitric acid, and (4) periodic acid. Each of these reagents produces a different and usually specific effect when it is allowed to react with a monosaccharide. We should now examine what these effects are.

22.6A BENEDICT'S OR TOLLENS' REAGENTS: REDUCING SUGARS

Benedict's reagent (an alkaline solution containing a cupric citrate complex ion) and Tollens' solution $[Ag(\overset{+}{N}H_3)_2\overset{-}{O}H]$ oxidize and thus give positive tests with *aldoses and ketoses.* The tests are positive even though aldoses and ketoses exist primarily as cyclic hemiacetals.

We studied the use of Tollens' silver mirror test in Section 16.13. Benedict's solution (and the related Fehling's solution that contains a cupric tartrate complex ion) give brick-red precipitates of Cu_2O when they oxidize an aldose. (In alkaline solution ketoses are converted to aldoses (Section 22.5), which are then oxidized by the cupric complexes.) Since the solutions of cupric tartrates and citrates are blue, the appearance of a brick-red precipitate is a vivid and unmistakable indication of a positive test.

$$
\begin{array}{c}
\overset{O}{\underset{\|}{C}H} \\
| \\
(CHOH)_n \\
| \\
CH_2OH \\
\textbf{Aldose}
\end{array}
$$

Cu^{2+} (complex) +   or $\longrightarrow$ $Cu_2O \downarrow$ + oxidation products

Benedict's solution (blue)

$$
\begin{array}{c}
CH_2OH \\
| \\
C = O \\
| \\
(CHOH)_2 \\
| \\
CH_2OH \\
\textbf{Ketose}
\end{array}
$$

(brick-red reduction product)

Sugars that give positive tests with Tollens' or Benedict's solutions are known as *reducing sugars,* and all carbohydrates that contain a *hemiacetal group* or a *hemiketal group* give positive tests. In aqueous solution these hemiacetals or hemiketals exist in equilibrium with relatively small, but not insignificant, concentrations of noncyclic aldehydes or α-hydroxy ketones. It is the latter two that undergo the oxidation, perturbing the equilibrium to produce more aldehyde or α-hydroxy ketone, which then undergoes oxidation until one reactant is exhausted.

Carbohydrates that contain only acetal or ketal groups do not give positive tests with Benedict's or Tollens' solution, and they are called *nonreducing sugars*. Acetals or ketals do not exist in equilibrium with aldehydes or α-hydroxy ketones in the basic aqueous media of the test reagents.

Reducing Sugar

Hemiacetal (R' = H;
or hemiketal, R' = CH_2OH)
(gives positive Tollens'
or Benedict's test)

Nonreducing Sugar

Alkyl group or another sugar

Acetal (R' = H;
or ketal, R' = CH_2OH)
(does not give a
positive Tollens' or
Benedict's test)

Problem 22.6

How might you distinguish between α-D-glucopyranose (i.e., D-glucose) and methyl α-D-glucopyranoside?

Although Benedict's and Tollens' reagents have some use as diagnostic tools [Benedict's solution can be used in quantitative determinations of reducing sugars (reported as glucose) in blood or urine], neither of these reagents is useful as a preparative reagent in carbohydrate oxidations. Oxidations with both reagents take place in alkaline solution, *and in alkaline solutions sugars undergo a complex series of reactions that lead to isomerizations* (Section 22.5).

22.6B BROMINE WATER: THE SYNTHESIS OF ALDONIC ACIDS

Monosaccharides do not undergo isomerization and fragmentation reactions in mildly acidic solution. Thus, a useful oxidizing reagent for preparative purposes is bromine in water (pH 6.0). Bromine water is a general reagent that selectively oxidizes the —CHO group to a —CO_2H group. It converts an aldose to an *aldonic acid*:

$$
\begin{array}{ccc}
\text{CHO} & & \text{CO}_2\text{H} \\
| & & | \\
(\text{CHOH})_n & \xrightarrow[\text{H}_2\text{O}]{\text{Br}_2} & (\text{CHOH})_n \\
| & & | \\
\text{CH}_2\text{OH} & & \text{CH}_2\text{OH} \\
\textbf{Aldose} & & \textbf{Aldonic acid}
\end{array}
$$

Experiments with aldopyranoses have shown that the actual course of the reaction is somewhat more complex than we have indicated above. Bromine water specifically oxidizes the β anomer, and the initial product that forms is a δ-aldonolactone. This compound may then hydrolyze to an aldonic acid, and the aldonic acid may undergo a subsequent ring closure to form a γ-aldonolactone.

β-D-Glucopyranose   D-Glucono-δ-lactone   D-Gluconic acid   D-Glucono-γ-lactone

22.6C NITRIC ACID OXIDATION: ALDARIC ACIDS

Dilute nitric acid—a stronger oxidizing agent than bromine water—oxidizes both the —CHO group and the terminal —CH_2OH group of an aldose to —CO_2H groups. These dicarboxylic acids are known as *aldaric acids.*

It is not known whether a lactone is an intermediate in the oxidation of an aldose to an aldaric acid; however, aldaric acids form γ- and δ-lactones readily.

Aldaric acid
(from an aldohexose)   γ-Lactones of an aldaric acid

The aldaric acid obtained from D-glucose is called D-glucaric acid.*

D-Glucose   D-Glucaric acid

*Older terms for an aldaric acid are a *glycaric* acid or a *saccharic* acid.

Problem 22.7

(a) Would you expect D-glucaric acid to be optically active?

(b) Write the open-chain structure for the aldaric acid (mannaric acid) that would be obtained by nitric acid oxidation of D-mannose.

(c) Would you expect it to be optically active?

(d) What aldaric acid would you expect to obtain from D-erythrose

$$
\begin{array}{c}
\text{CHO} \\
\text{H} \!-\!\!\!-\! \text{OH} \\
\text{H} \!-\!\!\!-\! \text{OH} \\
\text{CH}_2\text{OH}
\end{array}
$$

D-Erythrose

(e) Would it show optical activity?

(f) D-Threose, a diastereomer of D-erythrose, yields an optically active aldaric acid when it is subjected to nitric acid oxidation. Write Fischer projection formulas for D-threose and its nitric acid oxidation product.

(g) What are the names of the aldaric acids obtained from D-erythrose and D-threose? (See Section 5.13A.)

Problem 22.8

D-Glucaric acid undergoes lactonization to yield two different γ-lactones. What are their structures?

22.6D PERIODATE OXIDATIONS: OXIDATIVE CLEAVAGE OF POLYHYDROXY COMPOUNDS

Compounds that have hydroxyl groups on adjacent atoms undergo oxidative cleavage when they are treated with aqueous periodic acid (HIO_4). The reaction breaks carbon–carbon bonds and produces carbonyl compounds (aldehydes, ketones, or acids). The stoichiometry of the reaction is

$$
\begin{array}{c}
-\overset{|}{\underset{}{\text{C}}}-\text{OH} \\
\text{-----}\!\!\text{-----} \\
-\overset{|}{\underset{}{\text{C}}}-\text{OH}
\end{array}
+ HIO_4 \longrightarrow 2 -\overset{|}{\text{C}}\!\!=\!\!\text{O} + HIO_3 + H_2O
$$

Since the reaction usually takes place in quantitative yield, valuable information can often be gained by measuring the number of molar equivalents of periodic acid that are consumed in the reaction as well as by identifying the carbonyl products.*

Periodate oxidations are thought to take place through a cyclic intermediate:

---

* The reagent lead tetraacetate, $Pb(O_2CCH_3)_4$, brings about cleavage reactions similar to those of periodic acid. The two reagents are complementary; periodic acid works well in aqueous solutions and lead tetraacetate gives good results in organic solvents.

$$-\overset{|}{\underset{|}{C}}-OH \quad + IO_4^- \xrightarrow{(-H_2O)} \quad \overset{|}{\underset{|}{C}}\diagdown O \quad O^- \qquad -\overset{|}{C}=O$$

$$-\overset{|}{\underset{|}{C}}-OH \qquad\qquad\qquad \overset{|}{\underset{|}{C}}\diagup O \diagdown O \longrightarrow \qquad -\overset{|}{C}=O \quad + IO_3^-$$

Before we discuss the use of periodic acid in carbohydrate chemistry, we should illustrate the course of the reaction with several simple examples. Notice in these periodate oxidations that *for every C—C bond broken, a C—O bond is formed at each carbon.*

1. When three or more —CHOH groups are contiguous, the internal ones are obtained as *formic acid.* Periodate oxidation of glycerol, for example, gives two molar equivalents of formaldehyde and one molar equivalent of formic acid.

$$
\begin{array}{ll}
& \overset{\displaystyle H}{\underset{}{|}} \\
& H-C=O \qquad \text{(formaldehyde)} \\
\overset{\displaystyle H}{\underset{}{|}} & + \\
H-\overset{|}{C}-OH & \\
\text{-----}\overline{+}\text{-------} & O \\
H-\overset{|}{C}-OH + 2\,IO_4^- \longrightarrow & H-\overset{\|}{C}-OH \qquad \text{(formic acid)} \\
\text{-----}\overline{+}\text{-------} & + \\
H-\overset{|}{C}-OH & \\
\overset{}{\underset{\displaystyle H}{|}} & H-C=O \qquad \text{(formaldehyde)} \\
\textbf{Glycerol} & \overset{}{\underset{\displaystyle H}{|}}
\end{array}
$$

2. Oxidative cleavage also takes place when an —OH group is adjacent to the carbonyl group of an aldehyde or ketone (but not that of an acid or an ester). Glyceraldehyde yields two molar equivalents of formic acid and one molar equivalent of formaldehyde, while dihydroxyacetone gives two molar equivalents of formaldehyde and one molar equivalent of carbon dioxide.

$$
\begin{array}{ll}
& O \\
& \| \\
& H-C-OH \qquad \text{(formic acid)} \\
O & + \\
\| & O \\
C-H & \| \\
\text{-----}\overline{+}\text{-------} & H-C-OH \qquad \text{(formic acid)} \\
H-\overset{|}{C}-OH + 2\,IO_4^- \longrightarrow & + \\
\text{-----}\overline{+}\text{-------} & \\
H-\overset{|}{C}-OH & H-C=O \qquad \text{(formaldehyde)} \\
\overset{}{\underset{\displaystyle H}{|}} & \overset{}{\underset{\displaystyle H}{|}} \\
\textbf{Glyceraldehyde} &
\end{array}
$$

$$
\begin{array}{ll}
& \overset{\displaystyle H}{\underset{}{|}} \\
\overset{\displaystyle H}{\underset{}{|}} & H-C=O \qquad \text{(formaldehyde)} \\
H-\overset{|}{C}-OH & + \\
\text{-----}\overline{+}\text{-------} & \\
\overset{|}{C}=O \quad + 2\,IO_4^- \longrightarrow & O=C=O \qquad \text{(carbon dioxide)} \\
\text{-----}\overline{+}\text{-------} & + \\
H-\overset{|}{C}-OH & H-C=O \qquad \text{(formaldehyde)} \\
\overset{}{\underset{\displaystyle H}{|}} & \overset{}{\underset{\displaystyle H}{|}} \\
\textbf{Dihydroxyacetone} &
\end{array}
$$

3. Periodic acid does not cleave compounds in which the hydroxyl groups are separated by an intervening —CH_2— group, nor those in which a hydroxyl group is adjacent to an ether or acetal function.

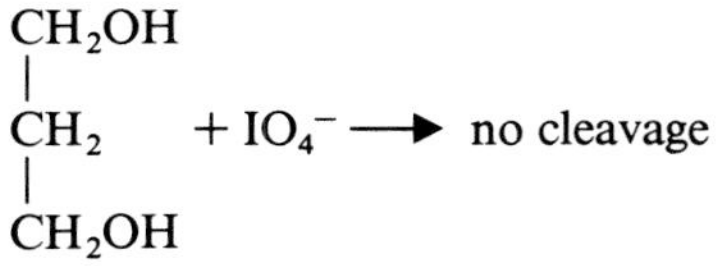

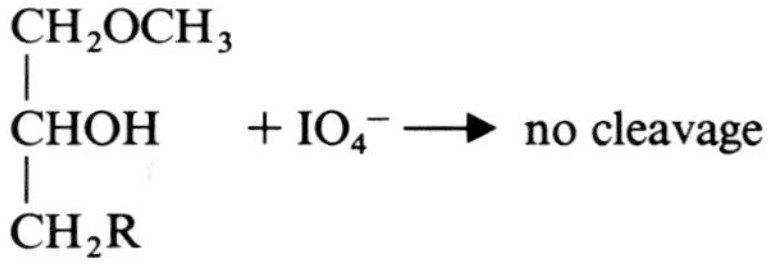

$$\underset{\substack{|\\ \\ |}}{\overset{CH_2OH}{\underset{CH_2OH}{CH_2}}} + IO_4^- \longrightarrow \text{no cleavage} \qquad \underset{\substack{|\\ \\ |}}{\overset{CH_2OCH_3}{\underset{CH_2R}{CHOH}}} + IO_4^- \longrightarrow \text{no cleavage}$$

Problem 22.9

What products would you expect to be formed when each of the following compounds is treated with an appropriate amount of periodic acid? How many molar equivalents of HIO_4 would be consumed in each case?

(a) 2,3-Butanediol

(b) 1,2,3-Butanetriol

(c) $CH_2OHCHOHCH(OCH_3)_2$

(d) $CH_2OHCHOHCOCH_3$

(e) $CH_3COCHOHCOCH_3$

(f) cis-1,2-Cyclopentanediol

(g) 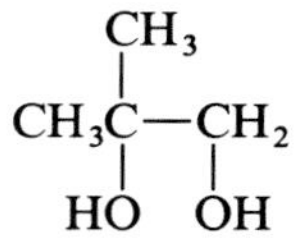 $CH_3\underset{\underset{HO}{|}}{\overset{\overset{CH_3}{|}}{C}}-\underset{\underset{OH}{|}}{CH_2}$

(h) D-Erythrose

Problem 22.10

Show how periodic acid could be used to distinguish between an aldohexose and a ketohexose. What products would you obtain from each, and how many molar equivalents of HIO_4 would be consumed?

22.7 REDUCTION OF MONOSACCHARIDES: ALDITOLS

Aldoses (and ketoses) can be reduced with sodium borohydride to compounds called *alditols.*

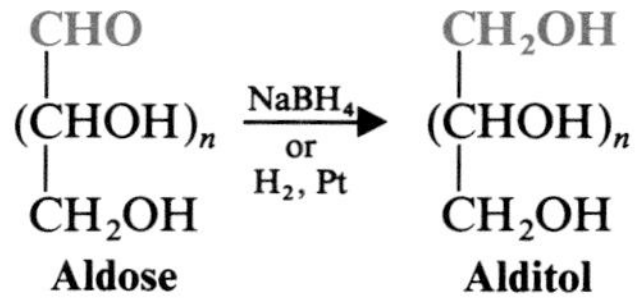

$$\underset{\text{Aldose}}{\overset{CHO}{\underset{CH_2OH}{(CHOH)_n}}} \xrightarrow[\substack{\text{or}\\ H_2,\,Pt}]{NaBH_4} \underset{\text{Alditol}}{\overset{CH_2OH}{\underset{CH_2OH}{(CHOH)_n}}}$$

Reduction of D-glucose, for example, yields D-glucitol.

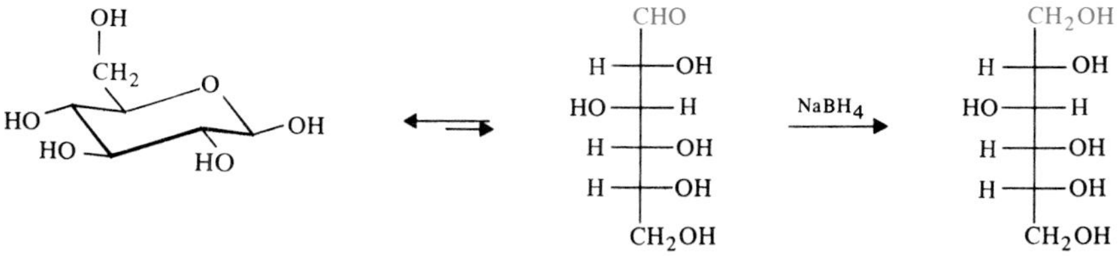

D-Glucitol
(or D-sorbitol)

Problem 22.11

(a) Would you expect D-glucitol to be optically active? (b) Write Fischer projection formulas for all of the D-aldohexoses that would yield *optically inactive alditols*.

22.8 REACTIONS OF MONOSACCHARIDES WITH PHENYLHYDRAZINE: OSAZONES

The aldehyde group of an aldose reacts with such carbonyl reagents as hydroxylamine and phenylhydrazine (Section 16.6). With hydroxylamine, the product is the expected oxime. With enough phenylhydrazine, however, three molar equivalents of phenylhydrazine are consumed and a second phenylhydrazone group is introduced at C-2. The product is called a *phenylosazone.*

$$
\begin{array}{cccc}
\text{H} & & \text{H} & \\
| & & | & \\
\text{C=O} & & \text{C=NNHC}_6\text{H}_5 & \\
| & & | & \\
\text{CHOH} & & \text{C=NNHC}_6\text{H}_5 & \\
| & & | & \\
(\text{CHOH})_n & + 3\ \text{C}_6\text{H}_5\text{NHNH}_2 \longrightarrow & (\text{CHOH})_n & + \text{C}_6\text{H}_5\text{NH}_2 + \text{NH}_3 + \text{H}_2\text{O} \\
| & & | & \\
\text{CH}_2\text{OH} & & \text{CH}_2\text{OH} & \\
\textbf{Aldose} & & \textbf{Phenylosazone} &
\end{array}
$$

Although the mechanism for osazone formation is not known with certainty, it probably depends on a series of reactions in which $\diagdown$C=N— behaves very much like $\diagdown$C=O in giving a nitrogen version of an enol.

$$
\begin{array}{ccc}
& \text{H H} & \\
& | \ \ | & \\
\text{CH}=\!\!\text{N}-\text{NHC}_6\text{H}_5 & \text{CH}-\text{N}-\text{N}-\text{C}_6\text{H}_5 & \\
\overset{\nearrow\text{H}^+}{|} & \| & \xrightarrow{(-\text{C}_6\text{H}_5\text{NH}_2)} \\
\text{H}-\text{C}-\text{OH} \underset{-\text{H}^+}{\rightleftharpoons} & \text{C}-\text{O}-\text{H} & \\
| & | &
\end{array}
$$

$$
\begin{array}{ccc}
\text{CH}=\!\!\text{NH} & & \text{CH}=\!\!\text{NNHC}_6\text{H}_5 \\
| & \xrightarrow{(+2\ \text{C}_6\text{H}_5\text{NHNH}_2)} & | \\
\text{C}=\!\!\text{O} & & \text{C}=\!\!\text{NNHC}_6\text{H}_5 + \text{NH}_3 + \text{H}_2\text{O} \\
| & & |
\end{array}
$$

Osazone formation results in a loss of the stereocenter at C-2 but does not affect other stereocenters; D-glucose and D-mannose, for example, yield the same phenylosazone:

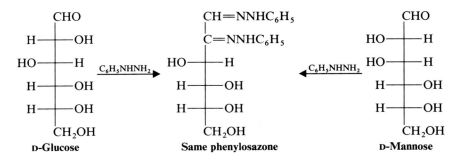

This experiment, first done by Emil Fischer, establishes that D-glucose and D-mannose have the same configurations about C-3, C-4, and C-5. Diastereomeric aldoses (such as D-glucose and D-mannose) that differ only in configuration at C-2 are called *epimers.**

Problem 22.12

Although D-fructose is not an epimer of D-glucose or D-mannose (D-fructose is a ketohexose), all three yield the same phenylosazone. (a) Using Fischer projection formulas, write an equation for the reaction of fructose with phenylhydrazine. (b) What information about the stereochemistry of D-fructose does this experiment yield?

22.9 SYNTHESIS AND DEGRADATION OF MONOSACCHARIDES

22.9A KILIANI-FISCHER SYNTHESIS

In 1885, Heinrich Kiliani (Freiburg, Germany) discovered that an aldose can be converted to the epimeric aldonic acids having one additional carbon through the addition of hydrogen cyanide and subsequent hydrolysis of the epimeric cyanohydrins. Fischer later extended this method by showing that aldonolactones obtained from the aldonic acids can be reduced to aldoses. Today, this method for lengthening the carbon chain of an aldose is called the Kiliani–Fischer synthesis.

We can illustrate the Kiliani–Fischer synthesis with the synthesis of D-threose and D-erythrose (aldotetroses) from D-glyceraldehyde (an aldotriose) in Fig. 22.6.

Addition of hydrogen cyanide to glyceraldehyde produces two epimeric cyanohydrins because the reaction creates a new stereocenter. The cyanohydrins can be separated easily (since they are diastereomers) and each can be converted to an aldose through hydrolysis, acidification, lactonization, and reduction with Na-Hg at pH 3–5. One cyanohydrin ultimately yields D-(−)-erythrose and the other yields D-(−)-threose.

We can be sure that the aldotetroses that we obtain from this Kiliani–Fischer synthesis are both D sugars because the starting compound is D-glyceraldehyde and its stereocenter is unaffected by the synthesis. On the basis of the Kiliani–Fischer synthesis we cannot know just which aldotetrose has both —OH groups on the right and which has the top —OH on the left in the Fischer projection formulas. However,

---

*The term *epimer* has taken on a broader meaning and is now often applied to any pair of diastereomers that differ only in the configuration at a single atom.

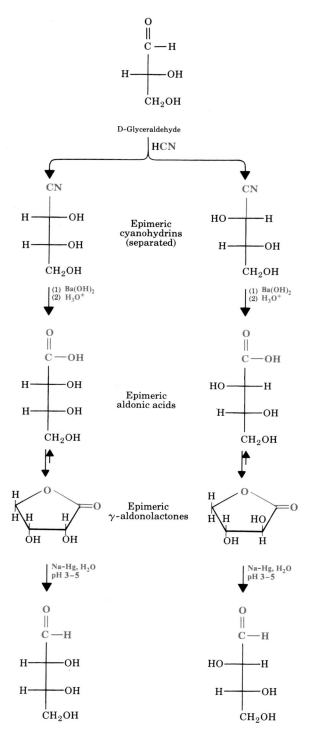

FIGURE 22.6 A Kiliani–Fischer synthesis of D-(−)-erythrose and D-(−)-threose from D-glyceraldehyde.

if we oxidize both aldotetroses to aldaric acids, one [D-(−)-erythrose] will yield an *optically inactive* product while the other [D-(−)-threose] will yield a product that is *optically active* (cf. Problem 22.7).

Problem 22.13 ————————————————————————————————

(a) What are the structures of L-(+)-threose and L-(+)-erythrose? (b) What aldotriose would you use to prepare them in a Kiliani–Fischer synthesis?

Problem 22.14 ————————————————————————————————

(a) Outline a Kiliani–Fischer synthesis of epimeric aldopentoses starting with D-(−)-erythrose (use Fischer projection formulas). (b) The two epimeric aldopentoses that one obtains are D-(−)-arabinose and D-(−)-ribose. Nitric acid oxidation of D-(−)-ribose yields an optically inactive aldaric acid, while similar oxidation of D-(−)-arabinose yields an optically active product. On the basis of this information alone, which Fischer projection formula represents D-(−)-arabinose and which represents D-(−)-ribose?

Problem 22.15 ————————————————————————————————

Subjecting D-(−)-threose to a Kiliani–Fischer synthesis yields two other epimeric aldopentoses, D-(+)-xylose and D-(−)-lyxose. D-(+)-Xylose can be oxidized (with nitric acid) to an optically inactive aldaric acid, while similar oxidation of D-(−)-lyxose gives an optically active product. What are the structures of D-(+)-xylose and D-(−)-lyxose?

Problem 22.16 ————————————————————————————————

There are eight aldopentoses. In Problems 22.14 and 22.15 you have arrived at the structures of four. What are the names and structures of the four that remain?

22.9B THE RUFF DEGRADATION

Just as the Kiliani–Fischer synthesis can be used to lengthen the chain of an aldose by one carbon atom, the Ruff degradation* can be used to shorten the chain by a similar unit. The Ruff degradation involves (1) oxidation of the aldose to an aldonic acid using bromine water and (2) oxidative decarboxylation of the aldonic acid to the next lower aldose using hydrogen peroxide and ferric sulfate. D-(−)-Ribose, for example, can be degraded to D-(−)-erythrose:

*Developed by Otto Ruff, a German chemist, 1871–1939.

$$\underset{\text{D-(−)-Ribose}}{\overset{\displaystyle\overset{O}{\|}}{\underset{CH_2OH}{}}} \xrightarrow[\text{H}_2\text{O}]{\text{Br}_2} \underset{\text{D-Ribonic acid}}{} \xrightarrow[\text{Fe}_2(\text{SO}_4)_3]{\text{H}_2\text{O}_2} \underset{\text{D-(−)-Erythrose}}{} + CO_2$$

Problem 22.17

The aldohexose D-(+)-galactose can be obtained by hydrolysis of *lactose,* a disaccharide found in milk. When D-(+)-galactose is treated with nitric acid, it yields an optically inactive aldaric acid. When D-(+)-galactose is subjected to a Ruff degradation, it yields D-(−)-lyxose (cf. Problem 22.15). Using only these data, write the Fischer projection formula for D-(+)-galactose.

22.10 THE D FAMILY OF ALDOSES

The Ruff degradation and the Kiliani–Fischer synthesis allow us to place all of the aldoses into families or "family trees" based on their relation to D- or L-glyceraldehyde. Such a tree is constructed in Fig. 22.7 and includes the structures of the D-aldohexoses, **1–8**.

Most, but not all, of the naturally occurring aldoses belong to the D family with D-(+)-glucose being by far the most common. D-(+)-Galactose can be obtained from milk sugar (lactose); but L-(−)-galactose occurs in a polysaccharide obtained from the vineyard snail, *Helix pomatia.* L-(+)-Arabinose is found widely, but D-(−)-arabinose is scarce, being found only in certain bacteria and sponges. Threose, lyxose, gulose, and allose do not occur naturally, but one or both forms (D or L) of each have been synthesized.

22.11 FISCHER'S PROOF OF THE CONFIGURATION OF D-(+)-GLUCOSE

Emil Fischer began his work on the stereochemistry of (+)-glucose in 1888, only 12 years after van't Hoff and Le Bel had made their proposal concerning the tetrahedral structure of carbon. Only a small body of data was available to Fischer at the beginning: Only a few monosaccharides were known, including (+)-glucose, (+)-arabinose, and (+)-mannose. [(+)-Mannose had just been synthesized by Fischer.] The sugars (+)-glucose and (+)-mannose were known to be aldohexoses; (+)-arabinose was known to be an aldopentose.

Since an aldohexose has four stereocenters, 2^4 (or 16) stereoisomers are possible — *one of which is (+)-glucose.* Fischer arbitrarily decided to limit his attention to the

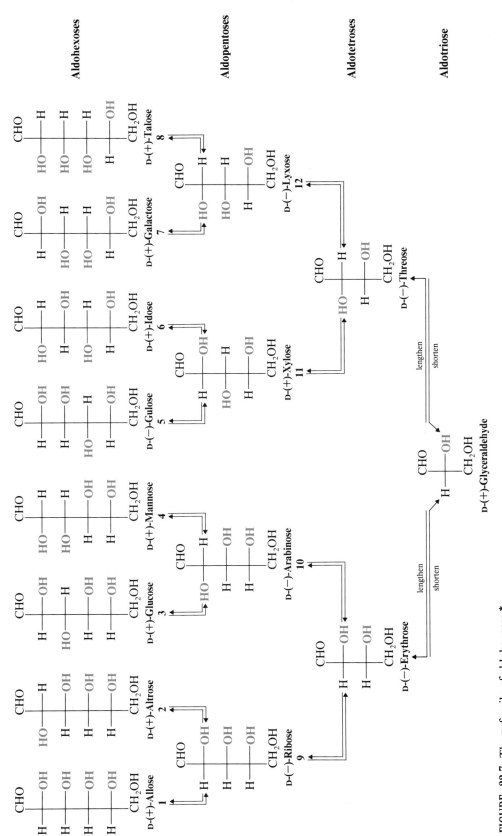

FIGURE 22.7 The D family of aldohexoses.*

*A useful mnemonic for the D-aldohexoses: All altruists gladly make gum in gallon tanks. Write the names in a line and above each write CH_2OH. Then, for C-5 write OH to the right all the way across. For C-4 write OH to the right four times, then four to the left; for C-3, write OH twice to the right, twice to the left, and repeat; C-2, alternate OH and H to the right. (From L. F. Fieser and Mary Fieser, *Organic Chemistry*, Reinhold, New York, 1956, p. 359.)

eight structures with the D configuration given in Fig. 22.7 (structures **1–8**). Fischer realized that he would be unable to differentiate between enantiomeric configurations because methods for determining the absolute configuration of organic compounds had not been developed. It was not until 1951, when Bijvoet (Section 5.13A) determined the absolute configuration of L-(+)-tartaric acid [and, hence, D-(+)-glyceraldehyde] that Fischer's arbitrary assignment of (+)-glucose to the family we call the D family was known to be correct.

Fischer's assignment of structure **3** to (+)-glucose was based on the following reasoning:

1. Nitric acid oxidation of (+)-glucose gives an optically active aldaric acid. This eliminates structures **1** and **7** from consideration because both compounds would yield *meso*-aldaric acids.

2. *Degradation of (+)-glucose gives (−)-arabinose, and nitric acid oxidation of (−)-arabinose gives an optically active aldaric acid.* This means that (−)-arabinose cannot have configurations **9** or **11** and must have either structure **10** or **12**. It also establishes that (+)-glucose cannot have configuration **2**, **5**, or **6**. This leaves structures **3**, **4**, and **8** as possibilities for (+)-glucose.

3. A Kiliani–Fischer synthesis beginning with (−)-arabinose gives (+)-glucose and (+)-mannose; nitric acid oxidation of (+)-mannose gives an optically active aldaric acid. This, together with the fact that (+)-glucose yields a different but also optically active aldaric acid, establishes structure **10** as the structure of (−)-arabinose and eliminates structure **8** as a possible structure for (+)-glucose. Had (−)-arabinose been represented by structure **12**, a Kiliani–Fischer synthesis would have given the two aldohexoses, **7** and **8**, one of which (**7**) would yield an optically inactive aldaric acid on nitric acid oxidation.

4. Two structures now remain, **3** and **4**; one structure represents (+)-glucose and one represents (+)-mannose. Fischer realized that (+)-glucose and (+)-mannose were epimeric (at C-2), but a decision as to which compound was represented by which structure was most difficult.

5. Fischer had already developed a method for effectively *interchanging the two end groups* (CHO and CH$_2$OH) *of an aldose chain.* And, with brilliant logic, Fischer realized that if (+)-glucose has structure **4**, an interchange of end groups *will yield the same aldohexose:*

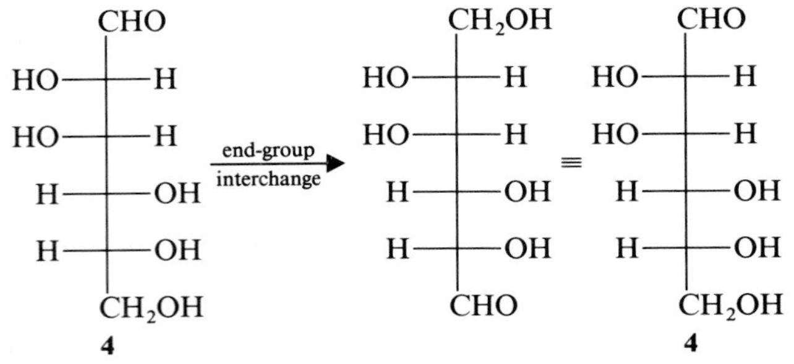

On the other hand, if (+)-glucose has structure **3**, *an end-group interchange will yield a different aldohexose,* **13**:

22.11 FISCHER'S PROOF OF THE CONFIGURATION OF D-(+)-GLUCOSE

```
    CHO                      CH2OH              CHO
H ──┼── OH              H ──┼── OH      HO ──┼── H
HO ─┼── H    end-group  HO ─┼── H      HO ──┼── H
H ──┼── OH   interchange H ──┼── OH  ≡  H ──┼── OH
H ──┼── OH             H ──┼── OH     HO ──┼── H
    CH2OH                   CHO               CH2OH
      3                                        13
                                            L-Gulose
```

This new aldohexose, if it were formed, would be an L-sugar and it would be the mirror reflection of D-gulose. Thus its name would be L-gulose.

Fischer carried out the end-group interchange starting with (+)-glucose and *the product was the new aldohexose* **13**. This outcome proved that (+)-glucose has structure **3**. It also established **4** as the structure for (+)-mannose, and it proved the structure of L-(+)-gulose as **13**.

The procedure Fischer used for interchanging the ends of the (+)-glucose chain began with one of the γ-lactones of D-glucaric acid (cf. Problem 22.8) and was carried out as follows:

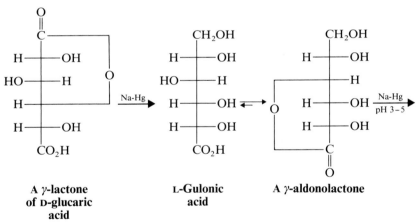

A γ-lactone   L-Gulonic   A γ-aldonolactone
of D-glucaric   acid
  acid

```
                              CH2OH          O
                                             ‖
                          H ──┼── OH     H──C──H
                          HO ─┼── H     HO ─┼── H
                          H ──┼── OH  ≡  H ──┼── OH
                          H ──┼── OH    HO ─┼── H
                              C──H          CH2OH
                              ‖
                              O
                          L-(+)-Gulose
                               13
```

Notice in this synthesis that the second reduction with Na-Hg is carried out at pH 3 – 5. Under these conditions, reduction of the lactone yields an aldehyde and not a primary alcohol.

Problem 22.18

Fischer actually had to subject both γ-lactones of D-glucaric acid (Problem 22.8) to the procedure just outlined. What product does the other γ-lactone yield?

22.12 DISACCHARIDES

22.12A SUCROSE

Ordinary table sugar is a disaccharide called *sucrose*. Sucrose, the most widely occurring disaccharide, is found in all photosynthetic plants and is obtained commercially from sugar cane or sugar beets. Sucrose has the structure shown in Fig. 22.8.

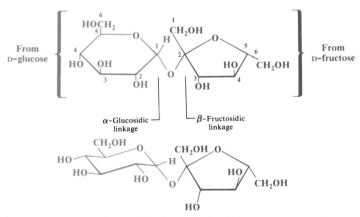

FIGURE 22.8 Two representations of the formula for (+)-sucrose (α-D-glucopyranosyl β-D-fructofuranoside).

The structure of sucrose is based on the following evidence:

1. Sucrose has the molecular formula $C_{12}H_{22}O_{11}$.
2. Acid-catalyzed hydrolysis of 1 mol of sucrose yields 1 mol of D-glucose and 1 mol of D-fructose.

$$
\begin{array}{c}
\overset{6}{\text{HOCH}_2} \quad \text{O} \quad\quad \text{OH} \\
\text{Fructose} \\
(\text{as a } \beta-\text{furanose})
\end{array}
$$

3. Sucrose is a nonreducing sugar; it gives negative tests with Benedict's and Tollens' solutions. Sucrose does not form an osazone and does not undergo mutarotation. These facts mean that neither the glucose nor the fructose portion of sucrose has a hemiacetal or hemiketal group. Thus, the two hexoses must have a glycoside linkage that involves C-1 of glucose and C-2 of fructose, for only in this way will both carbonyl groups be present as full acetals or ketals (i.e., as glycosides).

4. The stereochemistry of the glycoside linkages can be inferred from experiments done with enzymes. Sucrose is hydrolyzed by an *α-glucosidase* obtained from yeast but not by *β*-glucosidases. This hydrolysis indicates *an α configuration at the glucoside portion.* Sucrose is also hydrolyzed by *sucrase,* an enzyme known to hydrolyze *β*-fructofuranosides but not *α*-fructofuranosides. This hydrolysis indicates a *β configuration at the fructoside portion.*

5. Methylation of sucrose gives an octamethyl derivative that, on hydrolysis, gives 2,3,4,6-tetra-*O*-methyl-D-glucose and 1,3,4,6-tetra-*O*-methyl-D-fructose. The identities of these two products demonstrate that the glucose portion is a *pyranoside* and that the fructose portion is a *furanoside.*

The structure of sucrose has been confirmed by X-ray analysis and by an unambiguous synthesis.

22.12B MALTOSE

When starch (Section 22.13A) is hydrolyzed by the enzyme *diastase,* one product is a disaccharide known as *maltose* (Fig. 22.9).

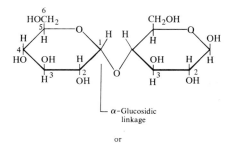

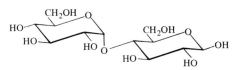

FIGURE 22.9 Two representations of the structure of the *β* anomer of (+)-maltose, 4-*O*-(*α*-D-glucopyranosyl)-*β*-D-glucopyranose.

1. When 1 mol of maltose is subjected to acid-catalyzed hydrolysis, it yields 2 mol of D-(+)-glucose.

2. Unlike sucrose, *maltose is a reducing sugar;* it gives positive tests with Fehling's, Benedict's, and Tollens' solutions. Maltose also reacts with phenylhydrazine to form a monophenylosazone (i.e., it incorporates two molecules of phenylhydrazine).

3. Maltose exists in two anomeric forms; α-(+)-maltose, $[\alpha]_D^{25} = +168°$, and β-(+)-maltose, $[\alpha]_D^{25} = +112°$. The maltose anomers undergo mutarotation to yield an equilibrium mixture, $[\alpha]_D^{25} = +136°$.

Facts 2 and 3 demonstrate that one of the glucose residues of maltose is present in a hemiacetal form; the other, therefore, must be present as a glucoside. The configuration of this glucosidic linkage can be inferred as α, because maltose is hydrolyzed by α-glucosidases and not by β-glucosidases.

4. Maltose reacts with bromine water to form a monocarboxylic acid, maltonic acid (Fig. 22.10a). This fact, too, is consistent with the presence of only one hemiacetal group.

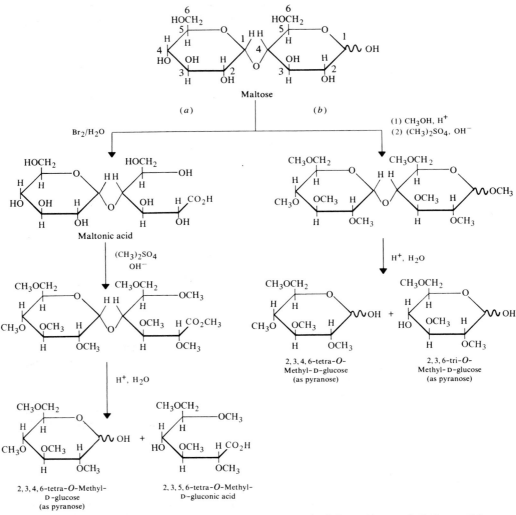

FIGURE 22.10 (a) Oxidation of maltose to maltonic acid followed by methylation and hydrolysis. (b) Methylation and subsequent hydrolysis of maltose itself.

5. Methylation of maltonic acid followed by hydrolysis gives 2,3,4,6-tetra-*O*-methyl-D-glucose and 2,3,5,6-tetra-*O*-methyl-D-gluconic acid. That the first product has a free —OH at C-5 indicates that the nonreducing glucose portion is present as a pyranoside; that the second product, 2,3,5,6-tetra-*O*-methyl-D-gluconic acid, has a free —OH at C-4 indicates that this position was involved in a glycosidic linkage with the nonreducing glucose.

Only the size of the reducing glucose ring needs to be determined.

6. Methylation of maltose itself, followed by hydrolysis (Fig. 22.10*b*), gives 2,3,4,6-tetra-*O*-methyl-D-glucose and 2,3,6-tri-*O*-methyl-D-glucose. The free —OH at C-5 in the latter product indicates that it must have been involved in the oxide ring and that the reducing glucose is present as a *pyranose*.

22.12C CELLOBIOSE

Partial hydrolysis of cellulose (Section 22.13C) gives the disaccharide cellobiose ($C_{12}H_{22}O_{11}$) (Fig. 22.11). Cellobiose resembles maltose in every respect except one: the configuration of its glycosidic linkage.

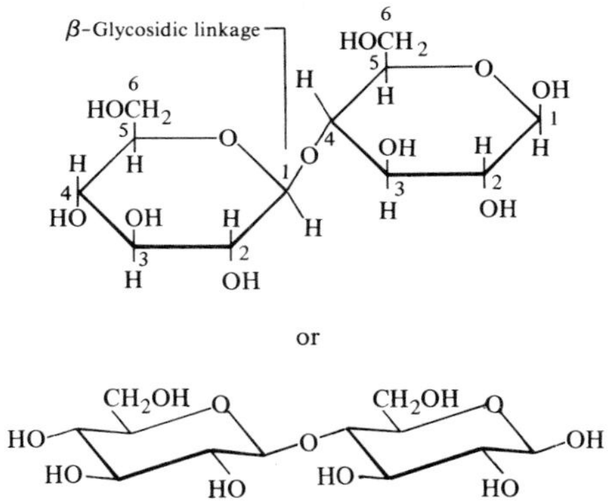

FIGURE 22.11 Two representations of the β anomer of cellobiose, 4-*O*-(β-D-glucopyranosyl)-β-D-glucopyranose.

Cellobiose, like maltose, is a reducing sugar that, on acid-catalyzed hydrolysis, yields two molar equivalents of D-glucose. Cellobiose also undergoes mutarotation and forms a phenylosazone. Methylation studies show that C-1 of one glucose unit is connected in glycosidic linkage with C-4 of the other and that both rings are six membered. Unlike maltose, however, cellobiose is hydrolyzed by *β-glucosidases* and not by α-glucosidases: This indicates that the glycosidic linkage in cellobiose is β (Fig. 22.11).

22.12D LACTOSE

Lactose (Fig. 22.12) is a disaccharide present in the milk of humans, cows, and almost all other mammals. Lactose is a reducing sugar that hydrolyzes to yield D-glucose and D-galactose; the glycosidic linkage is β.

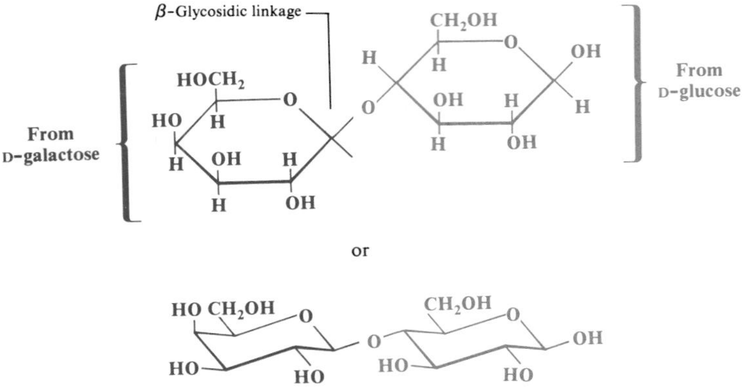

FIGURE 22.12 Two representations of the β anomer of lactose, 4-O-(β-D-galactopyrano-syl)-β-D-glucopyranose.

22.13 POLYSACCHARIDES

Polysaccharides, also known as **glycans,** consist of monosaccharides joined together by glycosidic linkages. Polysaccharides that are polymers of a single monosaccharide are called **homopolysaccharides;** those made up of more than one type of monosaccharide are called **heteropolysaccharides.** Homopolysaccharides are also classified on the basis of their monosaccharide units. A homopolysaccharide consisting of glucose monomeric units is called a **glucan;** one consisting of galactose units is a **galactan,** and so on.

Three important polysaccharides, all of which are glucans, are starch, glycogen, and cellulose. Starch is the principal food reserve of plants; glycogen functions as a carbohydrate reserve for animals; and cellulose serves as structural material in plants. As we examine the structures of these three polysaccharides, we shall be able to see how each is especially suited for its function.

22.13A STARCH

Starch occurs as microscopic granules in the roots, tubers, and seeds of plants. Corn, potatoes, wheat, and rice are important commercial sources. Heating starch with water causes the granules to swell and produce a colloidal suspension from which two major components can be isolated. One fraction is called *amylose* and the other *amylopectin.* Most starches yield 10–20% amylose and 80–90% amylopectin.

Physical measurements show that amylose typically consists of more than 1000 D-glucopyranoside units *connected in α linkages* between C-1 of one unit and C-4 of the next (Fig. 22.13). Thus, in the ring size of its glucose units and in the configuration of the glycosidic linkages between them, amylose resembles maltose.

Chains of D-glucose units with α-glycosidic linkages such as those of amylose tend to assume a helical arrangement (Fig. 22.14). This arrangement results in a compact shape for the amylose molecule even though its molecular weight is quite large (150,000–600,000).

Amylopectin has a structure similar to that of amylose (i.e., α,1 : 4 links), with the exception that in amylopectin the chains are branched. Branching takes place between C-6 of one glucose unit and C-1 of another and occurs at intervals of 20–25 glucose units (Fig. 22.15). Physical measurements indicate that amylopectin has a

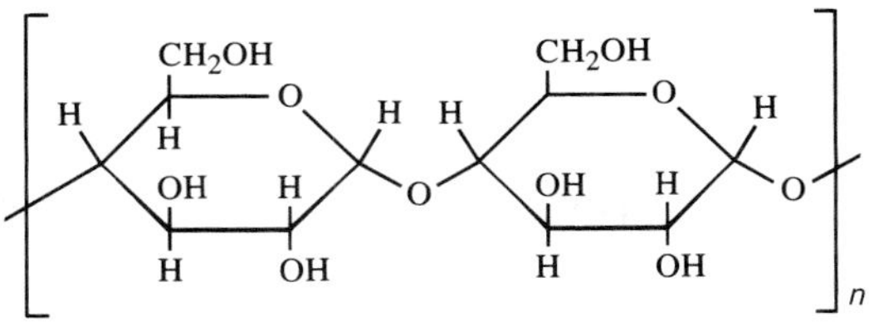

$$n > 1000$$

FIGURE 22.13 Partial structure of amylose, an unbranched polymer of D-glucose connected in $\alpha,1:4$-glycosidic linkages.

FIGURE 22.14 Amylose. The $\alpha,1:4$ linkages cause it to assume the shape of a left-handed helix. (Figure copyrighted © by Irving Geis. From D. Voet and J. G. Voet, *Biochemistry*, Wiley, N.Y. 1990, p. 256. Used with permission.)

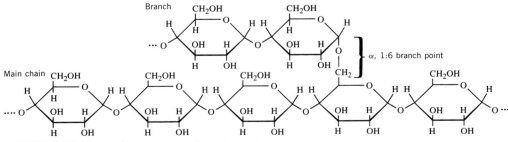

FIGURE 22.15 Partial structure of amylopectin.

molecular weight of 1–6 million; thus amylopectin consists of hundreds of interconnecting chains of 20–25 glucose units each.

22.13B GLYCOGEN

Glycogen has a structure very much like that of amylopectin; however, in glycogen the chains are much more highly branched. Methylation and hydrolysis of glycogen indicates that there is one end group for every 10–12 glucose units; branches may occur as often as every 6. Glycogen has a very high molecular weight. Studies of glycogens isolated under conditions that minimize the likelihood of hydrolysis indicate molecular weights as high as 100 million.

The size and structure of glycogen beautifully suit its function as reserve carbohydrate for animals. First, its size makes it too large to diffuse across cell membranes; thus, glycogen remains inside the cell where it is needed as an energy source. Second, because glycogen incorporates tens of thousands of glucose units in a single molecule, it solves an important osmotic problem for the cell. Were so many glucose units present in the cell as individual molecules, the osmotic pressure within the cell would be enormous—so large that the cell membrane would almost certainly break.* Finally, the localization of glucose units within a large, highly branched structure simplifies one of the cell's logistical problems: that of having a ready source of glucose when cellular glucose concentrations are low and of being able to store glucose rapidly when cellular glucose concentrations are high. There are enzymes within the cell that catalyze the reactions by which glucose units are detached from (or attached to) glycogen. These enzymes operate at end groups by hydrolyzing (or forming) $\alpha, 1:4$ glycosidic linkages. Because glycogen is so highly branched, a very large number of end groups are available at which these enzymes can operate. At the same time the overall concentration of glycogen (in moles per liter) is quite low because of its enormous molecular weight.

Amylopectin presumably serves a similar function in plants. The fact that amylopectin is less highly branched than glycogen is, however, not a serious disadvantage. Plants have a much lower metabolic rate than animals—and plants, of course, do not require sudden bursts of energy.

Animals store energy as fats (triacylglycerols) as well as in glycogen. Fats, because they are more highly reduced, are capable of furnishing much more energy. The metabolism of a typical fatty acid, for example, liberates more than twice as much energy per carbon as glucose or glycogen. Why then, we might ask, has Nature developed two different repositories? Glucose (from glycogen) is readily available and is highly water soluble.† Glucose, as a result, diffuses rapidly through the aqueous medium of the cell and serves as an ideal source of "ready energy." Long-chain fatty acids, by contrast, are almost insoluble in water and their concentration inside the cell could never be very high. They would be a poor source of energy if the cell were in an energy pinch. On the other hand, fatty acids (as triacylglycerols) because of their caloric richness are an excellent energy repository for long-term energy storage.

---

*The phenomenon of osmotic pressure occurs whenever two solutions of different concentrations are separated by a membrane that will allow penetration (by osmosis) of the solvent but not of the solute. The osmotic pressure (π) on one side of the membrane is related to the number of moles of solute particles (n) the volume of the solution (V) and the gas constant times the absolute temperature (RT): $\pi V = nRT$.

†Glucose is actually liberated as glucose-6-phosphate (G6P), which is also water soluble.

22.13C CELLULOSE

When we examine the structure of cellulose, we find another example of a polysaccharide in which nature has arranged monomeric glucose units in a manner that suits its function. Cellulose contains D-glucopyranoside units linked in 1 : 4 fashion in very long unbranched chains. Unlike starch and glycogen, however, the linkages in cellulose are *β-glycosidic linkages* (Fig. 22.16). This configuration of the anomeric carbon atoms of cellulose makes cellulose chains essentially linear; they do not tend to coil into helical structures as do glucose polymers when linked in an $\alpha, 1 : 4$ manner.

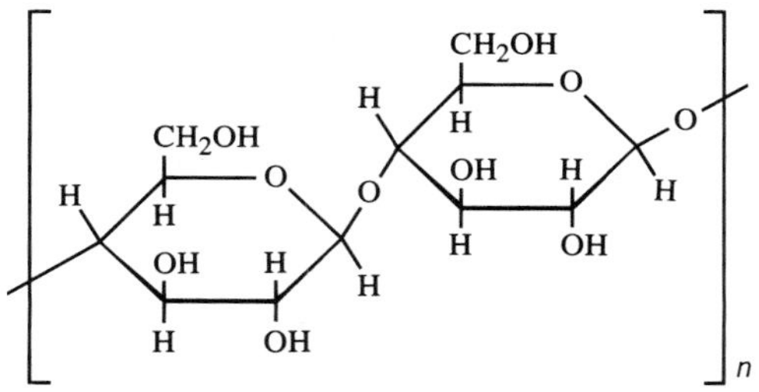

FIGURE 22.16 A portion of a cellulose chain. The glycosidic linkages are $\beta, 1 : 4$.

The linear arrangement of β-linked glucose units in cellulose presents a uniform distribution of —OH groups on the outside of each chain. When two or more cellulose chains make contact, the hydroxyl groups are ideally situated to "zip" the chains together by forming hydrogen bonds (Fig. 22.17). Zipping many cellulose chains together in this way gives a highly insoluble, rigid, and fibrous polymer that is ideal as cell-wall material for plants.

This special property of cellulose chains, we should emphasize, is not just a result of $\beta, 1 : 4$ glycosidic linkages; it is also a consequence of the precise stereochemistry of D-glucose at each stereocenter. Were D-galactose or D-allose units linked in a similar fashion, they almost certainly would not give rise to a polymer with properties like cellulose. Thus, we get another glimpse of why D-glucose occupies such a special position in the chemistry of plants and animals. Not only is it the most stable aldohexose (because it can exist in a chair conformation that allows all of its bulky groups to occupy equatorial positions), but its special stereochemistry also allows it to form helical structures when α linked as in starches, and rigid linear structures when β linked as in cellulose.

> Another interesting and important fact about cellulose: The digestive enzymes of humans cannot attack its $\beta, 1 : 4$ linkages. Hence, cellulose cannot serve as a food source for humans, as can starch. Cows and termites, however, can use cellulose (of grass and wood) as a food source because symbiotic bacteria in their digestive systems furnish β-glucosidases.

Perhaps we should ask ourselves one other question: Why has Nature "chosen" D-(+)-glucose for its special role rather than L-(−)-glucose, its mirror image? Here an answer cannot be given with any certainty. The selection of D-(+)-glucose may simply have been a random event early in the course of the evolution of enzyme catalysts. Once this selection was made, however, the stereogenicity of the active sites of the enzymes involved would retain a bias toward D-(+)-glucose and against L-(−)-

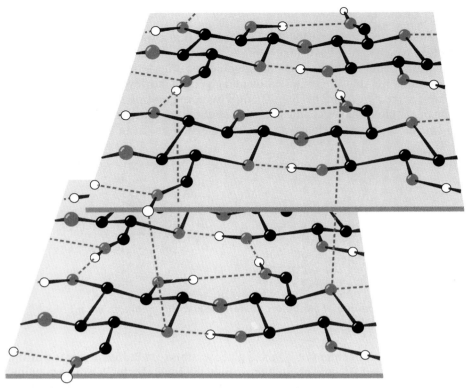

FIGURE 22.17 A proposed structure for cellulose. A fiber of cellulose may consist of about 40 parallel strands of glucose molecules linked in a $\beta,1:4$ fashion. Each glucose unit in a chain is turned over with respect to the preceding glucose unit, and is held in this position by hydrogen bonds (dashed lines) between the chains. The glucan chains line up laterally to form sheets and these sheets stack vertically so that they are staggered by one half of a glucose unit. (Hydrogen atoms that do not participate in hydrogen bonding have been omitted for clarity.) (From D. Voet and J. G. Voet, *Biochemistry,* Wiley, New York 1990, p. 255. Used with permission.)

glucose (because of the improper fit of the latter). Once introduced, this bias would be perpetuated and extended to other catalysts.

Finally, when we speak of Nature selecting or choosing a particular molecule for a given function, we do not mean to imply that evolution operates on a molecular level. Evolution, of course, takes place at the level of organism populations, and molecules are selected only in the sense that their use gives the organism an increased likelihood of surviving and procreating.

22.13D CELLULOSE DERIVATIVES

A number of derivatives of cellulose are used commercially. Most of these are compounds in which two or three of the free hydroxyl groups of each glucose unit have been converted to an ester or an ether. This conversion substantially alters the physical properties of the material, making it more soluble in organic solvents and allowing it to be made into fibers and films. Treating cellulose with acetic anhydride produces the triacetate known as "Arnel" or "acetate," used widely in the textile industry. Cellulose trinitrate, also called "gun cotton" or nitrocellulose, is used in explosives.

Rayon is made by treating cellulose (from cotton or wood pulp) with carbon disulfide in a basic solution. This reaction converts cellulose to a soluble xanthate:

$$\text{Cellulose—OH} + CS_2 \xrightarrow{\text{NaOH}} \overset{\displaystyle S}{\underset{\displaystyle \|}{\text{cellulose—O—C—S}^-\text{Na}^+}}$$

Cellulose xanthate

The solution of cellulose xanthate is then passed through a small orifice or slit into an acidic solution. This operation regenerates the —OH groups of cellulose causing it to precipitate as a fiber or a sheet.

$$\overset{\displaystyle S}{\underset{\displaystyle \|}{\text{Cellulose—O—C—S}^-\text{Na}^+}} \xrightarrow{\text{H}_3\text{O}^+} \text{cellulose—OH}$$

Rayon or cellophane

The fibers are *rayon;* the sheets, after softening with glycerol, are *cellophane.*

22.14 OTHER BIOLOGICALLY IMPORTANT SUGARS

Monosaccharide derivatives in which the —CH_2OH group at C-6 has been specifically oxidized to a carboxyl group are called **uronic acids.** Their names are based on the monosaccharide from which they are derived. For example, specific oxidation of C-6 of glucose to a carboxyl group converts *glucose* to **glucuronic acid.** In the same way, specific oxidation of C-6 of *galactose* would yield **galacturonic acid.**

D-Glucuronic acid   D-Galacturonic acid

Problem 22.19

Direct oxidation of an aldose affects the aldehyde group first, converting it to a carboxylic acid (Section 22.6B), and most oxidizing agents that will attack 1° alcohol groups will also attack 2° alcohol groups. Clearly, then, a laboratory synthesis of a uronic acid from an aldose requires protecting these groups from oxidation. Keeping this in mind, suggest a method for carrying out a specific oxidation that would convert D-galactose to D-galacturonic acid. (*Hint:* See Section 22.5C.)

Monosaccharides in which an —OH group has been replaced by —H are known as **deoxy sugars.** The most important deoxy sugar, because it occurs in DNA, is **deoxyribose.** Other deoxy sugars that occur widely in polysaccharides are L-rhamnose and L-fucose.

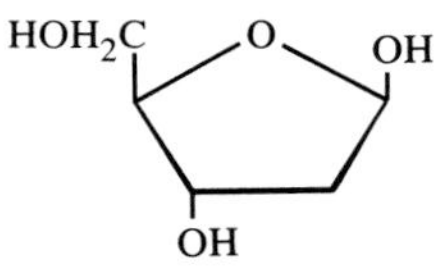

β-2-Deoxyribose 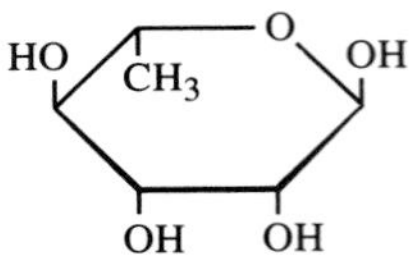   α-L-Rhamnose   α-L-Fucose
(6-deoxy-L-mannose)   (6-deoxy-L-galactose)

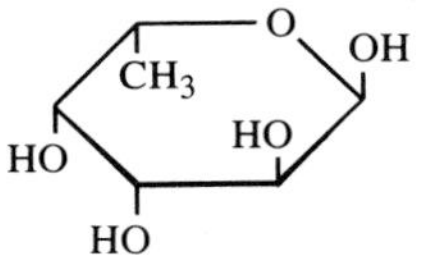

22.15 SUGARS THAT CONTAIN NITROGEN

22.15A GLYCOSYLAMINES

A sugar in which an amino group replaces the anomeric —OH is called a glycosylamine. Examples are β-D-glucopyranosylamine and adenosine (see following figures).

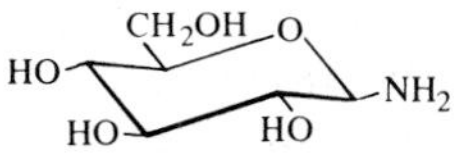

β-D-Glucopyranosyl amine 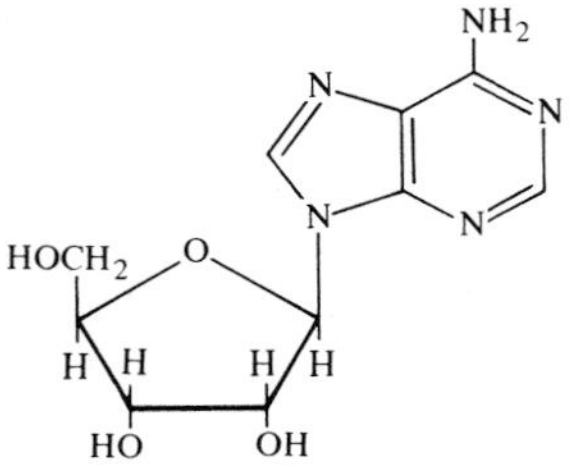   Adenosine

Adenosine is an example of a glycosylamine that is also called a **nucleoside.** Nucleosides are glycosylamines in which the amino component is a pyrimidine or a purine (Section 19.1B) and in which the sugar component is either D-ribose or 2-deoxy-D-ribose (i.e., D-ribose minus the oxygen at the 2 position). Nucleosides are the important components of RNA (ribonucleic acid) and DNA (deoxyribonucleic acid). We shall describe their properties in detail in Section 25.2.

22.15B AMINO SUGARS

A sugar in which an amino group replaces a nonanomeric —OH group is called an **amino sugar.** An example is D-**glucosamine.** In many instances the amino group is acetylated as in **N-acetyl-D-glucosamine. N-Acetylmuramic acid** is an important component of bacterial cell walls (Section 24.10).

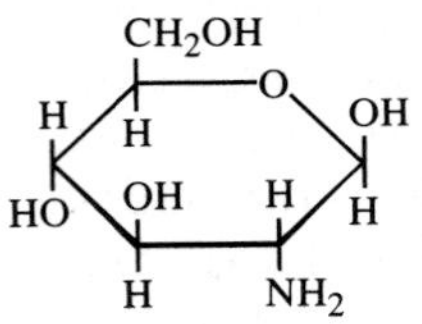

β-D-Glucosamine 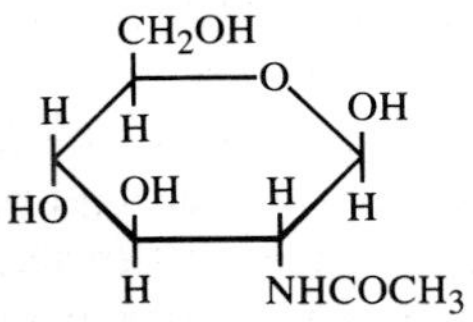   β-N-Acetyl-D-glucosamine   β-N-Acetylmuramic acid
(NAM)   (NAG)

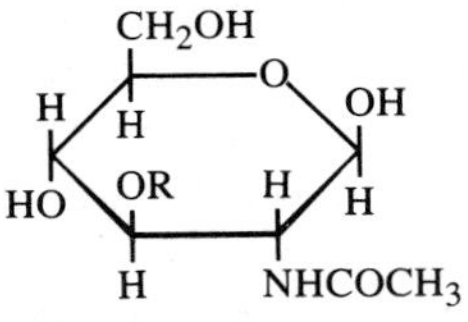

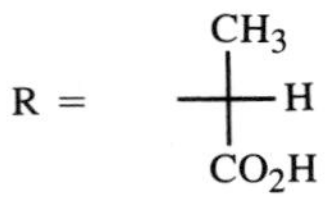

D-Glucosamine can be obtained by hydrolysis of **chitin,** a polysaccharide found in the shells of lobsters and crabs and in the external skeletons of insects and spiders. The amino group of D-glucosamine as it occurs in chitin, however, is acetylated; thus, the repeating unit is actually *N*-acetylglucosamine (Fig. 22.18). The glycosidic linkages in chitin are β,1 : 4. X-ray analysis indicates that the structure of chitin is similar to that of cellulose.

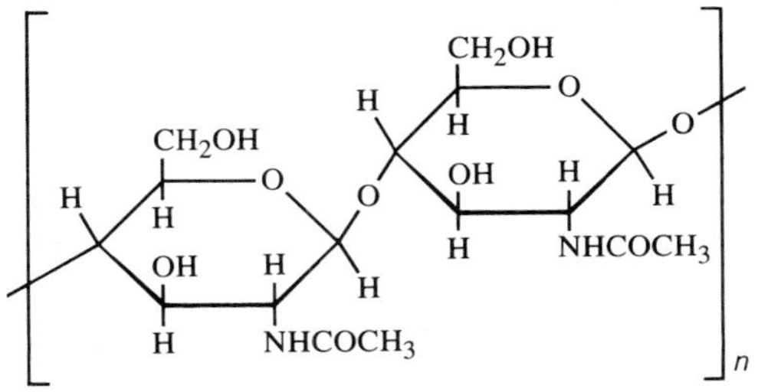

FIGURE 22.18 A partial structure of chitin. The repeating units are *N*-acetylglucosamines linked β,1 : 4.

D-Glucosamine can also be isolated from **heparin,** a sulfated polysaccharide that consists predominately of alternating units of D-glucuronate-2-sulfate and *N*-sulfo-D-glucosamine-6-sulfate (Fig. 22.19). Heparin occurs in intracellular granules of mast cells that line arterial walls, where, when released through injury, it inhibits the clotting of blood. Its purpose seems to be to prevent runaway clot formation. Heparin is widely used in medicine to prevent blood clotting in postsurgical patients.

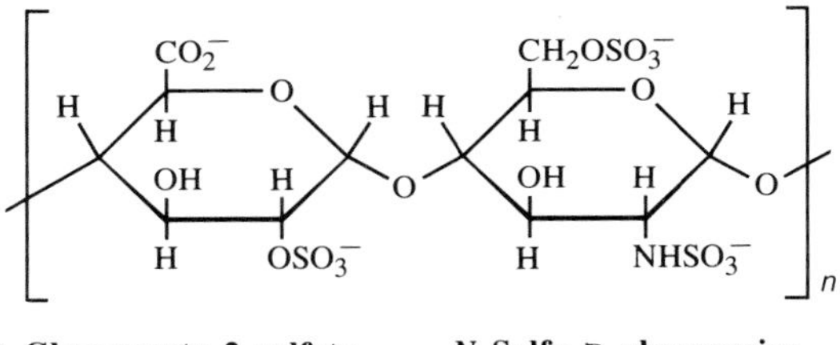

D-Glucuronate-2-sulfate   *N*-Sulfo-D-glucosamine-
                                       6-sulfate

FIGURE 22.19 A partial structure of heparin, a polysaccharide that prevents blood clotting.

22.16 GLYCOLIPIDS AND GLYCOPROTEINS OF THE CELL SURFACE

Prior to 1960, it was thought that the biology of carbohydrates was rather uninteresting; that, in addition to being a kind of inert filler in cells, carbohydrates served only as an energy source, and in plants as structural materials. Research of the last 30 years has shown, however, that carbohydrates joined through glycosidic linkages to lipids (Chapter 23) and to proteins (Chapter 24), called **glycolipids** and **glycoproteins,** respectively, have functions that span the entire spectrum of activities in the cell. Indeed, most proteins are glycoproteins, and the carbohydrate content of glycoproteins can vary from less than 1% to greater than 90%.

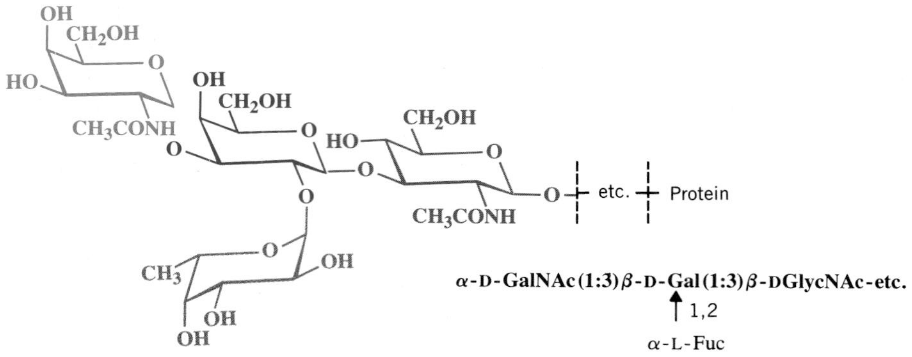

α-D-GalNAc(1:3)β-D-Gal(1:3)β-DGlycNAc-etc.

↑ 1,2

α-L-Fuc

Type A determinant

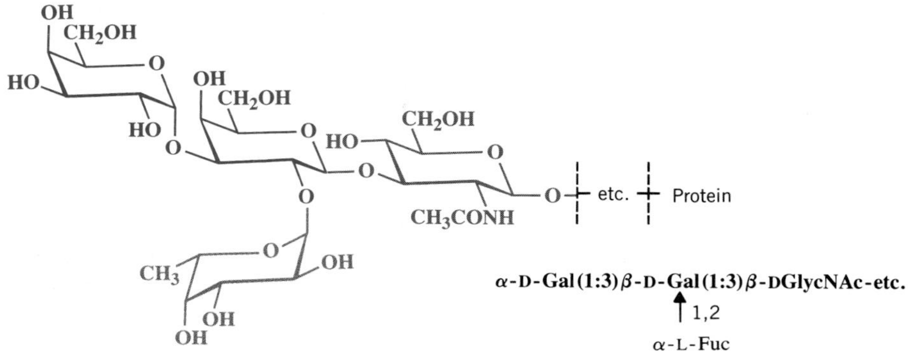

α-D-Gal(1:3)β-D-Gal(1:3)β-DGlycNAc-etc.

↑ 1,2

α-L-Fuc

Type B determinant

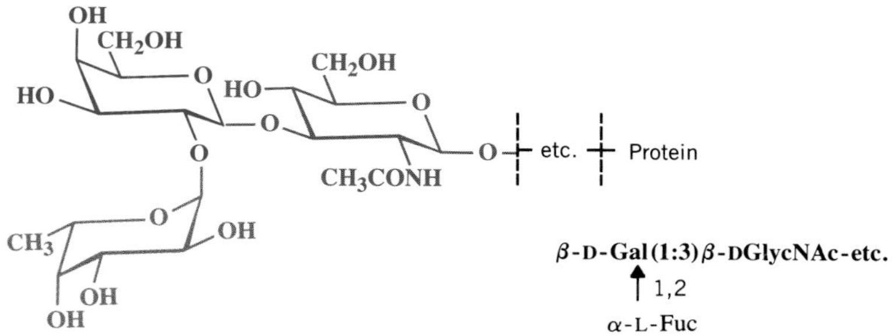

β-D-Gal(1:3)β-DGlycNAc-etc.

↑ 1,2

α-L-Fuc

Type H determinant

FIGURE 22.20 The terminal monosaccharides of the antigenic determinants for types A, B, and O blood. The type H determinant is present in individuals with blood type O and is the precursor of the type A and B determinants. These oligosaccharide antigens are attached to carrier lipid or protein molecules that are anchored in the red blood cell membrane (see Fig. 23.8, for a depiction of a cell membrane.) Ac = acetyl, Gal = D-galactose, GalNAc = N-acetyl-galactosamine, GlycNAc = N-acetyl-glucosamine, Fuc = Fucose.

Glycolipids and glycoproteins on the cell surface (Section 23.6A) are now known to be the agents by which cells interact with other cells and with invading bacteria and viruses. The human blood groups offer an example of how carbohydrates, in the form of glycolipids and glycoproteins, act as biochemical markers. The A, B, and O blood types are determined, respectively, by the A, B, and H determinants on the blood cell surface. (The odd naming of the type O determinant came about for complicated historical reasons.) Type AB blood cells have both A and B determinants. These determinants are the carbohydrate portions of the A, B, and H **antigens.**

Antigens are characteristic chemical groups that cause the production of **antibodies** when injected into an animal. Each antibody can bind at least two of its corresponding antigen molecules causing them to become linked. Linking of red blood cells causes them to agglutinate (clump together). In a transfusion this agglutination can lead to a fatal blockage of the blood vessels.

Individuals with type A antigens on their blood cells carry anti-B antibodies in their serum; those with type B antigens on their blood cells carry anti-A antibodies in their serum. Individuals with type AB cells, have both A and B antigens, but have neither anti-A nor anti-B antibodies. Type O individuals have neither A nor B antigens on their blood cells but have both anti-A and anti-B antibodies.

The A, B, and H antigens differ only in the monosaccharide units at their nonreducing ends. The type H antigen (Fig. 22.20) is the precursor oligosaccharide of the type A and B antigens. Individuals with blood type A have an enzyme that specifically adds an N-acetylgalactosamine unit to the 3-OH group of the terminal galactose unit of the H antigen. Individuals with blood type B have an enzyme that specifically adds galactose instead. In individuals with type O blood, the enzyme is inactive.

Antigen–antibody interactions like those that determine blood types are the basis of the immune system. These interactions almost always involve the chemical recognition of a glycolipid or glycoprotein in the antigen by a glycolipid or glycoprotein of the antibody.

22.17 CARBOHYDRATE ANTIBIOTICS

One of the important discoveries in carbohydrate chemistry was the isolation (in 1944) of the carbohydrate antibiotic called *streptomycin*. Streptomycin is made up of the following three subunits:

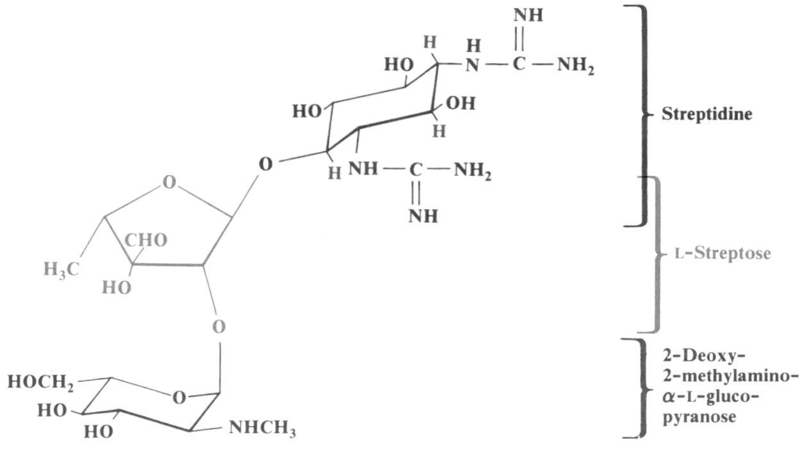

All three components are unusual: The amino sugar is based on L-glucose; streptose is a branched-chain monosaccharide; and streptidine is not a sugar at all, but is a cyclohexane derivative called an amino cyclitol.

Other members of this family are antibiotics called kanamycins, neomycins, and gentamicins (not shown). All are based on an amino cyclitol linked to one or more amino sugars. The glycosidic linkage is nearly always α. These antibiotics are especially useful against bacteria that are resistant to penicillins.

Additional Problems

22.20 Give appropriate structural formulas to illustrate each of the following:

(a) An aldopentose
(b) A ketohexose
(c) An L-monosaccharide
(d) A glycoside
(e) An aldonic acid
(f) An aldaric acid

(g) An aldonolactone
(h) A pyranose
(i) A furanose
(j) A reducing sugar
(k) A pyranoside
(l) A furanoside

(m) Epimers
(n) Anomers
(o) A phenylosazone
(p) A disaccharide
(q) A polysaccharide
(r) A nonreducing sugar

22.21 Draw conformational formulas for each of the following: (a) α-D-allopyranose, (b) methyl β-D-allopyranoside, and (c) methyl 2,3,4,6-tetra-*O*-methyl-β-D-allopyranoside.

22.22 Draw structures for furanose and pyranose forms of D-ribose. Show how you could use periodate oxidation to distinguish between a methyl ribofuranoside and a methyl ribopyranoside.

22.23 One reference book lists D-mannose as being dextrorotatory; another lists it as being levorotatory. Both references are correct. Explain.

22.24 The starting material for a commercial synthesis of vitamin C is L-sorbose (see following reaction); it can be synthesized from D-glucose through the following reaction sequence:

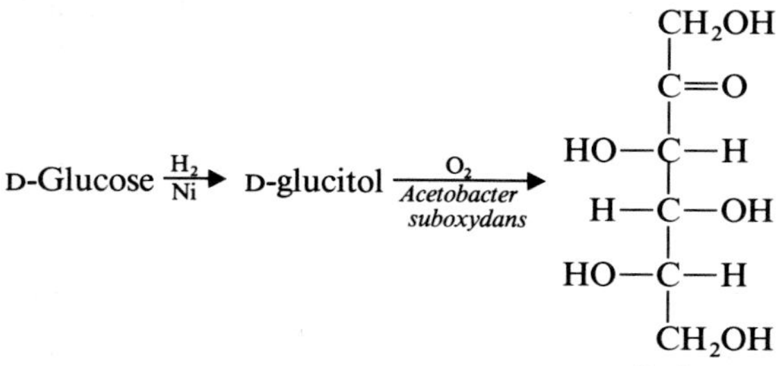

$$\text{D-Glucose} \xrightarrow[\text{Ni}]{\text{H}_2} \text{D-glucitol} \xrightarrow[\substack{\text{Acetobacter} \\ \text{suboxydans}}]{\text{O}_2}$$

CH$_2$OH
|
C=O
|
HO—C—H
|
H—C—OH
|
HO—C—H
|
CH$_2$OH

L-Sorbose

The second step of this sequence illustrates the use of a bacterial oxidation; the microorganism *Acetobacter suboxydans* accomplishes this step in 90% yield. The overall result of the synthesis is the transformation of a D-aldohexose (D-glucose) into an L-ketohexose (L-sorbose). What does this mean about the specificity of the bacterial oxidation?

22.25 What two aldoses would yield the same phenylosazone as L-sorbose (Problem 22.24)?

22.26 In addition to fructose (Problem 22.12) and sorbose (Problem 22.24) there are two other 2-ketohexoses, *psicose* and *tagatose*. D-Psicose yields the same phenylosazone as D-allose (or D-altrose); D-tagatose yields the same osazone as D-galactose (or D-talose). What are the structures of D-psicose and D-tagatose?

ADDITIONAL PROBLEMS

22.27 **A**, **B**, and **C** are three aldohexoses. Compounds **A** and **B** yield the same optically active alditol when they are reduced with hydrogen and a catalyst; **A** and **B** yield different phenylosazones when treated with phenylhydrazine; **B** and **C** give the same phenylosazone but different alditols. Assuming that all are D-sugars, give names and structures for **A**, **B**, and **C**.

22.28 D-Xylitol is a sweetener that is used in sugarless chewing gum. Starting with an appropriate monosaccharide, outline a possible synthesis of D-xylitol.

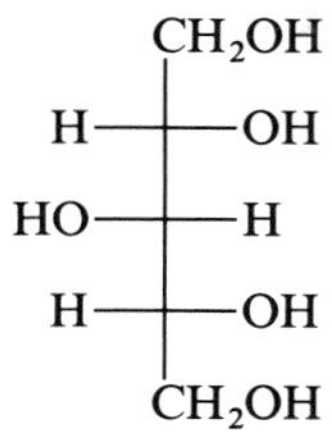

$$
\begin{array}{c}
\text{CH}_2\text{OH} \\
\text{H} \quad\rule[0.5ex]{2em}{0.4pt}\quad \text{OH} \\
\text{HO} \quad\rule[0.5ex]{2em}{0.4pt}\quad \text{H} \\
\text{H} \quad\rule[0.5ex]{2em}{0.4pt}\quad \text{OH} \\
\text{CH}_2\text{OH}
\end{array}
$$
D-Xylitol

22.29 Although monosaccharides undergo complex isomerizations in base (cf. Section 22.5), aldonic acids are epimerized specifically at C-2 when they are heated with pyridine. Show how you could make use of this reaction in a synthesis of D-mannose from D-glucose.

22.30 (a) The most stable conformation of most aldopyranoses is one in which the largest group—the —CH$_2$OH group—is equatorial. However, D-idopyranose exists primarily in a conformation with an axial —CH$_2$OH group. Write formulas for the two chair conformations of α-D-idopyranose (one with the —CH$_2$OH group axial and one with the —CH$_2$OH group equatorial) and provide an explanation.

22.31 (a) Heating D-altrose with dilute acid produces a nonreducing *anhydro sugar* (C$_6$H$_{10}$O$_5$). Methylation of the anhydro sugar followed by acid hydrolysis yields 2,3,4-tri-*O*-methyl-D-altrose. The formation of the anhydro sugar takes place through a chair conformation of β-D-altropyranose in which the —CH$_2$OH group is axial. What is the structure of the anhydro sugar and how is it formed? (b) D-Glucose also forms an anhydro sugar but the conditions required are much more drastic than for the corresponding reaction of D-altrose. Explain.

22.32 Show how the following experimental evidence can be used to deduce the structure of lactose (Section 22.12D).

  1. Acid hydrolysis of lactose (C$_{12}$H$_{22}$O$_{11}$) gives equimolar quantities of D-glucose and D-galactose. Lactose undergoes a similar hydrolysis in the presence of a *β-galactosidase*.
  2. Lactose is a reducing sugar and forms a phenylosazone; it also undergoes mutarotation.
  3. Oxidation of lactose with bromine water followed by hydrolysis with dilute acid gives D-galactose and D-gluconic acid.
  4. Bromine water oxidation of lactose followed by methylation and hydrolysis gives 2,3,6-tri-*O*-methylgluconolactone and 2,3,4,6-tetra-*O*-methyl-D-galactose.
  5. Methylation and hydrolysis of lactose gives 2,3,6-tri-*O*-methyl-D-glucose and 2,3,4,6-tetra-*O*-methyl-D-galactose.

22.33 Deduce the structure of the disaccharide *melibiose* from the following data:

  1. Melibiose is a reducing sugar that undergoes mutarotation and forms a phenylosazone.
  2. Hydrolysis of melibiose with acid or with an *α-galactosidase* gives D-galactose and D-glucose.
  3. Bromine water oxidation of melibiose gives *melibionic acid*. Hydrolysis of melibionic

acid gives D-galactose and D-gluconic acid. Methylation of melibionic acid followed by hydrolysis gives 2,3,4,6-tetra-*O*-methyl-D-galactose and 2,3,4,5-tetra-*O*-methyl-D-gluconic acid.

4. Methylation and hydrolysis of melibiose gives 2,3,4,6-tetra-*O*-methyl-D-galactose and 2,3,4-tri-*O*-methyl-D-glucose.

22.34 Trehalose is a disaccharide that can be obtained from yeasts, fungi, sea urchins, algae, and insects. Deduce the structure of trehalose from the following information:

1. Acid hydrolysis of trehalose yields only D-glucose.

2. Trehalose is hydrolyzed by α-glucosidases but not by β-glucosidases.

3. Trehalose is a nonreducing sugar; it does not mutarotate, form a phenylosazone, or react with bromine water.

4. Methylation of trehalose followed by hydrolysis yields two molar equivalents of 2,3,4,6-tetra-*O*-methyl-D-glucose.

22.35 Outline chemical tests that will distinguish between each of the following:

(a) D-Glucose and D-glucitol   (d) D-Glucose and D-galactose

(b) D-Glucitol and D-glucaric acid   (e) Sucrose and maltose

(c) D-Glucose and D-fructose   (f) Maltose and maltonic acid

(g) Methyl β-D-glucopyranoside and 2,3,4,6-tetra-*O*-methyl-β-D-glucopyranose

(h) Methyl α-D-ribofuranoside **(I)** and methyl 2-deoxy-α-D-ribofuranoside **(II)**

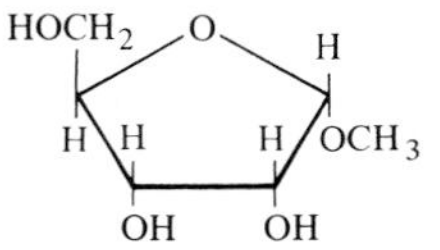

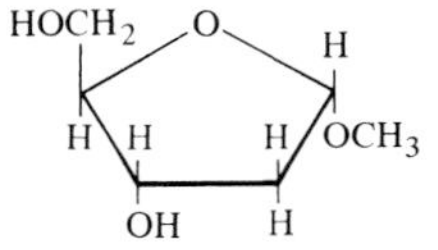

22.36 A group of oligosaccharides called *Schardinger dextrins* can be isolated from *Bacillus macerans* when the bacillus is grown on a medium rich in amylose. These oligosaccharides are all *nonreducing*. A typical Schardinger dextrin undergoes hydrolysis when treated with an acid or an α-glucosidase to yield six, seven, or eight molecules of D-glucose. Complete methylation of a Schardinger dextrin followed by acid hydrolysis yields only 2,3,6-tri-*O*-methyl-D-glucose. Propose a general structure for a Schardinger dextrin.

22.37 *Isomaltose* is a disaccharide that can be obtained by enzymatic hydrolysis of amylopectin. Deduce the structure of isomaltose from the following data:

1. Hydrolysis of 1 mol of isomaltose by acid or by an α-glucosidase gives 2 mol of D-glucose.

2. Isomaltose is a reducing sugar.

3. Isomaltose is oxidized by bromine water to isomaltonic acid. Methylation of isomaltonic acid and subsequent hydrolysis yields 2,3,4,6-tetra-*O*-methyl-D-glucose and 2,3,4,5-tetra-*O*-methyl-D-gluconic acid.

4. Methylation of isomaltose itself followed by hydrolysis gives 2,3,4,6-tetra-*O*-methyl-D-glucose and 2,3,4-tri-*O*-methyl-D-glucose.

22.38 *Stachyose* occurs in the roots of several species of plants. Deduce the structure of stachyose from the following data:

1. Acidic hydrolysis of 1 mol of stachyose yields 2 mol of D-galactose, 1 mol of D-glucose, and 1 mol of D-fructose.

ADDITIONAL PROBLEMS

2. Stachyose is a nonreducing sugar.

3. Treating stachyose with an α-galactosidase produces a mixture containing D-galactose, sucrose, and a nonreducing trisaccharide called *raffinose*.

4. Acidic hydrolysis of raffinose gives D-glucose, D-fructose, and D-galactose. Treating raffinose with an α-galactosidase yields D-galactose and sucrose. Treating raffinose with invertase (an enzyme that hydrolyzes sucrose) yields fructose and *melibiose* (cf. Problem 22.33).

5. Methylation of stachyose followed by hydrolysis yields 2,3,4,6-tetra-*O*-methyl-D-galactose, 2,3,4-tri-*O*-methyl-D-galactose, 2,3,4-tri-*O*-methyl-D-glucose, and 1,3,4,6-tetra-*O*-methyl-D-fructose.

22.39 *Arbutin,* a compound that can be isolated from the leaves of barberry, cranberry, and pear trees, has the molecular formula $C_{12}H_{16}O_7$. When arbutin is treated with aqueous acid or with a β-glucosidase, the reaction produces D-glucose and a compound **X** with the molecular formula $C_6H_6O_2$. The ^{1}H NMR spectrum of compound **X** consists of two singlets, one at δ 6.8 (4H) and one at δ 7.9 (2H). Methylation of arbutin followed by acidic hydrolysis yields 2,3,4,6-tetra-*O*-methyl-D-glucose and a compound **Y** ($C_7H_8O_2$). Compound **Y** is soluble in dilute aqueous NaOH but is insoluble in aqueous NaHCO$_3$. The ^{1}H NMR spectrum of **Y** shows a singlet at δ 3.9 (3H), a singlet at δ 4.8 (1H), and a multiplet (that resembles a singlet) at δ 6.8 (4H). Treating compound **Y** with aqueous NaOH and $(CH_3)_2SO_4$ produces compound **Z** ($C_8H_{10}O_2$). The ^{1}H NMR spectrum of **Z** consists of two singlets, one at δ 3.75 (6H) and one at δ 6.8 (4H). Propose structures for arbutin and for compounds **X**, **Y**, and **Z**.

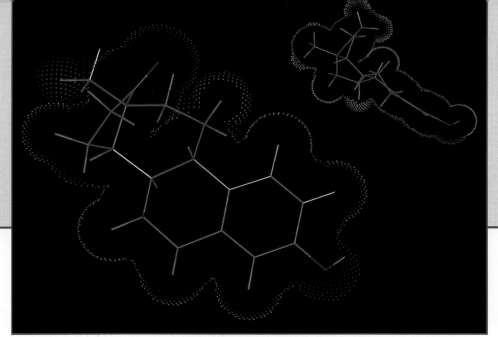

Estrone (see Section 23.4C).

CHAPTER

23

LIPIDS

23.1 INTRODUCTION

Lipids are compounds of biological origin that dissolve in nonpolar solvents, such as chloroform or diethyl ether. The name lipid comes from the Greek word *lipos,* for fat. Unlike carbohydrates and proteins, which are defined in terms of their structures, lipids are defined by the physical operation that we use to isolate them. Not surprisingly, then, lipids include a variety of structural types. Examples are the following:

A fat or oil
(a triacylglycerol)

Menthol
(a terpene)

Vitamin A
(a terpenoid)

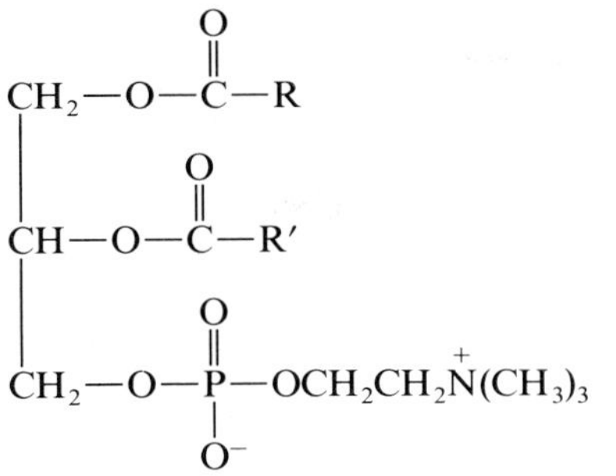

$$CH_2-O-\overset{\overset{O}{\|}}{C}-R$$

$$CH-O-\overset{\overset{O}{\|}}{C}-R'$$

$$CH_2-O-\overset{\overset{O}{\|}}{\underset{\underset{O^-}{|}}{P}}-OCH_2CH_2\overset{+}{N}(CH_3)_3$$

A lecithin
(a phosphatide)

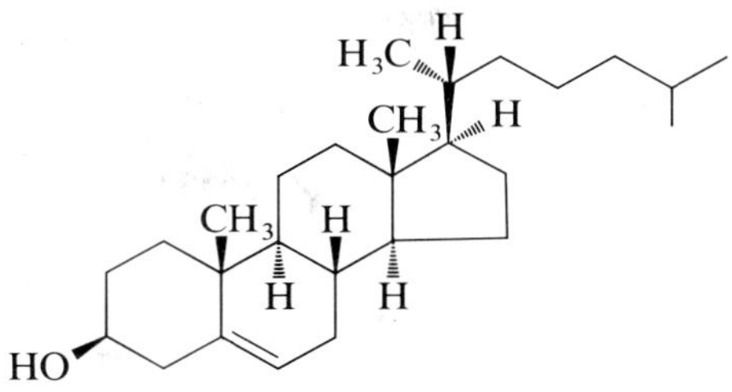

Cholesterol
(a steroid)

23.2 FATTY ACIDS AND TRIACYLGLYCEROLS

Only a small portion of the total lipid fraction consists of long-chain carboxylic acids. Most of the carboxylic acids of biological origin are found as *esters of glycerol,* that is, as **triacylglycerols** (Fig. 23.1).*

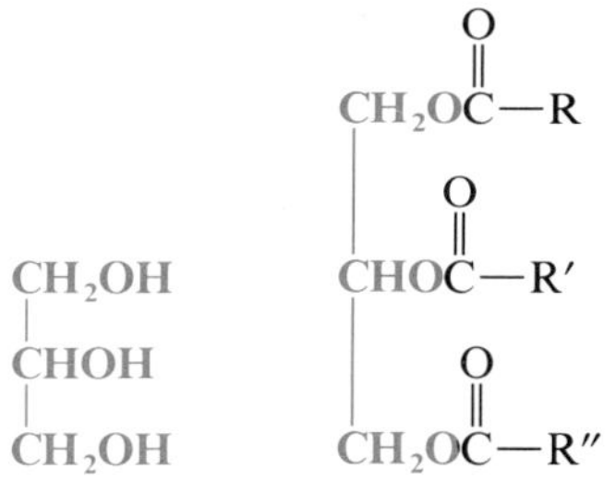

$$CH_2OH$$
$$CHOH$$
$$CH_2OH$$
(a)

$$CH_2O\overset{\overset{O}{\|}}{C}-R$$
$$CHO\overset{\overset{O}{\|}}{C}-R'$$
$$CH_2O\overset{\overset{O}{\|}}{C}-R''$$
(b)

FIGURE 23.1 (*a*) Glycerol. (*b*) A triacylglycerol. The groups R, R', and R" are usually long-chain alkyl groups. R, R', and R" may also contain one or more carbon–carbon double bonds. In a triacylglycerol R, R', and R" may all be different.

Triacylglycerols are the fats and oils of plant or animal origin. They include such common substances as peanut oil, soybean oil, corn oil, sunflower oil, butter, lard, and tallow. Triacylglycerols that are liquids at room temperature are generally called **oils;** those that are solids are called *fats.* Triacylglycerols can be **simple triacylglycerols** in which all three acyl groups are the same. More commonly, however, the triacylglycerol is a **mixed triacylglycerol** in which the acyl groups are different.

---

* In the older literature triacylglycerols were referred to as triglycerides, or simply as glycerides. In IUPAC nomenclature, because they are esters of glycerol, they should be named as glyceryl trialkanoates, glyceryl trialkenoates, and so on.

Hydrolysis of a fat or oil produces a mixture of fatty acids:

$$
\begin{array}{c}
\text{CH}_2\text{—O—C(=O)—R} \\
\text{CH—O—C(=O)—R}' \\
\text{CH}_2\text{—O—C(=O)—R}''
\end{array}
\xrightarrow[\text{(2) H}_3\text{O}^+]{\text{(1) OH}^-/\text{H}_2\text{O, heat}}
\begin{array}{c}
\text{CH}_2\text{—OH} \\
\text{CH—OH} \\
\text{CH}_2\text{—OH}
\end{array}
+
\begin{array}{c}
\text{RCO}_2\text{H} \\
\text{R}'\text{CO}_2\text{H} \\
\text{R}''\text{CO}_2\text{H}
\end{array}
$$

A Fat or oil   Glycerol   Fatty acids

TABLE 23.1 Common fatty acids

	mp (°C)
Saturated Carboxylic Acids	
$\text{CH}_3(\text{CH}_2)_{12}\text{CO}_2\text{H}$ Myristic acid (tetradecanoic acid)	54
$\text{CH}_3(\text{CH}_2)_{14}\text{CO}_2\text{H}$ Palmitic acid (hexadecanoic acid)	63
$\text{CH}_3(\text{CH}_2)_{16}\text{CO}_2\text{H}$ Stearic acid (octadecanoic acid)	70
Unsaturated Carboxylic Acids	
Palmitoleic acid (*cis*-9-hexadecenoic acid)	32
Oleic acid (*cis*-9-octadecenoic acid)	4
Linoleic acid (*cis,cis*-9,12-octadecadienoic acid)	−5
Linolenic acid (*cis,cis,cis*-9,12,15-octadecatrienoic acid)	−11

TABLE 23.2 Fatty acid composition obtained by hydrolysis of common fats and oils[a]

| | AVERAGE COMPOSITION OF FATTY ACIDS (mol %) | | | | | | | | | | | |
| | SATURATED | | | | | | | | UNSATURATED | | | |
FAT OR OIL	C_4 BUTYRIC ACID	C_6 CAPROIC ACID	C_8 CAPRYLIC ACID	C_{10} CAPRIC ACID	C_{12} LAURIC ACID	C_{14} MYRISTIC ACID	C_{16} PALMITIC ACID	C_{18} STEARIC ACID	C_{16} PALMITOLEIC ACID	C_{18} OLEIC ACID	C_{18} LINOLEIC ACID	C_{18} LINOLENIC ACID
Animal Fats												
Butter	3–4	1–2	0–1	2–3	2–5	8–15	25–29	9–12	4–6	18–33	2–4	
Lard						1–2	25–30	12–18	4–6	48–60	6–12	0–1
Beef tallow						2–5	24–34	15–30		35–45	1–3	0–1
Vegetable Oils												
Olive						0–1	5–15	1–4		67–84	8–12	
Peanut							7–12	2–6		30–60	20–38	
Corn						1–2	7–11	3–4	1–2	25–35	50–60	
Cottonseed						1–2	18–25	1–2	1–3	17–38	45–55	
Soybean						1–2	6–10	2–4		20–30	50–58	5–10
Linseed							4–7	2–4		14–30	14–25	45–60
Coconut		0–1	5–7	7–9	40–50	15–20	9–12	2–4	0–1	6–9	0–1	
Marine Oils												
Cod liver						5–7	8–10	0–1	18–22	27–33	27–32	

[a] Data adapted from John R. Holum, *Organic and Biological Chemistry*, Wiley, New York, 1978, p. 220, and from *Biology Data Book*, Philip L. Altman and Dorothy S. Ditmer, Eds., Federation of American Societies for Experimental Biology, Washington, DC, 1964.

Most natural fatty acids have **unbranched chains** and, because they are synthesized from two-carbon units (Special Topic L), **they have an even number of carbon atoms.** Table 23.1 lists some of the most common fatty acids and Table 23.2 gives the fatty acid composition of a number of common fats and oils. Notice that in the unsaturated fatty acids in Table 23.1 **the double bonds are all cis.** Many naturally occurring fatty acids contain two or three double bonds. The fats or oils that these come from are called **polyunsaturated fats or oils.** The first double bond of an unsaturated fatty acid commonly occurs between C-9 and C-10, the remaining double bonds tend to begin with C-12 and C-15 (as in linoleic acid and linolenic acid). The double bonds, therefore, *are not conjugated.* Triple bonds rarely occur in fatty acids.

The carbon chains of saturated fatty acids can adopt many conformations, but tend to be fully extended because this minimizes steric repulsions between neighboring methylene groups. Saturated fatty acids pack efficiently into crystals, and because van der Waals attractions are large, they have relatively high melting points. The melting points increase with increasing molecular weight. The cis configuration of the double bond of an unsaturated fatty acid puts a rigid bend in the carbon chain that

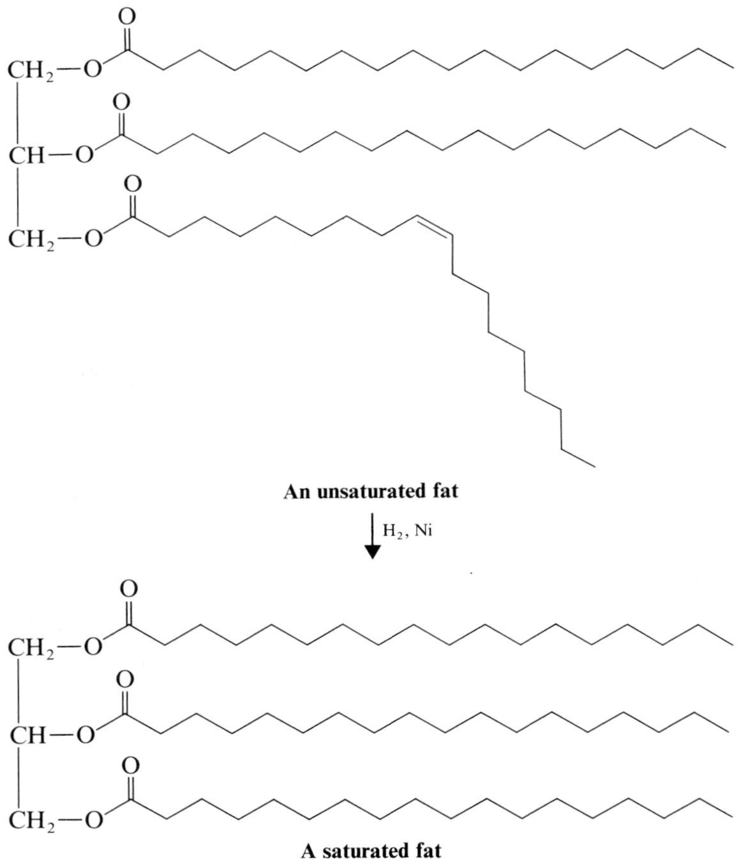

An unsaturated fat

$\downarrow$ H$_2$, Ni

A saturated fat

FIGURE 23.2 Two typical triacylglycerols, one unsaturated and one saturated. The cis double bond of the unsaturated triacylglycerol interferes with efficient crystal packing and causes it to have a lower melting point. Hydrogenation of the double bond causes an unsaturated triacylglycerol to become saturated.

interferes with crystal packing, causing reduced van der Waals attractions between molecules. Unsaturated fatty acids, consequently, have lower melting points.

What we have just said about the fatty acids, applies to the triacylglycerols as well. Triacylglycerols made up of largely saturated fatty acids have high melting points and are solids at room temperature. They are what we call *fats*. Triacylglycerols with a high proportion of unsaturated and polyunsaturated fatty acids have lower melting points. They are *oils*. Figure 23.2 shows how the introduction of a single cis double bond affects the shape of a triacylglycerol and how catalytic hydrogenation can be used to convert an unsaturated triacylglycerol into a saturated one.

23.2A HYDROGENATION OF TRIACYLGLYCEROLS

Solid commercial cooking fats are manufactured by partial hydrogenation of vegetable oils. The result is the familiar "partially hydrogenated fat" present in so many prepared foods. Complete hydrogenation of the oil is avoided because a completely saturated triacylglycerol is very hard and brittle. Typically, the vegetable oil is hydrogenated until a semisolid of appealing consistency is obtained. One commercial advantage of partial hydrogenation is to give the fat a longer shelf-life. Polyunsaturated oils tend to react by autoxidation (Section 7.10B) causing them to become rancid. One problem with partial hydrogenation, however, is that the catalyst isomerizes some of the unreacted double bonds from the natural cis arrangement to the unnatural trans arrangement.

23.2B BIOLOGICAL FUNCTIONS OF TRIACYLGLYCEROLS

The primary function of triacylglycerols in animals is as an energy reserve. When triacylglycerols are converted to carbon dioxide and water by biochemical reactions (i.e., when triacylglycerols are *metabolized*), they yield more than twice as many kilocalories per gram as do carbohydrates or proteins. This is largely because of the high proportion of carbon–hydrogen bonds per molecule.

In animals, specialized cells called **adipocytes** (fat cells) synthesize and store triacylglycerols. The tissue containing these cells, adipose tissue, is most abundant in the abdominal cavity and in the subcutaneous layer. Men have a fat content of about 21%, women about 26%. This fat content is sufficient to enable us to survive starvation for 2–3 months. By contrast, glycogen, our carbohydrate reserve, can provide only one day's energy need.

All of the saturated triacylglycerols of the body, and some of the unsaturated ones, can be synthesized from carbohydrates and proteins. Certain polyunsaturated fatty acids, however, are essential in the diets of higher animals.

The amount of fat in the diet, especially the proportion of saturated fat, has been a health concern for many years. There is compelling evidence that too much saturated fat in the diet is a factor in the development of heart disease and cancer.

23.2C SAPONIFICFATION OF TRIACYLGLYCEROLS

Alkaline hydrolysis (i.e., saponification) of triacylglycerols produces glycerol and a mixture of salts of long-chain carboxylic acids:

$$\begin{array}{ccc}
\underset{\displaystyle \text{CH}_2\text{O}\overset{\text{O}}{\overset{\|}{\text{C}}}\text{R}}{} & & \underset{\displaystyle \text{CH}_2\text{OH}}{} \quad \text{R}\overset{\text{O}}{\overset{\|}{\text{C}}}\text{O}^- \;\; \text{Na}^+ \\
| & & | \\
\text{CHO}\overset{\text{O}}{\overset{\|}{\text{C}}}\text{R}' + 3\,\text{NaOH} \xrightarrow{\text{H}_2\text{O}} & \text{CHOH} + & \text{R}'\overset{\text{O}}{\overset{\|}{\text{C}}}\text{O}^- \;\; \text{Na}^+ \\
| & & | \\
\text{CH}_2\text{O}\overset{\text{O}}{\overset{\|}{\text{C}}}\text{R}'' & & \text{CH}_2\text{OH} \quad \text{R}''\overset{\text{O}}{\overset{\|}{\text{C}}}\text{O}^- \;\; \text{Na}^+ \\
& \textbf{Glycerol} & \textbf{Sodium carboxylates} \\
& & \textbf{"soap"}
\end{array}$$

These salts of long-chain carboxylic acids are **soaps,** and this saponification reaction is the way most soaps are manufactured. Fats and oils are boiled in aqueous sodium hydroxide until hydrolysis is complete. Adding sodium chloride to the mixture then causes the soap to precipitate. (After the soap has been separated, glycerol can be isolated from the aqueous phase by distillation.) Crude soaps are usually purified by several reprecipitations. Perfumes can be added if a toilet soap is the desired product. Sand, sodium carbonate, and other fillers can be added to make a scouring soap, and air can be blown into the molten soap if the manufacturer wants to market a soap that floats.

The sodium salts of long-chain carboxylic acids (soaps) are almost completely miscible with water. However, they do not dissolve as we might expect, that is, as individual ions. Except in very dilute solutions, soaps exist as **micelles** (Fig. 23.3). Soap micelles are usually spherical clusters of carboxylate ions that are dispersed throughout the aqueous phase. The carboxylate ions are packed together with their negatively charged (and thus, *polar*) carboxylate groups at the surface and with their

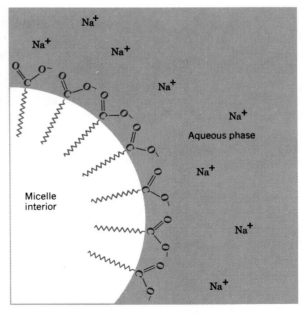

FIGURE 23.3 A portion of a soap micelle showing its interface with the polar dispersing medium.

nonpolar hydrocarbon chains on the interior. The sodium ions are scattered throughout the aqueous phase as individual solvated ions.

Micelle formation accounts for the fact that soaps dissolve in water. The nonpolar (and thus, **hydrophobic**) alkyl chains of the soap remain in a nonpolar environment—in the interior of the micelle. The polar (and therefore, **hydrophilic**) carboxylate groups are exposed to a polar environment—that of the aqueous phase. Because the surfaces of the micelles are negatively charged, individual micelles repel each other and remain dispersed throughout the aqueous phase.

Soaps serve their function as "dirt removers" in a similar way. Most dirt particles (e.g., on the skin) become surrounded by a layer of an oil or fat. Water molecules alone are unable to disperse these greasy globules because they are unable to penetrate the oily layer and separate the individual particles from each other or from the surface to which they are stuck. Soap solutions, however, *are* able to separate the individual particles because their hydrocarbon chains can "dissolve" in the oily layer (Fig. 23.4). As this happens, each individual particle develops an outer layer of carboxylate ions and presents the aqueous phase with a much more compatible exterior—a polar surface. The individual globules now repel each other and thus become dispersed throughout the aqueous phase. Shortly thereafter, they make their way down the drain.

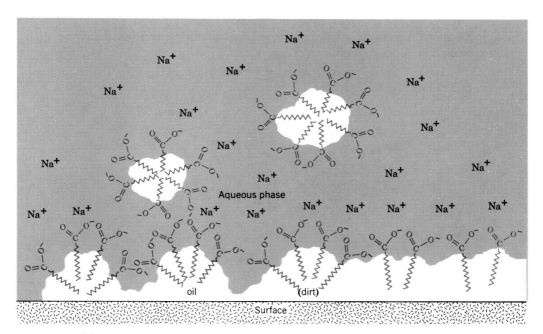

FIGURE 23.4 Dispersal of oil-coated dirt particles by a soap.

Synthetic detergents (Fig. 23.5) function in the same way as soaps; they have long nonpolar alkane chains with polar groups at the end. The polar groups of most synthetic detergents are sodium sulfonates or sodium sulfates. (At one time, extensive use was made of synthetic detergents with highly branched alkyl groups. These detergents proved to be nonbiodegradable, and their use was discontinued.)

$$CH_3(CH_2)_nCH_2SO_2O^- \ Na^+$$

Sodium alkanesulfonates

$$CH_3(CH_2)_nCH_2OSO_2O^- \ Na^+$$

Sodium alkyl sulfates

$$CH_3CH_2(CH_2)_n\overset{\overset{\displaystyle CH_3}{|}}{CH}-\!\!\!\bigcirc\!\!\!-SO_2O^- \ Na^+$$

Sodium alkylbenzenesulfonates

FIGURE 23.5 Typical synthetic detergents ($n = 10$).

Synthetic detergents offer an advantage over soaps; they function well in "hard" water, that is, water containing Ca^{2+}, Fe^{2+}, Fe^{3+}, and Mg^{2+} ions. Calcium, iron, and magnesium salts of alkanesulfonates and alkyl hydrogen sulfates are largely water soluble and, thus, synthetic detergents remain in solution. Soaps, by contrast, form precipitates—the ring around the bathtub—when they are used in hard water.

23.2D REACTIONS OF THE CARBOXYL GROUP OF FATTY ACIDS

Fatty acids, as we might expect, undergo reactions typical of carboxylic acids. They react with $LiAlH_4$ to form alcohols, with alcohols and mineral acid to form esters, and with thionyl chloride to form acyl chlorides:

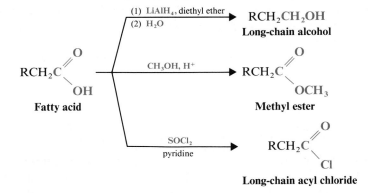

23.2E REACTIONS OF THE ALKYL CHAIN OF SATURATED FATTY ACIDS

Fatty acids are like other carboxylic acids in that they undergo specific α-halogenation when they are treated with bromine or chlorine in the presence of phosphorus. This is the familiar Hell–Volhard–Zelinski reaction.

$$\underset{\textbf{Fatty acid}}{RCH_2\overset{\overset{\displaystyle O}{\|}}{C}OH} + \ \underset{(2) \ H_2O}{\overset{(1) \ X_2, \ P_4}{\longrightarrow}} \ RCH\overset{\overset{\displaystyle O}{\|}}{\underset{\underset{\displaystyle X}{|}}{C}}OH + HX$$

23.2F REACTIONS OF THE ALKENYL CHAIN OF UNSATURATED FATTY ACIDS

The double bonds of the carbon chains of fatty acids undergo characteristic alkene addition reactions:

$$CH_3(CH_2)_nCH{=}CH(CH_2)_mCO_2H$$

$$\xrightarrow[\text{Ni}]{H_2,} CH_3(CH_2)_nCH_2{-}CH_2(CH_2)_mCO_2H$$

$$\xrightarrow[\text{CCl}_4]{Br_2,} CH_3(CH_2)_nCHBrCHBr(CH_2)_mCO_2H$$

$$\xrightarrow[\text{(2) NaHSO}_3]{\text{(1) OsO}_4} CH_3(CH_2)_n\underset{\underset{OH}{|}}{CH}{-}\underset{\underset{OH}{|}}{CH}(CH_2)_mCO_2H$$

$$\xrightarrow{HBr} \begin{array}{c} CH_3(CH_2)_nCH_2CHBr(CH_2)_mCO_2H \\ + \\ CH_3(CH_2)_nCHBrCH_2(CH_2)_mCO_2H \end{array}$$

Problem 23.1

(a) How many stereoisomers are possible for 9,10-dibromohexadecanoic acid?
(b) The addition of bromine to palmitoleic acid yields primarily one set of enantiomers, (±)-*threo*-9,10-dibromohexadecanoic acid. The addition of bromine is an anti addition to the double bond (i.e., it apparently takes place through a bromonium ion intermediate). Taking into account the cis stereochemistry of the double bond of palmitoleic acid and the stereochemistry of the bromine addition, write three-dimensional structures for the (±)-*threo*-9,10-dibromohexadecanoic acids.

23.3 TERPENES AND TERPENOIDS

People have isolated organic compounds from plants since antiquity. By gently heating or by steam distilling certain plant materials, one can obtain mixtures of odoriferous compounds known as *essential oils.* These compounds have had a variety of uses, particularly in early medicine and in the making of perfumes.

As the science of organic chemistry developed, chemists separated the various components of these mixtures and determined their molecular formulas and, later, their structural formulas. Even today these natural products offer challenging problems for chemists interested in structure determination and synthesis. Research in this area has also given us important information about the ways the plants, themselves, synthesize these compounds.

Hydrocarbons known generally as **terpenes** and oxygen-containing compounds called **terpenoids** are the most important constituents of essential oils. Most terpenes have skeletons of 10, 15, 20, or 30 carbon atoms and are classified in the following way:

NUMBER OF CARBON ATOMS	CLASS
10	Monoterpenes
15	Sesquiterpenes
20	Diterpenes
30	Triterpenes

One can view terpenes as being built up from two or more C_5 units known as *isoprene units*. Isoprene is 2-methyl-1,3-butadiene. Isoprene and the isoprene unit can be represented in various ways.

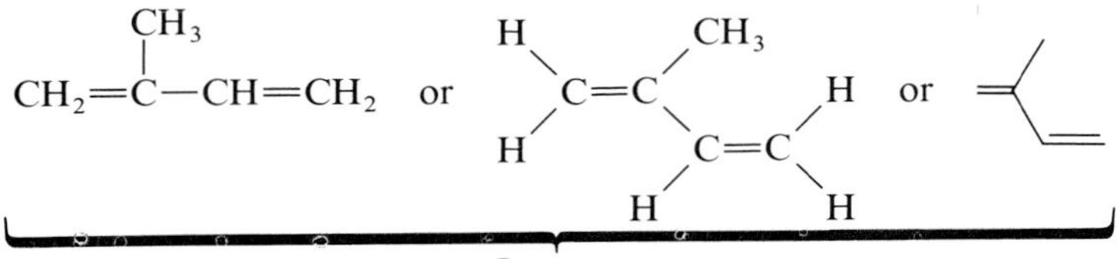

Isoprene

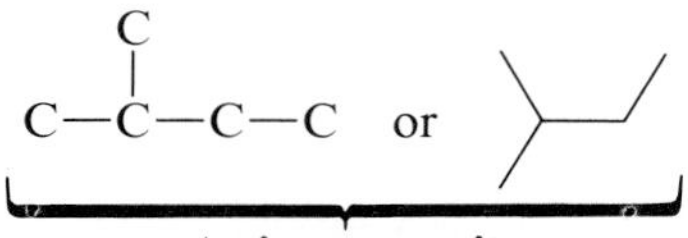

An isoprene unit

We now know that plants do not synthesize terpenes from isoprene (Special Topic L.3). However, recognition of the isoprene unit as a component of the structure of terpenes has been a great aid in elucidating their structures. We can see how, if we examine the following structures.

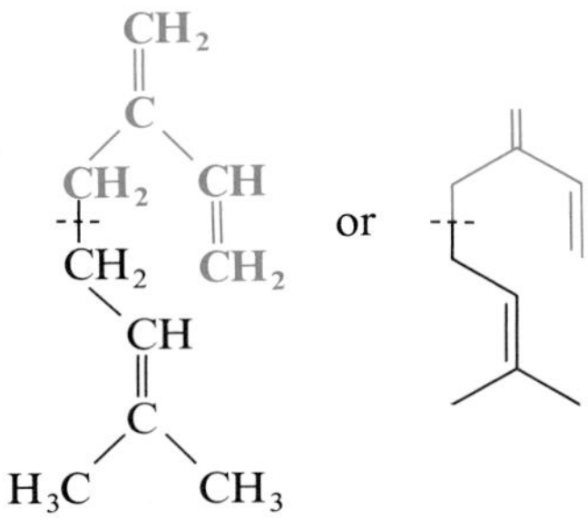

Myrcene
(isolated from bay oil)

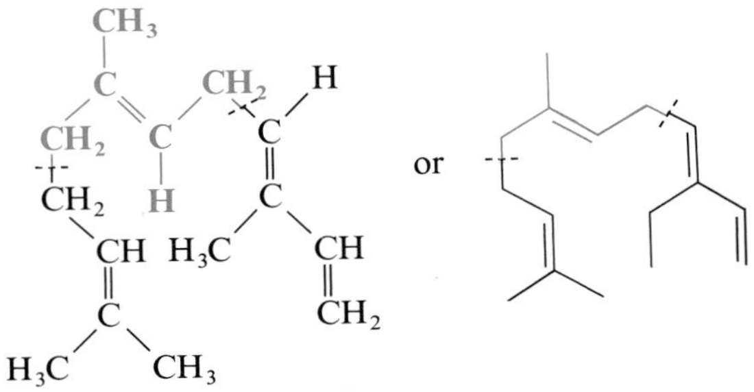

α-Farnesene
(from natural coating of apples)

Using dashed lines to separate isoprene units, we can see that the monoterpene (myrcene) has two isoprene units; and that the sesquiterpene (α-farnesene) has three. In both compounds the isoprene units are linked head to tail.

$$
\begin{array}{ccc}
\text{C} & & \text{C} \\
\text{C}-\text{C} & & \text{C}-\text{C} \\
\text{C} & \text{C}-\vdash\text{C} & \text{C}
\end{array}
$$

(head)   (tail)   (head)   (tail)

Many terpenes also have isoprene units linked in rings, and others (terpenoids) contain oxygen.

Limonene
(from oil of lemon or orange)

β-Pinene
(from oil of turpentine)

Geraniol
(from roses and other flowers)

CH₃

Menthol
(from peppermint)

Problem 23.2

(a) Show the isoprene units in each of the following terpenes.   (b) Classify each as a monoterpene, sesquiterpene, diterpene, and so on.

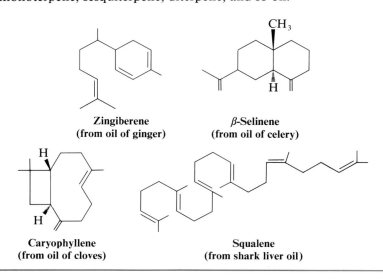

Zingiberene
(from oil of ginger)

β-Selinene
(from oil of celery)

Caryophyllene
(from oil of cloves)

Squalene
(from shark liver oil)

Problem 23.3

What products would you expect to obtain if each of the following terpenes were subjected to ozonization and subsequent treatment with zinc and water?

(a) Myrcene   (c) α-Farnesene   (e) Squalene

(b) Limonene   (d) Geraniol

Problem 23.4

Give structural formulas for the products that you would expect from the following reactions:

(a) β-Pinene + hot $KMnO_4 \longrightarrow$ (c) Caryophyllene + HCl $\longrightarrow$

(b) Zingiberene + $H_2 \xrightarrow{\text{Pt}}$ (d) β-Selinene + 2 THF:$BH_3 \xrightarrow[\text{(2) } H_2O_2, \text{ OH}^-]{}$

Problem 23.5

What simple chemical test could you use to distinguish between geraniol and menthol?

The carotenes are tetraterpenes. They can be thought of as two diterpenes linked in tail-to-tail fashion.

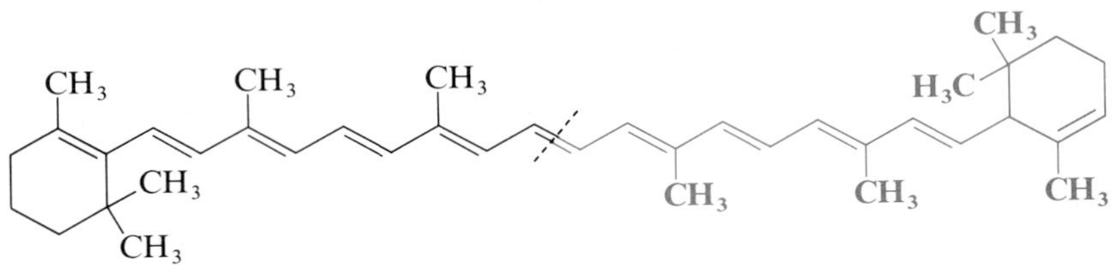

α-Carotene

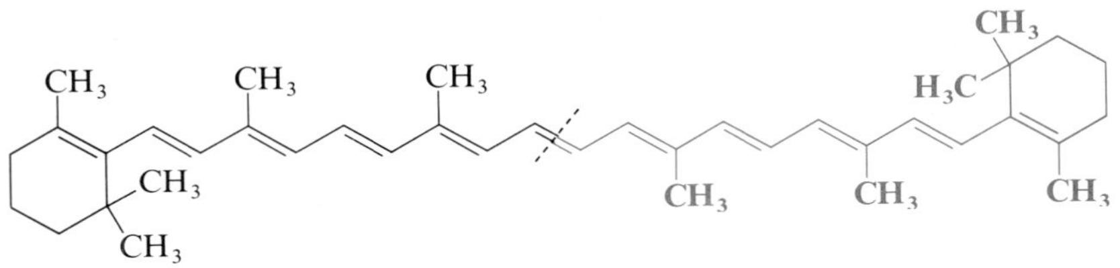

β-Carotene

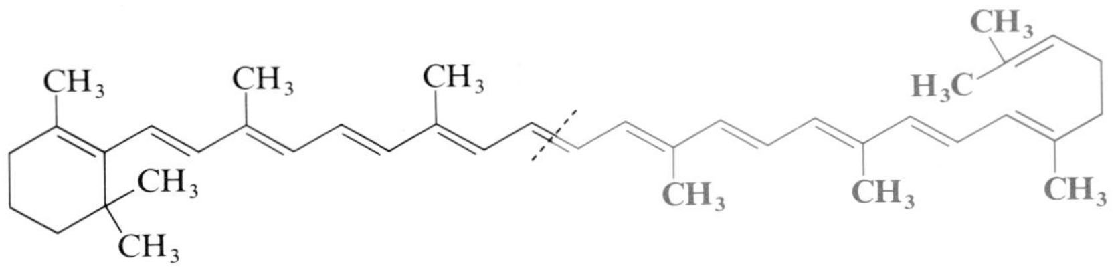

γ-Carotene

The carotenes are present in almost all green plants. All three carotenes serve as precursors for vitamin A, for they all can be converted to vitamin A by enzymes in the liver.

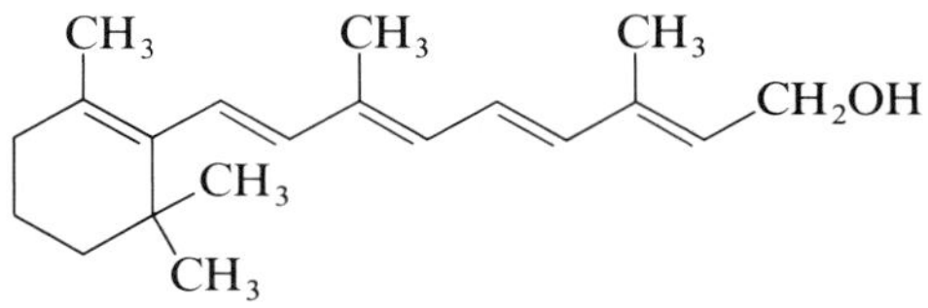

Vitamin A

In this conversion, one molecule of β-carotene yields two of vitamin A: α- and γ-carotene give only one. Vitamin A is important not only in vision but in many other ways as well. For example, young animals whose diets are deficient in vitamin A fail to grow.

23.3A NATURAL RUBBER

Natural rubber can be viewed as a 1,4-addition polymer of isoprene. In fact, pyrolysis degrades natural rubber to isoprene. Pyrolysis (Greek: *pyros,* a fire, + *lysis*) is the heating of something in the absence of air until it decomposes. The isoprene units of natural rubber are all linked in a head-to-tail fashion and all of the double bonds are cis.

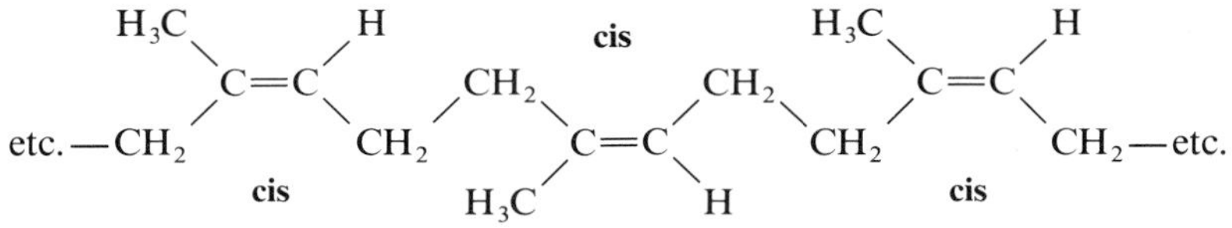

Natural rubber
(*cis*-1,4-polyisoprene)

Ziegler–Natta catalysts (Special Topic B) make it possible to polymerize isoprene and obtain a synthetic product that is identical with the rubber obtained from natural sources.

Pure natural rubber is soft and tacky. To be useful, natural rubber has to be *vulcanized.* In vulcanization, natural rubber is heated with sulfur. A reaction takes place that produces cross-links between the *cis*-polyisoprene chains and makes the rubber much harder. Sulfur reacts both at the double bonds and at allylic hydrogen atoms.

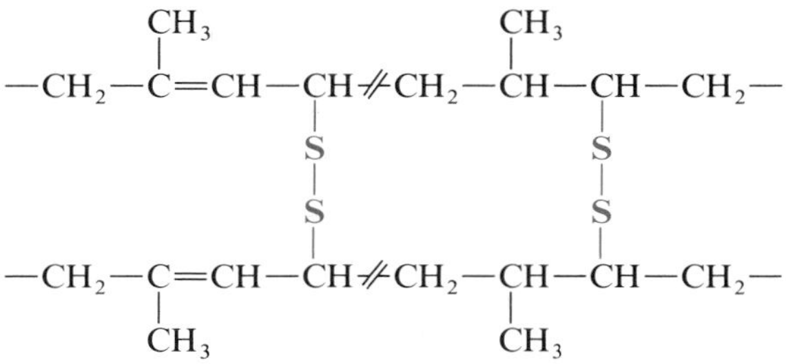

Vulcanized rubber

23.4 STEROIDS

The lipid fractions obtained from plants and animals contain another important group of compounds known as **steroids**. Steroids are important "biological regulators" that nearly always show dramatic physiological effects when they are administered to living organisms. Among these important compounds are male and female sex hormones, adrenocortical hormones, D vitamins, the bile acids, and certain cardiac poisons.

23.4A STRUCTURE AND SYSTEMATIC NOMENCLATURE OF STEROIDS

Steroids are derivatives of the following perhydrocyclopentanophenanthrene ring system.

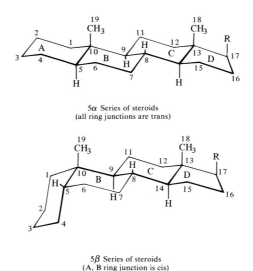

The carbon atoms of this ring system are numbered as shown. The four rings are designated with letters.

In most steroids the **B,C** and **C,D** ring junctions are trans. The **A,B** ring junction, however, may be either cis or trans and this possibility gives rise to two general groups of steroids having the three-dimensional structures shown in Fig. 23.6.

5α Series of steroids
(all ring junctions are trans)

5β Series of steroids
(A, B ring junction is cis)

FIGURE 23.6 The basic ring systems of the 5α and 5β series of steroids.

The methyl groups that are attached at points of ring junction (i.e., those numbered 18 and 19) are called **angular methyl groups** and they serve as important reference points for stereochemical designations. The angular methyl groups protrude above the general plane of the ring system when it is written in the manner shown in Fig. 23.6. By convention, other groups that lie on the same general side of the molecule as the angular methyl groups (i.e., on the top side) are designated as β **substituents** (these are written with a solid wedge). Groups that lie generally on the bottom (i.e., are trans to the angular methyl groups) are designated as α **substituents** (these are written with a dashed wedge). When α and β designations are applied to the hydrogen atom at position 5, the ring system in which the **A,B** ring junction is trans becomes the 5α series; and the ring system in which the **A,B** ring junction is cis becomes the 5β series.

Problem 23.6

Draw the two basic ring systems given in Fig. 23.6 for the 5α and 5β series showing all hydrogen atoms of the cyclohexane rings. Label each hydrogen atom as to whether it is axial or equatorial.

In systematic nomenclature the nature of the R group at position 17 determines (primarily) the base name of an individual steroid. These names are derived from the steroid hydrocarbon names given in Table 23.3.

TABLE 23.3 Names of steroid hydrocarbons

R	NAME
—H	Androstane
—H (with —H also replacing $\overset{19}{-CH_3}$)	Estrane
$-\overset{20}{C}H_2\overset{21}{C}H_3$	Pregnane
$-\overset{20}{C}HCH_2\overset{23}{C}H_2\overset{24}{C}H_3$ with $\overset{21}{C}H_3$	Cholane
$-\overset{20}{C}H\overset{22}{C}H_2\overset{23}{C}H_2\overset{24}{C}H_2\overset{25}{C}H\overset{26}{C}H_3$ with $\overset{21}{C}H_3$ and $\overset{27}{C}H_3$	Cholestane

The following two examples illustrate the way these base names are used.

5α-Pregnan-3-one

5α-Cholest-1-en-3-one

We shall see that many steroids also have common names and that the names of the steroid hydrocarbons given in Table 23.3 are derived from these common names.

Problem 23.7

(a) Androsterone, a secondary male sex hormone, has the systematic name 3α-hydroxy-5α-androstan-17-one. Give a three-dimensional formula for androsterone. (b) Norethynodrel, a synthetic steroid that has been widely used in oral contraceptives, has the systematic name 17α-ethynyl-17β-hydroxy-5(10)-estren-3-one. Give a three-dimensional formula for norethynodrel.

23.4B CHOLESTEROL

Cholesterol, one of the most widely occurring steroids, can be isolated by extraction of nearly all animal tissues. Human gallstones are a particularly rich source.

Cholesterol was first isolated in 1770. In the 1920s, two German chemists, Adolf Windaus (University of Göttingen) and Heinrich Wieland (University of Munich), were responsible for outlining a structure for cholesterol; they received Nobel Prizes for their work in 1927 and 1928.*

Part of the difficulty in assigning an absolute structure to cholesterol is that cholesterol contains *eight* tetrahedral stereocenters. This feature means that 2^8 or 256 possible stereoisomeric forms of the basic structure are possible, *only one of which is cholesterol.*

5-Cholesten-3β-ol
(absolute configuration of cholesterol)

*The original cholesterol structure proposed by Windaus and Wieland was incorrect. This became evident in 1932 as a result of X-ray diffraction studies done by the British physicist J. D. Bernal. By the end of 1932, however, English scientists, and Wieland himself, using Bernal's results, were able to outline the correct structure of cholesterol.

Problem 23.8

Designate with an asterisk the eight stereocenters of cholesterol.

Cholesterol occurs widely in the human body, but not all of the biological functions of cholesterol are yet known. Cholesterol is known to serve as an intermediate in the biosynthesis of all of the steroids of the body. Cholesterol, therefore, is essential to life. We do not need to have cholesterol in our diet, however, because our body can synthesize all we need. When we ingest cholesterol, our body synthesizes less than if we ate none at all, but the total cholesterol is more than if we ate none at all. Far more cholesterol is present in the body than is necessary for steroid biosynthesis. High levels of blood cholesterol have been implicated in the development of arteriosclerosis (hardening of the arteries) and in heart attacks that occur when cholesterol-containing plaques block arteries of the heart. Considerable research is being carried out in the area of cholesterol metabolism with the hope of finding ways of minimizing cholesterol levels through the use of dietary adjustments or drugs (Sect. L.5).

23.4C SEX HORMONES

The sex hormones can be classified into three major groups: (1) the female sex hormones, or **estrogens,** (2) the male sex hormones, or **androgens,** and (3) the pregnancy hormones, or **progestins.**

The first sex hormone to be isolated was an estrogen, *estrone.* Working independently, Adolf Butenandt (in Germany at the University of Göttingen) and Edward Doisy (in the United States at St. Louis University) isolated estrone from the urine of pregnant women. They published their discoveries in 1929. Later, Doisy was able to isolate the much more potent estrogen, *estradiol.* In this research Doisy had to extract *4 tons* of sow ovaries in order to obtain just 12 mg of estradiol. Estradiol, it turns out, is the true female sex hormone, and estrone is a metabolized form of estradiol that is excreted.

Estrone
[3-hydroxy-1,3,5(10)-
estratrien-17-one]

Estradiol
[1,3,5(10)-estra-
trien-3,17β-diol]

Estradiol is secreted by the ovaries and promotes the development of the secondary female characteristics that appear at the onset of puberty. Estrogens also stimulate the development of the mammary glands during pregnancy and induce estrus (heat) in animals.

In 1931, Butenandt and Kurt Tscherning isolated the first androgen, *andosterone.* They were able to obtain 15 mg of this hormone by extracting approximately 15,000 L of male urine. Soon afterwards (in 1935), Ernest Laqueur (in Holland) isolated another male sex hormone, *testosterone,* from bull testes. It soon became clear that testosterone is the true male sex hormone and that androsterone is a metabolized form of testosterone that is excreted in the urine.

Androsterone
(3α-hydroxy-5α-androstan-17-one)

Testosterone
(17β-hydroxy-4-androsten-3-one)

Testosterone, secreted by the testes, is the hormone that promotes the development of secondary male characteristics: the growth of facial and body hair; the deepening of the voice; muscular development; and the maturation of the male sex organs.

Testosterone and estradiol, then, are the chemical compounds from which "maleness" and "femaleness" are derived. It is especially interesting to examine their structural formulas and see how very slightly these two compounds differ. Testosterone has an angular methyl group at the **A,B** ring junction that is missing in estradiol. Ring **A** of estradiol is a benzene ring and, as a result, estradiol is a phenol. Ring **A** of testosterone contains an α,β-unsaturated keto group.

Problem 23.9

The estrogens (estrone and estradiol) are easily separated from the androgens (androsterone and testosterone) on the basis of one of their chemical properties. What is the property and how could such a separation be accomplished?

Progesterone
(4-pregnene-3,20-dione)

Progesterone is the most important *progestin* (pregnancy hormone). After ovulation occurs, the remnant of the ruptured ovarian follicle (called the *corpus luteum*) begins to secrete progesterone. This hormone prepares the lining of the uterus for implantation of the fertilized ovum, and continued progesterone secretion is necessary for the completion of pregnancy. (Progesterone is secreted by the placenta after secretion by the *corpus luteum* declines.)

Progesterone *also suppresses ovulation,* and it is the chemical agent that apparently accounts for the fact that pregnant women do not conceive again while pregnant. It was this observation that led to the search for synthetic progestins that could be used as oral contraceptives. (Progesterone, itself, requires very large doses to be effective in suppressing ovulation when taken orally because it is degraded in the intestinal tract.) A number of such compounds have been developed and are now widely used. In addition to norethynodrel (cf. Problem 23.7), another widely used synthetic progestin is its double-bond isomer, *norethindrone.*

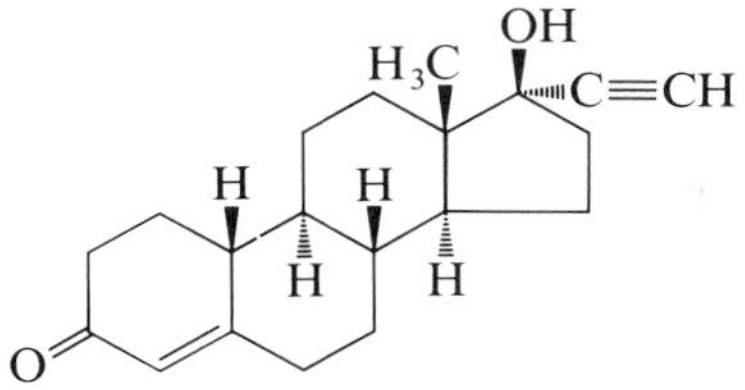

Norethindrone
(17α-ethynyl-17-β-hydroxy-4-estren-3-one)

Synthetic estrogens have also been developed and these are often used in oral contraceptives in combination with synthetic progestins. A very potent synthetic estrogen is the compound called *ethynylestradiol* or *novestrol.*

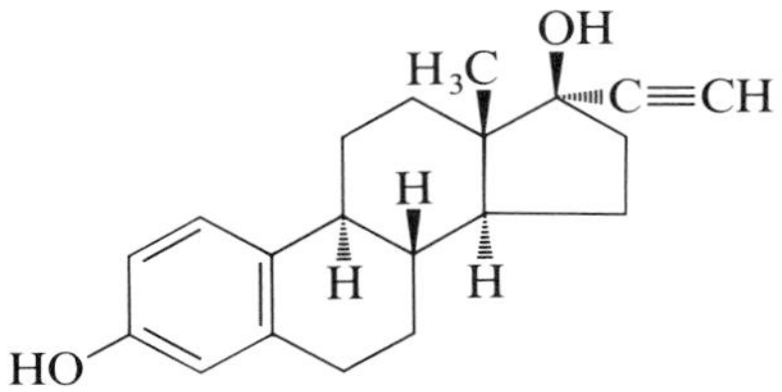

Ethynylestradiol
[17α-ethynyl-1,3,5(10)-estratriene-3,17β-diol]

23.4D ADRENOCORTICAL HORMONES

At least 28 different hormones have been isolated from the adrenal cortex. Included in this group are the following two steroids:

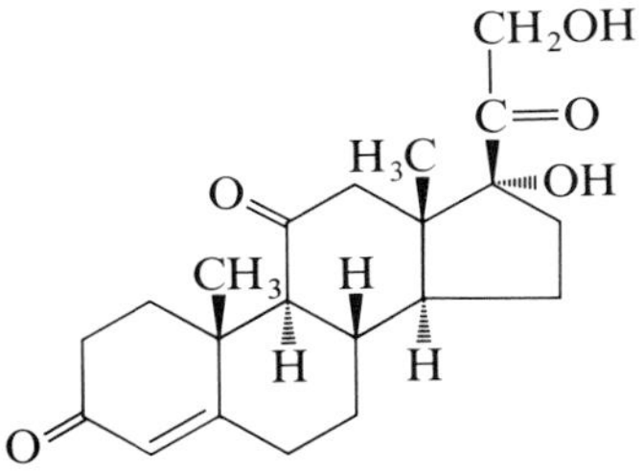

Cortisone
(17α,21-dihydroxy-4-pregnene-
3,11,20-trione)

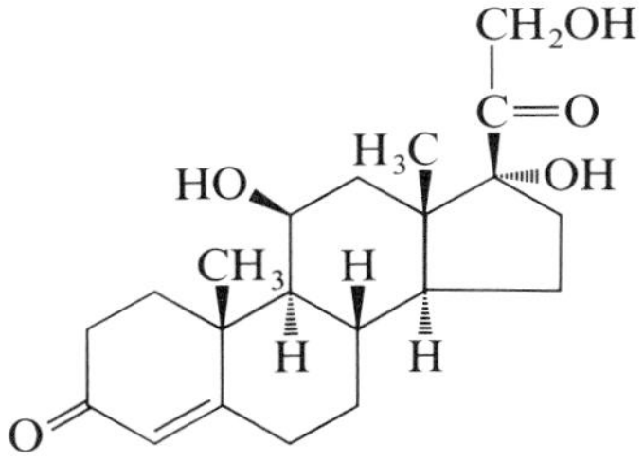

Cortisol
(11β,17α,21-trihydroxy-4-pregnene-
3,20-dione)

Most of the adrenocortical steroids have an oxygen function at position 11 (a keto group in cortisone, for example, and a β-hydroxyl in cortisol). Cortisol is the major hormone synthesized by the human adrenal cortex.

The adrenocortical steroids are apparently involved in the regulation of a large number of biological activities including carbohydrate, protein, and lipid metabolism, water and electrolyte balance, and reactions to allergic and inflammatory phenomena. Recognition of the antiinflammatory effect of cortisone and its usefulness in the treatment of rheumatoid arthritis, in 1949, has led to extensive research in this area. Many 11-oxygenated steroids are now used in the treatment of a variety of disorders ranging from Addison's disease, to asthma, and to skin inflammations.

23.4E D VITAMINS

The demonstration, in 1919, that sunlight helped cure rickets — a childhood disease characterized by poor bone growth — began a long search for a chemical explanation. Soon it was discovered that irradiation of certain foodstuffs increased their antirachitic properties and, in 1930, the search led to a steroid that can be isolated from yeast, called *ergosterol*. Irradiation of ergosterol was found to produce a highly active material. In 1932, Windaus (Section 23.4B) and his co-workers in Germany demonstrated that this highly active substance was vitamin D_2. The photochemical reaction that takes place is one in which the dienoid ring **B** of ergosterol opens to produce a conjugated triene:

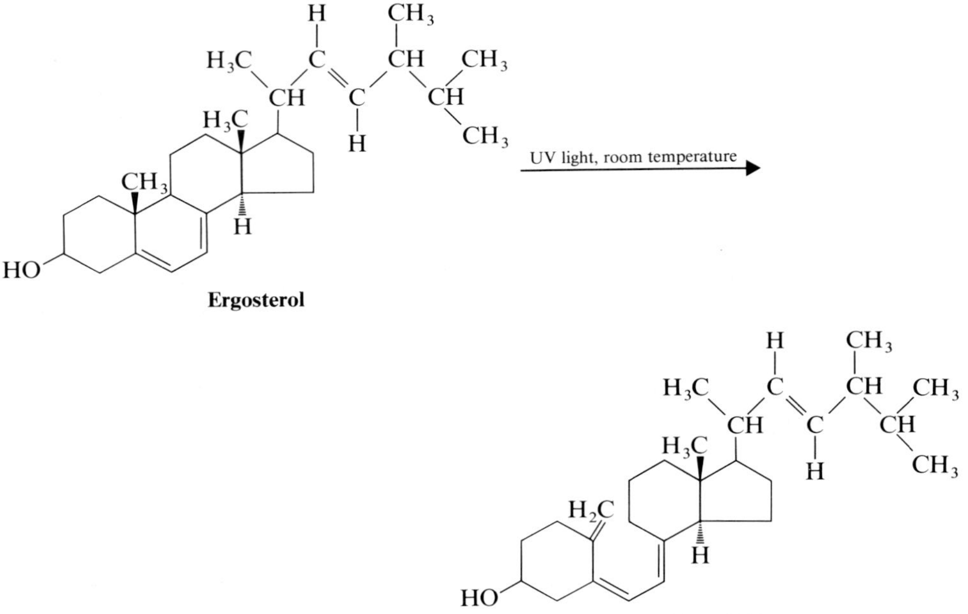

Ergosterol

UV light, room temperature

Vitamin D₂

23.4F OTHER STEROIDS

The structures, sources, and physiological properties of a number of other important steroids are given in Table 23.4.

23.4G REACTIONS OF STEROIDS

Steroids undergo all of the reactions that we might expect of molecules containing double bonds, hydroxyl groups, keto groups, and so on. While the stereochemistry of steroid reactions is often quite complex, it is many times strongly influenced by the

TABLE 23.4 Other important steroids

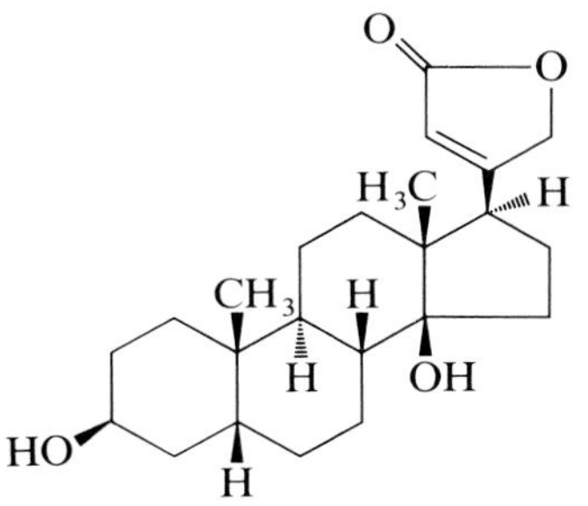

Structure	Description
Digitoxigenin	Digitoxigenin is a cardiac aglycone that can be isolated by hydrolysis of digitalis, a pharmaceutical that has been used in treating heart disease since 1785. In digitalis, sugar molecules are joined in acetal linkages to the 3-OH group of the steroid. In small doses digitalis strengthens the heart muscle; in larger doses it is a powerful heart poison.
Cholic acid	Cholic acid is the most abundant acid obtained from the hydrolysis of human or ox bile. Bile is produced by the liver and stored in the gallbladder. When secreted into the small intestine, bile emulsifies lipids by acting as a soap. This action aids in the digestive process.
Stigmasterol	Stigmasterol is a widely occurring plant steroid that is obtained commercially from soybean oil.
Diosgenin	Diosgenin, is obtained from a Mexican vine, *cabeza de negro,* genus *Dioscorea.* It is used as the starting material for a commercial synthesis of cortisone and sex hormones.

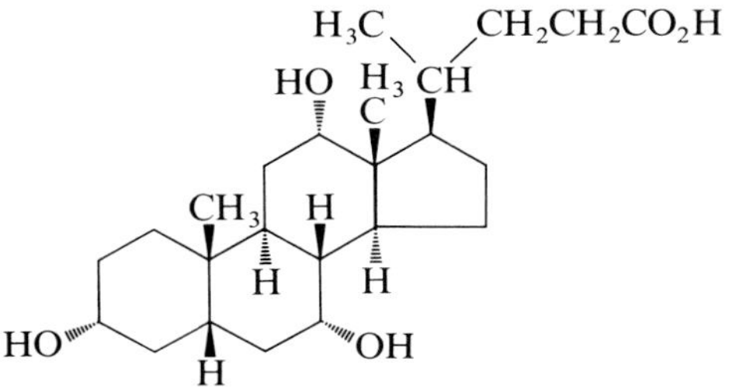

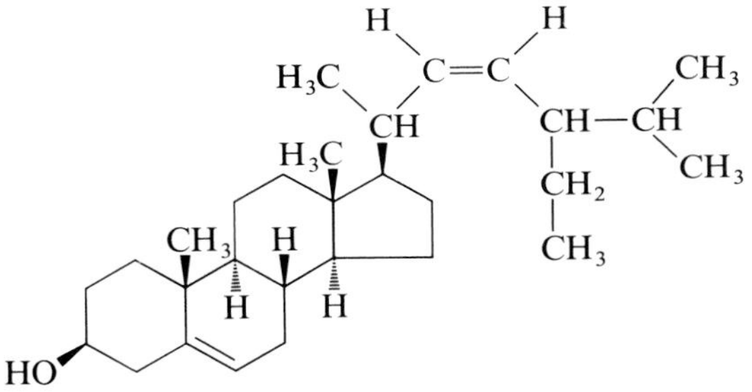

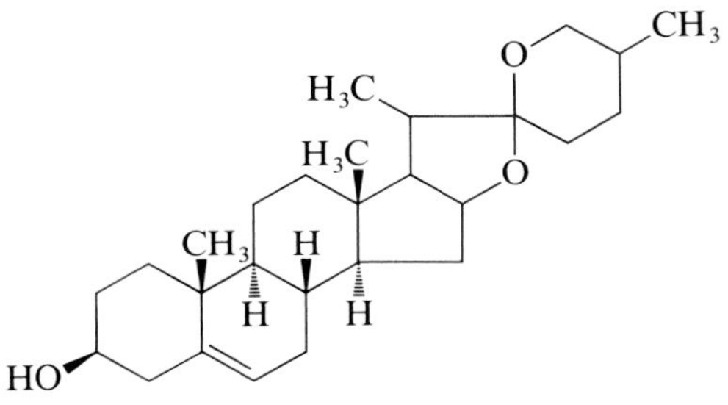

steric hindrance presented at the β face of the molecule by the angular methyl groups. Many reagents react preferentially at the relatively unhindered α face, especially when the reaction takes place at a functional group very near an angular methyl group and when the attacking reagent is bulky. Examples that illustrate this tendency are shown in the following reactions.

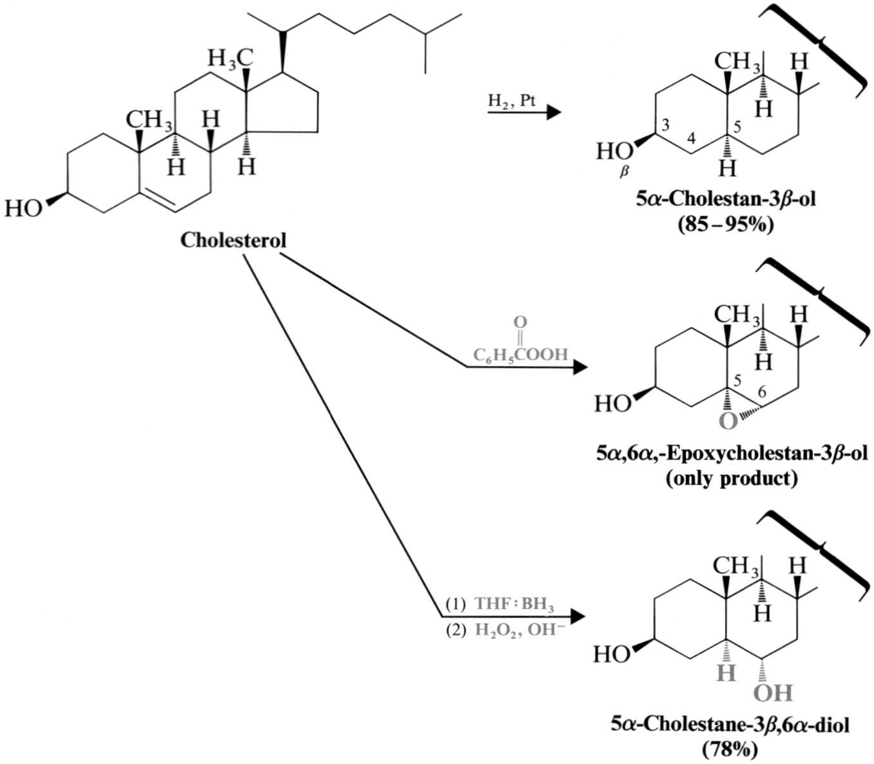

Cholesterol

H_2, Pt →

5α-Cholestan-3β-ol
(85–95%)

C_6H_5COOH →

5α,6α,-Epoxycholestan-3β-ol
(only product)

(1) THF:BH$_3$
(2) H$_2$O$_2$, OH$^-$
→

5α-Cholestane-3β,6α-diol
(78%)

When the epoxide ring of 5α,6α-epoxycholestan-3β-ol (see following reaction) is opened, attack by chloride ion must occur from the β face, but it takes place at the more open 6 position. Notice that the 5- and 6- substituents in the product are *diaxial* (Section 9.6).

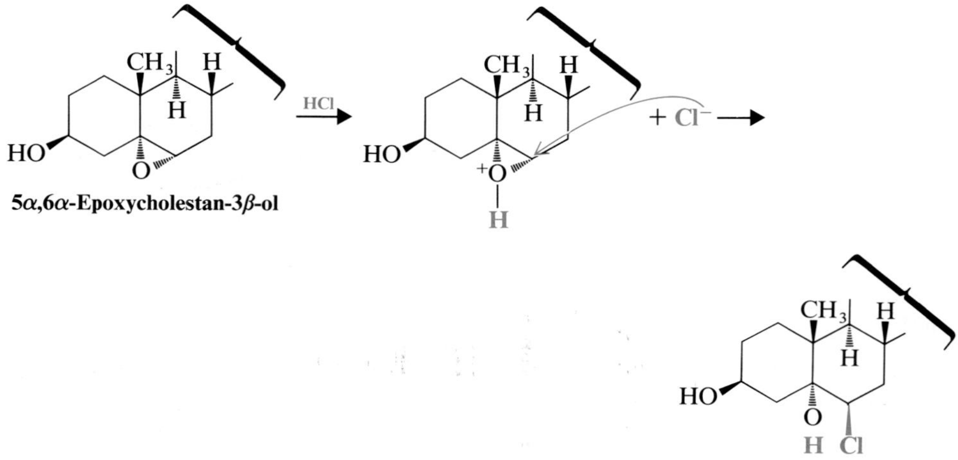

5α,6α-Epoxycholestan-3β-ol

HCl → + Cl$^-$ →

Problem 23.10

Show how you might convert cholesterol into each of the following compounds:

(a) 5α,6β-Dibromocholestan-3β-ol

(b) Cholestane-3β,5α,6β-triol

(c) 5α-Cholestan-3-one

(d) 6α-Deuterio-5α-cholestan-3β-ol

(e) 6β-Bromocholestane-3β,5α-diol

The relative openness of equatorial groups (when compared to axial groups) also influences the stereochemical course of steroid reactions. When 5α-cholestane-3β,7α-diol (see following reaction) is treated with excess ethyl chloroformate (C_2H_5OCOCl), only the equatorial 3β-hydroxyl becomes esterified. The axial 7α-hydroxyl is unaffected by the reaction.

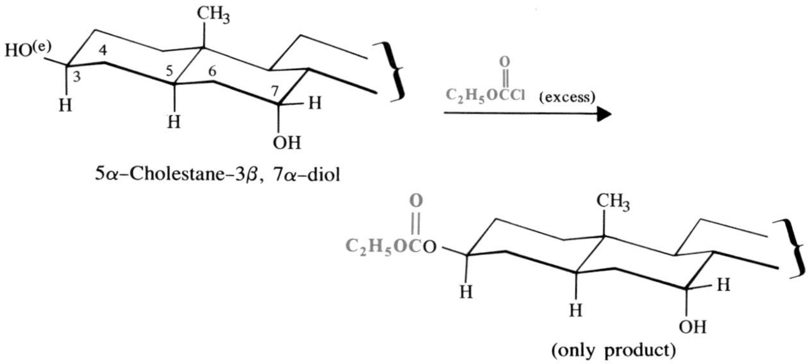

5α–Cholestane-3β, 7α–diol

C_2H_5OCCl (excess)

(only product)

By contrast, treating 5α-cholestane-3β,7β-diol with excess ethyl chloroformate esterifies both hydroxyl groups. In this instance both groups are equatorial.

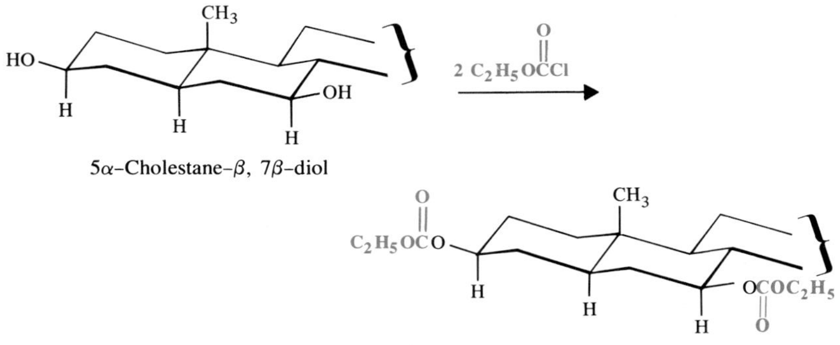

5α–Cholestane-β, 7β–diol

2 C_2H_5OCCl

23.5 PROSTAGLANDINS

One very active area of current research is concerned with a group of lipids called prostaglandins.* Prostaglandins are C_{20}-carboxylic acids that contain a five-membered ring, at least one double bond, and several oxygen-containing functional groups. Two of the most biologically active prostaglandins are prostaglandin E_2 and prostaglandin $F_{1α}$.

*The 1982 Nobel Prize in physiology or medicine was awarded to S. K. Bergström and B. I. Samuelson (of the Karolinska Institute, Stockholm, Sweden) and to J. R. Vane (of the Wellcome Foundation, Bechenham, England) for their work on prostaglandins.

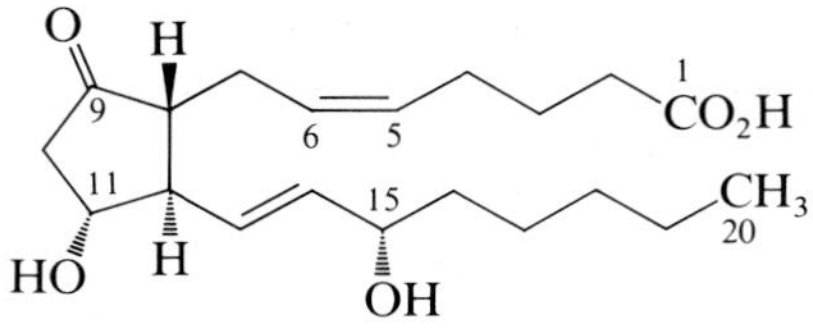

Prostaglandin E₂*
(PGE₂*)

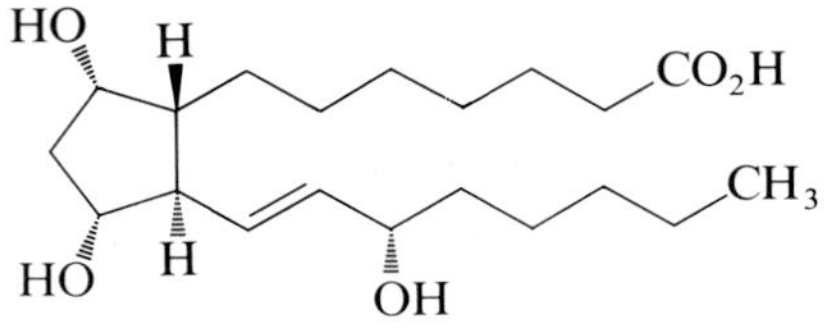

Prostaglandin F₁ₐ
(PGF₁ₐ)

Prostaglandins of the E type have a carbonyl group at C-9 and a hydroxyl group at C-11; those of the F type have hydroxyl groups at both positions. Prostaglandins of the 2 series have a double bond between C-5 and C-6; in the 1 series this bond is a single bond.

First isolated from seminal fluid, prostaglandins have since been found in almost all animal tissues. The amounts vary from tissue to tissue but are almost always very small. Most prostaglandins have powerful physiological activity, however, and this activity covers a broad spectrum of effects. Prostaglandins are known to affect heart rate, blood pressure, blood clotting, conception, fertility, and allergic responses.

The recent finding that prostaglandins can prevent formation of blood clots has great clinical significance, because heart attacks and strokes often result from the formation of abnormal clots in blood vessels. An understanding of how prostaglandins affect the formation of clots may lead to the development of drugs to prevent heart attacks and strokes.

The biosynthesis of prostaglandins of the 2 series begins with a C_{20} polyenoic acid, arachidonic acid. (Synthesis of prostaglandins of the 1 series begins with a fatty acid with one fewer double bond.) The first step requires two molecules of oxygen and is catalyzed by an enzyme called *cyclooxygenase*.

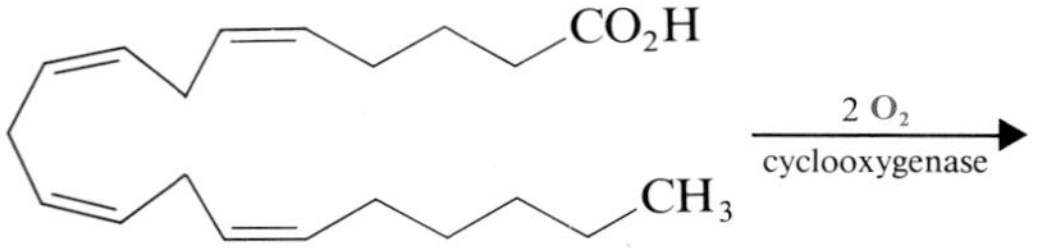

Arachidonic acid

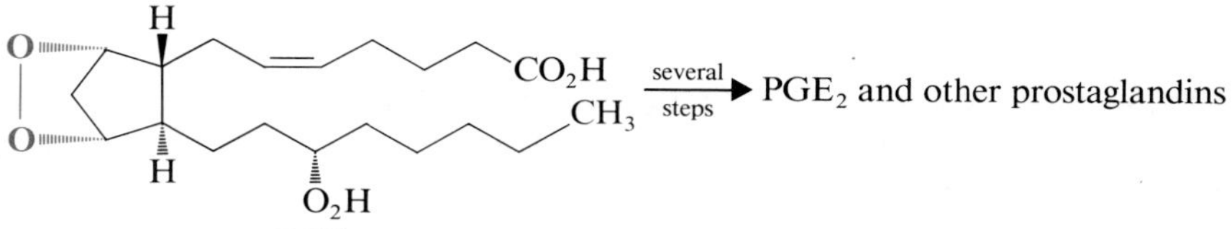

PGG₂
(a cyclic endoperoxide)

---

*These names are code designations used by workers in the field; systematic names are seldom used for prostaglandins.

The involvement of prostaglandins in allergic and inflammation responses has also been of special interest. Some prostaglandins induce inflammation; others relieve it. The most widely used antiinflammatory drug is ordinary aspirin (cf. Section 21.8). Aspirin blocks the synthesis of prostaglandins from arachidonic acid, apparently by acetylating the enzyme cyclooxygenase, thus rendering it inactive. This reaction may represent the origin of aspirin's antiinflammatory properties. Another prostaglandin (PGE_1) is a potent fever-inducing agent (pyrogen), and aspirin's ability to reduce fever may also arise from its inhibition of prostaglandin synthesis.

23.6 PHOSPHOLIPIDS AND CELL MEMBRANES

Another large class of lipids are those called *phospholipids*. Most phospholipids are structurally derived from a glycerol derivative known as a *phosphatidic acid*. In a phosphatidic acid, two hydroxyl groups of glycerol are joined in ester linkages to fatty acids and one terminal hydroxyl group is joined in an ester linkage to *phosphoric acid*.

$$
\begin{array}{l}
\underset{\|}{\overset{O}{}} \\
CH_2OCR \\
\quad \overset{O}{\underset{\|}{}} \\
CHOCR' \\
\quad \overset{O}{\underset{\|}{}} \\
CH_2-O-P-OH \\
\qquad | \\
\qquad OH
\end{array}
$$

From fatty acid

From phosphoric acid

A phosphatidic acid
(a diacylglyceryl phosphate)

23.6A PHOSPHATIDES

In *phosphatides,* the phosphate group of a phosphatidic acid is bound through another phosphate ester linkage to one of the following nitrogen-containing compounds.

$$HOCH_2CH_2\overset{+}{N}(CH_3)_3 \quad HO^- \qquad HOCH_2CH_2NH_2 \qquad HOCH_2-\overset{\overset{+}{N}H_3}{\underset{H}{\overset{|}{C}}}{}^{\cdots\cdots}CO_2^-$$

Choline   **2-Aminoethanol**   L-**Serine**
                 (ethanolamine)

The most important phosphatides are the **lecithins,** the **cephalins, phosphatidyl serines,** and the **plasmalogens** (a phosphatidyl derivative). Their general structures are shown in Table 23.5.

Phosphatides resemble soaps and detergents in that they are molecules having both polar and nonpolar groups (Fig. 23.7*a*). Like soaps and detergents, too, phosphatides "dissolve" in aqueous media by forming micelles. There is evidence that in biological systems the preferred micelles consist of three-dimensional arrays of "stacked" bimolecular micelles (Fig. 23.7) that are better described as **lipid bilayers.**

TABLE 23.5 Phosphatides

Lecithins

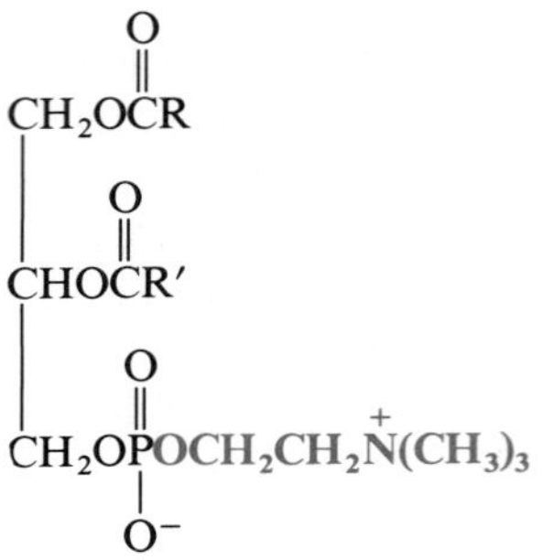

$$CH_2OCR$$
(with =O above the C)

$$CHOCR'$$
(with =O above the C)

$$CH_2OPOCH_2CH_2\overset{+}{N}(CH_3)_3 \qquad \textbf{(from choline)}$$
(with =O above the P and O^- below)

R is saturated and R′ is unsaturated

Cephalins

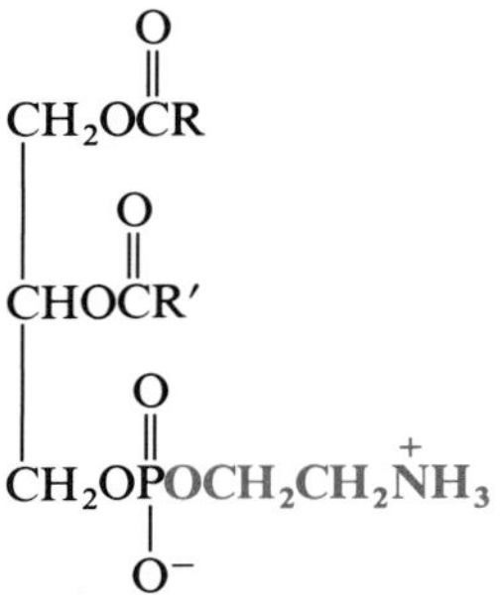

$$CH_2OCR$$
(with =O above the C)

$$CHOCR'$$
(with =O above the C)

$$CH_2OPOCH_2CH_2\overset{+}{N}H_3 \qquad \textbf{(from 2-aminoethanol)}$$
(with =O above the P and O^- below)

Phosphatidyl Serines

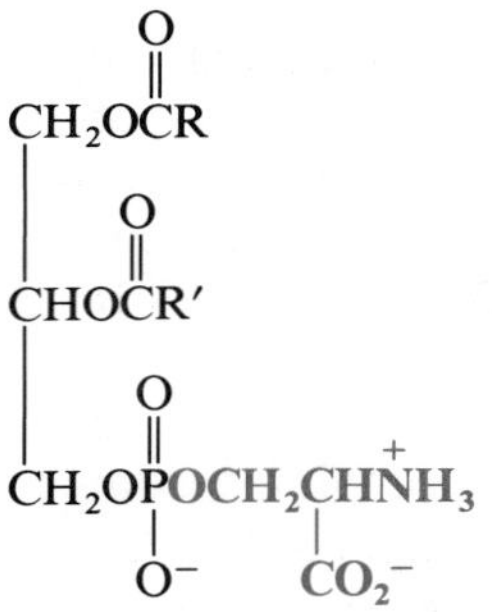

$$CH_2OCR$$
(with =O above the C)

$$CHOCR'$$
(with =O above the C)

$$CH_2OPOCH_2\overset{+}{C}HNH_3 \qquad \textbf{(from L-serine)}$$
(with =O above the P, O^- below the P, and CO_2^- below the CH)

R is saturated and R′ is unsaturated

Plasmalogens

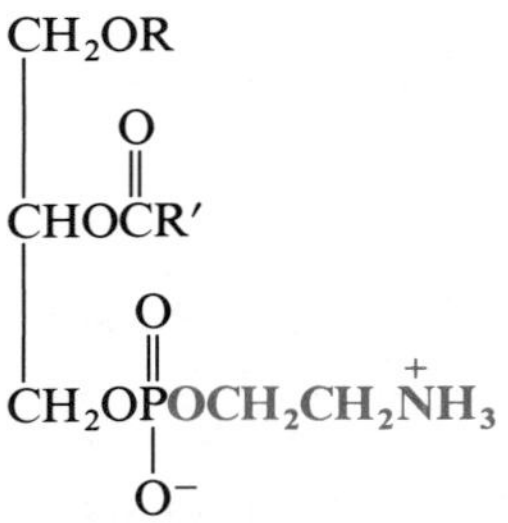

$$CH_2OR$$

$$CHOCR'$$
(with =O above the C)

$$CH_2OPOCH_2CH_2\overset{+}{N}H_3 \qquad \textbf{(from 2-aminoethanol)} \qquad \text{or} \qquad OCH_2CH_2\overset{+}{N}(CH_3)_3 \qquad \textbf{(from choline)}$$
(with =O above the P and O^- below)

R is $-CH{=}CH(CH_3)_nCH_3$ (this linkage is that of an α,β-unsaturated ether)
R′ is that of an unsaturated fatty acid

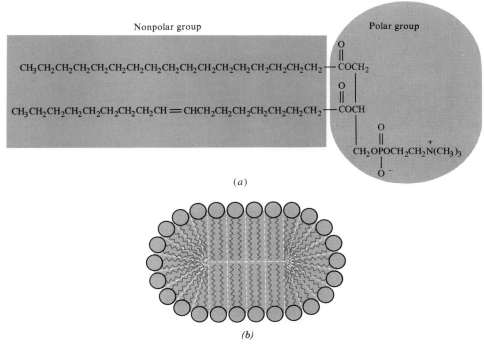

Nonpolar group   Polar group

(a)

(b)

FIGURE 23.7 (a) Polar and nonpolar sections of a phosphatide. (b) A phosphatide micelle or lipid bilayer.

The hydrophilic and hydrophobic portions of phosphatides make them perfectly suited for one of their most important biological functions: They form a portion of a structural unit that creates an interface between an organic and an aqueous environment. This structure (Fig. 23.8) is found in cell walls and membranes where phosphatides are often found associated with proteins and glycolipids (Section 23.6B).

Problem 23.11

Under suitable conditions all of the ester (and ether) linkages of a phosphatide can be hydrolyzed. What organic compounds would you expect to obtain from the complete hydrolysis of (a) a lecithin, (b) cephalin, (c) a choline-based plasmalogen? [*Note:* Pay particular attention to the fate of the α,β-unsaturated ether in part (c).]

23.6B DERIVATIVES OF SPHINGOSINE

Another important group of lipids is derived from **sphingosine,** the derivatives are called **sphingolipids.** Two sphingolipids, a typical *sphingomyelin* and a typical *cerebroside,* are shown in Fig. 23.9.

On hydrolysis, sphingomyelins yield sphingosine, choline, phosphoric acid, and a C_{24} fatty acid called lignoceric acid. In a sphingomyelin this last component is bound to the $-NH_2$ group of sphingosine. The sphingolipids do not yield glycerol when they are hydrolyzed.

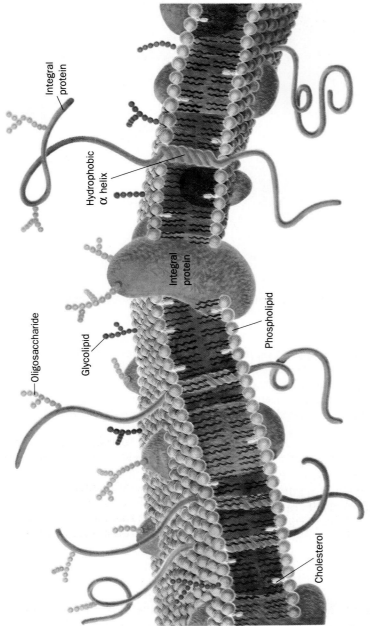

FIGURE 23.8 A schematic diagram of a plasma membrane. Integral proteins (*orange*) are embedded in a bilayer composed of phospholipids (*blue spheres with two wiggly tails;* shown, for clarity, in much greater proportion than they have in biological membranes) and cholesterol (*yellow*). The carbohydrate components of glycoproteins (*yellow beaded chains*) and glycolipids (*green beaded chains*) occur only on the external face of the membrane. (From D. Voet and J. G. Voet, *Biochemistry,* Wiley, N.Y., 1990 p. 286. Used with permission.)

Integral protein

Hydrophobic α helix

Integral protein

Oligosaccharide

Glycolipid

Phospholipid

Cholesterol

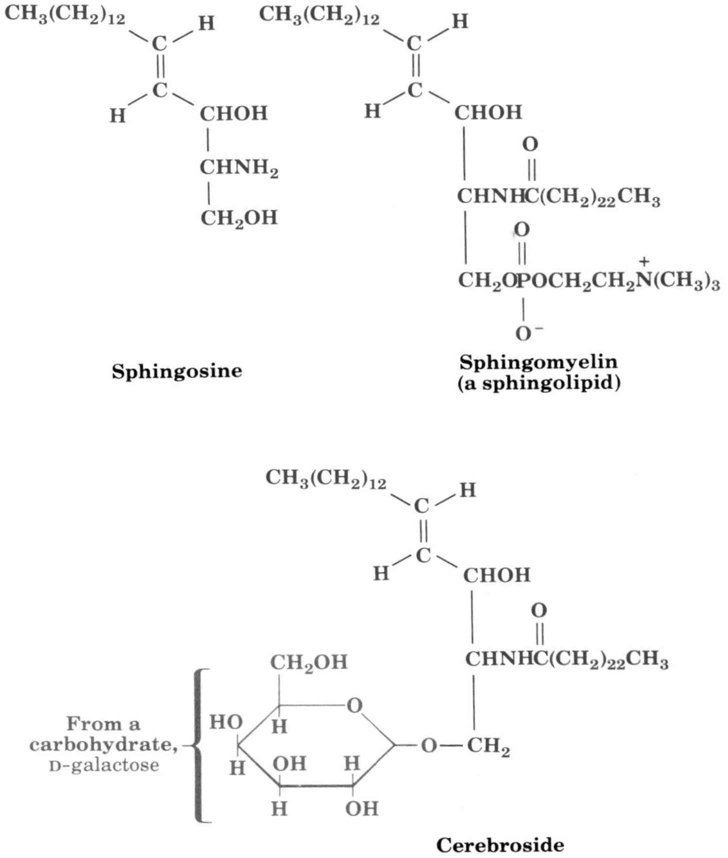

$$CH_3(CH_2)_{12}\!-\!\underset{H}{\overset{}{C}}\!=\!\underset{H}{C}$$

Sphingosine

(structure: $CH_3(CH_2)_{12}$–CH=CH–CHOH–CHNH$_2$–CH$_2$OH)

Sphingomyelin
(a sphingolipid)

(structure: $CH_3(CH_2)_{12}$–CH=CH–CHOH–CHNHC(CH$_2$)$_{22}$CH$_3$ with O, then CH$_2$OPOCH$_2$CH$_2\overset{+}{N}$(CH$_3$)$_3$, O$^-$)

From a
carbohydrate,
D-galactose

Cerebroside

(structure: $CH_3(CH_2)_{12}$–CH=CH–CHOH–CHNHC(CH$_2$)$_{22}$CH$_3$, with O–CH$_2$, CH$_2$OH, HO, H, OH, H, H, OH, O)

FIGURE 23.9 A sphingosine and two sphingolipids.

The cerebroside shown in Fig. 23.9 is an example of a **glycolipid**. Glycolipids have a polar group that is contributed by a *carbohydrate*. They do not yield phosphoric acid or choline when they are hydrolyzed.

The sphingolipids, together with proteins and polysaccharides, make up **myelin,** the protective coating that encloses nerve fibers or **axons.** The axons of nerve cells carry electrical nerve impulses. Myelin has been described as having a function relative to the axon similar to that of the insulation on an ordinary electric wire.

23.7 WAXES

Most waxes are esters of long-chain fatty acids and long-chain alcohols. Waxes are found as protective coatings on the skin, fur, or feathers of animals, and on the leaves and fruits of plants. Several esters isolated from waxes are the following:

$$CH_3(CH_2)_{14}\overset{O}{\overset{\|}{C}}OCH_2(CH_2)_{14}CH_3$$
Cetyl palmitate
(from spermaceti)

$$CH_3(CH_2)_n\overset{O}{\overset{\|}{C}}OCH_2(CH_2)_mCH_3$$
$n = 24$ and 26; $m = 28$ and 30
(from beeswax)

$$HOCH_2(CH_2)_n\overset{O}{\overset{\|}{C}}\!-\!OCH_2(CH_2)_mCH_3$$
$n = 16 - 28$; $m = 30$ and 32
(from carnauba wax)

Additional Problems

23.12 How would you convert stearic acid, $CH_3(CH_2)_{16}CO_2H$, into each of the following?

(a) Ethyl stearate, $CH_3(CH_2)_{16}CO_2C_2H_5$ (two ways)

(b) *tert*-Butyl stearate, $CH_3(CH_2)_{16}CO_2C(CH_3)_3$

(c) Stearamide, $CH_3(CH_2)_{16}CONH_2$

(d) *N,N*-Dimethylstearamide, $CH_3(CH_2)_{16}CON(CH_3)_2$

(e) Octadecylamine, $CH_3(CH_2)_{16}CH_2NH_2$

(f) Heptadecylamine, $CH_3(CH_2)_{15}CH_2NH_2$

(g) Octadecanal, $CH_3(CH_2)_{16}CHO$

(h) Octadecyl stearate, $CH_3(CH_2)_{16}\overset{\displaystyle O}{\overset{\displaystyle \|}{C}}OCH_2(CH_2)_{16}CH_3$

(i) 1-Octadecanol, $CH_3(CH_2)_{16}CH_2OH$ (two ways)

(j) 2-Nonadecanone, $CH_3(CH_2)_{16}\overset{\displaystyle O}{\overset{\displaystyle \|}{C}}CH_3$

(k) 1-Bromooctadecane, $CH_3(CH_2)_{16}CH_2Br$

(l) Nonadecanoic acid, $CH_3(CH_2)_{16}CH_2CO_2H$

23.13 How would you transform myristic acid into each of the following?

(a) $CH_3(CH_2)_{11}\underset{\displaystyle Br}{CH}CO_2H$

(b) $CH_3(CH_2)_{11}\underset{\displaystyle OH}{CH}CO_2H$

(c) $CH_3(CH_2)_{11}\underset{\displaystyle CN}{CH}CO_2H$

(d) $CH_3(CH_2)_{11}\underset{\displaystyle NH_3^+}{CH}CO_2^-$

23.14 Using palmitoleic acid as an example and neglecting stereochemistry, illustrate each of the following reactions of the double bond.

(a) Addition of bromine   (c) Hydroxylation

(b) Addition of hydrogen   (d) Addition of HCl

23.15 When oleic acid is heated to 180–200 °C (in the presence of a small amount of selenium), an equilibrium is established between oleic acid (33%) and an isomeric compound called elaidic acid (67%). Suggest a possible structure for elaidic acid.

23.16 Gadoleic acid ($C_{20}H_{38}O_2$), a fatty acid that can be isolated from cod-liver oil, can be cleaved by hydroxylation and subsequent treatment with periodic acid to $CH_3(CH_2)_9CHO$ and $OHC(CH_2)_7CO_2H$. (a) What two stereoisomeric structures are possible for gadoleic acid? (b) What spectroscopic technique would make possible a decision as to the actual structure of gadoleic acid? (c) What peaks would you look for?

23.17 When limonene (p. 1055) is heated strongly, it yields 2 mol of isoprene. What kind of reaction is involved here?

23.18 α-Phellandrene and β-phellandrene are isomeric compounds that are minor constituents of spearmint oil; they have the molecular formula $C_{10}H_{16}$. Each compound has a UV absorption maximum in the 230–270-nm range. On catalytic hydrogenation, each compound yields 1-isopropyl-4-methylcyclohexane. On vigorous oxidation with potassium permanganate, α-phellandrene yields $CH_3\overset{O}{\overset{\|}{C}}CO_2H$ and $CH_3\underset{\underset{CH_3}{|}}{C}HCH(CO_2H)CH_2CO_2H$. A similar oxida-

tion of β-phellandrene yields $CH_3\underset{\underset{CH_3}{|}}{C}HCH(CO_2H)CH_2CH_2\overset{O}{\overset{\|}{C}}CO_2H$ as the only isolable prod-

uct. Propose structures for α- and β-phellandrene.

23.19 Vaccenic acid, a constitutional isomer of oleic acid, has been synthesized through the following reaction sequence:

1-Octyne $+$ NaNH$_2$ $\xrightarrow{\text{liq.}}{\text{NH}_3}$ $\textbf{A}$ $(C_8H_{13}Na)$ $\xrightarrow{ICH_2(CH_2)_7CH_2Cl}$

$\textbf{B}$ $(C_{17}H_{31}Cl)$ $\xrightarrow{NaCN}$ $\textbf{C}$ $(C_{18}H_{31}N)$ $\xrightarrow{KOH,H_2O}$ $\textbf{D}$ $(C_{18}H_{31}O_2K)$ $\xrightarrow{H_3O^+}$

$\textbf{E}$ $(C_{18}H_{32}O_2)$ $\xrightarrow{H_2,Pd}{BaSO_4}$ vaccenic acid $(C_{18}H_{34}O_2)$

Propose a structure for vaccenic acid and for the intermediates $\textbf{A}$ – $\textbf{E}$.

23.20 ω-Fluorooleic acid can be isolated from a shrub, *Dechapetalum toxicarium,* that grows in Sierra Leone. The compound is highly toxic to warm-blooded animals; it has found use as an arrow poison in tribal warfare, in poisoning enemy water supplies, and by witch doctors "for terrorizing the native population." Powdered fruit of the plant has been used as a rat poison, hence ω-fluorooleic acid has the common name "ratsbane." A synthesis of ω-fluorooleic acid is outlined here. Give structures for compounds $\textbf{F}$ – $\textbf{I}$.

1-Bromo-8-fluorooctane $+$ sodium acetylide $\longrightarrow$ $\textbf{F}$ $(C_{10}H_{17}F)$ $\xrightarrow{(1)\ NaNH_2}{(2)\ I(CH_2)_7Cl}$

$\textbf{G}$ $(C_{17}H_{30}FCl)$ $\xrightarrow{NaCN}$ $\textbf{H}$ $(C_{18}H_{30}NF)$ $\xrightarrow{(1)\ KOH}{(2)\ H^+}$ $\textbf{I}$ $(C_{18}H_{31}O_2F)$ $\xrightarrow{H_2}{Ni_2B\ (P\text{-}2)}$

$$F-(CH_2)_8\underset{H}{\diagdown}C=C\underset{H}{\diagup}(CH_2)_7\overset{O}{\overset{\|}{C}}OH$$

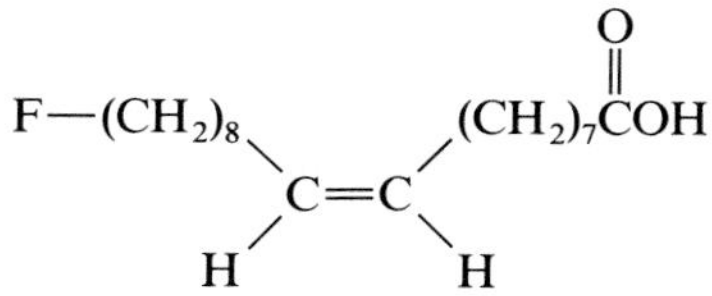

ω-**Fluorooleic acid**
(46% yield, overall)

23.21 Give formulas and names for compounds $\textbf{A}$ and $\textbf{B}$.

5α-Cholest-2-ene $\xrightarrow{C_6H_5\overset{O}{\overset{\|}{C}}OOH}$ $\textbf{A}$ (an epoxide) $\xrightarrow{HBr}$ $\textbf{B}$

(*Hint:* $\textbf{B}$ is not the most stable stereoisomer.)

23.22 One of the first laboratory syntheses of cholesterol was achieved by R. B. Woodward and his students at Harvard University in 1951. Many of the steps of this synthesis are outlined here. Supply the missing reagents.

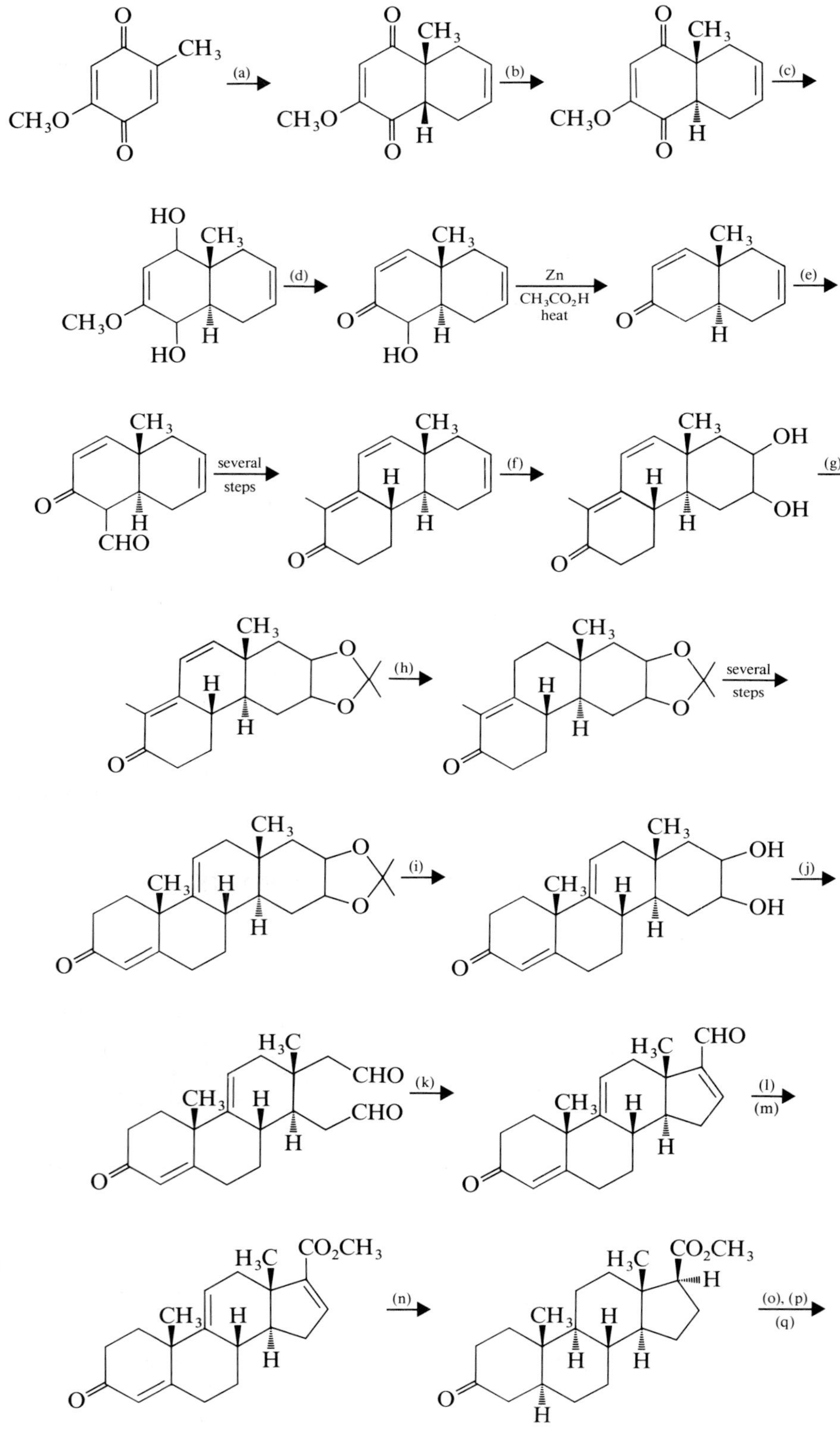
(a)
(b)
(c)
(d)
Zn
CH3CO2H
heat
(e)
several steps
(f)
(g)
(h)
several steps
(i)
(j)
(k)
(l)
(m)
(n)
(o), (p)
(q)

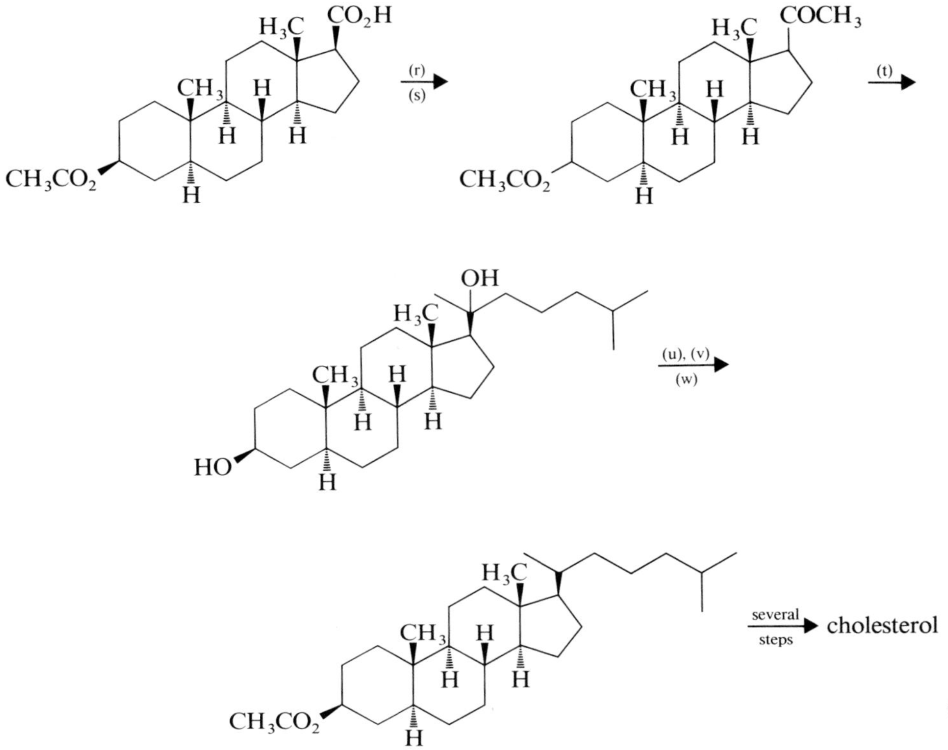

ADDITIONAL PROBLEMS

23.23 The initial steps of a laboratory synthesis of several prostaglandins reported by E. J. Corey (Section 4.15C) and his co-workers in 1968 are outlined here. Supply each of the missing reagents.

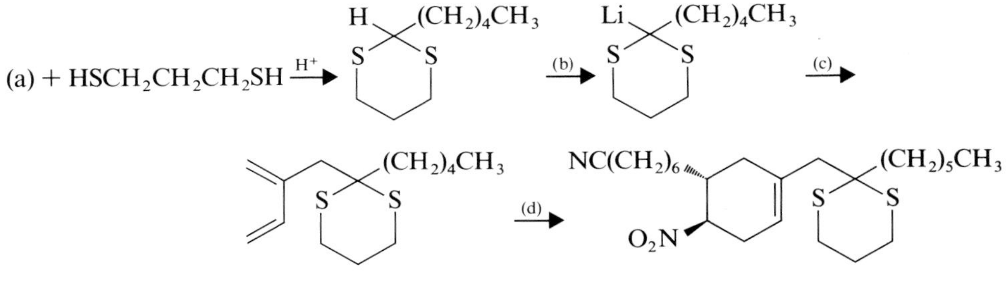

(e) The initial step in another prostaglandin synthesis is shown in the following reaction. What kind of reaction—and catalyst—is needed here?

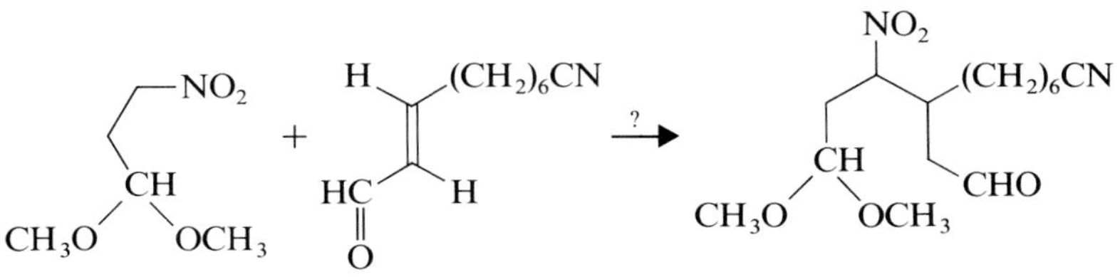

23.24 A useful synthesis of sesquiterpene ketones, called *cyperones,* was accomplished through a modification of the following Robinson annulation procedure (Section 17.9B)

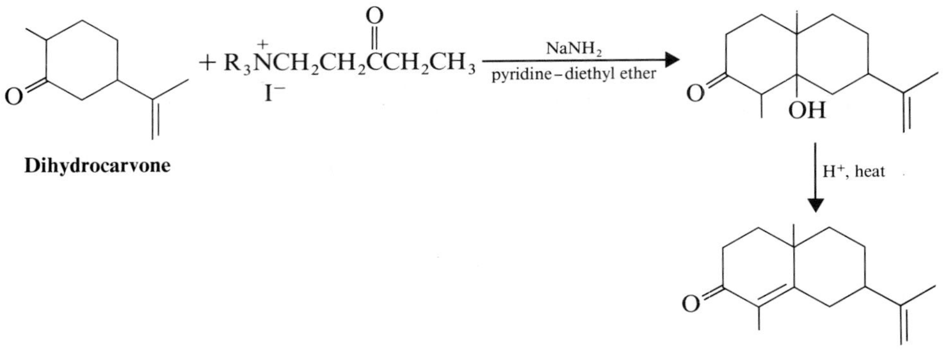

$$+ \; R_3\overset{+}{N}CH_2CH_2\overset{O}{\overset{\|}{C}}CH_2CH_3 \;\; \underset{\text{pyridine–diethyl ether}}{\overset{\text{NaNH}_2}{\longrightarrow}}$$

I⁻

Dihydrocarvone

H⁺, heat

A cyperone

Write a mechanism that accounts for each step of this synthesis.

SPECIAL TOPIC

L

THIOL ESTERS AND LIPID BIOSYNTHESIS

L.1 THIOL ESTERS

Thiol esters can be prepared by reactions of a thiol with an acyl chloride.

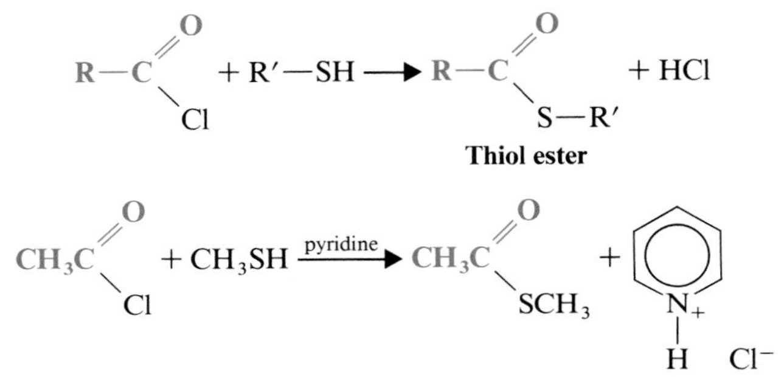

$$R-C\underset{Cl}{\overset{O}{\backslash}} + R'-SH \longrightarrow R-C\underset{S-R'}{\overset{O}{\backslash}} + HCl$$

Thiol ester

$$CH_3C\underset{Cl}{\overset{O}{\backslash}} + CH_3SH \xrightarrow{\text{pyridine}} CH_3C\underset{SCH_3}{\overset{O}{\backslash}} + \underset{\overset{|}{N_+}}{\bigcirc}$$

$$\overset{|}{H} \quad Cl^-$$

Although thiol esters are not often used in laboratory syntheses, they are of great importance in syntheses that occur within living cells. One of the important thiol esters in biochemistry is "acetyl coenzyme A."

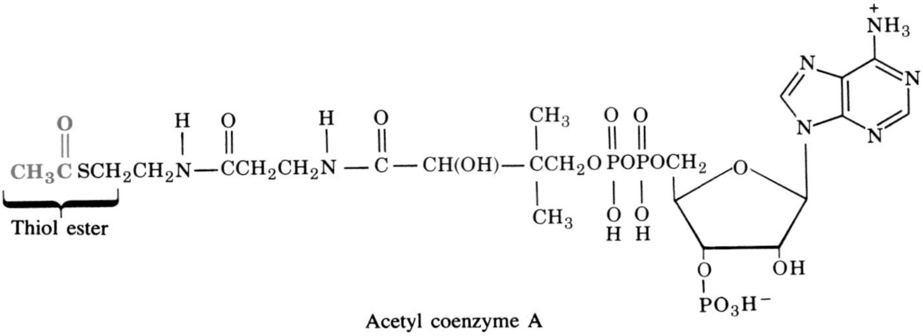

Acetyl coenzyme A

The important part of this rather complicated structure is the thiol ester at the beginning of the chain; because of this, acetyl coenzyme A is usually abbreviated as follows:

$$CoA-S\overset{O}{\overset{||}{C}}CH_3$$

and coenzyme A, itself, is abbreviated:

$$CoA-SH$$

1079

In certain biochemical reactions, an *acyl* coenzyme A operates as an *acylating agent;* it transfers an acyl group to another nucleophile in a reaction that involves a nucleophilic attack at the acyl carbon of the thiol ester. For example:

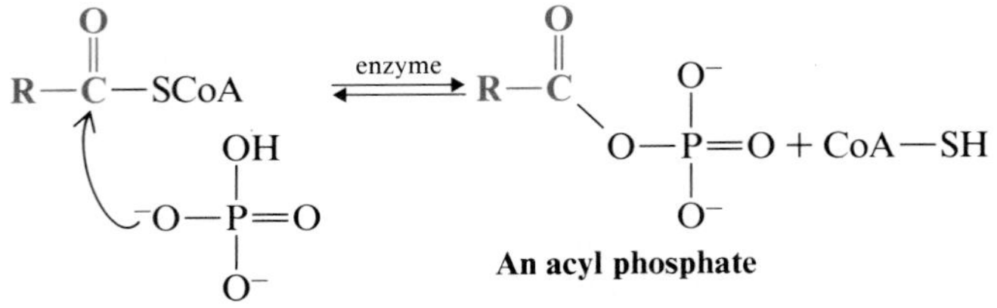

An acyl phosphate

This reaction is catalyzed by the enzyme *phosphotransacetylase.*

The α hydrogens of the acetyl group of acetyl coenzyme A are appreciably acidic. Acetyl coenzyme A, as a result, also functions as an *alkylating agent.* Acetyl coenzyme A, for example, reacts with oxaloacetate ion to form citrate ion in a reaction that resembles an aldol addition.

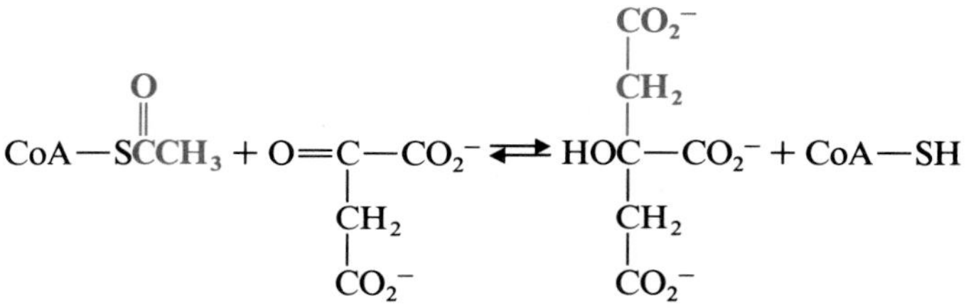

| Oxaloacetate ion | Citrate ion |

One might well ask, "Why has nature made such prominent use of thiol esters?" Or, "In contrast to ordinary esters, what advantages do thiol esters offer the cell?" In answering these questions we can consider three factors:

1. Resonance contributions of type (b) in the following reaction stabilize an ordinary ester and make the carbonyl group less susceptible to nucleophilic attack.

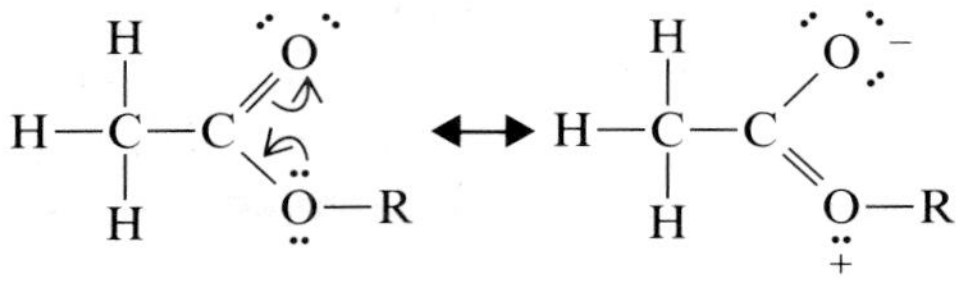

(a) (b)
**This structure makes
an important contribution**

By contrast, thiol esters are not as effectively stabilized by a similar resonance contribution because structure (d) among the following ones requires overlap between the $3p$ orbital of sulfur and a $2p$ orbital of carbon. Since this overlap is not large, resonance stabilization by (d) is not as effective. Structure (e) does, however, make an important contribution—one that makes the carbonyl group more susceptible to nucleophilic attack.

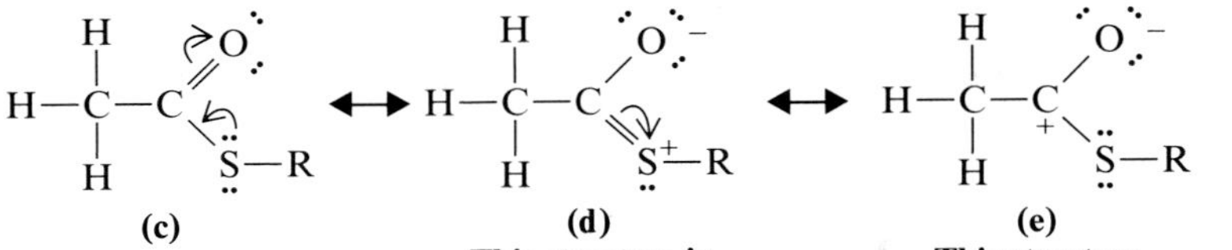

(c) **(d)**
This structure is
not an important
contributor

(e)
This structure
makes the carbonyl
carbon atom susceptible
to nucleophilic attack

2. A resonance contribution from the similar structure (g) makes the α hydrogens of thiol esters more acidic than those of ordinary esters.

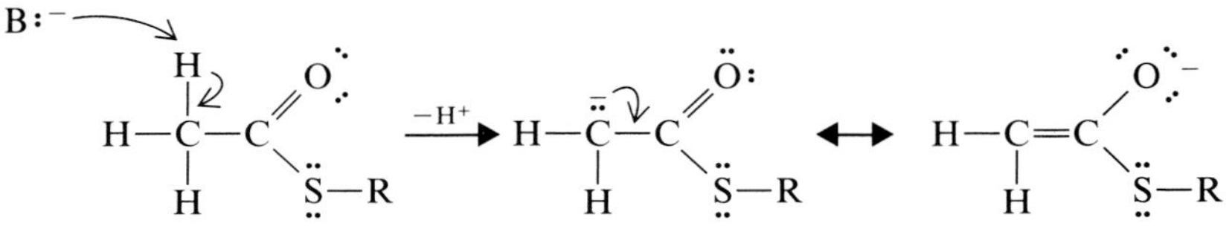

(f) **(g)**
This structure's
contribution stabilizes
the anion of a thiol ester

3. The carbon–sulfur bond of a thiol ester is weaker than the carbon–oxygen bond of an ordinary ester; ⁻SR is a better leaving group than ⁻OR.

Factors **1** and **3** make thiol esters effective *acylating agents;* factor **2** makes them effective *alkylating* agents. Thus, we should not be surprised when we encounter reactions similar to the following one:

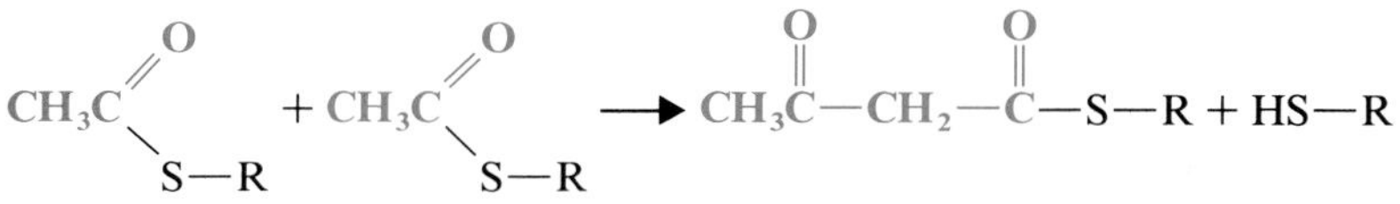

In this reaction 1 mol of a thiol ester acts as an acylating agent and the other acts as an alkylating agent (cf. Section L.2).

L.2 BIOSYNTHESIS OF FATTY ACIDS

The fact that most naturally occurring fatty acids are made up of an even number of carbon atoms suggests that they are assembled from two-carbon units. The idea that these might be acetate ($CH_3CO_2^-$) units was put forth as early as 1893. Many years later, when radioactively labeled compounds became available, it became possible to test and confirm this hypothesis.

When an animal is fed acetic acid labeled with carbon-14 at the carboxyl group, the fatty acids that the animal synthesizes contain the label at alternate carbon atoms beginning with the carboxyl carbon:

$\overset{*}{C}H_3CO_2H$ $\quad CH_3\overset{*}{C}H_2CH_2\overset{*}{C}H_2CH_2\overset{*}{C}H_2CH_2\overset{*}{C}H_2CH_2\overset{*}{C}H_2CH_2\overset{*}{C}H_2CH_2\overset{*}{C}H_2CH_2\overset{*}{C}O_2H$

Feeding
carboxyl-
labeled
acetic acid
($C^* = {}^{14}C$) $\cdots$

yields palmitic acid labeled at these positions

Conversely, feeding acetic acid labeled at the methyl carbon yields a fatty acid labeled at the other set of alternate carbon atoms:

$\overset{*}{C}H_3CO_2H$ $\overset{*}{C}H_3CH_2\overset{*}{C}H_2CH_2\overset{*}{C}H_2CH_2\overset{*}{C}H_2CH_2\overset{*}{C}H_2CH_2\overset{*}{C}H_2CH_2\overset{*}{C}H_2CH_2\overset{*}{C}H_2CO_2H$

Feeding methyl-labeled acetic acid · · ·   **yields palmitic acid labeled at these positions**

The biosynthesis of fatty acids is now known to begin with acetyl coenzyme A:

$$CH_3\overset{\overset{\displaystyle O}{\|}}{C}-S-CoA$$

The acetyl portion of acetyl coenzyme A can be synthesized in the cell from acetic acid; it can also be synthesized from carbohydrates, proteins, and other fats.

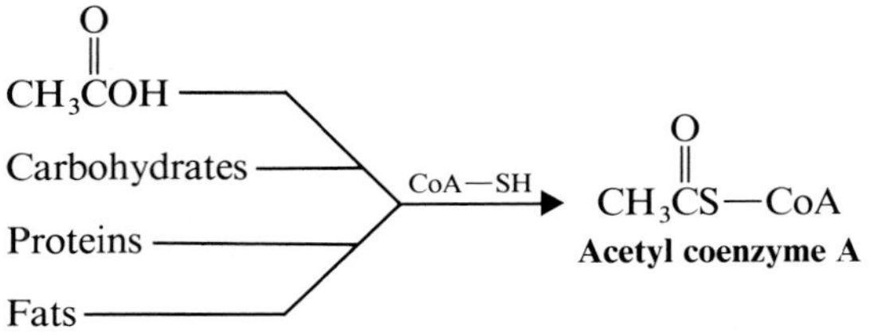

$$CH_3\overset{\overset{\displaystyle O}{\|}}{C}OH$$
Carbohydrates
Proteins
Fats
$\xrightarrow{CoA-SH}$ $CH_3\overset{\overset{\displaystyle O}{\|}}{C}S-CoA$
Acetyl coenzyme A

Although the methyl group of acetyl coenzyme A is already activated toward condensation reactions by virtue of its being a part of a thiol ester (Section L.1), nature activates it again by converting it to *malonyl coenzyme A.*

$$CH_3\overset{\overset{\displaystyle O}{\|}}{C}S-CoA + CO_2 \underset{\text{acetyl CoA carboxylase*}}{\rightleftharpoons} HO\overset{\overset{\displaystyle O}{\|}}{C}CH_2\overset{\overset{\displaystyle O}{\|}}{C}S-CoA$$
Acetyl CoA   **Malonyl CoA**

The next steps in fatty acid synthesis involve the transfer of acyl groups of malonyl CoA and acetyl coenzyme A to the thiol group of a coenzyme called *acyl carrier protein* or ACP—SH.

$$HO\overset{\overset{\displaystyle O}{\|}}{C}CH_2\overset{\overset{\displaystyle O}{\|}}{C}S-CoA + ACP-SH \rightleftharpoons HO\overset{\overset{\displaystyle O}{\|}}{C}CH_2\overset{\overset{\displaystyle O}{\|}}{C}S-ACP + CoA-SH$$
Malonyl CoA   **Malonyl-S-ACP**

$$CH_3\overset{\overset{\displaystyle O}{\|}}{C}S-CoA + ACP-SH \rightleftharpoons CH_3\overset{\overset{\displaystyle O}{\|}}{C}S-ACP + CoA-SH$$
Acetyl CoA   **Acetyl-S-ACP**

Acetyl-S-ACP and malonyl-S-ACP then condense with each other to form acetoacetyl-S-ACP:

---

*This step also requires 1 mol of adenosine triphosphate (Section 22.1B) and an enzyme that transfers the carbon dioxide.

SPECIAL TOPIC L

$$\underset{\text{Acetyl-S-ACP}}{CH_3\overset{O}{\overset{\|}{C}}S-ACP} + \underset{\text{Malonyl-S-ACP}}{HO\overset{O}{\overset{\|}{C}}CH_2\overset{O}{\overset{\|}{C}}S-ACP} \rightleftarrows \underset{\text{Acetoacetyl-S-ACP}}{CH_3\overset{O}{\overset{\|}{C}}CH_2\overset{O}{\overset{\|}{C}}S-ACP} + CO_2 + ACP-SH$$

The molecule of CO_2 that is lost in this reaction is the same molecule that was incorporated into malonyl CoA in the acetyl CoA carboxylase reaction.

This remarkable reaction bears a strong resemblance to the malonic ester syntheses that we saw earlier (Section 20.4) and it deserves special comment. One can imagine, for example, a more economical synthesis of acetoacetyl-S-ACP, that is, a simple condensation between 2 mol of acetyl-S-ACP.

$$CH_3\overset{O}{\overset{\|}{C}}S-ACP + CH_3\overset{O}{\overset{\|}{C}}S-ACP \rightleftarrows CH_3\overset{O}{\overset{\|}{C}}CH_2\overset{O}{\overset{\|}{C}}S-ACP + ACP-SH$$

Studies of this last reaction, however, have revealed that it is highly *endothermic* and that the position of equilibrium lies very far to the left. By contrast, the condensation of acetyl-S-ACP and malonyl-S-ACP is highly exothermic, and the position of equilibrium lies far to the right. The favorable thermodynamics of the condensation utilizing malonyl-S-ACP comes about because *the reaction also produces a highly stable substance: carbon dioxide.* Thus, decarboxylation of the malonyl group provides the condensation with thermodynamic assistance.

The next three steps in fatty acid synthesis transform the acetoacetyl group of acetoacetyl-S-ACP into a butyryl (butanoyl) group. These steps involve (1) reduction of the keto group (utilizing NADPH* as the reducing agent), (2) dehydration of an alcohol, and (3) reduction of a double bond (again utilizing NADPH).

Reduction of the Keto Group

$$\underset{\text{Acetoacetyl-S-ACP}}{CH_3\overset{O}{\overset{\|}{C}}CH_2\overset{O}{\overset{\|}{C}}S-ACP} + NADPH + H^+ \rightleftarrows \underset{\beta\text{-Hydroxybutyryl-S-ACP}}{CH_3\overset{OH}{\overset{|}{C}}HCH_2\overset{O}{\overset{\|}{C}}S-ACP} + NADP^+$$

Dehydration of the Alcohol

$$\underset{\beta\text{-Hydroxybutyryl-S-ACP}}{CH_3\overset{OH}{\overset{|}{C}}HCH_2\overset{O}{\overset{\|}{C}}S-ACP} \rightleftarrows \underset{\text{Crotonyl-S-ACP}}{CH_3CH=CH\overset{O}{\overset{\|}{C}}S-ACP} + H_2O$$

Reduction of the Double Bond

$$\underset{\text{Crotonyl-S-ACP}}{CH_3CH=CH\overset{O}{\overset{\|}{C}}S-ACP} + NADPH + H^+ \rightleftarrows \underset{\text{Butyryl-S-ACP}}{CH_3CH_2CH_2\overset{O}{\overset{\|}{C}}S-ACP} + NADP^+$$

These steps complete one cycle of the overall fatty acid synthesis. Their net result is the conversion of two acetate units into the four-carbon butyrate unit of butyryl-S-ACP. (This conversion requires, of course, the crucial intervention of a molecule of carbon dioxide.) At this point, another cycle begins and the chain is lengthened by two more carbon atoms:

* NADPH is *nicotinamide adenine dinucleotide phosphate (reduced form)*, a coenzyme that is very similar in structure and function to NADH, Section 13.13.

Condensation

$$\underset{\text{(four carbon atoms)}}{CH_3CH_2CH_2\overset{\overset{\displaystyle O}{\|}}{C}S-ACP} + HO\overset{\overset{\displaystyle O}{\|}}{C}CH_2\overset{\overset{\displaystyle O}{\|}}{C}S-ACP \longrightarrow$$

$$CH_3CH_2CH_2\overset{\overset{\displaystyle O}{\|}}{C}CH_2\overset{\overset{\displaystyle O}{\|}}{C}S-ACP + CO_2 + ACP-SH$$

Reduction

$$CH_3CH_2CH_2\overset{\overset{\displaystyle O}{\|}}{C}CH_2\overset{\overset{\displaystyle O}{\|}}{C}S-ACP \xrightarrow{\substack{NADPH\ NADP^+ \\ +H^+}} CH_3CH_2CH_2\overset{\overset{\displaystyle OH}{|}}{C}HCH_2\overset{\overset{\displaystyle O}{\|}}{C}S-ACP$$

Dehydration

$$CH_3CH_2CH_2\overset{\overset{\displaystyle OH}{|}}{C}HCH_2\overset{\overset{\displaystyle O}{\|}}{C}S-ACP \xrightarrow{(-H_2O)} CH_3CH_2CH_2CH=CH\overset{\overset{\displaystyle O}{\|}}{C}S-ACP$$

Reduction

$$CH_3CH_2CH_2CH=CH\overset{\overset{\displaystyle O}{\|}}{C}S-ACP \xrightarrow{\substack{NADPH\ NADP^+ \\ +H^+}} \underset{\text{(six carbon atoms)}}{CH_3CH_2CH_2CH_2CH_2\overset{\overset{\displaystyle O}{\|}}{C}S-ACP}$$

Subsequent turns of the cycle continue to lengthen the chain by two-carbon units until a long-chain fatty acid is produced. The overall equation for the synthesis of palmitic acid, for example, can be written as follows:

$$CH_3\overset{\overset{\displaystyle O}{\|}}{C}S-CoA + 7\ HO\overset{\overset{\displaystyle O}{\|}}{C}CH_2\overset{\overset{\displaystyle O}{\|}}{C}S-CoA + 14\ NADPH + 14\ H^+ \longrightarrow$$

$$CH_3(CH_2)_{14}CO_2H + 7\ CO_2 + 8\ CoA-SH + 14\ NADP^+ + 6\ H_2O$$

One of the most remarkable aspects of fatty acid synthesis is that the entire cycle appears to be carried out by a complex of enzymes that are clustered into a single unit. The molecular weight of this cluster of proteins, called *fatty acid synthetase,* has been estimated as 2,300,000.* The synthesis begins with a single molecule of acetyl-S-ACP serving as a primer. Then, in the synthesis of palmitic acid, for example, successive condensations of seven molecules of malonyl-S-ACP occur with each condensation followed by reduction, dehydration, and reduction. All of these steps, which result in the synthesis of a C_{16} chain, take place before the fatty acid is released from the enzyme cluster.

The acyl carrier protein has been isolated and purified; its molecular weight is approximately 10,000. The protein contains a chain of groups called a *phosphopantetheine group* that is identical to that of coenzyme A (Section L.1). In ACP this chain is attached to a protein (rather than to an adenosine phosphate as it is in coenzyme A):

---

* As isolated from yeast cells. Fatty acid synthetases from different sources have different molecular weights; that from pigeon liver, for example, has a molecular weight of 450,000.

Pantothenic acid   2-Aminoethanethiol

$$\text{Protein}\!-\!O\!-\!\overset{\displaystyle O}{\underset{\displaystyle OH}{\overset{\|}{P}}}\!-\!O\!-\!CH_2\!-\!\overset{\displaystyle CH_3}{\underset{\displaystyle CH_3}{C}}\!-\!CH(OH)\!-\!\overset{\displaystyle O}{\overset{\|}{C}}\!-\!NH\!-\!CH_2\!-\!CH_2\!-\!\overset{\displaystyle O}{\overset{\|}{C}}\!-\!NH\!-\!CH_2\!-\!CH_2\!-\!SH$$

Phosphopantetheine group

20.2 Å

The length of the phosphopantetheine group is 20.2 Å, and it has been postulated that it acts as a "swinging arm" in transferring the growing acyl chain from one enzyme of the cluster to the next (Fig. L.1).

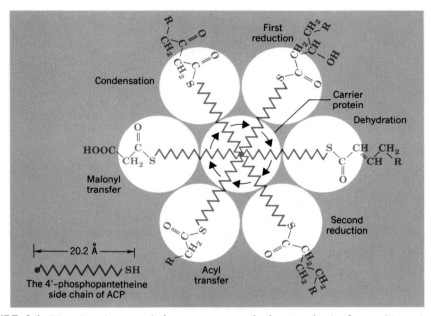

FIGURE L.1 The phosphopantetheine group as a swinging arm in the fatty acid synthetase complex. (Adapted from A. L. Lehninger, *Biochemistry*, Worth, New York, 1970, p. 519. Used with permission.)

L.3 BIOSYNTHESIS OF ISOPRENOIDS

The basic building block for the synthesis of terpenes and terpenoids (Section 23.3) is 3-methyl-3-butenyl pyrophosphate. The five carbon atoms of this compound are the source of the "isoprene units" of all "isoprenoids." The pyrophosphate group is a group that nature relies upon for a vast number of chemical processes. In the reactions that we shall soon see the pyrophosphate group functions as a natural "leaving group."

$$CH_2\!=\!\overset{\displaystyle CH_3}{\overset{|}{C}}\!-\!CH_2\!-\!CH_2\!-\!O\!-\!\overset{\displaystyle O}{\underset{\displaystyle OH}{\overset{\|}{P}}}\!-\!O\!-\!\overset{\displaystyle O}{\underset{\displaystyle OH}{\overset{\|}{P}}}\!-\!OH$$

3-Methyl-3-butenyl pyrophosphate

SPECIAL TOPIC L

3-Methyl-3-butenyl pyrophosphate is isomerized by an enzyme to 3-methyl-2-butenyl pyrophosphate. The isomerization establishes an equilibrium that makes both compounds available to the cell.

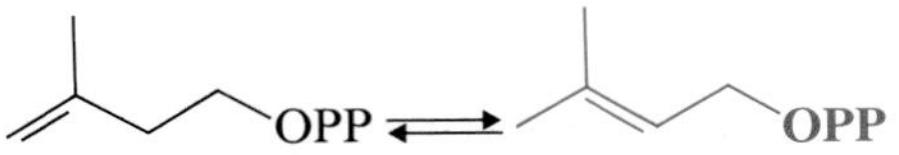

**3-Methyl-3-butenyl   3-Methyl-2-butenyl   OPP = Pyrophosphate
pyrophosphate   pyrophosphate**

These two C_5 compounds condense with each other in another enzymatic reaction to yield the C_{10} compound, geranyl pyrophosphate. The first step involves the formation of an allylic cation.

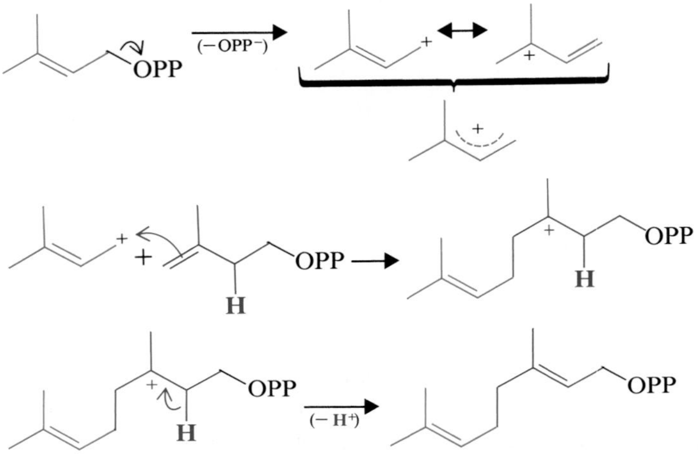

Geranyl pyrophosphate

Geranyl pyrophosphate is the precursor of the monoterpenes; hydrolysis of geranyl pyrophosphate, for example, yields geraniol.

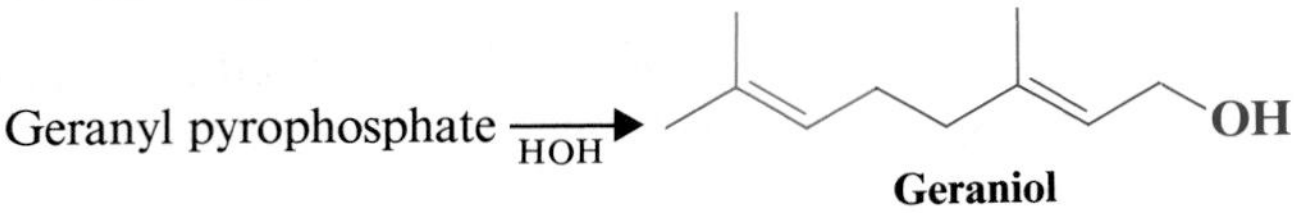

Geranyl pyrophosphate $\xrightarrow{\text{HOH}}$

Geraniol

Geranyl pyrophosphate can also condense with 3-methyl-3-butenyl pyrophosphate to form the C_{15} precursor for sesquiterpenes, farnesyl pyrophosphate.

Geranyl pyrophosphate

$-OPP^-, -H^+$

Farnesyl pyrophosphate

other sesquiterpenes

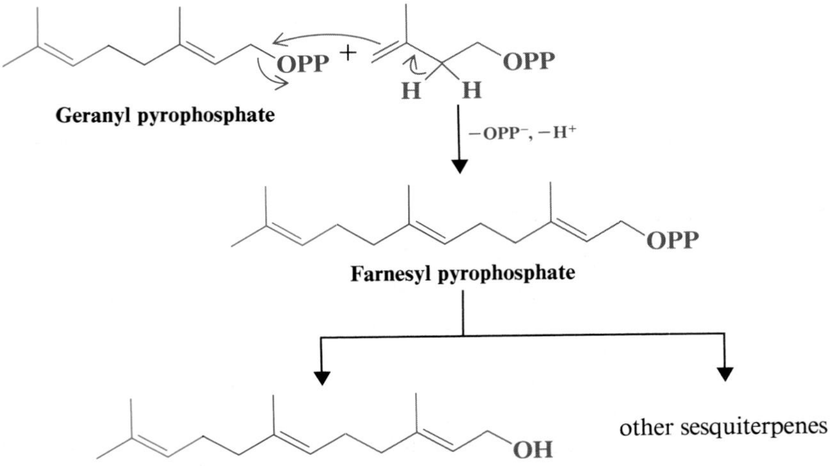

Farnesol

Farnesol has been isolated from ambrette oil. It has the odor of lily of the valley. Farnesol also functions as a hormone in certain insects and initiates the change from caterpillar to pupa to moth.

Similar condensation reactions yield the precursors for all of the other terpenes (Fig. L.2). In addition, a tail-to-tail reductive coupling of two molecules of farnesyl pyrophosphate produces squalene, the precursor for the important group of isoprenoids known as *steroids* (cf. Sections 23.4 and L.4).

Monoterpenes ◄── Geranyl pyrophosphate
(**C₁₀**)   (**C₁₀-pyrophosphate**)

3-methyl-3-butenyl
pyrophosphate

Sesquiterpenes ◄── Farnesyl pyrophosphate ──► Squalene
(**C₁₅**)   (**C₁₅-pyrophosphate**)   (**C₃₀**)

3-methyl-3-butenyl
pyrophosphate

Diterpenes ◄── C₂₀-Pyrophosphate   Lanosterol
(**C₂₀**)   (**cf. p. 1090**)

Tetraterpenes   Cholesterol
(**C₄₀**)   (**a steroid**)

FIGURE L.2 The biosynthetic paths for terpenes and steroids.

Problem L.1

When farnesol is treated with sulfuric acid, it is converted to bisabolene. Outline a possible mechanism for this reaction.

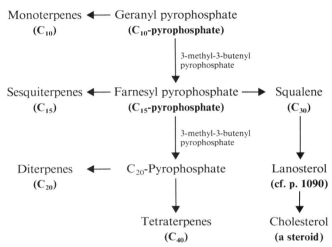

Farnesol $\xrightarrow{\text{H}_2\text{SO}_4}$

Bisabolene

L.4 BIOSYNTHESIS OF STEROIDS

We saw in the previous section that the C_5 compound, 3-methyl-3-butenyl pyrophosphate, is the actual "isoprene unit" that nature uses in constructing terpenoids and carotenoids. We can now extend that biosynthetic pathway in two directions. We can show how 3-methyl-3-butenyl pyrophosphate (like the fatty acids) is ultimately derived from acetate units, and how cholesterol, the precursor of most of the important steroids, is synthesized from 3-methyl-3-butenyl pyrophosphate.

In the 1940s, Konrad Bloch of Harvard University used labeling experiments to demonstrate that all of the carbon atoms of cholesterol can be derived from acetic acid. Using *methyl-labeled* acetic acid, for example, Bloch found the following label distribution in the cholesterol that was synthesized.

Bloch also found that feeding *carboxyl-labeled* acetic acid led to incorporation of the label into all of the other carbon atoms of cholesterol (the unstarred carbon atoms of the formula just given).

Subsequent research by a number of investigators has shown that 3-methyl-3-butenyl pyrophosphate is synthesized from acetate units through the following sequence of reactions:

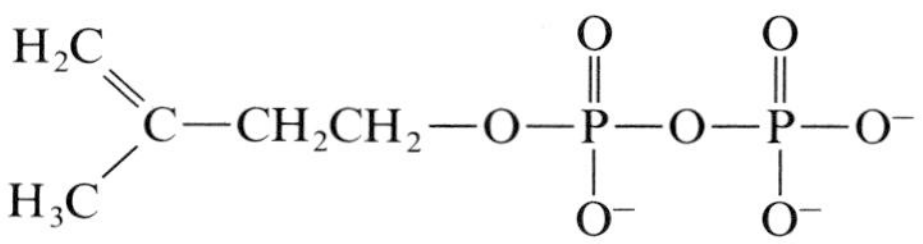

$$H_2C \diagdown \atop H_3C \diagup C—CH_2CH_2—O—\overset{\overset{\displaystyle O}{\|}}{\underset{\underset{\displaystyle O^-}{|}}{P}}—O—\overset{\overset{\displaystyle O}{\|}}{\underset{\underset{\displaystyle O^-}{|}}{P}}—O^-$$

(C$_5$)
3-Methyl-3-butenyl pyrophosphate

The first step of this synthetic pathway is straightforward. Acetyl CoA (from 1 mol of acetate) and acetoacetyl CoA (from 2 mol of acetate) condense to form the C$_6$ compound, β-hydroxy-β-methylglutaryl CoA. This step is followed by an enzymatic reduction of the thiol ester group of β-hydroxy-β-methylglutaryl CoA to the primary alcohol of mevalonic acid. The enzyme that catalyzes this step is called HMG-CoA reductase (HMG = β-hydroxy-β-methyl-glutaryl) and this step is the rate-limiting step in cholesterol biosynthesis. The key to finding this pathway was the discovery that mevalonic acid was an intermediate and that this C$_6$ compound could be transformed into the five-carbon 3-methyl-3-butenyl pyrophosphate by successive phosphorylations and decarboxylation.

Then 3-methyl-3-butenyl pyrophosphate isomerizes to produce an equilibrium mixture that contains 3-methyl-2-butenyl pyrophosphate, and these two compounds condense to form geranyl pyrophosphate, a C$_{10}$ compound. Geranyl pyrophosphate subsequently condenses with another mole of 3-methyl-3-butenyl pyrophosphate to form farnesyl pyrophosphate, a C$_{15}$ compound. (Geranyl pyrophosphate and farnesyl pyrophosphate are the precursors of the mono- and sequiterpenes, cf. Section L.3.)

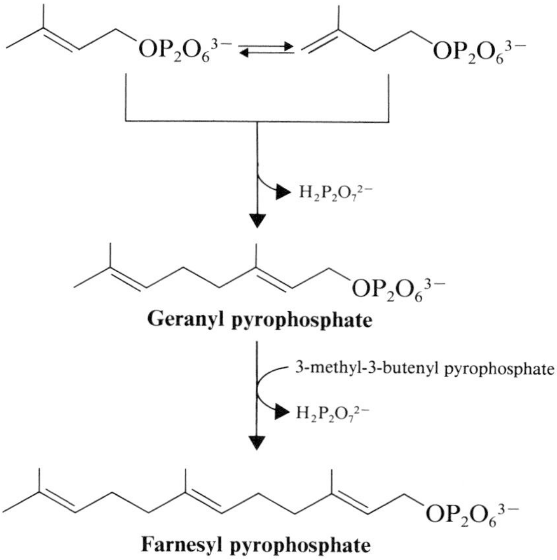

Geranyl pyrophosphate

Farnesyl pyrophosphate

Two molecules of farnesyl pyrophosphate then undergo a reductive condensation to produce squalene.

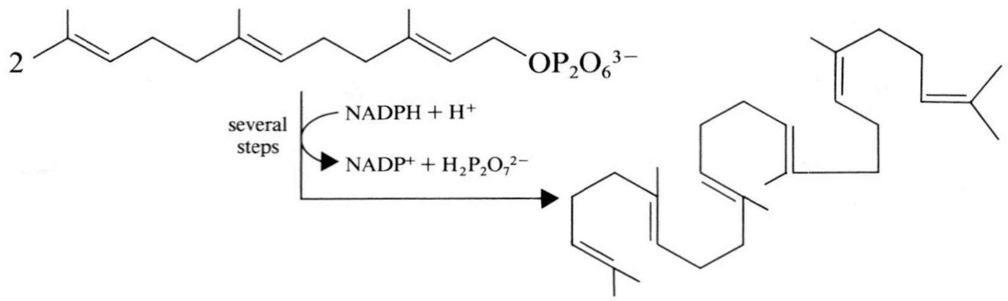

Squalene

Squalene is the direct precursor of cholesterol. Oxidation of squalene yields squalene 2,3-epoxide, which undergoes a remarkable series of ring closures accompanied by concerted methyl and hydride migrations to yield lanosterol. Lanosterol is then converted to cholesterol through a series of enzyme-catalyzed reactions.

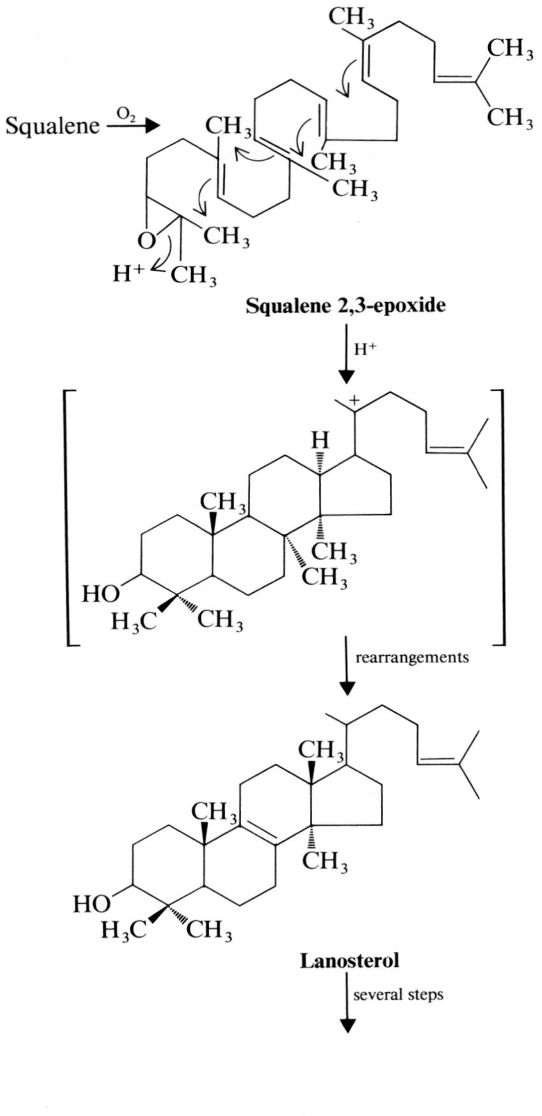

Squalene 2,3-epoxide

Lanosterol

Cholesterol

L.5 CHOLESTEROL AND HEART DISEASE

Because cholesterol is the precursor of steroid hormones and is a vital constituent of cell membranes, it is essential to life. On the other hand, deposition of cholesterol in arteries is a cause of heart disease and artherosclerosis, two leading causes of death in humans. For an organism to remain healthy, there has to be an intricate balance between the biosynthesis of cholesterol and its utilization, so that arterial deposition is kept at a minimum.

For some individuals with high blood levels of cholesterol, the remedy is as simple as following a diet low in cholesterol and in fat. For those who suffer from the genetic disease **familial hypercholesterolemia** (FH), other means of blood cholesterol reduction are required. One remedy involves using the drug *lovastatin* (also called *mevinolin*).

Mevalonate ion

Lovastatin

Lovastatin, because part of its structure resembles mevalonate ion, can apparently bind at the active site of HMG-CoA reductase (p. 1089), the enzyme that catalyzes the rate-limiting step in cholesterol biosythesis. Lovastatin acts as a competitive inhibitor of this enzyme and thereby reduces cholesterol synthesis. Reductions of up to 30% in serum cholesterol levels are possible with lovastatin therapy.

Cholesterol synthesized in the liver is either converted to bile acids that are used in digestion or it is esterified for transport by the blood. Cholesterol is transported in the blood and taken up in cells, in the form of lipoprotein complexes named on the basis of their density. **Low density lipoproteins (LDL)** transport cholesterol from the liver to peripheral tissues. **High density lipoproteins (HDL)** transports cholesterol back to the liver where surplus cholesterol is disposed of by the liver as bile acids. High density lipoproteins have come to be called "good cholesterol" because high levels of HDL may reduce cholesterol deposits in arteries. Because high levels of LDL are associated with the arterial deposition of cholesterol that causes cardiovascular disease, it has come to be called "bad cholesterol."

Bile acids that flow from the liver to the intestines, however, are efficiently recycled to the liver. Recognition of this has led to another method of cholesterol reduction, the ingestion of resins that bind bile acids and thereby prevent their reabsorption in the intestines.

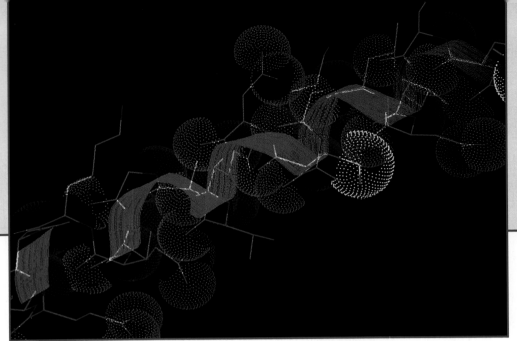

Alpha helix of a protein (see Section 24.8).

CHAPTER
24
AMINO ACIDS AND PROTEINS

24.1 INTRODUCTION

The three groups of biological polymers are polysaccharides, proteins, and nucleic acids. We studied polysaccharides in Chapter 22 and saw that they function primarily as energy reserves, as biochemical labels on cell surfaces and, in plants, as structural materials. When we study nucleic acids in Chapter 25 we shall find that they serve two major purposes: storage and transmission of information. Of the three groups of biopolymers, proteins have the most diverse functions. As enzymes and hormones, proteins catalyze and regulate the reactions that occur in the body; as muscles and tendons they provide the body with the means for movement; as skin and hair they give it an outer covering; as hemoglobins they transfer all-important oxygen to its most remote corners; as antibodies they provide it with a means of protection against disease; and in combination with other substances in bone they provide it with structural support.

Given such diversity of functions, we should not be surprised to find that proteins come in all sizes and shapes. By the standard of most of the molecules we have studied, even small proteins have very high molecular weights. Lysozyme, an enzyme, is a relatively small protein and yet its molecular weight is 14,600. The molecular weights of most proteins are much larger. Their shapes cover a range from the globular proteins such as lysozyme and hemoglobin to the helical coils of α-keratin (hair, nails, and wool) and the pleated sheets of silk fibroin.

And yet, in spite of such diversity of size, shape, and function, all proteins have common features that allow us to deduce their structures and understand their properties. Later in this chapter we shall see how this is done.

Proteins are **polyamides** and their monomeric units are about 20 different α-amino acids:

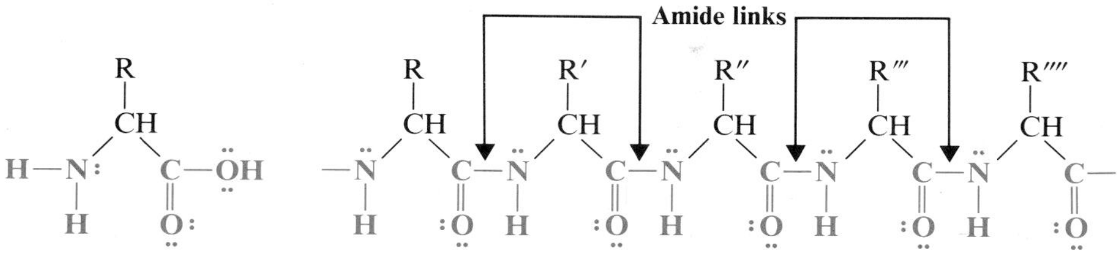

An α-amino acid   A portion of a protein molecule

Cells use the different α-amino acids to synthesize proteins. The exact sequence of the different α-amino acids along the protein chain is called the **primary structure** of the protein. This primary structure, as its name suggests, is of fundamental importance. For the protein to carry out its particular function, the primary structure must be correct. We shall see later that when the primary structure is correct, the polyamide chain folds in certain particular ways to give it the shape it needs for its particular task. This folding of the polyamide chain gives rise to higher levels of complexity called the **secondary** and **tertiary structure** of the protein.

Hydrolysis of proteins with acid or base yields a mixture of the different amino acids. Although hydrolysis of naturally occurring proteins may yield as many as 22 different amino acids, the amino acids have an important structural feature in common: With the exception of glycine (whose molecules are achiral), almost all naturally occurring amino acids have the L configuration at the α carbon.* That is, they have the same relative configuration as L-glyceraldehyde:

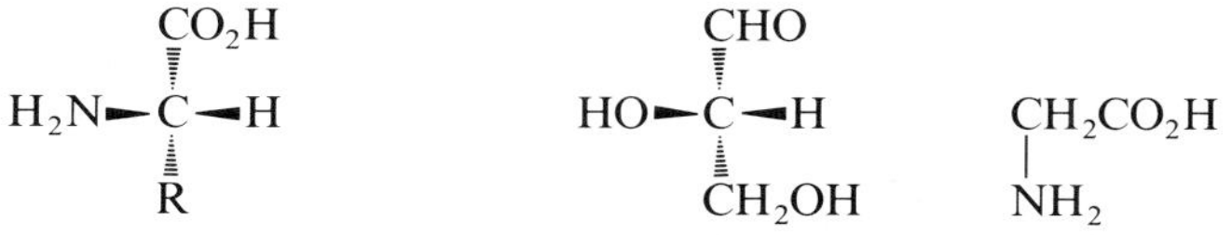

An L-α-amino acid   L-Glyceraldehyde   Glycine
[usually an (S)-α-amino acid]   [(S)-glyceraldehyde]

24.2 AMINO ACIDS

24.2A STRUCTURES AND NAMES

The 22 α-amino acids that can be obtained from proteins can be subdivided into three different groups on the basis of the structures of their side chains, R. These are given in Table 24.1.

Only 20 of the 22 α-amino acids in Table 24.1 are actually used by cells when they synthesize proteins. Two amino acids are synthesized after the polyamide chain is intact. Hydroxyproline (present mainly in collagen) is synthesized from proline, and cystine (present in most proteins) is synthesized from cysteine.

---

*Some D-amino acids have been obtained from the material comprising the cell walls of bacteria, and by hydrolysis of certain antibiotics.

TABLE 24.1 L-Amino acids found in proteins

$$H_2N \overset{\displaystyle CO_2H}{\underset{\displaystyle R}{\vert\!\!-\!\!\vert}} H \quad \text{or} \quad R \overset{H}{\underset{NH_2}{\blacktriangleright C}} -CO_2H$$

STRUCTURE OF R	NAME[a]	ABBRE-VIATION	pK_{a_1} α-CO$_2$H	pK_{a_2} α-NH$_3^+$	pK_{a_3} R GROUP	pI
Neutral Amino Acids						
—H	Glycine	Gly	2.3	9.6		6.0
—CH$_3$	Alanine	Ala	2.3	9.7		6.0
—CH(CH$_3$)$_2$	Valine[e]	Val	2.3	9.6		6.0
—CH$_2$CH(CH$_3$)$_2$	Leucine[e]	Leu	2.4	9.6		6.0

—CHCH$_2$CH$_3$
   |
   CH$_3$
	Isoleucine[e]	Ile	2.4	9.7		6.1

—CH$_2$—⬡	Phenylalanine[e]	Phe	1.8	9.1		5.5
—CH$_2$CONH$_2$	Asparagine	Asn	2.0	8.8		5.4
—CH$_2$CH$_2$CONH$_2$	Glutamine	Gln	2.2	9.1		5.7
—CH$_2$ (indole structure)	Tryptophan[e]	Trp	2.4	9.4		5.9

HOC(=O)—CH—CH$_2$
   HN   CH$_2$
      CH$_2$
 (complete structure)
	Proline	Pro	2.0	10.6		6.3

—CH$_2$OH	Serine	Ser	2.2	9.2		5.7

—CHOH
   |
   CH$_3$
	Threonine[e]	Thr	2.6	10.4		6.5

—CH$_2$—⬡—OH	Tyrosine	Tyr	2.2	9.1	10.1	5.7

HOC(=O)—CH—CH$_2$
   HN   CH
     CH$_2$ OH
 (complete structure)
	Hydroxyproline	Hyp	1.9	9.7		6.3

TABLE 24.1 (continued)

$$\begin{array}{c} CO_2H \\ H_2N\!\!-\!\!\!\!-\!\!\!\!-H \\ | \\ R \end{array} \quad \text{or} \quad \begin{array}{c} H \\ R\!\!-\!\!\overset{|}{C}\!\!-\!\!CO_2H \\ | \\ NH_2 \end{array}$$

STRUCTURE OF R	NAME[a]	ABBRE-VIATION	pK_{a_1} α-CO_2H	pK_{a_2} α-NH_3^+	pK_{a_3} R GROUP	pI
$-CH_2SH$	Cysteine	Cys	1.7	10.8	8.3	5.0
$-CH_2-S$ $\quad$ $\mid$ $-CH_2-S$	Cystine	Cys-Cys	$\left\{\begin{array}{l}1.6\\2.3\end{array}\right.$	$\left\{\begin{array}{l}7.9\\9.9\end{array}\right.$		5.1
$-CH_2CH_2SCH_3$	Methionine[e]	Met	2.3	9.2		5.8
R Contains an Acidic (Carboxyl) Group						
$-CH_2CO_2H$	Aspartic acid	Asp	2.1	9.8	3.9	3.0
$-CH_2CH_2CO_2H$	Glutamic acid	Glu	2.2	9.7	4.3	3.2
R Contains a Basic Group						
$-CH_2CH_2CH_2CH_2NH_2$	Lysine[e]	Lys	2.2	9.0	10.5[b]	9.8
$-CH_2CH_2CH_2NH-\overset{\overset{NH}{\|}}{C}-NH_2$	Arginine	Arg	2.2	9.0	12.5[b]	10.8
$-CH_2\!\!-\!\!\underset{\underset{H}{\|}}{\boxed{N}}$	Histidine	His	1.8	9.2	6.0[b]	7.6

[a] e = essential amino acids.
[b] pK_a is of protonated amine of R group.

This conversion of cysteine to cystine requires additional comment. The —SH group of cysteine makes cysteine a *thiol* (Special Topic I). One property of thiols is that they can be converted to disulfides by mild oxidizing agents. This conversion, moreover, can be reversed by mild reducing agents.

$$2\ R\!-\!S\!-\!H \underset{[H]}{\overset{[O]}{\rightleftharpoons}} R\!-\!S\!-\!S\!-\!R$$

Thiol $\qquad\qquad$ **Disulfide**

$$2\ HO_2CCHCH_2SH \underset{[H]}{\overset{[O]}{\rightleftharpoons}} HO_2CCHCH_2S\!-\!SCH_2CHCO_2H$$

Disulfide linkage

$$\underset{\text{Cysteine}}{\underset{NH_2}{|}} \qquad \underset{NH_2}{|} \qquad \underset{\text{Cystine}}{\underset{NH_2}{|}}$$

We shall see later how the disulfide linkage between cysteine units in a protein chain contributes to the overall structure and shape of the protein.

24.2B ESSENTIAL AMINO ACIDS

Amino acids can be synthesized by all living organisms, plants and animals. Many higher animals, however, are deficient in their ability to synthesize all of the amino acids they need for their proteins. Thus, these higher animals require certain amino acids as a part of their diet. For adult humans there are eight essential amino acids; these are designated with the superscript e in Table 24.1.

24.2C AMINO ACIDS AS DIPOLAR IONS

Since amino acids contain both a basic group ($-NH_2$) and an acidic group ($-CO_2H$), they are amphoteric. In the dry solid state, amino acids exist as **dipolar ions,** a form in which the carboxyl group is present as a carboxylate ion, $-CO_2^-$, and the amino group is present as an aminium group, $-NH_3^+$. (Dipolar ions are also called **zwitterions.**) In aqueous solution, an equilibrium exists between the dipolar ion and the anionic and cationic forms of an amino acid.

$$
\overset{+}{H_3N}CHCO_2H \underset{+H^+}{\overset{-H^+}{\rightleftharpoons}} \overset{+}{H_3N}CHCO_2^- \underset{+H^+}{\overset{-H^+}{\rightleftharpoons}} H_2NCHCO_2^-
$$
$$
\qquad\quad | \qquad\qquad\qquad\quad | \qquad\qquad\qquad |
$$
$$
\qquad\quad R \qquad\qquad\qquad\quad R \qquad\qquad\qquad R
$$

Cationic form	**Dipolar ion**	**Anionic form**
(predominant in		(predominant in
strongly acidic		strongly basic
solutions, e.g.,		solutions, e.g.,
at pH 0)		at pH 14)

The predominant form of the amino acid present in a solution depends on the pH of the solution and on the nature of the amino acid. In strongly acidic solutions all amino acids are present primarily as cations; in strongly basic solutions they are present as anions. At some intermediate pH, called the *isoelectric point* (p*I*) the concentration of the dipolar ion is at its maximum and the concentrations of the anions and cations are equal. Each amino acid has a particular isoelectric point. These are given in Table 24.1.

Let us consider first an amino acid with a side chain that contains neither acidic nor basic groups—an amino acid, for example, such as alanine.

If alanine is present in a strongly acidic solution (e.g., at pH 0), it is present mainly in the following cationic form. The pK_a for the carboxyl group of cationic form is 2.3. This is considerably smaller than the pK_a of a corresponding carboxylic acid (e.g., propanoic acid) and indicates that the cationic form of alanine is the stronger acid. But we should expect it to be. After all, it is a positively charged species and therefore should lose a proton more readily.

$$
\begin{array}{cc}
CH_3CHCO_2H & CH_3CH_2CO_2H \\
| & \\
\overset{+}{N}H_3 & \\
\end{array}
$$

Cationic form of alanine	**Propanoic acid**
p$K_{a_1} = 2.3$	p$K_a = 4.89$

The dipolar ion form of an amino acid is also a potential acid because the $-NH_3^+$ group can donate a proton. The pK_a of the dipolar ion form of alanine is 9.7.

$$CH_3CHCO_2^-$$
$$|$$
$$NH_3$$
$$+$$
$$pK_{a_2} = 9.7$$

The isoelectric point (pI) of an amino acid such as alanine is the average of pK_{a_1} and pK_{a_2}.

$$pI = \frac{2.3 + 9.7}{2} = 6.0 \qquad \text{(isoelectric point of alanine)}$$

What does this mean about the behavior of alanine as the pH of a strongly acidic solution containing it is gradually raised by adding a base (i.e., OH⁻)? At first (pH 0) (Fig. 24.1), the predominant form will be the cationic form. But then, as the acidity reaches pH 2.3 (the pK_a of the cationic form, pK_{a_1}), one half of the cationic form will be converted to the dipolar ion.* As the pH increases further—from pH 2.3 to pH 9.7—the predominant form will be the dipolar ion. At pH 6.0, the pH equals pI and the concentration of the dipolar ion is at its maximum.

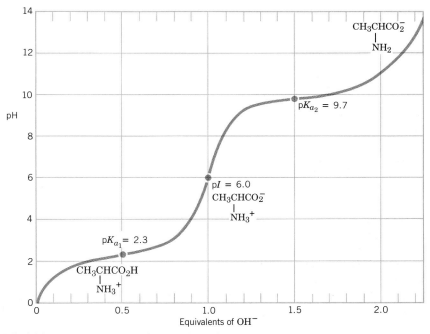

FIGURE 24.1 A titration curve for CH_3CHCO_2H.
$$|$$
$$NH_3$$
$$+$$

*It is easy to show that for an acid:

$$pK_a = pH + \log \frac{[acid]}{[conjugate\ base]}$$

When the acid is half-neutralized, [acid] = [conjugate base] and $\log \dfrac{[acid]}{[conjugate\ base]} = 0$; thus pH = pK_a.

$$CH_3CHCO_2H \underset{H^+}{\overset{OH^-}{\rightleftarrows}} CH_3CHCO_2^- \underset{H^+}{\overset{OH^-}{\rightleftarrows}} CH_3CHCO_2^-$$

$$\overset{|}{\underset{+}{NH_3}} \qquad \overset{|}{\underset{+}{NH_3}} \qquad \overset{|}{NH_2}$$

Cationic form   **Dipolar ion**   **Anionic form**
$(pK_{a_1} = 2.3)$ $(pK_{a_2} = 9.7)$

When the pH rises to pH 9.7 (the pK_a of the dipolar ion), the dipolar ion will be half-converted to the anionic form. Then, as the pH approaches pH 14, the anionic form becomes the predominant form present in the solution.

If the side chain of an amino acid contains an extra acidic or basic group, then the equilibria are more complex. Consider lysine, for example, an amino acid that has an extra $-NH_2$ group on its ε carbon. In strongly acidic solution, lysine will be present as a dication because both amino groups will be protonated. The first proton to be lost as the pH is raised is a proton of the carboxyl group ($pK_a = 2.2$), the next is from the α-aminium group ($pK_a = 9.0$), and the last is from the ε-aminium group.

$$\overset{+}{H_3N}(CH_2)_4CHCO_2H \underset{H^+}{\overset{OH^-}{\rightleftarrows}} \overset{+}{H_3N}(CH_2)_4CHCO_2^- \underset{H^+}{\overset{OH^-}{\rightleftarrows}}$$

$$\overset{|}{\underset{+}{NH_3}} \qquad\qquad \overset{|}{\underset{+}{NH_3}}$$

Dicationic form of   **Monocationic**
lysine   **form**
$(pK_{a_1} = 2.2)$ $(pK_{a_2} = 9.0)$

$$\overset{+}{H_3N}(CH_2)_4CHCO_2^- \underset{H^+}{\overset{OH^-}{\rightleftarrows}} H_2N(CH_2)_4CHCO_2^-$$

$$\overset{|}{NH_2} \qquad\qquad \overset{|}{NH_2}$$

Dipolar ion   **Anionic form**
$(pK_{a_3} = 10.5)$

The isoelectric point of lysine is the average of pK_{a_2} (the monocation) and pK_{a_3} (the dipolar ion).

$$pI = \frac{9.0 + 10.5}{2} = 9.8 \qquad \text{(isoelectric point of lysine)}$$

Problem 24.1

What form of glutamic acid would you expect to predominate in: (a) strongly acid solution? (b) strongly basic solution? (c) at its isoelectric point (pI 3.2)? (d) The isoelectric point of glutamine (pI 5.7) is considerably higher than that of glutamic acid. Explain.

Problem 24.2

$$\overset{\displaystyle NH}{\overset{\|}{-NH-C-NH_2}}$$

The guanidino group $-NH-\overset{\overset{\displaystyle NH}{\|}}{C}-NH_2$, of arginine is one of the most strongly basic of all organic groups. Explain.

24.3 LABORATORY SYNTHESIS OF α-AMINO ACIDS

A variety of methods have been developed for the laboratory synthesis of α-amino acids. We shall describe here three general methods, all of which are based on reactions we have seen before.

24.3A DIRECT AMMONOLYSIS OF AN α-HALO ACID

$$R-CH_2CO_2H \xrightarrow[(2)\ H_2O]{(1)\ X_2,\ P_4} RCHCO_2H \xrightarrow{NH_3\ (excess)} R-\underset{\underset{+}{NH_3}}{\overset{}{CHCO_2^-}}$$

(with X below the first product)

This method is probably used least often because yields tend to be poor. We saw an example of this method in Section 18.9.

24.3B FROM POTASSIUM PHTHALIMIDE

This method is a modification of the Gabriel synthesis of amines (Section 19.5A). The yields are usually high and the products are easily purified.

Potassium   **Ethyl chloroacetate**
phthalimide

(97%)   **Glycine**   **Phthalic**
                       (85%)   **acid**

A variation of this procedure uses potassium phthalimide and diethyl α-bromomalonate to prepare an *imido* malonic ester. This method is illustrated with a synthesis of methionine.

Diethyl α-bromomalonate

Phthalimidomalonic
ester

$$\text{phthalimide}-N-\underset{\underset{CO_2C_2H_5}{|}}{\overset{\overset{CO_2C_2H_5}{|}}{C}}CH_2CH_2SCH_3 \xrightarrow{\text{NaOH}}$$

$$\underset{\overset{||}{O}}{C}-NH\underset{\underset{CO_2^-}{|}}{\overset{\overset{CO_2^-}{|}}{C}}CH_2CH_2SCH_3 \xrightarrow[(84-85\%)]{\text{HCl}}$$

$$CH_3SCH_2CH_2\underset{\underset{+}{\overset{|}{NH_3}}}{CH}\overset{-}{C}O_2 + CO_2 +$$

DL-Methionine

Problem 24.3

Starting with diethyl α-bromomalonate and potassium phthalimide and using any other necessary reagents show how you might synthesize: (a) DL-leucine, (b) DL-alanine, and (c) DL-phenylalanine.

24.3C THE STRECKER SYNTHESIS

Treating an aldehyde with ammonia and hydrogen cyanide produces an α-amino nitrile. Hydrolysis of the nitrile group (Section 18.3) of the α-amino nitrile converts the latter to an α-amino acid. This synthesis is called the Strecker synthesis.

$$\overset{\overset{O}{||}}{RCH} + NH_3 + HCN \longrightarrow \underset{\underset{NH_2}{|}}{RCH}CN \xrightarrow{H_3O^+,\ heat} \underset{\underset{+}{\overset{|}{NH_3}}}{RCH}CO_2^-$$

$$\alpha\text{-Amino} \qquad\qquad \alpha\text{-Amino}$$
$$\text{nitrile} \qquad\qquad\quad \text{acid}$$

The first step of this synthesis probably involves the initial formation of an imine from the aldehyde and ammonia, followed by the addition of hydrogen cyanide.

$$\overset{\overset{O}{||}}{RCH} + :NH_3 \rightleftharpoons \underset{}{RCH}\overset{\overset{O^-}{|}}{\underset{+}{N}H_3} \rightleftharpoons RCH\overset{\overset{OH}{|}}{N}H_2 \xrightarrow{-H_2O}$$

$$RCH{=}NH \xrightarrow{CN^-} \underset{\underset{CN}{|}}{RCH}-NH^- \xrightarrow{H^+} \underset{\underset{CN}{|}}{RCH}-NH_2$$

Sample Problem

Outline a Strecker synthesis of DL-tyrosine.

Answer:

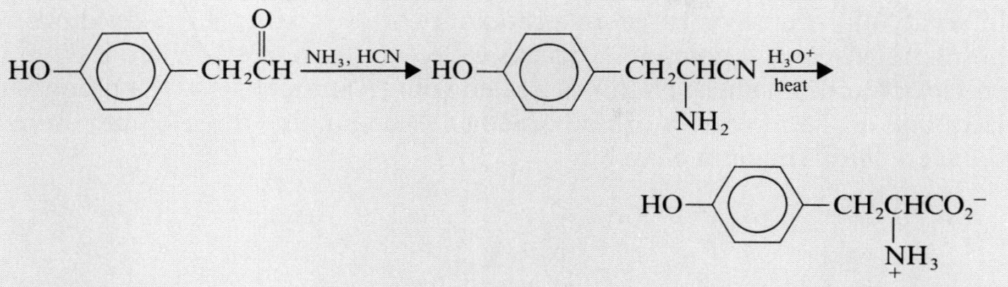

DL-Tyrosine

Problem 24.4

(a) Outline a Strecker synthesis of DL-phenylalanine. (b) DL-Methionine can also be synthesized by a Strecker synthesis. The required starting aldehyde can be prepared from acrolein (CH_2=CHCHO) and methanethiol (CH_3SH). Outline all steps in this synthesis of DL-methionine.

24.3D RESOLUTION OF DL-AMINO ACIDS

With the exception of glycine, which has no stereocenter, the amino acids that are produced by the methods we have outlined are all produced as racemic forms. In order to obtain the naturally occurring L-amino acid we must, of course, resolve the racemic form. This can be done in a variety of ways including the methods outlined in Section 19.3.

One especially interesting method for resolving amino acids is based on the use of enzymes called *deacylases*. These enzymes catalyze the hydrolysis of *N-acylamino acids* in living organisms. Since the active site of the enzyme is chiral, it hydrolyzes only *N*-acylamino acids of the L configuration. When it is exposed to a racemic modification of *N*-acylamino acids, only the derivative of the L-amino acid is affected and the products, as a result, are separated easily.

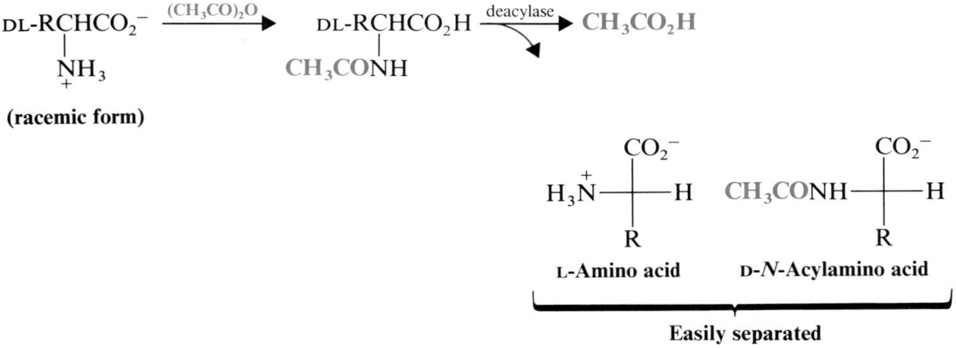

(racemic form)

L-Amino acid   D-*N*-Acylamino acid

Easily separated

24.3E STEREOSELECTIVE SYNTHESES OF AMINO ACIDS

The ideal synthesis of an amino acid, of course, would be one that would produce only the naturally occurring L-amino acid. This ideal has now been realized through the use of chiral hydrogenation catalysts derived from transition metals (Special Topic J). A variety of catalysts has been used. One developed by B. Bosnich (of the University of Toronto) is based on a rhodium complex with (R)-1,2-bis(diphenyl-phosphino)propane, a compound that is called "(R)-prophos." When a rhodium complex of norbornadiene (NBD) is treated with (R)-prophos, the (R)-prophos replaces one of the molecules of norbornadiene surrounding the rhodium atom to produce a *chiral* rhodium complex.

$$H_3C \quad \overset{H}{\underset{(C_6H_5)_2P}{\diagdown}} C - CH_2 \diagup P(C_6H_5)_2$$

(R)-Prophos

$$[Rh(NBD)_2]ClO_4 + (R)\text{-prophos} \longrightarrow [Rh((R)\text{-prophos})(NBD)]ClO_4 + NBD$$

Chiral rhodium complex

Treating this rhodium complex with hydrogen in a solvent such as ethanol yields a solution containing an active *chiral* hydrogenation catalyst, which probably has the composition $[Rh((R)\text{-prophos})(H)_2(EtOH)_2]^+$.

When 2-acetylaminopropenoic acid is added to this solution and hydrogenation is carried out, the product of the reaction is the *N*-acetyl derivative of L-alanine in 90% enantiomeric excess. Hydrolysis of the *N*-acetyl group yields L-alanine. Because the hydrogenation catalyst is chiral, it transfers its hydrogen atoms in a stereoselective way. This type of reaction is often called an **asymmetric synthesis** or **enantioselective synthesis.**

$$CH_2 = C - CO_2H \quad \xrightarrow[\quad H_2 \quad]{[Rh ((R)\text{-prophos}) (H)_2(solvent)_2]^+} \quad H_3C \overset{H}{\diagdown} C - CO_2H$$

NHCOCH_3 (left), NHCOCH_3 (right)

2-Acetylaminopropenoic acid → *N*-Acetyl-L-alanine

$$\xrightarrow[\quad]{(1)\ OH^-,\ H_2O,\ heat\ (2)\ H_3O^+} \quad H_3C \overset{H}{\diagdown} C - CO_2^-$$

$$\underset{+}{NH_3}$$
L-Alanine

This same procedure has been used to synthesize several other L-amino acids from 2-acetylaminopropenoic acids that have substituents at the 3 position. Use of the (R)-prophos catalyst in hydrogenation of the (Z)-isomer yields the L-amino acid with an enantiomeric excess of 87–93%.

$$\underset{R}{\overset{H}{\diagdown}} C = C \underset{NHCOCH_3}{\overset{CO_2H}{\diagup}} \quad \xrightarrow[(2)\ OH^-,\ H_2O,\ heat\ then\ H_3O^+]{(1)\ Rh((R)\text{-prophos})\ (H)_2(solvent)_2]^+,\ H_2} \quad R \overset{H}{\diagdown} C - CO_2^-$$

$$\underset{+}{NH_3}$$
L — Amino acid

Z-3-Substituted 2-acetylaminopropenoic acid

24.4 ANALYSIS OF AMINO ACID MIXTURES

Enzymes can cause α-amino acids to polymerize through the elimination of water:

$$\overset{+}{H_3N}-CH-\overset{\overset{\displaystyle O}{\|}}{C}-O^- + \overset{+}{H_3N}-CH-\overset{\overset{\displaystyle O}{\|}}{C}-O^-$$
$$\underset{R}{\big|} \qquad\qquad \underset{R'}{\big|}$$

$$\downarrow {\scriptstyle[-H_2O]}$$

$$\overset{+}{H_3N}-CH-\overset{\overset{\displaystyle O}{\|}}{C}-NH-CH-\overset{\overset{\displaystyle O}{\|}}{C}-O^-$$
$$\underset{R}{\big|} \qquad\qquad \underset{R'}{\big|}$$

A dipeptide

The —CO—NH— (amide) linkage that forms between the amino acids is known as a **peptide bond** or **peptide linkage.** Amino acids, when joined in this way (as opposed to being free), are called **amino acid residues.** The polymers that contain 2, 3, a few (3–10), or many amino acid residues are called **dipeptides, tripeptides, oligopeptides,** and **polypeptides,** respectively. Proteins are molecules that contain one or more polypeptide chains.

Polypeptides are **linear polymers.** One end of a polypeptide chain terminates in an amino acid residue that has a free —NH$_3$$^+$ group; the other terminates in an amino acid residue with a free —CO$_2$$^-$ group. These two groups are called the **N-terminal** and the **C-terminal residues,** respectively.

$$\overset{+}{H_3N}-CH-\overset{\overset{\displaystyle O}{\|}}{C}\left(\!\!-NH-CH-\overset{\overset{\displaystyle O}{\|}}{C}\!\!\right)_{\!n}-NH-CH-\overset{\overset{\displaystyle O}{\|}}{C}-O^-$$
$$\underset{R}{\big|} \qquad\qquad \underset{R'}{\big|} \qquad\qquad \underset{R''}{\big|}$$

$$\underbrace{\qquad\qquad}_{\text{N-Terminal residue}} \qquad\qquad \underbrace{\qquad\qquad}_{\text{C-Terminal residue}}$$

By convention, we write peptide and protein structures with the N-terminal amino acid on the left and the C-terminal residue on the right.

$$\overset{+}{H_3N}CH_2\overset{\overset{\displaystyle O}{\|}}{C}-NHCHCO^- \qquad\qquad \overset{+}{H_3N}CH\overset{\overset{\displaystyle O}{\|}}{C}-NHCH_2CO^-$$
$$\underset{\underset{\overset{\displaystyle |}{H_3C}\quad CH_3}{CH}}{} \qquad\qquad \underset{\underset{\overset{\displaystyle |}{H_3C}\quad CH_3}{CH}}{}$$

$$\begin{array}{cc} \text{Glycylvaline} & \text{Valylglycine} \\ \text{(Gly}\cdot\text{Val)} & \text{(Val}\cdot\text{Gly)} \end{array}$$

The tripeptide glycylvalylphenylalanine can be represented in the following way:

$$\overset{+}{H_3N}CH_2\overset{\overset{\displaystyle O}{\|}}{C}-NHCH\overset{\overset{\displaystyle O}{\|}}{C}-NHCHCO^-$$

Glycylvalylphenylalanine
(Gly·Val·Phe)

When a protein or polypeptide is refluxed with 6 M hydrochloric acid for 24 h, hydrolysis of all of the amide linkages usually takes place, and this produces a mixture of amino acids. One of the first tasks that we face when we attempt to determine the structure of a polypeptide or protein is the separation and identification of the individual amino acids in such a mixture. Since as many as 22 different amino acids may be present, this could be a formidable task if we are restricted to conventional methods.

Fortunately, techniques have been developed, based on the principle of elution chromatography, that simplify this problem immensely and even allow its solution to be automated. Automatic amino acid analyzers were developed at the Rockefeller Institute in 1950 and have since become commercially available. They are based on the use of insoluble polymers containing sulfonate groups, called *cation-exchange resins* (Fig. 24.2).

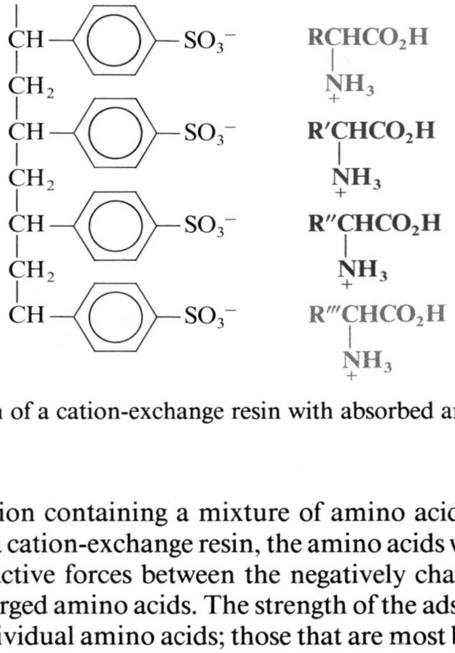

FIGURE 24.2 A section of a cation-exchange resin with absorbed amino acids.

If an acidic solution containing a mixture of amino acids is passed through a column packed with a cation-exchange resin, the amino acids will be adsorbed by the resin because of attractive forces between the negatively charged sulfonate groups and the positively charged amino acids. The strength of the adsorption will vary with the basicity of the individual amino acids; those that are most basic will be held most strongly. If the column is then washed with a buffered solution at a given pH, the individual amino acids will move down the column at different rates and ultimately become separated. At the end of the column the eluate is allowed to mix with **ninhydrin,** a reagent that reacts with most amino acids to give a derivative with an intense purple color (λ_{max} 570 nm). The amino acid analyzer is designed so that it can measure the absorbance of the eluate (at 570 nm) continuously and record this absorbance as a function of the volume of the effluent.

A typical graph obtained from an automatic amino acid analyzer is shown in Fig. 24.3. When the procedure is standardized, the positions of the peaks are characteristic of the individual amino acids and the areas under the peaks correspond to their relative amounts.

Ninhydrin is the hydrate of indane-1,2,3-trione. With the exception of proline and hydroxyproline, all of the α-amino acids found in proteins react with ninhydrin to give the same intensely colored purple anion (λ_{max} 570 nm). We shall not go into the mechanism

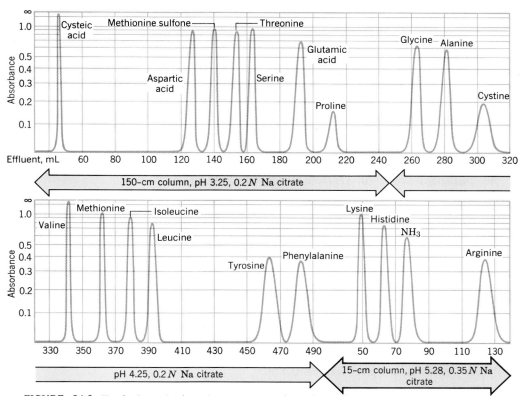

FIGURE 24.3 Typical result given by an automatic amino acid analyzer. [Adapted with permission from D. H. Spackman, W. H. Stein, and S. Moore, *Anal. Chem.*, **1958**, *30*, 1190. Copyright © by the American Chemical Society.]

here, but notice that the only portion of the anion that is derived from the α-amino acid is the nitrogen.

Indane-1,2,3-trione   **Ninhydrin**

Purple anion

Proline and hydroxyproline do not react with ninhydrin in the same way because their α-amino groups are part of a five-membered ring.

24.5 AMINO ACID SEQUENCE OF POLYPEPTIDES AND PROTEINS

Once we have determined the amino acid composition of a protein or a polypeptide, we should then determine its molecular weight. Various methods are available for doing this, including chemical methods, ultracentrifugation, light scattering, osmotic pressure, and X-ray diffraction. With the molecular weight and amino acid composition we shall now be able to calculate the *molecular formula* of the protein; that is, we shall know how many of each type of amino acid are present as amino acid residues in each protein molecule. Unfortunately, however, we have only begun our task of determining its structure. The next step is a formidable one, indeed. We must determine the order in which the amino acids are connected; that is, we must determine the **covalent structure (or primary structure) of the polypeptide.**

A simple tripeptide composed of 3 different amino acids can have 6 different amino acid sequences; a tetrapeptide composed of 4 different amino acids can have as many as 24. For a protein composed of 20 different amino acids in a single chain of 100 residues, there are $20^{100} = 1.27 \times 10^{130}$ possible polypeptides, a number much greater than the number of atoms estimated to be in the universe (9×10^{78}).

In spite of this, a number of methods have been developed that allow the amino acid sequences to be determined and these, as we shall see, have been applied with amazing success. In our discussion here we shall limit our attention to two methods that illustrate how sequence determinations can be done: **terminal residue analysis** and **partial hydrolysis.** In Section 25.6A we shall study an easier method.

24.5A TERMINAL RESIDUE ANALYSIS

One very useful method for determining the N-terminal amino acid residue, called the **Sanger method,** is based on the use of 2,4-dinitrofluorobenzene (DNFB).* When

*This method was introduced by Frederick Sanger of Cambridge University in 1945. Sanger made extensive use of this procedure in his determination of the amino acid sequence of insulin and won the Nobel Prize for chemistry for the work in 1958.

a polypeptide is treated with DNFB in mildly basic solution, a nucleophilic aromatic substitution reaction takes place involving the free amino group of the N-terminal residue. Subsequent hydrolysis of the polypeptide gives a mixture of amino acids in which the N-terminal amino acid bears a label, *the 2,4-dinitrophenyl group.* As a result, after separating this amino acid from the mixture, we can identify it.

Problem 24.5

The electron-withdrawing property of the 2,4-dinitrophenyl group makes separation of the labeled amino acid very easy. Suggest how this is done.

Of course, 2,4-dinitrofluorobenzene will react with any free amino group present in a polypeptide including the ε-amino group of lysine. But only the N-terminal amino acid residue will bear the label at the α-amino group.

A second method of N-terminal analysis is the *Edman degradation* (developed by Pehr Edman of the University of Lund, Sweden). This method offers an advantage over the Sanger method in that it removes the N-terminal residue and leaves the remainder of the peptide chain intact. The Edman degradation is based on a labeling reaction between the N-terminal amino group and phenyl isothiocyanate, C_6H_5N=C=S (see following reactions). When the labeled polypeptide is treated with acid, the N-terminal amino acid residue splits off as an unstable intermediate that undergoes rearrangement to a phenylthiohydantoin. This last product can be identified by comparison with phenylthiohydantoins prepared from standard amino acids.

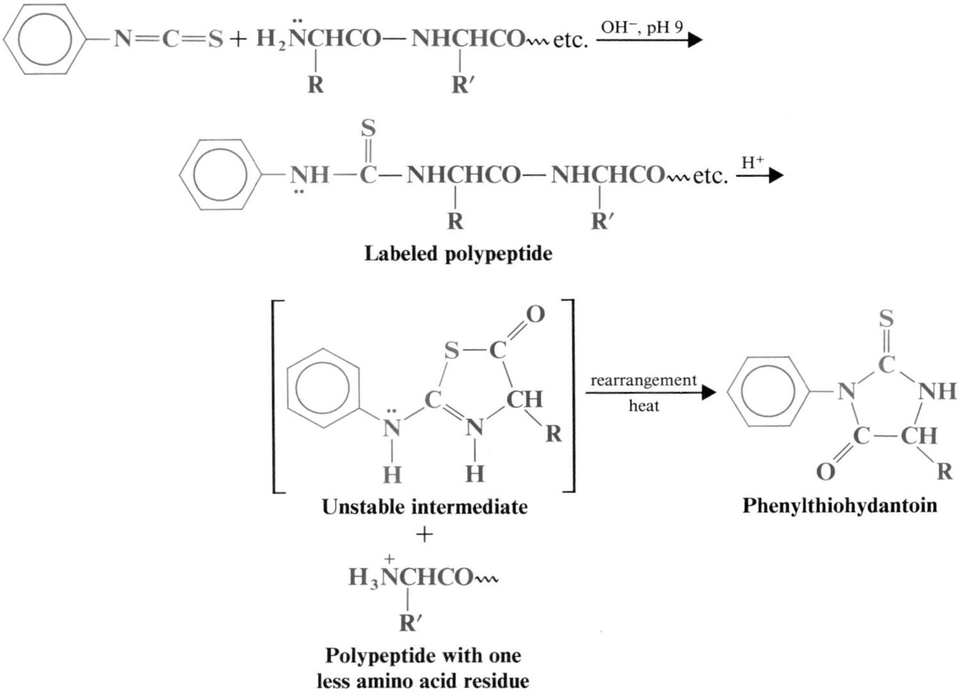

Labeled polypeptide

Unstable intermediate

Phenylthiohydantoin

+

$H_3\overset{+}{N}CHCO$∿
|
R'

Polypeptide with one
less amino acid residue

The polypeptide that remains after the first Edman degradation can be submitted to another degradation to identify the next amino acid in the sequence, and this process has even been automated. Unfortunately, Edman degradations cannot be repeated indefinitely. As residues are successively removed, amino acids formed by hydrolysis during the acid treatment accumulate in the reaction mixture and interfere with the procedure. The Edman degradation, however, has been automated into what is called a **sequenator.** Each amino acid is automatically detected as it is removed. This technique has been successfully applied to polypeptides with as many as 60 amino acid residues.

C-Terminal residues can be identified through the use of digestive enzymes called *carboxypeptidases.* These enzymes specifically catalyze the hydrolysis of the amide bond of the amino acid residue containing a free $-CO_2H$ group, liberating it as a free amino acid. A carboxypeptidase, however, will continue to attack the polypeptide chain that remains, successively lopping off C-terminal residues. As a consequence, it is necessary to follow the amino acids released as a function of time. The procedure can be applied to only a limited amino acid sequence, for at best, after a time the situation becomes too confused to sort out.

Problem 24.6

(a) Write a reaction showing how 2,4-dinitrofluorobenzene could be used to identify the N-terminal amino acid of Val · Ala · Gly. (b) What products would you expect (after hydrolysis) when Val · Lys · Gly is treated with 2,4-dinitrofluorobenzene?

Problem 24.7

Write the reactions involved in a sequential Edman degradation of Met · Ile · Arg.

24.5B PARTIAL HYDROLYSIS

Sequential analysis using the Edman degradation or carboxypeptidase becomes impractical with proteins or polypeptides of appreciable size. Fortunately, however, we can resort to another technique, that of **partial hydrolysis.** Using dilute acids or enzymes, we attempt to break the polypeptide chain into small fragments, ones that we can identify using DNFB or the Edman degradation. Then we examine the structures of these smaller fragments looking for points of overlap and attempt to piece together the amino acid sequence of the original polypeptide.

Consider a simple example: We are given a pentapeptide known to contain valine (two residues), leucine (one residue), histidine (one residue), and phenylalanine (one residue). With this information we can write the "molecular formula" of the protein in the following way, using commas to indicate that the sequence is unknown.

Val$_2$, Leu, His, Phe

Then, let us assume that by using DNFB and carboxypeptidase we discover that valine and leucine are the N-terminal and C-terminal residues, respectively. So far we know the following:

Val (Val, His, Phe) Leu

But the sequence of the three nonterminal amino acids is still unknown.

We then subject the pentapeptide to partial acid hydrolysis and obtain the following dipeptides. (We also get individual amino acids and larger pieces, i.e., tripeptides and tetrapeptides.)

Val·His + His·Val + Val·Phe + Phe·Leu

The points of overlap of the dipeptides (i.e., His, Val, and Phe) tell us that the original pentapeptide must have been the following:

Val·His·Val·Phe·Leu

Two enzymes are also frequently used to cleave certain bonds in a large protein. *Trypsin* preferentially catalyzes the hydrolysis of peptide bonds in which the carboxyl group is a part of a lysine or arginine residue. *Chymotrypsin* preferentially catalyzes the hydrolysis of peptide bonds at the carboxyl groups of phenylalanine, tyrosine, and tryptophan. It will also attack the peptide bonds at the carboxyl groups of leucine, methionine, asparagine, and glutamine. Treating a large protein with trypsin or chymotrypsin will break it into smaller pieces. Then, each smaller piece can be subjected to an Edman degradation or to labeling followed by partial hydrolysis.

Problem 24.8

Glutathione is a tripeptide found in most living cells. Partial acid-catalyzed hydrolysis of glutathione yields two dipeptides, Cys·Gly, and one composed of Glu and Cys. When this second dipeptide was treated with DNFB, acid hydrolysis gave N-labeled Glu. (a) Based on this information alone, what structures are possible for glutathione? (b) Synthetic experiments have shown that the second dipeptide has the following structure:

$$\overset{+}{H_3}NCHCH_2CH_2CONHCHCO_2^-$$
$$\underset{CO_2^-}{|} \qquad \underset{CH_2SH}{|}$$

What is the structure of glutathione?

Problem 24.9

Give the amino acid sequence of the following polypeptides using only the data given by partial acidic hydrolysis.

(a) Ser, Hyp, Pro, Thr $\xrightarrow[H_2O]{H^+}$ Ser·Thr + Thr·Hyp + Pro·Ser

(b) Ala, Arg, Cys, Val, Leu $\xrightarrow[H_2O]{H^+}$ Ala·Cys· + Cys·Arg + Arg·Val + Leu·Ala

24.6 PRIMARY STRUCTURES OF POLYPEPTIDES AND PROTEINS

The covalent structure of a protein or polypeptide is called its *primary structure* (Fig. 24.4). By using the techniques we described in the previous sections, chemists have

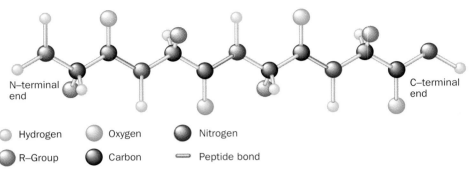

| ⬤ Hydrogen | ⬤ Oxygen | ⬤ Nitrogen |
| ⬤ R–Group | ⬤ Carbon | ⟸ Peptide bond |

FIGURE 24.4 A representation of the primary structure of a tetrapeptide.

had remarkable success in determining the primary structures of polypeptides and proteins. The compounds described in the following pages are important examples.

24.6A OXYTOCIN AND VASOPRESSIN

Oxytocin and vasopressin (Fig. 24.5) are two rather small polypeptides with strikingly similar structures (where oxytocin has leucine, vasopressin has arginine and where oxytocin has isoleucine, vasopressin has phenylalanine). In spite of the similarity of their amino acid sequences, these two polypeptides have quite different physiological effects. Oxytocin occurs only in the female of a species and stimulates uterine contractions during childbirth. Vasopressin occurs in males and females; it causes contraction of peripheral blood vessels and an increase in blood pressure. Its major function, however, is as an *antidiuretic;* physiologists often refer to vasopressin as an *antidiuretic hormone.*

The structures of oxytocin and vasopressin also illustrate the importance of the disulfide linkage between cysteine residues (Section 24.2A) in the overall primary structure of a polypeptide. In these two molecules this disulfide linkage leads to a cyclic structure.*

Problem 24.10 ————————————————————

Treating oxytocin with certain reducing agents (e.g., sodium in liquid ammonia) brings about a single chemical change that can be reversed by air oxidation. What chemical changes are involved?

24.6B INSULIN

Insulin, a hormone secreted by the pancreas, regulates glucose metabolism. Insulin deficiency in humans is the major problem in diabetes mellitus.

The amino acid sequence of bovine insulin (Fig. 24.6) was determined by Sanger in 1953 after 10 years of work. Bovine insulin has a total of 51 amino acid residues in two polypeptide chains, called the A and B chains. These chains are joined by two disulfide linkages. The A chain contains an additional disulfide linkage between cysteine residues at positions 6 and 11.

*Vincent du Vigneaud of Cornell Medical College synthesized oxytocin and vasopressin in 1953; he received the Nobel Prize in 1955.

Oxytocin

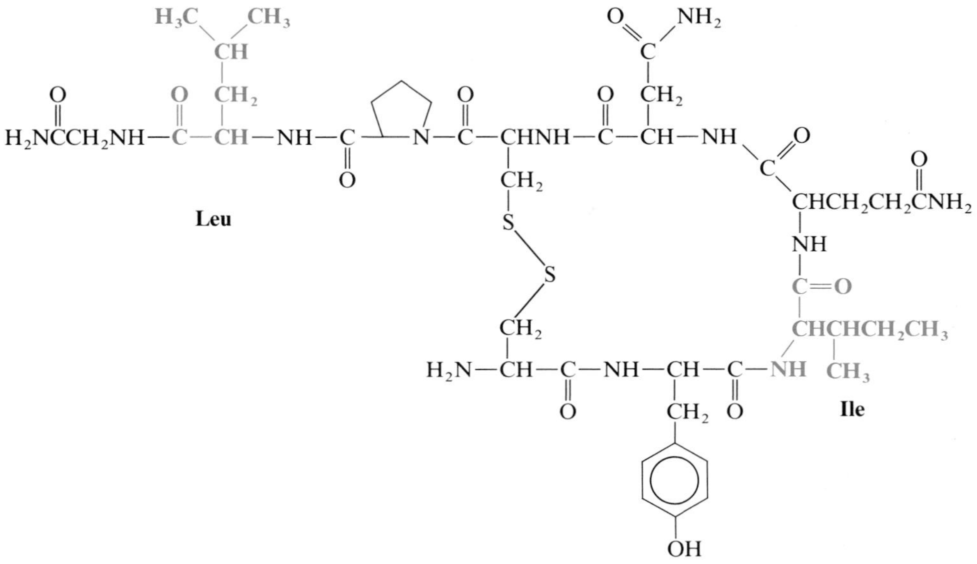

Vasopressin

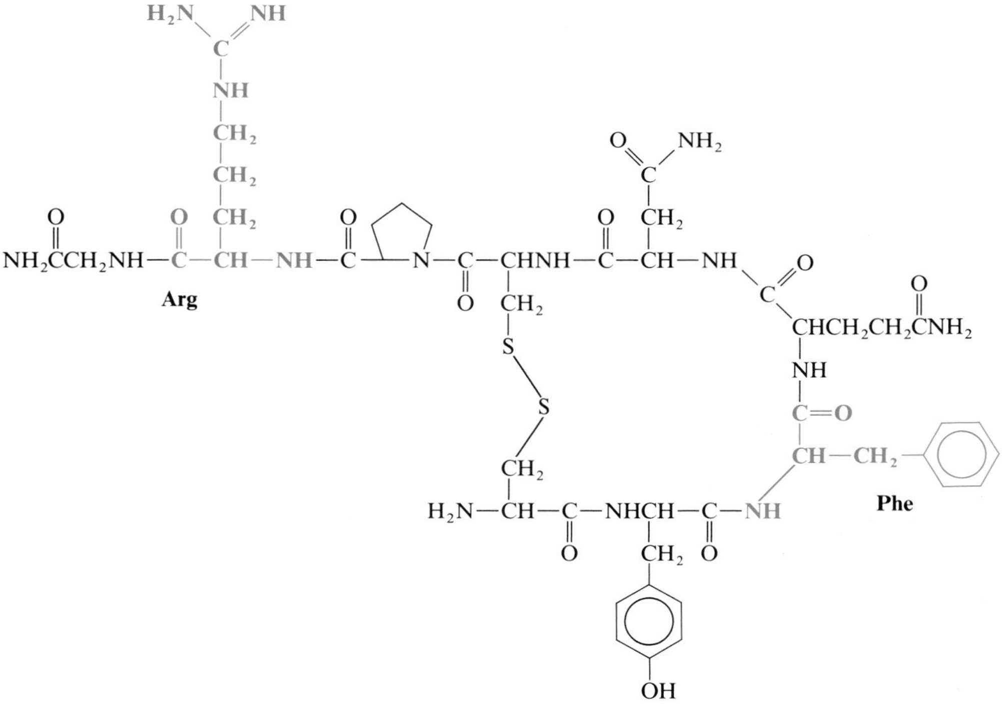

FIGURE 24.5 The structures of oxytocin and vasopressin.

Human insulin differs from bovine insulin at only three amino acid residues: Threonine replaces alanine once in the A chain (residue 8) and once in the B chain (residue 30), and isoleucine replaces valine once in the A chain (residue 10). Insulin from most mammals has a similar structure.

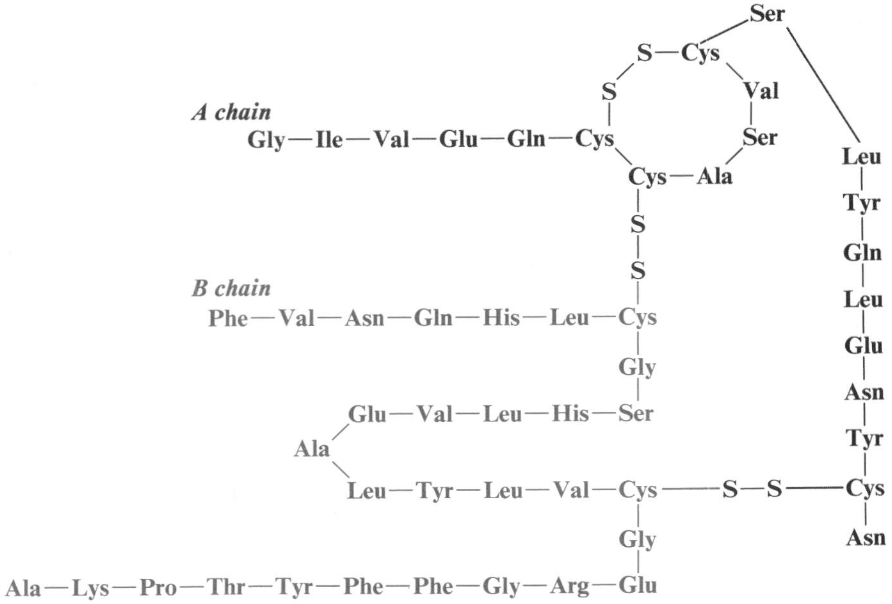

FIGURE 24.6 The amino acid sequence of bovine insulin.

24.6C OTHER POLYPEPTIDES AND PROTEINS

Successful sequential analyses have now been achieved with hundreds of other polypeptides and proteins including the following:

1. **Bovine ribonuclease.** This enzyme, which catalyzes the hydrolysis of ribonucleic acid (Chapter 25), has a single chain of 124 amino acid residues and four intrachain disulfide linkages.

2. **Human hemoglobin.** There are four peptide chains in this important oxygen-carrying protein. Two identical α chains have 141 residues each, and two identical β chains have 146 residues. The genetically based disease sickle-cell anemia results from a single amino acid error in the β chain. In normal hemoglobin, position 6 has a glutamic acid residue, while in sickle-cell hemoglobin position 6 is occupied by valine.

Red blood cells (erythrocytes) containing hemoglobin with this amino acid residue error tend to become crescent shaped ("sickle") when the partial pressure of oxygen is low, as it is in venous blood. These distorted cells are more difficult for the heart to pump through small capillaries. They may even block capillaries by clumping together; at other times the red cells may even split open.

Children who inherit this genetic trait from both parents suffer from a severe form of the disease and usually do not live past the age of two. Children who inherit the disease from only one parent generally have a much milder form.

Sickle-cell anemia arose among the populations of central and western Africa where, ironically, it may have had a beneficial effect. People with a mild form of the disease are far less susceptible to malaria than those with normal hemoglobin. Malaria, a disease caused by an infectious microorganism, is especially prevalent in central and western Africa.

Mutational changes such as those that give rise to sickle-cell anemia are very common. Approximately 150 different types of mutant hemoglobin have been detected in humans; fortunately, most are harmless.

3. **Bovine trypsinogen and chymotrypsinogen.** These two enzyme precursors have single chains of 229 and 245 residues, respectively.

4. **Gamma globulin.** This immunoprotein has a total of 1320 amino acid residues in four chains. Two chains have 214 residues each; the other two have 446.

24.7 POLYPEPTIDE AND PROTEIN SYNTHESIS

We saw in Chapter 18 that the synthesis of an amide linkage is a relatively simple one. We must first "activate" the carboxyl group of an acid by converting it to an anhydride or acid chloride and then allow it to react with an amine:

$$R-\overset{O}{\underset{||}{C}}-O-\overset{O}{\underset{||}{C}}-R + R'-NH_2 \longrightarrow R-\overset{O}{\underset{||}{C}}-NHR' + R-CO_2H$$

Anhydride   **Amine**   **Amide**

The problem becomes somewhat more complicated, however, when both the acid group and the amino group are present in the same molecule, as they are in an amino acid and, especially, when our goal is the synthesis of a naturally occurring polyamide where the sequence of different amino acids is all-important. Let us consider, as an example, the synthesis of the simple dipeptide alanylglycine, Ala·Gly. We might first activate the carboxyl group of alanine by converting it to an acid chloride, and then we might allow it to react with glycine. Unfortunately, however, we cannot prevent alanyl chloride from reacting with itself. So our reaction would yield not only Ala·Gly but also Ala·Ala. It could also lead to Ala·Ala·Ala and Ala·Ala·Gly, and so on. The yield of our desired product would be low, and we would also have a difficult problem separating the dipeptides, tripeptides, and so on.

$$CH_3CHCO^- \xrightarrow[\text{(2) } H_3\overset{+}{N}CH_2CO_2^-]{\text{(1) } SOCl_2} CH_3CHCNHCH_2CO_2^- + CH_3CHCNHCHCO_2^-$$

Ala   Gly   Ala·Gly   Ala·Ala

$$+ CH_3CHCNHCHCNHCHCO_2^- + CH_3CHCNHCHCNHCH_2CO_2^-$$

Ala·Ala·Ala   Ala·Ala·Gly

24.7A PROTECTING GROUPS

The solution of this problem is to "protect" the amino group of the first amino acid before we activate it and allow it to react with the second. By protecting the amino group we mean that we must convert it to some other group of low nucleophilicity — *one that will not react with a reactive acyl derivative.* The protecting group must be carefully chosen because after we have synthesized the amide linkage between the first amino acid and the second, we will want to be able to remove the protecting group without disturbing the new amide bond.

A number of reagents have been developed to meet these requirements. Two that are often used are *benzyl chloroformate* and di-*tert*-butyl carbonate.

$$C_6H_5CH_2{-}O{-}\overset{\overset{\large O}{\|}}{C}{-}Cl \qquad\qquad (CH_3)_3C{-}O{-}\overset{\overset{\large O}{\|}}{C}{-}O{-}C(CH_3)_3$$

Benzyl chloroformate **Di-*tert*-butyl carbonate**

Both reagents react with the following amino groups to form derivatives that are unreactive toward further acylation. Both derivatives, however, are of a type that allow removal of the protecting group under conditions that do not affect peptide bonds. The benzyloxycarbonyl group (abbreviated Z-) can be removed by catalytic hydrogenation or by treating the derivative with cold HBr in acetic acid. The *tert*-butyloxycarbonyl group (abbreviated Boc-) can be removed through treatment with HCl or CF_3CO_2H in acetic acid.

Benzyloxycarbonyl Group

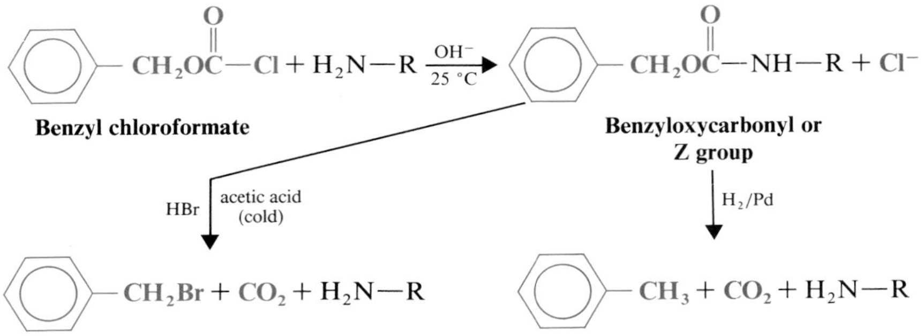

$$(CH_3)_3CO\overset{\overset{\large O}{\|}}{C}OC(CH_3)_3 + H_2N{-}R \xrightarrow[25\ ^\circ C]{\text{base}} (CH_3)_3CO\overset{\overset{\large O}{\|}}{C}{-}NHR + (CH_3)_3COH$$

Di-*tert*-butyl carbonate

***tert*-Butyloxycarbonyl or Boc group**

$$\downarrow \text{HCl or } CF_3CO_2H \text{ in acetic acid, } 25\ ^\circ C$$

$$(CH_3)_2C{=}CH_2 + CO_2 + H_2N{-}R$$

The easy removal of both groups (Z- and Boc-) in acidic media results from the exceptional stability of the carbocations that are formed initially. The benzyloxycarbonyl group gives a *benzyl cation;* the *tert*-butyloxycarbonyl group yields, initially, a *tert*-butyl cation.

Removal of the benzyloxycarbonyl group with hydrogen and a catalyst depends on the fact that benzyl–oxygen bonds are weak and are subject to hydrogenolysis at low temperatures.

$$C_6H_5CH_2{-}O\overset{\overset{\large O}{\|}}{C}R \xrightarrow[25\ ^\circ C]{H_2,\ Pd} C_6H_5CH_3 + HO\overset{\overset{\large O}{\|}}{C}R$$

A benzyl ester

24.7B ACTIVATION OF THE CARBOXYL GROUP

Perhaps the most obvious way to activate a carboxyl group is to convert it to an acyl chloride. This method was used in early peptide syntheses, but acyl chlorides are actually more reactive than necessary. As a result, their use leads to complicating side reactions. A much better method is to convert the carboxyl group of the "protected"

amino acid to a mixed anhydride using ethyl chloroformate, $Cl-\overset{\overset{O}{\|}}{C}-OC_2H_5$.

$$Z-NHCH\overset{\overset{O}{\|}}{C}-OH \xrightarrow[\text{(2) ClCO}_2\text{C}_2\text{H}_5]{\text{(1) (C}_2\text{H}_5)_3\text{N}} Z-NHCH\overset{\overset{O}{\|}}{-}\overset{\overset{O}{\|}}{C}-O-\overset{\overset{O}{\|}}{C}-OC_2H_5$$
$$\qquad\quad\underset{R}{\big|} \qquad\qquad\qquad\qquad\qquad \underset{R}{\big|}$$

"Mixed anhydride"

The mixed anhydride can then be used to acylate another amino acid and form a peptide linkage.

$$Z-NHCH\overset{\overset{O}{\|}}{C}-O-\overset{\overset{O}{\|}}{C}OC_2H_5 \xrightarrow{\overset{H_3\overset{+}{N}-CHC\overset{-}{O}_2}{\underset{R'}{\big|}}}$$
$$\qquad\quad\underset{R}{\big|}$$

$$Z-NHCH\overset{\overset{O}{\|}}{C}-NHCHCO_2H + CO_2 + C_2H_5OH$$
$$\qquad\quad\underset{R}{\big|} \qquad\qquad \underset{R'}{\big|}$$

Dicyclohexylcarbodiimide (Section 18.8E) can also be used to activate the carboxyl group of an amino acid. In Section 24.7D we shall see how it is used in an automated peptide synthesis.

24.7C PEPTIDE SYNTHESIS

Let us examine now how we might use these reagents in the preparation of the simple dipeptide, Ala·Leu. The principles involved here can, of course, be extended to the synthesis of much longer polypeptide chains.

$$CH_3CHCO_2^- + C_6H_5CH_2O\overset{\overset{O}{\|}}{C}-Cl \xrightarrow[25\ °C]{OH^-} CH_3CH-CO_2H \xrightarrow[\text{(2) ClCO}_2\text{C}_2\text{H}_5]{\text{(1) (C}_2\text{H}_5)_3\text{N}}$$
$$\quad\underset{\overset{|}{\underset{+}{NH_3}}}{\big|} \qquad\qquad\qquad\qquad\qquad\qquad\qquad \underset{NH}{\big|}$$
$$\qquad\qquad\qquad\qquad\qquad\qquad\qquad\qquad\qquad\qquad \underset{C=O}{\big|}$$
$$\qquad\qquad\qquad\qquad\qquad\qquad\qquad\qquad\qquad\qquad \underset{C_6H_5CH_2O}{\big|}$$

Ala   Benzyl chloroformate   Z-Ala

$$CH_3CH-\overset{\overset{O}{\|}}{C}-O\overset{\overset{O}{\|}}{C}OC_2H_5 \xrightarrow[\text{Leu}]{\overset{\overset{+}{NH_3}}{(CH_3)_2CHCH_2CHCO_2^-}}$$
$$\quad\underset{NH}{\big|} \qquad\qquad\qquad\qquad\qquad\qquad CO_2 + C_2H_5OH$$
$$\quad\underset{C=O}{\big|}$$
$$\quad\underset{C_6H_5CH_2O}{\big|}$$

Mixed anhydride
of Z-Ala

$$CH_3CH-\overset{\overset{\displaystyle O}{\|}}{C}-NHCHCO_2H \xrightarrow{H_2/Pd}$$

with NH, C=O, $C_6H_5CH_2O$, CH_2, CH, H_3C, CH_3 substituents

Z-Ala·Leu

$$CH_3\overset{\overset{\displaystyle O}{\|}}{C}NHCHCO_2^- + \langle\bigcirc\rangle-CH_3 + CO_2$$

with $\overset{+}{NH_3}$, CH_2, CH, H_3C, CH_3 substituents

Ala·Leu

Problem 24.11

Show all steps in the synthesis of Gly·Val·Ala using the *tert*-butyloxycarbonyl (Boc-) group as a protecting group.

Problem 24.12

The synthesis of a polypeptide containing lysine requires the protection of both amino groups. (a) Show how you might do this in a synthesis of Lys·Ile using the benzyloxycarbonyl group as a protecting group. (b) The benzyloxycarbonyl group can also be used to protect the guanidino group, $-NH\overset{\overset{\displaystyle NH}{\|}}{C}-NH_2$, of arginine. Show a synthesis of Arg·Ala.

Problem 24.13

The terminal carboxyl groups of glutamic acid and aspartic acid are often protected through their conversion to benzyl esters. What mild method could be used for removal of this protecting group?

24.7D AUTOMATED PEPTIDE SYNTHESIS

Although the methods that we have described thus far have been used to synthesize a number of polypeptides including ones as large as insulin, they are extremely time consuming. One must isolate and purify the product at almost every stage. Thus, a real advance in peptide synthesis came with the development by R. B. Merrifield (at Rockefeller University) of a procedure for automating peptide synthesis. Merrifield received the Nobel Prize in chemistry in 1984 for this work.

The Merrifield method is based on the use of a polystyrene resin similar to the one we saw in Fig. 24.2, *but one that contains* $-CH_2Cl$ *groups* instead of sulfonic acid groups. This resin is used in the form of small beads and is insoluble in most solvents.

The first step in automated peptide synthesis (Fig. 24.7) involves a reaction that attaches the first protected amino acid residue to the resin beads. After this step is complete, the protecting group is removed and the next amino acid (also protected) is condensed with the first using dicyclohexylcarbodiimide (Section 18.8E) to activate its carboxyl group. Then, removal of the protecting group of the second residue readies the resin-dipeptide for the next step.

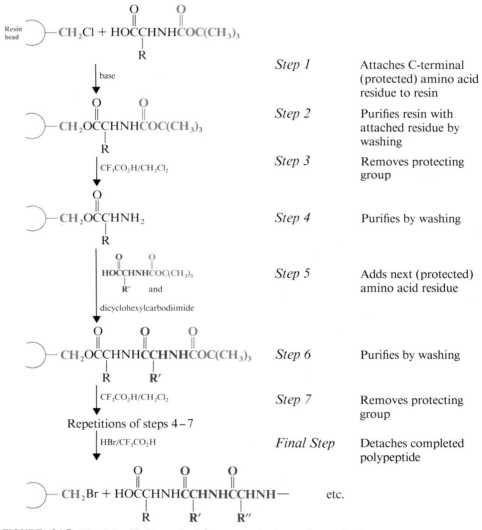

Step 1 — Attaches C-terminal (protected) amino acid residue to resin

Step 2 — Purifies resin with attached residue by washing

Step 3 — Removes protecting group

Step 4 — Purifies by washing

Step 5 — Adds next (protected) amino acid residue

Step 6 — Purifies by washing

Step 7 — Removes protecting group

Final Step — Detaches completed polypeptide

FIGURE 24.7 The Merrifield method for automated protein synthesis.

The great advantage of this procedure is that purification of the resin with its attached polypeptide can be carried out at each stage by simply washing the resin with an appropriate solvent. Impurities, because they are not attached to the insoluble resin, are simply carried away by the solvent. In the automated procedure each cycle of the "protein-making machine" requires only 4 h and attaches one new amino acid residue.*

The Merrifield technique has been applied successfully to the synthesis of ribonuclease, a protein with 124 amino acid residues. The synthesis involved 369 chemical reactions and 11,931 automated steps—all were carried out without isolating an intermediate. The synthetic ribonuclease not only had the same physical characteristics as the natural enzyme; it possessed the identical biological activity as well. The overall yield was 17%, which means that the average yield of each individual step was greater than 99%.

Problem 24.14

The resin for the Merrifield procedure is prepared by treating polystyrene, $\left(-CH_2CH-\right)_n$ with C_6H_5 as the substituent, with CH_3OCH_2Cl and a Lewis acid catalyst. (a) What reaction is involved? (b) After purification, the complete polypeptide or protein can be detached from the resin by treating it with HBr in trifluoroacetic acid under conditions mild enough not to affect the amide linkages. What structural feature of the resin makes this possible?

Problem 24.15

Outline the steps in the synthesis of Lys·Phe·Ala using the Merrifield procedure.

24.8 SECONDARY AND TERTIARY STRUCTURES OF PROTEINS

We have seen how amide and disulfide linkages constitute the covalent or *primary structure* of proteins. Of equal importance in understanding how proteins function is knowledge of the way in which the peptide chains are arranged in three dimensions. Involved here are the secondary and tertiary structures of proteins.

24.8A SECONDARY STRUCTURE

The **secondary structure** of a protein is defined by the local conformation of its polypeptide backbone. These local conformations have come to be specified in terms of regular folding patterns called *helices, pleated sheets,* and *turns.* The major experimental technique that has been used in elucidating the secondary structures of proteins is X-ray analysis.

When X-rays pass through a crystalline substance they produce diffraction patterns. Analysis of these patterns indicates a regular repetition of particular structural units with certain specific distances between them, called **repeat distances.** X-ray

---

*Protein synthesis in the body catalyzed by enzymes and directed by DNA/RNA takes only 1 min to add 150 amino acids in a specific sequence (cf. Section 25.5).

analyses have revealed that the polypeptide chain of a natural protein can interact with itself in two major ways: through formation of a **β-pleated sheet** and an **α helix.***

To understand how these interactions occur let us look first at what X-ray analysis has revealed about the geometry at the peptide bond itself. Peptide bonds tend to assume a geometry such that six atoms of the amide linkage are coplanar (Fig. 24.8). The carbon–nitrogen bond of the amine linkage is unusually short, indicating that resonance contributions of the type shown here are important.

$$\text{N—C} \overset{O}{<} \longleftrightarrow \overset{+}{\text{N}}=\text{C}\overset{O^-}{<}$$

The carbon–nitrogen bond, consequently, has considerable double-bond character (~40%) and rotations of groups about this bond are severely hindered.

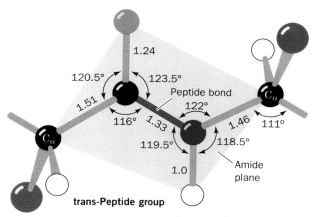

FIGURE 24.8 The geometry and bond lengths of the peptide linkage. The six enclosed atoms tend to be coplanar and assume a "transoid" arrangement. (From D. Voet and J. G. Voet, *Biochemistry,* Wiley, New York, 1990, p. 145. Used with permission.)

Rotations of groups attached to the amide nitrogen and the carbonyl carbon are relatively free, however, and these rotations allow peptide chains to form different conformations.

The transoid arrangement of groups around the relatively rigid amide bond would cause the R groups to alternate from side to side of a single fully extended peptide chain:

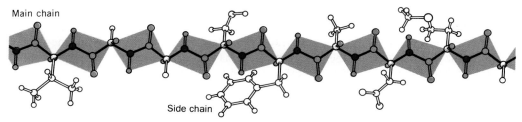

*Two American scientists, Linus Pauling and Robert B. Corey, were pioneers in the X-ray analysis of proteins. Beginning in 1939, Pauling and Corey initiated a long series of studies of the conformations of peptide chains. At first, they used crystals of single amino acids, then dipeptides and tripeptides, and so on. Moving on to larger and larger molecules and using the precisely constructed molecular models, they were able to understand the secondary structures of proteins for the first time.

Calculations show that such a polypeptide chain would have a repeat distance (i.e., distance between alternating units) of 7.2 Å.

Fully extended polypeptide chains could conceivably form a flat-sheet structure with each alternating amino acid in each chain forming two hydrogen bonds with an amino acid in the adjacent chain:

Hypothetical flat–sheet structure

This structure does not exist in naturally occurring proteins because of the crowding that would exist between R groups. If such a structure did exist, it would have the same repeat distance as the fully extended peptide chain, that is, 7.2 Å.

Slight rotations of bonds, however, can transform a flat-sheet structure into what is called the *β*-pleated sheet or *β* configuration (Fig. 24.9). The pleated-sheet structure gives small- and medium-sized R groups room enough to avoid van der Waals repulsions and is the predominant structure of silk fibroin (48% glycine and 38% serine and alanine residues). The pleated-sheet structure has a slightly shorter repeat distance, 7.0 Å, than the flat sheet.

Of far more importance in naturally occurring proteins is the secondary structure called the *α* helix (Fig. 24.10). This structure is a right-handed helix with 3.6 amino acid residues per turn. Each amide group in the chain has a hydrogen bond to an amide group at a distance of three amino acid residues in either direction, and the R groups all extend away from the axis of the helix. The repeat distance of the *α* helix is 1.5 Å.

The *α*-helical structure is found in many proteins; it is the predominant structure of the polypeptide chains of fibrous proteins such as *myosin,* the protein of muscle, and of *α-keratin,* the protein of hair, unstretched wool, and nails.

Helices and pleated sheets account for only about one half of the structure of the average globular protein. The remaining polypeptide segments have what is called a **coil** or **loop conformation.** These nonrepetitive structures are not random, they are just more difficult to describe. Globular proteins also have stretches, called **reverse turns** or **β bends,** where the polypeptide chain abruptly changes direction. These often connect successive strands of *β* sheets and almost always occur at the surface of proteins.

Figure 24.11 is a schematic representation of an enzyme, human carbonic anhydrase, showing how segments of *α* helix and *β* sheets intervene between reverse turns and nonrepetitive structures.

The locations of the side chains of amino acids of globular proteins are usually those that we would expect from their polarities.

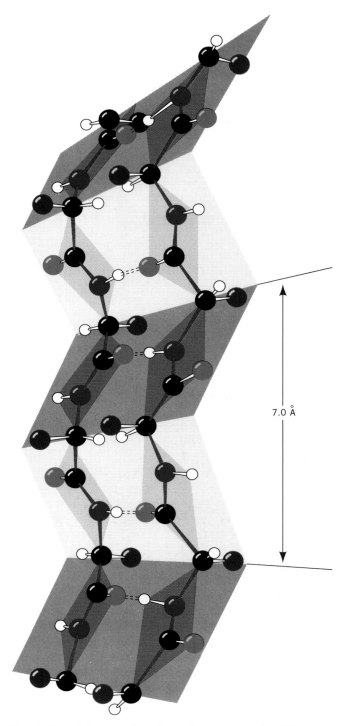

7.0 Å

FIGURE 24.9 The β-pleated sheet or β configuration of a protein. (Figure copyrighted © by Irving Geis. From D. Voet and J. G. Voet, *Biochemistry,* Wiley, New York, 1990, p. 153. Used with permission.)

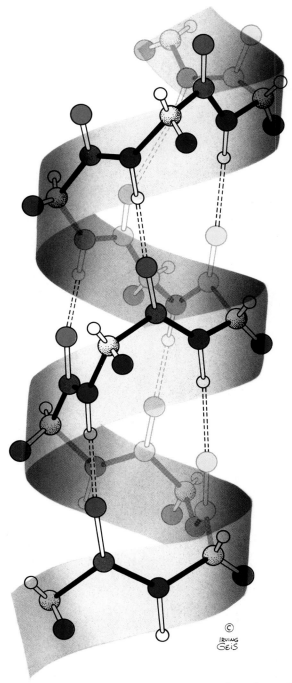

FIGURE 24.10 A representation of the α-helical structure of a polypeptide. Hydrogen bonds are denoted by dotted lines. (Figure copyrighted © by Irving Geis. From D. Voet and J. G. Voet, *Biochemistry,* Wiley, New York, 1990, p. 149. Used with permission.)

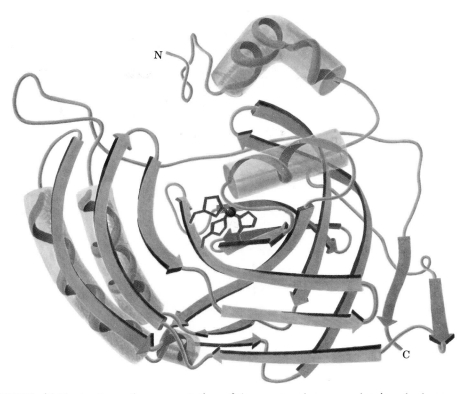

FIGURE 24.11 A schematic representation of the enzyme, human carbonic anhydrase. Alpha helices are represented as cylinders and strands of β-pleated sheets are drawn with an arrow pointing toward the C-terminus of the polypeptide. The side chains of three histidine residues (shown in blue) coordinate with a zinc atom (gray). Notice that the C-terminus is tucked through a loop of the polypeptide chain, making carbonic anhydrase a rare example of a native protein in which the polypeptide chain forms a knot. (From D. Voet and J. G. Voet, *Biochemistry,* Wiley, New York, 1990, p. 171.)

1. Residues with **nonpolar, hydrophobic, side chains,** such as *valine, leucine, isoleucine, methionine, and phenylalanine* are almost always found in the interior of the protein, out of contact with the aqueous solvent. (These hydrophobic interactions are largely responsible for the tertiary structure of proteins that we discuss in Section 24.8B.)

2. Side chains of **polar residues with + or − charges,** such as *arginine, lysine, aspartic acid, and glutamic acid,* are usually on the surface of the protein in contact with the aqueous solvent.

3. **Uncharged polar side chains** such as those of *serine, threonine, asparagine, glutamine, tyrosine, and tryptophan* are most often found on the surface, but some of these are found in the interior as well. When they are found in the interior, they are virtually all hydrogen bonded to other similar residues. Hydrogen bonding apparently helps neutralize the polarity of these groups.

Certain peptide chains assume what is called a **random coil arrangement,** a structure that is flexible, changing, and statistically random. Synthetic polylysine, for example, exists as a random coil and does not normally form an α helix. At pH 7, the ε-amino groups of the lysine residues are positively charged and, as a result, repulsive forces between them are so large that they overcome any stabilization that would be gained through hydrogen bond formation of an α helix. At pH 12, however, the ε-amino groups are uncharged and polylysine spontaneously forms an α helix.

The presence of proline or hydroxyproline residues in polypeptide chains produces another striking effect: Because the nitrogen atoms of these amino acids are part of five-membered rings, the groups attached by the nitrogen—α-carbon bond cannot rotate enough to allow an α-helical structure. Wherever proline or hydroxyproline occur in a peptide chain, their presence causes a kink or bend and interrupts the α helix.

24.8B TERTIARY STRUCTURE

The tertiary structure of a protein is its three-dimensional shape that arises from further foldings of its polypeptide chains, foldings superimposed on the coils of the α helixes. These foldings do not occur randomly: Under the proper environmental conditions they occur in one particular way—a way that is characteristic of a particular protein and one that is often highly important to its function.

Various forces are involved in stabilizing tertiary structures including the disulfide bonds of the primary structure. One characteristic of most proteins is that the folding takes place in such a way as to expose the maximum number of polar (hydrophilic) groups to the aqueous environment and enclose a maximum number of nonpolar (hydrophobic) groups within its interior.

The soluble globular proteins tend to be much more highly folded than fibrous proteins. However, fibrous proteins also have a tertiary structure; the α-helical strands of α-keratin, for example, are wound together into a "super helix." This super helix has a repeat distance of 5.1-Å units indicating that the super helix makes one

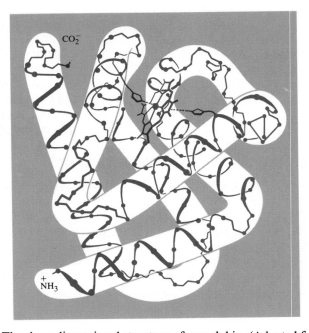

FIGURE 24.12 The three-dimensional structure of myoglobin. (Adapted from R. E. Dickerson, *The Proteins II*, H. Neurath, Ed., Academic Press, New York, 1964. p. 634. Used with permission.)

complete turn for each 35 turns of the α helix. The tertiary structure does not end here, however. Even the super helices can be wound together to give a ropelike structure of seven strands.

Myoglobin (Fig. 24.12) and hemoglobin (Section 24.11) were the first proteins (in 1957 and 1959) to be subjected to a completely successful X-ray analysis. This work was accomplished by J. C. Kendrew and Max Perutz at Cambridge University in England. (They received the Nobel Prize in 1962.) Since then many other proteins including lysozyme, ribonuclease, and α-chymotrypsin have yielded to complete structural analysis.

24.9 INTRODUCTION TO ENZYMES

All of the reactions that occur in living cells are mediated by remarkable biological catalysts called enzymes. Enzymes have the ability to bring about vast increases in the rates of reactions; in most instances, the rates of enzyme-catalyzed reactions are faster than those of uncatalyzed reactions by factors of $10^6 - 10^{12}$. For living organisms, rate enhancements of this magnitude are important because they permit reactions to take place at reasonable rates, even under the mild conditions that exist in living cells (i.e., approximately neutral pH and a temperature of about 35 °C.)

Enzymes also show remarkable **specificity** for their reactants (called **substrates**) and for their products. This specificity is far greater than that shown by most chemical reactions. In the enzymatic synthesis of proteins, for example (through reactions that take place on ribosomes, Section 25.5D), polypeptides consisting of well over 1000 amino acid residues are synthesized virtually without error. It was Emil Fischer's discovery, in 1894, of the ability of enzymes to distinguish between α- and β- glycosidic linkages (Section 22.12) that led him to formulate his **lock-and-key hypothesis** for enzyme specificity. According to this hypothesis, the specificity of an enzyme (the lock) and its substrate (the key) comes from their geometrically complementary shapes.

The enzyme and the substrate combine to form an **enzyme – substrate complex.** Formation of the complex often induces a conformational change in the enzyme that allows it to bind the substrate more effectively. This is called an **induced fit.** Binding the substrate also often causes certain of its bonds to become strained, and therefore more easily broken. The product of the reaction usually has a different shape from the substrate, and this altered shape, or in some instances, the intervention of another molecule, causes the complex to dissociate. The enzyme can then accept another molecule of the substrate and the whole process is repeated.

$$\text{Enzyme + substrate} \rightleftharpoons \underset{\text{complex}}{\text{enzyme–substrate}} \longrightarrow \text{enzyme + product}$$

Almost all enzymes are proteins.* The substrate is bound to the protein, and the reaction takes place, at what is called the **active site.** The noncovalent forces that bind the substrate to the active site are the same forces that account for the conformations of the proteins themselves: van der Waals forces, electrostatic forces, hydrogen bonding, and hydrophobic interactions. The amino acids located in the active site are arranged so that they can interact specifically with the substrate.

---

* We now know that certain RNA molecules can also act as enzymes. The 1989 Nobel Prize for Chemistry went to Sidney Altman (of Yale University) and to Thomas R. Cech (of the University of Colorado, Boulder) for this discovery.

Reactions catalyzed by enzymes are completely **stereospecific,** and this specificity comes from the way enzymes bind their substrates. An α-glucosidase will only bind the α form of a glucoside not the β form. Enzymes that metabolize sugars bind only D-sugars, enzymes that synthesize proteins bind only L-amino acids, and so on.

While enzymes are absolutely stereospecific, they often vary considerably in what is called their **geometric specificity.** By geometric specificity we mean a specificity that is related to the identities of the chemical groups of the substrates. Some enzymes will accept only one compound as its substrate. Others, however, will accept a range of compounds with similar groups. Carboxypeptidase A, for example, will hydrolyze the C-terminal peptide from all polypeptides as long as the penultimate residue is not arginine, lysine, or proline, and as long as the next preceding residue is not proline. Chymotrypsin, a digestive enzyme that catalyzes the hydrolysis of peptide bonds, will also catalyze the hydrolysis of esters.

$$R-\overset{\overset{\displaystyle O}{\|}}{C}-NH-R' + H_2O \xrightarrow{\text{chymotrypsin}} R-\overset{\overset{\displaystyle O}{\|}}{C}-O^- + H_3\overset{+}{N}-R'$$

Peptide

$$R-\overset{\overset{\displaystyle O}{\|}}{C}-O-R' + H_2O \xrightarrow{\text{chymotrypsin}} R-\overset{\overset{\displaystyle O}{\|}}{C}-OH + HO-R'$$

Ester

A compound that can alter the activity of an enzyme is called an **inhibitor.** A compound that competes directly with the substrate for the active site is known as a **competitive inhibitor.** We learned in Section 19.11, for example, that sulfanilamide is a competitive inhibitor for a bacterial enzyme that incorporates p-aminobenzoic acid into folic acid.

Some enzymes require the presence of a **cofactor.** The cofactor may be a metal ion as, for example, the zinc atom of human carbonic anhydrase (Fig. 24.11). Others may require the presence of an organic molecule, such as NAD^+ (Section 13.13), called a **coenzyme.** Coenzymes become chemically changed in the course of the enzymatic reaction. NAD^+ becomes converted to **NADH.** In some enzymes the cofactor is permanently bound to the enzyme, in which case it is called a **prosthetic group.**

Many of the water-soluble vitamins are the precursors of coenzymes. Niacin (nicotinic acid) is a precursor of NAD^+, for example. Pantothenic acid is a precursor of coenzyme A (Special Topic L).

Niacin   **Pantothenic Acid**

24.10 LYSOZYME: MODE OF ACTION OF AN ENZYME

Lysozyme is made up of 129 amino acid residues (Fig. 24.13). Three short segments of the chain between residues 5–15, 24–34, and 88–96 have the structure of an α helix; the residues between 41–45 and 50–54 form pleated sheets, and a hairpin turn

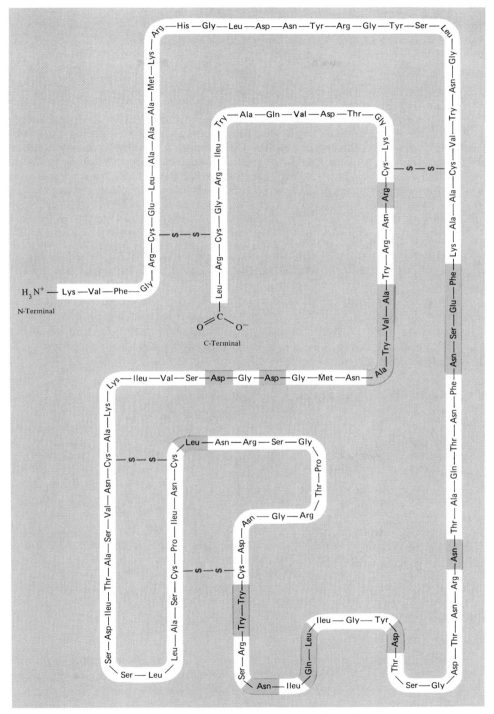

FIGURE 24.13 The covalent structure of lysozyme. The amino acids that line the active site of lysozyme are shown in color.

occurs at residues 46–49. The remaining polypeptide segments of lysozyme have a coil or loop conformation.

The discovery of lysozyme is an interesting story in itself:

One day in 1922 Alexander Fleming was suffering from a cold. This is not unusual in London, but Fleming was a most unusual man and he took advantage of the cold in a characteristic way. He allowed a few drops of his nasal mucus to fall on a culture of bacteria he was working with and then put the plate to one side to see what would happen. Imagine his excitement when he discovered some time later that the bacteria near the mucus had dissolved away. For a while he thought his ambition of finding a universal antibiotic had been realized. In a burst of activity he quickly established that the antibacterial action of the mucus was due to the presence of an enzyme; he called this substance lysozyme because of its capacity to lyse, or dissolve, the bacterial cells. Lysozyme was soon discovered in many tissues and secretions of the human body, in plants and most plentifully of all in the white of an egg. Unfortunately Fleming found that it is not effective against the most harmful bacteria. He had to wait seven years before a strangely similar experiment revealed the existence of a genuinely effective antibiotic: penicillin.

This story was related by Professor David C. Phillips of Oxford University who many years later used X-ray analysis to discover the three-dimensional structure of lysozyme.*

Phillips' X-ray diffraction studies of lysozyme are especially interesting because they have also revealed important information about how this enzyme acts on its substrate. Lysozyme's substrate is a polysaccharide of amino sugars that makes up part of the bacterial cell wall. An oligosaccharide that has the same general structure as the cell wall polysaccharide is shown in Fig. 24.14.

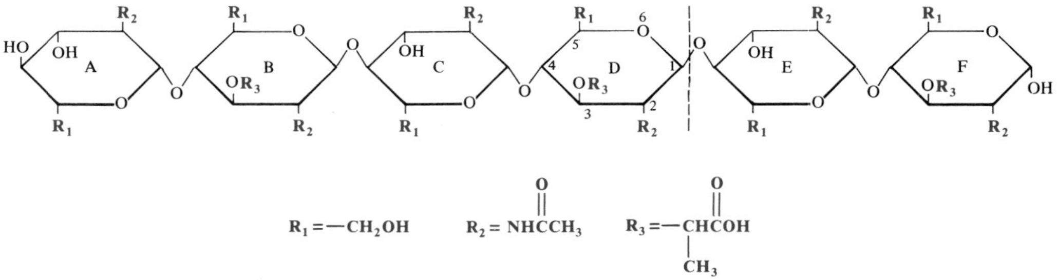

$R_1 = -CH_2OH$ $R_2 = NHCCH_3$ (O above) $R_3 = -CHCOH$ (O above, CH_3 below)

FIGURE 24.14 A hexasaccharide that has the same general structure as the cell wall polysaccharide on which lysozyme acts. Two different amino sugars are present: rings A, C, and E are derived from a monosaccharide called N-acetylglucosamine; rings B, D, and F are derived from a monosaccharide called N-acetylmuramic acid. When lysozyme acts on this oligosaccharide, hydrolysis takes place and results in cleavage at the glycosidic linkage between rings D and E.

By using oligosaccharides (made up of N-acetylglucosamine units only) on which lysozyme acts very slowly, Phillips and his co-workers were able to discover how the substrate fits into the enzyme's active site. This site is a deep cleft in the lysozyme structure (Fig. 24.15a). The oligosaccharide is held in this cleft by hydrogen bonds, and, as the enzyme binds the substrate, two important changes take place: The cleft in

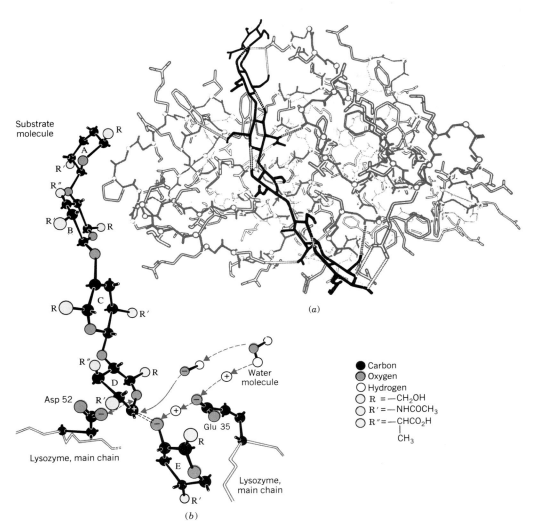

FIGURE 24.15 (*a*) This drawing shows the backbones of the lysozyme-substrate complex. The substrate (in this drawing a hexasaccharide) fits into a cleft in the lysozyme structure and is held in place by hydrogen bonds. As lysozyme binds the oligosaccharide, the cleft in its structure closes slightly. (Adapted with permission from *Atlas of Protein Sequence and Structure,* 1969, Margaret O. Dayoff, Ed. National Biomedical Research Foundation, Washington, DC, 1969. The drawing was made by Irving Geis, based on his perspective painting of the molecule, which appeared in *Scientific American,* November 1966. The painting was made of an actual model assembled at the Royal Institution, London, by D. C. Phillips and his colleagues, based on their X-ray crystallography results.) (*b*) A possible mechanism for lysozyme action. This drawing shows an expanded portion of part (*a*) and illustrates how hydrolysis of the acetal linkage between rings **D** and **E** of the substrate may occur. Glutamic acid (residue 35) donates a proton to the intervening oxygen atom. This causes the formation of a carbocation that is stabilized by the carboxylate ion aspartic acid (residue 52). A water molecule supplies an OH⁻ to the carbocation and H⁺ to glutamic acid. (Adapted with permission from *The Three-Dimensional Structures of an Enzyme Molecule,* by David C. Phillips, Copyright © Nov. 1966 by Scientific American, Inc. All rights reserved.)

the enzyme closes slightly and ring **D** of the oligosaccharide is "flattened" out of its stable chair conformation. This flattening causes atoms 1, 2, 5, and 6 of ring **D** to become coplanar; it also distorts ring **D** in such a way as to make the glycosidic linkage between it and ring **E** more susceptible to hydrolysis.*

Hydrolysis of the glycosidic linkage probably takes the course illustrated in Fig. 24.15*b*. The carboxyl group of glutamic acid (residue number 35) donates a proton to the oxygen between rings **D** and **E**. Protonation leads to cleavage at the glycosidic link and to the formation of a carbocation at C-1 of ring **D**. This carbocation is stabilized by the negatively charged carboxylate group of aspartic acid (residue number 52), which lies in close proximity. A water molecule diffuses in and supplies an OH^- ion to the carbocation and a proton to replace that lost by glutamic acid.

When the polysaccharide is a part of a bacterial cell wall, lysozyme probably first attaches itself to the cell wall by hydrogen bonds. After hydrolysis has taken place, lysozyme falls away leaving behind a bacterium with a punctured cell wall.

24.11 SERINE PROTEASES

Chymotrypsin, trypsin, and elastin are digestive enzymes secreted by the pancreas into the small intestines to catalyze the hydrolysis of peptide bonds. These enzymes are all called **serine proteases** because the mechanism for their proteolytic activity (one that they have in common) involves a particular serine residue that is essential for their enzymatic activity. As another example of how enzymes work, we shall examine the mechanism of action of chymotrypsin.

Chymotrypsin is formed from a precursor molecule called chymotrypsinogen, which has 245 amino acid residues. Cleavage of two dipeptide units of chymotrypsinogen produces chymotrypsin. Chymotrypsin folds in a way that brings together histidine at position 57, aspartic acid at position 102, and serine at position 195. Together, these residues constitute what is called the **catalytic triad** of the active site (Fig. 24.16). Near the active site is a hydrophobic binding site, a slitlike pocket that preferentially accommodates the nonpolar side chains of Phe, Tyr, and Trp.

After chymotrypsin has bound its protein substrate, the serine residue at position 195 is ideally situated to attack the acyl carbon of the peptide bond. This serine residue is made more nucleophilic by transferring its proton to the imidazole nitrogen of the histidine residue at position 57. The imidazolium ion that is formed is stabilized by the polarizing effect of the carboxylate ion of the aspartic acid residue at position 102. (Neutron diffraction studies, which show the positions of hydrogen atoms, confirm that the carboxylate ion remains as a carboxylate ion throughout and does not actually accept a proton from the imidazole.) Nucleophilic attack by the serine leads to an acylated serine through a tetrahedral intermediate. The new N-terminal end of the cleaved polypeptide chain diffuses away and is replaced by a water molecule.

Regeneration of the active site of chymotrypsin is shown in Fig. 24.17. In this process water acts as the nucleophile, and, in a series of steps analogous to those in Fig. 24.16, hydrolyzes the acyl–serine bond. The enzyme is now ready to repeat the whole process.

---

*R. H. Lemieux and G. Huber, while with the National Research Council of Canada, showed that when an aldohexose is converted to a carbocation the ring of the carbocation assumes just this flattened conformation.

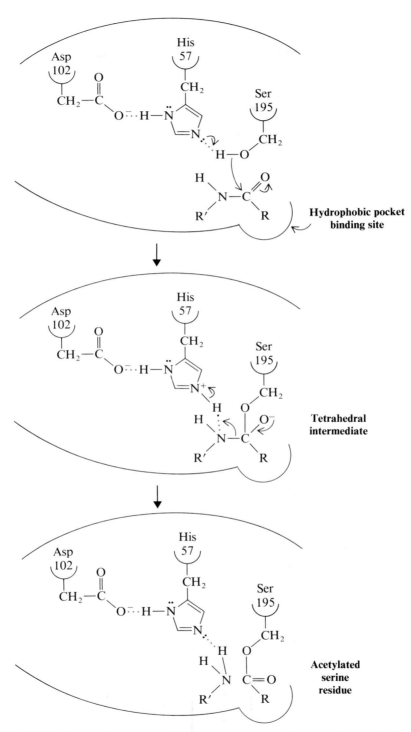

FIGURE 24.16 The catalytic triad of chymotrypsin causes cleavage of a peptide bond by acylation of the serine residue 195 of chymotrypsin. Near the active site is a hydrophobic binding site that accommodates nonpolar side chains of the protein.

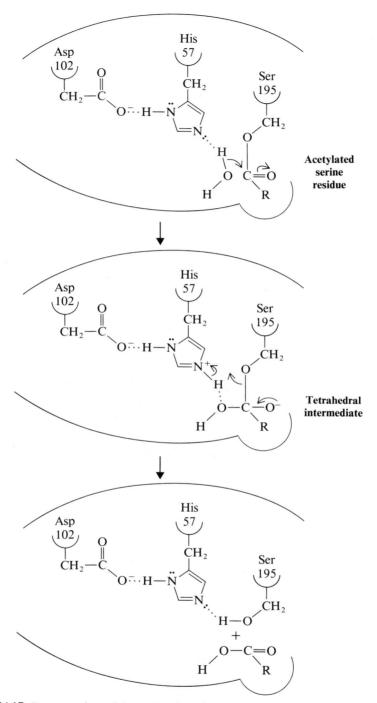

FIGURE 24.17 Regeneration of the active site of chymotrypsin. Water causes hydrolysis of the acyl-serine bond.

There is much evidence for this mechanism that, for reasons of space, we shall have to ignore. One bit of evidence deserves mention, however. There are compounds such as **diisopropylphosphofluoridate (DIPF)** that irreversibly inhibit serine proteases. It has been shown that they do this by reacting only with Ser 195.

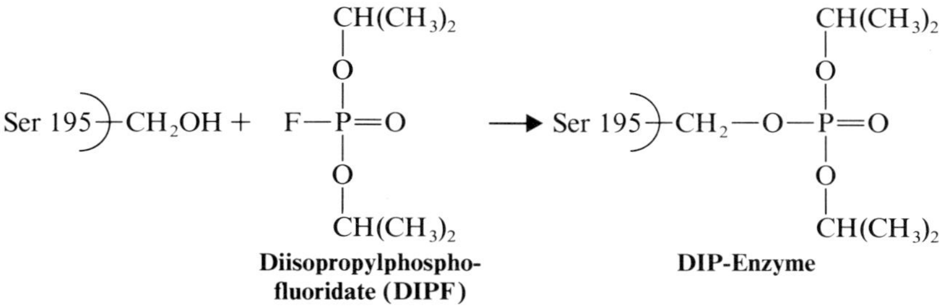

$$\text{Ser 195} \!\!-\!\! CH_2OH + F\!\!-\!\!\underset{\underset{O}{|}}{\overset{\overset{CH(CH_3)_2}{|}}{\underset{}{\overset{|}{P}}}}\!\!=\!\!O \longrightarrow \text{Ser 195}\!\!-\!\!CH_2\!\!-\!\!O\!\!-\!\!P\!\!=\!\!O$$

Diisopropylphospho-
fluoridate (DIPF) · DIP-Enzyme

Recognition of the inactivating effect of DIPF came about as a result of the discovery that DIPF and related compounds are powerful **nerve poisons.** (They are the "nerve gases" of military use, even though they are liquids, dispersed as fine droplets, and not gases.) Diisopropylphosphofluoridate inactivates **acetylcholinesterase** (Section 19.14) by reacting with it in the same way that it does with chymotrypsin. Acetylcholinesterase is a **serine esterase** rather than a serine protease.

24.12 HEMOGLOBIN: A CONJUGATED PROTEIN

Some proteins, called **conjugated proteins,** contain as a part of their structure a nonprotein group called a **prosthetic group.** An example is the oxygen-carrying protein, hemoglobin. Each of the four polypeptide chains of hemoglobin is bound to a prosthetic group called *heme* (Fig. 24.18). The four polypeptide chains of hemoglobin are wound in such a way as to give hemoglobin a roughly spherical shape (Fig.

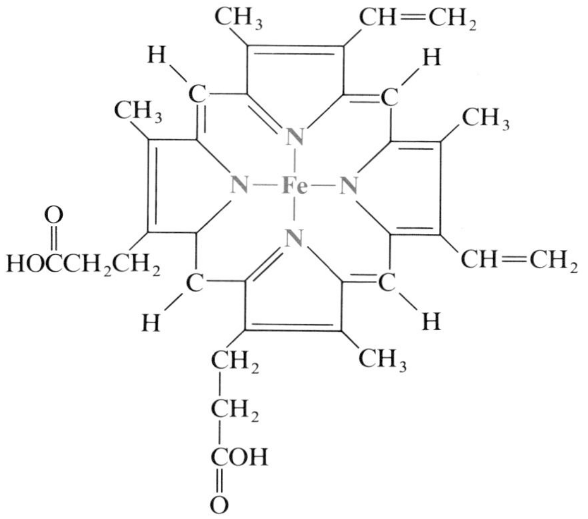

FIGURE 24.18 The structure of heme, the prosthetic group of hemoglobin. Heme has a structure similar to that of chlorophyll (Fig. 22.1) in that each is derived from the heterocyclic ring, porphyrin. The iron of heme is in the ferrous (2+) oxidation state.

24.19). Moreover, each heme group lies in a crevice with the hydrophobic vinyl groups of its porphyrin structure surrounded by side chains of hydrophobic amino residues. The two propanoate side chains of heme lie near positively charged amino groups of lysine and arginine residues.

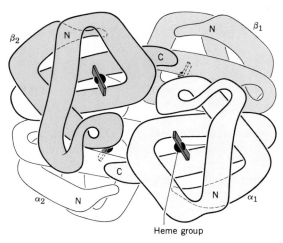

FIGURE 24.19 The hemoglobin molecule.

The iron of the heme group is in the 2 + (ferrous) oxidation state and it forms a coordinate bond to a nitrogen of the imidazole group of histidine of the polypeptide chain. This leaves one valence of the ferrous ion free to combine with oxygen as follows:

$$
\begin{array}{c}
N \quad \overset{\displaystyle O_2}{\underset{\displaystyle Fe}{|}} \quad N \\
N \quad\quad\quad N \\
N\,(\text{imidazole})
\end{array}
$$

**A portion of oxygenated
hemoglobin**

The fact that the ferrous ion of the heme group combines with oxygen is not particularly remarkable; many similar compounds do the same thing. What is remarkable about hemoglobin is that when the heme combines with oxygen the ferrous ion does not become readily oxidized to the ferric state. Studies with model heme compounds in water, for example, show that they undergo a rapid combination with oxygen but they also undergo a rapid oxidation of the iron from Fe^{2+} to Fe^{3+}. When these same compounds are embedded in the hydrophobic environment of a polystyrene resin, however, the iron is easily oxygenated and deoxygenated and this occurs *with no change in oxidation state of iron*. In this respect, it is especially interesting to note that X-ray studies of hemoglobin have revealed that the polypeptide chains provide each heme group with a similar hydrophobic environment.

Additional Problems

24.16 (a) Which amino acids in Table 24.1 have more than one stereocenter? (b) Write Fischer projection formulas for the isomers of each of these amino acids that would have the L configuration at the α carbon. (c) What kind of isomers have you drawn in each case?

24.17 (a) Which amino acid in Table 24.1 could react with nitrous acid (i.e., a solution of $NaNO_2$ and HCl) to yield lactic acid? (b) All of the amino acids in Table 24.1 liberate nitrogen when they are treated with nitrous acid except two; which are these? (c) What product would you expect to obtain from treating tyrosine with excess bromine water? (d) What product would you expect to be formed in the reaction of phenylalanine with ethanol in the presence of hydrogen chloride? (e) What product would you expect from the reaction of alanine and benzoyl chloride in aqueous base?

24.18 (a) On the basis of the following sequence of reactions, Emil Fischer was able to show that (−)-serine and L-(+)-alanine have the same configuration. Write Fischer projection formulas for the intermediates **A**–**C**.

$$(-)\text{-Serine} \xrightarrow[CH_3OH]{HCl} \textbf{A} \ (C_4H_{10}ClNO_3) \xrightarrow{PCl_5} \textbf{B} \ (C_4H_9Cl_2NO_2) \xrightarrow[\text{(2) } OH^-]{\text{(1) } H_3O^+, H_2O, \text{ heat}}$$

$$\textbf{C} \ (C_3H_6ClNO_2) \xrightarrow[\text{dil. } H_3O^+]{Na\text{-}Hg} \text{L-(+)-alanine}$$

(b) The configuration of L-(−)-cysteine can be related to that of L-(−)-serine through the following reactions. Write Fischer projection formulas for **D** and **E**.

$$\textbf{B} \text{ [from part (a)]} \xrightarrow{OH^-} \textbf{D} \ (C_4H_8ClNO_2) \xrightarrow{NaSH}$$

$$\textbf{E} \ (C_4H_9NO_2S) \xrightarrow[\text{(2) } OH^-]{\text{(1) } H_3O^+, H_2O, \text{ heat}} \text{L-(+)-cysteine}$$

(c) The configuration of L-(−)-asparagine can be related to that of L-(−)-serine in the following way. What is the structure of **F**?

$$\text{L-(−)-Asparagine} \xrightarrow[\substack{\text{Hofmann} \\ \text{rearrangement}}]{NaOBr/OH^-} \textbf{F} \ (C_3H_7N_2O_2)$$

$$\textbf{C} \text{ [from part (a)]} \xrightarrow{\quad} \underset{NH_3}{\uparrow}$$

24.19 (a) DL-Glutamic acid has been synthesized from diethyl acetamidomalonate in the following way: Outline the reactions involved.

$$\underset{\substack{\textbf{Diethyl acetamido-} \\ \textbf{malonate}}}{CH_3\overset{\overset{\displaystyle O}{\|}}{C}NHCH(CO_2C_2H_5)_2} + CH_2{=}CH{-}C{\equiv}N \xrightarrow[C_2H_5OH]{NaOC_2H_5}$$

(95% yield)

$$\textbf{G} \ (C_{12}H_{18}N_2O_5) \xrightarrow[\substack{\text{reflux 6 h} \\ \text{(66\% yield)}}]{\text{concd HCl}} \text{DL-glutamic acid}$$

(b) Compound **G** has also been used to prepare the amino acid DL-ornithine through the following route. Outline the reaction involved here.

$$\textbf{G} \ (C_{12}H_{18}N_2O_5) \xrightarrow[\substack{68 \text{ °C, 1000 psi} \\ \text{(90\% yield)}}]{H_2, \ Ni} \textbf{H} \ (C_{10}H_{16}N_2O_4, \text{ a } \delta\text{-lactam}) \xrightarrow[\substack{\text{reflux 4 h} \\ \text{(97\% yield)}}]{\text{concd HCl}}$$

$$\text{DL-ornithine hydrochloride } (C_5H_{13}ClN_2O_2)$$

(L-Ornithine is a naturally occurring amino acid but does not occur in proteins. In one metabolic pathway L-ornithine serves as a precursor for L-arginine.)

24.20   Bradykinin is a nonapeptide released by blood plasma globulins in response to a wasp sting. It is a very potent pain-causing agent. Its molecular formula is Arg_2, Gly, Phe_2, Pro_3, Ser. The use of 2,4-dinitrofluorobenzene and carboxypeptidase show that both terminal residues are arginine. Partial acid hydrolysis of bradykinin gives the following di- and tripeptides:

$$Phe \cdot Ser + Pro \cdot Gly \cdot Phe + Pro \cdot Pro + Ser \cdot Pro \cdot Phe + Phe \cdot Arg + Arg \cdot Pro$$

What is the amino acid sequence of bradykinin?

24.21   Complete hydrolysis of a heptapeptide showed that it had the following molecular formula:

$$Ala_2, Glu, Leu, Lys, Phe, Val$$

Deduce the amino acid sequence of this heptapeptide from the following data.

1.   Treatment of the heptapeptide with 2,4-dinitrofluorobenzene followed by incomplete hydrolysis gave, among other products: valine labeled at the α-amino group, lysine labeled at the ε-amino group, and a dipeptide, DNP—Val·Leu (DNP = 2,4- dinitrophenyl-).
2.   Hydrolysis of the heptapeptide with carboxypeptidase gives an initial high concentration of alanine, followed by a rising concentration of glutamic acid.
3.   Partial enzymatic hydrolysis of the heptapeptide gave a dipeptide (A) and a tripeptide (B).
     a. Treatment of A with 2,4-dinitrofluorobenzene followed by hydrolysis gave DNP-labeled leucine and lysine labeled only at the ε-amino group.
     b. Complete hydrolysis of B gave phenylalanine, glutamic acid, and alanine. When B was allowed to react with carboxypeptidase, the solution showed an initial high concentration of glutamic acid. Treatment of B with 2,4-dinitrofluorobenzene followed by hydrolysis gave labeled phenylalanine.

24.22   Synthetic polyglutamic acid exists as an α helix in solution at pH 2–3. When the pH of such a solution is gradually raised through the addition of base, a dramatic change in optical rotation takes place at pH 5. This change has been associated with the unfolding of the α helix and the formation of a random coil. What structural feature of polyglutamic acid, and what chemical change, can you suggest as an explanation of this transformation?

*24.23   Part of the evidence for restricted rotation about the carbon–nitrogen bond in a peptide linkage (see Section 24.9A) comes from ^1H NMR studies done with simple amides. For example, at room temperature and with the instrument operating at 60 MHz, the ^1H NMR spectrum of N,N-dimethylformamide, $(CH_3)_2NCHO$, shows a doublet at δ 2.80 (3H), a doublet at δ 2.95 (3H), and a multiplet at δ 8.05 (1H). When the spectrum is determined at lower magnetic field strength (i.e., with the instrument operating at 30 MHz), the doublets are found to have shifted so that the distance (in hertz) that separates one doublet from the other is smaller. When the temperature at which the spectrum is determined is raised, the doublets persist until a temperature of 111 °C is reached; then the doublets coalesce to become a single signal. Explain in detail how these observations are consistent with the existence of a relatively large barrier to rotation about the carbon–nitrogen bond of DMF.

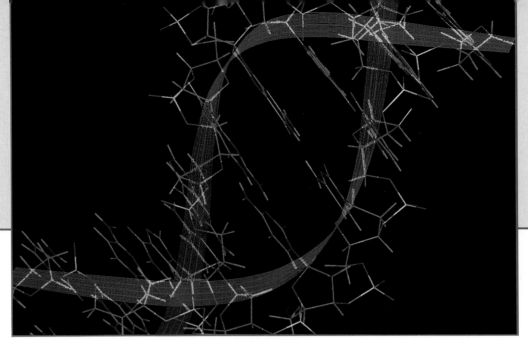

DNA (see Section 25.4).

25

NUCLEIC ACIDS AND PROTEIN SYNTHESIS

. . . I cannot help wondering whether some day an enthusiastic scientist will christen his newborn twins Adenine and Thymine.

F. H. C. Crick*

25.1 INTRODUCTION

The **nucleic acids,** deoxyribonucleic acid (DNA) and ribonucleic acid (RNA), are, respectively, the molecules that preserve hereditary information and that transcribe and translate it in a way that allows the synthesis of all the varied proteins of the cell. These biological polymers are sometimes found associated with proteins and in this form they are known as **nucleoproteins.**

Much of our still incomplete knowledge of how genetic information is preserved, how it is passed on to succeeding generations of the organism, and how it is transformed into the working parts of the cell has come from the study of nucleic acids. For these reasons, we shall focus our attention on the structures and properties of nucleic acids and of their components, **nucleotides** and **nucleosides.**

*Who along with J. D. Watson and Maurice Wilkins shared the Nobel Prize in 1962 for their proposal of (and evidence for) the double helix structure of DNA. (Taken from F. H. C. Crick, "The Structure of the Hereditary Material," *Sci. Am.,* 1954, *191,* 20, 54–61.)

25.2 NUCLEOTIDES AND NUCLEOSIDES

Mild degradations of nucleic acids yield their monomeric units, compounds that are called **nucleotides.** A general formula for a nucleotide and the specific structure of one, called adenylic acid, are shown in Fig. 25.1.

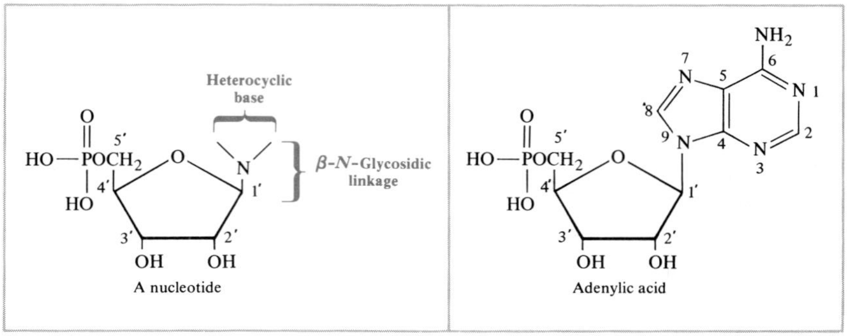

(a) (b)

FIGURE 25.1 (a) General structure of a nucleotide obtained from RNA. The heterocyclic base is a purine or pyrimidine. In nucleotides obtained from DNA, the sugar component is 2'-deoxyribose, that is, the —OH at position 2' is replaced by —H. The phosphate group of the nucleotide is shown attached to the C-5'; it may instead be attached to the C-3' atom. The heterocyclic base is always attached through a β-glycosidic linkage at C-1'. (b) Adenylic acid, a typical nucleotide.

Complete hydrolysis of a nucleotide furnishes:

1. A heterocyclic base, either a purine or pyrimidine.
2. A five-carbon monosaccharide, either D-ribose or 2-deoxy-D-ribose.
3. A phosphate ion.

The central portion of the nucleotide is the monosaccharide and it is always present as a five-membered ring, that is, as a furanoside. The heterocyclic base of a nucleotide is attached through an N-glycosidic linkage to C-1' of the ribose or deoxyribose unit and this linkage is always β. The phosphate group of a nucleotide is present as a phosphate ester and it may be attached at C-5' or C-3'. (In nucleotides, the carbon atoms of the monosaccharide portion are designated with primed numbers, i.e., 1', 2', 3', etc.)

Removal of the phosphate group of a nucleotide converts it to a compound known as a **nucleoside** (Section 22.15A). The nucleosides that can be obtained from DNA all contain 2-deoxy-D-ribose as their sugar component and one of four heterocyclic bases, either adenine, guanine, cytosine, or thymine:

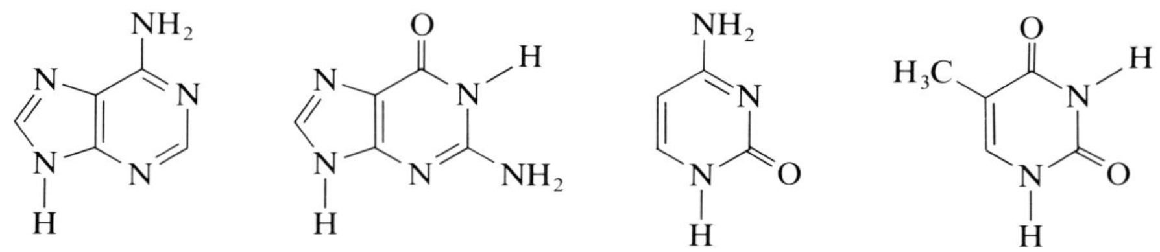

Adenine (A) Guanine (G) Cytosine (C) Thymine (T)

◄——— Purines ———► ◄——— Pyrimidines ———►

The nucleosides obtained from RNA contain D-ribose as their sugar component and either adenine, guanine, cytosine, or uracil as their heterocyclic base.*

Uracil
(a pyrimidine)

The heterocyclic bases obtained from nucleosides are capable of existing in more than one tautomeric form. The forms that we have shown are the predominant forms that the bases assume when they are present in nucleic acids.

Problem 25.1

Write the structures of other tautomeric forms of adenine, guanine, cytosine, thymine, and uracil.

The names and structures of the nucleosides found in DNA are shown in Fig. 25.2; those found in RNA are given in Fig. 25.3.

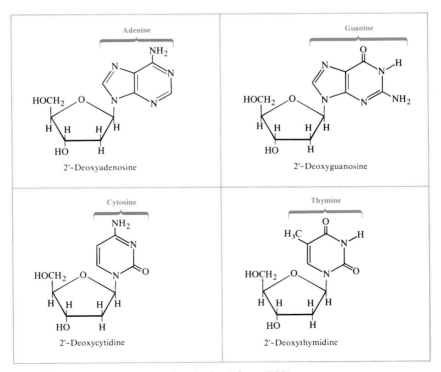

FIGURE 25.2 Nucleosides that can be obtained from DNA.

*Notice that in an RNA nucleoside (or nucleotide), uracil replaces thymine. (Some nucleosides obtained from specialized forms of RNA may also contain other, but similar, purines and pyrimidines.)

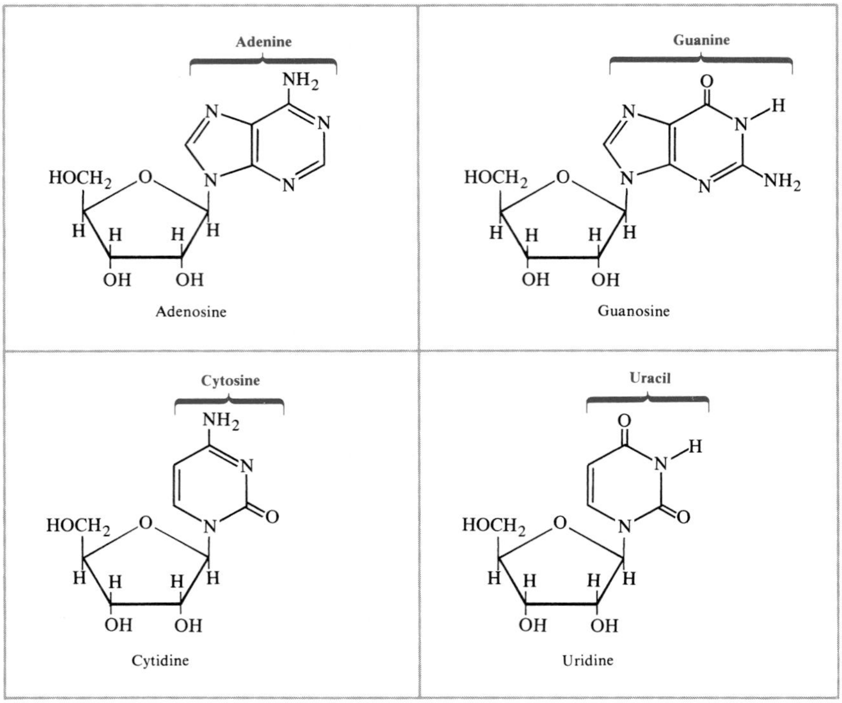

FIGURE 25.3 Nucleosides that can be obtained from RNA.

Problem 25.2

The nucleosides shown in Figs. 25.2 and 25.3 are stable in dilute base. In dilute acid, however, they undergo rapid hydrolysis yielding a sugar (deoxyribose or ribose) and a heterocyclic base. (a) What structural feature of the nucleoside accounts for this behavior? (b) Propose a reasonable mechanism for the hydrolysis.

Nucleotides are named in several ways. Adenylic acid (Fig. 25.1), for example, is sometimes called 5'-adenylic acid in order to designate the position of the phosphate group; it is also called adenosine 5'-phosphate, or simply adenosine monophosphate (AMP). Uridylic acid is called 5'-uridylic acid, uridine 5'-phosphate, or uridine monophosphate (UMP), and so on.

Nucleosides and nucleotides are found in places other than as part of the structure of DNA and RNA. We have seen, for example, that adenosine units are part of the structures of two important coenzymes, NADH and coenzyme A (Special Topic L). The 5'-triphosphate of adenosine is, of course, the important energy source, ATP (Section 22.1B). The compound called 3',5'-cyclic adenylic acid (or cyclic AMP) (Fig. 25.4) is an important regulator of hormone activity. Cells synthesize this compound from ATP through the action of an enzyme, *adenyl cyclase.* In the laboratory, 3',5'-cyclic adenylic acid can be prepared through dehydration of 5'-adenylic acid with dicyclohexylcarbodimide.

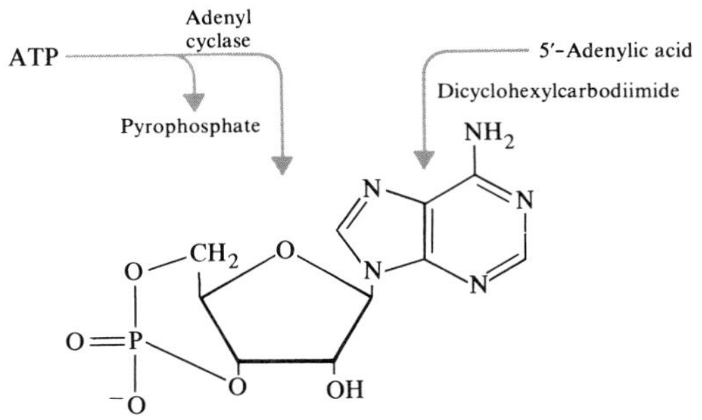

FIGURE 25.4 3′,5′-Cyclic adenylic acid and its biosynthesis and laboratory synthesis.

Problem 25.3 ─────────────────────────────────

When 3′,5′-cyclic adenylic acid is treated with aqueous sodium hydroxide, the major product that is obtained is 3′-adenylic (adenosine 3′-phosphate) rather than 5′-adenylic acid. Suggest an explanation that accounts for the course of this reaction.

25.3 LABORATORY SYNTHESIS OF NUCLEOSIDES AND NUCLEOTIDES

A variety of methods have been developed for the synthesis of nucleosides. One technique uses reactions that assemble the nucleoside from suitably activated and protected ribose derivatives and heterocyclic bases. An example is the following synthesis of adenosine:

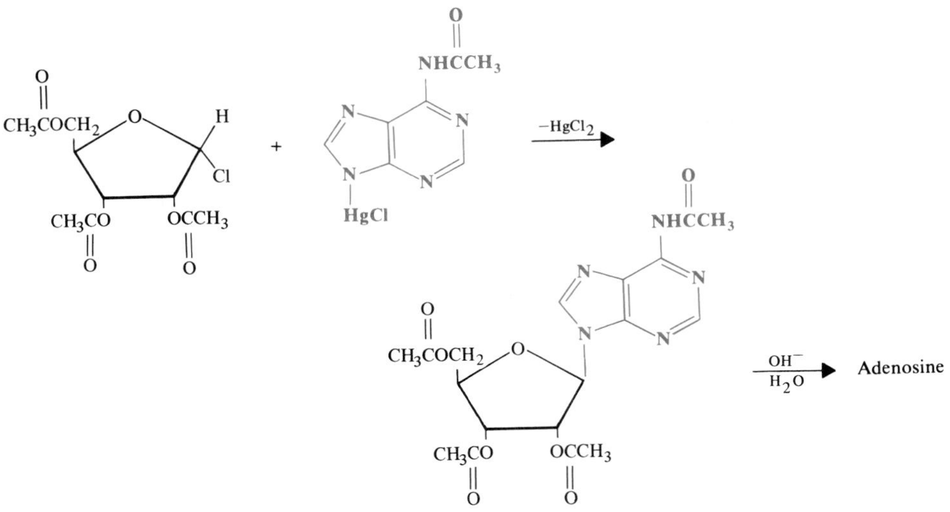

Another technique involves formation of the heterocyclic base on a protected ribosylamine derivative:

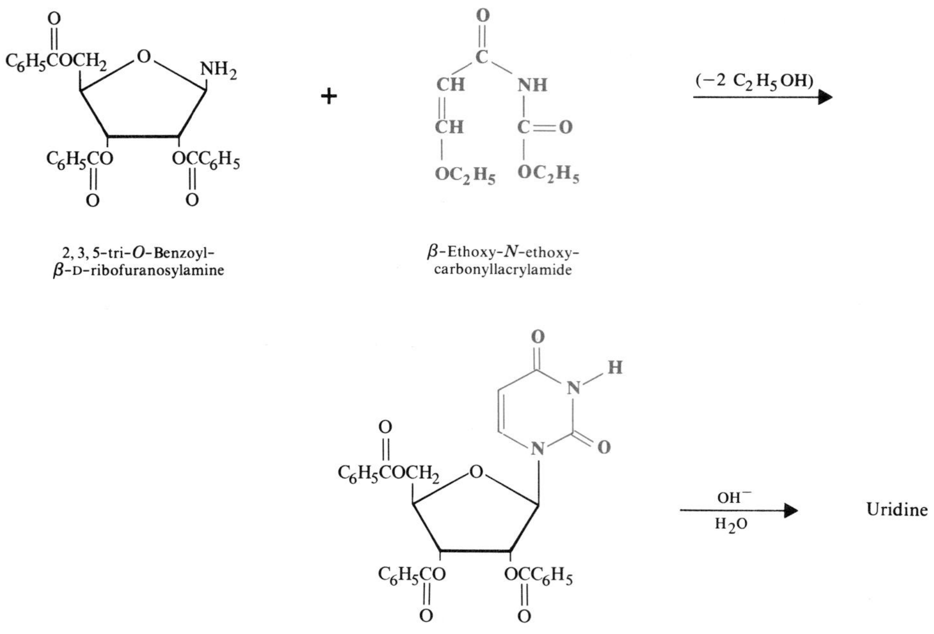

2, 3, 5-tri-O-Benzoyl-
β-D-ribofuranosylamine

β-Ethoxy-N-ethoxy-
carbonyllacrylamide

Uridine

Problem 25.4

Basing your answer on reactions that you have seen before, propose a likely mechanism for the condensation reaction in the first step of the preceding uridine synthesis.

Still a third technique involves the synthesis of a nucleoside with a substituent in the heterocyclic ring that can be replaced with other groups. This method has been used extensively to synthesize unusual nucleosides that do not necessarily occur naturally. The following example makes use of a 6-chloropurine derivative obtained from the appropriate ribofuranosyl chloride and chloromercuripurine.

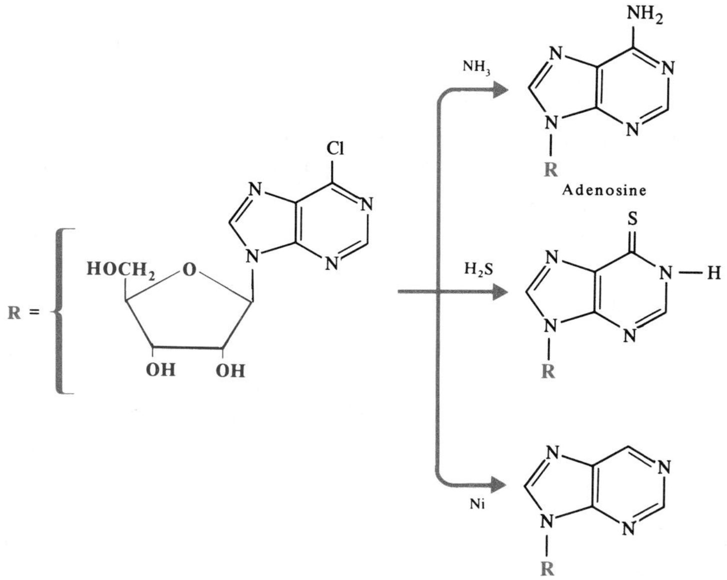

Adenosine

Numerous phosphorylating agents have been used to convert nucleosides to nucleotides. One of the most useful is dibenzyl phosphochloridate.

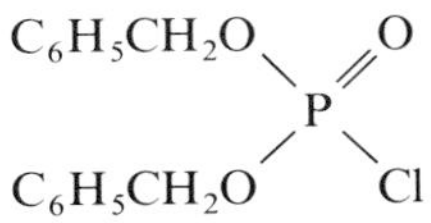

$$C_6H_5CH_2O \diagdown \quad \diagup O$$
$$P$$
$$C_6H_5CH_2O \diagup \quad \diagdown Cl$$

Dibenzyl phosphochloridate

Specific phosphorylation of the 5'-OH can be achieved if the 2'- and 3'-OH groups of the nucleoside are protected by an isopropylidene group (see following figure).

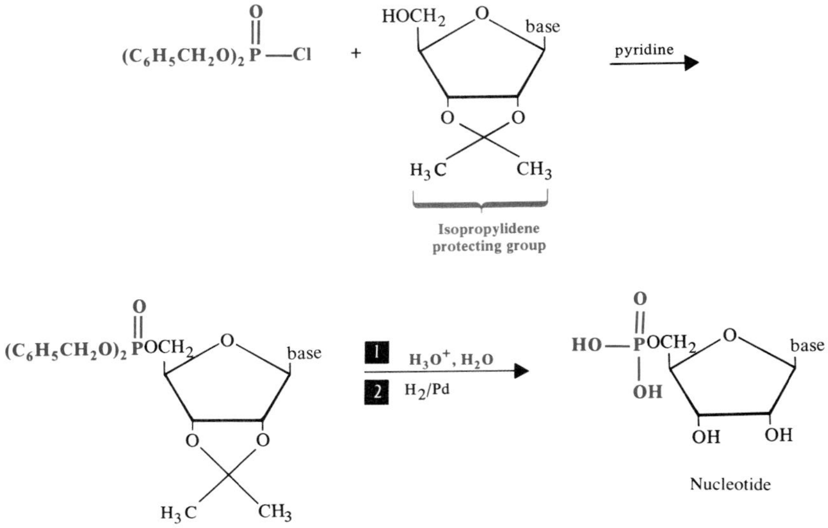

Isopropylidene
protecting group

Nucleotide

Mild acid-catalyzed hydrolysis removes the isopropylidene group, and hydrogenolysis cleaves the benzyl phosphate bonds.

Problem 25.5

(a) What kind of linkage is involved in the isopropylidene-protected nucleoside and why is it susceptible to mild acid-catalyzed hydrolysis? (b) How might such a protecting group be installed?

25.3A MEDICAL APPLICATIONS

In the early 1950s, Gertrude Elion and George Hitchings (of the Wellcome Research Laboratories) discovered that 6-mercaptopurine had antitumor and antileukemic properties. This discovery led to the development of other purine derivatives and related compounds, including nucleosides, of considerable medical importance.* Three examples are the following.

---

* Elion and Hitchings shared the 1988 Nobel Prize for their work in the development of chemotherapeutic agents derived from purines.

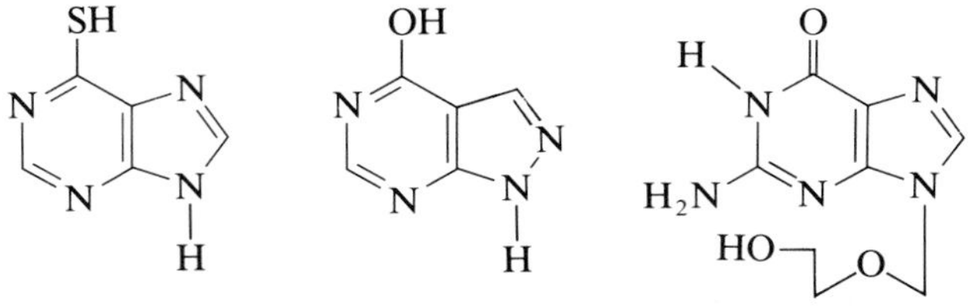

6-Mercaptopurine   Allopurinol   Acyclovir

6-Mercaptopurine is used in combination with other chemotherapeutic agents to treat acute leukemia in children, and almost 80% of the children treated are now cured. Allopurinol, another purine derivative, is a standard therapy for the treatment of gout. Acyclovir, a nucleoside that lacks two carbon atoms of its ribose ring, is highly effective in treating diseases caused by certain herpes viruses, including *herpes simplex* type 1 (fever blisters), type 2 (genital herpes), and varicella-zoster (shingles).

25.4 DEOXYRIBONUCLEIC ACID: DNA

25.4A PRIMARY STRUCTURE

Nucleotides bear the same relation to a nucleic acid that amino acids do to a protein; they are its monomeric units. The connecting links in proteins are amide groups; in nucleic acids they are phosphate ester linkages. Phosphate esters link the 3′-OH of one ribose (or deoxyribose) with the 5′-OH of another. This makes the nucleic acid a long unbranched chain with a "backbone" of sugar and phosphate units with heterocyclic bases protruding from the chain at regular intervals (Fig. 25.5). We would indicate the direction of the bases in Fig. 25.5 in the following way:

$$5' \longleftarrow A-T-G-C \longrightarrow 3'$$

It is, as we shall see, the **base sequence** along the chain of DNA that contains the encoded genetic information. The sequence of bases can be determined through techniques based on selective enzymatic hydrolyses. The actual base sequences have been worked out for a number of nucleic acids (Section 25.6).

25.4B SECONDARY STRUCTURE

It was the now-classic proposal of Watson and Crick (made in 1953 and verified shortly thereafter by the X-ray analysis of Wilkins) that gave a model for the secondary structure of DNA. The secondary structure of DNA is especially important because it enables us to understand how the genetic information is preserved, how it can be passed on during the process of cell division, and how it can be transcribed to provide a template for protein synthesis.

Of prime importance to Watson and Crick's proposal was an earlier observation (late 1940s) by E. Chargaff that certain regularities can be seen in the percentages of heterocyclic bases obtained from the DNA of a variety of species. Table 25.1 gives results that are typical of those that can be obtained.

Chargaff pointed out that for all species examined:

1. The total mole percentage of purines is approximately equal to that of the pyrimidines, that is, (%G + %A)/(%C + %T) ≃ 1.

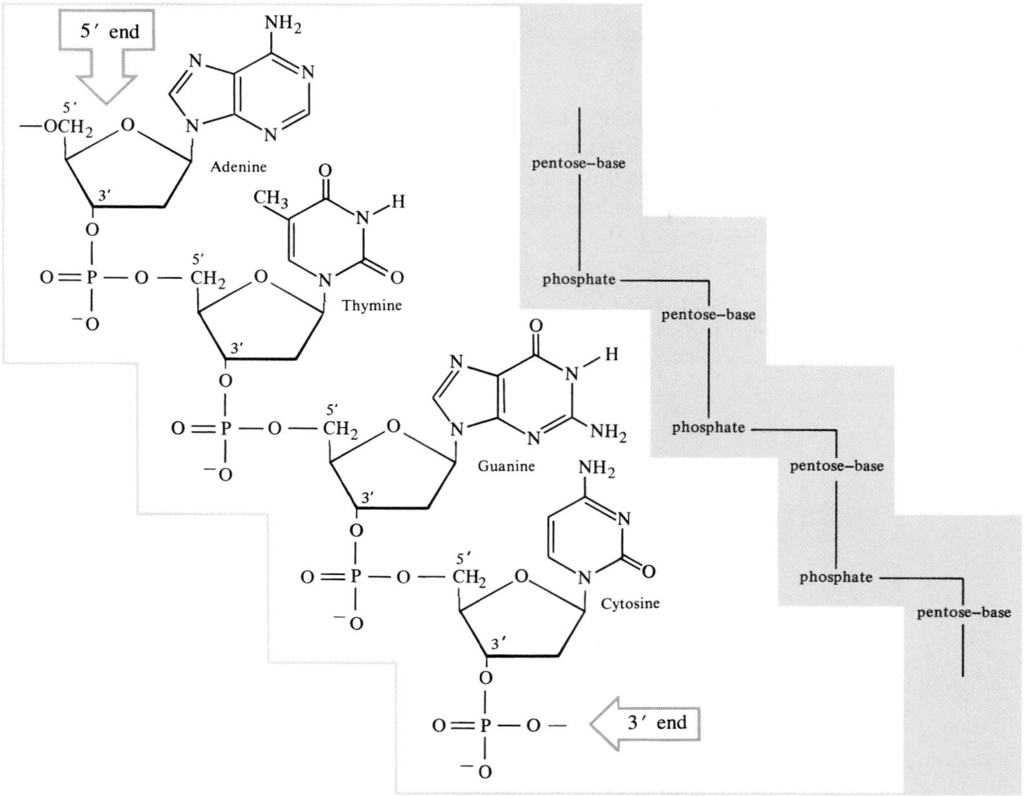

FIGURE 25.5 Hypothetical segment of a single DNA chain showing how phosphate ester groups link the 3'- and 5'-OH groups of deoxyribose units. RNA has a similar structure with two exceptions: A hydroxyl replaces a hydrogen atom at the 2'-position of each ribose unit and uracil replaces thymine.

TABLE 25.1 DNA composition of various species

SPECIES	BASE PROPORTIONS (mol %)							
	G	A	C	T	$\dfrac{G+A}{C+T}$	$\dfrac{A+T}{G+C}$	$\dfrac{A}{T}$	$\dfrac{G}{C}$
Sarcina lutea	37.1	13.4	37.1	12.4	1.02	0.35	1.08	1.00
Escherichia coli K12	24.9	26.0	25.2	23.9	1.08	1.00	1.09	0.99
Wheat germ	22.7	27.3	22.8[a]	27.1	1.00	1.19	1.01	1.00
Bovine thymus	21.5	28.2	22.5[a]	27.8	0.96	1.27	1.01	0.96
Staphylococcus aureus	21.0	30.8	19.0	29.2	1.11	1.50	1.05	1.11
Human thymus	19.9	30.9	19.8	29.4	1.01	1.52	1.05	1.01
Human liver	19.5	30.3	19.9	30.3	0.98	1.54	1.00	0.98

[a] Cytosine + methylcytosine.
From *Principles of Biochemistry* by A. White, P. Handler, and E. L. Smith. Copyright © 1964 by McGraw–Hill, Inc. Used with permission of McGraw–Hill Book Company, New York.

2. The mole percentage of adenine is nearly equal to that of thymine (i.e., %A/%T ≃ 1) and the mole percentage of guanine is nearly equal to that of cytosine (i.e., %G/%C ≃ 1).

Chargaff also noted that the ratio that varies from species to species is the ratio (%A + %T)/(%G + %C). He noted, moreover, that while this ratio is characteristic of the DNA of a given species, it is the same for DNA obtained from different tissues of the same animal, and does not vary appreciably with the age or conditions of growth of individual organisms within the same species.

Watson and Crick also had X-ray data that gave them the bond lengths and angles of the purines and pyrimidines of model compounds. In addition, they had data from Wilkins that indicated an unusually long repeat distance, 34 Å, in natural DNA.

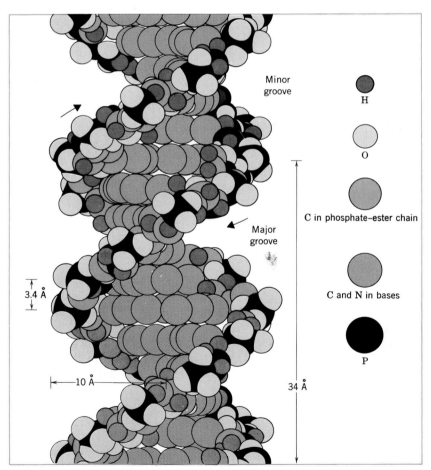

FIGURE 25.6 A molecular model of a portion of the DNA double helix. (Adapted from *Chemistry and Biochemistry: A Comprehensive Introduction* by A. L. Neal. Copyright © 1971 by McGraw–Hill Inc. Used with permission of McGraw–Hill Book Company, New York.)

Reasoning from these data, Watson and Crick proposed a double helix as a model for the secondary structure of DNA. According to this model, two nucleic acid chains are held together by hydrogen bonds between base pairs on opposite strands. This double chain is wound into a helix with both chains sharing the same axis. The base pairs are on the inside of the helix and the sugar–phosphate backbone on the outside (Fig. 25.6). The pitch of the helix is such that 10 successive nucleotide pairs give rise to one complete turn in 34 Å (the repeat distance). The exterior width of the spiral is about 20 Å and the internal distance between 1′-positions of ribose units on opposite chains is about 11 Å.

Using molecular scale models, Watson and Crick observed that the internal distance of the double helix is such that it allows only a purine–pyrimidine type of hydrogen bonding between base pairs. Purine–purine base pairs do not occur because they would be too large to fit, and pyrimidine–pyrimidine base pairs do not occur because they would be too far apart to form effective hydrogen bonds.

Watson and Crick went one crucial step further in their proposal. Assuming that the oxygen-containing heterocyclic bases existed in keto forms, they argued that base pairing through hydrogen bonds can occur in only a specific way:

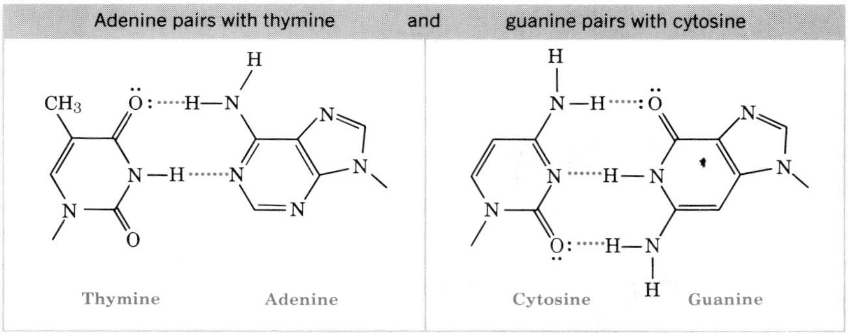

Adenine pairs with thymine   and   guanine pairs with cytosine

Thymine   Adenine   Cytosine   Guanine

The bond lengths of these base pairs are shown in Fig. 25.7.

Specific base pairing of this kind is consistent with Chargaff's finding that the %A/ %T ≃ 1 and that the %G/%C ≃ 1.

Specific base pairing also means that the two chains of DNA are complementary. Wherever adenine appears in one chain, thymine must appear opposite it in the other; wherever cytosine appears in one chain, guanine must appear in the other (Fig. 25.8).

Notice that while the sugar–phosphate backbone of DNA is completely regular, the sequence of heterocyclic base pairs along the backbone can assume many different permutations. This is important because it is the precise sequence of base pairs that carries the genetic information. Notice, too, that one chain of the double strand is the complement of the other. By knowing the sequence of bases along one chain, one can write down the sequence along the other, because A always pairs with T and G always pairs with C. It is this complementarity of the two strands that explains how a DNA molecule replicates itself at the time of cell division and thereby passes on the genetic information to each of the two daughter cells.

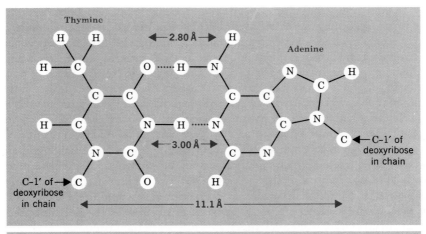

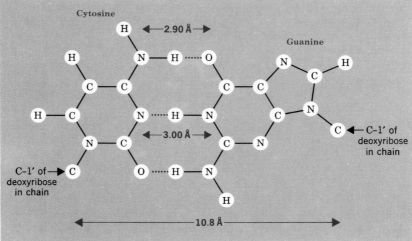

FIGURE 25.7 Dimensions of thymine–adenine and cytosine–guanine base pairs. The dimensions are such that they allow the formation of strong hydrogen bonds and also allow the base pairs to fit inside the two phosphate–ribose chains of the double helix. [Adapted from L. Pauling and R. B. Corey, *Arch. Biochem. Biophys.,* **1956,** *65,* 164.]

25.4C REPLICATION OF DNA

Just prior to cell division the double strand of DNA begins to unwind at one end. Complementary strands are formed along each chain (Fig. 25.9). Each chain acts, in effect, as a template, for the formation of its complement. When unwinding and duplication is complete, there are two identical DNA molecules where only one had existed before. These two molecules can then be passed on, one to each daughter cell.

Problem 25.6

(a) There are approximately 6 billion base pairs in the DNA of a single human cell. Assuming that this DNA exists as a double helix, calculate the length of all

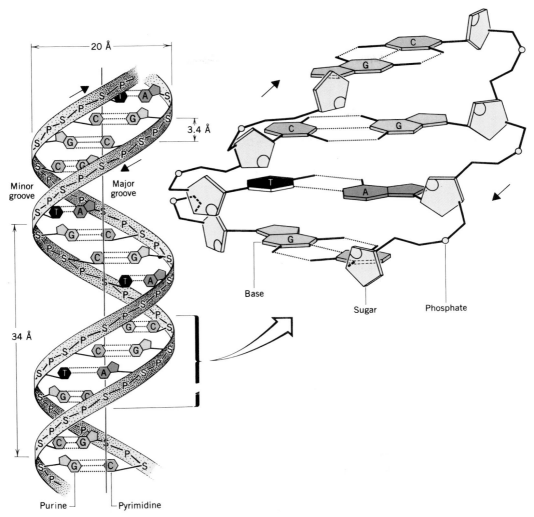

FIGURE 25.8 Diagram of the DNA double helix showing complementary base pairing. The arrows indicate the $3' \rightarrow 5'$ direction.

the DNA contained in a human cell. (b) The weight of DNA in a single human cell is 6×10^{-12} g. Assuming that the earth's population is about 3 billion, we can conclude that all of the genetic information that gave rise to all human beings now alive was once contained in the DNA of a corresponding number of fertilized ova. What is the total weight of this DNA? (The volume that this DNA would occupy is approximately that of a raindrop, yet, if the individual molecules were laid end to end, they would stretch to the moon and back almost eight times.)

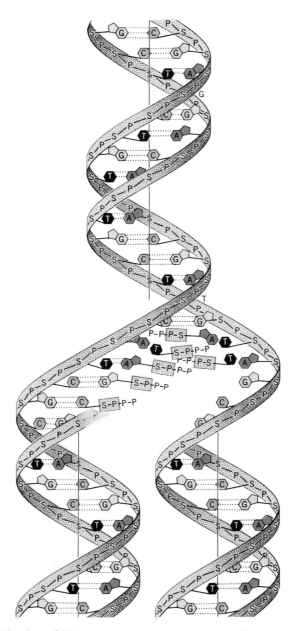

FIGURE 25.9 Replication of DNA. The double strand unwinds from one end and complementary strands are formed along each chain.

Problem 25.7

(a) The most stable tautomeric form of guanine is the lactam form. This is the form normally present in DNA and, as we have seen, it pairs specifically with cytosine. If guanine tautomerizes to the abnormal lactim form, it pairs with thymine instead. Write structural formulas showing the hydrogen bonds in this abnormal base pair.

| **Lactam form** | **Lactim form** |
| of guanine | of guanine |

(b) Improper base pairings that result from tautomerizations occurring during the process of DNA replication have been suggested as a source of spontaneous mutations. We saw in part (a) that if a tautomerization of guanine occurred at the proper moment, it could lead to the introduction of thymine (instead of cytosine) into its complementary DNA chain. What error would this new DNA chain introduce into *its* complementary strand during the next replication even if no further tautomerizations take place?

Problem 25.8

Mutations can also be caused chemically, and nitrous acid is one of the most potent chemical **mutagens.** One explanation that has been suggested for the mutagenic effect of nitrous acid is the deamination reactions that it produces with purines and pyrimidines bearing amino groups. When, for example, an adenine-containing nucleotide is treated with nitrous acid, it is converted to a hypoxanthine derivative:

| **Adenine** | **Hypoxanthine** |
| nucleotide | nucleotide |

(a) Basing your answer on reactions you have seen before, what are likely intermediates in the adenine $\longrightarrow$ hypoxanthine interconversion? (b) Adenine normally pairs with thymine in DNA, but hypoxanthine pairs with cytosine. Show the hydrogen bonds of a hypoxanthine–cytosine base pair. (c) Show what errors an adenine $\longrightarrow$ hypoxanthine interconversion would generate in DNA through two replications.

25.5 RNA AND PROTEIN SYNTHESIS

Soon after the Watson–Crick hypothesis was published, scientists began to extend it to yield what Crick called "the central dogma of molecular genetics." This dogma stated that genetic information flows from:

$$\text{DNA} \longrightarrow \text{RNA} \longrightarrow \text{proteins*}$$

* There are viruses, called retroviruses, in which information flows from RNA to DNA. The virus that causes AIDS is a retrovirus.

The synthesis of protein is, of course, all important to a cell's function because proteins (as enzymes) catalyze its reactions. Even the very primitive cells of bacteria require as many as 3000 different enzymes. This means that the DNA molecules of these cells must contain a corresponding number of genes to direct the synthesis of these proteins. A gene is that segment of the DNA molecule that contains the information necessary to direct the synthesis of one protein (or one polypeptide).

DNA is found primarily in the nucleus of the cell. Protein synthesis takes place primarily in that part of the cell called the *cytoplasm*. Protein synthesis requires that two major processes take place; the first takes place in the cell nucleus, the second in the cytoplasm. The first is **transcription,** a process in which the genetic message is transcribed on to a form of RNA called messenger RNA (mRNA). The second process involves two other forms of RNA, called ribosomal RNA (rRNA) and transfer RNA (tRNA).

25.5A MESSENGER RNA SYNTHESIS — TRANSCRIPTION

Protein synthesis begins in the cell nucleus with the synthesis of mRNA. Part of the DNA double helix unwinds sufficiently to expose on a single chain a portion corresponding to at least one gene. Ribonucleotides, present in the cell nucleus, assemble along the exposed DNA chain pairing with the bases of DNA. The pairing patterns are the same as those in DNA with the exception that in RNA uracil replaces thymine. The ribonucleotide units of mRNA are joined into a chain by an enzyme called *RNA polymerase.* This process is illustrated in Fig. 25.10.

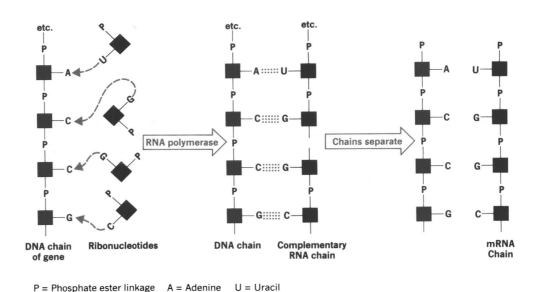

P = Phosphate ester linkage A = Adenine U = Uracil

■ = Deoxyribose C = Cytosine

■ = Ribose G = Guanine

FIGURE 25.10 Transcription of the genetic code from DNA to mRNA.

Problem 25.9

Write structural formulas showing how the keto form of uracil (Section 25.2) in mRNA can pair with adenine in DNA through hydrogen bond formation.

After mRNA has been synthesized in the cell nucleus, it migrates into the cytoplasm where, as we shall see, it acts as a template for protein synthesis.

25.5B RIBOSOMES — rRNA

Scattered throughout the cytoplasm of most cells are small bodies called ribosomes. Ribosomes of *Escherichia coli (E. coli),* for example, are about 180 Å in diameter and are composed of approximately 60% RNA (ribosomal RNA) and 40% protein. They apparently exist as two associated subunits called the 50S and 30S subunits (Fig. 25.11); together they form a 70S ribosome.* Although the ribosomes are at the site of protein synthesis, rRNA itself does not direct protein synthesis. Instead, a number of ribosomes become attached to a chain of mRNA and form what is called a **polysome.** It is along the polysome — with mRNA acting as the template — that protein synthesis takes place. One of the functions of rRNA is to bind the ribosome to the mRNA chain.

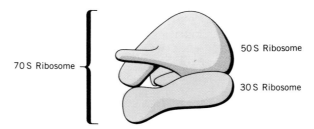

50 S Ribosome

70 S Ribosome

30 S Ribosome

FIGURE 25.11 A 70S ribosome showing the two subunits.

25.5C TRANSFER RNA

Transfer RNA has a very low molecular weight when compared to that of mRNA or rRNA. Transfer RNA, consequently, is much more soluble than mRNA or rRNA and is sometimes referred to as soluble RNA. The function of tRNA is to transport amino acids to specific areas of the mRNA of the polysome. There are, therefore, at least 20 different forms of tRNA, one for each of the 20 amino acids that are incorporated into proteins.†

The structures of most tRNAs have been determined. They are composed of a relatively small number of nucleotide units (70–90 units) folded into several loops or arms through base pairing along the chain (Fig. 25.12). One arm always terminates in the sequence cytosine–cytosine–adenine. It is to this arm that a specific amino acid becomes attached *through an ester* linkage to the 3'-OH of the terminal adenosine.

*S stands for svedberg unit; it is used in describing the behavior of proteins in an ultracentrifuge.

†Although proteins are composed of 22 different amino acids, protein synthesis requires only 20. Proline is converted to hydroxyproline and cysteine is converted to cystine after synthesis of the polypeptide chain has taken place.

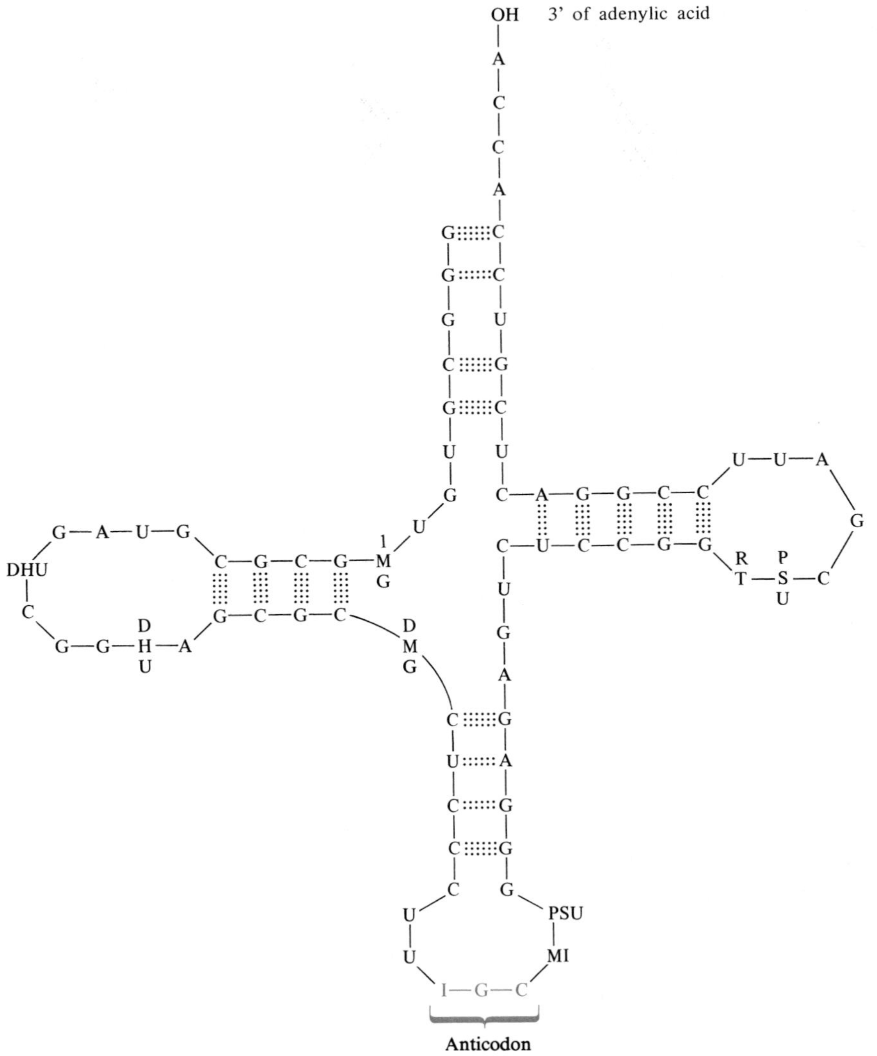

FIGURE 25.12 Structure of a tRNA isolated from yeast that has the specific function of transferring alanine residues. Transfer RNAs often contain unusual nucleosides. PSU = pseudouridine, RT = ribothymidine, MI = 1-methylinosine, I = inosine, DMG = N^2-methylguanosine, DHU = 4,5-dihydrouridine, 1 MG = 1-methylguanosine.

This attachment reaction is catalyzed by an enzyme that is specific for the tRNA and for the amino acid. The specificity may grow out of the enzyme's ability to recognize base sequences along other arms of the tRNA.

At the loop of still another arm is a specific sequence of bases, called the **antico-don.** The anticodon is highly important because it allows the tRNA to bind with a specific site—called the **codon**—of mRNA. The order in which amino acids are brought by their tRNA units to the mRNA strand is determined by the sequence of codons. This sequence, therefore, constitutes a genetic message. Individual units of that message (the individual words, each corresponding to an amino acid) are triplets of nucleotides.

25.5D THE GENETIC CODE

Which triplet on mRNA corresponds to which amino acid is called the genetic code (see Table 25.2). The code must be in the form of three bases, not one or two because there are 20 different amino acids used in protein synthesis but there are only four different bases in mRNA. If only two bases were used, there would be only 4^2 or 16 possible combinations, a number too small to accommodate all of the possible amino acids. However, with a three-base code, 4^3 or 64 different sequences are possible. This is far more than are needed, and it allows for multiple ways of specifying an amino acid. It also allows for sequences that punctuate protein synthesis, sequences that say, in effect, "start here" and "end here."

Both methionine (Met) and N-formylmethionine (Met$_{formyl}$) have the same mRNA code (AUG); however, N-formylmethionine is carried by a different tRNA from that which carries methionine. N-Formylmethionine appears to be the first

TABLE 25.2   The messenger RNA genetic code

AMINO ACID	BASE SEQUENCE $5' \rightarrow 3'$	AMINO ACID	BASE SEQUENCE $5' \rightarrow 3'$	AMINO ACID	BASE SEQUENCE $5' \rightarrow 3'$
Ala	GCA	His	CAC	Ser	AGC
	GCC		CAU		AGU
	GCG				UCA
	GCU	Ile	AUA		UCG
			AUC		UCC
Arg	AGA		AUU		UCU
	AGG				
	CGA	Leu	CUA	Thr	ACA
	CGC		CUC		ACC
	CGG		CUG		ACG
	CGU		CUU		ACU
			UUA	Trp	UGG
Asn	AAC		UUG	Tyr	UGG
	AAU				UAC
		Lys	AAA		UAU
Asp	GAC		AAG		
	GAU			Val	GUA
		Met	AUG		GUG
Cys	UGC				GUC
	UGU	Phe	UUU		GUU
			UUC		
Gln	CAA			Chain initiation	
	CAG	Pro	CCA		
			CCC	Met$_{formyl}$	AUG
Glu	GAA		CCG		
	GAG		CCU		
Gly	GGA				
	GGC			Chain termination	UAA
	GGG				UAG
	GGU				UGA

amino acid incorporated into the chain of proteins in bacteria, and the tRNA that carries Met$_{formyl}$ appears to be the punctuation mark that says "start here." Before the polypeptide synthesis is complete, N-formylmethionine is removed from the protein chain by an enzymatic hydrolysis.

$$CH_3SCH_2CH_2CHCO_2H$$
$$|$$
$$NH$$
$$|$$
$$C{=}O$$
$$|$$
$$H$$

N-Formylmethionine

We are now in a position to see how the synthesis of a hypothetical polypeptide might take place. Let us imagine that a long strand of mRNA is in the cytoplasm of a cell and that it is in contact with ribosomes. Also in the cytoplasm are the 20 different amino acids, each acylated to its own specific tRNA.

As shown in Fig. 25.13, a tRNA bearing Met$_{formyl}$ uses its anticodon to associate with the proper codon (AUG) on that portion of mRNA that is in contact with a ribosome. The next triplet of bases on this particular mRNA chain is AAA; this is the codon that specifies lysine. A lysyl-tRNA with the matching anticodon UUU attaches itself to this site. The two amino acids, Met$_{formyl}$ and Lys, are now in the proper position for an enzyme to join them in peptide linkage. After this happens, the ribosome moves down the chain so that it is in contact with the next codon. This one, GUA, specifies valine. A tRNA bearing valine (and with the proper anticodon) binds itself to this site. Another enzymatic reaction takes place attaching valine to the polypeptide chain. Then the whole process repeats itself again and again. The ribosome moves along the mRNA chain, other tRNAs move up with their amino acids, new peptide bonds are formed, and the polypeptide chain grows. At some point an enzymatic reaction removes Met$_{formyl}$ from the beginning of the chain. Finally, when the chain is the proper length the ribosome reaches a punctuation mark, UAA, saying "stop here." The ribosome separates from the mRNA chain and so, too, does the protein.

Even before the polypeptide chain is fully grown, it begins to form its own specific secondary and tertiary structure (Fig. 25.14). This happens because its primary structure is correct—its amino acids are ordered in just the right way. Hydrogen bonds form, giving rise to specific segments of α helix, pleated sheet, and coil or loop. Then the whole thing folds and bends; enzymes install disulfide linkages, so that when the chain is fully grown, the whole protein has just the shape it needs to do its job.

If this protein happens to be lysozyme, it has a deep cleft, or jaw, where a specific polysaccharide fits. And if it is lysozyme, and a certain bacterium wanders by, that jaw begins to work; it bites its first polysaccharide in half.

In the meantime, other ribosomes nearer the beginning of the mRNA chain are already moving along, each one synthesizing another molecule of the polypeptide. The time required to synthesize a protein depends, of course, on the number of amino residues it contains, but indications are that each ribosome can cause 150 peptide bonds to be formed each minute. Thus, a protein, such as lysozyme, with 129 amino acid residues requires less than a minute for its synthesis. However, if four ribosomes are working their way along a single mRNA chain, the polysome can produce a lysozyme molecule every 13 seconds.

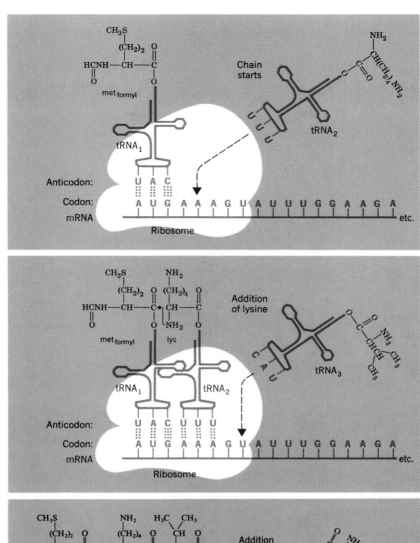

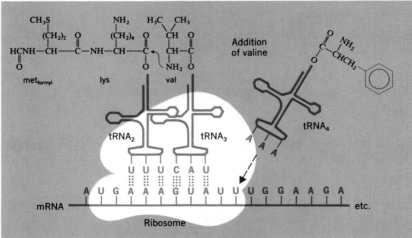

FIGURE 25.13 Step-by-step growth of a polypeptide chain with messenger RNA acting as a template. Transfer RNAs carry amino acid residues to the site of mRNA that is in contact with a ribosome. Codon–anticodon pairing occurs between mRNA and RNA at the ribosomal surface. An enzymatic reaction joins the amino acid residues through an amide linkage. After the first amide bond is formed the ribosome moves to the next codon on mRNA. A new tRNA arrives, pairs, and transfers its amino acid residue to the growing peptide chain, and so on.

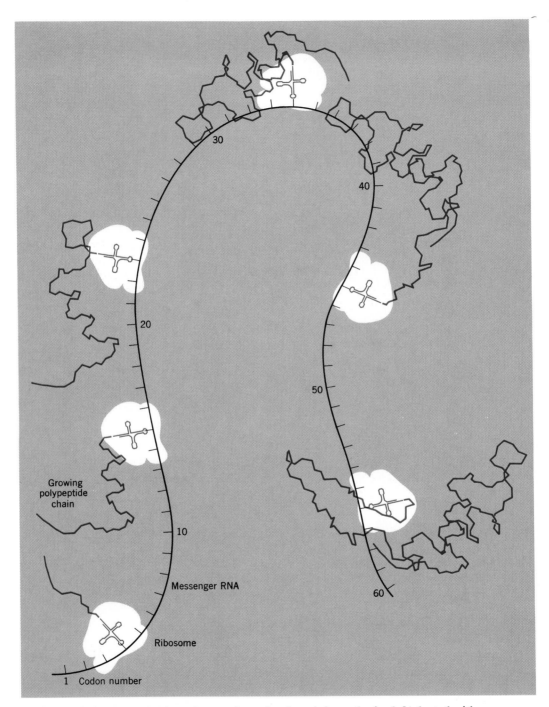

FIGURE 25.14 The folding of a protein molecule as it is synthesized. [Adapted with permission from D. C. Phillips, "The Three-Dimensional Structure of an Enzyme Molecule." Copyright © 1966 Scientific American, Inc. All rights reserved.]

But why, we might ask, is all this protein synthesis necessary—particularly in a fully grown organism? The answer is that proteins are not permanent; they are not synthesized once and then left intact in the cell for the lifetime of the organism. They are synthesized when and where they are needed. Then they are taken apart, back to amino acids; enzymes disassemble enzymes. Some amino acids are metabolized for energy; others—new ones—come in from the food that is eaten and the whole process begins again.

Problem 25.10

A segment of DNA has the following sequence of bases:

$$\ldots A \ C \ C \ C \ C \ C \ A \ A \ A \ A \ T \ G \ T \ C \ G \ldots$$

(a) What sequence of bases would appear in mRNA transcribed from this segment? (b) Assume that the first base in this mRNA is the beginning of a codon. What order of amino acids would be translated into a polypeptide synthesized along this segment? (c) Give anticodons for each tRNA associated with the translation in part (b).

Problem 25.11

(a) Using the first codon given for each amino acid in Table 25.2, write the base sequence of mRNA that would translate the synthesis of the following penta-peptide:

$$Arg \cdot Ile \cdot Cys \cdot Tyr \cdot Val$$

(b) What base sequence in DNA would transcribe a synthesis of the mRNA?
(c) What anticodons would appear in the tRNAs involved in the pentapeptide synthesis?

Problem 25.12

Explain how an error of a single base in each strand of DNA could bring about the amino acid residue error that causes sickle-cell anemia (Section 24.6C).

25.6 DETERMINING THE BASE SEQUENCE OF DNA

The basic strategy used to sequence DNA resembles the methods used to sequence proteins (Section 24.5). Because molecules of DNA are so large, it is first necessary to cleave them into smaller, manageable fragments. These fragments are sequenced individually, and then by identifying points of overlap, the fragments are ordered so as to reveal the nucleotide sequence of the original nucleic acid.

The first part of the process is accomplished by using enzymes called **restriction endonucleases.** These enzymes cleave double-stranded DNA at specific base sequences. Several hundred restriction endonucleases are now known. One, for example, called *Alu*I, cleaves the sequence AGCT between G and C. Another, called

*Eco*RI, cleaves GAATTC between G and A. Most of the sites recognized by restriction enzymes have sequences of base pairs with the same order in both strands when read from the 5′ direction to the 3′ direction. For example:

$$5' \longleftarrow G-A-A-T-T-C \longrightarrow 3'$$
$$3' \longleftarrow C-T-T-A-A-G \longrightarrow 5'$$

Such sequences are known as **palindromes.** (Palindromes are words or sentences that read the same forward or backward. Examples are "radar", or "Madam, I'm Adam.")

Sequencing of the fragments (called restriction fragments) can be done chemically (a method described below) or with the aid of enzymes. The first chemical method was introduced in 1977 by Allan M. Maxam and Walter Gilbert of Harvard University; the first enzymatic method was introduced in the same year by Frederick Sanger.*

25.6A CHEMICAL SEQUENCING

The double-stranded restriction fragment to be sequenced is first enzymatically tagged at the 5′ end with a phosphate group containing radioactive phosphate. After this, the strands are separated and isolated. Next, the labeled, single-stranded fragment is treated with reagents that attack specific bases, modifying them in a way that allows cleavage of the chain next to the specific bases. For example, if we had a chain like the following (reading from 5′ → 3′, left to right),

$$^{32}P-GCAATCACGTC$$

treating the fragment with hydrazine (NH_2NH_2) in 1.5 M NaCl, will (in a way that we cannot go into here) attack cytosine residues so that subsequent treatment with piperidine (Section 19.1B) will cause cleavage at the 5′ side of C residues. This will produce the following set of 5′-labeled fragments.

$$^{32}P-GCAATCACGT$$
$$^{32}P-GCAATCA$$
$$^{32}P-G$$

These fragments can then be separated by a technique called **gel electrophoresis** (Fig. 25.15). A sample containing a mixture of the fragments is placed at one end of the thin strip of a gel made up of a polyacrylamide $[\!-\!CH_2CHCONH_2\!-\!)_{\overline{n}}]$. The gel is designed to separate the radiolabeled fragments when a voltage difference is applied across the ends of the gel. The fragments move through the gel at different rates depending on the number of negatively charged phosphate groups that they contain and on their size. The smaller fragments move faster. After separation, the gel is placed in contact with a photographic plate. Radiation from a fragment containing a radioactive 5′-phosphate causes a dark spot to appear on the plate opposite where the fragment is located in the gel. The exposed plate is called an **autoradiograph** and this technique is called **autoradiography.** Unlabeled fragments from the middle of the chain are present, but these do not show up on the plate and are therefore ignored.

---

* Gilbert and Sanger shared the Nobel Prize in 1980 with Paul Berg for their work on nucleic acids. Sanger (Section 24.5) who pioneered the sequencing of proteins had won an earlier Nobel Prize in 1958 for the determination of the structure of insulin.

25.6 DETERMINING THE BASE SEQUENCE OF DNA

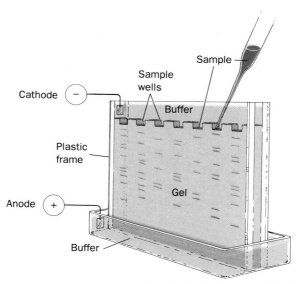

FIGURE 25.15 An apparatus for gel electrophoresis. Samples are applied in the slots at the top of the gel. Application of a voltage difference causes the samples to move. The samples move in parallel lanes. (From D. Voet and J. G. Voet, *Biochemistry,* Wiley, New York, 1990, p. 97. Used with permission.)

The DNA to be sequenced may be cleaved next to specific pairs by subjecting it in separate aliquots to four different treatments. In addition to cleavage next to **C only,** mentioned earlier, there are reagents that will cleave on the 5′ side of **G only,** on the 5′ side of **A and G,** and on the 5′ side of **C and T.** After cleavage, the separate aliquots are subjected to simultaneous electrophoresis in four parallel tracks of the gel. After autoradiography, results like those in Fig. 25.16 allow reading of the DNA sequence directly from the gel.

Starting from the bottom: There is a dark spot in the A + G track but none in the G track. This indicates that the smallest labeled fragment was A. The same pattern occurs at the second level indicating another A. The third level up is dark in the C track and light in the C + T track, indicating C as the third base in the sequence. The fourth is A again, and so on. The process is so regular that computerized devices are now used to aid in reading gels.

Developments in DNA sequencing have been so rapid that DNA sequencing of the gene corresponding to a protein is now the easier method for determining a protein's amino acid sequence. (Since the genetic code is known, we can deduce the amino acid sequence of the protein from the base sequence of the DNA that codes for the protein.) A recent high point in DNA sequencing was the determination of the entire 172,282 base pair sequence of Epstein – Barr virus (human herpes virus). Plans are now being made to sequence the 2.9 billion base pairs of the 100,000 genes that constitute the human genome. This task is so large, however, that even if a sequencing rate of 1 million base pairs a day can be achieved, it will take almost 10 years to complete.

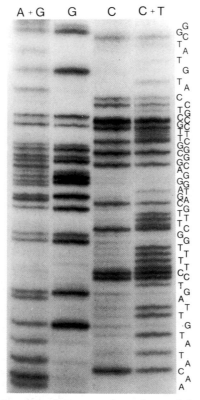

FIGURE 25.16 An autoradiograph of a sequencing gel containing fragments of a DNA segment that was subjected to chemical sequencing. The DNA was labeled with ^{32}P at its 5′ end. The deduced sequence of the DNA fragment is written beside the gel. Since the shorter fragments are at the bottom of the gel, the 5′ ⟶ 3′ direction in the sequence corresponds to the upward direction in the gel. (Courtesy of David Dressler, Harvard University Medical School. From D. Voet and J. G. Voet, *Biochemistry,* Wiley, New York, 1990, p. 832. Used with permission.)

25.7 LABORATORY SYNTHESIS OF OLIGONUCLEOTIDES

A gene is a blueprint for a protein that is encoded in a particular sequence of base pairs of DNA. What do the individual genes do, and how do they do it? These are the kinds of questions being addressed by biologists and biochemists today. In doing so, they are using a completely new approach to studying genetics, called **reverse genetics.** The traditional approach to genetics involves randomly altering or deleting genes by inducing mutations in an organism, and then observing the effects in its progeny. With higher organisms, such as vertebrates, there are serious disadvantages to this approach. The generations are inconveniently long, the number of offspring are few, and the most interesting mutations are usually lethal, making them difficult to propagate and study.

The approach of reverse genetics is to start with a cloned gene and to manipulate it in order to find out how it functions. One approach to this manipulation is to synthesize strands of DNA (oligonucleotides with about 15 bases) that are complementary to particular portions of the gene. These synthetic oligonucleotides, called **antisense nucleotides,** are capable of binding with what is called the **sense** sequence of the DNA. In doing so, they can alter the activity of the gene, or even turn it off entirely. For example, if the sense portion of DNA in a gene read:

$$A—G—A—C—C—G—T—G—G$$

The antisense oligonucleotide would read:

$$T—C—T—G—G—C—A—C—C$$

The ability to deactivate specific genes in this way holds out great medical promise. Many viruses and bacteria, during their life cycles, use a method like this to regulate some of their own genes. The hope, therefore, is to synthesize antisense oligonucleotides that will seek out and destroy viruses in a person's cells by binding with crucial sequences of the viral DNA or RNA. Synthesis of such oligonucleotides is an active area of research today and is directed at many viral diseases, including AIDS.

Current methods for oligonucleotide synthesis are similar to those used to synthesize proteins, including the use of automated solid phase techniques (Section 24.7D). A suitably protected nucleotide is attached to a solid phase called a "controlled pore glass" or CPG (Fig. 25.17) through a linkage that can ultimately be cleaved. The next protected nucleotide in the form of a **phosphoramidite** is added, and coupling is brought about by a coupling agent, usually 1,2,3,4-tetrazole. The phosphite triester that results from the coupling is oxidized to phosphate triester with iodine, producing a chain that has been lengthened by one nucleotide. The **dimethoxytrityl (DMTr)** group used to protect the 5′ end of the added nucleotide is removed by treatment with acid and the steps **coupling, oxidation, detritylation** are repeated. (All the steps are carried out in nonaqueous solvents.) With automatic synthesizers the process can be repeated at least 50 times and the time for a complete cycle is 40 min or less. After the desired oligonucleotide has been synthesized, it is released from the solid support and the various protecting groups, including those on the bases, are removed.

25.8 THE POLYMERASE CHAIN REACTION

The polymerase chain reaction (PCR) is an extraordinarily simple and effective method for amplifying DNA sequences. Beginning with a single molecule of DNA, the polymerase chain reaction can generate 100 billion copies in a single afternoon. The reaction is easy to carry out; it requires only a few reagents, a test tube, and a source of heat.

The PCR has already had a major effect on molecular biology. It is being used in medicine to diagnose infectious and genetic diseases. One of the original aims in developing the PCR was to use it in increasing the speed and effectiveness of prenatal diagnosis of sickle-cell anemia (Section 24.6C). It is now being applied to the prenatal diagnosis of a number of other genetic diseases, including muscular dystrophy and cystic fibrosis. Among infectious diseases, the PCR has been used to detect cytomeglovirus and the viruses that cause AIDS, certain cervical carcinomas, hepatitis, measles, and Epstein – Barr disease.

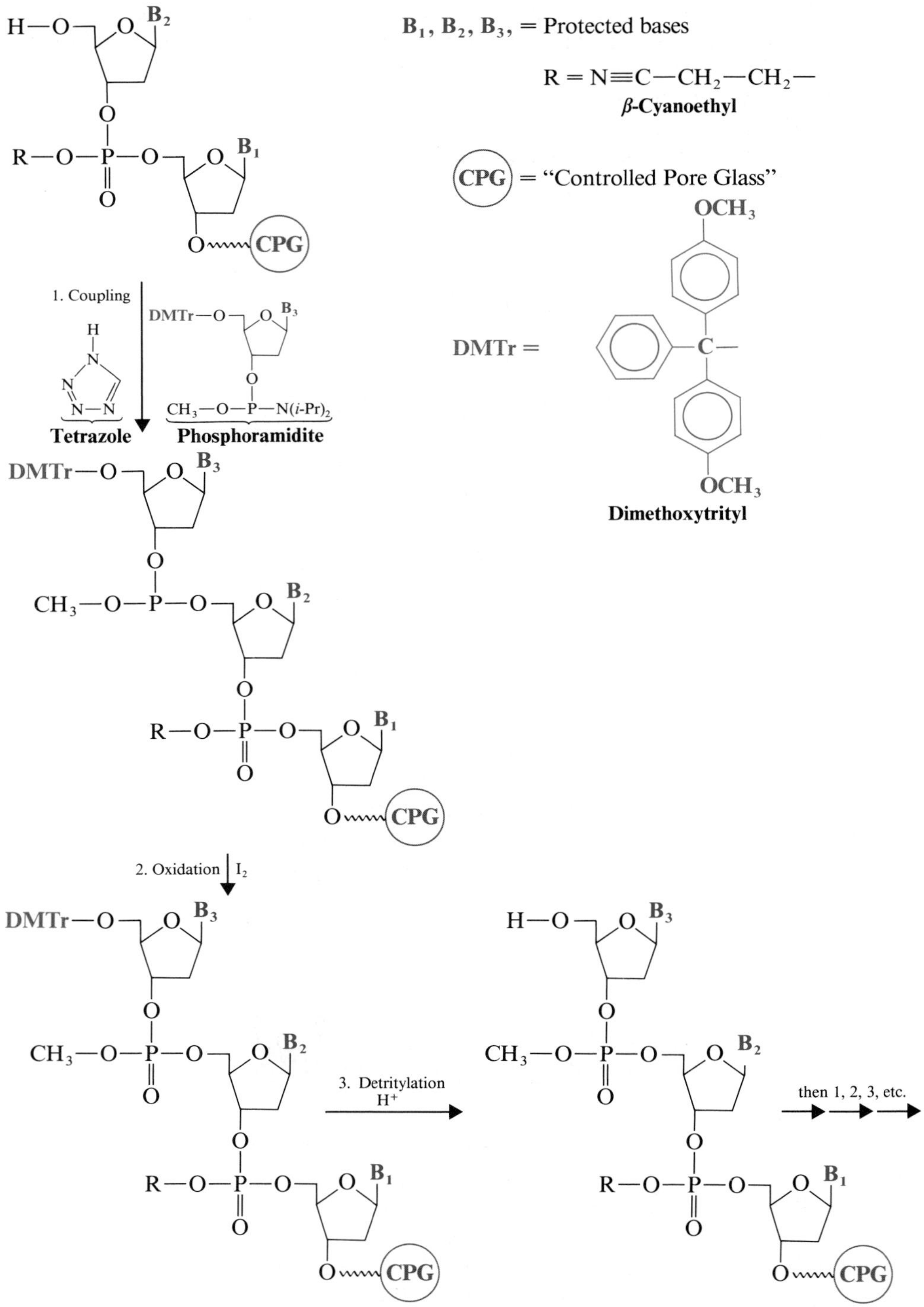

FIGURE 25.17 The steps involved in automated synthesis of oligonucleotides using the phosphoramidite coupling method.

25.8 THE POLYMERASE CHAIN REACTION

The PCR has been used in forensic sciences, in human genetics, and in evolutionary biology. The DNA sample that is copied may have come from a drop of blood or semen, or from a hair left at the scene of a crime. It may even have come from the brain of a mummy or from a 40,000-year-old wooly mammoth.

The PCR was invented by Kary B. Mullis and developed by him and his co-workers at Cetus Corporation. It makes use of the enzyme DNA polymerase, discovered in 1955 by Arthur Kornberg and his associates at Stanford University. In living

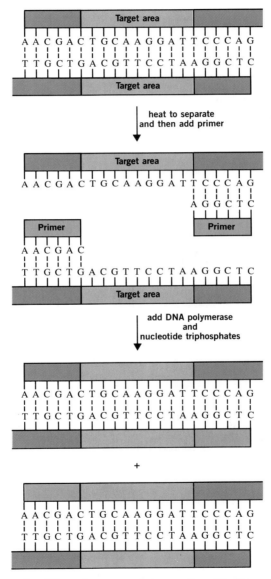

FIGURE 25.18 One cycle of the polymerase chain reaction. Heating separates the strands of DNA of the target to give two single-stranded templates. Primers, designed to complement the nucleotide sequences flanking the targets, anneal to each strand. DNA polymerase, in the presence of nucleotide triphosphates, catalyzes the synthesis of two pieces of DNA, each identical to the original target DNA.

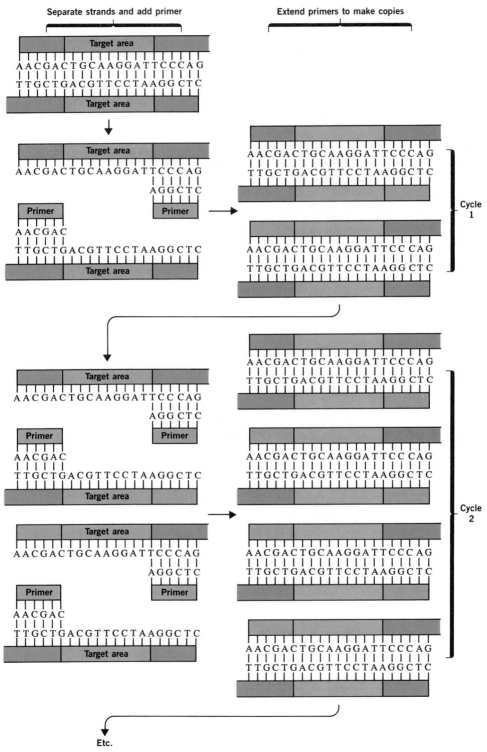

FIGURE 25.19 Each cycle of the polymerase chain reaction doubles the number of copies of the target area.

cells, DNA polymerases help repair and replicate DNA. The PCR makes use of a particular property of DNA polymerases: Their ability to attach additional nucleotides to a short oligonucleotide "primer" when the primer is bound to a complementary strand of DNA called a template. The nucleotides are attached at the 3′ end of the primer and the nucleotide that the polymerase attaches will be the one that is complementary to the base in the adjacent position on the template strand. If the adjacent template nucleotide is G, the polymerase adds C to the primer; if the adjacent template nucleotide is A, then the polymerase adds T, and so on. Polymerase repeats this process again and again as long as the requisite nucleotides (as triphosphates) are present in the solution, until it reaches the 5′ end of the template.

Figure 25.18 shows one cycle of the PCR in the way that it is usually carried out. Knowledge of the nucleotide sequence of the target of the PCR is not necessary. However, one must know the sequence of a small stretch on each side of the target in order to synthesize two single-stranded oligonucleotides (of ~20 nucleotides) that will act as the primers. The primers have to have nucleotide sequences that are complementary to the flanking sequences on each strand of DNA.

At the outset of the PCR, the double-stranded (duplex) DNA is heated to separate its strands. The primers (one for each strand) are added and annealed to their respective flanking sequences. DNA polymerase and nucleotide triphosphates are then added and the polymerase causes each primer to become extended across the target sequence of each strand. If the extension of a given primer is long enough, it will include the sequence complementary to the other primer. Consequently, each new extension product can, after the strands are separated, act as the template for another cycle.

Each cycle doubles the amount of target DNA (Fig. 25.19). This means that the amount of DNA increases exponentially. After n cycles, the amount of DNA will have increased 2^n times. After 10 cycles, there is roughly 1000 times as much DNA; after 20 cycles, roughly 1 million times as much. Application of the PCR is extremely rapid and has been automated; 25 cycles can be carried out in 1 hour.

SPECIAL TOPIC

M

PHOTOCHEMISTRY OF VISION

The chemical changes that occur when light impinges on the retina of the eye involve several of the phenomena that we have studied in earlier chapters. Central to an understanding of the visual process at the molecular level are two phenomena in particular: the absorption of light by conjugated polyenes and the interconversion of cis–trans isomers.

The retina of the human eye contains two types of receptor cells. Because of their shapes, these cells have been named *rods* and *cones.* Rods are located primarily at the periphery of the retina and are responsible for vision in dim light. Rods, however, are color-blind and "see" only in shades of gray. Cones are found mainly in the center of the retina and are responsible for vision in bright light. Cones also possess the pigments that are responsible for color vision.

Some animals do not possess both rods and cones. The retinas of pigeons contain only cones. Thus, while pigeons have color vision, they see only in the bright light of day. The retinas of owls, on the other hand, have only rods; owls see very well in dim light, but are color blind.

The chemical changes that occur in rods are much better understood than those in cones. For this reason we shall concern ourselves here with rod vision alone.

When light strikes rod cells, it is absorbed by a compound called rhodopsin. This initiates a series of chemical events that ultimately results in the transmission of a nerve impulse to the brain.

Our understanding of the chemical nature of rhodopsin and the conformational changes that occur when rhodopsin absorbs light has resulted largely from the research of George Wald and co-workers at Harvard University. Wald's research began in 1933 when he was a graduate student in Berlin; work with rhodopsin, however, began much earlier in other laboratories.

Rhodopsin was discovered in 1877 by the German physiologist Franz Boll. Boll noticed that the initial red-purple color of a pigment in the retina of frogs was "bleached" by the action of light. The bleaching process led first to a yellow retina and then to a colorless one. A year later, another German scientist, Willy Kuhne, isolated the red-purple pigment and named it, because of its color, *Sehpurpur* or "visual purple." The name visual purple is still commonly used for rhodopsin.

In 1952, Wald and one of his students, Ruth Hubbard, showed that the chromophore (light-absorbing group) of rhodopsin is the polyunsaturated aldehyde, 11-*cis*-retinal and a protein called opsin (Fig. M.1). The reaction is between the aldehyde group of 11-*cis*-retinal and an amino group on the chain of the protein and involves the loss of a molecule of water. Other secondary interactions involving —SH groups of the protein probably also hold the *cis*-retinal in place. The site on the chain of the protein is one on which *cis*-retinal fits precisely.

The conjugated polyunsaturated chain of 11-*cis*-retinal gives rhodopsin the ability to absorb light over a broad region of the visible spectrum. Figure M.2 shows the

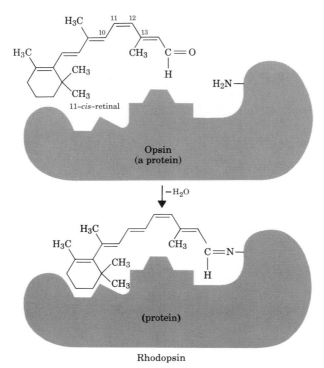

FIGURE M.1 The formation of rhodopsin from 11-*cis*-retinal and opsin.

absorption curve of rhodopsin in the visible region and compares it with the sensitivity curve for human rod vision. The fact that these two curves coincide provides strong evidence that rhodopsin is the light-sensitive material in rod vision.

When rhodopsin absorbs a photon of light, the 11-*cis*-retinal chromophore isomerizes to the all-trans form. The first photoproduct is an intermediate called bathorhodopsin, a compound that has about 35 kcal mol^{-1} more energy than rhodopsin. Bathorhodopsin then, through a series of steps, becomes metarhodopsin II (also all-trans). The high energy of the all-trans chromophore–protein combination causes it to change its shape. Two things happen as a result; a cascade of enzymatic reactions culminates in the hydrolysis of cyclic GMP (a guanosine analog of cyclic

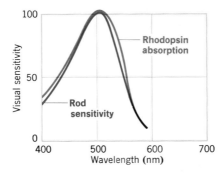

FIGURE M.2 A comparison of the visible absorption spectrum of rhodopsin and the sensitivity curve for rod vision. [Adapted from S. Hecht, S. Shlaer, and M. H. Pirenne, *J. Gen. Chem. Physiol.*, **1942**, *25*, 819.]

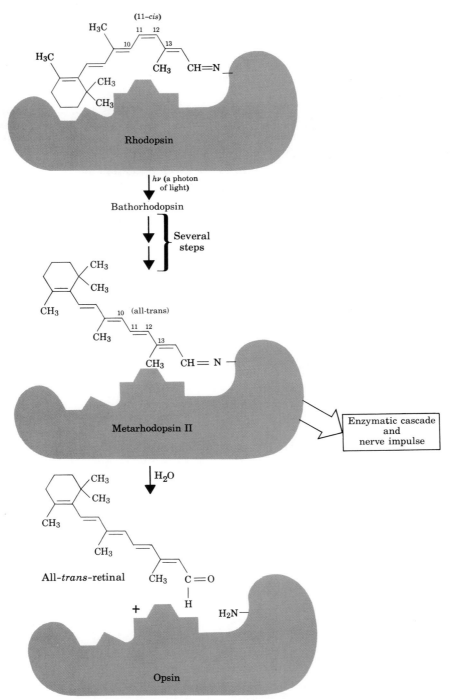

FIGURE M.3 The important chemical steps of the visual process. Absorption of a photon of light by the 11-*cis*-retinal portion of rhodopsin generates a nerve impulse as a result of an isomerization that leads, through a series of steps, to metarhodopsin II. Then hydrolysis of metarhodopsin II produces all-*trans*-retinal and opsin. This illustration greatly oversimplifies the shape of rhodopsin; the retinal portion is actually embedded in the center of a very complex protein structure. For a much more detailed representation of the structure of rhodopsin, and for a description of how a cascade of reactions results in a nerve signal, see L. Stryer, "The Molecules of Visual Excitation," *Scientific American,* **257,** 32 (1987).

AMP, Section 25.2) and, as a consequence of its formation, the transmission of a neural signal to the brain. The chromophore is ultimately hydrolyzed and expelled as all-*trans* retinal. These steps are illustrated in Fig. M.3.

Rhodopsin has an absorption maximum at 498 nm. This gives rhodopsin its red-purple color. Together, all-*trans*-retinal and opsin have an absorbance maximum at 387 nm and, thus, are yellow. The light-initiated transformation of rhodopsin to all-*trans*-retinal and opsin corresponds to the initial bleaching that Boll observed in the retinas of frogs. Further bleaching to a colorless form occurs when all-*trans*-retinal is reduced enzymatically to all-*trans*-vitamin A. This reduction converts the aldehyde group of retinal to the primary alcohol of vitamin A?

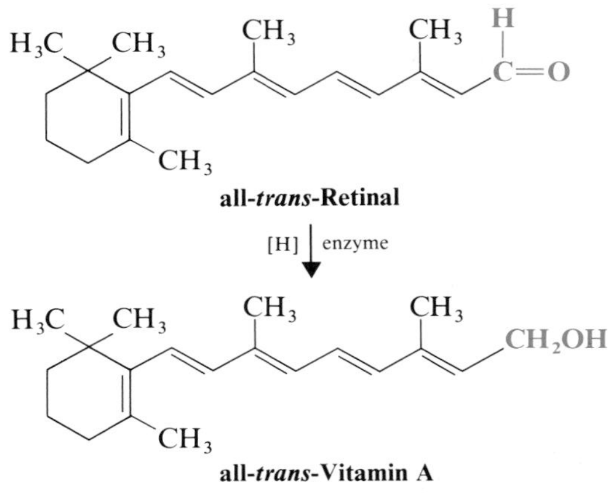

all-*trans*-Retinal

[H] enzyme

all-*trans*-Vitamin A

SPECIAL TOPIC

N

NUCLEOPHILIC SUBSTITUTION REACTIONS — A DEEPER LOOK

N.1 S_N2 REACTIONS: THE ROLE OF ION PAIRS

For many years, the Ingold mechanism (Section 6.8) was widely accepted as the only mechanism for bimolecular nucleophilic substitution reactions. In recent years, however, evidence has been advanced to support another possible mechanism: One involving *ion pairs.* The ion pair mechanism seems to be particularly important in those nucleophilic substitutions called *solvolyses;* however, it may operate in other S_N2 reactions. *A solvolysis is a reaction in which the nucleophile is a molecule of the solvent* (solvent + *lysis:* cleavage by solvent).

> Solvolytic reactions are often described as being pseudo-first order since, by convention, the concentration of the solvent is not included in the rate expression. Even if it were included, we might not be able to detect a variation in rate with a change in concentration of the solvent since the solvent concentration is usually very large and is, therefore, essentially constant. As we shall see, however, some solvolyses are actually bimolecular nucleophilic substitution reactions and occur with complete inversion of configuration.

> The first clear demonstration of ion pair involvement in solvolytic reactions was given by S. Winstein (of the University of California, Los Angeles).

Two examples of solvolytic reactions for which ion pair mechanisms have been proposed are the hydrolysis and acetolysis of methylheptyl sulfonates.

Hydrolysis of a 1-Methylheptyl Sulfonate

Acetolysis of a 1-Methylheptyl Sulfonate

Both of these reactions have been shown to take place with *complete inversion of configuration.*

On the basis of kinetic evidence (beyond the scope of our treatment here), it has been proposed that these reactions take place with the rapid, but reversible, formation of an *"intimate"* (or tight) ion pair, followed by a slow reaction with a solvent molecule. An intimate ion pair, is an ionic intermediate in which the cation and anion are in close proximity and are not separated by solvent molecules.

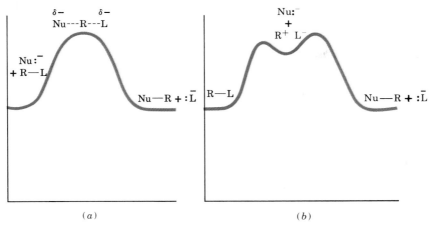

The intimate ion pair retains the configuration of the original sulfonate. However, when it reacts with the solvent, the displacement takes place from the backside and produces an inversion of configuration. In all likelihood, inversion occurs because the intimate ion pair still has partial bonding between the carbon and the leaving group, and attack of the nucleophile must occur from the backside in the same manner as for an S_N2 reaction of a neutral compound.

The difference between the Ingold mechanism and the ion pair mechanism is most apparent in their potential energy diagrams (Fig. N.1). In the one-step displacement mechanism there is a single transition state; in the ion pair mechanism there are two transition states and the ion pair occupies an energy minimum lying between them.

FIGURE N.1 Potential energy diagrams for the one-step mechanism (the Ingold mechanism) for an S_N2 reaction (*a*), and for the intimate ion pair mechanism (*b*).

At the time of this writing, not enough evidence is available to distinguish between these two mechanistic possibilities for most S_N2 reactions. However, with either mechanism the stereochemistry of S_N2 reactions is clear: S_N2 reactions, whether they take place in one step or through the formation of ion pairs, *occur with inversion of configuration.*

N.2 ION PAIRS AND S_N1 REACTIONS

When 1-phenylethyl chloride reacts with water in aqueous acetone, that is, the reaction rate is first order; it depends only on the concentration of 1-phenylethyl chloride and is essentially independent of the concentration of water.

$$\text{Rate} = k \left[\underset{\text{C}_6\text{H}_5\text{CHCH}_3}{\overset{\text{Cl}}{|}} \right]$$

The stereochemistry of the reaction is shown here.

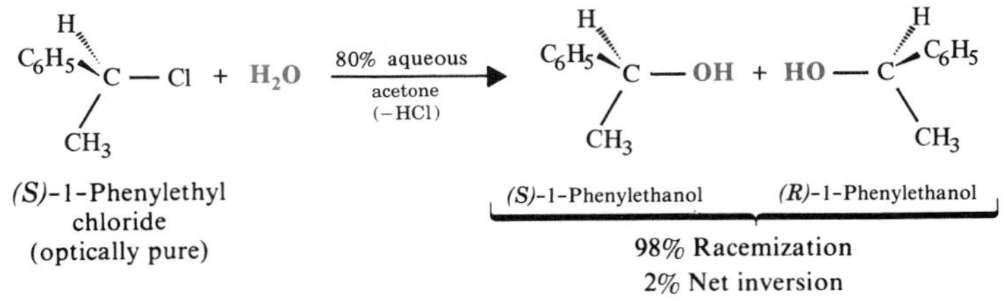

$$\underset{\substack{(S)\text{-1-Phenylethyl} \\ \text{chloride} \\ \text{(optically pure)}}}{\overset{\text{H}_{\cdots}}{\underset{\text{CH}_3}{\text{C}_6\text{H}_5}}\text{C}-\text{Cl}} + \text{H}_2\text{O} \xrightarrow[\substack{\text{acetone} \\ (-\text{HCl})}]{\text{80\% aqueous}} \underset{\substack{(S)\text{-1-Phenylethanol}}}{\overset{\text{H}_{\cdots}}{\underset{\text{CH}_3}{\text{C}_6\text{H}_5}}\text{C}-\text{OH}} + \text{HO}-\underset{\substack{(R)\text{-1-Phenylethanol}}}{\overset{\text{H}}{\underset{\text{CH}_3}{\text{C}_6\text{H}_5}}\text{C}}$$

98% Racemization
2% Net inversion

We see from this equation that the reaction of 1-phenylethyl chloride of the (S) configuration gives a product, 1-phenylethanol, of which 51% has the opposite (R) configuration and 49% has the same (S) configuration. In other words, 51% of the 1-phenylethyl chloride molecules have had their configuration inverted by the reaction, while the remainder (49%) have retained their original configuration. We describe this situation by saying that the reaction has taken place with 98% *racemization* and 2% *net* inversion.

We can account for the fact that this reaction is first order if we assume that the rate-determining step (or slow step) for the reaction involves the organic halide alone. A general mechanism is the following:

Step 1 $\quad \text{R}-\text{X} \xrightarrow{\text{slow}} \text{R}^+ + \text{X}^-$

Step 2 $\quad \text{R}^+ + \text{H}_2\text{O} \xrightarrow{\text{fast}} \overset{+}{\text{R}}\text{OH}_2$

Step 3 $\quad \overset{+}{\text{R}}\text{OH}_2 \xrightarrow[-\text{H}^+]{\text{fast}} \text{ROH}$

Step 1, the formation of a carbocation, is the slow step. Step 2 is a rapid reaction of the carbocation with water and step 3 is the rapid loss of a proton.

Since step 1 involves the organic halide alone (we are, for the moment, neglecting the involvement of solvent molecules), the overall rate of the reaction must correspond to the rate of this step,

$$\text{Rate} = k[\text{RX}]$$

and the reaction as a whole must show first-order kinetics.

A more detailed mechanism (shown in the following figure) illustrates one way in which we can account for the overall stereochemistry of the hydrolysis of 1-phenylethyl chloride.

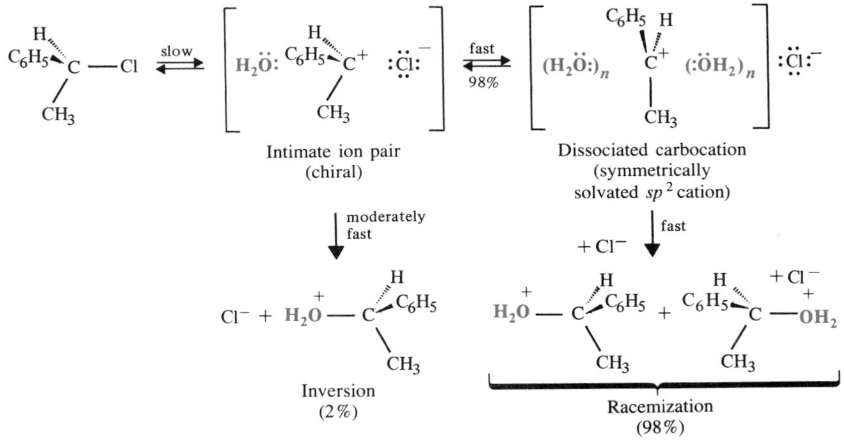

Here we see the important part played by solvent molecules and we also see the formation of two different cationic intermediates: an intimate ion pair and a more dissociated carbocation. The intimate ion pairs are formed first and their carbocations are solvated only on their back sides. A relatively small number of the intimate ion pairs collapse to give an inverted product. However, since the developing cation in this reaction is a relatively stable *benzylic* carbocation, most of the intimate ion pairs survive long enough to become more dissociated. The positive carbon atoms of the dissociated carbocations are sp^2 hybridized and they are solvated on both the front and back sides. They react equally rapidly with water molecules at either face to give a racemic modification of the protonated alcohol.

Some evidence, however, suggests that a third type of cationic intermediate called a "solvent-separated" ion pair may intervene between the intimate ion pair and the dissociated carbocation in reactions of this type. A solvent-separated ion pair, as its name suggests, is one in which a molecule of solvent is situated between the carbocation and the anion. There is also evidence that solvent-separated ion pairs may preferentially react with the intervening solvent molecule by a mechanism that operates with *retention of configuration:*

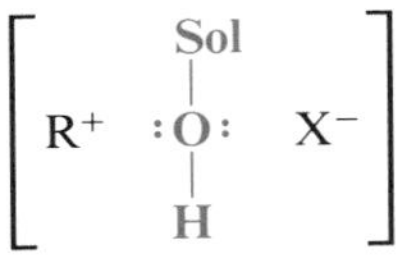

**A solvent-separated
ion pair**

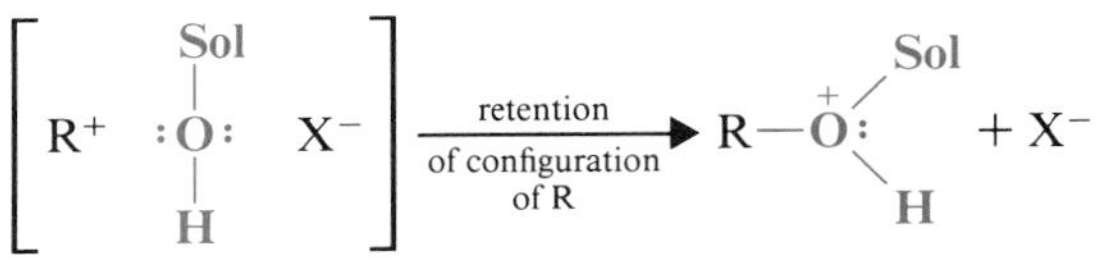

Therefore, it is possible that not all of the racemic product comes from dissociated carbocations and that more than 2% of the reaction may take place through intimate ion pairs. Part of the racemic product may result from a balanced collapse of intimate ion pairs (with inversion) and of solvent-separated ion pairs (with retention).

N.3 SUMMARY OF S_N REACTION MECHANISMS AT A SATURATED CARBON

Nucleophilic substitution reactions may very well take place through a spectrum of mechanisms ranging from a one-step displacement mechanism at one end and a mechanism involving fully dissociated carbocations at the other. Intervening between these limits may be mechanisms involving at least two kinds of ion pairs, intimate ion pairs and solvent-separated ion pairs. We can represent this spectrum as shown in Fig. N.2.

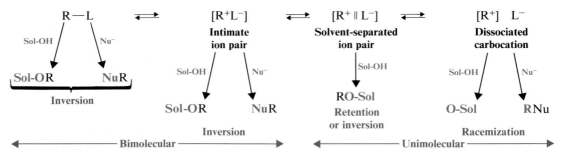

FIGURE N.2 A spectrum of mechanisms for nucleophilic substitution reactions.

Whether a reaction gives a first-order or second-order rate equation will depend on just which of these mechanisms operates. We will obtain a second-order rate equation for those reactions that take place by a one-step displacement mechanism (the Ingold mechanism) or through an intimate ion pair since, in these instances, the rate-determining step is bimolecular. We describe these reactions as being bimolecular or S_N2 reactions.

The mechanism involving an intimate ion pair is a true bimolecular reaction since the transition state of the rate-determining step,

$$R^+ L^- + Nu\colon \longrightarrow NuR + L^-$$

or

$$R^+ L^- + \text{Sol-OH} \longrightarrow \text{Sol}-\overset{+}{\underset{H}{O}}-R + L^-$$

involves two species: the intimate ion pair and the nucleophile or solvent.

We will obtain a first-order rate equation for those reactions that involve dissociated carbocations or solvent-separated ion pairs, for in these reactions the rate-determining step is unimolecular. We describe these reactions as being unimolecular or S_N1.

The only exception to these generalizations is a solvolysis. A solvolysis can be *bimolecular* because the transition state of its rate-determining step can involve two species: the substrate and the solvent. Such a solvolysis, however, will show *pseudo-first-order kinetics* because the solvent concentration is very large and is, consequently, essentially constant.

The stereochemical possibilities for nucleophilic substitution reactions are summarized in Table N.1.

TABLE N.1   The stereochemistry of nucleophilic substitution reactions

MECHANISM	SUBSTRATE	REPRESENTATION	STEREOCHEMISTRY
S_N2	(R—L) **Alkyl halide, tosylate, etc.**	R—L	Nucleophilic attack by the solvent or the nucleophile from the back side gives an inverted product by a one-step displacement mechanism
S_N2	(R⌣L) **Intimate ion pair**	$[R^+L^-]$	Nucleophilic attack by the solvent or the nucleophile from the back side gives an inverted product
S_N1	Sol | (R⁺) O (L⁻) | H **Solvent-separated ion pair**	$[R^+\|L^-]$	Nucleophilic attack by the solvent from the front side occurs with retention of configuration. (Attack by another nucleophile may occur with inversion)
S_N1	$\left(\begin{array}{c}\text{Sol}\\\|\\\text{O}\\\|\\\text{H}\end{array}\right)_n$ (R⁺) $\left(\begin{array}{c}\text{Sol}\\\|\\\text{O}\\\|\\\text{H}\end{array}\right)_n$ (L⁻) **Dissociated carbocation**	$[R^+]\ L^-$	Nucleophilic attack by the solvent or the nucleophile from the front or back side gives a racemic product

N.4 NEIGHBORING GROUP PARTICIPATION IN NUCLEOPHILIC SUBSTITUTION REACTIONS

Not all nucleophilic substitutions (Sections N.1–N.3) take place with racemization or with inversion of configuration. Some take place with overall *retention of configuration.*

One factor that can lead to retention of configuration in a nucleophilic substitution is a phenomenon known as *neighboring group participation.* Let us see how this operates by examining the stereochemistry of two reactions in which 2-bromopropanoic acid is converted to lactic acid.

$$CH_3CHCO_2H \longrightarrow CH_3CHCO_2H$$

Br	OH
2-Bromopropanoic acid	**Lactic acid**

When (S)-2-bromopropanoic acid is treated with concentrated sodium hydroxide, the reaction is *bimolecular* and it takes place with *inversion of configuration.* This, of course, is the normal stereochemical result for an S_N2 reaction.

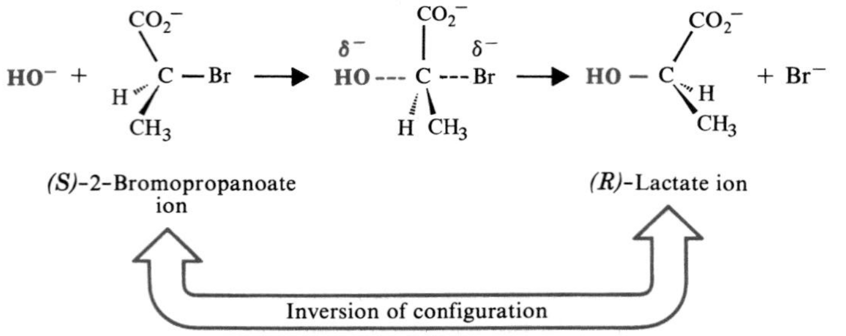

(S)-2-Bromopropanoate
ion

(R)-Lactate ion

Inversion of configuration

However, when the same reaction is carried out with a low concentration of hydroxide ion in the presence of Ag_2O, it takes place with an overall *retention of configuration.* In this case, the mechanism for the reaction involves the participation of the carboxylate group. In step 1 (see following reaction) an oxygen of the carboxylate group attacks the stereocenter from the backside and displaces bromide ion. (Silver ion aids in this process in much the same way that protonation assists the ionization of an alcohol.) The configuration of the stereocenter inverts in step 1, and a cyclic ester called an α-lactone forms.

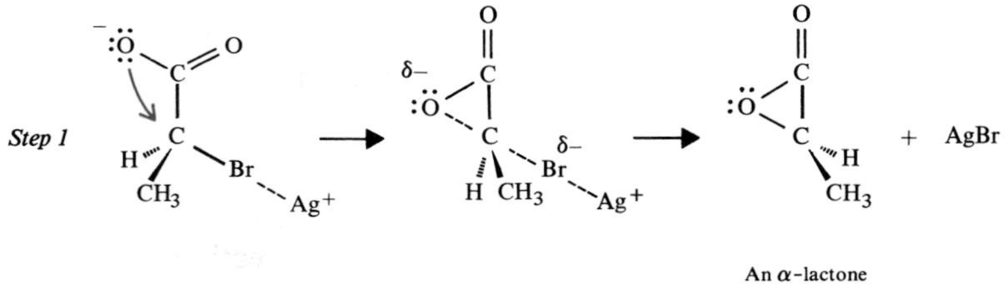

Step 1

+ AgBr

An α-lactone

The highly-strained three-membered ring of the α-lactone opens when it is attacked by a water molecule in step 2. *This step also takes place with an inversion of configuration.*

Step 2

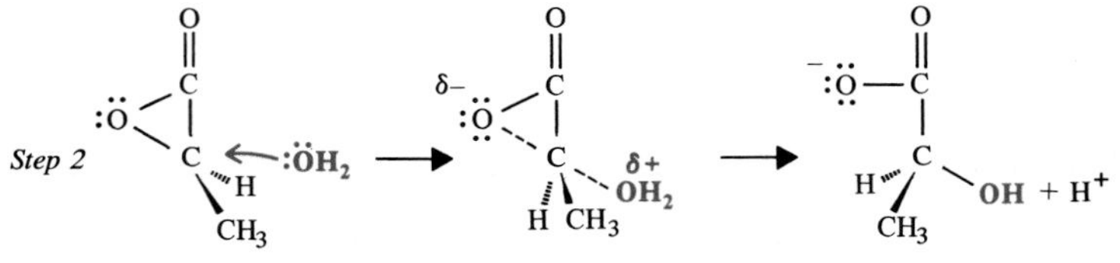

The net result of two inversions (in steps 1 and 2) is an overall *retention of configuration.*

Problem N.1

The phenomenon of configuration inversion in a chemical reaction was discovered in 1896 by Paul von Walden. (Configuration inversions are still called

Walden inversions in his honor.) Walden's proof of configuration inversion was based on the following cycle:

HO$_2$CCH$_2$CHClCO$_2$H
(−)-Chlorosuccinic acid

Ag$_2$O
H$_2$O

KOH
PCl$_5$

HO$_2$CCH$_2$CH(OH)CO$_2$H
(−)-Malic acid

HO$_2$CCH$_2$CH(OH)CO$_2$H
(+)-Malic acid

KOH
PCl$_5$

Ag$_2$O
H$_2$O

HO$_2$CCH$_2$CHClCO$_2$H
(+)-Chlorosuccinic acid

The Walden cycle

(a) Basing your answer on the preceding discussion, which reactions of the Walden cycle are likely to take place with overall inversion of configuration and which are likely to occur with overall retention of configuration? (b) Malic acid with a negative optical rotation is now known to have the (S) configuration. What are the configurations of the other compounds in the Walden cycle? (c) Walden also found that when (+)-malic acid is treated with thionyl chloride (rather than PCl$_5$), the product of the reaction is (+)-chlorosuccinic acid. How can you explain this result? (d) Assuming that the reaction of (−)-malic acid and thionyl chloride has the same stereochemistry, outline a Walden cycle based on the use of thionyl chloride instead of PCl$_5$.

Neighboring group participation can also lead to *cyclization reactions.* Epoxides, for example, can be prepared from 2-bromo alcohols by treating them with sodium hydroxide. This reaction involves the following steps:

OH
|
R—CH—CHR'
|
:Br:

$\xrightarrow{OH^-}$

:Ö:⁻
|
R—CH—CH—R'
|
:Br:

$\longrightarrow$

O
/ \
RCH—CHR' + :Br:⁻

Problem N.2

(a) How would you synthesize a 2-halo alcohol (a halohydrin) from an alkene? (b) Show how you could use this method to synthesize propylene oxide from propylene.

When neighboring group participation occurs during the rate-determining step for a reaction, the rate is often markedly increased. This effect, called *anchimeric assistance* (Greek *anchi + meros,* meaning neighboring parts), can be seen in the relative rates of S$_N$1 solvolysis reactions of isobutyl chloride and 2-phenyl-1-chloropropane. When 1-chloro-2-phenylpropane undergoes S$_N$1 solvolysis, it reacts more

CH$_3$
|
CH$_3$CHCH$_2$Cl
Isobutyl chloride

CH$_3$CHCH$_2$Cl
1-Chloro-2-phenylpropane

rapidly than isobutyl chloride. The phenyl group is thought to assist in the ionization step by stabilizing the transition state leading to the phenonium ion intermediate. The methyl group of isobutyl chloride is apparently unable to provide a similar kind of assistance when it undergoes solvolysis.

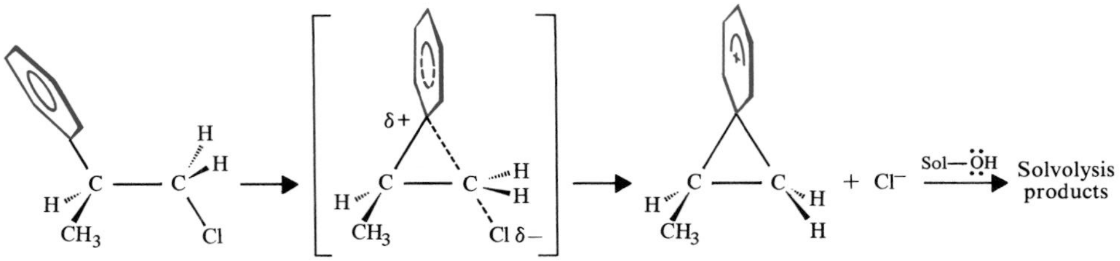

Transition state   A phenonium ion

Problem N.3

The phenonium ion formed as an intermediate in the previous reaction strongly resembles the arenium ions we saw in electrophilic substitution reactions. What relative order of reactivity would you expect the following compounds to show: 1-chloro-2-phenylpropane; 1-chloro-2-(*p*-nitrophenyl)propane; 1-chloro-2-(*p*-hydroxyphenyl)propane; 1-chloro-2-(*p*-methylphenyl)propane.

Neighboring group participation and anchimeric assistance are important in many reactions that are catalyzed by enzymes.

Problem N.4

In 1949, D. J. Cram published the first of a series of papers on the solvolysis of 1-methyl-2-phenylpropyl tosylates, **A** and **C**. These reactions displayed a remarkable stereospecificity: When the optically active tosylate **A** was heated in acetic acid, the reaction yielded almost exclusively the optically active acetate **B**. On the other hand, heating the optically active tosylate **C** in acetic acid gave the racemic acetate, **D** and **E**. Provide an explanation for these results.

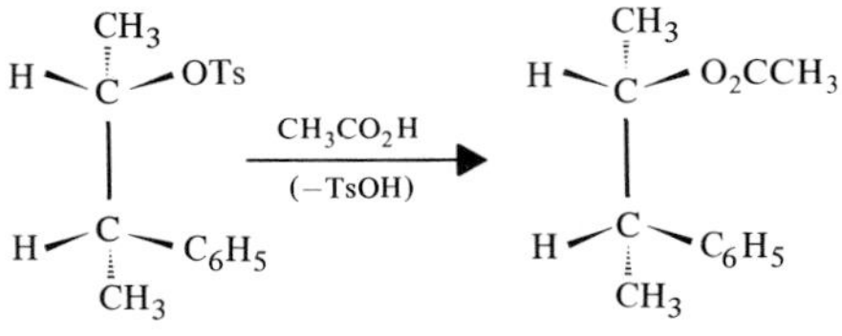

A

B
Optically active

SPECIAL TOPIC N

Racemic modification

SPECIAL TOPIC

O

REACTIONS CONTROLLED BY ORBITAL SYMMETRY

O.1 INTRODUCTION

In recent years, chemists have found that there are many reactions where certain symmetry characteristics of molecular orbitals control the overall course of the reaction. These reactions are often called *pericyclic reactions* because they take place through cyclic transition states. Now that we have a background knowledge of molecular orbital theory—especially as it applies to conjugated polyenes (dienes, trienes, etc.)—we are in a position to examine some of the intriguing aspects of these reactions. We shall look in detail at two basic types: *electrocyclic reactions* and *cycloaddition reactions.*

O.2 ELECTROCYCLIC REACTIONS

A number of reactions, like the one shown here, transform a conjugated polyene into a cyclic compound.

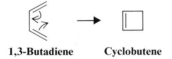

1,3-Butadiene   **Cyclobutene**

In many other reactions, the ring of a cyclic compound opens and a conjugated polyene forms.

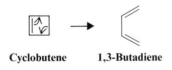

Cyclobutene   **1,3-Butadiene**

Reactions of either type are called *electrocyclic reactions.*

In electrocyclic reactions, σ and π bonds are interconverted. In our first example, one π bond of 1,3-butadiene becomes a σ bond in cyclobutene. In our second example, the reverse is true; a σ bond of cyclobutene becomes a π bond in 1,3-butadiene.

Electrocyclic reactions have several characteristic features:

1. They require only heat or light for initiation.
2. Their mechanisms do not involve radical or ionic intermediates.
3. Bonds are made and broken in *a single concerted step involving a cyclic transition state.*
4. The reactions are *highly stereospecific.*

The examples that follow demonstrate this last characteristic of electrocyclic reactions.

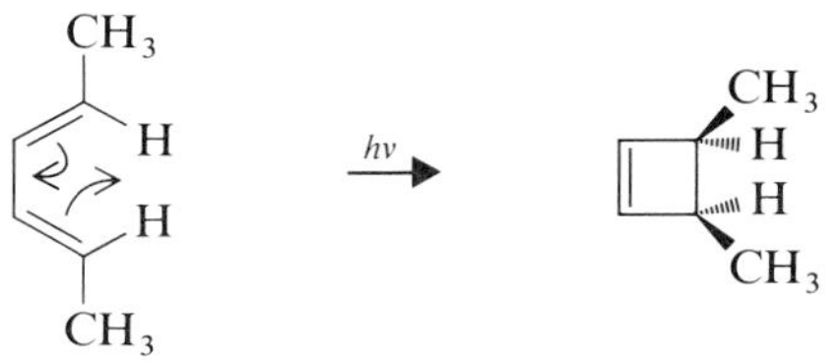

trans,trans-2,4-Hexadiene

cis-3,4-Dimethylcyclobutene

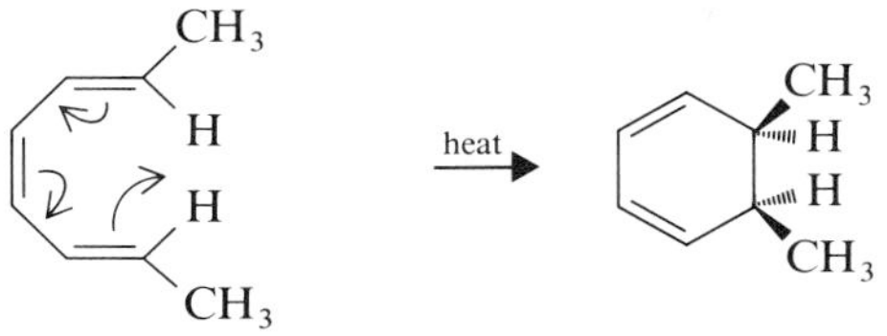

trans,cis,trans-2,4,6-Octatriene

cis-5,6-Dimethyl-1,3-cyclohexadiene

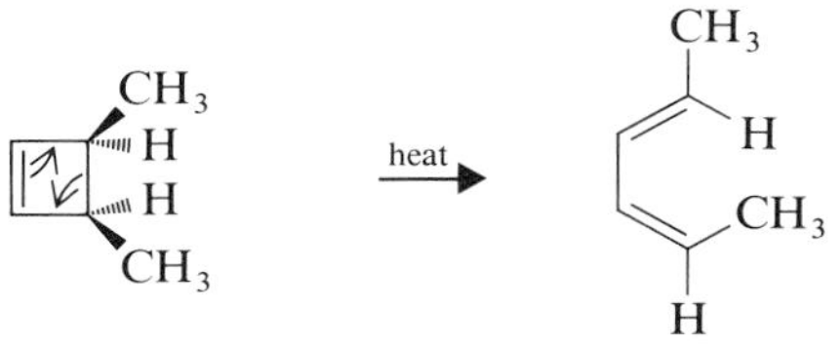

cis-3,4-Dimethylcyclobutene

cis,trans-2,4-Hexadiene

In each of these three examples, a single stereoisomeric form of the reactant yields a single stereoisomeric form of the product. The concerted photochemical cyclization of *trans,trans*-2,4-hexadiene, for example, yields only *cis*-3,4-dimethylcyclobutene; it does not yield *trans*-3,4-dimethylcyclobutene.

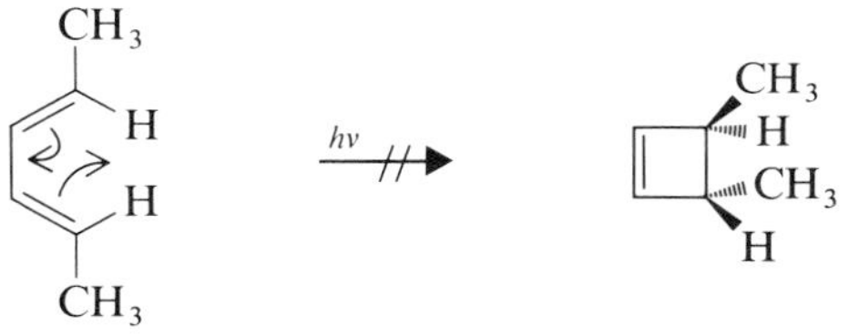

trans,trans-2,4-Hexadiene

trans-3,4-Dimethylcyclobutene

(not formed)

The other two concerted reactions are characterized by the same stereospecificity.

The electrocyclic reactions that we shall study here and the concerted cycloaddition reactions that we shall study in the next section were poorly understood by chemists before 1960. In the years that followed, several scientists, most notably K. Fukui in Japan, H. C. Longuet-Higgins in England, and R. B. Woodward and R. Hoffmann in the United States provided us with a basis for understanding how these reactions occur and why they take place with such remarkable stereospecificity.*

All of these men worked from molecular orbital theory. In 1965, Woodward and Hoffmann formulated their theoretical insights into a set of rules that not only enabled chemists to understand reactions that were already known but that correctly predicted the outcome of many reactions that had not been attempted.

---

* Hoffmann and Fukui were awarded the Nobel Prize in 1981 for this work.

SPECIAL TOPIC O

The Woodward–Hoffmann rules are formulated for concerted reactions only. Concerted reactions are reactions in which bonds are broken and formed simultaneously and, thus, no intermediates occur. The Woodward–Hoffmann rules are based on this hypothesis: *In concerted reactions molecular orbitals of the reactant are continuously converted into molecular orbitals of the product.* This conversion of molecular orbitals is not a random one, however. Molecular orbitals have symmetry characteristics. Because they do, restrictions exist on which molecular orbitals of the reactant may be transformed into particular molecular orbitals of the product.

According to Woodward and Hoffmann, certain reaction paths are said to be *symmetry allowed* while others are said to be *symmetry forbidden.* To say that a particular path is symmetry forbidden does not necessarily mean, however, that the reaction will not occur. It simply means that if the reaction were to occur through a symmetry-forbidden path, the concerted reaction would have a much higher energy of activation. The reaction may occur, but it will probably do so in a different way: through another path that is symmetry allowed or through a nonconcerted path.

A complete analysis of electrocyclic reactions using the Woodward–Hoffmann rules requires a correlation of symmetry characteristics of *all* of the molecular orbitals of the reactants and product. Such analyses are beyond the scope of our discussion here. We shall find, however, that a simplified approach can be undertaken, one that will be easy to visualize and, at the same time, will be accurate in most instances. In this simplified approach to electrocyclic reactions we focus our attention only on the *highest occupied molecular orbital (HOMO) of the conjugated polyene.* This approach is based on a method developed by Fukui called the *frontier orbital method.*

O.2A Electrocyclic Reactions of $4n$ π-Electron Systems

Let us begin with an analysis of the thermal interconversion of *cis*-3,4-dimethylcyclobutene and *cis,trans*-2,4-hexadiene shown here.

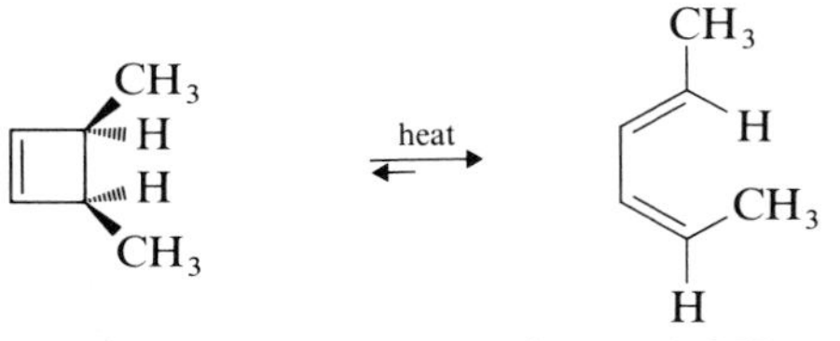

cis-3,4-Dimethylcyclobutene   cis,trans-2,4-Hexadiene

Electrocyclic reactions are reversible, and so the path for the forward reaction is the same as that for the reverse reaction. In this example it is easier to see what happens to the orbitals if we follow the *cyclization* reaction, *cis,trans*-2,4-hexadiene ⟶ ς-3,4-dimethylcyclobutene.

In this cyclization one π bond of the hexadiene is transformed into a σ bond of the cyclobutene. But which π bond? And, how does the conversion occur?

Let us begin by examining the π molecular orbitals of 2,4-hexadiene and, in particular, let us look at *the HOMO of the ground state* (Fig. O.1).

The cyclization that we are concerned with now, *cis,trans*-2,4-hexadiene ⇌ *cis*-3,4-dimethylcyclobutene, requires heat alone. We conclude, therefore, that excited states of the hexadiene are not involved, for these would require the absorption of light. If we focus our attention on Ψ_2—the HOMO of the ground state—we can

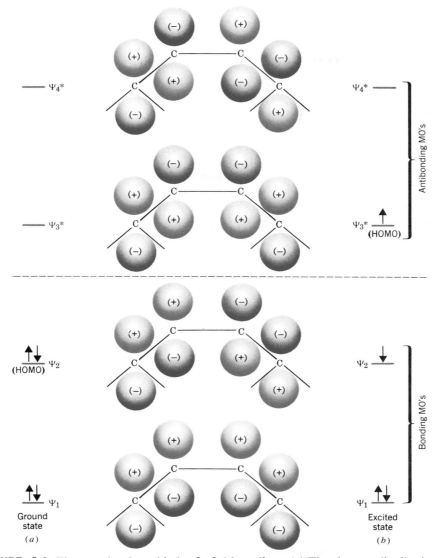

FIGURE O.1 The π molecular orbitals of a 2,4-hexadiene. (*a*) The electron distribution of the ground state. (*b*) The electronic distribution of the first excited state. (The first excited state is formed when the molecule absorbs a photon of light of the proper wavelength.) Notice that the orbitals of a 2,4-hexadiene are like those of 1,3-butadiene shown in Fig. 12.5.

see how the *p* orbitals at C-2 and C-5 can be transformed into a σ bond in the cyclobutene.

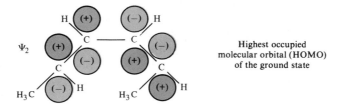

A bonding σ-molecular orbital between C-2 and C-5 is formed when the *p* orbitals *rotate in the same direction* (both clockwise, as shown, or both counterclockwise, which leads to an equivalent result). The term *conrotatory* is used to describe this type of motion of the two *p* orbitals relative to each other.

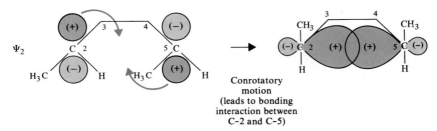

Conrotatory motion (leads to bonding interaction between C-2 and C-5)

Conrotatory motion allows *p*-orbital lobes of the *same phase sign* to overlap. It also places the two methyl groups on the same side of the molecule in the product, that is, in the cis configuration.*

The pathway with conrotatory motion of the methyl groups is consistent with what we know from experiments to be true: The *thermal reaction* results in the interconversion of *cis*-3,4-dimethylcyclobutene and *cis,trans*-2,4-hexadiene.

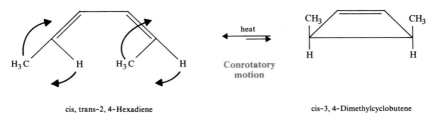

cis, trans-2, 4–Hexadiene   Conrotatory motion   cis–3, 4–Dimethylcyclobutene

We can now examine another 2,4-hexadiene ⇌ 3,4-dimethylcyclobutene interconversion: one that takes place under the influence of light. This reaction is shown here.

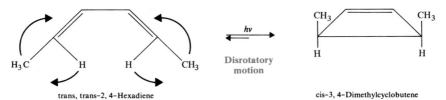

trans, trans-2, 4–Hexadiene   Disrotatory motion   cis–3, 4–Dimethylcyclobutene

In the photochemical reaction, *cis*-3,4-dimethylcyclobutene and *trans,trans*-2,4-hexadiene are interconverted. The photochemical interconversion occurs with the methyl groups rotating in *opposite directions,* that is, with the methyl groups undergoing *disrotatory motion.*

* Notice that if conrotatory motion occurs in the opposite (counterclockwise) direction, lobes of the same phase sign still overlap, and the methyl groups are still cis.

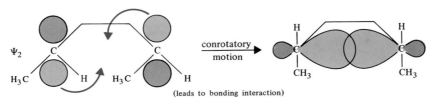

(leads to bonding interaction)

SPECIAL TOPIC O

The photochemical reaction can also be understood by considering orbitals of the 2,4-hexadiene. In this reaction, however — since the absorption of light is involved — we want to look at the first *excited state* of the hexadiene. We want to examine Ψ_3^*, because in the first excited state Ψ_3^* *is the highest occupied molecular orbital.*

Highest occupied molecular orbital of the first excited state

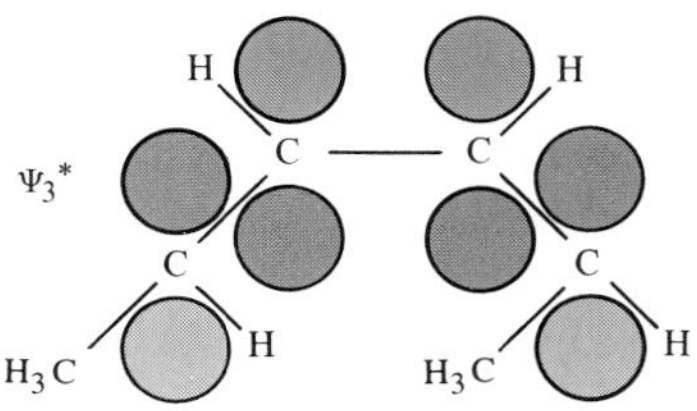

We find that disrotatory motion of the orbitals at C-2 and C-5 of Ψ_3^* allows lobes of the same sign to overlap and form a bonding sigma molecular orbital between them. Disrotatory motion of the orbitals, of course, also requires disrotatory motion of the methyl groups and, once again, this is consistent with what we find experimentally. The *photochemical reaction* results in the interconversion of *cis*-3,4-dimethylcyclobutene and *trans,trans*-2,4-hexadiene.

Disrotatory motion
(leads to bonding
interaction between
C-2 and C-5)

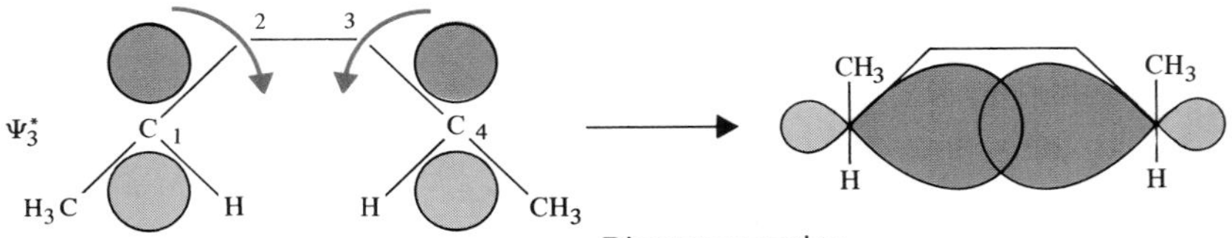

Since both of the interconversions that we have presented so far involve *cis*-3,4-dimethylcyclobutene, we can summarize them in the following way:

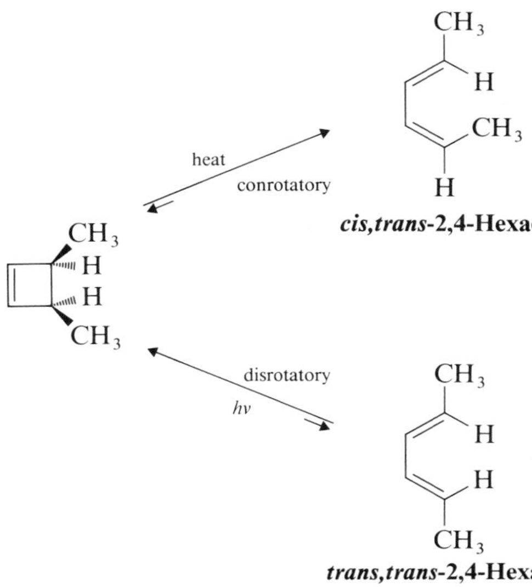

cis,trans-2,4-Hexadiene

trans,trans-2,4-Hexadiene

We see that these two interconversions occur with precisely opposite stereochemistry. We also see that the stereochemistry of the interconversions depends on whether the reaction is brought about by the application of heat or light.

The first Woodward–Hoffmann rule can be stated as follows:

1. **A thermal electrocyclic reaction involving $4n$ π electrons (where $n = 1, 2, 3,$ . . .) proceeds with conrotatory motion; the photochemical reaction proceeds with disrotatory motion.**

Both of the interconversions that we have studied involve systems of 4π electrons and both follow this rule. Many other $4n$ π-electron systems have been studied since Woodward and Hoffmann stated their rule. Virtually all have been found to follow it.

Before we leave the subject of $4n$ π-electron systems let us illustrate an application of the rule with one other example.

When *trans*-3,4-dimethylcyclobutene is heated, ring opening occurs and *trans,trans*-2,4-hexadiene is formed.

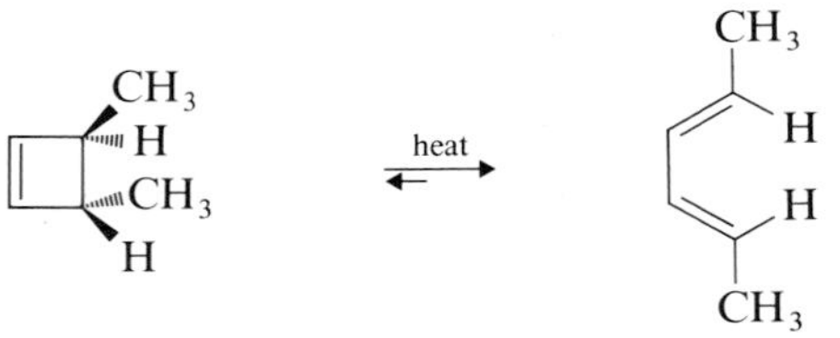

trans-3,4-Dimethylcyclobutene   *trans,trans*-2,4-Hexadiene

According to the Woodward–Hoffmann rule, this thermal reaction of a 4π-electron system should occur with *conrotatory motion, and this is precisely what happens. trans*-3,4-Dimethylcyclobutene is transformed into *trans,trans*-2,4-hexadiene.

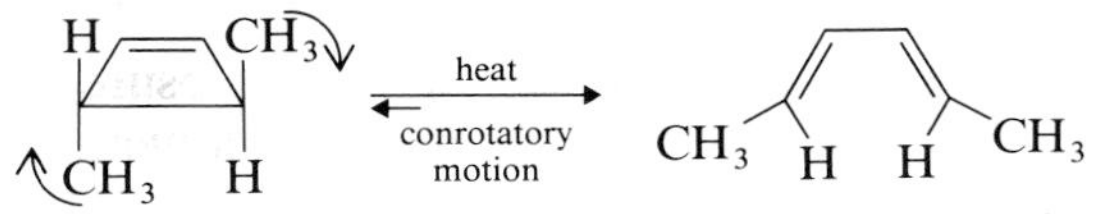

trans,trans-2,4-Hexadiene

Problem O.1

In the previous example, another conrotatory path is available. This path would produce *cis,cis*-2,4-hexadiene. Can you suggest a reason that will account for the fact that this path is not followed to any appreciable extent?

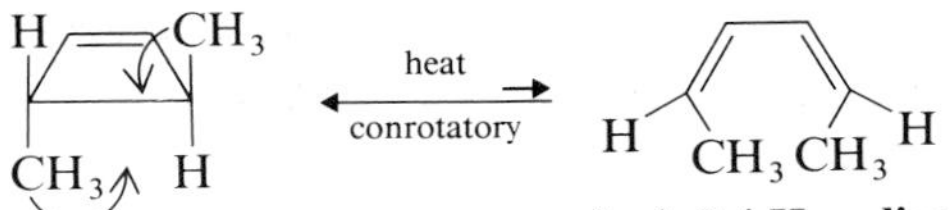

cis,cis-2,4-Hexadiene

Problem O.2

What product would you expect from a concerted photochemical cyclization of *cis,trans*-2,4-hexadiene?

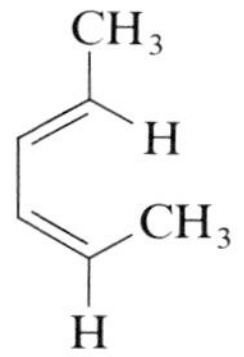

SPECIAL TOPIC O

CH$_3$
H
CH$_3$
H

cis,trans-2,4-Hexadiene

Problem O.3

(a) Show the orbitals involved in the following thermal electrocyclic reaction.

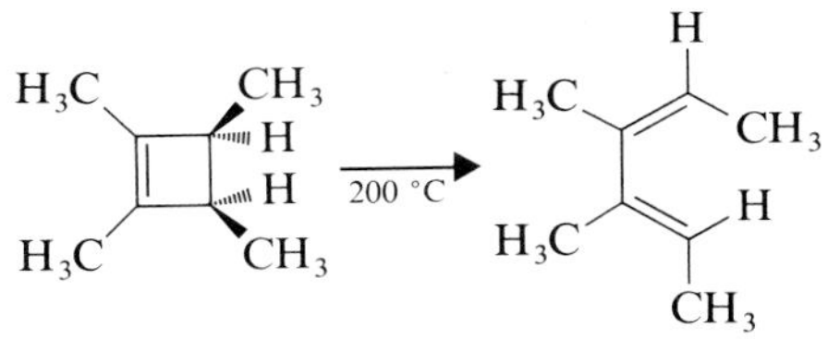

H$_3$C   CH$_3$
H
H   200 °C
H$_3$C   CH$_3$

H
H$_3$C   CH$_3$
H
H$_3$C
CH$_3$

(b) Do the groups rotate in a conrotatory or disrotatory manner?

Problem O.4

Can you suggest a method for carrying out a stereospecific conversion of *trans,trans*-2,4-hexadiene into *cis,trans*-2,4-hexadiene?

Problem O.5

The following 2,4,6,8-decatetraenes undergo ring closure to dimethylcyclo-octatrienes when heated or irradiated. What product would you expect from each reaction?

(a) 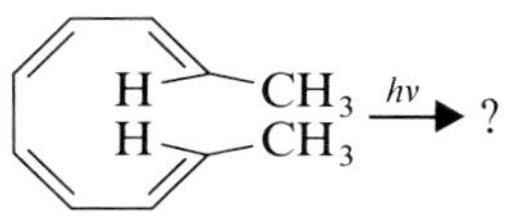 H—CH$_3$ H—CH$_3$ hv → ?

(b) 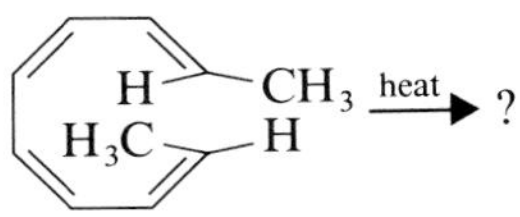 H—CH$_3$ H$_3$C—H   heat → ?

Problem O.6

(a) For each of the following reactions, state whether conrotatory or disrotatory motion of the groups is involved and (b) state whether you would expect the reaction to occur under the influence of heat or of light.

(a) 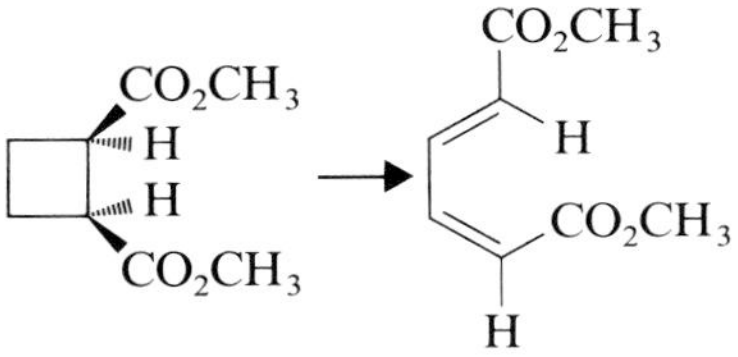 CO$_2$CH$_3$
H
H
CO$_2$CH$_3$
→
CO$_2$CH$_3$
H
CO$_2$CH$_3$
H

(b)

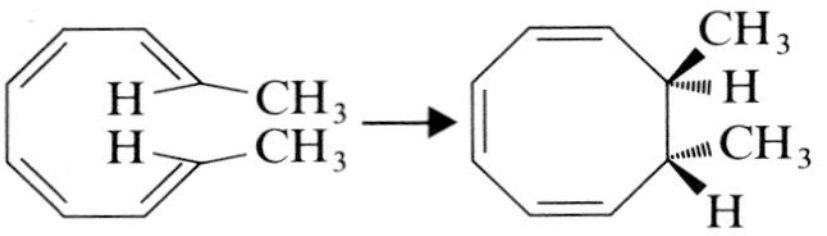

(c)

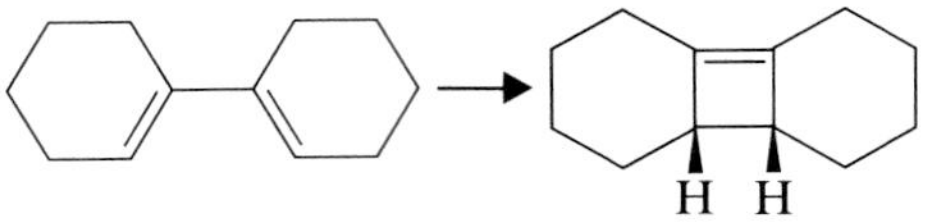

0.2B Electrocyclic Reactions of $(4n + 2)$ π-Electron Systems

The second Woodward–Hoffmann rule for electrocyclic reactions is stated as follows:

2. **A thermal electrocyclic reaction involving $(4n + 2)$ π electrons (where $n = 0, 1, 2, \ldots$) proceeds with disrotatory motion; the photochemical reaction proceeds with conrotatory motion.**

According to this rule, the direction of rotation of the thermal and photochemical reactions of $(4n + 2)$ π-electron systems is the opposite of that for corresponding $4n$ systems. Thus, we can summarize both systems in the way shown in Table O.1.

TABLE O.1   Woodward–Hoffmann rules for electrocyclic reactions

NUMBER OF ELECTRONS	MOTION	RULE
$4n$	Conrotatory	Thermally allowed, photochemically forbidden
$4n$	Disrotatory	Photochemically allowed, thermally forbidden
$4n + 2$	Disrotatory	Thermally allowed, photochemically forbidden
$4n + 2$	Conrotatory	Photochemically allowed, thermally forbidden

The interconversions of *trans*-5,6-dimethyl-1,3-cyclohexadiene and the two different 2,4,6-octatrienes that follow illustrate thermal and photochemical interconversions of 6 π-electron systems ($4n + 2$, where $n = 1$).

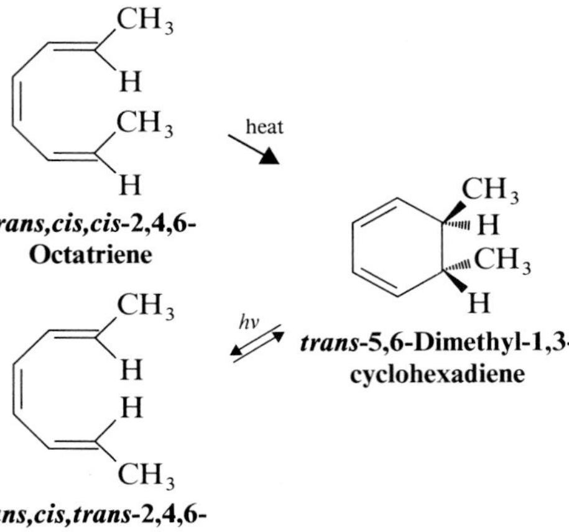

trans,cis,cis-2,4,6-
Octatriene

trans,cis,trans-2,4,6-
Octatriene

heat

hv

trans-5,6-Dimethyl-1,3-
cyclohexadiene

In the following thermal reaction, the methyl groups rotate in a disrotatory fashion.

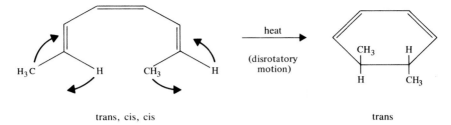

In the photochemical reaction, the groups rotate in a conrotatory way.

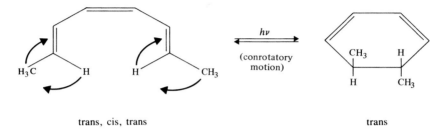

We can understand how these reactions occur if we examine the π molecular orbitals shown in Fig. O.2. Once again, we want to pay attention to the highest occupied molecular orbitals. For the thermal reaction of a 2,4,6-octatriene, the highest occupied orbital is Ψ_3 because the molecule reacts in its ground state.

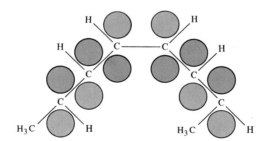

Ψ_3 of *trans, cis, cis,*-2, 4, 6–Octatriene

We see in the following figure that disrotatory motion of orbitals at C-2 and C-7 of Ψ_3 allows the formation of a bonding sigma molecular orbital between them. Disrotatory motion of the orbitals, of course, also requires disrotatory motion of the groups attached to C-2 and C-7. And, disrotatory motion of the groups is what we observe in the thermal reaction: *trans,cis,cis*-2,4,6-octatriene ⟶ *trans*-5,6-dimethyl-1,3-cyclohexadiene.

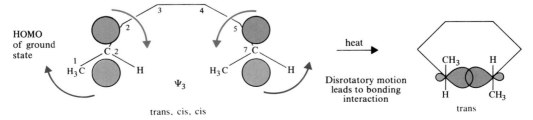

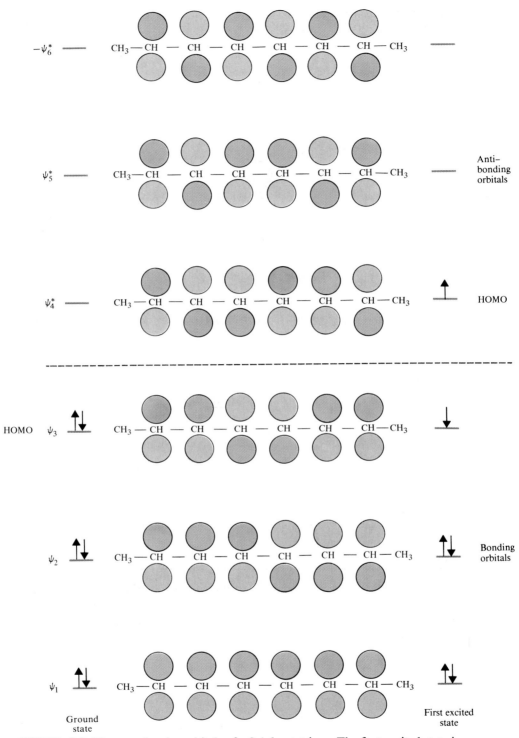

FIGURE O.2 The π molecular orbitals of a 2,4,6-octatriene. The first excited state is formed when the molecule absorbs light of the proper wavelength. (These molecular orbitals are obtained from calculations that are beyond the scope of our discussions.)

When we consider the photochemical reaction, *trans,cis,trans*-2,4,6-octatriene ⇌ *trans*-5,6-dimethyl-1,3-cyclohexadiene, we want to focus our attention on Ψ_4^*. In the photochemical reaction, light causes the promotion of an electron from Ψ_3 to Ψ_4^*, and thus Ψ_4^* becomes the HOMO. We also want to look at the symmetry of the orbitals at C-2 and C-7 of Ψ_4^*, for these are the orbitals that form a σ bond. In the interconversion shown here, conrotatory motion of the orbitals allows lobes of the same sign to overlap. Thus, we can understand why conrotatory motion of the groups is what we observe in the photochemical reaction.

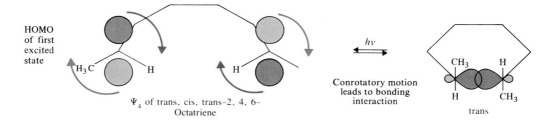

HOMO of first excited state

Ψ_4 of trans, cis, trans-2, 4, 6–Octatriene

hv

Conrotatory motion leads to bonding interaction

CH₃   H

H   CH₃

trans

Problem 0.7

Give the stereochemistry of the product that you would expect from each of the following electrocyclic reactions.

(a) [structure with CH₃, H, H, CH₃] heat ⇌

(b) [structure with CH₃, H, H, CH₃] *hv* ⇌

Problem 0.8

Can you suggest a stereospecific method for converting *trans*-5,6-dimethyl-1,3-cyclohexadiene into *cis*-5,6-dimethyl-1,3-cyclohexadiene?

Problem 0.9

When compound **A** is heated, compound **B** can be isolated from the reaction mixture. A sequence of two electrocyclic reactions occurs; the first involves a 4 π-electron system, the second involves a 6 π-electron system. Outline both electrocyclic reactions and give the structure of the intermediate that intervenes.

[structure A with H, H] heat→ [structure B with H, H]

A   B

O.3 CYCLOADDITION REACTIONS

There are a number of reactions of alkenes and polyenes in which two molecules react to form a cyclic product. These reactions, called *cycloaddition* reactions, are shown next.

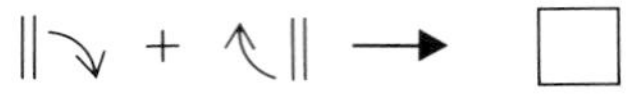

A [2 + 2] cycloaddition

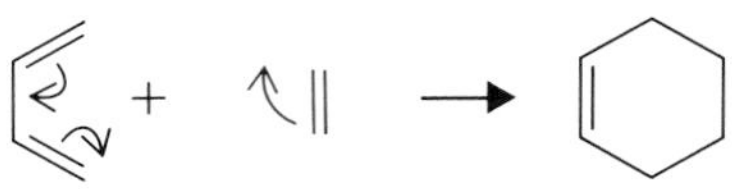

Alkene   Alkene   Cyclobutane

A [4 + 2] cycloaddition

Diene   Alkene   Cyclohexene
         (dienophile)   (adduct)

Chemists classify cycloaddition reactions on the basis of the number of π electrons involved in each component. The reaction of two alkenes to form a cyclobutane is a [2 + 2] cycloaddition; the reaction of a diene and an alkene to form a cyclohexene is called a [4 + 2] cycloaddition. We are already familiar with the [4 + 2] cycloaddition, because it is the Diels – Alder reaction that we studied in Section 12.10.

Cycloaddition reactions resemble electrocyclic reactions in the following important ways:

1. Sigma and pi bonds are interconverted.
2. Cycloaddition reactions require only heat or light for initiation.
3. Radicals and ionic intermediates are not involved in the mechanisms for cycloadditions.
4. Bonds are made and broken in a single concerted step involving a cyclic transition state.
5. Cycloaddition reactions are highly stereospecific.

As we might expect, concerted cycloaddition reactions resemble electrocyclic reactions in still another important way: The symmetry elements of the interacting molecular orbitals allow us to account for their stereochemistry. The symmetry elements of the interacting molecular orbitals also allow us to account for two other observations that have been made about cycloaddition reactions:

1. *Photochemical [2 + 2] cycloaddition reactions occur readily while thermal [2 + 2] cycloadditions take place only under extreme conditions.* When thermal [2 + 2] cycloadditions do take place, they occur through radical (or ionic) mechanisms, not through a concerted process.
2. *Thermal [4 + 2] cycloaddition reactions occur readily and photochemical [4 + 2] cycloadditions are difficult.*

O.3A [2 + 2] Cycloadditions

Let us begin with an analysis of the [2 + 2] cycloaddition of two ethylene molecules to form a molecule of cyclobutane.

$$2 \; \underset{CH_2}{\overset{CH_2}{\|}} \longrightarrow \begin{matrix} H_2C-CH_2 \\ | \quad\quad | \\ H_2C-CH_2 \end{matrix}$$

SPECIAL TOPIC O

In this reaction we see that two π bonds are converted into two σ bonds. But how does this conversion take place? One way of answering this question is by examining the frontier orbitals of the reactants. The frontier orbitals are the HOMO of one reactant and the LUMO of the other.

We can see how frontier orbital interactions come into play if we examine the possibility of a *concerted thermal* conversion of two ethene molecules into cyclobutane.

Thermal reactions involve molecules reacting in their ground states. The following is the orbital diagram for ethene in its ground state.

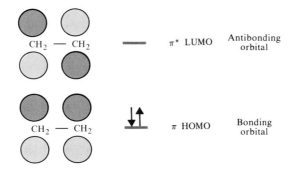

The ground state of ethene

The HOMO of ethene in its ground state is the π orbital. Since this orbital contains two electrons, it interacts with an *unoccupied* molecular orbital of another ethene molecule. The LUMO of the ground state of ethene is, of course, π^*.

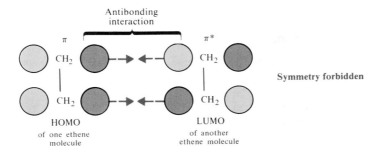

We see from the previous diagram, however, that overlapping the π orbital of one ethene molecule with the π^* orbital of another does not lead to bonding between both sets of carbon atoms because orbitals of opposite signs overlap between the top pair of carbon atoms. This reaction is said to be *symmetry forbidden*. What does this mean? It means that a thermal (or ground state) cycloaddition of ethene would be unlikely to occur in a concerted process. This is exactly what we find experimentally; thermal cycloadditions of ethene, when they occur, take place through nonconcerted, radical mechanisms.

What, then, can we decide about the other possibility — a photochemical [2 + 2] cycloaddition? If an ethene molecule absorbs a photon of light of the proper wavelength, an electron is promoted from π to π^*. In this excited state the HOMO of an ethene molecule is π^*. The following diagram shows how the HOMO of an excited state ethene molecule interacts with the LUMO of a ground state ethene molecule.

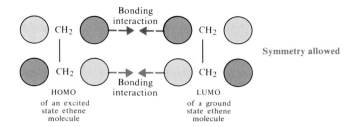

HOMO of an excited state ethene molecule — Bonding interaction — LUMO of a ground state ethene molecule — Symmetry allowed

Here we find that bonding interactions occur between both CH_2 groups, that is, lobes of the same sign overlap between both sets of carbon atoms. Complete correlation diagrams also show that the photochemical reaction is *symmetry allowed* and should occur readily through a concerted process. This, moreover, is what we observe experimentally: Ethene reacts readily in a *photochemical* cycloaddition.

The analysis that we have given for the [2 + 2] ethene cycloaddition can be made for any alkene [2 + 2] cycloaddition because the symmetry elements of the π and π^* orbitals of all alkenes are the same.

Problem O.10

What products would you expect from the following concerted cycloaddition reactions? (Give stereochemical formulas.)

(a) *cis*-2-Butene $\xrightarrow{h\nu}$

(b) *trans*-2-Butene $\xrightarrow{h\nu}$

Problem O.11

Show what happens in the following reaction:

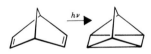

0.3B [4 + 2] Cycloadditions

Concerted [4 + 2] cycloadditions—Diels–Alder reactions—are *thermal reactions.* Considerations of orbital interactions allow us to account for this fact as well. To see how, let us consider the diagrams shown in Fig. O.3.

Both modes of orbital overlap shown in Fig. O.3 lead to bonding interactions and both involve *ground states* of the reactants. The ground state of a diene has two electrons in Ψ_2 (its HOMO). The overlap shown in part (a) allows these two electrons to flow into the LUMO, π^*, of the dienophile. The overlap shown in part (b) allows two electrons to flow from the HOMO of the dienophile, π, into the LUMO of the diene, Ψ_3^*. This thermal reaction is said to be symmetry allowed.

In Section 12.10 we saw that the Diels–Alder reaction proceeds with retention of configuration of the dienophile. Because the Diels–Alder reaction is usually concerted, it also proceeds with retention of configuration of the diene.

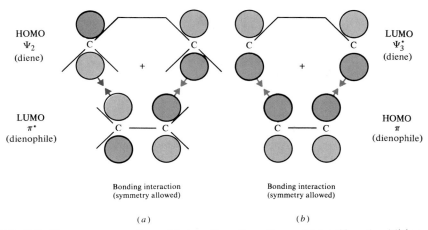

FIGURE O.3 Two symmetry-allowed interactions for a thermal [4 + 2] cycloaddition. (*a*) Bonding interaction between the HOMO of a diene and the LUMO of a dienophile. (*b*) Bonding interaction between the LUMO of the diene and the HOMO of the dienophile.

Problem O.12 ——

What products would you expect from the following reaction?

Problem 0.13

What are compounds **3**, **4**, and **5** in the following reaction sequence?

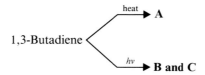

*Problem 0.14

Propose structures for compounds **A**, **B**, and **C**.

1,3-Butadiene
 — heat → **A**
 — hv → **B and C**

*Problem 0.15

What are the intermediates **A** and **B** in the following synthesis of basketene?

Cyclooctatetraene — heat ⇌ **A** (C_8H_8) — heat → **B** ($C_{12}H_{10}O_3$)

— hv → … — two steps → … ≡ …

Basketene

ANSWERS TO
SELECTED PROBLEMS

Chapter 1

1.8 (a), (b), (d), (e), (g) tetrahedral; (c), (i) trigonal planar; (f), (h) linear.

1.10 (a) $\xrightarrow{\text{H—Br;}}$; (b) $\xrightarrow{\text{I—Cl;}}$; (c) H_2, $\mu = 0$; (d) Cl_2, $\mu = 0$.

1.11 The bond moments cancel.

1.15 Trigonal planar structure causes bond moments to cancel.

1.18 (a) and (d), (e) and (f).

1.32 (a) An sp^3 orbital; (b) an sp^3 orbital.

1.38 The carbon atom of the methyl cation is sp^2 hybridized and uses sp^2 orbitals to form bonds to each hydrogen. The carbon also has a vacant p orbital.

Chapter 2

2.6 (a) RCH_2OH; (b) R_2CHOH; (c) R_3COH

2.12 Molecules of trimethylamine cannot form hydrogen bonds to each other, whereas molecules of propylamine can.

2.14 (a) Alkyne; (d) aldehyde.

2.19 (c) Tertiary; (e) secondary.

2.20 (a) Secondary; (c) tertiary.

2.21 (b) $CH_3CH_2CH_2OH$ (e) $CH_3CH_2CH_2CH_2X$ (l) $CH_3N(CH_3)CH_2CH_3$

2.22 (b) Ethylene glycol; (f) propionic acid

2.24 Ester

Chapter 3

3.4 (a) $[H_3O^+] = 0.0915\ M$ (b) % Ionized $= 91.5$

3.5 (a) $pK_a = 7$, (b) $pK_a = 5$, (c) The acid with $pK_a = 5$ is stronger

3.7 Aniline is the weaker base.

3.9 (a) $CHCF_2CO_2H$ is stronger. (d) CH_2FCO_2H is stronger.

3.12 (a) $:\!\ddot{N}H_2^-$; (c) $:H^-$; (e) $CH_3\ddot{O}\!:^-$; (f) H_2O

3.14 (a) H_2SO_4; (c) $CH_3NH_3^+$; (e) CH_3CH_3; (f) CH_3CO_2H

3.20 (a) $pK_a = 3.752$; (b) $K_a = 10^{-13}$

Chapter 4

4.6 (d) 7-Methylbicyclo[4.2.1]nonane

4.15 (a) $CH_3CHClCHClCH_2CH_3$ (k) $CH_3CH(CH_3)CH_2CH_2CH_2Cl$ (m) $CH_3C(CH_3)_2CH_2Cl$ (n) $CH_3CH(CH_3)CH_2CH_3$

4.16 (a) 3,4-Dimethylhexane; (f) cyclopentylcyclopentane.

4.17 (a) Neopentane (or 2,2-dimethyl-propane); (d) cyclopentane.

4.18 $\underset{\displaystyle CH_3}{CH_2{=}CCH_2CH_3}$, $\underset{\displaystyle CH_3}{CH_3C{=}CHCH_3}$, and $\underset{\displaystyle CH_3}{CH_3CHCH{=}CH_2}$

4.26 (c)

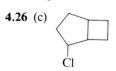

Cl

4.29 (d) Chloroethane; (e) ethanol.

4.32 (c) *trans*-1,4-Dimethylcyclohexane.

Chapter 5

5.1 Chiral: (a), (e)–(h); achiral: (b)–(d).

5.6 (b)–(d).

5.13 75% (*S*)-(+)-2-Butanol and 25% (*R*)-(−)-2-butanol.

5.14 (a) Diastereomers; (b) diastereomers; (c) diastereomers; (e) yes; (f) no.

5.15 (a) **A** alone would be optically active.

5.20 (a) No; (b) yes; (c) no; (d) no; (e), (f) diastereomers.

5.26 (a) Enantiomers; (d) diastereomers; (g) two molecules of the same compound; (j) enantiomers; (n) constitutional isomers; (p) diastereomers; (q) enantiomers.

Chapter 6

6.1 (a) $CH_3CH_2\ddot{O}H$; (c) $:NH_3$; (e) $^-:C\equiv N:$

6.2 *cis*-3-Methylcyclopentanol.

6.5 (a) $CH_3CH_2OC(CH_3)_3$

6.8 (a) NH_2^-; (b) RS^-; (c) PH_3

6.13 (a) $CH_3CH_2CH_2CH_2Br$ because it is a primary halide; (c) $CH_3CH_2CH_2Br$ because bromide ion is a better leaving group.

6.15 (b) $(CH_3)_3CBr + H_2O \longrightarrow$
$(CH_3)_3COH + HBr$
because water is a more polar medium than CH_3OH.

6.19 Reaction (2) because the substrate for the S_N2 reaction is a methyl halide.

6.24 (a) CH_3NH^- because it is the stronger base.

Chapter 7

7.1 (a) $\Delta H° = -25$ kcal mol^{-1}, (c) $\Delta H° = +9.5$ kcal mol^{-1}.

7.14 Good yields can be obtained when all of the hydrogen atoms of the compound are equivalent.

7.17 (b) Diastereomers. (c) no, the (R,S) isomer is a meso form; (e) yes, because diastereomers have different physical properties.

7.18 (b) All fractions are optically inactive.

Chapter 8

8.1 (a) 2-Methyl-2-butene; (d) 4-methylcyclohexene.

8.5 (a) one; (b) one; (c) no; (d) no; (e) two.

8.10 (a) 2-Butene, the more highly substituted alkene. (b) *trans*-2-butene.

8.31 (c), (e), and (i) can exist as cis–trans isomers.

8.34 (a) cis–trans Isomerization. This happens because at 300 °C the molecules have enough energy to surmount the rotational barrier of the carbon–carbon double bond. (b) *trans*-2-Butene because it is more stable.

8.39 (a) *cis*-1,2-Dimethylcyclopentane; (b) *cis*-1,2-dimethylcyclohexane.

8.42 (a) IHD = 4; 2 double bonds; (b) 2 rings.

Chapter 9

9.1 2-Chloro-1-iodopropane.

9.13 (a) *meso*-2,3-Butanediol.

9.19 (c) Cyclopentanol; (i) cyclopentene.

9.29 2-Methylpropene > propene > ethene.

9.32 4-Methylcyclohexene.

9.34

$$\underset{CH_3C=CHCH_2CH_2C=CHCH_2CH_2CCH=CH_2}{\overset{\overset{\displaystyle CH_3}{|}\qquad\quad\overset{\displaystyle CH_3}{|}\qquad\quad\overset{\displaystyle CH_2}{||}}{}}$$

9.39 (a) Propyne decolorizes Br_2/CCl_4; (d) 1-Butyne gives a ppt. with $Ag(NH_3)_2OH$

Chapter 10

10.2 Ethylene glycol is more highly associated, because having two —OH groups it can form more hydrogen bonds.

10.25 The reaction is an S_N2 reaction and, therefore, nucleophilic attack takes place more rapidly at the primary carbon atom.

10.30 (a) 3,3-Dimethyl-1-butanol; (e) 1-methyl-2-cyclopenten-1-ol.

10.37 (a) $CH_3Br + CH_3CH_2Br$; (c) $BrCH_2CH_2CH_2CH_2Br$

Chapter 11

11.1 (c) A change from -2 to 0; (d) an oxidation; (e) a reduction from $+6$ to $+3$.

ANSWERS TO SELECTED PROBLEMS

11.5 (a) PCC/CH_2Cl_2;
(b) $KMnO_4$, OH^-, H_2O, heat;
(c) H_2CrO_4/acetone;
(d) (1) O_3 (2) Zn, H_2O.

11.18 (a) $C_6H_5CH{=}CH_2$, H_2O, H^+, and
heat, or $C_6H_5CH{=}CH_2$, $Hg(O_2CCH_3)_2$,
H_2O, then $NaBH_4$, OH^-;
(e) $C_6H_5CH_2CO_2H$, $LiAlH_4$, diethyl ether;
(h) C_6H_6, Br_2, $FeBr_3$, then Mg, Et_2O, then
ethylene oxide, then H_2O.

11.23 $CH_3CH_2COCH_3 + NaC{\equiv}CH$, then
H_3O^+

Chapter 12

12.1 (a) $^{14}CH_2{=}CH{-}CH_2{-}X +$
$X{-}^{14}CH_2{-}CH{=}CH_2$; (c) in equal
amounts.

12.6 (b) 1,4-Cyclohexadiene is an isolated
diene.

12.13 (a) 1,4-Dibromobutane +
$(CH_3)_3COK$, and heat;
(g) $HC{\equiv}CCH{=}CH_2 + H_2$, Ne_2B (P-2).

12.16 (a) 1-Butene + N-bromo-
succinimide, then $(CH_3)_3COK$ and heat;
(e) cyclopentane + Br_2, hv, then
$(CH_3)_3COK$ and heat, then N-
bromosuccinimide.

12.18 (a) $Ag(NH_3)_2OH$; (c) H_2SO_4;
(e) $AgNO_3$ in alcohol.

12.25 This is another example of rate
versus equilibrium control of a reaction.
The endo adduct, **G**, is formed faster, and
at the lower temperature it is the major
product. The exo adduct, **H**, is more stable,
and at the higher temperature it is the
major product.

Chapter 13

13.1 (a) None; (b) none.

13.5 Tropylium bromide is a largely ionic
compound consisting of the cycloheptatrienyl (tropylium) cation and a bromide anion.

13.21 The nitrogen atoms at positions 1-,
3-, and 7- are of the pyridine type. The
nitrogen at position 9- is of the pyrrole type.

13.27 Compound **V** is the cyclooctatet-

raenyl dianion, a 10 π electron aromatic
system.

13.28 (a)–(d) Would not be aromatic;
(e)–(h) would be aromatic.

Chapter 14

14.3 **A**, o-Bromotoluene; **B**, p-bromo-
toluene; **C**, m-bromotoluene; **D**, benzyl
bromide.

14.5 (a) One; (b) two; (c) one; (d) three;
(e) two; (f) three.

14.10 A doublet (3H) downfield; a quartet
(1H) upfield.

14.11 (a) CH_3CHICH_3; (b) CH_3CHBr_2;
(c) $CH_2ClCH_2CH_2Cl$

14.15 (a) $C_6H_5CH(CH_3)_2$;
(b) $C_6H_5CH(NH_2)CH_3$;

(c)

14.20 Phenylacetylene.

14.22

F

14.23 **G**, $CH_3CH_2CHBrCH_3$
H, $CH_2{=}CBrCH_2Br$

14.33 **R** is bicyclo[2.2.1]heptane.

14.36 **X** is m-xylene.

Chapter 15

15.2 $HO{-}NO_2 + HO{-}NO_2 \rightleftharpoons$
$\qquad H_2O^+{-}NO_2 + {}^-O{-}NO_2$
$H_2O^+{-}NO_2^+ \rightleftharpoons H_2O + NO_2^+$

15.7 (a) benzene +

15.20 Introduce the chlorine into the benzene ring first, otherwise the double bond will undergo addition of chlorine when ring chlorination is attempted.

15.23 (a) 5-Acetyl-2-methylbenzene-sulfonic acid; (c) 2,4-dimethoxynitro-benzene; (e) 4-hydroxy-3-nitrobenzene-sulfonic acid.

15.27 (a) Toluene, $KMnO_4$, OH^-, heat, then H_3O^+, then Cl_2, $FeCl_3$; (b) toluene, CH_3COCl, $AlCl_3$, then isolate para isomer; (c) toluene, HNO_3, H_2SO_4, then isolate para isomer, then Br_2, $FeBr_3$.

15.30 $p\text{-}NO_2C_6H_4O\text{—}\overset{\displaystyle O}{\overset{\|}{C}}C_6H_5$ and

$o\text{-}NO_2C_6H_4O\text{—}\overset{\displaystyle O}{\overset{\|}{C}}C_6H_5$

15.33

I

Chapter 16

16.2 (a) 1-Pentanol; (c) pentanal; (e) benzyl alcohol.

16.6 A hydride ion.

16.17 (b) $CH_3CH_2Br + (C_6H_5)_3P$, then strong base, then $C_6H_5COCH_3$;
(d) $CH_3I + (C_6H_5)_3P$, then strong base, then cyclopentanone;
(f) $CH_2=CHCH_2Br + (C_6H_5)_3P$, then strong base, then C_6H_5CHO.

16.24 (a) $CH_3CH_2CH_2OH$
(c) $CH_3CH_2CH_2OH$
(h) $CH_3CH_2CH=CHCH_3$
(j) $CH_3CH_2CO_2^-NH_4^+ + Ag\downarrow$
(l) $CH_3CH_2CH=NNHCONH_2$
(n) $CH_3CH_2CO_2H$

16.35 (a) Tollens' reagent; (e) Br_2/CCl_4; (f) Tollens' reagent; (h) Tollens' reagent.

16.41

X is

16.42 **Y** is 1-phenyl-2-butanone; **Z** is 4-phenyl-2-butanone.

Chapter 17

17.1 The enol form is phenol. It is especially stable because it is aromatic.

17.4 Base is consumed as the reaction takes place. A catalyst, by definition is not consumed.

17.6 (a), (b), (d), (f), (h), (i).

17.10 (b) $CH_3\overset{\displaystyle O}{\overset{\|}{C}}CH=C(CH_3)_2$

17.11 $C_6H_5CHO + OH^- \xrightarrow[\text{heat}]{CH_3CHO}$

$C_6H_5CH=CHCHO$

17.14 (b) $CH_3NO_2 + H\overset{\displaystyle O}{\overset{\|}{C}}H \xrightarrow{OH^-}$

$HOCH_2CH_2NO_2$

17.23 (a) $CH_3CH_2CH(OH)\underset{\underset{\displaystyle CH_3}{|}}{C}HCHO$

(b) $C_6H_5CH=\underset{\underset{\displaystyle CH_3}{|}}{C}CHO$

(k) $CH_3CH_2CH(OH)C_6H_5$

(l) $CH_3CH_2CH(OH)C\equiv CH$

17.28 **B** is $CH_3\overset{\displaystyle O}{\overset{\|}{C}}\text{—}\underset{\underset{\displaystyle OH}{|}}{\overset{\overset{\displaystyle CH_3}{|}}{C}}\text{—}CH_3$

Chapter 18

18.2 (a) CH_2FCO_2H; (c) CH_2ClCO_2H; (e) $CH_3CH_2CHClCO_2H$;

(g) $CF_3\text{—}\bigcirc\text{—}CO_2H$

18.6 (a) $C_6H_5CH_2Br + Mg +$ diethyl ether, then CO_2, then H_3O^+;
(c) $CH_2=CHCH_2Br + Mg +$ diethyl ether, then CO_2, then H_3O^+.

18.7 (a), (c), and (e).

18.10 In the carboxyl group of benzoic acid.

ANSWERS TO SELECTED PROBLEMS

18.15 (a) $(CH_3)_3CCO_2H + SOCl_2$, then NH_3, then P_4O_{10}, heat; (b) $CH_2=C-CH_3$
$\quad\quad\quad\quad\quad\quad\quad\quad\quad\quad\quad\quad\quad\quad\quad\quad\quad\quad | $
$\quad\quad\quad\quad\quad\quad\quad\quad\quad\quad\quad\quad\quad\quad\quad\quad\quad\quad CH_3$

18.24 (a) CH_3CO_2H
(c) $CH_3CO_2CH_2(CH_2)_2CH_3$
(e) $p\text{-}CH_3COC_6H_4CH_3 +$
$\quad\quad o\text{-}CH_3COC_6H_4CH_3$
(g) CH_3COCH_3
(i) $CH_3CONHCH_3$
(k) $CH_3CON(CH_3)_2$
(m) $(CH_3CO)_2O$
(o) $CH_3CO_2C_6H_5$

18.30 (a) $NaHCO_3/H_2O$; (c) $NaHCO_3/H_2O$; (e) OH^-/H_2O, heat, detect NH_3 with litmus paper; (g) $AgNO_3/alcohol$.

18.35 (a) Diethyl succinate; (c) ethyl phenylacetate; (e) ethyl chloroacetate.

18.39 **X** is diethyl malonate.

Chapter 19

19.5 (a) $CH_3(CH_2)_3CHO + NH_3 \xrightarrow{H_2, Ni}$
$\quad\quad\quad\quad\quad\quad\quad\quad CH_3(CH_2)_3CH_2NH_2$

(c) $CH_3(CH_2)_4CHO + C_6H_5NH_2 \xrightarrow{H_2, Ni}$
$\quad\quad\quad\quad\quad\quad\quad\quad CH_3(CH_2)_4CH_2NHC_6H_5$

19.6 The reaction of a secondary halide with ammonia is almost always accompanied by some elimination.

19.8 (a) Methoxybenzene + HNO_3 + H_2SO_4, then $Fe + HCl$; (b) Methoxybenzene + $CH_3COCl + AlCl_3$, then $NH_3 + H_2 + Ni$; (c) toluene + Cl_2 and light, then $(CH_3)_3N$; (d) p-nitrotoluene + $KMnO_4 + OH^-$, then H_3O^+, then $SOCl_2$ followed by NH_3, then $NaOBr$ (Br_2 in $NaOH$); (e) toluene + N-bromosuccinimide in CCl_4, then KCN, then $LiAlH_4$.

19.14 p-Nitroaniline + Br_2 + Fe, followed by $H_2SO_4/NaNO_2$ followed by CuBr, then Fe/HCl, then $H_2SO_4/NaNO_2$ followed by H_3PO_2.

19.37 **W** is N-benzyl-N-ethylaniline.

Chapter 20

20.4 (a) $CH_3CHCOCO_2C_2H_5$
$\quad\quad\quad\quad | $
$\quad\quad\quad\quad CO_2C_2H_5$

(b) $HCCH_2CO_2C_2H_5$ (with C=O at top)
$\quad\quad\overset{\displaystyle O}{\overset{\displaystyle \|}{}}$

20.7 *O*-alkylation that results from the oxygen of the enolate ion acting as a nucleophile.

20.9 (a) Reactivity is the same as with any S_N2 reaction. With primary halides substitution is highly favored, with secondary halides elimination competes with substitution, and with tertiary halides elimination is the exclusive course of the reaction. (b) Acetoacetic ester and 2-methylpropene. (c) Bromobenzene is unreactive toward nucleophilic substitution.

20.29 (b) **D** is racemic *trans*-1,2-cyclopentane-dicarboxylic acid, **E** is *cis*-1,2-cyclopentane-dicarboxylic acid a, meso compound.

20.38 (a) $CH_2=C(CH_3)CO_2CH_3$
(b) $KMnO_4$, OH^-, H_3O^+
(c) CH_3OH, H^+
(d) CH_3ONa, then H^+
(e) and (f)

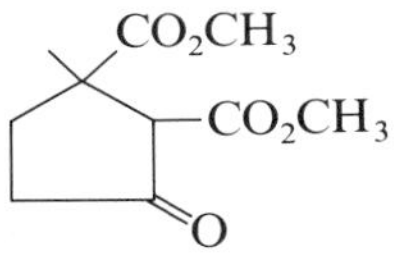

and

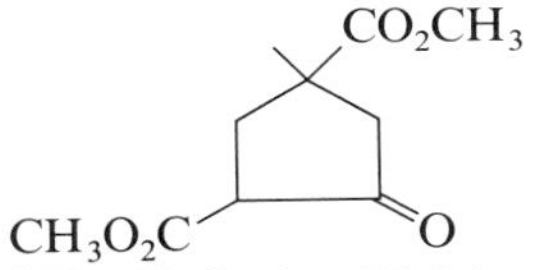

(g) OH^-, H_2O, then H_3O^+
(h) heat $(-CO_2)$
(i) CH_3OH, H^+
(j) Zn, $BrCH_2CO_2CH_3$, diethyl ether, then H_3O^+
(k)

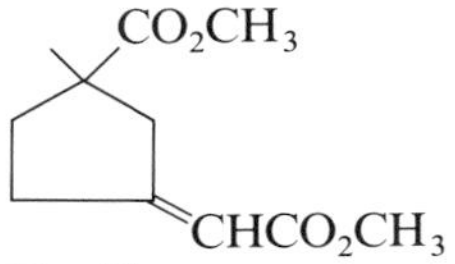

(l) H_2, Pt
(m) CH_3ONa, then H^+
(n) $2 NaNH_2 + 2 CH_3I$

Chapter 21

21.3 (d), (e), and (f) are all stronger acids than H_2CO_3 and would be converted to soluble sodium salts by aqueous $NaHCO_3$.

21.4 (a) The *para*-sulfonated phenol.

21.7 (a)

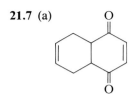

21.9 (a) OCH$_3$; (b) NO$_2$

NHCH$_3$

NO$_2$

(c) NHC$_6$H$_5$

NO$_2$

NO$_2$

21.22 Z is 3-methyl-2-buten-1-ol.

Chapter 22

22.1 (a) Two; (b) two; (c) four.

22.5 Acid catalyzes hydrolysis of the glycosidic (acetal) group.

22.9 (a) 2 CH$_3$CHO, one molar equivalent HIO$_4$
(b) HCHO + HCO$_2$H + CH$_3$CHO, two molar equivalents HIO$_4$
(c) HCHO + OHCCH(OCH$_3$)$_2$, one molar equivalent HIO$_4$
(d) HCHO + HCO$_2$H + CH$_3$CO$_2$H, two molar equivalents HIO$_4$
(e) 2 CH$_3$CO$_2$H + HCO$_2$H, two molar equivalents, HIO$_4$

22.18 D-(+)-Glucose.

22.23 One anomeric form of D-mannose is dextrorotatory ($[\alpha]_D = +29.3°$), the other is levorotatory ($[\alpha]_D = -17.0°$).

22.24 The microorganism selectively oxidizes the —CHOH group of D-glucitol that corresponds to C-5 of D-glucose.

22.27 A is D-altrose; **B** is D-talose, **C** is D-galactose.

Chapter 23

23.5 Br$_2$ in CCl$_4$ would be decolorized by geraniol but not by menthol.

23.12 (a) C$_2$H$_5$OH, H$^+$, heat or SOCl$_2$, then C$_2$H$_5$OH
(d) SOCl$_2$, then (CH$_3$)$_2$NH
(g) SOCl$_2$, then LiAlH[OCC(CH$_3$)$_3$]
(j) SOCl$_2$, then (CH$_3$)$_2$CuLi

23.15 Elaidic acid is *trans*-9-octadecenoic acid.

23.19 A is CH$_3$(CH$_2$)$_5$C≡CNa
B is
CH$_3$(CH$_2$)$_5$C≡CCH$_2$(CH$_2$)$_7$CH$_2$Cl
C is
CH$_3$(CH$_2$)$_5$C≡CCH$_2$(CH$_2$)$_7$CH$_2$CN
E is CH$_3$(CH$_2$)$_5$C≡CCH$_2$(CH$_2$)$_7$CH$_2$CO$_2$H
Vaccenic acid is

$$CH_3(CH_2)_5 \diagdown \qquad \diagup (CH_2)_9CO_2H$$
$$C=C$$
$$H \diagup \qquad \diagdown H$$

23.20 F is FCH$_2$(CH$_2$)$_6$CH$_2$C≡CH
G is FCH$_2$(CH$_2$)$_6$CH$_2$C≡C(CH$_2$)$_7$Cl
H is FCH$_2$(CH$_2$)$_6$CH$_2$C≡C(CH$_2$)$_7$CH$_2$CN
I is FCH$_2$(CH$_2$)$_7$C≡C(CH$_2$)$_7$CO$_2$H

Chapter 24

24.5 The labeled amino acid no longer has a basic —NH$_2$ group; it is, therefore, insoluble in aqueous acid.

24.8 Glutathione is
H$_3$NCHCH$_2$CH$_2$CONHCHCONHCH$_2$CO$_2$H
       | |
      CO$_2^-$ CH$_2$SH

24.20 Arg·Pro·Pro·Gly·Phe·Ser·Pro·Phe·Arg

24.21 Val·Leu·Lys·Phe·Ala·Glu·Ala

Chapter 25

25.2 (a) The nucleosides have an *N*-glycosidic linkage that (like an *O*-glycosidic linkage) is rapidly hydrolyzed by aqueous acid, but one that is stable in aqueous base.

25.3 The reaction appears to take place through an S$_N$2 mechanism. Attack occurs preferentially at the primary 5′-carbon atom rather than at the secondary 3′-carbon atom.

Periodic Table of the Elements

Periods →

Key

- atomic mass — 12.011
- electronegativity — 2.5
- [He]2s²2p² — electronic configuration
- symbol — C
- 6 — atomic number
- name — Carbon

Group I A

1 1.0079 2.2 1s **H** 1 Hydrogen									
2 6.941 1.0 [He]2s **Li** 3 Lithium	**II A** 9.01218 1.5 [He]2s² **Be** 4 Beryllium								
3 22.98977 1.0 [Ne]3s **Na** 11 Sodium	24.305 1.2 [Ne]3s² **Mg** 12 Magnesium	**III B**	**IV B**	**V B**	**VI B**	**VII B**	**VII**		

Period 4

III B	IV B	V B	VI B	VII B			
39.0983 0.9 [Ar]4s **K** 19 Potassium	40.08 1.0 [Ar]4s² **Ca** 20 Calcium	44.9559 1.2 [Ar]3d4s² **Sc** 21 Scandium	47.88 1.3 [Ar]3d²4s² **Ti** 22 Titanium	50.9415 1.5 [Ar]3d³4s² **V** 23 Vanadium	51.996 1.6 [Ar]3d⁵4s **Cr** 24 Chromium	54.9380 1.6 [Ar]3d⁵4s² **Mn** 25 Manganese	55.847 1.6 [Ar]3d⁶4s² **Fe** 26 Iron
							58.9332 1.7 [Ar]3d⁷4s² **Co** 27 Cobalt

Period 5

85.4678 0.9 [Kr]5s **Rb** 37 Rubidium	87.62 1.0 [Kr]5s² **Sr** 38 Strontium	88.9059 1.1 [Kr]4d5s² **Y** 39 Yttrium	91.22 1.2 [Kr]4d²5s² **Zr** 40 Zirconium	92.9064 1.2 [Kr]4d⁴5s **Nb** 41 Niobium	95.94 1.3 [Kr]4d⁵5s **Mo** 42 Molybdenum	98.906 1.4 [Kr]4d⁶5s **Tc** 43 Technetium	101.07 1.4 [Kr]4d⁷5s **Ru** 44 Ruthenium	102.9055 1.5 [Kr]4d⁸5s **Rh** 45 Rhodium

Period 6

132.9054 0.9 [Xe]6s **Cs** 55 Cesium	137.33 1.0 [Xe]6s² **Ba** 56 Barium	138.9055 1.1 [Xe]5d6s² *****La** 57 Lanthanum	178.49 1.2 [Xe]4f¹⁴5d²6s² **Hf** 72 Hafnium	180.9479 1.3 [Xe]4f¹⁴5d³6s² **Ta** 73 Tantalum	183.85 1.4 [Xe]4f¹⁴5d⁴6s² **W** 74 Tungsten	186.207 1.5 [Xe]4f¹⁴5d⁵6s² **Re** 75 Rhenium	190.2 1.5 [Xe]4f¹⁴5d⁶6s² **Os** 76 Osmium	192.22 1.6 [Xe]4f¹⁴5d⁷6s² **Ir** 77 Iridium

Period 7

(223) 0.9 [Rn]7s **Fr** 87 Francium	226.0254 1.0 [Rn]7s² **Ra** 88 Radium	227.0278 1.0 [Rn]6d7s² †**Ac** 89 Actinium	(261) [Rn]5f¹⁴6d²7s² **Unq** 104 Unnilquadium	(262) [Rn]5f¹⁴6d³7s² **Unp** 105 Unnilpentium	(263) [Rn]5f¹⁴6d⁴7s² **Unh** 106 Unnilhexium			

* Lanthanides — Period 6

140.12 1.1 [Xe]4f²6s² **Ce** 58 Cerium	140.9077 1.1 [Xe]4f³6s² **Pr** 59 Praseodymium	144.24 1.1 [Xe]4f⁴6s² **Nd** 60 Neodymium	145 1.1 [Xe]4f⁵6s² **Pm** 61 Promethium	150.4 1.1 [Xe]4f⁶6s² **Sm** 62 Samarium	151.96 1.0 [Xe]4f⁷6s² **Eu** 63 Europium	157.25 1.1 [Xe]4f⁷5d6s² **Gd** 64 Gadolinium

† Actinides — Period 7

232.0381 1.1 [Rn]6d²7s² **Th** 90 Thorium	231.0359 1.1 [Rn]5f²6d7s² **Pa** 91 Protactinium	238.029 1.2 [Rn]5f³6d7s² **U** 92 Uranium	237.0482 1.2 [Rn]5f⁴6d7s² **Np** 93 Neptunium	(244) 1.2 [Rn]5f⁶7s² **Pu** 94 Plutonium	(243) 1.2 [Rn]5f⁷7s² **Am** 95 Americium	(247) ≈1.2 [Rn]5f⁷6d7s² **Cm** 96 Curium

TABLE 14.3 Approximate proton chemical shifts

TYPE OF PROTON	CHEMICAL SHIFT, δ (ppm)
1° Alkyl, RCH_3	0.8–1.0
2° Alkyl, RCH_2R	1.2–1.4
3° Alkyl, R_3CH	1.4–1.7
Allylic, $R_2C=C-CH_3$ (with R)	1.6–1.9
Benzylic, $ArCH_3$	2.2–2.5
Alkyl chloride, RCH_2Cl	3.6–3.8
Alkyl bromide, RCH_2Br	3.4–3.6
Alkyl iodide, RCH_2I	3.1–3.3
Ether, $ROCH_2R$	3.3–3.9
Alcohol, $HOCH_2R$	3.3–4.0
Ketone, $RCCH_3$ (C=O)	2.1–2.6
Aldehyde, RCH (C=O)	9.5–9.6
Vinylic, $R_2C=CH_2$	4.6–5.0
Vinylic, $R_2C=CH-R$	5.2–5.7
Aromatic, ArH	6.0–9.5
Acetylenic, $RC\equiv CH$	2.5–3.1
Alcohol hydroxyl, ROH	0.5–6.0[a]
Carboxylic, RCOH (C=O)	10–13[a]
Phenolic, ArOH	4.5–7.7[a]
Amino, $R-NH_2$	1.0–5.0[a]

[a] The chemical shifts of these protons vary in different solvents and with temperature and concentration.

TABLE 14.4 Approximate carbon-13 chemical shifts

TYPE OF CARBON ATOM	CHEMICAL SHIFT, δ (ppm)
1° Alkyl, RCH_3	0–40
2° Alkyl, RCH_2R	10–50
3° Alkyl, $RCHR_2$	10–50
Alkyl halide or amine, $-C-X$ (X = Cl, Br, or $N-$)	10–65
Alcohol or ether, $-C-O$	50–90
Alkyne, $-C\equiv$	60–90
Alkene, $C=$	100–170
Aryl	100–170
Nitriles, $-C\equiv N$	120–130
Amides, $-C-N-$ (C=O)	150–180
Carboxylic acids, esters, $-C-O$ (C=O)	160–185
Aldehydes, ketones, $-C-$ (C=O)	182–215

BIBLIOGRAPHY OF SUGGESTED READINGS

J. G. MacConnell and Robert M. Silverstein, "Recent Results in Insect Pheromone Chemistry," *Angew. Chem. Int. Ed. Engl.,* **1973,** *12,* 644.

Chapter 10

H. C. Brown, *Organic Syntheses via Boranes,* Wiley, New York, 1975.

H. C. Brown, *Hydroboration,* Benjamin, New York, 1962.

H. C. Brown and P. J. Geoghegan, Jr., "Solvomercuration–Demercuration. I.," *J. Org. Chem.,* **1970,** *35,* 1844.

G. Zweifel and H. C. Brown, "Hydration of Olefins, Dienes, and Acetylenes, via Hydroboration," *Organic Reactions* Vol. 13, Wiley, NY, 1963.

N. Isenberg and M. Grdinic, "A Modern Look at Markovnikov's Rule and the Peroxide Effect," *J. Chem. Educ.,* **1969,** *46,* 601.

S. Patai, Ed., *Chemistry of the Hydroxyl Group,* Wiley, New York, 1971.

S. Patai, Ed., *Chemistry of the Ether Linkage,* Wiley, New York, 1967.

L. B. Clapp, *The Chemistry of the OH Group,* Prentice–Hall, Englewood Cliffs, NJ, 1967.

W. P. Weber and G. W. Gokel, "Phase Transfer Catalysis," *J. Chem. Educ.,* **1978,** *55,* 350 (Part I) and 429 (Part II).

R. West and T. J. Barton, "Organosilicon Chemistry," *J. Chem. Educ.,* **1980,** *57,* 334.

H. C. Brown, "The Borane Adventure—Past, Present and Future," *Isr. J. Chem.,* **1985,** *25,* 84.

G. W. Kabalka, "Incorporation of Stable and Radioactive Isotopes via Organoborane Chemistry," *Acc. Chem. Res.,* **1984,** *17,* 215.

Special Topic B

R. P. Quirk, "Stereochemistry and Macromolecules," *J. Chem. Educ.,* **1981,** *58,* 540.

F. W. Billmeyer, *Textbook of Polymer Science,* 3rd ed., Wiley, New York, 1984.

L. R. G. Treloar, *Introduction to Polymer Science,* Springer–Verlag, New York, 1970.

J. Chem. Educ., **1981,** *58* Nov. (An entire issue devoted to polymer chemistry.)

Special Topic C

M. Jones, Jr., "Carbenes," *Sci. Am.,* **1976,** *276,* No. 2, 101.

J. Hine, *Divalent Carbon,* Ronald Press, New York, 1964

G. L. Closs, "Structures of Carbenes and the Stereochemistry of Carbene Additions to Olefins," *Topics in Stereochemistry,* Vol. 3, Wiley, New York, 1968.

W. E. Parham and E. E. Schweizer, "Halocyclopropanes from Halocarbenes," *Organic Reactions,* Vol. 13, Wiley, New York, 1963.

H. E. Simmons, T. L. Cairns, S. A. Vladuchick, and C. M. Hoiness, "Cyclopropanes from Unsaturated Compounds, Methylene Iodide, and Zinc–Copper Couple," *Organic Reactions,* Vol. 20, Wiley, New York, 1973.

Chapter 11

H. C. Brown, "Hydride Reductions: A 40-Year Revolution in Organic Chemistry," *Chem. Eng. News,* **1979,** *24,* March 5.

Chapter 12

J. March, *Advanced Organic Chemistry,* 3rd ed., Wiley, New York, 1985, pp. 24–37.

A. Liberles, *Introduction to Molecular Orbital Theory,* Holt, Rinehart, and Winston, New York, 1966.

M. Orchin and H. H. Jaffé, *The Importance of Antibonding Orbitals,* Houghton Mifflin, Boston, 1967.

J. Sauer, "Diels–Alder Reactions, Part I," *Angew. Chem. Int. Ed. Engl.,* **1966,** *5,* 211; "Part II," *Angew. Chem. Int. Ed. Engl.,* **1967,** *6,* 16.

Chapter 13

J. March, *Advanced Organic Chemistry,* 3rd ed., Wiley, New York, 1985, pp. 37–64.

G. M. Badger, *Aromatic Character and Aromaticity,* Cambridge University Press, 1969.

R. Breslow, "Antiaromaticity," *Acc. Chem. Res.,* **1973,** *6,* 393.

F. Sondheimer, "The Annulenes," *Acc. Chem. Res.,* **1972,** *5,* 81.

L. J. Schaad and B. A. Hess, "Hückel Theory and Aromaticity," *J. Chem. Educ.,* **1974,** *51,* 640.

J. Aihara, "A New Definition of Dewar-Type Resonance Energies," *J. Am. Chem. Soc.,* **1976,** *98,* 2750.

R. G. Harvey, "Activated Metabolites of Carcinogenic Hydrocarbons," *Acc. Chem. Res.,* **1981,** *14,* 218.

C. Glidewell and D. Lloyd, "The Arithmetic of Aromaticity," *J. Chem. Educ.,* **1986,** *63,* 306.

BIBLIOGRAPHY OF SUGGESTED READINGS

Chapter 14

P. L. FUCHS and C. A. BUNNELL, *Carbon-13 NMR Based Organic Spectral Problems,* Wiley, New York, 1979.

G. C. LEVY and G. L. NELSON, *Carbon-13 Nuclear Magnetic Resonance for Organic Chemists,* Wiley, New York, 1972.

L. J. BELLAMY, *The Infrared Spectra of Complex Molecules,* 3rd ed., Wiley, New York, 1975.

J. D. ROBERTS, *An Introduction to Spin–Spin Splitting in High Resolution Nuclear Magnetic Resonance Spectra,* Benjamin, Menlo Park, CA, 1961.

F. A. BOVEY, *Nuclear Magnetic Resonance Spectroscopy,* Academic Press, New York, 1969.

J. D. ROBERTS and M. C. CASERIO, *Basic Principles of Organic Chemistry,* 2nd ed., Benjamin, Menlo Park, CA, 1977, Chapters 9 and 27.

R. M. SILVERSTEIN, G. C. BASSLER, and T. C. MORRILL, *Spectrometric Identification of Organic Compounds,* Wiley, New York, 1991.

J. R. DYER, *Applications of Absorption Spectroscopy of Organic Compounds,* Prentice–Hall, Englewood Cliffs, NJ, 1965.

J. D. ROBERTS, *Nuclear Magnetic Resonance,* McGraw–Hill, New York, 1959.

E. R. ANDREW, "NMR Imaging," *Acc. Chem. Res.,* **1983**, *16,* 114.

Special Topic D

W. F. MacLAFFERTY, *Interpretation of Mass Spectroscopy,* 2nd ed., Benjamin, Reading, MA, 1973.

Chapter 15

J. MARCH, *Advanced Organic Chemistry,* 3rd ed., Wiley, New York, 1985, Chapter 11.

G. A. OLAH, *Friedel–Crafts and Related Reactions,* Vol. I, Wiley, New York, 1963.

W. R. DOLBIER, JR., "Electrophilic Additions to Alkenes," *J. Chem. Educ.,* **1969**, *46,* 342.

E. C. TAYLOR and A. McKILLOP, "Thallium in Organic Synthesis," *Acc. Chem. Res.,* **1970**, *3,* 338.

Chapter 16

C. A. BUEHLER and D. E. PEARSON, *Survey of Organic Synthesis,* Wiley, New York, 1970.

H. O. HOUSE, *Modern Synthetic Reactions,* 2nd ed., Benjamin, New York, 1972.

S. PATAI, Ed., *The Chemistry of the Carbonyl Group,* Vol. 1, Wiley, New York, 1966.

S. PATAI AND J. ZABICKY, Eds., *The Chemistry of the Carbonyl Group,* Vol. 2, Wiley, New York, 1970.

E. VEDEJS, "Clemmensen Reduction of Ketones in Anhydrous Organic Solvents," *Organic Reactions,* Vol. 22, Wiley, New York, 1975.

M. W. RATHKE, "The Reformatsky Reaction," *Organic Reactions,* Vol. 22, Wiley, New York, 1975.

C. H. HASSALL, "The Baeyer–Villiger Oxidation of Aldehydes and Ketones," *Organic Reactions,* Vol. 9, Wiley, New York, 1957.

Chapter 17

A. J. NIELSON and W. J. HOULIHAN, "The Aldol Condensation," *Organic Reactions,* Vol. 16, Wiley, New York, 1968.

G. H. POSNER, "Conjugate Addition Reactions of Organocopper Reagents," *Organic Reactions,* Vol. 19, Wiley, New York, 1972.

Special Topic E

T. MUKAIYAMA, "The Directed Aldol Reaction," *Organic Reactions,* Vol. 28, Wiley, New York, 1982, p. 203.

I. KUWAJIMA and E. NAKAMURA, "Reactive Enolates from Enol Silyl Ethers," *Acc. Chem. Res.,* **1985**, *18,* 181.

G. STORK and P. F. HUDRLIK, "Isolation of Ketone Enolates as Trialkylsilyl Ethers, *J. Am. Chem. Soc.* **1968**, *90,* 4462.

H. J. REICH, "Functional Group Manipulation Using Organoselenium Reagents," *Acc. Chem. Res.,* **1979**, *12,* 22.

D. L. J. CLIVE, "Selenium Reagents for Organic Synthesis," *Aldrichimica Acta,* **1978**, *11,* 43.

D. LIOTTA, "New Organoselenium Methodology," *Acc. Chem. Res.,* **1984**, *17,* 28.

Chapter 18

S. PATAI, Ed., *The Chemistry of Carboxylic Acids and Esters,* Wiley, New York, 1969.

L. F. FIESER and M. FIESER, *Advanced Organic Chemistry,* Reinhold, New York, 1961, Chapters 11, 23, and 24.

S. PATAI, Ed., *The Chemistry of Amides,* Wiley, New York, 1969.

C. D. GUTSCHE, *The Chemistry of Carbonyl Compounds,* Prentice–Hall, Englewood Cliffs, NJ, 1967.

Special Topic F

J. K. STILLE, *Industrial Organic Chemistry,* Prentice–Hall, Englewood Cliffs, NJ, 1968.

BIBLIOGRAPHY OF SUGGESTED READINGS

Chapter 19

G. B. KAUFFMAN, "Isoniazid-Destroyer of the White Plague," *J. Chem. Educ.,* **1978,** *55,* 448–449.

S. PATAI, Ed., *The Chemistry of the Amino Group,* Wiley, New York, 1968.

L. F. FIESER and M. FIESER, *Advanced Organic Chemistry,* Reinhold, New York, 1961, Chapters 14 and 21.

H. K. PORTER, "The Zinin Reduction of Nitroarenes," *Organic Reactions,* Vol. 20, Wiley, New York, 1973.

H. ZOLLINGER, *Diazo and Azo Chemistry,* Wiley, New York, 1961.

L. A. PAGUETTE, *Principles of Modern Heterocyclic Chemistry,* Benjamin, New York, 1968.

Special Topic G

L. A. PAGUETTE, *Principles of Modern Heterocyclic Chemistry,* Benjamin, New York, 1968.

Chapter 20

C. R. HAUSER and B. E. HUDSON, "The Acetoacetic Ester Condensation and Certain Related Reactions," *Organic Reactions,* Vol. 1, Wiley, New York, 1942.

H. O. HOUSE, *Modern Synthetic Reactions,* Benjamin, New York, 1965, Chapters 7 and 9.

W. McCRAE, *Basic Organic Reactions,* Heyden and Son, Ltd., London, 1973, Chapters 3 and 4.

J. P. SCHAEFER and J. J. BLOOMFIELD, "The Dieckmann Condensation," *Organic Reactions,* Vol. 15, Wiley, New York, 1967.

G. JONES, "The Knoevenagel Condensation," *Organic Reactions,* Vol. 15, Wiley, New York, 1967.

T. M. HARRIS and C. M. HARRIS, "The γ-Alkylation and γ-Arylation of Dianions of β-Dicarbonyl Compounds," *Organic Reactions,* Vol. 17, Wiley, New York, 1969.

A. G. COOK, *Enamines: Synthesis, Structure, and Reactions,* Dekker, New York, 1969.

V. BOEKELHEIDE, "[2n] Cyclophanes: Paracyclophane to Superphane," *Acc. Chem. Res.,* **1980,** *13,* 67.

J. K. WHITESELL, "New Perspectives in Asymmetric Induction," *Acc. of Chem. Res.,* **1985,** *18,* 280.

Special Topic H

G. A. SWAN, *An Introduction to Alkaloids,* Wiley, New York, 1967.

T. A. GEISSMAN and D. H. G. CROUT, *Organic Chemistry of Secondary Plant Metabolism,* Freeman, Cooper and Co., San Francisco, 1969, Chapters 16–19.

H. HART and J. L. REILLY, "Oxidative Coupling of Phenols," *J. Chem. Educ.,* **1978,** *55,* 120.

Chapter 21

J. F. BUNNETT, "The Remarkable Reactivity of Aryl Halides with Nucleophiles," *J. Chem. Educ.,* **1974,** *51,* 312.

S. PATAI, Ed., *Chemistry of the Hydroxyl Group,* Wiley, New York, 1971.

Special Topic J

J. SCHWARTZ and J. A. LABINGER, "Patterns in Organometallic Chemistry with Application in Organic Synthesis," *J. Chem. Educ.,* **1980,** *57,* 170.

M. ORCHIN, "HCo(CO)₄, The Quintessential Catalyst," *Acc. Chem. Res.,* **1981,** *14,* 259.

J. E. ELLIS, "The Teaching of Organometallic Chemistry to Undergraduates," *J. Chem. Educ.,* **1976,** *53,* 2.

J. P. COLLMAN, "Patterns of Organometallic Reactions Related to Homogeneous Catalysis," *Acc. Chem. Res.,* **1968,** *1,* 136.

J. P. COLLMAN, "Disodium Tetracarbonylferrate —A Transition-Metal Analog of a Grignard Reagent," *Acc. Chem. Res.,* **1975,** *8,* 342.

Special Topic K

D. L. RABENSTEIN, "The Chemistry of Methylmercury Toxicology," *J. Chem. Educ.,* **1978,** *55,* 292.

J. R. HOLUM, *Topics and Terms in Environmental Problems,* Wiley, New York, 1977.

Chem. Eng. News, **1983,** June 6. (An entire issue devoted to Dioxin.)

R. E. BEYLER and V. K. MEYERS "What Every Chemist Should Know about Teratogens—Chemicals that Cause Birth Defects," *J. Chem. Educ.* **1982,** *59,* 759.

F. H. TSCHIRLEY, "Dioxin," *Sci. Am.,* **1986,** *254,* No. 2, 29.

Chapter 22

R. J. BERGERON, "Cycloamyloses," *J. Chem. Educ.,* **1977,** *54,* 204.

L. N. FERGUSON et al., "Sweet Organic Chemistry," *J. Chem. Educ.,* **1978,** *55,* 281.

BIBLIOGRAPHY OF SUGGESTED READINGS

G. B. KAUFFMAN and R. P. CIULA, "Emil Fischer's Discovery of Phenylhydrazine," *J. Chem. Educ.,* **1977,** *54,* 295.

C. R. NOLLER, *Chemistry of Organic Compounds,* 3rd ed., Saunders, New York, 1965, Chapter 18.

D. E. GREEN and R. F. GOLDBERGER, *Molecular Insights into the Living Process,* Academic Press, New York, 1967, Chapters 2 and 3.

C. S. HUDSON, "Emil Fischer's Discovery of the Configuration of Glucose," *J. Chem. Educ.,* **1941,** *18,* 353.

R. BARKER, *Organic Chemistry of Biological Compounds,* Prentice–Hall, Englewood Cliffs, NJ, 1971, Chapter 5.

I. TABUSHI, "Cyclodextrin Catalysis as a Model for Enzyme Action," *Acc. Chem. Res.,* **1982,** *15,* 66.

A. CERAMI, H. VLASSARA, and M. BROWNLEE, "Glucose and Aging," *Sci. Am.,* **1987,** *256,* No. 5, 90.

R. BENTLEY and J. L. POPP, "Configurations of Glucose and Other Aldoses," *J. Chem. Educ.,* **1987,** *64,* 15.

D. VOET and J. G. VOET, *Biochemistry,* Wiley, New York, 1990, Chapter 10.

Chapter 23 —————

D. KOLB, "A Pill for Birth Control," *J. Chem. Educ.,* **1978,** *55,* 591.

L. F. FIESER, "Steroids," *Bio-organic Chemistry: Readings from Scientific American,* M. Calvin and M. Jorgenson, Eds., Freeman, San Francisco, 1968.

E. E. CONN, P. K. STUMPF, G. BREUENING, and R. H. DORI, *Outlines of Biochemistry,* 5th ed., Wiley, New York, 1987.

J. R. HANSON, *Introduction to Steroid Chemistry,* Pergamon Press, New York, 1968.

F. M. MENGER, "On the Structure of Micelles," *Acc. Chem. Res.,* **1979,** *12,* 111.

R. BRESLOW, "Biomimetic Control of Chemical Selectivity," *Acc. Chem. Res.,* **1980,** *13,* 170.

S. HAKOMORI, "Glycosphingolipids," *Sci. Am.,* **1986,** *254,* No. 5, 44.

D. VOET and J. G. VOET, *Biochemistry,* Wiley, New York, 1990, Chapter 11.

Special Topic L —————

W. S. JOHNSON, "Nonenzymic Biogenetic-like Olefin Cyclizations," *Acc. Chem. Res.,* **1968,** *1,* 1.

C. D. POULTER and H. C. RILLING, "The Prenyl Transfer Reaction. Enzymatic and Mechanistic Studies of 1′–4 Coupling Reaction in Terpene Biosynthetic Pathway," *Acc. Chem. Res.,* **1978,** *11,* 307.

J. W. CORNFORTH, "Terpenoid Biosynthesis," *Chem. Br.,* **1968,** *4,* 102.

J. B. HENDRICKSON, *The Molecules of Nature,* W. A. Benjamin, Menlo Park, CA, 1965.

Chapter 24 —————

N. M. SENOZAN and R. L. HUNT, "Hemoglobin: Its Occurrence, Structure, and Adaptation," *J. Chem. Educ.,* **1982,** *59,* 173.

R. BRESLOW, "Artificial Enzymes," *Science,* **1982,** *218,* 532.

J. R. HOLUM, *Elements of General and Biological Chemistry,* Wiley, New York, 1991, Chapters 16 and 20.

The following articles from *Bio-organic Chemistry: Readings from Scientific American,* M. Calvin and M. Jorgenson, Eds., Freeman, San Francisco, 1968:

P. DOTY, "Proteins," p. 15.

W. H. STEIN and S. MOORE, "The Chemical Structure of Proteins," p. 23.

E. O. P. THOMPSON, "The Insulin Molecule," p. 34.

M. F. PERUTZ, "The Hemoglobin Molecule," p. 41.

E. ZUCKERKANDL, "The Evolution of Hemoglobin," p. 53.

D. C. PHILLIPS, "The Three-Dimensional Structure of an Enzyme Molecule," p. 67.

H. D. LAW, *The Organic Chemistry of Peptides,* Wiley, New York, 1970.

D. E. GREEN and R. F. GOLDBERGER, *Molecular Insights into the Living Process,* Academic Press, 1967, Chapters 4 and 5.

E. E. CONN, P. K. STUMPF, G. BRUENING, and R. H. DORI, *Outlines of Biochemistry,* 5th ed., Wiley, New York, 1987, Chapter 4.

R. E. DICKERSON and I. GEIS, *The Structure and Action of Proteins,* Harper and Row, New York, 1969.

M. D. FRYZUK and B. BOSNICH, "Asymmetric Synthesis. Production of Optically Active Amino Acids by Catalytic Hydrogenation," *J. Am. Chem. Soc.,* **1977,** *99,* 6262.

W. S. KNOWLES, "Asymmetric Hydrogenation," *Acc. Chem. Res.,* **1983,** *16,* 106.

B. MERRIFIELD, "Solid Phase Synthesis," *Science,* **1986,** *232,* 341.

J. REBEK, "Model Studies in Molecular Recognition," *Science,* **1987,** *235,* 1478.

R. F. DOOLITTLE, "Proteins," *Sci. Am.,* **1985,** *253,* No. 4, 88.

V. T. D'SOUZA and M. L. BENDER, "Miniature Organic Models of Enzymes," *Acc. Chem. Res,* **1987,** *20,* 146.

D. VOET and J. G. VOET, *Biochemistry,* Wiley, New York, 1990, Chapters 4, 6, 7, and Part III.

BIBLIOGRAPHY OF SUGGESTED READINGS

Chapter 25 ────────────

J. D. WATSON, *Molecular Biology of the Gene,* 2nd ed., Benjamin, New York, 1970.

The following articles in *Bio-organic Chemistry: Readings from Scientific American,* M. Calvin and M. J. Jorgenson, Eds., Freeman, San Francisco, 1968:

F. H. C. CRICK, "The Structure of the Hereditary Material," p. 75.

R. W. Holley, "The Nucleotide Sequence of a Nucleic Acid," p. 82.

R. A. WEINBERG, "The Molecules of Life," *Sci. Am.,* **1985,** *253,* No. 4, 48.

G. FELSENFELD, "DNA," *Sci. Am.,* **1985,** *253,* No. 4, 58.

J. E. DARNELL, "RNA," *Sci. Am.,* **1985,** *253,* No. 4, 68.

G. B. ELION, "The Purine Path to Chemotherapy," *Science,* **1989,** *244,* 41.

A. M. MAXAM and W. GILBERT, "A New Method for Sequencing DNA," *Proc. Natl. Acad. Sci. USA,* **1977,** *74,* 560.

E. UHLMANN and A. PEYMAN, "Antisense oligonucleotides: A New Therapeutic Principle," *Chem. Rev.,* **1990,** *90,* 544.

H. M. WEINTRAUB, "Antisense RNA and DNA," *Sci. Am.,* **1990,** *262,* No. 1, 34.

K. B. MULLIS, "The Unusual Origin of the Polymerase Chain Reaction," *Sci. Am.,* **1990,** *262,* No. 4, 56.

N. ARNHEIM and C. H. LEVENSON, *Chem. Eng. News,* **1990,** *68,* No. 40, 36.

D. VOET and J. G. VOET, *Biochemistry,* Wiley, New York, 1990, Part V.

Special Topic M ────────────

R. HUBBARD and A. KROPF, "Molecular Isomers in Vision," *Bio-organic Chemistry: Readings from Scientific American,* M. Calvin and M. Jorgenson, Eds., Freeman, San Francisco, 1968.

R. H. JOHNSON and T. P. WILLIAMS, "Action of Light upon the Visual Pigment Rhodopsin," *J. Chem. Educ.,* **1970,** *47,* 736.

E. L. MENGER, Ed., "Special Issue on the Chemistry of Vision," *Acc. Chem. Res.,* **1975,** *8,* (3), 81–112.

L. STRYER, "The Molecules of Visual Excitation," *Sci. Am.,* **1987,** *257,* No. 1, 42.

Special Topic N ────────────

W. H. SAUNDERS, JR. and A. F. COCKERILL, *Mechanisms of Elimination Reactions,* Wiley, New York, 1973.

W. H. SAUNDERS, JR., "Distinguishing between Concerted and Nonconcerted Eliminations," *Acc. Chem. Res.,* **1976,** *9,* 19.

D. J. RABER and J. M. HARRIS, "Nucleophilic Substitution Reactions at Secondary Carbon Atoms," *J. Chem. Educ.,* **1972,** *49,* 60.

R. A. SNEEN, "Organic Ion Pairs as Intermediates in Nucleophilic Substitution and Elimination Reactions," *Acc. Chem. Res.,* **1973,** *6,* 46.

F. G. BORDWELL, "How Common are Base Initiated, Concerted 1,2-Eliminations?" *Acc. Chem. Res.,* **1972,** *5,* 374.

Special Topic O ────────────

K. N. HOUK, "The Frontier Molecular Orbital Theory of Cycloaddition Reactions," *Acc. Chem. Res.,* **1975,** *8,* 361.

R. W. WOODWARD and R. HOFFMAN, *The Conservation of Orbital Symmetry,* Academic Press, New York, 1970.

INDEX

					He
					4.0026
					$1s^2$
					He 2
					Helium

III A	IV A	V A	VI A	VII A	
10.81	12.011	14.0067	15.9994	18.9984	20.179
2.0	2.5	3.1	3.5	4.1	
$[He]2s^2 2p$	$[He]2s^2 2p^2$	$[He]2s^2 2p^3$	$[He]2s^2 2p^4$	$[He]2s^2 2p^5$	$[He]2s^2 2p^6$
B 5	**C** 6	**N** 7	**O** 8	**F** 9	**Ne** 10
Boron	Carbon	Nitrogen	Oxygen	Fluorine	Neon
26.9815	28.0855	30.97376	32.06	35.453	39.948
1.5	1.7	2.1	2.4	2.8	
$[Ne]3s^2 3p$	$[Ne]3s^2 3p^2$	$[Ne]3s^2 3p^3$	$[Ne]3s^2 3p^4$	$[Ne]3s^2 3p^5$	$[Ne]3s^2 3p^6$
Al 13	**Si** 14	**P** 15	**S** 16	**Cl** 17	**Ar** 18
Aluminum	Silicon	Phosphorus	Sulfur	Chlorine	Argon

I B	II B	III A	IV A	V A	VI A	VII A	
58.70	63.546	65.38	69.72	72.59	74.9216	78.96	79.904	83.80

	I B	II B						
58.70	63.546	65.38	69.72	72.59	74.9216	78.96	79.904	83.80
1.8	1.8	1.7	1.8	2.0	2.2	2.5	2.7	
$[Ar]3d^8 4s^2$	$[Ar]3d^{10}4s$	$[Ar]3d^{10}4s^2$	$[Ar]3d^{10}4s^2 4p$	$[Ar]3d^{10}4s^2 4p^2$	$[Ar]3d^{10}4s^2 4p^3$	$[Ar]3d^{10}4s^2 4p^4$	$[Ar]3d^{10}4s^2 4p^5$	$[Ar]3d^{10}4s^2 4p^6$
Ni 28	**Cu** 29	**Zn** 30	**Ga** 31	**Ge** 32	**As** 33	**Se** 34	**Br** 35	**Kr** 36
Nickel	Copper	Zinc	Gallium	Germanium	Arsenic	Selenium	Bromine	Krypton
106.4	107.868	112.41	114.82	118.69	121.75	127.60	126.9045	131.30
1.4	1.4	1.5	1.5	1.7	1.8	2.0	2.2	
$[Kr]4d^{10}$	$[Kr]4d^{10}5s$	$[Kr]4d^{10}5s^2$	$[Kr]4d^{10}5s^2 5p$	$[Kr]4d^{10}5s^2 5p^2$	$[Kr]4d^{10}5s^2 5p^3$	$[Kr]4d^{10}5s^2 5p^4$	$[Kr]4d^{10}5s^2 5p^5$	$[Kr]4d^{10}5s^2 5p^6$
Pd 46	**Ag** 47	**Cd** 48	**In** 49	**Sn** 50	**Sb** 51	**Te** 52	**I** 53	**Xe** 54
Palladium	Silver	Cadmium	Indium	Tin	Antimony	Tellurium	Iodine	Xenon
195.09	196.9665	200.59	204.37	207.2	208.9804	(209)	(210)	(222)
1.4	1.4	1.5	1.4	1.6	1.7	1.8	2.0	
$[Xe]4f^{14}5d^9 6s$	$[Xe]4f^{14}5d^{10}6s$	$[Xe]4f^{14}5d^{10}6s^2$	$[Xe]4f^{14}5d^{10}6s^2 6p$	$[Xe]4f^{14}5d^{10}6s^2 6p^2$	$[Xe]4f^{14}5d^{10}6s^2 6p^3$	$[Xe]4f^{14}5d^{10}6s^2 6p^4$	$[Xe]4f^{14}5d^{10}6s^2 6p^5$	$[Xe]4f^{14}5d^{10}6s^2 6p^6$
Pt 78	**Au** 79	**Hg** 80	**Tl** 81	**Pb** 82	**Bi** 83	**Po** 84	**At** 85	**Rn** 86
Platinum	Gold	Mercury	Thallium	Lead	Bismuth	Polonium	Astatine	Radon

158.9254	162.50	164.9304	167.26	168.9342	173.04	174.967
1.1	1.1	1.1	1.1	1.1	1.1	1.1
$[Xe]4f^9 6s^2$	$[Xe]4f^{10}6s^2$	$[Xe]4f^{11}6s^2$	$[Xe]4f^{12}6s^2$	$[Xe]4f^{13}6s^2$	$[Xe]4f^{14}6s^2$	$[Xe]4f^{14}5d 6s^2$
Tb 65	**Dy** 66	**Ho** 67	**Er** 68	**Tm** 69	**Yb** 70	**Lu** 71
Terbium	Dysprosium	Holmium	Erbium	Thulium	Ytterbium	Lutetium
(247)	(251)	(254)	(257)	(258)	259	260
≈1.2	≈1.2	≈1.2	≈1.2	≈1.2		
$[Rn]5f^9 7s^2$	$[Rn]5f^{10}7s^2$	$[Rn]5f^{11}7s^2$	$[Rn]5f^{12}7s^2$	$[Rn]5f^{13}7s^2$	$[Rn]5f^{14}7s^2$	$[Rn]5f^{14}6d 7s^2$
Bk 97	**Cf** 98	**Es** 99	**Fm** 100	**Md** 101	**No** 102	**Lr** 103
Berkelium	Californium	Einsteinium	Fermium	Mendelevium	Nobelium	Lawrencium